# 卷　四

# 外文论文集

Part One：Confucianism and its Contemporary Implication

Part Two：Cross-Cultural Conversation

Part Three：Confucianism as Mega Tradition in China

Part Four：Confucianism in the World

# Contents

## 卷四　外文论文集

### Part One: Confucianism and its Contemporary Implication



### Part Two: Cross-Cultural Conversation

**Part Three: Confucianism as Mega Tradition in China**

## Part Four: Confucianism in the World

# Part One: Confucianism and its Contemporary Implication

## A Second Enlightenment: Confucianism in a Changing World Cultural Order

**Roger T. Ames University of Hawai'i**

### The Perfect Storm

It is the best of times and it is the worst of times. In the beginning decades of the twenty-first century, exponential scientific and technological innovations have given human beings the opportunity to live lives of extraordinary comfort and convenience. At least in the developed world, we live longer and we live better than ever before, and it gets even better with every passing day. But limiting this human opportunity to the developed world is a boundary of our own making. As a species, we now have the science to clean the water and produce the food so that no child on the planet need go to bed sick or hungry. If only we had the social intelligence and the political will, we could in our time be embarking upon a halcyon epoch of increasing peace and prosperity.

At the same time, we are living in a moment of increasing urgency. The darkness of a perfect storm of global proportions is gathering on the horizon that will immanently threaten our familiar ways of living if not ultimately the very survival of humanity as a species. Ours is a world beset by climate change, by extreme weather events, by an ever accelerating increase in population, by gross income inequities, by food and water shortages, by environmental degradation, by looming pandemics, by energy shortage, by international terrorism, by nuclear proliferation, by consumer waste, and by growing legions of the hopeless poor. Perhaps the most disturbing element in the overall picture is the nearly vertical trajectory in the galloping pace of precipitous change as it approaches a tipping point that takes us past any possibility of return.

There seem to be at least four underlying conditions that are defining of this galloping predicament. First, human beings and our way of being in the world are complicit in some immediate way for the malaise. Secondly, this predicament does not recognize or respect national or social boundaries. Crises such as pandemics and global warming have a global reach and affect everyone regardless of nationality or status. Thirdly, there is an organic relationship that obtains among this set of pressing problems, rendering them zero-sum—all or nothing. This means of course that the problems cannot be addressed and solved seriatim by individual players. Rather, we are facing a largely human-precipitated predicament that can only be engaged wholesale by a world community acting in concert. In these pages I will argue that this increasingly dire situation can only be addressed and arrested by effecting a global-scale radical change in human intentions, values, and practices. And to our shame perhaps our best hope is it will be necessity itself rather than any enlightened awareness on the part of the human community that will serve as the imperative for change.

While this perfect storm has been gathering both globally and locally, over the past several decades a dramatic reconfiguration of the world's economic and political order has been occurring that is now affecting us all in this age of global interdependence. Over this past generation, the rise of Asia, and particularly of China, has precipitated a sea change in the prevailing economic and political order. For example, in the quarter century since its founding in 1989, the Asia Pacific Economic Cooperation (APEC) that now consists of twenty-one Asia-Pacific nations with forty percent of the world's population has shifted world wealth and power from a beleaguered Europe to an increasingly thriving Asia. The GDP in the region has more than tripled and trade has increased by over 400%. For more than thirty years, the Chinese economy has being growing at an annual double-digit rate of ten, eleven, twelve, thirteen percent, enabling it to overtake Japan as the second largest economy in the world with the prediction that it will eclipse the American lead within a decade. In 2010, a G8 comprised of the world's strongest yet declining economies that could claim less than 50 percent of world production became the G20 with 90 percent of world output, and China as the factory of the world has taken up a place of privilege and influence squarely in the middle of these dominant nations.

Development generally and the global impact of China's own growth more specifically, is producing a range of changing economic and political patterns that are relatively easy to track. But what about cultural change? What difference does this dramatic reconfiguration of economic and political dominance make for an elite world cultural order that has long been dominated by a powerful liberalism? And what will be the role of traditional Chinese customs and values in the evolution of a newly emerging cultural order?

Within China, we have over the past decades witnessed a dramatic rise of "Schools of Canonical Learning" (*guoxueyuan* 國學院) across college campuses. And internationally at the best institutions of higher learning across America and the globe we have seen the proliferation of now more than four hundred Chinese government-funded "Confucius Institutes" (*Kongzi xueyuan* 孔子學院) that are committed to promoting literacy on traditional Chinese culture. It is clear that Chinese culture is being actively promoted both domestically and internationally by a collaboration of academic and political forces within China itself. And we know that Chinese culture celebrates the relational values of deference and interdependence. That is, relationally constituted persons are to be understood as embedded in and nurtured by unique, transactional patterns of relations, a conception of person that contrasts rather starkly with the more familiar model of discrete, rational, self-determining, autonomous, and self-interested individuals that we have come to associate with liberal democracy. Will a Chinese ethic that locates moral conduct within a thick and richly textured pattern of family, community, and natural relations challenge and change the international culture? Will these family-centered values under the rapidly evolving conditions in evidence today precipitate a new cultural world order?

James P. Carse provides us with a distinction between finite and infinite games that might be useful in beginning to think through how Confucian values could make a difference in a newly emerging cultural order.[①] For Carse in formulating this distinction, "games" is really an analogy for the human experience broadly. The focus of finite games is on the agency of single actors who engage in a game played according to a finite set of rules that in a finite time guarantee a resolution—that is, a winner and a

---

① James Carse. *Finite and Infinite Games*. New York: Ballantine, 1987.

loser. Finite games thus have a finite beginning and end, and are played to win. The pervasiveness of what has become an ideology of individualism and the liberal values that attend it makes finite games a familiar model of the way in which we are inclined to think about our daily transactions as particular persons, as corporations, and as sovereign states, where such finite games seem relevant to most human activities that entail competition such as sports, business, education, foreign affairs, and so on.

Infinite games are different. There are no discernible beginnings or endings to infinite games. The focus is on strengthening relationships rather than competition among single actors, and the ultimate goal is simply human flourishing and the enjoyment of continuing to play. Further, infinite games are played according to rules that can be altered to serve the purpose of continuing the game when it appears that resolution is a possibility. The relationship among family members might be good example of the infinite games we play, where a mother is resolutely committed to continuing to strengthen the relationship she has with her son so that together they can manage whatever increasingly complex problems their lives lived together might present. In the case of infinite games, the interdependence of relationships means that the success and prosperity of mother and son is coterminous and mutually entailing—they either succeed or fail together. Infinite games are always win-win or lose-lose.

When we look for the cultural resources necessary to respond to the global and national predicament described above as a perfect storm, we might anticipate the need for a shift in values, intentions, and practices that takes us from the preponderance of finite games played among self-interested, single actors to a pattern of infinite games played through the strengthening of relationships within families, communities, corporations, and polities necessary to overcome what are the shared problems of our day. And it is a common place that Chinese culture broadly—Confucianism, Buddhism, and Daoism as well—begin from values, intentions, and conduct that is grounded in a recognition of the primacy of vital relationships that is the hallmark of infinite games. The values of Confucianism are one cultural resource that might enable humanity to weather the perfect storm and to emerge from it on a halcyon sea.

**Getting Past the Ideology of Individualism**

We must confront a perfect storm that is gathering on the human horizon, and must acknowledge the need for a profound change in human values, intentions, and practices. We need to move precipitously from the mentality of single actors and finite games to the recognition of the primacy of vital relationality that underlies the values of interdependence and diversity characteristic of infinite games. In order to do this, we need to address a major underlying and entrenched conceptual problem that is exacerbating our current malaise.

There is a default individualism that is appealed to first in defining what it means to be a moral person, and thus, for this moral person to act justly. This foundational individualism with its roots deep in the Western philosophical narrative dilutes our sense of moral responsibility by allowing us to describe, analyze and evaluate individual persons—psychologically, politically, and morally—in isolation from others. The enlightenment assumption that defines persons ideally as free, autonomous, rational, and properly self-interested individuals is ubiquitous in much if not most of modern Western moral and political philosophy.

This putative foundational individual is not only an ontological fiction, but moreover, because this individual so defined provides the moral and political grounding for a libertarian economic system that can no longer be seen to be a cure for most of the world's ills, this fiction has become an insidious one. Indeed, it can be fairly argued that it is this same libertarian economic system justified as it is by appeal to individual liberty and autonomy that, far from being the cure for the world's ills, has come to aggravate and to exacerbate the disease itself.

The concept of the autonomous individual that underlies modern moral and political philosophy has at least two malevolent effects. First, it enables libertarian capitalists, growing in their numbers in the U.S., Europe, and Asia, to claim moral purchase in justifying an unfettered human freedom as the basis and ultimate source of political justice, and on that basis, to then reject any conception of justice that retards such freedom as fundamentally immoral. The notion of the individual so defined thus continues to provide a moral basis for a more or less *laissez-faire* global free market capitalist economy that is compounding exponentially the gross inequities in human well-being within and between modern nation states. And as long as the conservatives, liberals, communitarians, and socialists alike continue to ground their objections to libertarianism in their own version of the same autonomous individual, the libertarian will always be able to counter their challenges and remain above moral reproach.

The second related reason that the concept of the autonomous individual is pernicious is its pervasiveness in the consciousness of Western intellectuals. The foundational individual is entrenched at a depth that makes it almost impossible for them to see any alternative to an individualism so defined except that of a more or less faceless collectivism in a decidedly post-Marxist era. Indeed, the assumption that the essential characteristics and actions of human beings are best understood by regarding them as fundamentally free, autonomous, and rational individuals has itself become a default, uncritical ideology.

Such an individualism not only fails to provide us access to a sufficiently robust understanding of shared life in family and community, but further stands in tension with the empirical fact of associated living. Indeed, such a fictive individualism ignores the intimacy, mutuality, and particularity that is invariably defining of relations in real families. In failing to accommodate family roles lived through richly textured and constantly changing patterns of both natural and socially constructed differences, abstract individualism itself becomes reductive and violent by enforcing conformity at the unacceptable expense of excising real diversity and its creative possibilities.

**A Second Enlightenment: From the Ideology of Individualism to Confucian Role Ethics**

Confucianism has a focus-field, narrative conception of person that provides just such a robust alternative to liberal individualism. We might want to reflect upon the *sui generis* regimen of "Confucian role ethics" to argue that lives lived in our evolving roles as children and parents, as beneficiaries and benefactors, are too intimately bound up with one another to allow for the divisive and fragmenting assumptions that ground liberal individualism. We live associated lives, and are irreducibly social not only in the transactions that constitute our unique narratives, but in our most basic, role-informed sense of personal identity. The omnipresent responsibilities of family life not only direct our attention to the pressing current and future concerns of the day, but they also provide us with a historical and narrative sense of where we have come from, and in important degree, tell us who we are.

Within the interpretive framework of Confucian philosophy, associated, interpersonal living is taken to be an uncontested, empirical fact. Every person lives and every event takes place within a vital natural, social, and cultural context. Association being a fact, our different roles lived within family and society are nothing more than the stipulation of specific modes of associated living: mothers and grandsons, teachers and neighbors. But while we must take associated living as a simple fact, the consummate conduct that comes to inspire and to produce virtuosity in these stipulated roles lived in family, community, and the cultural narrative broadly—that is, Confucian role ethics—is an achievement; it is what we are able with imagination to make of the fact of association.

The meaning of the family is implicated in and dependent upon the productive cultivation of each of its members, and by extension, the meaning of the entire cosmos is implicated in and dependent upon the productive cultivation of each person within family and community. Personal worth is the source of human culture, and human culture in turn is the aggregating resource that provides a context for each person's cultivation. While certainly having important theoretical implications, the enduring power of this Confucian project is that it proceeds from a relatively straightforward account of the actual human experience. It is a pragmatic naturalism in the sense that, rather than relying upon metaphysical presuppositions or supernatural speculations, it focuses instead on the possibilities for enhancing personal worth available to us here and now through enchanting the ordinary affairs of the day. A grandmother's love for her grandchild is at once the most ordinary of things, and the most extraordinary of things.

Confucius by developing his insights around the most basic and enduring aspects of the ordinary human experience—family reverence, deference to others, friendship, a cultivated sense of shame, education, community, and so on—has guaranteed their continuing relevance. One characteristic of Confucianism that is certainly there in the words of Confucius himself and that has made his teachings so resilient in the Chinese tradition, is its porousness and adaptability. His contribution was simply to take ownership of the cultural legacy of his time, to work assiduously to understand and to extend this legacy with his own best thoughts, to adapt this wisdom of the past to his own present historical moment in addressing the pressing issues of his time, and then to recommend to next generation that they do the same.

The personal model of Confucius that is remembered in the *Analects* does not purport to lay out some generic formula by which everyone should live their lives. Rather, the text recalls the narrative of one special person: How he in his relations with others cultivated his humanity, and how he lived a fulfilling life, much to the admiration of those around him. Indeed, in reading the *Analects*, we encounter the relationally constituted Confucius making his way through life by living his many roles as best he can: as a caring family member, as a strict teacher and mentor, as a scrupulous and incorruptible scholar-official, as a concerned neighbor and member of the community, as an always critical political consultant, as the grateful progeny of his progenitors, as an enthusiastic heir to a specific cultural legacy, indeed, as a member of a chorus of joyful boys and men singing their way home after a happy day on the river Yi. He offers us historical models rather than principles, and exhortations rather than imperatives. The power and lasting value of his insights lie in the fact that these ideas are intuitively persuasive, and readily adaptable to the conditions of ensuing generations, including our own.

Indeed, invoking the Chinese natural cosmology as context, what makes Confucianism more empirical than empiricism—that is, what makes Confucianism a *radical* empiricism—is the fact that it respects the uniqueness of the particular, and the need for a generative wisdom that takes this uniqueness into account in anticipating a productive future. Rather than advancing grand universal principles and assuming a taxonomy of natural kinds grounded in some notion of strict identity, Confucianism is modest in proceeding from always provisional generalizations made from those *particular* historical instances of successful living, the specific events recounted in the narrative of Confucius himself being a case in point. It is generation upon generation across the centuries that has broadened and extended the Confucian way, and that has in our own time made the East Asian Confucian cultures a world resource for cultural change.

# The Confucian Revival of Traditional Values and China's Modernity

**Prof. Dr. Jana S. Rošker, Faculty of Arts, Ljubljana University**

## Introduction

The revitalization of the Chinese tradition remains one of the most important theoretical currents in contemporary Chinese theory. Due to its potentially stabilizing social function and its harmonious compatibility with capitalism, many scholars① see it as the Asian equivalent of Max Weber's "protestant ethic". In modern Sinology, this view is known as the "post-Confucian hypothesis":

Indeed, many scholars have invoked Confucianism as an important cultural cause of East Asia's economic success. In particular, scholars such as Berger and Tu have gone so far as to propose what is called the post-Confucian thesis, i.e.: that Confucianism has not only facilitated economic development in East Asian countries, but also has enabled these countries to create a different kind of capitalism and take a different path to modernity than the West (Kwon, 2007, 55).

Lee Hong-jung describes the potential of the Confucian tradition in terms of its constitutive role within the concept of so-called "Asian values":

Characteristic Asian values were transmuted into state-led economic models, playing a significant role in the economic development of Asian countries. Familism promoted strong cooperation among blood relatives, and created small- and mid-size family businesses based on Confucian familism and family ethics. These family businesses gradually developed to become the framework of Asian capitalism. Community spirit is also a key Asian value. By maintaining strong ties based on community spirit and solidarity, Asian populations have contributed to the economic development of the region. Promoting education, the most im-

---

① For example, see Feng Yaoming, 1992, 227, Wang Hui, 2000, 40.

portant Asian value, also stems from Confucianism which teaches that it is better to educate one's children than to give them wealth. This tenet has helped pave the way to economic development. The emphasis on education has also raised management capabilities and technological expertise, and has facilitated economic development through improved productivity (Lee Hong-jung, 2003, 32).

The representatives of the Modern Confucian movement were generally convinced that the successful development of modern East Asian societies was due primarily to a specific modernization model, known as "Confucian capitalism"(e.g. Kahn, 1979, Vogel, 1979). This model is characterized by a strong state leadership with a well-developed administrative structure, a hierarchical social structure and a well-developed network of social relations, and an emphasis on education. It also stresses virtues such as diligence, reliability and persistence, together with cooperation, loyalty and a strong sense of affiliation to one's own community or organisation (ibid).

Tu Weiming is a contemporary modern Confucian scholar who has published a number of important studies on Chinese modernization and its links with the Modern Confucians. As Heiner Roetz points out, Tu's analysis of modernization is not based on a negative critique of the ethics of the Enlightenment:

A constant point of reference in Tu's writings is the European Enlightenment and its model of "modernity." However, he concedes that any ethics that wishes to build on something other than its exploitability by authoritarian regimes must come to terms with the standards of the Enlightenment. There is no possibility of a "radically different ethics" (Roetz, 2008, 367).

What Tu instead criticizes in Western Enlightenment models is their excessive reliance on individualism and instrumental rationality (2000: 207). In his view, these two "fundamental pillars" of modernization are responsible for the estrangement from Nature and the human alienation, which prevails in modern societies. He sees a possibility for influencing a renewed conceptualization of the modern era in the Chinese and, especially, the Confucian traditions. He supports his argument with the concept of "multiple modernities":

In both the Western and non-Western worlds, the projected transition from tradition to modernity never occurred. As a norm, traditions continue in modernity. Indeed, the modernizing process itself is constantly shaped by a variety of cultural forms rooted in distinct traditions (Tu, 2000, 198).

This concept also confirms his belief that East-Asian or Chinese modernization should not be equated with Westernization. In fact, "modernity" is no longer antithetical to "tradition"; on the contrary, traditions constitute the essential meaning of current modernities. The Confucian tradition, which Tu sees as a form of religion, is definitely capable of creating a model of modernity that would not lead to the alienation and determination which the Western model of modernization has produced in its societies. In its "broad humanistic spirit", Tu sees the possibility for an economic development that can co-exist with state-building (institutionalization), social stability and cultural identity (Tu 2000: 212). The arrogance of Western culture which conceives of "its own" present as the future for all other cultures is not only in bad taste, but also completely misplaced. Like most other Modern Confucians, Tu denies that Confucian ethics hinders modernization; on the contrary, they can accelerate this process. The fact that the Chinese tradition never succeeded in developing the conditions for industrialization and a modern economic system does not preclude it from doing so in a different historical context. However, the question of modernity is still subject to debate within the cultural, civilizational, national or ethnic spaces it takes as its units of analysis; this may be justifiable when viewed from a global perspective, but appears quite differently when viewed from the inside. The problems of Eurocentrism, its foundation in capitalism as a dynamic force and attendant problems of modernity are not simply problems between nations and civilizations, but problems that are internal to their constitution (Dirlik, 2000, 26).

Heiner Roetz points out the problematic nature of these suppositions (Roetz 2008: 371). Bearing in mind that original Confucianism had a negative view of the concept of pure benefit or profit (li), the East Asian "economic miracle" acclaimed by most Modern Confucians is best exemplified in the explosive development of the P. R. China. However, it is impossible to ignore the fact that China's rapid rise as a global superpower was also due to certain factors, such as a development policies which have resulted in a series of ecological disasters. This hardly resembles the Confucian ideal of "moral rule" based on "self-cultivation" and the harmonious unification of "inner sage and external ruler". On the contrary, many ideologies in the contemporary Chinese state are founded on a neo-liberalism, which is rooted in turn in the very concepts that have always been criticized by the Confucians. In fact, these elements are viewed as typical products of the Western modernization model, which is based on excessive individualism and instrumental rationality[①].

In their nostalgic exaltation of the bond with Nature and the holistic, organic unity of man and the natural order, Roetz finds certain parallels between Modern Confucian discourses on modernization and the European romantic reaction to the Enlightenment. These European intellectual currents were an attempt to return to the original bond between the individual and their natural and social environment and a form of resistance against the new domination of technology, which implied an atomizing, mechanistic view of life.

If we consider these parallels, what we are dealing with are not Western versus Asian or Chinese cultural alternatives, but rather a culturally non-specific dialectic of the same global modernization process. The agonies of China in the course of more than a century of ongoing modernization (nachholende Modernisierung) repeat the agonies of the West, and her responses repeat the Western ones, not only with respect to Romanticism, but also in terms of the philosophy of life (Lebensphilosophie) or, in our day, communitarianism (ibid, 372).

**1. Modernity with Chinese characteristics**

China found itself in a critical situation at the dawn of the previous century, when the two thousand year rule of Confucianism gradually (but radically) started losing its dominance. Following the Opium wars (1842-44) it was clear that the Confucian ideology was outdated and that it could no longer serve the conditions of the new era, which was defined by the economic, politic and philosophical contact with the colonial superiority of the Western forces. As a result of the confrontation with the Western forces the mid $19^{th}$ century Chinese intellectuals debated modernisation as a period of transformation and separation from the traditional political, economic and axiology paradigms, which have until then credibly defined the social reality of the so-called central empire.

① However, as noted above, the state ideologies of presentday P. R. China are still rooted in the same Confucian tradition which prevailed in traditional China in the form of the dominant state doctrine and which followed Xunzi's interpretation of the original teachings. Taiwanese Modern Confucians instead mainly follow the neo-Confucian (i. e. Mengzi's) model of Confucianism.

If we try to analyse this process from the 'general' theoretical premises of modernity① and at this attempt to recall the central paradigms that have - in the Euro-American sociological, cultural and philosophical discourses - decisively influenced philosophical reflection, we also have to look at the classical definition, which was established by Hegel, and later developed through the socio-theoretical assumptions of Marx and later expanded upon by Weber, early Lukács and older representatives of the Frankfurt school. These discourses were based on the absolutist criticism of the intellect and thus led to a self-referential cul-de-sac; afterwards alternative theoretical projects with a self-critical foundation of modernity and the aid of a different, language based understanding of the term 'intellect' developed. This linguistic spin led to two different starting points for the explanation of modernity. The first starting point was shown in the post-modern 'surpassing' of the normative understanding, and the second in the intersubjective transformation of the classical term (Habermas, 1998, 195). In the prevailing Western understanding we do not focus merely on the explanation of a specific social situation (which is usually shown as criticism of the intellect), but on the terminological spectrum of modernity, which also includes the connotation of the 'conscious discontinuity of the new from the old' or the modern from the traditional.

When discussing modernisation processes in China, we of course need to know that we are dealing with a series of consecutive phases that lasted for a few decades each and that were-each in their own way-connected either to the specifics of Chinese tradition, or with the problems of accepting and transforming 'non-Chinese' forms of production, reproduction and life styles. If we thus try to transfer the above described theoretical starting points to the reflection of the 'modern' period and axioms of 'modernisation' in China, we have to pay attention to the following characteristics:

1. In China modernisation in the sense of an all encompassing political, economic

---

① Because the term 'Modernity', which in general denotes the period of such social transformations, was developed within Euro-American theories, the definition of 'general' theoretic evolutions within this frame (once again) deals with the theoretical development of the so-called West. Of course, we should draw attention to the fact that this is not a discussion on the period of modernity in the sense of a concrete, rounded period of the so-called classic modernity, i. e. the Western 'new era', but the period of modernity as a process of general social transformation or social revival linked to certain characteristic conditions that dictate modernisation (for instance Enlightenment or the dominant role of the intellect in philosophy or industrialisation in economy). This era is marked by processes that took place differently in various cultural environments or traditions, but always in connection with the transformation of the specific conditions of traditional societies.

and cultural process and its theoretical reflection were always influenced by the invasion of Western military and technological supremacy; thus it is no coincidence that Western technology, political systems and culture became a referential frame for the modernisation of China (Geist, 1996, 13).

2. From this it is obvious that the theoretical reflection is defined through the equation of tradition with Chinese, and modernisation with Western culture.

3. Historically, the debate on modernisation in China took place within the frame of classic Chinese discursive methodology, which is defined by traditional binary categories: in the context of modernisation 19th and early 20th century Chinese rhetoric tried to clarify the relation between modernity (the West) and tradition (China) through the binary category of 'essence (ti)' and 'function (yong)'. In the nineteenth century Zhang Zhidong's slogan which advocated a the preservation of the Chinese Essence (ti) and the application of Western Function (yong)① gained a wide spread popularization among many Chinese intellectuals (Rošker, 2008, 96). This reveals the attempt to preserve Chinese tradition regardless of the modernisation which was understood exclusively as accepting Western technology and administration. In the twentieth century the contemporary theoretician Li Zehou changed this assumption around, when he switched the two counter poles of the binary opposition (ibid, 179); he considered modernisation to be a transformation of essence in the sense of general social consciousness, production and lifestyles.

4. The inner logic of traditional Chinese society was intra systemic (Moritz 1993: 60) in the sense that ensuring stability and the centralisation of social communities represented priority. The past not only served as the central point from which they would reflect the present, but also as a signpost for the future (ibid, 61).

5. Enlightenment in the sense of broadening the ideological domination of reason, which was seen as essential to modernisation, did not find its dynamic and modification potential in its own philosophical history, but in the adaptation of Western philosophical traditions.

Modernisation as defined by the above mentioned characteristics, did not represent a 'natural' process in China (Luo Rongqu, 2008, 1), nor did it represent a process that would be defined merely by the internal dynamics of the autochthonous development of the Chinese society. In the 19th century it appeared as a necessity for

① 中學為體，西學為用.

radical changes in the existing political and economic system, which no longer fitted the terms and demands of the period. We cannot overlook the fact that the modernisation process in China was governed by their contacts with overseas lands; in this sense the European colonial past defined these processes. On the other hand 18th and 19th century China faced a deep inner crisis, the dimensions of which were greater and reached into the traditional structure of society and the state much deeper than in the normally occurring cyclic rises and falls of dynasties. This means that the radical reform of values, production manners and the economic and political system were necessary even without any contacts with the West. This reform would not be comparable to the 'Western' type[①] modernisation and we can only guess what China would look like today if it performed this reform 'on its own' -i.e. using only its own economic, political and philosophical sources as its base.

What is important for our debate is the fact that these sources have survived until the present day, even though they no longer hold the role of prevailing ideologies. Over the last century we have witnessed a revival of the various Chinese histories and pasts, even though it seemed that they were already destroyed by modernity and thrown onto the waste sites of survived ideologies. This revival is not a denial of modernity, for it takes place under its banner. Modern Confucians never showed the desire to return to the pre-modern period. Today's modern Confucians do not consider globalisation a victory or domination of the Eurocentric modernity, but a challenge for its historization (Dirlik, 2001, 17) in the sense that tradition should be harmonised with the present.

**2. Daring reforms, ambitious renovations and passionately naïve movements**

The first modernisation attempt was represented by the so-called *One hundred*

---

① We should draw attention to the fact that the Eurocentric discourses of the dominating Western social sciences still focus on the Western paradigms of social development. These discourses lead to the logical conclusion that China would never experience an industrial revolution because its production and technology never reached a level of development necessary for this to occur. However, the research that has led to the well known theory (in sinology) called "origins of capitalism in China" (Zhongguo zibenzhuyi mengya) has clearly shown that the production means (production technology) in China was at a sufficiently high level for an industrial revolution to take place already in the 12th century. This did not take place because the structure and composition of the traditional Chinese political and economic system did not enable such transfer-amongst other reasons also because China- unlike Europe-did not face an economic crisis.

days reform (Rošker 2008, 97), which is in China also known as the Wuxu reform[①] and which fell victim to the last relicts of the conservative authorities in the gradually disintegrating empire.

The first (transformation) took place when Kang Youwei and Liang Qichao led the 100 days reform, to 1927, when the first Civil war broke out. In the half century between the 1840 Opium war and 1898, the Chinese ruling elites attempted no serious social reform. The so-called Chinese studies as substance, Western studies for practical use or *Zhongxue wei ti Xixue wei yong*, effectively prevented profound social transformations of any kind. The 100-Days Reform was a product of the failure of this policy of introducing Western technology without changing society fundamentally. The attempts at reforming China's political system failed with the collapse of the Qing Dynasty in 1911 and the elites' inability to establish a workable republic shortly afterwards (Hua Shiping, 2001, 3).

The idea and political turning point in Chinese modernisation is represented by the *May Fourth Movement* (*Wu si yundong*), which started in 1919 with the student demonstrations against what China considered to be unjust decisions of the Versailles peace treaty. Over the next few years this grew into an all Chinese movement of the so-called 'new intellectuals'[②], who stood for radical cultural and idea reforms in Chinese society (ibid). This movement, the broader influence of which is historically known as the New Culture Movement (*Xin wenhua yundong*) and which contemporary theoreticians often equate with the beginning of Chinese enlightenment, included patriotic and nationalist elements and strongly criticised or even completely rejected Chinese tradition, especially its Confucian state doctrine. According to Li Zehou (1996, 568) the two components were complementary at the start, even though it might appear at first glance that they are in opposition to each other. In his opinion the enlightenment tradition of the May Fourth Movement gradually disintegrated because the years that followed demanded the mobilisation of all physical, economic and philosophical forces in order to prepare for the inner revolution and to fight against

---

① For a more detailed explanation of the philosophical and ideological basis of this reform see Rošker 2008, 97.

② These were mainly intellectuals (of both genders), who studied in Europe or Japan, or at least at one of the modern universities that adopted the Western curriculum.

the foreign aggressors and preserve the sovereignty of China (ibid). 'socialist centralism, in which minorities were submitted to the majority and in which the lower levels followed the higher ones' (ibid) prevailed. According to Li this principle represented a revolutionary heritage, which was based, advertised and mediated at great length, until it gained general social status and became a part of the general social awareness... and this is what I wish to show in my thesis, according to which enlightenment suffocated under the weight of the national solution. This is a historical fact that cannot be changed[①](ibid).

This thesis by Li Zehou is relatively wide spread in the contemporary theory; however, we should consider whether the reason for the failure of this enlightenment project truly lies merely in the political constellation of the time. According to Li Huiru this external factor did not have a direct influence on the loss of the direct philosophical heritage and modernisation potential of the movement itself. In his opinion the reason for this should be sought mainly in the fact that the May Fourth Movement was not an enlightened movement to start off with. Liu Huiru summarised (1993, 48), that the ? incongruence between 'what is said ' and 'what is actually thought', that was consciously used by the intellectuals in the May Fourth Movement, proved to be a tried out and well known strategy in Chinese tradition, the origin of which can be found in Confucian pragmatism. From the virulence of the tradition that was apparently sentenced to death, it should be clearly noticeable that their negation (proclaimed towards the outside) did not mean that the tradition was truly surpassed, for in reality it hindered its transformation.

The critical negation of the past ideas and practices would need to include the attempts to liberate themselves from the unreflected tradition. The fact that the May Fourth activists questioned this previously unquestionable sacral authority indicates a series of enlightenment elements; however, they did not try hard enough to establish a generally binding instance of reason that would surpass the declarative level and create a truly new discourse. Thus it comes as no surprise that this greatly praised cultural reformation movement, the main task of which was to raise modern awareness, was considered by numerous theoreticians to be incapable of producing a new line of phi-

① 革命的傳家寶，被廣泛地長期地論證，宣傳，教育，並推行給全社會，成為某種普遍狀態和普遍意識…這就是我所說的'救亡壓倒啟蒙'. 這是1個歷史事實，誰也沒法再去改變這一行程.

losophy (ibid, 49) that would not be merely limited to new methods of explanation and understanding the past and evaluations of new future strategies, but would include the possibilities of creatively overcoming the usual borders of cognition and reflection on the given reality.

A superficial understanding of the tradition, which was naturally not enough to truly surpass it, was linked to the superficial and idealised image of 'science', which was supposed to be the carrier of the all-mighty and unmistakable mind and would, following the negation of its own tradition appear as a surrogate that would overcome the transcendental homelessness and the loss of one's cultural identity. The following thesis by Wang Fuwu clearly shows the naivety of the 'modern' intellectuals of the time:

Science is composed of the principles of causality and identity. In the case of life, neither belief nor attitude can avoid the magical forces of these two principles. This leads us to believe that science can save any problem life can throw at us①. (Wang Furu, in Hu Shi, 1990, 127)

All similar starting points, notions and norms of the May Fourth Movement, which were expressed through the various slogans, and which on the declarative level demanded to be widely acknowledged, were never truly legitimized through a discursive argument, which is a necessary precondition for any type of enlightenment. In this sense we should agree with Liu Huiru (1993, 55), who saw it as some sort of 'non-enlightened enlightenment'.

The idea of reason as the core of modernisation and progress is of course closely connected to the ideas of subjectivity and individualism. The concept and political endeavours of the May Fourth Movement focused on freeing the individual from the domination of the traditional system, in which the monitoring institutions of the state and its bureaucratic system on one hand and the owners of production means (land owners) and their clan connections on the other, were closely connected. These institutions did not monitor merely external spheres (public and political spheres, institutionalised nepotism and corruption, political and economic clan connections and strategies), but also internal ones (formal and true relations between clan members). The

---

① "科學是憑籍'因果'和'齊一'兩個原理而構造起來的；人生問題無論為生命之觀念，或生活之態度，都不能逃出這兩個原理的金剛圈，所以科學可以解決人生問題".

Confucian society was based (and still is) on the notion that society has priority over the individual. Intellectuals active within the May Fourth Movement tried their utmost to turn around this relation. This can be clearly seen in their stance for the freedom of the individual, equal opportunities for all and especially free love, which of course did not mean a sexual revolution, but merely the possibility of arranging marriages and a free choice of partners regardless of the needs and interests of the clans to which the two potential partners belonged.

Since its establishment in 1949 the People's Republic of China has been developing and implementing various modernisation concepts. During the first decade they mainly imitated the Soviet model, which placed socialist industrialisation in the forefront. After 1956 the Chinese government endeavoured to come up with its own modernisation model, at which it focused predominantly on agriculture; in the field of autochthonous modernisation of politics and culture this period witnessed the 'Great Proletarian Cultural Revolution' experiment. Following the death of Mao Zedong and the introduction of economic liberalisation the endeavours to overcome the antagonistic abyss between capitalist reality and socialist values was at first expressed in the ideologies of 》Socialism with Chinese characteristics《 and concepts such as 》socialist market economy《.

Such 'modernisation' models emerged from the traditional inseparability of society and state. This was a holistic system in which neither politics nor economy represented a separate sphere①. The domination of the state in economy thus already traditionally presented one of the basic characteristics of traditional society. In this system the concept of private property was always relatively irrelevant, for the possibility of

① Since the Han dynasty onwards (206 BC-220AD), the state had the authority to actively get involved in agricultural relations, i. e. the base of the production system in a traditional society. This not merely dealt with the introduction of numerous state monopolies in various production fields, but also with the efficiency of the inheritance principle, which merged moral and family/clan motives with the interests of the state, which ensured its fiscal and budgetary power by preserving the highest possible number of independent farming economies, while preventing their decline (which was conditioned by the division of assets through inheritance deeds), by linking the owners of the production means (i. e. landowners) to the state by offering them state positions if they managed to prove that they have accepted the ideological axioms of the Confucian state. Only once this position was obtained was it possible to successfully overcome the dangers linked to the scattered main investment (i. e. arable land) as a result of the inheritance system (compare Moritz 1993: 64).

fulfilling its inherent potential for the liberation and contrast development was usually limited to a minimum. Throughout the history of the Chinese state all attempts to concentrate arable land failed as did all attempts by individuals to pull their ownership from state control. Thus, on the level of society property was manifested as that of a clan, which of course-alongside ideological and moral factors-made it harder to transfer or alienate. Moritz (1963, 65) stated that the nationalisation processes of production capacities and forces in the People's Republic of China had a completely different cultural and historical background as well as a completely different cultural meaning as the similar processes that took place in Eastern Europe after WWII. Any attempt to divide Chinese history into chronologically consecutive, distinctive epochs merely by property (or production) criteria, which does not take into account the essential characteristics of social reality in this traditional society, will fail to lead to logically consistent results. The effects of creating continuity linked to the state remain hidden. The holistic effect of the state in space-in the sense of *imperium mundi*-comes in pair with its holistic effect in time (ibid, 66).

In opposition to previous phases this new renovation, based on the laws of market economy, did not lead to a longer lasting mass movement, which would appropriate at least the illusion that it is based on the ideas of Enlightenment, i.e. that it fulfils a certain theoretical assumption of modernisation. This fact is hardly surprising when we consider that the economic liberalisation lead by Deng Xiaoping over the last two decades of the $20^{th}$ century (following the death of Mao Zedong), was predominantly a result of a government decree; a great difference from the 'classic' (i.e. Western) modernisation model can be seen already in this aspect. On the other hand, a short and spontaneous mass movement occurred during the gradual economic liberalisation, and this fought for parallel political 'democratisation'. This occurred even though the given situation was reflected upon on other levels and political criticism was often shown in the form of a search for new cultural expressions. The reform oriented into the gradual introduction of the market-capitalist economy, started in 1978 under the leadership of Deng Xiaoping. Similar to the first two society modernisation transformations, Deng's reforms also started in the fields that were not closely connected to what we understand under the expression culture: as is most commonly the case, it dealt primarily with technology and economy. Hua Shiping (2001, 4) stated that the increasingly successful reforms were often political reflected in the cultural field; this position was clearly indicated by the phenomena of the 'Cultural fever' (*Wenhua re*) and the 'Great debate on culture' (*Wenhua da taolun*).

Of course the enlightenment movement existed in Modern Chinese theory; in fact it belonged to the central theoretical reflections of Chinese social reality①; the reason why this reflection never became a part of mass movements can be found in the fact that government institutions managed to discharge the intellectuals' critical potential not only through repressive measures, but also - and especially - through the professionalization of the theory. In the post 1989 period the Chinese intellectuals were forced to rethink their historic experiences.

A large majority of intellectuals in humanities and social sciences renounced their new enlightenment style which defined them in the 1980s; this either resulted from the pressure put upon them by the environment or in some cases they reached this decision themselves. Following their discussions linked to the problems of intellectual work, they started to focus on more specialised research, and clearly redirected into the professionalization of their work. In the beginning they based this transformation on Weber's theories on the professionalization of research, which can be understood as a way of finding excuses for themselves in the harsh situation that emerged in the post 1989 period. After 1992, the process of market transformation accelerated the appearance of essential social stratifications. This tendency was obviously in accordance to the inner professionalization of research; the development of professionalization and institutionalisation of intellectual life gradually led to a fundamentally changed role of intellectuals. Most intellectuals from the 1980s were gradually transformed into experts, scholars and professionals.②(Wang Hui, 2000, 4)

This tendency did not result merely in the alienation of intellectuals from the state and its structures of political decision making, but also in their dispersion; in modern day China intellectuals no longer exist as a homogenous social group (ibid).

---

① In most cases the epistemological sources that formed the base for the new Chinese enlightenment theory emerged from the Euro-American (predominantly liberal) economic, political science and legal theories. In the historic perspective it is evident that the New Enlightenment thought processes served as the base ideology for economic reforms (Wang Hui 2000: 16)

② Chinese original:《出於環境的壓力，大部分人文和社會科學領域的知識分子放棄了1980年代啟蒙知識分子方式，通過討論智識規範問題何從事更為專業化的學術研究，明顯地轉向了職業華的知識運作方式》.

Over the last fifteen years of the 20th century Chinese intellectuals reacted to this new situation in different ways. While the minority tried to stick to the critical theory and believed that informing citizens is a traditional task to be carried out by intellectuals, most turned towards a narrow, but in the strictly applicative view, 'useful' scientific specialisation within their profession, or into the search for a modernisation method which would fulfil the 'vacuum of values' that most intellectuals believed prevailed in society at the time.

**3. The rehabilitation of tradition and the challenges of modernization**

The revitalization of the complex traditions of Chinese philosophical thought during the 20th century has assumed increasing relevance and significance in recent decades. In the first half of the 20th century, this tendency could be observed in the works of many of the leading modern Chinese philosophers who were searching for ways to renew the methodological and theoretical aspects of the Chinese tradition, and especially of the pre-modern philosophy which followed the Neo-Confucian revival. In addition to Xiong Shili and Feng Youlan, who are certainly among the most visible representatives of this current, we should also mention Liang Shuming, Zhang Junmai and He Lin. Fang Dongmei's contribution is likewwise important, though he never explicitly adhered to the Modern Confucian movement and considered himself, in his innermost convictions, to be not only a Confucian, but also a Daoist and a Buddhist (Bresciani 2001: 23). In fact, he not only taught many of the main figures of the 3rd generation of Modern Confucians, but also many leading contemporary Daoists, such as Chen Guying (1997: 96). We should also bear in mind that the term Confucianism (ru xue) often denotes traditional Chinese thought in general, even though the Neo-Confucians of the Song and Ming Dynasties, who created the theoretical framework that underpins Modern Confucianism, formally distanced themselves from Daoism, Buddhism and similar, more mystical, less rational traditions, even going so far as to view the proponents of these systems as their philosophical "enemies". At the same time, one of the greatest theoretical shifts in Neo-Confucian philosophy was due precisely to the integration of many important Daoist and Buddhist concepts and methods into the framework of classical Confucianism①. It was the assimilation of those very ideas that orthodox classical Confucian doctrine deemed dangerous, improper (fei zheng) and even "heretical", which to a great extent defined the reform of classical Confucian thought which, already at that time, had ossified and become far too formalized. These Buddhist and Daoist impulses saved Confucianism from collapse in the period from the $10^{th}$ to the $14^{th}$ centuries, and succeeded in transforming the classical state-building doctrine into a system of thought that deserved once again to be called "philosophy"②. In their attempts to synthesise Euro-American and Chinese philosophies and modernize the Chinese philosophical tradition, many other Modern Confucian thinkers also focused on various traditional discourses which do not belong to the framework of Confucianism in a narrow sense③. As a final point, we must also take into account the differences between the original Chinese notions and their semantic connotations that originate in the translations of these notions into Indo-European languages. The expression "ru xue" is translated as "Confucianism" (also in the term "Modern Confucianism"), and thus automatically connotes Confucius (Kong fuzi, Kongzi) and the various historical phases of the Confucian teachings. But "ru xue" ac-

---

① For example, the concepts of the subject and object of recognition (neng-suo), originating in Buddhist epistemology, which were often applied even by the most rationalistic philosophies within the School of Structure (li xue). Even Zhu Xi, the leading figure this school, incorporated several Daoist ideas and procedures into his own philosophy (e. g. the idea of the ultimate pole or taiji, the concept of non-action or wu wei, etc), whereas the theories of the more idealistic current ("The School of Mind", Xin xue) were practically based upon Buddhist and Daoist onto-epistemologies.

② It is difficult to say to what extent this process was a conscious one, but the contemporaneous integration and"discharging" of Buddhist and Daoist philosophy certainly constituted a challenge for Neo-Confucian philosophers. By the $10^{th}$ century, the formalized classical Confucian doctrine was an empty husk, and was studied and mastered only in order to pass the official state examinations, which for the successful candidates (and their clans) gave access to political power. But because this doctrine was incapable of satisfying the intellectual needs of the educated classes, these classes turned to the study of Daoist and Buddhist philosophies, a tendency which threatened both Confucianism as such, and the entire ideological system on which the traditional state institutions were based. In this sense, the Neo-Confucian reform was absolutely necessary for the preservation of Confucianism, in terms of its function as the main social, ethical and philosophical system of thought in China.

③ Modern Confucians rarely relied on Daoism, and understandably so, for this current emerged not only in order to preserve cultural identity, but also with the goal of modernizing and "saving" the institutional framework of Chinese society. The anarchic classics of Daoism are eminently unsuited for such goals. That said, several Modern Confucian philosophers have devoted considerable effort to the study and integration of Buddhist thought into their own theories (e. g. Xiong Shili and Mou Zongsan).

tually signifies "the teachings of the scholars", which means that this expression does not exclude a-priori any of the major influences on the history of Chinese thought. In fact, what Confucian and Daoist philosophy, as well as sinized Buddhism all share is this idea of traditional Chinese philosophy as the "teachings of the scholars"①.

The trend towards revitalizing Confucianism was already evident at the start of the famous debate on science and metaphysics (kexue yu xuanxue) in 1923, in which a group of young theoreticians led by Zhang Junmai challenged the naïve and superficial May 4th enthusiasm for Euro-American models of modernity with a series of closely-reasoned counter-arguments and objections (Bunnin 2002: 27).

A scholarly revival involving new interpretations of ancient Confucian, Daoist, Mohist, Legalist, and Buddhist texts was of vital importance, but the main inspiration from traditional Chinese thought derived from the great Neo-Confucian syntheses of the Song and Ming dynasties, especially those found in the writings of Zhu Xi (1130-1200) and Wang Yangming (1472-1529). The subtlety and scope of their philosophical intelligence and the tension between Zhu Xi's realism and and Wang Yangming's focus on Mind offered considerable margins for modern reflective interpretations of their work (ibid.)

These thinkers thus proceeded with a dual approach: on the one hand, reformulating certain key approaches of traditional (Confucian) thought which they believed were capable of transcending the prevailing ideological trends, thereby preserving Chinese cultural identity, while at the same making their own original contributions to the development of a philosophical and theoretical dialogue between Euro-American and Chinese cultures. This current, which after 1949 to a great extent defined the spirit of Taiwanese, but also (though at first only partially, and latently) mainland modernization, engaged in a wide-ranging effort to revitalize traditional (primarily Confucian and even moreso, Neo-Confucian) thought by means of new input and stimulation from Western philosophical systems. In its general tension towards syntheses, the spirit of German idealism was especially important, while among its more

① In considering specific features of traditional Chinese philosophy that are common to all schools of ancient and classical Chinese thought, of primary importance are the concept of transcendent immanence (or immanent transcendence), binary structured holism which functions by means of binary categories (for example yin-yang, you-wu, ti-yong, ming-shi etc), as well as the principle of complementarity which represents the method of interactions between both implied antipodes.

theoretical components considerable attention was also given to the contents and approaches of the Viennese school. However, in their search for antidotes and alternatives to social alienation (in Asian modernization, as well) and the "vacuum of values", these theorists instead looked primarily to the framework of classical Confucian thought.

Lingering in a state of self-affirmation and self-transformation, it faced a series of powerful, unprecedented challenges throughout the century. At the end of the century, even though Confucianism had already been relegated to the "ashpit of history" as a political institution[①], it ultimately found peace and its own place in the world as a philosophy. (Cheng, Chung-Ying, 2003, 160)

With the explosive development of the policy of economic openness and the liberalization that accompanied it, this current has also been gradually revitalized in P.R. China over the last two decades.

The question of cultural renewal created considerable turmoil in Chinese intellectual circles when it first appeared during the Qing dynasty. In a period marked by a constant state of crisis, many Chinese intellectuals were attracted by the gloss of modern material cultures and wanted China to enter into this Brave New World as soon as possible. In their view, traditional Chinese culture was backwards and old fashioned and had to be eliminated. The voices of the Modern Confucians were thus completely silenced by this barrage of new ideas. That China had pursued a form of modernization in which the negative aspects of its own culture predominated, and in which it also risked being expropriated by "external forces" was something that only became evident in recent years. In short, cultural renewal had gone in a completely wrong direction and now found itself at a dead end. The return to its own tradition thus once again became a topic of debate, leading to the "rediscovery" of Modern Confucianism and its intrinsic value by Chinese intellectuals.

**4. Conclusion**

The so-called Confucian revival that manifests itself in the philosophical stream

---

① The thesis of the defeat of Confucianism has yet to be fully verified. Ideological elements of this ancient tradition are still evident not only in the Chinese educational system and in the axiological framework of rights and duties within the family, but also in the hierarchies of professional politics and modern economic structures.

of Modern Confucianism is one of the most significant elements within the new Asian ideologies of modernization. An important consequence of the current transnationalization of capital is that, perhaps for the first time in the history of capitalism, the capitalist mode of production appears as an authentically global abstraction that is no longer limited to its specific historical origins in Europe. Hence, the narrative of capitalism is no longer an exclusively European narrative, and for the first time non-European capitalist societies are also making their own claims on the history of capitalism and modernization.

The philosophical current of Modern Confucianism (xin ruxue) was developed during the $20^{th}$ century in China and other East Asian regions that were traditionally influenced by Confucian thought, as for instance South Korea, Japan and Singapore. It forms the most influential and important stream of thought in contemporary East Asian theory and represents a crucial part of the new prevailing theoretical systems in the P.R. China. It is defined as the search for a synthesis between Western and traditional East Asian thought, in order to elaborate a system of ideas and values capable of resolving the social and political problems of the modern, globalized world. Hence, it is important not only to examine the main Modern Confucian philosophical approaches, ideas and methods, but also to explore the political, social and ideological backgrounds of the so-called Confucian revival and its connections with the ideological foundations of East Asian modernity.

The appearance of the 'vacuum of values' in modern China, its problematization and connection to the partially violent, partially by the modernisation processes determined transformation of the structure, role and function of social knowledge, is a good example for the consequences of explosive social transformations. All these issues raise the question of whether the Confucian modernization model is really capable of generating a non-individualistic version of modernity. In verifying this hypothesis, further research might show that the purported relation between modernity and individualism which international modernization theories have always viewed as "inevitable" or "intrinsic" is little more than an outcome of Western historical paradigms.

Thus, the research in the Confucian revival can tell us a great deal both about the times we live in, and the fate in contemporary societies of one of the most important philosophical legacies in the world, while also revealing the role of so-called "Non-Western" intellectual traditions in contemporary philosophical and cultural discourses.

Although many books and articles on this topic are available in Chinese, academic studies in Western languages are still few and far between. Because Modern Confucian efforts to revitalize and reconstruct traditional Confucian thought can be seen as an attempt to counter the dominant ideological trends and preserve Chinese cultural identity, the future Western Sinological research in this field will also hopefully

contribute to the development of theoretical dialogues between "China" and "Europe".

**SOURCES AND LITERATURE**

Bresciani, Umberto. 2001. *Reinventing Confucianism-The New Confucian Movement*. Taipei: Taipei Ricci Institute for Chinese Studies.

Bunnin, Nicholas. 2002. Introduction. IN: *Contemporary Chinese Philosophy* (ed. Cheng Chung-Ying in Bunnin, Nicholas). Oxford: Blackwell Publishers. 1-15.

Chen Guying 陳鼓應. 1998. Chen Guying ping dangdai xin rujia 陳鼓應評當代新儒學 *IN*: *Taiwanzhi zhi zhexue geming-zhongjie sanzhong wenhua weiji yu ershi shiji zhi gaobie* 台灣之哲學革命-仲介三種文化危機與二十世紀之告別 (ed. Wang Yingming). *Taibei*: *Shuxiang wenhua shiye*. 95-98.

Cheng Chung-ying 成中英, 2003: Confucianism: Twentieth Century. IN:

*Philosophy*, *Chinese - Encyclopedias* (ed.: Cua, Antonio S.). New York: Routledge. 160 - 172

Dirlik, Arif. 2001, Postmodernism and Chinese History. Boundary 4 (28), pp. 19-60

Feng Yaoming 馮耀明. 1992. Cong《zhitong》dao《qucheng》- dangdai xin ruxue yu xiandaihua wenti 從《直通》到《曲成》—— 當代新儒學與現代化問題. *Hanxue yanjiu*. 10/2. 227-251

Habermas, Jürgen, 1973. Legitimationsprobleme im Sp? tkapitalismus. Frankfurt/Main: Suhrkamp.

Hu, Shi 胡適. 1990. Hu Shi wencun 胡適文存 (Hu Shi's Essays). 2. zv. Taibei: Yuandong chuban she.

Hua, Shiping. 2001. Introduction: Some paradigmatic Issues in the Study of Chinese Political Culture. In: Hua Shiping (ed.), Chinese Political Culture 1989-2000. London/New York: M.E. Sharp, East Gate Books, pp. 3-17.

Kahn, Hermann. 1979. *World Economic Development*: 1979 *and beyond*. Boulder: Westview Press.

Kwon, Keedon. 2007. Development in East Asia and a Critique of the Post-Confucian Thesis. *Theory and Society*. 36/1. 55-83.

Lee Hong-jung, 2003: Development, Crisis and Asian Values. *East Asian Review*. 15/2. 27-42.

Li, Minghui 李明輝. 2001. Dangdai ruxuede ziwo zhuanhua 當代儒學的自我轉化.(The Self-Transformation of Contemporary Confucianism). Beijing: Zhongguo shehui kexue chuban she.

Li, Zehou 李澤厚. 1996. Zou wo zijide lu 走我自己的路.(Going my own Way). Taibei: Sanmin shudiuan.

Liu, Huiru. 1993. Die 4. Mai Bewegung aus heutiger Sicht. IN: Pohl, Karl-Heinz, Wacker, Gudrun in Liu Huiru (eds.), Chinesische Intellektuelle im 20. Jahrhundert: Zwischen Tradition und Moderne. Hamburg: Institut für Asienkunde, pp. 37-55.

Luo, Rongqu 羅榮渠 (ed.). 2008. Cong 'Xihua' dao 'xiandaihua' 從? 西化? 到現代化.(From Westernization to Modernization). Hefei: Huangshan shu she.

Moritz, Ralf. 1993. Denkstrukturen, Sachzw? nge, Handlungsspielr? ume-Die chinesische Intelligenz im Konflikt der Ordnungsmuster. IN: Pohl, Karl-Heinz, Wacker, Gudrun in Liu Huiru (eds.), Chinesische Intellektuelle im 20. Jahrhundert: Zwischen Tradition und Moderne. Hamburg: Institut für Asienkunde, pp. 9-108.

Roetz, Heiner. 2008. Confucianism between Tradition and Modernity, Religion, and Secularization: Questions to Tu Weiming. *Dao - Journal for Comparative Philosophy*. 2008/7. 367-380.

Tu, Weiming. 2000. Implications of the Rise of ? Confucian? East Asia. In: *Daedalus*. 129/1. 195-219

Ro? ker, Jana S. 2008. Searching for the Way: Theory of Knowledge in pre-Modern and Modern China. Hong Kong: Chinese University Press.

Sandel, Michael. 1984. The Procedural Republic and the Unencumbered Self. Political Theory. 12 (1)1, pp. 81-96.

Scalapino, Robert A. 2002. Democracy in Taiwan and Asia-Advances and Challenges. IN: Chow, Peter C. Y. (eds.), Taiwan's Modernization in Global Perspective. Westport, Connecticut-London: Praeger, pp. 29-44.

Taylor, Charles. 1985. What's Wrong with Negative Liberty? Philosophy and the

Human Sciences：Philosophical Papers. 2. zv. Cambridge：Cambridge University Press，pp. 211-229.

Vogel，Ezra F. 1979. *Japan as number one*. Cambridge，MA：Harvard University Press.

Wang，Hui 汪暉. 2000. Dangdai Zhongguode sixiang zhuangkuang yu xiandaixing wenti 當代中國的思想狀況與現代性問題（Contemporary Chinese Thought and the Question of Modernity）. Taiwan shehui yanjiu. 37（1），pp. 1-43

# Confucius and Globalization

**Ambassador Constantin Lupeanu**

## HISTORY

Confucius (September 28, 551 -March 4, 479 BC) is worshipped by 2,565 years for being the greatest thinker, statesman and educator of the Chinese nation. He was born in what is now Shandong province in the Principality Lu, from an extramarital union, his father being a septuagenarian. There are not Chinese who may not have heard of Confucius, nor a person who knows to read books that would not read and not memorized more or les quotes from the work of only 12.700 character book, Lunyu, The Analects, a synthesis of his conception of the world and life.

This paper contains the review of the master concept about the world and is focused on the relation between Confucius and his disciples.

It is obvious, Confucius has interacted with the young, wore dialogue, leading them to find their own way forward.

What counts is the Confucian thought has been built step by step, with a few adherents in the beginning, surely the seventy disciples steadfast, to which were joined by other scholars and philosophers and ended up being elevated to the rank of a doctrine of the Chinese Empire.

Confucianism dominated for centuries and millennia of Chinese thinking, and by spreading the Chinese language, dominates also other races and peoples' thinking in Asia.

Since 1687, after editing Analects in Latin, China began to be known not only by porcelain, silk and tea, but also by this doctrine, considering that the Confucian thinking is proper to every Chinese. Scholars like Leibnitz, Jung and many other European intellectuals have studied among the firsts, the works of Confucius and were influenced by them.

Extrapolating, in today's world of increasingly close connections, you would hardly find an intellectual, in any country in the world, who may not have read Confucius.

In the top of a hundred personalities of the world which have decisively influenced the history of humanity, prepared by an intellectual from the USA in the last century, Confucius occupies fifth place. One of the first five people on Earth, from the beginnings of civilization and to this day! This classification is significant, coming from outside of Chinese world, from outside of China, Asia and even Europe! Philosophical thinking of the influence of Confucius is found not only in the political sphere or in the sphere of culture, but also in life, in people's mentality and behavior. Who read and assimilated Confucius, regardless on what continent lives, is closer to wisdom and civilization.

Here's the value this overwhelming human personalities, which is a Chinese language has a meaningful name, Kong, which can be interpreted in various ways. Confucius has imposed strict order and regulation ethics in every human life and society, from top to bottom, starting with the king and ending with the humblest of subjects. Lunyu Confucius teachings refers to the main areas of life such as: politics, friendship, love, music, etc. In how to lead people, referring to the three basic factors for running a country, Confucius was asked by a disciple at what factor would opt out, if you take into consideration: the people, the food and the host, and his answer is enlightening. He responded without hesitation that you can opt out of the military. Indeed, Confucianism means peace and development!

**VISION**

His work is vast and covers the early Chinese and Mankind civilization. Its footprint, its ethics and philosophical thinking can be found in The Five classic books, Shijing, Shujing, Liji, Yuejing, and Chunqiu.

Confucius was a superior man, one of the few people full of heavenly light of the planet, arrived to change for the better the society and the man.

Pragmatic character, he has sought a balance between heaven and earth, for a favorable world for all.

His thinking has exerted an overwhelming influence, first on the Chinese world, later on the whole Extremely Orient and today almost everywhere in the world.

Let s proclaim Confucius the real father of globalization.

No one has ever thought that it's a world as today's modern concept, comprised of three milestones: shu - more population, fu - wealth, jiao -education.

Globalization has brought together as a concept and theory of modern life without barriers and without any restrictions after his precept: all men are brothers, 四海之内皆兄弟 *Sihaizhinei jie xiongdi*. And after doctrines like: ren-kindness or humanity (the highest of the Confucian virtues), xin - honor, honesty, yi - justice, li - ceremonial, xiao - love within each family, the love of parents for children and children's love for their parents, zhong, loyalty, zhongyong, doctrine of the mean, and more.

But above all, the fundamental concern is to learn to be human, to enfold us with kindness.

Confucian spirituality includes the size, the component of the self, community and tradition. Auto-cultivation represents the foundation of the whole edifice. Man must concern themselves to engage in a healthy body, a soul and a spirit, high grown. Auto-cultivation takes its nourishment from tradition, from the family and society, from the energy of the surrounding nature, but also from the heavenly power.

Confucius thought of a dignified world at a whole, the respect for oneself and respect and understanding of the rest of humanity. The community is very important for the success of the auto-cultivation. As for tradition, Confucius put price on harmony and consensus, and reject the conflicts, the wars.

**PRACTICAL IMPLEMENTATION**

Schools of confucianism are counted:Confucianism in the Han dynasty, Neo-Confucianism, Contempo rary Confucianism, Korean Confucianism,Japanese and Singaporean Confucianism, and European or World Confucianism, becoming more visible with the beginning of the 21st century.

Confucianism does not include elements known in religion as well as Christianity. Confucianism is a system of ethics, to which have added various rituals. The vision is based on respect of children for parents, high esteem paid to elders and authority, appreciation of learning, protocol and ceremony.

The world is ruled by virtue, based on a ceremonial, with judgment and misdeeds are fined. From here, the distinction from the Christian idea which urges: Do not stay against the devil, and if someone hits your right cheek, you turn also the other cheek, Matthew, 5-39. Confucius advises: Respond or answer to hatred with integrity and to virtue by virtue, Lunyu, 14: 34. Into Yijing, The Book of Changes, hexagram Heng, Duration, to three nine, is written: If you do not keep your virtue brings humiliation. Prediction of danger. Let us not forget that Confucius designed Yijing as a manual of individual refresher perfecting improvement and a guide of the conduct of life, divination being only an outside coat of her. And referring to the moral value of Shijing said: No even one bad thought.

**EVERYWHERE IN THE WORLD**

On these precepts of Confucius we can take today peoples and cultural exchanges, visits all over the globe, in exceptional circumstances.

We can exemplify.

The culture of each nation is established on the relationship based on his own life, rules on certain moral qualities, traditions, on a system of customs and cultural elements, related to aspects of human existence in its essential hypostases, between birth and extinction. And the tradition is a way to think and to live. Extended experience of tradition, gives length, action, commitment, time, etc.

The world is a culture a summum of national cultures of each nation. As we define the words, both in European languages and Chinese language speech, dialogue is exchanges of words between two or more persons, exchange of information and opinions between people, regardless of their role and place in society and in the world.

Dialogue can be, more often spontaneous, but also authorized dialogue, where certain individuals representing institutions of a state or a union of states. The very idea of dialogue reflects the transition from isolated or closed cultures, to the cultures than know and accept the existence of other forms of culture, to the cultures prepared to receive new things, to the cultures prepared to offer what has to be more specific and more good, useful to mankind, to the culture of partnership.

From the whole definitions currently existing in the world, according to the Organization of International Labor (OIL), any type of dialog is an act of volunteer information, consultation and negotiation amongst equal partners.

Any culture shall be defined and complemented by the dialogue with other cultures.

A few years ago, the year 2010 has been declared International Year of Rapprochement between cultures, in favor of dialogue and promotion of the diversity of cultural expressions, the recognition of their own culture and mutual respect. We are for accepting an infinities of cultural values and for the need for dialogue, in the interest of further progress, and for the enhance of human values. Let us remember how Confucius visited 2500 years ago, in difficult travelling conditions, often at the risk of his life, a good part of the feudal states of his time, and his efforts are also discernible in our days, since Confucian thought has spread everywhere in the world.

Communication between people, as well as teaching, beyond the barriers of caste, race, language, etc. is essential and form a sturdy base for peaceful cohabitation, for peace in the world.

UNESCO has among the main objectives to promote worldwide awareness, cultural, ethnic, linguistic and religious diversity, highlighting common values. The 21st century is marked by cutting-edge technology and globalization, and these involve transformations of life and even profound changes in the majority countries. So, what are the supportive, beneficial cultural policies? The extent to which, people and non-governmental and state bodies may result in positive developments? How to be promoted on a priority basis the culture of value?

Cultural exchanges, frequent contacts, the Internet and other digital electronic and technical means enable and streamline the mutual knowledge, improve the opportunities of learning from the discoveries of others. We must not forget that globalization at any price and under any conditions should cancel their own cultural specificity of each people, and may lead to uniformity, can fail in time however.

That's why the Confucian morals, urging and recognition of all nations and races through precept: all men are brothers, 四海之内皆兄弟 *Sihaizhinei jie xiongdi*, help the progress of the modern world, going forward. Confucius' doctrine is obsolescent, it's not outdated. Although Confucian works are the same, each new generation finds in them appropriate answers to questions of their time.

**ROMANIAN COMPREHENSION**

Allow me to refer in a few words the Romanian dimension of culture. One of the prominent poets and thinkers of the 20th century, Lucian Blaga, characterised the culture as follows:

Through culture, existence enriches with its the deepest variant. Culture is the visible expression of the figure, the body of this variant. Culture is therefore more closely to the definition of man than its physical conformation, or at least all that closely.

And between the elements that compose the culture, the art is the most eloquent expression of human creativity. Art can be reckoned quintessential supreme expression of culture.

Another learned, Simion Mehedin? i, logically make distinction between civilization and culture, seeing that they were independent developments, hence a weak civilization, a disorganized society, with loud enough, you may know the high culture, as well as there are well developed civilization where culture is pale or non-existent.

Therefore, he writes in his book Civilization and culture: The pole of civilization and culture rarely coincide. Everyone can reach a high level of civilization if borrows others'work. High culture is a phenomenon much more doable. It involves not only the rich and great wealth work of reflection, but also a fine feeling, which translates into an attitude of a higher level ethics and aesthetics.

After him, culture is the summum of all things spiritual, intellectual, ethical and aesthetic, and a civilization as the summum of all technical creations that help human adaptation to the environment. His explanation is as true as it is suggestive:

As the leaf has two sides: one amazing, towards the sun, the other darker, returned to earth (but very important, because through this herb breathes and nurture), so the life of humanity has two aspects: one civilization, i. e. telluric-physical technique; another heavenly-culture, or the summum of all spiritual products, through which man seeks to balance as fully with the rest of creation and, in general, with the moral universe that encompasses it. Both these aspects are inseparable and simultaneous, consecutive, not successively, as claim historical morphology of Spengler.

After these two Rumanian thinkers, Constantin Noica reworks the Romanian world through a few specific words: self, utterance, human nature and others, that invest with potentiality of entering inside the substance itself, and through them, he considers that we, Romanians can tell something new to the worls, within ans inside the world.

**CULTURAL DIALOGUE IN THE WORLD**

Currently, it is known that there is a fairly substantial European and global, world wide cultural dialogue.

The dialogue has always existed, and especially after the discovery of the so-called new world, in Asia and the Americas. After the second world war, in the USA it has been argued multiculturalism, understanding of minorities cultures, affirmation of the culture of all entities within the boundaries, while Europe has put the emphasis on inter-culturality, i.e. recognition of the existence of this interpenetration of culture and belonging to different communities and countries all over the world.

The concept adapted to the level of Europe and the entire world, cultural dialogue is a process of information, consultation and permanent exchanges between states and people or groups of people, with the aim of reaching understandings regarding enhancement of certain variables, macro-cultural level, both inside and micro-cultural, and to refresh and enrich the culture of humanity.

How to guide mankind in the century we have just entered? What principles should be adopted for the construction of new-type relations, in which culture and civilization to prevail and lead to a better life?

The dialogue between cultures is necessary, inevitable. The dialogue does not require discussion, but exploring what other offers, the assimilation of what is good, valid and the proximity between cultures and between people, in a way of special production melting private, particular into universal and of the completeness of the wagon body with what is particular, original, noble and worthy of being retained. Such a dialogue is the path of hermeneutics of the modern world and contemporary scholars, where there is an intimate connection between understanding and implement, between theory and practice philosophy. Hermeneutics is relevant for cross-cultural studies, as the antidote to the clash of some civilizations.

It is obvious that the solid principles, to represent the interests of all-equal countries, regions, races, religions, etc., to be accepted by all the people, and to enrich cultural dialogue within all of us.

The doctrine of Confucius meets such requirements. That is precisely why, for the debate today, Confucius, world peace and development, Confucius, contemporary culture and dialogue within civilizations are welcome and they will have a strong echo not only intellectual in the world, but also in the political-military environments, technical-scientific and economic.

Confucianism means spiritual cultivation. Predictions of Confucius about the development of mankind help to build a better world, an ideal world. Terra belongs to all of us. The leaders all over the world must be promoted through virtue and proven skills. The teachings of Confucius buid a clean, harmonious culture for us.

Humanity and honesty, love and forgiveness, harmony and justice etc, in a path of globalization that does not make smoothing us, but to preserve the peculiarities. Here's what Confucius teaches, and where these principles were put into practice, they have paid off. They constitute the basis of Confucian cultural harmony, propose a humanistic spirit. We see them not only like the essence of cultural dialogue, as well as the universal panacea to resolve the complicated conflicts in the world today, to maintain harmony and peace in the world.

Therefore, we can conclude:

-Civilization and culture are getting essentials. One concerns the material world; the other is the exclusive nature of mind, but both are essential in shaping human and of a new world.

-Inside each step of human development, alongside with civilization we also find and culture.

-Culture and civilization are interwoven. They converge in the unity of life, because the material (civilization) technique and the technique of mind (the culture) are connected to each other, depend on each other and develops some of the others, and the transition from one to the other is often imperceptible. The drive of life embraces both.

The doctrine of Confucius represents the way of learning, the path of love, of justice, of modesty, the middle way throughout the globe, the method that may collect us and keep us together, but in the same time we can be ourselves, and therefore the Confucius way is imperishable.

That is why China is a hotbed, the powerful outbreak of civilization!

**Romania, Bucharest, 2014, Summer**

# New China on Confucian Canvas: Reflections on Characteristics of Chinese Socialism

**Ragnar Baldursson**

The influence of Confucianism on Chinese culture, human relations, politics and Chinese thinking in general, can be compared to the influence of Christianity in Western Countries or Islam in the Islamic World. It constitutes a kind of a cultural background noise penetrating the thought patterns and perception of reality of everyone affected by it.

After more than a century of social turmoil, reconstruction and modernization, the Chinese Society is still a Confucian society in many aspects. Even though it is no longer a predominantly agricultural society,

Confucian ethics prevail in human relations and many of the goals of the political establishment can be defined with reference to Confucian tradition. This is not surprising, considering China's size, huge population and strength of China's long cultural tradition.

In fact, it is not conceivable that China's political upheavals in the 19th and 20th centuries, and the modernization of its economy in recent decades could have erased its cultural background. Thus, modern China can be described as a New China painted on an old Confucian canvas in fresh and vibrant colors.

It is only to be expected, that when Chinese people discuss social issues, politics or even personal issues with Westerners, there often is curious disconnection in the conversation revealing a misunderstanding on fundamental issues. And because of the nature of the misunderstanding, which is obscured by the cultural background, people often start arguing irrelevant points, which makes it difficult to reach an intelligent conclusion.

**Political Impermanence**

A Westerner explaining the advantages of Western Democracy to a Chinese official usually does not realize that the Chinese don't insist on the perfectness of China's political system. Hardly anyone believes that the present regime will last forever.

Thousands of years of historical experience have taught the Chinese people that every regime is subject to cyclical development of growth and decay just like any other process. This is why Confucian scholars give different political advice to officials according to prevailing political conditions. The task of a good official is quite different in times of good governance and peace, 天下有道, or times characterized by chaos, corruption and social unrest, 天下大乱.

The organizational structure of a government is not as important as the moral content and purpose of its governance. According to Confucianism it is the actions and effect of the governance on the welfare and safety of the general public, which decides the legitimacy of a political regime, rather than its formal structure. An effective political structure helps to carry out policies and ensure smooth development of the society in a complicated situation, but it is not decisive.

**Western Tools of Change**

At the end of the Qing dynasty, in late 19th century and at the beginning of 20th century, many prominent Chinese intellectuals believed that Western Liberalism and Democracy was the key to renovating China. But it is doubtful if the nature of their belief in Liberalism was the same as that of Western Liberalists who looked at Liberalism as the final blueprint for political development in the future. More likely the Chinese "Liberalists" looked at Liberalism as a useful tool to reform China rather than an all-embracing doctrine for all the future.

As a matter of fact, most of the Chinese Liberalists became disillusioned with Western Liberalism after the First World War and the Treaty of Versailles in 1919, when the Democratic Countries in Western Europe agreed to transfer German assets and territories in China to Japan. The radical Chinese intelligentsia soon turned to other doctrines for national salvation. Socialism or Communism soon became rather popular because of the influence of the newly established Soviet Union, which promised a different political path based on a "scientific social theory" that would take China towards Socialism, which was claimed to be a more advanced social system than Capitalism.

It is doubtful if the pioneers of Chinese Socialism really believed in all the aspects of the Marx-Leninist doctrine. In retrospect, the idea of a perfectly balanced and classless communist society, which would herald the end of historical development, seems quite alien to traditional Chinese thinking. The metaphysical belief in the existence of the historical culmination of political development in a perfect, or almost perfect, political system goes against the traditional Chinese view on historical development characterized by cyclical rise of new political regimes on the back of social unrest and chaos after the fall a previous dynasty. It is true that the Taiping revolution was based on some similar assumptions about the future, but it did not exactly succeed in that regard.

It now seems obvious that the leaders of the Chinese Communist revolutionary movement viewed communism as a tool for reforming China rather than a goal in it self or an ideological gospel that could not be changed.

The task at hand was to change China from a backward agricultural society into a modern industrial power, raising China from poverty and humiliation to its traditional positions as a leading world power.

When the ideological tool did not deliver the requested results, it was modified for the task at hand. This is a major reason for frequent revisions in the doctrine of Chinese Marxist ideology making it more pragmatic than the Occidental schools of Marxism.

**Political Dogma with Confucian Characteristics**

The difference between the dogma of Chinese and Western Marxism does not only stem from the Chinese pragmatic approach to political theories. There are many similarities between Chinese traditional thought and the philosophical premises of Marxism. Karl Marx himself pointed this out in an article published in Neue Rheinische Zeitung, in February1850, where he claims that "*It may well be that Chinese Socialism is related to European Socialism, just as Chinese philosophy is related to Hegelian philosophy.*"

The Chinese Scholar, Tsong-I Dow (Tou) made a study on the philosophical similarities between Confucianism and Marxism in a book published in 1977 by the University Press of America (Confucianism vs. Marxism: An Analytical Comparison of the Confucian and Marxian Theories of Knowledge-Dialectical Materialism). In this book Professor Tou shows that there are in fact many similarities between these two theories. He concludes that this is indeed a major factor in the conversion of many Chinese Confucianists to Marxism.

These similarities made it possible for Chinese radicals to adopt Marxism as an ideology without transforming their Confucian way of thinking as radically as many have supposed.

Furthermore, at the beginning of the communist movement in China, only a few Marxist texts had been translated into Chinese. Most of them had been translated from Japanese, and an attempt had been made to make them easier to understand by using some traditional Chinese Concepts. For instance, the Chinese word for "revolution" is *geming*, 革命, which has a strong traditional reference. Strictly, it should be translated as "Separation from Destiny" or "Losing the Mandate" of Heaven to govern the state, i.e. losing the capacity to rule. Losing the Mandate of Heaven meant that the government had lost the trust of its people, leading to social chaos, natural calamities, rebellions and insecure borders. Overthrowing such a government was right and proper, because it did not fit the concept of real government. Such a situation could only be rectified by the establishment of a new regime, which enjoyed the support of the people, bringing prosperity, peace and security to its subjects. In Confucianism this can be called "rectification of names", 正名, (see the Analects, XIII 3 and XII 11 for reference).

It can be argued, that the Liberation of China in 1949 constituted a rectification of names, establishing a new government with the support of its subjects, giving freedom to the people to carry out the tasks inherent in the name of their class. More recently, the emphasis on unification of China can also be described as rectification of names.

Thus, the early Chinese communists interpreted Marx-Leninism with reference to traditional Chinese thinking and philosophy. Debate on revolutionary policies and Marxist theory frequently turned into a debate on the correctness or relevance of ancient schools of Chinese philosophy. Confucian ideas would be dressed up in Marxist jargon or Marxist philosophy would be discussed using quotations from the Chinese classics. This practice continued to the very end of the Mao era in seventies.

**Red Peasant Revolution**

In spite of the Marxist rhetoric, the Chinese Communist Revolution was basically a Peasant Revolution. Li Dazhao (1888 -1927), the co-founder of the Chinese Communist Party together with Chen Duxiu (1879-1942) held that the peasantry would become the main force of the socialist revolution in China. This emphasis on the revolutionary role of the Chinese peasantry by Li Dazhao and his ideas on the dialectical interaction of social and material forces where influenced by traditional Chinese philosophy.

The theory of peasants playing a major role in a socialist revolution went against the Marx-Leninist orthodoxy, which emphasizes the role of the industrial proletariat. The stress on the importance of the peasants as a revolutionary force was not well received by the leadership of the Third International and the Communist Party of the Soviet Union. The Chinese Communist Party was ordered to focus on the cities and the countryside was neglected with disastrous results for the Chinese Communists. When the Chinese Communist Party got caught up in the power struggle between Trotsky and Stalin in 1927, it was all but wiped out. The communists were forced into the countryside, were it eventually came under the leadership of Mao Zedong.

It may be argued that, when Mao Zedong took over the leadership of the Chinese Communist Party in 1935, Marxism with Chinese Characteristics became the main ideology of Chinese Communist movement. Later it became known as Mao Zedong Thought, but many of its characteristics where manifest earlier.

After Mao's takeover there was no longer any doubt about the importance of the peasantry. The Chinese revolution turned into a Red Peasant Revolution. Thus the restructuring of "New China on the Confucian Canvas" of China's past got a new momentum with socialist slogans under the red festive banners of the communism.

In this context, it might be mentioned that the red colour has a different symbolic meaning in China than in the West where it stands for fierce struggle and bloodshed. In China the colour "red" is the festive colour of celebrations and brides on the way to their wedding.

**Dialectics**

In general, Chinese are dialectically thinking. The Chinese do not doubt the universality of contradictions as a driving force behind all change or development. This is in accordance with the Chinese concepts of Yin and Yang, which coexist within everything. There is a constant change in balance between these two aspects during the life cycle of all phenomena. The nature and mechanisms of these changes are explained in the Book of Change in rather obscure language.

Mao Zedong used Marxist terminology to modify and explain these ideas in his philosophical essay "On Contradictions", in 1937, which had a huge impact on the development of Chinese Socialism and the Communist Party of China. Mao uses concrete and easily understandable examples of the interaction of the two aspects of contradictions. Furthermore, he differentiates between different types of contradictions turning them into practical instruments of his policies.

It is probable that Chinese concept of internal contradictions as the force behind development and change, was brought to Europe by Jesuits in the 18th century. This in turn may have given rise to the emergence of dialectical theory among German Philosophers, including Hegel, which was later brought back to China through Marxism.

Mao's theory on contradictions does not seem to contradict the dialectical concepts of Yin and Yang or the Book of Change, even though the terminology is different. However, it does differ from the Marx-Leninist dialectics, especially as presented by Soviet theoreticians during the Stalin era.

The Hegelian dialectical process can be presented by three dialectical stages of development: a thesis, where internal changes in quantity give rise to antithesis, which contradicts or negates the theses by a change in quality through synthesis. This formulation indicates the absence of internal contradiction during the initial stage of change in quantity. Mao refutes this by stating that *difference constitutes a contradiction* in his article "On Contradictions".

This seemingly trivial difference in terminology constitutes a fundamental difference in philosophical theory. Furthermore, Mao put forward the political idea of "contradictions within the people" which should be handled in a different way to antagonistic contradictions. This made it possible for the Chinese Communists to form wide alliances between different political forces or social classes while admitting the inherent contradictions between them. Furthermore, it made it possible to resolve disputes and contradictions within the party leadership without branding one site of a dispute as class enemies or agents of world capitalism.

**Serving the People**

The slogan *Serve the People*, 为人民服务, coined by Mao Zedong is no doubt the best known political instruction of the late Chairman, which is still frequently quoted by his successors. It is the most resilient remnant of the Maoist ideology.

The clear and simple message of serving the people is easily understandable and accepted by most people. However, it is doubtful if everyone really understands the significance of this slogan. Some may even see it as an instruction for the service industry to be service minded towards its customers.

During the Cultural Revolution the slogan *Serve the People* was seen as a general moral instruction for every citizen to act in service of other people and the interest of society. This usage of the slogan comes close to the meaning of the Confucian concept of *Renyi*, 仁义, which refers to good and morally correct actions. Thus, the Cultural Revolution can maybe be seen as a futile experiment in turning the majority of people into persons of superior morality (君子). At the same time, those who continued to act in accordance with their private interests (小人), where branded "Class Enemies".

Recently, some Chinese leaders have made a slight modification in the slogan in order to focus on its significance, 为民服务, leaving out the character, 人, which does not change the meaning but forces people to think about its significance.

Mao Zedong first used the slogan in 1944 in a speech he held in the memory of Zhang Side, a soldier of the Guards Regiment of the Central Committee of the Chinese Communist Party, who died carrying out his duties on behalf of the revolutionary government in Yanan. "If we have shortcomings, we are not afraid to have them pointed out and criticized, because *we serve the people*." It is obvious that he is referring to the soldiers and officials of the revolutionary government.

The identification of *Serve the People* as the objective of the Government is basically a modern periphrasis of the Confucian principle of *Treasuring the People*, 民为贵, (Mencius), identifying the people as the most important element in the state. Mao's slogan echoes Sun Yatsen's principle, *The State is for the Public*, 天下为公, which could also be translated as "The World should be for the Public". And more recently, in the year 2003, Chairman Hu Jintao found it necessary to remind the CPC that its political power is based on the people, *Put the People First*, 以人为本.

The proclamation of *Serve the People* as the main role of a communist government goes against the Marx-Leninist concept of the *Dictatorship of the Proletariat*, whereby the main task of the state is defined as repression of hostile classes.

Mao introduced the concept of *People's Democratic Dictatorship* in 1949, to express his idea of the *Supremacy of the People* in the state. However, because of an ideological shift to the left and pressure from the political debate with the Soviet Union, the concept of the Dictatorship of the Proletariat was later put into the constitution of China. But in 1982 China reverted back to the formulation of the *People's Democratic Dictatorship*.

Thus, in spite of fierce attacks on Confucianism in the early decades of the People's Republic of China, it may be argued that the mandate to rule China is based on the Confucian principle of the *People being the Most Valuable* asset of the state, 民为贵; or the words of Confucius, "Without the trust of the people, there is nothing", 民无信不立, (the Analects of Confucius, 12.7).

**Challenging Destiny**

While Mao' ideology was clearly influenced by Chinese traditional thinking and Confucianism, there is no doubt he was also affected by Western radicalism and Marxism in particular. But in spite of the Marx-Leninist rhetoric, his ideas and policies can usually be explained with reference to Chinese history and traditional Chinese ideologies or concepts, some of which are not Confucian in origin. Sometimes he would refer to Legalist tradition, 法家, Daoism, 道家, or other ancient Chinese schools of thought.

For instance, there is no doubt that Mao Zedong was aware of the traditional meaning of the Chinese term for revolution, 革命, *Separation from Destiny*. However, he insisted on making *Continuous Revolution* a guiding principle for his regime, a constant factor, which would continue after he had taken power. Taken literally in the Chinese, the idea of*Continuous Separation from Destiny*, 继续革命, seems to be a contradiction in terms. But Marxism has a similar concept, *Permanent Revolution*, 不断革命, advocated by Trotsky in opposition to Stalin in the Soviet Union.

When Mao first raises the theory of *Continuous Revolution* in the debate against Soviet Union in 1958 there does seem to be some similarity to Trotskyism. In one respect these theories are in agreement, that is, on the danger of a counter-revolution from within lead by counter-revolutionary party officials or "bourgeoisie continuing to attempt capitalist restorations after they have been overthrown from power" (The Political report to the $9^{th}$ Congress of CCP, 1969). However, there are some fundamental differences in these two theories. Trotsky viewed the peasantry as a politically unreliable class, which would turn against the revolution, and he believed that Socialism in One Country was a practical and theoretical impossibility.

In retrospect, it seems possible, that the purpose of Mao's *Continuous Revolution* was indeed to *challenge destiny* like to the concept indicates in Chinese. He believed that the regime was in danger of internal degeneration, which would lead to its collapse in the same way as previous regimes. By continuous revolution, social development would be accelerated and the government would be continuously renewed. Thus the destiny of previous regimes might be avoided. From the dialectical viewpoint of traditional Chinese thought this is somewhat like trying to conquer death.

*Ragnar Baldursson is an Icelandic Diplomat presently working in China. He studied Beijing* 1975-1979, *graduating in philosophy from Beijing University in* 1979. *Thus he became the first student from West Europe undergraduate student to graduate from a Chinese University after the Cultural Revolution. This essay expresses he personal views and reflection.*

# Representing Tradition: An Analysis of Tu Weiming's Confucianism

**Ralph Weber (URPP Asia and Europe, University of Zurich)**

Over the last few decades, Tu Weiming (杜维明) has been an exceptionally vocal and most prominent representative of the Confucian tradition, perhaps even its foremost representative if measured against impact in institutions on a global scale. This is a widely accepted characterization. Whenever Tu delivers a speech or is otherwise introduced by third parties, the characterization as "representative" of Confucianism is near at hand. Being a representative amounts to the claim or even the right or duty of a person to stand for, speak, or act on behalf of some group of people, an institutional body or-as in the present case-something as clear or vague as a tradition.

Representation comes in different shapes and styles and it is thus that we say that a guardian *represents* the ward and a parliamentarian the people of a district or that an athlete *represents* a country at an international competition and a sales representative a company towards its customers. The representative may be free to represent as he or she deems fit or may be (or merely feel) bound by a clearly specified mandate. In many instances, it is interests that are being represented, whereby these interests do not necessarily have to be confined to those of existing human communities or institutions. Sometimes interests of non-human animals find themselves represented, and so do the interests of past or future generations. This also makes it clear that those represented do not have to be aware that they are being represented, let alone endorse how they are being represented. The case of representing a tradition is still different, since the notion of a tradition is notoriously difficult to grasp. It is hence rather unclear who or what is being represented and in what sense one could come to think that it is interests that are being represented. Perhaps being a representative of a tradition means to have the authority to define the tradition and to determine what it is that is being represented.

There are at least three different ways of approaching the question of whom or what represents a tradition. One way would be to adopt an insider view and to discuss what the tradition itself considers to be a representative of the tradition. With regard to the Confucian tradition, this would probably require some conceptual work on the notion of *daotong* 道统. There exists much scholarly literature on this notion and I do not seek to contribute to that literature. A second way is to look at the question of representation of a tradition from the outside, say, from the viewpoint of sociology, history or philosophy. In this paper, a recent debate in social epistemology on the question of true succession in a tradition is revisited and discussed. The positions defended in the debate allow us to sketch a theoretical framework against which we can question whether Tu Weiming is a true successor to Confucius or a representative of Confucianism, whether these two are the same or rather different questions, and whether the question is rightly posed if one is after understanding how Tu Weiming represents Confucianism if and to the extent that he is indeed representing it. A third way is to examine the matter of fact representation of a tradition to institutional bodies, the interested public, followers of the tradition, etc. In this paper, I will sketch some of the forums in which Tu Weiming has acted as a 'representative' of Confucianism and scrutinize what 'Confucianism' it is that he has chosen to represent. To this end, I shall analyse two sets of his writings (ten scholarly articles all written before 1979 and one introductory overview of about ninety pages on Confucianism written 1993), each addressing a different audience, but each out to represent Confucianism in one or another way. The goal of this exercise is not to judge how warranted, accurate or original Tu's representation of the Confucian tradition is, but to gain further understanding of how traditions are actually represented in the contemporary world, whose peace and development is the stated main concern of the present academic conference commemorating the 2565$^{th}$ anniversary of Confucius' birthday.

## I. TRUE SUCCESSORS AND REPRESENTATIVES

### § 1: A Confucian Precursor Debate (1980-88)

Although separated by several years, three articles appeared in *Philosophy East and West* in the 1980s, each later article referring to the earlier one(s) in what might be understood as a sort of mini-debate. The first article was written by Philip Ho

Hwang, who sought to challenge a reading of Confucius as a philosopher of human nature in the same vein, albeit perhaps more implicit and concise, as Mencius. Confucius rather should be understood "as a man of action whose philosophy was not based on any theory of human nature, but on what human beings *do*."① Hwang objects to a traditional historical argument that followed Mencius' own profession of him being the "'true' successor of Confucius" and that later in the Song dynasty made him into the second sage. The textual basis is in *Mengzi* 2A:2 and reads in Legge's translation, which Hwang uses:

可以仕則仕,可以止則止,可以久則久,可以速則速,孔子也。皆古聖人也,吾未能有行焉;乃所願,則學孔子也。

When it was proper to go into office, then go into it; when it was proper to keep retired from office, then keep retired from it; when it was proper to continue in it long, then continue in it long; when it was proper to withdraw from it quickly, then withdraw quickly:-that was the way of Confucius. These were all sages of antiquity, and I have not attained to do what they did. But what I wish to do is to learn to be like Confucius.

For Hwang, this is a very weak basis for saying that Mencius professed to be Confucius' *true successor*. Given the specific wording of this passage and also the fact that Mencius comes to say *this* in *Mengzi* 2A:2 only after having been pressured repeatedly into taking a stand as to whether he is a sage like Confucius was a sage, Hwang certainly has a point. For Hwang, the main dividing issue regards the theory of human nature. Confucius, he writes, "was not much interested in any theory of human nature or any problems related to human nature," and those who argue otherwise and from there conclude that Mencius "represented an advance over Confucius" or "took a big step forward" with regard to the theory of human nature trip into the pitfall of believing Mencius' self-presentation of standing also in this specific regard in a longer tradition. In fact, Hwang concludes, Mencius "misrepresented Confucius in a very important sense."②

In direct response to Hwang, Martin Lu challenged the denial of true succession

① Philip Ho Hwang, "A New Interpretation of Confucius," Philosophy East and West 30, no. 1 (1980): 45.

② Hwang, 1980, 52-53.

contending "that there is a solid theoretical foundation for Mencius' claim and its acceptance by Confucian scholars that the former was a true successor of Confucius."① Lu objects to Hwang on two accounts, one regarding the specific contents of Confucius' and Mencius' views on human nature and one concerning the conceptualization of true succession. The first is less persuasive. Lu takes Hwang's exclusive focus on the *Lunyu* as mistakenly narrow and claims that the inclusion of the *Daxue* and the *Zhongyong* as expressions of Confucius' views on human nature would have made it obvious that Mencius is offering a *different* but more elaborate analysis of the *same* issue of human nature and therefore justly is considered a true successor. The close link between the *Daxue* and the *Zhongyong* and the historical person of Confucius and his views seems difficult to sustain. What to do, for instance, with Youzi and Zengzi quarrelling about what the Master really said, as is also recorded in the *Liji* (Tan Gong)? Clearly, true succession was already in dispute among the very first generation of Confucius' disciples.② But, more importantly, Lu appears to have misunderstood Hwang's claim from the outset. He argues that it is simply wrong to expect Mencius to offer "a duplicate version of Confucius's view" on human nature and natural to assume development.③ But Hwang is not denying development on the basis that they both had the same view on human nature, nor is he saying that they should have had the same view in order to have Mencius qualify for a true successor. Hwang is saying that Confucius was not interested in having a view on human nature. A *theory* of human nature was not among his concerns, whereas it was among Mencius' concerns. So to be a true successor and to warrant talk of development, Mencius and Confucius should at least have been concerned with the same things, but in Hwang's opinion they were not.

Lu's response to Hwang is more interesting for its theoretical work on what true succession could possibly imply. Lu is certainly right to dismiss a view of a "genuine successor-master relationship" as necessitating the two to hold identical "ideas and doctrines," since a "successor is always allowed room for development and innova-

---

① Martin Lu, "Was Mencius a True Successor of Confucius?," *Philosophy East and West* 33, no. 1 (1983): 79.

② In the Mencius, several disciples (but not Zengzi) are said to have been willing to accept Youzi as their new master because of his resemblance to Confucius (*Mengzi* 3A:4).

③ Ibid.

tion."[1] In his considerations, Lu comes to frame the issue of true succession in different terminology, thereby opening up a variety of conceptualizations. At one instance, he writes that what is really at stake is "whether the embryonic ideas of the *Analects* [Lunyu] on the matter are *amenable* to further development along Mencius' line."[2] A criterion for amenability is given in that the matter in question "can be better understood from Mencius' theoretical perspective than from other parallel theories."[3] The parallel theory that Lu has in mind is of course Xunzi, whose thought on human nature Lu (following D. C. Lau) thinks less "*consonant* with Confucius' ideas" than Mencius' thought is.[4] Yet, amenability perhaps and consonance surely could also be ascertained between the thought of two thinkers completely unaware of each other. This is not what true succession should mean for Mencius and Confucius, and Lu accordingly speaks of Mencius as a "*faithful* follower of Confucius."[5] The element of faith offers a second criterion besides "the *adoption* of some central ideas", where it seems that adoption stands for developing ideas that remain consonant (adaptation rather than adoption might have been more accurate).[6] The second criterion is "eagerness in commitment on the part of Mencius to carry on and transmit the flame of the master's philosophical torch."[7] Lu does not mean to confine the master's philosophical torch to philosophical doctrine narrowly understood, but Mencius is said to share "the master's moral commitment" towards the centrality of humanity as a moral ideal.[8] More precisely, Mencius' professed will "to learn to be like Confucius" encompasses the "*emulation of the master's personality* and general moral principles and commitment."[9] It has of course often been emphasized that this moral commitment is part and parcel of the Confucian philosophical doctrine, and a carrying on and transmitting of an abstracted set of philosophical principles would be pointless. But emulating the master's personality seems not only putting the benchmark very high, but also

---

① Ibid.

② Ibid., 80 (my emphasis).

③ Ibid., 81.

④ Ibid., 80 (my emphasis).

⑤ Ibid., 81 (my emphasis).

⑥ Ibid. (my emphasis).

⑦ Ibid.

⑧ Ibid.

⑨ Ibid., 79 (my emphasis).

offering a model that appears not to find support e.g. in *Lunyu* 11:4 by the master himself.① In the end, we are still left in the dark as to what true succession would exactly amount to in the case of Confucius and Mencius as well as more generally.

John N. Williams's article takes up Hwang and Lu and offers an argument with regard to Confucius and Mencius (Mencius turns out not to be a true successor), but it is more centrally interested in the "relation that is sometimes called 'true succession'."② Williams also speaks out against the idea that a true successor would have to uphold ideas and doctrines identical with those of the master, which would straightforwardly be "plagiarism" or the outcome of the rare coincidence of two minds having arrived at the same view.③ True succession, Williams asserts, presupposes that "the successor is *influenced* by the predecessor" and-what is a further and in my view more controversial claim-that the "central ideas" of successor and predecessor "are *not* identical"; they must differ in their "central ideas", while they might have similar views in "peripheral" aspects.④ Yet, while differ they must, they are not allowed to differ to the extent of holding *inconsistent* views. Based on these and other observations, Williams comes to offer an analysis of true succession in terms of necessary and sufficient conditions:

B is a true successor of A if and only if

(a) The central ideas of B were developed after those of A.

(b) The central ideas of A are consistent with those of B.

(c) B understood the ideas of A.

(d) A would, *ceteris paribus*, have developed more or less the same central ideas as those actually developed by B.

(e) The central ideas of A are not identical with those of B.

This, at best, is a rather intricate set of conditions. (b) and (e) seem to give ex-

---

① *Lunyu* 11:4: 子曰:回也非助我者也,於吾言無所不說。[D.C. Lau: The Master said, ? Hui is no help to me at all. He is pleased with everything I say.]

② John N. Williams, "Confucius, Mencius, and the Notion of True Succession," *Philosophy East and West* 38, no. 2 (1988): 157.

③ Ibid., 158.

④ Ibid. This strikes me as very far from how traditions and succession in them often empirically work, where true succession would be reserved for the person who differs in peripheral aspects, but holds on to the central ideas. It seems important that Williams at one point frames his topic as being about "intellectual successors." See: Ibid., 157.

pression to the idea of the successor and the predecessor holding different, but not inconsistent views. But what are we to make of the "more or less" in (d)? Does (d) not put much emphasis on the power of contextual factors in the development of the central ideas from A to B and little emphasis on that A and B might have intellectually reacted differently to those contextual factors? From what perspective should one distinguish central from peripheral ideas? And how could one check whether (c) holds true? Would that check not in turn rely again on matters such as the consistency of their central ideas? And is it really inconceivable that B would hold *some few* inconsistent central ideas, which make his central ideas being not identical with those of A? How plausible is the idea of (e), holding *different* views on central ideas that (b) do not amount to an inconsistency between the central ideas of A and B? Finally, at what point does the difference that warrants a claim for development become so large that it is more appropriate to speak of a new tradition rather than a succession of an older tradition? Again, in the end, despite Williams's welcome attempt at offering a set of criteria for determining true succession, we are left with more questions than answers.① For one thing, Williams seems to dither between an interest in "*a* true successor" and "*the* true successor",② but which of these one is after makes a lot of difference, as the recent debate in social epistemology on traditions and true successors illustrates.

**§ 2: The Recent Debate in Social Epistemology (2013-14)**

Crediting Williams's as "one of the very few philosophical articles on true succession and related issues", David-Hillel Ruben has recently sparked a debate in the journal *Social Epistemology* by relating the topic to the matter of social disputes over true

---

① Williams's conceptualization of true succession suffers from a set of assumptions having to do with the fuzziness of ? central ideas", so that "consistency" in them becomes a slippery affair. The conceptualization would perhaps benefit from spelling out more clearly what is meant by consistency and in what regard consistency is sought. Williams is determined to argue that "true succession is *not a transitive relation*", which he undergirds by saying that consistency as such is not transitive, which it seems is true enough if no respect is determined along which the transitivity is measured, but if indeed the consistency regards the *same* respect across cases, then it would seem that an argument for consistency as being transitive could be produced. See: Ibid. , 161.

② Ibid. , cf. 157 and 161.

succession in the context of traditions.[①] Ruben states his guiding question most succinctly in the abstract of his article:

How can different parties to a dispute in aesthetics, history, politics or religion, either individuals or groups, each claim, apparently with at least some justification, that it, but not its rival(s), is the true or authentic successor or later representative for some earlier group or individual, or that it, but not its rival(s) stands in the same authentic tradition as the earlier one?[②]

The question raises several different issues, since we are still unclear whether a true successor and a representative are the same thing, while the mere "stand[ing] in the same authentic tradition" very clearly introduces a new aspect. The new aspect is peripheral to the concerns of the present paper, and I will not pursue it here, but it should be mentioned that Ruben in his article sometimes speaks about membership in a tradition, i.e. about "the legitimacy of belonging to a particular tradition."[③] Claiming membership for someone in a tradition is surely different from claiming someone to be a representative of the tradition or a true successor of a master predecessor.

Ruben discusses Williams at some length as a foil against which to formulate his own position. In terms of true succession, Ruben defines the matter as about "faithfulness" and "qualitative similarity" in "beliefs and practices":

A later person or group is more faithful to an earlier person or group, or is its true successor (and not vice versa), the more the latter's beliefs and practices are qualitatively similar to the earlier's beliefs and practices (and not vice versa). Qualitative similarity is a symmetric idea, but true succession or faithfulness is asymmetric.[④]

In stark contrast to Williams, it would seem that for Ruben identity in central ideas or "beliefs and practices" guaranteed the highest possible degree of qualitative similarity and hence of true succession. Ruben is also explicit that whereas he takes true succession to be a "backwards-looking" idea, Williams has conceptualized it as

---

① David-Hillel Ruben, "Traditions and True Successors," *Social Epistemology* 27, no. 1 (2013): 32-46.

② Ibid., 32.

③ Ibid., 33.

④ Ibid., 37. The second bracket remark ("and not vice versa") makes in my view no sense precisely because qualitative similarity is a symmetric idea, as Ruben says it is.

"forward-looking," particularly in light of condition (d).① Ruben ends his observations on true succession by claiming it to be (as Williams claimed it to be) a non-transitive relation,② and adding that it is a "many-one" relation, by which he means that "many distinct groups or thinkers, with different thoughts, ideas, practices, or whatever, might all be true successors of or faithful to A."③ This is an odd statement for Ruben to make since asserting such a relation seems to preclude providing any answer to the guiding question about social dispute over who is and who is not a true successor. Given that Ruben himself admits that "true succession and faithfulness come in degrees" and given his conceptualization of true succession as *the more faithful the more qualitatively similar*, it is rather unlikely that there could be several true successors of A.④It is telling that Ruben in the context of true succession as a "many-one" relation slips into talking about "*a* true successor" whereas his guiding question clearly and rightly is about "*the* true successor."⑤Perhaps Ruben is so quick in accepting true succession to be a "branching concept" because he understands it based on qualitative similarity only.⑥ A later individuals or group with no awareness of the earlier individual or group but in terms of beliefs and practices very much alike for him qualifies as true or authentic successor-but they do not stand in the same tradition. With traditions, Ruben writes, "there must be a causal component in addition to the similarity component."⑦Ruben explains:

They [the latter person or group] do what they do or believe what they do in part because that is what the earlier person did or believed. The 'because' in this is a causal idea.⑧

---

① Ibid., 37-38.

② The bases for Williams's and Ruben's claims for non-transitivity are of course different, since they hold very different views of true succession.

③ Ibid., 39.

④ Ibid., 36. Later in the text, Ruben takes up the same issue with an astonishing insistence since one wonders why it might be so important to argue for the unlikely case of having two groups who can equally lay claim to being true successors. It does not help that Ruben states that "B's and C's beliefs and practices might be equally qualitatively similar to A's, although different from one another's", for it is entirely left in the dark how one would weigh between the alleged similarities and differences, as Ruben himself comes to admit. See: Ibid., 43-44.

⑤ Ibid., cf. 32 and 39.

⑥ Ibid., 39.

⑦ Ibid., 41.

⑧ Ibid.

The beliefs and practices might be passed down from parent to child, learned by emulation, imitation, explicit teaching or whatever. Or, there might only be a text shared by the earlier and the latter groups. Or, in some cases, physical inheritance might be the kind of causal bond that is required, perhaps in the case of groups like Jews or the Romany. ①

Unfortunately, Ruben decides not to elucidate the latter subject any further. It would have been interesting to learn, for example, how a text should be shared by the earlier and later individuals and groups to constitute a tradition, and how that would help determine the true representative. One and the same text (e.g. the Bible) sometimes serves as causal condition in several competing traditions, and the text might play the binding role Ruben describes only in combination with an explicit teaching, physical inheritance and other elements.

Ruben's article ends with the question of dispute and a rather puzzling conclusion, as he comes to state a series of persuasive points directed against the idea of qualitative similarity, which fails to help determining the true successor or representative of a tradition. He also admits that the case of having to later rival groups with equally similar beliefs and practices is not interesting. One cannot but wonder why he chose to give all these issues so much consideration if *this* is the conclusion that he arrives at. Changing freely from talk about true succession, the representation of tradition, to membership in a tradition, Ruben appends an interesting paragraph with a new set of issues to consider:

It is doubtful whether anything useful can be said in a general way about just how qualitatively similar the beliefs and practices of the persons or groups B and C must be, either to each other's or to A's, in order to count as sufficiently similar to conclude that the persons or groups A, B, and C all belong to the same tradition. Each tradition may set the limits of permissible variation for itself, so that the criteria for membership become internal. Moreover, these criteria may not be agreed between the two groups, each of which claims to belong to the same tradition. Each tradition may not speak with a single voice about the limits of permissible variation. Finally, the criteria are themselves susceptible to change over time, since the criteria are them-

① Ibid., 42.

selves really only further beliefs of the groups. ①

The debate that followed the publication of Ruben's article took place online at the journal's own debate forum called *Social Epistemology Review and Reply Collective*. It was Williams himself who was the first to reply to Ruben, but others were quick to join in, and in what follows, I should like to mention some important clarifications made during the ensuing debate. ②

Williams takes the opportunity to sound out the differences between his and Ruben's account of true succession. Whereas Ruben speaks of "beliefs and practices", Williams was solely concerned with ideas. ③ He further points out that "unlike 'tradition', 'true successor' is a term of praise", and concedes to Ruben the better explanation for non-transitivity of true succession. ④ Most importantly, Williams distinguishes the question of true succession from the one of membership in an "intellectual tradition", standing by his opinion that in the former the successor must have made some "valuable advancement" over the predecessor to qualify as a "true" successor,

---

① Ibid., 44.

② John Williams, "David-Hillel Ruben's 'Traditions and True Successors': A Critical Reply," Social *Epistemology Review and Reply Collective* 2, no. 7 (2013): 40-45; David-Hillel Ruben, "Reply to Williams," *Epistemology Review and Reply Collective* 2, no. 8 (2013): 8-9; John Williams, "Further Reflections on True Successors and Traditions," *Epistemology Review and Reply Collective* 2, no. 9 (2013): 12-16; David-Hillel Ruben, "Reply to Williams' Reply," *Epistemology Review and Reply Collective* 2, no. 10 (2013): 21-22; Samuel Lebens, "True Successors and Counterfactual Approval," *Epistemology Review and Reply Collective* 2, no. 10 (2013): 26-32; Jonathan Payton, "Ruben's Account of Traditions and True Successors: Two Modifications and an Extension," *Epistemology Review and Reply Collective* 2, no. 11 (2013): 40-46; Samuel Lebens, "Counterfactual Approval and Idiosyncratic Counterfactual Approval," *Epistemology Review and Reply Collective* 2, no. 11 (2013): 65-69; David-Hillel Ruben, "More on True Succession and Tradition: Replying to Lebens and Payton," *Epistemology Review and Reply Collective* 2, no. 12 (2013): 29-31; Jonathan Payton, "Keeping Successorhood and Inheritance Apart: A Reply to Lebens and Ruben," *Epistemology Review and Reply Collective* 3, no. 1 (2013): 14-19; Martin Beckstein, "Traditions and True Successors: A Few Pragmatic Considerations," *Epistemology Review and Reply Collective* 3, no. 3 (2014): 30-36; David-Hillel Ruben, "Internal and External Perspectives: Reply to Martin Beckstein," *Epistemology Review and Reply Collective* 3, no. 3 (2014): 55-56; Martin Beckstein, "Addressing Ruben's 'Internal and External Perspectives'," *Epistemology Review and Reply Collective* 3, no. 5 (2014): 35-36; David-Hillel Ruben, "A Further Reply to Beckstein," *Epistemology Review and Reply Collective* 3, no. 6 (2014): 94.

③ Williams, "A Critical Reply," 41.

④ Ibid., 43.

which is precisely what makes it different from mere membership.[1] Ruben's rejoinder picks up on Williams's "normative idea" of true succession as advancement and rightly asks for the sort of tribunal that is required to judge "whether something is or is not a theoretical advance"; for Ruben it is not difficult to imagine a later "retrograde or degenerate version" that justly is considered to be a true successor.[2] Williams, of course, is not prepared to subsume such unpraiseworthy successors under the label of true succession.[3] Martin Beckstein introduces an interesting distinction, arguing against Williams's requirement of valuable advancement, but proposing that what is required is "a timely update."[4]

### § 3: Assessing the Debate in Light of the Confucian Tradition

The debate in social epistemology may help approach the question of representation in the case of the Confucian tradition. For one thing, we might want to inquire into what kind of tradition the Confucian tradition exactly is and what surely it is not. In the debate on true succession, a variety of examples has been used, ranging from the initial paradigm case of Confucius and Mencius, to Socrates and Plato, the very different "paradigm example" for Ruben of game championship, Hegel and Marx, the early and the late Wittgenstein, George Washington and Barack Obama, Karl Popper and later Popperians, and even Ruben himself and the readers of his article. The list suggests that it might be advisable to separate the question of intellectual succession in one or another regard and the one of true succession as concerns who is *the* authentic representative for a specific tradition. Still, there are also different kinds of traditions, which might require different yardsticks, as Samuel Lebens has pointed out, who wishes to distinguish between "*intellectual traditions*" on the one side and "*religious*, *cultural*, and/or *national* traditions" on the other.[5] It is also Lebens who has introduced into the debate the notion of authority, when he temporarily considers

---

① Ibid., 44.

② Ruben, "Reply to Williams," 9.

③ Williams, "Further Reflection," 15. Beckstein advises to follow Williams in this, since "no person or group will ever raise a claim to true successorhood by asserting to have developed a retrograde (or degenerate) version of the earlier set of beliefs and/or practices." See: Beckstein, "Pragmatic Considerations," 32.

④ Beckstein, "Pragmatic Considerations," 32.

⑤ Lebens, "Counterfactual Approval," 66.

the example of George Washington and Barack Obama (which Jonathan Payton objects to as not constituting a tradition[①]), from which he comes to highlight the importance of "offices of authority" in political and religious traditions, particularly "a certain chain of transmission in authority."[②] Lebens's example is the "Jewish tradition," for which the neat and elegant analyses and conditions produced in the debate on true succession might simply not work, because it seems that such real traditions are "much more difficult to tame."[③] Lebens adds:

Certain traditions view certain historical personages as authoritative. So, when disputes emerge between competing splinter groups, they are almost bound to appeal to the counterfactual approval of those authoritative personages, however idiosyncratic and subjective that approval might be.[④]

This line of reasoning is also pushed by Beckstein, who-as quoted above-rejected to accept retrograde or degenerate versions of an earlier set of beliefs and/or practices since "no person or group will ever raise a claim to true successorhood" on such a basis.[⑤] It is telling for this recent debate in social epistemology that exactly at the point where the debate seemed to move towards including a better sense and understanding of living traditions Ruben in his replies to Lebens and Beckstein retracts to a distinction between an internal and an external perspective on tradition, claiming that he was interested in the external perspective only, in what he also calls an "'objective' perspective."[⑥] This is dissatisfying and a bit ironic since Ruben himself-as also quoted above-introduced the internal perspective in his conclusion of the debate-inspiring original article ("…criteria for membership become internal"). Beckstein is certainly right in insisting on the importance of external *and* internal perspectives and on the possibility of merging them.[⑦]

It is not that the question who is a true successor or a representative of a tradition (or even a mere member) is without use or intellectual appeal if assessed from an ex-

① Payton, "Reply to Lebens and Ruben," 14-15.

② Lebens, "Counterfactual Approval," 67.

③ Ibid., 68.

④ Ibid., 68-69.

⑤ Beckstein, "Pragmatic Considerations," 32.

⑥ Ruben, "Reply to Martin Beckstein," 55.

⑦ Beckstein, "Internal and External Perspectives," 35.

ternal perspective only, even though Ruben himself-it deserves repetition-explicitly considers the use "doubtful" at best when it comes to assessing traditions.[①] Its use for the investigation of concrete cases might however be considerably impaired. A purely transcendental external examination seems to operate aloof from the very world that it seeks to address. In view of the world in which disputes over the question who can lay claim to being the true successor (or being the real representative) arise, it is true some external perspective must be brought into play, since from any one internal perspective the case might be decided before it is examined. Mind that there are many settings in which representatives of traditions meet and do exactly what they are said to do, namely represent their respective traditions, and where the plurality of traditions, each having internal criteria to decide about true succession and the other issues, is no less than an acknowledged fact. Such acknowledgment, however, presupposes that there are indeed external perspectives of some relevance. One way is to arrive at an external perspective by relying on rationality. Another way to arrive at an external perspective is to examine several internal perspectives and see in what ways they relate to each other so as to warrant talk of them as constituting traditions in some same sense. The latter way has the benefit of appearing less aloof, more relevant to the world that our debates should want to address. In any case, it seems that the phenomena of true succession and the representation of tradition, especially inasmuch as they refer not only to theory but also to actual practices of representation and actual claims of true succession, have thus far received insufficient attention. By turning to a concrete case of a commonly acknowledged representative (i.e. Tu Weiming) of a commonly acknowledged tradition (i.e. Confucianism) and asking how exactly it is that the former represents the latter, this paper seeks to contribute to the theoretical debates in social epistemology, to be sure, but also addresses the matter from a markedly more practical side.

## II. HOW DOES TU WEIMING REPRESENT THE CONFUCIAN TRADITION?

### § 5: Textual Analyses

It would be tempting to analyse all of Tu's writings for just how Confucianism is represented in them as a tradition. Given the amount of writing that Tu has produced

---

① Ruben, "Traditions and True Successors," 44.

in his long career, this would be a Herculean task. But it is unclear whether it would be helpful. Such an analysis would belie the fact that Tu, like any good writer, obviously tailors his writing to the specific audience that he is out to address and offers a version of the Confucian tradition that he continues changing as he continues making sense of it and studying it. There are many genres of texts by Tu addressing a variety of audiences and worthy of further analysis, and a fully analysis no doubt should include as many as possible: scholarly writing in English; scholarly writing in Chinese; texts for the United Nations and related organizations such as UNESCO; dialogues with 'representatives of other traditions'; interviews in glossy magazines and newspaper articles; audio and video material, etc. In what follows, I will merely analyse two different sets of writings, each of which quite evidently seeks to address a different audience and each of which has been written at a different point in time of Tu's academic career.

(1) *Humanity and Self-Cultivation* (1979)

The writings to be analysed (cf. Appendix A1) have all been published before 1979. All of them are in terms of genre scholarly writing, mostly published in academic journals and edited volumes. It would seem that, insofar as Tu seeks to represent the Confucian tradition in these writings, the sort of representation would have to be the one of a Confucian scholar operating in a contemporary, largely American, academic environment. The audience is clearly preconceived by the chosen publication organs as itself scholarly and academic.

The results of the different analyses (cf. A2, A3) are not very surprising for the reader familiar with Tu's writings. Some names that appear frequently under this analysis (e.g. Zhu Xi, Qian Mu) would certainly turn out to be less conspicuous in an overall picture of Tu's oeuvre. Their prominence is due to writings in the sample with a specific focus on them. Other than that, the picture showcases Tu's favourite Confucian personae. What might be of particular import is the occurrence of names of scholars associated with Western academia: Immanuel Kant, Soren Kierkegaard, Max Weber, Gabriel Marcel, Robert Bellah, Herbert Fingarette, and there would be many other names if we were to include the names occurring less than five times (cf. A3). Some of these names are certainly referred to in order to draw out a contrast and thus give profile to the Confucian tradition. Others, however-and these are especially telling for how Tu represents Confucianism-are used to articulate the idiosyncratic version of Confucianism that Tu presents (Gabriel Marcel, Robert Bellah) to his audiences. In fact, the amount to which Tu adopts vocabulary from his teachers and immediate academic peers in the United States to give expression to his version of the Confucian tradition can hardly be overestimated. The most striking example is his adoption of expressions similarly deployed by Wilfred Cantwell Smith (mentioned twice in the sample), as illustrated in what follows on the basis of Smith's *Faith and Belief: The Difference between Them* (1987): "to become creatively involved" (p. 5), ? faith, then, is engagement" (p. 5), ? existential commitment" (p. 66), ? self-transformational character of the action" (p. 74), "taking an existentially decisive step" (p. 74), "cosmic self-commitment" (p. 120), "to be Jewish is to be human" (p. 136), "critical corporate self-consciousness" (p. 148). Tu uses "communal critical self-consciousness" and has taken the notion "learning to be human" to be the very expression of what Confucianism as well as other religious traditions are about, the *differentia specifica* of Confucianism being its emphasis on education.

(2) "Confucianism" in *Our Religions* (1993)

*Presentation before Representation*

In Arvind Sharma's introductory volume to the seven world religions, the Confucian tradition is already presented in several important ways before Tu and his chapter enters the scene. On the cover, it is said that each "religion" is introduced by a "preeminent schola[r] from each tradition", which is saying quite a bit since it makes clear that in the editor's or the publishing house's understanding, each religion makes for one tradition (Hindu, Buddhist, Confucian, Daoist, Jewish, Christian, and Islamic), while it would be equally possible to understand each religion as quite naturally composed of several traditions (e.g. the Greek Orthodox, the Catholic, the Protestant Christian traditions). At the back side of the volume, one learns further that the publication is an outcome of the 1993 Parliament of the World's Religions and the eminent philosopher of religion and advocate of religious pluralism John Hicks is quoted praising the book for "that each of the great world religions is described by someone who is committed to that religion and lives within it, but who is at the same time fully at home in the modern Western academic study of religion … insiders who can speak to outsiders on the common wavelength of our contemporary academic culture." This is the characterization of the volume that is also presented by the editor in his introduction, but the editor is more explicit that the contributors are not only experts that happen to be members of the respective tradition, but that they are understood to represent that tradition: "…each author belong to the tradition he is writing about, he speaks not only *of* his tradition, but his standing in the field enables him also to speak *for* it."[①] Representation is here claimed because of the scholar's "standing in the field", by which is meant the academic study of religions, and one might conjecture that the scholars are taken in their capacity as representing their traditions specifically for this field, while it must remain unclear whether they are also understood as representing their traditions at large, say, over against all academic fields or even beyond academia over against all possible groups outside of their tradition, and whether they would be understood as representing their tradition over against the members of their tradition.

*Tu's Representation of the Confucian Tradition as a World Religion*

The chapter is fairly long, almost ninety pages, and Tu offers a rather comprehensive discussion of the Confucian tradition in terms of the topics addressed (cf. Appendix B1) and the names of Confucians mentioned and introduced (cf. B2)-although surely any discussion and list of names included is likely to face rightful objection. In what follows, I focus on two issues of representation that I find particularly conspicuous in this specific chapter of Tu.

The first issue has to do directly with the presentation of the Confucian tradition as a world religion. Tu is clearly representing Confucianism as a world religion and the text is full of formulations such as "Confucian spirituality", "the Confucian persuasion", "Confucian faith", "Confucian belief", "Confucian scriptural tradition,", etc. To be sure, this is a characterization of Confucianism that Tu (following Tang Junyi, Mou Zongsan, and others) has propagated himself for a long time before writing this chapter. It remains one of his key points in what he takes Confucianism to be. In the text, in an attempt to explain how Confucianism is rightly part in the volume on world religions but also differs from the other included religions, Tu presents some of his well-known characterizations about how exactly Confucianism is religious, but not itself an "organized," "institutionalized," or "worship-centered religion" (pp. 145 and 147). Confucius, he declares, "was neither a prophet with privileged access to the

---

① Arvind Sharma, "Introduction," in *Our Religions*, ed. Arvind Sharma (New York: HarperCollins, 1993), xi.

divine nor a philosopher who has already seen the truth, but a teacher of humanity who is an advanced fellow traveler on the way to self-realization" (p. 185). Still, Confucian thinkers are "profoundly religious" due to the role of "Heaven as a source for moral creativity, meaning of life, and ultimate self-transformation" (p. 145). "Significantly different" from Christianity, Buddhism, or Islam, Confucianism rests on a "calling comparable in intensity of feeling and seriousness of purpose to any of the great world religions" (pp. 145-46). There is a "transcendent dimension" to Confucianism, since "the human Way is sanctioned by Heaven" (p. 203). When presenting some "salient features of the Confucian spiritual orientation," Tu makes it clear that he is fully aware of his audience and for whom he is representing Confucianism in this chapter: "… we may wonder what significance this distinctively Confucian spiritual orientation really has for students in the comparative study of religion (p. 198). Confucianism defies "the conceptual apparatuses widely employed in religious studies", which Tu says is "obvious," while of course he is precisely out to give expression to the Confucian tradition as a world religion for the benefit and understanding of students in religious studies (in vocabulary drawn from scholars working in this field as reference above). The extent to which Tu is ready to present Confucianism as a *religion* is manifest in the way he chooses to end his chapter, which is by offering a "New Confucian articulation of faith, as inspired by Confucius, Mencius, Tung-Chung-shu, Chu His, Wang Yang-ming, and the New Confucians" (p. 221).① The i-

① The text of this "articulation of faith" has been published earlier in 1988 in a special issue of *Life Magazine* on the meaning of life and deliberately takes "the modern West as its point of departure". It reads: "Copernicus decentered the earth, Darwin relativized the godlike image of man, Marx exploded the ideology of social harmony, and Freud complicated our conscious life. They have redefined humanity for the modern age. Yet they have also empowered us, with communal, critical self-awareness, to renew our faith in the ancient Confucian wisdom that the globe is the center of our universe and the only home for us and that we are the guardians of the good earth, the trustees of the Mandate of Heaven that enjoins us to make our bodies healthy, our hearts sensitive, our minds alert, our souls refined, and our spirits brilliant. We are here because embedded in our human nature is the secret code for Heaven's self-realization. Heaven is certainly omnipresent, may even be omniscient, but is most likely not omnipotent. It needs our active participation to realize its own truth. We are Heaven's partners, indeed cocreators. We serve Heaven with common sense, the lack of which nowadays has brought us to the brink of self-destruction. Since we help Heaven to realize itself through our self-discovery and self-understanding in day-to-day living, the ultimate meaning of life is found in our ordinary, human existence" (pp. 221-222).

dea he takes from Zhang Zai and his "Western Inscription", which Tu has elsewhere described and also describes in this chapter as an "article of faith," "a Confucian declaration of faith" (p. 171). Tu formulating his own up-dated version of a Confucian articulation of faith is perhaps one of the most self-conscious acts one finds throughout all his writings of himself being a representative of the tradition.

That the formulation is said to be inspired by "Confucius, Mencius, Tung Chung-shu, Chu Hsi, Wang Yang-ming, and the New Confucians" is slightly surprising for the inclusion of Zhu Xi, the prominence it gives to Dong Zhongshu, the absence of Zhang Zai, etc. and warrants further examination. It brings up the question *who* Tu takes to represent the Confucian tradition most authentically, in order words, whether there is a gap between his presentation of a unitary Confucian tradition and his own idiosyncratic construction of that tradition. Here are some prima facie observations:

6. The Five Classics do not receive much attention, apart of course from the *Zhongyong* and the *Daxue*, which do get some attention, but not as much as could have been expected from Tu's other writings. Besides to these two chapters of the *Liji*, there is no citation let alone reference to any passage from the Five Classics. Tu, however, offers a short discussion of the Five Classics as representing five visions: metaphysical, political, poetic, social and historical (pp. 195-197). The Song-Ming Confucian venture point of Tu's construction of a Confucian tradition is further corroborated by his description of the *Analects* as "the most revered sacred scripture in the Confucian tradition" (p. 183).

7. Tu seems to be concerned to offer a balanced view of the Confucian tradition, but he comes to emphasize his idiosyncratic reading by way of depth that he gives to the presentation of single thinkers. It is no mere accidental slip when he comes to speak of the "original Confucian intention, as envisioned by Confucius and Mencius" (p. 214), as the amount of references in the overall presentation affirms (cf. B3 and B4). Tu sides with Mencius, as is well known, and not so much with Xunzi, for whom we find neither a citation nor a reference. The presentation of Xunzi in Tu's chapter is particularly interesting. At the surface (cf. B1 and B2) it receives only slightly less attention than the one of Mencius. But in the text itself three times it is mentioned that Xunzi held different views from Mencius (and it is pointed out how Xunzi may have been a bridge towards later authoritarian versions of Confucianism). Each time, the immediately preceding or following sentence emphasizes a commonali-

ty between Mencius and Xunzi: both "underscored the centrality of self-cultivation" (p. 159); both "believed in the perfectibility of all human beings through self-cultivation, in humanity and rightness as cardinal virtues, in humane government as the kingly way, in social harmony, and in education" (p. 160). This way of presenting Mencius and Xunzi's views softens their differences considerably. Emphasizing their differences more prominently might have led to an acknowledgement of several different Confucian traditions.

8. Having presented the Confucian tradition as based on common core values and as exposing common salient features, Tu is understandably concerned to underplay differences. His characterization of the Confucian vision as "anthropocosmic" (a term he adopts form Benjamin Schwartz) may serve as an example. This is how Tu begins the last paragraph in the subsection on Xunzi: "Mencius and Hsün Tzu deepened and broadened the Confucian project to such an extent that the Master's views on human nature and the Way of Heaven, which were rarely understood by his immediate disciples, became fully expounded into a coherent 'anthropocosmic' vision" (p. 160). That coherence is of course precisely what Mencius and Xunzi's *different* views on human nature are often taken to challenge. Something similar happens when Tu ascribes to Zhu Xi an "anthropocosmic vision" (expressed in his "Treatise on Humanity"), then posits Lu Xiangshan as Zhu Xi's major challenger, but presents Lu as having had a "holistic 'anthropocosmic' insight" (p. 176). In the section on "the modern transformation of the Confucian tradition", Tu again insists on "characterizing the Confucian vision as anthropocosmic" (p. 207). In light of this observation, it seems that terms such as "anthropocosmic" are surely a distinctive feature of what Tu takes Confucianism to be about, but they also serve as an umbrella under which to subsume (and put into the background) differences within the Confucian tradition. It the chapter, Tu very frequently speaks about "the Confucian project". This formulation certainly points away from an expert talking about a tradition and its features and towards a representative offering something that might be taken up by others, a "living tradition" that has contemporary relevance.

9. The chapter also discusses the third epoch of Confucianism and mentions the names of its main protagonists, including Tu's own teachers, but it completely glosses over what any of them actually has said. Given the enormous amount of books and other writings by the hands of Mou Zongsan or Tang Junyi, this is astonishing. There

is not one citation, not even a reference to any specified text by any 20th century New Confucian. [As an aside, it might be added that this observation-with the exception of some writing on Xiong Shili and some scattered remarks and short articles on Tang Junyi and Mou Zongsan-also holds true in view of Tu's entire oeuvre.]

**Conclusions**

The offered textual analyses have been very preliminary. The main outcome of the investigation into how Tu represents the Confucian tradition in view of the debates on true succession and representatives of traditions is the addition of further variables: the domain of representation and the addressed audience.

The debates in social epistemology have largely focused on two variables. The criterion of consistency involves two variables, e.g. the central views of A and B, and the same holds true for all of Williams's sufficient and necessary conditions. What is left out in this way of framing true succession and representation is the fact that B is not simply a true successor of A, but is so only in the eyes of C and in view of a specific domain. The case of representation makes this evident. If we take the Catholic Church for an example, then surely the Pope is a representative, but so are priests, non-ordained Catholic theologians, and in some settings even non-Christian scholars of Christianity or the one believing member in an otherwise atheist family. For a representative to be successful in his or her representation, it is absolutely necessary to enjoy authority in the domain of representation in the eyes of those who constitute the audience for the act of representation. In the case of a representative of a tradition and members of that tradition, the former needs to be acknowledged as an authority in the eyes of the latter, and in such a situation we find opening in front of us the vast realm of *authority* understood as passive obedience or an exercise of autonomy (or, indeed, a mixture of both). The authority exercised by the representative stands and falls with each act of representation, depending on matters such as the audience's expectations, institutional backing, etc.

Confucianism is an interesting case for investigating the question of authority involved in its representation as a tradition, since it lacks the institutionalized organization that other religious traditions boast (the priest represents the Catholic Church not only because of his expertise in the domain of representation, but also because he *is* the priest). In the absence of such institutional backing (at least today), it seems that the representative of the Confucian tradition is thrown back onto the authority that comes with reputation and standing in the eyes of the concerned audience and perhaps with offering a "timely update", as Beckstein put it. There is currently not much scholarship on how authority is exercised by Confucian scholars and how exactly they come to represent the tradition in specific situations. But some sort of "timely update" seems to play a role, although also this aspect hinges on the specific audience: a reactionary vision might in some circles be the most "timely update" imaginable. In any case, whether a representative succeeds in offering an appealing version of a tradition to a concerned audience does not merely depend on the consistency of his or her central views with those of a presupposed originator or an earlier representative, not merely with how well B is judged to understand the ideas of A, but also with the constitution (power structure, identity, interests, expectations, etc.) of the addressed audience. To gloss over that dimension and to consider it simply part of the "extraneous circumstances" of true succession and representation of tradition (not part of the hard philosophical problem, so to say) might amount to no less than altogether failing to take the phenomenon seriously enough.

**Appendices: Textual Analyses**

A. Humanity and Self-Cultivation (1979)

A1. Analysed Texts

10. "The Creative Tension between Jen and Li," in *Philosophy East and West* 18, no. 1-2 (1968): 29-39. Also HSC, 5-16.

11. "The Unity of Knowing and Acting-From a Neo-Confucian Perspective," in Philosophy: Theory and Practice, ed. T. Mahadevan, *Proceedings of the International Seminar on World Philosophy*, 7-17 December, Madras, 1970, 190-205. Also HSC 83-101.

12. "Mind and Human Nature (Review Article)," in *The Journal of Asian Studies* 30, no. 3 (1971): 642-647. Also HSC, 111-118.

13. "The Neo-Confucian Concept of Man," in *Philosophy East and West* 21, no. 1 (1971): 79-87. Also HSC, 71-82.

14. "Li as Process of Humanization," in *Philosophy East and West* 22, no. 2 (1972): 187-201. Also HSC, 17-34.

15. "Reconstituting the Confucian Tradition (Review Article)," in *The Journal*

*of Asian Studies* 33, no. 3

(1974): 441-454. Also HSC, 119-137.

16. "Inner Experience: The Basis of Creativity in Neo-Confucian Thinking," in Artists and Tradition, Uses of the Past in Chinese Culture, ed. Christian Murck, The Art Museum, Princeton: Princeton University, 1976, 9-15. Also HSC, 102-110.

17. "The Confucian Perception of Adulthood," in *Daedalus: Journal of the American Academy of Arts and Sciences* 105, no. 2 (1976): 109-123. Also HSC, 35-56.

18. "On the Mencian Perception of Moral Self-Development," in *The Monist* 61, no. 1 (1978): 72-81. Also HSC, 57-68.

19. "The 'Moral Universal' from the Perspective of East Asian Thought," in *Morality as a Biological Phenomenon*, ed. Gunther S. Stent, Dahlem Konferenzen, Berlin: Abakon-Verlagsgesellschaft, 1978, 187-207.

A2. Sentence-Long Direct Quotes in Main Text

1. **Analects 46**

1:4, 1:9, 1:12, 2:4 [2], 3:3 [2], 3:23, 4:8, 5:28, 6:30, 7:2; 7:6, 7:8, 7:19, 7:23, 7:30 [2] , 8:2, 8:7, 9:3, 9:5, 9:10, 9:18, 9:21, 9:23, 9:28, 12:1 [4], 13:21, 14:12, 14:18, 14:35, 14:43, 14:44, 15:3, 15:24 [2], 15:29, 16:7, 17:9, 17:19, 18:6 [2]

2. **Mencius 28**

2A:6 [4], 4B:12, 6A:4, 6A:6 [3], 6A:7, 6A:8, 6A:10, 6A:11, 6A:14 [2], 6A:19, 6B:15 [2], 7A:1 [2], 7A:4 [2], 7A:21, 7A:38, 7B:25, 7B:37 [3],

3. **Zhongyong 15**

Ch. 8, 9, 13:3, 13:4, 14:3, 14:5 [2], 20, 22 [3], 23, 25, 26, 32

4. **Wang Yangming 6**

5. **Cheng Yi 5**

6. **Zhang Zai 3**

7. **Zhu Xi 3**

8. **Cheng Hao 2**

9. **Daxue 2**

10. **Gabriel Marcel 2**

6. **Zhou Dunyi 2**

**One reference to:**

Étienne Balazs; Wing-tsit Chan; Herbert G. Creel; F.A. Jenner; James Legge;

Lu Xiangshan; Tang Junyi; Wang Pin; Xunzi

A3. Mentions in main body of text (of Persons mentioned at least five times)

B. "Confucianism" in *Our Religions* (1993)

B1. Structure of Presentation

What Is the Confucian Way?

Defining Confucian Spirituality

Self as Creative Transformation

Community as a Necessary Vehicle for Human Flourishing

Nature as Home

Heaven as the Source of Ultimate Self-transformation

The Formation of the Confucian Tradition

Confucianism as an East Asian Way of Life

Historical Context

The Life of Confucius

The First Epoch of the Confucian Way

Mencius: The Paradigmatic Confucian Intellectual

Hsün Tzu: The Transmitter of Confucian Scholarship

The Confucianization of Politics

Tung Chung-shu: Mutuality between Heaven and Humanity

Confucian Ethics in the Age of Buddhism and Taoism

The Second Epoch of the Confucian Way

The Anthropocosmic Vision (CHOU TUN-I; CHANG TSAI; CH'ENG HAO AND CH'ENG I; CHU HSI; LU HSIANG-SHAN)

Forming One Body with All Things (HSü HENG; LIU YIN AND WU CHENG; WANG YANG-MING)

Sagely Learning in East Asia

Core Values as Embodied in Confucian Sacred Texts

The *Analects* as the Embodiment of Confucian Ideas

The Mencian Idea of the Five Relationships (FATHER-SON; RULER-MINISTER; HUSBAND-WIFE; OLD-YOUNG; FRIEND-FRIEND)

Confucian Critique of the "Three Bonds"

The Five Classics as Five Visions

The Salient Features of the Confucian Spiritual Orientation

Learning to Be Human

This-Worldliness

Transcendence in Immanence

Human-Relatedness

The Modern Transformation of the Confucian Tradition: The Dynamics of the Family

The Third Epoch of the Confucian Way

Contemporary Relevance

The Confucian Form of Life

Future Prospects

Recommended Reading

Notes

B2. Confucians Mentioned by Name in the Chapter, Arranged Chronologically

Confucius (551-479 BC)

[Disciples of Confucius]

Mencius (390-305 BC)

Hsün Tzu (298-238 BC)

Tung Chung-shu (ca. 179-ca. 104 BC)

Li Ao (772-84)

Han Yü (768-824)

Hu Yüan (993-1059)

Sun Fu (992-1057)

Fan Chung-yen (989-1052)

Wang An-shih (1021-1086)

Ou-yang Hsiu (1007-1072)

Su Shih (1036-1101)

Ssu-ma Kuang (1019-1086)

Shao Yüng (1011-1077)

Chou Tun-i (1017-1073)

Chang Tsai (1020-1077)

Ch'eng Hao (1032-1085)

Ch'eng I (1033-1107)

Chu Hsi (1130-1200)

Lu Hsiang-shan (1139-1192)

Chao Ping-wen (1159-1232)

Wang Jo-hsü (1172-1248)

Hsü Heng (1209-1281)

Liu Yin (1249-1293)

Wu Cheng (1249-1333)

Hsüeh Hsüan (1392-1464)

Wu Yü-pi (1391-1469)

Ch'en Hsien-chang (1428-1500)

Wang Yang-ming (1472-1529)

Wang Chi (1498-1583)

Yi T'oegye (1501-1570)

Ki Taesung (1527-1572)

Li Chih (1527-1602)

Yi Yulgok (1536-1584)

Liu Tsung-chou (1578-1645)

Sun Ch'i-feng (1584-1675)

Huang Tsung-his (1610-1682)

Ku Yen-wu (1613-1682)

Yamazaki Ansai (1618-1682)

Kumazawa Banzan (1619-1691)

Wang Fu-chih (1619-1692)

Ogyū Sorai (1666-1728)

Tai Chen (1723-1777)

Hsiüng Shi-li (1885-1968)

Liang Shu-ming (1893-1988)

Chang Chün-mai (1886-1969)

T'ang Chün-i (1909-1978)

Hsü Fu-kuan (1903-1982)

Mou Tsung-san (1909-[1995])

B3. Text quoted in full

Analects / Lunyu

**2:4** (trans. D.C. Lau)

At fifteen I set my heart on learning; at thirty I firmly took my stand; at forty I came to be free from doubts; at fifty I understood the Decree of Heaven; at sixty my ear was attuned; at seventy I followed my heart's desire without overstepping the line.

**2:21** / Book of Documents / Shujing

Simply by being a good son and friendly to his brothers a man can exert an influence upon government.

**3:24** (trans. D.C. Lau)

The border official of Yi requested an audience, saying, "I have never been denied an audience by any nobleman who has come to this place." The followers presented him. When he came out, he said, "What worry have you, gentlemen, about the loss of office. The empire has long been without the Way. Heaven is about to use your Master as the wooden tongue for a bell [to rouse the empire]."

**6:28** (Wing-tsit Chan)

A man of humanity, wishing to establish his character, also establishes the character of others, and wishing to enlarge himself, also helps others to enlarge themselves. To be able to take the analogy near at hand (for understanding others) may be called the method of realizing humanity.

**7:3** (trans. D.C. Lau)

It is these things that cause me concern: failure to cultivate virtue, failure to go deeply into what I have learned, inability to move up to what I have heard to be right, and inability to reform myself when I have defects.

**7:19** (trans. D.C. Lau)

Why did you not simply say something to this effect: he is the sort of man who forgets to eat when he engages himself in vigorous pursuit of learning, who is so full of joy that he forgets his worries and who does not notice that old age is coming on?

**8:7** (trans. D.C. Lau)

[Zengzi: The truly profound person] must be broadminded and resolute, for his burden is heavy and his road is long. He takes humanity as his burden. Is that not heavy? Only with death does his road come to an end. Is that not long?

**9:5**

Since the death of King Wen [founder of the Chou dynasty], does not mission of culture (*wen*) rest here in me? If Heaven intends this culture to be destroyed, those who come after me will not be able to have any part of it. If Heaven does not intend this culture to be destroyed, then what can the men of K'uang do to me?

Quoted again (trans. D.C. Lau)

When under siege in K'uang, the Master said, "With King Wen dead, is not culture (*wen*) invested here in me? If Heaven intends this culture to be destroyed, those who come after me will not be able to have any part of it. If Heaven does not intend this culture to be destroyed, then what can the men of K'uang do to me?

**14:34**

When Confucius was asked: "Should one not return malice with kindness?" he replied, "If you return malice with kindness, what will you return kindness with? Therefore, return malice with uprightness (justice), but return kindness with kindness."

**14:41**

When Tzu-lu was stopping at the Stone Gate for the night, the gate keeper asked him, "Where are you from?" Tzu-lu said, "From Confucius." "Oh, is he the one who knows that it cannot be done and still does it?"

**15:28**(trans. Wing-tsit Chan)

"It is the human that can make the Way great, and not the Way that can make the human great."

**18:5** (D.C. Lau)

*Chieh Yü, the Madman of Ch'u, went past Confucius, singing,*

*Phoenix, oh phoenix!*

*How thy virtues has declined!*

*What is past is beyond help,*

*What is to come is not yet lost.*

*Give up, give up!*

*Perilous is the lot of those in office today.*

Confucius got down from his carriage with the intention of speaking with him, but the Madman avoided him by hurrying off, and in the end Confucius was unable to speak with him.

**18:6** (D.C. Lau)

Ch'ang-shu and Chieh-ni were cultivating their fields together. Confucius was passing that way and told [his disciple] Tzu-lu to ask them where the river could be forded. Ch'ang-shu said, "Who is the one holding the reins in the carriage?" Tzu-lu said, "It is K'ung Ch'iu [Confucius' given name]." "Is he the K'ung Ch'iu of Lu [Confucius' native state]?" "Yes." "Then he already knows where the river can be forded!" Tzu-lu asked Chieh-ni. Chieh-ni said, "The whole world is swept as though by a torrential flood. Who can change it? As for you, instead of following one who flies from this man or that man, is it not better to follow those who flee the world all together?" And with that we went on covering the seed without stopping. Tzu-lu went to Confucius and told him about the conversation. Confucius was lost in thought for a while and said, "One cannot herd with birds or beasts. If I do not associate with humankind, with whom shall I associate? If the Way prevailed in the world, there would be no need for me to change it."

**19:24** (trans. D.C. Lau)

Shu-sun Wu-shu made defamatory remarks about Chung-ni [Confucius]. Tzu-kung said, "He is simply wasting his time. Chung-ni cannot be defamed. In other cases, men of excellence are like hills which one can climb over. Chung-ni is like the sun and the moon which one has no way of climbing over. Even if someone wanted to cut himself off from them, how could this detract from the sun and the moon? It would merely serve the more to show that he did not know his own measure."

Mencius / Mengzi

**2A:6** (trans. D.C. Lau)

No man is devoid of a heart-mind sensitive to the suffering of others. Such a sensitive heart-mind was possessed by the Former Kings and this manifested itself in humane government. With such a sensitive heart-mind behind humane government, it was as easy to rule the world as rolling it on your palm.

**2B:2** (trans. D.C. Lau)

There are three things which are acknowledged by the world to be exalted: rank, age and virtue. At court, rank is supreme; in the village, age; but for assessing the world and ruling over the people it is virtue.

How can a man, on the strength of the possession of one of these, treat the other two with arrogance? Hence a prince who is to achieve great things must have subjects he does not summon. If he wants to consult them, he goes to them. If he does not honor virtue and delight in the Way in such a manner, he is not worthy of being helped towards the achievements of great things. … Today there are many states, all equal in size and virtue, none being able to dominate the others. This is simply because the rulers are given to employing those they can teach rather than those from whom they can learn.

**3A:4** (trans. D.C. Lau)

There are those who use their minds and there are those who use their muscles. The former govern; the latter are governed. Those who govern are supported by those who are governed.

Hou Chi [the minister in charge of agriculture] taught the people how to farm and grow the five kinds of grain. When these ripened, the people multiplied. This is the way of the common people: once they have a fully belly and warm clothes on their back they degenerate to the level of animals if they are allowed to lead idle lives, without education and discipline.

This gave the sage King further cause for concern, and so he appointed Hsieh as the Minister of Education whose duty was to teach the people human relationships: love between father and son, duty between ruler and subject, distinction between husband and wife, precedence of the old over the young, and faith between faiths.

**4A:5** (trans. D.C. Lau)

There is a common expression, "The Empire, the state, the family." The Empire has its basis in the state, the state in the family, and the family in one's own self.

**4A:18** (trans. D.C. Lau)

Kung-sun Ch'ou said, "Why does a gentleman not take on the teachings of his own son?" "Because in the nature of things," said Mencius, "it will not work. A teacher necessarily resorts to correction, and if correction produces no effect, it will end by losing his temper. When this happens, father and son will hurt each other instead. 'You teach me by correcting me, but you yourself are not correct.' So father and son hurt each other, and it is bad that such a thing should happen. In antiquity people taught one another's sons. Father and son should not demand goodness from each other. To do so will estrange them, and there is nothing more inauspicious than estrangement between father and son.

If a prince treats his ministers as his hands and feet, they will treat him as their belly and heart. If he treats them as his horses and hounds, they will treat him as a mere fellow-countryman. If he treats them as mud and woods, they will treat him as an enemy.

**4B:11** (trans. D.C. Lau)

The great man (a profoundly moral person) need not keep his word nor does he necessarily see his action through to the end. He aims only at what is right.

**7A:4** (trans. D.C. Lau)

All the ten thousand things are there in me. There is no greater joy for me than to find, on self-examination, that I am true to myself. Try your best to treat others as you would wish to be treated yourself, and you will find that this is the shortest way to humanity.

**7B:25** (trans. D.C. Lau)

Those who command our liking are called good (*shan*).

Those who are sincere with themselves are called true (*hsin*).

Those who are sufficient and real are called beautiful (*mei*).

Those whose sufficiency and reality shine forth are called great (*ta*).

Those whose greatness transforms itself are called sagely (*sheng*).

Those whose sageliness is beyond our comprehension are called spiritual (*shen*).

The Great Learning / Daxue

**Opening Statement** (trans. Daniel K. Gardner)

The ancients who wished to illuminate "brilliant virtue" all under Heaven first governed their states. Wishing to govern their states, they first regulated their families. Wishing to regulate their families, they first cultivated their personal lives. Wishing to cultivate their personal lives, they first rectified their hearts and minds. Wishing to rectify their hearts and minds, they first authenticated their intentions. Wishing to authenticate their intentions, they first refined their knowledge. The refinement of knowledge lay in the study of things. For only when things are studied is knowledge refined; only when knowledge is refined are intentions authentic; only when intentions are authentic are hearts and minds rectified; only when hearts and minds are rectified are personal lives cultivated; only when personal lives are cultivated are families regulated; only when families are regulated are states governed; only when states are governed is there peace all under Heaven. Therefore, from the Son of Heaven to the common people, all, without exception, must take self-cultivation as the root.

The Doctrine of the Mean / Zhongyong

**Ch. 13** (trans. Wing-tsit Chan)

There are four things in the Way of the profound person, none of which I have been able to do. To serve my father as I would expect my son to serve me: that I have not been able to do. To serve my ruler as I would expect my ministers to serve me: that I have not been able to do. To serve my elder brothers as I would expect my younger brothers to serve me: that I have not been able to do. To be the first to treat friends as I would expect my friends to treat me: that I have not been able to do.

**Ch. 22** (trans. Wing-tsit Chan)

Only those who are absolutely sincere can fully develop their nature. If they can fully develop their nature, they can fully develop the nature of others. If they can fully develop the nature of others, they can then fully develop the nature of things. If they can fully develop the nature of things, they can then assist in the transforming and nourishing process of Heaven and Earth. If they can assist in the transforming and nourishing process of Heaven and Earth, they can thus form a trinity with Heaven and Earth.

**Ch. 26** (trans. Wing-tsit Chan)

The sky [Chan: heaven, RW] before us is only this bright, shining mass; but when viewed in its unlimited extent, the sun, moon, starts, and constellations are suspended in it and all things are covered by it. The earth before us is but a handful of soil; but in its breadth and depth, it sustains mountains like Hua and Yüeh without feeling their weight, contains the rivers and seas without letting them leak away, and sustains all things. The mountain before us is but a fistful of straw; but in all the vastness of its size, grass and trees grow upon it, birds and beasts dwell on it, and stores of precious things [minerals] are discovered in it. The water before us is but a spoonful of liquid, but in all its unfathomable depth, the monsters, dragons, fishes, and turtles are produced in them, and wealth becomes abundant because of it.

Han Feizi

**zhong-xiao chapter**

The minister serves the king, the son serves the father, and the wife serves the husband. If the three are followed, the world will be in peace; if the three are violated, the world will be in chaos.

Dong Zhongshu

**Han Shu** (as quoted in)

…rectifying rightness without scheming for profit; enlightening the Way without calculating efficaciousness.

Zhou Dunyi

**An Explanation of the Diagram of the Great Ultimate** (trans. Wing-tsit Chan)

When the reality of the Ultimate on Non-being and the essence of yin, yang, and the Five Phases come into mysterious union, integration ensues. *Ch'ien* (Heaven) constitutes the male element, and k'un (Earth) constitutes the female element. The interaction of these two vital forces engenders and transforms the myriad things. The myriad things produce and reproduce, resulting in an unending transformation.

Human beings alone receive (the Five Phases) in their highest excellence, and therefore they are most sentient. Their physical forms appear, and their spirit gives rise to consciousness. The five moral principles of their nature (humanity, rightness, propriety, wisdom, and faithfulness) are aroused by, and react to, the external world and engage in activity; good and evil are distinguished; and human affairs take place.

**Penetrating the Book of Changes** (trans. Wing-tsit Chan)

[Qi as] an originating power, an inward spring of activity, an emergence not yet visible, a critical point at which one's direction toward good or evil is set.

The virtue of loving is called humanity, that of doing what is proper is called rightness, that of putting things in order is called propriety, that of penetration is called wisdom, and that of abiding by one's commitments is called faithfulness. Those who are in accord with their nature are sages. Those who return to their nature and adhere to it are worthies. And those whose subtle emanation cannot be seen and whose [goodness] is abundant and all-pervasive without limit are humans of the spirit.

Zhang Zai

**Western Inscription** (trans. Wing-tsit Chan)

Heaven is my father and Earth is my mother, and even such a small creature as I finds an intimate place in their midst. Therefore that which fills the universe I regard as my body and that which directs the universe I consider as my nature. All people are my brothers and sisters, and all things are my companions… Even those who are tired, infirm, crippled, or sick; those who have no brothers or children, wives or husbands, are all my brothers [and sisters] who are in distress and have no one to turn to. When the time comes, to keep him from harm-this is the care of a son. To rejoice in Heaven and to have no anxiety-this is filial piety at its purest.

One who knows the principles of transformation will skillfully carry forward the undertakings [of heaven and Earth], and one who penetrates spirit to the highest degree will skillfully carry out their will. Do nothing shameful in the recesses of your own house and thus bring no dishonor to them. Preserve your mind and nourish your nature and thus (serve them) with untiring effort.

Wealth, honor, blessing, and benefits are meant for the enrichment of life, while poverty, humble station, and sorrow are meant to help me to fulfillment. In life I follow and serve [Heaven and Earth]. In death I will be at peace.

**Correcting Youthful Ignorance** (trans. Wing-tsit Chan)

The integration and disintegration of vital energy is to the Great Vacuity as the freezing and melting of ice in water. If we realize that the Great Vacuity is identical with vital energy, we know that there is no such thing as non-being. Therefore, when discussing the ultimate problems of the nature of things and the Way of Heaven, the sages limit themselves to the marvelous changes and transformation of yin and yang and the Five Phases (of Metal, Wood, Water, Fire, and Earth). The doctrine of those superficial and mistaken philosophers who draw the distinction between being and non-being is not the way to investigate principle to the utmost.

From the Great Vacuity, there is Heaven. From the transformation of vital energy, there is the Way. In the unity of the Great Vacuity and vital energy, there is nature (of human beings and things). And in the unity of the nature of consciousness, there is the mind-and-heart.

By enlarging our heart-minds, we can enter into all the things in the world [to examine and understand their principles]. As long as anything is not yet entered into, there is still something outside our heart-minds. The heart-minds of ordinary people are limited to the narrowness of what is seen and what is heard. The sages, however, fully develop their nature and do not allow what is seen or heard to fetter their heart-minds. They regard everything in the world to be their own selves. This is why Mencius said that if we exert our heart-minds to the utmost, we can know nature and Heaven. Heaven is so vast that there is nothing outside of it. Therefore the heart-mind that leaves something outside is not capable of uniting itself with the heart-mind of Heaven. Knowledge coming from seeing and hearing is knowledge obtained through contact with things. It is not knowledge obtained through our moral nature. Knowledge obtained through our moral nature does not originate from seeing or hearing.

Cheng Hao

**Er cheng yi shu** (Wing-tsit Chan)

A book on medicine describes paralysis of the four limbs as absence of humanity (jen). This is an excellent description. Persons who embody humanity regard Heaven, Earth, and the myriad things as one body. To them there is nothing that is not themselves. Since they have recognized all things as themselves, can there be any limit to their humanity? If things are not part of the self, naturally they have nothing to do with it. As in the case of the paralysis of the four limbs, the vital energy no longer penetrates them and, as a result, they are no longer part of the self.

Zhu Xi

**Treatise on Humanity** (trans. Wing-tsit Chan)

The moral qualities of the heart-mind of Heaven and Earth are four: origination, flourish, advantage, and firmness. And the principle of origination unites and controls them all. In their operation they constitute the course of the four seasons, and the vital energy of the spring permeates all. Therefore in the human heart-mind there are four moral qualities-namely humanity (*jen*), rightness (*i*), propriety (*li*), and wisdom (*chih*)-and humanity embraces them all. In their emanation and function, they constitute the feeling of love, respect, being right, and discrimination between right and wrong-and the feeling of commiseration pervades them all.

[Humanity] as constituting the Way (Tao) consists of the fact that the heart-mind of Heaven and Earth to produce things is present in everything. Before feelings are aroused, this substance is already existent in its completeness. After feelings are aroused, its function is infinite. If we can truly practice love and preserve it, then we have in it the spring of all virtues and the root of all good deeds. This is why in the teachings of the Confucian school, the student is always urged to exert anxious and unceasing effort in the pursuit of humanity. Lu Xiangshan

**The Complete Works** (trans. Wing-tsit Chan)

The four directions plus upward and downward constitute the spatial continuum (*yü*). What has gone by in the past and what is to come in the future constitute the temporal continuum (*chou*). The universe (these continua) is my heart-mind, and my heart-mind is the universe. Sages appeared tens of thousands of generations ago. They shared this heart-mind; they shared this principle. Sages will appear tens of thousands of generations to come. They will share this heart-mind; they will share this principle. Over the four seas sages appear. They share this mind; they share this principle.

This principle existing throughout the universe is hidden from nothing and nothing can escape from it. Heaven and Earth are what they are because they follow this principle without partiality. Human beings coexist with Heaven and Earth as the three ultimates. How can we be selfish and disobey principle? Mencius said, "First build up the nobler part (the 'great body') of your nature then the interior part cannot overcome it." It is because we fail to build up the nobler part of our nature that it is overcome by the inferior part. In consequence we violate principle and become different from Heaven and Earth.

Wang Yangming

**Inquiry on the Great Learning** (trans. Wing-tsit Chan)

The great man [for our purpose, it should be read in the gender neutral sense of a broadly minded 'profound person'] regards Heaven, Earth, and the myriad things as one body. He regards the world as one family and the country as one person. As to those who made a cleavage between objects and distinguish between the self and others, they are small men.

That the great man can regard Heaven, Earth, and the myriad things as one body is not because he deliberately wants to do so, but because it is natural to the humane nature of his heart-mind that he do so. Forming one body with Heaven, Earth, and the myriad things is not only true of the great man. Even the heart-mind of the small man is no different. Only he himself makes it small. Therefore when he sees a child about to fall into a well, he cannot help a feeling of alarm and commiseration. This shows that his humanity forms one body with the child. It may be objected that the child belongs to the same species. Again, when he observes that pitiful cries and frightened appearance of birds and animals about to be slaughtered, he cannot help feeling an "inability to bear" their suffering. This shows his humanity forms one body with birds and animals. It may be objected that birds and animals are sentient beings as he is. But when he sees plants broken and destroyed, he cannot help a feeling of pity. This shows his humanity forms one body with plants. It may be said that plants are living things as he is. Yet, even if he sees tiles and stones shattered and crushed, he cannot help a feeling of regret. This shows his humanity forms one body with tiles and stones. This means that even the heart-mind of the small man necessarily has the humanity that forms one body with all. Such a heart-mind is rooted in the Heaven-endowed nature, and it is naturally intelligent, clear, and not beclouded. For this reason it is called the "brilliant virtue."

Peter Berger

**"An East Asian Development Model?"**

For several years now the so-called post-Confucian hypothesis has enjoyed a certain vogue. It is essentially simple: both Japan and the newly industrialized countries of East Asia belong to the broad area of influence of Sinitic civilization, and there can be no doubt that Confucianism has been a very powerful force in all of them. The hypothesis is that the key variable in explaining the economic performance of those countries is Confucian ethics-or post-Confucian ethics, in the sense that the moral values in question are now relatively detached from the Confucian tradition proper and have become more widely diffused. Historical evidence on the spread of Confucian education and ideology is very relevant to this hypothesis, but equally important is empirical research into the sway of Confucian-derived values in the lives of ordinary people, many of whom have never read a Confucian classic and have little education, Confucian or other. Robert Bellah has coined the happy phrase "bourgeois Confucianism" to distinguish this from the "high" Confucianism of the Mandarin elite of traditional China. The work currently being done by S. G. Redding and his associates at the University of Hong Kong on the norms of Chinese entrepreneurs is informed by precisely this point of view.

I'm strongly inclined to believe that, as evidence continues to come in, this hypothesis will be supported. It is inconceivable to me that at least some of the Confucian-derived values intended by the hypothesis-a positive attitude to the affairs of this world, a sustained lifestyle of discipline and self-cultivation, respect for authority, frugality, and overriding concern for stable family life-should not be relevant to the work ethic and the overall social attitudes of the region. At the same time, I strongly suspect that Confucianism is by no means the only cultural and religious factor in play. Other factors will have to be explored.

B4. References

1. **Analects 39**

2.4 [3], 2:21, 3.24 [2], 4:15, 5:6, 5:26, 5:28, 6:21, 6:28, 7:2 [2], 7:3, 7:8, 7:13, 7:15, 7:19, 7:20, 7:23, 7:28 [2], 8:7, 9:4, 9:5 [2], 9:8, 9:13, 12:1, 14:24, 14:34, 14:41, 14:46 [2], 15:28, 18:5, 18:6, 19:24-trans. Lau: 13 / trans. Waley: 1 / trans. Chan: 4 /trans. Legge: 4

2. **Mencius 24**

1B8, 2A:6, 2B:2 [2], 3A:4 [5], 3B:2 [2], 3B:9, 4A:5, 4A:18, 4B:2, 4B:3, 4B:19, 5A:2, 5A:5, 7A:1, 7A:4 [2], 7B:14, 7B:25-trans. Lau: 14

3. **Tu Weiming 10**

"Embodying the Universe", "Confucius and Confucianism", "Confucianism in an Historical Perspective", "Confucian Tradition in Chinese History", "Liu Yin's Confucian Emeritism", Centrality and Commonality, "The Rise of Industrial East Asia", "Towards a Third Epoch", "The Search for Roots in Industrial East Asia", Life Magazine

4. **Dong Zhongshu 5**

"An Explanation of the Diagram of the Great Ultimate" [1], "Penetrating the Book of Changes" [4]-trans. Chan: 5

5. **Doctrine of the Mean 4**

Ch. 13 [2], 22, 26-trans. Chan: 3

6. **Zhang Zai 4**

"The Western Inscription", Correcting Youthful Ignorance [3]-trans. Chan: 4

7. **Lu Xiangshan 4**

Complete Works 11:1a, 22:5a [2], 34:5b-trans. Chan: 4

8. **Great Learning 2**

Ch. 1 [2]

9. **Daniel K. Gardner 2**

Chu Hsi and the Ta-hsüeh [2]

10. **Herbert Fingarette 2**

Secular as Sacred [2]

11. **Max Weber 2**

The Religion of China [2]

12. **Wing-tsit Chan 2**

Source Book [2]

13. **Cheng Hao 2**

Er Cheng yi shu [2]-trans. Chan: 2

14. **Wang Yangming 2**

"Inquiry on the Great Learning", Instructions for Practical Living-trans. Chan: 2

15. **Disc. White Tiger Hall 2**

"San gang liu ji", "Jia qu"

16. **Peter Berger 2**

"An East Asian Development Model?" [2]

**One reference to:**

Yi T'oegye, Ten Diagrams on Sage Learning (trans. Michael C. Kalton)

**References**

Beckstein, Martin. "Traditions and True Successors: A Few Pragmatic Considerations." *Epistemology Review and Reply Collective* 3, no. 3 (2014): 30-36.

Beckstein, Martin. "Addressing Ruben's 'Internal and External Perspectives'." *Epistemology Review and Reply Collective* 3, no. 5 (2014): 35-36.

Hwang, Philip Ho. "A New Interpretation of Confucius." *Philosophy East and West* 30, no. 1 (1980): 45-55.

Lebens, Samuel. "True Successors and Counterfactual Approval." *Epistemology Review and Reply Collective* 2, no. 10 (2013): 26-32.

Lebens, Samuel. "Counterfactual Approval and Idiosyncratic Counterfactual Approval." *Epistemology Review and Reply Collective* 2, no. 11 (2013): 65-69.

Lu, Martin. "Was Mencius a True Successor of Confucius?" *Philosophy East and West* 33, no. 1 (1983): 79-86.

Payton, Jonathan. "Ruben's Account of Traditions and True Successors: Two Modifications and an Extension." *Epistemology Review and Reply Collective* 2, no. 11 (2013): 40-46.

Payton, Jonathan. "Keeping Successorhood and Inheritance Apart: A Reply to Lebens and Ruben." *Epistemology Review and Reply Collective* 3, no. 1 (2013): 14-19.

Ruben, David-Hillel. "Traditions and True Successors." *Social Epistemology* 27, no. 1 (2013): 32-46.

Ruben, David-Hillel. "Reply to Williams." *Epistemology Review and Reply Collective* 2, no. 8 (2013): 8-9.

Ruben, David-Hillel. "Reply to Williams' Reply," *Epistemology Review and Reply Collective* 2, no. 10 (2013): 21-22.

Ruben, David-Hillel. "More on True Succession and Tradition: Replying to Lebens and Payton." *Epistemology Review and Reply Collective* 2, no. 12 (2013): 29-31.

Ruben, David-Hillel. "Internal and External Perspectives: Reply to Martin Beckstein." *Epistemology Review and Reply Collective* 3, no. 3 (2014): 55-56.

Ruben, David-Hillel. "A Further Reply to Beckstein." *Epistemology Review and Reply Collective* 3, no.

6 (2014): 94.

Sharma, Arvind. "Introduction." In *Our Religions*, ed. Arvind Sharma. New York: HarperCollins, 1993, xi.

Smith, Wilfred Cantwell. *Faith and Belief: The Difference between Them*. Oxford: Oneworld, 1998.

Tu, Weiming. "Confucianism." In *Our Religions*, ed. Arvind Sharma. New York: HarperCollins, 1993, 141-227.

Williams, John N. "Confucius, Mencius, and the Notion of True Succession." *Philosophy East and West* 38, no. 2 (1988): 157-171.

Williams, John. "David-Hillel Ruben's 'Traditions and True Successors': A Critical Reply." *Social Epistemology Review and Reply Collective* 2, no. 7 (2013): 40-45.

Williams, John. "Further Reflections on True Successors and Traditions." *Epistemology Review and Reply Collective* 2, no. 9 (2013): 12-16.

# Confucius's Ethical Doctrine of "Mean" and Environmental Conservation

**Thandar Moe**

## Introduction

Chinese philosophy chiefly concerned with ethical and social in character. The task of philosophy is to cultivate human to become sage in the Chinese culture. As a significant philosophical tradition, Confucianism emphasizes the balance between individual integrity and social harmony. Moreover, Chinese philosophical traditions also represent the harmonious co-existence between humankind and nature. Hence, Confucian philosophy also takes account of environmental ethics through its inclusiveness of Heaven, Earth and the Human order. Confucius regards nature itself as holistic, all things in nature depending on each other and forming an organic whole. These form the traditional Chinese trinities which configure the ultimate harmony. In Chinese traditions, human being is considered as a part of nature or an existence within it. For that reason, it is assumed that people and nature are closely bound in primary relationship harmoniously without conflicts. Especially, relations between people and the natural world are also play the crucial role in Confucian ethics.

The Chinese traditional thoughts chiefly tend to be nature-centered or eco-centric while they also suggested the moral cultivation of its social members in which the individual self is urged to merge into the natural or social environment as a whole. At this point, the concept of "Mean", *chung-yung* (中庸) in Chinese, will be focused in this research because

it should be reconsidered as a significant moral guidance that can apply to show the way how to control human's greed and to conserve the natural environment. The term *chung-yung*, literally "centrality and universality," has been translated as moderation, the Mean, mean in action, normality, universal moral order, and so forth. In other words, it has the meaning of 'central harmony' or 'middle way' which means avoiding the extreme actions and finding or acting the balanced course.

In the presentations and suggestions of some leading scholars and environmentalists, the serious environmental issues were shown that the world has been degraded since hundreds of years ago in order that wild life species have been devastated and its ecosystem upset and the world climate is also are changed into warmer and warmer at present. The average sea level has risen by an annual rate of nearly 2mm since 1960 with the rate increasing to about 3mm per year between 1993 and 2003. Consequently, Arctic sea-ice has dramatically thinned by 40 per cent in the summers of the most recent decades (compared to their thickness at the start of the twentieth century). It was the first load warming about climate change.

Besides, another world environmental problem is "natural greenhouse effect". People are putting a lot of carbon in the atmosphere and it causes the changes of the temperature of the planet as well as ozone layer thinner and thinner. In addition to it, El Nino affects the weather round the world. Roughly every three to five years, the sea and atmosphere in and around the centre of the Pacific Ocean undergo a change. On particular, El Nino conditions are associated with warmer than usual surface temperatures at sea, which affect the temperature of the atmosphere, ocean currents and, in general, weather throughout the globe.

The present condition of earth is declining in every aspect, because of human? s greed to consume its valuable resources. How can human manage to restore the earth? s terrible condition? Thus, human being is responsible for repairing and restoring the degradation of the planet earth, our home. However, since scientific technology proceeds its advancement rapidly, human has used up valuable natural resources to create luxury goods for getting more comfortable life. As a result, human? s greed and desire are escalating to purchase them. To lessen this misleading tendency, there is in need of controlling the irrational conducts of human beings. In view of that the adequate ethical principle with respect to nature is needed to control misleading attitudes and irrational behaviour of human beings.

For that reason, the role of philosophical contribution for changing that situation becomes significant. Especially, philosophical ethics needs to reconsider or finding out its new way for the purpose to apply effectively in environmental conservation. Many scholars and environmentalists call attention to those human beings who are regarded as the major sources of these issues. This means that the responsibility of human beings towards environmental conservation and sustainable development of co-existence between humankind and natural world is called for urgently at this time. Ethics has experienced a revolution, since the last decade, resulting in the 'transformation of the basis of ethical debate since ancient Greece. Nevertheless, the issue of ethical responsibility has broadened to encompass the whole ecosphere because of the rapid changing of the natural environment which has given rise to environmental issues in our time.

The first to consider the philosophical implications of the ecological crisis realized that the issue is fundamentally a spiritual one. Hence the remedy must also be essentially spiritual. Thus human beings need to rethink and reconsider their attitude and their way of life. Perhaps, it is not deniable fact that the self-centered attitude of human being is at the heart of this issue. In this respect, it can be raised up an important reason moved forward the self-centered attitude of human beings that is Dualism that reduces things to objects for consciousness is at work in humanism and reduces nature to raw material for humankind. Hence, solution and purpose can be attained only through establishing a more ? non-dual relationship in ecological terms, with the earth which is our home as well as our mother. In other words, there is in needs of the adequate principle which is able to keep the central harmony between the co-existence of humankind and natural world. At this point, the Confucian concept of *chung-yung*, means "? central harmony or ? middle way" is noteworthy in order that it will be focal philosophical conception in this research because it is able to suggest some adequate ethical values and practical guidance to control human's greed and to conserve the environment.

**1. The Significant Role of Confucianism in Chinese Philosophy**

**1.1. A Brief Traditional Account of Early Chinese History**

In the Chinese history, it is found that the Chinese people had to face with tremendous economic and social change and political disorder. This period is called "the period of warring states". The Chinese philosophy seemed to appear for finding the solution of the problem of peace and tranquility of the whole country in the time war. China has a peace and unification for the first time in her history in the state of Ch in. Chinese philosophy emphasizes on the social relation and the political and moral problems of the people. Therefore, Chinese civilization and culture rest upon a philosophical basis shaped primarily by the principles of Confucianism, Taoism and Neo-Confucianism. In Confucianism, its emphasis is to cultivate human-heartedness and the social virtues of all individual beings. The lives and institutions of the Chinese people have been guided by these philosophies for more than twenty five hundred years. In Confucius time, there were political and social disorder, disintegration and widespread breakdown of morality in China. Therefore his attention directed towards the social reformation of his country. At this time, he seemed to know that the Chinese people had to face with the poverty, political abuse and hardship so that he seemed to try to aid the government and the problems and difficulties of the ordinary people. Since he saw the cause of the misery of people was the bad administration of the rulers, he set his attention to make the correction of society. Therefore, the social and political philosophy of Confucius is both conservative and revolutionary. Hence, it is noteworthy that Confucius was the first private teacher in China and he founded the "*Ju*" school. He spent his life time for teaching his philosophies and among his several thousands of students; several tens become famous scholars and thinkers in order that he is recognized as the ideal figure of the teachers in Chinese traditions.

**1.2. The Impact of Confucius's Personal Life on his Philosophy**

Confucius was born in 551 B.C.E. in the small feudal state of *Lu*. His family name was *K'ung*, his personal name *Ch'iu*. Confucius is the Latinized form of "*K'ung Fu-Tzu*" or "Master *K'ung*", and this name is commonly used in referring to him in Chinese. He had sunk to a position of poverty and insignificance by the time of his birth. His father died when he was very young, this experience taught him how to struggle alone with the problem of securing an education and making his way in the world.

In his time, China was divided into a number of small feudal states which were constantly bickering or making war upon each other or upon the barbarian tribe that pressed the Chinese people on all the sides. Most of all kings in China, who had once given peace and stability to the nation, were weak and ineffective before the might of the more powerful feudal lords. All was violence and disorder among the ruling class and there seemed to be no higher power, temporal or spiritual to which human beings might appeal.

Confucius tried to set about to bring order and peace to his society at that time. With energy and utter selflessness, he managed to find employment for his native state of *Lu*. When his father died, he was only three years old. He was brought up under the care and instruction of his widowed mother. Because of the death of his father, his family was poor but he had acquired skills in many things. At the age of fifteen, he devoted himself to learning and gained a reputation for knowledge and propriety.

In 528 B. C. E., after the loss of his mother, he abandoned his public employment. During the three years' mourning, he refrained from sensual indulgences and activities and devoted himself to the study of ancient history, literature and institution. And then he began his career as a public teacher, and came to command public attention and the respect of the great. In 518 B.C.E., he was sent to *Lo*, the Royal capital of *Chou*, and to observe the relics of imperial greatness. Upon returning to *Lu*, he continued his teaching, and his fame increased greatly. He attracted a great variety of aspiring young followers who eager to be instructed in the classics, in conduct and in government.

At the age of fifty two, he entered the court of *Lu*, and soon he reached height official rank. However, as a result of political intrigue, he was forced to resign his post. His success was a short lived. In his old age he retired to devoted himself. He died in 479 B.C.E.

Although he sought political success, high great achievement was in education. Confucius and his teachings were little respected and less practiced by the everybody of his day and for centuries the Confucian school reminded only one among many rival schools of philosophy with its greatest strength in the area of Confucius's native state of *Lu*. But gradually Confucius's humanism began to triumph over the superstition and mysticism of other doctrines, his idealistic emphasis on virtue, kindness and learning to attract more than the harsh and cynical philosophies of other states.

At last, in the second century B. C. E, Confucianism was declared the official creed of the nation and the Classics become the principle, if not the sole, study of all schools and statesmen. Through the centuries the teaching of Confucius continued not only to be reversed in China, but also to extort a tremendous influence in Korea and Japan.

His greatness can be measured by the extent, intensity, and duration of his influence on Chinese life. For almost twenty-five centuries, he dominated China's intellectual life. His doctrines were accepted as state teaching; his works were regarded as the Cardinal Books to be studied by the students in school; his cardinal virtues were regarded as the norms of society. The teaching of Master *K'ung*, or Confucius, replete with wisdom and common sense, molded the national characters and touch every corner of human society. About the significant role of Confucianism in Chinese culture, in the book of "*A Philosopher for the Ages*", Xu Yuanxian said these words; Without Confucius Chinese culture would be like water without a source; like trees without root."[2]

Confucius view on superior person is that the superior person is attentive to small details. He tries everywhere to be careful in speech and action and is careful that his words correspond to his deeds and vice versa.

One must have great effort and study to become sincere. One must study the way to be sincere assiduously. For Confucius, understanding leads to sincerity and sincerity leads to understanding. Understanding and education are to be understood as moral understanding and moral education. The goal of both is *Jen*, genuine humanity. *Jen* means "humanity".

Sincerity is the knowledge of where we stand. It is integrity, absence of falsehood, absence of artificiality.

According to Confucius, The truly superior person does not stand out. The superior person follows a middle course of doing small things well. So he is like water that refreshes, but has no distinctive taste. The truly good person harmonizes quietly, modestly. He does not call attention to himself or to the quality of his acts. He builds no monuments to himself. According to Confucius, the superior person brings order to the world without noise or show. So he compares as the operations of Heaven have neither sound nor smell.

In Chinese philosophy, the prominent characteristic is that everyone must be in his proper place and with his proper responsibilities and duties. Confucianism has dominated in Chinese thought throughout the ages. Theodore de Barry said that;

No other individual in Chinese history has go deeply influenced the life and thought of his people, as a transmitter, teacher and creative interpreter of the ancient culture and literature, and as a molder of the Chinese mind and character. The other ancient philosophies, the religious systems of Taoism and Buddhism, all have known their days of glory and neglect; but the doctrine of Confucianism, since their general recognition in the first century before Christ, have never ceased to exert a vital influence on the nation down to our own century. Many Chinese have professed themselves to be Taoists, Buddhists, even Christians, but seldom have they ceased at the same time to be Confucians.[3]

Since the time of its general acceptance, Confucianism has become an inseparable part of the society and thought of Chinese tradition as a whole. Confucian tradition is not the canon of a particular sect but the literary heritage of the whole of China.

**2. The Role of Ethics in Environmental Conservation**

Ethics is concerned with the study of human conduct. Ordinarily, ethics and morality are used interchangeably. Environmental ethics is an applied ethics that examines the moral basis of environmental responsibility. In recent times, everyone becomes to agree that all people should be environmentally responsible for environmental conservation and sustainable development of natural world as well as human culture.

Therefore, ethical theory is needed to resolve the several environmental issues and it often concerned with international action. Important as ethical theory is personal reorientation or commitment too. Solution will need to be considered solution; an, contemporary problems call for more than theory if they are to be solved, and for more than d often international action and policies are involved. Both theory and practice needs values outside of human subjects, while the objective of environmental ethics is more biologically and not anthropocentric. It also challenges the separation of science and ethics, and tries to reform a science that finds nature value free and ethics that assumes that only humans count morally. Environmental ethics tries to escape relativism in ethics, and to discover centuries of hard science and humanist ethics that there is little compassion for animals. Human beings are today confronted with the diverse problems in different areas of social, political, economic, etc. and environment. The problems in the human affairs are not strange to say because they have emerged with the stage of organized societies in history.

Nowadays human beings face the environmental problems in addition to the problems of human affairs. In the early time of history there may not be such problems because the population is not as much as today and the environment in which they live may provide the basic needs of the human beings well. Today? s exploding world population threatens with extinction an ailing environment. Though there may be many causes which give rise to environmental degradation the essential cause may be rapid population growth because of population increase more pollution is generated, more habitats are destroyed and more natural resources are used up. So, ecological-minded persons are attempting to change current life style of consumerism and exploitation of the natural resources by introducing an environmental ethics as a guide. That ethics must not be theoretical but an applied ethics which is based on eco-centrism than ego-centrism.

Then, the questions what is the real cause of exploitation of nature? Is it the development of sciences and technologies? The answer is that human beings over greed based on egoism is the main culprit in the current crises. Hence, the moral-minded persons suggest that such exploitation of nature give a way to caring and preserving the environment by the method of self-control and self-sacrifice. In the West, last thirty years ago, the environmentalists substitute new "Holistic Thought" in the place of traditionally accepted mechanistic thought. The holistic thought holds that everything has value and the world in the nature is based on systematic process and relation. The world and living beings are like system biology in which all parts are mutually related and supporting. The theory emphasizes participative rather than exploitative relationship between living beings and their environments.

The word "climate change" is the most frequently heard word from the various media. It is just one of the different numbers of effects of world environmental degradation.

Population of both urban and rural cannot escape from these effects of environmental degradation.

Moreover, the damage done by the burning of vast areas of equatorial forests has become an added problem for worries. The depletion helps extra ultraviolet rays to enter the earth's protective atmosphere resulting in divergent consequences. i. e, it leads to more skin cancers, low crop productivity, reduced fish stocks and significant climatic changes. And acid Rain is another cause for the ruin of forests and the killing of fish in dead lakes. In addition, countless species of microscopic creatures and plants are found, apart from animals and humans that are victims of thoughtless destruction of forest and oceans, and are disappearing forever. They are the potential contributors to the General Balance of Nature, if left untouched, with the depletion of the ozone layer. Left to themselves, plants manage to modify the climate over the oceans that ensure their survival as a microscopic species. If such macroscopic phenomena are gone, rainfall and sunshine reaching the surface are all likely to be affected and everyday comfort of people will be altered subsequently. If deforestation and over fertilization are left unchecked, pollution and soil destruction would continue. The age of machinery changed the capitalist expansion and abstract money from soil, first in the cities and later in the country itself for better or worse. Page Michale said in *The Tao of Power* as follows;

"A city is similar to a human body with its own metabolism. Given a city overdevelopment, it comes to resemble a cancerous growth with its cells multiplying in an uncontrolled manner. Urban planners are hopelessly fighting a losing battle like the antibodies in a cancerous tissue"

In all developing nations news cities are being built. A great number of people from the rural areas flock to these cities tremendously. Their movements cause overcrowding, create conditions for disease, infant mortality and squalor. It is predicted that cities of twenty million inhabitants would appear in the next century. It becomes increasing clear that the urban planners are not ready to begin to service their populations in any proper way for such conurbations. In Chinese, Confucius and Taoism are also in line with in keeping the nature and human nature.

**3. Western Worldview and Environmental Ethics**

The main cause of environmental degradation that occurred in the world hundreds of years ago was due to the Western world-view. The Western world-view developed directly from the scientific revolution of the 17th and 18th centuries. This world view dealing with Science, economics, politics, technology, art, philosophy, health, education as well as conservation and the current discussions about environmental ethics-all those are affected by and reflect the beliefs, values, and methodologies which are associated with their world-view.

The Western world-view has been spectacularly successful over the last three centuries; the major crises afflicting the world today may be viewed an evidence of its fundamental weaknesses. It can be regarded as model of reality. The critical characteristics of the modern scientific world-view are separation and dissociation. The foundations for the scientific paradigm as laid down by Cartesian logic by differentiating mind and body, subject and object, value and fact, spirit and matter. Most important is that Cartesian duality set human beings apart from and over nature. Thus, to open the way for a relationship that is primarily exploitative and manipulative. Ethical thought developed in Western societies has been greatly weakened by the positivist influence of Descartes and others.

These elemental ideas still underlie common attitudes, even in the case of environmental conservation and the place of ethics in everyday life. At the same time, instrumental values play a predominant yet often unrecognized role in Western and Westernized societies. Instrumental values deals with the utility of things, as opposed to their intrinsic value. Thus, persons, objects, actions, and all aspects of the natural world tend to be evaluated in terms of their use. It is not uncommon for narrow instrumental values to be cited in support of an ethical position, that is, by all other criteria, ethically untenable.

Thus the status of ethics in society at large, and in conservation, is complicated, which impedes intellectual and practical progress. Many professional conservationists have an intuitive feeling that ethics is a vital part of conservation thinking, yet are unclear about the how, what, and why it is involved. This confusion is a direct result of the Western Intellectual tradition based on separation and dissociation.

On the contrary point of view, Aldo Leopold is one of the champions of ecological awareness. Leopold's perceptions spell out clearly new values which bind human beings to the land. An example of a new ethical insight is Leopold s Ethic: A land ethic then, reflects the existence of an ecological conscience and this in turn reflects a conviction of individual responsibilities for the health of the land. Health is the capacity for self-renewal. Conservation is our effort to understand and preserve this capacity.

According to Henryk Skolimowski, we should first of all recognize the fact that nature is not to be trampled upon and that "all other beings were not created for our use, but that nature is alive and we are part of it, and that all other beings are our follow creatures in creation". This ethical insight leads, he says, to the idea of the *sanctity of life or reverence of life*.

*Responsibility* is another intrinsic value of ecological ethics. Responsibility is part of the meaning of reverence *responsibility* is an ethical principle in the sense that, if you understand the unity of life, and that you are part of it, then you must take *responsibility* for life. Thus the right understanding of the world and the understanding of the sanctity of life implies responsibility for it.

Another intrinsic value of ecological ethics is *frugality*. Frugality is not to be confused with negation or poverty. Frugality is a positive value, a form of richness. To understand the right of others to live is to limit our unnecessary wants. A motto reads: "*Anything we have that is more that we need is stolen from the person who has less than he needs*". The Greek philosopher Aristotle was aware of the beauty of frugality when he wrote: "*The rich person is not only the one who owns much but also one who needs little.*" Frugality is important in this age and day when excess seems to be mistaken for excellence. It is especially relevant to the consumerism that is mistakenly interpreted as development.

*Eco-justice* (Ecological Justice) is another value. Eco-justice means justice for all. The concept of ecojustice covers a more extensive domain; that it includes the idea of responsibility towards all things living and non-living and the perception of the interconnectedness of all things.

Therefore, according to Skolimowski, *Reverence*, *responsibility*, *frugality* and *eco-justice* form the minimal core of intrinsic values for right conservation and sustainable development. They are ideal signposts and imperatives for action.

Besides, Robert Mellert is crucial of the industrial world which he says operates with a Frontier Mentality, an attitude described by economist Kenneth Boulding, historian Roderick Nash and others.

The Frontier Mentality is characterized by three precepts.

1. The world has an unlimited supply or resources for human use (not necessarily to be shared by a life form). In other words, "there is always more and it is all ours".

2. Second, human are apart from Nature, rather than a part of it.

3. Nature is something to conquer. Technology has become the tool by which

human subdue (control) nature and that it is also answer to many conflicts between human society and nature.

The frontier Mentality has been part of human thinking for many tens of thousands of years, perhaps all of human society. The Frontier Mentality sees human as separate from nature and superior to all of life forms. Many societies have continually sought to dominate nature. The Frontier Mentality is the dominant belief structure or paradigm of modern society but if humans persist in this way of life it will lead to the destruction of the earth and extinction of all forms of life. It has to be replaced and soon by a sustainable ethics according to Mellert. Sustainable ethics holds that the Earth has a limited supply of resources and that human beings are a part of nature and not in any superior to it. The main concept of sustainable ethics is that: "there is not always more". To develop a sustainable society we must learn that an infinite increase of material consumption in a finite world is not at all feasible. We must learn that ever-increasing production and consummation can only damage the life-giving environment. The important realization will led to new resource consumption strategies such as:

4. Curtailing excessive use of resources.

5. Reuse and recycling of all materials.

6. The use of more renewable resources (e.g.) sunlight, wind) and fewer non-renewable resources (coal and oil)

7. The control of population growth. Sustainable ethics embraces a respect for the land, air, water and all living things, including other people in other lands and in future generations.

In the above argument of the West are concerned with the problems of relation between human beings and his natural environment. Therefore, the basic idea of environmental ethics can be found in the Western traditions.

**4. Eastern Worldview and Environmental Ethics**

Eastern philosophy is characterized by four main aims in governed, namely a cosmological unity, a concern with the realities that lie behind everyday appearances, with self-deliverance and with ethical behaviour.

Nevertheless, one of the most important characteristic of the Eastern world view is the awareness of the unity and mutual interrelation of all things and events. In Eastern world view experiences of all phenomena in the world as manifestations of an oneness which is a very primary cause of all things, but nevertheless it can be called the wholeness in each individual or particular are unified as its parts. All things are seen as interdependent and inseparable parts of this cosmic whole. All are seen as different manifestations of the same ultimate reality.

In this respect, Eastern thought resolutely believes in the interconnectedness of all things and of the need to escape from the limits of individualism, which is connected with bodily pleasure and the illusion of separateness.

**4.1 *Theravāda* Buddhism and Environmental Ethics**

Buddhism is a religion with a strong empathy towards Nature. In fact Buddhism is a religion that was born in the forest so to speak, because Buddhism maintains that Truth can only be found in natural surroundings far from human habitats where greed, hatred, anger and delusion prevail. Moreover great events in Gautama Buddha? s life all took place in a forest or a park. He was born in a grove of Sal trees in *Lumbini* Park. He saw four omens in Mingala Park that inspired Him to renounce mundane life to lead the life of a recluse. He practiced austerity for six years in the forest and achieved enlightenment while meditating under the shade of a Bodi tree in *Buddhagaya*. He preached His first sermon in the Deer Park at *Migadawun*. His monasteries were located in places like the bamboo forest of *Weluwun* or the banyan forest of *Nigrodharuma*. He passed away and achieved *Nibbāna* in the Sal forest of *Kusinagara*. Nature in its pristine state encourages serenity of spirit. The Buddha obviously could not have achieved enlightenment in a bustling and noisy city where the purpose of life is to fulfill many desires of human beings.

Buddhism is not a philosophy of environmental conservation; environmental conservation was not its goal. Its goal is more sublime. But it is conservation -minded as its core. There are no explicit teachings on the environment but its foundation principle, the Law of *Kammā* together with the tenets that follow from this law provide conservation norms and values which are as true today as they were more than, 2, 500years ago.

The Law of *Kamma* is the fundamental principle of Buddhism. "The literal meaning of the word *Kamma* is something that is done or a deed. It also means a mental state that is instrumental in doing the deed, good or bad, wholesome or unwholesome.

According to this law each living being is the result of his thought, words and deeds throughout the cycle of birth and rebirth till we are liberated when we achieve the state of *Nibbāna*. Thus, depending on our *kamma* or what we have done, we are born and die again and again as sentient beings. Buddhists therefore believe that in the endless cycle of birth and rebirth, we may not always be born human. We may be born as celestial beings or as lower forms of life. Anyone can be born as an animal or an insect. So, most Myanmar Buddhists will not deliberately squash a bug or kill a small insect. We are thus taught to respect all forms of life. In the *Jataka*, birth stories of the Buddha, Myanmar children learn how the Buddha Himself went through the round of birth and rebirth as deer, quail, peacock, fish elephant, monkey and so forth. This tradition teaches us that all life is interconnected and that each one of us animal, human or otherwise is the result of our *Kamma*.

This respect for life as part of the Buddhist moral code is again to be found in the Five Precepts, which enjoins us not to kill, not to steal, not to commit sexual misconduct, not to lie and not to indulge in intoxicants. All Buddhists are called upon to observe at least these Five Precepts which are based on the Principle of Reciprocity. That is, do unto others what you would have them do unto you. These precepts against stealing can be interpreted widely as not taking more than what you actually need or deserve. It is moral prescription that helps one to control greed. Greed is one of the main causes of exploitation not only of others but of nature as well. So the Five Precept indeed teach us not only to respects all forms of life but also to control lust and greed. This can be assimilated as a norm for both environmental ethics and sustainable development. Other great thinkers have maintained that respect for life is a foundation value upon which important ethical systems can be established. "For Gandhi the foundation value was *ahimsa* or non-violence. For Schweitzer it was reverence for life".[8]

Then there is the "*Mijjimapadpaddā*", the Middle Way preached by the Buddha in His First Sermon after Enlightenment. He exhorts His five disciples to avoid the two extremes-the hedonistic life of sensuous luxury and a life of self-torment and self-denial. He preached what could be interpreted as "frugality and contentment" but with a far deeper meaning. For, this is the Noble Path that will certainly lead us to liberation. In the meanwhile it is the best guide to a moral life in this mundane world. The practice of the *Mijjimapadpaddā*, which was later, enunciated as the Eightfold Noble Path, is indeed the correct and proper guide to sustainable development. The exhortations, to do what is right (Right Action or *Samā Kāmanta*) and earn an honest living, Right Livelihood (*Samsā ājiva*), are especially relevant to sustainable development and consumerism.

Besides, the four sublime states (*Brahmavihāra*) may be named moral norms of the Buddhist ethics. They are pure love (*Mettā*), compassion (*Karunā*), sympathetic joy (*Muditā*) and equanimity (*Upekkhā*).

*Mettā* or loving-kindness is extending unlimited, universal love and good-will (*mettā*) to all living beings without any kind of discrimination, just as a mother loves her only child. *Karunā* is for all beings who are suffering, in trouble and affliction; translated as "compassion or pity". The third sublime state is *Muditā* (Sympathetic Joy) in other success, welfare and happiness. The chief characteristic of sympathetic joy is happy acquiescence in other s prosperity and success. Sympathetic joy embraces all prosperous beings and is the congratulatory attitude of a person. It tends to eliminate any dislike. *Upekkhā* (equanimity) in all vicissitudes of life, *Upekkhā* embraces the good and the bad, the loved and the unloved, the pleasant and unpleasant equally.

Therefore, *Mettā* embraces all beings, *Karunā* embraces suffers, *Muditā* embraces the prosperous and *Upekkhā* embraces the good and the bad, the loved and the unloved, the pleasant and unpleasant equally.

*Mettā* or loving kindness to all beings maintains that all beings are interconnected and interrelated. If we have faith in this, and Nature at this point is making it very clear that it is so, then the concept of *Mettā* is most appropriate state of mind to guide us in our relationship with the world and with other sentient beings. It is a norm, which hold equally well for an ethic of environmental conservation and sustainable development and as a social and moral guide in the world.

The Buddha's Teachings are full of compassion and selflessness. Interpreted in social terms they imply tolerance and equality. The essence of Buddhism means less greed, less hatred, less ignorance and more selflessness and generosity. And these are values essential for the well being of the world and all who live in and depend on it.

Buddhism contributes to protect the living beings and the natural phenomena. Buddha's teaching of the Four Cardinal values, keeping of the Five Precepts and to respect all forms of life show not to disturb all natural phenomena as possible as human can. Buddha also preaches to control human's greed and keep selflessness which are existing in the inner of the mind. Therefore the Four Cardinal Value is the chief, the key, the primary, the most important, the most essential virtue in Myanmar Buddhist Ethics.

**4.2. Hinduism and Environmental Ethics**

From the perspectives of many world religions, human beings, ' exploitation of nature' is unjust, immoral and unethical. For example, in the ancient past Hindus and Buddhist were careful to observe moral teachings to the treatment of nature. But, according to Dwivedi in this age of globalization the material orientation of the West has affected the cultures of the East. Dwivedi maintains that it is time to reawaken the ancient cultural and religious wisdom that once prevailed in India that evoked respect for Nature.

This ancient wisdom can provide at least three fundamental mainstays to help humans cope in a technological society. First, it defends the individual's existence against the depersonalizing effects of the techno-industrial process. Second, it forces the individual to recognize human failure and combine realism with idealism. Third while technology gives the individual the physical power to create or to destroy the world, religious and ethical teachings and traditions give moral strength to grow in virtue, by nurturing restraint, humility and liberation from self-centeredness. Directly or indirectly such cultural and cognitive beliefs can be a powerful source for environmental conservation and protection. The great religious of the world, each in their own way, offer a unique set of moral values and rules to guide human beings in their relationship with the environment.

**The Sanctity (holiness) of life in Hinduism**

The principle of the sanctity of life is clearly ingrained (deeply fixed) in the Hindu Religion. Only God has absolute sovereignty over all creatures. Thus, human beings have do dominion over their own lives or non-human life. This is explicitly stated in the *Vedic* teachings.

In the *Yajur Veda*, it is said that the sacredness holiness of God's creation means no damage may be inflicted (cause to suffer) on other species without adequate (complete) justification. Therefore, all lives, human and non-human are equal value and all have the same right to existence. According to the *Atharva Veda*, the Earth is not for human beings alone for other creatures as well.

The most important aspect of Hindu theology concerning to treatment of animal life is the belief that the Supreme Being was Himself incarnated in the form of various species God was incarnated first in the form of a fish then a tortoise, a boar, lion, monkey and a cow. Further, Hindu belief in the cycle of birth and rebirth where a person may come back as an animal or a bird gives these species not only respect but also reverence. This provides a solid foundation for the doctrine of ahimsa- non-violence against animals and human beings alike. God's grace can be received by not killing his creatures or harming his creations.

As early as in the time the Reg Veda, tree worship was quite popular and universal. The tree symbolized the various attributes of God. The Reg Veda regarded plants as having Divine Powers and healing properties. Trees were considered as being animate and feeling happiness and sorrow. It is still popularly believed that every tree has "tree deity ", who is worshipped with prayers and offerings of water, flower, sweet and encircled by sacred threads. The cutting of trees and destruction of flora were considered a sinful act.

The effectiveness of any religion in protecting the environment depends upon how much faith its believers have in its precepts and injunctions.

In the Hindu religion which is practiced as Dharma (way of life) many of its precepts became ingrained in the daily life and social institutions of the people. Hindu scriptures revealed a clear conception of the ecosystem. There had been codes of conduct (dharma) and humanity's relationship to nature. An important part of that conduct is maintaining proper sanitation.

Hindus considered the cremation of dead bodies and maintaining the sanitation of the human habitat as essential acts Water is considered by Hindus as powerful media of purification and also as a source of energy. The healing property and medicinal value of water has been universally accepted.

Hindu religion teaches a renunciation of worldly goods and preaches against materialism and consumerism. Such teachings could act as a great source of strength for Hindu societies in the struggle to achieve sustainable development.

In Hinduism, the principle of the sanctity of life is deeply fixed and love of the flora is very explicit. According to it, only God had sovereignty and God creates all. So, the people? s paying respect of His created things shows their love of God. Under Hinduism, people must avoid destroying the living beings and non-living things; all must be in their proper order of God, Mahatama Gandi said, "Nature had enough for everybody's needs but not for everybody? s greed." Gandi was a great believed in drawing upon the rich variety of spiritual and cultural heritages of India. How *satyagraha* movement, Chipko movement could easily be turned into a point for the awaken spirit of Hinduism.

**4.3. Taoism and Environmental Ethics**

Taoism is more than just a philosophy. It is one of the basics of Chinese culture and religion. In order to find peace and contentment of human, it must follow the "way" or "*Tao*" in Taoism. So it becomes "way of human" that is human morality, conduct or truth. Chinese tradition tends to be nature-centered or ecocentric in which the individual self is urged to merge into the natural or social environment as a whole. Especially, in regarding to environmental conservation, the basic principle of Taoism that emphasizes the true way of human being should be in harmony with the law of Nature is noteworthy. For Lao Tzu, the way to act for a human is to preserve the nature. Human? s goal is to achieve and to know laws of the nature. Human must be humble and content. By having and doing the law of nature is having and performing with *Tao*.

Concerning the natural environment, Chuang Tzu said human should keep nature as it is. According to him, "We should not change what is natural into something that is artificial" [13]But human? s nature is full of greed and desire. Human must control them to a certain limits. If human does not control his greed and pleasure he will not have happiness. As Lao Tzu said, "People believed that they can obtain happiness if their desires are satisfied. But when they try to satisfy too many desires, they obtain an opposite result. Thus, man should be contented with what one has and not to dry to satisfy too many desires. Similarly one should have only a little knowledge. Knowledge enables people to know more about the objects of desires and serves as a means to gain these objects with increasing knowledge people come to know about the objects of desire. They are therefore no longer contented with what they have, and as much cannot obtain happiness."[11]

Thus, human must control his greed and desires. He should avoid the extreme of consuming all natural sources or transforming them into consumes goods. Not using them at all for human beings is another extreme. Human must avoid those extremes. So, people should hold the method of Myanmar saying, "There must be a way for a squirrel to pass as well as a right for a beehive to exist."[12]People must use the natural resources only for what he needs. There is Western saying that when a person has more than he needs he is stealing from someone who has less than he needs.

The Taoist critique of the self opposes self-ness with the realization of *Tao*. The individual self and the other self are different versions of the same thing. Hence, in Taoism human being as well as all other beings containing ecological world are the same existence. The Taoist concept of "*wu-wei*", not over doing, will be discussed here to control human? s greed and to conserve the environment. *Wu* means to avoid overdoing and *wei* is doing what is necessary; in order to differentiate what is necessary and what is not necessary to do one must know its nature. The basic principle of Taoism is that one should be in harmony with the laws of nature. It is a theoretical guide line for human beings to follow and the method to be applied is *wu-wei*. *Wu-wei* does not mean to waste time or to delay time to do but to avoid over doing without necessity. It means that human must choose the proper time, place and conditions to do by his intelligence. Human must not do before its proper time falls. Attempting or endeavoring before the right time comes is one extreme; it is a kind of wasting energies. But delaying or wasting time to act even when the proper time falls is another extreme; it is a kind of delusion or doubt and out of alert. Knowing and doing that method is applying the *wu-wei* in practice. It means that one should be in harmony with, not against the fundamental laws of the universe. According to Taoists, the goal of human is to seek to become one with nature and it is virtue for all human being. In fact, the planet earth came into being not only for human being, but also for other living beings including wild life.

According to the basic principle of Taoism is to live in line with laws of nature, human must be harmony with nature or the process of the whole universe, and not to disturb its origin. Human must not against the fundamental laws of the universe.

In this respect, the naturalistic or eco-centered attitude of Eastern philosophy is more appropriate rather than the anthropocentric or ego-centered attitude of Western philosophy to find out a way of avoiding extreme egoism. Chuang Tzu said that "The duck? s legs are short, but if we try to lengthen, the duck will feel pain. The crane's legs are long but if we try to shorter, the crane will feel grief. "*Wu-wei* means "avoiding 'overdoing' or unnecessary things". This concept can support the conservation of the balance of ecological world in its superficial meaning. However it can be extended to the guidance for controlling human's desire and promoting the attitude of contentment. Then this attitude can be extended in the mutual relationship between human being and his natural environment. Therefore the Taoists method of *wu-wei* can be considered as one of the important approaches to resolve the above several problems which are human beings confront into this global age.

In the Taoist context, respect or reverence, attunement, and humility connote practicing the Tao in which humans are dependent like other creatures. Hence, Taoism advocates a life of simplicity. In the life of simplicity, cleverness or artificiality is abandoned, selfishness is minimized, and sensual desire is reduced. In other words, if one will act according to the principle of *wu-wei*, then he never act like over doing and he is capable to control his over desire in order that he can cultivate his ethical virtues such as respect or reverence, attunement, and humility. Nevertheless, the Taoist principle of *wu-wei* is capable to contribute the ecological virtue ethics for environmental conservation by its *wu-wei* which brings forth a middle way that is devoid of the extreme egoism and extreme altruism. In this respect, the eco-centered attitude of Taoist naturalism brings forth a consensus of opinion on the human responsibilities for the environmental issues of today s world. According to it all of the natural phenomena are under the determination of the law of nature. Therefore, all living beings have responsibilities to preserve their life themselves in order that it can be capable to keep the harmony with nature.

The above arguments of the East and West are concerned with the problems of relation between human and his natural environment. Therefore, the basic idea of environmental ethics can be found in the Eastern as well as Western thought.

In Eastern thought to preserve nature, not to destroy the environments and ecosystem have been advocated as the basic idea of human ethics. In Hinduism, the principle of the sanctity of life is deeply fixed and love of the flora is very explicit. According to it, only God had sovereignty and God creates all. So, the people's paying respect of His created things shows their love of God. Under Hinduism, people must avoid destroying the living beings and non-living things; all must be in their proper order of God.

Similarly Buddhism contributes to protect the living beings and the natural phenomena in ethical sense. Buddha's teaching of the "Four Cardinal values", keeping of the "Five precepts" and to respect all forms of life. This means that one of the basic moral conducts of human being implies that one should not destroy the natural phenomenon. Buddha also teaches to control human's greed and practice selflessness.

### 5. Confucianism's Concept *Chung-yung* (中庸) and Environmental Ethics

As a Chinese traditional thought, like Taoism, Confucianism also tends to be nature-centered or eco-centric in which the individual self is encouraged to merge into the natural or social environment as a whole. Here, the concept of "Mean" or in Chinese, *chung-yung* (中庸), will be focused in this research because it is able to suggest a significant ethical values that can apply to control human's greed and to conserve the natural environment. The term *chung-yung*, literally "centrality and universality," has been translated as moderation, the Mean, mean in action, normality, universal moral order, and so forth.[15] In other words, it has the meaning of central harmony or ? middle waywhich means avoiding the extreme actions and finding or acting the balanced course. Confucius said that The superior man [exemplifies] the Mean (*chung-yung*). The inferior man acts contrary to the Mean.[16]

Both the universe and the superior person follow the "Mean" or *chung-yung*. *Chung* means center, equilibrium, balance and *yung* means harmony. Thus, the way of *Chung-yang* involves a sense of justice and fairness, a spirit of tolerance, a state of harmony, a sense of propriety, an intuition of correct behavior, a knack of knowing and doing what is right in a particular situation, motivated by *jen* and guided by *li*.

Inquiry on the Great Learning:

"The great man regards Heaven and Earth and the myriad things as one body. He regards the world as one family and the country as one person… That the great man can regard Heaven, Earth and myriad things as one body is not because he deliberately wants to do so, but because it is natural to the humane nature of his mind that he do so. Forming one body with Heaven, Earth, and the myriad things is not only true of the great man. Even the mind of the small man is no different. Only he himself makes it small. Therefore when he sees a child about to fall into a well, he cannot help a feeling of alarm and commiseration. This shows that his humanity (*Jen*) forms one body with the child. It may be objected that the child belongs to the same species. Again, when he observes the pitiful cries and frightened appearance of birds and animals about to be slaughtered, he cannot help feeling an "inability to bear" this suffering. This shows that his humanity forms one body with birds and animals. It may be objected that irds and animals are sentient beings as he is. But when he sees plants broken and destroyed, he cannot help…feeling…pity. This shows that his humanity forms one body with plants. It may be said that plants are living thing as he is. Yet even when he sees tiles and stone. This means that even the mind of the small man necessarily has the humanity that forms one body with all. Such a mind is rooted in his Heaven-endowed nature, and is naturally intelligent, clear and not beclouded. For this reason it is "clear character".

For Confucians to fully realize themselves, it is not enough to become a responsible householder, effective social worker, or conscientious political servant. No matter how successful one is in sociopolitical arena, the full measure of one? s humanity cannot be accommodated without a reference to Heaven. The highest Confucian ideal is the "unity of human and Heaven," which defines humanity not only in anthropological terms but also in

cosmological terms. In the ***Doctrine of the Mean*** (*Chung-yang*), the most authentic manifestation of humanity is characterized as "forming a trinity with Heaven and Earth."

Confucius taught that humanity exists in an inter-relationship between heaven and earth. 'Heaven' is seen as the guiding force, giving direction to change and progress, while 'earth' provides the natural context and seasonal changes. Humanity has a moral task to work in balance with these other two forces.

Heaven is my father and Earth is my mother, and even such a small creatures I find an intimate place in their midst. Therefore that which fills the universe I regard as my body and that which directs the universe I consider as my nature. All people are my brothers and sisters, and all things are my companions. [18]

Underlying and unifying this triad of heaven, earth and humanity is the notion of *qi* (pronounced chee in English, as in 'cheetah'). This is understood as the material life force of the universe that runs through all things, integrating human beings with nature and driving the continuous process of change and creativity. This Confucian understanding of the universe as a holistic unity emphasizes the responsibility of every person to behave respectfully and with care to contribute to the general wellbeing of creation, acting as an orderly part of a collective effort. In this way the interests of humanity are served by looking after the interests of all of nature.

Confucians know that the earth is alive. We observe its presence, appreciate its beauty and participate in its creativity. We therefore share its richness and fecundity with all life on the "Blue Planet". This process is set within the greater context of humanity and Heaven.

Hence Confucians maintain that human beings should control and restrict their desires, so that natural resources can be rationally exploited and utilized, and their production and consumption kept in balance. Confucius himself resolutely opposed the misuse of resources.

The principle spiritual exercise of Confucianism is self-cultivation whose practice leads to true selfhood. Through following this virtue, we embrace or enable family cohesiveness, social solidarity, national integrity, and world peace. It provides an authentic possibility of transcending selfishness, nepotism, parochialism, ethnocentrism, nationalism, regionalism, and anthropocentrism.

Success in this matter is dictated by an ethic of responsibility informed by a transcendent vision. We do not become "spiritual" by departing from or transcending above our earth, body, family, and community, but by working through them. Indeed, our daily life is not merely secular but a response to an onto-cosmological decree. Since the Mandate of Heaven that enjoins us to take part in the great enterprise of cosmic transformation is implicit in our nature, we are Heaven's partners, and thus we can embody the creativity and spirituality of heaven through personal self-knowledge.

In this respect, the morally true conduct is decided by the right-minded one: the virtuous person is the standard and measure of things. The highest good for human, then, is self-realization which means one realizes his/her true self (the rational part). The virtuous person will act often in the interest of his friends and of his country, and if need be, will even die for them. He will surrender money, honour, and all the goods. Human is a social being and willing to live with other.

Humanity as a partner with both Heaven and Earth Confucianism sees humankind to have a deep and cosmic significance. This significance manifests itself in partnership with both Heaven and Earth forming the classic Chinese trinity of Heaven Earth and Humankind, together manifesting the true embodiment of nature itself. In the *Doctrine of the Mean* it is succinctly captured the essence of this cosmological thinking:

"Only those who are the most sincere [authentic, true and real] can fully realize their own nature. If they can fully realize their own nature; they can fully realize human nature. If they can fully realize human nature, they can fully realize the nature of things. If they can fully realize the nature of things, they can take part in the transforming and nourishing process of Heaven and Earth. If they can take part in the transforming and nourishing process of Heaven and Earth, they can form a trinity with Heaven and Earth."[19]

The idea of the unity of Heaven and Humanity implies four inseparable dimensions of the human condition: self, community, nature and Heaven. The full distinctiveness of each enhances rather than impedes, a harmonious integration of the others. The self, as a centre of relationships, establishes its identity by interacting with community variously understood, from the family to the global village and beyond. A sustainable harmonious relationship between the human species and nature is not merely an abstract ideal, but a concrete guide for practical living. Confucians believe that our human nature comes from Heaven and that the Way of Heaven is accessible through self-knowledge. They also believe that to understand the Mandate of Heaven we must continuously cultivate ourselves. This completes the triad of Heaven, Earth and humankind. Nature is as an unending process of transformation rather than a static presence, and as such is a source of inspiration by which we understand the dynamism of Heaven.

Therefore, saving the environment requires more than physical preservation; it calls for reverence and duty to the environment's greater self, nature. This extension of humanity carries ethical concerns for the environment. This is the distinguishing feature of Confucian ecological ethics: it does not give humans dominion over nature, nor does it sacrifice human development at the altar of pristine nature. Confucians maintain the oneness of humankind and nature, the harmony and unity between the two.

According to Toynbee, the twentieth century's intoxication with technology has led to the poisoning of our environment and has created the possibility that humanity may destroy itself. He believes that any solution to the current crisis depends on self-control. Mastery of the self, however, cannot be achieved through either extreme self-indulgence or extreme asceticism. The people of the twenty-first century must learn to walk the middle path, the way of moderation. [20] While Liang merely hinted at the possibility of alternative visions

In considering the individuality of the person, the Eastern philosophers do not divorce them from society as well as nature. They have synthesis outlook but the Western philosophers consider absolute individuality or individuality totally separate from nature and society. Since the Eastern thought has a synthesis outlook of individuality and society as well as individuality and nature (i.e. they believe that human's moral codes are determination of nature, and human's action are mutually related with nature) its outlook contributes to the protection and development of environment.

**Conclusion**

In the history of culture, accordingly to the development of sciences and technology human beings have changed the natural environment in the wrong way for human? s needs and utilities. The natural environment is destroyed and changed for human social welfares. Accordingly, the rain forests of the world are destroyed and the natural resources are extremely used up and become to be depleted. Consequently, the today's world of humankind is threatened by the problem of ecological imbalance which occur the several natural disasters.

As mentioned above, most environmental problems are the consequences of human's extreme egoism, greed and ignorance. Thus for restoring or sustaining the world ecological balance, human beings have to take overall responsibility. However, there is in need of a common opinion in order to resolve these environmental issues. To find out the appropriate approach for it, the mutual understanding and respect for respective cultures are needed to develop the tendency of co-existence among all countries in the world. In other words, all human beings have to control their extremes of self-centered attitude and cultivate the attitude of reverence for others in which either human being or other living creatures in nature are included.

At this point, the naturalistic or eco-centered attitude of eastern thoughts include Chinese philosophy is more appropriate the anthropocentric or ego-centered attitude of most western thoughts in order to find out a best way of avoiding extreme egoism. Particularly, the aim of Confucius philosophy is to have well organized or ideal society which bases on unity among Community, Earth and Heaven. Therefore, Confucius disliked intensely the human beings who abused the beautiful gift of the Heaven by violating the balance and harmony laid down by it. Thus, he strongly encouraged to control the extreme desires of human beings and to cultivate ourselves to follow the principles of Heaven and to have a harmonious relation among the triad of Heaven, Earth and Humankind.

In that case, the question how to cultivate right attitudes and conducts of human beings and what is the suitable method for it probably be brought to our attention. At this point, it can be raised up a suitable method which is known as "*chung-yung*" of Confucius's thought. *Chung-yung* is action of moderation or method of universal moral order and to have a notion of balance and harmony. The most authentic manifestation of humanity, the Confucius's *Chung-yung*, is characterized as "forming a trinity with Heaven and Earth." In the *Doctrine of the Mean* it is said that "Attaining equilibrium, heaven and earth will be in their right places and all things will come into being." In handling relations between the human and natural worlds, people need to observe the principle of equilibrium, so that the vitality and harmony of nature, the ecological balance of the natural environment, can be maintained properly.

According to Confucius, in the relation of human being and natural environment human behaves recklessly and exploits the nature. A sage who is human but attains the highest stage and he lives in accordance with laws of Heaven and Earth. Confucius seems to teach that if someone want to cultivate his/her moral standard, he/she must behave like sage or must follow the *chung-yung*, the middle way to take central harmony, which enables to control the extreme desire or greedy nature of human beings. The *chung-yung* enables to give adequate moral guidance for humankind that is how to live in accordance with the laws of nature without superseding.

In the same way, Buddhism, as a significant eastern thought like Confucianism, also contributes to protect the living beings and the natural phenomena in ethical sense. Buddha's teachings of the "Four Cardinal Virtues" and "Five precepts" are worthwhile philosophical contribution to respect all forms of life. All Buddhists are called upon to observe at least these Five Precepts which are based on the ? Principle of Reciprocity. This means that one of the basic moral conducts of human being implies that one should not destroy the natural phenomenon because natural world and the world of all living beings are coexist by means of correlation in Buddhist thought. Buddha also teaches to control human's greed and to practice selflessness. Similar to Confucius's *Chung-yung*, there is also the Middle Way in Buddhism called "*Mijjimapadpaddā*" which was preached by the Buddha in His First Sermon after Enlightenment. In this sermon He exhorts His five disciples to avoid the two extremes-the hedonistic life of sensuous luxury and a life of self-torment and self-denial.

Just as Confucius paves the way to live in harmony with social relation as well as nature, Aristotle and the Buddha also construct a harmonious way of deeds. Aristotle's way is known as "Golden Means" which aims at to achieve moral value. According to Aristotle, in doing actions human beings must keep temperate act which refers that excess and deficiency are vices. A mean is one which lies between two vices, excess and deficiency. As for example, the feelings of fear and confidence are vices or two extremes, but courage is a mean state. Thus, as for Aristotle, to have right action we must have means state or to behave in accordance with Golden Means.

According to Taoists, the goal of human is to seek to become one with nature and it is virtue for all human being. In fact, the planet earth came into being not only for human being, but also for other living beings including wild life. Hence, in Taoism human being as well as all other beings containing ecological world are the same existence. The Taoist concept of "*wu-wei*", not over doing, will be discussed to control human's greed and to conserve the environment. It is a theoretical guide line for human beings to follow and the method to be applied is *wu-wei*. *Wu-wei* does not mean to waste time or to delay time to do but to avoid over doing without necessity. It means that human must choose the proper time, place and conditions to do by his intelligence. Human must not do before its proper time falls. Attempting or endeavoring before the right time comes is one extreme; it is a kind of wasting energies. But delaying or wasting time to act even when the proper time falls is another extreme; it is a kind of delusion or doubt and out of alert. Knowing and doing that method is applying the *wu-wei* in practice.

Though the four worldly great persons, Aristotle, Buddha, Lao Tzu and Confucius established the moderate way of human conducts as a right principle in their thoughts the aims are not the same. Aristotle's intention is for moral virtue in social life. Even though the Buddha's goal is for the attainment of *Nibbanā* in next or final life, this way can also be applied in mundane affairs of present life in its level of secular world in which social and environmental conservation are also involved. The basic principle of Taoism is that one should be in harmony with the laws of nature. Confucius's aspiration is for the present life of community and physical environment.

In some Eastern and Western thought, to preserve and not to destroy the environments and ecosystem have been advocated as the fundamental idea of human ethics since ancient times. Nevertheless, it can be said that the self-centered attitude of human being is at the heart of the environmental issues. Particularly, the anthropocentric tendency or extreme humanistic way of thinking of humankind is primary cause. By means of the ethical guidance came from the Confucian conception of Mean or *Chung-yung*, it will be able to lessen human's extreme desires and to awaken the awareness of conserving the natural environment.

The highest Confucian ideal is the "unity of human and Heaven," which defines humanity not only in anthropological terms but also in cosmological terms. In the *Doctrine of the Mean* (*Chung-yung*), the most authentic manifestation of humanity is characterized as "forming a trinity with Heaven and Earth.

The ecological tendency of Confucian ethics enable to give the moral conscience of people in which several relationships between individuals as well as humankind and nature are suggested such as between one person and another, one generation and another, an individual and society, people and nature, partial interests and overall interests, immediate interests and long-term interests. The crossroads of two centuries presents a fitting occasion to pause and reconsider the eternal theme of how to achieve harmony between human civilization and nature. At this time, it is the adequate occasion offered great opportunity to have real understanding the crucial role of ecological harmony between humankind and natural world through the application of Confucian ethical doctrine of the "Mean in this ? greening century.

**Notes**

1Wing-Tsit Chan(trans. & Compl.). (1973). *A Source Book in Chinese Philosophy*. Princeton, New Jersey: Princeton University Press. pp.98-99.

2Xu Yuanxing, (2007) *Confucius -A philosopher for the Ages*. China: International press. p-28.

3Wm. Theodore de Barry (1964) *Sources of Chinese Tradition*. New York and London: Columbia University Press, p.15.

4Page Michael (1988) *The Tao of power*. London: Green print an imprint of the Merlin press Ltd. P 49.

5Heneryk Skolimowski (1993) *Reverence for life* in (eds) Engle. R.J and /J.G Engel. London: Ethics of Environment and Development University of Arizona Press. P.223,

6 Daw Kyi Kyi Hla. (2010). *The Ethics of Environmental Conservation*. Yangon: Myanmar Academy of Arts and Sciences. p.23.

7Ashin Thittila. (1992). *Essential Themes of Buddhist Lectures*. Yangon: Department of Religious Affairs. p.176.

8 Heneryk Skolimowski (1993) *Reverence for life* in (eds) Engle. R.J and /J.G Engel. London: Ethics of Environment and Development University of Arizona Press. p.222.

9Ashin Thittila. (1992). *Essential Themes of Buddhist Lectures*. Yangon: Department of Religious Affairs. p.77.

10 O.P. Dwivedi. *Satyagaraha for Conservation*: Awakening the Spirit of Hin-

duism in (eds)J. Ronald Engle and Joan Gibbs Engel, Ethics of Environmental Development (ed). pp. 201-211.

11 Fung Yu-Lan. (1966). *A Short History of Chinese Philosophy*. New York: Macmillan Publishing Co., Inc. p. 96

12 Myanmar saying

13 Fung Yu-Lan. (1966). *A Short History of Chinese Philosophy*. New York: Macmillan Publishing Co., Inc. p. 100.

14 H. G. Creel. (1953). *Chinese Thought (from Confucius to Mao Tse-Tung)*. USA, Chicago: University of Chicago Press. p36.

15 Wing-Tsit Chan (trans. & Compl.). (1973). *A Source Book in Chinese Philosophy*. Princeton, New Jersey: Princeton University Press. pp. 98-99.

16 Ibid.

17 Ibid., pp. 659-60.

18 Chang Tsai (Zhang Zai). (1963). "The Western Inscription," in Wing-tsit Chan, trans., *A Source Book of Chinese Philosophy*. Princeton: Princeton University Press. p. 497.

19 Tu Wei-ming. (1989). *Centrality and Commonality: An Essay on Confucian Religiousness*. Albany, NY: State University of New York Press. p. 77.

20 Ikeda Daisaku. (1966). *A New Humanism*. New York: Weatherhill. p. 120.

References

1. Chang Tsai (Zhang Zai), "The Western Inscription," in Wing-tsit Chan, trans., *A Source Book of Chinese Philosophy* (Princeton: Princeton University Press.

2. Creel, H. G. (1953) *Chinese Thought*. New York: Printed in the United State of America Press.

3. Daisaku Ikeda (1966) *A New Humanism*. New York: Weatherhill.

4. K. Sri Dhammananda (1989) *How to Live Without Fear & Worry*. Kuala Lumpur, Malaysia: Publication of the Buddhist Missionary Society.

5. Dwivedi, O. P. *Satyagaraha for Conservation*: Awakening the Spirit of Hinduism in (eds)J. Ronald Engle and Joan Gibbs Engel, Ethics of Environmental Development (ed).

6. Fung Yu-Lan (1966) *A Short History of Chinese Philosophy*. New York: A Division of Macmillan Publishing Co., Inc.

7. Kyi Kyi Hla, Daw (2010) *The Ethics of Environmental Conservation*. Yangon:

U Sein Min Secretary, Journal Publication Committee, Myanmar Academy of Arts and Sciences.

8. Michael, Page (1988) *The Tao of power*. London: Green print an imprint of the Merlin press Ltd.

9. Skolimowski, Heneryk (1993) *Reverence for life* in (eds) Engle. R. J and /J. G Engel. London: Ethics of Environment and Development University of Arizona Press.

10. Thittila, Ashin (1992) *Essential Themes of Buddhist Lectures*. Yangon: Department of Religious Affairs.

11. Wing-Tsit Chan(trans. & Compl.). (1973). *A Source Book in Chinese Philosophy*. Princeton, New Jersey: Princeton University Press.

12. Xu Yuanxing, (2007) *Confucius-A philosopher for the Ages*. China: International press.

13. hongyong (Doctrine of the mean), XXII. See Tu Wei-ming, Centrality and Commonality:An essay on Confucian Religiousness (1989) (Albany, NY: State University of New York Press.

# The Value of Confucian Eco-Perspective for Environmental Protection

Yao Xinzhong (Prof. at Renmin University of China)

Are there any philosophical resources within the Confucian tradition that can be used for our reconstruction of human-nature relationship? Many people have pointed to the Confucian concept of *tian ren he yi* 天人和一 or the harmonious unity between nature and humanity as a significant contribution to modern environmental philosophy. In the assessment of the ecological implications of this Confucian concept articulated in early Confucian texts①, this paper argues that, different from a commonly held interpretation that Confucian eco-perspective is simply a fusion of humanity and nature, it is in fact composed of two contradictory orientations, one *ren* 人-centred (roughly anthropocentric) and the other *tian* 天-centric (nature-centric in a specific sense), which correspond generally to the two major camps of environmental philosophy in the twentieth century. It is proposed that these two orientations have different yet related functions: the *tian*-centred understanding establishes a metaphysical and religious framework for Confucian eco-ethical norms, in which ecological prohibitions and policies are built into the political structure, while the *ren*-centred orientation provides Confucians with a practical value and meaning for protecting environment. The former is the core or foundation, while the latter is the application or superstructure. However it is further argued that early Confucian masters did not end their consideration of human-nature relationship with a dualistic philosophy; rather they searched for the way of how these two 'centres' could be unified as one holistic principle to provide a theoretical and practical guidance for our understanding of the posi-

① Primarily in the recordings of the teachings of early Confucian masters, particularly Confucius (Kongzi, 551-479 BCE), Mengzi (385? -312? BCE) and Xunzi (310-219? BCE).

tion of humans in the universe.

**Anthropocentrism and Ecocentrism**

Modern environmental philosophy is an amalgamation of a variety of philosophical, ethical and religious claims and arguments essentially concerning the relationship between humans and eco-environment. In general two fundamental principles dominate the discussion of twentieth century environmental issues, one anthropocentric and the other ecocentric. The former represents the mainstream of traditional as well as modern philosophy in the West, claiming that all environmental problems must be understood and solved in the light of humanity's own interests and for human benefits, while the latter, represented by such theories as earth ethics and animal rights, protests against the anthropocentric paradigm, insisting that eco-system has its own rights and value, and therefore commands moral respect①. This understanding prompts some philosophers to place the blame of most profound environmental problems squarely on the anthropocentrism that sees everything and values everything from the human point of view, and to argue that guided by anthropocentric philosophy we humans have been so easily prepared to look after our own interests in any circumstance, frequently at the expenses of environment, and to extend the care and concern from humans at the centre to the environment only if this would do good to ourselves. Developed along with this criticism, an eco-philosophy called 'deep ecology' emerges to displace the human being from the centre of the moral universe②. It is proposed that whole natural configurations of animals and plants, namely ecosystems, have their intrinsic values independent of human existence and employment. The moral respect that 'deep ecology' and other 'new' philosophies require for Nature and natural environment lays the foundation for an eco-ethics known as eco-centrism.

Diametrically opposing to each other, two kinds of environmental philosophy developed from these two principles have nevertheless been in a constant interaction, which is the driving force of environmental awareness and eco-friendly policies in

---

① For example, Holmes Rolston, III, *Philosophy Gone Wild*: *Essays in Environmental Ethics*, Buffalo, 1986, Prometheus Books.

② For deep theology, see Arne Naess *Ecology*, *Community and Lifestyle*. Cambridge, 1989, CUP, and Bill Devall, George Sessions, *Deep Ecology*: *Living as if Nature Mattered*, Salt Lake City, 1985, Peregrine Smith Books.

western countries. However at the same time we must also see that the artificial opposition between anthropocentrism and eco-centrism is a typical refection of the way of dualistic thinking and is no more than a revision of the traditional object-subject dualism, which are not necessarily the sole contents of an environmental philosophy. Alternatives have existed that may shed light on our rethinking of human-nature relationship, and Confucianism is no doubt one of them for constructing an environmental philosophy in which excessive pairs of anthropocentric understandings and eco-centric theories are juxtaposed to expatiate on the interrelatedness and interdependence of humanity and nature.

**Confucian Eco-Principle**

Is there anything that can be called 'eco-ethics' or environmental philosophy in the Confucian tradition? As a traditional school of thought, Confucianism does not have a systematic doctrine as such. However, there are many ideas and arguments that can be seen as elements of an environmental perspective that sees human-nature relationship as dynamic, interrelated, and interdependent. For example, Confucian masters deliberated on the anthropo-cosmic interrelationship in which humans were given prime responsibilities, and provided a holistic reconstruction of the organic universe that is empowered by material force (*qi* 氣). When examining these elements, however, we find that underlying them is an understanding that humans and their natural circumstances (represented by the Chinese word 'tian', temperately translated as 'Heaven') must be harmonised rather than opposed to each other. This is what we call 'the unity of humanity and Heaven', *tian ren he yi*.

Is this fundamental Confucian commitment anthropocentric or eco-centric? Two kinds of the answer to this question have been proposed by modern scholars when they come to tackle this question. One suggests that the Confucian unity of Heaven and humans is essentially human-centred, because Confucians place the greatest emphasis on human matters and human responsibility, and the Confucian ideal is to establish the grant unity (*da tong*) in human society. There is no doubt that Confucian masters primarily considered human own interests in their metaphysical and cosmological understandings, but at the same time they also contributed human success to the following of cosmic norms, which in one sense can be said to be of nature-centrism. The second view of modern scholars with regard to the Confucian *tian ren he yi* is that this principle is neither anthropocentric nor nature-centric, but anthropo-natural unity. It seems that scholars in this position catch the essence of Confucian doctrines, and rightly point out that Confucians seek the meaning and value in the unity and harmony of humans and nature, rather than in their dichotomy or opposition. Interpreted as such the Confucian understanding of anthropo-cosmic relationship stimulates so much imagination among modern environmental activists and thinkers who believe that it outlines for us a new philosophy and new action-guideline for dealing with environmental problems. However scholars who support this position have not paid sufficient attention to the complicated nature of the Confucian eco-perspective. At the surface it seems that *tian ren he yi* does not make any claim on either side, humanity or nature. However, looking at various expressions of tian-human relations, we can see clearly that this perspective is not unitary; it contains both anthropocentric and eco-centric elements, two seemingly contradictory perspectives contained in one system. Are they really contradictory? If they are, then how can they be put into one principle that forms the core of the Confucian metaphysical, epistemological and ethical doctrines?

To answer these questions we must come to understand that these two parts are in fact meant at different levels, one at the metaphysical level and the other at practical and ethical level, and they are integrated into one principle through the flexible interpretations of *tian* by the Confucians.

There are metaphysical and natural dimensions in the contents and extensions of the Chinese word *tian*, which can be roughly represented by Heaven and Nature. As Heaven, tian is meant to be the ultimate being or power or force that provides the human and natural worlds with a spiritual and metaphysical source and sanction. Therefore the unity of humanity and Heaven in this sense is meant for a religious and metaphysical ideal in which humans follow the mandate of heaven (tian ming) to achieve their own destiny. As Nature, on the other hand, tian (frequently together with di, the earth) stands for the world that exists outside humanity but provides humans with necessary circumstances and material conditions. In this sense the unity between humans and nature is meant for an ecological and ethical norm that guides human activities.

**Tian-centric Perspective**

Different interpretations of *tian* lead to different understandings of tian-ren relationship, which in turn results in different positions of humans in this relationship. In the metaphysical and religious realms, tian or Heaven or Nature is always seen at the centre of its relation with humans. Either as the supreme agent (or Lord) who generates human beings as well as ten thousand things, or as the ultimate power that guarantees the universe runs its own course, tian, spiritual Heaven or the natural entity, dominates, and its/his discipline humans must follow. The value and meaning humans may gain from their relationship with *tian* come from obedience of the heavenly law or mandate. In this 'uneven' relationship a 'tian-centrism' is generated which has significant implications for Confucian understanding of eco-philosophical issues, and accounts for the spiritual meaning of Confucian eco-norms and principles. Only by placing Confucian eco-perspective on its metaphysical ground can we understand how an eco-centric dimension can be derived from a fundamentally religious commitment, and why Confucian eco-norms must not be seen as simple prohibitions and temporary measures.

Firstly *tian* is the cause or reason of the world and human beings. It is believed that tian produces all the people and establishes laws for them ('天生烝民,有物有則',《诗经·大雅·荡之什·蒸民》), and that tian initiates and sustains the generation and regeneration of the universe. Based on these understandings it is suggested that all existences and beings have a sacred nature, and that humans have no right to abuse them. Therefore the Confucian prohibitions with regard to environment are not simply political policies and for human benefits. Rather they arise from their belief in the creative power of tian and its spiritual values.

Secondly, it is believed that tian produces ten thousand things by its own laws and endows changes with a rhythm. These laws are manifested in the succession of four seasons and in the process of cosmic evolution, which Confucius described as: 'There are the four seasons going round and there are the hundred things coming into being' ('四时行焉,百物生焉'《论语·阳货》). Therefore humans must adjust their behaviour according to the same regularity. As far as environment is concerned, 'in conformation with seasons' (以其时,《礼记·祭义》) is a fundamental Confucian norm against which an action is judged. This norm is articulated throughout Confucian classics and consummates particularly in 月令 section of the *Book of Rites*. These regulations should be seen as a response to the supreme authority of *tian*, and as part of the mysterious interaction between spiritual Heaven and humans (天人感应).

Thirdly *tian* is taken as the source of moral power or virtue (*de* 德), which humans must extend to other people as well as to natural beings and things. Confucius claimed that *Tian* had begot 'virtue' in him ('天生德于予',《论语·述而》). The core of the moral power or virtue is ren or benevolence. We humans should treat other people in 'benevolence'. In the same token we should also treat animals and plants with benevolence. This is what Mengzi called for 'being benevolent towards the people and taking care of all things' 仁民爱物'(《孟子·尽心上》). Taking care of things is an eco-norm, but this norm is not a political design. It is a logic extension of being benevolent to the people. If 'being benevolent to the people' is what tian has bestowed to everyone and is humans' innate nature, then 'taking care of things' is also what tian has imparted to us and is our innate nature. In this sense we can say that all Confucian eco-norms are extended from the centre where tian occupied the commanding position.

Fourthly, as the supreme authority Tian commands respect both in religious and in ethical terms. Confucians in fact take the respect of the laws or mandate of Heaven as one of the criteria by which junzi or gentlemen or persons of virtue are differentiated from *xiaoren* 小人 or morally underdeveloped persons ('君子有三畏：畏天命，畏大人，畏圣人之言。小人不知天命而不畏也，狎大人，侮圣人之言.'《论语·季氏》) Here 'standing in awe' of the Mandate of Heaven is both religious and eco-ethical. The people who stand in awe of the heavenly mandate would conscientiously respect what natural laws command and would be in harmony with all creatures and things, while those who do not would mostly likely behave against natural laws and therefore damage environment.

Fifthly, tian is the ultimate end of human cultivation and services. Only after humans have understood

their own nature thoroughly can they understand Tian and serve Tian①. Aimed at being part of tian, humans are required to cultivate their own nature, which underlies all the prime motives of Confucian action plans. Humans are required to extend their own nature, by which they can extend the nature of other beings and things, which in turn enables them to be able to participate the transformation and generation of Heav-

① D. C. Lau (tr.) *Mencius*, 7A:1, Penguin Classics, 1969.

*en and Earth, and therefore to be able to stand with them in a trinity*①.

Anthropocentric perspective

The *tian*-centrism has laid foundation for Confucian eco-perspective, enabling Confucians to think of human-nature relationship in metaphysical terms. Fundamentally ethical by nature, however, Confucian philosophy comes to speculate on the concrete matters that arise from the human interaction with the variety of natural phenomena. This brings us to the ethical and political level on which Confucian eco-perspective is constructed.

Different from its European counterpart, Confucian philosophy does not merge itself in the meditation on cosmic essence and laws. Confucian metaphysical consideration is, to the best, speculative by nature and instructive in function. It is primarily meant to provide a precondition or foundation for various ethical and political schemes, rather than a meta-ethics itself. Therefore we have progressed only half way by pinpointing the metaphysically tian-centric understanding. If we intend to draw a holistic picture of the Confucian perspective we have to go further to examine its practical arena, where humans initiate and eco-system is subjected to the human requirements.

Many scholars note that Confucianism is essentially a humanistic tradition because it is concerned primarily with the solution of human problems and searches for the ideal way of life. However, they have not clearly explained how the Confucian *tian ren he yi*, a tian-based cosmological principle, has become essentially anthropocentric. Tu Wei-ming once draws us a Confucian diagram in which the self is at the centre, and is then extended to the family, community, society, state and the universe. This applies both to individual human beings and to the human race as a whole. As individuals, each human is born with a value and a responsibility, for which he/she must fulfil, while as the human race, humanity has a value higher than that of an animal or thing. When hearing that the stable was burnt down, Confucius first cared about the people who worked at the stable, rather than about horses ('厩焚。子退朝，曰："伤人乎?"不问马'《论语·乡党》). This humanistic philosophy has been carried out through all Confucian classics, and leads to a conviction that humans are the spirit of

① *The Doctrine of the Mean*, *Chapter* 22. *See* Wing-tsit Chan (ed.), *A Source Book in Chinese Philosophy*, Princeton University Press, 1963, p. 108.

ten thousand things(‘惟人万物之灵’《尚书·周书·泰誓上》);and that humanity is the summit of the virtues of Heaven and earth, the combination of yin and yang, and the finest force of the Five Elements(‘故人者其天地之德,阴阳之交,五行之秀气也’《礼记·礼运》)。

Since humans are on the top of the creature ladder, then they are by logic endowed with the ability and capability to control the process of social as well as natural evolution. There is no doubt a positive side of human control and interference of the natural world, because it is meant to protect it. Human control and interference, however, are primarily for the benefits of humans, and are therefore utilitarian in function. Mengzi made it plain that all measures for protecting environment, such as following the seasons and prohibiting overlumbering, are for the interests of human community and society, and eco-concern is in essence a concern of human own benefits: ‘As you do not interfere with the busy seasons in the fields, then there will be more grain than the people can eat; if you do not allow nets with too fine a mesh to be used in large ponds, then there will be more fist and turtles than they can eat; if hatchets and axes are permitted in the forests on the hills only in the proper seasons, then there will be more timber than they can use’(不违农时,谷不可胜食也;数罟不入洿池,鱼鳖不可胜食也;斧斤以时入山林,材木不可胜用也;谷与鱼鳖不可胜食,材木不可胜用,是使民养生丧死无憾也;养生丧死无憾,王道之始也。《孟子·梁惠王上》)

In the minds of Confucians, it is highly recommendable to protect rather than disrupt the natural growth of natural things: not to end the lives of plants prematurely(不夭其生)and not to interrupt the maturation of aquatic animals(不绝其长), which seems to indicate that Confucian eco-norms imply that the eco-system has its intrinsic value. However, this is a misunderstanding. Not like Buddhism where universal compassion is applied to all living things, Confucianism does not specify that compassion should be extended to non-human beings as they are. Natural beings and eco-matters are of value only in their relations with humans, and in their being good to human society. Just as we can see clearly in the case of Xunzi, seemingly eco-protective measures are, in the end, only to provide more food and materials for the people: ‘By plowing in spring, weeding in summer, harvesting in autumn and storing up in winter, the four activities are not out of the proper seasons; thus the production of the five grains is not interrupted, and the people have more than enough to eat. The ponds, lakes, pools, streams, and marshes being strictly closed during the proper season is the reason that fish and turtles are in plentiful abundance and the people have surplus for other uses. The cutting and pruning, the growing and planting, not being out of their proper seasons is the reason the mountain forests are not denuded and the people have more than enough timber.（春耕、夏耘、秋收、冬藏，四者不失时，故五谷不绝，而百姓有余食也。污池渊沼川泽，谨其时禁，故鱼鳖优多，而百姓有余用也。斩伐养长不失其时，故山林不童，而百姓有余材也。《荀子·王制》）

The anthropocentric nature of Confucian eco-protective measures suggests that Confucians would support environment protection if it is useful and good for the people, but they could, potentially, also support the abuse or exploitation of natural resources if this was required to feed the people and to provide them with sufficient, for example, firewood and timber. This might be one of the reasons why in Chinese history there were no consistent policies with regard to environment protection, and natural resources were subject to overexploitation, although its was aware of the necessity of protecting them.

Another feature of Confucian anthropocentrism is that it is profoundly moralised. In contrast to Western anthropocentric philosophy where humans become mighty and superior because of reason (early Greek philosophy), soul (Christian philosophy) or knowledge (modern empiricist philosophy), Confucians believe that humans are superior to natural beings such as animals only because of their moral sense. Mengzi specifically points out that there is little by which humans are differentiated from beasts, which those of virtues retain while the morally underdeveloped have lost（'人之异于禽兽者几希。小人去之，君子存之'《孟子·离娄下》）. How can each of us preserve this distinguishing feature of humans as humans? This question leads them to place a great emphasis on the self-cultivation, and call for the people in superior positions to cultivate themselves before requiring others who are below them to follow.

Confucian anthropocentric perspective has a psychological potential to become anthropo-ecological co-existing and co-flourishing. Starting from humans at the centre, Confucians extend their moral understanding to natural existences and phenomena, and construct an interactive human-nature relationship. Applying this understanding to human-nature relationship, Confucians tend to make use of empathy to speculate the interrelatedness of humans and natural existences. Animalised plants deserve human respect, because they are believed to have a spirit or soul. Mountains and rivers are believed to be able to feel painful or happy, and this is taken as the reason for protecting them from being damaged. Most of all, Confucians apply their ideas of moral duties and virtues to how humans should treat natural beings and things. Mengzi first developed the inner side of Confucian benevolence and extended this internal moral feeling to non-human beings, arguing that once having seen animals alive, a Confucian gentleman could not bear to see them die, and once having heard their cry, he could not bear to eat their flesh'(君子之於禽兽也,见其生,不忍见其死;闻其声,不忍食其肉《孟子·梁惠王上》)。Wang Yangming (1472-1529) of the Ming Dynasty further developed this into a Confucian perspective on the unity of human beings and all things in the universe. He took the benevolent heart as the starting point and finally reached the one body of humankind and the world. He argued that the Confucian benevolence was to be one body with the universe. When one saw a child about to fall into a well, he argued, one could not help feeling alarm and compassion. This fact showed that one's benevolence formed one body with the child. Further, when one observed the pitiful cries and frightened appearance of birds and animals about to be slaughtered, one could not help feeling an 'inability to bear' their suffering. This fact, he again argued, showed that his benevolence led him to unify with the birds and animals. Even when one saw plants broken and destroyed, one could not help feeling pitiful. This fact showed that his benevolence led him to be in a unity with the plants too. Even when one saw tiles and stones shattered and crushed, one could not help feeling regret. This fact showed that his benevolence formed one body with tiles and stones①.

It is in this kind of reasoning, human-nature relationship is essentially personalised and moralised. The bad behaviour that has caused damage to environment is described as 'not benevolent' (*bu ren* 不仁); the action that has led to the overexploitation of natural resources not according to their seasons is called 'bu yi' (not righteous), while the killing of animals and cutting off trees randomly is condemned as '*bu xiao* 不孝' (not filial piety 曾子曰:'樹木以時伐焉,禽獸以時殺焉。夫子曰:"斷一樹,殺一獸,不以其時,非孝也"《礼记·祭义》。). In this moralised consciousness, Confucians finally developed a holistic vision of the world, in which all people are taken as one's brothers and sisters and all things as one's companions ('民胞物与'《张载·西

---

① *Wang Yangming Quanji*, Shanghai Guji chubanshe, 1992, p. 968. See Wing-tsit Chan (ed.) *A Source Book in Chinese Philosophy*, Princeton University Press, 1963, pp. 659-660.

铭》)。These moral terms produced a powerful effect on prohibiting the abuse of eco-system and on environment protection. They also added an extra weight to human responsibility towards environment. This evidences again that anthropocentrism does not necessarily lead to the opposition between humans and nature. Rather, in an ethical framework, it can produce an eco-awareness that natural environment is itself meaningful and valuable, in which eco-centrism and anthropocentrism are finely combined and balanced.

**Confucian Perspective in Modern Environment Philosophy**

In face of environmental problems, philosophers and activists investigate the cause and reason for these problems, in which they find the conflict and opposition between anthropocentrism and eco-centrism. Environmental philosophy moves from practical consideration to metaphysical understandings, and some philosophers argue that in order to rid us of the risk of environmental disasters, we must first rid ourselves of the anthropocentric philosophy that guides our behaviour. While acknowledging that there is a good point in the examination of environmental problems in terms of anthropocentrism and eco-centrism, we must understand that humans and nature or eco-environment are locked in one relationship, and we cannot totally isolate one from the other. No absolute anthropocentric philosophy would make sense without associating humans with their metaphysical and natural sources; nor eco-centric theory would be effective if eco-system was placed against human interests. In this aspect, Confucianism can be an alternative, since it seeks meaning and value in the harmony between tian (Heaven or nature) and humans, rather than in their opposition.

It is not a Confucian view that *tian* and *ren* are totally equal and balanced. Although Confucians in history have not constructed a proper environmental philosophy as we see in the modern world, it does have both anthropocentric and eco-centric elements, which through reconstruction can become an eco-perspective meaningful to the modern world. There are contradictions between these two parts. According to the metaphysical understanding, all beings and things in Nature have their intrinsic positions irrespective of their value to human beings. In this sense respect of environment is part of the respect required in 'being' itself, and the protection of eco-system is embedded in the process of generation and regeneration (生生). On the other hand, humans are regarded as the highest representation of the cosmic power, with a prime responsibility for the world, and natural beings and things are meaningless without being examined in association with human civilisation. This is essentially a human-centred doctrine. In its positive side, this doctrine requires human beings to be responsible not only to humans themselves but also to the environment in which they live and act. However in its negative aspect, we can see clearly that whatever humans do, they are after their own interests, to meet their own needs and to satisfy their own desires first. This inevitably causes a lot of environmental problems. Therefore to make the Confucian perspective relevant to the modern world, we must reduce its negative extension, while maximising its positive values.

Understood as one principle with two orientations, Confucian eco-perspective can make some contribution to modern environmental philosophy. Firstly it rejects either extreme of anthropocentrism or eco-centrism as an independent perspective for the solution of environmental problems; instead it subjects both to a higher principle in which human society and eco-system have each their own values and positions. Secondly it refuses to accept purely abstract views concerning human-nature harmony, and confirms that harmony must come from interaction and interdependence of humans and their environment. Thirdly it rejects the static unity of humanity and nature in which humans and natural environment exist and operate in parallel and without mutual interference; rather it is seriously concerned with the prospect of human development in which a dynamic harmony between human action and ecological adjustment. It is these three perspectives that we must take into account in our reconstruction of a proper relationship between the human realm and the environmental world.

# Part Two: Cross-Cultural Conversation

## Confucianism and Humanism: Chances for a Global Humanism in the Conflict of Cultures[①]

Helwig Schmidt-Glintzer 施寒微

**English Summary**

Whereas in China there is a long tradition to conceive mankind as a great family there are in the West still concepts alive who propose a hierarchy between Western (white) and non-Western societies. The historical experience of China and particularly the Confucian tradition provides examples of overcoming such arrogant behaviour. Starting from a concept of a society putting the individual as well as its social context in the centre the paper proposes a theory of humanism compatible with the continuation of different cultures. It will also proof that there are ways to accommodate a Confucian attitude with the European heritage. Although it seems improbable that we find a common concept of heaven 天 it is not only feasible but necessary for the future of mankind that we establish means of communication and discourse to overcome obstacles and hindrances in aiming at a peaceful world.

**Preliminary Remarks**

That man is wolf to man has long been a commonplace. The justification for this view was not so much supplied by man's biological constitution and genetic disposition. It was rather European civilization, which had proved to be decisive of

---

① This paper is based on my contribution "Chances for a Global Humanism in the Conflict of Cultures", in: Jörn Rüsen, Hrsg., Approaching Humankind. Towards an Intercultural Humanism. Göttingen 2013, S. 250-266, but fundamentally revised.

mankind's fate over the last few centuries that provided the basis for the success of this assessment of man. While Immanuel Kant had still linked the concept of enlightened autonomy with an awareness of communal life①, Thomas Hobbes (1588-1679) had already resolved goodness "into the process of self-preservation and self-enhancement on the part of the individual's social behaviour".② Alois Hahn has summed this up as follows:

"[…] the state of socialization among men has to be regarded as *bellum omnium contra omnes*-everybody seeks their own advantage and uses all others as a means to that end.③ It is obvious that such an individualistic anthropology-everybody has 'a right to everything'④-as the realization of *homo homini lupus*⑤at the very beginning of modernity could not possibly encourage a positive theory of self-realization.⑥"

In general the rise of Europe and the ensuing 'Europeanization' of the world went along with a dehumanization of the racial or cultural other, and in spite of this it did not clash with the love of nature, of animals or with romantic love, all of which experienced-in a kind of compensatory move - a new heyday. Enemy-concepts went hand in hand with European expansion, in spite of a long-lived Enlightenment discourse. And yet, and this is another aspect of European Enlightenment, fairly early on the European policy of violence and conquest also came under severe criticism.⑦

**Man at the Centre**

The idea of a new humanism is based on merely an extended knowledge of mankind and its history, and it focuses its attention on man as a member of the entire hu-

---

① Cf. Theunissen, Michael: *Selbstverwirklichung und Allgemeinheit. Zur Kritik des gegenwärtigen Bewußtseins*, Berlin 1982, p. 7; cf. Haas, Alois M: "Selbstverwirklichung, in: *Georges Bloch Annual* 13/14 (2006/2007): 545-565, p. 549.

② Theunissen: ibid.

③ Hobbes, Thomas: *Vom Menschen*, *Vom Bürger*, Hamburg 1994, p. 83.

④ Ibid., p. 82.

⑤ Ibid., p. 59.-Haas draws particular attention to Jüngel, Eberhard: "Zum Wesen des Friedens. Frieden als Kategorie theologischer Anthropologie, in: Jüngel, Eberhard: *Ganz werden*, Tübingen 2003, pp. 1-39, besonders 3. *Homo homini lupus*, pp. 18-22.

⑥ Haas, Alois M.: op. cit., p. 549.

⑦ Cf. Pierre Kodjio Nenguié: "Rasse, Alterität und Humanität: Anmerkungen über die Afrikapolitik der Goethezeit. Zu Karl von Eckartshausens *Isogin und Celia*, *eine Geschichte von einem unserer schwarzen Brüder aus Afrika*, *von einem Mohren* (1786), in: *Das achtzehnte Jahrhundert* 33. 1 (2009): pp. 26-41.

man race. This inclusive trope is very ancient and finds its most pronounced expression in the Chinese tradition where it historically manifests itself in the genre of biography.[①] But it is also to be found in the Stoa and the discourse of natural rights in the early Modern Age. Such a new humanism is dominated by the principle of viewing all humans as part of the same species, and it considers all the variations of the attempts that have been made to exclude people from human society: Such acts of exclusion are obviously as unavoidable as they are an occasion for reflecting upon the possibility of inclusion or, where this proves to be impossible, of reconciling 'humanity' with a certain guarded distance.

The humanism referred to in this context is grounded in the basic human capacity for empathy, which to destroy has been attempted time and again and at all levels. Especially for the process of drilling soldiers some kind of negative conditioning has become the standard procedure, but it also figures in the rhetoric justifying torture as the ultimate means for state agencies to obtain information. The discourse of criminal psychology in the 18$^{th}$ century, the link between Enlightenment discourse and the formation of man belong in this context,[②] as much as the utter willingness to fight and kill on the part of the German officer corps with its 'humanist' education.[③]

The new humanism, however, is guided by the principle of including all humans without exception while at the same time being conscious of the fact that this claim is constantly under threat. The hope for this humanism is founded on the assumption that peaceful negotiation of conflicts will become the norm. The need for difference in the search for identity and for self-assertion, even at the price of denigrating the Other or entire groups of people, are accepted as part of reality. This acceptance is accompanied by the absolute resolve always to set off against it the capacity for empathy. This means that in education also it will be important to instil a 'culture of empathy'. At the same time this process will require institutions and, more generally, su-

---

① Mann, Susan: "Scene-Setting: Writing Biography in Chinese History, in: *The American Historical Review* 114.3 (June 2009): 631-639.

② Cf. Schott, Heinz: "'Born Criminals', 'Degenerates' and 'Psychopaths'. On the History of Criminal Psychology in Germany, in: *Transactions in Medicine & Heteronomous Modernization*, Tokyo 2009, pp. 33-47.

③ Cf. also the scrupulous reflection by Himmler, Katrin: *Die Brüder Himmler: eine deutsche Familiengeschichte*, Frankfurt/Main 2005.

pra-individual agencies in order to be able to minimize evil. ①

Another dimension to be considered in this context is the way we treat our dead, because "without a culture of burial and remembrance there can be no humaneness". ② This comes under the category of care in general, but then in a more special sense it means the care we take of the dead as well as of children since both birth and death are an integral part of human existence. Robert Harrison's observation that man only became human after having been driven out of paradise is highly pertinent. It is important to foster this conviction, which in Max Weber's words resembles what in the case of China has been labelled as "inner-worldliness", as well as the insight that man is man and not God. ③ In this regard there is wide agreement between Christian and Chinese religiousness, because after all the awareness of a lost Golden Age formed the basis of the Confucian world view. It is therefore not surprising that the Neoconfucians should have attempted to ascribe to the Confucian tradition "a strained relationship with the world". ④ Thus it is not our concern to regain paradise. On the contrary, it is life in the here and now that gets affirmed. At the same time it has to be acknowledged that there are asymmetrical processes of change that move at different rates of speed, which results in there being winners and losers of modernization. Thus the temporal dimension has always to be taken into account.

I am therefore proposing the following thesis: it is only by acknowledging the "clash of civilizations", to use Samuel Huntington's formula, that there is a chance of realizing a global humanism. This means that we also have to know how to deal with inequality, with guilt and fate, with responsibility and to whom it is to be attributed, but in an equal measure with forms of compensation, of forgetting, of forgiveness, of

---

① Cf. Thomä, Dieter: "Gespiegelte Perspektiven, in: *Frankfurter Allgemeine Zeitung* 147 (29. June 2009): 6 as a review of Breithaupt, Fritz: *Kulturen der Empathie*, Frankfurt/Main 2009. -Rizzolatti, Giacomo/Sinigaglia, Corrado: *Empathie und Spiegelneurone. Die biologische Basis des Mitgefühls*, Frankfurt/Main 2008.

② Robert Harrison in interview with Köhler, Andrea, in: *Neue Zürcher Zeitung* 146 (27./28. June 2009): 31.

③ Cf. Jüngel, Eberhard: "'Wir sollen Menschen und nicht Gott sein. Das ist die summa'. Zum Wesen des Christentums, in: *Weltreligionen. Verstehen, Verständigung, Verantwortung*, ed. by Karl Kardinal Lehmann, Frankfurt/Main 2009, pp. 113-134.

④ Cf. Metzger, Thomas A. : *Escape from Predicament. Neo-Confucianism and Chinas Evolving Political Culture*, New York 1977.

expiation and of pardon.[①] This will also be a matter of opening up possible choices of action with practical consequences. Such a comprehensive approach will enable us to conceive of the conflict of interests and the potential of the sciences in terms of a unified knowledge that is modelled on the ancient concept of *humanitas*, and thereby make our principles of action subservient to the requirement of a 'humane' life of the entire world community.

**Humanism: More than a period-term**

It should be agreed that-ever since each point of the globe can be reached within a few hours and since the early-warning interval of intercontinental missiles and intelligent high-precision weapons has dwindled to a very short time-it is now a matter of urgent necessity to reconstitute the older idea of *one* humanity on a global scale. One should therefore take into consideration whether the concept of humanism might not form a bridge between earlier discourses on humanity on the one hand and new ideas for the future under novel conditions on the other. This attempt might be aided by the fact that not only in the European tradition, but also in the cultures of East Asia that were influenced by Chinese thought, specific concepts of humanity and humanism have been evolved that could be joined together to form a new idea of humanism in an intercultural perspective. In Chinese culture the tradition of preserving human memory and personal history that is evidenced by the genre of biography might form a point of departure for such an enterprise as well as the customary role of the scholar, who with the sounds of the Zither emulates the harmony of the spheres, and who with brush, ink and paper inscribes himself in the intellectual tradition, and through doing both strives to perfect the formation of his personality. These activities, one could argue, come perhaps closest to realizing something one could designate as humanism. However, since it is a fact that the discourse of humanity, the concept of world literature, of world peace or even of "eternal peace"[②] was initially a result of the European Enlightenment, which brought in its wake an unprecedented domination of the

---

① Cf. Kodalle, Klaus-Michael: *Annäherungen an eine Theorie des Verzeihens*, Stuttgart 2006.

② Cf. Kant's essay of 1795 "Zum ewigen Frieden. Ein philosophischer Entwurf.

world,[①] we have to start with Europe. This is not to deny that in the history of mankind there have been similar processes of globalization, understood as the "intensification and acceleration of cross-border transactions accompanied by their extension in space" (Ulrich Menzel).[②] To name but one example: The rationalization period during the epoch of separate states that resulted in the foundation of the unitary Chinese empire in 221 B.C. was notable for a similar dynamic and ever since the $6^{th}$ pre-Christian century generated similar concepts of humanity and universality.

**Doubt and the disappointment of war**

As already pointed out above, it only makes sense to talk of global humanism if at the same time the existence of conflicts is acknowledged. Another aspect that is novel in the $20^{th}$ and $21^{st}$ centuries compared with all other previous processes of globalization resides in the fact that the globality we have now attained is irreversible, at least as far as we can imagine. It is true that processes of globalization have always alternated with critical counter-movements-something which can also be expected for the present or the near future and which has often been due to the circumstance that as a rule there are always winners and losers in the process of globalization. However, there are some signs that for the benefit of most people-if not for the survival of the species-it is necessary and sensible to do everything we can in order to avoid relapsing into a period of time before our present technological achievements, while at the same time reaffirming and guaranteeing the value system of universal human rights.

One obstacle to this is due to the concept of humanism itself, because from early on it had been systematically confined to European culture and was thereby withheld from mankind in its entirety as well as certain individuals, even though some thinkers

---

① It is no surprise that the idea of universality should originate in that part of the world from which the dynamics of change proceeded.

② Menzel, Ulrich: "Tausend Jahre Globalisierung im Rückblick aus der aktuellen Globalisierungsdebatte, in: Schmidt-Glintzer, Helwig (Ed.): *Neue Blicke auf alte Karten und die Dynamik der europäischen Kulturgeschichte*, Wiesbaden 2007, p. 137-209, hier p. 139.-intensification" means "that such cross-border activities are developing more rapidly than those that remain within national boundaries." (Ulrich Menzel).

like Kant, Herder and Humboldt emphatically sought to encompass all of the human race.① The failure of this project led to a disappointed humanism.② Thus Sigmund Freud in 1915 was justified to speak of the "disappointment of war".③ The concept also came under criticism from another perspective. In the lecture notes from a propaedeutic seminar on Schiller's *Letters on the Aesthetic Education of Man*, dated 4 November 1936, the following statement can be found:

"What does humanism want? The spiritual perfection of man?" For this one would have to know first what man is and what his perfection or imperfection consists in.④

This was said at a time when men who had had the benefit of a 'humanist' education were planning the Shoa, so that Albert Camus was right in remarking that "today's executioners are, as everyone knows, humanists. Therefore one cannot … be sufficiently distrustful of the humanitarian ideology."⑤

In spite of the prevailing tendency in the 20th century to discredit the concept of humanism, certain thinkers have tried to reconceptualise humanism. This was done in

---

① The confinement to national culture can also be found in Hans Georg Gadamer's on "The meaning of the humanist tradition". Cf. Gadamer, Hans-Georg: *Wahrheit und Methode*, 2nd ed., Tübingen 1965, pp. 1-39, esp. p. 6 below and p. 7 above. -I do not wish to gloss over counter-positions such as that of Giambattista Vico (1669-1744). Cf. Vico Giambattista: *Die neue Wissenschaft über die gemeinschaftliche Natur der Völker*. Edition from 1744 translated and introduced by E. Auerbach with an epilogue by W. Schmidt-Biggemann, Berlin/New York 22000.

② Accordingly to this an understanding of what is alien is not impossibly although seldom achieved. Cf. on this Osterhammel, Jürgen: *Die Entzauberung Asiens*, Munich 1998, pp. 24-25.

③ Cf. Freud, Sigmund: "Zeitgemäβes über Krieg und Tod (1915), in: Sigmund Freud, *Studienausgabe*, vol. IX, Frankfurt/Main 1974, pp. 33ff. -It is recommended to everybody to study the period around 1914 when the century that has not yet ended actually begins. Just read Thomas Mann's "Gedanken im Krieg" or simply consult the second volume of the journal "Neue Rundschau" from that first year of war.

④ Heidegger, Martin: *übungen für Anfänger. Schillers Briefe über die ästhetische Erziehung des Menschen*, ed. by Ulrich von Bülow. (= Marbacher Bibliothek 8), Marbach am Neckar 2005, p. 10.

⑤ Camus, Albert: "Die Guillotine. Betrachtungen zur Todesstrafe, in: idem: *Fragen der Zeit*, Hamburg 1960, p. 177. See also Himmler: *Die Brüder Himmler. Eine deutsche Familiengeschichte*. - Sartre's debate of the concept of humanism is also important, beginning with his mockery in his novel *La Nauseé* from 1938 right up to his later statements. -cf. Wroblewsky, Vincent von: "Wie humanistisch ist Sartres Existentialismus? in: Faber, Richard and Rudolph, Enno (Eds.), *Humanismus in Geschichte und Gegenwart*, Tübingen 2002, pp. 119-137.

the face of the Moscow trials or the Shoa, and Maurice Merleau-Ponty remarked that "the realization of humanity utterly depends on the successful creation of meaning initiated by humans in and through history", even though this does not guarantee any progress towards more humanity.① Theologians like Eberhard Jüngel have countered this kind of despondency by referring to the coming of God's kingdom as a realistic utopia. Maintaining the four relations of man with God, his social and natural environment as well as with himself not only plays an important role in Christian theological discourse,② but also has a determining influence on the religiosity of other cultures such as in China. And the very recognition of other beings in their otherness emanating from the insight that in all its relations the human subject, especially with regard to its connection to God, must never aspire to be *like God*, is a central of all religions throughout history.

**The new humanism in posttraditional societies**

A new humanism will not be able to confine itself to only recognizing certain abstract norms of behaviour, but it must also acknowledge the concrete needs and requirements of posttraditional societies, which comprises their self-interpretation in the light of their own specific tradition. We also assume that "human community has really become established without being limited to a specific nationality".③ In this context the demand that "the self-realization required from us [⋯] today [⋯] [is made concrete] in the way we are concerned about hunger in the world or world-peace."④ But this appeal is not sufficiently far-reaching. The concern for the whole is a necessary but not a sufficient reason. This is evident quite clearly in the Chinese example where currently the unity of the world is being proclaimed as the basis of all explanations of the world and the production of meaning, as in the concept of religion as defined by Zhuo Xinping.⑤ This demands an insight into multifarious interests, the recognition of which can only be attained through participation; what is at stake here is not just the insight into this connection as such, but also a change of the cognitive

---

① Cf. *Historisches Wörterbuch der Philosophie*, vol. 3, column 1229-1230.

② Jüngel, Eberhard: op. cit. (in: Karl Lehmann), p. 126.

③ Theunissen: op. cit., p. 45.

④ Theunissen: ibid.

⑤ Cf. Schmidt-Glintzer, Helwig: *Wohlstand, Glück und langes Leben. Chinas Götter und die Ordnung im Reich der Mitte*, Frankfurt/Main 2009, p. 240.

process itself that has to be brought about. It must be accepted that we are incapable of putting ourselves in the shoes of every other because as human beings we are of limited capacity.

**The individual and its world**

I am referring at this juncture to the theory of *normative individualism* (Dietmar von der Pfordten) and confront it with the demands of human rights, both in a historically reconstructive as well as a synchronous perspective relevant to our own present. It would be worthwhile to empirically verify this theoretical construct in a comparative perspective from the 16th century onward, taking into account its various social, governmental and institutional specifities. In von der Pfordten's view the 17th century from its very beginnings has been dominated by one "central idea" which has contributed to the "development of constitutional government, the rule of law as well as human rights", which is summed up in the idea of a *normatively legitimated individualism*, i.e. "the idea that the use of political power in the final resort can only be justified through its being legitimated by every individual involved."① After surveying some specific theories of how to justify political decision-making he develops his *Three-Zone Theory of Political Justice*.② After having examined a number of terms like law, freedom, human abilities, self-preservation, and preference, the concept of *interest* becomes of crucial relevance for him.③ In his Three-Zone theory there are certain interests which only depend on individuals, then there are others which are exclusively dependent on communities, whereas in a third zone there exist interests which are only partially dependent on communities.④ In the Chinese context this discourse could be further pursued by reconstructing the reflections upon the relationship between the "common good" (*gong* 公) and personal or particular interest (*si* 私). With regard to Buddhism a similar tension would have to be negotiated between the monastic community, the individual monk and society at large.

In addition to negotiating between communal and individual interests the distinction between a state under the rule of law and a tyrannical regime is relevant, howev-

① von der Pfordten, Dietmar: *Rechtsethik*, Munich 2001, p. 293.

② Ibid.: pp. 436ff.

③ Ibid.: p. 441.

④ Ibid.: p. 452.

er in the sense of gradual differences between both,[①] and not in the shallow sense propagated these days by party politicians. When von der Pfordten defines a state under the rule of law in terms of "the observation of human rights, the principle of democracy, the principle of majority rule, legal protection and compensation in the case of disappropriation etc."[②], then all pre-modern states fall outside the category of rule of law. This also raises the question of which individual rights define the standard by which this can be judged. As John Rawls has argued, hierarchical and thereby illiberal societies can recognize liberal societies and vice versa. Nonetheless the hierarchical societies have to fulfil three minimal conditions:[③]"*firstly* they have to be peaceful and non-expansionist; *secondly* their legal system has to be guided by a notion of justice that is orientated towards safeguarding the common good, and which can plausibly and credibly demonstrate that this common good reflects the interests of all members of society.-The People's Republic of China is a prominent example of such a society."[④]

**Four preconditions for humanism as a guiding concept**

The *first precondition* for a new humanism therefore consists in recognizing the networks created in the process of globalization as the elements enabling understanding and management, especially considering that they are forms of subjective affiliation. The League of Nations, the United Nations and the human rights debate, but also international networks, non-governmental organizations and initiatives[⑤] as well as forms of transnational security alliances come under this category. The idea of humanity is indissolubly linked with the long-past experience of global wars such as the Thirty Years' War, the first real world war properly speaking, and most certainly with the so-called First World War in the 20th century, and it is reflected in the mention of the inalienability of human dignity in the constitution of the Federal Republic

---

① Ibid. : p. 524.

② Ibid. : p. 524

③ Schubert, Gunter: "Zwischen Konfuzius und Kant. Ansätze zur Operationalisierung eines interkulturellen Menschenrechtsdialogs mit Ostasien, in: idem (Ed.): *Menschrechte in Ostasien. Zum Streit um die Universalität einer Idee II*, Tübingen 1999, p. 19-51, p.4 3.

④ Cf. Schubert, Gunter: op. cit., p. 43.

⑤ An example of this is the 'Clinton Global Initiative' founded in 2005 by the former President of the USA Bill Clinton. Cf. "Das bessere Gesicht Amerikas, in: *Der Spiegel* 14 (2006): 116-117.

of Germany of 1949. However, humanism is also associated with numerous wars of liberation, including the liberation of Germany from its self-imposed Nazi-loyalty.

The *second precondition* is formed by recognizing the fact that in European Modernity the concept of humanity that was deemed to be universal has remained 'incomplete' because on the one hand even enlightened societies can be profoundly inhumane,[①] but above all because incompleteness is the constituent element of humanism in the first place. If, for instance, in an edition of the *American Historical Review* the reasons are listed for why the rate of murder and manslaughter in the USA is so much higher than in Europe,[②] then the topic of the vastly different conditions influencing humanism throughout the world is addressed, which is always associated with ideas of freedom.[③]

The *third precondition* consists in recognizing that not only humanism but any other kind of identity formation and sense-making is a referral to its own specific prehistory and thereby poses the question-and I am here expanding Merleau-Ponty's theory-whether there can be a human past which is capable of integrating its own past events in the manner of collective memories. This also applies to the past of 'victims' and 'winners'. At this point one also is compelled to ask to what extent collectives are capable of being held responsible, because they are much more susceptible to delusions than individuals and therefore are not completely accountable, in the sense of Friedrich Nietzsche's dictum: "Madness is quite rare with individuals, but in the case

---

① The deficit associated with this also consists in the relevant debates only taking place within certain cultures. Cf. Höffe, Otfried: *Vernunft und Recht. Bausteine zu einem interkulturellen Rechtsdiskurs*, Frankfurt/Main 1996, p. 53.

② The "Problem of American Homicide, in: *American Historical Review* 11.1 (February 2006): 75-114.

③ This historicity is constitutive of all cultures. It would therefore be relevant to connect the concept of humanism with the traumata of other cultures. In his book, *A Nation among Nations. America's place in World History*. Thomas Bender has argued against the concept of "American Exceptionalism" and emphasized: "If we can begin to think about American history as but one local instance of a general history, as one history among others, not only will historical knowledge be improved, but the cultural foundations of a much-needed cosmopolitanism will be enhanced. We do not want to reinforce a narrow and exclusive notion of citizenship, but encourage and sustain a cosmopolitan citizenry, at once proud nationals and humble citizens of the world, quoted after http://hnn.us/articles/23913.html [04/17/2006].

of groups, parties, peoples and eras it is the rule."[①] By inverting this argument, it is all about the question if collectives are not *per se* ambivalent, and are thus capable of being humane just as much as they are inhumane.

The *fourth precondition* is formed by a much-needed revision of the concept of religion or, respectively, by overcoming the peculiar distance between humanism and religion.[②] For a long time humanism was seen as a "turning away from the Beyond" and a "turning towards the here and now,"[③] and it is therefore no coincidence that the relationship between humanism and Christianity, but especially the "relation between humanism and the Reformation", [④] should have been variously debated and been the subject of a lot tension.[⑤] Over against Etienne Gilson, who designated the Renaissance as the "Middle Ages without God", Enno Rudolph insists on calling the Renaissance "God without the Middle Ages". The humanist ideal of education prevalent during that epoch-Rudolph estimates this to have covered the period from 1300 to 1600 - according to him was the "emancipation of the individual from the tutelage imposed from outside".[⑥]

These then are the *four preconditions*, and what is at stake here is the *condition humaine* within the ambit of a global concept of mankind that essentially lives by accepting the variety and the social conditioning as well as the individuality and uniqueness of men, including their historicity. Of these four preconditions I would like to

---

① Nietzsche, Friedrich: "Jenseits von Gut und Böse, in: *Werke*, vol. 2, ed. von Karl Schlechta, Munich 1966, p. 637.

② We should like to warn, however, against easy remedies, since difference is most clearly manifested between religions, which justifiably try to resist the process of levelling in a highly complex society. Very illustrative of this is the comment on the world-ethos project of Hans Küng by Klaus Berger: *Von der Schönheit der Ethik*, Frankfurt/Main 2006, pp. 24f.

③ *Religion in Geschichte und Gegenwart*, 1st ed., "Humanismus", column 191, (published Tübingen 1912).

④ This is the introduction to Kampschulte, F. W.: *Die Universität Erfurt in ihrem Verhältnisse zu dem Humanismus und der Reformation. Erster Theil: Der Humanismus*, Trier 1858, p. VII.

⑤ That 'relations' of humanism and Christianity have always been 'conflictual' is an argument also propounded by Stegemann, Ekkhard W.: "Das unaufhebbar Befremdliche am Menschlichen. Einige Gedanken über Humanismus und Christentum, in: Faber, Richard/Rudolph, Enno (Eds.), *Humanismus in Geschichte und Gegenwart*, Tübingen 2002, pp. 167-186, here p. 167.

⑥ Rudolph here is referring to Blumenberg, Hans/Kristeller, P. O.: *Humanismus und Renaissance*, Munich 1973 and more others. Rudolph, Enno: "Der Renaissance-Humanismus als Epochenstifter, in: Faber/Rudolph: *Humanismus in Geschichte und Gegenwart*, pp. 3-15, esp. p. 3.

*make a few specific remarks on the last one.* ①

**Humanism in functional terms**

In this sense a global new humanism cannot afford to be just a continuation of the European concept of humanism. Much though the idea of humanism may be linked with character formation and education as in the Latin term *studia humaniora* that has been in use in Germany since the 17th century, it nevertheless remains closely associated with "a spiritual attitude that is making it clear that it is modelling the striving of the Modern Age for humanity on the example of the ancient Greeks and Romans."② What can be meant by 'global humanism' considering the definitions given so far? It is certainly not what Julian Nida-Rümelin understands by a "renewed humanism" which merely consists of invoking other previous stages of humanism, such as the humanist movement of the late Middle Ages and the early Modern Age or the neo-humanism of the 19th century. Nida-Rümelin also thinks that a "new definition as regards its content" is required and is thus focussing on "the fundamental dimension of culture": social interaction, communication, self-determination, self-formation, aesthetic and musical education.③ In addition to this he is concerned with rationality, liberty and responsibility④ plus "humanistic revolutions" from Plato to the present. If we wanted to run the whole gamut of such ideas, and if we decided to take up Sartre's "Existentialism is a Humanism" ("*L'existentialisme est un humanisme*") as well as ring all the changes of the discourse on nihilism from Nietzsche to Gottfried Benn we

---

① In this context I am expressly referring to Jörn Rüsen's contribution "Die Erziehung des Menschengeschlechts-ein Rückblick in die Zukunft der Vergangenheit, in: Schmidt-Glintzer, Helwig (Ed.): *Aufklärung im 21. Jahrhundert*, Wiesbaden 2004, pp. 67-92.

② "Humanismus", in: *Historisches Wörterbuch der Philosophie*, vol 3, column 1217-1230, s. v. column 1217.-The recourse to Classical Antiquity led to new coinages like "neo-humanism" (F. Paulsen) and "third humanism" (L. Helbing), and, throughout the 19th and 20th centuries, to a variety of specializations such as "pragmatic, technical, national, modern, real, social, socialist, existentialist, personal, Christian humanism."

③ Nida-Rümelin, Julian: *Humanismus als Leitkultur. Ein Perspektivenwechsel*, ed. by Elif Özmen, Munich 2006, p. 26.

④ Ibid. p. 30.

would still remain within the confines of European thought.① If we really want to arrive at a concept of humanity that would be globally accepted, this would have to be based on notions of humaneness from diverse cultures.② Because too much self-centred confidence would be at best nothing but emotional enthusiasm, as Gotthold Ephraim Lessing remarks in his work "Die Erziehung des Menschengeschlechts" ("On Educating the Human Race") from 1780 ( § § 85ff.). However, can it possibly be our purpose, and above all, is it realistic to expect that "men do what is good [⋯] because it is good" ( § 85)?

**The Obstinacy of Cultures**

Of course, as has already been indicated, one does come across the spirit of self-critique besides that of arrogance in the writings about other peoples throughout the early Modern Age. This became more accentuated since the end of the $18^{th}$ century. At the same time a certain arrogance vis-à-vis the human race started to manifest itself.

Thus one of the preconditions for a new humanism is to be open to what the other thinks about oneself. This ,however, is a mere starting point, and it is conditional upon ourselves enquiring after the tradition of the other.③ In the process we will make the experience that Lessing has formulated in § 38 of his work "Die Erziehung des Menschengeschlechts" (1780)④ according to which our limited focus will not just be returned back on our own tradition, but in addition it will be widened in such a way that we

---

① In this context I do not wish to refer to the European rhetoric of superiority of the last two hundred years, and also do not wish to invoke the concepts of separatism or exclusionism of all other non-European cultures, but I do want to point out very briefly that even the concepts of 'European' or 'Asian' themselves are constructs representing a one-sided view of the world.

② The opposite perspective to this would be to simply designate the Other as evil and attempt to eradicate it-something that has been reflected upon a lot but has been justifiably and above all plausibly rejected.

③ If only we had got that far already so that we in Europe could talk about the Chinese literary tradition in the same way that Chinese Germanists and Romanists are capable of talking about German, Italian or French literature.

④ The child that had been sent to foreign parts encountered other children who knew more, who lived more decently, and it was shamed into thinking: Why do I not know this, too? Why do I not live like this, too? Could they not have taught me this in my father's house? Could they not have brought me up like this, too? Then it looked at its schoolbooks again, for which it had long ago developed an aversion, in order to put the blame on its school books. But behold! It recognized soon that the books are not to blame, that it only has got itself to blame for not knowing these things and not living this kind of life."

can better understand ourselves. Our concern is therefore with both our own tradition as well as with that of the other, and consequently with the contingency of our own position, and only with acknowledging this trans-cultural humanism will be viable. ①

Whatever it is that still remains recognizable beyond all the differences is the continuity of what we will designate as *humanum*, i.e. the principle that human beings are generally capable of reciprocal recognition, love and empathy. In order to make possible the education of mankind in this spirit towards self-formation, mutual recognition, general accountability, and-to employ a modern concept-a global civil society, the process of globalization itself has to be critically reflected upon. This does not imply that we wish to deny those values we usually connect with the concept of humanism any degree of universality, but every culture has to come to the realization that it has to arrive at the idea of humanity and human rights from within its own context. ②

However, we always have to reckon with institutions, self-perceptions, demands, and therefore the recourse to being human alone is no solution. This is no surprise, because human beings consist of more than just their basic equipment. Man is a cultural creature. This is exactly the context where it makes sense to conceive of humanism in the terms of one's own tradition, but only to the extent that mankind still perceives itself as a unity, whereby the claim to universality is not just limited to its Enlightenment sense, and that its various traditions and their provenance are remembered and reflected upon. ③

---

① In this work "Philosophischer Glaube (Frankfurt/Main 1958, p. 80) Karl Jaspers has described this situation as follows: "The consequence of such a faulty perspective (the perspective of the historically formed unconditionality of one's own belief in a universal truth for all) is the self-deception about what I really am and desire, is intolerance (not accepting anything except one's own dogmatic view) and the inability to communicate (not listening what others have say, not being willing to have one's own view questioned." Cf. Wen-chao Li, *Die christliche China-Mission im 17. Jahrhundert*, Stuttgart 2000, p. 311.

② This is also emphasized by Otfried Höffe, cf. Höffe, Otfried: *Vernunft und Recht. Bausteine zu einem interkulturellen Rechtsdiskurs*, Frankfurt/Main 1996, p. 83.

③ In this context I would like to propound four theses: *Firstly*, human beings have always accepted their kind, and the abhorrence of the Other is secondary phenomenon. -*Secondly*, reflecting upon the part is not unique to the European cultural tradition, but other cultures also have their history, their historiography, and their traditions of symbolic meaning. -*Thirdly*, there s no reasonable argument for justifying the precedence of one cultural tradition over another. -*Fourthly*, we assume-and I think justly-the universality of human rights as we know them: Of course it is totally unresolved by which means this utopia can be achieved.

Reflection upon and remembrance of the past as well as reciprocal recognition and agreement upon common values are all faced with the undeniable problem that all humans come from cultural backgrounds that are highly different. These differences in their turn are the result of multiple and partially explicable causes and effects. Therefore a global realization of humanism can only be imagined as a process conducted on the spirit of mediation and justice.

In order to facilitate communication this requires the clarification of one's own humanistic tradition, concepts of humanity, as well as ideas of freedom, self-determination and necessity. This will only be successful and practicable if, besides diachronically studying the various traditions, we maintain a synchronous discourse. How could this function in practice? I shall give an example of this.

**The Clash of cultures and the demographic factor**

There have always been and always will be clashes of culture. But there are also lines of conflict within each culture. In this context the debate conducted in Europe comes to mind when period-terms became linguistic weapons. The debate on the Gothic period in Germany, which is reflected in titles like "Die Renaissance, das Verhängnis der deutschen Cultur" ("The Renaissance, the Doom of German Culture") by Richard Benz (Jena 1915) is a case in point by way of demonstrating how such concepts carried a normative charge in their function as linguistic weapons.[①] This equally applies to the concept of Baroque and numerous others, but also to such phenomena as iconoclastic movements, especially during the period of the *Kulturkampf* when Germany was riven by strife among the major religious denominations. There are numerous ways conflicts can be conceived and carried out, and all cultures have devoted some thought to this. Sigmund Freud concludes his text from 1915 about "The Disappointment of War" with this statement:

"It will remain a mystery why national individuals should despise, hate, abhor one another, even in peace-time, and every nation the other. I cannot explain this. It seems as if in such a case all moral restraints on the part of the individuals become removed when they form part of a majority or even of millions of people, and only the

---

① On the "spirit of the Gothic period" cf. Claussen, Peter Cornelius/Mondini, Daniela (Eds.): "Wohin weht der ? Geist der Gothik" über einen Stilbegriff der Deutschen Moderne, in: *Georges-Bloch-Jahrbuch des Kunsthistorischen Instituts der Universität Zürich* 9/10 (2002/03): 223-347.

most primitive, primal and crudest mental attitudes are left over. Such a sorry state of affairs will perhaps only be altered in the course of some later development. But a modicum of truthfulness and sincerity among men, and between the people and those who govern them might pave the way for such a change."[①]

In all these considerations one should be mindful of the fact that the idea of humaneness, the basic element of any concept of humanism, only seems to have become a necessity after its actual disappearance. But it has already been mentioned at the beginning that we live in a post-paradisiacal era.

① Freud: op. cit., pp. 47-48.

# Imaging "A Confucian-Islamic Connection"

**SUZUKI NorioPh. D. (Professor, Aichi University, Japan)**

In 1993, Samuel P. Huntington argued on "the Confucian-Islamic connection" in his "The Clash of Civilizations?" His main concern was its military one. So he wrote "a central focus of conflict for the immediate future will be between the West and several Islamic-Confucian states". The first question is where are "several Islamic-Confucian states" in the world, and what has happened after two decades is maybe second one. In fact Huntington had no deep understanding of ideas and images on "the Confucian-Islamic connection". But a real image of the Confucian-Islamic connection must be reconsidered in thecontext of peace and construction in this world. What kind of factors we need to think about "the Confucian-Islamicconnection"? Both of the Confucianism and Islam are not "religions", that is the first. The concept of "religion" is a kind of special phenomenon of Christianity. Both of them are also defined as an absolute separation of human being and the other. "Ji Lu asked about serving the spirits of the dead. The Master said, "While you are not able to serve men, how can you serve their spirits?" Ji Lu added, "I venture to ask about death?" He was answered, "While you do not know life, how can you know about death?"(Xian Jin: 12). Both of them have the unique stance to "philosophy". Once Jacques Derrida told that there is no "philosophy" in China, at Shanghai. We should think on Derrida's words in the context of "the Confucian-Islamic connection".

**1. The End of History and The clash of the Civilizations**

End of the last century, the image "post-Cold War" of the world were made by two books, *The End of history* by Francis Fukuyama and *The Clash of the Civilizations* by Samuel Huntington. Both were compared often. Fukuyama wrote that "the History ends" and the democracy becomes "the absolute goodness". As for Huntington, "the History does not end." Because "the dominant civilization does not sustain but it determines the form of government of the human race." Each thinking axis is different. So, it is not much sense to compare in fact.

Which one has received more attention? *The Clash of Civilizations*.

It was prophesied in the world of the near future, that "Western civilization" and "the Confucian-Islamic connection" eventually crash. It was criticized as an exaggerated fantasy. It may be, however, that was easy to be understood as a strategic world image. Therefore, the image like below has been sprayed all over the world.

……A new form of arms competition is thus occurring between Islamic-Confucian states and the West. In an old-fashioned arms race, each side developed its own arms to balance or to achieve superiority against the other side. In this new form of arms competition, one side is developing its arms and the other side is attempting not to balance but to limit and prevent that arms build-up while at the same time reducing its own military capabilities. (Huntington1993)

Huntington's words had been forgotten now, however, he left an image of post Cold War that is alive like a Cheshire Cat in the Middle East and Asia Pacific. Well, but we should not forget his main concern was the United States to the end as Dabashi insists anyway.

……. . While both Huntington and Fukuyama have targeted foreigners, Muslims and Asians in particular, as the locus of their attack, it is blatantly obvious that it is the emerging demographic changes inside the United States that concerns them most. Huntington has been particularly successful in appearing to be globally concerned, to the degree that the Persian translation of his essay, "The Clash of Civilization," has prompted the then Iranian President Mohammad Khatami to propose to the United Nations a "Dialogue of Civilizations." Huntington of course is far less concerned about the Islamic or the Asian world, about which he knows absolutely nothing, than in the frightful, for him, demographic changes inside the United States. (Dabashi2009)

**2. Islamic Civilization as an image**

Huntington was the director of John Olin Institute for Strategic Studies, Harvard University. In the summer of 1993, an article called "The Clash of Civilizations?" has been published on Foreign Affairs. A point of view "the clash of civilizations" is in fact an idea of Bernard Lewis originally, however, Huntington described it as a strategic world image. It is doubtful whether there is rationality in its description. But, it gave the people a clear image of the post-Cold War. Strategically the clarity of this image is a bottom line.

Huntington described the intervention and aggression and so on by the nation state as "the Clash of Civilizations." What was his intention? Representing of a big tension of the world instead of the Cold War. The Cold War was assumed an image of a big war, like World War III. So what happens after the crash? The winner puts under the control of other civilization.

Currently, somewhat, the political environment has changed after the age of Huntington's. At the end of the last century, the images of the Islamic civilization were mainly the Iranian Islamic Revolution with Orientalism sense. Of course, we know very well that Islamic civilization with its great contributions to theology, jurisprudence, philosophy, science, architecture and literature is itself under attack from such movements. Islamic civilization's dynamism and energy is in stark contrast to the narrow restrictions of the Islamist perspective.

And through the 30 years after the revolution, those images are confused changing variety. Until the end of 20th century, the intellectual project to over come the Orientalist prism offers more than just an end to the exclusion of Islam, as Said seductively wrote:

……For the first time, the history of imperialism and its culture can now be studied as neither monolithic nor reductively compartmentalized, separate, distinct. True, there has been a disturbing eruption of separatist and chauvinist discourse whether in India, Lebanon, or Yugoslavia, or in Afrocentric, Islamocentric, or Eurocentric proclamations; far from invalidating the struggle to be free from empire, these reductions of cultural discourse actually prove the validity of the fundamental liberationist energy that animates the wish to be independent, to speak freely, and without the burden of unfair domination. (Said1993)

But after 9/11, Muslims in all over the world are run after by the self-proof of that they are not the terrorists, and it is harder than before to restructure the rich resource of the Islam civilization.

" Islam is a religion of peace, " Sherman Jackson, co-founder of the American Learning Institute for Muslims (ALIM), writes. "This is certainly the mantra that has inundated us from almost every quarter since the horrifying events of September 11, 2001"(Jackson 2007). He continues:

From president George W. Bush to local, national and even international Muslim spokespersons, the peaceful nature of Islam has been reiterated time and again. Of course, this has not gone unchallenged. Skeptics, polemicists, even opportunists of various stripes, have repeatedly warned against accepting too uncritically what they hint at being a "new found, politically correct" depiction of religion that includes, inter alia, a scripturally mandated institution of armed violence and a holy book that exhorts its adherents, at least on the face of it, to "slay 'them' wherever you find them." Today, years after the tragedy, emotions and rhetoric on both sides have subsided a bit. But there is still a perduring suspicion among many Americans—including many Muslim Americans—when it comes to the question of Islam, violence and relationship between Muslims and non-Muslims.

As Bobby S. Sayyid wrote, "Islam is the thinnest of phrases in Muslims' final vocabulary. It is this thinness which makes it difficult to contest. Ultimately, for Muslims, Islam is another word for 'Goodness incarnate' " and "Islam is another name for the hope of something better" (Sayyid 2003). In this context, we will see that the term "Bad Muslims" is a contradiction in terms, as would be the term "virtuous tyrant."

So, now, the extremity of "Bad Muslims" is "Islamic State (IS)." Their actions contradict the faith system of Islam. In the name of Islam, IS have repeated Western imperialism has done.

What is "Islamic State (IS)"? According to *the Wall Street Journal*, Islamic State-previously known as Islamic State of Iraq and al-Sham-is the successor organization to al Qaeda in Iraq, started by Abu Musab Al Zarqawi a few years before the 2003 U.S.-led invasion of the country. AQI pledged allegiance to Osama bin Laden's al Qaeda in 2004, and its Sunni fighters devoted themselves to attacking American forces and terrorizing the Shiite-led government in Baghdad that took over after Saddam Hussein's ouster (*WSJ* Jun 12, 2014).

What's in a Name? There are various discussions between Muslim on this naming.

The mufti's senior adviser, Dr. Ibrahim Negm, told that "we felt that it would not be fair for the religion of Islam to be described through this inhumane type of violence." And Dr. Tawfik Hamid, an Islamic thinker and a senior fellow at the Potomac Institute for Policy, said "the reality is that its nameis IS —Islamic State. It's better to confront this reality rather than try to hide it and call it by another name." To Hamid, the only way to salvage the image of Islam is to face the underlying issue of radicalism. "These people aren't inventing things," he said. "I don't think overall this mission will succeed without clearly and honestly addressing the root of the problem, which is the violent teachings that are provided in some traditional, old-style Islamic books. Islamophobia will disappear if we provide alternative teachings." (*VICE* News September 4, 2014)

The image of the Confucian civilization is represented by Chinese culture mainly. Reconstructing movement of Confucianism is more pronounced in recent years. Confucianism used be just one of Chinese "culture" in the time of Huntington, however, at present, as the Confucius Institutes can be seen in the all over the world, Confucianism is heavily involved in the real world politics because of Chinese public diplomacy and so on. Now, Confucianism is a soft power and the important part of Chinese global strategy.

**3. Civilization, culture and religion/secular**

In Huntington's discussion, friction and the collision of various ethnic state and national states were overlooked. In a word, the culture is not so considered. The civilization and the culture are vaguely used as a concept.

What is the difference in the concept of the civilization and the culture?

Needless to say, the civilization is "urbanization." In a certain civilization, the physical production by the technology and the means develop and urbanization advances on average. The various pattern of "urbanization" exists in the world. It is necessary to add that the "information network" is spreading at the present day. Therefore, the "crash of civilizations" means the "collision" of "urbanization" and "information network" pattern. The problem is which "urbanization" pattern becomes dominant as a result of the "collision".

Then, do the cultures collide? A culture has the characteristic of the civilization partially. Any culture is various. A culture accompanies complex feelings. And, there is an individual side where the custom and life are led. It is not possible to talk about a culture thoroughly. A culture is also various even in case of being in one country.

Such various cultures are covered with the one civilization. The civilization disregards the difference between Paris and New York as long as there is no interest the politics and economics it even if Paris and New York have cultural differences.

A civilization is enhanced according to its standard of urbanization. Then, it collides with other civilizations. And, it influences each other, and each signs is left. The culture has diversity first. The civilization fears the end. The culture is pleased with outbreak.

It is not possible to separate from the civilization and the culture. Braudel considered, "the civilization is an area of the culture". Wallerstein says, "the civilization is a specific chain of the outlook on the world, the lifestyle, the organization, and the culture".

It is people that discuss "future" of the civilization who think that their civilizations have been powerfully developed until the present age. It is an extremely important theme for people, a strategist like Huntington and the founders of modern Japanese nation-state, who thought how own civilization should advance. Oppositely, Kunio Yanagita and Shinobu Orikuchi and so on in Japan, who are interested in the culture, Edward Said and Noam Chomsky might be also the same.

Then how about the perception of secularism?

The Islamic civilization and the Confucian civilization are common in the meaning that a certain kind of belief system is related to the real politics. Actually, "secularism," it would be said "separation of church and state," phenomenon in modern politics is a special form in "Western Europe Christianity civilization". Therefore, the Islamic civilization and the Confucian civilization are in a phase originally different from such "secularism" a phenomenon.

It is needless to say that in the assumption of "Western Europe civilization" that Huntington says, there are modern political various principles such as "secularism", "democracy", "bourgeois society", "market", and "nation state" and so on. Because "Islam and Confucian connection" has its norms and principles different from various standards of "Western Europe civilization", the "Collision" is coming. There is room for argument of course, one thinks the "Collision" is a sign of the decline of "Western Europe civilization" or not.

Talal Asad has posed some interesting questions in his discussion on secularism:

……I do not deny that religion, in the vernacular sense of that word, is and historically has been important for national politics in Euro-America as well as in the rest of the world. Recognition on this fact will not doubt continue to prompt useful work. But there are questions that need to be systematically addressed beyond this obvious fact. How, when, and by whom are the categories of religion and the secular defined? What assumptions are presupposed in the acts that define them? Does the shift from religious political order to one that is governed by a secular state simply involve the setting aside of divine authority in favor human law? (Asad 2003)

Asad addressed that latter question in relation to a particular place and a particular time, that is Colonial Egypt. Asad writes that a secular state "is not one characterized by religious indifference, or rational ethics—or political toleration" (Asad 2003). Then he looked at aspects of *Shari'a* reform in Colonial Egypt as both the precondition and the consequence of secular processes of power.

Global wide problematiques on secularism have many counterforces, including Christianity, Islamism, Confucianism, Shinto-ism and so on. These religious counterforces and secularism are not equal, however: they depend on historical and situational conditions. When considering the discussion of secularism in Richard Dawkins's *The God Delusion* (Dawkins 2006), the opposite sides are not only churches or Christian power but also Islamism, Confucianism etc.

So, how should we focus on the ongoing conflict between Islamism/Confucianism and secularism in the contemporary Muslim/Chinese world? In general, we could use the term "Islamism/Confucianism" to mean the political activism based on the belief that all human life must be guided by Islamic/Confucian principles, and use "secularism" as a sociological trend that seeks to separate political and civil affairs from the religion. But is it true that such conflict exist? Are Islamism/Confucianism the counter concept against secularism? What is the difference between United States being seen by citizens as blessed by God and Iran as guided by modern interpretations of doctrines of Islam/Confucianism?

Especially, the problem of this secularization is important in the Islamic world.

Since the 1980s and up until now, Islamism occupied a central position in both political discourse in Muslim countries and scholarly discussion among Islamic studies scholars. However, there are still doubts about establishing the framework for such discussions as that "Islamist political challenges work against secular national governments." Of course, we can continue to discuss on the current situation and dynamism of Islamist movements in Indonesia, Turkey, Central Asia (post-Soviet Union), and other so called Muslim countries, with special reference to the different intellectual, sociological, economic, and political backgrounds, and the philosophical and political struggles over Islamic law in contemporary nation-states with Muslim majority. But it is doubtful the central issue is the conflict between "Islamists" and "secularists." Because of "secularists" in thosenation-states are not secular at all in the sense used by Dawkins(2006).

As is well-known, from the early nineteenth century, most of the Muslim countries adopted the Western civil code as their model and the rulers replaced most of their traditional laws with those of Western origin. But the situations of having civil code without "civism" and laws of Western origin without Western-style jurisprudential resources in their Muslim societies have not functioned well. This may be a factor to consider when looking at the dramatic growth of Islamism during the 1980s and 2000s and demands by Islamists that Islamic law and its codification, especially family law, regain some of its influence in most Muslim nation-states. In brief, transplanted Western laws and judicial systems are necrotizing at present, but that is not the problem of the conflict between Islamists and secularists at all. Islam as an alternative is one of the options.

According to the Islamic teachings, Jesus is not God, and there is an absolute discontinuity between God and humankind. It is very clear for Muslims that Jesus is a noble human prophet like Muhammad. Thus, the meaning of "secularism" in Islamic context must be quite different from the Euro-American one. We should not think of "the secular" as the space in which everyday human life gradually emancipates itself from the controlling power of "religion", namely Christianity, and thus displaces religion. In modern European thought, it is this assumption that allows us to think of religion as "infecting" the secular domain or as replicating within it the structure of theological concepts. "The concept of "the secular" today is part of a doctrine called secularism" (Asad 2003). In other words, the question of "secular" may have no meaning in this world for Muslims, who believe that God is the absolute Other.

In this sense, Confucianism is not a "religion." The famous following sentences in the Analects of Confucius clearly express it:

"Ji Lu asked about serving the spirits of the dead. The Master said, "While you are not able to serve men, how can you serve their spirits?" Ji Lu added, "I venture to ask about death?"He was answered, "While you do not know life, how can you know about death?"(Xian Jin:12). 季路問事鬼神。子曰:「未能事人,焉能事鬼?」敢問死。曰:「未知生,焉知死?」

**4. Vagueness of "Japanese civilization"**

Huntington is setting "Japanese civilization" besides "Western Europe civilization", "Islam civilization", and " Confucian civilization", etc. It is after the 19th century that the civilization theory was active in Japan. At that time, Japan was in a period of transition to Western civilization from the Confucian civilization. At present, the civilization is discussed again in Japan than the culture. Obviously, this is a phenomenon that was responsive to the reconstruction of the economic power of China.

Modern Japan is dependent on Western civilization. However, some of Japanese hope to survive the Japanese language and Emperor. It will be because they want to leave some kind of Japan identity indicators. If you think about the dimension of culture, Japan identity has been self-destruct once already in 1945. The Japanese culture went out of use once in 1945, so it is subordinate to the United States and exists in inertia.

Huntington wrote that Japan civilization is afraid to be isolated Between Sino-US confrontation, with a noncommittal hesitation might be shown. However, Japan does not enter a new plot in the scenario of the collision of the civilization that Huntington drew. The reason for that Japan has already gone out of use, actually.

The end of the 20th century, Huntington was concerned about the connection with the Confucian civilization and Islamic civilization. Mid-20th century, American strategists we had been concerned, it was the connection with the Islamic world and Japan. Western civilization was concerned about what of the connection with the Islamic world and Japan?

Are there any links between Islamic discourses and modern Japan? This is because when non-Westerners "think" about an alternative world order, they are not necessarily thinking of modern Western Christian world. Instead, Islamic discourses influence their thinking by providing guidance about what this alternative could be, such as "Islam is the solution," a typical slogan used by Islamists all over the world against Westernization.

A World War II report by the US Office of Strategic Services (OSS) entitled

"Japanese Infiltration Among the Muslims Throughout the World" (OSS 1943), documented US concern over Japanese policy toward Muslim majority regions. During World War II, US intelligence officials were very concerned about Japanese infiltration of Muslim majority regions, most of which were still occupied by West. This report claimed that Japan had successfully implemented a policy of courting Muslim nations, starting at the turn of the century, in order to serve its own strategic ends. The OSS (predecessor of CIA) detailed the methods Tokyo employed to befriend such Muslim political groups -even as far as spreading word to Muslim nations that Mikado, Emperor Hirohito might convert to Islam and that Islam could become Japan's state religion. The report's summary stated, "She (Japan) has expended on it (Muslim policy) many years of patient labor and has assigned to it some of her ablest political and military leaders. Her cunning and opportunism, her flexible approach and unscrupulous manipulation of the facts have borne fruit in many lands"(OSS 1943).

The report claimed that some Japanese strategies used a combination of anti-Western and anti-communist views, together with economic power, to appeal to those Muslim majority regions. According to the report, Tokyo also emphasized the flexible nature of Japanese religion, Shinto, in order to suggest that many Japanese might convert to Islam. The report states that Japan could appeal to Muslim missionary zeal by hinting at the opportunity of large-scale conversions among the Japanese. The research and analysis branch of OSS wrote:

Instead of posing as the magnanimous protector of Islam, Japan can make a plausible showing as an eager seeker after the truth. Under these circumstances, rumors judiciously planted here and there that the Emperor might consider turning Muslim, are bound to take root and spread. Millions of sanguine believers have fallen for the promise that Islam is about to become the world's greatest power with the Mikado as Caliph. (OSS 1943)

This report also noted that Japan began befriending Muslim majority regions and countries during the 1880s. After the Russo-Japanese War (1904-1905), Japan courted the Muslims more openly, and as early as 1906, rumors started to circulate that the Emperor was preparing to make Islam Japan's state religion. That was true in a sense; however, the options included not only Islam but also Christianity. But such a conversion did not come about; instead, Japanese government of the time came up with the artificial state religion of Shinto. After World War I, the OSS report said, "once again word spreads abroad that thousands of Japanese have gone over to Islam, that Japan as a whole is ripe for conversion, and that the Mikado himself is on the verge of embracing the vigorous faith of Muhammad" (OSS 1943).

The OSS speculated that Tokyo's Muslim policy was spearheaded by members of the Black Dragon Society (Kokuryukai), a group of Japanese Pan-Asianist, and Muslim policy was formalized with the singing of the Muslim Pact in 1900 or 1909, which stipulated that the participants were to promote faith in Islam. Signatories were said to include UCHIDA Ryohei, president of Kokuryukai, TOYAMA Mitsuru, who was the "inspiration behind secret societies," INUKAI Tsuyoshi, who would later become prime minister, and pan-Islamic writer Abdurrashid Ibrahim. According to the documents, the Kokuryukai would be directing the activities of a Japanese, named SAKUMA Teijiro, who was of same generation as Okawa Shumei, a Japanese nationalist, pan-Asian thinker and Islamic scholar, who set up a Muslim evangelical center in Shanghai in 1923 called "The Society of Light" in order to promote Islam in China.

The report also pointed to a number of Muslim publications, groups and mosques that were set up in Japan around this time, and it notes that for years Tokyo had been successful at attracting Muslim students to visit Japan for study tours. The report claimed that Japan had been conducting"persistent undercover activity" in neighboring countries: "As a result, the Muslim territories of Russia and China have felt the impact of subversive operations enjoying the blessing of Japan." (OSS 1943)

The report noted that Japan was portraying its expansion into Southeast Asia as a means of liberating those countries from the "Anglo-American tyranny." "In short it (the Muslim policy) is backed by the most dynamic elements in Japan, on the ascendant since the turn of the century." The report concluded with "Suggested counter activity" (OSS 1943).

Modern Japan is characterized by "religious" indifference; however, the State Shintoism is not the "religious" problem in Japan. Shintoism is not at the heart of the problem of "religion and state" in modern Japan at all, primarily because Shinto is not a "religion" to the Japanese people. In Japan, "religion" means Christianity and the word was adopted for diplomatic purposes in the early days of Meiji era. Modern State Japan, in the late 19th century, imported and adopted many words and concepts such as "nation", "state" and "religion" as it became Westernized.

In a sense, "Japan" and "Japanese" were also constructed during that era. Fitting within the structure of modern state Japan, and the Mikado (the Emperor), the modern *Tennoh* ('hevenly sovereign') system for a modern Japanese nation, was an important concept designed by the so-called Meiji Reform founders, ITOH Hirobumi and the others in order to construct a coherent national state. But why did modern Japan called itself as an "empire"? It did so in part because the Japanese concept of nation already included other ethnic groups within Japanese territory, such as the Ainu and Ryukyu people. After the Sino-Japanese War of 1894-95 and the Russo-Japanese War, it was especially important for Mikado to be the supreme authority for the Japanese nation as well as other Asian nations. For Japanese nationalists, like UCHIDA Ryohei, TOYAMA Mitsuru, it was not difficult to think of Japanese nationalists as equivalent to pan-Asianism.

As the OSS has observed, the Mikado was the supreme existence not only for Japanese; Muslims all over the Asia had a positive image of Mikado. Japanese nationalism had created a multinational Mikado system. Otherwise, the logic of Japanese "empire" could not be sustained at all and the modern Japanese empire faced an anomalous situation. Although, in the first stage of modernization of Japan, the modern *Tennoh* should make up one nation from complex pre-Japanese groupsm the concept of modern Japanese gradually expanded as 'teikoku shinmin' (Japaneseempire subjects) including Okinama, Korean, Chinese and so on. In addition to this problem, it was difficult to explain how the succession of the Mikado would work, because of the Meiji Mikado had been invented as a modern Mikado by Meiji Reform founders after a kind of 'coup in Court' in the middle of the 19th century. He was not a traditional Mikado.

ORIGUCHI Shinobu published his essays in "Daijosai no hongi (The real meaning of the *daijosai* (succession ceremony of the Mikado)", and "Shinto ni arawareta minzokuronri (the logic of Japanese nation in Shintoism)" 1928. These essays have been extraordinarily influential in Japan these days, especially with regard to succession of Mikado. Briefly, Origuchi's view are as follows; sacred power comes to the Emperor through the entry into his body of the soul or *mitama* みたまof the imperial house. The legitimacy of the imperial line, dating back to the descent of the divine grandchild *Ninigi-no-Mikoto*, depends not so much on hereditary blood succession as on the complete and correct transference of the imperial *mitama* from the old Emperor to his successor. This transference is accomplished by the ritual of the *daijosai*, which is a symbolically enactment of the implanting and gestation of the imperial soul in its new vessel.

The imperial *mitama*, in Origuchi's view, resembles in some degree the ancient Shinto *tama*, which was believed to reside in its host, imparting to him/her life and energy, but not personality. When the *tama* grew weaker, or left the body, the host must fall sick and eventually die. But Origuchi reminds us that the boundary between life and death was by no means clear-cut in ancient Shinto belief. Even after bodily death, the *tama* was still subject to recall, by special magic songs and dances, so that life might once more be infused into the dead body. To this end the body was placed in a "mortuary hut," known as *mogari* もがり, where for a stated period the magic songs, dances, and ritual calls were performed, which might induce the *tama* to return. Only if the body failed to return to life at the end of the period was the final funeral performed.

But the case of the imperial *mitama*, Origuchi notes, is special in that during this period of intermediary waiting, the soul must be transferred from the body of the old Emperor to that of the new. It does not, as in the case of the souls of ordinary people, simply leave the body and depart for another world. The new Emperor's body is a *tamashii no iremono* (a vessel for a soul), ready waiting to receive the soul of his predecessor.

According to Origuchi's explanation, it can be said Mikado succeeds to the world order, not only for Japanese nation, but for several nations under the Japanese Empire. The point is that the Mikado is not a god. He/she is a kind of prophet. He/she is the special vessel for God's word and that is the basis of the legitimacy of the Mikado's powers. How could Mikado get the words and power from the Other (God)? There is a very similar process and structure for the succession of prophets in Islam and there is also some circumstantial evidences that, Origuchi recognized, shows similarities to some Islamic doctrines regarding prophecy and *Tawhid*, the unity of Allah; he may also have been influenced by OKAWA Shumei, Japanese political theorist and writer, and IZUTSU Toshihiko, an outstanding authority in the metaphysical philosophical schools of Islamic doctrines, and so on.

The important point in this argument is Origuchi's concept of the Mikado combined with *mikotomochi*. "*Mikotomochi*" is literally "bearer of the honorable word". A *mikotomochi* was a court official dispatched to a provincial post by imperial order. The belief that the Emperor's authority as a sovereign was vested in his being the recipient of *mikoto* sent from above by the *Amatsumkami* (*Kami*of heaven). *Kami* is a God of gods, and *Amatsukami* refers to *Kami* residing in the Plain of High Heaven (*Takamanohara*), who were born in *Takamanohara* but later descended to the land of Japan. Therefore, even the Emperor himself served as a *mikotomochi* — has existed since ancient times. By extension, mikotomochi refers to any person who travels on behalf of the Emperor in order to communicate the 'honorable words' of the *Amatsukami*.

On the other hand, *Kunitsukami*, generally refers to those *kami* native to the land of Japan, together with the spirits and powerful families who existed in Japan. *Kunitsukami* are also considered equivalent to the chthonic *kami* called *chigi*.

According to the *Kojiki* (or *Records of Ancient Matters*, the oldest surviving book in Japan), there are five types of *kami* in the heavens: namely *Amenominakanushi no kami*, *Takamimusuhi no kami*, *Kamimusuhi no kami*, *Umashiashikabihikoji no kami*, and *Amenotokotachi no kami*. These five are called "separate kami of heaven" (*kotoamatsukami*); however, this separation is similar to the phenomenon of having different names for God in Islam. Each kami is not a particular individual existence; it is an expression of the essence.

The Emperor of Japan is not a God originally. Japanese civilization also shares the idea of an absolute break with God and human beings, like Islamic civilization and Confucian civilization.

**5 Rescue plan of Western Europe civilization**

Huntington preached that he should undertake preservation measures of "Western civilization".

In near future, the relative power of Western Europe is gradually decreases to the power of non-Western regions. So what are Huntington's provisions for "Crash of civilizations"? Huntington wrote as follows (Huntington1993):

……If these are plausible hypotheses, however, it is necessary to consider their implications for Western policy. These implications should be divided between short-term advantage and long-term accommodation. In the short term it is clearly in the interest of the West to promote greater cooperation and unity within its own civilization, particularly between its European and North American components; to incorporate into the West societies in Eastern Europe and Latin America whose cultures are close to those of the West; to promote and maintain cooperative relations with Russia and Japan; to prevent escalation of local inter-civilization conflicts into major inter-civilization wars; to limit the expansion of the military strength of Confucian and Islamic states; to moderate the reduction of Western military capabilities and maintain military superiority in East and Southwest Asia; to exploit differences and conflicts among Confucian and Islamic states; to support in other civilizations groups sympathetic to Western values and interests; to strengthen international institutions that reflect and legitimate Western interests and values and to promote the involvement of non-Western states in those institutions.

And as for the longer term other measures;

……Western civilization is both Western and modern. Non-Western civilizations have attempted to become modern without becoming Western. To date only Japan has fully succeeded in this quest. Non-Western civilizations will continue to attempt to acquire the wealth, technology, skills, machines and weapons that are part of being modern. They will also attempt to reconcile this modernity with their traditional culture and values. Their economic and military strength relative to the West will increase. Hence the West will increasingly have to accommodate these non-Western modern civilizations whose power approaches that of the West but whose values and interests differ significantly from those of the West. This will require the West to maintain the economic and military power necessary to protect its interests in relation to these civilizations. It will also, however, require the West to develop a more profound understanding of the basic religious and philosophical assumptions underlying other civilizations and the ways in which people in those civilizations see their interests. It will require an effort to identify elements of commonality between Western and other civilizations. For the relevant future, there will be no universal civilization, but instead a world of different civilizations, each of which will have to learn to coexist with the others.

Such Huntington's measures were not reflected in the Bush father and son and Clinton after 1993 at all. Huntington thought that the United States faces the danger of "Crash of civilizations". Huntington's discussion was a kind of "Proposal of American patriotism."

The civilization has been classified a lot up to now. Spengler undertook the impact in World War I that divided Europe into the friend or foe. The history went back, and the eight civilizations on world history was classified into Egypt, Babylonia, India, China, Greece Rome, Arabia, the West, and Mexico. Toynbee has increased this 8 to 26. He arranged 16 had been ruined sooner or later. It was assumed that having remained at the end was five (a Western Europe Christianity civilization, Eastern Europe, a Byzantine civilization, an Islam civilization, a Hinduism civilization, and the Far Eastern civilization). Huntington only followed this.

In making of a new civilization composition, there is a meaning for giving the new image to the post Cold War world. However, after the Cold war, capitalism and the open market have globalized. Urbanization and the information network have already been advanced in all over the world. Did "Western Europe civilization" bring the globalization? Yes, the globalization itself is a kind of the US-made ideology that the Corporation should extend all over the world with denying the nation-state-system. So what kind of war we are facing to?

**6 The Crash of civilizations and the New World War**

If "Crash of civilizations" is replaced with something with the war, Huntington's discussion is comprehensible. However, what kind of war is possible in the age of fading out the nation-states? The civilization theory and the war theory that does not ask this are meaningless in the 21st century.

How wins the war, that is the assumption of Clausewitz's war theory. And he thought the war is the continuance of politics. Carl Schmitt wrote politics is to decide who is the enemy and the war invents an original rule in the decision of politics. Wallerstein thought that the war and capitalism occurred in the heartland on which the surplus concentrated, because "Heartland on which the surplus concentrates" makes up the state apparatus and wheels of government. The violence device can disturb the formation of state, so Gilles Deleuze and Félix Guattari wrote that originally the war and the nation would be the different one.

In the real world, balance and the tension proceed, then, there are two new situations to be more complex and difficult to make the relation between the war and politics. One is the "Cold war." It is because "Deterrent" becomes the pronoun of the back of the war. Another one is rampancy of "Suicide bombing". The civilization does not collide with the civilization in the suicide bombing but the civilization and the individual will stab each other. Huntington's civilization theory cannot understand

"Suicide bombing."

There is terrorism from the beginning of the history. It is possible to say that French Revolution is an origin of modern terrorism. However, how do we see the terrorism since 9.11? At present, neither "Western Europe civilization" nor "Confucian-Islamic connection" completely has "theory" and "strategy" on the terrorism.

Terrorism is politics and it is a war, too. Terrorism and the guerrilla are politics and they are also the wars. It is contradicted to fight to seal terrorism. Then, the terrorism of Islam radicals is considered to be "belief" for a while. It is usual understanding to say the "belief," when one reads the terrorism of Islam and the confrontation of Europe and America. "Suicide bombing" has been described in conjunction with the faith and belief.

However, it is "Western Europe civilization" to support the terrorism physically in fact. "Islam State (IS)" that develops in Northern Iraq and Syria is just a monster that "Western Europe civilization (the United States and Israel)" has produced to begin with now. It is an uncivilized cohesion body.

Origins of the "Crash of civilizations" and "Islam State" are "Western Europe civilization."Russian General Gerasimov reports the feature of the war of the 21st century as follows:

In the 21st century we have seen a tendency toward blurring the lines between the states of war and peace. Wars are no longer declared and, having begun, proceed according to an unfamiliar template. The experience of military conflicts -including those connected with the so-called colored revolutions in north Africa and the Middle East - confirm that a perfectly thriving state can, in a matter of months and even days, be transformed into an arena of fierce armed conflict, become a victim of foreign intervention, and sink into a web of chaos, humanitarian catastrophe, and civil war…….. /Of course, it would be easiest of all to say that the events of the "Arab Spring" are not war and so there are no lessons for us - military men - to learn. But maybe the opposite is true - that precisely these events are typical of warfare in the 21st century./In terms of the scale of the casualties and destruction - the catastrophic social, economic, and political consequences - such new-type conflicts are comparable with the consequences of any real war./The very "rules of war" have changed. The role of non-military means of achieving political and strategic goals has grown, and, in many cases, they have exceeded the power of force of weapons in their effectiveness./The focus of applied methods of conflict has altered in the direction of the broad use of political, economic, informational, humanitarian, and other non-military measures—applied in coordination with the protest potential of the population. All this is supplemented by military means of a concealed character, including carrying out actions of informational conflict and the actions of special operations forces. The open use of forces -often under the guise of peacekeeping and crisis regulation -is resorted to only at a certain stage, primarily for the achievement of final success in the conflict./From this proceed logical questions: What is modern war? What should the army be prepared for? How should it be armed? Only after answering these questions can we determine the directions of the construction and development of the armed forces over the long term. To do this, it is essential to have a clear understanding of the forms and methods of the use of the application of force.…….( "*Military-Industrial Kurier*" on February 27, 2013)

Gerasimov wrote about how "a perfectly thriving state can, in a matter of months and even days, be transformed into an arena of fierce armed conflict, become a victim of foreign intervention, and sink into a web of chaos, humanitarian catastrophe, and civil war." So the very "rules of war" have changed like this, how about the meaning of the clash of civilizations? Perhaps the original form of civilization war in the new century has already come to appear.

**7 Meaning of the Confucian-Islamic connection**

Huntington thought that the Confucian-Islamic connection conflicted with "Western Europe civilization". It is because there is danger that China offers Iran the nuclear weapons technology and the missile. Huntington has not inquired anything about Confucianism and Islam itself. Afterwards, "Western Europe civilization" restrained the military force in the Islam civilization. And the military assistance to Israel was systematically continued. The war to Afghanistan and Iraq could not stop completely. Leaders of neo-conservative assume the democratization of the Middle East to be a purpose of Iraq War. This purpose rationalized the all means. The war against Iraq was started by false, that there were the weapons of mass destruction. Only the elite has to understand the truth. The truth is good for the people without information. This "double the truth" is features of neo-conservative "Western Europe civilization".

"Western Europe civilization" had a large influence in "Islam civilization" in ten years afterwards. CIA made and FBI managed Al-Qaeda, and "War on terrorism" was an indeed convenient excuse for a military enhancing "Western Europe civilization" in the post Cold war. Actually, enhancing the militarization in the Islamic world promoted Westernization of the Islamic World. And the United States made up "Islam State (IS)" as a cohering negative side of "Western Europe civilization." Obama administration has not any strategy that destroys "Islam State," because IS may be just a realization of an extreme self-image reflects in the mirror of "Western Europe civilization".

On the other hand, the formation of the connection with "Islam civilization" has been obstructed to "Confucian civilization" by this "War on terrorism". That connection has just started a first step.

The contact of "Western Europe civilization" and "Islam civilization" has been based by militarization. However, the contact of "Confucian civilization" and "Islam civilization" should be expected the opposite action, for "peace making." "Western Europe civilization" will disintegrate militarily, however, "the Confucian-Islamic connection" requests a kind of liberation for de-militarization. And the connection has the possibility of contributing to the construction of a new world order with the Confucian-Islamic value standard.

**8 New Asia Norms and Intellectual networks**

The resource of "Western Europe civilization" and "Islam civilization" was various, cultural differences. Oppositely, the causes of the decline of "Confucian civilization" were to have ruined this various, cultural differences.

Confucian civilization has been widely shared in East Asia. However, it was the situation until the 17th century. About 400 years throughout to modern, each in China, Korea, Japan, Confucian civilization had developed separately. Now, to think about the reconstruction of Confucian civilization, it may need to rethink the regional space of it. Asia, the region name is recalled immediately. But the concept "Asia" and "Orient" is the one that created with the rivalry with "Western Europe civilization". As well as the concepts of "Asia" and "Orient," "Confucian civilization" has been reconstructed in the post-modern nation state system recently.

Currently, the redefinition of the Asia is required. One of the factors for that request, there is a presence of China, which is achieving significant economic growth in the early 21st century. So it is also correlated with the issues on the definition of China: Is China the Asia? The presence of China is diluted when the Asia is noted, the presence of the Asia is marginalized when China is highlighted. It is that the floating image with a vague definition in both cases. This is also related to the question "the US is whether the Asia." Therefore, the situation of Asia is very complicate in fact.

Asia is the concept of expansion and contraction of the speech subject to try to issue it by the intent. The EU can indicate the presence by certain parameters. Asia can not do like that.

For example, when it is about to be spoken by "the intended" that "beyond the political boundaries of the nation-state of each, to build the political space of the imaginary one, and to dismantle the state-centric in the inward manner, to resist the hegemony of Western Externally," Asia is presented as meaningful as such. There are many of the speeches of "thinking from Asia," "building of world history image from Asia." For attempting to give the representation of postcolonial Asia images, fleeing from Orientalist thinking, however, if it is asked whether possible Asia treats as "one world history", it means that to meet a variety of quickly disproved. After all, it is hard to define the Asia, because that there are various possibilities for the redefinition of the Asia.

The word Asia is nothing but a complex of images. Economically, socially, Asia is a concept that has a functional reality of some sort. In addition, the diffusion of certain information is taking place mutual infiltration of the media. However, it is not enough to bring about a qualitative change of the more quantitative expansion of information to build their Asian identity. Kenneth Waltz was formulated image in three dimensions of "human, national and international system." The concept of region is located in the middle of "order" and "anarchy". For the purposes of whether to see how the world, a region level, does not play only auxiliary functions only.

It can be assumed "to die for their country". Though, it is difficult to imagine "to die for the Asia". But if "state" itself is a kind of "imagined communities", <region> image may become a high cohesive image of supranational assembling beyond the "state". Share of the various elements are required to be recognized for <region> is the representation of a set of organic like "nation". We need time together with the sharing of experience and memory than anything else. Memory, which is currently shared in the Asia, is storage as a colony in the 19th century imperialist countries.

And, it is the memories of the war in the Asia-Pacific Ocean region in the 20th century.

In the 19th century, Western imperialism extended and Asia was divided. Japan, late imperialist countries, did not want to use the word <imperialism>. Japan tried to put under the control of the area over to the northeastern part of China from the Korean Peninsula by the word <regionalism>. Western powers have had with the awareness of imperialism, it is because was a derivative of Western civilization. Japan was not self-proclaimed imperialism. <Regionalism> was conveniently over to imperialist aggression justified.

Once, Kishore Mahbubani asked that "Can Asians think?" Asia is not self-defined originally. Therefore, re-definition of <Asia> is difficult. It is difficult also building <Asian> identity. By Asian himself, redefine the <Asia>, it must be con sidered to clarify the role and *global* positioning. Nevertheless, the question that is really complicated even come to overlap automatically there.

There is an idea "Asia as the method" of Takeuchi Yoshimi. It might be useful for reconstructing the Confucianism in the Asia at the present. According to Takeuchi, the concept named Asia does not direct a region. The Asia is a certain kind of sense of self that the reaction caused in the process of expanding European powers toward the East. The resistance power to the power of the Western Europe civilization is caused by the consciousness of the Asian.

There is no border in the Confucian civilization. It recollects there is not a border in the Asian concept either. An Asian concept is effective for Japan and South Korea to make a relative stance not only on the West but also on China. It is not only in China that the Confucian civilization symbolizes. The expression of Confucian civilization in Asia might be more appropriate. It is necessary to take the idea "Asia as the method" to reconstruct the Confucian civilization. In addition, if it expands cooperation with the Islam civilization, we will be able to discuss on the universality of "Confucian-Islamic connection".

"Confucian civilization" has the possibility to be developed with the universality over the Asian concept. It subsumes "Western Europe civilization". Of course a great amount of energy and time are necessary for the reconstructing of such "Confucian civilization".

"The Rebalancing Strategy " of the United States is basically an adjustment of a military balance. However, "Confucian civilization" should review its root of thought for the strategic shift from the "Western Europe civilization". Once Jacques Derrida said that "there is no philosophy in China" at Shanghai. "Philosophy" is a key concept of most remarkably characterizing "Western Europe civilization". It is related to the role that "philosophy" carried out to a fundamental problem of the Christianity doctrine. In "Islam civilization," it also occupies an important position. "Philosophy" has carried out the function to connect the relation between Greece speculation and Absolute God.

First of all, it is necessary to reconstruct the thought that subsumes this "Philosophy". "Confucian-Islamic connection" is the most important thing for that.

In constructing, "Confucian-Islamic connection," what can we "think" in Islamic context?

An approach to Islamism now being used by Susan Buck-Morss, Political Philosopher at Cornell, is acquiring a new significance:

…..By attempting to silence Islam as a political discourse, by reducing it to a religious practice, Bush is in effect closing off public discussion of how the many varieties of Islamism are challenging and extending the discursive field of political resistance. Such a discussion, however, is there to be engaged within the *global* public sphere, as opposed to our own provincial one, and there is urgency to do so. But this urgent task requires, paradoxically, taking time, the time to read not only news reports and journalistic comments that record and react to the kaleidoscope of daily events, but scholarly articles and books, whole books written by critical theorists like Akbar Ahmed, Leila Ahmad, Mohammed Arkoun, Talal Asad, Ahmet Davutoglu, Saba Mahmood, Ziba Mir-Hosseini, Abdelwahab El-Messiri, Ali Mirsepassi, Ali Moussalli, Bobby Sayyid, Hisham Sharabi, Azzam Tamimi, Bassam Tibi. These scholars(who is no way speak with one voice) have been trained in the West where many are citizens; most live and teach here. They are fluent in the traditions of Husserl's and Heidegger's phenomenology, Foucault's analyses of power and truth, Gramsci's work on organic intellectuals, Derrida on deconstruction, the radical democracy of Laclau and Mouffe, the cultural studies of Birmingham school, the postcolonialism of Spivak and Bhabha, and the critical theories of Adrno, Horkheimer, Benjamin, and Harbermas. They have been writing for Western audiences for at least the past decade, engaged in the crucial task of making clear how Western phenomena such as secularization, modernization, and nationalism change, not their conceptual meaning as they move from the West to non-West, but their material referent, and with it, their political value…….(Buck-Morss 2003)

There now exist global Muslim Intellectual networks composed of this new generation of scholars and others within the global public sphere; however, the audiences are very limited. Buck-Morss continues on an innovative political use of Islamic discourses: "Paradoxically (dialectically?), once Islam was free from traditional institutional arrangements, emptied of any political use yet still widely dispersed within cultural life, it became available for articulations of political resistance to the postcolonial order"(Buck-Morss 2003).

She also insists that "We, as critical theorists, need to make Western audiences aware that Islamism as a political discourse embraces far more than the dogmatic fundamentalism and terrorist violence that dominate in the Western press" (Buck-Morss 2003). In spite of her claim, Islamism discourses are still classified into a certain special field by "Culture Talk": that of *Orientalism*:

……Islamic discourses are also a powerful source of critical debate in the struggle against the undemocratic imposition of the so-called new world order by the United States and against the economic and ecological violence of neo-liberalism, the fundamentalist orthodoxies of which fuel the growing divide between rich and poor. Secularization, however, is no guarantee against dogmatic beliefs, and even foundational religious texts are open to multiple interpretations. Islamism has become a site within civil society of social movements that struggle in the most diverse ways to come to grips with the inequities of modern life, and that have developed within the period of dominance by the West. This is a West that for Islamists included the atheistic, materialistic Soviet Union that so faithfully mimicked the model of Western modernization, along with the Western-Orientalist judgment of Islam as an irredeemable obstruction to historical progress. (Buck-Morss 2003)

I think methodologically, that also a new approach to Confucianism would be capable of a similar way. Then, it may be necessary to reconstruct the "Confucian-Islamic connection" in the new Asian concept in order to withstand the Clash of civilizations.

In the last part of the paper of Huntington, there are sentences as the following: "It will also, however, require the West to develop a more profound understanding of the basic religious and philosophical assumptions underlying other civilizations and the ways in which people in those civilizations see their interests." We should be aware of the words "religious" and "philosophical." The concepts of those words themselves are guiding the fundamental recognition of Western civilization. It is necessary that it should be reconsidered fundamentally first, those concepts that form the basis of modern Western society.

It is a well-known passage such as the following in the Analects of Confucius: Zi Lu said, "The ruler of Wei has been waiting for you, in order with you to administer the government. What will you consider the first thing to be done?" The Master replied, "What is necessary is to rectify names." 子路曰:「衛君待子而為政,子將奚先?」子曰:「必也正名乎!」

# 恥之於人大矣-"Great is the Use of Shame to Man"[①]

**Amira Katz-Goehr (The Hebrew University of Jerusalem)**

Regrettably, the writing of my talks for this conference and for the last conference of 2009 coincided with two wars in the country from which I come. Both took place in the tiny, poverty stricken Gaza strip, a forlorn land, home to a huge population, militarily occupied for many years, then besieged and forever left in a state of underdeveloped misery.

There can be no victory in any war: the defeat is on both sides. But in the war-ridden history of my country, I think that this time, our moral defeat is of unprecedented dimensions. It is here that I will take up my talk.

When the images of atrocities of this third Gaza war started appearing on the screens, you may initially have found yourselves speechless. However, one word which seems to me of some substance among the more conventional ones ('horrible', 'awful', 'intolerable' etc.)is 'shame' and its derivations - shameful, shameless, ashamed.

After a couple of days of emotionally useless outbursts, and leaving aside all possible political and existential questions, the word 'shame' keeps suggesting itself and demands further consideration. [I will repeat this, as it is such considerations that I deal with in what follows.] Is it just a vague, abstract marker for expressing rage and grief? Or does it stand for things which require more substantial attention? If yes, was it I myself who was and is ashamed? Is the 'thing' itself shameful? Am I ashamed for my compatriots, or for things like this happening in the world? Is it a feeling of personal responsibility? It seems that all of these deliberations are somehow bundled into

---

① . 孟子,7B7. *Mencius*, translated with an Introduction by D. C. Lau. Penguin Books (1970). p. 183

the root of this one word. And again, whatever this term incorporated or meant, it clearly expresses an unmitigated, immediate response of disapproval and disgust.

So this 'paper', the writing of which coincided with the events of war, is not a non-partisan exposition nor can its tone be dispassionate as befits an academic dissertation.

In my talk at the last Confucian conference of 2009, under the shadow of very similar war clouds (the second Gaza war), I attended to a Confucian analect, the most obvious one dealing with the dilemma of Law and Morality. It is the 'concealment case' where family morality, the root of all morality, overrides the law. At the time, following Zhu Xi's commentary, I salvaged the 'little' word 'zhi'《直》('straightness', 'honesty') so as to expose it as a marker for a direct attitude of 'heart', when there is no need of further deliberation in taking a problematic decision. I presented it as a missing links in the discussion of Legality and Morality, not so much with the intent of giving [unrealistic] priority to the one at the expense of the other, but rather with the emphasis on the disparity between the two which we, in parts of our modern world, are made to believe might 'harmoniously' coexist.

Today, I would like to see whether a similar observation might be relevant to the term *chi* 耻 and its 'relatives': *xiu* 羞, *ru* 辱, *can* 惭, *kui* 愧, *jian* 贱。

It has often been claimed, but long disputed, that Chinese culture is a 'shame culture', associated with the individual's sense of not complying with or abiding by social norms, by comparison to the 'Western' Judeo-Christian culture which is described as a 'guilt culture' (Ruth Benedict, Wolfram Eberhard, Max Weber), burdened with divine law, sin and punishment. The distinction implicitly views 'shame' as a somewhat 'thinner', 'lighter' emotion which can be attributed mainly to being seen by others, to losing face or to being disgraced, and less to being innerly afflicted, guilt-ridden and driven to regret, penitence and confession.

This aspect of the relative superficiality of the sense of shame, hinging on being [externally] seen or looked at, is also implicitly suggested by contemporary philosophers such as Gabriele Taylor and Bernard Williams.

Conversely, depending on one's point of view - the sense of shame might be taken morally as 'thicker', wider of scope, since it relates to society at large and refrains from the over psychologized, individualistically-inclined man's search for his self.

Indeed the Confucian ideal society, according to its classical writings, is one based on rites, on proper behavioral norms internalized by its members-an utopian state of affairs where law becomes redundant. Western culture, on the other hand, is based on law and ethical codes emanating from an external divine source as sanction. Breaking the Law originally meant disobedience to a divine force (and later to the state and its constitution), the legitimizing authority of its system of laws, justice and morality. Western law is in a sense negative - it imposes avoidance of bad behavior by the threat of punishment.

Looking at some examples from the [Confucian] Four Books with this distinction in mind, and attending to the varied translations which try to cope with rendering the concept of shame, one immediately becomes aware that the distinction is more complex and not quite as clearcut.

The few examples I chose to present here, have been picked out not so much with the intent of displaying an optimal translation of the meaning of a term, or a comprehensive report on the 'Master's views' on shame (or else, on judging where to use which rendered term) but so as to emphasize the inner aspect of the Confucian sense of shame, as a spontaneous, involuntary reaction of internal moral unease. Although it relates to self cultivation, it can be a sense not only independent of being observed from outside, but also independent of as if being 'observed' by fixed, supposedly acceptable norms. It is something which may happen in one's four quarters, while 'sitting on one's own' (慎其獨 in《大學》and《中庸》).

Obviously, distinguished scholars have paid specific and detailed attention to these aspects of shame in the Confucian classical texts. Antonio S. Cua and Andrew H. Plaks have exhaustively written, the first on the

ethical significance of the shame experience①, and the latter on the place of emotion in self cultivation②.

My starting point, vaguely embodied in the profuse questions set at the beginning

① . Antonio S. Cua, "The Ethical Significance of Shame: Insights of Aristotle and Xunzi," in *Philosophy East and West*, Volume 53, no. 2 (2003). pp. 147-202. Cua mainly deals with shame in the *Xunzi* and Aristoteles, but also touches upon the *Analects* and the *Mencius*.

② . Andrew H, Plaks, "Xin 心 as the Seat of the Emotions in Confucian Self-Cultivation," in ? *Love, Hatred,? and Other Passions*, ed. Paolo Santangelo and Donatella Guida (Leiden, Brill (2006). pp. 113-125.

I will quote from both scholars' work in the final version of this essay

of my essay, is to look at a few of the Confucian examples side by side with these questions which I find difficult to sort out. I will also refer shortly to the term and concept of shame in my own language - Hebrew, reverting to its classical source - the Bible. It will be of some interest to check how the biblical passages incorporating 'shame' (*busha*) with its various synonyms are translated into Chinese in some of its Old Testament versions.

Of course, when we try to understand a Chinese term and consider its equivalence or dissimilarity in nuance (and evolving concept) in our languages, we'd do well to compare its various renderings. I'll start here by attending to a few examples of translations into English. The variations in the english translations of 'shame'(*chi* 恥), its synonyms and related words (*xiu* 羞, *kui* 愧, *can* 慚, *ru* 辱, *jian* 賤) into 'shame', 'disgrace', 'humiliation', etc., might in addition hint at one of the sources of blurred conception when qualifying cultural ways of thought (e.g. shame and guilt cultures).

I will begin with analect 1.13, admittedly not the most important one for my exposition, but instructive as to problems of translation and potential misconceptions.

*Analects* 1.13

1. 13. 有子曰:「信近於義,言可復也;恭近於禮,遠恥辱也;因不失其親,亦可宗也。」

James Legge[①]: [The philosopher Yu said, 'When agreements are made according to what is right, what is spoken can be made good.] When respect is shown according to what is proper, one keeps far from shame and disgrace.

Arthur Waley[②]: ...In your obeisances cleave to ritual, and you will keep dishonor at bay.

D.C. Lau: Yu Tzu said, "[To be trustworthy in word is close to being moral in that it enables one's words to be repeated.] To be respectful is close to being observant of the rites in that it enables one to stay clear of disgrace and insult.

Chichung Huang[③]: Only when your respectfulness is close to the rituals can you keep humiliation away.

---

① . *Confucius*; Confucian *Analects*, *The Great Learning and the Doctrine of the Mean*. Translation by James Legge. New York: Dover Publications (1971)

② . *The Analects of Confucius*. Translated and annotated by Arthur Waley. London: Unwin Hyman (1988)

③ . *The Analects of Confucius*. Literal Translation with an Introduction and Notes by Chichung Huang. Oxford University Press (1997)

Simon Leys[①]: Master You said, '[if your promises conform to what is right, you will be able to keep your word.] If your manners conform to the ritual, you will be able to keep shame and disgrace at bay. The best support is provided by one's own kinsmen.

As we can see right away, the choice of translated words, is varied [nothing remarkable in this], other than Legge and Leys both of whom use 'shame and disgrace' for the two Chinese terms - *chi* 恥 and *ru* 辱. Of more interest is the fact that two of the translators - Waley and Huang, use one English word - 'dishonor' and 'humiliation' respectively, for rendering the two Chinese characters. A compound in the Analects? Surely the two characters stand for two different states of mind - *chi* for the inner sense of shame and *ru* for suffering external disgrace, both for one's negligence of ritual *li* 禮 [for respect or manners which have not been properly internalized and thus falsely performed. Feeling ashamed here would hint at some unease of inner contradiction when acting as if according to manner but perhaps insincerely].

I'll only add here that the distinction between *chi* 恥 and *ru* 辱 appears also in analect 13.20, so that notice should be taken of the different aspects of these two words:

13. 20. 子貢問曰:「何如斯可謂之士矣?」子曰:「行己有恥,使於四方,不辱君命,可謂士矣。」曰:「敢問其次。」曰:「宗族稱孝焉,鄉黨稱弟焉。」曰:「敢問其次。」曰:「言必信,行必果,硜硜然小人哉! 抑亦可以為次矣。」曰:「今之從政者何如?」子曰:「噫! 斗筲之人,何足算也。」

Legge: Tsze-kung asked, saying, 'What qualities must a man possess to entitle him to be called an officer?' The Master said, 'He who in his conduct of himself maintains a sense of shame, and when sent to any quarter will not disgrace his prince's commission, deserves to be called an officer.'

Lau: [Tzu-kung asked, "What must a man be like before he can be said truly to b a Gentleman?"] The Master said, "A man who has a sense of shame in the way he conducts himself and, when sent abroad, does not disgrace the commission of his lord can be said to be a Gentleman.

Waley: is held back by scruples... ...Does not disgrace his prince's commission

---

① *onfucius - The Analects*. Translated by Simon Leys. New York; London: W. W. Norton & Co. Ltd (1997)

[omit: huang: in conducting himself he has a sense of shame he does not fail the sovereign's mission...]

Leys - ...he who behaves with honor , and, being sent on a mission to the four corners of the world, does not bring disgrace on his lord, deserves to be called a gentleman.

Legge and Lau stick here to'a sense of shame', but Waley and Leys do not, perhaps because of the connection to the official character of the man to be defined - an 'Officer' or 'Gentleman' *shi* 士. In any case we cannot fail noticing here the close, but separate presence of *chi* and *ru*, denoting the two aspects of inner and external shame.

It is also important to note that *chi* and *ru* [although referring here to a *shi* 士] appear here as the first qualifiers of the scholar-official/Gentleman, even before the important *xiao* 孝 and *ti* 悌'filial' and 'fraternal' (in Legge's translation) and before 'keeping one's words' - 言必信. Also, 'shame' and 'disgrace'are given directly 行己有恥, without a more'definitional' form - the way they are called (宗族稱孝焉,鄉黨稱弟焉) i.e. seen from the outside. The end of the analect, 'The rulers today are not worthwhile mentioning', probably also implies that they are shameless.

And now to the two seminal paragraphs - well known to everyone - the one - Lunyu (2.3), which is an abstract formulation of the more concrete 'concealment case', analect 1.13 [of the last conference]. It is concerned with the ideal way of rule [involving shame]. The other is Mencius 2A6, dealing directly with shame as one of the four innate, natural inclinations of the heart, and as part of the *Mencius* substantial discourse on human nature.

Although these paragraphs are more abstract 'summaries' of both texts' doctrine, formulated in high rhetoric, they serve as a good introduction to shame's 'in-between' function, relating the core emotion to the more general framework /essence of a moral system.

2.3 子曰:「道之以政,齊之以刑,民免而無恥;道之以德,齊之以禮,有恥且格。」

Legge: The Master said, 'If the people are led by laws, and uniformity sought to be given them by punishment, they will try to avoid *the punishment*, but have no sense of shame.

If they be led by virtue, and uniformity sought to be given them by the rules of propriety, they will have the sense of shame, and moreover will become good.'

Lau: The Master said, 'Guide them by edicts, keep them in line with punishments, and the common people will stay out of trouble but will have no sense of shame. Guide them by virtue, keep them in line with the rites, and they will besides having a sense of shame, reform themselves.'

Leys: The Master said, 'Lead them by political maneuvres, restrain them with punishments: the people will become cunning and shameless. Lead them by virtue, restrain them with ritual: they will develop a sense of shame and a sense of participation."

Legge and Lau translate *chi* with sense of shame. Leys uses 'shameless' in the first case, and 'sense of shame' in the second. Waley writes, [lose all] self respect.

It is often of interest to find connections between adjacent analects, even when they do not clearly concern themselves with one particular subject (as for example, when various disciples ask the Master to elaborate on one particular issue - *ren* 仁, *xiao* 孝 and the like).

I look here at analect 2.4 in connection with the previous one:

2.4「吾十有五而志于學,三十而立,四十而不惑,五十而知天命,六十而耳順,七十而從心所欲,不踰矩。」

Legge: At seventy, I could follow what my heart desired, without transgressing what was right.

waley: I could follow the dictates of my own heart; for what I desired no longer overstepped the boundaries of right.

Lau: at seventy I followed my heart's desire without overstepping the line.

Leys: '...at seventy, I follow all the desires of my heart without breaking any rule.'

Huang: overstepping the rules of propriety.

We have here in the combined reading of the two analects, the *Lun Yu*'s frequent, but unique, mixture of a general, politico-philosophical declaration - here on the ideal way of governance - with the very brief [moving] [auto]biographical sketch of the Master, describing his personal intellectual-moral development.

Positing the two analects side by side, does not just 'exemplify' the abstract by a concrete 'case' (of course not forgetting, that of the Master), but, as in many other places in the Analects, it inspires the reader by means of its ethico-literary fusion, bridging the distance between theory and reality, between the more 'public' and the personal.

The implication (of the combined reading) in my view is that shame in 2.3 is not to be taken just as a useful educational tool of social control. If it were just that, the difference between this way of ruling the people as opposed to the legalistic methods mentioned in the analect, would not be that dramatic. Surely 'shame' here in the context of the grand principles of virtue and ritual implies a more substantial emotion leading to self cultivation and reform, to becoming good.

The sequence of the two analects suggests another important consideration: that when the Master follows the desires of his own heart without breaking a rule, he does not merely find peace within himself vis-a-vis any norms. By norms, understand, in the 19th century sense, something not so absolute at all, rather than as in the latin, *Norma*. He rather finds peace within an ideal moral fabric identifiable as universal virtue *de* 德 and its accompanying ritual *li* 禮 (and perhaps as described in the previous analect [2.3]).

The element of shame suggested in analect 2.3, even if sounding to our ears rather meagre, as a direct (even if complex) emotion, might be an effective arbiter when we enter the domain of conflicting relative norms and value systems.

And from here to some notes on Mencius' discourse on human nature.

The writings on Mencius' discourse on man's good nature( 性善說) are voluminous indeed, and I will limit myself only to a few notes on the passages relevant to my topic, again, mainly from the point of view of translation [and its possible implications].

Let us remind ourselves that 'shame' in the *Mencius* is one of the 'four hearts', 'four tendencies/inclinations of the heart', 'germs' or 'sprouts' - depending on the translation one chooses to adopt - being of the same importance as the three others, and in fact occupying the second place after the 'heart of compassion'.

These four 'hearts' - the other two being 'respectfulness' and [a sense of] 'right and wrong' - guarantee man's potential/capacity for humanity or morality provided they are continuously sought after and nurtured. Their 'naturalness' or inborn-ness does not imply a detachment from the world.

Inherent within the 'four inclinations' are self diminution, humility and the withdrawing of the self whilst attending to 'the other'. [In this respect, they stand apart from traits of character discussed in the classics, e.g. vigor, power, courage, all of which focus on and (in a way) glorify the self.]

I commence here with the general statement of the human heart's sensitivity to the suffering of others, the heart universal to all men, as is described in chapter 2A6, and then proceed on to the paragraphs dealing with human nature, with particular reference to the sentences dealing with shame.

2A6 孟子曰:人皆有不忍人之心。先王有不忍人之心,斯有不忍人之政矣,以不忍人之心,行不忍人之政,治天下可運之掌上。。。

Lau:Mencius said, No man is devoid of a heart sensitive to the suffering of others. Such sensitive heart was possessed by the former kings and this manifested itself in compassionate government. With such a sensitive heart behind compassionate government, it was as easy to rule the empire as rolling it on your palm. (p.82)

Legge: Mencius said, 'All man have a mind which cannot bear to *see the sufferings of others*. The ancient kings had this commiserating mind, and they as a matter of course, had likewise a commiserating government. When with a commiserating mind was practised a commiserating government, to rule the kingdom was *as easy a matter* as to make anything go round in the palm. [italics in original text]. (p.201)

Again the commiserating heart is connected to the ideal way of government. Shameless are the rulers with no shame (derived from (*Analect* 13.20).

Hereafter comes Mencius' ''validation' of man's innate good nature - it is the well-known story of the young child on the verge of falling into a well, a sight which would move anyone to compassion. And its conclusion:

2A6 [ continues]由是觀之,無惻隱之心非人也,無羞惡之心非人也,無辭讓之心非人也,無是非之心非人也。惻隱之心仁之端也;羞惡之心義之端也;恭敬之心禮之端也;是非之心智智端也.

Lau: From this it can be seen that whoever is devoid of the heart of compassion is not human, whoever is devoid of the heart of shame is not human, whoever is devoid of the heart of courtesy and modesty is not human, and whoever is devoid of the heart of right and wrong is not human. The heart of compassion is the germ of benevolence; the heart of shame, of dutifulness... (p.82-83)

Legge: From this case we may perceive that the feeling of commiseration is essential to man. that the feeling of shame and dislike is essential to man, that the feeling of modesty and complaisance is essential to man, and that the feeling of approving and disapproving is essential to man. The feeling of commiseration is the principle of benevolence. The feeling of shame and dislike is the principle of righteousness... (p. 202-203)

The term for 'shame' here is *xiu* (羞) and not *chi* (恥). [However, *chi* is used in the Mencius elsewhere.] The *Hanyu da cidian* (漢語大詞典) gives *xiu* a number of meanings, starting with its older uses in the *Zuozhuan* and in the *Shujing*, for sacrifice, sacrificing, delicacies, etc.① In the *yijing xiu* appears with the meaning of shame - 恥辱②, and it does so similarly elsewhere in the *Mencius* [《公孫丑上》]. *Xiu* is additionally defined as having the nuance of embarrassment and being shy: 難為情,慚愧③. The more external 'despise' or 'being despised', 'belittle/d' (嘲弄,侮辱) are also given as definitions of *xiu*.

The issue is discussed again even more categorically in *Mencius*, 6A6:

6A6 惻隱之心人皆有之,羞惡之心人皆有之。。。惻隱之心仁也;羞惡之心義也;恭敬之心禮也;是非之心智也。仁義禮智,非由外鑠我也,我固有之也,弗思耳矣,故曰,求則得之,舍則失之。。。

Lau, p.161: The heart of compassion is possessed by all men alike; likewise the heart of shame, the heart of respect, and the heart of right and wrong. The heart of compassion pertains to benevolence, the heart of shame to dutifulness, the heart of respect to the observance of the rites, and the heart of right and wrong to wisdom.

...are not welded on to me from the outside; they are in me originally. Only this has never dawned on me. (p.163)

*Xiu* in these essential paragraphs, stands together with *wu* 惡 - hatred/dislike, to hate/dislike. *Xiu-wu* 羞惡 is explained as: 對自己或別人的壞處感到羞恥厭情 - shame and disgust at defects/flaws of oneself or others. The *Menius* English translations I've looked at don't provide real solutions as to how the two relate to each other. D.C. Lau translates *xiuwu* 羞惡 both in 2A6 and in 6A6 into one word - 'shame'. He used

---

① . I'd just mention here the Hebrew 'ch'atat', a name of a biblical special sacrifice, which was offered for a sin [one] committed unintentionally. This might insinuate that shame in both languages has a 'religious' origin, and relates to atonement and offerings (in Chinese, also to fear -'pa' [怕] which is given as one of the nuances of *xiu*).

The name 'Ch'atat' originates from the root 'ch'et' (???) - 'sin', as does the verb 'lech'ate' - to clean; the sacrifice offered to redeem sin is meant to cleanse.

② . Note the interesting quotation:《易。恆》不恆其德,成承之羞。

③ . This again finds its parallel in Hebrew where both words for 'shame' and 'bashfulness' are rooted in the three root-letters - ???.

'disgrace and insult' translating *chiru* 耻辱 in *Analects* 1.13 (perhaps conceiving of the two characters in that particular context as implicating something more external.) His use of 'shame' here fits the more intimate and 'lofty' emotion, similar in weight to the other three natural tendencies of the heart - compassion (one word in his translation for two in the Chinese), courtesy and modesty, [sense of] right and wrong. James Legge translates *xiuwu* into shame and dislike, without putting into italics (his usual practice) what the object of dislike might be. Irene Bloom in a new *Mencius* version of 2009 writes shame and aversion. All three use 'shame' interchangeably for both *xiu* and *chi* 恥.

Interesting from the point of view of translation is also Legge's moderation of the categorical statement in 2A6 無羞惡之心非人也 when he translates, " shame and dislike is essential to man", deviating from the original, as well as differing from Lau's and Bloom's translations, which deprive humanity from man devoid of the four tendencies or 'sprouts'. And one wonders whether the statement is too harsh for the great sinologist/translator, a Congregationalist missionary?

[Another interesting problem of translation, which goes much further than the rendering of terms, is posed by the two different (semantically-philosophically) formulations of the following formulations:

惻隱之心仁之端也;羞惡之心義之端也...

惻隱之心仁也;羞惡之心義也…

[I will attend to it in the final version of this essay.]

The more substantial point as far as we are here concerned, is the different connection established in the *Mencius* between 'shame' and *yi* 義 - 'righteousness', 'the right thing to be done', 'duty', when transforming the *Lunyu*'s relating of shame, *chi* 恥 to ritual, *li* 禮. This relation has been established In analect 1.13, which I have just quoted above: "If your manners conform to the ritual (禮), you will be able to keep shame and disgrace at bay". This 'transformation' enhances the importance of the emotion as a function not only of doing things according to internalized *li*, but according to what is right - *yi*, a pillar of morality only second to *ren* 仁.

Surely, the emotion described here as the germ of *yi* points to an inner feeling, the feeling of shame and perhaps an accompanying sense of disgust, as indicated by *wu*, a 'sprout', in a way spontaneous, which nevertheless responds to the world and is not detached from it. It is enmeshed in a social and ethical framework, and potentially has a part in paving one's way to a right moral judgement.

It is an appropriate point here to turn back to the *Analects* of which quite a number of sayings closely relate to my initial questions about the sense of shame. These sayings (both in the *Analects* and in the *Mencius*), repeatedly posit the dilemma of serving in a country which lost its way. They normally deal with historical paragons of virtue or with contemporary lesser figures, forced to decide whether to serve, to resign, to become recluses or exiles where circumstances are such. Since shame goes along with such situations where extreme choice has to be made - the question of the meaning of the emotion posits itself yet again.

*Analects*

8.13 子曰:「篤信好學,守死善道。危邦不入,亂邦不居。天下有道則見,無道則隱。邦有道,貧且賤焉,恥也;邦無道,富且貴焉,恥也。」

Waley - The Master Said, Be of unwavering good faith, love learning, if attacked be ready to die for the good Way. Do not enter a State that pursues dangerous course, not stay in one where the people have rebelled. When the Way prevails in your own land, count it a disgrace to be needy and obscure; when the way does not prevail in your land, then count it a disgrace to be rich and honored.

Lau: 'Have the firm faith to devote yourself to learning, and abide to the death in the good way... Show yourself when the way prevails in the Empire, but hide yourself when it does not. It is a shameful matter to be poor and humble when the Way prevails in the state, Equally, it is a shameful matter to be rich and noble when the Way falls into disuse in the state.'

Are these words of advice clearcut? Is it a simple matter of serving or not serving a state where the way prevails or where it does not? Or is it even a categorical call to disappear when the way is lost? The analect with its terms and concepts of sacrifice, 'way' or/and 'Way', 'state', 'empire', demonstrates different levels of morality and politics, and confuses public and personal feelings of shame - 'a shameful matter' writes Lau; 'things to be ashamed of' is Legge's decision. The nuance of 'disgrace' [for 恥 here] seems to be the favored translation.

Waley spells Way with a capital-W in both parts of the analect. Lau spell the first - [small w] way, the second - [capital W] Way. And although he translates 'a shameful matter', the feeling of the analect is more personal; emphasized here is the shame one feels more than the behavior which is disgraceful. Legge personifies the first 'way', writing: '... holding firm to death, he is perfecting the excellence of his **course**.' This is vague. In the second part, though, he dampens the 'way' writing: '...When right principles of government prevail in the kingdom, he will show himself; when they are prostrated, he will keep concealed.' Does he resort to this rendition in order to distinguish between Way and way?

For my part, I read some sort of antithesis or contradiction into the analect where the first part encourages dying for the good way, and the second, advises us not to enter a country in chaos or else not to take up a position therein. Is the unease here the living and serving in a state which has lost the Way in some 'universal' sense, a moral breakdown which causes the shame, and not just the 'principles of government'?

We may observe 'shame' here as a personal awareness of contradictions: the unease of living and serving in one's own erring environment, or, in the 'times of Confucius', when it applies more directly to a network of loyalties between minister and ruler. It is a shame at one's own responsibility. In some way, the analect reflects a shame both personal and collective.

Next, a direct question about shame:

14.1 1. 憲問恥。子曰:「邦有道,穀;邦無道,穀,恥也。」

Lau: Xian asked about the **shameful**. The Master said, It is shameful to make salary your sole object, irrespective of whether the way prevails in the state or not.

Waley: Yuan Ssu asked about compunction. The Master said, When a country is ruled according to the Way, (the gentleman) accepts rewards. But when a country is not ruled according to the Way, he shows compunction in regard to rewards.

Huang Chicung: .asked about shame. … it is a shame.

Leys - shame... to serve a state that has lost the Way - this is shameful indeed.'

Lau shifts the emphasis from shame of serving to shame of pursuing benefit. He might be doing so following various other sayings relating shame to materialistic ambitions and lack of modesty.

And here, a third example of shame evolving in an actual political reality, quoted in the *Mencius* from the mouth of King Hui of Liang. I mention it here because the use of the term is personal - Mencius' conversations with the king are intimate and psychologically sophisticated①. Shame is mentioned by Mencius' first interlocutor right in the first chapter of the book. King Hui of Liang, a ruler not up to and undeserving the title of [true] King, is in control of a small state, but nurtures aspirations of unrealistic military campaigns and conquests:

1A5 梁惠王曰:"晋国,天下莫强焉,叟之所知也。及寡人之身,东败于齐,长子死焉;西丧地于秦七百里;南辱于楚。寡人耻之,愿比死者一洒之,如之何则可?"

Lau: King Hui of Liang said, 'As you know, the state of Jin was second to none in power in the Empire. But when it came to my own time we suffered defeat in the east by Qi when my eldest son died , and we lost territory to the extent of seven hundred li to Qin in the west, while to the south we were humiliated by Chu. I am deeply ashamed of this and wish, in what little time I have left in this life, to wash away all this shame. How can this be done? (p.53)

Legge:...and on the south we have sustained disgrace at the hands of Chu. I have brought shame on my departed predecessors, and wish on their account to wipe it away once for all.

We are presented here with the public face of 'shame' - national shame resulting from a loss of prowess. Although' shame' is pronounced by the King, the term is a misnomer, demanding a kind of 'rectification of names', and hence is immediately disputed by Mencius. The King's Shame' is here taken for granted in a response to prevailing ways of thinking and norms, but far from any natural inner ''germ' and its ensuing moral search and judgement. It is shame for the wrong reason or misguided tenet. Not only does it reveal unrealistic considerations, but an unworthy aim on the part of the king. As the little kingdom has no chance of victory over its powerful neighboring states, it will all result in nothing but suffering to its people. The aspirations are wrong in the first place, and hence the philosopher's reaction:

孟子對曰:地方百里,而可以王。王如施仁政於民,省刑罰。。。

Lau: ' A territory of a hundred li square,' answered Mencius, 'is sufficient to enable its ruler to become a true King. If you Majesty practices benevolent government towards the people...'

Or in Legge's more festive timbre:

---

① . See also the fascinating dialogue in chapter 1A7, where Mencius analyses step by step the King's feelings, leading him to understand his motives, not without embarrassing, almost shaming him.

Mencius replied, 'With a territory which is only a hundred li square, it is possible to attain to the royal dignity...'

An optimistic note, apposite for concluding my 'Chinese Shame' exposition.

Still, just to solidify the position of this unassuming term, I'll add here two conclusive sayings, one of which partly serves in the title of this essay:

Mencius, 7A6: 人不可以無恥。無恥之恥,無恥矣。

Lau: Mencius said, 'A man must not be without shame, for the shame of being without shame is shamelessness indeed.' (p.183)

Legge: Mencius said, ' A man may not be without shame. When one is ashamed of having been without shame, he will afterwards not have occasion to be ashamed. (p.451)

Definitely a succinct statement in Chinese, and still, given to such different renditions!

7A7 孟子曰:恥之於人大矣。惟機變之巧者,無所用恥焉。不恥不若人,何若人有?

Lau: Mencius said, 'Great is the use of shame to man. He who indulges in craftiness has no use for shame. If a man is not ashamed of being inferior to other men, how will he ever become their equal?'(p.183)

[The second part of the saying does not sound right.]

Legge: Mencius said,'The sense of shame is to a man of great important. Those who form contrivances and versatile schemes distinguished for their artfulness, do not allow their sense of shame to come into action (p. 451)

Voluntary, controllable shame?

In the last section of my essay, I bring a few quotations from the Hebrew Bible. The biblical as well as the modern Hebrew provide us with a few synonyms for 'shame' which more or less correlate to the English 'shame', 'disgrace', 'humiliation'. My initial purpose in looking at the Bible was to try and find there, in its 'shame vocabulary' more about the intricacy of the term. While looking at the book (which I must admit, is not my daily reading material), I was surprised by some of the particular characteristics of the circumstances and bearers of 'shame'.

Another curiosity was the striking lack of 'shame' in the Pentateuch, besides, of course, for its dramatic appearance at the beginning of Genesis - the 'non-shame' paradisiac existence of Adam and Eve (although described after their fall). When they lose their innocence, naturally their shame is personal, although symbolic of every person's fear of being seen naked, i.e. as it were, exposed to the eyes of God, for ever unable to hide or evade his laws. In spite of the existence of the concept of shame at the very beginning of the Bible (ch. 2.25), the word hardly reappears (I find only a couple more mentions of shame in the five books of the Torah.) The uncertain chronology of the Bible might account for this, but it is beyond the scope of this piece.

Nevertheless, a further search in the Concordance brings up many mentions of shame, mostly in the books of the prophets Jeremiah, Isaiah and Ezekiel. Although my first reading suggests principally manifestations of 'national shame', i.e. shame experienced or to be experienced by peoples (either the Hebrews or their enemies), I will also quote here a few of the more personal expressions of shame.

Added are also the phrases in their Chinese translations, variously those of Karl Friedrich August Gutzlaff (1838) and Samuel Isaac Joseph Scereschewsky (1910) (both of whom translated the Bible from the Hebrew), as well as of Robert Morrison (1815) and [the translation known as] the Union Version (1823). The Hebrew words for shame and its synonyms are variously translated into 羞,愧,慚愧,辱,'unsystematically' so, as far as I could ascertain. Much less common is 恥,the most prevalent term in the classical Chinese writings.

First, some examples of 'personal shame'[①]:

*Genesis* 2.25

And they were both naked, the man and his wife, and were not ashamed.

Gutzlaff:且夫婦二人並裸而不愧矣

Schereschewsky:亦無愧焉

Morrison:伊兩人即夫婦為赤身而不羞也。

Union version:亞當與妻並裸,亦無愧焉。

*Genesis* 30.23

And she conceived, and bare a son; and said, God hath taken away my reproach

Gutzlaff.:又 * 懷孕生子,曰,上帝已洗去我羞矣。

Schereschewsky.:已雪我恥

Morrison:…受孕而生一子,曰,神取去我辱矣。

Union version:曰,上帝已洒我耻矣。

*Genesis* 34.14

① . All English quotations are taken from the *King James Bible* (online).

Gutzlaff：夫子云：人未受斷勢皮，而嫁妹與之不得行焉。乃自取辱矣。

Schereschewsky：自取辱耳.

‘Prophetical’ shame

***Isaiah* 45:16**

They shall be ashamed, and also confounded, all of them: they shall go to confusion together *that are* makers of idols.

Gutzlaff：慚羞（twice）

Union version：他的眾敵承然羞辱。。。。。而將不被羞辱。。。

***Jeremiah* 17:13**

O LORD, the hope of Israel, all that forsake thee shall be ashamed, *and* they that depart from me shall be written in the earth, because they have forsaken the LORD, the fountain of living waters.

Gutzlaff：皇上帝以色列族所望者，諸凡棄主者必愧羞也，且去主者因離皇上帝，正是活水之源，其必。。。

Schereschewsky：主與以色列所望，凡棄主者，本必蒙羞恥，我乃活水之源 …

Union version：皆必見羞也。

***Jeremiah* 20:11**

But the LORD *is* with me as a mighty terrible one: therefore my persecutors shall stumble, and they shall not prevail: they shall be greatly ashamed; for they shall not prosper: *their* everlasting confusion shall never be forgotten.

Gutzlaff：其永愧不忘。

shereschewsky：甚為愧一一抱恥蒙羞永不見忘。

***Jeremiah* 51:51**

We are confounded, because we have heard reproach: shame hath covered our faces: for strangers are come into the sanctuaries of the LORD'S house.

Gutzlaff：是以我聞其辱，則愧而羞滿面焉。故此皇上帝云，日期將來我刑其偶像，在遍國

因聞才辱則暫羞滿着我面

Schereschewsky:我聞辱言之言，則愧一不勝，羞慚滿面。。

***Ezekiel* 43:10**

Thou son of man, shew the house to the house of Israel, that they may be ashamed of their iniquities: and let them measure the pattern.

gutzlaff：羞（twice）

Scheres.：使彼因其罪言罪——，自覺愧 zha

***Ezekiel* 43:11**

And if they be ashamed of all that they have done, shew them the form of the house, and the fashion thereof, and the goings out thereof, and the comings in thereof, and all the forms thereof, and all the ordinances thereof, and all the forms thereof, and all the laws thereof: and write *it* in their sight, that they may keep the whole form thereof, and all the ordinances thereof, and do them.

'Personal-national' shame

***Ezra* 9:6**

And said, O my God, I am ashamed and blush to lift up my face to thee, my God: for our iniquities are increased over *our* head, and our trespass is grown up unto the heavens.

Shame in the Bible is expressed by the Prophets. It is spoken at their people who have gone morally astray, and in that way have betrayed their covenant, the commandments and laws of the Almighty. The prophet takes upon himself and relays the shame of the group. Shame in many of its forms is defined according to demands and ordinances taken upon themselves by the Prophets and the people of Israel. Shame in the biblical story is naturally ascribed to the community, and so can be described as being fostered as a corner-stone in building the narrative of a people. [This section is to be elaborated in the final version of this essay].

Back now to our own days and the beginning of this essay. I started my essay with the crude old distinction between shame and guilt cultures, deriving it in part from the idea of running a society along the Confucian ideal of rule of virtue and ritual (*de* and *li* 德，禮) or alternatively by rule of law, ['western' culture] initially sanctioned by divine authority, and later [with the Enlightenment and belief in reason], by constitutions based on human rights.

In times of political turmoil and crisis, when national cohesion is both encouraged and imposed from above and self-imposed as if automatically, personal shame seems to dwindle, or at least be hidden from the public eye. The 'sprout' of shame tends to dry and even if some of it survives in one's own "four quarters", the narrow local 'norms' of the collective take over and not only press hard on the individual's emotional built-up, but potentially on his ability to distinguish right from wrong. But it is also true that at such points the 'sprout' or 'germ', the heart might still call out, seemingly spontaneously, but from a deep well enriched by the pure water of basic humanity. Vague as it is, shame erupts.

I will end here with the 'heart' and its 'inclinations', an elusive concept, but never one forsaken by all. Under such extreme circumstances as I have described in my introductory words, the heart or 'sprout' of shame can be drowned in the sea of political interests, ideologies, swelling legal systems and organs of state. All this, I know, sounds extremely na? ve, and is perhaps just desperation.

This morning when writing these last lines, I happened to read in my daily newspaper a very personal piece, a kind of summary of the war which ended with a ceasefire some four days ago. It was penned by one almost lone and persisting voice, who bravely, almost daily, accompanied the war which 'turned his stomach' (shame does not only make one blush [and also remember 羞恶]). The word 'shame' is twice repeated in his article: first, the shame felt by the writer (who has been targeted as the [second] most hated person in our country) for his self-deluding readership, which has reacted the way it has and hissed daily at his critical and reprimanding words; and secondly, when pondering [among other things] the impossibility of staying aloof (or not being shocked in his own words) in face of such atrocities, by reiterating the prerogative to feel compassion and **to be ashamed.**

Confucian as well as Hebrew writings, be they what they are, remind us again and again of the heart and the Way:

*Analects*

7.29 子曰:"仁遠乎哉? 我欲仁,斯仁至矣。"

Leys: "The Master Said: Is goodness out of reach? As soon as I long for goodness, goodness is at hand."

15.29 子曰:"人能弘道,非道弘人"

Leys: The Master said: "Man can enlarge the Way. It is not the Way that enlarges man."

***Deuteronomy* 30:11-13**

For this commandment which I command thee this day, it *is* not hidden from thee, neither *is* it far off.

It *is* not in heaven, that thou shouldest say, Who shall go up for us to heaven, and bring it unto us, that we may hear it, and do it?

Neither *is* it beyond the sea, that thou shouldest say, Who shall go over the sea for us, and bring it unto us, that we may hear it, and do it?

*Jeremiah* 31:31-33

Behold, the days come, saith the LORD, that I will make a new covenant with the house of Israel, and with the house of Judah.

Not according to the covenant that I made with their fathers in the day that I took them by the hand, to bring them out of the land of Egypt, which my covenant they brake, although I was an husband unto them, saith the Lord.

But this shall be the covenant, that I will make with the house of Israel, After those days, saith the Lord, I will put my law in their inward parts, and write it in their hearts, and will be their God, and they shall be my people.

(King James Bible)

Regrettably these words associate either with a far bygone golden epoch [of wise Chinese thinkers], or with ancient utopian visions of the end of days [of the Hebrew prophets].

# Values—Limits of Economic Rationality and Imperialism of Culture

Christian Krijnen (VU University Amsterdam)

## I. Economic Imperialism of Culture?

Perhaps there have been at least as many attempts to answer philosophical questions by means of an approach belonging to one or another special science as there have been attempts by philosophy to defend her right to an authentically philosophical approach. Questions about the nature of man and his world, culture, are especially at stake. However, the matter of *reductionism* does not just play a role in the relation between the special sciences and philosophy: within the special sciences themselves too there has been much resistance to the urge for expansion of certain approaches to the detriment of others (this holds outside science too: one can think of the resistance the anti-globalization movement offers to 'neo-liberalism').

Currently it is not just biology, but also (partly in connection with biology) *economics* which is trying to break out of its original range, and claims to be developing *a universal theory of human behavior* (cf. paradigmatically Becker 1976, Part I). And why not, actually? Humans have to act, even if only for reasons of physical existence, therefore they have to choose, hence bring about an optimal relation, in one or another sense and in one or another way, between the 'costs' and 'benefits' of behavior (that is to say, if we conceive of human behavior as a rational activity and not merely a natural process). Economics is about optimal relations qua maximal 'utility'. From this point of view rational behavior is determined by economic principles. If this is the case it stands to reason to think that the economic approach is capable of offering a universal or a basic theory of human behavior.—To be sure, the protagonists of such a theory accept 'non-economic' aspects, which are said to be relevant; although from a methodological point of view it remains unclear what this relevance could mean, since the point of the thematic expansion of economics precisely consists in determining the phenomena by means of concepts that are characteristic of the economic approach; hence from the point of view of the economic approach, non-economic aspects strictly speaking either are given boundary conditions (exogenous variables) or they are unknowable (and therefore irrelevant).

In the literature this economic variant of a universal theory of behavior is known as *economic imperialism* (Radnitzky/Bernholz [Eds.] (1987); Sappinen 2003); without a doubt Gary Becker is its most important spokesman.① This is not at all to say that economic imperialism is uncontroversial within the economic sciences: the opposite is the case (Sappinen 2003, pp. 18, 94ff.; Manstetten 2000, pp. 100ff.; Frambach 1996, pp. 107ff.; Biervert/Wieland 1990). Nevertheless it is very influential, in the other social sciences as well. Here the 'rational-choice-model' (RCM) is frequently employed to explain social phenomena. However, the RCM formally speaking is the approach of neo-classical economic theory, i.e. the (despite all criticism) standard setting form of micro-economics. This approach is rightly entitled that of the homo oeconomicus (Kirchgässner 1991; Manstetten 2000).

By taking a closer look at the presuppositions of economic imperialism I want to show that for reasons of principle it can offer neither a universal theory of action nor a basis for such a theory. Take note: these considerations are *not* a criticism of the conception of economic rationality as it is interpreted in 'economic theory', *but they criticize a particular interpretation of this rationality, namely that of economic imperialism*. On the topic of the elaboration of my claim against economic imperialism and its place in the discourse on the RCM the following three remarks.

(1) I assume a familiarity with the RCM and the neo-classical concept of rationality.② Notions such as 'abstraction', 'given preferences', 'methodological individualism' and 'the maximization of utility' play an important role in this; moreover physics turns out to function as a methodological paradigm for the neo-classical approach.

---

① On economic imperialism recently cf. Sappinen (2003), compare also Manstetten (2000, pp. 96ff.) or supporters such as McKenzie/Tullock (1978) and Bowmaker (2005), with the telling subtitle: 'a complete guide to life, death and misadventure'.

② For a succinct presentation of the essentials of the neo-classical approach to human behaviour see, for example, McKenzie/Tullock (1978, chap. 1); Manstetten (2000); Perloff (2001, pp. 73ff.).

Under the title of 'rational choice' the neo-classical economic conception of rational behavior has figured for some decades now as a general theory of rationality;[①] strictly speaking the economic model of explanation is the RCM.[②] In the final analysis the RCM says the following.[③]

1. Through their behavior humans try to maximize their *utility*. Rationality is essentially the calculation of utility. Utility is the final decisive motive for human action.

1. Action is the action of *individuals* satisfying their *self-interest*. The acting subject has his self-interest as his sole aim.

2. Self-interest means something like the *preferences* (desires) of the acting subject.

3. This subject has an ordered (and consistent) whole of *given* preferences;

4. he is *informed* about the probabilities of satisfying his preferences through his actions, hence he has a number of 'beliefs';

5. and he is able to *calculate* the (expected) utility of his actions.

This also means, among other things, that rational behavior in the sense of the RCM is *instrumentally* rational behavior: behavior that realizes given goals (preferences, desires) in a utility-maximizing way, that is to say that it puts the available means (actions) to their optimal use. It is a form of rational behavior that does not include reflection on the goals themselves, or to put it more accurately: it precludes reflection—*the rationality of goals is for methodological reasons not taken into consideration; they cannot be 'rationally' justified in terms of the model.*[④]

(2) The basis ideas of the RCM that have just been mentioned give rise to rather

---

① From this point of view the RCM has an economic essence (Bievert/Wieland 1990, p. 19). Neo-classical micro-economics determines economic behaviour in terms of choices based on rational self-interest. Depending on the perspective, of course the opposite holds as well: from the point of view of content the RCM is a formal moment of economic rationality neo-classically conceived.

② For example cf. Becker (1993, p. 396), Sen (1977, p. 323) or Mki (2002, p. 237ff.).

③ There is enormous variation within the RCM and its literature is without bounds, but every specification of the RCM follows the 'economic' logic of action that characterizes the RCM. Cf. the authors mentioned in the text for criticisms of the RCM, but also, for example, Archer/Tritter (2000) or Hollis (1994).

④ Simon (1983, p. 8) puts it drastically: "Reason is wholly instrumental. It cannot tell us where to go; at best it can tell us how to get there."

many questions; they are criticized frequently *within* the discourse of economics itself. However, it is of importance to my claim that such criticism is of a primarily *empirical* nature. As far as the criticisms are concerned there are two leading tendencies.

The first tendency emphasizes that human behavior is more *complex* than the 'physicallistically' oriented RCM is able to bring out. Notions such as creativity in particular, the setting of and being concerned with goals and social action in a constantly changing ('open') environment are brought to bear on the RCM (cf. Chick 1998; Dow 1999; Johnson/Duberley 2000).—Even if critics emphatically put forward *normative* elements in human behavior against the RCM, such as 'commitment' (Sen 1977), 'values' (Etzioni 1988, chap. 6 in particular), 'agency' or 'affiliation' (Nelson 1994), their criticism remains empirical, that is to say methodologically bound up with the point of view of empirical science. From this point of view the assumptions of the RCM turn out to be 'unrealistic': empirically unfounded (this also holds for critics such as Elster (1983; 1984; 1989a), Kahnemann (2003) or an 'apostate' such as McKenzie (1983, e.g. 32f.)[①]).

The *reflexive* argument—that is central to my criticism—does not play any significant role for these critics. However, just like these critics I am of the opinion that the concept of rationality of the RCM is too narrow, that it cannot address human behavior in an inclusive way—that the RCM fails as a *universal* theory of behavior, because it does not do sufficient justice to human behavior (with respect to its rationality).

The second tendency emphasizes that the RCM is not an adequate theoretic *construct* for explaining human behavior: In an influential essay Friedman (1953) said goodbye to the claims of the assumptions of economic models of representing reality; according to Friedman the validity of a model depends on the success of the predictions the model enables us to make (Becker (1976, p.7) or McKenzie/Tullock (1978, p.6) also take this view). It is not even of importance whether subjects consciously

---

① McKenzie even conceives of the sphere of the origin of preferences as 'the non-rational' (1983, pp. 32ff.). Etzioni too prematurely concedes the concept of rationality to the RCM. As against this, it will become clear that notions such as 'freedom', 'values' and 'justification' have an intrinsic relation to the concept of rationality. Hence Brodbeck's opposition of rationality to freedom makes for a distorted picture (2000, § 5.8, cf. especially pp. 254ff.). In short: a *broader* concept of rationality is required.

obey the logic of the RCM: the model methodologically speaking treats subjects as if they are subject to this logic; strictly speaking the difference between rationality 'in reality' and 'in theory' is irrelevant to the 'economic approach': humans are homines oeconomici by definition. [①] Hence one successful critical strategy consists of showing that predictions do not come true sufficiently, or do not come true at all. [②]

(3) Having said this I now come to the elaboration of my claim. The point on unsuccessful predictions gives us a start. From the science-theoretic point of view, to be sure, the question is if theories can be justified even by successful predictions. For if we admit that a prediction made on the basis of a model has come true, it does not follow that this result may not be explained by another model. This *fundamental proof-theoretic deficiency* is of great importance. For critics such as Sen, Etzioni, Elster, Nelson[③] or the later McKenzie propagate an *other* structure of human behavior, whereas the phenomenon that is to be explained, human behavior, is the *same*. They say that only within a structure of this other kind such a thing as utility maximizing is possible. It does not just follow from this that the RCM apparently starts from assumptions it does not itself justify, or is even able to justify (assumptions which, according to the critics, do not even allow for scientific justification), but at the same time it follows that the RCM cannot be the core of a universal theory of behavior. (The question about the amount of realism of the assumptions of the model, therefore, has also been decisively answered.)

It is also true, however, that the critics have only provided fragments of this other structure (values, commitment, agency, affiliation, etc.), since they lack the *reflexive* basis that is necessary for giving shape to such a structure and to determine the concomitant concepts sufficiently. Therefore it is of great importance to make this reflexive foundation the explicit topic of investigation, to be more precise: to debate it

---

① From this point of view method has an objective meaning (on this topic cf. the essays by Krijnen in Krijnen/Kee (2009); assumptions *are* realistic if they can be *shown* to be fruitful. The only point is the *justification* of their realist character. In what way 'unrealistic' assumptions are supposed to explain actual behaviour is one of the riddles whose solution consists of a correction to the question. (Manstetten 2000, p. 119, note 2) does not take sufficient account of this.)

② Cf. Biervert/Wieland (1990, pp. 22ff.), Dow (1999, pp. 10ff.), Elster (1983; 1984; 1989b), Etzioni (1988), Nelson (1994) or Sen (1977; 1990, pp. 263ff.).

③ Nelson (1994) also advocates a structure that is much more complex than utility maximizing provides, namely a structure that includes qualitative notions such as 'agency' and 'affiliation'.

with the RCM; for the broader concept of rationality will then be the result of an *immanent critique of the* RCM (*qua universal conception of rationality*): *we find it by thinking about the presuppositions that belong to the* RCM *itself*. The problems raised by problematizing the RCM are not of a kind that allows them to be solved 'empirically' or 'mathematically': they pertain to the sense and meaning of the RCM as such. It will also become clear that non-quantitative concepts are required for understanding the possibility of human behavior and quantifying with respect to it.

**II. The Being Given of Preferences and the Validity-Reflexive Formation Process**

In this section I want to show that preferences are not just 'given'; they are part of a reflexive formation process that has the validity of those preferences as its topic (II.1). Hence human behavior is characterized by a fundamentally different structure from the one proposed by the RCM. I will first sketch this other structure and then discuss its necessity (II.2). If this other structure turns out to be necessary, then it must as a matter of course also be the foundation of the behavior of the RCM theoretician; a contradiction arises between form and content of the RCM qua *universal* theory of action (II.3).

1. The Being Given of Preferences

Among other things the RCM presupposes that those involved are sufficiently informed about their preferences (needs, interests, goals, and so on). However, judgements on our preferences may well be deficient because of all kinds of cognitive, emotional or social 'confusion'. All kinds of processes that have to do with understanding, judging and criticizing our preferences, then, belong to what is known as the basis of utility calculation. Obviously preferences are not merely given, they are *evaluated*. From a logical point of view this evaluation can only be made on the basis of *another* criterion (therefore the foundations of utility calculation are not to be determined by utility theory). This process of evaluation may lead to the reconsideration of ('given') preferences and orderings of preferences. It follows that the concept of 'preference' (or one of its substitutes) is not a purely empirical (descriptive) concept: it is a *reflexive* (normative) concept, at least to the extent that a preference functions as a *goal of action*. Self-understanding, self-criticism and self-determination are intrinsic to 'rational behavior'. However, a reflexive structure of this kind is not conceived of by the RCM; qua universal theory of behavior on the contrary it unthinkingly posits utility maximizing as the purpose of action. The RCM does not provide reflection on individual goals of actions (preferences, interests, etc.), since goals are merely 'given' according to the model—*qua* goals they remain not reflected on; a methodological disclosure of goals is out of the question as a matter of principle. As against that it will become apparent in the following that goals are neither simply given nor stable: they are always possible objects of reflection.①

Historically speaking, to be sure, 'rationality' has always also been associated with arithmetic and calculation, but the term 'rationality' historically speaking also refers to a more fundamental meaning: rationality as foundation and justification. As a disposition of man (animal rationale) rationality signifies the competence to have reasons for beliefs (regardless which), the ability to justify beliefs (regardless whether that justification is sufficient or not). Competence of this kind is not limited to the validity of the means, but also includes the validity of goals; hence human behavior is not merely heteronomous (determined by natural and cultural constellations), but autonomous (self-determining) too. Limiting rationality to *instrumental* rationality is *unrealistic*; it does not sufficiently pertain to man's rationality; rather the exclusively instrumental view makes absolute one particular aspect of rationality. The value of an action is not merely dependent on the result or the object of our will, it also depends on a certain formal structure of rational activity (known as 'practical reason'). Our practical reason does not only lead our behavior in the sense that it takes care that we realize our goals optimally; it also leads our behavior in an essentially *different* sense: it prescribes compulsory rules of behavior and goals. In so doing it at the same time puts a whole of principles or criteria at our disposal that makes it possible for us to examine rules on the basis of which we act and the goals we strive for within the framework of these rules.

---

① Because of this the debate about Becker's views regarding the stability of preferences (cf. Bievert/Wieland 1990, p. 23; Manstetten 2000, pp. 97ff.; Sappinen 2003, pp. 115ff.) is irrelevant to the argument elaborated in the text. As a matter of principle preferences are subject to critical reflection, i. e. on the basis of criteria that themselves neither have a natural nor a cultural origin, namely criteria that pertain to the meaning of behaviour itself (being criteria of this kind they are not preferences in the sense of the economic sciences); they are methodologically determined by validity-reflection. —The debate on the amount of realism of the assumptions of the RCM is no more relevant, since the RCM, whether in its 'empirical' or in its 'rational' variant, cannot be the basis of a *universal* theory of human behaviour. The dimension of reflection, intrinsic to human behaviour, is lacking in both varieties.

2. The Validity-Reflexive Formation Process

If the examination of our goals of action is part of a reflexive process in this way, then one of the most important assumptions of the RCM (qua universal theory of action) becomes completely problematic: that the over-arching goal of human behavior is *utility* (which is conceived of as sensory).

(1) First of all everyone of us 'naturally' pursues his happiness and his advantage as a matter of course; utility/happiness is (at most) a natural final goal, a goal *given by nature*, of human behavior. That is why it is not a goal of which it makes sense to demand a generally committing force, in the sense that everyone *ought* to pursue it. This natural final goal doubtlessly entails rather many imperatives of action: technical imperatives, i.e. rules on the basis of which we choose the necessary means for reaching one goal or another; it also entails pragmatic imperatives, i.e. rules which we must obey so that we do not ourselves stand in the way of the fulfillment of our natural need for happiness. *Instrumental* rationality in the final analysis is nothing but this type of rationality. It is a form of rationality which, to quote Kant, is only 'hypothetically' valid: on the basis of a non-necessary condition (*if* it is the case that a, then b). This is not at all to say that the relation between goal and the means to it is not objectively or 'categorically' valid, but to say that the whole relation is only hypothetically valid, since it includes the proviso that the set goal be objectively valid. (Everyone who wants to be rich has to…; but does or should everyone want to be rich? Everyone who wants to reach old age has to…; but does or should everyone want to reach old age?)

(2.1) Secondly it has become apparent in the above that human behavior as rule-oriented behavior is not just a natural process. Neither is it only a consequence of preferences and desires in the economic sense; for the possibility to understand, examine and evaluate the goals for which we strive is a part of our behavior. Humans do not simply have goals, preferences, desires or the like that are to be realized as effectively and efficiently as possible for one reason or another; rather it is the case that humans take their goals into critical consideration, accept or reject them; hence we are always concerned with the *objective validity* of our goals (and means).

Apparently our behavior relates to validity, both regarding our goals as well as their realization. With this we subject ourselves to a set of validity principles (values, ideas) that ought to be normative for our thinking and action. From this point of view human beings are not just instrumentally rational and out for their own advantage, focused on their 'life' interests, but even *in* the satisfaction of such life interests insight plays a decisive role in their thinking and action: our thinking and action ought to be *valid* thinking and action, we aim for objective validity. Even if we're wondering if our behavior is 'useful', we're wondering whether our thinking and action are valid. Our thinking and action are by no means 'naturally' valid.

This concern with values, rules or ideas is of eminent significance if we want to know what human behavior is. That is why I will take a closer look at some salient issues by means of illustration, limiting myself to the sphere of willing as willing is the foundation of our action (according to the RCM too). The following points are decisive.

(a) As living creatures we are dependent on various natural conditions: we have 'life interests', our natural need for happiness enforces fundamental goals and objects on our will.

(b) 'Willing', however, seen as reasonable activity (reasonable desire), as willing never is without content: we always will something, our will as will always has an object. If at this point we follow Kant's instructive line of thought, then it turns out to be important that that object does not also function as *ground* for our act of willing, as a *reason* for our willing. Willing qua reasonable desire—more broadly: willing, striving, behaving, acting in a rational sense—takes place on the basis of 'concepts', 'rules', 'goals' and so on. Therefore in our behavior not only do specific objects play a role, but something 'general' as well: a 'motive', a 'reason'. Our will is not just 'materially' determined by the object, it is also determined by a rule of behavior, a so-called 'maxim'. Everyone of us has such 'subjective' rules of behavior. *As* rules for our behavior they are a product of our 'practical reason': we give them to ourselves, for whatever reason (if they are forced on us by others it is up to us to accept them).

(c) However, it is by no means the case that we just 'have' such rules, maxims: having these rules is no sufficient reason for their validity. There is no doubting for us that some rules are valid, and others are invalid. And it goes without saying that this holds for the rules aimed at our 'life interests', our happiness and well-being, too: the maxims on the basis of which we act are *validity-different*, that is to say: they may be valid or they may be invalid—regardless of whether technical, pragmatic or those rules we call 'moral' are at stake.

(d) The validity value (quality) of an action depends on the validity value of the maxim, for the maxim, being a rule for action, is the *ground* of our behavior.① Rational behavior is behavior based on grounds, behavior based on reasons (of which we need not be aware), not just an instinctive response.

(e) Since human behavior is conceived of (by the RCM too) as 'reasonable' or 'rational' behavior, and is therefore characterized by a concern with validity (natural processes as such are validity indifferent), both the possibility and the necessity of *validity reflection* belong to such behavior. Being rational or reasonable creatures, we are both capable of judging our goals as well as the means we use to realize those goals. Our reason is even able to provide criteria for judging, for how else would we judge these goals and means if not on the basis of criteria of judging?

(f) It is an undeniable *fact* that we *evaluate* our thinking and action (to dispute this fact is to confirm it). Evaluation presupposes criteria. Perhaps in the first instance these are traditional criteria, criteria we possess on the basis of some or other psychological, social, historical, etc. grounds. But we evaluate these types of criteria as well—we are only capable of doing so on the basis of other criteria.

(g) The validity of our criteria (rules for behavior, norms and so on) is a topic for debate, the validity of the criterion of 'utility', or, in a hedonistic variant, 'pleasure', to take one example. Some criteria are forced on us by 'nature', others by 'culture'. Latching on to current terminology we might call these types of criteria *life values*: they signify what is useful if we try to do as much justice as possible to our life interests; whether our behavior is good or bad depends on the fact if this behavior is conducive to our 'life'. There certainly is a kernel of truth in this kind of view—but it does not contain the essence. For behavioral rules of that kind *themselves* already refer to another type of behavioral rules. We must therefore introduce another type of rules: rules which we choose spontaneously, freely, that we give to ourselves, determine ourselves—no rules which are forced on us by nature or culture. Hence our behavior is directly determined by interests which we have qua 'rational' beings ('subjects'), interests which are responsive to 'reason' (autonomy), not by our life

① With a view to my argument it is unnecessary to elaborate a theory on the validity of maxims at present.

interests (heteronomy). Criteria of this kind are not valid on the basis of life interests, they are valid independently of this kind of conditions: they are *unconditionally valid qua self-regulation*. Such criteria are also known as *objective* values, *ideal* values, *unconditional* values, *autonomous* values, *cultural* values (in the universal sense), and so on.[①] The fact that we subject ourselves to values of this kind and therefore consider ourselves capable of determining ourselves, we prove constantly by our thinking and action. Hence we subordinate our life interests to interests that belong to our being subjects; we place them in a different framework; so we take a distance to our life interests, evaluate them and give them a place *within* the interests of our being subjects; hence 'life' is *integrated* within the sphere of unconditionality, reshaped by higher interests (interests that do not depend on nature or culture). It is this sphere which contains what it means to be a subject; it includes notions such as freedom and freedom of choice, for example.

(h) Behavior does not only has an 'external', 'observable' side, it also, and decisively so where the meaning of behavior is concerned, has an 'internal' side: a side that pertains to the *grounds* (reasons) of our behavior, the way we shape our lives. Rational behavior strictly speaking is nothing but the capability of determining oneself like that. The concept of rationality of the RCM does not provide an adequate picture of this.

(2.2) The reflexive argument includes the *necessity* of assuming that man is rational in the sense elaborated above. A rationality of that kind defines the cultural concept of man (i.e the concept of man as a cultural being).

Life has its demands. Nevertheless in our 'rational' behavior we always make a *claim* to validity. Behavior of that kind is so to speak a cultural expression (science, art, politics, religion, etc.); cultural phenomena are validity phenomena. By means of culture man shapes himself. If we shape ourselves, we subject ourselves to a whole of rules that leads our behavior; we are determined by values—at least we are if we conceive of values as conscious or unconscious determinants of orientation for human behavior, normative instances for our concern with the world and ourselves. At the same time we are value-determined in such a way, that we claim to transcend our life interests qua life interests (our behavior sometimes expressly goes against our life in-

---

① Cf. Krijnen (2001, 7.3.1; 2002) for more details.

terests). As a consequence we determine *ourselves* in such a way that our behavior obtains a quality that it does not have on the basis of 'life', on the basis of its being determined by life interests or life values; hence man's determinacy of life is elevated, integrated in its unconditional determination, i.e. in the capability and task that belong to him qua man. Precisely because of this capability and this task man is a 'subject'. As a subject man orients himself on values and leads a value-oriented life. To be sure man is also a living being, hence subject to the laws of nature. But since we *claim* to behave in a goal-oriented, planned way, we behave on the basis of values (goals, plans). Hence we transcend our natural determinacy (if only to continue our biological existence). Because we attempt to realize *goals*, orient ourselves on *values*, we take a distance to our natural determinacy, and try to do justice to higher interests, interests that have not been predetermined by life (the distance to life would then be lost again): interests that concern the *validity* of our behavior. Our life finds itself at the service of values, not vice versa. In this way man is a subject. As a subject he orients himself on values.

Being rational creatures humans do not simply 'have preferences'. To be sure human behavior genetically speaking is primarily driven by natural instincts, by the natural pursuit of survival. But even *in* the striving to remain alive there are claims connected to the control and shaping of those natural instincts.① Survival demands behavior that abides by certain rules, it demands rule determinacy of human beings. Hence man is subject to *rules* in his survival, particularly if he is after his 'advantage' and tries to lead a life of 'utility'. He does not simply vegetate biologically; such an estimate is rather the result of an *abstraction* that *isolates* one aspect of human life. Our biological existence obtains a stamp of the life world by this regulation. A multiplicity of interests pervades the life world of man: the regulation of those interests is highly differentiated and intensified; our life world very much is a 'rule-bound' world. Even on this level of the life world *man to a large extent shapes himself* (self-formation), even if it is just 'utility', 'advantage' or 'normal behavior' and so on which is at issue here. Utility, advantage, normality and so on are *criteria* for behavior. Someone who fulfils these criteria will live 'agreeably'. To live agreeably, to have pleasure, to

---

① Cf. the debates that are conducted within utilitarianism on the long and short term 'consequences' of behaviour that is determined by the pursuit of pleasure.

satisfy one's desires (in the economic, hence *sensory* sense) demands immense control over our natural instincts; behavior that makes life agreeable transcends instinctive actions to a profound degree, since it is concerned with a whole of social rules. —Nevertheless this type of self-formation is determined by the interests of *life*, by life interests. *Conditional* self-formation is what is at stake here. Unconditional self-formation, however, is free from life interests of that kind, in the sense that those interests are not determining *grounds* for behavior; they are not *directly* determining for human behavior (heteronomy): human behavior is *self-determined* behavior, behavior determined by its own meaning (autonomy). Self-determined behavior is concerned with its own unconditional possibility and task; behavior that is not determined by life, but behavior which is concerned with unconditional validity: with respect to ourselves we behave as creatures that shape their *own* existence, as *independent* creatures. Because of this self-formation, which is in an eminent sense determined by ideas, we move our life interests to a secondary plane. The satisfaction of life interests is a goal of our behavior, but it is not its *final goal*—its final goal is our self-formation qua value-determined (idea-determined) behavior, to be more exact: qua determinacy by values which are defining moments of our being subjects. Here, in a strict sense, we determine our own behavior; life as a natural phenomenon has been *subordinated* to the possibility and task of unconditional self-formation.

Only because of a structure of this kind are we capable of conceiving of human behavior as *accountable* behavior, not lastly where the result of behavior hence its validity evaluation is concerned: is our behavior valid or invalid? Reflection is a part of human behavior. Behavior is behavior in a particular situation on the basis of rules (maxims, values, ideas, etc.). Rules of this kind themselves are evaluated too (accepted, rejected). A rule is valid if it is a specification of an unconditional task (and therefore has a place within the spectrum of the value sphere concerned), if it is part of the determinations that define or determine being a subject itself (and are therefore independent of any particular situation). In this way we behave as subjects, in this way we are free and accountable for our actions.

Human behavior is concerned with validity, but it is also validity-different; that is why it is part of our behavior that we *want to be sure* that our behavior is valid. We do not just exhibit behavior, but we claim that our behavior is *valid* (this holds for any value whatever—qua orientation determinant—which determines that validity: utility, pleasure, beauty, truth, and so on). In our behavior we are concerned with values; moreover we evaluate the validity content our behavior has. In so doing

1. we do not just commit ourselves to a criterion ('utility' for instance) through our concern with value.—In the language of the RCM: our behavior is not just instinctive or vegetative acting but it is 'rational' (utility-maximizing).

2. We moreover want to know if our behavior fulfils the criterion (whether our behavior is 'useful').—In the language of the RCM: is our behavior 'rational' (utility maximizing)?

3. We even wonder whether this criterion is a valid criterion for our behavior (is 'utility' a valid criterion?).—In the language of the RCM: is the concept of 'rationality' (utility maximizing) a valid one?

All of this is part of human behavior, because it is part of the *concept* of human behavior (this concept also includes theoretical validity-reflection: is our *knowledge* of the validity of that criterion valid?). The rationality of human behavior is essentially more complex than the RCM suggests.[①] The dream of the RCM as a *universal* theory of human behavior ought to have been done with a long time ago.[②]

On this point the critics are right. However, it is also of importance to see through the complexity of human behavior, particularly through the reflexive structure of this behavior; for only through that do we obtain a *foundation* for our talk of 'values', 'commitment', 'agency', etc. On the basis of the above argument we come to the following classification.

1. Preferences in the economic sense are 'goods' ('objects', 'objects of

---

① A philosophical analysis comes to a result that is the diametrical opposite of Xenos's (1989, p. 78); since according to Xenos economic rationality is "potentially independent of value rationality altogether" it does not stand in need of "value rationality." This conception of economic rationality in particular turns out to be an abstraction.

② With a view to the simplistic conception of human behaviour that the RCM espouses, it is unsurprising that according to a number of critics the RCM nolens volens gives up one of its assumptions, namely the idea of choice, and lands itself in a determinism (Manstetten 2000, pp. 100 ff.; McKenzie 1983, pp. 28 ff., and so on). In so doing economics becomes a kind of physics of human behaviour, in the form of a Skinnerian behaviourism for example. Preferences are given; there is no room for choice: man is completely determined by his natural and cultural situation; he only calculates the action, he is only instrumentally rational, that is to say, strictly he is not at all rational, since that kind of instrumentality is an *isolating abstraction* of rationality.

choice').[①]

2. These goods are not desired for their own sakes; they are part of a *structure of rules* that is normative for the acting subject.

1. This setting of a norm in the first instance is normative on the basis of *life values*.

2. Life values, however, only have meaning within the framework of autonomous values ('ideal values', 'unconditional values'): values whose validity is not based on something else ('life'), but which are valid *in themselves*. Man as a subject autonomously subjects himself to those values: not for reasons that are directly determined by the interests of life, but for reasons that are determined by his *subjectity*. Autonomous values, then, *directly* determine man as a subject; the interests of life are not pushed aside, they are integrated in this autonomous framework, hence they are *reshaped*.

To this extent, the concept of *self-interest*, which is of such great significance to the RCM, is a striking concept—if the concept is not limited to its sensory aspect, but takes seriously the ideal aspect of human behavior. Hence scientists—like Robbins (1935, 12f.) or Becker—who only conceive of man as a being determined by instincts or drives that operates rationally (calculating in the economic sense), do not have an *inclusive* conception of human behavior: human behavior is essentially determined by values, it essentially has an ideal nature.[②]

3. Application of the RCM to Itself

According to the above analysis human behavior does not just consist of life-oriented calculations of utility; rather a calculation of that kind is always embedded in a process of reflection that founds that calculation. Hence the calculation of utility is reshaped by autonomous values and in so reshaping it, it is connected to another dimension of meaning. If this is so—then it must be true as well for the behavior of the *RCM theoretician*. It follows that qua *universal* theory of action the RCM must be capable of making plausible the behavior of its theoreticians in terms of the RCM. Does

---

① On this point cf. III. 2. 1.

② On this topic cf. my criticism of explanatory conceptions of human behaviour founded in biology (1999a; 1999b; 2001, 6. 3. 3. 2). —On the significance of man's animalistic nature for economic science cf. the analyses by Levine (1976).

it succeed?

By his behavior the theoretician of the RCM produces a theory 'RCM'. Without him there would be no such theory. Why did scientists who defend the RCM choose this theory? What utility, what pleasure or sensory need do they satisfy by this choice? Money, status? Or do they choose the RCM as *scientists*, because they are convinced of the *truth* of the RCM? Do they reject alternative theories (such as the one proposed here), because this theory makes them uneasy, or because this alternative theory is *false*? Does it follow that, as scientists, they are *directly* concerned with the truth: does truth function as an orientation determinant for their behavior? Don't they examine their behavior (and the behavior of competing scientists) with a view to the *value* of truth (since values are orientation determinants for human behavior)? Why should the opponents of the RCM be convinced by the adherents of the RCM? Because it pleases the adherents of the RCM or because it is advantageous to their career? Or because they are convinced of the *validity* of the RCM? Is it agreeable to be refuted? Is that fact relevant with respect to *choosing* a theory? Shouldn't a theory be chosen on *other grounds*: grounds of theoretic validity, of truth?

The preference for a theory is by no means *given* but the result of a *process of appropriation aimed at validity*, a 'founded' conviction. That is why that preference is embedded in an entire net of validity grounds and is evaluated within that framework; for scientific knowledge claims to be founded knowledge that is supported by reasons:[①] it is knowledge on the basis of values, on closer inspection, knowledge on the basis of a whole of values that we may call 'truth'. Because of *its own* claim to validity the theoretician of the RCM is concerned with that whole of values. The RCM certainly does not claim to be an instinctive reaction or a dogmatic thesis, it claims to be a scientific theory.

But if the RCM is not even able to give a sufficient explanation of the behavior

① So it is not even necessary to follow Biervert/Wieland (1990, p. 22) in citing controversial criteria of demarcation, such as Popper's criterion of falsification, and then point out that the economic approach to rational behaviour has a "totalisierte Unfähigkeit zum Irrtum." For in elaborating the reflexive argument it has become clear that the economic approach certainly is falsifiable and not at all "logically speaking immune." From the point of view of formal logic that approach is incapable of explaining the axioms of its model in terms of the model itself. From this point of view too—the choice of the axioms—the model founders qua universal theory of action.

that makes up its own theory formation—then how can it be a *universal* theory of human behavior? Let's move on to the second point of my criticism!

**III. Quantifying Preferences and Their Quality**

(1) Within the neo-classical view of human behavior 'utility', 'improving one's lot' and so on, just like the notion of 'self-interest', are conceived of *empirically* (i. e. as being sensory in nature). Moreover within the neo-classical view goals get a quantitative determination. Because 'utility' is conceived of quantitatively, the calculation of utility in the neo-classical sense is possible: the quantifiability of utility is one of the necessary conditions of neo-classical economics. Is utility quantifiable *qua goal of human behavior*?

As mentioned already, 'rationality' is often associated with the human capability of calculating. Particularly in the empiricist tradition of philosophy—the tradition utilitarianism belongs to—such an operational concept of rationality is definitive. Rationality, reason and so on obtain an algorithmic character. However, the philosophical tradition also knows a more inclusive meaning of rationality. In that case rationality stands for the justificatory capabilities of the subject: subjects are able to justify (found) their opinions, beliefs, actions and so on. From this point of view ratio concerns every 'goal-oriented', 'planned', 'considered' activity of man: it is an activity based on grounds (and those grounds *may be* grounds that have to do with calculation and economic utility, but they may also be other grounds).

From a utilitarian point of view human behavior deteriorates into a kind of arithmetic, into a rational process of calculation, as Bentham paradigmatically and influentially showed with his hedonistic calculus. This calculus turns out to be connected to a multiplicity of problems, problems that have also determined the development of utilitarianism.[①]

These problems include the problem of the *calculation of utility*. It is a problem

---

① Cf. for example Goodin (1991); Hfffe (1979, pp. 120ff.; 1992); Snoeyenbos/Humber (1999); Wagner (1992, §§ 13ff.).—However, it is typical of the self-understanding of the adherents that the approach of utilitarianism is fundamentally 'all right' and its problems only of a technical nature. Snoeyenbos and Humber, for instance, show up time and again the aporetic character of the utilitarian attempts; hence, it is highly surprising that they still hold utilitarianism to deliver an adequate foundation of human behaviour—without giving so much as the beginnings of a possible solution! This has little to do with science, but all the more with religious beliefs.

that has been much discussed, particularly within the economic sciences. Even if the RCM does not directly aim for the maximum utility 'for everyone', but rather for the maximum utility for the individual—the problems of calculation are analogous. With a view to the following it is of importance that these problems cannot be exhaustively discussed within the framework of the questions that are characteristic of the discourse: the question as to the comparability of goods/preferences (material vs. immaterial), or of subjects (intra- and inter-personal comparisons of utility), the question about the cardinal or just the ordinal measurability of utility, the question about the objective validity of the unit of measurement used, and so on. Why not? In the proposed solutions, insofar as they are relevant to the RCM, it is tacitly presupposed, *that preferences qua goals of human behavior are quantifiable* (regardless of whether it concerns cardinal or ordinal measurability);① that is to say, that an object of behavior qua orientation determinant ('goal', 'value', 'interest') has quantity. Without this presupposition there is no calculation of utility, without the calculation of utility there is no RCM, at least not as a 'universal' or 'foundational' explanation of human behavior. Is it a valid presupposition?

In what follows it will turn out that it is once again a manifestation of the RCM's *deficient reflexivity*, that quantitative determinacy is ascribed to preferences qua goals of action. This ascription is unsurprising, since the RCM is intrinsically related to axiomatic thinking. Hence its own assumptions, the 'axioms', are only presupposed; hence *within the framework* of the model the validity and determinacy of its fundamental concepts remain assumptions which cannot be justified. From this point of view the model is a variant on the influential 'Euclidean', deductive-axiomatic rationality. For this type of rationality there is basic knowledge that need not be proved, but which is evidently valid. It is unproblematically taken up as a starting point and functions as a foundation for all other knowledge; the latter is gained from

① I neither agree with Manstetten (2000, p. 74) to the extent that the ordinal determination of utility is not of a quantitative nature, nor that the concept of 'utility' loses it quantitative determination in a framework of preference theory (preferences in Robbins's sense or revealed preferences in Samuelson's sense) (p. 76). The quantitative determination of utility is only modified. This modification, however, entails specific problems pertaining to the possibilities of calculation.

the former by a linear process of proof.[①] For the calculus of the RCM this means that the RCM does not just presuppose general-logical meanings (and logical operations), but presupposes the same for the specific meanings that make that calculus into the one of the RCM. The presuppositions of the RCM itself, qua *universal theory of behavior*, remain at least unclear; they are beliefs that are not perspicuous, and insufficiently determined in respect of their validity, not to say dogmas (think of fundamental concepts such as 'behavior', 'choice', 'utility', 'preference', and so on). Due to its axiomatic starting points the RCM deprives the 'theoretical behavior' we call knowledge of its dimension of ground and foundation of validity.

(2.1) To elucidate the non-quantitative character of preferences qua goals of action, I will by way of introduction first discuss an analogous problem within the history of epistemology, namely the problem of the validity of knowledge, to be more precise: of the attempt to understand the validity of knowledge quantitatively: in degrees of the (un)clarity of the image of an object'. As opposed to that truth turns out not to have gradations (Kant), not to admit of more or less (Frege). Truth is not determined quantitatively. To be sure, there is more than one true statement, but this quantity is irrelevant to the truth of those statements (a true statement, so to speak, is valid only once). The truth of this or that statement rather is a matter of quality ('what'): there is no quantitative hence relative difference between truth and falsehood (more, less) but an absolute difference: something is either true or false (or partially true, or partially false, but again without gradations).[②]

It is not hard to see that the quantitative conception of truth derives from sensory experience, or from physics. Like hot/cold consist of a greater/lesser amount of molecular movement, knowledge consists of a greater or a lesser amount of truth. Knowledge, however, is not a natural phenomenon, it is a *phenomenon of meaning*: true and false knowledge are both phenomena of meaning, and they are so to the same degree. The difference between them is not a difference of greater or lesser meaning.

---

① On the fundamental problems of founding this type of rationality, cf. Krijnen (2008, pp. 14ff.).

② That the truth of statements may also be thought about in terms of probability, changes nothing, to the extent that then too the distinction made applies; for the probability of a statement is not itself probable, or else there is the threat of an asymptote tending to 0, which is to say that nothing is being said.

Here we do not have a sensory (physical or psychological) substrate, that would have greater presence in the case of truth, and lesser presence in the case of falsehood. The difference between true and false knowledge rather is the adequate or inadequate shaping of our theoretical representations according to the principles, criteria, values, grounds of (valid) knowledge. —This holds in the case of our behavior as well!

Being a 'rational activity' human behavior is not just a natural process, but it is also concerned with a whole of 'ideas', 'rules', 'maxims', 'concepts', 'goals', and so on. Hence behavior is concerned with validity. Since we have called the orientation determinants of human behavior 'values', we can also say that human behavior is necessarily *concerned with values*. Only because of the subject's concern with values it is possible to speak of an object that is 'wanted' or 'preferred' (in the economic sense). Such an object is itself something that, in respect of being a goal or a preference of action, is related to a value. 'Nature' and 'value' come together in the preferred object. Through their connection a meaningful reality comes about: a true proposition, the cultural institute that is science as the (purported) set of such propositions, love and friendship, economic organizations, states and governments, works of art and religions, and so on—in a word: everything we know as *culture*, as cultural reality. Even subjects of action pursuing maximum utility, create culture in the above sense of culture (nature concerned with values and related to values). For 'utility' determines their behavior; the 'chosen actions' are concerned with the goal or the value 'utility'. Through this concern with values they create a meaningful reality; in this case a world constituted (i.e. determined in its objectivity) by the value of 'utility'. It is a world that consists of goods in the sense of 'cultural goods'. Preferences in the sense of the RCM and neo-classical economics are goods of this kind:① objects that are preferred, hence objects that are concerned with value and therefore value-laden—*as* preferred objects they are never merely natural objects.

(2.2) With the help of this rudimentary insight into human behavior we are able to examine critically the quantifying aspect of the RCM, to the extent that the RCM claims to offer a *universal* theory of behavior.

---

① For example, cf. Perloff (2001, p. 75) to whom white or black underwear are examples of "tastes or preferences." McKenzie/Tullock (1978, pp. 8ff.) mention "desires" and "values" such as "beer," "pretzels," but also "immaterial" objects, such as reading Shakespeare or attending church.

Because the value (the 'goal') constitutes the good or the preference (in the economic sense), this value—unlike what happens in the RCM—cannot function in the *plural*. The value, the orientation determinant of our behavior, only exists in the singular (where 'singular' must not be understood in the quantitative sense). It is only because goods, of which there are many in the quantitative sense (so numerical ordering, calculation is possible), are constituted by a value, only because objects have meaning *as* preferences, *as* desired or intended objects through a value, that they *are* goods or preferences (in the economic sense). If, in our behavior, we are concerned with the One value, we create a world consisting of goods, we create culture. We shape this world through the value that directs our behavior. There are goods only on the basis of this concern with values, only on the basis of values can there be a multiplicity of goods, and are we able to count goods. To put it classically and in the context of practical philosophy: only because *the* Good is the goal of all behavior, are there goods at all. Without *the* Good, there are no goods; the Good is the condition of the possibility of goods, it is the principle, that is to say moment of the concept of their validity, hence of their determination (if it is not *valid* that a is, then a *is* not).

This unity of the ground of goods—not of preference as one of the goods, but as a goal/value/point of orientation for behavior—is unique in the non-quantitative meaning of the word. For *conceptual* reasons there is no multiplicity of this unity, for as a multiplicity of that unity that multiplicity would have to be constituted by that unity. From this point of view we are not dealing with a multiplicity of grounds of behavior, but with a unique ground that *makes itself concrete*, so that a multiplicity of concreta that are constituted by that ground, comes about: goods. Just like there are many truths, but every truth is valid only once, there are many good actions that are good only once, many beautiful products (works of art) which are beautiful only once; they are concreta, concretizations, goods of the One True, Beautiful and Good; *qua* truth, *qua* good, *qua* beautiful those goods are validity- or determinacy-functionally dependent on them.

Preferences qua values, then, are not countable (generally speaking: numerically determinable). Numerical unity and multiplicity have the structure of a series of units that are exactly demarcated (delimited) one from the other. Such a structure apparently is not what we are dealing with on the level of value as principle. Strictly speaking we aren't dealing with such a structure either on the level of *goods*, for goods are characterized by their concern with values. If we ignore that concern with values, and only conceive of goods quantitatively, then we deny their value-determinacy—which, however, is defining of the good as good; hence we abstract from a moment that determines goods as such. Through this isolating abstraction, it is true, we would have quantitative entities at our disposal, but oddly enough we would not have goods, for they are determined by value. Value determinacy is validity determinacy, and validity determinacy is of a qualitative nature: true/false, good/bad, beautiful/ugly, efficient/inefficient, and so on. Such value-determined alternatives are by no means merely 'given preferences'.

Preferences qua goods cannot be a coincidental, rule-free or natural ragbag of something that is originally without relations. Preferences are what they are always and only because of their value determinacy, within the framework of a 'meaningful coherence'. Whereas the RCM because of its methodological orientation on mechanistic physics conceives of preferences/goods as isolated elements, hence conceptually making them into numerically manageable quantities, preferences/goods as such aren't 'atoms', but value-determined entities, phenomena of meaning, hence integrated in a structure of value and the meaning constituted by it.[①] The assumption of their not being concerned with values, the assumption of something that exists in isolation in and for the calculation, on the contrary precisely is the condition of possibility for their calculation. However, *this assumption is itself a concern with values* that constitutes a meaningful coherence, namely the utility calculation of the RCM. That calculation is possibly only *on the basis* of meaning and value. It follows that the RCM can neither offer a 'universal theory of behavior', nor the foundations of such a theory; the concern of behavior and its object with meaning and value remains unconsidered

---

① From a Heideggerian point of view Brodbeck has said this as follows: possibilities for action are no "Zustände in einem logisch starren Raum," but they are "Interpretationen" (2000, p. 12), "Einzelereignisse" only exist on the basis of a "Weltmodell" (p. 16); in the social sciences in particular we do not have a "jüngfraulichen Stoff des empirischen Materials," we only have interpretations (p. 31 and onwards). This interpretationism—which is currently better known as social constructivism—can, however, not cover everything, for it is delimited by the objective structure of meaning (for a view that is critical of Heidegger's, cf. Krijnen 2001, 6.3.3.3.2; 2004).

for methodological reasons. ①

This way it becomes clear that human behavior cannot be reduced to natural determinates, for it has a value-referential character, or in the language of the theory of consciousness an 'intentional' character. Preferences are not 'masses', their identity is not a 'substance', etc. 'Great' thoughts and 'great' deeds are by no means extremely extended (sometimes a great action is even the omission of an action), but actions or thoughts which are to a remarkable extent concerned with value, are 'valuable'; actions do not 'follow' like a natural effect follows a natural cause; and someone who thinks that being 'quick on the uptake' is just a temporal neural process, has neglected the concern our thinking has with the value of 'truth' (someone who quickly says the wrong things, isn't quick on the uptake: 'quick' here is a 'value concept', not a 'natural concept'). Human behavior can be understood as a concretization of a value. Hence a science that wants to determine human behavior *universally*, does not possess any concept of 'atomic ultimate units'; preferences/goods are not stable 'givens', phenomena of value aren't atoms. Rather they are value-determined, hence value-functionally structured. By appealing to this structure behavior is explained, not by means of a calculus that has a structure analogous to the one natural laws have. ② Validity constellations *as* validity constellations are neither determined temporally, nor spatially; so they have no numerical determinacy; *as* validity constellations they are value-determined.

---

① Value determinacy cannot be quantified, but can be 'operationalized'. Operationalizing values reduces them to indicators, to be more precise: to sensory indicators. This may be a legitimate process within the framework of a particular interest of knowledge. However, the operationalization becomes problematic as soon as indicators are thought to be the matter itself—cf. the RCM in the shape of a universal theory of action. To the extent that the object of economics may be presented as an 'order', that object certainly is mathematicizable, but mathematics is not constitutive for the object of economics (this is another matter where physics is concerned). By mathematizing the object, economics subjects it to an approach that is independent of its special nature as an economic object, and addresses it solely with a view to the notion of an 'ordering'.

② For criticism with respect to the limits of quantifiability from a consciousness-theoretical point of view cf. Düsing (2005, pp. 114ff.) on the conclusions that have been drawn on the basis of Libet's experiments. Düsing's criticism is relevant to the above argument in the sense that the temporality of decision processes makes it impossible to fix the time of a 'decision' exactly. Similar arguments may be found in the work of Husserl or Hönigswald. For a critical look at the concept of time in neo-classical economics, cf. Georgescu-Roegen (1976) or Brodbeck (2005).

Economic imperialism wants to offer a *universal* theory of action or a basis for it. That has turned out to be an invalid pretention. What, then, does the RCM explain? *Aspects* of human behavior, and not even the basic ones. Especially according to neo-classical economics human beings must choose. Choice, however, involves a relation to values (regardless which values they are, the value of 'utility' for example). Some-one who is not willing to give up the idea of the freedom of choice, is involved with values; someone who does give up the idea of freedom of choice, is unable to explain anything at all, not even the validity of his own theory. By means of the isolating abstraction of the RCM we do not gain any scientific insight into the foundations of human behavior—we need a different theory of rationality.

**References**

Archer, M., Tritter, J. (Eds.): *Rational choice theory: a critique*, London (Routledge) 2000.

Becker, G.: *The Economic Approach to Human Behavior*, Chicago (University of Chicago Press) 1976.

Becker, G.: "Nobel Lecture: The Economic Way of Looking at Behavior", in: *Journal of Political Economy*, 101 (1993), pp. 385-409.

Biervert, B., Wieland, J.: Gegenstandsbereich und Rationalitätsform der Ökonomie und der Ökonomik", in: B. Biervert, K. Held, J. Wieland (Hrsg.): *Sozialphilosophische Grundlagen ökonomischen Verhaltens*, Frankfurt/M. (Suhrkamp) 1990, pp. 7-32.

Bowmaker, S. (Ed.): *Economics uncut: a complete guide to life, death and misadventure*, Cheltenham/Northampton (Elgar) 2005.

Brodbeck, K.-H.: *Die fragwürdigen Grundlagen der Ökonomie. Eine philosophische Kritik der modernen Wirtschaftswissenschaften*, Darmstadt (Wissenschaftliche Buchgesellschaft) 2000.

Chick, V.: "On knowing one's place: the Role of Formalism in Economics", in: *Economic Journal*, 108 (1998), pp. 1859-69.

Dow, S.C.: *The Use of Mathematics in Economics*, 1999, http://www.ioe.ac.uk/esrcmaths/sheila1.html.

Düsing, K.: *Fundamente der Ethik. Unzeitgemäße typologische und subjektivitätstheoretische Untersuchungen*, Stuttgart-Bad Cannstatt (Fromann-Holzboog) 2005.

Elster, J.: *Sour Grapes*, Cambridge (Cambridge University Press) 1983.

Elster, J.: *Ulysses and the Sirens*, Cambridge (Cambridge University Press) 1984.

Elster, J. (1989a): *Solomonic Judgements. Studies in the Limitations of Rationality*, Cambridge (Cambridge University Press) 1989.

Elster, J. (1989b): "When Rationality Fails", in: *Solomonic Judgements*, 1989, pp. 1-35.

Etzioni, A.: *The Moral Dimension. Toward a New Economics*, New York (Free Press) 1988.

Frambach, H.: "Nutzen- und Tauschtheoretische Grundlagen in der Entwicklung der Neoklassik", in:

*Zeitschrift für Wirtschafts- und Sozialwissenschaften*, 116 (1996), pp. 85-117.

Friedman, M.: "The Methodology of Positive Economics", in: *Essays in Positive Economics*, Chicago (University of Chicago Press) 1953, pp. 1-43.

Georgescu-Roegen, N.: *Energy and Economic Myths. Institutional and Analytical Economic Essays*, New York et al. (Pergamon) 1976.

Goodin, R.E.: "Utility and the good", in: P. Singer (Ed.): *A companion to ethics*, Oxford (UK)/Cambridge (USA) (Blackwell) 1991, pp. 241-248.

Hfffe, O.: *Ethik und Politik. Grundmodelle und -probleme der praktischen Philosophie*, Frankfurt/M. (Suhrkamp) 1979.

Hfffe, O.: "Einleitung", in: O. Hfffe (Hrsg.): *Einführung in die utilitaristische Ethik*, 2. verb. Aufl., Tübingen (Francke) 1992, pp. 7-51.

Hollis, M.: *The Philosophy of Social Science*, Cambridge (Cambridge University Press) 1994.

Johnson, P., Duberley, J.: *Understanding Management Research. An Introduction to Epistemology*, London (Sage) 2000.

Kahneman, D.: "Maps of Bounded Rationality: Psychology for Behavioral Economics", in: *American Economic Review*, 93 (2003), pp. 1449-75.

Kirchg ssner, G.: *Homo oeconomicus. Das ökonomische Modell individuellen Verhaltens und seine Anwendung in den Wirtschafts- und Sozialwissenschaften*, Tübingen (Mohr Siebeck) 1991.

Krijnen, Ch. (1999a): "Das philosophische Problem ethischer Grundlagen und das Grundproblem der Evolutionären Ethik“, in: *Zeitschrift für philosophische Forschung*, 53 (1999), pp. 77-100.

Krijnen, Ch. (1999b): “Tiere ohne Rechte und Menschen mit Pflichten”, in: B. Busch, J.C. Joerden (Hrsg.): *Tiere ohne Rechte?*, Berlin et al. (Springer) 1999, pp. 83-99.

Krijnen, Ch.: *Nachmetaphysischer Sinn. Eine problemgeschichtliche und systematische Studie zu den Prinzipien der Wertphilosophie Heinrich Rickerts*, Würzburg (Königshausen & Neumann) 2001.

Krijnen, Ch.: “Wert“, in: M. Düwell, Ch. Hübenthal, M. H. Werner (Hrsg.): *Handbuch Ethik*, Stuttgart (Metzler) 2002, pp. 527-533.

Krijnen, Ch.: “Fundamentalontologische oder geltungsfunktionale Bestimmung von Sinn und Wert? Heidegger und der Neukantianismus“, in: P.-U. Merz-Benz, U. Renz (Hrsg.): *Ethik oder Ästhetik? Zur Aktualität der neukantianischen Kulturphilosophie*, Würzburg (Königshausen & Neumann) 2004, pp. 87-114.

Krijnen, Ch.: *Philosophie als System. Prinzipientheoretische Untersuchungen zum Systemgedanken bei Hegel, im Neukantianismus und in der Gegenwartsphilosophie*, Würzburg (Königshausen & Neumann) 2008.

Krijnen, Ch., Kee, B. (Eds.): *Economics and Management & Organisaties Studies: A Critical*

*Philosophical Introduction*, Deventer (Kluwer) 2009.

Levine, D.P.: *Economic Studies: Contributions to the Critique of Economic Theory*, London et al.

(Routledge) 1977.

M ki, U.: “Explanatory Ecumenism and Economic Imperialism”, in: *Economics and Philosophy* 18 (2002), pp. 235-257.

Manstetten, R.: *Das Menschenbild der Ökonomie. Der homo oeconomicus und die Anthropologie von Adam Smith*, Freiburg i. B./München (Alber) 2000.

McKenzie, R.B.: *The limits of economic science*, Dordrecht (Kluwer-Nijhoff) 1983.

McKenzie, R.B., Tullock, G.: *The New World of Economics. Explorations into the Human Sciences*, Illinois (Irwin) 1978.

Nelson, J.A.: “I, Thou and Them: Capabilities, Altruism, and Norms in the Economics of Marriage”, in: *American Economic Review*, 84 (1994), pp. 126-131.

Perloff, J. M.: *Microeconomics*, 2nd ed., Boston et al. (Addison Wesley) 2001.

Radnitzky, G., Bernholz, P. (Eds.): *Economic Imperialism. The Economic Method Applied Outside the Field of Economics*, New York (Paragon) 1987.

Robbins, L.: *On the Nature and Significance of Economic Science*, 2. ed., London (Macmillan) 1935.

Sappinen, J.: *Stretching the Scope of Economics—On the Nature and Impact of Gary Becker's Economics Imperialism*, Lappeenranta (Lappeenranta University of Technology Studies in Business Administration) 2003.

Sen, A.: "Rational Fools: A Critique of the Behavourial Foundations of Economic Theory", in: *Philosophy and Public Affairs*, 6 (1977), pp. 317-344.

Sen, A.: Interview, in: R. Swedberg (Ed.): *Economics and Sociology, Redefining their Boundaries*, Princeton (Princeton University Press) 1990, pp. 249-267.

Simon, H.: *Reason in Human Affairs*, Oxford (Blackwell) 1983.

Snoeyenbos, M., Humber, J.: "Utilitarianism and Business Ethics", in: R. Frederick (Ed.): *A companion to business ethics*, Oxford (UK)/Cambridge (USA) (Blacwell) 1999, pp. 17-29.

Wagner, H.: *Die Würde des Menschen. Wesen und Normfunktion*, Würzburg (Königshausen & Neumann) 1992.

Xenos, N.: *Scaricity and Modernity*, London (Routledge) 1989.

# Self-reflection as Method to Approach Thinking and Being: Is Contradiction the Essence of Being?

**Claudia Bickmann (University of Cologne, Germany)**

Self-reflection, self-understanding and self-determination was the origin and major method of European thought development. As Aristotle asserts: the unity of being and thinking is not just given-as in nature,-but it has to be achieved-by self-reflection or self-determination. The method of self-reflection as a way to address thinking and being in most European philosophical traditions was even regarded as synonym for philosophy itself. It remained influential till the science oriented Analytical Philosophy became the dominant method of Western thinking. The self-reflecting approach to major questions of thinking and being was transformed into a merely formal or logical method for the justification of arguments. The concept of spirit (Geist) or thinking should no longer be based on a self-reflecting method, but rather became an observable object of Neuro-science.

Hereby the idea of a whole as an integrative horizon of nature and spirit was lost likewise. Due to our human capacities to merely perceive and understand the given phenomena of the spatiotemporal world, the concept of being as a whole should no longer be a possible object of empirical knowledge.

Now we might take over the chance to enter a new phase of mutual learning by searching for a common ground and by trying to integrate the strength and the irreducible insides of each other reciprocally.

I will put a theme into the centre of my analysis, which has become a prominent topic in both traditions, namely the question of *whether or not contradiction might be the essence of being*.

We take the hypothesis of the in-itself-contradicting nature of being as a starting point. As it seems, we find similar dualities in nearly all world philosophies: Yin and yang, freedom and necessity, nature and spirit etc. We ask: How can we avoid to just dogmatically presuppose this duality without any justification for these two irreducible dimensions of being as a whole? Without any justification scepticism and relativism cannot be avoided. The validity or evidence of this thesis could simply be interrogated, in order to overcome the included metaphysical premises.

Thus we face the problematique of either dogmatically posit a highest duality or sceptically deny it. In order to avoid both extremes our task will be to enlighten the premises of our thinking and acting in order not to take any duality for granted or as a matter of our believes.

I will advance in three steps:

First I will analyse the problematique to understand the irreducibility of the extremes.

Secondly I will indicate that reflecting the embeddedness of freedom and necessity will reveal a triangular structure: a third dimension is needed to understand their interrelatedness.

Thirdly we will shed light on three different models answering the question of how the extremes might be united.

**Ⅰ. The in-itself contradicting essence of being**

a. In nearly all world philosophies an elementary insight is prevailing:

Even though our human nature is based on reason and morality, we usually hesitate when being asked: How to define and explain what knowledge or cognition might be? And with regard to our actions we will ask: What does it mean to act morally?

As we shall see, we are not only confronted with the methodological challenge of how to analyse and understand thinking and acting; but we will also have to answer the question of how to understand the in-themselves contradicting types of causality here involved: namely *causality by nature* and *causality by the law of freedom*.

And finally, with regard to these two types of causality we will have to answer the question, of how they are intertwined within ourselves and within the world as a whole. Thus we will have to ask for the common ground of reason and morality.

But the question arises: Do we really need an explicit concept of reason and morality before knowing how to perceive, understand or explain the phenomenal world or how to act morally in the supernatural, a moral world? Was the predominantly methodological approach within Western philosophy maybe even a failure with regard to the value-orientation of our practical reason-prevailing in most Asien traditions? Didn't it lead to a predominance of theoretical philosophy-neglecting the questions of a fulfilled life? As a possible answer, one could just simply indicate, that while our human reason guides morality, morality cultivates our nature.

But if simultaneously we have to concede, that human nature is not morally by itself, but has to be cultivated and inspired by a reasonable guidance and by education, we have to admit, that humans, as Confucius and Kant hold, are themselves responsible for the rules of their social and personal lives-in order to substitute the missing instincts of their physical nature.

Thus the awareness of a possible hiatus between the natural sources of our existence and the need for the cultivation of our capacities based on moral reasons became an essential topic in nearly all cultures and world-philosophical traditions.

Hereby the concept of the highest good, as anticipated in the idea of the One or the Dao or the supernatural substratum should indicate, how (and according to which 'ethos' or 'telos') human nature should develop itself, if harmony between our natural striving for happiness (in the empirical world) and the unconditioned capacity to create a world under moral rules should be obtained.

Since such rules are not just given by our physical nature, as if nature had equipped us already with a coherent concept of morality,-morality has to be developed according to our ideas of justice, freedom and peace in order to achieve individual and social wealth. Here causality by freedom is prevailing.

And while our knowledge acquirement of the cause-effect relations is related to the given phenomena in space and time, morality and hope are linked to merely *expected effects of our activities* or an *expected state of the world*,-thus they are reaching far beyond the knowledgeable state of our existence in a future time to come.

Morality as based on our free will is bound to normative rules of our behaviour. The guiding principle governing our normative moral rules can be expressed in a law, according to which our actions should be the source of a state of human existence, in which mutual freedom and respect to one another will be guaranteed.

And since within the field of morality freedom is the source of our behaviour, according to which every person should act in a way, that the maxim of his actions may serve as basis for an universal law-we have to infer from the universality of such a moral rule, that moral causality is possible only due to the unconditioned ground within us, called freedom.

In difference to the law of nature, to natural causality, which is linked to phenomena of the given world and thus to be grasped by external causes,-moral causality - based on our free will-is possible only because of this unconditioned fundament within us, called freedom of our will. If we would consider that the phenomenal world would be the all-determining, all-encompassing framework of our actions, morality could not be explained. With regard to the two contradicting types of causality, causality by nature and causality by our free will, we find the idea of an in-itself-contradicting nature of being in a micro- and a macro cosmic perspective in nearly all world philosophies. Interpreted as Yin and Yang, as nature and spirit, freedom and necessity-the polarity of our nature seems to be an essential axiom in nearly all world philosophies.

Within European thought-development from Plato to Hegel and Heidegger neither should the empirical, the natural law, determine our free will, nor should our free will contradict the rules of nature.

b. Thus the challenge was to integrate both conflicting laws of causality in an all-encompassing horizon, in which all spheres of our individual, social and cosmic life could be regarded as just two sides of being as a whole. This should mean:

a) With regard to our individual lives we should regard freedom and necessity, spirit and nature not only as two conflicting but also complementary dimensions of our personal lives;

b) Within the social order we should regard ourselves as equipped with the creative power to build a society based on moral and juridical rules;

c. Thirdly within the cosmic whole we should understand our human nature-as equipped with its capacity to live in accordance with the rules of nature; while-as a price of our freedom-we simultaneously are free to neglect the natural demands for care, cultivation and conservation.

The idea of a compossibility between the two complementary, colliding or even contradicting types of causality was unquestioned within the main stream of Western philosophy-from the early Greeks to Leibniz, Kant till Heidegger - as similarly interpreted in different Asian traditions: in Confucianism, Buddhism or Taoism.

—Leibniz still interpreted the idea of the all-encompassing original monadic system as the pre-established realm of harmony between freedom and necessity, spirit and nature. Both dimension were understood as just two poles of the cosmic whole.

—And while Descartes-at the beginning of modern times-sharply cut the link between the extremes of nature and spirit by inaugurating a hiatus between the realm of thinking ('res cogitans') and the realm of things ('res extensa');

—Spinoza reintegrated anew the two poles by arguing for the idea of an originating substance-grounding the two contradicting sides.

—Kant reconsidered the inevitable hiatus between these two spheres within his 'dialectics of pure reason': Inevitably, as he holds, human reason faces the unavoidable destiny to strive for the unconditioned within us (freedom) and outside of us: as the founding principle of freedom and necessity,-while his senses and his understanding are limited to the spatial-temporal world. Thus, what might be valid within the phenomenal world, cannot be valid within the intelligible, the supernatural world (et vice versa): Within the realm of freedom the idea of the unconditioned guides our sense for morality and our hope for a world under moral rules - in the three dimensions of an unconditioned within us (our self or our souls), besides us (within the realm of a social an juridical order as well as in the natural order) and finally outside of us (with regard to a founding principle of freedom and necessity-named over-sensual substratum-the sphere of transcendence etc.). Since freedom is not given by our nature, but has to be achieved and realised only by our acts of self-determination of our will and thus can only be strived and acted for, we can never take it for granted. The law of freedom rather has to be regarded as a cultural achievement.

But as Kant holds, insofar as there is only one human reason, expressing itself in different ways (manners), namely within the sphere of the empirically bound spatial temporal world on the one side and within the non-empirical spatiotemporal unbound sphere of the unconditioned, the realm of freedom, on the other side, the antinomy of pure reason with itself is the inevitable consequence. But, as Kant further holds, reason would destroy itself, if the concept of reason would be *in-itself contradicting*,-thus we have clearly to distinguish between the two different spheres in which we find ourselves as human beings:

We cannot limit ourselves as natural beings to space and time, if we want to understand the sphere of the unconditioned, namely morality; and inversely, we cannot regard ourselves as pure spiritual beings, spatial temporally unlimited, if we want to understand our physical nature as the preconditioned ground for our human activities.

Thus we will have to distinguish clearly：

Even if the result might be, that our nature is in itself contradicting,-as presupposed in most Asian and European philosophies from the ancient Greeks till Schelling and Hegel,-the concept of the in-itself contradicting nature of human beings cannot be itself contradicting. This means, we cannot at same time posit the thesis of the in- itself contradicted nature of human mankind and simultaneously deny it.

As a consequence, Kant indicated, that the two types of causality, natural and moral causality, cannot follow the same principles, - because of the possible contradiction and collisions between these two causalities. Thus if they might even contradict rather than harmonize, our approach to the wanted harmony between our natural desires and the moral order to strive for, may even be useless - unless we enter the method of self-reflection：figuring out how far our reason might reach in order to understand the wholeness of the whole without dogmatically positing the apodicticity of a possible principle such as the principle of God, the highest good, of the One, of the absolute substance or the concept of the oneness of the Dao.

**II. Anticipating the future effects of our actions：The Contingency-gap**

Now, given the case that we act according to moral rules, the *effects* of our moral actions are not predictable-inasmuch as all future events and consequences of our actions and non-actions cannot be anticipated by reason：

Since we cannot *know* in advance, weather the than given circumstances will coincide with the wanted effect of our actions,-because it is not guaranteed by our free will, we only may *hope* for the best effect of our actions. We only will have to presuppose that the given circumstances may *harmonise* with the wanted effect of our actions in principal.

Thus a third capacity comes into play, if we want to understand how reason and morality, knowledge and moral behaviour are intertwined：

Besides our capacity of knowledge acquirement-as the capacity to perceive, to understand and to explain the phenomenal world and the capacity to act according to moral rules,-we thirdly have to presuppose the capacity *to anticipate* the consequences and effects of our doings. The anticipation of possible consequences or effects of our actions presupposes the *idea of a whole*, in which our knowledge (bound to the *the* past), our recognition of the given circumstances of our actions in *presence*, and finally our capacity to anticipate *future events*-linked to the regulative idea of a whole, in which past, presents and future are synoptically integrated.

This capacity to tentatively anticipate the future effects may be named: *the capacity to hope*. With our hopes we enter the sphere of the unknown, linked to the limitations of our knowledge within the given spatial temporal world and our lack of knowledge with regard to the future consequences of our actions. Hereby we presuppose the idea of a whole-integrating all time-sequences: the past events, the given situation and the anticipated effects of our actions.

In nearly all world cultures and epochs of the history of mankind we find different strategies to fill the gap between our knowledge of the given state of being and the merely anticipated state of a possible future or world to come.

、**III. Three models to face the Contingency of the Unpredictable:**

1*rst Model: Mythology as a method of 'analogous thinking'*

The different myths or tales of the origin of nature and mankind maybe understood as a way to interpret or explain the unknown by reference to the known, in order to be able to predict future events or the future state of the world. The method applied may be called: analogous thinking. Analogues thinking transfers a given relation between two well-known elements to an unknown relation, whereby we only know the effects, but not yet the causes to the effects.

Analogous thinking does not interpret the causes according to a cause-and-effect relation, which is the result of perceptions, hypothesis-building and then anticipating or predicting the consequences of the observed state of being, but rather tries to understand the given phenomena as an expression or manifestation of causes, familiar to the logic of actions: the given events or states of being-are interpreted in analogy to human actions-as consequences of supernatural laws or activities of a divine being.

Based on a projection of the known to the unknown, human relationships served as a paradigm to understand the laws of nature and the cosmos as a whole: Personifications and projections built the methodological framework to interpret the origin of the originating forces and laws.

And since in most mythological concepts or schemes the cause-effect relation was based on an analogy between the divine or supernatural law and their manifestations in nature and society - according to the purposiveness or intentionality of human actions and intentions, an anticipation of future events should be possible.

2nd *Model*: *Religion as a method of 'representational, imaginative thinking'*.

Religion may be named as a second model to interpret the unknown phenomenal world or the inexplicable events by reference to an intelligible causality. In most religious traditions the idea of a personification of the Divine was prevailing. A noumenal, a divine being (like Abraham, Moses, Confucius, Jesus or Mohamed, the Persian Zarathustra or Brahman and Buddha) should be considered as paradigm of a wise person mediating between the origin of supernatural, intelligible world and the finitude of the created world. The creating power of the universe was supposed to be equipped with wisdom and almightiness likewise for the better understanding of the natural and intelligent ground of being as a whole and a possible anticipation of a future state of being. Purposiveness and intentionality should be named as a source of its power to understand the cosmic and the social order as a whole.

Thus our knowledge of these originating powers simultaneously should help to understand and to predict our destiny in future times

The idea was: that our lives are not merely limited to the finitude of the given spatiotemporal world, but rather be able to reach far beyond these limitations to a sphere of transcendence. Since only by reference to a transcendent principle we would be able to understand the possibility to go beyond our personal lives and open the horizon of intersubjectivity in our social lives. The capacity to create the world under moral rules should indicate, that humans were not just regarded as natural beings but rather as citizens of a super-natural, a divine world. The sphere of transcendence, in which we find ourselves as human beings,-Heidegger would identify this going beyond ourselves as our 'being-in-the-world',-must not necessarily be based on religion, but may be revealed already by our capacity to anticipate *a whole of all interrelated aspects of the natural and intelligible lives*, in which we find ourselves capable of acting intentionally.

This human capacity to transcend the spatiotemporal limits of our natural existence finds its expression in our cultural, our moral nature. Within the realm of freedom, human mankind is capable to anticipate the idea of a cosmos as a whole and to strive for equilibrium between his natural and intelligible qualities.

3rd *Model*: *Science as method of modelling 'cause- and effect-relations' for the explication and prediction of phenomena.*

a. Within the history of mankind a third decisive capacity was developed to anticipate the Unpredictable: by exploring the cause-effect relations through observations, descriptions and explanations of the given phenomena in space and time. By reference to the principle of causality the 'cause and effect-relations' should be explained, whereby the hypotheses about the possible causes and effects should be proved-verified or falsified-by experimental reproductions and no longer be dependent on mere assumptions, beliefs or our mere hopes for the underlying supernatural forces to intervene. Whatever may be named a cause or an effect within the phenomenal world should prove its evidence by reference to an observable relation within the empirical world.

Thus during Renaissance the holy book, the bible, was replaced by observing, describing and studying the laws of nature (Keppler, Galilei, Newton). Cause-related predictions of future events or phenomena should help to anticipate the unsecure future events to occur.

With the Copernican shift within European thought development it seems that a new hiatus between reason and morality within the sphere of science and the realm of morality was initiated. Causality by nature

and causality by freedom should no longer be bound to a unifying supra-natural substratum.

Let us sketch a short light on the dynamics of the development between the contradicting and complementary spheres:

*b. Kant's limitation of the claims of natural sciences: 'Empirical realism' presupposes 'transcendental idealism'.*

With regard to the observable facts in space and time, as Kant holds, there is no way to affirm the necessity between the relation of cause and effect-except by presupposing a form of our under-standing, which provides an a priori guarantee to affirm the necessity of the relation between the two related phenomena. Since by inference through empirical induction uncertainty remains, and therefore the question: why the observed facts should necessarily follow on to the other, we have to presuppose an a priori preconditioned subjective form of our understanding, which may guarantee the necessity of the relation between cause and effects. Thus transcendental idealism is presupposes in any empirical Realisms.

As Kant argues:

"Accidental observations, made in obedience to no previously thought-out plan, can never be made to yield a necessary law, which alone reason is concerned to discover." (I. Kant, Critique of pure Reason, transl. K.Smith, B XIII).

With regard to 'transcendental idealism' we have to be aware of the following possible misunderstanding: Kant did not presuppose, that the two given facts should necessarily be connected in our accidental observations, but that they should belong together necessarily according to our transcendental unity of apperception; since otherwise the 'law by nature' would be contradicting in itself.

Within the development of natural sciences: Kant's critical-his transcendental shift-was refuted as a merely metaphysical hypothesis, unable to be grounded by empirical observations. But as Kant would argue: What has to be understood as the preconditioned - the a priori - ground for any empirical observation or analysis, cannot itself be an object of our empirical analysis.

c. But the scientific approach became prevailing. Here the observable natural phenomena should serve as proof criterion for the validity of the respective hypotheses. Simultaneously the justification of a theory by reference to the phenomenal evidence should not just lead to a better understanding of the laws of nature, but simultaneously help to exclude the non-observable phenomena from any scientific approach. Within the horizon of natural sciences the capacity of explaining a phenomenon by reference to natural cause and effect relations and to predict an event or phenomenon became the exclusive methodological paradigm. During the 20th century even the humanities should explain our intentions or spiritual attitudes or even our moral behaviour according to the paradigm to explain natural phenomenona etc.

For Kant the concept of knowledge was strictly confined within the limits of the phenomenal world. But for his integrative theory this restriction of our knowledge to objects given in space and time did not exclude to presuppose such supernatural causes like the idea of a divine or highest being or the freedom of our will-from being regarded as a possible object of cognition and of our coherent thinking. They simply should not be regarded as empirical facts: Since intentions, dispositions, intuitions, feelings or imaginations are inaccessible to spatiotemporal observations, they should no longer be regarded as adequate objects of natural sciences. But since for Kant our free will and the idea of the world on the moral rules was not to be reduced to any scientific approach, the realm of freedom and morality, linked to the unconditional ground within us remained the irreducible source of human existence.

d. Modern sciences successively eliminated the concept of purposiveness and the idea of the free will, our other mental states by establishing a predominantly reductionist approach: reducing these phenomena to an object of Neuro-Sciences. Thus the basis of any knowledge-acquirement was the explicit abstraction from all dimensions-inaccessible to our observations in space and time.

The success of this models was guaranteed by experimental reproductions: whereby the initial premises could be isolated and kept stable within different experiments in order to find the general rule or to predict the further events by deducing from the respective premises.

Thus certainty was no longer depending on the 'certainty' of our believes (myths or religion); but should be guaranteed by a method of knowledge acquirement, which was capable of proving its validity by experimental reproductions on the basis of logical and mathematical laws on the one side and the possible observations in space and time on the other side.

The price of the reductionist scientific approach was high, namely the extinction and elimination of the dimensions of our mental states, like intentionality or our free will.

e. A complementary field of scientific research was inaugurated.

In the first phase of the development within the 17th and 18th century starting with Herder, Humboldt, Schleiermacher etc. the idea was not only to understand and interpret the internal dimensions of our minds but also all those phenomena, which cannot be explained by reference to general - to natural - rules such as individuality, the particularities or specificity of the phenomenal world.

And while Herder brought ahead the historical consciousness of all different epochs of history by giving credit to the different cultural heritages and traditions, Humboldt tried to understand the historically bound development of the different languages.

Thus the field of humanities was inaugurated during the 18th century in European History as the complementary sphere to deal with the specificities, individualities or contingencies of the phenomenal world: here our access was possible by interpreting and understanding these phenomena in an hermeneutical way.

With W. Dilthey's distinction: "Explaining and understanding", the two realms of natural sciences and the field of humanities should follow different aims by reference to their methodological characters.

Dilthey expressed the hiatus between the 'natural sciences' and the 'fields of humanities' by the two different methodological approaches: the empirically based hypothetical method to deduce the predicted events or facts from general principles and premises on the one side and the interpretation of the individuality of the given phenomenona in literature, art by hermeneutical methods on the other side.

f. During the latest decades of the 20s century natural sciences and humanities successively converged methodologically:

The great success of dynamic mathematical theory to analyse and predict the even highly individualised phenomena by means of the computer-guided algorithms was successively adapted and imitated within the field of humanities.

As example: meteorology became more and more precise to predict the a higly-individualised phenomenon the weather forecast.

Or within field of economics-the explanation of individual or social behaviour seemed to be possible by reference to so-called game theories, able to calculate with models of highly individualised economical decisions.

In recent years the framework of highly distinguished algorithms to describe the highly individualised phenomena took over in major fields of the humanities.

Predictions with a high degree of precision should help to analyse and understand even human behaviour. Besides the parameters of game theory - evolutionary anthropology opened the floor for a reduction of our individual and social behaviour to a behaviourist approach. Decision-making was no longer interpreted as an expression of clear and justifiable reasons, but rather as an effect of striving forces of our unconscious needs and behavioural patterns. As predominantly externally motivated-our behaviour in nearly all fields of research of humanities became the object of an empirical theory, whereby our free will was reduced to a simple choice between different alternatives. Thus natural sciences became a paradigm even within the field of humanities and replaced the formerly dominant hermeneutical methods.

And while hermeneutics maybe named the last discipline to presuppose the unity of a whole in order to understand the parts or specifities of the particular entities, the concept of a whole was almost lost by replacing hermeneutics by a behaviorist approach. The hermeneutic method-as a method to reveal the sense or the meaning of an entity by reference to its purposiveness-was criticised not arguing precise enough; no justification-procedure by clear arguments could be given by the method of hermeneutics. Thus the interpretation of a text, a piece of music, history or even a whole philosophical theory, should be under-stood as a mere subjective enterprise.

Only clearly separable micro-arguments might be object of possible justifications-verification of falsification - by the means of clearly defined logical systems, should prevail especially within the Anglo-Saxon analytical philosophy. As it seems there was no space any more for a hermeneutical method even with in the horizon of philosophy. Context-free analytical argumentations became the dominant paradigm and spread out in nearly all areas of our social life.

g. But an astonishing dialectics occurred within the field of modern natural sciences: In his late philosophy W. v. O. Quine pledged for the idea of the wholeness as prior to the knowing of an object. Natural philosophers like Virilio or Maturana,-or even quantum physicists like Werner Heisenberg and Carl Friederich v. Weizsäcker stressed the importance of a concept of spirit as the elementary quality of the atoms-in a micro- or macrocosmic perspective. Hence Heisenberg and C. F. von Weizsäcker in the middle of the 20th century asserted: Nature in essence might be spiritual; spirit might be the essence of nature.

A parallel tendency we may find within the field of analytical philosophy:

The formerly rejected themes like 'ontology' or 'metaphysics' now advanced anew to a central topic of a 'concept analysis', whereby 'a priori-arguments' are prevailing again.

And while within the field of humanities 'rational choice arguments' indicate assimilation to the methods of the successful natural sciences; scientists on the other side become more and more prudent with regard to the validity and universality of the natural laws they had detected without any reference to the holistic framework of the argument.

The hereby-indicated convergence of the different scientific systems nevertheless marks the tendency to overcome the hiatus between the two spheres.

And while the natural sciences opened towards the integration of the concept of individuality; the humanities-formerly based on interpretation and understanding of individual phenomenona like language, history or art in an hermeneutical way-successively adapted the methods of natural sciences.

But while natural sciences reintegrated a concept of teleology, which was lost by a mere concentration on the linearity of the cause-and effect relations,-the humanities paid a high price by describing, interpreting and explaining human behaviour according to scientific models, adapting the criteria of observability and predictability of human behaviour.

Neuro-sciences took over in order to better understand our mental activities. The adapted reductionist method to describe mental states by reference to the analysis of brain activities as an object of Neuro-sciences became dependent on a concept of consciousness-which formerly was developed within different philosophical systems like in transcendental analysis, phenomenology of theory of consciousness.

Thus the convergence between *the causality by nature and the causality by freedom* has a high price within the field of humanities:

The understanding of human cognition and behaviour as reduced to a functional perspective endangers our self-understanding as value-oriented free human beings. The capacity of self-determination and self-reflection-essential for our existence in general and for the philosophical enterprise in particular-looses it's function to orientate, integrate, to considerably anticipate a future common social and political order. Thus philosophy itself is endangered, if we do not return to its original substance: to self-reflection, self-determination and even more: to self-critique.

**IV. Complementarity between the traditions**

We finally may come back to our initial question of whether we might assume a complementary or a conflicting relation between Western Philosophies at New-Confucianism.

If we concede, that the reduction of the humanities to a natural sciences and hereby the loss of a unifying ground between spirit and nature, freedom and necessity etc. is a the very late development within European philosophy, we may find some more similarities between Chinese and Western philosophy by reference to the early stages of European thought development.

Neo-Confucianism nowadays strongly argues for an integrative horizon to reflect upon the distinctions, dualities or polarities between the irreducible spheres - which maybe found in nearly all cultural traditions.

As a result of our analysis we may state, that the openness of the Chinese Neo-Confucianism towards an integration of the different cultural, philosophical and spiritual traditions may serve as a helpful attitude to avoid the one-sidedness of the respective approaches and open the floor for a mutual understanding, for self-reflection and self-critique as the basis of a successful interchange of our philosophical traditions and a fruitful communication in the future difficult times to come.

With regard to the Western philosophy we may state:

Neither should our theoretical ambitions be the predominant way to understand human nature or even nature as a whole, nor should relativism and scepticism dominate the field of humanities.

The idea of a unifying horizon named 'our being-in-the world', as Heidegger presupposed,-or even more morally bound-understood as the idea of the highest good, as 'Ren' or 'Heaven', in which our natural striving for happiness is intertwined with the idea of a world under moral rules, is indispensable, if we want to avoid a reductionists approach, by reducing the spiritual and cognitive dimensions to causality by nature.

In all these different ways to understand the unity of human nature, we may find a similar human intention, to first of all enter common ground in order to better understand the irreducible differences between our cultural, religious socially bound traditions.

Martin Heidegger's critique of the objectivising reductionist scientific approach to spiritual and cognitive phenomena strongly rejected the predominance of natural sciences-taking over the lead in nearly all spheres of human existence. In his later works he strongly sympathised with the Buddhist' and Taoist' awareness of the concept of humanity. The Asian traditions, as he understood, still maintained the human capacity to enlighten our self- and world-understanding by a predominant all-integrative horizon of thinking and acting.

*b. The result of my theses may be resumed as follows*:

With regard to the idea of a common ground, Western philosophy has to enter a new phase of scrutiny and self-reflection in order to pave the way for the regular idea of the unconditioned ground within us, besides us and outside of us. Only by reference to the unconditioned ground within us, freedom might be justified. And only by transcending the limits and premises of our specific traditions and world-views we may enter a phase of development, in which 'independent thinking',-'in itself coherent thinking' and the 'thinking from the point of view of the others' may reach a common ground for a fruitful dialogue in the future times to come.

And while theoretical analysis-understood merely as a means and not as an aim in itself,-has been elaborated and become a highly distinguished part of Western philosophy since the ancient Greeks, and become a fruitful part of the world heritage for the further development of mankind, the idea of a universal ground of thinking and being, as maintained within the modern Chinese philosophy, that can be regarded as an inspiring impulse for the Western philosophies to regain the necessary unifying ground for the making of moral and peaceful world.

Hereby self-reflection-as an essential source and method of European Philosophy-has to be renewed-in order to better understand the deficits and failures with regard to most non-European nations and traditions,-which they still fail to integrate in their own horizon of scrutiny.

# How to Educate Man in Order to Become Human? Revisiting the Western Philosophy of Education (Plato-Kant-Dewey) to Get into a Dialogue with Confucianism

**Michael Spieker (Academy for Civic Education, Tutzing and Freiburg University/Germany)**

In this paper, I would like to present some arguments concerning three theses about education (Bildung). The three theses are:

20. Bildung of human beings always means to educate both body and soul, and in no way to develop only intellectual abilities. Bildung is possible because human beings are malleable and it is necessary, because otherwise they would not be different from animals.

21. In the intellectual dimension, Bildung“ is supposed to aim at the development of critical power of judgement. The inviolable dignity of every individual must be its measure and orientation.

22. In order to facilitate a rich and flourishing life, “Bildung” has to be built upon a principle of openness. It should neither affirm the past nor the present.

I would like to explain these theses by passing through the epochs of Western philosophy starting with Plato in Ancient Greece, moving on to Immanuel Kant's modern concept of the individual and education and finally coming to John Dewey's thoughts on democracy and education. Of course, this is only a selection and therefore needs preliminary remarks about our method. We should at least consider this approach to philosophy as a methodic problem, even if we cannot resolve it in the shortness of time. Already Plato and Aristotle saw that philosophy itself has a history. So, one thought follows certain preceding thoughts for certain reasons and they again are followed by other thoughts. Therefore, philosophy is different at different times. In every epoch, philosophy has its specific tasks and gives specific answers. Thus, it does not make sense to isolate single sentences from different epochs and to assemble them, because either the sentences remain incomprehensible or appear ill-founded. Consequently, our path through the history of Western thinking about ? Bildung“ is not directly meant to be a recommendation for our present time. The path is rather meant to give us those concepts as a background in order to enable us to think ourselves about "Bildung" in our present time. As Heidegger put it: by thinking the already thought we prepare ourselves to the thoughts that have to be thought yet. By choosing this approach we have to be especially aware of the epochal differences of each of the concepts. Strictly speaking, Plato, Kant and Dewey talk about three very different issues. Plato's philosophy speaks about paideia and trophe. Kant talks about "Bildung" and Dewey about education. In the following part, we try to see what differences and common elements there are.

23. Plato's paideia"Bildung" and education are important topics in almost all of Plato's writings. He always asks if and how we can learn or teach something. Opposing his philosophy against contemporary sophists, he asks who is responsible for education and how a good order of the soul of every single human being and of the state as a whole can be attained. In the centre of Plato's thoughts about this topic, there is an allegory in his dialogue on the constitution of the state (Politeia), the allegory of the cave.① Plato introduces this allegory as showing the "effect of education and the lack of it on our nature".②

It is remarkable that Plato does not just introduce an allegory of education but simultaneously an allegory of the lack of education. Education and the lack of it seem to belong always together in human nature. This approach already hints at the understanding of education as a process. Thus, education is not a fixed state but rather a movement from the lack of education to education. Consequently, movement is an important motif in the allegory of the cave.

The allegory starts with prisoners in a cave chained in a way that their legs and necks are fixed. They can only see shadows at the wall in front of them. These prisoners neither can contact each other nor can they turn around to see where the shadows come from. They would not even realize that what they see are shadows, but they would perceive them as real and objective.

---

① Plato, Republic 514a-519d.

② Plato, Republic 514a.

But although the prisoners are chained, Plato explains that they are not completely motionless. They compete with each other guessing which shadow is about to appear and predicting which one will follow. The prisoners "assign credit and prestige" to those who guess most quickly.[①] Therefore, already in the cave there is science, its aim being prognosis based on a jury of human beings and their consensus.

Yet, there is an entirely different world for the prisoner who is freed, who turns and walks towards daylight. He recognizes that the figures he had seen at the wall are only shadows of puppets, which some puppeteers display in front of a fire. So, what they once thought to be immediate and out of itself now appears to be caused by something and thus to have its reasons. In the imagery of the allegory these are the puppeteers and the fire. However, the fire is not a primordial beginning either. It has to be lighted first. Also the puppets are just images of a preceding model or pattern. The one who is free and who is ready to depart from the cave will see: He had lived in a world of mere illusion, when he thought that the shadows he perceived did make up reality, that the immediate was already true. Only if we consider something from its first cause, we can judge rightly and behave accordingly. This prime cause is the original goodness of the good.

However, one cannot asscend to the highest level of the 'Ideas' by oneself. In order to be freed and to turn the gaze there is somebody else needed, someone who guides through the darkness of the cave. He is even able to force the prisoner to depart, but not by discipline and violence.[②] Rather, he forces the him by force of better arguments, by taking away reasons or giving them. If a departure takes place, the entire soul must move.[③] Therefore, it is not just an intellectual exercise, but a turn of the entire person. As a consequence, the desired knowledge is not simply a contemplative vision, but activates the philosopher. He will return to the cave as a teacher and legislator in order to establish a good order.

At the heart of this good order, which one can recognize by the reign of justice, is education. Legislation pays most attention to it. The education of children is at the beginning of Plato's Politeia as well as at the beginning of his Nomoi. Here, Plato u-

---

① Plato, Republic 516c.

② Plato, Republic 515c.

③ Plato, Republic 518c.

ses the term 'trophe', which actually means nourishment. Thus, the first step of education consists of nourishing the children's soul. This kind of education already starts in the mother's womb. The pregnant woman makes her child move in certain ways. Later, education continues with gymnastics for the body and 'mousike' for the soul. In Ancient Greece, 'mousike' not only meant vocal and instrumental music but also poetry. Thereby, adolescents should live in a world of images that embody the ideal of good order. For example, nurses should not tell stories in which bad acting leads to happiness or in which the gods were jealous and self-centered. As human beings learn by imitation, educators should be well-educated and well-behaved themselves. The grown-up person must educate himself. He must dominate his passions. Then, a child can learn from him, when it is adequate to follow one's passions and when it is not. Only if a child is well nourished in this way it can get on to 'paideia'. In 'paideia' we find higher mental capabilities like mathematics, rhetorics or dialectics. The basic law of the Platonic state says that everyone should be lead, according to his or her abilities, to his or her specific optimum. The unity of just order maintains the differences of the human beings and lets develop different talents. Therefore, the 'intellectual way' is not a way for everbody. But the one who pursues this way has to educate and control his affects first.

If somebody approaches these sciences, maybe because of his or her special abilities, but without having a mental state in good order, his or her abilities will lead to distress. In the first place, there has to be affective self-control. Otherwise, higher levels of knowledge only lead to hybris. Thus, trophe aims at the responsivity of reason confirming true convictions that have been established since early childhood by reasons. This, however, guarantees that everbody can live in a just manner, and not only the one who pursue the higher way to paideia. Plato even says that the others are more educated than the 'intellectuals' because they often are smooth talkers but do not act accordingly.①

Still, education and 'Bildung' are not limited to the affirmation of tradition. On the contrary, following strictly the good can sometimes mean to break with tradition and to claim something that most people would consider absurd. Plato gives an exam-

---

① Plato, Laws 689c.

ple of how the manner of performing gymnastics has changed.[①] Of course, runners and wrestlers are naked, because it is generally considered convenient. But fifty year before, one could not imagine to do so without being laughed at. The educated person has to show courage, to be laughed at if he has recognized that something is good. He will hang on to it even if he encounters obstacles. We can see clearly the interaction between individual and society. It is the single person that as a legislator provides a good order of the polis. And it is the polis, by its institution, that allows the individual to grow and develop. This interaction is the basis for forming abilities out of natural dispositions and for approaching the idea of human perfection, which immediacy does not permit.

24. Kant's 'Bildung' For Immanuel Kant dignity is essential in his determination of the human being. The freedom of his nature of reason makes everybody a unique individual. His pure ability-to-be gives everybody a right that obligates everybody else to respect his freedom. But looking at Kant's determination of dignity and right there remains the question how this infinite dignity can be mediated into the realm of finiteness. Kant's categorical imperative phrases one element of this mediation by defining the conditions of the possibility of freedom. It becomes evident that freedom has to be universal. Freedom is given to the finite being as a task and not as a possession. That is why freedom can only be understood as an imperative.

But what are the empirical conditions of realisation of this imperative? We will have a look at Kant's anthropology, which contains a philosophy of education in his lectures "On Paedagogy". Kant starts with a programmatic sentence: "The human being is the only creature that has to be educated." (Kant 1963: 9). Education, according to him, is always separated into two fields: care or maintenance and "Bildung" or moral cultivation. The first one serves the mere bringing up of the human being, his natural education. In order to develop his rational abilities there has to be "Bildung" in addition to nursing and bringing up. According to Kant, the principle of education must be the "idea of humanity"[②], which should therefore shape all curricula. This idea is necessarily general. Otherwise it would not be subject in the formation of rationality. This idea, however, is not abstract containing for example the least com-

---

① Plato, Republic 452a-e.

② Kant 1963: 14, translation by the author.

mon denominator of human beings. It is rather the contrary. The idea is utmost concrete, as its content is freedom of the rational human being. The possibility to be something is the essence of the human being. So, when Kant calls this dignified, he recognizes that this ability is real. Being a condition of all individuality, this ability is not separated from individuality. Therefore, it is concrete. As the condition itself is unconditioned Kant calls this condition an idea. ①

Consequently, education achieves its aim if it does not only impart a variety of competences but if it leads to an unconditioned but yet thinkable core, which can be understood as foundation of human action. However, the ability to understand principles proves itself in its execution and not in mere contemplation. Therefore, the idea becomes 'regulatory', it is not constitutive for cognition.

To the human being as a creature of nature an idea is only accessible in a mediated manner. That is why an idea cannot be realized perfectly. Mediation can bring along deviations and mistakes: "Man can become man through education only. He is only what education makes him. It is to be noted that man is educated only by man, and by those men who are educated themselves. Defects, therefore, in the discipline and instruction of some men make them poor educators of their pupils. If a being of a superior nature were to assume the care of our education, we would then see what man could become."②

The idea of humanity lies in its reason. Reason is the faculty of discernment that is able to distinguish itself from itself and thereby lets the individual become general. Then, he does no longer pursue his mere short-term self-interest without having consequences in mind, but he is rather aware of his own limited perspective and because of this awareness he is able to transcend his perspective towards something general for everybody. This rational/reasonable faculty that has to be developed within the individual has a simple name: thinking. As already Platon said, thinking cannot be implemented into the human being from outside. ③ If there is no thinking, there cannot enter any thinking. Only thinking itself is able to start thinking. Thus, education is a strictly subject-oriented process. It is impossible to mould it into an object. As a con-

① Cf. Kant's Critique of Pure Reason, 1. edition p. 365.

② Kant 1904: 107-108.

③ Plato, Republic 518b-c.

sequence, education and educational faculty point to the foundation of human dignity-subjectivity. Kant phrases it in his writing "What does it mean to orient oneself in thinking": "Orienting is in the proper meaning of the word: from a given region of the world to find (in the four we divide the horizon) the other, namely the rise. I now see the sun in the sky, and I know that it is now noon, so I know to find the south, west, north and east. For this purpose (Behuf) but I definitely need to feel a difference in my own subject, namely the right and left hand. I call it a feeling (Gefühl), because these two sides outward show in intuition no noticeable difference."① Even if the human being is given all instruments for orientation, it has always to position itself on a map and only from this point it is able to orient itself.

In his "Anthropology from a Pragmatic Point of View" Kant describes, what belongs to thinking, even though he makes clear that there cannot be perfect thinking among human beings: "Wisdom, as the idea of practical use of reason that conforms perfectly with the law, is no doubt too much to demand of human beings. But also, not even the slightest degree of wisdom can be poured into a man by others; rather he must bring it forth from himself. The precept for reachin git contains three maxims: 1) Think for oneself, 2) Think into the place of th other (in communication with human beings), 3) Always think consistently with oneself. "②

In Kant's concept of autonomous thinking we can hear his claim for self-determinedness of his "Answer to the Question: What is Enlightenment": "Sapere aude! Have courage to use your own understanding!" But where can self-determinedness be fulfilled? Its fulfilment is the public use of reason. So, it aims at politics and needs institutions. Otherwise, a free use of reaon is not possible. To think autonomously, however, does not simply mean to put the label 'individual' on every thought. It means to question all opinions and ideas without prejudices in search of reasons. That is how they become thoughts. In relation to the idea of dignity this means not to take it as a given property or attribute and to be content with it but to recognize that it is based on an ability that wants to be activated. If someone thinks from the perspective of somebody else, he distinguishes himself from himself and thus as an individual becomes universal. The idea also points to the communicability of autonomous thinking.

---

① Kant 2014:

② Kant 2006: 94.

It must rely on general shared reasons and cannot be a sort of 'private thinking'. Kant calls it enlarged thinking. To think unanimously with oneself not only means logical consequence and consistency, but also concordance of speech and action. Where an I thinks that it thinks reasonably but does not want to act according to reason, it is not in unity with itself but divided in itself. Although we cannot go into detail we would like to mention that for Kant the contribution made by nature and history is more important than any humanly possible contribution. This, however, does not change the aim of education neither its importance. Enlightenment and moralisation① are the only way to realize and to protect human dignity by acknowledging that dignity is general and by forming the will to freedom. Without human dignity the idea of right would be void. Hence, according to Kant education is not only condition for human dignity but already its realization.

But what does Kant mean when he talks about leading citizens to morality? Kant' view of his time might help to understand. He writes: "To a high degree we are, through art and science, cultured. We are civilized-perhaps too much for our own good-in all sorts of social grace and decorum. But to consider ourselves as having reached morality-for that, much is lacking. The ideal of morality belongs to culture; its use for some simulacrum of morality in the love of honor and outward decorum constitutes mere civilization. So long as states waste their forces in vain and violent self-expansion, and thereby constantly thwart the slow efforts to improve the minds of their citizens by even withdrawing all support from them, nothing in the way of a moral order is to be expected. For such an end, a long internal working of each political body toward the education of its citizens is required. Everything good that is not based on a morally good disposition, however, is nothing but pretense and glittering misery. "②

Being cultured and civilized, according to Kant, does not prevent from forming an immoral system. And it is possible to lead a decent life although one pursues expansion of one's own power of disposition instead of developping inner freedom. What does hinder the development of a free order of the state? Kant diagnoses the "violent self-expansions" of the state and its underlying urge to territorial extension as the main

① Cf. Kant 1963: 17.

② Kant 1963b: 20. (Idea for a Universal History from a Cosmopolitan Point of View).

reason. Today, there is less of it, but it seems to be substituted by the imperative of economic expansion. Terms like globalisation and factual constraints are part of this new kind of expansion. The economic imperative dictates today what is fit and proper. Also this economic imperative is categorical. It not only commands what has to be done, but also creates a new relation to the self. This self, however, in its dignity is not menaced by exploitation or abuse from outside, but exploits itself on business purposes. The state, says Kant, hinders constantly what would be necessary: "the slow efforts to improve the minds of the citizens".

How can we recognize an educated mode of thinking? It has got a faculty of judgement that works in two directions. Either it knows something universal and subsumes the particular under it or it sees something particular and finds the appropriate universal. The first approach calls Kant 'determining', the second 'reflecting' (KdU A XXVf.). In view of the individual, it means that the principle of existence must be brought to mind. If we know the principle we have to figure out what is appropriate for it and what is not. Being rational would actually mean to agree with one's own conditions of the possibility. Thus, the freedom of the human being must not get into contradiction to itself. It has rather to develop according to its concept. As a consequence, an individual acknowledges itself as well as the others as rational beings. Only reflexion can judge if a certain political practice serves the development of inner freedom or does not. Kant states that it is a long way to get to this reflexion. Then, a "moral" society would be formed in accordance with universal reason. Moral attitude thus depends on reasonableness/rationality and not on any non-communicable opinions or judgments. They would not be "public concern". Kant states responsibility for developing universal reason as a public concern, although the state plays at the same time a critical role.

In this respect, education lays the foundation of a free state. This foundation, however, is neither based on a moral substance of individuals nor on homogeneity. On the one hand, to create homogeneity would mean to negate differences, on the other hand, to touch on the substance of an individual would mean to break into the being of a person. Neither of it is allowed in a free state. A concept of education which would aim at such an idea would at the same time need to create a new human being. Instead, the foundation consists of a moral subjectivity of the individual that is structured by a logic of recognition. The individual is therefore constituted by others, as already his dependence on education shows. That is why he is open to and dependent on demands and expressions of respect by others. To demand and to respect are both elements to form and to educate a subject. We may call a person educated if he has the courage to use his critical power of judgment und to act according to his knowledge. Sometimes, he has to act against common sense and may appear "indecent", although in reality he remains faithful to his dignity.

25. Dewey's democratic educationTo treat John Dewey in one line with Plato and Kant might seem astonishing regarding his judgements concerning the tradition of western philosophy. Dewey thought of the history of western philosophy as being dualistic and static and thereby contrary to life's ever changing dynamic and to the openness of man's life. So he wanted to leave behind what he conceived to be the history of metaphysics. But Dewey's judgements on philosophy's tradition are problematic at best, if not simply wrong. ① However it is not our task to refute his theses here. We also do not want to look further on the contradiction of dismissing tradition and portraying oneself as innovator on the one hand and the fact that just this dismissal and the style of innovation itself is a core-characteristic of modern western philosophy. Instead, we want to consider Dewey's hints at the praxis of education that is up-todate. These ideas of Dewey are compatible with Plato's and Kant's foundation of education and culture.

Openness is the central motif in Dewey's philosophy of education. This means the capability of concrete individuals to realise and to master varying challenges at different times and places in a constructive way. Problem solutions can be called constructive whenever they reconcile the interests of all instead of serving only the interests of a partial group and if they allow to build more intense community among free and equal men. This idea of growth means that the individual's self gets widened through his interactions. The social self is not an atomistic part, but it is the whole of society itself. But in Dewey's view education is a threat to this openness for experience of an

① For example when Dewey talks about Plato: "He never got any conception of the indefinite plurality of activities which may characterize an individual and a social group, and consequently limited his view to a limited number of classes of capacities and of social arrangements." (Dewey 1916: 102) On the contrary Plato's picture of the state tries to capture just the multiplicity of man's talents and the tripartition is introduced not as a representation of the actual situation but as a picture in order to gain insight in the overall structure.

ever changing future: "Each generation is inclined to educate its young so as to get along in the present world instead of with a view to the proper end of education: the promotion of the best possible realization of humanity as humanity. Parents educate their children so that they may get on; princes educate their subjects as instruments of their own purposes. Who, then, shall conduct education so that humanity may improve? "① The main problematic is education and culture affirming the present. This affirmation, set in one time for all times to come, hinders men in adjusting to the ever changing problems of his time.

The aim of education is seen by Dewey in improving humanity. This does not mean some short-term utility of man for unchanging ends but it signifies the free cultivation of ethical life in a community. It is the task of education to facilitate this life. In order to allow for this, education cannot be seen as a mere preparation for a life that is other to the process of education itself or which begins after one is educated. Rather, education has to realize itself, what it is meant to prepare for. The same goes for the educators: only who educates himself, can be an educator for others. Furthermore, education that shall facilitate growth in a diversified world has itself to value diversity and pluralism in the talents and characters of those who are to be educated.

To meet those demands already early education has to be renewed. Children's participation must be realised already there. Only by this provision can we do justice to the fact that it is the individual self as such that educates itself in a social situation. Therefore it needs room for developing itself. Herein Dewey saw the essence of democracy: "A society which makes provision for participation in its good of all its members on equal terms and which secures flexible readjustment of its institutions through interaction of the different forms of associated life is in so far democratic. Such a society must have a type of education which gives individuals a personal interest in social relationships and control, and the habits of mind which secure social changes without introducing disorder."②

Instead of being abstract-individualistic or collectivist democratic education leads to individuals that develop in their own person a deep interest in the well-being of the community. They acknowledge their traditions as their own and they want to take

---

① Dewey 1916: 111.

② Dewey 1916: 115.

part in renewing them so that they meet the demand of their present time. Education and cultivation are the means through which one gets experience in one's tradition. This is the way to avoid disorder and yet to renew a society. "[S]ocial efficiency as an educational purpose should mean cultivation of power to join freely and fully in shared or common activities."①

Teaching is not only about transferring knowledge or building an acquaintance to a certain canon, but it shall strengthen practical knowledge, which is called a form of thinking by Dewey himself. So thinking itself is a practical activity, because there can be no activity without having a purpose and having purposes is a matter of thinking. - Even if it is not a theoretically reflected thinking. This relates to the need to overcome the sharp division of literary-aesthetic cultivation and industrial-vocational education. Only where this is overcome the dominance of elites is broken, a dominance that is made possible through this division. Liberation from domination can only be accomplished by education and cultivation and not by some decree of a government. True democracy that strives for a flourishing of each individual can only be reached by a reorientation of education.

Education itself has to be pluralistic. If it followed only a literary-aesthetic ideal, it became an instrument of domination and not liberation. Not only the individual right to freedom but also prudence demands this pluralism for growth of a community depends on the diversity of its members and on the creativity that rises out of it.

Learning in schools should not be restricted to the classroom and to books or tablets. This would result only in a "bookish" knowledge (Dewey). Learning has to be conjoined with manifold activities and with the world outside the classroom. Thereby learning can be part of moral education, because no one would become a moral agent by being given a sermon or by repeating paragons of moral behaviour. So Dewey outlines the institutional structure of an educational system that puts into practice what has been a key element in Plato and Kant already: namely to develop the wholeness of man and to strengthen his reasonable self-determination by his critical thinking.

26. Outlook From this reconstruction of one western strand of philosophy of education we might start to come to an understanding of uniting and differential aspects in the eastern and western tradition. At least one point might have become clear so

① Dewey 1916: 144.

far: The western tradition is in no way dualistic or one-sided rationalist from the beginning. As the need for education has shown: Even the self is from the beginning on always conceived of as being a social self-although there has always been a parallel strand of thinkers who thought the self was an unencumbered and atomistic being. From a western perspective two questions arise when confronting this to an eastern tradition: How do we approach the self and where would be the place of critique in Confucian philosophy? Or to put it other terms: How can thinking and acting that is inspired by the Confucian tradition help to create a flourishing of humanity?

Bibliography

Dewey, John 1916: Democracy and education: An introduction to the philosophy of education. New York.

Kant, Immanuel 1904: The Educational Theory of Immanuel Kant. Transl. and ed. by Edward Franklin Buchner, Philadelphia and London.

Kant, Immanuel 1963: Ausgewählte Schriften zur Pädagogik und ihrer Begründung. Besorgt von Hans-Hermann Groothoff, Paderborn.

Kant, Immanuel 1963b: Idea for a Universal History from a Cosmopolitan Point of View. In: Immanuel Kant: On History, edited, with an introduction by Lewis White Beck. Translated by Lewis White Beck, Robert E. Anchor, and Emil L. Fackenheim. Indianapolis, pp. 11-26.

Kant, Immanuel 2006: Anthropology from a Pragmatic Point of View. Transl. by Robert B. Louden, Cambridge.

Kant, Immanuel 2014: What Does it Mean to Orient Oneself in Thinking? Translation by Daniel Fidel Ferrer, https://archive.org/details/KantOrientFerrerMarch2014.

# Confucianism as a Fusion of Knowledge and Life

**O. Migunova**

Specificity study of Confucianism is determined by the particular cognitive paradigm of subject-object relations. In contrast to the classical Western epistemological paradigm, where the existence of the subject outside the object is the guarantee of impartiality and objectivity of the research, Confucian cognitive model is based on the premise of the absence of a distance between them. This fundamental difference is determined by the fact that Confucianism has always been a multi-dimensional phenomenon focused on life. Confucianism sought to influence the life and even more-to penetrate every pore of life. Confucian truths are not the same that the abstract-universal scientific truths about life "in general", they are the forms of "personal knowledge" obtained by personal effort. This effort is simultaneously epistemological and moral act, and has for each concrete human being (a researcher) not only impersonal cognitive sense, but also intimate and existential meaning. For Confucianism, only the truth, which is extracted and felt by man personally, is the real truth. The main objective of Confucianism is the formation of character, and "learning to be human". The study of Confucianism, in its own terms, inevitably entails change of one's character, values, behaviors and moral practices. In ideal, a man studying Confucian teaching has become a Confucian proponent practicing Confucian way. In such a case, the start point and destination of reflection is not an abstract subject, not an abstract cognitive ability like Cartesian *cogito*, but human being living here-and-now in the real world, and thinking about the mundane world, in short, a real living person. This attitude, properly speaking, was expressed by neo-Confucian idea of the heart/mind as a unity of cognitive and affective dimensions of human cognition, as contemplative and at the same time compassionate-active began, in conjugating of which a man apprehends himself as a moral being. Then, knowledge translates into the deeds, in moral action, in human-heartedness which conscious that it does good. Thus, cognition is certified by the application. Confucianism is attained through moral self-cultivation, and this is the main purpose of it as a "living" tradition, as a way of life. The unity of knowledge and deeds is the condition of human being's transfiguration, and leads to transformation of human being condition, to unity *neisheng* and *waiwang* (内圣外王)— "sageliness within and kingliness without".

**THE MIRROR OF THE WORLD**

According to European tradition, which goes back to Descartes and Locke, philosophy is often compared to a mirror of the objective world. A similar analogy exists in the history of Chinese thought, classical Chinese philosophy is often called the "mirror of Chinese civilization". His *History of Chinese Philosophy* Fung Yu-lan (冯友兰) opens by words that "the place which philosophy has occupied in Chinese civilization has been comparable to that of religion in other civilizations"①. However, such a statement is a half of the truth. No less true to say that in many ways Chinese civilization is influenced by the philosophical and primarily Confucian thought, and — if not in real, but in its ideal dimension — it is a mirror of Chinese philosophy. In the long history of its existence, Confucianism formed the spiritual origins of Chinese civilization, to use the accurate definition of Li Zehou (李泽厚), its "psychocultural matrix" and dominant traits of "chineseness".

China's history is the history of ideocratic state. The idea never developed here for the sake of the idea itself, its purpose was to affect life in all its manifestations — from public to private ones. Of course, this was associated with a particular understanding of the role of philosophy and its vocation, and more broadly — the role of the conscious factor in the life, which continues to be treated as an inseparability of conscious and unconscious, the spiritual and the material, the subjective and the objective, the natural and the social. Such a comprehension, of course, does not mean any violence of abstract speculative schemes over the real life. Speaking about the role of the conscious factor in the Chinese world-picture, I mean the role of the idea of correspondence "everything with everything", including accordance of conscious human actions to natural sociocosmic order of the universe, or — to say more precisely — to their comprehension of this order generated by metaphysical Confucian discourse.

---

① *Fung Yu-lan*. A Shot History of Chinese Philosophy // Selected Philosophical Writings of Fung Yu-lan.-Beijing: Foreign Languages Press, 2008, p. 193.

But the main purpose of wisdom, as it was formulated by Chinese sages and scholars of different times was not so much to obtain positive knowledge about the outer world and human being for the sake of "simple to know" but in the moral elevation of man through self-improvement with help from knowledge extracted by him. Anthropocosmic harmony, the nature of which is universal onto-ethical one, is not conceived achievable outside of Confucian self-improvement practices in the ways of the conscious building of life in the movable accordance with the rhythms of sociocosmic transformations.

One of the most profound minds of the Chinese thought of the twentieth century, Liang Shuming (梁漱溟, 1898 — 1988) emphasized that philosophy in its essence (meaning of it primarily Confucianism as historically dominant direction of Chinese thought) is not so much an abstract theoretical system as a special way of the world-comprehending and values-comprehending that form the semantic basis of a certain lifestyle. In the words of Tu Weiming(杜维明), Confucianism is a way of conceptualizing of special life form, a specific organization of mental life and habits of the heart[①]. In the late twentieth century they are already talking about specific *Confucian way of life* that characterizes the East Asia region, and about specific Asian form of modernity — modernity, characterized by specific forms of sociality manufactured by centuries-old influence on man and his life Confucian values and Confucian worldview. Noteworthy, that in our days under conditions of planetary challenge, which is embodied by an anthropological crisis in the modern West, the value of Confucianism as a life form ceases to be narrowly regional, and begins to discover in itself the traits of planetary existential alternative.

However, that mirror about which I have told above, has become not quite clear, philosophy looks confused in front of the challenges of the modern transformational sociocultural processes, having lost its inherent role of the civilizational spiritual basis, which was adequate to its time. Chinese philosophical thought, complain its representatives, turned into the area of abstract specialized knowledge, detached from life. Philosophy and life has ceased to meet each other, they became look like something existing at different temporal and semantic dimensions. The Patriarch of the

① *Tu Weiming*. The Global Significance of Concrete Humanity. Essays on the Confucian Discourse in Cultural China. - New Delhi: Centre for Studies in Civilizations, 2010, p. 108.

new Confucianism Liang Shuming bitterly wrote: "our contemporaries are not enough experienced feelings of Confucianism", between theoretical reflection about life and life itself arose a gap. And this gap between philosophical reflection and the practice is becoming more significant owing to the penetration in China major paradigmatic principles and knowledge arsenals of Western discourse. Emphasizing Confucianism as one of the main directions of modern Chinese thought, many scholars are concerned about the loss of its adherence to the fundamental statement "unity of knowledge and action". Of course, the revival of Confucianism in China is obvious, but there is a danger that it may remain only an object of special studies for narrow circle of specialists and adherents, a certain system of historical knowledge①.

Of course, such a perspective distorts the original spirit of Confucianism and its mission. One of the leading representatives of contemporary Confucianism Cheng Chung-ying(成中英) ascertains its disintegration on "doctrine" (*xue* 学) and "school" (*jia* 家), identifying in it areas that are focused on either "value" or "knowledge"②. Other modern Confucian Yu Yingshi (余英时)complains that Confucianism has transformed now into a "discourse", and in no way connected with the life practices of ordinary people③. Thus, the rebuke of modern Confucianism in the "academism" is nearly common. Meanwhile, Confucianism has always claimed to be something more significant — to be "Life-teaching", i.e. the guide to life, the organic alloy of worldview and life practices. Such a vision of own destiny was built on the premise of substantial unity of spirit and bodily forms, expressed in life practice, on the premise that spirit and matter, philosophy and life are modalities of single indivisible reality, "parts" of which are opposed to each other only in reflection.

It is known that an idea of "accordance" or "correspondence" is fundamental one in the Chinese worldview. A certain pragmatism of Chinese mentality is connected with that idea of accordance due to which the theoretical discourse become necessary and important for the Chinese people, in the words of Russian researcher L. S. Va-

---

① *Го Циюн*(郭齐勇). Исследования современного конфуцианства в КНР // Проблемы Дальнего Востока, 2008, № 1, с. 124-125.

② *Cheng Chung-ying*. An Onto-hermeneutic Interpretation of Twentieth-Century Chinese Philosophy: Identity and Vision // *Cheng Chung-ying and Nicholas Bunnin* (eds.). Contemporary Chinese Philosophy. - Oxford: Blackwell Publishers, 2002, p. 13.

③ 余英时。现代儒学论。上海:上海人民出版社,1998,第 4-6 页。

siliev, only "if it is required by life itself"[1]. Indeed, traditionally utilitarian attitude to the theory is usual for China, but at the same time — it is usual no less to recognize its paramount importance for life itself as its guide began. The principle according to which the life is always right, lays the blame for the any discrepancies embodied in the dissonances and disharmonies of life itself, on philosophy. The historical fate of Confucianism in the last century is an eloquent example (and effect) of such psychocultural installation. But on the other hand, the more hopes and the more responsibility are entrusted with the philosophy in moments of overcoming historical bifurcations. This explains us the unprecedented role of ideas in society as regulator of worldly human actions for the sake of anthroposociocosmic equilibrium, that is of harmony.

**TEACHING AS LEARNING TO BE HUMAN**

To regain once lost influence on the life, one must immerse yourself in this life. I think this implies a particular understanding of modern Confucianism as "a new way of conceptualizing the form of life, the habits of the heart under... the influence of Confucian education for centuries"[2]. The role which Confucianism gives to education in the broader sense of the word, reveals to us its place in the spiritual life of mankind.

The matter is that Confucian master teaches not "ideas", not "thoughts", not concepts and categories, but *existentials*. Moreover, in reality, he does not "teaches" but transmits it. And at least, this transmission requires a "sympathetic comprehension" or some comprehension as compassion (i. e. the situation when the result of comprehension should be compassion, the result of mental action should be a moral state). It is important to understand. Humaneness-*ren* is not an abstract category, this is conceptualization of onto-ethical principles/norms of human life, so the teacher does not transmits to the disciple knowledge as a sum of useless certainties, but "forms" for him the world-relatedness model and life conduct model. As stated in *Lüshi Chunqiu* (吕氏春秋), "... it is called learning without instruction, teaching without words"[3], this is what Mencius called "nurturing the spirit", this is what mod-

---

① *Vasiliev L. S.* The Problems of the Genesis of the Chinese Thought. (Priblemi genezisa kitaiskoi misli). - Moskwa, 1989, c. 247.

② *Tu Weiming*. The Global Significance of Concrete Humanity. Essays on the Confucian Discourse in Cultural China, p. 108.

③ *Lüshi Chunqiu*(吕氏春秋), XVII, 2.

*ern Confucianism calls "building character"*[①].

Thus, Confucianism is not only teaching, but also the education system. Disciple isn't taught but is nurtured, and he/she is nurtured by the learning process. Teaching, learning, educating, — are the categories related as well to knowledge, as to education (education as transmission). Noteworthy that in Chinese language these practices are marked in one character-*jiao yu* (教育), meaning simultaneously knowledge, education, and nurture. Confucian education system assumes that "knowledge" is learned as not an amount of abstract information, but as a definite life program, and psychocultural matrix of interaction with the world, as a kind of responding matrix, resounding ability, behavior standards, in a word, as the spirit of Confucianism, or Confucian *Dao*. And since each event is unique, so each individual application of this matrix by single person in every single situation is a validation exercises for teaching's vitality, a mode of teaching spirit's "adaptation" to the life and the mode of its life-assertiveness. Speaking paradoxically, in their ultimate forms the spirit is life, and hence, Confucian spirit is identical with the Confucian way of life. That is why the Confucian spirit can be revived, embodying it in the life. This comprehending of the spirit and life as inseparability (non-duality) reflects one of the fundamental units of the new Confucianism to overcome the dichotomous thinking, which is so typical to Western discourse. Teaching nourishes life, and life nourishes the doctrine. Only when the application was held, a transmission (*daotong*) was held too. The identity of the teaching's transmission is not proved in the classroom, but in the life, although it should be noted that Confucianism sees the class activity as a form of life, and education as the "cultivation of the Way" (*Zhongyong*,中庸).

At the same time, the idea that education is possible only as self-discipline and moral self-improving, and not as the result of external influence, is strongly developed in Confucianism. One ancient parable comes to my mind. An old peasant who came back home late at night from the field complained to the householders that he is so tired because he was "helping the shoots to grow" the whole day long. In this story which contains clearly an ironic background, a deep insight is expressed about the impossibility or naivety of assumption that inner growth may be something other than self-growth. That is why Confucianism is "learning to be", which means "learning to

---

① *Tu Weiming*. Op. cit., p. 100.

be human" in the process of self-efforts. In this context "to be" means the process of becoming. It is crucial to realize that from the Confucian point of view to be human does not mean to be born a humaniform being but *to become* a human being, that is, to nurture and cultivate in the self a humaneness-*ren*, which is not, according to Confucian teaching, some separate quality, or even the quality of the qualities ("mega-quality"), but the essence, the nature of human being, his or her "whatness" and "suchness". Namely at this point the inseparability of teaching and life (teaching/learning and living/being) is found out very distinctively: someone is not a passive object of educating from "outside"; when he or she starts to learn on their own to be human, then life and teaching merge.

**TEACHING AS A WAY**

But the ways to be human in this life are diversified and plural. For a disciple who has entered on the Confucian way first step in learning to be human is namely *learning*; for the master the Confucian way to be human is *teaching*. In his case to teach-is no less the way of "learning". Teaching turns to him a fundamental spiritual experience, for appeals not only to a partial cognitive abilities of disciple, but to the integrity of his person. This communication of teacher with disciple turns into deep personal transformation and in the same time is the situation of learning because someone "repeating old, knows new"[①]. The conjugation of these two modalities gives in total *daotong*. The doctrine is embodied and lives not so much in the compendiums and treatises, as in living bearers, who are personified by the Confucians; also doctrine is individualized in human actions (behavior) and destinies. Human being is "two" (二), and it means that his "whatness" —- *ren* — is human-relatedness and that due to it *daotong* can be realized. The substance of this relatedness is a moral one which is all-penetrating. Confucian teaching exists in this circulation of moral relationships being thus a form of human life inseparable from the man.

Of course, in ideal, Confucians hope that a new generation of moral transfigured humanity must arises through a series of sequential transmissions of the teaching from generation to generation. It should represent a new phase of the ethico-cosmic evolution of mankind, the birth of *homo ethicus*. Confucian ethics, the quintessence of

---

① *Lun yu* (论语), 2: 11.

which is the humaneness-*ren*, should give rise to a new global type of sociality, which will be based on moral interpersonal relationships. In fact, it should be a triumph of moral metaphysics.

Ultimately, Confucianism is able to act in all plenty of its modalities — as a doctrine, as a teaching, as a learning (apprenticeship), as matrix/standard of moral behavior (a doctrine, a teaching, learning, living, being); and as self-improvement, self-cultivation, etc. The ability of Confucianism as a special form of life be embodied in many different modalities perfectly conveys its inclusiveness, dynamism, and high energies of the potential of becoming contained in it. But more important to note that this set is not the sum of forms which can exist independently from each other. It is the unity, the existence of which provides the movement of human beings along the path of self-cultivation, and of nurture of humaneness-*ren* through the daily practice of interpersonal interaction.

Self-improvement requires "the other" because it is only possible in interaction, and both the teacher and the disciple are such an "other" to each other in equal measure. Moral relations are primary in the process of education, and more broadly — in the process of cognition. As a result, Confucianism becomes emotionally "experiencing knowledge" (Tu Weiming), and existential living knowledge. Existential living and emotionally experiencing knowledge is wisdom, but it is impossible to teach to be a sage, the sage can only to become. To be a sage is not a state, it is a process, a special form of life. The sage is capable to practice a deep experiences of intimate belonging and connectedness with the people, world, universe, in its entirety and inexhaustibility. Thus, Confucian wisdom is not book knowledge, but living life of the living interaction people with people, disciples and teachers, father and son, husband and wife, manager and managed, the citizen and the state, and all them together with the society, the nature and the cosmos.

I believe that in the process of the revival of Confucianism, as an exclusively Chinese form of world-relatedness, the developing of ideas, concepts and existentials must be accompanied by elaboration of corresponding, i.e. Confucian form of personal identity, which should be adequate to the Chinese modernity. I see this as a way of formation of contemporary new Confucianism as a fusion of knowledge and deeds, philosophy and life.

# Confucianism and Contemporary Culture and Dialogue Among Civilizations

**Poonam Surie (Indian Council of World Affairs)**

The twenty first century has been marked with economic discontinuities and crises and shifts in the play of the balance of power, confrontations of religious groups and cross-border terrorism. A chronic insecurity and sense of gloom engulfs us. Natural disasters add to the insecurity as witnessed by the Tsunami, earthquakes and floods in many parts of the world. Man- made disasters threaten us just as much as natural ones. The distortion of nature's path has lead to tragedy on more than a few occasions. In such a time, we need to have a collective means of grappling with the very real problems of today. The problems of materialism versus human values.

If we succeed in looking toward a flourishing of humanity, and a hope for future generations, we will have made a start. No one country can isolate itself on this in today's world of globalization and interconnectedness. A dialogue has become impending and urgent.

How do different cultures with different histories, different traditions and different religious orientations find convergent points of interest and the platform for a common conversation? How do they even understand the language of trust and how do we penetrate the hard exterior of nationalist sentiment is the question. These are the questions which urgently need addressing. No country should force its ideology on others; no country should interfere in the internal affairs of a sovereign state. In such a situation, how do we find common threads, common needs and common platforms for understanding, cooperation and collaboration… That is the question.

Realpolitik shapes politics across the world, and it is not only domestic challenges but also global factors which shape these decisions. In this scenario, it is important that we temper our decisions with, for example Confucian values and benevolence so that new conditions can be created which rejuvenate ties and they develop a new vitality. Relations between countries are multidimensional and need to take into account much more than mere territorial issues, economic issues and trade etc. A relationship developed in this humane way would be enduring and long lasting. There could be in this situation, enhanced diplomatic activity and defence dialogues in addition to political discussions and agreements. The Confucian way is the harmonious way where humans care and consider their neighbours to be as dear as members of their own family. Such an approach would ensure that problems are tackled in a positive atmosphere. From an inward looking ideology, one would take an outward looking stance with the world.

In this world of interdependence, global institutions have to be set up which deal with multidimensional issues and involve many countries. The basis of all agreements is a respect for sovereignty but there are many issues which need to be resolved keeping this sovereignty in mind.

No country wants to interfere in another country's affairs. However, non interference needs to be redefined in this modern, globalized world. Labour laws, monetary and other institutions which act as checks for unfair competitive practices, for example, need to be developed today. Migrants and labour which moves from country to country needs specific laws which impinge on all countries. Not only do we need each others' markets but a host of other issues like resources, climate change, cyber security, energy cooperation and maritime issues all are common problems. Negotiations between countries need the humane touch and the need for understanding each other's cultures. Today, Asia needs long term peace and prosperity for building a new and forward looking future. One which can sustain this peace and interdependence for long term stability.

In the recent years we have seen a shift in the balance of power from the West to the East. China and India have become important countries for the world and for each other. It is important for people of both the countries to understand each other in order to have a common ground and a common platform on which to discuss the very real problems facing them today. Competition notwithstanding, not only China and India but many other countries have to develop ways of collaboration and cooperation. Together the two most populous countries of the world can take on the world and become a force to be reckoned with. All this will not happen if we do not have respect for each other, if we do not have self confidence. Self cultivation and independence in thought is important, at the same time engaging with each other in a benevolent way.

Patience and a great deal of understanding are necessary.

In fact, this is the new era of President Xi Jinping in China and Prime Minister Narendra Modi in India. President Xi said in a public address that peace is of the essence, it is like air and sunshine. It is with a great deal of anticipation that we hope that the newly elected Indian Prime Minister Modi has ushered in an era of peace and prosperity.

The two countries China and India have a great deal to learn from each other. Historical ties of Buddhism have created a backdrop on the basis of which the present relations have been cemented and ties strengthened and will hopefully continue to do so. The common aims of economic development, eradicating poverty, social welfare, reduction in inequality all need to be addressed not only by these two countries but also much of the developing world. In such a scenario, we would do well to cooperate and collaborate.

There is a bit of India in every Chinese home because of the legacy of Buddhism which travelled across the Silk Route through traders across difficult terrain and was brought back from India by the great travelers who visited her centuries ago. These were travelers such as Faxian and Xuanzang whose records are valuable sources of Indian history of that period. Figures like Kumarajihva and Bodhidharma contributed to the marriage of cultures. In such a situation, the two countries have much in common and can develop even greater ties by adopting a stance which is sympathetic and engaging. The Chinese classic 'Journey to the West' is based on the story of Xuanzang's travels to India. It is a classic which every Chinese child has read in school.

The first thing to be realized is that a dialogue need not be combative and conflictual in nature but can start from a premise that consensus and agreement will be the order of the day. A dialogue of civilizations may work slowly unlike quickfix remedies such as military or political intervention but its results will be long term and hopefully, permanent.

The two predominant tenets which work for people in the current context in countries across the globe are the influence of Westernization and the sense of rootedness to the cultures that they belong to. These can sometimes pull us in different directions but if we think deeply we realize that who we are is in large measure due to what we become after years, maybe centuries of history, the gradual passing down of traditions, customs, values and thoughts across the generations to the present generation. We as citizens of different countries become globalized, keeping our inherent and individual characters intact. Hence, we don the mantle of the world while being who we are, still intact inside. Therefore a dialogue will of necessity underscore our respective beliefs and values. Only after we have understood ourselves will we understand the need for understanding others.

In the words of Prof Tu Weiming: 'We are now confronted with two seemingly contradictory forces, both of which define the human condition for the twentieth century. The first is globalization. Westernization evolved into modernization, and all civilizations, large and small, old and new, have been affected by this process. The assumption was made that cultural and even religious differences would lose their significance because the globalizing process would homogenize everything. This assumption is now being challenged by the other major trend of thought of the twentieth century: The search for roots. This trend, in contrast to the first, could be called "localization," or a quest for a sense of primordial ties and rootedness'. ①

Indeed the rootedness in our local cultures should colour our view of the world and make it our own.

Based on many years of civilizational encounters, one can say that in the world of today, it has become imperative to devise ways of extending our reach to people across the globe. Natural resources (as has been observed and studied by scientists, sociologists and various watchdog groups across the world, as well as governments) are scarce and rapidly being depleted with the vast increase in population, with fast paced industrial progress and by the use of these resources as we set out to define our wants in terms of increased needs bordering sometimes on luxury. In this world of limited resources, we are not faced with an option of war and conflict. It is to our advantage that we devise solutions that attempt to maximize benefits to humanity, choose optimal solutions as far as pricing of goods and commodities is concerned and use infra-

---

① [The Dialogue of Civilizations: A Conversation with Tu Weiming,. " *Http://www. ikedacenter. org/thinkers-themes/thinkers/tu-interview* ]. N. p. , n. d. Web. 6 June 2014. <http%3A%2F%2Fwww. ikedacenter. org%2Fthinkers-themes%2Fthinkers%2Ftu-interview%20%5D.>.

structure in a way that we use the comparative advantage of countries in an effective way. Cross border terrorism, maritime security, energy security all are important issues today.

If we try to find shared principles and objectives and even common threats we can look for common and shared solutions. We can use our collective intelligence to utilize resources in the best possible way for the world, marginalize and fight the disease of extremism and terrorism, try to minimize the use of force and violence and the destruction of life and property. Then we will be on the right track.

Dialogue among civilizations, looked at from a perspective of the common good of humankind is a way of doing away with the power-centric approach and adopting one based on compassion and benevolence for all. It goes without saying that nationalist sentiments will be strong and uppermost in the minds of leaders and governments. However, keeping sovereignty and nationalist sentiments intact and still having a dialogue is the challenge.

In this dialogue of civilizations could be involved artists, writers, scholars, educators, thinkers who are representatives of their respective cultures and civilizations. Such a dialogue would be conducive to mutual understanding, tolerance, peaceful coexistence and international cooperation and security. It would also help in promoting the peaceful resolution of conflicts and disputes and reconciling tensions between countries, between different cultures and religions. Alongside, and coterminous with this could be the advancement of scholarly debate and academic research which would lead to a deeper understanding of people from different cultures and civilizations and thus to peace in the world.

A dialogue of civilizations would of necessity be concerned with pluri-culturalism and the varied cultural differences between civilizations. It would seek to find ways of understanding different cultures so that they can be looked at from the perspective of people from different countries. In understanding our culture we can experience the urge to study other cultures and can find a way to communicate with others. This dialogue between cultures should be one of a constant and evolving nature. History plays a part as well since culture is a continuous and seamless entity shaped by past events and beliefs. Religion, traditions, social practices and rituals, common beliefs which lend credence to the common feeling of nationalism and patriotism, all play a part in shaping the language which can be used in this dialogue.

To grapple with the problems of modern society, one must find ways of coming up with solutions which not only look at the new and modern social and political milieu in avante garde ways but also combine them with traditional values and philosophies. And moreover, the ancient philosophies of different civilizations and cultures could be borrowed from each other and cross cultural solutions devised which would provide answers to the problems of the countries of the world.

This brings us to the ancient philosophies across civilizations of the world. One of the ancient Chinese philosophies which is still as relevant today as it was since ancient times in China is Confucian philosophy. If we go deep into this, we can come up with ways in which Confucian philosophy can be used to temper the conversation between people from different cultures. Confucian philosophy talks about benevolence, filial piety, love, compassion, the importance of aptitude based education, personal improvement and growth, ethics and environment issues. Each of these concepts taken in their entirety and coloured with the different shades of the hues of civilizations across the world can give us valuable insights into the communication process that is an integral part of a dialogue. Cut and dry relationships, boxed reasoning which takes into account only material paradigms, the often forgotten compassion behind human centered concepts, all these need to be studied carefully and then complemented with the humane aspects of traditional philosophies and developed into tools for dialogues.

In the world of today, consensus building, mediation and persuasion are more likely to succeed than mere power tactics and bullying by force. Confucian thought propounds that people use mediation and arbitration by the elderly or seniors of society rather than take recourse to law and court. It may show us how to avoid extreme actions like war and settle disputes in a dignified way rather than create discord. The results could be a win win situation for all people and all countries concerned so that there is harmonious coexistence.

Confucius believed in a society governed by the principles of '*li*' (right behavior) and not '*fa*' (law). According to Daoism, the key to life was the way to find compromise by choosing the path between opposing forces and this finds a resonance in Confucian philosophy because it believes in harmony and finding the golden mean.

The Indian philosopher Chanakya said in his famous treatise '*The Arthashastra*' that the defining force behind the foreign policy of a country is self interest. As we study the civilizational dialogues we need to remember that nationalism is by implication the supporting basis of all conversation between countries. In view of this we need to find common threads, common values and interests which would be a starting point for these countries to develop deeper and more meaningful ties, at the same time keeping their nationalist sentiments intact.

Let us take each of the Confucian concepts separately. Benevolence means that we look at our fellow human beings with compassion and take decisions based on the common good of the people of a family, the community, the society and the country. Taken in a wider perspective it means that we consider those policies that are beneficial to the people of not only one's own country but of the wider world community. One should look beyond one's own country and one's own interests. Compassion is also important when dealing with other countries and forms a good and solid basis for long term friendship and good relations. As far as filial piety is concerned, the relationships between father and son, elder brother and younger brother, parent and child can be translated into similar relationships in society. These can be seen to be relevant if one looks at ruler and subjects, elder colleague and younger colleague, husband and wife, the elders in a community and the younger members of the community and so on.

The most important element of Confucianism, though, is education and learning. Confucius advocated intellectual honesty, modesty and open mindedness, advocating education across all sections of society. The commitment to merit meant able and educated people at the helm of the government and in bureaucracy. Education meant equal opportunity across classes, social mobility and offering jobs based on intelligence, learning and ability. [①]

Skill development is a part of educating young people today and they could be taught vocational skills such that they are able to flourish as productive members of the community.

The important ideas behind Confucius' philosophy are thus '*Ren*' (*Jen*), '*Li*', '*Xiao*' (*Hsiao*) and '*Zhongyong*' (Wade Giles: *Chung Yung*). '*Ren*' (*Jen*) as we know is love, '*Li*' the rules of proper conduct, '*Xiao*'(*Hsiao Chung*) or filial piety, whereas '*Zhongyong*' (*Chung Yung*) is the doctrine of the mean or harmony or the u-

---

① Shaohua Hu, 'Confucianism and Contemporary Chinese Politics'. Wagner College, *Politics and Policy*, Volume 35, No 1 (2007): pp 136-153. Pub. Blackwell Publishing Inc

niversal moral order. In other words being thrifty, having a conscience and being poised in one's behavior constitute, among other things, good '*Li*'. The individual is free to decide the '*li*' that would be best under the circumstances. As far as '*Xiao*' (*Hsiao*) is concerned, 'those who love their parents dare not show hatred to others. Those who respect their parents dare not show rudeness to others.'①

Confucian thought gives practical everyday solutions to the problems facing society as against the Western notion of rationality and the Indian notion of spirituality. However, in Indian philosophy as well, the epics such as the Bhagvad Gita and the Mahabharata actually deal with practical problems in the life of people and the solutions in their finite lifetimes. In Vedic philosophy we have the Sublime Age when people do everything for the common good and peace and prosperity reigns in the land. This is called the *Satyug* as against *Kalyug*, or the Machine Age when everyone looks at his or her own advantage and becomes self centered and selfish and where materialism takes over all of humanity. In a way, great thinkers have since ancient times been trying to find an ideal state where everyone is benevolent and morally sound so that humanity flourishes.

In Daoism, Chinese Buddhism and Confucianism as well, the great Dao is a state which we must strive for in order to achieve the ultimate peace on earth. This is when people consider all good to be for the common good and the fight against all evil as the common aim so that everyone strives to do things that are beneficial to everyone.

"When the Great Dao prevails, the world belongs to all. The people elect men of talents, virtue and ability (for rulers). They advocate sincerity and cultivate friendship. Thus men do not regard as their parents only their own parents, nor treat as their children their own children. A competent provision is made for the aged until their death, and employment of the able bodied, and a means of education for the young. The widowers, widows, orphans, childless men, and those who are disabled by disease are all efficiently maintained. Each man has his mate and each woman her home. Goods, though not to be wasted, are not necessarily kept privately. Disliking idleness, people work, but not alone with a view of their own advantage. In this way selfish schemes are repressed and find no way to arise. Robbers, thieves and rebels do not exist. Hence the outer door remains open and not shut. This is the stage of Great

---

① Tien Tzu op. cit. ibid 276

Harmony"①.

Thus ancient philosophies show us how in the world of today with its inherent materialism we can learn from these traditional value systems.

Confucian thought deals with the way humans should cope with different situations. For example, if one is faced with a situation where war is inevitable, then you have to go to war, however much you believe in peace and benevolence. In the great Indian epic *Mahabharata* God Krishna said to Arjuna on the battlefield that if you have to take a tough decision and even if the people you are dealing with are your own brothers and close family members then you have to take the side of truth and fight for it.

Taking the Confucian triad as our basepoint, we can think of different cultures as Confucian families and members of society and taking the whole world as our community, try to use this philosophy and take the side of truth and morality. We would aid those countries that we feel are morally right and support them. Moreover, we would help to develop relationships between the members of the community where they can help each other and their less fortunate brethren in a way that society reaches the Utopia that Confucius talks about. At the same time, each member of the community and the society can be grounded and rooted to their cultures in a moral way so as to have a strong character and stand up for their own moral values.

Civilizational pluralism means that we realize that there are different civilizations that have varied ways of thinking, different value systems, and patterns of behaviour and that we accept the existence of differences between them. Cultural differences are based on historical truths, on traditions and customs and socio-economic factors. Such differences also exist, for example within the ethnic communities as in China, religious groups in India, people belonging to tribes such as in East Africa. The civilizational rituals such as the coming of age dances and customs of certain tribes in Africa and India, are an example of this. There are many ways in which people come face to face with these differences. The important point is that we should celebrate the differences and understand that all cultures are different. 'LI' or rituals are important in Confucianism. Rituals, as we know in real life take on a meaning which is very im-

---

① Jingpan, Chen. "Chapter 4,'The Aim of the Teaching of Confucius, Section A, 'According to the Analects',." Confucius as a Teacher. Beijing: Foreign Languages, 1994. 194. Print.]

portant.

It is important for countries to have people to people exchanges, conferences and seminars, academic exchanges, collaboration and partnerships in technical and scientific fields, cultural exchanges in the field of art, music, dance, literature, poetry etc. It is through the explored and unexplored areas of the ethos of society; the art, the world of fiction, the esoteric world of music and the explored and unexplored pages of deep thought that we realize the differences between cultures and civilizations. Thus understanding one's own culture is important in order to understand the differences between different cultures. Civilizational pluralism does not mean homogeneity but a wondrous variety and diversity of thought and an awareness that the fabric of the variety of local, horizontally bound cultures together make the warp and weft of the tapestry of a civilization.

As we become global citizens and look at life through the prism of Westernization, we must realize that it is important to understand that globalization should not mean merely adopting western values and customs. Our historical backgrounds, our family structures, our values are uniquely shaped by where we come from and how we became the persons that we are. For example, a software engineer who now lives in the USA but originally came from India makes an effort to understand the working conditions of the country where he or she now lives in. Similarly, people who travel and work across the world, are aware of the cultural differences of their working and living environment and strive to adapt and adjust to them. This also holds true as far as tourism is concerned. An awareness of local customs is important to understand the country. For example, in China, the family is the unit of social structure and very often, business is carried out by a network of family and friends, and *guanxi* is an important part of the structure. Similarly, *mianzi* or face saving is a typical Confucian Chinese characteristic and plays an important part in society.

Indeed, an inter-civilizational dialogue has to be based on mutual understanding. The term '*entrare*'

(enter into another world) was used by an Italian philosopher Giambattista Vico to refer to the effort required in encounters between cultures In other words, civilizations have to engage with each other and develop a deep understanding of each others' ethos. If we look at the world and at different cultures from an open and objective viewpoint, we realize that the worldviews of different civilizations are not antagonistic but complement each other. [①]

Let us first examine the definition of civilization. If we look at the definition of a city, as defined by the ancient Greek philosopher Plato the nature, meaning and purpose of a city is that it is a place where people with civic virtues and a moral code live. [②]

Hence a city is not merely a place where one gets shelter, food and material objects. A city is a place where people engage and help each other, where we find our spaces overlapping with spaces of other people and where communities live together, communicating and living a life of close communion. People learn to be civil and hence developed the term civilization. A civilization is thus infinitely greater than the sum total of its communities, its states, its districts, its religious communities and their cultures. It embodies a history, a philosophy, a social evolution, a love of literature, art, the philosophy of living. Civilizations are living, feeling and growing entities. They are not merely cut and dry communities of people but involve people who are caring, who make an effort to engage with other members of the community and grow spiritually. The Indian civilization has a long history of upheavals, of attacks and counter attacks and yet all in all, it embodies an ethos, a philosophy of giving, of sharing, of selflessness and compassion. It means the great and learned people who were born in this land instilled in us the love of learning and our endless spiritual enfoldment.

Other great civilizations are much the same. The Chinese considered the components of the cosmos to be in harmony with each other and Confucius is as much a part of the Chinese civilization as the mountains and rivers that flow in her bosom. Confucian thought believes that human beings care for each other, have compassion and are deeply enmeshed in relationships with other members of the community and if this is so, then the whole community will flourish. On the other hand, Confucian thought also made it possible to view everyday problems with a practical approach.

Gandhi describes a civilization as "that mode of conduct which points out to hu-

---

① Victor Segesvary_Dialogue. pdf] [Dialogue of Civilizations- An Introduction to Civilizational Analysis- Victor Segesvary, Mikes International, The Hague, Holland, 2004. Page 14. http://www. federato. org/mikes_bibl. html. ISSN 1570-0070. ISBN 90-8501-008-X]

② Victor Segesvary_Dialogue. pdf] [Dialogue of Civilizations- An Introduction to Civilizational Analysis-Victor Segesvary, Mikes International, The Hague, Holland, 2004. Page 2. http://www. federato. org/mikes_bibl. html. ISSN 1570-0070. ISBN 90-8501-008-X]

mans the path of duty. Performance of duty and observance of morality (or ethics) are convertible terms. To observe morality is to attain mastery over our mind and our passions. In so doing, we come to know ourselves." ①

In fact, I believe that civilizational paradigms are also reflective of the deeper spiritual and divine

powers of the earth and therefore impinge on environmental issues as well. Hence all of us who belong to civilizations have the duty of keeping intact her precious resources not only for the present but for future generations as well. This involves looking at humanity from a humane and compassionate viewpoint and that is where Confucian philosophy becomes meaningful in a dialogue of civilizations.

The next question that arises is what is a dialogue. A dialogue is a conversation between people in which each one is certain about what he or she wants to say and is willing to hear the other one out patiently and is at the same time open to learning from others. A dialogue is not just a one way street but actually a meeting of minds, with one person trying to understand the other person. Thus a dialogue would be "the globalization of learning, the cultivation of a global civility animated by a sense of justice and ethical standards." And, also "What undergirds and sustains this aim is the vision of a shared cosmopolitan civility, a vision oriented toward "truth" and the "good life" respecting the diversity of life-forms. ②

The Western way of thinking has been perceived, rightly or wrongly, as being self centered and individualistic. The Asian value systems traditionally have a much more humancentered approach. For example, Confucian thought is based on family, community and society, a shared civility and ethical values. Confucian philosophy started with '*ren*' or goodness. It can be interpreted to be a way of life; as an attitude to other people. Being sympathetic, compassionate and understanding towards other human beings was the essence of Confucius' philosophy.

---

① Victor Segesvary_Dialogue. pdf] [Dialogue of Civilizations- An Introduction to Civilizational Analysis- Victor Segesvary, Mikes International, The Hague, Holland, 2004. Page3. http://www.federato. org/mikes_bibl. html. ISSN 1570-0070. ISBN 90-8501-008-X]

② DIALOGUE AMONG CIVILIZATIONS: ITS MEANING AND PURPOSE (Fred Dallmayr, University of NotreDame) [http://balvantparekhcentre. org. in/index. htm][ http://balvantparekhcentre. org. in/1st% 20Balvant% 20Parekh% 20Distinguished% 20Lecture% 20by% 20fred% 20dallmayr% 20%20on%2021%20may%2009. htm

"If the people be led by laws, and uniformity sought to be given them by punishments, they will try to avoid the punishment but have no sense of shame. If they be led by virtue, and uniformity be sought them to be given them by '*li*' or rules of proper conduct, they will have a sense of shame and moreover will become good." (The Analects, 2.3)[①]

Confucius also talks about a perfect gentleman or *chuntzi*. This is a superior man. The superior man should 'Study extensively, and love the true learning. He should earnestly put his learning into practice, and be sincere to himself and others. He should not speak more than he is able to fulfill, and he should also be ready to be rectified by good teachers, and be constrained by virtues.'

"There are three things which the superior man guards against. In youth, when the physical powers are not yet settled, he guards against lust. When he is strong and the physical powers are full of vigour, he guards against quarrelsomeness. When he is old, and the animal powers are decayed, he guards against covetousness." (The Analects, 16,7)

Confucian philosophy can be the base of a dialogue of civilizations on many planes. First and foremost, the sense of benevolence is the prism through which people should look at other civilizations. This is an important first step in the process towards a dialogue. Without a compassionate attitude, it is not be possible to look at others in a way that creates an open and ready playing field for a discourse on important issues affecting us today. This can be done believing that each individual is enmeshed in society and is part of a whole and that we live life not merely as individual entities but as parts of a community that believes in giving and caring. The family is the most important unit of community and benevolence extends across the family to immediate relatives, colleagues, neighbourhood, community, society and then the country. The benevolence would then permeate across borders to other countries and then finally would encompass the whole world.

This implies a feeling of caring and sharing the burdens of the problems and difficulties arising out of living a life in today's society. For example, if a father does something wrong, the son tries to shield him. He does not ridicule him in public.

---

① Jingpan, Chen. "Cf The Analects or Lun Yu, J. Legge's Translation in Chinese Classics." *Confucius as a Teacher*. Trans. J. Legge. Vol. 1. Beijing: Foreign Languages, 1994. 62. Print.

Mother and father together care for the family and try to look after the needs of special members of their extended family with special care. These may be elders, widows, widowers, needy unmarried women or poor relatives. In a similar way, a dialogue of civilizations could take into account the needs of specifically needy countries, just as one looks after people in a family.

Confucius had a lot to say about education, self cultivation, human welfare, economic and social justice, legitimacy and nonlegitamacy of profit seeking and a sense of public responsibility and public service. We need to remember that self discipline is the key to many things in life including governance. In a dialogue of civilizations therefore, Confucian philosophy can play a vital role.

As against the Marxist theory of class struggle, Confucian philosophy talks of harmony and peace. Peace is a natural concomitant to prosperity and well being, to flourishing of humans and to their development and growth. Hence growth in terms of intellectual vigour, scientific and technological research, medical breakthroughs are much more likely to take place during peaceful times. Peace is a powerful catalyst in the process of development. Premier Li Keqiang, visiting India in May 2013 mentioned that only if China's neighbourhood is peaceful can China do well.

Confucianism talks of ethical norms and values. These guide human action in all fields and in all cultures, in a way that is closely linked to the value system of the culture. The value systems of a culture and the religious beliefs are what guides culture and creates an adhesive which binds a society together.

To understand cultures, one's own as well as other cultures is thus important in order to build bridges between them. Opening up minds to the rest of the world, to other beliefs and civilizational traits is a big step forward in one's growth first as an individual and secondly, as a people. In the interconnected world of today, if we lag behind in this important exercise, we may be doing ourselves a great disservice.

Traditions, myths and rituals are a binding force within societies and therefore within civilizations. ①

For example, in India every year, the ritual of immersing the God Ganesh adds

---

① Victor Segesvary_Dialogue. pdf] [Dialogue of Civilizations- An Introduction to Civilizational Analysis- Victor Segesvary, Mikes International, The Hague, Holland, 2004. Page 24, 25. http://www.federato.org/mikes_bibl.html. ISSN 1570-0070. ISBN 90-8501-008-X

fervor and meaning to the lives of people all over the country. There is a feel good factor as well as the religious fervor of a collective belief and celebration, especially the symbolic triumph of good over evil. The ritual of *havan* is performed on important days whether they are auspicious occasions, for purifying the home, or the passing away of family members. Here again the symbolic act of burning special wood and herbs in a fire adds meaning to the family collectively and also marks the occasion and adds a legitimacy since witnesses are present in the form of friends and family. Similarly, the Chinese ritual of sweeping the tombs of ancestors is a powerful symbol bringing home to people the fact that ancestors are to be remembered. This ritual adds in its own way to the thought that life is a continuous process and that the past is linked to the present and to the future as well. It also reminds people about the Confucian philosophy of filial piety and the importance of family.

Similarly, myths give a sense of grounding to people since these myths have been passed down over the centuries from generation to generation and give a sense of stability and continuity in civilizations. It is important to remember that there are many myths that act as a bulwark against which we base our many of our values and actions. For example, in India, Sita (the wife of God Ram) is known for her chastity and her devotion to Ram. Largely based on this myth, women in India still revere their husbands and continue to be devoted to them even after their demise. Widow remarriage is not common and devotion to one's husband often extends to the thought that in the afterlife, the husband will once again be reunited with the wife and that for seven lives they will be together thereafter.

Rituals and myths are called shared collective memories. In performing rituals and believing in myths, the people feel a sense of collective belonging and identity. This is important because a feeling of cohesiveness among the people adds to the many factors that go toward sharing a civilization. Once we accept that every culture has its own values, its own religiosity, its own character and its own ethos, it becomes easier to accept differences, recognize that the distances can be bridged and contact established between people.

Often the Western world, particularly the Americans and Europeans look at our civilizations with their own yardsticks. They cannot understand our family structures, the intense way in which all family is interlinked, the feeling of being part of a collective whole where the individual in a family or a community is concerned. In this context it has already been mentioned certain informal arrangements like unwritten contracts, an understanding between family and friends of business deals, the concept of face saving and the network of family and friends who help in innumerable ways. This resonates in Confucian thought where social relationships are very important.

Thus we realize that points of agreement and disagreement have to be worked upon so that the dialogue of civilizations established by such means (after developing an understanding of the cultures of different civilizations) has numerous contexts in which the dialogue can work. If the contexts are of a transcivilizational as opposed to a transnational nature, then the world could be a more peaceful place and all nations can benefit from this exchange.

One of the Confucian concepts which has great relevance today is ethics in the modern world. Ethics, whether in the field of business or medicine or in everyday life is important and sets a standard by which people work in an efficient way in society. Business ethics translates into '*shang de*' in Mandarin and those committed to ethical business practice are known as '*Ru Shang*' or 'Confucian trader.' Being *Ru Shang* is said to be the road to success. *Guan xi* (relationships) and *Mian zi* (saving face) are deeply embedded into the system of relationships. *Guan xi* has been called 'social capital' as relationships are created which are

long term and are based on trust.

In the business world ethical standards are not important only for themselves as set by leaders but as an example to be followed by the junior members of the team. It has been found that if a company is run in an ethical way, the employees feel more secure and are likely to feel more loyal to the establishment. There is also likely to be less absenteeism and quitting of jobs. People understand that the company is being run on ethical lines and that is a feel good factor and somewhere along the line they feel secure in the belief that they will also be treated fairly. Confucius said that profit should not be the only motive behind running a business. This implies that the surplus generated by selling goods or services be set aside for furthering the cause of society as a sort of charity towards less fortunate members of society, or for training those people who would later join the productive team in society and earn so that they can support themselves and their families. Also, the money can be given to non-governmental organizations which in turn spend it on educating members of society or improving their lives in whatever way they can. Some of this is reflected in corporate social responsibility

In China today, as indeed in other countries, it needs to be remembered that running business using ethical means is important. There have been numerous instances recently in China in which profit has been the overarching concern. Numerous such cases have come in the public eye thanks to media reports. An example is the melamine milk case and the machine oil case (where it was sold as edible oil). Here consumers can act as whistle blowers and help in clamping down on such businesses. The well known management guru Peter Drucker talks about Confucian values being the value system of modern management with authority, strong leadership, hierarchy, interdependence and personal ethics. Confucian ethics underlie much of Drucker's writing on management.

"Confucian ethics …is a universal ethic in which the same rules and imperatives of behavior hold for every individual. There is no "social responsibility" overriding individual conscience, no cost benefit calculation, no greater good or higher measure than the individual and his behavior. In the Confucian ethics the rules are the same for all. But there are different general rules, according to the five basic relationships of independence, which for the Confucian embrace the totality of individual interactions in civil society: superior and subordinate (or master and servant); father and child; husband and wife; older brother and younger siblings, friend and colleague. Right behavior-which in the English translation of Confucian ethics is usually called sincerity-is that individual ethics that is truly appropriate to the specific relationship of mutual dependence because it optimizes benefit for both parties. Other behavior is 'insincere' and therefore wrong and unethical. It creates dissonance instead of harmony, exploitation instead of benefits, manipulation instead of trust." ①

With a globalized business world, Confucian values and ethics and in addition the harmonious society using mediation and arbitration in business matters can thus help in a dialogue between members of the global business community.

In medical ethics as well, it is important that medicine be practiced by strict ethi-

---

① Peter F. Drucker. "Managerial Harmony: The Confucian Ethics of Peter F. Drucker" (Drucker, 1981, pp 166-167). Qtd in *Journal of Business Ethics*, Vol 51, No. 2, Edward J. Romar: 'Promoting Business Ethics'(May, 2004) pp 199-201. Pub by Springer. Stable URL: http://www.jstor.org/stable/25379185

cal standards. Private practitioners should be guided not by the profit motive but by the common good of society.

In the field of education, Confucius was way ahead of his time. He believed in teaching taking into account the aptitude of each student, and not just by rote. Education should arouse curiosity and should be based on principles which take into account the common good of all. For example, translated into contemporary terms research should be carried out for the sake of not just itself but so that it benefits humanity. Educational institutions could thus be harbingers of prosperity to countries if they taught in a way that would benefit society.

In this regard, history should be written taking into consideration not just nationalist sentiments, but according to a broader worldview so that students from a very young age learn to look at facts objectively. Also, education should be research based and invite inquisitiveness and curiosity in students, so that from a young age, they learn to go into the depth of subjects which would later help them in growing not only for themselves but as far as research for the good of humanity is concerned. Also, aptitude based education and education for all, irrespective of their social class and means is also a Confucian concept and will ultimately help in increasing the productivity of the labour as a means of production.

Zhao Tingyang's '*The Tianxia System*: The Philosophy for the World Institution' (2005) looks at how tradition in China can shape a future for China where it takes on a role not only as a builder of a harmonious society but also a harmonious world. Zhao recognizes the role of the Confucian past and uses it as a way of moving beyond the realm of what Hu Jintao had spoken about (a harmonious society) and into the realm of the Universe. Zhao moves to the space of public intellectuals to use the concept of *tianxia* or all under heaven 'thinking through the world in an all inclusive way' rather than thinking about the world in a regional or nationalistic way. Zhao, looking at Chinese philosophy for answers uses a passage from Chapter 54 of the 6th century BC Chinese classic *Dao de Jing*: "use the world [*Tianxia*] to examine the world *Tianxia*." World unity thus leads to world peace and world harmony. *Tianxia* being a utopia defines a global unity that is 'geographical, psychological, and institutional. Since there are no physical or ethical borders in Zhao's *Tianxia*, the main task in this holistic system is to use Confucian ethics to transform enemies into friends, "where 'transformation' seeks to attract people rather than conquer them." [①]

According to him then the *Tianxia* system is the solution to the world's problems; 'It is a new interpretation of Confucianism's hierarchical system that values order over freedom, ethics over law, and elite governance over democracy and human rights. Rather than looking to the U.N. as a liberal model for building world order from the bottom up as in Hu's harmonious world, Zhao thinks that global peace and prosperity can only be guaranteed in a top-down manner through a single world government institution.' [②]

It being a Utopian state, details of such a system are not provided, but Zhao looks to different civilizations to deal with global politics. 'But rather than different civilizations coexisting on the world stage, Zhao defines world order in terms of one unified Civilization (Wenming). Here, Zhao's *Tianxia* system is looking back to imperial China's "tributary system" that governed relations with its neighbours before the 20th Century.

Thus the *Tianxia* system is provided by scholars such as Zhao as the solution to the world's problems; interpreting in a different way the 'Confucianism's hierarchical system that values order over freedom, ethics over law, and elite governance over democracy and human rights.'

Whether this will in fact work is up for debate and has prompted many intellectuals and scholars to discuss the issue. Some feel that tolerance and equality is the answer to China's and the world's harmony while others have differing views. [③]

One of the Confucian concepts which is of relevance in today's world is its implication for environment issues. Confucian philosophy believes in a harmonious whole which if translated into environmental issues implies that we consider man 'in' nature as opposed to man 'and' nature. If we believe that man is one of the entities in the universe we should look upon nature as precious; rather than man opposed to nature. If

---

① Zhao Tingyang, "All under Heaven," China Security 4:2 (2008),Page 33]

② China's Strategic Futures, Author(s): William A. Callahan Source: Asian Survey, Vol. 52, No. 4 (July/August 2012), pp. 631. Published by: University of California Press Stable URL: http://www.jstor.org/stable/10.1525/ as. 2012. 52.4. 617 . Accessed: 28/05/2014 06:33

③ China's Strategic Futures. Author(s): William A. Callahan Source: Asian Survey, Vol. 52, No. 4 (July/August 2012), pp. 617-642Published by: University of California Press. Stable URL: http://www.jstor.org/ stable/ 10.1525/ as.2012. 52. 4.617 . Accessed: 28/05/2014 06:33

we believe that nature is not something to be controlled and mastered but as something of beauty which should be preserved for the future and nurtured, then the issue of environment becomes something that can be tackled in a different way.

Our natural resources should be kept intact and not destroyed for the sake of satisfying human greed. Urbanization needs to be carefully studied so as to not take away large tracts of land from agricultural use; pesticides and insecticides which are toxic should be replaced by organic and natural products and it should be remembered that the cycle of nature should be maintained as it was intended to. This is in keeping with the Vedic philosophy of environmental conservation as well. Here humans look upon other living beings as part of the cycle of nature and not as creatures meant to be controlled by man. If we believe in this Confucian concept, then the environment will be kept safe for future generations and not destroyed and mutilated for the use and abuse of humans.

If we realize that we live under one sky, look at the same stars and experience the same pleasure upon coming across a beautiful garden or looking at the ocean or at the beauty and poignance of the setting sun, we will find it easier to look at problems from a common viewpoint.

And hence it will be easier to carry on a dialogue.

"The first requirement of a successful dialogue among cultures is, therefore, that each human being relates to others in respect of his or her mutual cognitive or divine identity. If this cognitive aspect is treated as primary, then the "different cultural traditions," as Nicolaus of Cusa said, are an enrichment, not a threat.'①

The German "poet of freedom," Friedrich Schiller gave in lecture in 1789 "What Is, and to What End Do We Study, Universal History?," Schiller says to the students seated before him:

'Even that we found ourselves together here at this moment, found ourselves together with this degree of national culture, with this language, these manners, these civil benefits, this degree of freedom of conscience, is the result perhaps of all previ-

---

① The One and The Many, and The Dialogue Among Cultures by Helga Zepp-LaRouche, The Schiller Institute, ' Dialogue of Civilizations' in Fidelio Magazine, Vol XIII, No. 3, Fall 2004. A letter to India from the West. First appeared in Asia Annual, 2003,' published by the Multidisciplinary Institue of the Maulana Abul Kalam Azad Institute of Asian Studies, Calcutta, India. http://www.schillerinstitute.org/fid_02-06/2004/043_hzl_dial_cultures.html

ous events in the world: The entirety of world history, at least, were necessary to explain this single moment.'①

In other words different cultures have to look at a common divinity and realize that they live through the same rules of the laws of nature and look to a common sun for light and life. The civilizational histories of countries have influenced cultures across the world. Witness the Buddhist influence which came from India to China and to other countries of South East Asia and which has indirectly influenced Confucian thought. This reiterates that our endeavour should be to look at the world as one entity and to look at the people of the world from the perspective of a single pinhole of vision.

In the Hindu religion, the Upanishads show us the universal way. The Brahma is the all pervasive being who creates all of humankind and the Atma is the spirit of each and every person. "*ishawaram idam sarvam jagat kincha jagatvam jagat*" meaning that we are one and we are all. Dr. Karan Singh, noted Indian philosopher and social scientist talks about "*amritashya putra*"—"children of immortality" which stands for the race of human beings as a whole. In other words, each individual is connected to an 'infinite chain of humanity'. He also mentions the essential unity of all religions, of all spiritual paths, "*ekoham svat vipra bahuda vadanti*"—"the truth is One, the sages call it by different names"—as it is said in the Rig Veda. And another concept in the Upanishads is "*bahujana shukhaya bahujana hitaya cha*." At its highest, Hindu philosophy seeks "the welfare of all human beings and all forms of life on the planet.②

In the Bhagvad Gita, there are three states of human existence. Human beings move from *tamas* or darkness and inactivity to *rajas* or passion, excitement and overactivity to *satva*, or a refined and pure state where reason and spirituality are one. All humans should aspire to attain this state. This resonates in other religious discourses as well. The Confucian equivalent would be a human being who can cultivate himself or herself and behave in a balanced and reasonable way so that he or she can live in a

① Friedrich Schiller, "What Is, and to What End Do We Study, Universal History," in Friedrich Schiller, Poet of Freedom, Vol. II, ed. by William F. Wertz, Jr. (Washington, D.C., Schiller Institute, 1988), p. 263.

② Jan 20, 2004, The Hindustan Times, New Delhi ed.

harmonious way in society. And that as humans in society imply a complex network of relationships, they must be grounded on performance, knowledge, trust, responsibility and interdependence. The network should work to the mutual benefit of all.

So, eloquently stated, the real purpose of the dialogue is to find the universal science of human possibilities. And the people who would do so would be refined and morally sound individuals who move

ahead of narrow visions and look at problems from a wider perspective. ①

Confucianism states that trust, morality, integrity and respect for others are what counts in any society. According to Prof Tu, this can support harmonious relations among diversified communities.

In the present century we have seen economic crises and a host of other problems. Materialism and profit making are the mantra of today's societies. Human values have been downgraded and striving for personal wealth, humankind has forgotten compassion and benevolence. In this situation, we certainly have a lot to learn from Confucian ethics. Similarly, we can also learn a great deal from the traditions of India, especially from the teachings of the Upanishads and the Bhagavad Gita. Mahatma Gandhi, who is also known in India as the father of the nation, believed sincerely in the Bhagvad Gita and widened his horizon with insights taken from Christianity, Jainism, Buddhism and the Western world.

We can recall these well known words from the Gita:

Even as the unwise work selfishly in the bondage of selfish works,

Let the wise person work unselfishly for the good of all the world (3:25).

And again:

Those who ever follow my teachings and who have faith and goodwill,

find through pure work their freedom (3:31).

'And here is a passage from what is sometimes called the Gita's "*mahavakya*" and which Gandhi was particularly fond of recalling:

When a person surrenders to me

---

① The One and The Many, and The Dialogue Among Cultures by Helga Zepp-LaRouche, The Schiller Institute, ' Dialogue of Civilizations' in Fidelio Magazine., Vol XIII, No. 3, Fall 2004. A letter to India from the West. First appeared in Asia Annual, 2003,' published by the Multidisciplinary Institue of the Maulana Abul Kalam Azad Institute of Asian Studies, Calcutta, India. http://www.schillerinstitute.org/fid_02-06/2004/043_hzl_dial_cultures.html

all desires that come to the heart,

and by the grace of God finds divine joy,

his/her soul has indeed found peace (2:55).

This is "*bahmasthithi*," O Arjuna.①

Thus the ancient traditions of India and China can borrow from each other or they can complement each other.

The dialogue of civilizations is the antithesis to Samuel Huntington's thesis of the clash of civilizations. In 1993, Huntington's book,' The Clash of Civilizations and the Remaking of the World Order' created waves in the realm of political theorists. The book said that the post cold war conflicts would occur because of cultural rather than ideological differences. Whilst in the Cold War the conflict would have been likely to take place between the Capitalist West and the Communist Bloc, it now was most likely to occur between the world's major civilizations — identifying seven, and a possible eighth: (i) Western, (ii) Latin American, (iii) Islamic, (iv) Sinic (Chinese), (v) Hindu, (vi) Orthodox, (vii) Japanese, and (viii) the African. This cultural organization is in stark contrast to the notion of sovereign states in the contemporary world. This thesis has lead to debate and discussion across the world.

The theory of the clash of civilizations has been challenged and it partly is in relation to this that the concept of a dialogue of civilizations has emerged.

We would do well to remember once again the thoughts of Gandhi on cultures of the world. 'I do not want my house to be walled in on all sides and my windows to be stuffed. I want the cultures of all lands to be blown about my house as freely as possible. But I refuse to be blown off my feet by any'.

If we look at Gandhian thought we find a resonance in it of the great philosophers of the world. Gandhi rejected the basic premises of industrial civilization and offered a concrete proposal for reordering society that promised to do away with the ills associated with modern civilization. 'The cornerstone of his proposal is provided by his conception of uniqueness of being human. Rejecting all attempts to reduce the uniqueness of being human to biological, psychological, or sociological considera-

---

① 'The meeting of human and the divine' (2:72). [DIALOGUE AMONG CIVILIZATIONS: ITS MEANING AND PURPOSE (Fred Dallmayr, University of NotreDame) [http://balvantparekhcentre.org.in/index.htm]

tions, he sees the destiny of man to lie in his ethico-religious quest of self-transformation. But this quest for self- knowledge, far from being pursued in the isolation of Himalayan cave, occurs in the world of here and now and provides the basis for man's relationship with the outer world that is characterized by an organismic vision emphasizing inseparable unity, harmony and non-injury… The moral sensibility that lies behind Gandhi's condemnation of this civilization springs from his world-view. It is his world-view that gives a concrete shape to his moral perspective and defines its contents. Constituting an integral component of his world-view, Gandhi's moral perspective cannot be understood apart from his world-view.' ①

As far as environmental issues are concerned, we would do well to remember that if seen in the light of Vedic or Confucian philosophies, the whole universe being one and all individuals being part of that whole, it would make sense for countries to look at technologies which have a carbon footprint and polluting industries from a common perspective rather than from a nationalist viewpoint. If they are involved in a dialogue, they would strive to understand common issues and try to aid each other in developing alternative forms of renewable energy so that ultimately the whole of mankind would benefit.

In connection with this is an important corollary. The learning of languages, attending history lessons, tourism not only for one's personal pleasure but for the sake of observing the people of the country one is visiting and attempting to study and understand the ethos and what makes them tick is important. Language is an important tool bridging people. In this regard, an example is the Confucius institutes set up in countries around the world. By studying Chinese, people may want to visit China and may be drawn to the people and encouraged to further study the religious, political and socio-economic factors that go into the making of contemporary China today. This could be a step towards a dialogue of sorts between China and people from different countries.

Studying the music, art and literature of different cultures is important for the same reason. Art is a

reflection of the cultural ethos of a civilization that evolves over a historical peri-

---

① Articles on and by Gandhi, M. K Gandhi, www.mkgandhi.org/articles/hind_swaraj3.html Hind Swaraj, A Fresh Look by Jai Sharma

od of time. It speaks a language which expresses the angst and the concerns, the social issues plaguing the society as also the beauty and the warmth of its culture.

Similarly, music speaks for itself. Not only is it a way of connecting with people but it reflects their ethos and the beauty of the style it projects. Literature is an important component of the bridging process and connects people by informing them not only of the writers' thoughts, habits, the thought processes, but the current state of society, gender issues, the traditions, the historical threads and the language of the land. Cultural exchanges such as the exchange of artists, musicians, writers, poets, scholars and academicians is important as also such exchanges as for example, youth delegations, sports teams and Parlementarians and journalists. People are what make a difference and thus translated into actual action plans it would involve people from all walks of life interacting with each other. That would be the start of a dialogue of civilizations.

Thus translated in real and practical terms, a dialogue of civilizations could mean organizing symposia, conferences, debates, especially designed to encourage exchange between cultures and civilizations in the right spirit. Also, communication between experts in their respective fields, exchange of journals and academic papers and people to people exchanges are also important.

Therefore we see that in summing up a need for a dialogue of civilizations, it would be worth our while to study Confucian traditions and philosophy. We could perhaps set up a dialogue of civilizations by incorporating the ancient philosophies of different civilizations and arrive at a common understanding that would lead to a deeper trust between the countries of the world.

A couple of years ago while China, I visited the Indian style Buddhist shrine at Luoyang in Henan province. This temple stands next to the *Bai Masi*, the oldest Buddhist temple to come up in China where the two Indian monks Dharmaratna and Kashyap Matunga came from India centuries ago at the invitation of the then Chinese Emperor Ming Di. The Indian style Buddhist shrine was built by the Indian government as an agreement between the two governments at the time that the then Indian Prime Minister Vajpayee visited China. It stands testimony to the meeting of two great civilizations. It has a huge statue of the Buddha which was crafted and brought to China from India.

As I stood in front of the temple, I thought to myself: Where else would I find a better example of India and China collaborating than here, where Buddhism and Confucianism were present together! Where the peace of human introspection meets the compassion and benevolence of Confucius and where histories and cultures have merged to create a peaceful haven. It may well be that this is a tourist attraction and that creating an Indian style shrine next to a Chinese Buddhist temple would bring in the renminbi from all over the Buddhist world. But the fact remains that the two stand as a symbol of cooperation and friendship between the two countries.

Dialogues are started this way. We need to remember that and carry on meaningful conversations

between our countries and in so doing, try to make the world a better place for our future generations.

*Works cited*:

# Crossing Borders, Breaking Walls: An Indian Response to Confucius

**Prof Shubhra Tripathi (Dept. of Higher Education Govt. of Madhya Pradesh Bhopal)**

The most striking feature about India to a foreigner is her multiplicity of major world religions, deep rooted faiths including tribal faiths, spiritual traditions, all co-existing in harmony, despite sporadic clashes. Religion and faith are important to all spheres of life and development in India, including politics. A curious fact is that though followers of Confucianism and Daoism are miniscule in India, the two great Chinese *sage-gurus* are frequently quoted in tabloids and referred to by educated Indians. Confucius is a familiar figure to most educated Indians, although they are not so familiar with his teachings or thoughts.

Another curious fact is that despite centuries of harmonious cultural and trade interactions, both China and India still view each other with caution, diplomatically and politically. Yet another fact is that economic ties between the two are strengthening steadily. The time is therefore ripe to break 'walls' of caution and suspicion to strengthen national bonds for mutual benefit.

The paper seeks answers to questions: Will Confucian thoughts and preaching appeal to the deeply religious and faith- governed psyche of average Indians? Will promoting Confucian ideas and studies among Indian youth can succeed in 'breaking walls' where diplomacy has been unsuccessful? How can we spread Confucian traditions in India so as to promote peace and harmony between people of the two countries, driven by selfish materialistic interests resulting from technological and economic 'advancement'?

India and China are not only neighbours but also share several historical and cultural similarities. It is due to this fact that despite so many political and economic differences, both the countries are not able to deny each other's significance, and despite these differences, cultural relations between them have never waned. Both came into existence as strong and independent nations around almost the same time: India in 1947 and Peoples Republic of China in 1949. Both have ancient and prosperous civilizational past; both have their own well developed systems in the areas of religion, science and medicine which have existed for centuries. In the field of philosophy and spirituality, both the nations, India and China, have flourishing and insightful traditions since times immemorial. In India, several spiritual and religious traditions had taken shape, for example Hinduism, Buddhism and Jainism, and sustained human beings; similarly in China Daoism and Confucianism sustained the Chinese people. Do these happy coincidences or similarities end here? Certainly not! Even now both the countries are moving side by side on the path of "development."But does this "development" imply "progress" in the real sense of the word? Has not the mad rush for so called "development" or "progress" resulted in competition and contention between two nations instead of cooperation and cordiality? It seems a sad state of affairs. Diplomatic relations, bilateral talks and negotiations are marred by selfish motives and issues of mutual concern often recede into the background. Is there something that can check the incessant competitive spirit? Can anything save the two countries from their current plight and restore their former friendly relations of the past, when cultural and trade interactions had benefited both. The answer is an emphatic affirmative. I firmly believe that spreading the ancient wisdom of the *sage-gurus* of China like Confucius can certainly accomplish what diplomacy and politics could not. My conviction is founded on several facts. Let us examine what they are and how they can forge and strengthen friendly ties between India and China, thus contributing to global peace and harmony.

At the beginning of the paper I had raised three questions. The answers to those three questions are the factual basis of my conviction that Confucian thoughts can influence Indian psyche and promote better mutual understanding. Let me take the first questions first:

Will Confucian thoughts and preaching appeal to the deeply religious and faith-governed psyche of average Indians?

The youth in India today, is of two kinds, the first category is of those who are deeply religious, governed by a sense of spiritual and traditional propriety; the other class is of those, who under the influence of science technology, IT etc., questions the established beliefs and faiths. However, the numbers of such people are, comparatively speaking, very less. People who reject all faiths are there, but rare. Similarly, fanatics are also rare. The majority comprises of those educated youth who range from deeply religious to casually religious. India being a secular country, with many religions co-existing peacefully, this category of youth is tolerant of other religious and faiths, and often even appreciates them. People of all religions celebrate their festivals together. Therefore, this category of youth will certainly not be averse to Confucius' teachings. The educated youth, studying or working in large cities and metropolis is over burdened with responsibilities and is always on the lookout for fresh stress busters. Inspiring thoughts of Confucius are the right fodder for such over stressed youth, lost in the maze of this complex existence, vying for more and more materialistic gains. In a multicultural, multi-linguistic, multi-ethnic and multi-religious society, one more set of moral/ethical/ spiritual / religious ideas can be easily accommodated.

One may question the need for such an exercise. Aren't there enough storehouses of ancient wisdom from classics in India? True, there are, but not from China. The crucial issue here is to enhance friendly Sino - Indian cultural ties. The universality of Confucian thought and its humanism will certainly appeal to all Indians, particularly the youth in question, and in the process bring them closer to Chinese culture and Chinese people, thus initiating the process of 'breaking barriers— demolishing walls.'

The second question that I had raised was:

Will promoting Confucian ideas and studies among Indian youth can succeed in 'breaking walls' where diplomacy has been unsuccessful?

Though India has immense religious diversity, it is a secular country by constitution, and has an underlying unity in diversity. Since Hinduism is the religion of the majority in India, and Confucianism is not in opposition to it, we can safely presume that at least Hindus will not find it difficult to relate to it.

Apparently Hinduism and Confucianism appear very different from each other. Though they have similar philosophical beliefs, social order, and their overall view of life, Hinduism achieved this through the caste system and Confucianism attained this through meritocracy. Confucianism is not a religion in the most basic sense of the word, but may be termed a social and political philosophy, whereas Hinduism is a religious and social system based on spirituality. In Hinduism the goal of a person's life is to merge with the Brahma and achieve salvation or *moksha*. Confucianism is family based, which advocates placing others before you, and peace loving. Hinduism talks of renunciation of worldly things and relationships, and has the concepts of *Darma* - obedience to religious symbols or laws, *Karma* - Sum of good or bad deeds which determine a person's place in next life, transmigration of soul or *atma*, incarnation or *avtar* etc.

Confucian values are *Ren*, *Li*, *Xiao*. *Ren* means being 'respectful and loyal,' *Li* means 'treating all humans with courtesy and more respect to elders,' *Xiao* means respecting family always. There are four *Purushartha* or duties of a man in Hinduism. *Dharma*, or righteous path; *Artha* - pursuit of economical being prosperity; *Kama* - enjoyment of social, physical, and sexual pleasures; *Moksha* - salvation of the soul acheived by meeting caste responsibilities. Hinduism has many Gods and cults. The Holy Trinity. Brahma - the creator

Vishnu - Preserver of the world, Shiva - God of Fertility and Destruction.

However both Hinduism and Confucianism look into life's meaning and the actions of the people within a society as well as the social structure. Both philosophical systems deal with the aspect of a supreme being and a similar social hierarchy. Both Hinduism and Confucianism look to bettering the lives of the people within them. They look for the common good that will help enforce peace and brotherhood. Both of these belief systems go on a basis of making the people act accordingly helping to run government and set a stable mindset for its people. Both had strict policies of education and life and their social standing. Hinduism was based on it's caste system and hereditary in which the only way to better one's social position is to die with good karma. Confucianism's social hierarchy was based on the educational system and work ethic when it comes to determining a person's positon.

Though Hinduism and Confucianism have certain differences mentioned earlier, there are several similarities which will appeal to Hindus. Relating to Confucius, the person and his persona will therefore not be difficult. Confucius was a moral preacher, ethical master, philosopher etc., a *sage-guru* who later acquired a divine status. Such instances are not new to Hindus. Many *sage-gurus* are popular in India today, who are worshipped by people because of deep faith in their teachings. The Sai Baba of Shirdi, a small town in the state of Maharashtra, is an apt example. Even Rama, the prince of Ayodhya, an important Hindu deity, though an incarnation of God

Vishnu, is worshipped for his travails as a human being. So according divine status to noble and idealistic humans is not new to followers of Hinduism, the majority population of India. Another fact common to Confucius and God Rama is that both went into self - imposed exile, although for different reasons and under different circumstances. Even God Krishna, another *avtar* or incarnation of God Vishnu as human being, is worshipped by Hindus. However, this comparison cannot be stretched too far as the concept of *avtar* is different in Hinduism.

Although Confucianism cannot be called a religion as Hinduism, with the latter's belief in innumerable Gods and Goddesses, it does discuss 'afterlife', 'astrology' and the concept of 'Heaven.' Confucius observed:

Heaven sends down its good or evil symbols and wise men act accordingly.

Thus commonness of religious / philosophical perceptions will certainly promote mutual understanding and curb the tendency of viewing each other with suspicion. There are many other such instances in Confucianism which will serve the same purpose. Confucianism lays stress on cultivation of virtues:

The man of virtue makes the difficulty to be overcame his first business, and success only a subsequent consideration.

Let us take into consideration the two concepts mentioned here-'virtue' and 'success only a subsequent consideration.' First we examine the concept of "virtue" in Hinduism, which is termed *sanskara*. The *sanskaras* are qualities that any human being acquires since birth from his/her environment, family, society, etc. as a natural consequence of upbringing, education, circumstances in life etc. Thus *sanskaras* determined and shaped the personality of any individual. Men and women performed action *karma* according to their *sanskar*.

As far as the idea 'success only a subsequent consideration' is concerned, a similar idea is expressed in the *Bhagwad Gita*, a religio-philosophical treatise, which is a part of the epic the *Mahabharata*. In the epic God Krishna advises Arjuna to pursue the right action for its own sake and with complete indifference to success or failure In his *Introduction* to the translation of Confucius' *Analects*, D. C. Lau says,

Behind the pursuit of the ideal moral character lies the unspoken and therefore, unquestioned, assumption that the only purpose a man can have and also the only worthwhile thing a man can do is to become as good a man as possible. This is something that has to be pursued for its own sake and with complete indifference to success or failure." (xii)

This principle of pursuing the right action with complete indifference to success or failure has been called *nishkam karma* in the *Bhagwad Gita*. Thus we see that Confucius talked of virtue and action being crucial to his system of ethics; these can be equated with the concepts of *sanskar* and *nishkamkarma* in Hinduism.

The concept of 'righteous action' as propounded in the *Bhagwad Gita* is not almost, but quite similar to that exemplified by Confucius in *Li*. His ethical theory is founded on three significant aspects of human existence:

1. Ceremonies associated with sacrifice to ancestors and different deities.

2. Social and political institutions.

3. The conduction and etiquette of day to day behaviour.

Some scholars were of the opinion that *Li* originated from the Heaven, but as far as Confucius is concerned, he asserted the growth and development of *Li* through the actions of sage leaders of the past. John N. Berthraong and Evelyn N. Berthrong observe that "his role was to restore the way of the ancient sages rather than to propound some novel set of doctrines. However, as is often the case with great religions and cultural reformers, the more they seek to renew the past, the more they generate a new culture out of it."(3) In his analysis of *Li* he redefined the term to imply all kinds of righteous actions of men in order to shape an ideal society, instead of merely those which conformed to ceremonial standards. In the early days of Confucianism, *Li* implied taking proper action at the proper time; maintaining a balance between existing norms in order to perpetuate an ethical social fabric, and even at times, if required, violate them so as to accomplish ethical good.

Let us now take up Confucius' attitude towards ancestors. The first point mentioned earlier pertaining to his ethics was ceremonies associated with ancestor worship. Reverence for parents, elders and ancestors, is an important feature of Hindu culture. The Sanskrit word *pitra* means 'father' and in the plural also implies 'ancestors'. There are four debts or *rin* in Vedic Hinduism, which a man must repay before attaining salvation. One of them is *pitrarin* or the debt towards one's father and ancestors. A son repays this debt by marrying and begetting children, especially a son, in order to continue the family lineage. Besides this, there is an important traditional ritual which is performed by a son on the day of *sarvpitramoksha amavasya*. *Sarv* means' all', *pitra* means 'father' or 'ancestors,' *moksha* is 'salvation' and *ama-*

vasyais 'moonless night'. On a special *tithi* or date, a son performs *shradh*ceremony in order to achieve salvation for all the dead ancestors. These were just two prominent examples. There are many more customs and rituals to express reverence to ones living and dead ancestors. These examples clearly illustrate that Confucian ethics of respecting ancestors finds parallel in Hindu culture too. Therefore, the youth of India will not find it difficult to accept the teachings of Confucius.

The teachings of Confucius laid emphasis on maintaining a balance between existing norms to perpetuate an ethical social fabric, and violating them in case it was imperative, in order to attain ethical good. More or less the same inference emerges from the sermon of God Krishna to Prince Arjuna in the epic *Mahabharata*. Arjuna is in a dilemma over fighting with his kin and revered elders in war. Then God Krishna gives him a sermon, which is the *Bhagwad Gita*. Lord Krishna preaches that even though the opponents are blood relatives it is ethical to face them and defeat them. The example is akin to Confucius' idea of violating norms for righteousness, *dharmasansthapnarthaye* 'in order to establish dharma or righteousness.'

Confucius also talks of *Ren* which comprises of five basic virtues: seriousness, generosity, sincerity, diligence and kindness. In short it is the virtue of fulfilling one's responsibilities towards others, and is often taken to be synonymous with 'benevolence' or 'humaneness' and also translated as 'Goodness'. The concept of 'Goodness towards others' is *parmartha* in Hinduism.

Apart from personal ethics, Confucius also elaborated upon how to govern and administer effectively. Some of these thoughts find a parallel in Hinduism. For example, he believed in revival of the ordered society of earlier times. This ideal ordered society, where all are satisfied and happy is R*amrajya* in Hinduism. Similarly Confucius had proposed the revival of a unified royal state, whose rulers would succeed to power on the basis of merit. In Hindu tradition also there is a concept of *chakravarti samrat* 'an all-powerful king'. The only difference is that here the king acquires power by conquering several kingdoms. However, the concept of *ramrajya* is closer to Confucius' ideas about an ideal ruler who was devoted to his subjects; struggled to achieve personal perfection; spread his virtues among people by setting example, rather than by imposing laws.

Thomas Cleary, a Confucian scholar, in his *Foreword* to his translation of the *Analects* observes that, it is a basic source book for a wide range of advice an human affairs, from governing nations and managing enterprises, to dealing with society and getting along with friends, to maintaining family and mastering oneself his views on personality, social relations and the human condition are ever more incisive as history intensifies the gravity of the very concerns he voiced twenty five centuries ago. (x)

Comparing Hinduism and Confucianism in a well-researched article Jarod, Rebekah and Russell opine, Both Hinduism and Confucianism look into life's meaning and the actions of the people within a society, as well as the social structure. Both philosophical systems deal with the aspect of a supreme being and a similar social hierarchy. Both Hinduism and Confucianism look to bettering the lives of the people within them. They look for the common good that will help enforce peace and brotherhood. Both of these belief systems go on a basis of making the people act accordingly helping to run government and set a stable mind-set for its people. Both had strict policies of education and life and their social standing. Hinduism was based on its caste system and hereditary in which the only way to better one's social position is to die with good karma. Confucianism's social hierarchy was based on the educational system and work ethic when it comes to determining a person's position.

The foregoing account is just the tip of the iceberg. The more we compare Confucianism with Hindu beliefs and traditions, the more we will be convinced that they are not in opposition of each other, but are different ways of looking at the same aspects of human life and existence. Thus spreading Confucius thoughts among the younger generation will bring them closer not only to Confucius, but also to China, binding them with cultural ties. Once the ethical and moral thoughts of Confucius appeal to Indian youth and are accepted by them, they will have respect for the *sage guru* and also for Chinese culture. Hence the people will come closer willingly, promoting sharing of ideas, and mutual understanding, which is what I call "crossing borders - breaking down walls." This cultural exchange will I am sure achieve what diplomacy has not been able to.

The third question that I had raised was:

How can we spread Confucian traditions in India so as to promote peace and harmony between people of the two countries, driven by selfish materialistic interests resulting from technological and economic 'advancement'?

Once we are convinced that spreading knowledge about Confucius and his teachings will appeal to the youth of India and will be studied by them, which will in turn promote feelings of mutual understanding and brotherhood, the next logical step is how to go about it. It is not that the governments of the two countries do not realise this. Several efforts have been made in recent past and more are in the offing.

India is currently undergoing a phase of radical political change. Political changes are inevitably accompanied by changes, and even upheavals, in the socio-economic set up of the country. There is an urgent need to upgrade and reform the socio-economic, as well as political set up so as to lead the nation towards progress and prosperity. Developing cordial relations with neighbouring countries especially China, is an essential part of this agenda, China, till recent times, was an enigma to many educated Indians, an exotic but mysterious neighbour. In the global economic scenario, trade links have improved and the "walls" of mystery and mistrust are slowly crumbling. Commenting upon Sino-Indian relations in 2012, the Chinese Ambassador to India Zhang Yan said:

Relations between India and China have entered a fast track in recent years, and as two of the most ancient civilizations and fast growing economies in the world, India and China should join hands in building a world for future generations.

At such a time Confucius and his ethical - moral thoughts can play a vital role in giving impetus to the environment of harmony and peace, which is gradually building up, despite sporadic political and military differences, the teachings of Confucius, project him as an exemplary human being, the ultimate model of excellence, rather than a divine being, and so following his ethical code will surely benefit India and Indians.

The pertinent question is how to spread the knowledge, of Confucius' moral and ethical code among the Indian masses. Both Chinese and Indian governments have realized this already, and have taken some steps in this direction. In order to introduce Chinese culture in India the process of establishing Confucius Institutes has been initiated. There are teething troubles, as bureaucratic and diplomatic processes have to be followed, which require time and patience. But as we say "well begun is half done." The first Confucius Institute in India was inaugurated on 18 July 2013, and was set up at the Kalina campus of Mumbai University, in collaboration with Tianjin University of Technology. The aim of this exercise was not only to promote Chinese language, art and culture in the Indian Institution but also to start a student and faculty exchange programme between the two nations. Once the Indian teachers learn Chinese, as a future activity, they will go to teach Hindi in China.

Consul General Liu Youfa spoke highly of the effort made for the inauguration ceremony by the University of Mumbai, and wished the ceremony a big success on behalf of Mr. Wei Wei, Chinese Ambassador to India. In his speech, he mentioned that

more than 1,300 years ago, Master Xuanzang, a famous Chinese Buddhist monk, scholar, traveler and translator in the early Tang Dynasty, trekked to India for sutras and brought back home the thought of Buddhism. Today, we gather here to feel the charm of Chinese Confucianism, a legacy of great value left by the ancient Chinese ideologist and educator Confucius.

Mr. Liu further pointed out during the visit to India, Premier Li Keqiang accentuated that to deepen the cultural communication between China and India, as it is a channel of great importance to promote mutual understanding In the speech made by the Party Secretary of Tianjin University of Technology, Meng Qingsong said that he hoped and wished that, "Confucius Institute takes root in India, and it will sprout, blossom and bear fruit."

Welcoming the opening of Confucian Institutes in India and explaining their need, Charu Sudan Kasturi, an authority on Sino-Indian affairs wrote in an important national daily *The Telegraph*,

As more and more Indian and multinational companies build business ties with Chinese firms, professionals and organisations are looking to understand a culture that has historical relations with India Although several private institutions offering crash courses in Chinese have mushroomed in Indian cities in recent years, few have the resources of government-supported institutions.

Even the Chinese were as enthusiastic and determined as the Indians about opening the first Confucius centre at Mumbai University. Lin Xu, Director General of the National Office for Teaching Chinese as a Foreign Language, or Hanban, which is also responsible for China's global Confucius Institute programmes, said:

This agreement is a great event in Chinese education. It may take 20 years to promote the Chinese language in India, with patience, confidence, and perseverance in the next 20 years.

Lin Xu is also the Chief Executive of the Confucius Institute Headquarters, and she was hopeful about the Institutes', success in India, although two earlier attempts had not borne fruit. There were preliminary discussions and preparations between

Jawaharlal Nehru University, Delhi and Peking University. However, due to procedural complexities, the project could not take off. Similarly, another tie up was proposed between Vellore Institute of Technology, situated in the South of India. It faced some difficulties in hiring Chinese language teachers, but nevertheless runs a small study centre. Another university situated in Karnataka, which is growing by leaps and bounds, is Manipal University. It has been making intensive efforts to open a first ever Indian University campus in China. These are significant beginnings; more such institutes/ institutions are to come up. But the efforts will bear fruit only when there is aggressive persuasion from both the nations.

There had been another very important development a year before the setting up of Confucian Institute in Mumbai. In April 2012, the Central Board of Secondary Education, the nationwide body governing school education and having the largest number of schools associated with it, introduced Chinese language as one of the foreign language subject to be taught in 500 select schools of India. The plan is to increase this numbers to 11,500 middle schools. This was described as "first of its kind initiative" by The Hindu, a leading national newspaper in India. The Chinese government had offered to cover the expenses, including flight tickets, living costs and tuition, for 300 Indian teachers to undergo a six months training in top Chinese universities. Under the agreement, China also promised to support in developing Mandarin Chinese language curriculum and provide educational materials. India's Ambassador to China Dr. Subramanyam Jaishankar observed that the agreement was one of "exceptional and long - term significance."He further said that:

If Indian school students are provided opportunities to learn Mandarin, their understanding and appreciation of China and its culture will grow enormously. We will truly be shaping the thinking of future generations.

Though one of the reasons why these efforts are being made is that people around the globe need to communicate with China, who has risen as the foremost commercial giant, but a by-product of it is that the common people are coming closer to each other and developing universal brotherhood. Seema Guha, analysing Sino-Indian cultural ties for one of the leading newspapers Daily News Analysis, comments

Managing ties with a rising China will be one of India's biggest foreign policy challenges. The two giants will compete for dominance in Asia. . . . But the leaders of India and China are talking of growing together in peace. Though there has been no major progress in talks, the two have ensured peace along the 3000 km border.

India's relationship with China is a common feature in Indian media as it is an important national concern. More and more young Indians employed in various sectors are taking interest in China, often expressing their opinions in blogs, websites or print media. One such ardent observer of Sino-Indian relations Ashish Advani, expressed on TV, "Every time I read about Confucius or his teachings, I am fascinated by the dichotomy of his teachings. . . . Each time, I walk away with a sense of appreciation as well as a new set of doubts of when his teachings would help solve a problem. Another keen Indian blogger Chandrakant Maliya, discussing the influence of Confucian teachings on family and society in his blog says, "Confucius pleads for responsibility at every stage of life of an individual An individual must seek the path for betterment through social relationships and self-efforts."

Bhanoji Rao, formerly with the National University of Singapore and the World Bank, and Professor Emeritus, GITAM Institute of Foreign Trade, Visakhapatnam and a Visiting Faculty at Sri Sathya Sai Institute of Higher Learning, Deemed University, in Prasanthi Nilayam gives a pertinent view of the situation:

My oversimplified version of the essence of Confucian ethics comprises the following: Investment in education, high saving rates, meritocracy, respect for authority and rebellion against corruption. …. More than the 13 agreements signed recently by India and China, and much more than the targets for bi-lateral trade, India could benefit significantly and substantially by using the key ethical principles of Confucius, notwithstanding the highly probable rediscovery of an Indian saint or sage who has proclaimed the same or similar or even more potent set of ethical principles. It does not matter who said the good things, what they are, is what counts.

To sum up, India is on the threshold of sweeping changes in all spheres of national life. Harmonious relations with all her neighbours will help her in achieving not only economic advancement, but also all round progress and prosperity. In the view of Prof Yu Longyu, Director of Indian Studies Centre at Shenzhen University, if the hearts of two hundred and fifty billion people of China and India come together in love, ". . . what a great power it will be! It will be a power benefitting the people of India and China as well as world peace." Political diplomacy has been taking its own course; our leaders, both from India and China are taking care of that. What can we, the common people, coming together in a programme like this, bound by common interests of peace and brotherhood, do, to tie the 250 million people of India and China in a strong bond of love, in order to generate the great power that Prof Yu talks of? The easiest way is to forge cultural ties bringing people together in love and brotherhood, and what better beginning can be there than spreading the teachings of Confucius in India, because as Hendrik van Loon in his famous book *The Story of Mankind* says, Confucius is almost the only one among the great moral leaders who did not see visions, who did not proclaim himself as the messenger of a divine power; who did not at some time or another, claim that he was inspired by voices from above . . . . who believed in right living and righteous thinking without the hope of a reward but simply for peace of the soul that comes with good conscience.

**Notes and References**

Advani, Ashish. "Confucius Is Needed in India." Newsmax TV. Tuesday July 08, 2014.

http://www. newsmax. com/Advani/Confucius-India-rupee-economy/2012/05/23/id/439985/

Berthrong, John N. and Evelyn N. Berthrong. Confucianism : A Short Introduction Oxford : One World Publication. 2000.

Cleary, Thomas. The Essential Confucius: The Heart of Confucius' Teachings in Authentic I Ching Order, New York : Harper SanFrancisco. 1992.

Confucius. The Analects, Translated by D. C. Lau. Chinese University Press, 2010.

Guha, Seema. DNA Analysis "Sept 2009 New Delhi"Confucius Say India Smart, China Smarter. Friday, 11 September 2009

http://www. dnaindia. com/india/report-confucius-say-india-smart-china-smarter-1289231

Indian Express, Mumbai, Friday, 19 July 2013 "India's first Confucius Institute inaugurated."

http://archive. indianexpress. com/news/country-s-first-confucius-institute-opens-at-mu-today/1143195/

Jaishankar, Subramaniyam. ICF Monitor, 17 Sept 2012, "China paves the way for new Confucius Institutes in India, global demand rising."

Jarod, A, RebekahS. and Russell T. "Comparisons of Hinduism and Confucianism and philosophical systems including some underlying similarities in cementing a social hierarchy." Wikispaces

Kasturi, CharuSudan. "Confucius centres welcome, with rider ." The Telegraph, Calcutta. Tuesday, July 8, 2014

http://www.telegraphindia.com/1130725/jsp/frontpage/story_17154874.jsp#.U7u0wFWSxic

Lau, D. C. (Trans) The Analects of Confucius, Penguin Classics, Penguin Books Ltd. 1979.

Lin, Xu. ICF Monitor, 17 Sept 2012, "China paves the way for new Confucius Institutes in India, global demand rising."

Liu, Youfa. "Inauguration Ceremony of the Confucius Institute at the University of Mumbai

held in Mumbai, India."

http://english.hanban.org/article/2013-07/24/content_508661.htm

Loon, Hendrik van. The Story of Mankind. Amezon Books.

Maliya, Chandrakant. "Influence of Confucian teachings on Family and Society." Indian Blogger. 18 October 2010.

Meng, Qingsong. "Inauguration Ceremony of the Confucius Institute at the University of

Mumbai held in Mumbai, India."

http://english.hanban.org/article/2013-07/24/content_508661.htm

Pound, Ezra. "Confucius: The Unwobbling Pivot," The Great Digest: The Analects. New Directions Publishing Corporation. 1969.

Rao, Bhanoji. "Confucian ethics, China and India." Business Line, Business Daily from THE HINDU group of publications, ePaper. Tuesday, Nov 28, 2006

http://www.thehindubusinessline.in/2006/11/28/stories/2006112800590800.htm

He formerly with the National University of Singapore and the World Bank, is Professor Emeritus, GITAM Institute of Foreign Trade, Visakhapatnam and Visiting Faculty, Sri Sathya Sai Institute of Higher Learning, Deemed University, Prasanthi Nilayam. The organisation Prasanthi Nilayam is in South India, and belongs to a trust set up by the Sai Baba of Puttaparti, a religious guru. It is a huge group of institutes and organisations, including schools, colleges, charitable hospitals etc.

The Bhagavad-Gītā . Gita Press Gorakhpur.

The title 'Bhagwad Gita' means 'The Song of God,' (referring to the god Krishna) is the best-known section of the Hindu epic Mahābhārata, belonging to the $3^{rd}$ or $4^{th}$ century BCE. It is in Sanskrit, the classical (literary) language of ancient India. It is a philosophical dialogue between Prince Arjuna, the leader of the Pāndavas, and the god Krishna, who had assumed the human form or *avtar*, and was Arjuna's charioteer in the war.

Arjuna's dilemma at the moment when the battle was about to begin, was that he didn't want to fight because he feared killing his own kinsmen. He did not consider pursuing and achieving worldly rewards like victory and power worthwhile. As a good Hindu, he knew that the physical world, after all, is only an illusion.

Yu, Longyu. Speech of Thanks at "Saptakam," a dance programme organised by Indian Studies Centre of Shenzhen University, on 10 July, 2014.

Zhang, Yan. ICF Monitor, 17 Sept 2012, "China paves the way for new Confucius Institutes in India, global demand rising."

# Part Three: Confucianism as Mega Tradition in China

## Confucian Secularism in Theoretical and Historical Perspective

**Albert Welter (University of Arizona)**

### Introduction

The current paper began in a somewhat unlikely place, a project aimed at a translation and examination of a medieval (or early modern, depending on one's perspective) Chinese text dealing with the administration of Buddhism, compiled at the beginning of one of China's most illustrious periods, the Song dynasty (960—1279).① (For those unfamiliar with Chinese culture, the Song dynasty may be said to occupy a place in China and East Asia comparable to the role of France in the European context, establishing standards for artistic, literary, and cultural expression admired down to the present day). The Song brought a new sense of order to China predicated on a return to classical learning and the Confucian orientation that accompanied it, including answers to lingering questions regarding the role of Buddhism (and religion) in the Chinese context. During the course of my research into this text, I became interested in larger questions regarding the role of religion in China, whether there is

① The text in question, the *Da Song Seng shilue* 大宋僧史略(Topical History of the Buddhist Clergy complied in the Great Song dynasty), compiled by the Buddhist monk—literatus, Zanning (919—1001), is a review of Buddhist institutions and social practices in China, arguing for the legitimate role of Buddhism as an organ of the official Chinese bureaucracy. The current paper draws very little from the detailed examination that Zanning undertakes, but is very much in the background as a stimulus to my thoughts on the nature of Chinese secularism. I would like to take the opportunity to thank the Social Sciences and Research Council of Canada for supporting my research on this text.

something that might be called Chinese secularism, and the way in which Confucian principles articulate secularism and determine how religion, namely Buddhism, is adjudicated in the Chinese context. The current paper reflects my thoughts thus far on these matters.

**1. Secularism: The Confucian Dimension**

While definitions of secularism may differ, and the fact that secularism is nuanced by different contexts is an abiding theme of the current presentation, I start with a definition of secularism that is prevalent in many, if not most, western contexts.

Secularism is the principle of the separation of government institutions and persons mandated to represent the state from religious institutions and religious dignitaries. One manifestation of secularism is asserting the right to be free from religious rule and teachings, or, in a state declared to be neutral on matters of belief, from the imposition by government of religion or religious practices upon its people. Another manifestation of secularism is the view that public activities and decisions, especially political ones, should remain uninfluenced by religious beliefs and/or practices. ①

In the West, secularism draws inspiration from the intellectual roots provided by the Greek and Roman traditions, through philosophers such as Marcus Aurelius and Epicurus; from Enlightenment thinkers such as Diderot, Voltaire, Spinoza, and Locke, and from American founding fathers like Madison, Jefferson, and Thomas Paine. The purposes and arguments in support of secularism vary widely, but the secularization hypothesis generally argues that secularism is a natural consequence of modernization, as a society moves away from dependence on traditional religious values. Having said this, religion is not always displaced by secularism, and often occurs while maintaining an official state church or other state support of religion.

Current discussions of secularism are framed rather exclusively from western contexts. Examples are drawn from western societies, even when the examples in question are based on the experiences of ethnic and religious minorities in those societies.

---

① *Secularism & Secularity: Contemporary International Perspectives*, edited by Barry A. Kosmin andAriela Keysar (Hartford, CT: Institute for the Study of Secularism in Society and Culture [ISSSC], 2007).

Experiences drawn from the Muslim world and Islamic societies have been incorporated into this discussion in recent years, especially with the rise in importance of Islamic identity in the political arena in may of these societies. In the broader context of the discussion of secularism and its relation to religion, Islam falls into the same category of Abrahamic faiths, and while the experiences of Islam may inform us about interesting and important variants of Abrahamic faith—based models of secularism, it still does not extend our understanding of how secularism might operate in non—Abrahamic religious contexts. The importance of China and East Asia looms large in this overlooked aspect of secularism for a number of reasons.

The influence of the Confucian tradition throughout East Asian societies has been vast and extensive. Its secular humanist perspective is typically acknowledged, as is its inspiration on European enlightenment figures such as Voltaire, which helped to spawn secular traditions in the West. In spite of this commonly acknowledged perspective, there has been little discussion about what Confucian secularism actually constitutes. Even basic questions—is there a Confucian secularism? —fail to elicit uniform agreement. My paper explores various facets of Confucian tradition with an aim toward answering questions regarding whether or not Confucian traditions may be regarded as a species of secularism, and if so, what the nature/character of Confucian secularism is, and what if anything, distinguishes it from other types of secularism. Both theoretical and historical aspects are introduced and discussed. While George Jacob Holyoake (1817—1906) is widely credited as the first to coin the term "secularism" (*The Principles of Secularism*), many would contend that the genesis of the concept can be traced much earlier, and that the role of the Confucian tradition in forging at least a species of secularism has long been overlooked.

As secularism in the West was forged in relation/reaction to religious, specifically Christian traditions, my paper also addresses the role of Confucian secularism in the administration of religion, specifically Buddhism, in China. I argue that public and private realms were never thought of as distinct in China, but as part of a continuum of harmonious, if sometimes contested terrain where secular and sacred aims met. The paper explores how the administration of Buddhism in China informs us about a Confucian secularism, especially notions of a "public" sphere (following Habermas), and how distinctive these notions are in a Chinese context, where sharp distinctions between "public" and "private" break down in the face of an espoused harmony between secular and religious roles. In place of a "public sphere," I posit the notion of a "sphere of privilege" where interested parties are allowed access to the mechanisms of power and arenas of cultural privilege. In this way, I respond to questions about the nature of Confucian secularism by suggesting the unique species of secularism that Confucian and the Chinese tradition represents, where notions of the separation of church and state give way to administrative policies designed to manage religious forces, providing official support for sanctioned institutions and activities, and proscribing beliefs and activities that run counter to government aims.

**2. What Lies Beneath: Native Terminology Relating to "Religion" in China**

The term "religion" is a word borne in the West and exported around the globe with the advance of western institutions and the frames through which knowledge is referenced. As these western institutions and frames of reference were transplanted in lands and cultures far removed from their origins, they were adapted and assumed a normative quality, however understood. These newly acquired knowledge structures competed with latent cultural practices and norms that strove to find places within the new systems of modernity. One of the concepts where this is abundantly clear is in the case of "religion," and in an attempt to provide a comprehensive framework for understanding concrete manifestations of religion in the public sphere in various settings, both western and nonwestern, it is appropriate to begin by problematizing the notion of "religion" itself. The fact that "religion" is a problematic notion is hardly new. The fact that it is a term embedded in particular Western linguistic and cultural frameworks is often pointed out.[①]Richard King, for example, asserts:

The modern concept of "religion" carries with it certain key assumptions about the world that are … ultimately grounded in a hegemonic Euro—American myth about the origins of 'modernity' and the birth of the secular nation—state. These assumptions are not ideologically neutral but rather are encoded according to a specifically

① See, for example, Russell T. McCutcheon, *The Discipline of Religion: Structure, Meaning, Rhetoric*(London: Routledge, 2003); and Craig Martin, "Delimiting Religion," *Method and Theory in the Study of Religion* 21 (2009): 157—176.

European history of the world. ①

The long association of religion in the West with Christianity and other monotheistic traditions likewise influenced the ways in which the category of "religion" has normally been understood. ② Moreover, the use of the concept "religion" as presently understood is of quite late vintage, emerging in Western thought during the Enlightenment. ③ Lest we fall victim to blindly mapping our cultural concepts onto other, indigenous contexts, we must be mindful that we are imposing alien importations, along with the map of the world that we use to manage and control them.

The importation of the Western category of "religion" into the Chinese and broader East Asian cultural context offers a case in point on how alien concepts assumed normative status and competed with and against domestic notions. The nature of the Chinese language, comprised of characters or logographs (commonly referred to as ideograms) that convey semantics graphically rather than phonologically (i.e., symbols represent words rather than sounds—though many logographs are composed of compounds that contain both semantic meaning and phonological information), is intrinsically different from phoneme based language systems. Although it is possible to use

---

① "The Association of 'Religion' with Violence: Reflections on a Modern Trope," in John R. Hinnells andRichard King, eds., *Religion and Violence in South Asia: Theory and Practice* (London: Routledge, 2006), p. 235.

② Within the discipline of Religious Studies, "religion" is understood as a collection of cultural systems, belief systems, and worldviews that relate humanity to spirituality, often based on the supernatural, the word itself is from Old French *religion* meaning "religious community," and derives from Latin *religionem* (nom. *religio*) meaning "respect for what is sacred, reverence for the gods," "obligation, the bond between man and the gods." Through Christianity and other Abrahamic traditions, religion became exclusively associated with monotheistic faith in the one true God. Note also the observation by Malory Nye that "the concept of religion is a trope, or a typology … it is untranslatable into many languages that religious scholars work in … it bears little relation to any 'emic' discourses" ("Religion, Post—Religionism, and Religioning: Religious Studies and Contemporary Cultural Debates," *Method & Theory in the Study of Religion* 12: 451; cited in McCutcheon, The Discipline of Religion, p. 236). See also McCutcheon's discussion (pp. 252—253), where he observes that "*for languages unaffected by Latin, there is no equivalent term to "religion"*—unless, of course, we pompously assert that our local word captures something essential to the entire human species, thereby distinguishing local *word* from universal *concept* (i. e., although they do not call "it" religion, they still have It; …)" (italics in original). McCutcheon goes on to note how this assertion is made easier through the long history of European influence on other languages and cultures through trade and conquest.

③ Peter Harrison, *"Religion" and the Religions in the English Enlightenment* (Cambridge: Cambridge University Press, 1990): 1.

the pronunciations of Chinese characters as phonemes (i.e., for their sound quality) and reproduce the pronunciation of foreign words, the tendency is to translate the foreign word into Chinese logographs that most closely approximate the meaning. To give one quick example from the Buddhist tradition, which in an earlier era faced a similar gargantuan task oftranslating Sanskrit and terms from other Buddhist languages into Chinese, there is the important term prajñā, which refers to the "wisdom" associated in particular with Mahayana Buddhist insight into the nature ofreality as "empty" (sūnya). The transliterated form ofthis concept in modern Mandarin pronunciation is bore (using the Chinese characters 般若), but its older pronunciation in Middle Chinese as something akin to *panna*, *parna*, *or p[r]ana* still retains enough ofits phonological character to be recognizable as a transliterated form of prajñā.① The logographs themselves have no meanings remotely associated with meaning of *prajñā* as "wisdom."② As a translated, rather than transliterated term in Chinese *prajñā* is often rendered as zhi 智, or sometimes as the combined term zhihui 智慧, referring to wisdom in the classical Chinese tradition, and of ten associated with the wisdom of a sage in Confucianism. While translation supplies a readily understandable meaning for the term in a domestic context, it sacrifices the nuance of the Buddhist term that equates *prajñā* with the insight into the true nature of reality where all things are ephemeral in their existence and "empty" ofultimate value and significance, for a recognizable meaning that equates it with the social and political acumen of a sagely ruler who is benevolent (ren 仁), wise (zhi 智) and expert in the applications ofritual decorum (*li* 禮).③

---

① For the complexities associated with the pronunciation of this term in Middle Chinese see the discussion on H-Net online by Christoph Anderl: http://h-net.msu.edu/cgi-bin/logbrowse.pl? trx=vx&list=hbuddhism&month=1201&week=d&msg= mQ2tciWHx Zp2cz/SQyy6dA&user=&pw=

② *Bo* 般 (or its more common pronunciation of *ban*) is usually translated as "sort; kind; class; way;manner." *Re* 若 is normally translated as "dry grass," and in the more common pronunciation of *ruo* means "be like; seem," or as an initial particle, "if."

③ See, for example, the *Book of Mencius* 孟子 (Gong Sun Chou I 公孫丑上), where it is reported that when Confucius' disciple Zi Gong 子貢 asked Confucius if he was a Sage, Confucius responded, "A Sage is what I cannot rise to. I learn without satiety, and teach without being tired," to which Zi Gong said, "You learn without satiety—that shows your wisdom. You teach without being tired—that shows your benevolence. Benevolent and wise—Master, you are a Sage." (聖則吾不能，我學不厭而教不倦也。子貢曰：學不厭，智也；教不倦，仁也。仁且智，夫子既聖矣！); James Legge translation, Chinese Text Project (http://ctext.org/mengzi/gong-sun-chou-i).

While this is neither the time nor the place to go into the perils associated with translating terms from one language to another, it is appropriate to spend a few moments considering how some of the key terms for understanding what passes for religion in the Chinese context, how they are framed and what they imply. A linguist could obviously spend a great deal more time on this than I can, and what I introduce here is simply intended as a prelude to my larger discussion.

Like many of the categories of knowledge systems that entered East Asia as part of a general acceptance of modernization and Westernization, the term "religion" received standard formulation in a Sino—Japanese logographic term coined in Meiji Japan as *shūkyō* 宗教, pronounced in modern Chinese, *zongjiao*. The combination of these two logographs *zong* and *jiao* was almost entirely unprecedented, but each of the logographs taken independently had long — standing meanings in China and throughout East Asia. The combined logographs quickly formed a new category indicating the kind ofexclusive allegiance or devotion to a tradition common to the definition of religion in the West. While religion in the West was understood as part and parcel of an exclusive faith to a single and universal creator God, the concept of exclusivity, while not unknown in East Asia, was the exception rather than the rule. Nor was faith necessarily the primary concern, as *praxis* replaced *dox* as how one's relationship with a tradition was defined, and *praxis* in different traditions simultaneously was much more common than not. As the combined logographs *shūkyō* or *zongjiao* became the normative equivalent of "religion" in the East Asian context, the majority of practitioners began to see themselves as essentially "not religious," meaning "not religious in the Western sense of the term." This confusion, the association of religion with exclusive commitment based on faith, has marred the understanding of religion in the region down to the present day.

One way of suggesting a possible inherent meaning for "religion" in the Chinese (and Japanese) context, is to look at the latent native meanings of the logographs used to translate the Western term "religion." While it is not my intention to invoke an etymological reductionism in place of"religion" as an easy solution, I do content that an etymological analysis ofthe two logographs, zong 宗 and jiao 教 reveals latent native understandings lurking beneath the surface of the modern normative category *zongjiao*.

The logograph *zong* 宗 is comprised of two elements: an upper element (the "radical") 宀, signifying the "roof" of a building; and the lower element 示, which by itself is an independent logograph (pronounced *shi*) meaning "to show, reveal; to announce, report." Taken together, the upper element is taken as indicating the roof of an ancestral shrine, while the lower element indicates offerings presented to the ancestors while reporting (i.e., praying) to them. In short, the logograph zong is closely associated with the veneration of ancestors that forms the core of traditional Chinese expressions of religiosity.①

The logograph *jiao* 教 is likewise pregnant with embedded meanings that resonated in a traditional native context. It, too, can be broken down into two parts, a left element 孝 and a right element 文 (the "radical"), both of which form independent logographs when taken on their own. The left element, *xiao* 孝, refers to "filial piety," the cardinal Confucian virtue of respect for one's parents, exhibited through actions and attitudes exhibited both in this life and after they have departed, but broken down further into upper and lower sub—elements, one finds an abbreviated form of the character for "elder," *lao* 老, over the character for *zi* 子, "son" or "child." The right element, *wen* 文, contains a range of meanings: "letters, literature, writing, culture." Taken as a whole, *jiao* indicates the passing down of writings imbued with cultural values (i.e., traditions) from elders to children. It is hardly surprising to find Chinese, particularly Confucian undertones lurking in the etymological analysis of these logographs. The logographs themselves exhibit a native understanding of attitudes and behaviours that approximate our category "religion." The combination of these logographs as *zongjiao* reflects a newly coined term that transposes them into a Western category, one that has assumed normative status, but that is often confused by attitudes and actions suggested by their etymological origins.

"Sacred" and "secular" are also terms imported from the West for which no pre-

---

① The etymological explanations of Sino—Japanese logographs provided in this section are by and large consistent throughout numerous dictionaries and other linguistic reference works. I have generally relied on the explanations provided in Ogawa, Nishida, and Akatsuka, eds., Shin ji en 新字源 (Tokyo: Kadokawa shoten, 1988; original printed 1968).

cise Chinese or East Asian equivalents existed. ①"Sacred" was translated into Chinese using two logographs, *shensheng* 神聖. The first logograph, *shen* 神, is commonly used to refer to "god; spirit; spiritual being." The left element is a stylized form of the logograph *shi* 示, meaning "to show, reveal; to announce, report," discussed above. The right element, *shen* 申, originally indicated a "flash or bolt of lightning," and was associated with the god of thunder or the sky. Eventually, the combined elements acquired a broader meaning of god or deity, and by extension, any activity that surpasses human ability. The second logograph of *shensheng* 神聖 is arguably the more significant and interesting of the two. *Sheng* 聖 is comprised of two elements, a top element divided into left and right sub—elements, and a bottom element. The bottom element (the "radical") constitutes the independent logograph *wang* 王, indicating a "king or ruler." It is an important concept in the Chinese tradition which early on was preoccupied with discussions associated with what constitutes a true king, and the "kingly way" (*wangdao* 王道) of justice and virtue. The logograph itselfdepicts the division of the Chinese universe in terms of three realms as three horizontal lines 三, indicating (in descending order) the heavenly realm, human realm, and earthly realm, intersected by a vertical line 丨, which stands for the uniting and harmonizing influence of the king or ruler. Taken together, the logograph indicates the harmonious unification of the cosmos—heaven, earth, and humans—through the virtuous rule of the king. Without human moral effort, the natural course of heaven and earth will be disrupted, and the ensuing chaos will portend disaster for human society. It is the ruler's primary responsibility to insure moral rectitude through virtuous conduct, and the ruler serves as moral exemplar in this effort. The two upper sub—elements in the logograph *sheng* 聖 are also noteworthy for their contribution to the overall meaning. The left sub—element constitutes the independent logograph *er* 耳, indicating the

---

① The word "sacred" derives from the Latin *sacrum*, referring to the gods or anything in their power, and to *sacerdos*, "priest"; and *sanctum*, "to set apart." It was generally conceived spatially, as referring to the area around a temple. *Secular* and *secularity* derive from the Latin word *saecularis* meaning "ofa generation,belonging to an age." The Christian doctrine that God exists outside time led medieval Western culture to use *secular* to indicate separation from specifically religious affairs and involvement in temporal ones. This meaning has been extended to mean separation from any religion, regardless of whether it has a similar doctrine. One is reminded here, as well, that sacred/secular, along with private/public, Church/State, etc. ,are among the binaries upon which modern understandings of reality are constructed.

"ear" and the listening function associated with it. The right sub—element constitutes the logograph *kou* 口 , for "mouth" and the speaking activity associated with it. In its entirety, the logograph *sheng* represents the ruler who listens to heaven with his ear and articulates the message he receives with his mouth. *Sheng* is normally associated with the "sage" ofChinese tradition, who is attuned to the will of Heaven (conceived at times anthropomorphic, but mostly in non—anthropomorphic terms), and exemplifies its message through words and deeds. The great heroes of Chinese tradition, the so—called sage—kings of antiquity, exemplified the virtues of the sage through their exemplary behavior and heroic deeds. While the status of sage is beyond ordinary human accomplishment, it remained a powerful goal for ideal rule throughout Chinese history, and every ruler aspired to and was believed to receive heavenly sanction, *tianming* 天命 or "the mandate of Heaven," as a condition of their ascent.

The term "secular" is also comprised of two logographs in Chinese, *shisu* 世俗. The first logograph, *shi* 世, was originally written as 卅, indicating the Chinese character for the number ten 十, written three times, equaling the number "thirty" and standing for the notion of a "generation" that prevails in the world for roughly thirty years. In general, it represents the idea of"generation, era, or world," but of ten takes on the meaning of "hereditary."①The second logograph, *su* 俗, is comprised oftwo elements. The left element (the "radical") is a stylized representation of the logograph *ren* 人, meaning "human being or beings." The right element, *gu* 谷, is the character for "valley," but here it is used to indicate the sound or pronunciation of the logograph which has apparently changed over time. The logograph *su* 俗 is normally taken to mean "social customs, common, vulgar, or unrefined."

I am not trying to suggest that the etymological root—meanings indicated by these terms are the "correct" ones. To do so would impose a teleological fallacy to etymological meanings. Words are not static; their meanings evolve through temporal and spatial circumstance, and their etymologies only suggest from whence they derive. What I would suggest, however, is that the etymological analysis points not only

---

① Note, for example the use of *shi* 世 in the compound *shi jia* 世家 "hereditary houses," a common category in Chinese dynastic histories for incorporating the biographies from members ofillustrious families.

to past "dead" meanings, but also possibilities for how Chinese approximations for these concepts have been understood in the past and the meanings that they may again take on in future, as China embarks on a course to rediscover native traditions and shed itself of a cultural hegemony imposed by imported normative categories.

### 3. The Metaphor of Proximity: The Confucian Rejection of Universalism, the "Public Sphere", and the "Sphere of Privilege"

This section is a continuation of some background considerations to the discussion of religion and the public sphere in the Chinese context. If the previous section leaned toward problems associated with terms like "religion," "secular," and "sacred," this section involves issues relating to transposing the notion of a "public sphere" to a Chinese context. There are many ways this problem could be approached, and my discussion here represents but one attempt to provide some clarity to the issue. I begin with a characterization of the "public sphere" as it has been described in recent Western academic discourse.

Russell McCutcheon argues that modern European rhetorical innovations delimited religion as a private concept "in a way that was designed to sequester it from the state," creating the "public sphere" and the "private sphere," and establishing the "separation of church and state." However externalized, objectified, or reified as natural or eternal this order was suggested to be, there was nothing natural about it. Instead, it is a "fabrication" that segregates (or "straightjackets") the world, and although it might be a fabrication that benefited modern Europe, it is an ordering of the world that is hardly selfevident.①

According to Habermas,The bourgeois public sphere may be conceived above all as the sphere of private people come together as a public; they soon claimed the public sphere regulated from above against the public authorities themselves, to engage them in a debate over the general rules governing relations in the basically privatized but publicly relevant sphere of commodity exchange and social labor. *The medium of this political confrontation was peculiar and without precedent: people's public use of*

---

① McCutcheon, *The Discipline of Religion*, chapters 11 and 12, pp. 230—290; as described by Martin, "Delimiting Religion," pp. 173—174.

their reason (*öffentlich Rasonnement*). [①]

The public sphere as "a discursive space in which individuals and groups congregate to discuss matters of mutual interest and, where possible, to reach a common judgment,"[②] as "a theater in modern societies in which political participation is enacted through the medium of talk,"[③] or "a realm of social life in which public opinion can be formed,"[④] draws on well—known notions put forth by Habermas of a public sphere that mediates between a "private sphere" and the "Sphere of Public Authority."[⑤] According to Habermas, whereas "the private sphere comprised civil society in the narrower sense, that is to say, the realm of commodity exchange and of social labor,"[⑥] and the "Sphere of Public Authority" dealt with the State, or realm of the police, and the ruling class,[⑦] the public sphere crossed over both these realms and "[t]hrough the vehicle of public opinion it put the state in touch with the needs of society."[⑧] In this sense, according to Nancy Fraser, "the public sphere is an arena conceptually distinct from the state;" a "site for the production and circulation of discourses that can in principle be critical ofthe state."[⑨] The public sphere "is also distinct from the official economy; it is not an arena of market relations but rather one of discursive relations, a theater for debating and deliberating rather than for buying and selling."[⑩] These distinctions between "state apparatuses, economic markets, and demo-

---

① Jürgen Habermas (Thomas Burger, trans.) *The Structural Transformation of the Public Sphere: An Inquiry into a Category of Bourgeois Society* (Cambridge, Mass.: MIT Press, 1989; German edition, 1962), p. 27.

② Gerard Hauser, "Vernacular Dialogue and the Rhetoricality of Public Opinion," *Communication Monographs* 65—2 (June 1988): 83-107; p. 86.

③ Nancy Fraser, "Rethinking the Public Sphere: A Contribution to the Critique of Actually Existing Democracy," Social Text (Duke University Press, 1990) 25/26: 56-80.

④ Robert Asen, "Toward a Normative Conception of Difference in Public Deliberation," *Argumentation and Advocacy* 25 (Winter, 1999): 115-129.

⑤ Jürgen Habermas (Thomas Burger, trans.) *The Structural Transformation of the Public Sphere: AnInquiry into a Category of Bourgeois Society* (Cambridge, Mass.: MIT Press, 1989; German edition, 1962), p. 30.

⑥ Habermas, *The Structural Transformation of the Public Sphere*, p. 30.

⑦ Habermas, *The Structural Transformation of the Public Sphere*, p. 30.

⑧ Habermas, The Structural Transformation of the Public Sphere, p. 31.

⑨ Fraser, "Rethinking the Public Sphere," p. 57.

⑩ Fraser, "Rethinking the Public Sphere," p. 57.

cratic associations... are essential to democratic theory."[①] The people themselves came to see the public sphere as a regulatory institution against the authority of the state.[②] The study of the public sphere centers on the idea of participatory democracy, and how public opinion becomes political action. A basic premise of public sphere theory is a beliefin the efficacy of enlightened debate. Political action is instigated by public sphere debate; the only legitimate governments are those that listen to the public sphere.[③] "Democratic governance rests on the capacity of and opportunity for citizens to engage in enlightened debate."[④]

This characterization invites comment in several respects. The discussion is framed essentially around Habermas's characterization of a "public sphere" drawn from eighteenth century European bourgeois society. It is a category that presupposes a number of unique features pertaining to that society: participatory democracy, the role of public opinion, and attitudes toward citizen activism, not to mention the lack of regard for status (hierarchy) among participants, the domains of common ground over which private citizens could exercise authority, and ever expanding notions ofinclusivity that in principle could exclude no one, to name but a few. As a realm that mediates between the "private sphere" and the "Sphere of Public Authority," the "public sphere" can hardly be said to exist outside modern democracies, so the first question that must be addressed is the applicability of a notion of the "public sphere" to a pre—modern or non—western context. Clearly the term does not apply. Yet, to the extent that democratic forms of government provide a normative model against which modern governments are judged, one can hardly dismiss discussions of the "public sphere" out of hand, even in the Chinese context.[⑤] As with the case of democracy, even when it is not subscribed to, countries like China are frequently forced

---

① Fraser, "Rethinking the Public Sphere," p. 57.

② Habermas, *The Structural Transformation of the Public Sphere*, p. 27.

③ Seyla Benhabib, "Models of Public Space," in Craig Calhoun, ed., *Habermas and the Public Sphere* (Cambridge Mass.: MIT press, 1992), p. 87.

④ Hauser, "Vernacular Dialogue," p. 83.

⑤ The impact of Habermas is described by Weidong Cao, "The Historical Effect of Habermas in the Chinese Context: A Case Study of the Structural Transformation of the Public Sphere," *Frontiers of Philosophy in China*, Vol. 1, No. 1 (Jan., 2006), pp. 41—50.

in international forums to explain their actions against the norms that democratic value systems presuppose, so that even when China does not sanction a "public sphere" where democratic presumptions prevail, large portions of the rest of the world and even some of its own citizens presume that this is a model that China should aspire to. There are fewer arenas in China where this is more self—evident than in the arena of religion and the limits of China's tolerance toward its public display. The question thus turns to why there is such resistance to a "public sphere" in the Chinese context. How does Chinese thinking about things like a "private sphere" and the "sphere of public authority" work to inhibit the growth of a "public sphere"? To answer this question requires a shift away from the Western discourse surrounding a "public sphere" initiated by Habermas, and an entry into the Chinese discourse that delineates how arenas of influence are apportioned and managed through bureaucratic apparatuses in the Chinese context.

As pointed out by Oskar Negt and Alexander Kluge, the German term for "public sphere" in Habermas's title, *Öffentlichkeit*, includes a variety of meanings, but implies a spatial concept, social sites or arenas where meanings are articulated, distributed, and negotiated, as well as the collective body constituted by "the public."① The pubic sphere as spatial concept provides a good entry point for understanding how the Chinese rationalize and manage the flow of public discourse on criteria different from the model assumed by Habermas. While Habermas's model of the public sphere is predicated on the creation of free and open public spaces, sites or arenas where meanings are articulated, distributed, and negotiated, the Chinese model is built upon notions of symbolic spatial proximity, where distance from the center is viewed as a

---

① *Public Sphere and Experience: Toward an Analysis of the Bourgeois and Proletarian Public Sphere*(Minneapolis: University of Minnesota Press, 1993). According to Cao, "The Historical Effect of Habermas in the Chinese Context" (p. 44), Chinese scholars also disagreed on how to translate *Öffentlichkeit* into Chinese. Some thought it should be translated as *gonggong lingyu* 公共领域 (publicdomain/sphere/field/territory/area), some thought that it should be translated as *gonggong lunyu* 公共论域(domain/sphere/field of [critical] public discussion), while others thought it should be translated as *gonggong kongjian* 公共空间 (public space). The first alternative became the commonly accepted one. The second one (domain/sphere/field of [critical] public discussion) preserves the polemical nuances that Habermas associated with the "people's use of reason" (*öffentlich Rasonnement*) (*The Structural Transformation of the Public Sphere*, p. 27).

means to manage and control access and privilege. Chinese notions of"space" are thus managed on the basis of proximity that positions participants around a centrifugal force creating a symbolic social universe that arranges and manages articulated, distributed, and negotiated spaces in relation to each other. Access to power and privilege is managed through proximity to the center. This includes the power to express oneselfpublicly, i.e., to engage in public debate.

Chinese notions of proximity that govern access and privilege are firmly rooted in the Confucian tradition. These notions dominated the Chinese imperial state and continue to resonate down to the present under different guises. It is not that the Chinese were unaware of alternatives. The Confucian consensus emerged out of a welter of intellectualturmoil, termed the "hundred schools of thought" (*zhuzi baijia* 諸子百家) of the Spring and Autumn and Warring States periods of Chinese history (770－221 BCE). Among the schools of thought that challenged for supremacy was one instituted by the philosopher Mozi 墨子 (or Mo Di 墨翟; 470—ca. 391 BCE) and his disciples, who became known as Mohists (*mojia* 墨家). Mozi argued for a form of universalism whereby everyone is equal before Heaven, and ofstandards to be followed, "there is nothing better than following Heaven."① Mozi advocated that no distinctions based on kinship proximity were warranted, that freedom from partiality through "universal love" (*boai* 博愛) would rid the world of chaos and friction. The universal standard provided by Heaven created norms applicable to all alike, and all became equal before Heaven.

The Confucian consensus actively disputed the model endorsed by Mozi and his followers. Whereas Mohists saw in their universal standard the seeds of social harmony, Confucians viewed it as a pretext for chaos. It was unnatural, the Confucians argued, to love another's parents as much as one's own, or to regard the members of other's families as the equal to one's own. Human relationships naturally followed a spatial proximity determined by kinship ties: those closer to one on the kinship scale were more deserving of affection and regard than strangers at a distance. The hypothetical standard that rendered everyone equal violated the law of natural human in-

---

① *Mouzi* 墨子 Bk. 1, "On the Necessity of Standards" (*fayi* 法儀), section 4: 莫若法天. China Text Project (http://ctext.org/mozi/on—the—necessity—of—standards), consulted June 28, 2012.

stincts, where love or affection was apportioned on a sliding scale based on relative proximity. In the Confucian constellation, filial piety was transformed from bland respect for one's parents, to an ultimate mandate by which one's virtue was measured. Filial piety was thus not a voluntary choice, but a mandate written into the order of the universe, the violation of which threatened the natural law of Heaven. In this constellation, human relations became a finely tuned balancing act dictated by symbolic notions of proximity. Confucian texts provided the code books through which proximate human relations were understood and managed.

The influence of the Confucian kinship model did not stop with the family, but was superimposed on the framework of society as a whole whereby the entire population was regarded as the "Chinese family." The emperor, as patriarch of the nation, presided over the Chinese family, just as patriarchs presided over individual Chinese clans. Ministers of state proffered their obedience and respect to the emperor in a manner modeled on the filial respect learned as children toward one's parents. The deference ministers showed to the emperor was mitigated by the Confucian tradition of remonstration, whereby the minister also had a duty to respectfully guide imperial decision making to the point of actively disagreeing with the emperor if the situation warranted it. This was a privilege accorded only to Confucian educated advisors, who "earned" the right to remonstrate (i.e., express their "public" opinion, though the *public* in this case was restricted to the emperor and his court) through their command over the Confucian curriculum and the moral virtues it instilled in them. The hierarchy of the Chinese bureaucracy thus imitated the kinship proximity model that the Confucian tradition enshrined. Entrance into the bureaucratic constellation marked one as a privileged member of the ministerial family, where rank and position determined a relative scale to access and privilege. Gaining entrance to this world of access and privilege was an overwhelming preoccupation of the aspiring elite. ①

How do these notions affect the way religion has been managed in the Chinese context? In the following section, I touch briefly on how Buddhism was managed in

---

① The Confucian bureaucracy in pre-modern China approximates Habermas' description of the world of letters of courtly-noble society, whose influence extended to the public sphere in the world of letters (*literarische Öffentlichkeit*) (*The Structural Transformation of the Public Sphere*, *pp.* 29-30).

China, based on the notion of allowing and denying privileges based on the model of spatial proximity.

**4. Administrating Religion in China: The Example of Buddhism**

At the outset, I noted how definitions of secularism were intricately connected to religious expression, and how the management of religion in society was a major concern for secular governments and institutions. In the Chinese context the template for managing religion was established with the entrance of Buddhism into China. Over the centuries, Chinese administrative practices and policies were formed to manage Buddhist institutions and the Buddhist influence, and this served as a prototype for managing other religions as they became established in China.

Some years ago, the French Sinologist Jacques Gernet outlined a model for how Buddhism functioned in Chinese society based on material and economic criteria, the relevance of which is still evident.① While noting the great diversity that characterizes the Buddhist institutional presence in China, from great monasteries housing dozens of monks to village chapels and mountain hermitages with one or two inhabitants,② Gernet also calls attention to a similar diversity in terms of status:

Some monasteries are official places of worship and are recognized as such. They have received their name (*e* 額) by imperial bestowal as well as gifts of land, funds, servants, allotments of local families, and certain privileges. They are entitled to annual subventions from the court. Their monks have been selected and ordained by the emperor and are supervised by officially appointed clergy who are held accountable for their conduct. The other kind[s] of establishments are merely tolerated and are always the first to fall victim to repressions. These are private places of worship, serving the great families as well as the people.③

Following the distinction in status accorded Buddhist institutions, Gernet stipu-

---

① *Buddhism in Chinese Society: An Economic History from the Fifth to the Tenth Centuries*, translated by Franciscus Verellen (New York: Columbia University Press, 1995); originally published as *Les aspectsêconomiques du bouddhisme dans la sociêtê chinoise du Ve au Xe siècle* (Saigon: êcole Francaised'Extrême—Orient, 1956).

② Gernet, *Buddhism in Chinese Society*, p. 3.

③ Gernet, *Buddhism in Chinese Society*, p. 4. I have added the Chinese character for the temple name tabletconferred by the emperor (額), and changed the pronunciation from Wade—Giles o to pinyin *e*.

lates that there were three kinds of Chinese monks: "the official monk, maintained at state expense and responsible for the performance of ceremonies of the imperial cult"; "the private monk, fed and clothed by the great families"; and "the common monk who lived in the country side, either in isolation or as a member of a small group."① What Gernet indicates, in effect, is that there was great distinction between official and private monasteries, and that private monasteries were also divisible into two types: those constructed by officials and members of prominent families, and those erected to serve the interests of the common people. Great divides of privilege and power separated these three types of institutions and the monks who inhabited them. Rather than a single Buddhist institution in China, it is important to recognize the diversity among the types of institutions and monks who comprised the Buddhist world. The recognition of these distinctions weighed heavily on the fate of Buddhism in China. An imperial court that tolerated Buddhism and even one that identified with Buddhism was obliged to resist uncontrolled expansion of clergy and monastic constructions: expansion and construction perpetrated by imperial relatives and high officials, although highly visible, was difficult to control owing to the influence and privilege of the perpetrators; developments at the popular level occurred in response to diffuse forces and relatively anonymous patrons.②

Just as elite families coveted entrance into the privileged world of ministerial position in the government bureaucracy (ostensibly through the examination system, but also through "back—door" type connections), so did great families seek to convert their private monasteries into official establishments and exercised all their influence in order to do so. Similarly, clergy members whose ordinations had not been officially accredited benefited from imperial decrees sanctioning their ordained status. As Gernet notes: "This amounted to a steady and highly effective pressure exerted upon the religious policy of the court, tending to favor a development of Buddhism in China well beyond the bounds that governments might

---

① Gernet, *Buddhism in Chinese Society*, p. 4. To give an idea ofthe relative numbers of institutions housing each ofthese three types, Gernet refers to the *Bianzheng lun* 辯正論 (T 52, no. 2110) by Falin 法琳 (572—640) which enumerates for the Northern Wei dynasty (386—534): 47 great state monasteries; 839monasteries of princes, dukes, eminent families, etc.; and 30,000 or more monasteries built by commoners.

② Gernet, *Buddhism in Chinese Society*, p. 5.

have reasonably wished to impose on it."①

In short, while religions like Buddhism faced serious challenges to gain acceptance in China, there did exist legitimate avenues whereby Buddhist institutions and clergy were allowed access to privilege. Official monasteries and clergy served at the behest of emperor, and were recognized as legitimate members of the bureaucratic establishment. Clergy residing in monasteries sponsored by the great families, protected by the prestige of their patrons, also enjoyed a kind of privileged status and held out the hope of conversion to official status. In times of suppression, however, these monasteries were vulnerable to the vagaries of imperial policy and the protections afforded them by their patrons could easily evaporate. The "common" monasteries and the clergy who inhabited them were most vulnerable and least tolerated, but any of the private, nonofficial monasteries and clergy could be subject to closure at government whim. The elite Buddhism practiced at official monasteries, the reserve of a privileged few, was the "official" face of Buddhism and, as such, immune from persecution.

According to binary oppositions that divide reality into competing hierarchical spheres,② monastics and their institutions can hardly fit anywhere but on the religious/sacred/ church side, juxtaposed against the secular/ profane/ state, and with which there is little in common. What do we make of the Buddhist monastery as government institution, or members of the Buddhist clergy as officials in the government bureaucracy? Such arrangements strike the modern reader as medieval, at best, and relegated to a dark age of confusion where the natural lines of demarcation separating (i.e., protecting) religion (the irrational) from the state (the rational) are not in force.

What the Chinese example suggests is that the conceptual categories of Western modernity separating the sacred and secular are not the only "natural" means available to adjudicate between rational and irrational. This is not to suggest that binaries do not also apply to the Chinese context, as even passing familiarity to *yin/yang* ideology

---

① Gernet, *Buddhism in Chinese Society*, p. 5.

② Jacques Derrida describes meaning in the West as defined in terms of binary oppositions, "a violent hierarchy" where "one of the two terms governs the other" (*Positions*: Chicago: University of ChicagoPress, 1981, pp. 28—30).

attests. But borrowing the metaphor of proximity based on kinship, the Chinese paired their binaries to a model ofspatial proximity. This produced not strict oppositions *per se*, but graded distinctions of acceptance/ tolerance based on symbolic proximity to a central authority. It was this model that was used to adjudicate between the various Buddhisms that existed in the Chinese context as described by Gernet, to determine and legislate between acceptable Buddhist "rational" behavior and unacceptable "irrational" and superstitious behavior. This does not mean that China was exempted from the "violent hierarchy" that, according to Derrida, such binaries suggest,① but the model ofspatial proximity did serve to soften the violence as binaries were regarded as less absolute and more tolerant.

**5. Chinese Secularism and Religion, or Secularism with Chinese Characteristics?**

The experience of Buddhism in the Chinese context provides a clear glimpse into the principles guiding Chinese secularism and it's managing of religious affairs. While my specific comments here pertain to the Chinese state's management of Buddhism, the principles espoused are easily transferable to the management of other religious traditions and other religious activities. Even the officially atheist modern Chinese Communist Party's (CCP) policies on religion may be seen as heir to these principles. According to current policy, religious activities are officially permitted for five religious groups: Buddhism, Daoism, Islam, Catholicism and Protestant Christianity.② The activities of these groups are subject to CCP oversight, on the one hand, but they are also supported institutionally and financially. Members of officially acknowledged groups must abide by rules mandated by the CCP, including provisions regarding patriotism, and a key aspect of these groups is that they are regarded as patriotic associations.③ Accounting for religious adherents who are not included as members of CCP

---

① Ibid.

② There are far too many sources discussing the current state of religious practice in China, and government policies surrounding it, to list here. For a comprehensive, ifslightly dated overview, see the articles contained in Daniel L. Overmyer, ed., *Religion in China Today* (Cambridge: Cambridge University Press, 2003).

③ See, for example, Pitman B. Potter, "Beliefin Control: Regulation of Religion in China," in Overmyer, ed., *Religion in China Today*, pp. 11—31. Potter characterizes CCP policy as an attempt to manage a balance between socio—economic autonomy and political loyalty (pp. 12—13, 27), noting the inherent tension "[t]o the extent that policies on regulation of religion require a degree of subservience that is inconsistent with religious conviction, compliance will be elusive" (p. 29).

authorized groups is difficult and estimates vary widely, but the majority of religious practitioners (and by most estimates, the vast majority) operate in autonomous communities outside of state sanction and authority. Toleration for these groups varies according to the public vs. private nature of the activities engaged in (reprimands are less likely in the case of private, behind closed doors or "house" activities), and the vagaries of state tolerance. Beyond this are groups whose practices are labeled as "superstitious" (Falun Gong being the most noted example) and deemed to be intrinsically disruptive to the socialist aims and policies of the state and its citizens. Any activity so labeled is liable to be prohibited, at times forcefully, especially activities involving public performance.

It is easy to correlate modern CCP policy toward religion with traditional dynastic government policies toward Buddhism. Recall Gernet's tripartite division introduced above—"the official monk, maintained at state expense and responsible for the performance of ceremonies of the imperial cult"; "the private monk, fed and clothed by the great families"; and "the common monk who lived in the country side, either in isolation or as a member ofa small group"—and we see a semblance of CCP policy toward religion: officially authorized religious groups, autonomous private groups, and groups branded as active in "superstition." The concentric circles that radiate from the control mandated by central authority privilege an inside sphere, a "sphere of privilege," of sanctioned activities deemed to foster government aims, operating as legitimate organs of government policy. Beyond this, religious activities may be tolerated, but not officially sanctioned. Any activities deemed to defy official policy are subject to censure.

At the outset, I postulated a Western definition of secularism based on:

- The principle ofthe separation of government institutions from religious institutions and religious dignitaries;
- The right to be free from religious rule and teachings, or from the imposition by government of religion or religious practices upon its people;
- The view that public activities and decisions, especially political ones, should remain uninfluenced by religious beliefs and/or practices.

In contrast to this Western definition, I have characterized a Chinese secularism, or Secularism with Chinese Characteristics, in terms whereby:

- The administration of religion falls fully within the purview ofthe state;

• Sanction and support of religious institutions and activities are provided for, so long as they abide by dictates of state;

• A "public sphere" is controlled by the state, and a "sphere ofprivilege" provides for earned access to the arena of cultural discourse and influence.

**6. Concluding Reflections: Religion, Secularism, and "Modernity"**

The discussion of Chinese secularism and its relation to the administration of religion raise important questions regarding the nature of religion in relation to modernity, as commonly understood. The discussion of "modern" or "modernity" in relation to religion invokes the spirit of Weber, and Weber's formulations in this regard cast a long shadow over our understanding of modernity and its relation to tradition (especially religion), and the West's alleged uniqueness over the non—West, including China (the very essence of Weber's formulation of modernity).[①] Weber's formulation ofmodernity derives from European enlightenment notions of rationality and subjective freedom that grew out of Protestant Christianity and the rejection of "traditional" Christianity, or Catholicism, that preceded it. It essentially negates everything that is non—modern: the past (medieval Europe) and the other (Asia). By necessity, Asia and medieval Europe are lumped together as lacking rationality and subjective freedom—the essential components of Weber's modernity (actually "rationality" is the Weberian term; "subjective freedom" is the functional equivalent term used by Habermas). In the Weberian project the key concepts of modernity were products of Christian civilization, universalized as truths applicable to all times, all societies, and all civilizations.

Weber's notion of modernity was predicated on a notion of secularism that isolated and marginalized religion under the rubric of "separation of church and state," assigning religion a primarily private function and curtailing religious participation in the public sphere. By historicizing the Weberian project as a product of a particular time and a particular civilization (thus depriving it of its universalizing mission), we are forced to reconsider the fallacious underpinnings of Weber's "modernity" and how the conceptual framework deriving from it has tainted our understanding of the non—

① My thoughts on this topic have been informed by Wang Hui, "Weber and the Question of Chinese Modernity," in *The Politics of Imagining Asia* (Cambridge MA: Harvard University Press, 2011), pp. 264—306.

West, including China. In this regard, it is necessary (citing Habermas) to "{disassociate} 'modernity' from its modern European origins … and break the internal connections between modernity and the historical context of Western rationalism, so that processes of modernization can no longer be conceived as rationalization, [or] as the historical objectification ofrational structures."[①]

What does this have to do with our understanding of religion and secularism? Quite a lot, I would contend, for the separation or non—involvement ofreligion in the operation of the secular state is a normative principle of modern nation — states formed on the Western model, as is the subsequent privatization of religion. The Chinese model of Confucian secularism or secularism with Chinese characteristics seriously challenge the presuppositions of Western normative principles, allowing for, even encouraging, judicious participation of religious institutions and their representatives in the public sphere. Confucian secularist encouragement of religious participation does not tolerate the unbridled reign of subjective freedom, but sanctions responsible religious expression that openly subscribes to government aims and sees religious participation as a fulfillment of such aims. Access to the public sphere is privileged, entrance is determined by specific markers and conditions of acceptance. To the extent that Chinese governments incorporate traditional policies toward the administration of religious groups (and current CCP policies toward religion suggest that they do), we will see a new understanding of religion viz. a viz. the secular that challenges and supplants the hitherto normative pattern imposed by Western secularism.

By questioning the applicability of the Weberian project to cultures like China, we are questioning Weberian notions of modernity itself, based as it is on concepts of allegedly universal applicability that privilege uniquely Western developments. In this regard, we must understand our new mission: to explain how the concept of rationalization has been employed for all societies and historical periods as a conceptual and theoretical principle, how it has organized and regulated our view of social and cultural history, and how it has managed to align all historical data into a seamless historical discourse—one that marginalized most human experience, especially Asian. Wang

---

① Habermas, *The Philosophical Discourse of Modernity*, *trans.* by Frederick Lawrence (Cambridge, MA: The MIT Press, 1987), p. 2 [originally published in German as *Der Philosophische Diskurs der Moderne:ZwölfVorlesungen* (Suhrkamp Verlag, 1985)].

Hui's point is that the trope of Western modernization (following Weber) has been validated by a negation of the past and the non—West.[①] The rise of the non—West necessarily questions this premise, and confronting and challenging Weber is a step in this process. Beyond this, we must recognize a challenge to the entire European enlightenment project based on Hegel's "principle of subjectivity," the notion that individual autonomy constitutes the essence of man (sic.) and entails freedom from all forms ofexternal authority.[②] Religion, in the Chinese context, does not represent a notion of subjective freedom from all forms of external authority, a privileged privatesphere. To the contrary, it represents the potential for privileged access to the levers of public participation, for full and inclusive membership in the execution of state policy.

My own paper, in some small way, hopes to engage this process by analyzing linguistic and conceptual concepts that are important to notions of religion and secularism, key components of the modernization project, as linguistic and conceptual concepts in their natural Chinese habitat. Rather than invoking the normative frames of reference applied to "religion" and "secularism" as Western concepts based on Western modernization theory, I try to look at Chinese equivalent frames of understanding. Finally, I suggest that the Chinese frames of understanding not be simply relegated to a "past" or "other," Weberian markers of the absence of true "modernity," but viewed as indicators of an alternate modernity, not indebted to Western frames ofreference, with an accompanying alternate understanding of how relations between religion and secularism are adjudicated.

---

① *The Politics ofImagining Asia.*

② As characterized by Habermas, *Philosophical Discourse of Modernity*, p. 18 and p. 7.

# The Mawangdui Silk Manuscript *Yi zhi yi* 易之義 Revisited: Confucian, Daoist, or …?

**Bent Nielsen (University of Copenhagen, Denmark)**

How does the silk ms. text known as the *Yi zhi yi* add to our understanding of *Yi jing* 易經 studies in the late 3rd and early 2nd centuries BCE? What new information—if any—does the text provide? The *Yi zhi yi*—which I translate 'The Significance of the Changes' but perhaps better rendered as 'the appropriate significance of the Changes'—is a new text yet it contains passages also appearing in the received tradition of the Ten Wings.

In the present paper I will argue that the text we know as the *Yi zhi yi* was composed and/or edited as a part of a body of political-philosophical literature intended to offer a philosophy of government which would serve as an alternative not only to Legalism or Confucianism but more specifically, perhaps, to the Five Phases cosmology. This corpus is comprised of the *Zhou yi* 周易 and the *Lao zi* 老子 plus a number of texts that are new to us, among them the *Yi zhi yi*. The editors of the *Yi zhi yi* draw on a number of different sources or schools, and in my opinion neither 'Confucian' nor 'Daoist' is an adequate description of the contents. I find that the resemblances between the *Yi zhi yi* and the so-called Huang-Lao *yin-yang* 黄老陰陽 texts accompanying the two *Lao zi* ms. are more intriguing. Some of these resemblances have already been pointed out by Chen Guying. I wish to inquire further into the question.

For this purpose I have decided to focus on two pairs of contrasting concepts:

1. *Gang* 剛 and *rou* 柔, hardness and softness, concepts which are well-established in the received tradition. Does the *Yi zhi yi* contribute to our understanding of these concepts? And how do *gang* and *rou* in the context of the *Yi zhi yi* relate to the second pair:

2. *Wen* 文 and *wu* 武, culture and martiality? The concepts of *wen* and *wu* are en-

tirely absent from the received tradition of the *Yi jing* but figure prominently in the *Yi zhi yi*.

The text of the *yi zhi yi* is written on a piece of silk where it follows the *Xi ci zhuan* 繫辭傳, The Commentary on the Appended Phrases, and precedes the *Yao* 要, The Essentials. It totals some 45 columns, approximately 3,100 characters. Less than half of column 45 is legible as it runs into a badly damaged part of the silk ms. making it impossible to determine how and where the text ends. Relatively large parts of the first 13 columns are illegible; Liao Mingchun has stated that his and Chen Songchang's transcription of columns 9 through 13 is questionable. The text shows traces of having been divided into paragraphs by black circular punctuation marks. Initially—due to the fact that the text incorporates paragraphs of the 2nd part of the received *Xi ci zhuan*—Yu Haoliang believed the *Yi zhi yi* to be part of that text. It is now generally agreed that the *Yi zhi yi* is an independent text. Because the last columns of the text have suffered damage, it remains undecided whether or not there was a title and a character count appended at the end as is the case with many of the Mawangdui texts. The current title, *Yi zhi yi*, was supplied by Zhang Liwen basing himself on the first three words uttered by the master at the beginning of the text. Recently, Xing Wen has argued in favor of naming the text *Yi zan* 易贊, The Assistance (or the manifestation) of the Changes. Xing Wen has also presented a division of the text into five paragraphs which except for the first 19 columns follows a division into eight paragraphs suggested by Li Xueqin. A transcription of the *Yi zhi yi* was first made available in 1993 but a critical edition has yet to be published. Prof. Shaughnessy has presented the first (and so far the only) translation into English which appeared in late 1996. This translation has proved helpful in many respects.

The *Yi zhi yi* begins with a short section explaining hardness and softness in relation to *yin* and *yang* to which I shall return. Following this comes a listing of hexagram names and the associations they carry in the mind of the author(s) of the text. The hexagram names are enumerated in an order not previously known although a single brief sequence at the beginning follows the order of the received edition. Due to the defective condition of the silk only about half of the hexagram names are discernible, and the text is too fragmented to allow any conclusion as to the contents. However, the text does not appear to be quoting the *Yi* or any known commentary. As I believe Shaughnessy has observed, this paragraph reminds us of the *Xu gua* 序卦, The

Sequence of Hexagrams; it does, however, lack the sorites of that text. Both the lack of rhymes and the syntax seems to preclude we are dealing with mnemonics. Reading through the bits and pieces, expressions like 'guilt', 'death', 'fierce knights', 'abdication' etc. seems to suggest impending danger. This is reinforced at the end of the paragraph where the master quotes the line statements of a few hexagrams: 'Advancing anxiously', 'avoiding danger', 'danger, relatives are injured'. The entire paragraph is summed up with the line statements of hex. 21, *Shi he* 噬嗑, Biting, bottom and top lines, saying, '"carrying a cangue", inauspicious, "wearing foot fetters", auspicious. This is what it means.' Chen Guying has noted a pervasive awareness of and preoccupation with suffering and hardship in the text. He ascribes this to the somber sentiments among Confucian scholars as a result of the burning of the books in 213 BCE.

The next columns are in a far better condition and give the impression of a well-constructed essay. The paragraphs to which parallels exist in the received editions of the *Shuo gua* 說卦, Explaining the Trigrams, and the *Xi ci zhuan* fit in nicely. The three sections also found in the *Shuo gua* certainly appear in a more meaningful context in the *Yi zhi yi*. That these sections have little in common with the rest of the *Shuo gua* was already noted by the Japanese *Yi jing* scholar Matsui Rashu who died in 1822. The *Yi zhi yi* beginning with column 34 follows sections 2.5 through 2.8 of the received edition of *Xi ci zhuan* more or less closely apart from two columns explaining the features of the cultured man and an occasional interspersed remark, mostly on divination.

The *Yi zhi yi* has the master explaining the significance of the Changes, the use of the Changes, and the essentials of the Changes. The part on which I wish to focus concludes the explanation of the significance of the Changes with a discussion of the significance of the ten thousand things, the significance of Heaven, of earth, of martiality, and of culture. This discussion is conducted with numerous references to the concepts of hardness and softness, *gang* and *rou*.

Nowhere in the late Warring States' literature do the concepts of hardness (*gang*) and softness (*rou*) occur more prominently than in the received commentary tradition to the *Zhou yi*. While the pair is only absent from one of the texts known collectively as the Ten Wings, it occurs most frequently in the *Tuan zhuan*, The Commentary on the Decisions. In addition to commenting briefly on the Hexagram Statements which it follows, the *Tuan zhuan* mainly consists of explanations of the hexagram names and interpretations of the symbolism and relative positions of the hexagram lines. The *Tuan zhuan* uses *gang* and *rou* as technical terms for the solid and broken lines, and also, in a few cases, to characterize the nature of the constituent trigrams. The terms *yin* and *yang* occur only twice in the *Tuan zhuan* (commentary on hexagrams 11 and 12, *Tai* and *Pi*), in both instances referring to the constituent trigrams and not the lines:

The inner is *yang* and the outer is *yin*; the inner is strong and the outer is submissive; the inner is the nobleman and the outer is the commoner.

The inner is *yin* and the outer is *yang*; the inner is soft and the outer is hard; the inner is the commoner and the outer is the nobleman.

'Inner' refers to the lower trigram and 'outer' to the upper.

In the *Tuan zhuan* the soft and the hard interact in a number of ways variously described as *ying*, 'corresponding to', *yu*, 'meeting with', *fen*, 'separating', *jue*, 'interrupting', *bian*, 'changing into', *cheng*, 'riding on'.

Another of the Ten Wings, the *Xiao xiang zhuan*, The Commentary on the Small Images, commenting on the line texts adds to the list of technical terms 接 *jie*, 'receiving' and 際 *ji*, 'converging'.

As these examples demonstrate, the *Tuan zhuan* and the *Xiang zhuan* clearly use the terms 'hard' and 'soft' to refer to the solid and broken lines and—in a few exceptional cases—to the constituent trigrams. Of course, in later *Yi jing* exegesis it becomes customary to use the terms *yin* and *yang* to refer to both the lines and the trigrams, but in the *Tuan zhuan* and the *Xiang zhuan* the terms *yin* and *yang* are virtually absent. Altogether they occur three times each and only in the commentaries to the hexagrams nos. 1, 2, 11, and 12, the four hexagrams which make up the total possible combinations of the trigrams *Qian* and *Kun*, the epitome of *yin* and *yang*.

Does this perhaps suggest that when it comes to defining the lines of the hexagrams the terms *gang* and *rou* were in use prior to *yin* and *yang*? It is generally agreed that the *Tuan zhuan* and the *Xiang zhuan* belong to the older strata of the Ten Wings. Could these commentaries have been written before *Zhou yi* exegesis became infused with *yin yang* cosmology? It is noteworthy, I think, that the famous list of things that are *yang* and things that are *yin* concluding the silk ms. *Cheng*, Designations, does not mention *gang* and *rou*. How did the terms 'hard' and 'soft' come to refer to the hexagram lines in the first place? Two possible solutions present themselves.

In his seminal article published in 1980 Zhang Zhenglang suggested there may be a connection between numerals inscribed in groups of three and six on oracle bones and bronze vessels and the hexagrams of the *Yi jing*. Simplistically stated, Zhang argued that solid lines (*yang* lines) developed from odd numerals and broken lines (*yin* lines) from even numerals. The *Xi ci zhuan* does associate *yang* with odd and *yin* with even numbers. I have previously proposed how the *yin* and *yang* lines could have evolved from numerals. The concepts *gang* and *rou* may have been an intermediate stage in this development. The *Qu li*-chapter of the *Li ji* has a paragraph that clearly associates hard-soft with odd-even in a divination context:

For external matters (*i. e.* sacrifices related to the temple) use hard days and for internal matters (*i. e.* sacrifices related to the household) use soft days. As to the days for both oracle bone and plant stalk divination, those outside a week are called distant such-and-such days and those inside a week are called near such-and-such days.

The commentary says that 'hard days' are odd days and 'soft days' are even days in the ten-day week.

Alternatively, the use of the terms 'hard' and 'soft' may have come about as a description of the physical nature of the lines. In the Mawangdui ms. the soft hexagram lines differ from the broken lines of the received edition (another early Han ms. also has different broken lines). The *Yi zhi yi* aptly describes the hexagram lines in the very first column:

The master said, The significance of the Changes is *yin* and *yang*. There being six lines, they complete a pattern. The bent and crooked of them are soft, the straight of them are hard.

Returning for a moment to the received edition of the *Yi jing*, the meaning of *gang* and *rou* is extended somewhat in the *Xi ci zhuan*; already the opening paragraph places the concepts in a cosmological setting:

Heaven is exalted, earth is low, *Qian* and *Kun* are thus fixed.

Low and high are thereby arranged, the noble and the mean are thus positioned.

Movement and quiescence have constancy, hardness and softness are thus separated (or maybe decided).

*Gang* and *rou* no longer merely refer to the lines of the hexagrams—although the association is by no means lost. More examples from the *Xi ci zhuan* could be adduced but let us turn to the *Yi zhi yi*. Following the opening statement of the text quoted earlier, it says:

Six hard and no soft [lines], this is called the great *Yang*. {The next sentence is partly reconstructed:} This is [the significance of] Heaven. {After a lacunae of about 12 characters follows:} Six soft and no hard [lines]. This is the significance of the earth. Heaven and earth follow each other, *qi* and flavor obtain each other, *yin* and *yang* flow into form, hardness and softness complete {one character missing}.

Except for the somewhat unusual pairing of *qi* and *wei*, this is a fairly straightforward example of *Yi jing* and *yin yang* cosmological thinking. *Gang* and *rou* are used both in the concrete sense referring to the lines and in an extended sense probably meaning an embodiment of *yin* and *yang*. In column 34 of the *Yi zhi yi* a passage also occurring in the received *Xi ci zhuan* says, "*Yin* and *yang* join virtues and thus hardness and softness have body."

Columns 14 and 15 and the first twelve characters of column 16 contains what appears as paragraphs 1-3 of the received version of the *Shuo gua*, it says,

Therefore, establishing the way of Heaven is called *yin* and *yang*.

Establishing the way of the earth is called hardness and softness.

Establishing the way of man is called humaneness and righteousness.

There is a striking parallel to this in the *Yao*, The Essentials, the text written after the *Yi zhi yi* on the silk ms., and a text with which it shares many features:

Therefore, the Changes has the way of Heaven in it but it cannot by means of the sun and the moon, the stars and the planets be exhaustively designated, so it is done by means of *yin* and *yang*.

It has the way of earth in it but it cannot by means of water, fire, metal, earth, and wood be exhaustively designated, so it is regulated by means of softness and hardness.

It has the way of man in it but it cannot by means of father and son, prince and vassal, husband and wife, and attendants be exhaustively designated, so it is summarized by means of above and below.

In the triad Heaven, earth and man, *gang* and *rou* are associated with earth whereas *yin* and *yang* are connected with Heaven. Otherwise *gang* belongs to Heaven and *rou* belongs to earth.

The part of the *Yi zhi yi* text I wish to focus my attention on follows immediately after the passage also occurring in the received *Shuo gua*. This paragraph discusses the loss of hardness and the loss of softness in relation to the significance of the ten thousand things.

The Master said, The significance of the ten thousand things is that, if they are not hard then they cannot move, and if they cannot move then there is no aggression (here I tentatively read *gong*, 'to attack', for *gong*, 'achievement', as in the Mawangdui *Jing fa*, *Jun zheng*). But if they are constantly moving and not centered then ...

[This] is the loss of [hardness].

If they are not soft then they are not quiescent, and if they are not quiescent then they are not peaceful. But if they are quiescent for a long time and not moving then they sink.

This is the loss of softness.

Therefore,

*Qian*'s "haughty dragon" (1.6),

[*Da*] *zhuang*'s "butt the hedge" (34.3 & 34.6),

*Gou*'s snared horns (*cf.* 44.6),

*Ding*'s "broken leg" (50.4),

*Feng*'s emptiness and fullness (55),

These five line statements are [instances of] the loss of hardness, moving but not capable of being quiescent.

*Kun*'s "mare" (2.0),

*Xiao xu*'s "dense clouds" (9.0),

*Gou*'s "[walk to] and fro" (?) (44.1),

[*Jian*]'s pregnant woman (53.3),

*Zhun*'s "weeping blood" (3.6),

These five line statements are [instances of] the loss of *yin*, being quiescent but not capable of moving.

Therefore,

The significance of Heaven is hardness and strength, movement and sending forth (attacking?) and thus not resting. Its auspiciousness ensures the attacking. If there is no softness to relieve it, and it does not die, it will surely perish [anyway].

The moving *yang* perishes. Therefore, fire is not auspicious.

The significance of the earth is softness and weakness, sinking and quiescence and thus not moving. Its auspiciousness [ensures the peace. If there is no] hardness to ... it, it will be exhausted and humbled, abandoned and lost. Valuing *yin* is sinking. Therefore, water is not auspicious.

So the significance of martiality is to ensure attacking and make constant the dying;

the significance of culture is to ensure peace and make constant the exhausting (?).

Therefore,

to be soft yet not to bend, only then is there culture and thus capability for victory;

to be hard yet not to break, only then is there martiality and thus capability for peace.

The *Yi zhi yi* states that movement requires hardness and may result in some kind of change presumably brought about by an action of violence. Conversely, quiescence requires softness and may result in peace. However, the states of movement and quiescence cannot be perpetuated without causing the loss of hardness and softness. Unfortunately, the consequence of constant movement cannot be determined due to the defective condition of the silk ms. The consequence of quiescence and not moving is sinking. In the subsequent passage on earth, softness, quiescence, and not moving, it says, "Valuing *yin* is sinking. Therefore, water is not auspicious." In the parallel passage on Heaven, hardness, movement, and not resting, the conclusion is that, "The moving *yang* perishes. Therefore, fire is not auspicious."

Fire and water may refer to two of the Five Phases (or Agents), *Wu xing*; fire being correlated to the Zhou dynasty and water being adopted by the First Emperor of the Qin. If indeed the *Yi zhi yi*, as has been suggested, was put together after the fall of the Qin, it would have been painfully obvious to the editor(s) that sole reliance on either phase (or agent) was not auspicious. In the *Yao*, The Essentials, which also has a short passage that probably refers to the burning of the books in 213 BCE, it says, as I quoted earlier,

[The Changes] has the way of earth in it but it cannot by means of water, fire, metal, earth, and wood be exhaustively designated, so it is regulated by means of softness and hardness.

Instead of the theories of the mutual conquest sequence or the mutual production sequence of the Five Phases, the *Yi zhi yi* offers the philosophy of softness and hardness of the *Yi jing* tradition. The received edition of the Ten Wings does not mention *wu xing* at all. The *Yi zhi yi* has a passage that may be the master voicing his opinion on *wu xing* but again the defective condition of the silk ms. precludes further discussion. The text known as the *Er san zi wen*, The Disciples Asked, which is written on a different piece of silk where it follows the *Zhou yi* itself, also mentions *wu xing* but I think it is difficult to decide whether this refers to the Five Phases or the five kinds of conduct, humaneness, righteousness, ritual and so on.

These are the only references to the Five Phases in the texts accompanying the *Zhou yi* and *Lao zi* ms. In his study of the ms. accompanying the two *Lao zi* texts, Peerenboom argues, the fact that these texts do not mention the Five Phases,

favor[s] a late Warring State as opposed to a Han dating [because] by the Han, five phase theory is so widespread and closely linked to yin yang that one would expect the author to take note of, if not incorporate, the five phases into his own yin yang naturalism.

I believe the Mawangdui *Zhou yi* commentaries *Yi zhi yi* and *Yao* do take note of the theory of the Five Phases and reject it in favor of softness and hardness. But similar to movement being relieved or restrained by quiescence and vice versa, the softness of the earth needs to be relieved or restrained by the hardness belonging to Heaven and vice versa. If this does not happen, the consequence is, we are told in the *Yi zhi yi*:

The Changes says, "Wearing a cangue" (21.6), this is [an instance of] hardness and thus breaking.

As to "crying out; modesty" (15.2 & 15.6), this is [an instance of] softness and thus [bending].

This is opposed to the ideal situation which is described as

[*Dun*]'s "yellow ox" (33.2) is [an instance of] culture and thus understanding victory.

The Decision Phrase of *Huan* (59) is [an instance of] martiality and thus understanding peace.

*Kun*'s utmost virtue is [an instance of] softness and thus reversal to the square.

*Qian*'s utmost virtue is [an instance of] hardness and thus being capable of yielding.

The same notion may be found in the Three Prohibitions, *San jin* 三禁, of the Huang-Lao *yin-yang* ms. *Jing fa* 經法 (*The Constancy of laws*):

The Way of man is hard and soft; hardness [in itself] is not sufficient to employ and softness [in itself] is not sufficient to depend on.

The concepts of hard and soft also play a profound role in the cosmology of the Huang-Lao *yin-yang*

texts, e.g. The Way and the Rule, *Dao fa*, says:

The constant rules of Heaven are the four seasons, darkness and light, birth and killing, softness and hardness.

Some of the Huang-Lao *yin-yang* texts clearly prefer softness to hardness which is also evident in the *Lao zi*, e.g. The Name and Principle, *Ming li*, says:

Turning hardness into softness is living,

turning softness into hardness is attacking.

Valuing softness is auspicious,

valuing hardness is destruction.

This is not the case with the *Yi zhi yi* which advocates not only both softness and hardness but also both culture and martiality in dealing with the world. This is eloquently summed up as follows:

To be soft yet not to bend, only then is there culture and thus capability for victory;

to be hard yet not to break, only then is there martiality and thus capability for peace.

The *Yi zhi yi* goes on to discuss the merits of culture and martiality letting the master comment on the line statements of *Qian* and *Kun*; a single example will have to do:

The Changes says, "Yellow skirts. Principal auspiciousness." The master said, "This is said of possessing flourishing culture but not manifesting [it]. The cultured man wears on the inside his brightness and on the outside his dragon. He does not with his whiteness brighten people's blackness, therefore, his culture is nourished and displayed.

This inquiry into the concepts of *gang* and *rou* and *wen* and *wu* is by no means an exhaustive examination of the *Yi zhi yi*. However, I do believe it touches on an important aspect—a central idea in the text. The message seems to be that the appropriate and significant use of the Changes is regulating culture and martiality through proper understanding of the mechanics of softness and hardness. Certainly, the *Yi zhi yi* deserves much more attention than I have been able to give it here.

# Authenticity, Internalization and Efficacy: Contextualizing the Wuxing Text within the Confucian Philosophy of Education.

**Geir Siguresson (School of Humanities University of Iceland)**

This paper is part of a larger work seeking to unfold the notion of Confucian learning, education and humanization with a particular focus on Confucian 'ritual propriety,' *li* 禮.[①]The focus will be on concrete dimensions of aesthetic refinement and in particular on the relationship between ritual propriety and music in order to seek out the Confucian view of personalization and creativity in human action. Such dimensions call for a discussion of the Confucian view of the difference and mutual bearing of the internal and external modes of human behavior, a topic that is best represented by the *Wuxing* 五行 essay, an ancient philosophical document only recently unearthed in China, and so one aim of this paper is to appropriately contextualized this philosophical text within the Confucian philosophy of education.

Among Confucian thinkers, it is taken as a fundamental and important assumption that the process of learning does not begin in formal institutions, but in the family. It is through family relations that an individual gradually acquires a sense and understanding of her place, roles, obligations, and reasonable expectations as to what she may expect from others. While certainly entailing cultivation of one's person, such learning is not aim-directed in a simple sense as the relations and all that they engender are changing with time along with all those involved. Thus, the configuration of these relations as informed by *li* is in a continuous process of reevaluation. Roger

---

① For the most part, this paper constitutes a chapter in Siguresson (forthcoming 2015).

T. Ames speaks of *li* as "achieved propriety in one's roles and relations,"① thus emphasizing that *li* are first and foremost enacted in the dynamic context of family relations. Learning to become a social human being is what Confucian self-cultivation is all about, for one's identity is also to a considerable extent constituted by the roles, relations, and obligations one has as a member of a given group or, indeed, groups, for one is bound to have several overlapping identities depending on the context. My identity as a stepfather differs from my identity as a grandson or a teacher, and yet, all these identities make up what I am. How these identities differ is most clearly exemplified through the ways in which *li* is enacted in the relational profile particular to each of them. However, while there is certainly a blurry frame within which my enactment of *li* is expected to take place in each of my roles, I nevertheless have considerable scope to creatively personalize that enactment in each case.②

Book 10 of the *Lunyu* is a collection of detailed descriptions of Confucius's behavior in various formal and non-formal situations, the latter of which include his comportment while eating and sleeping, and even the way in which he mounts his carriage. These descriptions betray the extensive scope of *li* according to Confucius's own embodiment of it in real life. As Ames and Rosemont have noted, *li* applies to a way of life carefully choreographed down to appropriate facial expressions and physical gestures, a world in which a life is a performance requiring enormous attention to detail. Importantly, this *li*-constituted performance begins from the insight that personal refinement is only possible through the discipline provided by formalized roles and behaviors.③

*Li*, then, is something of an artwork of life to be accomplished through discipline and training, and is, as the *Lunyu* records, best exemplified by the life of Confucius himself. Note, however, that Confucius's comportment is not presented as constituting universal rules to be imitated. It is, on the contrary, highly personalized as manifesting the particular character traits of Confucius himself, and therefore a mode of action inimitable by others. Due to the perceived continuity between the inner and the

---

① Ames (2011), for example, p. 109, though he uses variations of this formulation throughout in his work.

② Cf. Ames (2011), p. 178.

③ Ames and Rosemont (1998), p. 52.

outer, every action enjoys its particularity as an action performed by that particular person in that particular circumstance and her particular phase of life. Consider, for instance, the following description of Baron von Landwagen from Ivan Goncharov's nineteenth century novel *Oblomov*, which might well be a description of a *li*-oriented manner of comportment:

He was exquisitely polite, never smoked in the presence of ladies, never crossed his legs, and severely criticized the young men when during a visit they allowed themselves to lean back in an arm-chair or raise their knees and boots on a level with their noses. He kept his gloves on even indoors, removing them only when he sat down to dinner. He dressed in the latest fashion and wore several ribbons in his buttonhole. He always drove in a carriage and pair and took great care of his horses: before stepping into the carriage, he first walked around it, examined the harness and even the horses' hoofs, and sometimes took out a white handkerchief and rubbed their flanks and backs to see whether they had been well groomed. He greeted acquaintances with a polite and affable smile, and strangers coldly at first, but his coldness was replaced by a smile as soon as they had been introduced to him, and his new acquaintance could always count on it in future. He discussed everything: virtue, high cost of living, science and society-and with equal precision; he expressed his views in clear-cut and well-balanced sentences, as though speaking in ready-made maxims written down in some textbook and circulated among society people for general guidance.①

The descriptions of Confucius in the *Lunyu* and elsewhere, and, for that matter, the description of Baron von Landwagen here, may indicate that the issue of *li* revolves merely around "correct" external behavior. Indeed, in the classical Chinese corpus, *li* is sometimes described as belonging to the external, that is to say, as conveying interhuman respect (*gong* 恭) in the social sphere in order to reach a state of harmony (*he* 和) between people. Peng Lirong 彭立荣, for example, quotes the following two passages from the *Lunyu* to point to the primary functions of *li*:

Master You said: "Achieving harmony [*he* 和] is the most valuable function of *li*. In the tradition [*dao* 道] initiated by the former kings, this produced elegance and both small and great affairs proceeded from there. But when things are not functioning, to harmonize things on the basis of [supposed] knowledge [*zhi* 知] of harmony

① Goncharov (1954), p. 219.

without regulating them through *li* is bound to fail."

The Master said: "What can I see in someone who, when holding an influential office, is not tolerant, when observing *li*, is not respectful, and, when overseeing the mourning rites, does not grieve."[①]

Both passages imply that the main function of *li* is to harmonize external interaction within society. But this implication is deceptive, and, in fact, a more complete reading of the former passage makes it evident that an exclusive concentration on the external—in other words, a kind of imposition of "harmony"—will not suffice. It must be done through *li*, precisely because *li*, in its best spirit, demands that the harmonizing action comes from within and is, therefore, authentic.

As is paradigmatic for apparent dichotomies in Chinese thought, the relationship between the "inner" (*nei* 内) and the "outer" (*wai* 外) is portrayed as one characterized by mutual influences and as strictly inseparable. It is probably Zhuangzi who provides the most succinct formulation of their inseparability in the ancient Chinese philosophical tradition with his notion of "inner sage and outer king" (*neisheng waiwang* 内聖外王).[②]However, the *Zhongyong* also says that [c]onsummating oneself is an instance of communal humanity [*ren* 仁] and consummating other things is an instance of wisdom [*zhi* 知]. This is bringing one's natural tendencies [*xing* 性] to a state of virtue [*de* 德] and is the way of integrating the inner [*nei* 内] and the outer [*wai* 外].[③]

The apparent schism between the inner and the outer is further brought to expression in the *Liji*'s discussion of music (*yue* 樂) and ritual (*li* 禮), where music is presented as belonging to the "inner" and ritual to the "outer"aspects of human life.[④]But even here the distinction is only provisional or, I am tempted to say, "pragmatically analytical." For *yue* and *li* belong together as complementary practices acquired by the people so that social order will be produced and maintained *by* the people: "*Li*, music, penal law [*xing* 刑] and government decrees [*zheng* 政] all aim at the same

---

① *Lunyu* 1.12 and 3.26 respectively. Cf. Peng Lirong (2003), p. 82.

② *Zhuangzi* 91/33/14.

③ *Liji* 32.23/146/5-6. Cf. also an interesting discussion of *neisheng waiwang* by Geldsetzer and Hong (1998), pp. 26-41. The authors tie it to Confucianism and the general line of thought in Chinese philosophy.

④ "Records of Music" ("Yueji" 樂記) chapter of the *Liji* 19.26/104/10-11.

thing, namely to assimilate the minds [*xin* 心] of the common people and produce order in the way."① Note that the former two relate to the practices of the people themselves, whereas the latter two, penal law and government decrees, are external administrative modes for effecting social order. Confucius, for his part, is quite clear on his own preference:

The Master said: "If led with government decrees [*zheng*] and controlled with penal law [*xing*], the common people will refrain [from committing crimes] but will be without a sense of shame. If led with moral virtue [*de*] and controlled through the observance of *li*, they will not only develop a sense of shame but will also order themselves."②

One of the most frequently cited passages from the *Lunyu*, one in which Confucius explains to the outraged Zilu why he would begin by correcting the application of names (*zhengming* 正名) if he were to rule the state, is clearer yet on the priority and the complementariness of *li* and *yue*:

When names are not applied correctly, language will not accord with things; when language does not accord with things, affairs will not be taken care of; when affairs are not taken care of, the observance of ritual propriety and the playing of music will not flourish; when the observance of ritual propriety and the playing of music do not flourish, government decrees [*zheng*] and penal law [*xing*] will not be on the mark; if government decrees and penal law are not on the mark, the common people will not know where to place their hands and feet.③

We have already seen that "not knowing where to place one's hands and feet" implies a situation of *anomie*, that is to say, one in which at least relatively established norms are unavailable. The point is that negligence of the social or cultural foundations of emotions and practices will result in a state of alienation between the people and those in power, which, in turn, results in a state of social *anomie*. In order to be a responsible and active citizen, one needs to have faith in one's society, enjoy the feeling of security, and, lastly, have certain emotional dispositions such as the belief in one's ability and possibility to take care of affairs, in short, some level of optim-

---

① "Records of Music" ("Yueji" 樂記) chapter of the *Liji* 19.1/98/17-18.

② *Lunyu* 2.3.

③ *Lunyu* 13.3.

ism.

The crux of a well-ordered, harmonious and dynamic society, then, consists in starting at the right end. And it is precisely one of the distinguishing particularities of the Confucian philosophy that it emphasizes the development of certain personal sensibilities as the foundation of society. This is why *li* and *yue* are considered prior to *zheng* and *xing*.

Now *yue* as music and *le* as joy or optimism are in fact expressed by the same character 樂. Their original identification can be traced back to the joy expressed in the music and dance during harvest celebrations in China's antiquity. Music is moreover indispensable to the sacrificial ceremonies for the ancestors and, in fact, constitutes certain parts of these ceremonies.①*Li* and *yue*, therefore, representing the moral and the artistic tradition, cannot be fully separated. As Confucius stresses, these are not mere external performances, but must be properly internalized in order to be truly functional: "When speaking time and again of ritual propriety, how could I just be talking about jade and silk? When speaking time and again of music, how could I just be talking about bells and drums?"②

The importance of the internalization of certain dispositions is alluded to throughout the Confucian corpus of the pre-Qin period. Nowhere, however, does it receive as detailed a discussion as in the recently discovered *Wuxing* 五行 document, or *The Five Kinds of Conduct*, a pre-Qin text possibly written by Confucius's grandson, Zisizi, or his students, and excavated in Mawandgui for the first time in 1973, and again at Guodian in 1994. The *Wuxing* emphasizes the distinction between conduct that is merely externally appropriate and conduct proceeding from within. In its first paragraph it says that "[w]here communal humanity [*ren* 仁] takes shape from within, it is called virtuous conduct [*de* 德]; where it does not take shape within, it is called mere (proper) conduct."③The same argumentative pattern is then repeated in the passage about *yi* 義(appropriate conduct), *li* 禮, *zhi* 智(wisdom), and *sheng* 聖(sagacity), all of which are core Confucian notions. An important implication here is that actions executed with skill and authenticity, on the one hand, or by sheer imita-

① Jin Shangli (2002), pp. 124f.

② *Lunyu* 17.11.

③ Li Ling (2003), p. 78 §1.

tion, on the other, are bound to be vastly and noticeably different. The latter will, quite literally, be hollow, as they are based on mere imitation of external form. Mencius, for instance, is in no doubt that one's physical deportment reveals most clearly what lies behind one's actions:

To the natural dispositions of exemplary persons [*junzi* 君子] belong communal humanity [*ren* 仁], appropriate conduct [*yi* 義], *li* 禮, and wisdom [*zhi* 智], which are rooted in their thoughts and feelings [*xin* 心]. These manifest themselves in the mildness of their faces, amplify themselves in their backs and extend to their limbs, which, in turn, instruct them without uttering a single word. ①

With regard to the *Wuxing* argument, Pang Pu has pointed out that the difference between the two kinds of conduct also indicates different stages of learning, whereby "if one has neither grasped it nor effected its formation in one's heart, all that remains is the embodiment of the action, which is then called simply 'action' (*xing* 行)."② In other words, imitation is merely second rate and perhaps only useful as a kind of drill for those in whom the Confucian moral skills have not yet taken shape.

The qualitative difference described in the opening lines of the *Wuxing*, *The Five Kinds of Conduct*, between "virtuous conduct," proceeding from within, and "mere (proper) conduct," being only external, consists in *de* 德, which may be translated provisionally as "virtue."③The five kinds of conduct are the familiar ones of *ren* 仁, *yi* 義, *li* 禮, *zhi* 知, and *sheng* 聖, of which the last, sagacity, is presented as the final stage of personal cultivation. ④ It is *de* 德, however, that enjoys a particular privilege as signifying the harmony between the five actions together: "If (all) five of the virtuous conducts are in harmony [*he* 和], one speaks of virtue [*de*]; if (only) four of the virtuous conducts are in harmony, one speaks of goodness [*shan* 善]. Goodness is the way of human beings; virtue is the way of *tian* 天."⑤

*De* obviously proceeds through some stages here, from describing the characteristics of a single action as such to the harmony that obtains between all of them togeth-

---

① *Mencius* 7A. 21.

② Pang Pu (2000), p. 30.

③ Cf. Li Ling (2002), p. 78 § 1.

④ Cf. Cook (2000), pp. 119f.

⑤ Li Ling (2002), p. 78, § 2.

er. But it is even more complicated than that. As Ames and Hall explain, *de* connotes in the early philosophical literature "the insistent particularity of things." The conventional translations of *de*, "virtue" or "power," they continue, define the particular as a focus of potency within its own field of experience … The earliest Confucian literature tended to limit its concerns to human experience, where this qualitative dimension of *de* more nearly suggests both "excellence" and "efficacy" as what we can truly be and do if we "realize (*zhi* [知])" the most from our personal careers as members of a specific community. ①

Elsewhere, they add to this:

Given the intrinsic relatedness of particulars in this conception of existence as process, *de* is both process and product both the potency and the achieved character of any particular disposition within the unsummed totality of experience. ②

This two semantic or connotative pairs of "excellence" and "efficacy," on one hand, and "process" and "product," on the other, are particularly germane to the complex meaning of *de* in the *Wuxing* passage. As excellence, it points to an achieved state of personal character, a product reaped from the process of learning. As efficacy, it signifies the external "potency" in that character's actions.

"Potency" has a twofold meaning here. First, it points to the ability to be able to make the most of one's circumstances, and obviously, a sage, who has appropriated all five kinds of conduct, is here the supreme virtuoso. The *Wuxing* expresses this by invoking the notion of timeliness: "A sage realizes [*zhi* 知] the way of *tian* 天. To realize it, and thereby put it into practice [*xing* 行], is appropriateness [*yi* 義]. To put it into practice in a timely manner [*shi* 時]is *de*."③

The second meaning of potency points to the transformative effects one is capable of having through one's comportment. The *Wuxing* uses an artistic, indeed, musical image to convey this idea:

[Opening with] the sound of bells and [concluding with] jade tubes is to possess *de* 德. The sound of bells is goodness [*shan* 善]. The timbre of jade is sagacity. Only those who possess *de* are able to [open with] the sound of bells and [conclude with]

① Ames and Hall (2001), pp. 64f.

② Ames and Hall (2003), pp. 59f.

③ Li Ling (2002), p. 79, § 17.

jade tubes.[1]

A similar passage occurs in the *Mencius*. In fact, it seems probable that Mencius is referring directly to the ideas presented in the *Wuxing*.[2] It is illuminating to look at the *Mencius* passage as well:

Bo Yi was the sage who was pure. Yi Yin was the sage who was responsible. Confucius was the sage whose actions were timely. Confucius may be said to have "assembled the great symphony."[3] "Assembling the great symphony" means to [open with] the sound of bells and [conclude with] jade tubes. The "sound of bells" means to begin with a rhythmic order [*tiao li* 脩理]; the "jade tubes" means to (carry through and) bring the rhythmic order to a conclusion. Beginning the rhythmic order is the affair of knowledge [*zhi* 智]; (carrying through and) bringing the rhythmic order to a conclusion is the affair of sagehood [*sheng* 聖]. Knowledge is comparable to skill and sagehood is comparable to strength. It is like when shooting an arrow from a distance of hundred paces: its getting there is a matter of your strength; its hitting the mark is not a matter of your strength.[4]

Having reached sagehood means possessing the virtuosity or potency to see things through to the end. Remember that, according to the *Wuxing*, one needs to have harmonized all the five conducts, among which sagacity is the ultimate stage, in order to rise above a "mere" *shan*ness 善 and become a *de*-inspired sage. Now *de* 德 is often presented as an almost mysterious power to govern and control without having to force things or, in government, resort to violence. In the *Lunyu*, Confucius describes the effects of *de* thus: "The *de* of the *junzi* 君子 is the wind, while the *de* of the petty person [*xiao ren* 小人] is the grass. When the wind blows, the grass necessarily bends."[5] *De* is often associated with musical impressions. Knoblock has noted that *de yin* (德音), literally "virtuous sound," is a common expression in the *Book of Odes* (*Shijing* 詩經). He explains this idea such "that the 'sounding' of the true 'inner power' produces change in all that hear it, [the *junzi*'s] charisma transforms all who know of him, just as a sound struck on one instrument produces sympathetic vibrations

---

① Li Ling (2002), p. 79, § § 10-11.

② See for example Xing Wen (2000), p. 77

③ Following Cook (2000), p. 128.

④ *Mencius* 5B. 1.

⑤ *Lunyu*, 12. 19.

wherever it extends."[①]This musical metaphor catches the image of the *junzi*, who, wherever he goes, effects transformations by "touching" people's sentiments through his way of living and interacting.[②]A true *junzi* can thus be recognized through his demeanor. The *Wuxing*, then, underscores the importance of internalizing the *de*-excellence, and of building in oneself a charismatic *de*-character for the sake of acquiring genuine efficacy.

However, the *Wuxing* repeatedly stresses the necessity of a joyful or optimistic disposition in order to be able to efficacious. In fact, the entire process of developing *de* requires certain inner sentiments that are therefore authentic. Consider, for instance, the second strip of the *Wuxing*:

If *junzi* have no heart-felt worries [*you* 憂], they will lack heart-felt wisdom [*zhi* 智]; if they lack heart-felt wisdom, they will not have heart-felt enjoyment [*yue* 說]; if they do not have heart-felt enjoyment, they will not have heart-felt feeling of security [*an* 安]; if they do not find security, they will not be optimistic [*yue* 樂]; if they are not optimistic, they will not have the potency to be efficacious [*de* 德].[③]

One should be wary of reading this as a linear causal development in which each successive stage signifies the completion of the previous one. The *de*-inspired *junzi* still has heart-felt worries, but he worries about the state of his community and, of course, about his own deeds and dispositions. Now the entire passage can be read as a socio-psychological account of the necessary conditions for a vibrant and effective society. Without the sensitivity necessary for enjoying things in one's immediate surroundings, for instance, without being able to savor the culinary specialties of one's home place, one cannot be at ease. One does not feel at home and lacks a feeling of security. And if there is no inner feeling of security, one is incapable of believing in one's own ability to improve the less perfect aspects of one's culture and society: in short, without optimism, one cannot be efficacious.

The "efficacy" contained in *de*, however, is not a mere ability to carry through actions to the end without considering the quality of the action as such. An excessive

---

① Knoblock (1994), vol. 2, 304f. n43. Cf. Cook (2000), p. 129: "The qualities of the sage are … jade-like in both luster and resonance manifest forms of external evidence that cannot fail to influence those who gaze upon their radiance or become captivated by the harmonious melody of virtue embodied."

② Cf. *Mencius*, 7A. 13.

③ Li Ling (2002), p. 78, § 2.

concentration on the power of the *de*-inspired *junzi* can be misleading. [1] One of our important gains from the *Wuxing* consists precisely in an unusually clear presentation of what *de* really consists in. *De* turns out to be the internalization of the supreme Confucian qualities of *ren* 仁, *yi* 義, *li* 禮, *zhi* 智, and *sheng* 聖. Consequently, there can be no presentation of a meaningful notion of "efficacy" in isolation from these qualities.

Of these, *ren*, which I have referred to as "communal humanity," is undoubtedly one of the most important. If *de* is the potency to initiate things and bring them to completion, *ren* makes sure that these things are worth initiating at all. The character for *ren* is composed of the characters for the human being (*ren* 人) and the numeral two (*er* 二). Hence, and as many have pointed out, *ren* 仁 stresses the unavoidably social aspect of human existence. A human being is never alone, is born of other human beings, and is not able to develop him-or herself without other human beings in short, without some sort of society the human being would not be human. *Ren* reminds us that our mode of living and our actions always involve other persons, thus implying a social or communal sense. As such a sense, it lends a vital qualitative direction to our behavior. Skill or efficacy in the sense of *de* is certainly of profound importance in the Confucian tradition, but if disengaged from the social sense of *ren*, it runs the danger of degenerating into a kind of means-end rational mode of action typical of the greedy, vain and egocentric "petty person" (*xiao ren* 小人) who seeks to manipulate situations exclusively for his or her own benefit. While, as Confucius points out, "there are occasions on which the *junzi* fails to act in accordance with *ren*, there are no occasions on which the petty person acts according to *ren*." [2] This complete lack of the sense of *ren* is precisely what makes such persons petty and distinguishes them from those who are *junzi*.

In the process of education and refinement, therefore, the sense expressed

---

① François Jullien, for instance, seems to give too much weight to "efficacy" and the "logic of manipulation" in Chinese thought, claiming, as I have already cited, that "[a]rt, or wisdom, as conceived by the Chinese, … lies in strategically exploiting the propensity emanating from that particular configuration of reality, to the maximum effect possible." (Jullien, 1995, p. 15) Though this is certainly an important aspect of the ancient Chinese world-orientation, Jullien makes it sound as if there is a kind of value-ignoring means-end rationality at play, however different it may be from the kind detected by Max Weber in Western culture.

② *Lunyu* 14. 6.

*through ren* must be present and evolving. Otherwise, the process will not lead to the formation of a *junzi*. This is also why Confucius asks, rhetorically: "What does someone who is not *ren* have to do with the observance of ritual propriety? What does someone who is not *ren* have to do with the playing of music?"[①] If the aesthetic experience of *li* and *yue* are to have any effects on the character development of the person, this can only be meaningful if it enhances and refines that person's sense of *ren*. Conversely, a person who is not *ren* is bound to perform both *li* and *yue* in a superficial and meaningless manner.

The process *qua* process of learning is described in the *Wuxing* both as analogous to and mediated through the experience of art, producing a particular kind of consciousness or sensibility that informs sagacious and exemplary behavior, which, again, has the effect of stimulating others to strive for their own cultivation. The aesthetic sense and aesthetic experience acquired through *li* and *yue* are therefore far removed from, say, the Western modernist notion of *l'art pour l'art* that was meant to liberate art from social commitments. On the contrary, a Confucian would maintain that art can never be disengaged from moral considerations, though this does not mean that the artist or performer must necessarily present some moral claims. It is rather, as Eliot Deutsch has pointed out, explaining the Chinese attitude to artistic creation, that "one [will] inevitably be disclosed in one's work as the kind of person one is."[②] One might further argue that considering the absence of body-soul dualism in the Chinese worldview, as well as the close interplay between the inner and outer, it is but to be expected that the (inner) character traits of a person are considered to be observable in that person's (outer) works and actions. Such a view clearly goes hand in hand with a development of a refined kind of discernment to evaluate persons' "authenticity" by observing their every move in the smallest detail.

*Li* and *yue* as learning experiences are meant to enhance one's engagement in the dynamic configuration of the social environment and foster an elevated sense of community by revealing the impossibility of personal development, according to the value of humanness within the framework of tradition, outside of society.

Further, a performance of *li* is always to some extent personalized and particu-

---

① *Lunyu* 3.3.

② Deutsch (1996), p. 86.

lar, depending on the person performing and the situation at hand. Therefore, it demands of the performer an endeavor to assess the situation and present a personal interpretation of the meaningful variables of the situation through a personalized performance. From another point of view, however, Confucians, no less than others, also expect those who perform rituals to do so according to preestablished patterns. Without such patterns, obviously, the rituals would be arbitrary and eventually lose the structure that preserves their identity as rituals. Invariance as an element of *li* has the educational function of continuously revealing, partially but significantly through the performer's hermeneutic creativity, new latitudes of the social meaning and message of the ritual. While performances of *li* are described in minute detail in various ancient writings, the descriptions do not include the exact meanings for the parties involved. These need be interpreted by each. And it is here that personalization and internalization come in. As pointed out by Wu Zongjie and Hu Meixin, [l]inguistic meaning arises when the participants reflect on [their] own identity and relationship with [their] circumstances through a dialogue with the situation. Therefore, meaning arises as situated understanding which is, and has to be, based on reflection on the dialogic relationship between [...] individual and the community.[①]

The generation of meaning, as Wu and Hu continue, "is always relative to local, historical and social, and personal context, and one may make different meaning at a different stage of one's life with one's evolving cultural identity."[②] Thus, there is necessarily a hermeneutic openness to the practice of *li* customs, an openness that demands individual creation of meaning on behalf of the practitioner. Otherwise, the customs are merely empty relics devoid of meaning.

As has been shown in these pages, *li* encompass both formal and informal kinds of conduct. From a pedagogical point of view, one might say with some simplification that the more formal aspects are to be applied at one's early stages of learning, while more spontaneous, personalized and informal patterns will emerge at advanced stages. The former has to do with appropriating one's cultural legacy; the latter with its expression, interpretation, and thus development. Tradition and culture must be continuously revised and reinterpreted in light of the novel circumstances arising in the con-

---

① Wu and Hu (2010), p. 108.

② Wu and Hu (2010), p. 108.

stant transformation to which we refer as "reality." And this revision and interpretation can only be done by us, as indicated in Confucius's saying that "[h]uman beings are able to broaden the tradition (*dao* 道); the tradition does not broaden human beings."①It is our task to carry the cultural legacy forward, and this is precisely what we do when we interpret and apply *li* appropriately and creatively, for this kind of "creativity emerges from the interdependence between person and world."②

References:

Ames, Roger T. (2011). *Confucian Role Ethics. A Vocabulary*. Hong Kong: The Chinese University Press.

Ames, Roger T. and David L. Hall. (2003). *Dao De Jing. "Making This Life Significant." A Philosophical Translation*. New York: Ballantine Books.

Ames, Roger T. and David L. Hall. (2001). *Focusing the Familiar. A Translation and Philosophical Interpretation of the Zhongyong*. Honolulu: University of Hawai'i Press.

Ames, Roger T. and Henry Rosemont Jr. (1998). *The Analects of Confucius. A Philosophical Translation*. New York: Ballantine Books.

Cook, Scott. (2000). "Consummate Artistry and Moral Virtuosity: the "Wu xing 五行" Essay and its Aesthetic Implications." Chinese Literature: Essays, Articles, Reviews 22, pp. 113-146.

Deutsch, Eliot. (1996). Essays on the Nature of Art. Albany: State University of New York Press.

Geldsetzer, Lutz and Hong Han-ding. (1998). Grundlagen der chinesischen Philosophie. Stuttgart: Reclam.

Goncharov. (1954). Oblomov. Translated by David Magarshack. Harmondsworth: Penguin. (2002). Li yi yue he de wenhua lixiang 禮宜樂和的文化理想. Chengdu:

Jullien, François. (1995). The Propensity of Things. Toward a History of Efficacy in China. Translated by Janet Lloyd. New York: Zone Books.

Knoblock, John. (1994). Xunzi. A Translation and Study of the Complete Works. 3 vols.

---

① *Lunyu* 15.29.

② Wang (2007), p. 282.

(2002). Guodian Chu jian jiao du ji 郭店楚簡校讀記. Beijing: Beijing daxue

Liji 禮記.(1992). A Concordance to the Liji. Edited by D. C. Lau and Chen Fong Ching. Hong

Lunyu 論語.(1966). A Concordance to the Analects of Confucius. Harvard-Yenching Institute Sinological Index Series. Supplement no. 16. Taibei: Chinese Materials and Research Aids 18

JinShangli 金尚理. Bashushushe. Stanford:StanfordUniversityPress.

LiLing 李零. chubanshe. Kong:CommercialPress. ServiceCenter,Inc.

Mencius 孟子. (1966). A Concordance to the Meng Tzu. Harvard-Yenching Institute Sinological Index Series. Supplement no. 17. Taibei: Chinese Materials and Research Aids Service Center, Inc.

Pang Pu 龐樸. (2000). Zhubo《Wuxing》pian jiaozhu ji yanzhou 竹帛<五行》篇校注及研究.

Taibei: Wanjuanlou tushu.

Peng Lirong. (2003). Ru wenhua shehuixue 儒文化社會學. Beijing: Renmin chubanshe.

Siguresson, Geir (forthcoming 2015). Confucian Propriety and Ritual Learning. A Philosophical Interpretation. Albany: State University of New York Press. Wu, Zongjie and Meixin Hu (2010) "Ritual Hermeneutics as the Source of Meaning: Interpreting the Fabric of Chinese Culture." China Media Research 6(2), pp. 104-113.

Xing Wen. (2000). "The 'Wanzhang' Chapter in the Mencius and the Bamboo Slip Wu Xing." Contemporary Chinese Thought 32, no. 1, pp. 63-78.

Zhuangzi 莊子. (1956). A Concordance to Chuang Tzu. Harvard-Yenching Institute Sinological Index Series. Supplement no. 20. Cambridge: Harvard University Press.

# Rule of Virtue and Rule of Law

**Gregor Paul (Karlsruhe Institute of Technology, Karlsruhe University, Germany)**

How to preclude, or at least minimize, abuse of political power? This is one of the most important questions in ethics and political philosophy. Most, if not all, answers can be subsumed under at least one of the following two alternatives. First, abuse of political power can and should be minimized by entrusting it to a certain kind of men, especially wise and good men, or-to put it somewhat differently-able persons of (great) virtue. Second, abuse of political power should be minimized by certain institutions, in particular by institutions of power division, and checks and balances of power. One of the most famous 'Western' respresentatives of the first conviction was Plato who delevoped the notion of the philosopher king. The most re-known representative of the second view was Popper who sharply criticized Plato. According to Popper, one should not ask, "Who should rule?", but "Which institutions should be built in order to minimize power abuse even then when culprits are in possession of power?" According to Popper, experience tells us that all human beings are liable to give in to the temptations of power. Popper firmly believed that Lord Acton was right in maintaining that "Power corrupts, and absolute power corrrupts absolutely." As to Chinese philosophical traditions, the *Lunyu* 論語, *Mengzi* 孟子, and *Xunzi* 荀子 demand that abuse of power should be avoided by following the norms of *ren* 仁 and (*ren*) *dao* (仁)道, i. e. humaneness and the way (of humaneness). To achieve this, these classics advocated a regime of wise and good men, namely sage-like men, noble and great persons, *shengren* 聖人, *junzi* 君子, or *daren* 大人. Persons in power who are not wise, intelligent, competent, or lack personal integrity-in short, who do not or cannot live up to the standards of intelligence, competence and humaneness should be helped by good and wise men and should accept such help. They should be open for just criticism (e.g., *jian* 諫), and their faults and errors should be criticized. This idea gave birth to a particular Chinese institution, the censorate. Its members should criticize, or admonish, ministers and emperors who, abusing power, gravely violated the norm of humaneness. In some cases, the idea that abuse of power could be avoided or reduced by wise and good advisors, and by the censorate succeeded, but in most cases it did not really work. The temptation of power proved too powerful-a fact, by the way, that evokes Oscar Wilde's beautiful *bon mot*: "I can resist everything except temptation".

Perhaps, some phrases from the *Xunzi* best sum up the classic Confucian notion of ideal and hence legitimate power. They declare *ren(dao)* 仁(道) [or 人道], and *yi* 義 the highest virtues and norms of human behavior. They say that whether one is a son of heaven depends on what kind of man he is. And they demand that human beings should be open for just criticism, and that one should not shrink from criticizing persons who violate humanity even if these persons are powerful rulers (or-what is also worthwhile mentioning-if they are your parents or teachers). According to the *Xunzi*, such a notion of ideal government can be realized (i) when people are adequately educated, (ii) when their positions in state and society reflect their abilities and moral qualities, and (iii) when they, because of their general education *and* a kind of aesthetical education, are (iv) able to accept their just position in the *inevitably hierarchical* society. Perhaps it is not superflous to expressly add that according to this notion hierarchy is determined by merit. ①

Except for the rather weak institution of the censorate, Chinese philosopher rarely argued for an institutional check of power. One of the few exceptions was Huang Zongxi 黃宗羲 (1610-1695). ②

---

① For more extensive and detailed accounts of my interpretations of pre-Qin Chinese philosophy, see my: (i) *Aspects of Confucianism*, Frankfurt a. M., New York: Lang, 1990. (ii) Menschenrechtsrelevante Traditionskritik in der Geschichte der Philosophie in China, in: G. Schubert, ed., *Menschenrechte in Ostasien*, Tübingen: Mohr-Siebeck, 1998, pp. 75-108. (iii) Global Ethics and Chinese Resources, in: Karl-Heinz Pohl und Anselm W. Müller, eds., *Chinese Ethics in a Global Context-Moral Bases of Contemporary Societies*, Leiden: Brill, 2002, pp. 78-92. (iv) Confucian notions of Criticism: An Important Contribution to a Valid Theory of Humaneness, in: TENG Wensheng und SHAN Chun, eds., *Confucianism and Its Current Missions*, Beijing: Jizhou Press, 2010, vol. 4, pp. 194-213. (v) Konfuzius und Konfuzianismus, Darmstadt: WBG, 2010.

② See W. Th. de Bary, *Waiting for the Dawn: A Palm for the Prince. Huang Tsung-Hsi's Ming-I tai-fang lu*, trans. and introd. by Wm. Theodore de Bary, New York: Columbia University Press, 1993.

Especially since the begin of the so-called 'War on Terror' and the War in Afghanistan in 2001, it has again become abundantly clear that, in order to effienciently cope with the problem of power abuse, versions of the first and second alternatives must be combined. However, political philosophies such as Plato's are nevertheless obsolete, for Plato advocated an idea of an ontologically and anthropologically justified slave society. Also, he argued for an almost totalitarian government of the elite. Further, his theology, his (ontological) idealism (which implied an ontological and anthropological dualism), and his (rationalistic) epistemology are simply untenable. The only thing that remains worthwhile considering, is the general idea that the 'right' men should be in power.

The classic Chinese theories of ideal government, especially as put forward in the *Lunyu*, *Mengzi*, and *Xunzi*, on the other hand, are also unsatisfactory. They do not tell us how to select the right ruler or-in more general terms-the right politicians, and they provide no ideas of how to efficiently and peacefully dispose with inhumane government.

Neither in 'Western' nor in Chinese history there ever existed a government by virtue that was morally or ethically acceptable. At least, I myself do not know of any actual government in human history that really deserves the name "rule by virtue".

As to the second alternative (namely, institutionalized power control by rule of law), even so-called advanced Western democracies as for instance US and German democracies have proved problematic. In the US, in spite of its democratic constitution, George W. Bush Jr. and his clique succeeded in initiating the second war in Iraq, re-establishing systematic torture, and establishing prisons like Guantanamo. They had people kidnapped and transferred to torture prisons in Eastern Europe. Their doings led to the killing of more than 100.000 innocent civilians, and now even unmanned drones are used for killing humans without caring much for what is called 'collateral damage'. If Al Gore and not George W. Bush had been elected president, such crimes against humanity would never have occurred. It is obvious that, in the US, the institutions, or mechanisms, of power division and checks and balances of power do not work, as they actually ought to work. In other words, in the US, extant laws and democratic institutions *can not* preclude that *one man* severely abuses his power. Plato's disgust for democracy as a way of deceiving the unintelligent and greedy masses can be understood, if one looks at the ways, US elections are led or wars are initiated and, in an utterly demagogic way, are publicly advertised. By the way, Aristophanes, in his comedy *The Knights* (*Ιππεῖς Hippeîs*), provides an as entertaining as insightful picture of demagogy. In our context however, the most important conclusion is that even a highly developed democracy characterized by a rule of law does not preclude grave abuse of power, but needs to be supplemented by *moral* rules that bar ruthless politicians from gaining power. ***Since war and peace may even depend on (the character of) one single man, it ought to be ascertained that only men of moral integrity could be elected.*** Simply put, it should be impossible that a George Bush and not an Al Gore becomes president.

In Germany, it is an open secret that it is not the people but political parties which actually hold power. They even select heads of important elementary schools and the more influencial TV journalists. Only recently, on the 25th of March in 2014, the German Constitutional Court, restricted such possibilities. When the German state parliament had to decide whether or not to support the Kosovo and the Afghanistan wars, many of its members voted against their conviction and thus also against the German constitution, according to which a member of parliament ought to follow his moral conviction. More philosophically put, he or she ought to act as morally autonomous person. But the referred to members were put under pressure by their party leaders and finally gave in to the temptations of power. While politicians demand that ordinary people pay more taxes and are satisfied with shortened wages, they themselves again and again decide to raise their own income.

The Edward Snowden case perhaps exemplarily shows that the laws that constitute democracy do not work the way they should. Most Germans are of the opinion that Snowden should be given asylum in Germany. The government, however, afraid of the US, is not willing to do this. On July 09 this year (2014) a German commented in the internet on the situation as follows: "It is strange that the people are of a different opinion [than the government] and that no democracy follows the will of the people".① The same applies to German foreign policy. A majority of the people disa-

① Ein Jahr Zeit !!!

Und die westlichen Wertegemeinschaften geben kein Asyl? Keiner? Da braucht es keine Worte mehr!!!!!

(Erst recht keine von Verschw? rungstheoretikern OST u. West)

Merkwürdig ist, das das Volk anderer Meinung ist u. der Volkswille in keiner Demokratie sich durchsetzt selbst nach Umfragen nicht !!!!!"

grees with the way the conflict between Russia and Ukraine is handled.

Though it is quite clear that representative government has its inbuilt shortcomings, the actual degeneration of German democracy, its deplorable status, so to say, cannot be justified by pointing out the difficulties of representative democracy.

Similar to the situation in the US, in Germany the systems of power division and power control simply do not function (any longer) in a sufficient way.

From all this follows that especially the basic democratic institutions of power division and power control must be improved, i.e., must be made more efficient, and must be complemented with procedures of making as sure as possible that only competent persons of moral integrity can become politically powerful. But how is this to achieve? How to avoid an unacceptable and inefficiently eleborate bureaucracy? How to avoid scrutinizing people, and the private life of people, in a way which would gravely violate their individual freedom, or even their dignity? How to avoid washing dirty loundry in public? How to select the able and good persons we need for ideal government without, in an unacceptable way, intruding in, and making public, their private lifes?

In my view, there is actually no alternative to (also) considering a person's private life, if he or she wants to be elected to power, for otherwise it would be impossible to know whether a person possesses moral integrity, whether he or she is trustworthy-or to put in this old-fashioned way-whether he or she is a virtuous person. Whoever seeks political power should therefore (be willing to) provide respective information (although such information should of course be sought tactfully and in a qualified manner). Otherwise people should simply refrain from pursuing a political career.

As to the moral criteria, politicians ought to satisfy, there are, of course, some measures that can be enacted comparatively easy. Whoever decides about war and peace, must himself or herself be forced to take respective personal risks. It is simply unacceptable that those who decide to lead a war are the last who can suffer from it. And the same applies to many other political decisions. Generally speaking, politicians should be forced to at least more or less following the same rules, and take the same risks, as other people. They need not be, and probably should not behave as, moral purists. But they certainly should be obliged to live up to their words, to not apply double standards etc. Respective rules could be institutionalized. One of the main points is again: whoever prefers just to do as he likes ought not to enter politics, or he or she must accept the legally established right that others publicly point out his or her untrustworthiness, unreliability, ruthless egoism, etc. To make it even clearer: ***There should be a class of moral rules, politicians must abide by. These rules should be institutionalized, and they should be made public.*** (One may be reminded of the fact that moral rules for physicians have been expressly established.) Whoever decides to enter politics, must know these rules, and must accept the consequences if he gravely violates them.

As I need not emphasize, the whole situation can be improved by general and compulsory moral education. *Everybody who wants to enter a political career should undergo human rights education and even pass respective examinations.* In Germany, almost every pupil is an ardent defender of ecological politics. This is simply the result of respective education. As to the contents of moral education, it should imply reflection on the following three principles: (i) Peace is more important than realization of truth. (ii) Religious convictions must not justify political decisions. (iii) The Golden Rule is a universally valid moral rule, and as a matter of consequence also valid for politicians.

Further, compulsory aesthetical education is needed. The idea is not foreign to German culture. Based on Immanuel Kant's *Critic of Aesthetical Judgment*, Friedrich Schiller developed a theory of aesthetical education. Among others, Herbert Marcuse further developed this theory.①

Aesthetical education is necessary to help bridging the gap between right insight on the one hand and right behaviour on the other. Even when we are aware that an argument is sound, if it contradicts our feelings and inclinations, we do not like to follow it, e.g., to behave or act accordingly. Therefore, from our childhood, our inclinations and feelings should be trained and modelled so as to give them the same direction as morality, or, in other words, so as to make them supportive of living up to our moral standards. In short: Aesthetical education is indispensible, since it can model us in a way that, (i) if we ought to behave morally or in a socially acceptable way, we like to behave so, and that, (ii) in following our inclinations, we, so to say, automatically act morally and socially acceptable. The question of how to design respective programmes of aesthetical education, is no philosophical task. It is rather a question

---

① See again my *Aspects of Confucianism*, Frankfurt a. M., New York: Lang, 1990.

of educational science, didactics, and educational politics. But to avoid the impression that the idea of realizing an aesthetical education is just empty talk, some indications may be appropriate. One can indeed be educated *to enjoy* abiding by moral or social norms, and to view violations *with disgust*. How? In the first place, the norms themselves can be aestheticalized, i.e., their realization should take place in a cultivated and refined way, or, in other words, they should be put into practice in a cultivated manner, embedded in a cultivated environment. This, in turn, would require education in arts, music, and in refined and sensible behaviour, including issues such as how to dress oneself. Evidently, politics, public media, families, and schools could contribute to such eduaction. These deliberations are well in keeping with Schiller's general ideas, but even more with the theory of aesthetical education, as put forward in the *Xunzi*. For Schiller-and the same applies to Kant, Freud, Marcuse and others in this tradition-start from conceiving of man as a psycho-somatic being, i.e., from an ontological and anthropological dualism. Though they tried to overcome this dualism by introducing a third faculty besides ratio and the senses, or a third part besides mind and body, namely the "faculty of pleasure" (the "Vermögen der Lust"), or the "desire to play" (the "Spieltrieb"), they did not really escape the dualistic notion of man and its questionable and dangerous implications. In particular, all the metaphysical problems of the ontologies and epistemologies involved remained. The *Xunzi*, on the other side, includes a theory of aesthetical education which can be reconstructed as an elaborate and detailed *empirical* (*not metaphysical*) doctrine of a *monistic* notion of men who (i) cannot but give way to certain feelings and desires, who, (ii) as a matter of consequence, should be allowed to give way to them, but (iii) at the same time be provided with means to do this in a (becoming) way that does not harm themselves or others. (iv) These means should be provided by learning and realizing *li* 禮. It is the empiricalness, the pragmatics, the 'realism', and the detailedness which make the *Xunzi*'s theory superior to the 'Western' approaches.

As to the improvement of traditional democratic institutions, in advanced democracies like Germany, (i) new parties should have a greater and fairer chance to succeed than they actually have; (ii) the role money plays in elections must be significantly limited; (iii) members of parliament must not be allowed to decide themselves over their allowances; (iv) even in a representative democracy there must be a possibility for certain cases of 'direct democracy,' inspite of all difficulties to realize such an idea, (v) as indicated, if a politician forces the people to take grave risks, the politician himself must take similar risks, etc.

My speculations about ideal government are based (i) on theories about the characteristics of ideal politicians, especially ideal sovereigns, ideal ministers, ideal political advisers and ideal bureaucrats, (ii) on theories about democratic institutions of power division and power control, (iii) on respective historical experience, and (iv) the conviction that one should also utilize the possibilities of so-called comparative cultural studies. Though cultures like the Chinese and European, or 'Western', cultures are in principle capable of developing on their own such theories and respective practices, in their attempts to improve their theories and practices, they can benefit from mutually utilizing each others contributions and experiences. Actually, all attempts of theoretical and practical improvements should utilize as many international data as possible.

I do not want to enter into a methodological discussion. I have done this elsewhere.① But it may be helpful to remember that international and intercultural discourse and theorizing is one of the best means for optimizing extant theories and for creating viable new theories. If this is done with necessary care, there is no danger of willful eclecticism, of cultural centrism or ethno-centrism, and no danger of cultural imperialism. There is also no danger that *viable* notions and norms of cultural identity would be called into question.

This is not to say that, if one restricted oneself to the study of Anglo-European philosophies, one would not come to conclusions similar to those one arrives at by also studying Chinese theories, but to say that it would certainly be more difficult. Actually, it was because of my studies of pre-Han Chinese philosophies, particularly the *Shujing* 書經, *Chunqiu Zuozhuan* 春秋左轉, *Lunyu*, *Mengzi*, *Xunzi*, *Mozi* 墨子, *Shangjun shu* 商君書, and *Han Feizi* 韓非子, that I became aware of the requirements of an adequate theory of ideal government. Since many others made the same experience, I regard this as an indication of the relevance of becoming aquainted with, and of analyzing and utilizing, Chinese ethics and political philosophies.

To provisionally sum up: traditional Anglo-European democratic theories of insti-

---

① See my: (i) Kulturelle Identität: ein gefährliches Phänomen? *Interkulturelle Philosophie und Ph? nomenologie in Japan*, ed. M. Lazarin, T. Ogawa und G. Rappe, München: iudicium, 1998, pp. 113-138. (ii) *Einführung in die Interkulturelle Philosophie*, Darmstadt: WBG, 2008.

tutional power division and power control should be complemented by theories of ideal politicians according to which politicians ought to be persons of moral integrity. Politicians should themselves do what they ask others to do, they should be trustworthy, reliable, and as far as possible behave in exemplary ways-but without becoming moral purists. Democracies should supplement their extant institutions by institutions that help meeting, or realizing, these requirements.

Leaving aside more or less deontological justifications, such developments would also be justified by pragmatic arguments, for they would significantly enhance the efficiency of government, and of politics in general. From early childhood through old age, we deeply dislike following orders by persons who themselves act differently. In international human rights discourse, whole states and governments escape argumentative discourse by just pointing out that the persons or institutions that criticize them have no moral right, i. e., no moral legitimation, to voice any criticism, for they themselves violate human rights, i.e., fail to live up to their own standards.

Supplementing extant notions of democratic power division and power control by norms and institutional checks of moral integrity, however, must not lead to even more personalized elections and politics. Hence, general education should much more emphasize the importance of valid argument. In other words, education should make clear that decisions should be based on, and justified by, valid arguments, and that the validity of arguments is independent from their genesis, especially from the persons who formulate them. Even in German academic circels, misology is widespread. Also, public moral criticism of politicians must accord with the extant norms of acceptable behavior, especically the norms of mutual personal respect, of politeness, decency and modesty. As the so-called Confucian classics emphasize, criticism and remonstrations (e. g., *jian*) should, as far as possible, be put forward in a becoming way. In Chinese history, personal criticism often focused on insignificant issues, and was unduely severe. During the so-called Cultural Revolution, the traditional Chinese ideal of criticism was perverting into an instrument of destroying people. In the West, certain forms of criticism ultimately led to a kind of witch hunt. Especially a person's dignity ought to be always respected.

Deficiencies notwithstanding, democratic theories and practices, especially those of power division and power control, are indispensible. The two traditional notions of ideal government must not be seen as mutually exclusive choices.

For example, it would be misleading to conceive of the 'Chinese' theories of ideal government as theories of government *exclusively* based on morality (or ethics), or as doctrines solely based on a notion of a "rule by virtue", while characterizing the respective 'Western' theories as advancing notions of mere government by law, thus simply contrasting the two traditions with each other. The 'Western' theories and practices of democracy, as well as of government by law, are (also) ultimately based on ethics, particularly on notions of universally valid human rights. The Chinese theories, on the other hand, have from the very beginning included juridical doctrines, and actual Chinese government has been from very old times also government by penal law. Further, from its very beginnings respective Chinese theories have been doctrines of ethical norms, e.g., the way (the *dao*) or humaneness (*ren*) rather than of "virtuous men." According to the classics, the ideal person(ality) is characterized by his or her following the way. It is not *vice versa*, i.e., it is not the ideal person that determines the way.

In many cultural traditions, and certainly in all states of the 21st century, ideal government has been or is conceived of as ultimately based on ethics or morality, though, on the part of the powerful, this often remained and remains mere lip service. Further, Chinese history itself provides an example that democratic institutions of power division and power control are indispensible for ideal government. Much too often, Chinese sovereigns, rulers, ministers, and bureaucrats have gravely abused power, causing much suffering, and even the death of huge numbers of people.

I have suggested how democratic institutions could and should be improved. It would lead too far to go into further details. Actually, this is rather the task of political, sociological, psychological, and juridical sciences, than a philosophical task.

I am well aware that my speculations are of a very general and, as I believe, common sensical kind. Hence one might regard them as somewhat trivial, especially if one thinks of the bulk of literature on democracy. But what is trivial, need not to be irrelevant. Coming to my conclusion, I emphasize again what I regard as the most important points in my speculations. (i) Ideal government requires both "rule by law" and "rule by virtue": democratic institutions and morally integer politicians. (ii) In developing respective theories and practices, both Anglo-European as well as Chinese philosophies and historical experiences should be utilized. (iii) This is not only possible, but actually necessary. An optimal approach would even take into account respective contributions from many more cultures. (iv) The Chinese contribution is significant. Neglecting this contribution, would aggravate the task. I would almost certainly never have identified certain problems of democracy, and conceived of possible solutions, if I had not read through the Chinese classics. (v) The value of the respective Chinese theories lies with their empiricalness, comprehensiveness and detailedness. This applies in particular to the referred to Chinese notions of (a) supremacy of peace over truth, (b) secular government, (c) indispensability of exemplary political life, i. e., political behavior characterized by personal integrity, honesty, truthfulness, etc., and (d) moral and aesthetical education. Emphasizing this, it should be clear again that I have in mind pre-Qin philosophy rather than later Chinese theories. Such metaphysical doctrines as *li xue* or modern Confucianism (*xin rujia* 新儒家) which include highly speculative ontologies, even ontologicalizing ethics, suffer from similar flaws and dangers as for instance Platonism, and hence do not offer viable alternatives or supplements to 'Western' theories and practices

# Dialectical Relationship between Rule of Virtue and Rule by Law

**Paolo Santangelo Sapienza (University of Roma)**

The evolution of Confucianism: The "rule of law", the "rule of virtue" and the "rule of human being", ambiguities and creativity in long-term debates on variations of anthropological dimensions of human beings.

We often raise questions on the flexibility and evolutions of ideologies: Confucianism is an example of a practical ideology has adapted itself to the great social changes from the times of its founder to the present day society. The five cardinal relations, *wugang* 五綱, as well as the contents of many instructions, reflected a certain kind of society in a certain period, and necessarily were adapted to the transformations during the centuries. In order to last longer the doctrine could not but be transformed according to the changes of society, hierarchy, mobility, etc. My reflections will start from the examination of the different meanings concerning the *fazhi-renzhi* 法治/人治 debates, and them I will shortly analyse some cases of construction of new anthropological dimensions in late imperial period.

The old order that Confucius intended to restore collapsed with the end of the Zhou dynasty. The contribution of Legalism to social-political efficiency was the creation of a written penal law that could be objectively applied to the whole population, and the establishment of a unique system in the country. Confucian alternative of government by moral suasion opposed Legalism and finally survived to it because considered human beings endowed with moral sense. The so called Imperial Confucianism was a compromise between the Legalist foundation of the Empire and the ideal rules by Rites (*lizhi* 禮治). The strength of law alone was not enough to get consensus, to control people and insure order and cooperation, because men respond also to their sense of justice and their ideals, and cannot be ruled only by the fear of punishment and the hope of prize. Thus Confucianism has contributed to human morality and social harmony by stressing the *moral need* of human beings and the *optimistic trust into in their education*. The priority of the principle of conscience on the principle of authority had been expressed by Confucius:

The Master said,"If the people be led by laws, and uniformity sought to be given them by punishments, they will try to avoid the punishment, but have no sense of shame. If they be led by virtue, and uniformity sought to be given them by the rules of propriety, they will have the sense of shame, and moreover will become good." 子曰:「道之以政,齊之以刑,民免而無恥;道之以德,齊之以禮,有恥且格。」

This directive is iterated in other passages of Confucian Classics that stress the priority of the ruler's virtue on the use of law, such as in the proposition "it was your greatly distinguished father, the king Wen, who was able to illustrate his virtue and be careful in the use of punishments."惟乃丕顯考文王,克明德慎罰, or "the sovereigns all made their virtue illustrious, and were cautious in the use of punishments" 罔不明德慎罰,亦克用勸。And again," If good men were to govern a country in succession for a hundred years, they would be able to transform the violently bad, and dispense with capital punishments". 善人為邦百年,亦可以勝殘去殺矣。"

*Lizhi* 礼治 and *dezhi* 德治 expressed the basis of the rule on morality, education and social practices, 为政以德, principles near the concept of *renzhi*: moral education can bring back the original goodness of human mind or can establish it by reinforcing the sense of shame. *Dezhi* is the ideal model of *renzhi*, and can be realised as far as rulers and officials are correct and respectful: rulers must be models for the rest of population, and teach people by their own behaviour. The Master said, "When a prince's personal conduct is correct, his government is effective without the issuing of orders. If his personal conduct is not correct, he may issue orders, but they will not be followed." 子曰:「其身正,不令而行;其身不正,雖令不從。」

This trend emphasised education, civilisation and persuasion 教化, against repression based on "hating evil"恶恶". The elaboration and diffusion of the consensus theories (Mencius but also Xunzi) together with the theory of the Heavenly Mandate were all elements for a limitation and softening of authoritarian power and the mere application of law. Above all, the prevalence of Mencian concept of original morality of human nature offered more space to the reflection on the extension of human conscience. In the Ming period Wang Yangming started his discourse on inner conscience from Mencius.

Thus the emphasis on morality rather than on an objective law has its own advantages on the growth of personal sense of responsibility, but it brings however also negative effects, at least from the modern point of view:

1) weakness of objective determination of duties and rights among all citizens;

2) danger of an unequal standard in interpersonal relations;

3) finally the risk of moralism, that is the*misuse of moral justification* in order to legitimate the wrongs of the powerful, or to destroy the image of the adversary or competitors. Moralism cannot rule interpersonal affairs, as it may easily generate conformism and hypocrisy and weaken individual creativity. In the history of humanity it often happens that in the name of morality itself minorities - that did not share the same principles with the majority - have been oppressed. In fact, from the political point of view, the emphasis on the virtue of rulers, the king or the officials ("明德"、"敬德"), is not a sufficient tool to exclude the abuse of an excessive power as it does provide neither theoretical nor practical limits to it.

In order to clarify the terms of the question, we notice that the spirit of the dispute on the "rule by man" 人治 in traditional society is different from the similar notion used in the present-day debates, as well as in China also the way *fazhi* 法治 is intended today-enforcement of a certain rule to protect the rights of the citizen - is to be distinguished from the way *fazhi* was intended by the ancient Chinese: in fact the Legalists' idea of *fazhi* equated to renzhi (rule by man)". In order to keep in mind the different interpretations of the above concepts even in traditional China and Europe, we should go back to the basic Chinese optimistic belief in the innate goodness of man (Mencius' original nature) or his reformation by education (Xunzi's theory of *capacity* to *become* good), versus the basic pessimistic Western attitude on man's evil (which can be exemplified in the notion of the "original sin").

***Renzhi*** did neither mean absence of law and rights, nor arbitrary and absolute power by few persons (*legibus soluti*). Thus, the contrast with *fazhi* was based on other values and criteria than our own. Law in Chinese tradition was prevalently penal law and was related to the *Fajia* school, so its concept is far from the modern Enlightenment idea of a law which limits the power of the king, and protects the citizen from the authority and power. In traditional China the main *ratio* was to enforce order against disorder rather than to protect the individual from the power of the ruler.

In fact, from the modern point of view, both *fazhi* and *renzhi/dezhi* endorse to different degrees a *paternalistic* conception of the state: rulers know better than their subjects and make laws to guide them.

In modern Western history the rule of law (*nomocracy*) refers to theoretical equality of all citizens who are subject to the law, including the ruler who is not above the law. It was contrasted with the older concept of "Divine right" according to which the ruler was not subject to earthly authority, as he derived the right to rule directly from the will of God.

Thus the dimension of the discussion in traditional China was different from nowadays debates. Some centuries after the fall of the Ming dynasty, the ambiguous role of law and its application in redressing justice is clearly envisaged by Yuan Mei, when he notices the conflict between a sense of humaneness and the duty to apply the law-which brings about suffering and death-and seems to be one of the pivotal themes of moral responsibility. In China, the official was at the same time considered a judge and bound to enforce the penal law in order to keep the social order. Yuan Mei had been official, with several duties, and thus his sensitivity made him reflect on this contradiction. In a story, he presents a moment of crisis for a high-ranking official, which leads him to rethink his life, and in his dream he visits the netherworld, where he is suddenly made aware of his behaviour:

The old monk smiled and said: "You have killed too many people and your fortune and official rank have already been used up to atone for your crimes. What use is there in asking?" The Assistant Minister said: "I may have killed many people, but they were meant to die according to the law. It's not my fault." The old monk said: "When you were handling a case, did you truly act according to the law alone, or did you also covet the favour of the powerful and seek career promotion?" 老僧笑曰:"汝殺人多矣,祿折盡矣,尚何問為。"侍郎曰:"我殺人雖多,皆國法應誅之人,非我罪也。"僧曰:"汝當日辦案時,果只知有國法乎,抑貪圖迎合固寵遷官乎?"

Interesting is that an original scholar like Yuan Mei, at the end of the 18 century, did not foster the reinforcement of *fazhi* in order to protect the weaker or equalize the rights, but moved in the direction of rehabilitating passions and desires, and also illegitimating the resort to "principles" and their unhuman application. Law was still perceived as means of punishment rather than a protection against power and arrogance, and principles and rites as the hypocritical moralistic tool to enforce the arrogance of power.

My hypothesis is that besides the objective rule of law (*fazhi*), and the moralist rule of virtue (*dezhi*), in the ambit and on the margins of Confucian debates, from the late Ming on, we can notice the development of another dimension, a more autonomous dimension in the rule of human being-different from the traditional *renzhi* concept. Here I will present a few elements whose concurrence is a symptom of this different attitude.

**1. The cult of** *qing* and the new anthropological personality according to Li Zhi

If *qing* 情 is a multifarious concept, rather ambiguous for Western culture remains also the use of notions such as *renqing* 人情. "The term *renqing* is a very complex notion, which can be translated in different ways as "human feelings, obligations and experiences", "personal relations", "social sentiments", "responsive relations of trust", "the gratitude or the favour or the helpfulness one owes to someone else". Thus it concerns not only *human emotions*, but also *social ties and behavioural interaction*, and may imply moral and sentimental norms ruling human relations, based on common sense. In a few words, the term may be used to express the fundamental and basic needs of people that reflect the innate morality of social organization, but also the subjectivity of feelings that should be carefully controlled in order to avoid mistakes, favoritism and excesses in front of others. Thus, this concept is a parameter for moral evaluation, relatively conforming to basic Confucian virtues. These "innate feelings" are the basis of good human nature, and do not need to be learned, because every human being can find them in his own heart. In fact, such a concept is so related to social interrelations that its psychological dimension is completely socially directed, and rather expresses the feeling of one image in others' opinion.

Feng Menglong, in his "History of Love" (*Qingshi*), wrote: "the Royal Way is based on "human social sentiments (*renqing*)"; without an understanding of them one cannot become king or emperor. 王道本乎人情。不通人情不能為帝王。And *renqing* 人情 is one of the most frequent expressions used by Lü Kun with some different nuances. In the following sentence he relates "law" and "social sentiments": 法者 御世宰物之神器,人君本天理人情而定之,人君不得與。"Law is a divine instrument to govern and regulate the world. The ruler establishes it, on the basis of heavenly principles and human social sentiments. He does not interfere." (Lü Kun, 呻吟語, 治道;

Araki Kengo: 189) One notices the pair of "heavenly principles and human social sentiments"天理人情, where human sentiments, meaning men's natural feelings in their social interaction are just as important as heavenly principles, or that both balance each other. Furthermore, it seems that Lü Kun here expresses not only the general consciousness that the rule of the law should be confucianised and moralised-as Dong Zhongshu had started to do during the Han dynasty -but also that the power of the political authority is limited by consuetudinary legal system and customs:人君不得與). Furthermore, Lü Kun himself uses the term *renqing* in two very similar sentences which express his cautiousness: "Human social sentiments are identical in every age and everywhere. Sages, in order to prevent excess [they become wanton], have especially established moderation as a moral criterion." 人情，天下古今所同。聖人防其肆，特為之立中以的之(呻吟語,應務,112); and again: "Human social sentiments are the same over time everywhere. Sages, fearing their excesses [that they become wanton], have especially established moderation in order to protect against them."人情,天下古今所同。聖人懼其肆,特為之立中以防之.(呻吟語, 治道 165). Moreover, Lü Kun writes that the rules of the Dynasty, social roles and positions, the Way of the sages cannot be in private favour (social sentiments). 朝廷法紀,做不得人情。天下名分,做不得人情。聖賢道理。。。(呻吟語,人情, 169). It means that the sentiments of friendship cannot interfere with the laws of the state and with the complex social relations that are at the basis of community life, because they may contain egoistic tendencies that are dangerous for the general interests of the state. Thus here law is more reliable than passions. However commonly shared feelings-but here he uses "people's sentiments" *minqing* - are irrepressible demands and cannot be totally repressed:

The feelings of the people cannot be totally repressed. If dikes are built to restrain water, once [the dikes] are broken, [water] will sweep by houses and move mountains. If a gun is used to hold fire, once [the gun] shoots, it will reduce stone to fragments and it will raze trees to the ground. Jie and Zhou repressed the feelings of the people they governed; instead Tang and Wu understood them. These are the principal causes of the existence or the collapse [of the State]. These are the things which concern the rulers of the world every waking hour. 民情甚不可鬱也.防以鬱水一決則漂屋推山.砲以鬱火一發則碎石破木.桀紂鬱民情而湯武通之.此存亡之大機也.有天下者之所夙夜孜孜者也?(呻吟語, 治道,186)

A new trend was surely opened by some thinkers of the School of Mind, whose moral 'relativism' and subjectivism was partially to be understood in the frame of Buddhist and Daoist influences. He Xinyin placed a good deal of weight on 'personal feelings and temperament' (*yìqì* 意氣), and, as he did not accept the identification of passions with selfishness and lack of morality, he considered them to be part of human nature (性而味,性而色,性而声,性而安逸,性也。). He reiterated Mencius' admonishment to the king to consider people's desires worthy of satisfaction; he went on to develop a conception of 'training desires' (*yù yù* 育欲), in which self fulfilment meant the fulfilment of the needs of others, and the desires of individual people became universalised. Li Zhi 李贄 (1527-1602), with his typical paradoxicality, not only recognized that the reviled desires were positive in nature, but he set about praising 'selfishness', as the spring of action and social welfare:

The human mind recognizes itself in its selfishness: without selfishness, there is no mind. He who works on the land must have an interest in the harvest so that he works diligently; he or she who works at home must have an interest in accumulating wealth in order to shrewdly manage household affairs; the student must have an interest in passing exams in order to study well. Likewise, if a functionary was not interested in his pay, he would not have sought the job. 夫私者,人之心也。人必有私,而後其心乃見;若無私,則無心矣。如服田者私有秋之穫,而後治田必力;居家者私積倉之穫,而後治家必力;為學者私進取之穫,而後舉業之治也必力。故官人不私以祿,則雖召之必不來矣[…].

As has already been noted, the Confucian tradition does not lack concrete recognition of the importance of the primary needs of individuals (examples range from the "Analects" to Zhu Xi) and this is even truer of the Legalist tradition. However the scope was undoubtedly delimited to the quantified need, and theoretically it was clear that food and procreation were legitimate needs, based on social requirements, while exceeding them was the egoistic search for profit, lust, greed (*si* 私, *li* 利, *tan* 貪) of the immoral people. Exemplary are the distinction between gluttony and hunger by Zhu Xi and Lü Kun's warnings. And yet it remains true that this represents the limitation and coding of desires: it reflects the idea of wisdom of a society based on a natural economy, with its protectionism, both economic and cultural; traditional Chinese society came within these characteristics, with the constant nightmare of hunger and the very high rate of infantile mortality. Consequently what we do not find is the absolute exaltation of desire as such - going as far as the modern provocative identification of man with the libidinally diffuse *desiring machine* -, a desire that is indeed never limited to, or rather, identified with needs and necessity. Needs are different from desires - whose essence does not consist of their realisation or their full satisfaction, but of their perpetual reproduction - even though they may be induced and acquired, precisely because the former are quantifiable and limited, while the latter are not; to reduce desire to a need means identifying happiness with the satisfaction of material needs, limiting it to certain well-defined goods and ignoring the function of *imagination* on which desire feeds. A certain overcoming of this concept can be singled out in Li Zhi. With his typical paradoxicality, Li Zhi extends He Xinyin's discourse on desires, and does not stop short at recognising the basic vital needs. He extends this category to desires which are positive in nature, he sets about praising "selfishness", as the starting point of any social process, by developing the arguments of the previous passage:

The wise have taught that "one succeeds through not being troubled [over-doing]" (*wuwei er cheng zhe* 無為而成者). But now the expression "not being troubled" has come to mean "absence of mind-heart" (*wuxin* 無心) [...]. If he does not use his mind-heart, the peasant leaves the field untilled, the craftsman works shoddily, and the scholar is not up to his job. How can something be obtained without the use of the mind? Commentators assure us that the so-called "absence of mind" is not a real lack of mind, but only an absence of selfish feelings (*wu sixin* 無私心). Yet the mind of man is characterized by "selfishness". The human mind recognizes itself in its selfishness: without selfishness, there is no mind. He who works on the land must have an interest in the harvest to work diligently; he or she who works at home must have an interest in accumulating wealth in order to shrewdly manage household affairs; the student must have an interest in passing exams in order to study well. Likewise, if a functionary was not interested in his pay he would not have sought the job [...] Desire for goods, for sexual satisfaction, for education, for a personal career, for the amassing of wealth; the desire to buy land or houses for one's descendants; the quest for geomantic things to bring good luck to one's children - all of these things are productive and keep life going in this world, all of these things are loved and practiced by the people, all of these things are known and openly discussed [...] The concrete principles of human relations are made up of clothing and food. Without these items there would be no relationships [...] Scholars should recognize the true essence that lies behind these relationships, and stop procrastinating about them [...]

It was thus an important fact that Li Zhi went beyond the mere formulation of moral obligations and prohibitions of Chinese tradition, but instead reiterated the priority of each man's vital needs and desires, by acknowledging the fundamental importance of personal stimulus in every activity. It can be considered the beginning of the transition from the 'subject of roles'-the Confucian definition of the individual in the society-to a 'subject of desires'. When he tells of profit, interest, self-advantage, clothes, sexual life, career, his scope is beyond the classical natural needs for living and procreation, and it concerns the projections, wishes and desires everybody nurtures, from the peasant to the scholar.

Li Zhi's ideas surpass the traditional Confucian effort to combine individual needs with social needs: in an opened and developed society, what is individually ("selfishly") yearned for is understood in its "necessity". The constant reference to man's fundamental appetites goes beyond the mere reference to concepts already known in antiquity, in order to attribute to the constitutive nature of certain desires an important dialectical function in social relations.

Li Zhi's was anything but isolated in his stance. There were also other authors whose positive attitude towards desires combined with their search for a comfortable and refined life to set them against the majority of scholars, who criticized the loosening of morals and condemned the dangers held by human feelings. Some decades before Li Zhi, Lu Ji 陸楫 (1515-1552) elaborated a type of liberal economic analysis that justified the pursuit of self-realization, and the luxury of rich families. According to Lu Ji, their spending was not only consonant with the Empire's morality and economy, it set off a process that once started would feed itself with the augmentation of wealth derived from mechanisms of consumption and production. Poor people would benefit from an increase in desires and a subsequent increase in the needs of the rich, finding jobs and earning money. This meant that the acquisition of expensive and prized merchandise (ornate palaces, horses and carriages, splendid gardens, luxurious clothing etc.) could not be judged as morally negative, in contrast with the prevailing praise for frugality. There were comforts for those who could afford them, and benefits for many others. His illustration was that people who ate sumptuous meals indirectly shared their wealth with peasants and the cook; people who wore magnificent clothes shared their wealth with merchants and the weavers.

Li Zhi also observes that "there is neither impurity in passions, nor purity in emptiness," and, holding up the two Han high functionaries named Cao Can 曹参（？ - 190 B.C) and Ji An 汲黯（ - 108 B.C.?) as examples, he propounds a policy of non-intervention（民實自治）based on loving life's pleasures.

Li Zhi criticizes just one form of real egoism, hypocritic moralism, with the same vehemence as he uses in his positive ruling of the fulfilment of human desires, and contrasts *xuedao* with *daoxue*. He quotes two examples taken from the "Analects" (*Lunyu*): in one case, Confucius gives different advices to his disciples depending on their character; reverence and reciprocity for Zhonggong and caution in speech to Si ma Niu. Then Li Zhi remarks:

Confucius never taught men to study his doctrine. Therefore if he had achieved his objectives, he would not have used himself as a model to the world. He is right in saying that when the wise man is at his peak, everything is in its rightful place. Men found their rightful place a long time ago, and if some have not it is due to the greedy and the arrogant who exploit people, or the "virtuous" torment them. "Virtuous" men are worried that nobody has lost their place in the world, and they wish for all they are worth to revive their own position. That is why they use virtue and rites to control men's minds, and political power and penal laws to fetter their bodies, so that they can really make them lose their status. 夫惟孔子未嘗以孔子教人學，故其得志也，必不以身為教于天下。是故聖人在上，萬物得所，有由然也。夫天下之人得所也久矣，所以不得所者，貪暴者擾之，而"仁者"害之也。"仁者"天下之失所也而優之，而汲汲焉欲貽之以得所之域。于是有德禮以格其心，有政刑以縶其四體，而人始大失所矣。

The thing that most offended his moral sensibilities was that the moralists deceived and harmed ordinary people: the hypocrisy of scholars and functionaries, while claiming to be altruistic, duped and aggrieved the population. He is also very aware of the danger inherent in all efforts that, in the name of a principle, claim to redeem humanity: he fears anybody who claims to root out evil from amongst men, considering such a person to be far more dangerous than any amoral or immoral person; such a man creates divisions amongst men, pitting one man against another, consciously or unconsciously using them as implements for certain "sacred" ideals:

Confucius never taught that others should follow him as a model. If he had done so, how could he have told his disciple Yan Yuan, who had questioned him on the virtue of humaneness, that this virtue depended on each and every individual alone? How could he have asserted that in ancient times scholars studied for their own personal advancement, and that what the superior man seeks is to be find in himself? It follows that if each man depends upon himself alone, the scholar has no need to turn to Confucius for guidance on the subject of humaneness; and if each and every individual depends on himself, there is no need to provide teachings for disciples. Such knowledge is without others and without ourselves.

These ideas remind Dai Zhen's 戴震 (1724-1777) criticism of the use of "principle" by some scholars and powerful men. Dai Zhen for instance warned against exploiting morality to cover up the arrogance of power: "The respectable one resorts to principles to criticize the humble, as well as the Senior uses it against the young and the higher against the lower."尊者以理責卑,長者以理責幼,貴者以理責賤..

Li Zhi expressed similar concepts in other passages of his works. He refused any model of heteronomous wisdom, because each of us must discover wisdom within ourselves, and he repudiates any pretext of possessing a monopoly on truth. If it is true that all men are good and wise, then they do not need either models or masters. All true wise men, including Confucius and Buddha, avoided forcing rules onto other men, because moral laws that come from the outside are hollow, deceiving words. Wise men have no special quality that may be passed on or taught to others. Hence the absurdity of the age-old question of continuity in the "passing on of the Way" that marked the course of the history of Confucianism; where there is humaneness, the Dao, the Way, may be found, just like water can be found everywhere on this earth; the Dao is not the realm of one particular master or another. Hence the distinction of morality - that is one's ability to rejoice over the greatness of men and to suffer for their vileness with the consciousness that both are his own greatness and vileness - from moralism - a system intended to justify one's choices and to blame others. Li Zhi - as well as other later thinkers (Huang Zongxi 黃宗羲,1610-1695, or Chen Que 陳確, 1604-1677, for instance) -, emphasises the personal experience that offers the primary criterion of *truth* and *right*, devaluating traditional imperatives and external models: Classics and the past can offer only hints that we have to develop and complement with *our own* experience and intuition. Consequent upon Li Zhi's fundamental optimism about human beings is his impression that all men are wise, regardless of social standing or cultural level, and that nobody has the right to impose anything on anyone. Consequently moral rules are not needed to be established, as each individual must live a life which is distinctive to him/herself, as every human being is different from others: good life is uncodifiable.

Li Zhi notes that superior and common men are as different from one another as fish are from water. Indeed, he felt that his non-conformist life and his often scandalous behaviour were compatible with being a wise man. In other words (according to Laozi) a man who "is happy with what everybody else refuses and is close to the Way", or a man who "tempers his lustre and mixes himself with dust". The evenings spent at the theatre or in the "district of flowers and willows" for which he was rebuked by Neo-Confucian moralists were a proof of his ability to living amongst common people without vaunting his own gifts, in accordance with the formula of the *Daodejing*.

In order to better understand Li Zhi's attitudes towards emotions and morality it is beneficial to refer to De Bary's definition of "negative and positive individualism", no matter one shares or not all his conclusions: Li Zhi's conception has both of these characteristics, the "negativity" of those who leave society because they are not able to adapt themselves to its compromises and its laws, and the "positiveness" of the defence he makes of human desires as an objective and generalized phenomena. It is true that Li Zhi did not propose any kind of juridical or political reform aiming at establishing the rights of individuals before the state like in the modern times. But it is equally true that this would have been an unusual way for things to proceed in China. Li Zhi's reiteration of the inviolability of man's basic and universal passions and desires was an effective recognition of a dominion that applied to every person who deserved respect and satisfaction. Even though there is no claim of having legal power, we may consider this an assertion of the full development of the human personality within the framework of traditional Chinese society.

The same may be said of his firm belief in equality between the sexes as far as intellectual ability is concerned. Naturally enough, there is nothing in his writings (nor is there in the writings of Lü Kun and Li Ruzhen) that refers to legal or political equality of rights between the sexes. Nevertheless, his assertions concerning "morality" and "principle" are at least as important as European enlightenment theories on human personality which have been developed by certain circles of eighteenth century intellectuals. In particular, Li Zhi places great importance on a number of universal passions and desires he considers as basic biological drives, as in the quoted passage.

In China certain trends contributed to the gradual development of an increasingly elaborate and complex image of the "individual". The individual was no longer considered only as a "subject" merely performing a given role, nor simply as part of the "people", in the best Mencian tradition, the populistic object of the king's concern and a necessary support for his legitimation. The person becomes the bearer of fundamental needs-demands, which must be recognized and respected by the state. In particular, the identification of "natural common desires" is an indication of an awareness that transcends the ethical delimitation of the powers of the king and the bureaucracy and becomes a form of "inviolability of natural rights" - in our conceptual terms - through the equating of "desires" with "needs".

In Li Zhi these natural tendencies and requirements form the basis of people's life in provocative contrast to deposed abstract orthodox principles. Contemporaneously passions and desires that "the man on the street" feels in everyday life belong to true customs and a true morality. There is as much to be learnt from humble people, such as peasants, potters and fishermen (*gengjia tao yu zhi ren* 耕稼陶渔) as from wise men. This universality and respectability of common individual desires constitutes the core of a branch of "individualism".

The impact of Li Zhi's ideas as well as the strong reaction of the orthodoxy made him an unconventional and troublesome personage. He has been labelled as an "anti-Confucian" or even Legalist, although he considered himself a Confucian writer and practicing. In fact he was both trans-valuing and reinvigorating Confucianism, embracing and rejecting parts of the Confucian tradition. Accused of three crimes, deviant views, sexual promiscuity and confusing Buddhism for Confucianism, with his life and death he witnessed how in fact the *kuangshi* 狂士 could be a kind of role model for young people from low and high-ranking families, dissatisfied with their lives, who either disdained to pursue a career as a bureaucrat or who had already failed their exams. Probably associated with his notion of original genuine child's soul, *tongxin* 童心, the concept of 'foolishness' (*chi* 痴, *kuang* 狂 and *pi* 癖, 呆/蠢/愚) with both the metaphorical meaning of 'lack or retardation of mental brightness and understanding', and the notion of 'lack of judgment and wisdom' in the sense of abnormal evaluation and madness gained a certain success as new models of personality in intellectual circles.

This phenomenon was manifested as part of the so called "cult of *qing* 情" or "cult of passions", and was an important intellectual and literary movement developed in the late Ming dynasty, aiming at revaluating the emotions against the traditional diffidence for passions and desires (*qing*). The anti-hero Baoyu, with his aversion for any kind of official ceremony and convention, his abnormal sensibility, his impractical and naïve mentality, his consciousness of being different from others, is a late example of this model of personality.

**B) Rehabilitation of "passions and desires"**

Another important convergent trend which contributed to the elaboration of a new anthropological personality was the rehabilitation of passions and desires, phenomenon that we already noticed in Li Zhi, and which has been well demonstrated by Pauline Lee. Yang Shen 楊慎 (1488-1559) was one of the first who stated the interrelation of *xing* and *qing* 性情不離: "Promoting nature and neglecting emotions one become dead ashes, while being involved by emotions and forgetting nature one become as animals. " 舉性而遺情何如曰死灰. 觸情而忘性何如曰禽獸. Other important evidences are Luo Qinshun and Chen Que.

Luo Qinshun 羅欽順 (1465-1547) stated "The fact that man has desires definitely derives from heaven. Some are necessary and cannot be repressed; some are appropriate and cannot be changed. If those that are irrepressible all conform to the principle of what is appropriate, how can they not be good? It is only heedlessly giving way to passions, indulging the desires, and not knowing how to turn back that is evil. Confucians of the past often spoke about eliminating or restraining human desires and thought it necessary to resort to severe means in order to repress them. But their mode of expression seems one-sided and exaggerated. The desires, together with pleasure, anger, sorrow and joy, are qualities of nature. Can pleasure, sorrow, anger and joy also be eliminated?"夫人之有欲固出於天. 蓋有必然而不容已. 且有當然而不可易者. 於其所不容已者而皆合乎當然之則夫安往而非善乎. 惟其恣情縱欲而不知反斯為惡爾. 先儒多以去人欲遏人欲為言蓋所以防其流者不得不嚴但語意似乎偏重夫欲與喜怒哀樂皆性之所有者喜怒衰樂又可去乎(*Kunzhi ji* 困知记 (SKQS), 卷下),

Chen Que 陈确(1604—1677) arrived to openly talk of desires: "basically there is no principle in human mind, as heavenly principle appears from human desire. When appropriate, desire is principle. Without desires can be said there would not be also principle. " ….人心本无天理,天理正从人欲中见,人欲恰好处,即天理也。向无人欲,

则亦并无天理之可言矣。(*Chen Que ji* 陈确集, 别集,5,聋言 4,无欲作圣辨).

We can sum up the process of rehabilitation of desires and passions as follows:

2. **Moral justification** 情 = 仁

*Qing* is considered source of morality (see also 真情)。。。私情化公。。。子有情于父,臣有情于君。推之种种相,俱作如是观。。。圣亦何仁义《情史》序(1) Also 故凡忠臣孝子,義士節婦,莫非大有情人。(*Yuerong bian*《悦容编》序.

3. **Vitalistic justification** 情 = 生

Life and reproduction in the universe are based on desires: 天地若无情,不生一切物。一切物无情,不能环相生。生生而不灭,由情不灭故。四大皆幻设,惟情不虚假。(《情史》, 序 1)情始于男女。(《情史》, 序 2). For Luo Rufang 羅汝芳. (1515-1588), the concept of *qing* 情 is inseparable from *sheng* 生.

4. **Nobility of pure emotions** 真情

"genuine love" is the innate and moral link which unites all beings:"自来忠孝节烈之事,从道理上做者必勉强,从至情上出者必真切。"情史・情贞类》叙.

5. **Active moral function of emotions** 情教

The "doctrine of love" or "sentimental education" is the way people are spontaneously induced to be virtuous, without any pressure of duty "我欲立情教,教诲诸众生。子有情于父,臣有情于君。推之种种相,俱作如是观。《情史》情史》序(1 吴人龙子犹序); 六经皆以情教也(序 2 江南詹詹外史述).

6. **Reversal of values**:

Tang Xianzu 湯顯祖 contrasts passions and principles 情 >< 理 (*Tang Xianzu Mudan ting ji tici* 湯顯祖牡丹亭記題詞). Moreover, in the "Peonies' Pavilion", in refusing to obey her father's order to leave her husband and go back to being just his daughter, Liniang defies the patriarchal system and wins. Tang Xianzu followed Li Zhi, who at that time argued that all human bonds should be aligned with the bond of husband and wife, not that of father and child. *Mudan ting* was undoubtedly influenced by this debate. Furthermore, according to Zhu Xi the cosmic energy (*qi*) - of which every being is composed - is differently pure: literati and male at the top the society were composed by the most pure *qi*, while people of lower strata and women were endowed with a less pure energy. The challenge to the world order and social-moral hierarchy was expressed in the revival and reappraisal of the statement of the poet Xie Ximeng 謝希孟, a disciple of the famous Neo-Confucian thinker Lu Xiangshan 陸象山 (1139-1193), to his master: "*The marvellous and splendid energy of the universe is always concentrated in the woman and not in man*"天地英靈之氣,不鍾于男人而鍾于婦人。This statement smacked of sacrilege and subversion, because it referred to the Neo-Confucian cosmological conception but overturned its universal order. On several occasions in his works, Feng Menglong cited Xie's proposition, with slight variations, although he was not the only one, and the rediscovery of this quotation and the rise of the new anti-rigorist and non-conformist trends of the late Ming period, made it proverbial also in the dynasty. This erosion of the correspondence between hierarchical order of society and moral prestige can be found in many writers at the end of the Ming dynasty. Zhang Dai 张岱 (1597-1689?) introduced some examples of artisans that had created some fortunes and had become so important to be treated at the same level of the officials and the gentry, and He Xinyin 何心隐 (1517-1579) encouraged this social mobility.

Moreover, in Feng Menglong's Preface to "The Mountain Songs" (*Shan'ge* 山歌) the reversal of values is expressed by resorting to the above mentioned pure and genuine emotions: "borrowing from the genuine love between man and woman as an antidote for the fake medicine of moralistic rules" (借男女之真情,發名教之偽藥)."

The above cases do not involve specifically the traditional scope of *renzhi* and *fazhi*, but in fact indirectly challenge them by questioning their *values and effectiveness*. In the "Mountain Songs", the "subversive" element of the lyrics is clear both in the content and the expository language: A picture of the world is often turned on its head and goes against common knowledge, and reveals the banality of certain clichés regarding gender differences and family. The representation of passions and desires offers an unusual perspective, if compared with the image coming from most of other official and private sources: the minimalist interpretation of love could be summed up in the statement "*love is like food*", but also "*love is like fire*", and it ephemeral and light nature emerges through "*the beloved is like a flower*". Thus, traditional sense of moral shame, *youchi* 有耻, is replaced by the fear of the severe and unjust social control. The search for a new language to express true and essential feelings leads to an apparent simplification of the phenomenon, an "anti-Romantic Romanticism": purposely avoiding any sublimation reduces love to everyday need and yet offers a gallery of both heroic and cynical, engaged and ephemeral cases. Love becomes a universal need beyond moral and social rules.

Finally, among others, another interesting element can be found in the late

18century, the *Zibuyu* 子不语, which questions the cognitive ability of men, the function and power of beliefs, the root of morality itself, responsibility. Thus Yuan Mei creates an epistemological challenge which even affects our ability to reconstruct the past and justify any absolute and authoritarian system of values. Like common people needs to resorts to spirits, monks and magicians, literati too look for analogous safety through their adherence to the Confucian system, and the belief in the retributive power of destiny and heaven. Evil pervades the world, as greed and snobbism reign even in the netherworld, and the difficulty in obtaining justice and avenging oneself is a widespread occurrence. Thus, hope in a superior's retribution is illusory. Stories present the coexistence of two contrasting subjective states: on the one hand, the wronged soul's indignation over a wrong committed against it and a sense of justice inspiring its revenge; on the other hand, the fear and tension experienced by the persecuted human being in the effort to avoid such punishment, which is often felt as unjust persecution because he does not feel guilty. This dual portrayal with the victim of injustice that becomes persecutor of innocents makes the reader question the concepts of responsibility and retribution, which are at the basis of the notion of destiny both in personal existence and in history. These situations, which moreover seem to present the difficulty of the realisation of retribution and justice, raise doubts regarding the possibility of ever achieving a satisfactory understanding of reality, on a laic role of justice, and on a basic tolerant attitude. This work represents a critical reconsideration of the basis of Confucian tradition, the *moral need* of human beings and the *optimistic trust in their education*.

All these writers contributed to the growth of new anthropological models. Life is based on desires, that determine common aspirations and practices of personality 共好而共習, so that for Li Zhi selfishness is the basis of individual desires and personality: "夫私者人之心也。人必有私而後其心乃見,若無私,則無心矣 (如好貨,如好色,如勤學,如進取,如多積金寶,如多買田宅為子孫謀,博求風水為子孫福蔭)。" Yet the mind of man is characterized by 'selfishness'. The human mind recognizes itself in its selfishness: without selfishness, there is no mind (Desire for goods, for sexual satisfaction, for education, for a personal career, for the amassing of wealth; the desire to buy land or houses for one's descendants; the quest for geomantic things to bring good luck to one's children)". The scope is beyond the classical natural needs for living and procreation, and it concerns the projections, wishes and desires everybody nurtures, from the peasant to the scholar. Desires are not justified only by the basic needs, but are the dynamic incentive for the common good, as well as the theoretical basis of the sense of justice and solidarity. Li Zhi's utilitarian morality combines the priority of basic needs with the recognition of the social utility of individual interests and ambitions: this contributes to the perception of a new personality, which is not bound by traditional ethics but promotes new individuals with personal desires and creativity. This concept of personality is strengthened by the defence of intellectual freedom: Li Zhi refuses any model of heteronomous wisdom, and he repudiates any pretext of possessing a monopoly on truth, because each human being can discover wisdom within him/herself: "the greedy and the arrogant who exploit people, is no worse than the 'virtuous' who torments them. 貪暴者擾之,而"仁者"害之也。Nobody should paternalistically worry about the others and the subjects' virtue: "'Virtuous' men are worried that nobody has lost their place in the world, and they wish for all they are worth to revive their own position. That is why they use virtue and rites to control men's minds, and political power and penal laws to fetter their bodies" "仁者"天下之失所也而優之,而汲汲焉欲貽之以得所之域。于是有德禮以格其心,有政刑以縶其四體,而人始大失所矣。This universality and respectability of common individual desires and independence from other's indoctrination constitute the core of a branch of "individualism". This new type of personality, independent and autonomous, with a moral without moralism, with legitimate desires and interests, was anthropologically different from the standard models, and thus it could not but be seen as "crazy and foolish".

Another question is why these new anthropological elements remained recessive in Chinese society, but this has been only partially studied. The above examples present models of personality which are different from the orthodox or the main stream of Confucianism. They enriched the debates inside this doctrine, and gave consistent answers to new questions and to social-economic transformation of Chinese society. This doctrine, opened to further developments, owing to its encouragements of perpetual self-transcendence, based on the *Analects* (Wei ling gong, 29) statement: "It is the human being that can extend the Way, not the Way that extends the human being." 人能弘道,非道弘人.

We may temporarily conclude with the following hypotheses on the vitality of Confucianism:

7. What was considered not-orthodox-Li Zhi for instance - can be recognised as a

fundamental contributor to the development of Confucianism.

8. The so called "cult of *qing*" shows how the same Confucianism produced tendencies which were

neither Puritanic nor self-restraining, and contributed to a new development of personality.

9. The inclusion of Western elements-such as Liberalism, Freudianism, Enlightenment, Renaissance thought-in the last decades is an important means of revitalising the Confucian doctrine in contemporary global society.

# Virtues and Relationships in the Mencius

**Richard Alfred Harmsworth King (University of Berns, Switzerland)**

There has been recently some debate as to the scope of the virtues-should they be finely divided for specific tasks, or taken to be broad dispositions covering wide ranges of behaviour. i This debate seems to me to be premature, in that the question of how to individuate virtues should be aired first: how do we or should we count virtues? Now one marked distinction between parts of the Chinese tradition and the Western one is provided by the virtues particular to certain relationships-between parents and children, between friends, between prince and minister. Clearly, this is one way virtues, at least some virtues *may* be counted. In this paper, I look at some texts in the *Mencius* to get a little clearer on these virtues and the relationships they come to bear in.

i For a discussion of how this question relates to early Confucian ethics, see Edward Slingerland, "The Situationist Critique and Early Confucian Virtue Ethics", Ethics, Vol. 121, No. 2 (January 2011), pp. 390-419.

ii Thus Aristotle also sees a contrast between what being a good human requires of us, and what being a good citizen demands; here one may compare the competing demands of one's social roles and of one's obligations as a rational being. This is sometimes seen, incorrectly, as a prerogative of the Stoics. Julia Annas argues that the Stoics combine two perspectives, often thought to be in conflict — the embedded perspective from within one's social context, and the universal perspective of the member of the moral community of rational beings. In Annas, Julia (2002). My Station and its Duties: Ideals and the Social Embeddedness of Virtue. *Proceedings of the Aristotelian Society* 102 (2): 109-23. The phrase "My station and its duties" in Annas' title refers to Bradley's Chapter 5 in his *Ethical Studies*, in which he argues, from a Hegelian perspective, that the fulfilment of duties demanded by social relations is never enough. (Bradley, F. H. (1988 [1876]) My Station and its Duties. In his *Ethical Studies*. *Oxford*: *Oxford University Press*.) *Cf*. *also* Sidgwick, *Henry* (1893) My station and its duties. *International Journal of Ethics*. 4(1): 1—17.

iii Cf. Plato *Meno* 72E—73A. Socrates asks what virtue is, and Meno replies that there is the virtue of man, woman and child. Socrates replies that where one thing was wanted, Meno had given him many. Aristotle thinks that both determinations of virtue in general are possible on the one hand in the *Ethics* (II6 1106b36—1107a2), but then in the *Politics*, where he talks much more about role specific virtue (I 13 1259b32—1260a4, III 4 1276b16—1276b34).

iv Cf. Nussbaum, Martha. "Non—Relative Virtues: An Aristotelian Approach." In The Quality of Life, eds., Martha C. Nussbaum and Amartya Sen. New York: Oxford University Press, 1993. I have argued against the applicability of this scheme of virtues to Chinese ethics in "Courage in Aristotle and Xunzi: an example of mapping thick ethical concepts", Bulletin of the Museum for Far Eastern Antiquities, forthcoming.

v Categorisation of virtue presents a certain problem for Aristotle-as either dispositions (246a10—17) or as relatives (246b3) in *Physics* VII 3, namely a good disposition relative to its proper affections (*pathê*). In the *Categories* virtue, and the individual virtues are qualities (8b29, 33, 15b19).

vi I have argued that this applies to the *Lunyu* also ("Ren in the Analects, Sceptical Prolegomena" Journal of Chinese Philosophy 2012).

vii Often attention is directed towards the developmental story or indeed a story of enhancement running between familial virtues-being a good son-to governmental virtues, e.g. in the *Lunyu* 6.30, and there are issues about conflict, of course.

In fact, such virtues should not surprise anyone concerned with understanding what virtue is. It is of course an open question what role understanding the nature of virtue has to play in virtue itself. Generally, virtues of character are actually used in relation to other people. We might say they are social. This is one reason that Aristotle thinks that God has no need of virtues of character. The only activity left is thought, and the corresponding virtue, wisdom, sophia, even for humans is the one that can be exercised without others, more or less; it is also, in his view, the closest to being divine we get. God is active, but not practical; we are bound to be practical, and our actions relate to others. In this sense justice is for Aristotle the whole of virtue relating to others. So virtue of character seems relational, on the one hand.

But on the other Socrates' virtue is *his* virtue, and no one else's. Thus it is his disposition to behave in a certain way. More broadly speaking, one advantage of talk about virtue is that one can distinguish, at least that is the hope, between those who are good and those who are bad. Individuals possess dispositions one can rely on. Thus whether or not they are being exercised, they are a quality of the human in question. And this applies to virtues belonging to those fulfilling a function. One person is good at the job, and that is a quality of theirs.

In fact Aristotle also thinks that there are virtues for the different roles in society-he even allows a degree of virtue to the slave. This follows from the fact that a city is a complex whole, and different people fulfil different functions within it. Nor is there invariably identity between the good citizen and the good human; ii only in a certain kind of polity does he think the good human is the good citizen. But he also, much more famously, defines virtue of character, quite generally. iii Thus he allows both a general account of virtue, and of the virtues specific to fulfilling certain functions excellently.

From the fact that all virtues are exercised relative to others it does not follow that virtues should be individuated by the different relations one has to other people. iv Aristotle in fact divides them up according to the ranges along which each excellent disposition represents the mean. Thus courage is a mean disposition relative to us of being afraid and taking risks. Clearly, such a virtue may have close connections to those entrusted with defending the city, as it actually does in Aristotle's scheme. But it is not *defined* as the virtue of one functional part of the city as it is in Plato's *Republic*.

These dispositions can then come into play within a relationship-being a good wife-but the relationship does not individuate the virtue. v Note also that 'friendship' philia, a term which ranges over excellent relationships extending from the familial to the political, is a virtue in Aristotle's eyes. There are different grades of friendship, depending on the character and motivation of those involved. There is here a general point to be made about virtues constituted in part by relations to others: the existence of these virtues depends not on one of the people so related, but on both. People are friends for the sake of pleasure, for example, Aristotle thinks, if both share this kind of motivation; and, even more clearly, the best kind of friendship requires virtue on both sides. In other words, virtuous friendship is not self—standing; virtues of the individual are presupposed.

But there is another aspect to the dependence of friendship: it is a relation, and both sides have to play their part for the relation to hold, let alone succeed. That is to say, being a good son is only possible if you have a good father, being a good subject is only possible if you have a good king. There is much more to be said about this; for one thing it seems not to hold in all generality, as we shall see when turn to Mencius.

This brief Aristotelian introduction serves to highlight a group of problems with understanding the structure of the traits such as *ren* 仁, *yi* 義, *li* 禮, *zhi* 知, which play such an important role in the Mencius. For on the one hand there are virtues-a termI use here very loosely as a way of collecting together *ren*, *yi*, *li*, *zhi*-which have to be exercised within a determined relationship or set of determined relationships, such as *ti* 悌, being a good younger brother-and others of which this is not true-*yi*, or *li*. Now, the fact that these last virtues do not apply only to one relationship does not mean that they are not relational.

One crucial distinction between Mencius and Aristotle is that Mencius does not conceive of the state (*guo*) or empire as a functional whole; nor is virtue seen as the excellent performance of function. vi So just how does Mencius individuate virtues? vii In this paper I wish to argue that virtues are not individuated entirely by relationships: some are and some are not. I leave aside here the question of the general account of virtue. viii In fact, some of the importance attached especially to *xiao* would appear to be that it serves as the first stem, the first support for living in accordance with one's obligations. In this way it can appear to have, if not an overarching importance, then at least that of the necessary first steps.

viii Such an account would have to deal with *ren*, which e.g. in 2a6 is seen by some as the source of the other virtues; and also with de, which is often in Mencius as elsewhere translated virtue. I will touch on some of the problems of duties or obligations below, which I think is closely related to *de* 德.

ix For universality and argument in 2a6, see my paper "Universality and argument in Mencius IIa6"

*Proceeding of the Aristotelian Society*, 2011 Vol. CXI.

x Lau nominalises it into "ill—mannered younger brother"; surely this is too weak-see my remarks above about the way of Yao and Shun being just *ti* and *xiao* (D.

C. Lau, *Mencius*. Penguin: Harmondsworth 1970). However, mention of manners is important in two respects. Firstly, it suggests a connection with rites: in 2a6 it is the heart of yielding and giving precedence which is the tip of the rites. Secondly, it raises the question of how morality and manners are to distinguished, if at all. I do not think Mencius draws a distinction. There is another distinction which Mencius does not make-between the capacity for morality and physical capacities. 6b2 works with a comparison between the ability to lift weights and the ability to act like Yao and Shun.

xi Scheffler 1997: 197 argues for a "non—reductionist" view of responsibilities arising from relationships (i.e. not only interaction gives rise to responsibilities) "one's relationships to other people give rise to special responsibilities to those people when they are relationships that one has reason to value." Scheffler, Samuel (1997) Relationships and Responsibilities. *Philosophy and Public Affairs* 26: 189—209.

xii Cf. Aristotle *Nicomachean Ethics* II 3 104b22—26: Virtue is a disposition for acting in the way one should, towards the people one should and when one should.

xiii Filial piety has been treated by a variety of a contemporary authors-see above all "Filial Piety in Chinese Thought and History." Edited by Alan K. L. Chan and Sor—hoon Tan London 2004 RoutledgeCurzon, also P.J.Ivanhoe, "Filial Piety as a Virtue," in Rebecca Walker and Philip J. Ivanhoe, eds., *Working Virtue: Virtue Ethics and Contemporary Moral Problems*, (Oxford University Press, December, 2007). Ivanhoe argues that justification for filial piety cannot lie in the past goods received from parents-the relationship is not one akin to barter; and some goods thus acquired, such as character cannot be sensibly "repaid". It is not clear to me that a virtue, if *xiao* is such, requires justification; there is little sign of justifying *xiaoti*, e.g. in the *Mencius*, or indeed the cardinal virtues in Plato's *Republic*. There is however, a more general problem, in that *ti*, and indeed other virtues of relationships, (see below on the *renlun*). On theories of justifying filial piety, see Keller, Simon (2006) Four Theories of Filial Duty. *Philosophical Quarterly* 56: 254—74.

xiv See "Does *xiao* come before *ren*?" Alan K. L. Chan. 2004 Filial Piety in Chinese Thought and History. Edited by Alan K. L. Chan and Sor—hoon Tan 2004 by RoutledgeCurzon, on Mencius esp. 159—60, Chan discusses the varying relationships between *xiao* and *ren* from the Lun Yu to NeoConfucianism. He notes that some of the passages in the Mencius about ren suggest that filial sons and humans who are ren are the same people (3a5). And if serving one's parents is the actuality (*shi*) of *ren* (4a27), then *xiao* would appear to be more important than *ren*.

No doubt virtues attach to individuals in *Mencius*, for example the different kinds of courage discussed in 2a2. But he is also concerned with abilities *neng* 能, conceived of as attaching to humans. This is what is showed about King Xuan of Qi in IA7.10—11. The King does indeed have the ability to feel pity. But I think that ability is in fact not suitable for understanding the kind of disposition a virtue is. Part of the problem is clear in IA7; for what Mencius wishes to show is that the King has the bare ability to have pity, a bare ability in the sense that a human *can* break a branch if ordered to do so, but *cannot* pick up a mountain. The concept of a disposition is much richer than this bare capacity. A disposition includes a tendency to act in the way required, but also requires past actions of the kind required.

An interesting text for the question of virtue and relationships is 6b2. Jiao of Cao asks Mengzi if anyone can act as a Yao or Shun. Mengzi replies that acting as such is the point. 奚有於是? 亦為之而已矣。"What has this to do with the matter? It all lies simply in acting as such." (Legge trans.)

The illustration for acting as Yao or Shun, if such it is, is ti 悌: all that you do is walk slowly and give precedence to your elders. That is something that anyone *can do*. They just do not do it.

徐行後長者謂之弟,疾行先長者謂之不弟。夫徐行者,豈人所不能哉? 所不為也。堯舜之道,孝弟而已矣。

"To walk slowly, keeping behind his elders, is to perform the part of a younger brother. To walk quickly and precede his elders, is to violate the duty of a younger brother. Now, is it what a man cannot do — to walk slowly? It is what he does not do. The course of Yao and Shun was simply that of filial piety and fraternal duty." (Legge trans.)

In order to establish the universalityix of the ability to act like Yao or Shun, a form of behaviour is presented which any human is capable of. There is no word here of motivation, or of understanding what you are doing: apparently, only actual behaviour is relevant. Legge translates *ti* 'the duty of a younger brother'.x This is perhaps an unhappy translation, but it does point to a feature of *Mencius*'s thought: relationships place you under obligations. Some difficult questions for anyone interested in virtue: Why do relationships place you under obligations? And are there obligations above and beyond those imposed by particular relationships? xi Are the obligations to other rational beings or humans, as such? And also: how do obligations relate to virtues? This last is a complicated question. A first, no doubt overly simple thought, might be that possession of a virtue *consists* in fulfilling obligations. xii Thus virtuous activity consists in performing your duty. This leaves open what the source of these obligations are-what imposes the obligations? Why do these obligations hold? In this text, all that implied about this is that humans *should* act like Yao and Shun-these are the models, one might think. And the way in which following these models provides obligations relates to parents and elders generally.

The final point that I wish to make about this text concerns xiaoti as the whole of the way of Yao and Shun: *Yao Shun zhi dao, xiaoti er yi yi* 堯舜之道,孝弟而已矣。"The way of Yao and Shun is filial piety and fraternal piety and that is all." On the surface this may seem to leave no room for the other virtues; at best it leaves unclear how all the others relate to *xiaoti*. xiii Various relations are conceivable-*xiaoti* may be derived from *ren* or it may represent the exercise of this. xiv If we were to accept this last suggestion, the question would then arise how we are to think of other exercises of *ren*. For example feeling pity towards a child, or the developed pattern of behaviour based on this, may be an exercise of *ren*, but can hardly be conceived of as xiaoti 孝弟.

xv Cf. Chen's comment 陳氏曰:「孝弟者,人之良知良能,自然之性也。堯舜人倫之至,亦率是性而已。豈能加毫末於是哉?」"Filial and fraternal piety are humans' good knowledge good abilities, their nature; Yao and Shun are the perfection of human relations, and just follow this nature, that is all. How can one add the smallest thing to this?" Note that *xiaoti* are taken to be abilities here. This comment refers of course to 7a15 which is discussed briefly below.

xvi One may well wonder why *xiao* is not explained here at all. The reason for this omission is not that it is merely part of a binome.

xvii James Legge, 1893. *The Chinese Classics with a translation* etc. by James Legge Vol. 1: The Confucian Analects, The Great Learning, The Doctrine of the Mean, The Works of Mencius. Oxford. Reprint Taipei: SMC 1992.

xviii Cf. the slightly different wording in Ia7.24 謹庠序之教,申之以孝悌之義,頒白者不負戴於道路矣。Legge translates, "Let careful attention be paid to education in schools, the inculcation in it especially of the filial and fraternal duties, and grey－

haired men will not be seen upon the roads, carrying burdens on their backs or on their heads." This makes it seem that xiaoti zhi yi is a phrase restricting kinds of "duties", namely those between brothers and fathers and sons. That is to say, *xiaoti* is subsumed under *yi*.

xix On Kuang Zhang, see D.C.Lau, Mencius, Harmondsworth, Penguin, 1970, Appendix 1, 211—213.

xx See 4a18.

xxi There is no hint here of any formal view of just what kinds are.

xxii Cf. *Lunyu* I 2, and Ivanhoe, Filial Piety

Thus one may think that xiaoti 孝弟 here are only examples chosen for the ease of displaying a trivial example; in fact, all virtues are meant by synecdoche. xv And the example is not so trivial after all, in that a particular relation to others is displayed in it. The possibility of acting as Yao and Shun depends on their "way" being exhausted by *xiaoti*. xvi On the one hand, anyone can perform the duty demanded here; walking more slowly than your elders is

indeed not difficult. But surely, one may object that in many cases of acting the difficulty lies in recognising what is to be done, and being disposed then always to do it. Not all situations are as clear as opening the door for your elders. Nor is everyone so disposed. Again, the point here is to provide an example of something anyone can do. But the weakness of this procedure is that it leaves unclear how more exacting duties can be recognised, indeed motivated and performed. But the example is not meant to answer all questions about virtue, or social organisation.

In 5a3 the question arises of why Shun, on becoming *Tianzi* 天子 looked after his younger brother Xiang, rather than punishing him for his attempts on his life. The reason for Mencius lies in *ti*:

曰:「仁人之於弟也,不藏怒焉,不宿怨焉,親愛之而已矣。親之欲其貴也,愛之欲其富也。封之有庳,富貴之也。身為天子,弟為匹夫,可謂親愛之乎?」"

"Mencius replied, A benevolent man does not lay up anger, nor cherish resentment against his brother, but only regards him with affection and love. Regarding him with affection, he wishes him to be honourable: regarding him with love, he wishes him to be rich. The appointment of Xiang to be the prince of You Bei was to enrich and ennoble him. If while Shun himself was sovereign, his brother had been a common man, could he have been said to regard him with affection and love?"

(Leggexvii trans.)

The goods at issue are here ones of office and honour, conferred on Xiang. The behaviour towards the brother, based on affection (*qin* 親) and love (ai 愛), arise from *desires* to make the brother honoured and rich. And, crucially, the moral quality of Xiang plays no role whatever in diminishing the obligations that the ties of brotherhood impose. Here it would appear that there is no reciprocity between the behaviour of the brothers: the relationship trumps virtue. But then one is left wondering how a relationship can display virtue, where other virtues are not being displayed within the relationship. In fact, the relationship is one sided: Shun, the model benevolent man, treats his brother in model fashion. Thus the display of *ti* is not reciprocal. Thus *ti* does not characterise a relationship, even though it is a virtue displayed within a relationship.

*Xiao* 孝 and *ti* 弟 are an important pair; both are, naturally, concerned with subordination, as has already become clear in the case of *ti*. In fact, the political import of the pair is clear in that a political context is common for the stories thye are involved in CHECK. Thus they are crucial in the *Mencius* both to education and to politics. Noticeably, neither is

mentioned for example in 2a6; and how they relate to *ren* for example is an interesting question. Some relevant texts are the following:

Ia3.4 謹庠序之教,申之以孝悌之養,頒白者不負戴於道路矣 xviii。

"Let careful attention be paid to education in schools, inculcating in it especially the filial and fraternal duties, and grey—haired men will not be seen upon the roads, carrying burdens on their backs or on their heads." (trans. Legge)

Here the benefits of these virtues are entirely instrumental, and not for the good of the bearers of these virtues, but for those they are subordinate to. But there is no need to think that the whole story about xiaoti is being told here. This applies also to the next text in which King Xuan of Qi is being encouraged to think of benevolent government as a way of realising his aims:

Ia5.3 王如施仁政於民,省刑罰,薄稅斂,深耕易耨。壯者以暇日修其孝悌忠信,入以事其父兄,出以事其長上,可使制梃以撻秦楚之堅甲利兵矣。

"If Your Majesty will indeed dispense a benevolent government to the people, being sparing in the use of punishments and fines, and making the taxes and levies light, so causing that the fields shall be ploughed deep, and the weeding of them be carefully attended to, and that the strong—bodied, during their days of leisure, shall cultivate their filial piety, fraternal respectfulness, sincerity, and truthfulness, serving thereby, at home, their fathers and elder brothers, and, abroad, their elders and superiors, you will then have a people who can be employed, with sticks which they have prepared, to oppose the strong mail and sharp weapons of the troops of Qin and Chu." (Legge trans.)

Here *xiao* and *ti* form part of a quartet of virtues said to arise out of a certain kind of government, namely a benevolent one (*ren zheng* 仁政). One might think that the relation between *ren* and *xiao* and *ti* is that they are brought about by it, that is, in others. Thus rather than looking for a logical relation between *ren* and other virtues, there seems to be a causal connection. Again, the benefit of these virtues is executive; helping Qi in its warfare with neighbouring states which had worsted it. Thus the value is not inherent in the virtues, but lies in the consequences they have, at least in this persuasion of the King of Qi.

Let us turn to *xiao* 孝 filial piety. Kuang Zhang (4b30)xix is said to be thought unfilial throughout all the states, but *Mencius* defends him, saying that he has none of the commonly recognised five kinds of unfiliality. Rather, he and his father argued about a matter of morality (*ze shan*). Mengzi says that this is bad for the relationship between father and son, although it is appropriate between friends. Thus what is right and wrong depnds on the

relationship of the people concerned. The question arises because of what "all the states" say about Kuang Zhang; Mencius' reply usesthe five things called unfilial commonly by the world (*shisu suo wei bu xiao* 世俗所謂不孝). These are:

1. Laziness in caring for father and mother (惰其四支,不顧父母之養).

2. Gambling and drinking (博弈好飲酒) instead of caring for father and mother.

3. Loving money and things, and wife and children (好貨財,私妻子) instead of caring for father and mother.

4. Following the desires of ear and eye (從耳目之欲), so that father and mother are disgraced.

5. Loving courage and fighting so much as to endanger father and mother 好勇鬥很,以危父母).

Mencius here argues against a common opinion, using, in turn, a set of standards claimed to be common usage. This is slightly puzzling. If the kinds of unfiliality are as commonly and clearly recognised as Mengzi says, then why do all the states attribute unfiliality to Kuang Zhang? This is perhaps not such a serious problem. Reputations are often not deserved. Mencius is criticising the gap between standards and reputation. Kuang Zhang does not deserve his reputation. Furthermore, there is no hint that this list is related to human nature in any way; while it may be easy to accept that certain forms of behaviour are natural between parents and children, the further specification of what is permitted and what is not relies on common views. For the argument to work the list of the ways of being unfilial has to be exhaustive: nothing else may count as being unfilial. All of these are forms of action; motivation is not mentioned-the point is not your attitude to your parents, but actual treatment. The basic duty in question is "caring for the nourishment of father and mother" (*gu fumu zhi yang* 顧父母之養); and of course, nourishment, *yang* 養 is to be taken in a very broad sense. Interestingly, the question of conflict between relationships arises-namely, favouring wife and children over one's parents. And, furthermore, reproving one another about the good is something precluded because such reproof leads to distancing (*li* 離) between themxx. Thus obligations depend on relationships; and the crucial question is whether or not these obligations are fulfilled, not whether one has such and such a disposition. Here, the obligation trumps the disposition.

One might argue that is not clear. The five kinds of unfiliality depend not on individual actions-the odd game of chess, the odd present for wife and children-but on habitual behaviour. The unfilial man is one with these tendencies, and he then of course exhibits this actual behaviour. The kindsxxi of unfilial behaviour are the ways in which filial behaviour can be prevented. In favour of this reading one may cite the second and fifth kinds-which are described as a love of goods and money and a love of valour. These are presumably standing tendencies.

But does Mengzi himself not admit that Kuang Zhang has done something inappropriate to filial behaviour, namely criticised his father? (We do not in fact know what passed between them.) He admits that his behaviour, reproving him as to goodness *ze shan* 責善, inflicts great injury on kindness (*fu zi ze shan*, *zei en zhi da zhe* 父子責善,賊恩之大者。). Why then does such 'moral criticism' 責善 not fall under the general rubric unfilial? One thought might be that such moral criticism does not affect the well—being of the parents, and so does not conflict with the basic duty of caring for the nourishment of father and mother. Another question concerns the status of *en*

恩, kindness here. The son has been unvirtuous, if we suppose that *en* falls under the virtues; merely not unfilial. He has offended against the kindness shown by his parents towards himself-in giving him life and looking after him. Put this way, this sounds pretty unfilial. But it may be that the decisive thing is that reproving his father is, while inappropriate, hardly due to his own failings of character. For the five kinds of unfiliality point to weaknesses of character.

Indeed, one might go further. Kuang Zhang in fact punishes himself for his crime against kindness. It is not said that this is what he thinks he has done, but it may be presumed that it is what Mengzi thinks he has done. And this is said to be something he "settled in his mind": this punishment-sending away wife and children so he received no 'nourishment' (*yang* 養) from them-expiates his crime. Thus Mencius' treating Kuang Zhang with ritual propriety *is* after all related to his character; he is someone who understands his crime, and that he has to atone for it, and then acts on this knowledge.

Thus in the case of Kuang Zhang, Mencius assessment of him, in the face of general opprobrium, relies on an appraisal of his character. Thus his filial behaviour is rooted in other aspects of character. But filial piety is often said to be the base from which character is developed, and hence ethically basicxxii. The developmental model in Mengzi is one of the most important aspects of his moral theory: we learn about the proper treatment of others through our upbringing in a family. The following very important text poses some riddles with regard to the place of 仁 ren in this scheme:

7a15 孟子曰:「人之所不學而能者,其良能也;所不慮而知者,其良知也。孩提之童,無不知愛其親者;及其長也,無不知敬其兄也。親親,仁也;敬長,義也。無他,達之天下也。」

"Mencius said, 'The ability possessed by men without having been acquired by learning is good ability, and the knowledge possessed by them without the exercise of thought is their good knowledge. Children carried in the arms all know to love their parents, and when they are grown a little, they all know to love their elder brothers. Filial affection for parents is the working of benevolence. Respect for elders is the working of righteousness. There is no other reason for those feelings — they belong to all under heaven.' (Legge trans., with some alterations)

Here *ren* "benevolence" seems to be identified with the relation between child and parents; the norm is to treat your parents as parents (Legge goes so far as to translate *qin* 親 as filial affection), whereas honouring your elders comes out as *yi* 義 righteousness or justice. The emphasis here is on extending (*ta* 達) this to the whole empire. The puzzle is that xiao and ti, which might seem to be the obvious names for the virtues at play here, are not used-instead we have much less specific terms.

Let us now turn briefly to some texts which discuss human relationships (*renlun* 人倫).:

4a2 孟子曰:「規矩,方員之至也;聖人,人倫之至也。欲為君盡君道,欲為臣盡臣道,二者皆法堯舜而已矣。不以舜之所以事堯事君,不敬其君者也;不以堯之所以治民治民,賊其民者也。

"Mencius said, 'The compass and square produce perfect circles and squares. By the sages, the human relations are perfectly exhibited. He who as a sovereign would perfectly discharge the duties of a sovereign, and he who as a minister would perfectly discharge the duties of a minister, have only to imitate — the one Yao, and the other Shun. He who does not serve his sovereign as Shun served Yao, does not respect his sovereign; and he who does not rule his people as Yao ruled his, injures his people."

Models or standards are very prominent in Mencius 4a, and here the idea is developed using a common craft analogy, as in 4a1.1, for the *shengren*, 聖人 the sage who is 'the perfection' (*zhi* 至) of the human relations, where compass and square are the same for circles and right angles. The analogy then culminates in Yao and Shun being taken as models. The only human relation named here is between prince and minister, and Yao and Shun serve as

the models for these respectively. It thus becomes clear that the sage *alone* does not exemplify the relationship, rather his way of performing the duties within this relationship are exemplary. Indeed, not following these worthies in these roles is said to evince a lack of respect for the other party. Clearly, as with the schools to which we turn in a moment, the wisdom of the sage is concerned with practical affairs, not the theory represented for example by Aristotelian sophia. Far from removing the sage from human relations, his wisdom exhibits the acme of relations. And it is concrete rulers, like the compasses and square, which serve as paradigms, not an abstract ideal. So if that is where all learning is aimed-the perfection of the human relationships-we would expect institutions of learning to concentrate on them. And that is exactly what we find:

3a3「設為庠序學校以教之:庠者,養也;校者,教也;序者,射也。夏曰校,殷曰序,周曰庠,學則三代共之,皆所以明人倫也。人倫明於上,小民親於下。

"Establish Xiang, Xu, Xue, and Xiao, all those educational institutions, for the instruction of the people. The name Xiang indicates nourishing as its object; Xiao, indicates teaching; and Xu indicates archery. By the Xia dynasty the name Xiao was used; by the Yin, that of Xu; and by the Zhou, that of Xiang. As to the Xue, they belonged to the three dynasties, and by that name. The object of them all is to illustrate the human relations. When those are thus illustrated by superiors, kindly feeling will prevail among the inferior people below." (Legge trans.)

Here the relations between those above, presumably the elites trained in the schools named here, serve as models for those below. Already in the case of *ti* and *xiao* we have remarked on the connection between upbringing and relationships, and the associated virtues. In this text, not only is this emphasised-as the especial area of the *xue*; the political function of the *lun* is made clear. If the *lun* are made clear (ming) among superiors, then the people subject to them will have *qin*, familial affection.

It is conceivable that the *renlun* here are relations between nobles, the old sense of ren; for the *renlun* are to be made clear only in those 'above'. This sense of *ren* is also quite possible in the last text we considered. And indeed here the preservation of *renlun* plays the role of distinguishing between the mass of the people and the "gentleman" *junzi* 君子: the former cast them away, the latter preserve them:xxiii

xxiii See also 6b10.5 今居中國,去人倫,無君子,如之何其可也? "Now we inhabit the Middle States: getting rid of the human relationships, having no gentlemen: what kind of a possibility is that?"

xxiv David Wong investigates the way in which partiality, can be seen as part of ethics in David Wong. 1989. Universalism versus love with distinctions. Journal of Chinese Philosophy 16: 251—72. He is followed by Kwong—loi Shun in *Mencius and Early Chinese Thought* Stanford 1997.

xxv Christina Sommers argues that an account of the special obligations to one's relations and community is very hard to give for Kantianism and Utilitarianism, which aim rather to tell us what are duties are towards everyone impartially than to explain something like filial obligation. (Sommers, Christina Hoff (1986) Filial Morality. *Journal of Philosophy* 83: 439—56.). She develops a theory (p.45) of "differential pull" (DP). According to the DP thesis, the ethical pull of a moral patient will always partly depend on how the moral patient is related to the moral agent on whom the pull is exerted. Sommers accepts however that there are constraints of non—interference between individuals, which hold between all individuals as such. Thus there are both universal obligations and constraints due to relationships.

4b28 孟子曰:「人之所以異於禽於獸者幾希,庶民去之,君子存之。舜明於庶物,察於人倫,由仁義行,非行仁義也。」

Not only that, but the human relationships also, if in a different way, serve to mark the difference between humans and beasts. Perhaps the point is that humans, unlike the beasts, have the capacity for these relationships, which is realised in the "gentleman", the elite, but not in others. The interesting thing about this view is not only that realising the relationships constitutes the elite, their morality would seem to lie in this. The next text seems to go against this reading whereby actual human relationships are confined to the gentlemen. For here the relationships increase the distance between humans and beasts.

4a4 后稷教民稼穡。樹藝五穀,五穀熟而民人育。人之有道也,飽食、煖衣、逸居而無教,則近於禽獸。聖人有憂之,使契為司徒,教以人倫:父子有親,君臣有義,夫婦有別,長幼有序,朋友有信。

"The Minister of Agriculture taught the people to sow and reap, cultivating the five kinds of grain. When the five kinds of grain were brought to maturity, the people all obtained a subsistence. But men possess a moral nature; and if they are well fed, warmly clad, and comfortably lodged, without being taught at the same time, they become almost like the beasts. This was a subject of anxious solicitude to the sage Shun, and he appointed Xie to be the Minister of Instruction, to teach the relations of humanity: how, between father and son, there should be affection; between sovereign and minister, righteousness; between husband and wife, attention to their separate functions; between old and young, a proper order; and between friends, fidelity." (Legge trans.)

This story tells how five relations were established among humans-presumably making up their 'way', dao, translated by Legge here as 'moral nature'; the five relations are separate from, indeed apparently unconnected to, sustenance (food, clothing, housing). But nor does this text imply that these relations are actually entered into by all humans, although they have the capacity to do so. For the actualisation of the relationships is a product of teaching, rather than a given of nature. Two of the relations are given the names of a virtues: that between prince and minister is called *yi*, righteousness, and that between friends is called *xin*, trust.

In conclusion, let me sum up some of the main points. We started from the observation that virtues of character are social, and noted that this does not mean that virtues have to be individuated by specific relationships. While this is of course what we do find in the *Mencius*, up to a point, in fact, the language of the virtues in the *Mencius* more complicated than that. This is clear from the case of Kuang Zhang. For he himself, although offending against *en*, kindness is treated with *limao*, correct etiquette by Mengzi. He falls under none of the kinds of unifilialty which are recognised, and these all imply defects of character. In other words, filiality is predicated on certain more basic character traits. Thus although filiality is a virtue relative to a specific other human, it attaches to the person themselves. This point is reinforced when one considers the possibility that brotherly duty can be adhered to by one brother and not the other, as the case of Shun and Xiang.

Shun is of course the concrete model for the *shengren*, the sage. The wisdom belonging to this status constitutes his position relative to others, and enables him to stand model for the human relations, above all for that between prince and minister. These relations are norms or models, not merely for the *junzi*, but also for the common people. This is of more political and ethical importance to *Mencius* than a complete enumeration of all such relations and virtues attaching to them. For many the problem posed by ethics in the Mencius lies in the fact that relationships are the basis for special obligations; in other words, we are not bound impartially. xxiv My focus here is on the problem of whether there are two kinds of virtues-ones which are involved in a life generally, and others which regulate specific relationships. xxv I think that in the *Mencius* two factors militate against a stable system dividing these two kinds of virtue. One si that ethics and politics as a whole is modelled on a certain understanding of family relationships, especially the father son relation. Thus even ren seems embedded in this relationship. The second point is really the converse of the first one. Just as all virtues emante from the family, so one see the specifically familial virtues, painted large as it were as the whole or acme of virtue.

In fact, the *Mencius* is very flexible in naming the virtues appropriate to each of the relationships. This flexibility, along with his emphasis on the individual case under consideration makes it difficult to reconstruct a system from the text of the *Mencius*. This is one of the attractive aspect of his moral philosophy, that it is not driven by a scheme, but the concrete cases, which after all make up the actuality of morality.

# Rights-Oriented Ethics in Confucianism

**Shan Chun (Dr. & Prof. China University of Political Science and Law)**

**Introduction**

The modern western term "economy" has three slightly differentiated senses in Chinese. Firstly, it indicates the administration of secular affairs and relieving people from poverty (*jing shi ji min*), a term employed mainly by Confucian scholars and bureaucratic officials in history, but now it has acquired the sense of social process of production, exchange and consumption. Secondly it connotes the production and distribution of food and commodities(*shi huo*), a term used by historians in their records of economic activities, mainly the production and exchange of good, throughout the whole span of imperial Chinese dynasties, and thirdly it has been serving as slang phrase "life sense"(*sheng yi*), a popular term among businessmen and ordinary people which literally implies "senses derived from cosmic liveliness" but revealed in daily lives of "the people under heaven"(*tian min*). These three terms in Chinese context somewhat ingeniously relating to the term of "economy" have exposed Chinese conceptions concerning Confucianism in particular to animated cosmology and natural justice which reveal a universal balance between rights and duties, which will serve as historical argument for right—oriented ethics in Confucianism .

**Food as Heaven's Mandate**

As the most prioritized item of all natural rights, Chinese would conventionally state that people have rights to food. This might have been otherwise categorized as substantial item of economic and social rights in modern human rights law or civil law in Chinese context which traditionally acknowledge food as the most durable and indispensable property of every family, but has been patently self—evident with Chinese plebeian. Chinese populace both from lower to higher social ranks and from ancient to contemporary would take this doctrine — People Taking Food as Their Heaven(*min yi shi wei tian*), in other words "food is the God for people", as their dogma universally paramount in either daily lives or social undertakings. We would frequent the saying in historical documents or regular admonishments among plebeian or officials that "with food stored at barn, famine would not intrude into hearts" (*cang zhong you liang*, *xin li bu huang* ), this adequately exemplifies Chinese ethical pragmatism which justifies their faith in heavenly mandate only that the latter guarantees their right for food as the most sacred. Of course, we would in other cases read stories about the Confucian scholars who prioritized spirituality to food, being martyrs for their ethical faith by self—chosen starvation like Bo Yi and Shu Qi.① At first glimpse this may seem to be different in their attitudes towards the concept of heaven, for many Confucian scholars heaven stands for divine moral more any anything under the heaven while the ordinary Chinese take food as their heavenly gifts since they engage in agriculture with good or bad harvest at the disposal of natural climate identical to heaven in Chinese context. What BoYi and Shu Qi would not agree is the social revolution, but social revolution is often the last resort for Chinese society to overthrow despotic rule which blatantly violates the heavenly principle in depriving people of their food and clothes or the basic means to survive. As Mencius explained the revolutionary situation which Bo Yi and Shu Qi experienced as: "The four seasons are formed by the revolution of heaven and earth in their rotations to replace days and nights reciprocally. Thus revolutions conducted by Saint Tang and King Wu in replacing their preceding rulers are justified by heaven's mandates as well as human morality. And these revolutions have their gorgeous natural and social implications."② To Chinese plebeian, food and clothes are the very representations of "human morality", while to Confucian scholars "humanity" and "righteousness" are the exact expressions of "heaven's mandates", and they are untied into the social revolution. As they both

---

① Bo Yi and Shu Qi were two brothers lived in China as the time of the transition from the Shang Dynasty to the Zhou Dynasty, who were opposed to the social revolution led by King Wen of Zhou and refused taking food from the revolutionary regime of the rebels who established Zhou Dynasty and chose to have died of starvation for their political and ethical commitments in defiance of revolution. They are worshipped as ethical and spiritual icons by some Confucian scholars.

② Deng Qiubai eds., *The Book of Changes in Modern Chinese*(bai hua yi jing), (Changsha: Yuelu Press, 1993) p. 304.

have their ultimate faiths in what heaven sacredly suggested in its natural rotation, the Chinese plebeian and Confucian scholars have much in common as believers in heaven's mandates.

Concerning the basic attributes to human beings, ancient Chinese would have agreed that clothes and foods invariably come first in their physical existence and then ensued "the rule of propriety and music"(*li yue zhi zhi*) as the form of civilization, which is also accepted as the "universal doctrines heavenly vertical and earthly horizontal"(*tian jing di yi*), the political legitimacy in Chinese social context. Such simple dialectics observed in their daily lives was enthusiastically discussed among ancient scholars, typically Confucian scholars, and coherently associated with cosmology, politics, ethics and law.

If we ascribe the civilization of the revealed truth in a dichotomy of God and Man to the western world dominated by Christianity, we would be equally reasonable to link the civilization of the "integration between heaven and human" (*tian ren he yi*) to Chinese mentality. Therefore when Chinese claim their rights to food and clothes they could naturally associate them to the natural rights consecrated by Heavenly Mandates(*tian ming*) that may ground Chinese to defy any administrative orders from the secular rulers. In order to secure their rule, the Chinese emperors not only depend on their armies to suppress their subject, but also justify their rule by paying religious respect to Heaven, as evidenced in the imperial buildings of Tian An Men Square, the center of Beijing which means the Gate to the Forbidden City Blessed by Heaven and the Temple of Heaven (*tian tan*) where is the exclusive altar for emperors to pray for heavenly protection and offer sacrifice for heavenly favors. Since the paramount attribute of Heaven is its divinity, that's why Chinese scholars directly translated Catholic into "the Heaven Master Religion"(*tian zhu jiao*). Chinese concept of Heaven, by analogy to western God, retains its one peculiar feature exclusive to Chinese, that is, every human being can be a heavenly incarnate himself, either by the discovery of self conscience or by conscientious enlightenment through external means. Thereupon Chinese scholarship, drastically distinctive to Aristotelian disciplines in politics, economics, biology, physics, psychology or ethics, manifests its genre in the domain between heaven and human, or briefed as scholarship between heaven and human(*tian ren zhi xue*), that is, all knowledge covering the whole span of knowledge from heaven to human come under the category of Chinese scholarship. And such specialty of scholarship would be accurately mirrored in the popular Confucian mottoes in their much—quoted phrases from an ancient Confucian scholar Zhang Zai, "To testify a cosmic heart between heaven and earth, to vindicate the heaven's mandate for all human beings, to accomplish the scholarship of ancient Saints and to bring about universal harmony for future generations."① These phrases constitute an intellectual fabric for traditional Chinese scholars in their understanding what we now call economics in its relations with cosmology, politics and ethics. Before economic rights are linked to food, commodities, clothes and accommodations, they are often prioritized in the notions of cosmological virtue, the timely season for farming—to think of the Temple for Farming(*xian nong tan*) which was built parallel to the east of the Temple of Heaven where emperors were expected to pray for good farming, for the authorized rule of administration and proper wealth accumulation and distribution. With these intricate messages in mind, one may adequately come to the true sense of what is generalized for Chinese scholarship in *The Book of Changes* (also *I Ching*): "The grand virtue between the heaven and earth is life and the grand treasure of the saint—kings is their positions. The preservation of their positions is based on humanity, the attraction of people comes from wealth, the administration of wealth and legislation to forbid people from doing illegal things are righteousness."② Some scholars believe that the concept of "wealth", once isolated from the context, conveys more sense than any other nouns to "economics" in the English word. As Dr. Chen Huan—chang explained for the similar passage with minor alterations in English translations:"But we must remember that the object of 'administering wealth' is man. Our reason for administering wealth is simply that men are living collectively and need wealth to support them. Man is our end, and wealth our means. From this we get as a definition: Economics is the science administering wealth according to the principle of justice, for the sake of men who live collectively."③ By omitting the grand virtue in the universe,

① Feng Youlan, *The Complete Works of San Song Tang by Feng Youlan*, (Zhengzhou: Henan People's Publishing House, 2000) Vol. 10, p. 135.

② Deng Qiubai eds., *The Book of Changes in Modern Chinese*(bai hua yi jing), (Changsha: Yuelu Press, 1993) p. 435.

③ Chen Huan—Chang, *The Economic Principles of Confucius and His School* (Published by Forgotten Books 2012, Originally Published 1911, Faculty of Political Science, Columbia University, New York), p. 49.

*i. e.* the cosmic virtue permeated between heaven and earth which originates, sustains, benefits and assists human beings in all dimensions, we may not be coherently convinced with the legitimacy of justice and moral basis of collective life. As economics is motivated by grand virtue of the universe and in the principle of righteousness, it cannot afford to separated human economic activities more from their social vocations than from their religious affiliations to the heaven and the earth, for which another Confucian classic amends with eight types of administration in the chapter of Grand Norms: "What are eight issues of administration? The first is food, the second commodities, the third sacrifice, the fourth citizen, the fifth education, the sixth justice, the seventh tribute diplomacy and the eighth army."[①] The above－mentioned two passages from both the *Book of Changes* (*yi jing*) and the *Book of History* (*shang shu*) disclose, as what I reflect, the big picture of economic rights of Confucian scholars in their mentality of heaven－human integration. And it has been simultaneously transplanted in the minds of ordinary Chinese in their conviction "people taking food as their heaven", which tells the paramount principle of the natural rights for people consecrated by heaven as well as the universal responsibilities imposed on the rulers also by heaven, as everyone knows that emperor is the son of heaven contrasted to the people of heaven. When observing Chinese history, we could easily come across these phrases derived from "people taking food as their heaven", such as the popular complaint goes "our heaven has fallen" (*wo de tian ta le*) whenever their lives are being threatened by a widespread famine. And such legitimate complaints originated from economic rights to food, commodities, clothes, accommodations, healthcare and pensions, *etc.* often proving to be spiritual catalyst to social revolts symbolized in the slogan "performing the political mission in Heaven's stead." (*ti tian xing dao*) One would not be surprised to read this statement in Chinese civil revolts in history that regularly associated their justified actions in attempting to overthrow the government headed by the son of heaven－the emperor. Since heaven was thought of as the determinate source dictating the good or bad harvest for farmers and thus the solid foundation of a stable society, it gradually acquired the religious, political and legal authorities of economic rights for Chinese, who have been in the capacity of farmers for the

---

① Zhou Bingjun eds., "Grand Norm", *The Book of History* (*bai hua shang shu, hong fan*), (Changsha: Yuelu Press, 1990), p. 99.

most part of their civilized history.

**Rights—Oriented Ethics Implied in *Jingtian* System**

The grand virtue of heaven, as popularly assumed in the Zhou Dynasty when Confucian school of thought was being established, was evidenced in both politics and law in terms of land allotment, being respectively illustrated as "worshipping for the grand virtue in safeguarding people" (*jing de bao min*) in governmental rule and "interpreting the grand virtue in circumspect jurisprudence in punishment"(*ming de shen fa*) and these concepts exercised an enormous influence on both Confucius and Mencius who creatively transformed them into their ethical principles of humanity(*ren*) and righteousness(*yi*). When Confucianism is frequently referred to as "the virtue of humanity and righteousness"(*ren yi dao de*) or "Confucius' humanity and Mencius' righteousness"(*kong ren meng yi*), it exposes Confucian ethical principles to human natural rights to survive with basic conditions of livelihood in the spirit of natural law in Chinese cultural context. And this is the exact social and semantic situation that Chinese put "natural rights" in the west as the "human rights consecrated by heaven's mandates."(*tian fu ren quan*)

For Confucian thinkers, the grand virtue of heaven manifests itself in universal ethics that guarantees all cosmic beings natural rights to exist, survive and prosper in a reciprocal "grand peace under heaven"(*tian xia tai ping*).① For human society, largely confined to farmers on the land yet under the heaven, a land administration policy would most represent such a grand virtue, or most pertinent to heaven's will or mandates. In fact, this land administration policy was depicted as "well—shaped land system"(*jing tian zhi*). "Well" is the word for a place where people can fetch water publicly, a symbol for universal right to survive with basic means of livelihood. But in Chinese pictographic, "well" is written in the shape of nine pieces or plots of land(井, *jing* is spelt in pronunciation for Chinese and well in meaning for English) and "well

① "The Grand Peace under the Heaven" were the political slogans for at least two great historical farmer rebellions in China, one occurred at the end of the Han Dynasty, the Yellow Turban Army (*huang jin jun qi yi*) was mobilized by the Dao of Grand Peace(*tai ping dao*) in their upheaval, and The Taiping Heavenly Kingdom Rebellion took place in the late years of the Qing Dynasty also in the name of "securing Grand Peace for all under heaven". These famous farmer rebellions are referred to as "great upheavals"(*da qi yi*), meaning they are justified by heaven's mandates to save the civilians from starvation and suppression in the years of bad harvest and heavy taxations.

—shaped land system" thus implies that among nine pieces, each piece consists of one hundred acres, only the central piece is public one as the source of government revenue and open for food and other good to exchange serving as prototype of ancient market for business, and the rest of eight pieces are assigned to eight families who offer their collective services for the public piece in the center of this nine—piece land system in well—shape as the interest of land lease. Compared to the system of tithe, this "well—shaped land system" tends more to farmers' benefits either for their manageable services to the government or for their exchanging goods. This land system implemented in the Zhou Dynasty, the most durable among all twelve dynasties of Chinese empires, covering the time—space from 1046 to 256 B.C., often serves as the ideal model of Confucian ethics in terms of economics or "administration of secular affairs and relieving people from poverty", and its moral sense was summarized by a modern Confucian scholar Huang Zongxi in that "The purpose of our saint—kings in well—shaped land system was to secure people in their daily lives and prolific offspring." ① In the similar clue to "well—shaped land system", Confucian scholars have been attentive consistently on "Three Main Themes Addressed in the Spring and Autumn Period"(*chun qiu san shi*), namely, purify virtue(*zheng de*), improve instruments(*li yong*), and enrich lives(*hou sheng*), and these themes could be further expounded as the grand virtue in the universe fairly investing all cosmic beings their natural rights to exist, all resources in the universe or the world under the heaven being fully employed in manifesting that grand virtue, and human livelihood being abundantly rich in quantity and quality. These are the ethical substances focused by Confucian scholars in their discussions about the rule of saint—kings and the golden times of human society. Since the "well—shaped land system" was adopted, implemented and supervised by the government, Confucian scholars imposed on the government the ethical obligations towards people in the proposed policies of "all estates and assets should be accumulated for people"(*wei min zhi chan*) and "national wealth should be properly stored among the plebeian."(*cang fu yu min*) These people's rights—oriented for their livelihood is known as the "people—centered Confucianism" (*ru jia min*

---

① Huang Zongxi: "A Ming Barbarian Waiting for A Visitor(*ming yi dai fang lu*)" in *The Complete Works of Huang Zongxi* (*Huang Zongxi quan ji*) (Hangzhou: Zhejiang Classic Press, 2005), Vol. 1, p. 25.

*ben zhu yi*) originated from famous principles proposed in *The Works of Mencius*: "People is the most valuable in the world, the deities for territory and grains, the symbol of the country, come the second, and monarch weighs the least important. Therefore it is the people that make monarch his throne, it is the monarch that makes dukes their ranks, and it is the duke that makes his ministers their positions. If the dukes endanger the country, just oust them; if the sacrifices are full and vessels for sacrifices are clean, yet the country is still devastated with drought and flood, then replace the deities with new ones."① This statement of Mencius is briefed as "the priority of people over their monarch."(*min gui jun qing*) And its modern interpretation was most noticeably echoed in the modern Chinese revolution led by Dr. Sun Yat—sen for his "Three Principles of the People"(*san min zhu yi*), i.e. nationalism, democracy, and the people's livelihood, but in Chinese, these three entries are all introduced by "people" as their predicative like "nationalism"(*min zu*),"democracy"(*min zhu*), and "people's livelihood"(*min sheng*), culminating in "the people's rights"(*min quan*) as political priority over "the monarch's power"(*jun quan*). There we could see the ideological origin of modern social revolution in Confucianism and its social institutions. In the "well—shaped land system", Confucian scholars saw the moral obligations of the government to secure the peoples' rights to fair land lease and the pursuit of happiness. When Mencius was sent for consult by Duke Tengwen for the importance of the "well—shaped land system", he told the messenger: "You are sent here under my tutorship and this shows that your ruler intends to adopt humanity—centered politics. You will never let him down! I believe humanity—centered politics must begin with the demarcated land. If the land is not demarcated appropriately, the well—shaped land will lose its fairness and injustice would appear in crop distribution. Therefore the tyrants and corrupting officials tend to abuse their powers in making a mess of land boundaries. To secure a rule of peace and stable revenue, public land should be clearly and fairly demarcated."② And in response to the request from Duke Qixuan, Mencius also proposed a famous moral precept for rulers that "happiness can

---

① Yang Bojun eds., "The Works of Mencius(*meng zi*)" *in The Four Books in Modern Chinese* (*bai hua si shu*)(Changsha: Yuelu Press, 1989), p. 456.

② Yang Bojun eds., "The Works of Mencius(*meng zi*)" *in The Four Books in Modern Chinese* (*bai hua si shu*)(Changsha: Yuelu Press, 1989), p. 399.

only be truly shared with people."(*yu min tong le*)For both economic rights and the pursuit of happiness, Confucian scholars always demand the rulers be obliged to make policies and see them implemented in securing them, or otherwise they are subject to criminal charges in violating peoples' rights, thus they invite their being morally despised and legitimately removed from their ruling positions as "a solitary public thief" (*du fu min zei*), and their theft in stealing public rights is the justification for the people to stage social revolution and conduct execution of these "public thieves". Thus, for Confucian scholars, the well—shaped land system can generate more political and social rights than just economic one. Moreover, the political and legal charms incubated in the well—shaped land system in the Zhou Dynasty were intentionally referred to whenever Confucian scholars feel obliged to remind the rulers not to boast their powers and riches at the cost of the ruled plebeian, being strikingly visible in the Han and Song Dynasties when the masses of people were pushed too hard as to the threshold of social revolts. Thus Zhang Zai, a famous Confucian scholar in the Song Dynasty, admonished the rulers that "The rule of the world under heaven would not be ultimately justified if not guided by the well—shaped land system. The administrative success in the Zhou Dynasty was nothing more than fairness demonstrated in its land system…What has been testified in the proverbs reveals the truth in its political economy as 'the affluence of civilians will never leave their monarchs in poverty, while the poverty of civilians always endangers the affluence of their monarchs."① He thought economic and social rights realized in wealth and affluence accumulated by ordinary people as benefited from the well—shaped land system constituted the moral base and social dynamics for the rule of the imperial government, and which, if weakened or spoilt by the rulers in their policies to cheat people their rights, would lead to social tragedies both for the rulers and plebeian. His comments and predictions were either instructive in reviewing the administrative collapse in the Han Dynasty in its late years or predictive in lamenting the exile of the government when the great Song Dynasty was invaded and forced to move its capital across the Yangzi River by the northern barbarians. For Confucian scholars like Zhang Zai, the political and legal

---

① Zhang Zai, "Theoretical Aspects of Confucian Scholarship in the Proprieties of Zhou Dynasty" (*jing xue li ku, zhou li*), in *The Anthology of Zhang Zai* (Beijing, Zhonghua Shuju Press,1978),pp. 248—249.

legacy in the well—shaped land system would never depreciate in guaranteeing peoples' rights and in performing positive duties of the government. And with such religious and political commitments Confucian scholars have been influential in inculcating Chinese rulers their duties to protect and enrich their people as their legitimate subjects in both ancient and modern times, with a moral sense of responsibility to administer their policies in accordance with peoples' rights and benefits.

**Political and Economic Rights in Confucianism**

The well—shaped land system, as an intermediary stage from the primitive fishing and hunting social system to the farming social system, was gradually replaced by land annexation and monopolization of landlords, warlords or ambitious yet powerful dukes even in the days when Confucian scholars were eclipsed by Legalists, Daoists and Mohists. But Confucian scholars would stick to that outdated system with ethical engagement in advocating their political and economic philosophy. This was especially so when Confucian scholars in the Han and the Song Dynasties attempted to stage political and economic rectification to the administrative corruption and land monopolization at hands of big landlords and imperial bureaucrats. The methodologies they employed in expounding their viewpoints are labeled as "creative transformation" (*jie ti fa hui*) and "metaphysical import explored in concise words"(*wei yan da yi*), that is, ideas of originality are more feasibly disseminated and accepted in association with pre—existed themes, and the hidden meanings are extensively apprehensible in abstract terms.

Based on the fact that China was basically an inland country of agriculture, where land was the real estate for ordinary people or plebeian farmers and crops both as food or cash associated with land were their livelihood resources. For them, all political and economic rights must be assured on their relations with land and labour. This is why Confucius was convincing in tutoring his disciples: "to rule a dukedom of one thousand chariots, one should administer affairs in diligence and earnest, his undertakings should be dictated to thrift expenditure and tender care of his subordinates, and the rulers should not spoil farmers' seasonable work on their won fields by levied service."① Some revolutionary commentators of modern China influenced by western dichotomy of class — struggle ("the ruling exploiting class and the ruled exploited

① Yang Baijun, "The Analects of Confucius(*lun yu*)", in the *Four Books in Modern Chinese* (*bai hua si shu*), (Changsha, Yuelu Press, 1989), p. 303.

class" in Chinese communist's wording) might depreciate the Confucian ethics by pointing out that such political and economic admonishments could help improve and consolidate the ruling class. Yet in Confucius' days, his moral teachings might indirectly serve the interests of the ruled working class, poor farmers in this case, by persuading the ruling class to commit themselves to safeguarding the political and economic rights of their civilians. Such legitimacy in politics and economics can be readily appreciated when referring to the concept of "hands—off" in "the respect rights of others" which says: "This study requires the state to treat persons equally, to respect their individual dignity and worth, and hence not to interfere with or impart their declared rights, whether they be physical security rights or rights to due process, equal protection, speech or political participation. This duty of respect has often been described as 'negative' in the sense of being a 'hands—off' duty. The broad idea is not to worsen an individual's situation by depriving that person of the enjoyment of a declared right."① What Confucius admonished the rulers not to spoil farmers' seasonable work on their won fields by levied services can be justified as the "negative rights" of the plebeian farmers which the government was obliged to adopt the "hands—off" policy in the form of what Roman philosopher Cicero called "negative duties" to refrain from perpetrating any harm. It also entails the positive duties of the rulers or the government to protect the "negative rights" the ruled or the plebeian farmers which equally alluded peoples' rights to education and fair distribution of market profits in the relative situations when Confucius was quoted as saying: "When Confucius arrived in Dukedom Wei, his disciple Ranyou came to his service. Confucius exclaimed, 'the Dukedom is so great with its populace!' Ranyou, then, asked: 'With such populace, what should the ruler do?' Replied Confucius, 'to make them rich.' Ranyou asked again, 'if they were made rich, should the ruler do anything more on that?' Again Confucius answered, 'to cultivate them by providing education service'."② "When Confucius asked Gongming Gu about the merits of Duke Gongshu Wen: 'I have heard that he refrains himself from speaking, smiling and obtaining, is

---

① Philip Alston and Ryan Goodman, *International Human Rights*, Text and Materials, The Successor to International Human Rights in Context: Law, Politics and Morals, (Oxford: Oxford University Press, 2013), p. 182.

② Yang Baijun eds., "The Analects of Confucius(*lun yu*)" in the *Four Books in Modern Chinese* (*bai hua si shu*), (Changsha, Yuelu Press, 1989), p. 345.

that true?' Gongming Gu responded, 'Not true. The Duke would speak when people won't be annoyed by his speech, would smile when people won't be distasteful of it, and would obtain profits when people agree them to be righteously distributed'. Confucius was moved by hearing this, 'That's it! Can it be any nicer?'" ① To provide education service for people and to obtain profits by righteous principles, these were moral duties Confucius suggested to impose on the rulers, which also illuminated the positive rights of the ruled that their rulers should take positive actions to assure them, or otherwise they might be accused of dereliction of their obligations. The impact of legal culture proposed in these negative rights of the people and positive duties of the ruling officials in Confucianism can be visibly felt nowadays in the web commentaries that "They'd better go home peddling toast sweet potatoes if officials fail to benefit people."(*dang guan bu wei min zuo zhu, bu ru hui jia mai hong shu*)② To benefit people, according to Confucianism, is the positive duties of the rulers, these might include the negative rights of the ruled or the people as well as positive rights demanding on their rulers. And in a conventional analogy, Chinese would name their own country "an expanded family"(*guo jia*), in which its people are the "children civilians"(*zi min*) and they morally and legitimately claim their civilians rights basically of livelihood, food, land, education and comfortable living from their rulers, the "parent officials"(*fu mu guan*) in this case. The relations between peoples' rights and rulers' duties are made clear in the articulation of Mencius: "If the royal kitchens are full of delicious meat, and their stables are full of strong horses, you still see the hungry people in the streets and even corpses of starvation in the wild, you may curse the rule as leading animals devouring people. If people were contemptuous of animals eating each other, how could they respect their rulers who cannot be exempt of leading animals devouring people in their administration? Are they still thought of as parent officials to their people? Confucius once commented, 'The inventor of human sacrifice in clay figures will suffer the misfortune of non—offspring!' If Confucius did not tolerate human being copied in sacrifice, how could we tolerate the politics of

---

① Yang Baijun eds., "The Analects of Confucius(*lun yu*)" in the *Four Books in Modern Chinese* (*bai hua si shu*), (Changsha, Yuelu Press, 1989), p. 350.

② A catch phrase in the very popular play of "*Stories of the Lowest Rank Officials*"(*qi ping zhi ma guan*) on Chinese play theatre.

*murdering people by way of starvation?*"① In his interpretation of Confucianism, Mencius enhanced Confucius' humanistic feelings in human dignity and rights to life to moral liabilities of the rulers as their parent officials, insinuating people as "children civilian" their economic, social and cultural rights that their "administrative parent" should provide and guarantee in the capacity of "household heads."(*jia zhang*) What both Confucius and Mencius proposed as their moral, political and legal principles were humanity and righteousness which Confucius based for his agenda to reform the "rule of propriety and music"(*li yue zhi zhi*) initiatively introduced by Duke Zhou and Mencius for his insistence on government's duties to assure peoples' rights to property(*wei min zhi chan*). These are the meat and potatoes of Confucianism in the form of Confucius—Mencius Doctrines(*kong meng zhi dao*).

**Human Dignity and Rights Creatively Transformed**

In the time of "big chaos under the heaven"(*tian xia da luan*) as the consequence of "the violations of propriety and the spoils of music"(*li huai yue beng*), both Confucius and Mencius criticized the inventors of the rule of propriety and music in the form of "humanity"(*ren*) and "righteousness"(*yi*), and in their critical speculations and creative interpretations, both Confucius and Mencius managed to transform the political and legal institutions based on propriety and music regimes into the doctrines of human dignity and economic and social rights. But 500 years later, when Buddhism and Daoism were gaining popular vogue among Chinese rulers and masses, Confucianism was forced to update itself into Neo—Confucianism, which witnessed Confucian doctrine of humanity in the form of "reason"(*Li* 理), similar in pronunciation with "propriety"(*li* 礼), but more abstract in metaphysical sense, and Mencius' doctrine of righteousness in the form of "heart"(*xin*), which bears much similarity in cosmic emotion with French thinker Pascal in his "the heart has reasons which the reason does not know."② According to Neo—Confucians in the Song and the Ming Dynasties, the principles advocated in both "reason" and "heart" were properly employed in interpreting the universalities among cosmic issues rather than particularities of experimen-

---

① Yang Baijun eds., "The Works of Mencius(*meng zi*)" in the *Four Books in Modern Chinese* (*bai hua si shu*), (Changsha, Yuelu Press, 1989), p. 374.

② See in Samuel Enoch Stumpf eds., *Socrates to Sartre, A History of Philosophy*, (Fifth Edition, McGraw—Hill, Inc. 1993), p. 208.

tal events, thus having alienated themselves far away from traditional Confucianism underscoring human dignity and economic and social rights. This intellectual alienation later provoked severe criticism among Confucian scholars, to think of Dai Zhen, the enlightened Confucian thinker in later Qing Dynasty, who blamed Neo－Confucianism as "the massacre of human life by reason"(*yi li sha ren*) , and most notably Lu Xun, a radical literature giant of contemporary China, for his commentary of Confucianism as "religion of devouring human life"(*chi ren de li jiao*).

Companied by these humanistic censure on Neo－Confucianism, one may naturally wonder how Confucianism could be so paradoxical as to decline from human dignity and rights claims in Confucius and Mencius into the fallacies what its critics ridiculed as "life－devouring ethics"? There were and perhaps always have been such cases or stories that Confucianism was viciously misinterpreted and enforced in the abuses of human rights by the imperial administration or their deal with the powerless civilians. But such Confucianism could be nothing more accurate than a fake one, being apples and oranges in essence despite their being fruit in name. Let's examine why Confucius underlines "*ren*" or humanity－the moral and spiritual identity to human in the same pronunciation "*ren*" and pictographic character "three human bodies"(仁，人＋二＝three people)－as his supreme philosophical principle, being associated with Chinese adages of "three people make the masses"(*san ren cheng zhong*)(the masses in Chinese character also has three people in combined form "众") and "the anger of the masses cannot be subdued,"(*zhong nu bu ke wei*) and "people armed with humanity is invincible."(*ren zhe wu di*) In the first instance, he justified humanity as the ethical doctrine to rectify the institutional regime of the rule of propriety and music, and secondly in its social implementations the doctrine can be transformed as "what I understand humanity is that you should establish people while you wish to establish yourself and make people prosper while make yourself prosper. If such principle is applied in daily chores the methodology of humanity will be proven valid in its gradual expansions."① Such doctrine and its social transformation concerning the balance of rights and duties can be analogous to "agape" in ethical principle and "live and let live" in social policies in the Christian west. When Mencius explained Confucius in his humanity doc-

---

① Yang Baijun eds., "The Analects of Confucius(*lun yu*)" in the *Four Books in Modern Chinese* (*bai hua si shu*), (Changsha, Yuelu Press, 1989), p. 322.

trine and social implementation he targeted his own Duke Lianhui with power in a tendency to violate the universal ethical principle of humanity: "Powerful Duke Lianghui just sets an evil example of violating humanity! A person of humanity should expand his love for those whom he loves to those whom he does not, while a person bereft of humanity expands his hatred for those whom he does not love to those whom he loves."① Therefore he claimed human rights for the ruled from the duties of the rulers, accusing powerful Duke Lianghui as a tort—feasor, insisting on his restituting accommodation yards for mulberries that feed silkworms to assure peoples their clothing, domestic animals their rights to reproduction to assure people meat to eat, work of the farmers on their well—shaped lands to assure them no starvation, school facilities for the ruled to assure them education and ethics. If people are guaranteed their rights in economic, social, and education deeds and aged care, they have no reason to object the rule of their saint—kings. By his commitment to humanity in rectifying the rule of propriety and music, I would rather rank Confucius to be humanitarian philosopher and Mencius to be human rights advocate, and my estimation about them could also be reinforced by Confucius' conviction that "the whole world is unified in humanity"(*tian xia gui ren*) and Mencius' doctrine in "the priority of people over their monarch." With this political doctrine based on rights—oriented ethics, both Confucius and Mencius were insightful in their harsh critiques on "the system of propriety and music"(*li yue zhi du*) in their days: "If not guided by humanity, can any person behave himself in accordance with propriety? If not guided by humanity, can any person behave himself in accordance with music?"② Sophist Chunyu Kun challenged Mencius by asking: "Is it the propriety stipulated by Duke Zhou that male and female is forbidden to touch by hands when passing something between them?" Mencius responded: "Yes." The sophist then asked: "Should one touch hands with his drowning sister—in—law by violating the forbidding propriety?" The came the answer from Mencius: "He might degenerate into a terrible wolf if not grasping the hands of his drowning sister—in—law. It is the propriety stipulated by Duke Zhou not to touch by

① Yang Baijun eds., "The Works of Mencius(*meng zi*)" in the *Four Books in Modern Chinese* (*bai hua si shu*), (Changsha, Yuelu Press, 1989), p. 454.

② Yang Baijun eds., "The Analects of Confucius(*lun yu*)" in the *Four Books in Modern Chinese* (*bai hua si shu*), (Changsha, Yuelu Press, 1989), p. 308.

hands when passing goods between male and female; but it is the justified adaptation for male to reach hands for his drowining sister—in—law." The sophist pushed hard on Mencius again: "Now the world is drowning in its violation of social orders, why should you refrain from getting involved?" Mencius replied thus: "If the world is drowning, I should rescue it with my political doctrine. The logic is analogous to help the drowning sister—in—law by hands. You could not expect me to rescue the drowning world by hands instead of political doctrines."① In Confucius, the established political system by Duke Zhou, or "the Rule of Propriety and Music(*li yue zhi zhi*)", was socially violated because it lacked the moral foundation in humanity for the society to abide by it, therefore humanity should be installed as the guiding principle for the system of propriety and music and "you should establish people while you wish to establish yourself and make people prosper while make yourself prosper" should be introduced as methodology in implementing that guiding principle based on humanity. For Mencius, the political doctrine to rescue "the drowning world" is implicated in "righteousness", which was assumed to save China from the "big chaos under heaven (*tian xia da luan*)" caused by powerful dukes in their "wars without righteousness in the Spring and Autumn Period(*chun qiu wu yi zhan*)". The politics of rectitude should be justified in the principle of righteousness which Mencius termed as "Dao of Saint—King and Politics of Humanity(*wang dao ren zheng*)", resulting in the establishment of political scenario of rights—oriented ethics compatible with "people—centered Confucianism." Therefore, the doctrine of righteousness was purposefully advocated by Mencius as to revolutionize the power—oriented politics initiated by Duke Zhou with his rule of propriety and music in a way "prefecture magistrates are prohibited from setting fires on civilian houses while civil plebeian are all justified in lighting lamps at their homes", this reversed metaphor properly insinuated the "rights—oriented ethics" in Confucian Differentiation between Righteousness and Benefits.② To my comprehension, this "rights—oriented ethics" in Mencius' political doctrine of right-

---

① Yang Bojun eds., "The Works of Mencius(*meng zi*)" in the *Four Books in Modern Chinese*(bai hua si shu) (Changsha: Yuelu Press, 1989), p. 413.

② The original popular metaphor to depict political tyranny in imperial China is "The magistrates are allowed to burn down houses while the common people are forbidden even to light lamps", but Prof. Feng reversed it in explaining Mencius revolutionary ideology prioritizing people's rights over officer's powers. See in Feng Youlan, *The Complete Works of San Song Tang by Feng Youlan*, (Zhengzhou: Henan People's Publishing House, 2000) Vol. 5, p. 364.

eousness bears identical legal spirit in "Everything which is not forbidden is allowed for ordinary citizen" and "Everything which is not allowed is forbidden for public authorities." And in this Confucian and British legal tradition, we can see clearly the predilection of people's rights over the governmental powers. My observation on Confucian rights—oriented ethics is also properly reflected by contemporary human rights scholar in the west with his appreciation on Mencius: "The Mencian idea that all humans are born good combined with the Hierarchical responsibility of rulers, could be used to criticize emperors, their ministers, and the court for the shortcomings of the people."① For the concept of righteousness, pronounced in Chinese as "yi", we could associate many entries in Chinese regarding peoples' rights in defiance of governmental powers, like "justified by faith"(*yin xin cheng* yi), "march of moral courage"(yi *yong jun jin xing qu*), the title of the Chinese National Anthem, "righteousness is prioritized over profit"(*jian li si* yi), "righteousness breeds bravery like bravery" (*jian* yi *yong wei*), and "righteousness makes obligation just"(*shi min ye* yi), etc. In all these cases, Mencian "righteousness" has revealed Confucian "humanity" in concrete implications, underscoring the rights of people to the eclipse of the powers of the government. Here I also want to specify the enduring impact of this rights—oriented ethics in Chinese political legacies in contemporary Chinese society. Not only Chinese Nationalist leader Dr. Sun Yat—sen adopted "the Three Principles of the People" as his top political agenda, but also Chinese Communist leader Mao Zedong advocated a lot in his political addresses to communist cadres with the motto "serve the people"(*wei ren min fu wu*), but unfortunately he could not reconcile this "rights—oriented ethics" with his "Marxist class struggle doctrine", and finally ruined this motto in "the Great Cultural Revolution" in spite of the fact that the motto is still inscribed on the courtyard screen on the entrance to Headquarters of Chinese Communist Party Central Committee and Chinese Government in the center of Beijing.

In a two—thousand—year space of Chinese history, the Confucian ideology based on Confucius' humanism and Mencius' human rights or Confucius' humanity and Mencius' righteousness or simply "The Doctrine of Confucius and Mencius"(*kong meng zhi dao*) in Chinese slang has influenced Chinese mentality too much as in their

---

① Jack Donnelly, *Universal Human Rights in Theory and Practice*, 3rd ed., (New York: Cornell University Press, 2013), p. 141.

evaluations of the rule of Chinese empires that it is never allowed to overstep the red line of humanity and people's rights, or "the exhaustion of humanity and righteousness"(*ren zhi yi jin*) in Confucian term, otherwise the people are authorized to overthrow the government and execute the rulers as the "solitary public thieves."(*du fu min zei*) And these political, economic, social and legal rights are called "natural rights", or "human rights consecrated by heaven's mandates", and have their origins in rights—oriented ethics of Confucianism and have been frequently verified by Chinese social revolutions. Such humanitarian and human rights ideology was mirrored in the traditional farmers' rebellions as "performing the political mission in heaven's stead"(*ti tian xing dao*) and in the modern democratic social revolution led Dr. Sun Yat—sen in his political doctrine "the Universal Commonwealth"(*tian xia wei gong*), which is the catch phrase in explaining Confucian "cosmic doctrine."(*da dao zhi xing*) If we like to examine more attentively we are sure to find that both Chinese Nationalists and Communists in modern China just proposed their political legitimacy in humanism and human rights, to be respectively attributive of "the Three Principles of the People" to the credit of its founder Dr. Sun Yat—sen, *i.e.* nationalism, democracy, and the people's livelihood for Chinese Nationalists , and of "the New Democracy"(*xin min zhu zhu yi*) for the Chinese Communists at their early stage which has its cultural resources in Confucian rights—oriented ethics in "assuming to be the new people"(*zuo xin min*) proposed in *the Great Learning*(*da xue*), one of the most popular classics in *the Four Books*(*si shu*) system. Apparently, this political legitimacy is the spiritual legacies cultivated in Confucianism and thereof was positively and enthusiastically echoed by Chinese people in the times of being authentically interpreted and sincerely applied. On mainland China since Deng Xiaoping introduced Reform and Open—Door Policy, we have witnessed his economic agenda "to let some people become rich", Jiang Zemin, as Deng Xiaoping's successor, for his theory in improving Maoism with "the Three Representatives"(*san ge dai biao*), *i.e.* the representative of the progressive production power, the representative of the advanced orientation of Chinese culture and the representative of the fundamental interest of the broad masses of the people, and after Jiang's retirement, Hu Jingtao advocated in his "the Three Fors"(*san wei*), *i.e.* the power is used for the people, feelings are expressed for the people, and profits are gained for the people. If the Chinese Communist leaders really mean what they propose, they are sure to be favored and respected by Chinese people, for they, by sticking to these political convictions, truly demonstrate their legitimacy in Chinese characteristics in combining Confucian values with Marxist ideology, western democracy, market economy and the rule of law. In contemporary China, when national agricultural production was relieved of any tax levied by Chinese government at any level, when shantytown in many old industrial cities would be reconstructed by government's budgets for those low—income inhabitants, when governmental dominated medical care was declared to cover all citizens and peasants, when all children in China have free access to nine—year schooling of obligatory education without any tuition fees and when barest minimum income were claimed to be guaranteed by national revenues for all inhabitants in the cities and towns, these policies and agendas are often promptly interpreted as "the projects of peoples' livelihood" (*min sheng gong cheng*) or "the projects winning peoples' heart" (*min xin gong cheng*). By the term of "livelihood" and "heart", we can dearly appreciate the merits of humanism and human rights in Confucianism in the form of "cosmic virtue" exhibited in "lives" and "who wins the heart of the people wins the world." (*de min xin zhe, de tian xia*) In Confucian mentality of integration between heaven and human, civil, political, economic, social and cultural rights are unified as people's rights, therefore Chinese characteristics of socialism or modernization could not be comprehensively cherished in separating these rights or in isolating its Confucian legacies with modern globalized values.

**Conclusion**

Some western scholars have noticed that the supremacy of human rights was been discussed among modern European thinkers on state protection of human rights beyond their own borders, and they even believe "these ideas can also be found in the works of philosophers in ancient China", definitely relating it to the mandate of heaven as the form of "sovereign accountability". ① Yet we should notice the mandate of heaven is a key term in Confucianism concerning religion, politics and law, to think of Confucius' commitment to heaven's mandate (*tian ming*), Mencius' self—appointed heavenly titles (*tian jue*) and plebeian rebel's "performing political mission in Heaven's stead", to name just a few in this case. In Chinese mentality, heaven is the

---

① See foot note 12 in "Responsibility to Protect Beyond Borders" by Luke Glanville, in *Human Rights Law Review*, printed by Oxford University Press, Volum 12, Number1, 2012. p. 5.

representative of human life, human ultimate concern, political legitimacy and legal authority as well as male nature in the female—male cosmos(*yin yang qian kun*). To be specific in politics and jurisprudence, such mentality is bound to prioritize the natural rights to life, liberty and conscience, which are invariably seen as the themes in Confucian rights—oriented ethics. If western scholars were amused by people's rights supremacy revealed in Chinese reflections on heaven's mandates, they should be more academically reminded of the humanism of Confucius and the religious commitments to human rights than political powers from Mencius in his illustrations of righteousness.

Western scholars might be equally astonished by the slow process in Chinese People's Congress to ratify the International Covenant on Civil and Political Rights though it ratified the International Covenant on Economic, Social and Cultural Rights in 2001. It is no surprise some of the western critics would be in an easy mood to state that Chinese government is more concerned with economic, social and cultural rights than civil and political rights, a tendency to be drastically alienated from its Confucian tradition. Such preference would be paradoxical in Chinese mentality, but it only seems to be so. My argument would be that if we bear in mind the intellectual fabric of Confucian integrity of heaven and human, Confucius' humanism and Mencius' human rights justified in righteousness are sure to manifest themselves in Chinese Communist political agenda like "the projects of peoples' livelihood" and "the projects winning peoples' heart" and "serving the people", *etc*. The reason that Confucianism has been influential among Chinese people in about more than two thousand years is that its humanity conviction and its ethics revealed in the priority of rights over powers have already been ingrained in Chinese identity. Therefore both Chinese Nationalists and Communists would never deny this "rights—oriented ethics" in Confucianism with their politics and its modern transformation in the form of democracy and market economy would become ever more harmonious with global trends in human rights civilization.

# Confucian persuasion, man and his relation to others: shu 恕 (empathy), ren 仁 (humanity) and cheng 誠 (authenticity)

**Tiziana Lippiello 李集雅 (Ca' Foscari University Venice)**

In Chinese literature the *locus classicus* of what in the West has been called "the golden rule" is a passage from the *Lunyu* 論語 (Analects) in which Zigong, one of Confucius' favourite disciples asks his Master about a principle that can guide man's behaviour:

Zigong asked: "Is there an adage that can guide us throughout our life?" The Master said: "It is *shu*! What you don't want done to yourself, do not do to others." (*Lunyu*, IV.15)

In the sentence "What you don't want done to yourself, do not do to others" (*ji suo bu yu*, *wu shi yu ren* 己所不欲,勿施於人) Confucius defined *shu* 恕, a character variably translated as "reciprocity", "consideration of others" or "do unto others as you would have others do unto you". *Shu* is one of the most widely debated and controversial assertions of Confucian ethics, not only because of the alleged analogy with the biblical "golden rule", but also because of its semantic richness, as we discover from reading the *Analects* and other Confucian writings. Confucius perceived in *shu* a basic requirement for anyone setting out to lead a virtuous life, in conformity with the *mores* of the sages of ancient times, as inherited and elaborated by Confucius and his followers.

*You* (friendship) and *ren* (benevolence, humanity) are other concepts recurring in *Lunyu* which highlight the importance of the relation to others in Confucianism.

I shall analyze these key concepts, which are familiar also in western culture, such as *shu*, *you* and *ren* and their interpretation by the Jesuits in their latin translations of the classics.

**PAPER** (max. 12.000 words)

Today I shall introduce a few cardinal principles of Chinese ethics, dating back to Confucius, the Master who set the rules and behavioural model of Chinese ethics.

I have chosen this subject because of the alleged analogy with the Christian golden rule especially in the words of Jesus according to Mathews 22 (repeated in Luke and Mark). In the Old Testament, as acknowledged in the Catholic canon, two fundamental passages deal with the Golden Rule. One is Tobia 4,15: "Do not do to others what you do not like for yourself", the other is "You will not revenge or feel resentment against your people's sons, but will love your people as yourself." (Levitic, 19,18). The first passage, the most recent of the two, is a clear negative formulation of the golden rule, whereas the second explicitly quotes the golden rule in its positive formulation: "[you] will love your people as yourself". ①

In fact, the Chinese golden rule, although it is expressed in negative and positive terms as in other traditions, cannot be compared to the biblical golden rule, at least in its earliest formulation as there is no mention or reference whatsoever to a God. It is man who is at the center of the Chinese golden rule and his relation with himself and

---

① On the golden rule in the Judaic—Christian world see Leopoldo Sandonà, "Forme della Regola d'oro nel mondo ebraico—cristiano", in Vigna, C. e Zanardo, S., *La regola d'oro come etica universale*, Milano, Vita e pensiero, 2005, pp. 3—36, p. 5. On the Chinese golden rule see Fung Yulan, *A Short History of Chinese Philosophy* (New York 1948), pp. 42—44; H. Fingarette, "Following the 'One Thread' of the *Analects*", *Journal of the American Academy of Religion*, 47 (1979), 35, pp. 373—405; R. E. Allinson, "On the Negative Version of the Golden Rule as Formulated by Confucius", *New Asia Academic Bulletin*", 3 (1982), pp. 305—315; Id., "The Confucian Golden Rule: A Negative Formulation", *Journal of Chinese Philosophy*, 12 (1985), 3, pp. 305—315; D. H. Hall and R. T. Ames, *Thinking through Confucius* (New York, Albany 1987), pp. 283—304; P. J., Ivanhoe, "Reweaving the 'One Thread' of the *Analects*", *Philosophy East and West*, 40 (1990), 1, pp. 17—30; D. S. Nivison, "Golden Rule Arguments in Chinese Moral Philosophy", in *The Ways of Confucianism* (La Salle, Open Court, 1996), pp. 59—76; Id., "Zhong (Chong) and *Shu*: Loyalty and Reciprocity", in A. S. Cua, ed., *Encyclopedia of Chinese Philosophy* (New York and London 2003), pp. 882—885, H. Roetz, *Confucian Ethics of the Axial Age. A Reconstruction under the Aspect of Breakthrough toward Postconventional Thinking*, (New York, Albany 1993), pp. 137—148. Wang Qingjie, "The Golden Rule and Interpersonal Care-From a Confucian Perspective", *Philosophy East and West*, 49 (1999), 4, pp. 415—438; Sin Yee Chan, "Can *Shu* Be the One Word that Serves as the Guiding Principle of Caring Action?", *Philosophy East and West*, 50 (2000), 4, pp. 507—524; B. Van Norden, "Unweaving the 'One Thread' of *Analects* 4:15", in Id., *Confucius and the* Analects (Oxford 2002), pp. 216—236; Bo Mou, "A Reexamination of the Structure and Content of Confucius' Version of the Golden Rule", *Philosophy East and West*, 54 (2004), 2, pp. 218—247. T. Lippiello, "A Confucian Adage for Life: Empathy (shu) in the Analects", in R. Malek S. V. D. and G. Criveller P. I. M. E., ed. by, *Light a Candle. Encounters and Friendship with China: Festschrift in Honour of Angelo S. Lazzarotto P. I. M. E*, Monumenta Serica, Sankt Augustin, 2010, pp. 73—97.

with the others.

In Chinese literature the *locus classicus* of what in the West has been called "the golden rule" is a passage from the *Lunyu* 論語 (Analects) in which Zigong, one of Confucius' favourite disciples, asks his Master about a principle that can guide man's behaviour:

子貢問曰:「有一言而可以終身行之者?」子曰:「其恕乎!」己所不欲,勿施於人。」

Zigong asked: "Is there an adage that can guide us throughout our life?" The Master said: "It is *shu*! What you don't want done to yourself, do not do to others." (*Lunyu*, 15,24)

Confucius considered *shu* a basic requirement for anyone setting out to lead a virtuous life, in conformity with the *mores* of the sages of ancient times, as inherited and elaborated by Confucius and his followers. *Shu* recurs again in the *Lunyu*, 4,15, where it imposes itself with greater force and incisiveness, together with another key concept of Confucian ethics, *zhong* 忠, which contributes to defining the semantic area of both terms.

子曰:「參乎! 吾道一以貫之。」曾子曰:「唯!」子出,門人問曰:「何謂也?」曾子曰:「夫子之道,忠恕而已矣。」

The Master said: "Shen! In my Way there is one thread binding all together." Zengzi said: "Indeed!" When the Master had left, the disciples asked: "What did he mean?" Zengzi [Shen] replied: "The Master's Way consists of *zhong* and *shu* and that's all."

In Matthews 22,35—40 we read:

"Master, which is the greatest commandment in the law?" Jesus answers: "*Love thy Lord as your God, with all your soul, and with all your mind*". That is the greatest commandment. It comes first. The second is like it: "*Love your neighbour as yourself.*" Everything in the Law and the prophets hangs on these two commandments.

Herbette Fingarette suggests an interesting, albeit controversial, interpretation of the relation between the "Confucian golden rule" as expressed in *Lunyu*, 4,15 and the Biblical golden rule. He maintains that the notion of *zhong* corresponds to what is expressed in the first commandment, "*Love thy Lord as your God, with all your soul, and with all your mind*", while *shu* corresponds to the second, "*Love your neighbour as yourself*". According to him the concept of the golden rule is expressed in similar terms in Chinese tradition. The scholar's interpretation is based on the reading of the *Lunyu*, 4,15 and in particular on the comments of Song scholars who interpreted *zhong* as the Way of Heaven and *shu* as the way of man:

忠者天道,恕者人道

*Zhong* is the way of Heaven, *shu* is the way of man. ①

Fingarette maintains that, just as in the teachings of Jesus the golden rule is composed of two components, the love of God and the love of one's neighbour, in a similar fashion, in the teaching of Confucius "the unifying principle" is made up of *zhong*, loyalty, absolute dedication to a transcendent principle, and *shu*, love of one's fellow man.

However, as we shall see, there is no transcendental principle in the Chinese golden rule: absolute dedication is meant as true devotion to oneself, to the other, to the *dao*.

*Zhong* 忠

Loyalty, absolute dedication

"Love thy Lord your God with all your soul, with all your mind"(Fingarette)

*Shu* 恕

Empathy

"Love your neighbour as yourself" (Fingarette)

***Shu* 恕 *andren* 仁 *in the Lunyu***

H. Fingarette provides the following explanation for *shu*:

*Shu* is intended to cause me to have concern for you, not to impose my tastes and inclinations on you. Therefore, to assess the situation appropriately in declining what I want, I must not imagine being in your place, I must do this in such a way as to see it *through your eyes*. To put it in a nutshell I must not imagine myself being in your situation; I must imagine *being you*.

*Shu* thus implies to have concern for the other, not to impose our tastes and inclinations on him, but rather to understand and follow his tastes and inclinations.

As we have seen *shu* is explained in *Lunyu*, 15,24 with the formula "What you don't want done to yourself, do not do to others"(己所不欲,勿施於人).

Zhu Xi, commenting on this passage, explains:

---

① Zhu Xi, *Sishu zhangju jizhu* 四書章句集註, Beijing, Zhonghua shuju 1983, p. 73.

推己及物，其施不窮，故可以終身行之。尹氏曰：「學貴於知要。子貢之問，可謂知要矣。孔子告以求仁之方也。推而極之，雖聖人之無我，不出乎此。終身行之，不亦宜乎？

Extend yourself to others, and what you do unto them will be inexhaustible. As a consequence, you will be able to practice it [empathy] for the whole of your life. Mr. Yin [Tun] said: "In learning, we value knowing the essentials. Zigong's query can be said to be about knowing the essentials. Confucius told him the way to pursue humanity, benevolence (*ren*). Extend yourself, and bring it [empathy] to perfection so that even the selflessness of the sages does not surpass it. Wouldn't it make good sense to practice this for the whole of your life?①

It is interesting to notice here that Zhu Xi mentions the "selflessness of the sages" as a paradigm of humanity, benevolence (*ren*) and that he explains empathy (*shu*) as a way to pursue humanity.

In particular, Master Cheng distinguishes *ren* from *shu* in commenting *Lunyu* 4, 15. He states:

程子曰：「以己及物，仁也；推己及物，恕也…」

Master Cheng said: "Moving from oneself to reach others is humanity (*ren*); extend yourself to others is empathy (*shu*).

*Lunyu* 6, 30, mentioning *ren* (humanity) provides a similar explanation, expressed in positive terms:

仁者，己欲立而立人，己欲達而達人。能近取譬，可謂仁之方也已。

The term *ren* means that when you desire to get established yourself, you help others to get established; and when you desire success for yourself you help others to succeed. The ability to take as analogy what is near at hand can simply be called the method of attaining humanity *ren*. ②

D. Gardner remarks that *ren* (humanity, benevolence), which he renders with "true goodness", is described in the *Lunyu* in many ways, such as: to be slow or modest in speech (12.3), to be resolute and firm (13.27), to be possessed of courage (14.4), to be free from worry (9.29), to delight in mountains (6.23); to subdue the self and return to propriety (12.1); to be respectful, tolerant, trustworthy, diligent, and

---

① Zhu Xi, p. 166; Daniel K. Gardner, *Zhu Xi's readings of the Analects. Canon, Commentary and the Classical Tradition*, New York, Columbia University Press, pp. 88—89.

② D. K. Gardner, *op. cit.*, p. 55.

kind (17.5); and to love others (12.22). "In this way", he states, "Confucius gives his followers-and readers— glimpses of various dimensions of true goodness."①

Zhu Xi comments that

以己及人,仁者之心也。於此觀之,可以見天理之周流而無閒矣。狀仁之體,莫切於此。

using oneself to approach others is the mind—and—heart of the person of true goodness. Looking at it from this point of view, we can see that the heavenly principle is all—pervasive. To sketch the substance of true goodness, nothing comes closer than this.②

Master Cheng is more exhaustive in explaining why it is so difficult to attain humanity. He writes that

醫書以手足痿痹為不仁,此言最善名狀。仁者以天地萬物為一體,莫非己也。認得為己,何所不至;若不屬己,自與己不相干。如手足之不仁,氣己不貫,皆不屬己。故博施濟眾,乃聖人之功用。

A book on medicine considers numbness of the hands and legs to be the absence of *ren* [true goodness]. This is an excellent description. A person of true goodness regards heaven, earth, and the myriad things as one body. They all are his own self. If he acknowledges them as the self, where does he not reach? But if they do not belong to the self, then naturally they are of no concern to the self-which is like the absence of *ren* in the hands and legs. If one's *qi* no longer penetrates them, none of them belongs to the self. It is for this reason that widely bestowing benefits and bringing relief to the multitude are the achievements of the sage.

Moreover:

仁至難言,故止曰:「己欲立而立人,己欲達而達人,能近取譬,可謂仁之方也已。」欲令如是觀仁,可以得仁之體。

True goodness is extremely difficult to talk about, and so here it merely says, 'that when you desire to get established yourself, you help others to get established; and when you desire success for yourself you help others to succeed. The ability to take as analogy what is near at hand can simply be called the method of attaining humanity *ren*.' He (Confucius) wished to have us understand *ren* in this way so that we

① D. K. Gardner, *op. cit.*, p. 53.

② Zhu Xi

could understand its substance.

Master Cheng continues:

論語言「堯舜其猶病諸」者二。夫博施者,豈非聖人之所欲?然必五十乃衣帛,七十乃食肉。聖人之心,非不欲少者亦衣帛食肉也,顧其養有所不贍爾,此病其施之不博也。濟眾者,豈非聖人之所欲。

The *Analects* on two occasions says: 'Even Yao and Shun would find this difficult'. Now to bestow benefits widely is indeed what a sage desires. And yet [Mengzi 1A.3 says that] people must be fifty to wear silk, and seventy to eat meat. In his mind—and—heart, a sage would surely want the young as well to wear silk and eat meat and would look upon such care [i.e. that advocated in Mengzi] as inadequate. He would find it difficult that his benefits had not been bestowed widely. Bringing relief to the multitude is indeed what a sage desires. [⋯]

Apparently Song scholars were more concerned with *ren* than with *shu*, which they considered a method or technique to achieve *ren*.

Zigong was able to apply himself to empathy, but *ren* was out of his reach; in fact, when he expressed to Confucius his intention of not doing to the others what he did not want for himself, Confucius said: "Zigong, you have not yet reached this point!" (賜也,非爾所及也。Lunyu, 5.12)

The Master thought that Zigong had not yet attained a natural "empathy". Master Cheng so interpreted this passage: "Zigong was able to apply himself to it, by not doing to others what he didn't want done to himself, but he had not reached the point to pursue it *naturally*.

Zhu Xi explains that empathy is a way to attain humanity, empathy and humanity stem from the same principle; Zigong could not attain empathy and therefore the Master said that he had not reached this point yet.

說文:「恕,仁也。」如己之心,以推諸仁,此求仁之道,故「恕」亦訓仁。恕,仁本一理,子貢未能至恕,故夫子以為非爾所己(論語,6.30)

Liu Baonan 劉寶楠 (1791—1855) commented:

如己之心,以推諸人,此求仁之道,故「恕」亦訓仁。恕、仁本一理,子貢未能至恕,故夫子以為非爾所及。他日問終身行之,又告以恕,皆此教也。

*Shu* and *zhong*

The Master explained to Ji Kangzi 季康子 (d. 469 BC), the head of the three most influential families of Lu, how a ruler should behave with the people in order to obtain their respect (*jing* 敬), dedication, loyalty (*zhong* 忠) and zeal (*qin* 勤).

季康子問:「使民敬,忠以勤,如之何?」子曰:「臨之以莊,則敬;孝慈,則忠;舉善而教不能,則勤。」

Ji Kangzi asked: "To make the people be respectful, loyal and zealous, what should one do?" The Master said: "Regard them with dignity, and they will be respectful. Be filial to your elders and caring to your juniors, and they will be loyal. Raise the good and instruct those who are unable, and they will be zealous. (*Lunyu*, II.20)

In the sentence "What you don't want done to yourself, do not do to others" (*ji suo bu yu, wu shi yu ren* 己所不欲,勿施於人) Confucius defined *shu* 恕, a character variably translated as "empathy", "reciprocity", "consideration of others" or "do unto others as you would have others do unto you". *Shu* is one of the most widely debated and controversial assertions of Confucian ethics, not only because of the alleged analogy with the biblical "golden rule", but also because of its semantic richness, as we discover from reading the *Analects* and other Confucian writings.

We can find *shu*, together with another cardinal virtue, *zhong*, also in the *Zhongyong* (On the practice of

the mean), a text ascribed to Zisi, Confucius' grandson. The *Zhongyong*, similar to the *Lunyu*, is a collection of maxims and anecdotes by different authors. Here it is Confucius again who pronounces the following words:

**忠恕**違道不遠,施諸己而不願,亦勿施於人。

One who is *zhong* and *shu* will never stray from the Way. What he does not wish done to him he does not do to others. (*Zhongyong* 中庸 , 13)

*Zhong* is commonly translated as "loyalty" but it is something more than that. *Zhong* basically means "loyalty", meant as loyalty to one's superior. According to H. Fingarette, *zhong* is loyalty and absolute dedication which transcends all individualism, the purely personal and encourages to achieve completeness, moral integrity, authenticity. It designates a psychological effort to be sincere, authentic to oneself and to others. *Zhong* thus means loyalty, however it is not intended as a blind obedience to a superior or one's peer, but as an absolute commitment to preserving the integrity of one's life, of one's social role. In fact Fingarette interprets *zhong* as "loyalty—fidelity" (*zhong—xin* 中信), meant as loyalty—fidelity to moral rules, to principles of justice dictated by Heaven, which he associates with God. Moreover, Fingarette emphasizes the role of *zhong* and *shu* as criteria for judging what is just and appropriate. This reading is suggested by a passage in the *Daxue* which defines the golden rule in terms of "measuring square":

所惡於上,毋以使下;所惡於下,毋以事上;所惡於前,毋以先後;所惡於後,毋以從前;所惡於右,毋以交於左;所惡於左,毋以交於右:此之謂**絜矩**之道。

What is called "measuring square" is [the carpenter's] square, that is the heart—and—mind. What my heart—and—mind wishes corresponds to what others wish. If I wish to show filial and brotherly love and be caring to the young, I will wish others, like me, show filial and brotherly love and be caring to the young [...]

Therefore the man of noble character perceives that the heart—and—mind of others and his own are similar. Hence he always uses his own heart—and—mind to measure the heart—and—mind of others, so that all will become tranquil. ①

This theory was developed in the 18th century by Dai Zhen 戴震 (1724—1777) on the basis of the conception of the original goodness of human nature formulated by the *Mengzi*. Dai Zhen stated that the ethical sense (*li* 理) belongs to the sage and coincides with his desires and expectations. The Sage is guided by a kind of moral intuition. ②

P. Ivanhoe in "Reweaving the 'one thread' of the Analects" (p. 21), remarks that H. Fingarette's analysis is based on a misunderstanding of zhong which, combined with *xin*, would mean something like "interpersonal good faith and loyalty", mediated by the *li* "rituals". Ivanhoe maintains that *zhong*, in the *Lunyu*, means "doing one's duty in service to others".

Xu Shen 許慎(c. 55-c. 149) in the *Shuowen jiezi* 說文解字 reads *zhong* as *jing* 敬

---

① *Daxue*, in Zhu Xi, *Sishu zhangju jizhu*, ch. 10, p. 10. See Li Jingde 黎靖德, *Zhuzi yulei* 朱子語類 (Beijing 1985), ch. 16, p. 361.

② 子贡问曰:「有一言而可以终身行之者乎?」子曰:「其恕乎! 己所不欲,勿施于人。」大学言治国平天下,不过曰「所恶于上,毋以使下, 所恶于下,毋以事上」,以位之卑尊言也;「所恶于前,毋以先后,所恶于后,毋以从前」,以长于我与我长言也;「所恶于右,毋以交于左,所恶于左,毋以交于右」,以等于我言也;曰「所不欲」,曰「所恶」,不过人之常情,不言理而理尽于此。惟以情情,故其于事也,非心出一意见以处之,苟舍情求理,其所谓理,无非意见也。未有任其意见而不祸斯民者。问:以意见为理,自宋以来莫敢致斥者,谓理在人心故也。今日理在事情,于心之所同然,洵无可疑矣;孟子举以见人性之善,其说可得闻欤?

*Mengzi ziyi shuzheng* 孟子字義疏證 (An Explication of the Meaning of Terms in Mengzi), *Xuxiu siku quanshu* 續修四庫全書, Shanghai 2002, chap. 1, pp. 21—22.

(respect, reverence), and he adds that "to give full realization to one's heart—and—mind is what is meant by *zhong* (盡心為忠). [①]

We find an explanation of *jinxin* also in *Mengzi* 孟子. *Jinxin* is the title of *Mengzi* VII A,1. The incipit of the chapter reads:

テマラモヤサ:。クアM二菻トユ゜。ヨユ二菻ヤ。Дヨユフ・モ。」。ヶ

For a man to give full realization to his heart—and—mind is for him to understand his own nature, and to understand his own nature is to understand Heaven." [②]

Wang Bi 王弼 (226—249) interprets it as to "fully realize one's feelings/emotions"(情之盡也)

Commenting on *Lunyu* IV, 15, Huang Kan 皇侃 (488—545) interpreted *zhong* as "to fully focus on one's heart and mind (*jin zhong xin ye* 盡中心也)

Zhu Xi probably followed Mengzi in saying: "to give full realization to one's heart—and—mind is what is meant by *zhong*" (*Jinxin wei zhong* 盡心為忠). He also used the locution "to do one's best, to exhaust oneself"(*jiejin* 竭盡);

Zhu Xi in his interpretation was inspired by the reading of the definition provided by Xu Shen (c 55— c. 149), who, in *Shuowen jiezi*, and explained that *zhong* meant "respect", "reverence" (*jing*). He glossed: to give full realization to one's heart—and—mind is what is meant by *zhong*. This amounts to saying that he who is *zhong* shows reverence as he performs his tasks with absolute devotion, dedicating the whole of himself.

Xu Shen 許慎 defines *shu* as *ren* (humanity, benevolence); [③]

Speaking of *shu* Mengzi is clear, he maintains that empathy is a way to attain benevolence:

強恕而行,求仁莫近焉。(孟子, VIIA,4)

"Strengthen your empathy and you will find that this is the shortest way to benevolence". (*Mengzi*, VIIA,4).

Wang Bi 王弼 (226—249) comments that *shu* implies to reflect on one's feeling in order to understand other people's feelings:

---

① Duan Yucai, *Shuowen jiezi zhu* (Shanghai 1984), chap. 10B, p. 25 b.

② *Jinxin* アMミト (To give full realization to one's heart—and—mind) is the title of *Mengzi*, 7A,1. See also D. C. Lau, *Mencius* (Hong Kong 1979, repr. 1984), p. 265 and B. W. Van Norden, *Mengzi. With Selections from Traditional Commentaries*, (Indianapolis/Cambridge 2008), p. 171.

③ Xu Shen, 10B. 28a.

**恕**:反情以同物也

To reflect on one's feelings in order to have sympathy with other beings (Wang Bi)

Huang Kan 皇侃 (488—545) interpreted *shu* in a similar way:

忖我以度於人也

To ponder on oneself in order to measure the others (Huang Kan)

Zhu Xi 朱熹 (1130—1200)

**恕**:推己

To extend oneself (in the sense of being empathetic to others) (Zhu Xi)

己所不欲,勿施於人 (*Lunyu*, XV,24)

What you don't want done to yourself, do not do to others.

As we have seen before, Feng Youlan, starting from the statement, "What you don't want done to yourself, do not do to others" (*ji suo bu yu*, *wu shi yu ren* 己所不欲,勿施於人) has interpreted *shu* as the negative formula of the golden rule, whereas *zhong* according to his opinion should represent the positive formula. Indeed in confucian texts we can find other concepts and formulas which reminds us the golden rule, although they are not identified with the two key concepts so far examined, that is *zhong* and *shu*. One of this passage is found in the Daxue, one of the four books of the Confucian tradition of the Song dynasty, a text traditionally to Master Zeng, one of Cofucius disciples. It reads:

大學:絜矩

所惡於上,毋以使下;所惡於下,毋以事上;所惡於前,毋以先後;所惡於後,毋以從前;所惡於右,毋以交於左;所惡於左,毋以交於右:此之謂**絜矩**之道。

What is called "measuring square" is [the carpenter's] square, that is the heart—and—mind. What my heart—and—mind wishes corresponds to what others wish. If I wish to show filial and brotherly love and be caring to the young, I will wish others, like me, show filial and brotherly love and be caring to the young [...] (*Daxue*)①

The measuring square corresponds to the formula "What you do not want done to yourself, do not do to others."

(Zhu Xi)

It is worth noticing how Chinese scholars made use of terms such the carpenter's

① Zhu Xi, *Sishu zhangju jizhu*, ch. 10, p. 10.

square which denotes how they felt the need to regulate human relations in the search of harmony with yourself and with the cosmos

Zhu Xi explained that *shu* corresponded to the carpenter's square(恕,亦是絜矩之意)and, moreover, he commented:

所谓絜矩者,矩者,心也,我心之所欲,即他人之所欲也。我欲孝弟而慈,必欲他人皆如我之孝弟而 慈。[...]是以君子见人之心与己之心同,故必以己度人之心,使皆得其平。

What is called "measuring square" is [the carpenter's] square, that is the heart—and—mind. What my heart—and—mind wishes corresponds to what others wish. If I wish to show filial and brotherly love and be caring to the young, I will wish others, like me, show filial and brotherly love and be caring to the young [...]

Therefore the man of noble character perceives that the heart—and—mind of others and his own are similar. Hence he always uses his own heart—and—mind to measure the heart—and—mind of others, so that all will become tranquil. ①

Once again, I would like to draw your attention on these two sentences in *Lunyu*, 6.30, *he shi yu ren*! **何事於仁** *Neng jin qu pi* **何事於仁**, in order to stress how Confucius in this passage someway identifies empathy with *ren*, and in fact he suggests that bestowing benefits and bringing relief to the people, are prerogatives of the Sage (as explained by Zhu Xi, see above p. 4).

子貢曰:「如有博施於民而能濟眾,如何? 可謂仁乎?」子曰:「**何事於仁! 必也聖乎! 堯,舜其猶病**諸! 夫仁者,己欲立而立人,己欲達而達人。能近取譬,可謂仁之方已。」*Lunyu*, VI,30.

Zigong asked: "What about him who is broadly generous with the people and is able to help the multitudes? Can we define this benevolence?" The Master said: "Why stop at benevolence? Such a person should surely be called a Sage! Even Yao and Shun would find such a task arduous! *The term "benevolence" means that when you desire to get established yourself, you help others to get established; and when you desire success for yourself you help others to succeed. The ability to take as analogy what is near at hand can simply be called the method of attaining benevolence.*" (*Lunyu*, 6.30)

What is the meaning of "The ability to take as analogy what is near at hand"(能進

① Li Jingde 黎靖德, *Zhuziyulei* 朱子語類 (Beijing 1985), ch. 16, p. 361.

取譬)(*Lunyu*, VI,30)?

It means, as Fingarette puts it, "to be able from what is close, i.e. yourself, to grasp analogy with the other person, and in that light to treat him as you would like to be treated. You must imagine being in the other person's place ; then, in that status, you are to ask yourself what you want or do not want done." This presupposes a mental exercise which is familiar to everybody: you imagine yourself in the other's shoes and become one with the other. Therefore you can see things as the other sees them, you can perceive and appreciate things as the other. And the greater effort you make to put yourself in the other's place, the more this condition belongs to you.

In ultimate analysis what is *zhong*? *Zhong* is loyalty and absolute dedication which transcends all individualism, the purely personal, in the hope to pursue completeness, moral integrity and sincerity. It is loyalty in the name of an ethical principle, the *dao* 道.

I believe that when Fingarette equates the Chinese golden rule to the Biblical golden rule he does not consider the fundamental difference between the Christian and the Chinese message.

The scholar claims that, just as in the teachings of Jesus the golden rule is made up of two essential components— the love of God and the love of one's neighbour— in a similar fashion in the teaching of Confucius "the unifying principle" is made up of *zhong*, loyalty, absolute dedication to a principle, that is the *dao*, and *shu*, love of one's fellow man. The basic difference between the Confucian precept and the biblical one lies in the identity of the transcendent principle

忠恕一以貫之:「忠者天道,恕者人道;忠者無妄,恕者所以行乎忠也。忠者體,恕者用,大本達道也。

*Zhong* and *shu* are pervaded by a single unifying principle. *Zhong* is the Way of Heaven, *shu* is the Way of man. *Zhong* means absence of hypocrisy, *shu* is how to put *zhong* into practice. *Zhong* is substance, shu is function. Thee are the great root and the realized Way (Zhu Xi, *Sishu zhangju jizhu*, pp. 72—73).

Cheng 誠 (authenticity)

There is another passage where Mengzi anticipates the interpretation of Song Confucians and particularly of Zhu Xi.

孟子曰:「萬物皆備於我也。反身而誠,樂莫大焉。強恕而行,求仁莫近焉。」

Mengzi said: "The ten thousand things are all brought to completion in me.

There is no greater joy for me than to find, on self—examination, that I am authentic. Strengthen your empathy and you will find that this is the shortest way to benevolence."

誠:實 (sincerity, genuineness, authenticity) 朱熹

This passage, partly quoted above (see p. 3) is found in the chapter *Jinxin* 盡心 ("To give full realization to one's heart—and—mind") of Mengzi. *Mengzi* VIIA, 4.

Zhu Xi glosses *cheng* 誠 as 實 (reality, sincerity, authenticity, genuineness). ①

Mencius paid attention to the inner sphere, he thought that *shu* was innate in us, we should only cultivate it in order to attain *ren*, *Wanwu* 萬物 ten thousand things in me.

1.反身 introspection

2.誠 authenticity

3.強恕 strengthen empathy as a way to attain *ren*

*Cheng* (authenticity) seems to be a condition necessary to attain empathy. We can find a clear description in the *Zhongyong*:

唯天下至誠,為能盡其性;能盡其性,則能盡人之性。能盡人之性,則能盡物之性;能盡物之性,則可以贊天地之化育:可以贊天地之化育,則可以與天地參矣。(中庸,22)

None but those who have attained the highest degree of authenticity— integral wholeness in the entire world have the capacity fully to realize their inborn nature. One who is able to fully realize his inborn nature can thereby bring to full realization the nature of other people; one who is able to bring full realization the nature of others is thereby able to bring to full realization the nature of all existing things; and one who is able fully to realize his inborn nature can thereby bring to full realization the nature of other people; one who is able to bring to full realization the nature of others is thereby able to bring to full realization the nature of all existing things; and one who is able to bring to full realization the nature of all existing things can partake thereby in the transformative and generative processes of Heaven and Earth. He who can partake in the transformative and generative processes of Heaven and Earth can stand, by virtue of this capacity, as a third term between them in the cosmic continu-

---

① Zhu Xi, *Sishu zhangju jizhu*, ch. 13, p. 350. Cf. tr. D. C. Lau, *Mencius* (Hong Kong 1979, repr. 1984), p. 265; B. W. Van Norden, translated by, *Mengzi, With Selections from Traditional Commentaries* (Indianapolis/Cambridge 2008), p. 172.

um. (Plaks, p. 22)

*Cheng* 誠

4. Authenticity, moral integrity

5. It is the moral perfection and implies the knowledge of the self and of the cosmos.

Here the *Zhongyong* introduces an element which was very much appreciated by the NeoConfucians in Song times but also by the Jesuits when they arrived in China: man's relation with heaven, with the cosmos.

誠者,天之道也。誠之者,人之道也。誠者,不勉而中,不思而得,從容中道:聖人也。誠之者,擇善而固執之者也。

A perfect state of integral wholeness can only be attributed to the Way of Heaven; the process of making oneself whole is, however, within the province of the Way of Man. 'Integral wholeness' means a state of centred balance requiring no striving, complete attainment requiring no mental effort. To strike the mean with absolute effortlessness is the mark of none but those of perfect cultivation. The process of 'making oneself whole', by contrast, requires choosing the good and holding fast to it with all one's strength. (A. Plaks, tr., p. 42)

To be true/authentic is the Way of heaven. To make oneself true/authentic is the Way of man. He who is true/authentic [i.e. whose virtue is naturally in accord with heavenly principle] maintains perfect balance without effort and apprehends without thinking; he is centered naturally and comfortably in the Way. Such is the sage! He who makes himself true chooses the good and hold to it firmly (Zhongyong, 20, tr. Gardner)①

Zhu Xi remarks that *cheng* means authenticity, being true to our endowment of human nature, to the virtues embodied therein. In Zhu Xi's words:

誠者,真實無妄之謂,天理之本然也。誠之者,未能真實無妄,而欲其真實無妄之謂,人事之當然也。聖人之德,渾然天理,真實無妄,不待思勉而從容中道,則亦天之道也。未至欲聖,則不能無人欲之私,而其為德不能皆實。故未能不思而得,則必擇善,然後可以明善;未能不勉而中,則必固執,然后可以誠身,此則所謂人之道也。

The *Zhongyong* continues by exhorting man to cultivate his interiority and also to

---

① *Ta hsüeh and Chung Yung* (*The Highest Order of Cultivation and On the Practice of the Mean*), Translated with an introduction and Notes by Andrew Plaks, Preface by Xinzhong Yao, London, Penguin Books, p. 42; See also D. K. Gardner, *The Four Books. The Basic Teachings of the Later Confucian Tradition*, Indianapolis/Cambridge, Hackett Publishing Company, 2007, p. 121.

bring to perfection all things in the phenomenal world.

誠者非自成己而已也,所以成物。成己,仁也;成物,知也。性之德也,合外内之道也。

Integral wholeness signifies not merely the process of making oneself complete and nothing more; rather, it constitutes the ground for bringing to completion all things with which one interacts in the phenomenal world. Making whole the individual self is the substance of man's essential humanity, just as the completion of all other things constitutes the ground of wisdom. This is the moral force inherent in one's inborn nature, the Way that unites the external and the internal aspects of being. And so, it behoves one to put it into practice unceasingly. (Plaks, pp. 45—46)

Truthfulness is not merely the completion of self and nothing more; by means of it other things become complete. Completion of the self is true goodness; completion of other things is wisdom. These are virtues belonging to human nature; these are the Way the unites external and internal. Thus, employ them according to circumstances and things will be as they should. (Gardner, tr., p. 126)

Zhu Xi remarks that, although *cheng* originates from the completion or perfection of the self, it belongs to human nature, it develops spontaneously and spontaneously can be extended to other beings. *Ren* is equated to "substance" (*ti* 體) whereas *zhi* (wisdom) to"function" (*yong* 用). In his words:

誠雖所以成己,然既有以自成;則自然及物,而道亦行於彼矣。仁者,體之存,知者用之發,是皆吾性之固有,而無內外之殊。既得於己,則見於事者,以時措之,而皆得其宜也。(四書章句集註,p. 34)

Du Weiming 杜維明 commented:

*The authenticity and moral integrity of the individual in the final analysis resides in the* dao *of man, the Way indicated by the ancient sages, the Way that runs like a thread through everything, uniting it.*

Only those in the earth who have reached this perfection can realize this transformation. The perfect virtue is such that can foretell the future… in conclusion the perfected man is like a spirit.

***Aureae mediocritatis constantia***

*Solum (in hoc) universo summe perfectus efficere potest conversionem (huius modi). Summe perfecti virtus (ea est, ut) possit praescire (futura).*

*Ideo summe perfectus (est) instar spiritus*

Matteo Ricci, Michele Ruggieri

可以贊天地之化育,則可以與天地参矣。

*iam poterit adiuvare ceolum et terram in productione* (*et*) *consevatione rerum*; *si potest adiuvare coelum* (*et*) *terram* (*in*) *productione* (*et*) *conservatione* (*rerum*) *iam* (*etiam*) *poterit cum coelo et terra ternarium principium* (*costituere*). (Matteo Ricci e Michele Ruggieri, p. 160)

*Sinarum Scientiae Political Moralis*

The Jesuit Prospero Intorcetta in his introduction to the translation of the *sishu* (Goa 1667) remarked that the great value of the *Zhongyong* was the spiritual benefit and prestige deriving from reading this small but very rich work for all those who use the maxims and teachings of the past in order to spread the knowledge of God.

*through the remaining thousand years of Chinese dynastic history, these slim volumes occupied the vital core of the intellectual patrimony shared by all members of the vast empire's educated elite*… (A. Plaks, Introduction, pp. XXVII—XXVIII).

An even when they were labelled by generations of reforms and revolutionaries as the embodiment of the old order and of the feudal system this served only to reaffirm their place at the heart of traditional Confucian life and values, leaving the treatises intact and ready or the rekindled intellectual attention they have enjoyed in recent decades throughout the Chinese—speaking world.

# Part Four: Confucianism in the World

## The Role of Portuguese Overseas Trade for the Spread of Confucianism and Chinese Culture in Europe

**Rui D'ávila Lourido**

Before the opening of the new maritime silk route, connecting Europe and Asia and carried out by the Portuguese in the late 15th century (Vasco da Gama's 1497/8 trip to India), China was practically unknown to Europeans. Knowledge about Asia was fragmented and wrapped up in fantasy, following medieval travelling descriptions, successively copied and folded in fanciful imagination, reproducing European myths about the East.

The 15th century Portuguese navigations started the first globalization of the Modern Era, by connecting and bringing closer the peoples of five continents (Europe, Africa, America, Asia and Oceania). Besides the intense mercantile movement between the West and the East, which allowed Europeans to achieve a great economical development, the Portuguese navigators brought the first European descriptions of China, produced by direct and extended observation of the Middle Kingdom①.

With the establishment of direct relations between Portugal and China, from 1513 onwards, Portuguese and European knowledge about China increases and becomes deeper.

---

① However, we must keep in mind that, before the 16th century, many travellers and missionaries had already entered China ever since the 9th century, having channelled some information to Europe. This is the case of the Nestorians in the 9th century and the Franciscans in the 13th century. See our article on the Silk Route in *Dicionário Temático da História de Macau -DITEMA*, [Macao Thematic and Historical Dictionary] 4 vols, University of Macau, 2012 (with other several Lourido's articles on Macao). Cf. Kenneth Scott Latourette, *A History of Christian missions in China*, New York, 1929

For the first time Europe possesses the exact information of: the real location and geographical dimension of China; the system of social and political organization of the Middle Kingdom; on the value of the famous precious Chinese products, long known and appreciated in Europe, and their production processes; the religious and philosophical currents developed in China; the meritocratic system of the public administration, the education and examination system.

It is in this context that the traditional Chinese culture modelled by Confucianism starts to become known and studied by Portuguese and other Europeans, especially Jesuits.

The traditional Chinese culture and the Confucian philosophical principles that characterize it are, in our opinion, spread and transmitted in Europe through two main different ways. Firstly, through the mercantile movement and its direct and indirect agents (navigators, traders and consumers), secondly, by texts of two different sources: civil or military on the one hand, with reports, letters and travel descriptions; on the other, texts of Christian origin, especially the letters from Jesuits living in China, under the jurisdiction of the Portuguese Patronage of the East, apologetical and pedagogical.

In this work, we want to point out the importance of the Portuguese mercantile network, associated with Asian networks, for the diffusion of Chinese traditional and Confucian culture. The great profitability of the commerce with China was crucial in motivating Portuguese and European elites to surpass the practical obstacles (distance-each go and return trip took more than a year, and sea risk-numerous shipwrecks due to weather conditions and piracy). The success of this trade led the King of Portugal and those from other states to create a great investment, in an attempt to achieve economical control over this business. For the mentality of that epoch, the dissemination of Christianity was, equally, a geo-strategic value, bringing prestige to the states that were able to send out missionaries.

Predictably, not only people and goods circulated in this maritime net directly connected to Portugal and Europe, but also ideas and new concepts of political, social and economic organization.

We will address the agents of this transference of knowledge, the precious Chinese products, paradigmatic of the sophisticated Chinese civilization and its technological evolution. We will emphasize the role of the texts that informed the West about the reality of Chinese material and cultural organization, responsible for the transmission of a new image of China. In this context, we will give special attention to *Relalcão da Grande Monarquia da China* [*Relation of the Great Monarchy of China*], by Álvaro Semedo①.

The mental framework of traditional Chinese culture moulded by Confucianism was one of the focus of Portuguese and European travellers, ever since the 16th century, especially scholars and missionaries, among them the Jesuits.

In general, the European perception of China was obviously shaped and influenced by the European mindset and social economic structure, having suffered a radical transformation through the centuries. If we want to have a broad idea about the evolution of European perception of China, we can synthetically (hence superficially and simplistically) indicate that, in spite of exceptions, the European perception has developed from an attitude of great respect, admiration and apologetical of navigators, adventurers, merchants, military men and Portuguese missionaries and other Europeans in the 16th and 17th century, towards a position of critical detachment in the 18th century, and later of rejection in the 19th century, by the European political and economic elite, made rich by the capitals accumulated in trade with Asia, particularly China. This aristocratic mercantile elite had invested in an emergent industrialization, so became in need of new and gentle markets to sell the cheap goods produced in series by the European industrial revolution. This social economic context motivated a gradual change of the previous paradigm, from regarding the Chinese as a sophisticated and exemplary civilization, to a depreciative view of Chinese traditional values. In mentality terms, it was important to transmit this depreciation of Chinese values, which came to allow the imposition of a political, economic and social model that would validate the Opium War under the pretext of civilizing other peoples in a colonial type posture.

In the West, the more traditionally spread vision failed to recognize, for a long time, the fundamental role of the first period of Portuguese presence in the seas of China (16th and 17th centuries) in the diffusion of Chinese culture and Confucianism in Europe, due to difficulties in the reading of Portuguese historic sources. We must not

---

① Álvaro Semedo (1586-1658), *Relacão da Grande Monarquia da China*, ed. Direcão dos Servicos de Educão e Juventude, Fundacão Macau, Macau, 1994.

forget that the western theorists of *Chinoiserie* (the influence of Chinese culture and art in Europe) set out their beginning from 1650①.

However, Confucian ideas had been diffused ever since the 16th century, through the sea route of the Cape of Good Hope, under Portuguese control, and through the sea route of Manila-America, under Spanish management②.

The Confucian thought was revolutionary to Europe, and described a society run by scholars on duty, military or civil, in the central and regional imperial administration of China. Now, in spite of all the historical, economic and social differences, the French educated elite would originate, in 18th century Europe, a movement of transformation in European mentalities-the Enlightment (in which Montesquieu, Voltaire and Rousseau were prominent), and it was partly inspired by Confucian ideas. As an example we may refer to copy of the book Alvaro Semedo, Relationship Monarchy of Greater China, read carefully, underlined and with marginal notes by Montesquieu. It is not surprising that one of the claims of the Enlightment was a greater role for European scholars in political and administrative matters, questioning the nomination

---

① The *Chinoiserie* is a somewhat imprecise and ambiguous description, because it covers a large time span (from 16th to 19th century), and covers a diversity of artistic styles (e.g. Baroque and Rococo to Rocaille), and a multiplicity of geographical influences (namely China, sometimes also Japan, India and Persia). The designation of *Chinoiserie*, originally referring to the type of drawings by Antoine Watteau, was later consecrated by Francäois Boucher, who extended the denomination of *Chinoiserie* to other artistic fields, such as architecture and sacred art. Generally speaking, the experts have considered that the *Chinoiserie* has four periods that would have begun around 1650 and lasted until around 1800. Cf. Rui D'ávila Lourido, "Chinese fashion crossed the oceans in the wake of the Portuguese trade with China, during the late Ming and early Qing dynasties", in *Face to Face: the transcendence of the arts in China and beyond. Historical perspectives*, pp. 355-369, edition of Centro de Investigaäo e Estudos em Belas Artes (CIEBA), Faculdade de Belas Artes da Universidade de Lisboa, with the sponsorship of Observatory for China, 2014, p. 365.

② To integrate the Portuguese diffusion of the Chinese culture in the West, and in the *Chinoiserie* movement we suggested two complementary periods. The first one cover the time Before Macau: with two sections of different intensity and influence: 1st section -1498 to 1513, from the arrival in India, to the arrival in China. Characterized by a scarce and indirect knowledge, as it was acquired by Portuguese sailors and merchants in the Indian Ocean and Southeast Asia, before the arrival to the South coast of China. 2nd section-1513 to 1557. Characterized by non-permanent contacts, mostly commercial, and a fragmented knowledge of Chinese culture. The second period start with the establishment of the Portuguese in Macau in 1557: it begins a deeper knowledge and a progressive assimilation of Chinese culture, by the Portuguese living in Macau, and a bigger diffusion of Chinese culture in Europe. Cf. Lourido, idem, p. 366.

criteria of kinship based on the lineages of old European nobility. These ideas followed their path and fermented the political and social environment that became beneficial to the French Revolution①.

In this work, we will focus on the first phase of the influence of traditional Chinese Confucian culture in Europe, which includes the time period from the $16^{th}$ to $17^{th}$ century.

In this stage, the diffusion agents were mainly navigators, merchants, soldiers and Portuguese and European missionaries, in the service of the Portuguese Crown or the Portuguese Patronage of the East, or from individual initiative, autonomously or semi-illegally, in search of better opportunities for enrichment and social ascent.

Both ways of contact with China (framed within the official initiatives of the Portuguese and Castellan Crowns, or non-official initiatives) motivated an enormous mercantile movement, and, in parallel, originated large sources of information that were rapidly transposed to writing form, having a decisive contribution for a deeper knowledge of China.

Two geographical compendiums and a botanic one are noteworthy in this first contact: *Suma Oriental* (written in Malacca, between 1513-1515), by Tomé Pires② and *O Livro do que viu e Ouviu no Oriente Duarte Barbosa* (written in Cannanore, around 1516)③; and an extensive botanic study, already scientific-spirited, the

① Cf. Jianfu Yu, "The influence and enlightenment of Confucian cultural education on modern European civilization", in Journal Frontiers of Education in China, Volume 4, Issue 1, pp 10-26, 2009

② Armando Cortesão, *A Suma Oriental de Tomé Pires e o livro de Francisco Rodrigues*, Ediāo Acta Universitatis Conimbrigensis, Coimbra, 1978., Rui Loureiro, *O manuscrito de Lisboa da "Suma Oriental" de Tomé Pires*, (*Contribuicão para uma edicão crítica*), s. l., Instituto Português do Oriente, 1996

③ Duarte de Barbosa, *Livro de Duarte de Barbosa*, cerca de 1516, published by Sebastião Trigoso, in the*Colecão de Noticias para a História e Geografia das Nacães Ultramarinas*, Lisbon, vol. II 1821. *The Book of Duarte Barbosa*, por Mansel Longworth Dames, Hakluyt Society, 2 vols, 1918-1921. Its critical and noted edition was by Maria Augusta da Veiga e Sousa, ed. Instituto de Investigacão Científica Tropical, 1996 (1o vol. with 282 p., and BN: CG. 16307 V.) [article in the *Studia* on critical edition, n. 47 1989, pp. 439-440. Also in Luís de Albuquerque, *Livro do que viu e Ouviu no oriente Duarte Barbosa*, Lisboa, 1989.

*Colóquio dos Simples e drogas da índia*, by Garcia da Orta (from around 1564)①. To these, we can add, namely, some of the descriptions from middle 16th and 17th centuries: the *Tractado em que se contam muito por estenso as cousas da China com suas particularidades...* (1569), by Gaspar da Cruz②; *Algumas coisas Sabidas da China*, by Galeote Pereira (c. 1553); Duarte de Sande (*De Missione Legatorum Iaponnensium*③), Fernäo Mendes Pinto (*Peregrinaäo*, 1614④), Priest Adriano de las Cortes (Relación⑤), António Bocarro ("Descriäo da Cidade do nome de D. S da China", 1635⑥), and António de Gouveia (*ásia Extrema*⑦). In order to grasp the view con-

---

① Garcia da Orta, *Colóquios dos Simples e drogas da índia*, facsimile of the 1891 edition, coordinated and noted by the count of Ficalho, Lisbon, Imprensa Nacional-Casa da Moeda, 1987.

② Gaspar da Cruz (frei), *Tractado em que se contam muito por estenso as cousas da China com suas particularidades, assi do reino d'Ormuz, composto por el posto por el padre frei Gaspar da Cruz da ordem de sam Domingos*, ed. André de Burgos, évora, 1569-70. Edited in 1989, in Enformacão das cousas da China, Textos do Século XVI, introduction and Reading of Raffaella D'Intino, Imprensa Nacional-Casa da Moeda. Critical edition of

③ Macau, 1590, it has an extensive chapter on China which, according to Rui Loureiro, would have been the first printed work with information about China, collected by the priests Michele Ruggieri and Matteo Ricci, in "Revista de Cultura" no31 (II série), ed. Instituto Cultural de Macau, p. 14, 1997

④ Edited in 1614, the information here contained would have been collected until the year of death of its author in 1583. Fernäo Mendes Pinto and the Peregrinaäo, Vol II: Restored Portuguese Text, by Elisa Lopes da Costa, ed. Fundaäo Oriente e Imprensa Nacional-Ediäo da Casa da Moeda, Lisboa, 2010.

⑤ Detailed manuscript text that describes the eventful trip of the author through the south of China between 1625 and 1626. He portrays a description of the social respect for scholars, education and cult forms. R. Loureiro, in "Revista de Cultura" no31 (II série), ed. Instituto Cultural de Macau, p. 37-40, 1997

⑥ António Bocarro, in his work: *Livro das Plantas de todas as Fortalezas, Cidades e Povoaöens do Estado da India Oriental com as descripçoens da altura em que estäo, e de tudo que há nellas, Artilharia, Presidio, gente de Armas, e Vassalos, rendimento, e despeza, fundos e baxos das Barras, Reys da Terra dentro, o poder que tem, e a paz, e a guerra, que guardäo, e tudo que está debaxo da Coroa de Espanha. Dedicado à Serenissima Magestade del Rey Filipe o IV das Espanhas, e III de Portugal Rey, e Senhor nosso*. It is currently preserved in the Public Library and Distrital Archive of évora. It was published by C. R. Boxer, *Macau na Época da Restauraäo (Macau three hundred years ago)*, Macau Imprensa Nacional, 1942. Edition by Isabel Cid in 3 volumes, Imprensa Nacional-Casa da Moeda, 1992.

⑦ It is a detailed description of the Jesuit activity in China between 1582 and 1644. António Gouveia, "ásia Extrema: Entra nella a Fé, promulga-se a Ley de Deos pelos padres da Companhia de Jesus", códices 49-V-1 e 49-V-2 Biblioteca da Ajuda. The first and second parts were published with introduction and notes by Horácio Peixoto Araújo, in *ásia Extrema*, Fundaäo Oriente edition, 1995. First part, Book I, and the second part, Books I to III, 2005.

*veyed by these texts, the reader can refer to several important contemporary researchers*[1]. Texts sent from China contain a very positive, complimentary perspective of China, not only as an immense empire in geographic terms, but also the richest ever found by the Portuguese, considering the diversity of peoples that constituted it, and the richness of the raw materials, the sophisticated technological innovations (silk, porcelain, paper, gunpowder, …) and the mercantile networks they controlled.

The great Jesuit sensibility towards understanding the Chinese Confucian traditional culture led its co-founder São Francisco Xavier to establish, even before the entrance of Jesuits in the Middle Kingdom[2], that only the brighter missionaries and those with deep knowledge of philosophy (especially dialectics) and science (especially astronomy) should be sent to China. It was believed that, besides the learning of Chinese language and writing, they would need great argumentative skills in order to exceed and seduce the mandarins[3]. Jesuits soon realized that in China power and social influence depended upon the level of knowledge of classic Confucian literature, which characterized the education system and the heedful Chinese culture. It was thus defined, in general lines, the adaptation program of Jesuits to the Chinese culture, as a better way for a deeper evangelization.

The Jesuits stood out from other religious orders by their capacity to adapt to the Chinese mental and social framework, which allowed them to be officially accepted within the Empire. Finally, in 1583, the Jesuits, resident until then only in Macau, received permission to live in another city of the province of Guangdong-Zhaoqing (Shiuhing), thus rewarding the efforts of S. Francisco Xavier, Priest Alexandre Val-

---

① Among others, Rui Loureiro, *Fidalgos Missionários e Mandarins*, *Portugal e a China no Século XVI*, Lisbon, ed. Fundaão Oriente, 2000. A. M. Martins do Vale, *Entre a Cruz e o Dragão. O Padroado Português na China no século XVIII*, ed. Fundaão Oriente, 2002, Lisboa. Rafaella D'Intino, *Enformaão Das Cousas Da China*, *textos do século XVI*, ed. Imprensa Nacional -Casa da Moeda. Pascale Girard, *Les Religieux Occidentaux en Chine à l' époque Moderne. Essai d' analyse textuellecomparé*, ed. Centre Culturel Calouste Gulbenkian, Lisboa-Paris, 2000

② São Francisco Xavier (1506-1552) died in the Chinese Island of Shangchuan, in 1552, waiting for permission to enter China. See Padre Manuel Teixeira, *Sanchoão. Morte de S. Francisco Xavier*, pp 32-33, Imprensa Nacional de Macau, Macau, 1941. Jean Charbonnier, *Histoire des chrétiens de Chine*, ed. Desclée, Paris, 1992, p. 79.

③ See A. M. Martins do Vale, *Entre a Cruz e o Dragão*…, p. 32.

ignano, Jesuit visitor, and, later, Priest Matteo Ricci, for the learning of Chinese language and writing, as well as the dressing code of Confucian scholars. Michele Ruggieri (羅明堅) and Matteo Ricci (利瑪竇) were the first European missionaries in the 16th century who could discuss and write in Chinese with Chinese intellectuals. Ricci arrived at Beijing in 1601 and he would be the most enthusiastic defender of the sinicization of Jesuit missionaries, as an improved method to the later evangelization of Chinese scholars. Ricci achieved such a degree of proficiency in Chinese that he became teacher of Chinese for several young people and 3 children of the Viceroy of Nanchang①. Nevertheless, other religious orders or missionaries non-dependent of the Portuguese Patronage of the East, disagreed and have proposed a greater distance between Catholic missionaries and Chinese culture②.

As the precious Chinese products (porcelain, silks, and others) stimulated the curiosity and fascination of Westerners towards Chinese culture, from early on the European and particularly the Jesuits had also started to use valuable European objects, through which technological sophistication and beauty they could display Europe's capacity and scientific development, as a way to attract the curiosity of the Chinese educated elite to Christian ideas. These objects sublimated, in some way, the Jesuits' weak skills over Chinese language and writing in the beginning of their stay in China. Accordingly, Matteo Ricci has shown, in the opening of the Jesuit residency of Zhaoqing, glass from Venice, watches, celestial and terrestrial globes, maps and European books③.

The diffusion of the Confucian thinking in the West had with Ricci a crucial moment, as he was the first European to translate into Latin, in 1594, the *Analectos* (*Lunyu*), the thoughts attributed to Confucius, as well as other classics from Chinese

---

① Pasquale M. D'élia, *Fonti ricciane*, I, p. CXVIII

② Such is the case of the Spanish Jesuit priest Alfonso Sanchez, founder of the mission in the Philippines, having visited Macau and Guangzhou in 1582. About the opposite visions see Jean Pierre Duteil, *Le mandat du ciel*, p. 13, 79 e segs.; Pasquale M. D'élia, *Fonti ricciane*, I, p. 169; Henri Bernard-Maître, S. J., *Aux portes de la Chine*, pp. 84-85.

③ Matteo Ricci produced, already in Beijing, the famous first planispheric map of China, with modern cartographic knowledge and legends in Chinese.

literature[①].

We point out in this Jesuit adaptation process to Chinese culture the inclusion and conversion of Chinese intellectuals such as: Li Chih-tsao (Leão), Hsu Kwang-chi (Paulo) and Yang T'ing-yun (Paulo). Additionally, the arrival to China of Jesuits with high scientific education leads to their recruiting as advisors in the service of the Imperial administration, such as the *Tribunal das Matemáticas* (Court of Mathematics), and it intensifies the process of knowledge exchange between Europe and China[②]. Furthermore, considering the dissemination and influence of Confucian culture in Europe, the Jesuit prolix epistolary legacy was particularly important. "Cartas Ânuas" (letters or annual reports) were very representative, and they gave, annually, a particularly complete description of the evangelic activities and concerns. In the missionaries' descriptions, we can find detailed reports of social habits and the Chinese Confucian traditional culture, many of them adopted in the daily life of the Catholic missions in China. The letters sent from China were regularly read during meals in Portuguese and European Catholic convents, in order to hold the attention of young candidates to priests and missionaries, who could eventually volunteer for the missions in China and Asia.

The translation of the Bible to Chinese is an important Jesuit achievement with the Pope Paul V, in 1615, who also authorizes the use, in mass, of the hat and Chinese ceremonial clothes.

The Confucian influence in the Catholic dressing code and rites practiced by the Jesuits was openly criticized by other European religious orders, who wanted to win power and Christian influence in China. They were particularly criticized for "allo-

---

① He also translated other 3 classics: *A grande escola* (*Da Xue*), *O livro de Mêncio* (*Mengzi*), and *Doutrina do Meio* (*Zhongyong*), Cf. Jean Charbonnier, *Histoire des chrétiens de Chine*, ed. Desclése, Paris, 1992, p. 102

② Among other Jesuits, Johann Adam Schall von Bell and Ferdinand Verbiest integrated the *Tribunal das Matemáticas*. The Jesuits conceived calendars, terrestrial and celestial maps (Schall, Verbiest, Magalhäes, Pereira, Rocha Espinosa, and others), "projected the Summer Palace (Castiglione) and even fortresses (Schall)", in painting Giuseppe Castiglione was representative in joining European technique to Chinese and imperial taste, see Horácio Araújo, "Companhia de Jesus", in *Missionação e Missionários na História de Macau*, p. 265, coordination by Maria Antónia Espadinha and Leonor Diaz de Seabra, Universidade de Macau, 2005

wing rites in honour of Confucius and ancestors"①. To this rivalry between religious orders in China, we should add the competition among European nations, who considered having missionaries of their nation in China as politically prestigious.② Accordingly, we can understand the persistency of the King of France, Louis XIV, in promoting the sending of French missionaries to Beijing, or the dispute of the Portuguese king D. João V over the Beijing diocese, and the Jesuit influence in the Imperial Court against French and Spanish opposition.

**The *Relation of the Great Monarchy of China*, by Álvaro Semedo:**

Among the numerous texts of this early period (16th and 17th centuries) of the diffusion of Chinese Confucian traditional culture, we have selected the *Relation of the Great Monarchy of China*, by the Jesuit ɑlvaro Semedo, written in 1637-40, after 22 years of life and observations in China③. We have chosen this *Relation* for three reasons. First, because it was one of the most circulated and translated texts of this period④, so it can show us the kind of information that arrived to Europe about China, and especially about traditional culture and Confucian thought. Secondly, because ɑlvaro de Semedo was an active participant in the defence of the attitude of acculturation of Jesuits to Chinese culture, against other opposite positions (such as those of the mendicant religious orders), which rejected in particular the reverence to Confucius

---

① Horácio Araújo, "Companhia de Jesus", in *Missionacão e Missionários na História de Macau*, p. 271, coordination by Maria Antónia Espadinha and Leonor Diaz de Seabra, Universidade de Macau, 2005

② See the extensive study by A. M. Martins do Vale, *Entre a Cruz e o Dragão. O Padroado Português na China no século XVIII*, ed. Fundacão Oriente, 2002, p. 539.

③ Álvaro Semedo (1586-1658), *Relacão da Grande Monarquia da China*, 1994.

④ Written in Portuguese, an excerpt was published in 1642, by Craesbeck, when Álvaro Semedo arrives to Rome. I have consulted the following originals in Italian libraries: *Historica relatione del gran regno della Cina...*, Rome, 1653. [BA. Vaticana, cota: Capponi IV 158]; Rome edition, sumptibus H. Scheus, 1643 (translation from Portuguese by Giattini): [Barberini, P. VIII. 38]; Bologne edition in 1678, [Racc. Gen. Storia VI. 213]. The first comprehensive edition is in Castellan (1642). The Italian edition (1643) was translated to French (1667). English edition (1655) and Dutch edition (1670). See note about the several editions of this work, by the sinologue Luís Gonzaga Gomes, editor of the first comprehensive Portuguese edition in 1956, and by António Aresta, coordinator of the 1994 edition, in ɑlvaro Semedo, *Relação da Grande Monarquia da China*, p. 7 e pp. 15-16.

carried out by Chinese Christians and validated by the Jesuits[①]. Thirdly, the *Relacão* by Álvaro de Semedo was chosen because of its detailed content in the description of China, as well as the description of the Confucius thought and its predominance in Chinese culture.

Synthetically, we can affirm that the *Relation of the Great Monarchy of China* was organized by its author in two parts. The first is called "Of the Temporal State of China", and it is a description of the main constitutive elements of Chinese civilization, with 286 pages, in the modernized 1994 edition, including a geographic description of the territory with its provinces and a description of the population and their habits, culture and religion. Semedo highlight the meritocratic and philosophical conception, with the Confucian education system and access to Imperial administration, the kind of books that the Chinese produce, science and liberal arts, aristocracy and justice system. The second part, between pages 289 and 410, was named "Of China's Christianity" and it describes its beginning, difficulties and development.

Semedo start with a very positive description, aware of the importance of Confucian thought in China.

First about the man: "This philosopher flourished 150 years before Christ. He was good-natured, quite driven to virtue, cautious, sententious and friend of common good". [②]

Semedo shows the difficult political and social context in Confucius lifetime, hardened by the fragmentation of China in several states -"Confucius wandered from state to state, searching for good governance, in an era unsuitable for philosophers to rule", "and he kept thinking about reforming the world, which, even then, was losing that sincerity, truthfulness and ancient way of living, with the introduction of

---

① Particularly when, in Rome in 1642-1643, as procurator of the Vice-province of China, he was ordered to answer the questions addressed by the mendicants and the Sacred Congregation of Fide Propaganda (Catholic organization founded in 1622 by the Roman Curia, who wanted to program and coordinate a missionary action in the five continents, Cf. Joseph Metzler, 《Foundation of the Congregation de Propaganda Fide》, pp. 85 and following). Semedo attributed the opposition of Franciscans and Augustinians to the fact that they had a short period of permanence in China, so they were unaware and did not understand Chinese culture, where Christians had to be tolerant towards local traditions. Cf. A. M. Martins do Vale, *idem*, p. 131.

② Álvaro Semedo, *idem*, *p.* 102. Semedo misled on the date of birth of Confucius who actually lived 551-479 BC.

modern habits.", adding "And thus governed in several states, because when he saw that in one, if he did not proceed according to his rules and advice, he would pass on to another, which was noticed by many other philosophers of that time, who, watching the wrong path things were taking, withdrew to their lands and became farmers, cultivating themselves, individually"①.

As China's recognition to Confucius, he indicates the distinctions and privileges offered to his direct descendants, still in the 17th century-"The closest of his descendants has adequate income and the title of chu heu, which is equivalent of marquis or duke.② The governor of the city where he was born is still, for his respect and particular honor, a member of his family. Finally, all those of his lineage, from their birth, benefit from special privileges from the King, being respected due to Confucius's virtue. This usage is still observed, today, although 1800 years have gone by."③

As for the impact of the philosophical ideas of Confucius, since antiquity until álvaro de Semedo's time, says the Jesuit: "He had many disciples who would follow him…"④ and "such grace and esteem and so great credit have achieved the books he wrote, and the sayings and sentences left by him, that not only they consider him a saint, master and doctor of the kingdom, but also all that is quoted from him is kept as a sacred thing, besides existing, in every city of the kingdom, public temples where he is revered with many ceremonies in planned dates, and in year of exams, one of the ceremonies consists of all the graduates paying him homage and recognizing him as master"⑤.

Naturally, as a scholar, Álvaro de Semedo considers the philosophical and literary work of Confucius compiled by his disciples fundamental to assess the impact of Confucian thought in Chinese society. Semedo reveals a detailed knowledge and describes to the European reader the works of Confucius -"books that he conceived: the

---

① Idem, *Ibidem*, p. 102.

② The most prestigious and powerful in noble hierarchy in Portugal, in the author's time.

③ Idem, *Ibidem*, p. 103

④ Idem, *Ibidem*, p. 102.

⑤ Idem, *Ibidem*, p. 103

first, called Yekim[1], deals with natural philosophy, generation and corruption of things and natural principles, philosophizing by means of numbers, signs and symbols and applying everything to moral and good government. The second, called Xukim[2], is composed of chronicles, considering the kings of Antiquity and their good government. The third Xikim[3], of ancient poetry, all about metaphors and poetic figures, disserts on the inclinations and human nature, and also several habits. The fourth, called Likim[4], deals with Rites and civil ceremonies of the ancient, and also things related to divine cult and religion. The fifth, called Chumchou[5], also focuses on the chronicle of the country, and contains the narration of the examples of several ancient kings, good and bad, to be imitated or avoided.

There are four other books which belong to Confucius and another philosopher called Mensiu[6] and thus, in these nine books, lies all the physical and moral doctrine,

---

① The *Zhouyi* 周易, also called *Yijing* 易經, or, shortly, *Yi* 易, is one of the most important Confucian Classics. It has not only influenced Confucian and especially Neo-Confucian thinking but is also deeply rooted in the Daoist tradition (Each of the "five" classics is a group of works rather than a single text). Cf. http://www.chinaknowledge.de/Literature/Classics/jingbu.html

② *Shangshu* 尚書 or Shujing 書經, or History book is a collection of speeches from the Shang and Western Zhou periods. It is one of the Five Confucian Classics. Cf. http://www.chinaknowledge.de/Literature/Classics/jingbu.html

③ The *Shijing* 詩經 or "Book of Songs" is one of the traditional Confucian classics. It is a collection of three different types of songs originating in the Shang 商 (17th to 11th cent. BC) and the early and middle Zhou period 周 (11th. cent.-221 BC), in 305 chapters. Of 6 chapters only the names are preserved (*Nangai* 南陔, *Baihua* 白華, *Huashu* 華黍, *Yougeng* 由庚, *Chongqiu* 崇丘, and *Youyi* 由儀). Cf. http://www.chinaknowledge.de/Literature/Classics/jingbu.html

④ The *Liji* 禮記 "Book of rites" is a collection of describing the social forms, administration, and ceremonial rites written during the late Warring States 戰國 (5th cent.-221 BCE) and Former Han 前漢 (206 BCE-8 CE) periods. The *Book of Rites*, along with the *Rites of Zhou* (*Zhouli*) and the *Book of Etiquette and Rites*(*Yili*), which are together known as the "Three Li (*San li*)," constitute the ritual (*li*) section of the Five Classics which lay at the core of the traditional Confucian canon. Cf. http://www.chinaknowledge.de/Literature/Classics/jingbu.html

⑤ The *Chunqiu* 春秋 "Spring and Autumn Annals" is the chronicle of the state of Lu 魯 between 722 and 479. It is the oldest and the only surviving type of chronicles from the early Eastern Zhou period 東周 (770-221 BC). The book gained such a high position in traditional literature that the whole period covered by it was called the Spring and Autumn period 春秋 770-5th cent. BCE). Cf. http://www.chinaknowledge.de/Literature/Classics/jingbu.html

⑥ Mencius ( 孟子, *Meng Zi*, most accepted dates: 372-289 BC; other possible dates: 385-303/302 BC), was born in the State of Zou, now forming the territory of the county-level cityof Zoucheng, Shandong province, only thirty kilometers south of Qufu, Confucius' birthplace. He was the most famous Confucian Chinese philosopher.

that all the kingdom studies and from where they take the points that are read or about which the compositions are done in degree exams.

They have about these books several commentaries and glosses, which are observed as laws of the kingdom, and cannot be questioned in public acts, because they have the power of text". Those nine books are sacred, and in them, in their glosses and commentaries lies all effort of study … understood and interpreted with application to each person, about how one should act by way of virtue, and to the kingdom, about how to administer by way of good rules. ①

About the philosophical principles and about the Confucian education system in China, ǎlvaro de Semedo was one the first to thoroughly describe them, but many scholars have analyzed them and they are well known. Less known is the relationship between them and their transmission through language, writing and the use of precious products and the values of virtue associated with many of these products.

**First, let us talk about Chinese language and writing:**

Álvaro Semedo dedicates chapter VI of his *Relation of the Great Monarchy of China* to Chinese language and calligraphy, indicating that Confucian tradition has appreciated both in the transmittance of its values, stressing their antiquity and unifying role, especially for having taken the language of the province of Beijing as the language of central administration around the country and one unique form of writing of tonal and ideographic characters. Says Semedo: "It is said that, at least, in his books, it is in use for more than 3.700 years. It is varied because there are diverse kingdoms integrating this crown and that did not belong to it, because they were in the hands of Barbarians like all the austral provinces and some northern. Nevertheless, the Chinese language comes to be just one called quonhoa② or language of mandarins because these, at the same time they introduced their government in other kingdoms, they also introduced their language, which is spoken today around the country, as Latin around Europe and, in spite of being universal, each of the regions keeps its own idiom."③

Chinese writing evolved from ideographic representation and by pictograms, to

① Semedo, *Ibidem*, p. 104.

② *Guanhua* 官话, Mandarin adopted as the national language, based on the Beijing dialect.

③ Semedo, *Idem*, p. 73

modern writing of straight line, whether complicated-as it is used in documents of the Ming and Qing dynasties and that speak of the Portuguese presence in China, or simplified-as is predominantly used in China today. This evolution was soon understood by the Portuguese living in China, and who like álvaro de Semedo have studied it and reported it "It is said that the author of those letters was Fohi [Fouhi or Fuei, 2852 a. C.] one of its first kings. At first, they were less, simpler and, in a way, similar to things they enunciated, since that [word] that is pronounced *ge* and means sun, was written with a circle and a diametrical line. After that, its shape was changed, the circle being turned into almost a square with the same line and continuing to mean, in the same way, sun". The Chinese calligraphy held the attention and admiration of Europeans, due to the aesthetic beauty of the line and the complexity and exoticism of this way of writing. álvaro de Semedo, after indicating the antiquity of Chinese writing "since more that 3.700 years ago until 1640, in which we write this Relation", proceeds affirming "I dare say that this is one of the most wonderful things of this kingdom, because in spite of those characters being numerous, almost everyone knows them relatively well, at least, enough for the practice of their crafts". Semedo, with his acute sense of observation, points out the pragmatic advantages of, in spite of the existence of different languages in the great Chinese Empire, all of them being represented by a unique system of characters "and, being peculiar of China, are also common in neighbouring countries, them giving, nevertheless, each one, the sounds of their own language, like we do with digits in numbers and with names of planets, which are the same in all the European languages but are pronounced differently. This is very convenient for embassies, documents and books"①.

Álvaro de Semedo has also enhanced the prestige of writing and its parallel with painting "Those who write well are greatly cherished. They value so much a good calligraphy as a good painting, and they do not hesitate in giving a lot of money for paintings of ancient well designed letters."② According to specialists, the line should express emotion, energy, rhythm and spirit, in order to be considered good writing. The virtuous character of the transmission of Confucian and traditional principles of the Chinese culture, of almost mythical respect towards writing, is equally referred to

① Idem, *ibidem*, p. 74

② Idem, *ibidem*, p. 77

by Semedo "The letters, besides being cherished, they are revered, so people do not tolerate to see a written paper on the floor. They pick it up immediately and, in schools for boys, there are places to store it, to be burned in due time, not by religion, as do the Turks, but by mere respect for letters"①.

**Role of the Chinese precious products and inherent transmission of Chinese values:**

As a way to draw attention and positively impress authorities, whether European or Chinese, it was common for the traveller or messenger, merchant or missionary, to offer precious products or useful objects, representative of Europe or China. When they left on mission to China they took some diplomatic gifts such as watches, beautiful books, artistically adorned maps and charts, among many other valuable items. When leaving on mission to the West, they would bring from China not only letters ad reports, but also several gifts, including curiosities, sophisticated useful products and precious products like silk, porcelain, jade, lacquer work, and many other. After 22 years in China Álvaro de Semedo was sent to Europe, and nominated "procurator" to defend the Jesuit points of view in Rome. Arriving in Portugal in 1640 and to Rome in 1642, he returned to China in 1644, where he died in 1658.

Jade

Confucius's followers concentrated in jade, or believed that it reflected, the five moral virtues (kindness, honesty, wisdom, courage and purity), whereas Taoists associated jade with the immortality of the wise. In China, it is known as Yu and it possesses a magical aura that plunges in the Neolithic and extends from Antiquity to the Modern Era, expressed in texts and poetry of those times. It was a stone that was used in the cult of ancestors, justified by its ability to delay body putrefaction, besides being a display of respect for the deceased. In addition, it was associated with the masculine principle (Yang). Only after the 17th century, when the Spanish discovered jade in America, this and the Chinese Yu were linked. Several archaeological findings confirm the elites' esteem for jade pieces, since the Neolithic.

With the participation of the Portuguese in Chinese mercantile routes and with the expansion of Macau, jade pieces also started to be part of their decorative house-

---

① Idem, *ibidem*, p. 78

hold products. The impact of jade as ornamental stone and jewel, quite appreciated by Chinese elite and by the emperor himself is pointed out, in 1637, by álvaro Semedo, who describes its inclusion as one of the main gifts of a tributary embassy to the Chinese emperor -"The most abundant and best [good] is a certain stone which they call Yaka, and extract from the kingdom of Yarken. The colour of the ordinary [common] is whitish and the finest is green, having reached a great price in China, but still a good value. With it they make several jewels for head ornamentation, and it is quite used in palaces. The belt with which the king awards the colaos [the highest mandarin of the supreme court] is decorated with the most beautiful of those stones, reason why nothing else can be applied in this ornament... On arriving in the presence of the king, the ambassadors are offered their gifts that contain this precious stone, in the quantity of a thousand arrobas, which is three hundred and thirty three Italian pounds, from which three hundred are of the finest..."①. This ability for observation is quite interesting, as Semedo's perception is accurate, jade being a symbol of authority. The emperor himself, in state ceremonies, would hold a bar of jade, which stood for absolute power (*Zhengui*) and on his belt, a pendant called *Tagui*. The hierarchy of state, the mandarinate, would also receive plates of jade according to their degree of importance, namely the *Huangui*, representing bravery, it was given to those who the Portuguese would identify as dukes; the *Xingui* would represent fidelity and trust as a quality of the marquis; the *Gonggui* signified submission as an attribute of counts; and the 4th and 5th class mandarins were invested with *Pubi*, a jade piece representing the duty to provide food and tranquillity to the population②. The importance of jade as a decorative element that elevates the social status of its owner took several European royal houses will then hold numerous objects made of jade. Not only the Portuguese kings, but also some others in Europe. Some of them became very famous and remain until today in their palaces. Among other Portuguese kings, the King João V ordered to decorate with Jade and other precious stones the walls of one chapel of the Church of S. Roque in Lisbon, in a display of royal power and wealth. As well as the Medicis also covered with jade the walls of the chapel of his Pitti palace

---

① Idem, *ibidem*, p. 51-52.

② José Jorge, *Notas sobre a Arte Chinesa*, Macau, Instituto Cultural de Macau, 1995, p. 106-108.

in Florence. We still can visit the majestic decoration of precious jade panels covering the walls of a room of S. Petersburg Hermitage Museum.

Other decorative objects

The Jesuit Álvaro Semedo stated, in 1637, his great admiration for the richness of China in several areas, including the precious stones, among which he pointed out "rubies, sapphires". He also complimented the work perfection of Chinese jewellery "Their gold works in jewellery, ornaments and jewels for ladies, for actual use or as curiosities, are known throughout the world"① and added on about the skills of artisans "… they are excellent, mainly, with earrings and gold and silver ornaments for women. They work wonders with strings. They took one to Goa that had three hundred knots, weighed only three golden ounces, a work so delicate that the knots disappeared from sight"②.

He also adds that these products are object of a great international demand, being easily sold -"They do not go out through one door but many, very wide and of great and perpetual commerce"③.

With the emergence of Macau, the Portuguese galliots transported a lot of lacquer work from that harbour to Japan, as in 1637, the 150 cates of lacquer evaluated in 52 tael. Still in this year, úlvaro Semedo gives out an appreciative reference to the Chinese furniture submitted to the process of lacquering "giving good use of the mentioned japan, a kind of varnish which is extracted from the tree original of that country and other surrounding countries. It is actually an excellent thing, by the perfection of the substance, as you can see in the pieces that came from there, and by the smoothness of its application, whether to new things or in restoring old ones, which are given back their primitive beauty"④.

**Portuguese pioneered spread of Chinese Cultural influence in Europe:**

The Portuguese Royal Court had a pioneering role (in the context of the Modern Age) in the dissemination in the European fashion of Chinese and Oriental luxury items and, what is more important of a new Oriental and exotic atmosphere. Particu-

---

① Semedo, *ibidem*, p. 32

② Idem, *ibidem*, p. 66

③ Idem, *ibidem*, p. 32

④ Idem, *ibidem*, p. 27

larly the consumption of tea, the use of silks and tapestries, porcelains, jewellery and other precious stones and exotic utilities.

But the kings and princes were not the only customers of decorative products and Chinese utilities; from very early, even before the foundation of Macau, some vice-king and the captains of the so called "China Voyage" or the governors of the cities under Portuguese control (as Goa, Malacca and Macau), and many noblemen and religious orders (the Jesuits stood out and place orders for their religious houses), and many elements of the merchant elite engaged and enriched by the "China's business" ordered armoured or emblazoned pieces with the representation of his coat of arms, or the family name.

The Chinese artistic products were regarded by western merchants and their intermediaries, not by its intrinsic artistic value, but as a commercial product capable of providing interesting profits by being sold to new Portuguese and Europeans customers. In this context, with the Portuguese expansion was created amongst the Portuguese and European elite the desire of possessing oriental cultural products. These valuable goods were not regarded by their original symbolic value, but as it provided a social status, reflecting the power and affordability of the buyer (the European noble man and bourgeois), attracted by the beauty and exoticism allure of a particular object. Naturally, the ordinary European client was unaware of the Chinese or oriental artistic criteria surrounding of an object, so this exported art was, many times of less aesthetic quality than that the objects made specifically for the use of the Chinese elite educated and knowledgeable. This leads to a demand that materialized in significant orders for artwork, which has increased significantly, from the late seventeenth century with the opening of the port of Canton to western trade and the future establishment of European companies with China, resulting in the diffusion of a new European fashion with Chinese influence, but also by the increase in/of Chinese workshops, mainly in Canton province, producing for this new European consumer market. The objects produced in large quantities, whether ordered by an identified buyer or not, may reflect a combined influence of classical tradition Chinese models with popular local tradition of a particular Chinese manufacturing centre, and furthermore, in the case of an order from a western customer, the objects was made attempting to integrate the features of the European model required. Such is the case of porcelain with the name or crest of Portuguese family, or the vestments and other religious ornaments, made in china[1].

Among the most important orders, are those of the Portuguese royal house, made after the celebrated Vasco da Gama's voyage that open the direct Sea Route to India. One of the essential sources for the study of this subject, are the inventories of the belongings of the palaces and royal chambers or "Cartas de Quitacão". D. Manuel I bought Chinese porcelain, jewellery and precious stones, objects of gold and silver, textiles, artistic furniture, exotic spices and amber[2]. In 1513 D. Manuel gave his wife (and Queen) D. Maria daughter of the Spanish Catholic Kings, a set of oriental products such as: Chinese porcelain, cloth, amber, benzoin and musk[3].

In the context of the sixteenth century European monarchs stood out, particularly, the Queen of Portugal, Dona Catarina de áustria[4]. She collected all sort of cultural oriental pieces, both regarding its nature and its origin, covering almost all peoples that Portuguese have contacted until then. In 1548, we know through the "discharge ordered by Queen Catarina and written by Francisco Velasques, nobleman of King's House, who was her jewellery stores in the year 1548 ", that the treasury of the queen already had a multitude of products of Oriental origin and Chinese in particular.

To illustrate this Portuguese pioneered spread of Chinese influence in Europe, are

---

① As in the dalmatic silk embroidered before the seventeenth century, in the Museu Nacional de Arte Antiga, in Lisbon, 10 pieces from the Museu de São Roque, or the travel lacquered and painted altar, see Maria Helena Mendes Pinto, *Via Orientalis*, Brussels, 1991, No. 139

② Portuguese king born in Alcochete, in 1469 and died in Lisbon, in 1521. Between 1511 (February) and 1514 (April) the "House of India" (customs house for overseas goods) registered 692 pieces of Chinese porcelain, and other Asian objects, precious and semiprecious stones. From these Asian shipments, D. Manuel offered in 1512, 12 Chinese porcelains and 20 painted fabrics to the Monastery of S. Jerónimos in Belém.

③ "Cartas de Quitacão del Rei D. Manuel", *Archivo Histórico Português*, Organization by A. Braamcamp Freire, vol I, Lisbon 1903, p. 75; P. Dias, 1995, p. 192, note 14; J. Meco, "A azulejaria e a Ceramica Escultórica nos Jerónimos", *Jerónimos. Quatro séculos de Pintura*, Lisbon, 1992, pp. 108-110, notes 3 and 4. João Brandão, *Grandeza e abastança de Lisboa em* 1522, Directed by João da Felicidade Alves, Lisbon 1990, pp. 97-103

④ borne in Torquemeda 1507, died in 1578 in Lisbon, she married D. João III King of Portugal in 1525. In 1531, an expedition with three ships, commanded by Manuel Botelho, was sent by the King D. João III, from Lisbon to India and China "... to sail during three years in direction to r China and to all parts of India trading for the Queen profit's [Dona Catarina]" cf. João P. O. Costa, *A descoberta da Civilizacão Japonesa pelos Portugueses*, Macau, 1985, p. 114

the pieces that remain in Portuguese Palaces and Museums, as well as in Europe's museums, since many of the collections of the Portuguese crown have been scattered and absorbed by other collections of royal and aristocratic houses of Europe. Especially in the collections of Spanish kings (from the Felipe's times), but many others, as the Archduke Fernando do Tirol received some Chinese pieces from 1520 to 1595, some parts of this collection are currently in the Kunsthistorisches Museum in Vienna. Also inside of the collections of Rodolfo II of Prague and in the collections of some Papal representatives in Portugal, as the Ricci da Montepulciano (1495-1574), or Francesco de Medici (1541-1587) we may find Chinese luxury products from Portuguese provenience①.

The impact of a new Oriental fashion, often of Chinese influence, spread by the Portuguese in Renaissance and Humanist Europe, may be gauged by the profusion of orders for Chinese and Asian decorative products, made by royal and aristocratic houses of Europe. In 1504 Felipe "The Beautiful", son of Emperor Maximiliano I, commissioned a set of tapestries "*a la manière de Portugal et de l'Indye*" (in Portugal and India manner of use). In 1510 Emperor Maximiliano I commissioned a tapestry of the same type. In 1513-16 Henry VIII of England ordered five exotic tapestries. Between 1545-1550 Cardinal Geovanni Ricci of Montepulciano (1495-1574) was a papal representative in Lisbon and carried on his return to Italy numerous Chinese and Asian porcelains and other precious products collected in Lisbon. When he settle in his palace in Rome on the Via Giulia, he inclusive ordered Francesco Salviati, after 1552, to depicted "in fresh" in their halls, some of the beautiful porcelains he purchase. Geovanni Ricci's inventory of 1561, identify 138 Chinese porcelains, and three Chinese paintings called "fantasy"②. The use of precious and semi-precious stones have a high decorative power, giving an sophisticate and exotic character to the atmosphere, took the Medici of Florence to profusely decorate with jade the chapel of his palace. When Bernier visit that chapel he describes it saying "We only see everywhere jachen or jade, which are these types of stone, that enriches the chapel of the Duke of Flor-

---

① See Julius von Schlosser, *Las camara artisticas y maravillosas del renacimiento tardío*, Madrid, Akal, 1988), and by Pompeo Zambeccari (who was a Pope representative in 1550-53)

② descriptions of these paintings in the palace, see S. Deswarte, 1991, pp. 124-26

ence"①. D. Fernando II of Tirol has obtain some precious and exotic products, from Lisbon, as the rolls of silk painted in China with landscapes and plant, zoomorphic and human elements, which are at present two in Vienna and the other two in Innsbruck, these anonymous rolls were produced during the Ming dynasty destined for export and were inspired by the paintings of the Sung dynasty②. In the *Museo Civico* in Bologna we can see a blue and white bowl, from the Ming dynasty exclusively decorated with Chinese elements of Jiaqing period -(16th century), offered to Pompeo Zambeccari (who was a Papal representative in Portugal from 1550-53), possibly by the King or Queen (King John III or Catherine). To prepare this gift to a suitable European use, it was ordered to made a gilded silver support (possibly by a silversmith of the royal house), with the Latin inscription "Pompeius Zambecarius Sulmonencis - Nuntius-Ad-Regem Lusitan. MD. L. IIII " (in which appears the name, place of birth, the reference of being a Papal representative in Portugal, and the date of 1554). This bowl exclusively decorated with Chinese elements, incorporates through its support the prototype of an eclectic linking between cultural elements of China with the West (Europe via Portugal and Italy), reflecting the wealth and financial power of a narrow circle of European Renaissance aristocrats.

**As an example of Chinese gifts offered by the kings of Portugal to non-European kings**, consisting by Chinese objects from the collections of the royal household, we may mention: "the gift that king Henry [*El Rey D. Henrique*], in glory, sent to the Xarife [leader]" of Morocco, in a uncertain date between 1577 and 1580. The diplomatic gifts always intend to impress the foreigners' authorities and demonstrate the Portuguese power on the sea routes that linked the Atlantic to India and China in the Far East. This gifts , integrated several oriental products including: "One conch (*Búzio*) from China of mother of pearl ornamented with silver golden, has as a foot in a form of a eagle with two mouths [and] eyes, and in the wing one marine horse",

① in *Voyages II*, , 1663. , p. 83

② Now in the Kunsthistorisches Museum, Schloss Ambras, inv. No. P8912 and P8913, view pictures and comments from Annemarie Jordan Gschwend, "The wonders of the East: curiosities of Renaissance collections in Portugal "in *A heranãa de Rauluchantim*, p. 115. See the remarks of H. M. Garner," Chinese Paitings of the Sixteenth Century at Schloss Ambras", *Oriental Art*, No. 22, 1976, pp. 262 -4; and R. Whitfield, "Chinese Paintings from the Collection of Archduke Ferdinand II, *Oriental Art*, No. 22, 1976, pp. 406-10

this conch (*Búzio*)was inside of one box of green velvet with gold ornaments and inside covered with crimson satin"; and prestige Chinese furniture: "A large Chinese table carved with mother of pearl and studded of silver around the edges, and many other silver applications. One table feet made of walnut and carved with gold and black. Straps of green velvet, and many other silver applications, as for shoes, buckles for belts and cloths"①.

With the Dynastic Union of Portugal with Spain (1580-1640) under the Felipes's Crown, the kings of Spain have visited sometimes the royal palaces of Portugal, and on their return to Spain, they transferred for their palaces in Spain (despite the autonomy of each country), many Chinese precious products from Portugal. If we examine the Chinese goods inventory, on the death of Spanish king Felipe II, we suspect that some of them have been collected in the palaces of the Portuguese crown, in particular the royal palace in Lisbon, such as silk dresses ("sayos y roupas") of various qualities, weapons, musical instruments, jewellery, lacquer, worked ivory, and 26 frames embroidery with gold and silk. Annemarie Jordan Gschwend believes "There is evidence that Felipe II of Spain took hold of such objects [exotic and oriental] belonging to the royal Portuguese collections, which were incorporated into its own collection in Spain or dispersed in the form of gifts, by their relatives in Hapsburg in Prague, Vienna or Innsbruck.

However, Spain could also get a large amount of cultural products coming from China, without passing through Lisbon. These products could be caught by the Spanish route, trough Philippines and Sud America, and were previously bought from Chinese merchants (from Fujian and Guangdong, as well as Portuguese from Macau), trading in Parian market in Manila.

In this context, the importation of decorative and utility objects had a great impact on mentalities in Europe, boosted the influence of oriental models, and the European perception of Eastern civilizations, and particularly of China, in the European society and fashion.

**European perception on China Culture in the 18th century**

The movement or Oriental state of mind, the Orientalism with Confucian

---

① D. António Caetano de Sousa, *Provas da História genealógica da Casa Real Portuguesa*, Coimbra, 1948, Evidence No. 171

thought, was inspirited some Europeans of the eighteenth century, especially the enlightenment opinion (as Montesquieu, 1689-1755, Voltaire, 1694-1778, Adam Smith, 1723-1790, and G.W. Leibniz, 1646 -1716). The Orientalism was perceived as tool to criticise the old European society. The Orientalism made the apology of the Confucian Chinese model, which was perceived in a mythical way, its rational religion and political structure and socio-economic structure of China, projecting their own views and rationalist proposals for a new Europe. Which these European intellectuality wanted to see succeed in a universal level. António Hespanha states that "what is really at the base of that Orientalism is not so much a fascination for a different world, but a passion for itself European proposals. ... Beginning universally as humanistic, the enlightenment ends with the creation of modern racism, based on intellectual and civilizational inequality" is thus stronger than the previous racism based on religion. In the late eighteenth and early nineteenth centuries, "China, that was once a model to be followed as a good example, may now be a bad example, and they begun to talk more about the artificial character, slavish immobilizing and superstitious of its institutions than their natural and rational nature"①. The previous apologetic view of China is now denounced as improper and deformed. The Chinese elements that had been widely used in European styles, from baroque to rococo, started to be avoid in the neoclassicism and its "naturalistic" programme, because they are now accused of serious sin of "artificiality"②. However, the influence of Chinese aesthetics (in the English interpretation) will continue to be felt in many gardens' design of the European elite parks, which move fast to Romanticism; as well as in the sumptuous and exquisite ambient given by sophisticated silks and Chinese decorative luxury pieces, in the European halls of some bourgeoisie and aristocracy palaces.

The evolution of the European perception of the Orient/East (the view from the other) was for centuries naturally tailored by the cultural, social and political context of the observer. In the case of a contemporary and European observer, its vision (shaped by its conceptual apparatus) is influenced by the political-ideological and social post-colonial framework. It is now consensual among inter-cultural studies, considering the historical texts that describe the "Other", most enlightening about the au-

---

① Hespanha, *O Orientalismo*, p. 17

② António Pimentel, "Chinoiserie", *Dicionário de Arte Barroca em Portugal*, 1987

thor (observer) than about the reality of the "Other" (observed subject). The Orientalism was also used as an instrument of ideological-political sectors of the European elite in the context of their own society, to strengthen its dominant social position. In a diplomatic level, Orientalism served the European states and their royal houses to emphasize their greatness and heroic history in comparison with others who initially had no direct access to China or the Orient.

**FINAL NOTES:**

The arrival of the Portuguese to China in 1513 started a new era for the relations between the West and the East. This globalization of the Modern Era innovated in three main levels: its expansion in geographic terms (for the first time in the history of mankind the communication to a global scale between the five continents could be done by a single ship), its economical development (by the possibility of mass transportation of mercantile products and the superiority of maritime safety over the terrestrial, which navigation represented for the manufacturing and industrial production) and the increase of cultural interaction (together with navigators, merchants and clergymen, there is a circulation of habits and ideas and a knowledge exchange).

In this work, we looked at the influence of Chinese culture in Europe, and the Confucian perspective that shapes it. We emphasized the role of the Portuguese oversea trade as an important means for the dissemination of Confucian ideas in Portugal and Europe, since the 16$^{th}$ century.

We confirmed the existence of several agents responsible for cultural inter influence, from navigators to merchants, from kings to their mediators, from the Portuguese and Chinese administrations to religious men in proselytizing and missionary action. We pointed out the Jesuits for their strategic ability to comprehend the Confucian culture and thought and its dissemination in the West, namely through letters, reports and books that were read in convents among European elites. Of these, we selected the *Relation of the Great Monarchy of China*, written by the Jesuit álvaro Semedo, because it was quite influential for European scholars and elites, particularly the humanists of the French Enlightment, such as Voltaire or Montesquieu.

Álvaro de Semedo gave a great contribution to the diffusion of Chinese Confucian principles of valuing an administration centralized in the hands of a professional elite of scholars, selected by an education system and exams according to their merit, in order to guarantee the quality and impartiality of their decisions.

We also analyzed the great influence of Chinese culture in the West, through the commerce of Chinese precious products, which had a peak in the 18th century and became a great European fashion traditionally known as *Chinoiserie*. We even suggested that the movement of influence of Chinese culture and of *Chinoiserie* must be extended to the first period of the presence of Portuguese ships in the Indic Ocean and the Seas of China.

Thus, we can conclude that the circulation of information about the traditional Chinese culture and of the Confucian mindset which supports it have intensified its dissemination, from the 16th century onwards, with unparalleled range in Europe. This led to a long road towards the affirmation of general principles like preferring a universal education system in a national scale, with a rigorous exam structuring as a basis for access to public administration, based on merit. Confucianism has inspired part of the European elite, intellectual or mercantile, to question the surviving theological principles of the Middle Ages, whether the criterion of affiliation to a noble family or the nobility social dependences as main means of access to central administration and the ruling power of states. The Confucian ideas of "Governance with virtue", of saving for high-raking positions those members showing great virtue and talent, and who socially promote knowledge, understanding and mutual trust, had a large repercussion and have contributed for a change in mentalities in Europe and the West.

# How Confucianism is Transmitted Across Cultural Boundaries: A Case from Seventeenth-century Japan

**Robert L. Chard (University of Oxford)**

If Confucianism is to play a role in global relations and the enhancement of intercultural understanding, it will need to become more widely influential throughout the world. This study will attempt no direct concrete proposals on how this might be accomplished, but will rather consider how Confucianism crosses cultural boundaries, and what happens to it when it does. One of Confucianism's significant features has been its ability to spread and take root in other regions beyond China, historically in East Asia-Korea, Vietnam, and Japan. How, and why, does Confucianism cross cultural boundaries? Inevitably, it changes, but do we sufficiently recognize how it changes? How different is Confucianism in different cultures, and exactly how did these differences come about?

The current study will approach this question through one specific example: the introduction of Confucian ritual forms in Japan, as reflected in the writings of the Chinese émigré Zhu Shunshui 朱舜水 (1600-1682), who lived in Japan from 1660 to 1682. In the category of ritual forms, I include everything that comes under the Chinese category of *li* 禮: ranging from performed rituals and rules of behavior to material objects such as ritual vessels, temple buildings, clothing, coffins, graves, and ancestral tablets. By studying these, I am emphasizing the visible, material manifestations of Confucianism, which I regard as being an essential part of what Confucianism is. In particular, ritual forms play a significant role in the transmission and reproduction of Confucianism both inside China and beyond, and their particular prominence in Japanese Confucianism is evident from Zhu Shunshui's writings.

It is apparent that Confucians in Japan took material ritual forms more seriously than Confucian-minded gentry in China would have done. It is this, I would argue, that exposes a key difference between the Confucianism of Japan and China. Zhu Shunshui, despite his usual politeness, occasionally expresses dissatisfaction with what he regards as the Japanese over-emphasis on ritual forms or misunderstandings of their true function, which for him was part of a larger failure to grasp what was truly important about Confucianism. His writings on the introduction of Confucian ritual forms in Japan give us a window into a direct encounter between the different Confucianisms of China and Japan in the seventeenth century, and reveal his own dissatisfaction with Japanese Confucianism and Confucians. I shall argue that it is the attitude towards ritual forms, or material Confucianism, that most clearly exposes key differences between the two, and that this specific case will offer clues as to how Confucianism and Confucian culture might cross cultural boundaries in the wider world today. The philosophical and ethical ideas of Confucianism, however worthy they may be in the abstract, cannot be decoupled from Confucian culture in China, and the case of seventeenth-century Japan suggests that this is even more the case if Confucianism is to spread beyond China in the modern world.

**Zhu Shunshui's assumptions**

We begin by considering a few points on Zhu Shunshui's general understanding of Confucian ritual forms, and how he conceived them within the context of the establishment of Confucian institutions in Japan. From this it is apparent that his understandings and priorities were not entirely in alignment with those of his Japanese hosts.

The first point to note is the prominence of precise, technical detail in the descriptions of ritual forms provided by Zhu. This is evident in his own writings, and in accounts by others of the advice he provided. Examples of the latter appear in the biography (*gyōjitsu* 行實) of Zhu composed by his Mito students Imai Kōsai 今井弘濟 (1652-1689) and Asaka Tanpaku 安積澹泊 (1656-1738). According to this document, which is one of the more important sources we have on the details of Zhu's life, in 1670 Mitsukuni asked him to draw up a set of plans for a "palace of learning" (*xuegong* 學宮), with all the buildings of a Confucian school, including a Confucius temple, which Zhu did under the title *Xuegong tushuo* 學宮圖說. Mitsukuni instructed craftsmen to create an intricate wooden model on the basis of these plans, at one-thirtieth the size of the full buildings, complete in every architectural detail. Zhu's personal intervention was frequently required when a particular feature lay beyond the knowledge of the craftsmen.[①] Mitsukuni also required Chinese sacrificial vessels conforming to the canonical models of antiquity, which Zhu was also able to produce according to the ancient forms and dimensions. In particular, he crafted a "tilting vessel" (*qiqi* 欹器), which, Zhu's biographers claimed, had been known only through illustrations since the Tang and Song dynasties, the ancient method of manufacture having been lost.[②]

Kōsai and Tanpaku are primarily concerned to praise Zhu's remarkable knowledge and technical skill. For us the key point is the high degree of precision in the design of ritual forms required by Mitsukuni and his Confucian scholars, as provided by Zhu. Much of this detail is preserved in a text titled *Shunsui Shushi danki* 舜水朱氏談綺, compiled by the Mito scholar Hitomi Bōsai ネヒメ器ヨ畔 (1638-1696), together with Kōsai and Tanpaku, one section of which includes material corresponding to the *Xuegong tushuo* (though it does not contain the title), narrative instructions in Japanese and drawings for the Confucian school buildings and sacrificial ritual vessels. Other parts of the text include instructions for a wide range of Chinese forms, Confucian and otherwise, ranging from clothing (the *yefu* 野服, "rustic garment", and *daofu* 道服, "Confucian garment"), coffins, graves, stelae, calling cards, menu and seating arrangements for formal banquets, and the (definitely non-Confucian) New Year offerings to the stove god (*zao shen* 竈神).[③]

This emphasis on material forms does not mean that the teachings and values of Confucianism were ignored by Japanese Confucians, but it is evident that considerable

---

① *Zhu Shunshui ji* 朱舜水集 (Beijing: Zhonghua Shuju, 1981), p. 619. Zhu's collected works lists only the title *Xuegong tushuo*, with a note saying that the piece itself, in Japanese, is included in the *Shunsui Shushi danki* 舜水朱氏談綺; see *Zhu Shunshui ji*, p. 611. The relevant material in the *Shunsui Shushi danki* is discussed immediately below.

② *Zhu Shunshui ji*, p. 620.

③ *Shunsui Shushi danki* 舜水朱氏談綺, compiled by Hitomi Bōsai 人見懋濟, Imai Kōsai 今井弘濟 (Imai Rosai 魯濟) and Asaka Tanpaku 安積澹泊, photoreproduction of Shinkei Shoho Ryūshiken Ibaraki Hōdō zōhan 神京書鋪柳枝軒茨城方道藏版 edition of 1707, published in China as *Zhushi Shunshui tanqi* マヒエヒヨエ十_ (Shanghai: Huadong Shifan Daxue Chubanshe, 1988), which will be the version cited in this paper. The school narrative instructions take up most of *kan* 2 (*chūkan* 中巻), pp. 132-210 (page numbers refer to the continuous pagination added in the Chinese edition), drawings on pp. 213-84, the sacrificial vessels and funeral banner on pp. 285-90; the stove god sacrifice is in *kan* 1 (*jō* 上) on pp. 121-2.

time and effort went into achieving correct forms to a high degree of precision and accuracy, suggesting that this was a priority for Zhu's hosts. A concern for correct ritual forms had always existed in China, of course, but there are occasional hints in Zhu's writings that he did not regard this as the true essence of Confucianism, and would have preferred that the Japanese attached less importance to these forms. One such indication occurs during the "brush conversations" (*biyu* 筆語, J. *hitsugo*) between Zhu and Oyake Seijun 小宅生順 (? 1637-1674), the Confucian scholar Mitsukuni sent to Nagasaki to find Zhu in the autumn of 1664. Three times Seijun asked Zhu about Confucian dress, in particular the "long garment" (*shenyi* 深衣, in this context the same as the *daofu* 道服 in the *Shunsui Shushi danki*), which he clearly regarded as the correct dress for Confucians.

Seijun, who was at pains to convince Zhu that Confucianism was thriving in Japan, mentioned the *shenyi* in one of the earliest exchanges between them, probably the first time they met: ①

[O]yake: In recent generations, Confucian ways (*jufū* 儒風) have grown daily more prevalent in our country. Teachers and their students often wear garments such as the Long Garment and the Rustic Garment (*yefu*), and demonstrate in imposing dignity the ways of the Zhu 洙 and Si 泗 Rivers. ② In fashioning these garments, we investigated the design in works such as the *Li ji* 禮記, the *Jiali* 家禮 of Master Zhu (Zhu Xi), and the *Helin yulu* 鶴林玉露 of Mr. Luo (Luo shi 羅氏, or Luo Dajing 羅大經, 1196-c. 1252). Different regions have different customs, and although we all practice this in accord with [Confucian] righteousness, the length and width [of these garments] are not comfortable on the human frame. I wonder if there are other traditions concerning the design and measure of these garments, and the correct way of

---

① There are two versions of this conversation. That in the *Zhu Shunshui ji*, from which much material has been cut, places this question and answer at the very beginning of their exchanges (*Zhu Shunshui ji*, p. 404). The other version is in a text titled *Saiyū shuroku* 西遊手録, Seijun's own more complete record of his trip to Nagasaki, in which the passage presented here appears only after an extended exchange of pleasantries, which seems to come from their first meeting. See Shōkōkan'in ユテリシ comp., *Shu Shunsui kiji zanroku* 朱舜水記事纂錄 (Tokyo: Yoshikawa Kōbunkan, 1914).

② Where Confucius was active, by extension the Confucian Way.

making them—could you enlighten me on this?[①]

For Seijun, wearing the *shenyi* or *yefu* was a key sign of the growing influence of Confucianism in Japan, and he is worried that they have not yet discovered the correct form of the garment. Zhu takes a quite different view. In his response, he bluntly rebuts Seijun's assertion about the growth of Confucianism in Japan. As a nation Japan is filled with human talent, wide in land area, and rich in material wealth, unmatched anywhere but in China, he says, yet it is deficient in civil (or non-martial) teachings (*wenjiao* 文教), "truly a matter of everlasting regret ('regret for ten thousand generations')" (*shi wei wandai zhi kexi* 實為萬代之可惜). And, Zhu is particularly disturbed by what he describes as a separation between academic learning and moral cultivation:

Dividing learning (*xue* 學) and self-cultivation (*xiu shen* 修身) into two separate forms of righteousness—this is something your servant understands even less. [You say that] Confucian ways have grown daily more prevalent. I make so bold as to ask: how many people have actually achieved equal excellence in both learning and good conduct? How many have actually produced writings that crown a generation? … As far as the design of the *shenyi* is concerned, this is merely to study the rough traces of the sages. The "Yuzao" 玉藻 writings [in the *Li ji*] are profound in meaning, and truly difficult to comprehend.[②] The *Jiali* merely assembles a multitude of conflicting arguments, and gives no fixed rule. When one wears the *shenyi*, one must always have a black cloth around the head, with a turban above it, and a wide sash at the waist, with dangling streamers falling the length of the lower garment. The color of the shoes should match that of the lower garment, and the shoe clasps should be neatly fastened. The clothing of your honored country has its own design; I fear I would not wish to change it without good reason.[③]

Zhu makes little attempt to soften what he regards as the stark difference between Seijun's understanding of Confucianism and his own. For Zhu, the Japanese

---

① Translation slightly modified from Zenan Shu, "Cultural and Political Encounters with Chinese Language in Early Modern Japan: The Case of Kinoshita Jun'an (1621-1698)," D. Phil. thesis, University of Oxford, 2009, p. 130; *Zhu Shunshui ji*, p. 404, and *Saiyū shuroku*, p. 2.

② "Yuzao": the text in the *Liji* 禮記 devoted to the minutiae of ritual dress and trappings.

③ Translation modified from Zenan Shu, "Cultural and Political Encounters," pp. 130-31; *Zhu Shunshui ji*, p. 404; *Saiyū shuroku*, p. 2.

had not really grasped what Confucianism really is: they lacked civil or refined education, or, as he tells Seijun on another occasion, "They are unable to love the learning of the sages" (*bu neng hao shengren zhi xue* 不能好聖人之學).[①] They do not understand the essential unity of textual learning and moral cultivation, a point Zhu makes elsewhere. For Zhu, the *shenyi* is unimportant, a "rough trace" of what the sages of antiquity were really about. A garment with a few basic features will do well enough, and Japanese Confucians can just as well wear the dress of their own country.

However, as we will see from the account of Zhu's interactions with Andō Seian below, at the time he met Oyake Seijun he already understood very well that Japanese Confucians took the details of the *shenyi* and other ritual forms seriously, and had accommodated himself to that fact. In further written conversations, Seijun continued to ask questions about Confucian dress, and Zhu voiced no further criticisms.[②] After going to Edo to take service under Mitsukuni in 1665, Zhu went to considerable lengths to provide Mitsukuni with an improved *shenyi*, and asked a friend to find a particular Chinese seamstress in Nagasaki named Second Lady Chen (Chen Erniang 陳二娘) who knew how to make the garment.[③] Whatever his own feelings, Zhu provided the precise technical instructions on Confucian ritual forms Mitsukuni and his other Japanese interlocutors required, which emphasizes the point that his actual transmission of cultural forms was driven and shaped much more from the Japanese side than it was by his own wishes and priorities. But what more can we say of his own priorities, and his basic premises regarding Confucian ritual forms and their function?

The first point to mention is that Confucian ritual forms are governed by the rules of ritual or propriety (*li* 禮), and Zhu regarded *li* as a fundamental property of civilization, which he conceived of as the possession of Chinese, Confucian *mores*. Such a linking between *li* and civilization did not originate with him, of course; it had existed since very early times, when outside peoples such as the Xiongnu were said to

---

① *Zhu Shunshui ji*, p. 412; *Saiyū shuroku*, p. 13.

② Two further questions about Confucian dress appear in *Zhu Shunshui ji*, pp. 407 and 417-8. Only the first of these is in *Saiyū shuroku*, pp. 5-6, which means that the third took place after Zhu went to Edo.

③ Letter reproduced in Xu Xingqing's compilation of Zhu's writings not in the *Zhu Shunshui ji*, see Xu Xingqing 徐興慶 comp., *Xinding Zhu Shunshui ji buyi* 新訂朱舜水集補遺 (Taibei: Taiwan Daxue Chuban Zhongxin, 2004), p. 102.

know nothing of propriety and righteousness (*bu zhi liyi* 不知禮義).[①] But, given that Zhu had travelled widely outside China, this discourse has special significance: he distinguishes between "states which know *li*" (*zhi li zhi guo* 知禮之國) and "states which do not (yet) know *li*" (*wei zhi li zhi guo* 未知禮之國), and says that he had chosen to come because he had been told that Annam (and also Korea) were "States which knew *li*."[②] And, he believed that "states which do not know *li*" (including Japan) had the capacity to transform into "states which know *li*" through Confucian education, and Japan had excellent potential for doing this.[③]

Second, Zhu makes clear in various letters that a high priority for him was to persuade Japanese rulers to establish schools in their domains, for the spread of Confucian education and moral transformation of their populations. Mitsukuni, at least, got as far as making plans and a wooden scale model of such a school, though the shogunate seems to have denied him permission to build it.[④] Mitsukuni's maternal nephew, Maeda Tsunanori 前田綱紀 (1643-1724), lord of Kaga 加賀 domain, who was also interested in Confucian learning, consulted Zhu on ritual matters and sent two young students to learn from Zhu, with the intention of starting a school. In a letter to Tsunanori's chief Confucian scholar, Kinoshita Jun'an 木下順庵 (1621-1698), Zhu provides one of his most complete discussions on the function of education. An enlightened ruler's first priority must be on education and establishing schools, he says; even in the earliest days of establishing a regime, when people's daily sustenance is still a struggle, starting schools will ensure that there will be more good people than bad, so that morality will thrive and good social order be achieved.[⑤]

A final, important premise underlying Zhu's understanding of Confucian ritual

---

① For example in the biography of the Xiongnu, *Shi ji* (Beijing: Zhonghua Shuju, 1959), p. 2879.

② *Zhu Shunshui ji*, p. 27.

③ Letter to Akashi Gensuke 明石源助, *Zhu Shunshui ji*, p. 83. I will investigate Zhu's ideas in the context of more general Chinese conceptions in a future study.

④ See the discussion in Kurakazu Masae 倉員正江, "Mito-han hen 'Dai Nihonshi hensan kiroku' ni miru chishikijin no kōryū to shuppan bunka no kenkyū" ヒヨ託キユセ治クユ　エアセハキセ邪・h」イへへ抱一ク)。ケ、ヒメ侃・ユラRネヒ、木ムミセソ(research report, Nihon Daigaku, 2006), where she suggests that the *bakufu* was uneasy that Zhu, as a Chinese, would take a leading role in the school.

⑤ *Zhu Shunshui ji*, pp. 201-2. See also the discussion of Zhu's Kaga students in Zenan Shu, "Cultural and Political Encounters," pp. 158-65 and 173-181.

forms was that they fall within the purview of the state, and hence have a fundamentally political dimension. In China, the formulation of correct ritual was a state matter, and attempts were made to regulate what rituals could be performed at what level of society, particularly during the Ming. Some court rituals, such as the sacrifices at the imperial ancestral shrines, were significant expressions of dynastic authority, and were often contested, most famously under the Jiajing emperor from 1524 onwards. High officials at court deployed their knowledge of the Confucian canon to advise on the forms of such ritual. All men of Zhu's time in China who identified themselves as "gentry" (*shi* 士) assumed that they were qualified to hold office, and even if not in office they had the duty to express opinions and advice on matters of government, and participate in projects which would benefit society around them, such as local charitable works.① Zhu thus took for granted the political nature of ritual forms, and his own role in defining and formulating them, on Chinese terms. It would be misleading to say that Japanese Confucians had no conception of the political dimension of ritual forms, but it is clear that their conceptions were not the same as Zhu's. An example of this is the five ancestral shrines for feudal lords (*zhuhou wu miao* 諸侯五廟) designed by Zhu for Tsunanori and Mitsukuni: for Zhu, these were a lesser counterpart of the imperial ancestral shrines, and an important emblem of the Japanese daimyō's authority; for Tsunanori and Mitsukuni, the emphasis was on expressing personal veneration of their ancestors. Hence Zhu's shrine designs were never actually built either in Kaga or Mito, and both lords used the Buddhist (or partly Buddhist) temples where the remains of their ancestors were kept.②

**Zhu Shunshui's work on rituals from 1660 to 1665**

A key figure in Zhu Shunshui's rise to prominence was Andō Seian 安東省菴 (1622-1701), with whom Zhu interacted on a regular basis from 1660 to 1665 while he was living in Nagasaki. The story of Zhu and Seian is well known; less well known is the extensive work on Confucian ritual forms undertaken by Zhu at Seian's request.

---

① See the discussion in Peter Bol, *Neo-Confucianism in History*, Harvard East Asian Monographs 307 (Cambridge, Mass.: Harvard University Asia Center, 2008), pp. 30-42, 220-26.

② For a more detailed account of this, see Robert L. Chard, "Zhu Shunshui's Plans for the Confucian Ancestral Shrines (*Zongmiao* 宗廟) in Kaga Domain," *Tōyō Bunka Kenkyūjo Kiyō* 164 (2013), pp. 21-52.

Seian was a man of the samurai class who devoted himself intensely to Confucianism, first studying with the Kyoto Confucian Matsunaga Sekigo 松永尺五 (1592-1657) from 1649 to 1653, before returning to his native Yanagawa to take up the post of domain Confucian scholar. From there he was able to travel to Nagasaki and interact with Chinese residents, and was eventually introduced to Zhu Shunshui in 1659, though they did not actually meet face to face until approximately a year later.①

It is worth noting that modern biographical accounts of Zhu state that he made initial contact with Seian in 1658, and resided permanently in Japan from 1659, following what was recorded in the biography (*gyōjitsu*) of Zhu by Imai Kōsai and Asaka Tanpaku.② As Zenan Shu has demonstrated, Seian's own descriptions of their early contact contradict this. In his eulogy of Zhu (*Dō Shu Sensei bun* 悼朱先生文), Seian states that he first learned of Zhu through a mutual acquaintance (a Chinese scholar and physician named Chen Mingde 陳明德, or Chen Rude 入德, Japanese name Egawa Nittoku 穎川入德, 1596-1674) after returning from a trip to Kyoto in 1659 (year 2 of the Manji period, Manji ninen 萬治二年).③ Nittoku conveyed a letter from Zhu to Seian, and also an extract from Zhu's account of his time in Annam.④ Deeply impressed, Seian wrote a polite letter in reply, but the two were unable to meet; the very evening Zhu received the letter, he learned that he was to take ship for Xiamen two days later (on the nineteenth day of the tenth month, 1659), leaving him no time to compose a response. He explained these circumstances to Seian in a long letter sent

---

① For a biography of Seian see Komoguchi Isao 菰口治 and Okada Takehiko 岡田武彦, *Andō Seian, Kaibara Ekiken* 安東省庵・貝原益軒 (Tokyo: Meitoku Shuppansha, 1985). One of the most detailed accounts of him in English, focusing on his relationship with Zhu Shunshui, is in Zenan Shu, "Cultural and Political Encounters," pp. 110-26.

② For the year 1658 see, for example, Ishihara Michihiro ハツセユオタイウ, *Shu Shunsui* ヨ・ユヒヨ (Tokyo: Yoshikawa Kōbunkan, 1961, reprinted 1989), pp. 289-290. The *gyōjitsu* version of events is in *Zhu Shunshui ji*, pp. 616-17.

③ See Zenan Shu, "Cultural and Political Encounters," pp. 119-21. As Shu's study may not be readily accessible, I will repeat her main evidence here.

④ *Dō Shu Sensei bun*, *Zhu Shunshui ji*, p. 735; three more identical versions of this document are included in various collections of Seian's writings, reproduced in *Andō Seian shū*: *ei'in hen*一イ翻ハ。ネCシツイDイDモ。セŽ, Part I, *Yanagawa bunka shiryō shūsei* チイホトサツルYチマシツウノ (Yanagawa: Yanagawa-shi 柳川市, 2002), pp. 360 and 487; the third is in *Andō Seian shū*: *ei'in hen*, Part II, in *Yanagawa bunka shiryō shūsei* 2.2 (Yanagawa: Yanagawa-shi, 2004), p. 372.

from China.[①] Seian records that Zhu returned from China the following year (i.e., 1660, not 1659 as conventionally stated), and elsewhere, in a preface he composed for Zhu's collected works, he states that Zhu returned from China to Nagasaki in "the third year of Manji" (Manji sannen 萬治三年).[②] As Zenan Shu argues, Seian's version of events carries more weight than Imai Kōsai and Asaka Tanpaku's account, since he was actually there at the time, and is less likely to have mis-remembered the year he returned from Kyoto.

Seian then joined with a number of others (most importantly the Confucian-minded lord of Ogi 小城, Nabeshima Naoyoshi 鍋島直能, 1623-1689, whose intervention seems to have been the deciding factor) in persuading the Nagasaki Commissioner Kurokawa Masanao 黒川正直 (1602-1680) to grant Zhu permission to settle permanently in Nagasaki. Seian became Zhu's student, giving half his salary for Zhu's support, and until 1665 went as frequently to Nagasaki as his duties allowed, usually twice a year.[③] In 1664 he proposed to Zhu that he ask the new ruler of Yanagawa (Tachibana Akitora 立花鑑虎, r. 1664-1696) for permission to allow Zhu to join him there, but Zhu counselled caution, fearing that the Nagasaki Commissioner might refuse permission, which in turn would have an adverse effect on the new and important relationship between Seian and Akitora.[④]

The formulation and introduction of Confucian forms was an ongoing area of activity for Zhu and Seian during their years together, and the work they did prefigured much of what Zhu was later to do for Mitsukuni, with a similar emphasis on visible rituals and forms. The work on ritual forms is reflected in Zhu's letters to Seian, and also in various of Seian's own writings, particularly in a text titled *Shinsō shūgo* 心喪

---

① Reply letter 1 to Seian, *Zhu Shunshui ji*, pp. 169-172.

② *Dō Shu Sensei bun*, *Zhu Shunshui ji*, p. 736 and *Andō Seian shū*, Part I, pp. 360 and 487, Part II, p. 373. For the preface see *Andō Seian shū*, Part I, p. 432. The version of the same preface in *Zhu Shunshui ji* gives the year as Manji 2 (p. 784); the text is otherwise identical, probably because the text was altered by Asaka Tanpaku to conform to the date he had determined for the *gyōjitsu*. The inconsistency between Manchi 2 and 3 is noted in Kurakazu Masae 倉員正江, "*Shunsui sensei bunshū* hensan jijō (yon): *Dai Nihonshi henzan kiroku* o chūshin ni ユヒヨマネノ昫トシッ。サセ邪・ツヌ饕イヒト」ウ——。コユユアセ邪・帠 h。サ、ミミ、ヒ," *Kinsei bungei kenkyū to hyōron* ス・タホトワソ、ネセuユ" 68 (2005), p. 98, note 2.

③ Eulogy to Zhu, *Zhu Shunshui ji*, p. 736. For Nabeshima's role see Ishihara, *Shu Shunsui*, p. 103.

④ Letter 7 to Seian, *Zhu Shunshui ji*, p. 158.

集語, written materials he received from Zhu and records of written conversations with him, which he compiled soon after Zhu's death in 1682. The material in all these documents derives largely from the period of closest interaction between the two men between 1660 and 1665. Meeting face to face only twice a year, they communicated regularly by letter. It is usually possible to identify which of Zhu's letters to Seian come from this period (those written from Edo after 1665 are much fewer in number and usually easy to recognize) but few of them can be dated more precisely, and since none of the available versions of Zhu's collected works arrange the letters in chronological order it is often a matter of guesswork to establish a sequence of letters on a particular topic. After 1665, when Zhu went to Edo, there is no sign in their correspondence of any continuation of collaborative work on ritual forms.

In Zhu's letters to Seian, overt dissatisfaction with Japanese Confucianism rarely appears. In the long letter Zhu sent from China in late 1659, he does note that Confucianism has not prospered in Japan despite the excellent qualities of the land and its people, and says this is because the Japanese do not devote themselves to study, and are too conscious of personal status to have the humility to learn from others. However, he words this criticism in far less direct a fashion than he was later to do with Oyake Seijun, and politely also blames the fact that communication between China and Japan has been impeded by prohibitions on the Chinese side, with the result that the Chinese who did come to Japan tended to be people of mean status. Even the few scholars among them were men who "did not have equal mastery of learning and conduct" (*xue xing bu jian* 學行不兼), a phrase reminiscent of his characterization of the split between learning and moral cultivation among Japanese Confucians in his conversations with Oyake Seijun.①

The work on ritual forms by no means makes up a major proportion of the content of Zhu's letters, which in itself is an indication that this was not a high priority in his plans for Seian's cultivation and Confucian attainment. When he does mention Confucian forms, it is evident that he was responding to queries and requests from Seian. Both Zhu's letters and Seian's *Shinsō shūgo* suggest that Seian's chief ritual interest was in Confucian funerals, including the design of Chinese coffins and mourning garments, though, like the Mito Confucians, he was also concerned with the cor-

① Reply letter 1 to Seian, *Zhu Shunshui ji*, pp. 169-70.

rect design of the "long garment" (*shenyi*). Though Zhu seems to have considered this sufficiently worthwhile to devote considerable time and effort to it, there are occasional signs in his letters that he did not regard this as being as important as Seian did.

One such sign comes in a letter that appears to date from 1660, very likely just before Zhu was granted permission to settle in Japan, since it chiefly concerns the Nagasaki Commissioner's request through Chen Mingde for Zhu to supply a personal history (*lüli* / *rireki* 履歷) and the edict from the Prince of Lu appointing Zhu to office in 1653.① At the very end of this letter, Zhu responds to what must have been a query from Seian about the *shenyi*:

As far as the design of the Long Garment is concerned, the diagrams in the *Xingli* [*daquan*] 性理[大全] are insufficient to use as a basis. Allow me to seek the assistance of a tailor (*caigong* 裁工) to search this out. However, this is the sort of matter which can be done at leisure. More urgent is to recite the words of [the sage-king] Yao, and put into practice the actions of Yao.②

As in his later conversation with Oyake Seijun, it is clear that he did not feel the *shenyi* to be of central importance in the practice of Confucianism.

Seian also requested written instructions for funeral sacrifices (*sangji* 喪祭), as is reflected in Zhu's response to him:

In the matter of funeral sacrifice, I accept your instruction (*cheng yu* 承諭), and of course will write a text on this. However, in the matter of writing a text, one first verifies it from the ancients, and after that relies on the wise men of later times. If there is the most trifling thing that is inappropriate, even though everyone in the present might esteem the text, if there is a single person even a hundred generations in the future who criticizes it, then it is not perfect. Thus we must proceed slowly. Wait until I am settled into my residence, and I will do it.③

---

① The personal history may be that preserved under the heading "Lüli" in the *Shinsō shūgo*, *Andō Seian shū*, Part II, pp. 338-41. For the Prince of Lu's edict of appointment, which Zhu prized as a conferral of official status, see the account in Ishihara, *Shu Shunsui*, pp. 60-66; the text of the document itself is in *Zhu Shunshui ji*, p. 34, and in *Shinsō shūgo*, *Andō Seian shū*, Part I, pp. 341-2, with a simple drawing of the document on p. 346.

② Seventh letter in reply to Andō Morinari (Seian), *Zhu Shunshui ji*, p. 178.

③ Letter 23 to Seian, *Zhu Shunshui ji*, p. 168.

A brief line in another letter also says that he will complete the detail work on funeral ritual once he has moved house; possibly this was written in the aftermath of the great Nagasaki fire of 1663 in which Zhu's home was destroyed.[①] Another letter asks Seian to send a copy of Zhu Xi's *Jia li* (*Wengong Jia li* 文公家禮) as soon as he can find it, so that Zhu can get started (*qi shou* 起手); if he can send the *Yi li* 儀禮 and Zhou li 周禮, all the better. Again he stresses the need for painstaking textual work, to ensure that the work is trusted. With the letter he sent a revised draft of the preface of the proposed text for Seian to look at.[②] Still another letter, obviously later, alludes to criticisms of the *Jia li*, but says that he must not speak of these until he has done careful research spanning from antiquity to the present, then he will "write this text" (*zhu ci shu* 著此書).[③] He also mentions having completed working through the *Xingli da quan* and *Jiali*.[④] It is evident that he was planning to compile a ritual manual of some sort, perhaps intended to cover only funerals as Seian had originally requested, though the number of texts being consulted might also suggest that the project had expanded to include a wider range of ritual. What Seian actually planned is not recorded, but it is possible that the Tachibana rulers of Yanagawa were asking for a manual on Confucian funeral ritual. Other daimyō were interested in Confucian funerals at around this time, and in 1666 Mitsukuni of Mito and Ikeda Mitsumasa 池田光政 (1609-1682) of Okayama distributed funeral ritual manuals based on Zhu Xi's *Jiali* to their populations, the *Sōsai giryaku* 喪祭儀略 and *Sōsai no gi* セ眈タ、ホべrespectively.[⑤] It is likely that Seian, and perhaps also the Tachibana rulers, had a similar idea that encouraging Confucian funerals would promote moral transformation and loyalty among their subjects. From Zhu's perspective, what is clear is that Seian was keen to get the job done, and that Zhu was repeatedly telling him that it should not be rushed.

There are also several mentions of making clothing, the "long garment" and

---

① Reply letter 9 to Seian, *Zhu Shunshui ji*, p. 179. For the fire and its impact on Zhu, see Ishihara, *Shu Shunsui*, pp. 112-13.

② Reply letter 25 to Seian, *Zhu Shunshui ji*, p. 193.

③ Letter 16 to Seian, *Zhu Shunshui ji*, p. 165.

④ Reply letter 10 to Seian, *Zhu Shunshui ji*, p. 179.

⑤ See the account in Azuma Jūji ホ眸ヨリカ, "Ikeda Mitsumasa to jukyō sōsai gireiウリフ・篋、ネネ蠖フ・シタベタñ," *Higashi Ajia bunka kōshō kenkyū* 翻・「・ク・「ホトサッスサ徂ムミセソ1 (2006), p. 91.

mourning garments, and coffins. Zhu could not make the garments himself, and was awaiting the arrival of a tailor from China with the necessary skills, but the man had been arrested by Qing officials and his arrival was delayed. Zhu says that he had sought out several other tailors, but none had the necessary knowledge; a reasonable approximation of the garments could be made, but they would not be sufficient to use as a template. He promises to get the *shenyi* and mourning garments made as soon as the tailor does arrive.[①] Eventually he was able to provide a sample of mourning garments, which Seian has received, though warns that they are still inadequate and require improvement. The *shenyi* is more difficult, and will require the arrival of the tailor (presumably the one detained by the Manchus), which will take half a year.[②]

In the case of the coffin, Zhu attempted to formulate the design himself. He mentions sending diagrams twice, the second of which seems to have been more elaborate, perhaps because the first was not detailed enough.[③] There was a carpenter Zhu sought out, but the man was too busy, so Zhu attempted to make one himself out of soft wood, and showed the result to a visitor from Yanagawa, but the pieces did not fit together well, and Zhu concluded that only a good craftsman could make one properly.[④] The final result of Zhu's efforts is probably the discussion and series of drawings of coffins from different sides preserved in Seian's *Shinsō shūgo*, under the heading "When I asked about the design of coffins, he made drawings and bestowed them on me" ("Wen guan zhi zuotu ci zhi" 問棺製作圖賜之).[⑤] This in turn was the basis for the identical instructions and drawings for coffins in the *Shunsui Shushi danki*.[⑥]

In general, Zhu seems to have been happy to assist Seian with the technicalities of ritual forms, and despite his oft-repeated reluctance to hurry matters, he does not repeat his view that this is not the essence of Confucianism, but rather recognizes the value of Confucian funerals in countering the overwhelming influence of Buddhism in Japan. One of his letters to Seian makes this clear, yet at the same time he tells Seian

① Letter 18 to Seian, p. 166.

② Reply letter 13 to Seian, pp. 182-3.

③ Letter 10 and reply letter 19 to Seian, *Zhu Shunshui ji*, pp. 160 and 188-9. In Letter 18 he asks Seian if the coffin has been made.

④ Reply letter 13 to Seian, p. 183.

⑤ *Andō Seian shū*, Part II, pp. 365-8.

⑥ *Shunsui Shushi danki*, pp. 97-102.

not to demand too much precision in ritual forms. He seems to be responding to something Seian told him about the way someone performed a Confucian funeral, but we do not know exactly what, and the person is not named. The letter begins:

Even at the time of a raging tide that none can withstand, there are those able to stand erect, sufficient to be a pillar in the midst of a torrent. In your honored country, deluded by the pernicious teachings (*xiejiao* 邪教, i.e. Buddhism), from which an entire generation cannot extricate itself, for there to be one who all of a sudden buries his parents according to the Way of the Sages, rather than deceiving his parents with the pernicious teachings, then we should ply the whip [in encouragement]. There is no need for us to ask whether or not he is in complete conformity with the rites (*jin he yu li* 盡合於禮). This surely is the significance of the "white cap" and "white knee-guards."① Do you insist on regulating them with the "twist your elder brother's arm…go gently" [argument]?② Have you not heard of "the one who returns West, I cherish with fair words?"③ It is only that there are too many flowery phrases in it, and it has too little sincerity of grief; this is where it is somewhat skewed.④ If there are points of major error, then criticize it. With regard to the fact that they were completely ignorant of how to make the coffin, the burial pit, and the grave lining, it seems that they were influenced by the *Jia li*, but unable to get anything genuine from it.

He goes on to praise two more people in different parts of Japan who have given their parents Confucian burials, and says, "From now on, when there are those who perform this, they will not cause such fright and alarm to prevailing custom" (*jing shi*

① I. e., a simple expression of mourning. This is a reference to the *Shi jing* song "Su guan" 素冠 in the Gui feng 檜風 section, which is a lament by one in extreme grief who yearns to see someone dressed in white cap, clothes, and knee-guards, seemingly someone else in a similar state of mourning.

② I. e., exact conformity with ritual regulations, deriving from a statement by Mencius, who criticized one of his disciples for proposing to advise King Xuan of Qi that one year's mourning would be better than not observing mourning at all, likening this to telling a man twisting his elder brother's arm to do it more gently, rather than teaching him about filial piety and fraternal devotion; *Mencius* 7a. 39.

③ An allusion to the *Shi jing* song "Fei feng" 匪風 of the Gui feng section, in reference to someone heading west to fight for the Zhou court, though here Zhu is using "return West" (*gui xi* 歸西) in the common contemporary sense to refer to someone dying.

④ Zhu seems to be referring to the funeral as described by Seian, or possibly a document or invocation used in it.

*hai su* 驚世駭俗).①

What I wish to stress here is that there is a difference between the two in relation to exacting accuracy in ritual forms: for Zhu, performing Confucian burials counters the influence of Buddhism and promotes Confucianism, and getting the forms approximately right with no major errors is enough. We do not see Seian's side of the story, but Zhu's letter does suggest that Seian had criticized someone for not performing a Confucian funeral correctly.

Zhu Shunshui and Andō Seian discovered in one another the ideal teacher and student respectively, and yet still we detect a subtle dissonance between them. Zhu did not regard ritual forms as being the essence of Confucianism, yet Seian persisted in questioning him on the precise details of funerals and other forms. How much this is attributable to Seian himself, and how much to the demands of the Tachibana lords of Yanagawa, is a question that awaits further research. However, through Zhu's writings we can see a difference between his Chinese Confucianism and Japanese Confucianism.

**Zhu Shunshui's work on rituals after 1665**

Once Zhu Shunshui was appointed as advisor and teacher to Tokugawa Mitsukuni in 1665, Confucian ritual forms became an even more significant area of activity for him. The material on this is extensive, far more than can be covered in this study, but it is possible to list some of the most important points in relation to this, before turning to one conspicuous example of a clash between the respective "Confucianisms" of Zhu and the Japanese in relation to one particular ritual form, the temple to Confucius.

The first point to mention has already been discussed above, the text *Shunsui Shushi danki* compiled by Mito Confucians on ritual forms and other Chinese knowledge, which gives us a good sense of the range of material passed on to them by Zhu, and the emphasis on visible ritual forms revealed there. This includes the *shenyi*, coffins, and other funeral-related forms very like those he gave to Andō Seian.

Another area of activity was Zhu's designs for the "Five Ancestral Shrines of the Feudal Lords" (*zhuhou wu miao* 諸侯武廟), which he first formulated for Maeda Tsu-

① Reply letter 19 to Seian, p. 188. The "*Jia li*" mentioned here as almost certainly Zhu Xi's *Jia li*.

nanori, ruler of Kaga domain, and Mitsukuni. I have written on this in some detail elsewhere, but for purposes of the current study two points are worth repeating.[①] First, Zhu was in the beginning most reluctant to take on the task, on grounds similar to those he expressed to Seian in respect of the manual on funeral ritual: the task was difficult and required extensive research by a group of scholars working together, and the slightest mistake would incur derision from future generations. The second point is that the shrines were never built in Kaga or in Mito, and observances to ancestors were instead maintained in Buddhist establishments. Likewise, though Mitsukuni had asked for a rehearsal of the ancestral sacrifices, and Zhu spent considerable time working on this, there is no record of the rehearsal ever being performed. This is attributable to the very different nature of Chinese and Japanese ancestral worship, particularly the function of a sovereign's ancestral shrines as an emblem of rulership, fundamental in China and taken for granted by Zhu, but lacking any real resonance in Japan.

Finally, we have the temple to Confucius, and the sacrificial ritual performed in it, the *shidian* 釋奠, or *sekiten* in Japanese. Zhu had included the Confucius temple as one component of his plans and scale model for a Confucian school, according to the usual Chinese pattern. Mitsukuni also asked Zhu to organize a rehearsal of the *sekiten*, which Zhu was much more willing to work on than he had the ancestral sacrifices.[②] The rehearsal was carried out, and two people associated with Zhu, Andō Seian and Hattori Kichū 服部其衷 (n. d.), both recorded that they had heard that all those observing this had been deeply moved, some to tears.[③] Zhu produced a text titled *Gaiding shidian yi zhu* 改定釋奠儀注, which seems to be his revised version of a *Shidian yi zhu* 釋奠儀注 sent to him by Hattori Kichū, which he is likely to have found in the large Sonkeikaku 尊經閣 library in Kaga.[④] Zhu prefaces his text by saying that he is not familiar with the Japanese domain and bureaucratic structure, and so

---

① Robert L. Chard, "Zhu Shunshui's Plans for the Confucian Ancestral Shrines (*Zongmiao* 宗廟) in Kaga Domain," cited above.

② As he states in a letter to Okumura Yasuteru 奥村德輝 of Kaga, *Zhu Shunshui ji*, p. 284.

③ Seian's eulogy of Zhu, *Zhu Shunshui ji*, p. 737.

④ Zhu's text is reproduced in *Zhu Shunshui ji*, pp. 602-11. The letter from Kichū is in Xu Xingqing comp., *Xinding Zhu Shunshui ji buyi*, pp. 125-126; he says he is sending Zhu a *Shidian tu* 釋奠圖 and a [*Shidian*] *yi zhu* [釋奠] 儀注, which could have been either Chinese or produced in Japan.

has set forth the Chinese imperial version of the ritual, which can be modified by analogy to suit Japanese circumstances. The main text includes a list of participants and the characteristics and qualification they should have, detailed instructions for the ritual itself, and a list of rules to be observed by all those in attendance. However, in Mito only the rehearsal was held in Zhu's time, never the formal ritual itself, even though *sekiten* and the similar *shi cai / sekisai* 釋菜 had been performed elsewhere in Japan for several decades.① And it was instituted in Kaga, using a tablet representing Confucius prepared by Zhu, which still survives.②

It is on the related matter of the Confucius temple that we find one of Zhu's strongest statements of disagreement with his Japanese hosts over a Confucian ritual form. This comes in a letter to the Mito Confucians Oyake Seijun and Hitomi Bōsai on Mitsukuni's plans to build a Confucius temple at some distance from the Mito capital. Zhu opens the letter with praise for Mitsukuni as an enlightened sovereign, whose every plan and policy is carefully considered, and who can be persuaded by reason if he is in danger of making an error. Seijun and Bōsai should not always keep silent in such a case. Zhu then alludes to previous discussion of the temple plans, saying that he had expressed the opinion that it was undesirable to situate the temple in a remote and isolated location, whereas Seijun and Bōsai had supported Mitsukuni in favoring a remote site to ensure its long-term survival in case of turmoil. Mitsukuni's caution is admirable, Zhu says, but he disagrees.

In the lengthy argument that follows, it is clear that Zhu's most important objection is the separation of the Confucius temple from the school; what he was hoping for was the incorporation of both into a "Palace of Learning" (*xuegong*), along the lines of his plans and the wooden scale model discussed above. He says:

In antiquity the establishment of a school was invariably in the capital of the state. All major affairs issued from there, and after that the Libation of Return (*yinzhi* 飲至)③ and rewards for merit [in battle] were conducted in the Grand Shrine

① A leading expert on the *sekiten* in Japan is James McMullen, who is now completing a book on the subject. The current paper owes a great deal to his advice and materials he has shared with me.

② Kondō Iwao 近藤磐雄, *Kaga Shō'unkō* 加賀松雲公 (Tokyo: Hano Tomoaki Shuppan, 1909) vol. 2, pp. 448-454, which includes a photograph of the tablet.

③ The sovereign or feudal lord's ritual announcement to the ancestral shrine that he has returned, usually from battle.

(Tai miao 太廟, the ruler's ancestral shrine). The presentation of enemy heads and captives was always in the Pangong 泮宮.[1] Thus, the temple to the sage should not be removed from the school.

In antiquity, titles were always granted at court, and punishments meted out in the market. It was not merely a matter of giving and taking away, but something shared with the populace, demonstrating that the King dared not concentrate power entirely in his own hands, and also a way of encouraging the world and polishing the dullards. And nothing is more important for encouraging the world and polishing dullards than the Palace of Learning. The son of a farmer may rise to the post of Minister of War or Minister of the Masses, and decide on appointments to official posts; the offspring of a family with the cap and tassels [of high office] may be transferred to the remote hinterland, as punishment for indulging a weak will. In the course of such rises and falls, people naturally are put in a position where they have no choice but to exert themselves to do good, and expunge all evil and pernicious thoughts. The state will rely on the effect of completed virtue and accomplished talent, and the family teach the regulations of intimacy and respect, of filial and fraternal devotion, so that models reach a state of optimal goodness. Therefore, the temple to the Sage should not be far removed from the school.[2]

This is Zhu's vision for Confucian institutions in Japan, based on an entirely Chinese conception of the ancient past. He conflates the contemporary Confucius temple with the ancient school and ritual buildings in the feudal states, as central, public institutions through which the lord displays the acts of rulership to his subjects. For Zhu, the school is the most important component in this, because it encourages the people to apply themselves to moral transformation. The meritocratic ethos underlying all this is spelled out; dramatic rises and falls in status are what inspire people to cultivate themselves. Of course he was preaching to the converted in the case of Seijun and Bōsai, but this meritocratic vision is rather far removed from the reality of seventeenth-century Japan. In practical terms, his conceptions were not in alignment with the needs of Mitsukuni, who at that time could contemplate founding a Confucius

---

① Supposedly the ancient feudal lord's equivalent to the royal *mingtang* 明堂 and *biyong* 辟廱, ritual building and school.

② *Zhu Shunshui ji*, p. 322.

temple if he wished to, as other daimyō in Japan had done before him, but founding an official domain school of the sort Zhu desired was much more difficult, and in fact turned out to be impossible during this period. ①

Zhu's letter goes on to advance three further objections to putting the temple in a remote location, all more practical considerations which were probably designed to sway Mitsukuni. First, he observes that twice-monthly incense offerings would be required, which would be logistically difficult if Mitsukuni and all his officials went together, and have to be cancelled in bad weather. A proxy might be appointed, but might not take the observances seriously enough. Either way, there was the risk that the offerings would fall into abeyance. Second, the major *sekiten* sacrifices would also pose a logistical burden. Mitsukuni and his officials would have to be present for ritual preparation of the sacrificial beasts on the previous day, so that special buildings to house them overnight would have to be constructed, at extra cost. Third, in the Japanese environment where Buddhism was dominant, there was the risk that participants might become exhausted travelling to and from the remote location, and develop negative feelings toward Confucianism. Or, they might become ill after staying in partially-sheltered buildings, and conclude that Confucius lacked all spiritual potency, in contrast to the Buddha's supposed miraculous powers. Mitsukuni's vigorous and earnest promotion of Confucianism had elicited some degree of support from his subordinates and populace, but the disadvantages of a remote temple risked driving them back to Buddhism. ②

Zhu then turns to the advantages of his own proposal to locate the temple in the city. He says that there is enough space for the temple and purification hall in the relevant space; the current number of students is small, and there is more than enough room in the purification hall to house them. If numbers should swell to the point where they cannot be housed, then people in general are likely to be pleased with the success of the school, and expansion will receive enthusiastic support. Then he says:

With the potent virtue and great undertakings of the High Lord (Mitsukuni) at

---

① See the discussion of this in Kurakazu Masae 倉員正江, "Mito-han hen 'Dai Nihonshi hensan kiroku' ni miru chishikijin no kōryū to shuppan bunka no kenkyū" 水戸藩編「大日本史編纂録(往復書案)に見る知識人の交流の研究, unpublished research report, Nihon Daigaku, 2006.

② *Zhu Shunshui ji*, pp. 322-3. This part of the letter is discussed in greater detail in Shu, pp. 135-6.

present, all the surrounding states will be roused to observe him, and even the capital will come to seek him as a model. If it indeed comes to pass that the people of the surrounding states are moved to take the actions of the High Lord as their target, then if he does the slightest thing wrong, then people will slack off and the Teachings of the Sage will not flourish. But if he implements everything according to the right way, then he will become the greatest contributor to the Teachings of the Sage, and the founding patriarch in the promotion of wisdom in Japan. Everyone in all directions will worship him like an ancestor, and he and Confucius together will go down forever, untarnished. What need is there for caution [in deciding the location of the Confucius temple]? As long as people's unworthiness does not reach the extent of a Sun Hao 孫皓 or Fu Sheng 符(苻)生,[1] they will never seek to destroy the temple; there is no need to take the trouble to worry too much over this.

I have only given an abbreviated sketch of the merits and disadvantages here, but [it is clear that] the temple and school require one another to this extent, and a remote location is as disadvantageous as it is. We have not reached the stage of multiple expenditures on gathering materials and recruiting craftsmen, appointing officials, or selecting households to be in charge of sweeping [the temple]. It is up to you two Elder Brothers to put yourselves to the trouble of conveying this in detail. Your Younger Brother has suffered from dizziness for many days in succession, and falls over at every step. If I recover a little, I will also rush to put this case in person.[2]

We tend to regard Zhu's time in Mito as a success. He was accorded great honor by Mitsukuni, making him probably the most prominent Chinese person in Japan during the seventeenth century. As we have seen, a range of sources demonstrates the extent of his influence in Mito and beyond. And yet, measured against his own hopes and expectations, Zhu cannot have been satisfied with the results of his work. The above letter is a striking example of this: his vision of the Confucius temple, integrated with a school and placed at the center of the political activity of the state, was never realized. Even the temple alone as Mitsukuni was not built, and the *sekiten* offerings to Confucius were rehearsed but never actually performed. Mitsukuni was genuinely

---

① Rulers of the Three Kingdoms Wu state and the Former Qin in the Sixteen Kingdoms period, both labeled by history as bad rulers, and both supporters of Buddhism.

② *Zhu Shunshui ji*, p. 323.

devoted to Confucianism, but in the cultural and political environment of Japan, so very different from that in China, made a mismatch between his needs and Zhu's vision inevitable.

**Conclusion**

This study has focused on one specific case to expose an encounter between Chinese and Japanese Confucianism in the seventeenth century. Chinese and Japanese Confucianism were not entirely separate phenomena—they were based on the authority of the same textual canon, used the same terminology and discourse, and inspired a similar degree of devotion. Confucians from both sides meeting one another would regard themselves as sharing the same identity. And yet, particularly when viewed in cultural, social, and political terms, differences are apparent, perhaps most clearly revealed in their different approaches to ritual forms, which in turn helps us understand how Confucianism might be transmitted globally in the modern world.

The Japanese Confucianism that Zhu encountered was developing within the sphere of political power, and responding to the urgent needs of rulers seeking new and better ways to maintain order in their domains. This is not to deny the existence of Confucianism outside the political sphere, and of course from the perspective of the history of ideas Japanese Confucianism is an area of lasting interest. Ultimately, though, it was the Confucianism developing around centers of political power that had the widest practical impact. It is here that we see how Confucianism begins to take hold in another civilization outside China. The political needs of lords such as Mitsukuni shaped and conditioned the nature of the Confucianism that developed under their control. They were rulers first, and Confucians second (if they can be described as Confucians at all), and their interest in Confucianism was only one partial aspect of their full range of activity.

What were their needs? Very generally, we can observe that even in the time of Mitsukuni Japan was only decades away from a period of many centuries of warfare and disorder. Mitsukuni's plan to situate the Confucius temple in a remote location to preserve it from attack in a time of turmoil is evidence of his unease about the sustainability of his own era of peace. Confucian moral values among the people would promote respect and loyalty, and thus order and stability. Abstract ideas and values would not have such an effect, but actual practices could, if people could be persuaded to adopt them. The visible ritual forms of Confucianism, especially funerals, could spread and take hold, or so the Confucian-minded lords hoped. It must have been with this in mind that Mitsukuni and Ikeda Mitsumasa disseminated manuals on Confucian funeral rituals among their populations. Visible forms—funerals, the *shenyi* worn by many Confucian scholars in Japan, the *sekiten* sacrifices at the Confucius temple—were deliberate displays of something different from the prevailing customs in Japan, which, Confucians hoped, others would emulate.

In the Japanese environment, Confucian ritual forms practiced by lords were striking and carried special significance, as when Mitsukuni and Mitsumasa gave their fathers Confucian burials. Such actions went against the current of general custom, and so required determination and commitment. The pressure would be strong to get the forms precisely right, so as not to create grounds for criticism and ridicule. And, if resistance proved too strong, the practice of forms might be seen as an impediment to effective government, creating an incentive to rein back on them; something like this might have been a factor in Mitsukuni's decision to retain Buddhist elements in the venues in which he venerated his ancestors.

By contrast, other areas of Confucian practice, such as individual moral cultivation and the study of texts, were private in nature, and would have attracted relatively little notice, in much the same category as a personal appreciation for paintings or poetry.

This divide between public and private, visible ritual forms and personal cultivation, would not have seemed a natural one to Zhu Shunshui. In the Chinese educated gentry class from which he came, such a divide scarcely existed at all. The observance of Confucian ritual forms, such as funerals and mourning, was a matter of course, practiced by all within the same milieu, and thus lacking the tension and significance they had in Japan. Confucian learning and moral cultivation carried over into public life, in that members of the gentry exchanged views on scholarship, and held exacting expectations about moral values as expressed through actions and speech, and regularly observed their peers and made judgments about their strengths and failings in this regard. The observance of ritual forms was just one aspect of this attainment, one more criterion by which a person might be judged. With his background, Zhu would have seen the whole of Confucianism as guiding personal cultivation toward the goal of transforming the individual, transforming the populace through moral education in schools, and achieving ideal government (as he described it, the Way of the True King, *wang dao* 王道). Precise adherence to ritual forms was part of the package, but was not weighted with the special significance it had in Japan.

From this specific case, we can make a wider observation: if the new Confucianism of China is to have global influence in the modern world, it must retain something of its traditional cultural forms, and through them somehow engage with the needs of other cultures. Such needs might be in (for example) ethics. Confucianism has a highly developed system of ethics, especially ways of thinking about how specific virtues can be understood, inculcated, and tested, and enabling the enrichment of Virtue Ethics as it has been developing over the last few decades in the West. For this to have anything more than an abstract, conceptual influence, some adaptation of the living culture of Confucianism might have to be introduced, to the extent that there could be people dedicated to Confucianism, like Mitsukuni and Andō Seian in seventeenth-century Japan, akin to religious believers, who could play a role in its transmission. Confucian ritual forms of some sort, appealing to people at large, might have to be involved. Exactly how this might work is something best left to those who have thought in greater depth about how Confucianism might be introduced in the West, but I offer it as a suggestion.

# China's Soft Power: Confucius Institutes and Confucianism

Anja Lahtinen (University of Helsinki)

## Introduction

The subject of this 5th Meeting on International Confucian Association is Confucianism. Its aim is take a look on how Confucianism influence in the twenty-first century China and what lessons can we learn from Confucianism today.

My article explores how Confucius Institutes serve as the tool of Chinese soft power. It also discusses Confucianism that brands Confucius Institutes and what ingredients Confucianism provides to government's policies. This article is a part of the becoming monograph contributed to Asian Studies. It draws theories from international relations and management theories. The central concept is soft power based on notion that cultural politics and foreign policies are intertwined. I have used a qualitative research and gathered research data that includes multiple types of data: literature, open interviews, discussions and observations. As I worked as a Director of Confucius Institute at the University of Helsinki in Finland from 1.2.2012 to 31.8.2014 I had the chance to deepen my understanding of contemporary China. In this job had an opportunity to meet and discuss with hundreds of people in connection to Confucius Institutes, not only Chinese and local staff in the institute, but also other Confucius Institutes' directors from all over the world in various meetings and conferences in China and elsewhere, people from Confucius Institutes Headquarters, Chinese higher education and Chinese embassies. In addition, I have analyzed CI's official and internal documents and reviewed Confucius Institute magazines and web-pages, as well as I have consulted Chinese and non-Chinese literature revealing the topic. This article presents my scholarly view on issues aiming at objectivity while I acknowledge that sought objectivity is always bound to researcher's own attitudes, values, and experiences. I recognize that this can be both an asset and limitation. However, I trust that this article demonstrates some of the challenges of China's soft power, Confucius Institutes and Confucianism in today's world.

In this article, the overall aim is to reveal how the world sees China's soft power and how Confucius Institutes serve as soft power tool presenting Chinese culture. To find out, there are three questions to answer. First, what is China's soft power to win minds and hearts in China's global reach? And, how China is perceived internationally? Second, what is the role and impact of the hundreds of Confucius Institutes as part of China's soft power and foreign policy? And, what are the challenges of Confucius Institutes? And third, to what extent Confucianism and Confucian values impact in contemporary China and what challenges government's cultural politics can expect in exercising its soft power cultural power?

In the following, first I take a look into China's foreign policy and its soft power with a focus on culture. Second, I analyze Confucius institutes as the tool of soft power. Then I present my findings and challenges of Confucius Institutes, and finally I discuss the role of Confucius Institutes and Confucianism as part of China's foreign policy in contemporary China.

China's Foreign Policy

Over 2000 years, Chinese approach in foreign relations was dominated by distinction of a Chinese "Us" and the non-Chinese "Others." China-centric universalism adopted the view where the Chinese emperor as the Son of the Heaven had the mandate of Heaven to rule All-under-Heaven (*Tianxia*). Both Confucianism and the Mandate of Heaven provided the foundations for the tributary system that shaped foreign policy and trade in Imperial China playing a great role in the History of East Asia. Neighboring "barbarian" tribes and kingdoms wanting to trade with China sent "tribute" missions that legitimized China's superiority and suzerainty via the ritual of *kow-tow*, which consisted of three kneeling before the emperor. The relationship with the "barbarians" meant that they had to accept the universal Chinese culture through China's moral example-though it occasionally employed force. ①

From 1978 reforms China concentrated on economic development and thus Deng

① Chen 2005: 37

Xiaoping laid a peaceful foreign policy strategy "hide its strength and bide its time" (*taoguang yanghui*).[①] Today, China is the second largest economy in the world, and for the reason, China is seeking greater influence in the world. As Huntington says, China's modern history defeat, subordination to Japan, humiliation by Western powers has produced China's desire for international respect as a great power.[②] He also said that global politics has become multi-polar and multi-cultural and in consequence the nature of power is changing.[③]

China's foreign policy is derived from the Five Principles of Peaceful Coexistence that consists of mutual respect for sovereignty and territorial integrity, mutual non-aggression, non-interference in each other's internal affairs, equality and mutual benefit, and peaceful coexistence. These principles were originally numerated in 1954, when China was seeking to extend relations with all non-socialist Third World countries. The core idea behind the Five Principles is sovereignty-meaning that one state has no right to interfere in the internal affairs of another state.[④] Today, China's foreign policy is characterized by multilateralism (*duobian zhuyi*), economic diplomacy and the good neighbor policy (*mulin zhengce*) adhered to the win-win (*shuangying*) strategy that is based on principles of equality, mutual trust and mutual benefits, and reciprocity. China's grand strategy has three objectives: first, preserve domestic order and well-being, second, defend against external threats to national sovereignty and territory, and third, attain and maintain geopolitical influence[⑤]

**Chinese Soft power**

International relations are about power, national interests, security, strategy, hegemony, economic interdependence, conflict and cooperation. Robert Keohane and Joseph Nye (1977) claimed that international relations could no longer be conceived as a geo-strategic competition among states as access to the education, mobile phones and internet has empowered the traditionally powerless and, in consequence,

---

① Suettinger 2004.

② Huntington 1996: 229.

③ Huntington. 1993.

④ Nathan Andrew and Robert S. Ross 1997. See also: Nathan, Andrew. Principles of China's Foreign Policy. http://afe.e asia.columbia.edu/special/china_1950_forpol_principles.htm. Accessed 3 July 2012.

⑤ Swaine and Tellis 2000.

the nature of power is changing[1] In his book *Bound to Lead: the Changing Nature of American Power* (1990), Nye defined soft power as the capability of a nation to achieve desired objectives through diplomatic persuasion by employing a deep knowledge of culture and history. He explained how a state can influence through persuasion or attraction, without using hard or coercive power such as military actions.[2] Nye's concept is evolving. Recently, he combines hard and soft power into a winning strategy claiming that "states under the globalization need the concept of 'smart power'-the intelligent integration and networking of diplomacy, defense, development, and other tools of so-called 'hard and soft' power".[3]

In 1990s, Nye's concept of soft power was introduced in China. Since, Chinese scholars, journalists and government analysts have analyzed Nye's concept of soft power. Discussions have developed Chinese perspectives on soft power. Some scholars (Zheng and Zhang In: Lai and Lu 2012:21) claim that Nye's conceptual division of soft power and hard power is too simple and "some of Nye's arguments are not in accordance with the reality of international politics" and "Nye sees some countries' admiration for American democracy and political values lead them automatically to follow US foreign policy".[4] Zhang (2005) finds many weaknesses of soft power, because it is difficult to measure in a quantitative way."[5] Lai and Lu claim that Nye's scope of soft power resources is not scientific enough as he does not make a clear distinction between soft power resources in international politics and other domains and his listings of soft power resources (such as American popular culture, films as TV programs, Europe's Nobel Prizes and overseas development assistance). In their view Nye's listings "do not have important implications for international politics or state behavior," because "sovereign states are still the major players in international relations, and national interests are the most important factor they consider when formulating foreign policy."[6] In consequence, Chinese scholars propose that power can be divided into hard power, soft power and *bargaining* power for an alternative inter-

---

① Keohane and Nye, 1977.

② Nye 1990.

③ Nye 2011: 209.

④ Zheng, Yongnian and Chi Zhang 2012: 21.

⑤ Zhang Xiaoming 2005.

⑥ Lai and Lu 2012: 25-26.

pretation and "that whether a power resource is soft or hard depends on the perceptions and *feelings* of various actors in specific situations."[①]

China has rapidly increased its profile in international affairs. In the pursuit of soft power, a mixture of economic diplomacy and cultural appeals aim to promote China's global and regional influence and to become a true global power.[②] Chinese soft power and its role is emphasized as a component of "peaceful rise" (*heping jueqi*) and "peaceful development" (*heping fazhan*) to cultivate its international image.[③] But, there are some problems in the concept that claims for tolerance and enhancement of dialogue amongst diverse civilizations. As Scott (2012) points out China employs a battery of tools, often calibrated with regards to audience. However, in his view these tools to improve China's soft power attractiveness can be productive, unproductive or counterproductive for China's ultimate grand strategy of achieving long term national rise within the international systems.[④]

**From Propaganda to Cultural Diplomacy**

China has always understood the importance of positive image abroad and the power of press. In the mid-1930s the Chinese Communist Party invited American journalist Edgar Snow to China to report on the civil war. The book *Red Star Over China* that Snow later wrote on Mao Zedong's struggle with the Nationalist forces was a worldwide success. After founding the People's Republic of China in 1949, the regime kept inviting selected journalists and academics to visit (selected parts of) China and write about it. Radio Beijing, taking over from Radio Yan'an, in 1941, broadcasted its programs in all languages and in the world as did Voice of America and BBC World Service. Over the decades, projected images presented China as a peace-loving socialist country and a victim of foreign aggression. In 1960, hundreds of thousands of young Westerners marched behind portraits of Mao waving the "little red book". In early 1970s, so-called "ping-pong" diplomacy and pandas started to pave a way for more outward looking China. In 1978, Deng Xiaoping's introduced the 'open-door policy' and economic reforms to open up and modernize China. His famous slogan "it

---

① Ibid: 21, 27.

② Freedman 2004: 35

③ Li Mingjiang. 2008.

④ Lai and Lu: 2012: 57.

doesn't matter if the cat is white or black, as long as it catches mice", attracted foreign investors-and surged. In 1985 Deng was chosen as "Man of the Year" by the international TIME Magazine. The Tiananmen crisis in 1989 severely damaged China's new and favorable reputation abroad. Two years later, the internal situation seemed under control. China's new leader, Jiang Zemin began efforts to influence international opinion by increasingly reaching out to foreign audiences in order to promote trade and investment and to further China's standing in the world.

"It's high time to make ourselves better understood by the world's people" says Professor Du Ruiqing, former president of the Xi'an International Studies University. In his view culture is a soft power that reduces the misunderstanding and hostilities between the people of different races as "Once they come to know the Chinese people better, they would find out that harmony is an essential part of the Chinese tradition and a country that highly values harmony will absolutely pose no threat to the rest of the world."And therefore," China should help people in other nations acquaint themselves with the Chinese culture, including its traditions, religions and particularly the Chinese way of thinking"[①] Culture as the core of soft power was first expressed by Fudan University Professor Wang Huning. In his article *Culture as National Soft Power* (1993) he wrote that Chinese culture is the main source of a state's soft power: "if a country has an admirable culture and ideological system, other countries will tend to follow it. …It does not have to use its hard power which is expensive and less efficient."[②]Thus, he developed the concept that can be termed "the soft power with Chinese characteristics."

Liu and Wang (2007) find that culture is frequently referred by Chinese leaders to enhance China's competitiveness in the international arena. In the 16th Chinese Communist Party (CCP) Congress in 2002, President Jiang Zemin advocated culture as a comprehensive national power in foreign politics.[③] Consequently, China's soft power promoting traditional Chinese culture and its values have become as part of foreign politics. In May 2004, the concept of soft power was exposed in the thirteenth

---

① China promotes its culture overseas to dissolve "China threat". May 28, 2006. http://english.peopledaily.com.cn/200605/28/eng20060528_269209.html. Accessed 26 June 2014.

② Wang 1993.

③ Jiang 2002.

group study session of the Politburo of the Chinese Communist Party (CCP). Two articles were published in *Outlook* (*liaowang*) the official weekly magazine. The first article discussed the Chinese model and the Beijing Consensus and the second one made the point that China's soft power comprising culture and ideology was becoming increasingly important. Thus, Premier Wen encouraged gaining international recognition and respect, utilizing the quintessence of its traditional culture with the emphasis of harmony. ① In 2006, President Hu Jintao in the Central Foreign Affairs Leadership Group meeting called to increase nation's international status and influence also through the culture. ②In July 2007, the Chinese People's Political Consultative Conference (CPPCC) Committee held a special session on 'cultural construction as the main approach for national soft power to meet domestic demands and enhance China's competitiveness in the international arena. ③ In 2010, the Party decided to deepen the reform of cultural institutions to enhance China's cultural soft power. In consequence, the Central Committee of the CCP called for greater development of culture and increase in national soft power through traditional culture, exports of cultural products, and external media initiatives. ④

In his book *Charm Offensive: How China's Soft Power is Transforming the World* (2008:167) Joseph Kurlantzick points out that Chinese traditional culture has the major role to play to "win minds and hearts while political values and economic attraction are considered essential components of the national strength."⑤ In recent years, it has been shown that China's rise rest not only on its economic power, but also on its soft power, and culture has been augmented as an important tool to augment China's soft power. "Many westerners' biases toward China result from their lack of understanding of the essence of the Chinese culture…" Thus, "China should revitalize its traditional culture, especially its traditional emphasis on social harmony, attract international students, and continue to set up Confucius Institutes abroad. ⑥

---

① Lai 2012. See also: http://dangxiao.jmu.edu.cn/show.asp? id=1156. Accessed 8 July 2013.

② Ma In: Li Mingjiang, 2008: 287-308.

③ Pan Yue, "Quanguo Zhengxie Zhaokai Zhuanti Xieshanghui" (CPPCC National Committee Convenes a Special Consultation Meeting), Renmin Ribao (People's Daily). In: Li Mingjiang, 2008.

④ Lai and Lu 2012: 22.

⑤ Kurlantzick 2008.

⑥ Lai2012: 85.

But, as Li Mingjiang (2008) says constant reference is made into culture and values Chinese soft power is still uncertain. He claims that there are few concrete suggestions on how the Chinese 'harmonious' worldview promoted by the government could restructure the world order, and how a harmonious world can be achieved.

**Confucius Institutes**

"*The Confucius Institute as an effective vehicle for cultural exchanges and important platform for reinforcing international friendships is where the China Dream, the dreams of all countries and the world dream come to convergence.*"

Liu Yandong

Vice Premier of the State Council of China

Chairperson of the Council of Confucius Institute Headquarters

(December 7, 2013)

At the Opening Session of the 8th Confucius Institute Conference, Madam Liu Yandong in her keynote speech "Join our Hands to Develop Confucius Institutes and Write New Chapters in People-to-People Exchange" greeted Chinese and foreign delegates from Confucius Institutes across the world. I was there, one of the delegates, I carefully listened her speech that assured "the high level commitment and full support of the Chinese government is bound to create new impetus for Confucius Institutes." She said "At the moment, the people of China are rallying around the China Dream, a vision of full achievement of a well-off society and the great rejuvenation of the Chinese nation". "The realization of the China Dream will bring about not just wellbeing for the people of in China, but also greater opportunities for world prosperity and win-win cooperation". And, " the Confucius Institutes as an effective vehicle for cultural exchanges and an important platform for reinforcing international friendships is where the China Dream, the dreams of all countries and the world dream of global peace and prosperity".

The first Confucius Institute was founded in 2004. The first Confucius Institute opened on 21 November 2004 in Seoul, South Korea, few months after establishing a pilot institute in Tashkent, Uzbekistan. Now 440 Confucius Institutes and 646 Confucius Classrooms are established in 120 countries and regions throughout five continents, totaling over one thousand.[1] Constitution and By Laws of Confucius Institutes states that "Confucius Institutes devote themselves to satisfying the demands of people from different countries and regions in the world who learn the Chinese language, to enhancing understanding of the Chinese language and culture by these peoples, to strengthening educational and cultural exchange and cooperation between China and other countries, to deepening friendly relationships with other nations, to promoting the development of multi-culturalism, and to construct a harmonious world". The Confucius Institutes conduct Chinese language instructions in Mandarin, using Standard Chinese Characters (Chapter 1). The Confucius Institutes provide the following services: Chinese language teaching; Training Chinese language instructors and providing Chinese language teaching resources; Holding the HSK examination (Chinese Proficiency Test) and tests for the Certification of the Chinese Language Teachers; Providing information and consultative services concerning China's education, culture, and so forth; Conducting language and cultural exchange activities between China and other countries (Chapter 2). The Confucius Institute Headquarters is a non-profit organization that has the independent status of a corporate body. It owns the proprietorship of the name, logo and brand of the Confucius Institutes. The Headquarters is the regulatory body that provides guidelines to the Confucius Institutes worldwide. The Headquarters is located in Beijing in the People's Republic of China.[2]

The Confucius Institutes are governed by the Office of Chinese Language Council International (Hanban), affiliated with the Ministry of Education of the People's Republic of China. The council is composed of members from 12 state ministries and commissions, namely, the General Office of the State Council, the Ministry of Education, the Ministry of Finance, the Overseas Chinese Affaires Office of the State Council, the Ministry of Foreign Affairs, the State Development and Reform Commission, the Ministry of Commerce, the Ministry of Culture, the State Administration of Radio Film and Television (China Radio International), the State Press and Publications Administration, the State Council Information Office (also known as the

---

① The Confucius Institute Journal, Volume 30, 01, Jan. 2014.

② Constitution and By-Laws of the Confucius Institutes. Confucius Institute Headquarters. http://english.hanban.org/node_7880.htm. Accessed 8 August 2014.

Office of Overseas Propaganda) and the State Language Work Committee. The duties of the Council include: Formulating and amending the Constitution and By-Laws of the Confucius Institutes, examining and approving the development strategies and plans of global Confucius Institutes, examining and approving annual reports and working plans of the Headquarters, and discussing issues of significance concerning the development of Confucius Institutes. ①

In 2013, the Confucius Institutes Headquarters spent USD 142 million, which represents a 25% increase from previous year. In 2012, the total global expenditure of Confucius Institutes in amounted to USD 396 million. This figure includes total spending on foreign cash payments, personnel expenses, teaching venues and utilities amounted to USD 199.7 million. In foreign cash payments, tuition revenue accounted for 34% of the amount. Total expenses from Chinese side was USD 196.3 million, mainly for wages and subsidies to dispatched directors, teachers and volunteers, and to support cultural exchanges by Confucius Institutes all over the world. Financial inputs from Chinese and international sources remain at a ratio of approximately 1:1. ②

Confucius institutes promote language, culture and friendliness. To learn Mandarin is "the must-have language." "Mandarin is trendy around the globe, and the establishment of Confucius Institutes is a natural response to the world's thirst," says Xu Lin, Chief of the National Office for Teaching Chinese as a Foreign Language (NOCFL) (Xinhua News 2006-10-02). Hartig (2012) says Confucius Institutes and Confucius Classrooms around the world are set to shape China's image. ③ As many observers Wey-Shen Siow (2011) finds that Confucius Institutes are the most visible symbols of China's growing soft power, and a tool for the country to expand its international influence and advance its public diplomacy agenda. ④ However, Ding and Saunders (2006) point out that in spite of rich cultural resources China lacks competitiveness in promoting its culture. They argue that although China's aim is to develop the "soft architecture" for China-related activities in local community and forge strategic alliances

① Ibid.

② The Annual Report 2012 of Confucius Institute Headquarter(Hanban).

③ Hartig, 2012.

④ Wey-Shen Siow 2011.

with business, industry, government and other institutions, "a true cultural revival in China is dependent on a relaxation of the political environment."[①] Starr (2009) claims that the establishment of the first Confucius Institute in Seoul in 2004 marked a new phase in China's political self-confidence. In his view, the choice of the first location of the Confucius Institute was not a random choice, but a message that China sent to the world was that China is back as the "central state" Zhongguo.[②] Whereas Gosset (2014) finds that Confucius Institutes reveals six of the main features defining Chinese renaissance-economic reemergence, speed of change, socio-political transformation, civilization revival, China's outward projection and the entry into the era of a "New Sinology."[③] James Paradise (2009) says that the institutes may increase China's "soft power" while he points out that real winners in partnerships are China's universities as Confucius Institutes facilitate communication and exchange with foreign academic institutions. Rui Yang (2010) links Confucius Institutes to China's global engagement and internationalization as they serve as platform for collaboration and exchange of higher education in projecting China's soft power.

**Challenges of Confucius Institutes**

The rapid expansion of the Confucius Institutes has internationally raised concerns of their goals and political influence. Many prestigious universities which opened Confucius Institute complain over their influence on academic freedom and a selective and politicized view of China. An organized opposition to the establishment of a Confucius Institute has been demonstrated at University of Melbourne, University of Manitoba, Stockholm University, and recently University of Chicago has been in headlines. *China U* by Marshall Sahlins (2013) brought the University of Chicago to light claiming that universities hosting a Confucius Institute have become engaged in the political propaganda and efforts of a foreign government. He urges prominent CI hosts to take a lead in changing the course to assure academic freedom and the universal ideal of free inquiry.

In June 2014, the American Association of University Professors issued a state-

---

① Ding and Saunders 2006:21.

② Starr 2009.

③ The Confucius Institutes and the Chinese Renaissance . http://www.huffingtonpost.com/david-gosset/the-confucius-institutes-_b_3819878.html. Accessed 26 June 2014.

ment urging American universities to cease their collaboration with Confucius Institutes.

Certainly, this indicates that there are different views and opinions between Chinese side and their hosts about the role and tasks of Confucius Institutes in a host university.

However, I learned that there are many problems which stem from issues which are intertwined with management and organizational aspects. Therefore, it may be useful to take a deeper look into those trying to understand their impact on overall operations in the institute. No matter my experience comes from one of the institute, my observations can be used also in analysis of other institutes' operations.

I used the McKinsey 7S framework, developed in the early 1980s by Tom Peters and Robert Waterman, to examine the areas which need attention in Confucius Institutes. The model includes seven internal aspects of an organization that need to be aligned if it is to be successful. The McKinsey 7S model involves seven interdependent factors: Strategy, Structure, Systems, Style, Staff, Skills, and Shared Values.

Strategy is about what the institute is trying to do. Confucius **Institute** provides educational services to promote Chinese language and culture, and research on China. Its strength is that it uses resources both from Hanban and host university whereas weakness is to adapt services to local conditions and lack of own researchers.

**Structure means** the way the organization is structured. Partnership structure is complex with different players. Confucius Institute is created through partnership between Hanban and the host university (foreign academic institution) on 50/50 basis. Hanban nominates the Chinese university (institution of higher learning), as an academic partner. Hanban contributes financially: start-up money and annual fee for the institute whereas the host university provides facilities and pays local staff. Academic partner institution is responsible for pre-selection of Chinese director and teachers from its staff and then to be sent to Hanban training before their dispatch to institutes all over the world. Hanban also pays annual fee to academic partner for its selection process and support for the appointed institute. The Confucius Institute is individually managed under the leadership of their own board of directors which include members of the host institution/local partner university and the Chinese partner university. The board meetings supposed to be held every year, but this seems not to happen always. Local director has the overall responsibility of the institute while Chinese director is appointed to "assist" host director in running the institute. They supposed to work in harmony. However, things can get quite complicated if two directors have different focus for the institute's operations. The purpose is to work on "local terms," but sometimes this is quite difficult due to the pressure from Chinese side to run more cultural activities. Local director may have little to say, as Hanban trained and financed Chinese director who comes from the Chinese partner university, holds the strings of institute's burse

**Systems** are more than processes of the institute. Confucius Institute is responsible for drawing up and managing its own budget and financial statement. Yet, there are two systems: Chinese and local one (part of host university's system). Hanban/Confucius Institutes Headquarters provides guidelines and funding annually based on approved budget by the Confucius Institute Headquarters. There are various restrictions on how their funds may be used. Furthermore, there is little flexibility to react quickly for any changes during ongoing program period. In parallel the institute runs its own budgetary system within host university's guidelines. Activities and procedures of the institute are engaged by the partnership structure and the client management system (Hanban and academic partner).

**Style** means culture, informed and uninformed rules. Along different systems different working styles prevail, Chinese and local one. Chinese working culture is hierarchical and quite controversy to more egalitarian style in the host country (common in Nordic countries). This shows in communication style, how to address and call each other, what and how to report and to whom, what means yes, how to say no, and what is regarded more important-focus on quantity (Chinese style) or on quality (host's style). Different working culture shows also in how to interpret and apply the rules and deadlines set by Confucius Institute Headquarters (Surprisingly it seems that Chinese are quite flexible while Nordic work culture is more strict in getting things done by deadline).

**Staff** is the people working in the institute. They are different kinds of people with different skills based on their capabilities and capacities, Chinese and non-Chinese with different working styles.

China sends Chinese director, teachers and volunteer teachers. Host universities hire director and other staff.

**Skills** mean individual working skills, and how we work together and what is our major focus.

As the number of Confucius Institutes has increased, Hanban has the shortage of teachers and directors. This shows sometimes in deficiency of skills of Chinese staff. Increasingly Hanban rely on volunteer teachers, mainly young graduates, even they are not qualified teachers, and they may be graduated from other discipline while they have no experience in teaching Chinese. Hanban also sends teachers who are not familiar with modern teaching methods and Chinese director who has neither management skills nor experience. Too often the institute's director has no possibility to interview candidates to find their suitability and motivation to work in particular host country and institute. Neither the candidate has possibility to find out whether this particular institute would be appropriate for him/her. How to assure the quality of teaching skills is problematic when the institute offers academically credited Chinese language courses in their host university. For the teacher the situation is also a challenge. How to teach in foreign country of what they have little knowledge and when the teacher is not able to use the language of the country while his/her ability to use English might be limited. Therefore, professional teacher development and their training for multilingual and multi-media teaching resources is one of the key issues to increase the quality of teaching.

**Shared Values** are central to the development of all the other critical elements. The institute's strategy, structure, systems, style, staff, and skills, all stem from why the organization was originally created and what it stands for. Hanban's Constitution and By-Laws of the Confucius Institutes is applicable to all Confucius Institutes worldwide (Chapter 1:3). Confucius Institutes shall abide by laws and regulations of the countries in which they are located, respect local cultural and educational traditions and social customs, and they shall not contravene concerning laws and regulations of China (Chapter 1: 6). Individual Confucius Institutes may constitute their own regulations and measures with this Constitution and By-Laws and submit to the Headquarters for archiving purpose (Chapter 8: 37). Then, the Confucius Institute Headquarters reserves the right to interpret this Constitution and By Laws (Chapter 8:39). There are no omnipresent shared values to guide the institutes. All partners are looking for benefits: host university benefit of Chinese language classes for students and earning China prestige. Confucius Institute benefits from the credibility and reputation of the host university. Chinese university as academic partner improves their domestic academic relevance as "international exchange", an index for evaluation of Chinese universities and colleges.

To summarize, the management of the institute is quite a challenge. The 7Ss analysis shows that strategy, structure, systems, style, skills, staff and shared values are not consistent and they do not support each other. This analysis, while it helps to identify what needs to be change, it is also important to address the critical role of coordination in organizational effectiveness.

**Discussion**

Indeed, China has done much to promote its soft power to win hearts and minds. Chinese soft power stresses culture and harmony whereas American soft power advocates the universal values of democracy and human rights. China has allocated substantially resources to cultivate a better image of China. Chinese government has expanded the capacity of its mass media in international communications and established over 400 Confucius Institutes all over the world targeting to increase the number to 500 institutes by the end of 2014. Confucius Institutes, supported by the Chinese government play increasingly important role in China's foreign policy serving as areas of public diplomacy for cultural exchange and international communication. However, it seems that the impact of China's increasing soft power resources to win minds and hearts in China's global reach and how China is perceived internationally is twofold. The number of Chinese language learners and cultural exchange has increased quite substantially. On the other hand, this positive development has not led to more positive ratings for the People's Republic as found in a survey by the Pew Research Center conducted in 39 countries among 37,653 respondents from March 2 to May 1, 2013. Overall, the U.S. enjoys a stronger global image than China. One of the major challenges for China's global image is that few believe the Chinese government respects the personal freedoms of its people. Another challenge for China's image is that around the world the prevailing view is that China acts unilaterally in world affairs, pursuing in its own interests and not taking into account the interests of other countries when making foreign policy decisions. Science and technology are China's most popular soft power. But the spread of Chinese ideas and customs and Chinese cultural products-such as music, movies and television-lack majority appeal. Chinese discourse on soft power reflects the fact that the Chinese socio-political system is not in conformity with the global political discourse and atmosphere within which political openness and pluralism are the dominant norms. The fact is that China is still undergoing a profound economic, social and political transition. It is clear that China's soft-power has yet to develop. ①

As Hanban declares the Confucius Institutes have become a platform for cultural exchanges between China and the world as well as a bridge reinforcing friendship and cooperation between China and the rest of the world and are much welcomed across the globe. ② Chinese diplomacy with the highest level Chinese leadership pays much attention to Confucius Institutes. They attend the Signing Ceremony of the Confucius Institutes as did President Xi Jinping in Samarkand Uzbek on September 9, 2013 and Premier Li Keqiang at Hanoi University in Vietnam on October 13, 2013. Liu Qibao, Member of the Political Bureau of the CPC Central Committee and Head of the Publicity Department of the CPC Central Committee paid a visit to Tel Aviv University in Israel on October 21, 2013 where he was talking with the Israeli students studying Chinese language there. And, very recently in July 17, 2014, in the presence of Chinese President Xi Jinping and his Brazilian counterpart Dilma Rousseff, Chief Executive of Confucius Institute Headquarters and Director General of Hanban Xu Lin respectively signed agreements on the joint establishment of Confucius Institutes with the heads of the Federal University of Ceara, the State University of Campinas and the Federal University of Pará.

In spite of these efforts, political and financial, Confucius Institutes may not be as widely known in a society as one could expect. Certainly, this results from various reasons. Using the 7Ss analysis it became clear that institutes needs change to make them more attractive and effective. However, this is not the only challenge of the institutes and of their partners. More profound thinking is needed for the change. As Mette Lendin says, cultural exchange is not only 'art' and 'culture' but also communicating a country's thinking, research, journalism and national debate. In this perspective, this wider concept include new priorities, such as the promotion of human

---

① America's Global Image Remains More Positive than China's. But Many See China Becoming World's Leading Power. Pew Research Center, July 18, 2013. See: www.pewglobal.org. Accessed 8 August 2014.

② About Confucius Institutes. http://english.hanban.org/node_10971.htm. Accessed 26 June 2014.

rights and the spread of democratic values, notions such as good governance, and the role of the media in civil society. Thus, the argument is that as long as intellectual dialogue of contemporary China with its challenges is discouraged, this limits China's soft power goals. As long as Confucius institutes gives power to ideological "watchdogs" to censure so called China sensitive issues, this has an impact on worldviews about China. As Nye says, the essence is how to use soft power *resources* and *behavior* to achieve desired outcomes.① Thus, the question is how attractive these are to others, and whether attraction can influence others to gain favorable outcomes. The key issue with soft power is that *what target thinks is most important*. Hence, the targets matters as much as the agents. As Nye says "soft power is a dance that requires partners".②

*Seeing mountains' climbing and rivers' curving,*

*I could see no way ahead,*

*Suddenly in the shade of the willows and amidst shining flowers,*

*a village appeared.*

This Song dynasty poem is a metaphor how Confucianism has been criticized and then revived from time to time. Confucius (551 B.C. to 479 B.C.) was a thinker, political figure, and educator. Fung Yu-lan, one of the great $20^{th}$ century authorities on the history of Chinese thought, compares Confucius' influence in Chinese history with that of Socrates in the West. Confucian values Filial Piety (*xiao*), Humanity (*ren*), and Ritual (*li*) are taught in the Four Books. Filial piety that is connected with ancestor worship is the root of humanity. Every human being has capacity to possess *ren* also interpreted as "goodness," "benevolence," and "love." *Li*, respect for ritual is interpreted as the proper way of doing things. Confucius advocated moral education in his teaching (Zhang 2004: 66, 178) His teachings in the *Lunyu* or *Analects* form the foundation of *junzi*-the educated man and how such an individual should live his life and interact with others, and the forms of society and government in which he should participate. Confucius presented the idea of harmony and harmonious society (*hexie shehui*). In China, thousands of years ago character "he", which means harmony and peace was carved on tortoise shells. Confucius extended the philosophical concept

① Nye 2004: 69-80.

② Nye 2011: 84.

"harmony without uniformity", meaning a world is full of differences and contradictions, but the righteous man should balance them and achieve harmony.

Throughout the 20th century, China's Communist leaders criticized Confucianism and denounced Confucius as the personification of China's "feudal" traditions, with anti-Confucianism campaigns, ranging from the 1912 New Culture Movement to the 1973 Criticize Lin, Criticize Confucius campaign during the Cultural Revolution when Confucianism was seen as an obstacle and throwback to the past.

Recently, China has set up Confucius Institutes. Confucianism and the Confucian classics are experiencing a revival. Yu Dan, professor of media studies at China's Beijing Normal University has popularized the Analects. Her book *Insights into Analects* (2006) remains on the bestseller lists. The book has also been criticized for being a product to serve current Chinese politics as it neglected Confucian spirit of political and social critique. Confucianism is back in fashion. In 2005, China started to advance social harmony, first in the domestic sphere and then at the United Nation's 60th anniversary summit in June where President Hu Jintao promoted multilateralism and harmony by building "a world where all civilizations coexist harmoniously and accommodate each other". ① The "Harmonious Socialist Society" serves also the goal building up *Xiaokang* (well-off) society by 2020 as a part of Hu Jintao's Scientific Development concept. White Paper on peaceful development issued by the Chinese government describes "harmony as the building of a peaceful and prosperous world as the ultimate goal of China's development". ②

What means politicization and commercialization of Confucian values and traditional Chinese culture to the society? Confucianism it is not a doctrine of the party, although the CCP embraces harmony. Marxism, the national ideology and market economy goes hand in hand. In pursuit of becoming rich, kind heathenness and compassion are not any more first in minds of Chinese people. It seems that today's revival of Confucianism and stress on Chinese culture and history and harmonious world serves the goals of foreign policy, constructing a new world order through diplomatic effort and idealized image of the country.

---

① http://www.un.org/webcast/summit2005/statements15/china050915eng.pdf, Accessed 8 August 2014.

② People's Daily, October 2, 2007. http://english.people.com.cn/90001/90776/6275744.html

Confucius' political beliefs were rooted in his belief that a good ruler would be self-disciplined who would govern his subjects by his own example. Confucius said "he who governs by means of his virtues is like the pole-star: it remains in its place while all the lesser stars do homage to it" (Lunyu 2.1) As Chinese American historian Yu Ying-shih says the ethical and philosophical system developed from the teachings of the Confucius (551-479 BC) is "all-encompassing," Freedom, equality, fraternity, human rights, and the rule of law are all universal values.[①] So are the five constant Confucian virtues of benevolence, righteousness, propriety, wisdom and good faith. Democracy is a universal value, so is the Confucian concept of the people being the foundation of society. In implementing universal values and working toward modernization and democratization, traditional Chinese culture can be a resource.

How to connect universal Confucian virtues to modern Chinese Dream[②] concept is a great task to the Chinese government. The challenges are many and bound to: How to resolve corruption, how economy can transfer its manufacturing and trade structures, how to balance the income gap, how to progress social development in aging society within urbanization process, how to increase transparency, and how to develop in sustainable manner to protect environment. How China handles these challenges are bound to how China's soft power develops. And finally, the key question is how Chinese soft power aiming to build friendship and partnerships and help to enhance global stability, is perceived in the world.-it's not just image-building.

**REFERENCES**

About Confucius Institutes. http://english.hanban.org/node_10971.htm. Accessed 26 June 2014.

America's Global Image Remains More Positive than China's. But Many See China Becoming World's Leading Power. Pew Research Center, July 18, 2013. See: www.pewglobal.org. Accessed 8 August 2014.

The Annual Report 2012 of Confucius Institute Headquarter (Hanban).

Chen, Zhimin. 2005. Nationalism, Internationalism and Chinese Foreign Policy. *Journal of Contemporary China*, 14 (42), February, 35-53.

---

① http://www.tang-prize.org/ENG/Publish.aspx? cnid = 320&p = 223. Accessed 8 August 2014.

② *Chinese Dream*. 2013.

China promotes its culture overseas to dissolve "China threat". May 28, 2006.

http://english. peopledaily. com. cn/200605/28/eng20060528_269209. html. Accessed 26 June 2014.

*Chinese Dream. Development Under New Leadership*. 2013. China Intercontinental Press.

Constitution and By-Laws of the Confucius Institutes. Confucius Institute Headquarters. http://english. hanban.org/node_7880.htm. Accessed 8 August 2014.

The Confucius Institute Journal, Volume 30, 01, Jan. 2014.

The Confucius Institutes and the Chinese Renaissance . http://www.huffingtonpost. com/david-gosset/the-confucius-institutes-_b_3819878. html. Accessed 26 June 2014.

Ding, S. and Saunders, R. A. 2006. Talking up China: An analysis of China's rising cultural power and global promotion of the Chinese language. *East Asia*, 23 (2), 3-33.

Fung Youlan. 1985. Zhongguo zhexue jianshi (A Concise History of Chinese Philosophy) Beijing: Beijing daxue chubanshe. pp. 211-222.

Freedman, Lawrence. 2004. *China as a Global Strategic Actor*. In: Buzan Barry and Rosemary Foot (eds.), Does China Matter? A Reassessment. London: Routledge, 21-36.

Gossett, David. The Confucius Institutes and The Chinese Renaissance. http://www. huffingtonpost. com /david-gosset/the-confucius-institutes-_b_3819878. html. Accessed 8 August 2014.

Hartig, Falk. 2012. Cultural diplomacy with Chinese characteristics: The Case of Confucius Institutes in Australia. Communication, Politics & Culture, 45, 256-276.

Hartig, Falk. Confucius Institutes and the Rise of China. *Journal of Chinese Political Science* , March 2012, Volume 17, Issue 1, pp 53-76.

Huntington, Samuel. 1996. The Clash of Civilizations and the Remaking of World Order. New York: Simon & Schuster.

Huntington, Samuel. 1993. Clash of Civilization. *Foreign Affairs*. Summer 1993. http://www. hks. har vard. edu/ fs/pnorris/Acrobat/Huntington_Clash. pdf. Accessed 25.1.2014.

Jiang Zemin. 2002. "Build a Well-off Society in an All-Round Way and Create a New Situation in Building Socialism with Chinese Characteristics". Full Text of Jiang

Zemin's Report at 16th Party Congress, Nov. 8, 2002. http://english.people.com.cn/200211/18/eng20021118_106985.shtml. Accessed 8 August 2014.

Keohane Robert Owen and Joseph S. Nye. 1977. Little Brown.

Kurlantzick, Joshua. 2008. *Charm Offensive: How China's Soft Power is Transforming the World*. New Haven: Yale University Press.

Lai, H. 2012. *The Soft Power concept and a rising China* In: Lai and Lu2012: 11. See also: http://dangxiao.jmu.edu.cn/show.asp? id=1156. Accessed 8 July 2013.

Lai, H. 2012. *China's Cultural Diplomacy*. In: Lai and Lu 2012:85.

Lai and Lu. (2012). Eds. *China's Soft Power and International Relations*. Routledge: London and New York.

Li, Mingjiang. 2008. China Debates Soft Power. *Chinese Journal of International Politics*, Vol. 2, 2008, 287-308.

Liu Qing and Wang Li-tao. 2007. Review Domestic Studies of Soft Power Theory in Recent Years. Journal of Jiangnan 2007-02. Social University. China.

Ma, Lisi. "Guanyu Woguo Jiaqiang Ruan Shili Jianshe de Chubu Sikao", (Preliminary Thoughts on Accelerating China's Soft Power Building). Dang de Wenxian (Literature of Chinese Communist Party), No. 7, pp. 35-38. In: Li Mingjiang, China Debates Soft Power. *Chinese Journal of International Politics*, Vol. 2, 2008, 287-308.

Marshall Sahlins. 2013. China U. *The Nation*, November 18, 2013.

People's Daily, October 2, 2007. http://english.people.com.cn/90001/90776/6275744.htmlPan, Yue. "Quanguo Zhengxie Zhaokai Zhuanti Xieshanghui" (CPPCC National Committee Convenes a Special Consultation Meeting). Renmin Ribao (People's Daily). In: Li Mingjiang, China Debates Soft Power. *Chinese Journal of International Politics*, Vol. 2, 2008, 287-308.

Nathan Andrew and Robert S. Ross. 1997. *The Great Wall and the Empty Fortress: China's Search for Security* (New York: W. W. Norton. Nathan, Andrew. Principles of China's Foreign Policy.

http://afe.easia.columbia.edu/special/china_1950_forpol_principles.htm. Accessed 3 July 2012.

Nye, Joseph. 1990. *Bound to Lead: The Changing Nature of American Power*

Nye, Joseph S, Jr. 2011. *The Future of Power*. Public Affairs: New York.

Paradise, J. F. 2009. China and international harmony: The role of Confucius Institutes in bolstering Beijing's soft power. *Asian Survey*, *XLIX*(4), 647-669.

Starr, Don. 2009. Chinese Language Education in Europe: the Confucius Institutes. European Journal of Education Special Issue: Chinese-European Cooperation in Education. Volume 44, Issue 1, pages 65-82, March 2009.

Suettinger, Robert. 2004. The Rise and Descent of Peaceful Rise. *China Leadership Monitor*, No. 12.

Swaine Michael and Tellis Ashley, 2000. *Interpreting China's Grand Strategy. Past, Present, and Future*. Rand: Washington.

Wang, Huning. 1993. "Culture as National Soft Power: Soft Power." *Journal of Fudan University*. March 1993.

Wey-Shen Siow, Maria. 2011. China's Confucius Institutes: Crossing the River by Feeling the Stones . *Asia Pacific Bulletin*, Number 91, January 6, 2011.

Yang, Rui. 2010. Soft power and Higher Education: An Examination of China's Confucius Institutes. Globalization, Societies, and Education, 8 (1).

Zhang, Xiaoming. 2005. An Analysis of Joseph Nye's "Soft Power" Concept. American Studies Quarterly, 2005-01. China.

ZhengYongnian and Chi Zhang. 2012. *"Soft Power" and Chinese soft power*. In: Lai and Lu 2012: 21. Internet

http://dangxiao.jmu.edu.cn/show.asp? id=1156. Accessed 8 July 2013.

http://english.hanban.org/node_7880.htm. Accessed 29 July 2014.

http://www.tang-prize.org/ENG/Publish.aspx? cnid=320&p=223. Accessed 8 August 2014.

http://www. un. org/webcast/summit2005/statements15/china050915eng. pdf, Accessed 8 August 2014.

# The Remaking of World Order and the Role of Chinese Universal Values

Guo Yi (Department of Philosophy, Seoul National University)

Future world order will be an integrated global civilization. Who can unite the world? Toynbee said: Chinese civilization!

He said, after the collapse of Roman Empire, the Western world has never retrieved the political unification. Since then, the Western political tradition is not cosmopolitanism, but nationalism. Therefore, the West cannot fulfill the political unification of the world.

At the end of 1970's, when China was in Culture Revolution, Toynbee made an unexpected judgment: the one will unite the world in the future is not a European Country, nor a Europeanized country, but China!

Why? On one hand, Chinese nation has rich historical experience; on the other, it has a long-standing world spirit.

In this presentation, I would like to interpret and prove this judgment.

## I. the Experience of Ancient Chinese Organicising World

Scholars noticed very early that, compared to other countries of the world, ancient China was very special. Liang Qichao called it "anti-countryism", "super-countryism", "cosmopolitanism"①. Liang Shuming also said: "China was not a country in a category of ordinary countries, but rather a super-country." ②His conclusion, drawn from multi-faceted study, was that China was quite unlike a country. Internally it lacked the capacity that a country should have, that is, politically it was passive and

① Liang Qichao, *History of Pre-Qin Plitical Thought*, chap. 1 (Zhonghua Book Company, 1996).

② Liang Shuming, *Liang Shuming Collected Works*, vol. 1, p. 26 (Shandong People's Publishing House, 1990).

laissez-faire: externally, it lacked international antagonism①. The English philosopher Russell believes: "China really was a cultural body, not a country." ②Their views are correct. In my opinion, this uniqueness of China, its difference from a country, is all due to it being a society where the world was seen as organicising.

Among the concepts held by Chinese ancients, one which largely corresponds to the Western words "world" and "globe" is [a two-character word which, literally translated, means] "tian xia (under sky)". The literal meaning of "under sky" is "everywhere under the sky", meaning every inhabited place. Given the geographical limits of the time, the Chinese ancients simply did not know that beyond China there existed other peoples and civilizations, so, at the beginning "under sky", in fact, meant all land in the China sphere. But the connotation of "under sky" [hereafter referred to as "Chinese world", meaning the Chinese vision of the world] and "world" [hereafter called "Western world"] have indeed differences. The latter means the limits of the space made up of different countries and regions; it is a loose system, with each part relatively independent, even mutually repellent, while the former is a united and complete body. Although we can say it is made up of different countries and regions, the different parts are subordinate to the unifying embrace of the Chinese world. That is to say, the concept that the Chinese world embodies is a world merging into an organic whole [hereafter referred to as the "organicising world". It is precisely in this sense that Liang Shuming said: "From the beginning Chinese have substituted for the concept of country the concept of the Chinese world."③

The reason "Chinese world" and "Western world" have different connotations lies in the differences between the states of socialisation of Chinese and Western civilization. After striding into the threshold of the civilised era, a stable and enduring core civilization gradually came into being in the vast spaces of China. The spread of this civilization to the surrounding still uncivilised regions naturally formed the Chinese-world" and "Chinese-organicising-world" concepts. In 221BC, Qin's unification also laid the basis for political unity. By comparison, until Europeans entered modern society, they never, in any major sense, conceived of the world as an organic whole, let

---

① Ibid, p. 158-160.

② Ibid, p. 26.

③ Ibid.

alone as a political entity, because they could not form a stable, enduring core civilization—although cultural exchanges existed among the various regions of Europe. Despite this, Europe's strivings and attempts to make itself an organic whole never ceased. In a certain sense, from ancient times, the wars between the various countries of Europe, including the two World Wars of the past century, are, in essence, similar to the annexation wars of the Spring and Autumn and Warring States period, including the Qin war to destroy the 6 states. What was different was that the European efforts to achieve an organic whole by means of war ended in failure, while the Chinese were extremely successful. From the viewpoint of moral values, these wars of invasion and annexation were unjust, but, from the viewpoint of historical value, they pushed forward, to varying degrees, the advance of socialisation. Besides the Qin wars of annexation actually uniting China, another clear proof is that, if the Second World War had not happened, the United Nations-this international organisation-would not have been established.

Ancient China's world was in substance a political and cultural community. Basically, it can be divided into two parts, a core area and a surround. The Chinese organicising world was manifest mainly in political and cultural aspects; its basic form being the political and cultural interaction between core area and surround., In it, the core area's political and cultural radiation and dissemination played the main role, with the core's receipt and absorption of the surround's political culture was secondary.

Looking at it from the study of embryology, this Chinese organicising world was achieved through a process of political merging bringing about a cultural merging, but, in the end, the extent and significance of the cultural merging far and away exceeded that of the political merging. Generally speaking, the process of organicisation of the Chinese world can be divided into three stages. And each stage began with a political merger.

The Five Emperors period to the Yin and Zhou dynasties was the first stage, with the "Many States" [feudal China] and "Four Barbarians" representing, respectively, the core area and surround that were organicising the world of that time.

The Chinese organicising world arose practically together with Chinese civilization. Archaeological excavations have established the many origins of Chinese civilization. Not only the Yellow River basin, but also the Yangtse, Liao and Pearl River basins, and even the south-western region were all birthplaces of Chinese culture. At the dawn of the civilised era, through a series of wars between tribes, a Huaxia race with Emperor Yan and the Yellow Emperor's tribes as core gradually formed. The various states of Huaxia were called the "Many States" [feudal China]. The various races of the surround were, as a group, called the "Four Barbarians", and, individually: in the east "Yi": in the north "Di": to the west "Rong": to the south "Man". Since the Many States were in the middle of the 4 barbarians it was called the "Middle State" [now translated as China], meaning the "Central State". That is to say, "Middle State" [China] was the general name for the various states established by the Huaxia race, and from the beginning did not mean a specially designated country. The Xia, Shang and Zhou [dynasties] of later times were countries established by the Huaxia race. One after another these successive dynasties became the main country of the "Many States" or "Middle State" [China].

Among the various nationalities of the time, or in the Chinese world of the time, or the whole world, the Huaxia race was the strongest, and represented the highest civilization, so it occupied a special position. The leader of its main country was called "King" and "Sky Son", and claimed to be king over all the Chinese world. Early in the time of Yao and Shun the Son of Heaven received regular tribute from the each state, laying the first foundation stones of the pattern of the Chinese organicising world. Later, Yu the Great's taming of the waters further strengthened and consolidated this. Historically, Yu's work was not just a case of flood control-of victory over natural disaster, it was also a great work of establishing boundaries and spreading civilization.. The area affected by his taming of the waters was called Yu's footprint. It may be said that wherever Yu's footprint went, Huaxia's civilization was sure to follow. According to *Zuo Zhuan*, *Fourth Year of Xiang Gong* [the *Zuo Zhuan* is a Commentary on the *Spring and Autumn Annals*]: "Yu's footprint spread widely, marking the nine territories". The Huaxia civilization, to varying degrees, influenced all the nine territories [the nine divisions of China under Yu the Great]. It can be seen from written record and archaeological excavation that the Xia-Shang civilization had already developed to a high degree, and was continuing to spread throughout the surround.

The second stage in the process of organicising of the Chinese world is from the period of enfeoffment at the beginning of the Western Zhou Dynasty. There were in the main three types of enfeoffment. In the first, the Zhou king enfeoffed relatives and meritorious councillors to traditional parts of Huaxia (the Central Plains region), that is-apart from the royal domain-the entire territory of the Huaxia race. Of course, one could not say this was an organicising of the Chinese world. The second was the Zhou dynasty's enfeoffment of members of the royal line and meritorious councillors to subjugated Yi princedoms and haunts, like Qi, Lu, Yan and Jin. This, in fact, was a colonial rule by the Huaxia race of the Yi. Through this type of colonial measure, Huaxia culture then spread relatively rapidly and permeated to the periphery of the surround, making it into a part of the core, or areas undergoing transition to the core. To a very large extent this enlarged the core region of the Chinese organicising world. The third type of enfeoffment was to border regions that had not been subjugated. To those, only local nobility were enfeoffed; no members of the royal line or meritorious councillors were sent to rule them: countries like Qin and Chu were of this type. This then strengthened the political control of the Zhou, and also promoted the organicising of the Chinese world. The situation at the time is as *The Book of Songs: Minor Odes: Northern Mountain* said: "Under the universal sky, there is no territory that is not part of the kingdom; in all territory to the far shores there is nothing without a councillor of the king." At the end of the Zhou Dynasty, the royal house weakened and diminished and the nobility rose, setting of a spate of annexation wars of the Spring and Autumn and Warring States Period, which hastened enormously the organicising of the Chinese world.

Qin Shi Huang's unification of China and the formation of a principal Han nationality marks the entry into a third stage of the Chinese organicising world. After formation of the unified empire Chinese culture continued to spread to more distant regions, and gradually became the main cultural stream of the East Asian region. At the same time, China's powerful momentum in such fields as culture, politics and economics also deeply influenced ancient East Asia's political and cultural domain. In this sense, we have good reason to include the whole of the East Asia region within the field of vision of ancient China's organicising world. Culturally, places like the Korean peninsula, Japan and Vietnam not only introduced Chinese written characters and various ceremonial and legal systems, they also introduced ideologies like Confucianism, Buddhism and Taoism resulting in their becoming the common basis of culture and thought in the entire East Asian region. Politically, in the Han and Tang periods, as relations between China and the states of East Asia moved steadily closer, a tributary system with China as suzerain gradually formed, like the relations that the feudal princedoms of the pre-Qin period had with Xia, Shang and Zhou. Which is to say, in the Chinese world of that time, the Central Plains empire formed the core region, with the other areas of East Asia the regions of the surround. So, the East Asia common body that we talk of today has ample historical cultural roots.

The organicisation of ancient China's world was achieved principally through 4 channels.

First came wars of annexation, e.g., a first stage of tangled wars among tribal alliances, a second of hegemonic struggles among the various states, and a third of the central authority's punitive expeditions against the political power of the national minorities and other small states, etc. Secondly, the channel of peaceful politics; the highest rulers of the core region used peaceful methods to effect political control over the surround, trying to bring the whole of the Chinese world into their sphere of influence, and create an organicising society. For example, the dynastic tributary system of the first stage, the enfeoffment system of the second, and the feudal tributary arrangement of the third stage, were all part of this. Thirdly, the channel of spreading culture. One side of this was the spread to the surround of the highly developed culture of the core area, raising the surround's cultural level; another was the core area's acceptance and absorption of the culture of surround, which, in turn, to a degree in turn, enriched and strengthened the culture of the core area. In other words, the culture of the surround is assimilated by the core region and the core region's culture is also, to a certain degree, dissimilated by the surround. Assimilation and dissimilation exchanging and enhancing each other, gradually merging the culture of core and surround into one. Fourthly, the channel of assimilation of nationalities. In ancient China the distinction between the nationalities of the core and surround was often undefined, to the point where sometimes the races of the surround had only to accept the core area's mainstream culture and actively participate in its political activities to become members of the cores region nationality. Of course, sometimes assimilation of nationalities was achieved by means of war. In Chinese history, it is not known how many national minorities were absorbed into the main one. In summary, following the strengthening of political and cultural movement between the core and surround and the partnership-like blending of nationalities, the core region constantly expanded, and with increased geographical knowledge and the growing frequency of contact among the nationalities, the surround also continually expanded.

**II. the characteristics of Ancient Chinese Organicising World**

Ancient China's organicising world had the following main characteristics.

First, many in one. Although China's world as an organic whole led to the weakening of localism-e. g., very many national minorities and their culture merged into the Huaxia Han race and its culture, thereby ceasing to be principals-the cultural distinctiveness and innate character of the each region did not disappear. In this respect, we can say that China's culture is multicultural. Not only was the Spring and Autumn and Warring States Period Chinese culture's most illustrious era, it was also a key period in the creation of the multicultural structure. According to region, we can divide the culture of the time into many different types, such as the Central Plain culture, Zou and Lu culture [parts of Shandong where Mencius & Confucius respectively were born], Yan and Qi culture [Hebei and north-east Shandong], Three Jins culture [the 3 states of Wei, Zhao & Han], Qin culture, Chu culture [Hunan, most of Hubei and part of Guizhou], Wu and Yue culture (Jiangsu and Guangdong), Ba and Shu culture [Sichuan] and so on and so forth. Among them, the Central Plains district was the great base camp of Huaxia culture, so naturally the ancient Central Plains culture was Huaxia culture's orthodox school. Zou and Lu were originally under the eastern Yi, but, from the great enfeoffments of Western Zhou, they promoted a comprehensive "Huaxia-isation" policy; and, after Western Zhou died out, it became the main fortress of Huaxia culture, to the point where people of the time said "Zhou customs were taken to the ultimate in Lu". Yan and Qi culture was a product of the combination of Huaxia and eastern Yi culture, Three Jins culture and Qin culture were a combination of Huaxia culture and Rong Di culture; as for Chu, Wu and Yue, and Ba and Shu, because they were quite far from the Central Plains region and their receipt of Huaxia culture was relatively slight, their innate national culture maintained quite high purity, even though cultural exchange was already quite frequent.

After Qin unification, although, historically, rulers have liked to promote a monocultural policy-such as Qin Dynasty promotion of its Legalist culture, Han Dynasty promotion of the study of the Yellow Emperor and Laozi [Taoism] that originated in Chu, and, in the time of the Han Dynasty Emperor Wu Di making "Rejection of the

100 schools, and respect only for Confucianism" national policy-nevertheless, in the main, the pre-Qin period had created a multicultural culture system that continued on. Even through to today, the difference in culture and language of the various areas is obvious. The extent of difference is probably no less than that among the countries of Europe, which amass to a similar size. The difference from Europe is that although though the dialects of the different areas have multitudinous differences, they use common written characters: this perhaps is the unique accomplishment of ancient China's organicising world.

The second main characteristic was that, at the same time as the regions maintained the individuality of their local cultures, those cultures entered also into a common territory. It cannot be doubted that the Confucianists, the Taoists, the Legalists and such were formerly regional cultural phenomena that, at an early stage, were comprehensively accepted by he Chinese, and together merged into China's great cultural river. In their respective areas such as moral principles, politics, outlook on life, literature and art each manifest an energy and gave rise to delightful contrasts. Later, Buddhism—created in India—spread to China; it also gradually entered the souls of Chinese, becoming a type of general cultural phenomenon and a major integral part of Chinese culture, and thereby greatly enriched and amplified the multicultural organic system.

Thirdly, in the multicultural organic system, the various cultures not only permeated each other, they were also able to get along harmoniously. In many regions of the world, different belief and religious groups, nationalities and countries often saw each other as enemies, and were irreconcilable, and even willing to start protracted religious wars. But in China, people with different beliefs not only got on with each other without any problem, they were able to draw on each other's experiences, and be magnanimous one to the other. The three teachings of Confucianism, Buddhism and Taoism were China's principal belief carriers. As for getting along together, historically, although they have competed to become the official ideology, in the main, competition was peaceful, rational and was not a spark for outbreaks of religious warfare. Take, for example, their ideas and theories; there was mutual absorption and mutual study among them. According to research, Confucianism and Taoism had a common origin. Later, although the two assumed a confrontational stance, the traces of their influence on each other remain very clear. Initially, Buddhism's entry was through matching concepts, which means that it borrowed Taoist concepts to penetrate China's thought world. In order to adapt to Chinese society, it also absorbed many Confucian moral principles. By the time of the Song and Ming Dynasties, Confucian scholars, while using Confucian ideals as their platform, were, at the same time, amply absorbing the two teachings of Buddhism and Taoism, thereby creating a paradigm of Neo-Confucianism.

**III. the Confucian "Worldism"**

What is the world spirit in ancient China? It was embodied in "worldism".

"Worldism" is an ideology corresponding to the Chinese organicising world. In sweeping terms, all advocacy and viewpoints that had a positive attitude toward the Chinese organicising world, can be summed up as "worldism". Looking at "*The Book of History*", "*The Book of Changes*", "*The Book of Songs*" and other early classics, "worldism", from the beginning, took the position of orthodoxy in Chinese culture. Later, although Chinese schools of learning and thought increased in number and complexity, in the main, they maintained a "worldism" stand. Among them, probably, Confucian "worldism" was the most complete system. Its main points were as follows:

(1) Tian (sky, Heaven, the source of myriad things) and mankind uniting as one 天人合一, the myriad things flowing from the same spring 万物同源-the philosophical basis of Confucian "worldism".

In the west, people try to change nature, which is to say, mankind and the natural world are in a confrontational mode. But the Chinese position is completely different. Early in the first stages of Chinese civilization the sky dominated the natural world and society; the actions of the people had to conform with the will of the sky, which is to say, between sky and man was a type of interlinking relationship, this is how the concept of sky and mankind uniting as one germinated.

Later, this concept was accorded philosophical interpretation. Laozi, through his cosmic theory, established his metaphysical system. He thought that in the process of creating the myriad things the way took its own natural being and gave it to the myriad things, and became their inherent character. Mankind should follow the example of the way, and live according to its natural basic character. Like Laozi, Confucius in his later years also probed the secrets of man's nature through Laozi's cosmic creation theory. The elder Confucius, after "Studying *Changes*", established "changes" as the highest metaphysical concept in his philosophical system. He believed the myriad things were created into life from the "changes". "Changes" was basically good, and, in the process of creating the myriad things, took its goodness and gave it to the myriad things. Later, Zisi and Mencius both thought the goodness of men came from the highest metaphysical concept of "sky".

Because philosophers used different concepts to express their understanding of the world's origin -Laozi called it the "way", Confucius in his later years called it "changes", and Zisi and Mencius called it sky, so we consider sky and mankind uniting in onc as having two meanings—a broad and a narrow. The narrow meaning points to an intimate inseparable relationship, while the broad was a general reference to the unity of world's original categories with mankind.

The concept of unity of Tian and mankind meant that mankind and the myriad things had the same origin, so mankind should cherish, and live with, them. By the time of Northern Song Dynasty, Zhang Zai 张载(1020-1077) pointed out explicitly: "The people and I are of the same womb, the myriad things and I likewise". Also, later, Wang Yangming 王阳明(1472-1529)said: "The great man takes Tian, earth and the myriad things as one body, he sees the world as one family, China as one person."

(2) Datong 大同 or the Great Harmonious Togetherness—the Confucian social ideal for the Chinese organicising world.

In *Liji* 礼记 or *The Record of Rites*, Confucius elaborated on his ideal society. It was a world for the common good—a "great harmonious togetherness" society:

"When the grand Dao or the Way is followed, a public spirit reigns in the world; people of virtue and talent are appointed; they speak with credibility and cultivate harmony. Thus people do not limit love to their own parents, nor treat as children only their own children. The aged are secured till death; the able-bodied are employed; the young are able to grow to maturity; there is compassion for the widows, orphans, childless, disabled and diseased, so they are all sufficiently maintained; men have their appropriate lot in life, and women homes; goods are neither wasted, nor hoarded; work is deemed proper but not just with a view to individual advantage. Thus scheming is repressed and cannot flourish. Nor do robbers, thieves, rebels and traitors appear, so front doors are left open. We call this the great harmonious togetherness."

Also, in *Spring and Autumn*, Confucius pursued in greater depth his advocacy of cosmopolitanism to unite the world. The book's first page says: "In the first year of the reign, spring, King Wen established the calendar". Added to this the *Gong Yang Annals Commentary on the Spring and Autumn Annals* explains: "Why is this calendar used by the Annals? Because it is an instrument of world unity."

There were two ways to implement the social ideal of Confucian "worldism". The first was social evolution. According to He Xiu, the sublime words of the *Spring and Autumn Annals* reflect the traces of three periods of evolution: firstly, a time of rebellion and confusion—both within one's own states, and externally with the other Xia: secondly, the rise to a peaceful period—with the interior now being all the Xia and the exterior the Yi and Di: and thirdly, peace and tranquillity—the world, far and near, big and small, as one, with Yi and Di joining the nobility. The second was the way of men improving themselves, like *The Great Learning*'s advocacy of the cultivation of moral character, managing the family, running the country, pacifying the world, with the cultivation of moral character as the key to achieving the great peace: "Things being investigated, knowledge became complete. Knowledge being complete, thoughts were sincere. Thoughts being sincere, hearts were then rectified, and persons were cultivated. Persons being cultivated, their families were regulated. Families being regulated, the states were rightly governed. States being rightly governed, the world was made tranquil and happy. From the son of heaven to the mass of the people, all must consider the cultivation of the person to be the root of everything."

(3) Wangdao 王道 or the kingly way-the way to realize wordism

No matter whether it was the pre-Qin period of many states, or the post-Qin- unification imperial period, Confucianists, consistently, were the most positive supporters and defenders of the Chinese organicising world. They were always able to break through narrow localism, and assume "worldism" as their responsibility.. Fan Zhongyan's famous sentence, "First worry about the world, then enjoy its fruits", portrays the Confucian feelings.

In the Spring and Autumn, and Warring States Periods, respect for the Zhou royal house, which represented "worldism", diminished by the day, and the nobility, which represented localism and nationalism, rose swiftly and violently. Against this, Confucius' position was: "When the world is the way, the ceremonies, music, government and the maintenance of order issue from the Emperor, when it is not, those things issue from the nobility"—*Analects of Confucius. The Ji Family.* He upheld "worldism" and opposed the nationalist attitude that was on everyone's lips. Confucius also said: "Implementation of the five principles is virtue in the world"— *Analects of Confucius. Yang Huo.* This states clearly that Confucius advocated respect, toleration, trust, earnestness and graciousness and so on—a series of moral categories whose aim was to establish law in the world for mankind.

By the Warring States Period, Mencius clearly advocated applying "virtuous government"德治 of the "kingly way"王道 to control the world, and opposed especially warlordism 霸道 that relied on armed struggle to secure advantage. The so-called "kingly way" and "warlordism" represented respectively "worldism" and nationalism.

(4) The Yi-Xia Argument — the cultural basis of Confucian "worldism".

Although, in the main, one can separate the Chinese organicising world into political and cultural levels, Confucianists, far and away stressed more the cultural. The Qing Confucian, Gu Yanwu, once said: "There are lost states, there are lost worlds. How do you distinguish between them? He answered: Where the dynasty and the names are changed, call them lost states; where there humanity and justice are blocked, and it leads to beasts feeding on people and people eating each other, call it a lost world."[①] Liang Shuming explained: "This is China's orthodox school of thought", "It is not the nation that is supreme, nor race, but culture."[②]

The notion that culture is supreme is also seen in Confucianists' Yi-Xia argument. The so-called Yi-Xia argument included principally two points. The first was "The great Xia defence against Yi". It stressed the difference between the two. In fact, in substance it stressed the difference between the two cultures, with the object of preserving the Huaxia civilization, so it would not be assimilated by Yi and Di culture. Secondly, "Use Xia to change the Yi", i.e. use advanced Huaxia culture to change and assimilate Yi and Di culture. So, just as scholars have pointed out, the Yi-Xia argument was a type of cultural separation, not a racial one. This type of thinking has had a gigantic influence in Chinese history; for example, the Mongols and the Manchus, after getting control of political power in China, all consciously accepted Han culture.

---

① Gu Yanwu, *Notes on the Daily Accumulation of Knowledge*, vol. 13, commencement.

② Ibid. note 2, p162.

(5) *He* [harmonious interaction] and not *tong* (bare togetherness or similarity)和而不同-the Confucian pluralist principle for the Chinese organicising world

Comparatively speaking, Westerners stress the opposition and contradiction between different things, but Chinese ancients stressed their harmony. In *The Analects of Confucius . Xue Er* Confucius said:" In using the ceremonies, *he* is precious". In *The Analects . Zilu* he also said: "The superior person is *he* and not *tong*. The inferior person is *tong* and not *he*". Here Confucius emphasises the difference between *he* and *tong*. So-called *he* is the uniting together of different things, arising out of a harmonious attitude. So-called *tong* refers to the adding of a type of thing, and looks very monotonous. . *He* and not *tong* is a basic theory of Confucionism; of course it fits the multicultural approach, and means, with respect to different civilizations, their joint containment and embrace.

Although Confucians stressed the Yi-Xia debate, they certainly did not advocate cultural chauvinism. They believed that national differences and peculiarities should be fully respected. *The Doctrine of the Mean* points out: "As for the ordinary Yi and Di, let them pursue their ways". In the Ming-Ching interregnum the great Confucian Wang Fuzhi even proclaimed : "A king does not restrain the Yi and Di". He fully affirmed multiculturalism and respect for national autonomy; he considered that, among the nationalities, each should preserve its customs, culture and systems; and they should live, and coexist, in peace, and respect and not interfere with one another.

Which is to say, Confucianists stressed the difference between Xia and Di from the point of view of cultural advancement and level of development, while, with respect to the cultural differences and individuality, they stressed multiculturalism.

## IV. The enlightenment from the ancient Chinese organicising world and Confucian "worldism"

At present, there are two relatively influential theories concerning reestablishment of world order: Fukuyama's theory of the end of history and Huntington's theory of the clash of civilization. Both are the product of Western nationalism and both violate Confucian principle of he and not tong. The former is tong and not he, while the "clash" of latter opposites he (harmonious).

The ancient Chinese view of an organicising world was, in fact, in a comparative sense, a type of globalisation. To sum up, the lessons of Chinese experience are undoubtedly helpful in advancing the healthy development of globalisation in the present era.

The most important thing is that the basic distinguishing feature of Confucian "worldism" was peace, harmony, and opposition to the use of force to achieve the Chinese organicising world. That means the ancient Chinese organicising world tells us that globalisation is something that can be achieved by peaceful means.

Therefore, according to Confucian worldism, the correct choice for reestablishment of world order under the background of globalization is 多元一体 (many in one) and 和而不同 he and not tong (to make the world integrated and harmonious without sameness).

In today's world, where the flames of war continue to burn, and terrorism is breaking out, Huntingdon's clash of civilizations theory has found favour among ordinary people. Now, how should one regard today's international situation? There are two principal reasons giving rise to today's clash of world civilizations. Firstly, the great civilizations of the world have developed through thousands of years relatively independently, and created their own unique character. Once these systems civilization systems, by nature very different, encounter each other in the current of globalisation it is extremely easy for them not to mutually adapt, to the point of clashes occurring. In this sense, a clash of civilizations will be a phenomenon very hard to avoid in the globalisation process. Secondly, taking America as leader of the Western countries, it lacks a clear understanding of the position it should take with respect to the above-mentioned world modernisation and globalisation processes, and to other civilizations in the new world order. It achieved modernisation earlier than other civilizations due to the impetus of its science and technology, and economy, and this has led it to think, mistakenly, that Western civilization as a whole is superior to others, and, from that, caused it to wrongly consider itself to be the superior civilization, interfere everywhere in other countries' affairs, impose it will on others, and throughout the globe push only western civilization. If this goes on, a clash between the civilization of Western countries and that of others will be hard to avoid.

But, this does not mean that a clash of civilization is inevitable. In the four traditional roads to the Chinese organicising world-wars of annexation, peaceful politics, spread of culture, and national assimilation, peaceful methods were paramount. It should be emphasised that, as Confucianists saw it, wars of annexation could be superseded by peaceful politics. The core of Confucian "worldism" was precisely to achieve it through peaceful means. The experience of Chinese ancients proves that this position can be realised.

Next, one must have a correct regard for how local knowledge converts to general world knowledge.

In the process of the unification in ancient China, Confucian, Taoist and Legalist thought, changing from local knowledge to general world knowledge. Based on their advantage, they played different roles in the different levels and areas of the united culture.

I believe the same things will happen in today's globalization. In terms of culture advantage, if culture can be divided into spiritual culture, institutional culture and material culture, I think the advantage of Chinese traditional culture lies in the spiritual culture, while the advantage of Western modern culture lies in the material culture. As for institutional culture, the Chinese and Western civilizations are equal. If the modern Western politics is democratic, the Chinese traditional politics is aristarchy or elite governance.

By the way, I must emphasize the difference between political unification and cultural unification. Generally speaking, the ancient Chinese organicising world was achieved through a process of political unification bringing about a cultural unification, but, at the end, the extent and significance of the cultural unification far and away exceeded that of the political unification.

The political unification can be achieved by both piece and force, but the cultural unification is always peaceful.

The political unification is contemporary, while the cultural unification is enduring. For instance, Qin Dynasty used force to unite China, but it only existed for 15 years. And then, Han Dynasty kept the unification by culture, especially by Confucianism.

The situation of the present world is very similar with Warring State Period. Thus the US is very possible to unite the world by force in the future. But if it wants to keep the unification, it must take the Confucian worldism to achieve the cultural unification. Otherwise, it will be the second Qin Dynasty.

### V. The Chinese Universal Values and Their Role in the Future Human Civilization

Like western civilization contributed to human being the universal values such as democracy, freedom, human rights, the major civilizations in the world all have revealed the universal values in different cultural domains.

There are four thought and cultural systems that can most embody the Chinese values, namely, Zhouyi 周易 or *the Book of Changes*, Daoism, Confucianism and Buddhism. Personally speaking, the core values of the four systems are:

Zhouyi — taihe 太和 tai he (the great harmoniousness)

Daoism — ziran 自然(origin-like, beginning-like)

Confucianism — renyi 仁义. ren: love, benevolence, humanity; yi: appropriate, righteousness.

Buddhism—cibei 慈悲. Ci: bringing everyone happiness; bei: removing everyone's pain.

The original meaning of he is response to singing, which indicates the emotional consistency between the two people. It is easy to derive the meaning of consent and cooperation, from which we can in turn derive the meaning of harmony. Tai he (the great harmony) puts he as the cosmic law. In *Tuan* of *Zhou Yi*, it says "the way of Qian is to change and transform, so that everything obtains its correct nature as appointed (by mind of Tian); and (thereafter the conditions of) great harmony are preserved in union. The result is what is advantageous, and correct and firm. Tian creates everything and the myriad states all enjoy repose." ("乾道变化,各正性命。保合大和,乃利贞。首出庶物,万国威宁。") Zhu Xi in his *zhouyi benyi* (*The Original Meaning of Zhou Yi*) put that "tai he is integration and harmony between Yin and Yang." Yin and Yang are two basic agents and forces in the universe, so tai he concerns cosmic laws. In the ancient literature, he has the meaning of integration, especially referring to the relationship between Yin and Yang. Thus, from the explanation of Zhu Xi, tai he has two meanings: one is unity of Yin and Yang; the other is harmony between them. Therefore, as the core value of *Zhou Yi*, tai he embraces two basic parts: one is unity, including unity of the Tian and human, unity of the Gods and human, unity of oneself and external world, and unity of subject and object; the other is the harmony of myriad things, including harmony between Tian and human, harmony between people, harmony in people's heart, and etc.

As is known to all, the law of the unity of opposites is the fundamental law of the Western dialectics, claiming that everything, as well as different things, contains contradiction. Unity and struggle in both parties of a contradiction promote movement, change and development. However, from the Chinese dialectics reflected by the conception of yin and yang in *Zhou Yi*, everything, as well as different things, contains two agents and forces, namely, yin and yang. The two forces are in harmony and united, promoting movement, change and development of all things. Therefore, this dialectics can be called "the law of the harmonious unity of yin and yang".

As a value, tai he entails the original connotations of he. The first is moderation and appropriateness. The second is adjustment and coordination between different things, which is opposite to tong (the same). The relationship between he and 同 tong (sameness) was a hot topic during Spring and Autumn Period. Many scholars are concerned with Shi Bo and Yan Ying's opinions. They both considered that he referred to harmony and integrity between different things, and tong, was the simple accumulation of the same things. Later, Confucius introduced he and tong into the moral category: "the superior man is he but not tong; the small man is tong but not he."①

The supreme notion of Laozi is Dao, taking Zi Ran as the law. He noted that "there was a state which formed chaotically. It existed before the sky and the earth. It is quiet, independent, and never changes its nature. It may be considered the mother of the myriad things. No one knows its name. I call it Dao. If forced to give it a name, I will call it the Great." "Man models himself after Earth, Earth models itself after Tian, Tian models itself after Dao, and Dao models itself after zi ran."② It means that zi ran embodies the core value of Taoism.

The original meaning of zi ran is beginning-like and origin-like. Laozi advocated that all things in the world, including human, the earth, Tian, and Dao, should follow their original nature. As for people's mental state, it should remain peaceful and plain.

Later, based on the notion of zi ran put forward by Laozi, Zhuangzi especially emphasized the spiritual state of zi ran. This is a form of freedom has a more profound meaning compared with the Western individual freedom, that is, the transcen-

---

① *The Analects*, 13:23.

② *The Guodian Bamboo Laozi*, Book A.

dental spiritual freedom and freedom of life.

All in all, as a value, zi ran manifests itself in freedom and peace in spirit, simplicity and honesty in morality, and wuwei (to govern by doing nothing, noninterference) in politics.

The core values of Confucianism had been summarized as ren (benevolence), yi (justice), li(courtesy), zhi (wisdom), xin(credibility) by Dong Zhongshu early in the Han Dynasty. To extract the essence, I think it should be ren and yi. Confucius and Mencius both explained ren as "loving man". Fan Chi asked what Ren is, Confucius answered "loving man"①. Mencius also said, "The people who are benevolent love man, and the people who are polite respect others."② In a word, "loving man" is enthusiasm, love and respect for life. There is no doubt that it is an inner experience. No wonder Mencius also said: "ren lies in people's heart."③

Confucianism stresses to put oneself in another's position. To be more specific, the notion of ren that Confucianism advocated embraces three levels: The first is cherishing and respecting people's own life, as Confucius said, "the man of ren will not seek life at cost of injuring their virtue. They will even sacrifice their lives to fulfill virtue."④ Escaping from death seems to be protecting life, but actually it is trampling on and humiliating life, for the substance of life does not lie in the body, but in the spiritual value of life. Therefore, devoting life when necessary is truly cherishing and respecting life, and is the real manifestation of ren. The second is love for your parents and brothers, "filial piety and fraternal submission is the root of ren."⑤ The third is love for all people. "Zigong asked, 'suppose there is a man who can extensively confer benefits on the people and assist all, what could you say of him? Might he be called ren?' Confucius said, 'he is more than a man of ren. He must be a sage!"⑥

Then how to achieve ren? For Confucius, it is a mental process in which people should learn to feel for others and put themselves into others' shoes. From a positive

---

① *The Analects*, 12:22.

② *Mencius*, 8:28.

③ *Mencius*, 11:11.

④ *The Analects*, 15:9.

⑤ *The Analects*, 1:2.

⑥ *The Analects*, 6:30.

perspective, "the man of ren is one who, desiring to sustain himself, sustains others, and desiring to develop himself, develops others. To be able to draw from one's self a parallel for the treatment of others, what may be called the way of ren."① From a negative perspective, "Zhonggong asked about ren. The Master said, 'when away from home, to behave as though you were receiving a great guest; to employ the people as though you were assisting at a great sacrifice; do not do to others what you do not wish yourself; do not vear resentment either in the state or in the family.'"②

Ren zheng (benevolent governance) is a very important part of ren in Confucianism. Confucius held that carrying out filial piety is a policy of ruling a country. Confucius said, "*The Book of History* says, 'filial piety! Be filial to your parents and kind to your brothers. These qualities are displayed in government.' This also is to engage in government. Why is it that only holding office can be said to be in government?"③ We know, Youzi ever said: "filial piety and fraternal submission are the root of ren." Thus, applying filial piety to politics is benevolent governance. However, the budding benevolence policy is just one aspect of Confucius' thought on politics and his political ideas can be expressed by de zhi (moral governance). Later, Mencius clearly put forward the notion of ren zheng (benevolent governance), which is inheritance and development of moral governance. The essence of it is min ben (people-orientation).

Yi is another core value of Confucianism. Yi implies appropriateness, duty and rightness, from which we can derive the sense of justice and fairness. If ren can be regarded as an inner desire, we can assume that yi comes from external factors, for its standard, Dao, is external.

All in all, as a value, ren yi covers the meaning of love, benevolent governance, people-orientation, justice, fairness and etc.

The biggest difference between Buddhism and other religions is that it advocates people can get relief through their wisdom rather than the external gods. People usually say "Prajnaparamita", which means people can be relieved from all the secular adversities and sufferings through the immense wisdom in their heart. According to

---

① *The Analects*, 6:30.

② *The Analects*, 12:2.

③ *The Analects*, 2:21.

the Buddhism doctrine, people not only need to save themselves, but also save all others, bringing salvation to all living creatures. In the words of Buddhism, this is ci bei.

It says in *Amitāyurdhyāna-sūtra* that " the Buddha's heart is ci bei." In *Mahāprajnāpāramitāsāstra* (*Great Treatise on the Perfection of Wisdom*), it is clearly pointed that "ci bei is the essence of Buddhism." In light of this, it is quite reasonable to take ci bei as the core value of Buddhism. Specifically, ci and bei have different meanings. Ci means loving all people and bringing them happiness; Bei is having compassion for all people and taking away their afflictions. Thus, like ren and yi in Confucianism, ci and bei in Buddhism are two values which are supplementary to each other.

The notion of ci bei in Buddhism is not confined to human. It covers all the living things including flowers, grass, trees, and even the nonliving things like mountains, water, earth and stones. It is similar to the Confucian notion of "all people are my brothers and sisters, all things are my companions" and is of significance for the protection of ecological environment nowadays.

As the Chinese core values, are tai he, zi ran, ren yi, ci bei universal? We can classify them into two categories. One is tai he and zi ran, as is discussed above, embodying the cosmic laws. Therefore, there's no doubt that they are universal. The other is ren yi and ci bei, reflecting human nature, thus its universal value could not be denied either.

**VI. The Better Politics**

It should be noted that the universal values from the Chinese civilization could supplement and correct the defects of the universal values from the Western civilization.

First, Chinese and Western universal values belong to different value categories. Obviously, tai He, zi ran, ren yi and ci bei are Chinese universal values that derive from different belief systems and belong to final values, while Western universal values like freedom, equality, democracy and human right can be attributed to common values like social values, political values, and etc.

In terms of culture advantage, if culture can be divided into spiritual culture, institution culture and material culture, I think the advantage of Chinese traditional culture lies in the spiritual culture, while the advantage of Western modern culture lies in the material culture. As for institution culture, the Chinese and Western civilizations are equal.

People may ask "Isn't the Western institution culture a big advantage?" The answer is yes in the current situation that the traditional Chinese institution culture is neglected. But if we discard prejudices, and explore the treasure of the Chinese traditional institution culture, we will find that the Chinese and Western civilizations are equal in this aspect and can complement each other. If the modern Western politics is democratic, the Chinese traditional politics is aristarchy or elite governance.

Churchill ever said: "The democratic institution is very bad, but other institutions are worse." It is usually transcribed as "the democratic institution is the least bad institution." In view that the democratic institution has been accepted by more and more regions in the world, we can further say that it is the best institution that still exists. But it doesn't mean democratic institution is an ideal political institution.

Therefore, in the era of globalization, can we establish a political institution better than democracy? The author proposes that in terms of framework, a new political institution should be built creatively on the basis of the combination of the Western democratic politics and the Chinese traditional elite politics.

During this process, the Confucian conception of "concentrating on rule of virtue supplementing by rule of law" deserve our attention.

In terms of the politicians' qualities, the Confucian idea of "sagely inside and kingly outside"内圣外王 should be adopted, just as Confucius said, "if a ruler makes his own conduct correct, what difficulty will he have in governing? If he cannot rectify himself, what has he to do with rectifying others."

In terms of political strategies, it's important to learn from Taoism, especially the political conception of wuwei (to govern by doing nothing, noninterference) in politics.

# The Contribution of Confucian Religion to Regional and Global Peace

Dr. Drs. Chandra Setiawan, M. M. , Ph. D

## I. Introduction

According to Thomas Hosuck Kang, Ph. D (1999) Confucianism is a universal system of human behavior. It includes religion, philosophy, psychology, sociology, anthropology, ethics, science, and all others. On the other hand, Tu Weiming, himself come down solidly on the side of saying that Confucianism is a religion with a considerable spiritual dimension. He emphasizes Confucianism is not a religion limited to a particular culture, race, or nationality (1993:10).

The experience of rapid development in East Asia, is has been increasingly recognized that Confucian commitments to self-improvement, family ties, education, and the social good may actually have facilitated economic and political modernization in East Asia societies.

Prof. Fosco Maraini, an Italian Japanologist as quoted by Bey, Arifin (1997: 175) in Bakar, Osman, Ed. , Nai, Cheng Gek (1997) has listed nine requirements for a society to absorb science and technology and hence, to modernize.

1). It does not experience serious racial, religious, linguistic, caste, cultural, and sexual divisions;

2). Its respect for learning and desire for information is traditional;

3). It is capable for grasping and appreciating the scientific is climate of though;

4). Its normal approach to life and its problems is pragmatic;

5). Its attitude to work is positive;

6). There is a widespread competitive spirit;

7). A stable social order;

8). Collaboration among individuals and organizations is habitual; and

9). Manual dexterity is common to many people

In short, in modern society the progress of humanity depends in a large measure on how effectively human beings organize themselves into groups, bid and small, and how efficiently the various groupings interact and cooperate among themselves to pursue the common good. With globalization (not just confined to the economic sense) steadily gathering way, the coming century will witness the proliferation of a greater variety of extra and supra-state organizations or of trans-national movements tackling such world-wide problems as energy crisis, food shortage, population explosion, and enivironmental protection. This development will drive civilizations into closer contact with one another than ever before for good or for evil.

Globalization that is faced by modern society holds the twin prospects of conflict and accomodation of values and beliefs of different civilizations. It is therefore necessary for people of different civilizational backgrounds to understand one another with tolerance and an open mind through dialogue, so that a common ground may be identified for cooperation, More significantly, seeking such a common ground is a neccesary step in the evolution of a global ethics needed for truly global society (Nai, Cheng Gek, 1997: 206).

**II. The Vision of Confucian for Peaceful World**

The Confucian vision of the Grand Unity Society (*datong shehui*) is the fundamental vision to create a peaceful world. The Confucius' vision of the future of mankind, the Great Harmony, the Grand Unity, is particularly relevant in the context of globalization. The Grand Unity emphasized at least the following ten values (Nai, Cheng Gek, 1997: 219):

(1) The democratic ideal

(2) Love and caring ( a loving culture)

(3) Trustworthiness

(4) Social solidarity (neighborliness)

(5) Benevolence ( the care for the disadvantages; altruism)

(6) Fairness and justice (meritocracy)

(7) Prudence

(8) Security

(9) Peace and harmony

(10)Social order (low crime rate)

The Ethical World- Confucius' vision is not limited to nation. He advocated the ideal of Grand Unity (*datong*) of the world's nations and the idea that the world is shared by all (*tianxia wei gong*).

**III. Moslem and Confucian Dialogue in Malaysia and Indonesia**

In 12-14 March 1995 the University of Malaya organized an international seminar on civilizational dialogue between Islam and Confucianism. It was a historic seminar according to Osman Bakar, because it was the first time on a large scale. The seminar was attended around a thousand people, mostly Malaysians of all races and religions. In this dialogue several speakers such as Tu Weiming mentioned the compatibility between Islam and Confucian tradition about Almighty, the source of power, idea, submission, and humility that allow us to free ourselves from slavery, greed, and anxiety and to pursue a desirable personal status with a new spiritual dimension embedded in one's daily life. In this dialogue there are concepts of ethics to be discussed such as the ethical of person, family, nation and world community. They also discussed the cardinal virtues: benevolence, filial piety, dedication, altruism, propriety, righteousness, wisdom and trustworthiness (Bakar, Osman, 1997).

I believe the dissemination of the seminar though media, book and the people that attended the dialogue already bring the positive outcome to strengthening the good relations between Islam and Confucian in Malaysia and neighboring countries such as Singapore and Indonesia.

Last year in Indonesia from 23 to 25 of August 2013 in order to facilitate a constructive dialogue between Confucian leaders and Moslem leaders and contribute to the creation of a culture of peace and harmony in a globalizing world, the Supreme Council for Confucian Religion in Indonesia (MATAKIN) in cooperation with Majelis Ulama Indonesia (MUI)/ The Indonesian Council of Ulama held the summit title, " Islam and Confucian Summit (ICS) 2013 in Jakarta, the capital city of Indonesia. The summit was attended by the Islam ulama and Confucian leaders from all the provinces in Indonesia and several countries, such as Malaysia, Singapore, Japan, Chinese-Taipei, and Hong Kong. The summit officially was opened by the vice President of Republic Indonesia, Prof. Boediono. In his keynote address Prof. Boediono stated that the dialogue of religious followers such as ICS can help in preventing conflict between groups and promote mutual understanding between religious followers. The dialogue between religious communities always become "fresh wind" in the middle of declining tolerance and conflict among group of ethnics in Indonesia and any places of the world. The summit agreed to make a commitment with the declaration title "Jakarta Message for a Peaceful world" as it is shown as an Appendix.

Even though most of Indonesian is Moslem, Indonesia is not an Islamic state. Therefore although Confucian in Indonesia is a minority, the Confucian can leave together harmoniously with most Moslem in Indonesia. I believe the ability and capacity of Confucian Indonesia to maintain in tolerance and harmony with other religious communities due to the contribution of Confucius teaching. For Prophet Kongzi (Confucius), a single person cannot live alone. Men are plural, more than two who are living together. Thus, men are by nature 'organization men'. Men are among men who live in the web of human relationships, e.g. parents and children, husband and wife, older and younger persons, friend and friend, and ruler and the people. What are the rules which regulate human relationships for harmony and peace to commence a happy life? The virtues, that are *ren* (benevolence/humaneness), *yi* (righteousness), *zhi* (wisdom), *li* (propriety), *yong* (courage) and *xin* (mutual trust). Through learning and self cultivation only a man can become a matured, civilized and well-cultured. To learn practicing virtue is to be done in life persistent as a part of spiritual devotion to *Tian*, God the Almighty, which become the source of the moral power of man in developing to answer the challenges and tests of worldly life. To be a Confucian (*Junzi*, gentleman) has to show that as a human being he/she holds the responsibilities to keep, care, survive, and develop virtues potentialities in his/her inner-self; love or benevolence, righteousness, propriety, and knowledge or wisdom are not infused into us from without. These virtues are already with us. Several sacred articles in Confucius teaching as follow:-"*Within the four-corners of oceans all humankinds are brothers and sisters*" (*Lun Yu XII*:5). -"*Do not do what you do not want others to do unto you*" (Lun Yu XV:24).-"*A benevolent man helps others to take their stand in that he himself wishes to take his stand, and gets others there in that he himself wishes to get there*" (Lun Yu VI:30.3).

By describing the example on how Confucian religion and tradition play important role and contribution in creating the peaceful society in ASEAN's member countries can be concluded that the Confucian religion and tradition has been developed not only so called 'the Confucian influenced countries such as China, Korea, Vietnam, and Japan, but also in the regional of ASEAN countries.

**IV. The Scope of Ideals Ethical**

There are four ideals in Kong Zi (Confucius) teaching, namely, (1) the ethical person, (2) the ethical family, (3) the ethical nation, and (4) the ethical world community of nations. The person, the family, the nation, and the world are related:" *The basis of the world is the nation; the basis of the nation is the family; and the basis of the family is the individual himself*" (Meng Zi/Mencius, IVA:5)

4.1. Ethical Person

The Ethical Person—It is known as the Gentleman (*junzi*). The individual should first cultivate his personal life by making his will sincere (*cheng yi*) and rectifying his mind (*zheng xin*) to be followed by efforts to regulate his family (*qi jia*), and bring order to the nation (*zhi guo*) and peace throughout the world (*pin tianxia*). The ethical person is a person of benevolence (*renzhe* or *renren*), of high morals (*de*), and of wisdom (*zhi*).

To be a good person, with heart and mind in perfect equilibrium, is a necessary condition of being *Junzi*. But this is not enough on its own. For Confucius, the *Junzi* is not only good, he must also be a great and noble person, always mindful of the affairs of the world, and he must have real drive and energy (Yu Dan, translated by Esther Tyldesley (2006), p.85).

Confucian ethics insists that the self be the centre of relationships, not in order to claim one's right, but to emphasis one's responsibilities, that daily behaviour be guided by the rules of propriety, not merely for restricting individuals, but more for cultivating the sense of holiness and mission in their hearts, and the knowledge is important for developing a good character, not primarily for conquering what is unknown, but for co-operating with others and for contributing to the harmony of the universe. Sel-cultivation (*xiu shen*) as the basis for governing the state and bringing peace to the world has been accepted as politically correct and therefore has deliberately been adopted as a means of re-establishing moral standards among students, as shown when the Graduates' society of Beijing University published its manifesto on self-cultivation in 1994, calling for all students to start with cultivating good habits and moral virtues. The combination of Confucian values and modern qualities creates a new title for business leaders, 'Confucian entrepreneurs' (*ru shang*), praising their Confucian virtues demonstrated in industrial and commercial activities, such as humaneness (*ren*), trustfullness (*xin*), sincerity (*cheng*) and altruism as quoted by Yao (2001: 276) from the People's Daily, 15 January 1998.

The idea of self-cultivation has helped Confucian values to regain the respect of Chinese people everywhere as an inspiration to knowledge, and be used as a guide to proper behaviour in all circumstances. Whether at home and among friends, and whether inside or outside their respective countries, all this could be in harmony with religious belief and practice. And, not least, this personal level of Confucianism could be a source of great wisdom that remains valid even for the modern world (Bakar, Osman, ed., 1997: 203-204).

Yao (2001) quoted that the anthropological, sociological, and political surveys all point to the pervasive presence of Confucian ethics in belief, attitude, and behaviour across all strata throughout China (Tu, 1996b:259); "Confucian culture is still work in the everyday lives of the Korean people, and it is now being renovated or reproduced" (Kim, 1996:203).

For the Indonesian Confucian, nobody would deny the teaching of Confucian religion relevant to today's social/personal and religious life. There are obvious signs indicating that aspects of the Confucian ethics are still useful and valuable, that the uniqueness of Confucian religiosity is being recognized as an important dimension of human spirituality, and that the Confucian on metaphysical views is considered conducive to the heathy growth of the global village. Kuncono (2013) quoted from Linda Kleebe Trevino (1995) "Business Ethics is about building of trust between people and organizations, an absolutely essential ingredient to conducting business successfully in longterm". Kuncono (2013) in his dissertation conclusion stated that Confucius ethics have significance positive impact toward entrepreneurial spirits, business ability and the performance of business.

4.2 Ethical Family

Good will is essential to being human, and it emerges first in caring for one's family. The family is regarded as the most important social unit in Confucianism; it must be regulated by codes of conduct based on the virtues.

Family values are indeed important for the stability and continuity of a modern society. Family continues to serve as a vital institution for social cohesiveness, moral education, spiritual growth. The Confucian position also means that the flourishing of family is a priority—seeking other personal goals such as the development of one's talents and interests at the expense of family harmony and flourishing is not endorsed by Confucianism. Confucian accept sexual equality between men and women in contemporary society. The Confucian position on the issue of men and women can be described as "politically equal and socially equitable". Politically, women have the same rights and same opportunities as men. Socially, however, Confucians would not press for "blind" indiscriminative social equally between men and women. From a care perspective, Confucians recognize that men and women may have different psychological and biological needs and capacities, and there should be different opportunities for them; socially Confucius emphasize equity rather than equality between men and women. Because the family is the origin and archetype of human care, Confucians place the family as a primary consideration of political philosophy, and promote the kind of care from within the family to society at large.

4.3 Ethical Nation

The nation should be governed by the highest moral standards. Confucian political teaching emphasize that governmental policies should be made from considerations of concrete social circumstances, not from abstract political principles. In the Confucian view, good society should be measured by how its people are being taken care of, and social policies should be caring and humane.

Lead the people by laws and regulate them by punishments, and they will avoid wrong-doing but will have no sense of shame. Lead the people with virtue and regulate them by the rules of propriety, and they will have a sense of shame and, moreover, will set themselves right.

The ruler is expected to practise benevolent government (*renzheng*) or ethical government (*dezheng*). He should be a person of rectitude: "*A ruler who governs his state by virtue is like the north polar star, which remains in its place whilde all the other stars revolve around it*"

When good men are in office, government is efficient, just as when the earth is fertile, plants flourish. Therefore, good government depends upon good men. Such men should be chosen on the basis of character. Good character is developed by following nature. By following nature, one acquires good will (Bahm, Archie J., 1992:

91).

Confucius suggest that the moral power (*de*) of the ideal ruler will eventually attract those living a faraway lands, bringing peace to the whole world and presumably doing way with the need for territorial boundaries between states:

"*I have always heard that what worries the head of a state or the chief of a clan is not poverty but the inequitable distribution of wealth, not the lack of population, but the lack of peace. For if wealth is equitably distributed, there will be no poverty, and where there is peace, there is no lack of population. And then, if people who live in far-off lands still resist your attraction, you must draw them to you by the moral power of your civilization; and then, having attracted them, make them enjoy your peace*" (16.1; *Leys, modified*).

The ideal ruler would win people's heart simply by his benevolence (*ren*), without relying on the use of force. Even if people do not seem immediately receptive to Confucian norms, the ruler should not worry. He should cultivate his own personal virtue, people will be inspired by his example, and eventually he will gain the allegiance of the whole world.

China's former president Hu Jintao has been actively promoting Confucian themes such as "harmony," "honesty", "loyalty". The Confucian idea of harmony means diversity in harmony, not blind conformity to official viewpoints. The Confucian foreign policy relies mainly on moral example, not threats of physical force.

In the Book of Verses it is written" '*The goal of country is the happiness of the people*". In the Book of Verse it is written: "*The chirping yellowbird is happy in the corner of a hill.*" *If the bird knows how to be happy, ought a man know less than a bird?*"

In the Book of Verses it is written: "*How admirable was King Wen! How exemplary his character! How much he appreciated the happiness of his realm". As a king, he was happy when good will (Ren) prevailed. As an administrator, he was happy with propriety. As a son, he was happy with respecting his father. As a father, he was happy in kindness to his son. When speaking to the people of the country, he was happy in being truthful* (Archie J. Bahm, 1992, pp. 134-135).

The demanding of the government to recognize the role of Confucian can be seen by the activity of Confucian institutions in Chinese communities in Hong Kong, Taiwan and South East Asia. A variety of Confucian organizations has been established aiming at restoring the religious functions of Confucian religion. For example, the Confucian Academy of Hong Kong (Kongjiao Xueyuan) and its three affiated schools list the following objectives in their constitution: (1) to strive for the Government's recognition of Confucianism as a religion; (2) to strive for designating Confucius's birthday as a national holiday; (3) to incorporate Confucian doctrines into the curricula of primary, secondary and tertiary education institutions; and (4) to encourage the establishment of Confucius Temples or Confucian Youth Centres in cities and towns far and wide across the country (Yao, 2001).

4.5 Ethical World Community of Nations

The teaching of Confucian religion can support and guide the proses of modernisation. There are three are especially of significance for the Confucian future: its concern about moral responsibilities, its emphasis on the important of transmission of values, and its humanistic understanding of life. It is believed that these values are the most important elements for Confucian relevance to the future, because they will make a significant contribution to an ethic of responsibility, give a new momentum to the establishment of a comprehensive education system, and help people in their search for ultimate meaning in a temporary life (Yao, 2001).

Humans are not merely political and economic animals. They are also moral beings, characterised by freedom of choice and by a sense of responsibility, being responsible for their own behaviour and being concerned not only with the process of an action but also with its motives and results. In a sense, we may say that one of the key issues in all the existent traditions in the world to attain a kind of balance between action and responsibility. Due to cultural differences, however, some traditions are more concerned with free choice and individual rights, while others deal more with responsibility. Confucianism is a tradition that places much emphasis upon human responsibility.

In a recent and important study of Japanese civilization, the sociologis S.N. Eisenstadt has suggested that more than other (post- modern societies), Japanese society coheres as a result of the remarkably high levels of trust that exist horizontally at the level of the community, and vertically in terms of one's relationship with the state, with one's employer, and so on. And like many other observers of contemporary Japan, Professor Eisenstadts locates the roots of this trust in the priority Confucianism attaches to maintaining correct relationships, both horizontally between persons and vertically between rulers and their subjects (Bell, Daniel A, ed, 2008: 41).

Confucian political philosophy emphasizes the role of moral virtue in society and advocates a "thick" notion of good society. A good society does not only prosper economically, but also virtuously. A good society is to be led by virtuous leaders supported by virtuous peope, for from the Confucian view only virtuous persons can adequately care for others and only virtuous lives are worth living. A good society is a caring society (Bell, Daniel A, ed., 2008: 192-193).

For Prophet Kongzi (Confucius), a single person can not live alone. Men are plural, more than two who are living together. Thus, men are by nature 'organization men'. Men are among men who live in the web of human relationships, e.g. parents and children, husband and wife, older and younger persons, friend and friend, and ruler and the people. What are the rules which regulate human relationships for harmony and peace to commence a happy life? They are virtues, that is *ren* (benevolence/humaneness), *yi* (righteousness), *zhi* (wisdom), *li* (propriety), *yong* (courage) and *xin* (mutual trust). Among them: *ren*, *yi*, *zhi*, *yong* and *xin* are all invisible; li is the only visible virtue. Another important characteristics of the Confucian virtues is their orientations: inward (*ren*) to the family, and outward (*yi*) to the society or nation. It should be understood that according to Confucius these orientations can not be vertical or horizontal, but reciprocal.

In LunYu 17:8 Prophet Kongzi (Confucius) said: "To love humanness (*ren*) without loving learning is liable to foolishness; To love intelligence (*zhi*) without loving learning is liable to deviation from the right path; To love faithfullness/sincerity (*xin*) without loving learning is liable to harmful behavior; To love forthrightness/honesty (*zhi*) without loving learning is liable to intolerance; To love courage (*yong*) without loving learning is liable to insubordination; To love unbending strength (*gang*) without loving learning is liable to lead to indiscipline".

**V. Closing Remark**

In Confucian Religion perspective demands that all people be treated with humanity (*ren*). All interaction must be based in *ren*, but specific actions are delineated within a clearly defined hierarchy (hierarchy is considered to be natural and essential to the creation of harmony). Key roles and corresponding virtues are outlined in the "Five Relationships", namely, those between parent and child, elder brother and younger brother, husband and wife, friend and friend, and ruler and subject. Each relationship has its specific roles and responsibilities: a parent owes a child education, care, and moral formation; a child owes a parent obedience, respect, and care in old age and after death. The parent/child relationship establishes the basic pattern for other relationships—thus, the virtue of filiality (*xiao*) is the basis for social structure. A husband and wife are to care for each other. The elder brother has responsibility for younger siblings who owe him deference (birth order is very clearly delineated in East Asian kinship terms). The relationship between ruler and subject parallels that of parent and child, for the ruler is to provide care and guidance, and the subject is to be obedient as well as loyal. Friends are to be loyal-this is the only relationship that has the potential of being between people of equal rank, but even here, a hierarchy of age is often reflected.

Although obedience and defense are demanded from subordinates within this structure of relationships, a good son, worthy wife, and loyal minister have a duty to remonstrate unethical behavior. All five relationships (as well as others, such as those between teacher and student, and employer and employee) have serious mutual responsibilities, and both familial and non-familial bonds are presumed to last a lifetime.

A Confucian always dream of becoming a *JunZi* (profound person/gentleman), a practitioner of love who does not show a group or a cluster, or a gang, but rather to be the one who is a practitioner of love (broadminded and resolute). Within oneself spreads the love which shows the loyalty to *Tian*/God Almighty is to love other people. Trust other people as brothers and sisters, therefore amongst different religion and faiths have to respect, accepting the differences, cooperate each other to struggle any parties that against human rights, practice discrimination, spread intolerance and violence. Especially in Indonesia, interfaith partnerships within the religious communities are important in designing innovative programs in promoting tolerance, mutual respect and understanding as the common ground for action-oriented interfaith partnerships. To educate and evolve youth in personal transformative experiences, especially those that build bridges of friendship, understanding, and harmonious integration transcending barriers of religion, ethnicity and social status. The Confucius' vision of the future of mankind, the Grand Unity will be always to be a great source of inspiration to build a better peaceful world.

**REFERENCES**

Bahm, Archie J. (1992). *The Heart of Confucius. Interpretation of Genuine Living and Great Wisdom*. California: Jain Publishing Company.

Bakar, Osman, Ed. , Nai, Cheng Gek (1997). *Islam and Confucianism A Civilization Dialogue*. Malaysia: University of Malaya Press

Bell, Daniel A (2008). *Confucian Political Ethics*. USA: Princeton University Press.

Kang, Hosuck (1997). *Confucius and Confucianism: Questions and Answers*. USA: Confucian Publications Washington, D.C.

Kuncono, Setio (2013). Pengaruh Etika Confucius terhadap Kewirausahaan, Kemampuan Usaha dan Kinerja Usaha Pedagang Eceran Etnis Tionghoa di Surabaya. *http://www.spocjournal.com/disertasi.html*

MATAKIN (2012), *Si Shu (Kitab Yang Empat). Kitab Suci Agama Khonghucu*. Jakarta: MATAKIN

Weiming, Tu *et. al*. editors (1993),"*The Confucian World Observed A Contemporary Discussion of Confucian Humanism in East Asi*a", Hawaii USA: University of Hawaii Press.

Yao, Xingzhong (2001),"*An Introduction to Confucianism*", UK: the University Press, Cambridge.

Yu Dan (2006). *Confucius from the Heart. Ancient Wisdom for Today's World* (translated by Esther Tyldesley). UK: Zhonghua Book Company.

Appendix

JAKARTA MESSAGE FOR A PEACEFUL WORLD

ISLAM AND CONFUCIAN SUMMIT

Jakarta, AUGUST 23-25 2013

On the occasion of the Islam and Confucian Summit to be held in Jakarta, Indonesia from 23rd to the 25th of August 2013, sponsored by Majelis Ulama Indonesia/MUI (Indonesian Council of Ulama) and Majelis Tinggi Agama Khonghucu Indonesia/MATAKIN (the Supreme Council for Confucian Religion in Indonesia), we the participants declare:

1. To commit ourselves with sincerity to foster peace, harmony and respect for religious diversity in our communities and around the World. Delegates will make an

effort to discuss with their own national governments a range of recommendations designed to strengthen Moslem and Confucian community and other various religious communities.

2. To promote mutual understanding among Moslems and Confucian and other faith communities across region and the whole world. We believe this Summit between Islam and Confucian is the beginning of a process of more direct and intensive communication between Islam and Confucian leaders in contributing to solve social problems at local, regional and national levels in respective countries, as well as to conceive bilateral or multi-lateral interfaith projects in poverty amelioration, drug-addiction elimination, and to build a more harmonious, trustworthy and peaceful future for the World.

3. To collect, collate and determine the similarities between Islam and Confucian religious teachings. The historical harmonious relationships between adherents of Moslems and Confucians are shown by many points of convergence, especially in the general area of social ethics and the unity of God. To encourage both Islam and Confucian worshippers to write scientific papers and share their findings and conclusions on a global stage as a contribution to create a more civilized and peaceful world.

4. To express our concerns for manipulative and corruptive cultures that are already adopted by individuals and governments' officials and even governments. Therefore, we recommend that ethical and moral values, such as sincerity, integrity, responsibility, trustworthiness be promoted in each lesson from primary and secondary high schools, to higher education institutions, as an Almighty God's decree that shall be executed in daily life, in order that the life of human beings is full of peace, harmony, empathy and brotherhood as one family under One God.

5. To arouse a spirit of unity and reconciliation in various places and countries of conflict and confrontation; equity and fair play in place of exploitation towards all human beings irrespective of color, gender, creed, religion, and ethnicity. To appeal for reduction of production weapons, and other equipments that are used to kill and destroy human being and humanity.

6. To encourage between Moslem and Confucian communities around the world to take initiative for proposing and organizing a collaboration project between interfaith leaders works on community empowerment and share common values: volunteerism, tolerance, respect, love and integrity.

7. To educate youth leaders to engage the youth in personal transformative experiences, especially those that build bridges of friendship, brother and sisterhood, understanding, and harmonious integration transcending barriers of religion, ethnicity and social status.

8. To call upon governments, interfaith non-government organizations, council of religions, and religious institutions to play a more significant role by taking the initiative in the future to forge vibrant and meaningful interfaith partnerships and programs for promoting universal principles, values from religions and culture to enrich the civilization dialogue with a view contributing to the non-violence, peace building, environmental care and harmonious integration transcending barriers of religion, ethnicity and social status.

9. Delegates express their strong appreciation to both councils of religions: Majelis Ulama Indonesia (MUI)/Indonesian Council of Ulama and Majelis Tinggi Agama Khonghucu Indonesia (MATAKIN)/The Supreme Council for Confucian Religion in Indonesia and the Government of Republic of Indonesia and to those participants who come from various countries for their support for Islamic and Confucian Summit and underline their support for further interfaith dialogue initiatives and continue the Summit periodically.

# The Rise of China and the Time of Africa: Gauging Afro-Sino Relations in the Light of Confucian Philosophy and African Ideals

**Cornel W du Toit**[①]

## INTRODUCTION

China has come of age and is spreading its influence. The Chinese are the most plentiful people on the globe and it is estimated that China will be the leading economic power by 2018. But it is also the time of Africa, triggered perhaps by the 1994 democratic elections in South Africa. Africa's time has come to shed its third world shackles, to introduce the African 'renaissance' and to take its place in the global arena. But Africa cannot muddle through all challenges on its own and China is seemingly instrumental in African economic emancipation. The sleeping giant has awoken and is seemingly catching up with lost time. China and Africa need each other albeit for different reasons. If this relationship is successful it can be the long awaited turning point for Africa. There are already more than a million Chinese citizens in Africa and Chinese construction programmes worth billions of dollars have already become legendary in most important African metropolises. The role played by China is perhaps one of the most significant and determinative events in post-colonial African. The question is whether Chinese influence may be the magic factor to fire up economic growth, and eradicate poverty, disease and illiteracy in Africa. Africa's colonial past has made it sceptic towards foreign influence and the question is if China's economic and cultural involvement will truly benefit the African cause.

Considering the Afro-Sino interaction the basic question is what both countries

---

① This paper is allowed to print by The HTS Journal. The author is Head, Research Institute for Theology and Religion, University of South Africa. E-mail: dtoitcw@unisa.ac.za;

need and can offer to ensure a lasting and fruitful relationship. Many mistakes were made in the long history of Western involvement in Africa. Western influence, although well entrenched in Africa, is ostensibly waning (considering only the diminishing commercial ties) and it would be short-sighted of any nation interacting with Africa to ignore past blunders. But Chinese involvement in Africa requires a tour de force of diplomacy, planning and sound business acumen. Africa is divided in 54 states (represented in the AU), has no common language, is plagued by political unrest and war, threatened by Christian-Muslim divide in the North, suffers from unstable governments and corruption, plagued by illness and disease, deprived of good infrastructure, and so the list goes on and on. In spite of these challenges Chines involvement in Africa seems to be a success and is making a difference.

Africa has rich resources to offer but lacks infrastructure, skills, education, jobs, unity, and specifically peace. China has skills, monetary muscle, human capital, work ethic, and the historical experience of conquering poverty and attaining the skills to use a liberal market economy to their advantage. China needs resources to maintain and grow its mammoth economy. The optimistic NEPAD-programme proposed by former South African president Thabo Mbeki never came off the ground because of economic constraints. Chinese involvement may change the scene and perhaps help to realise some of the much needed infrastructure.①

But more is at stake than economic relations. Economic involvement at such a gigantic scale inevitably involves an array of other factors. Some of these concern African cultural values, Africa's voice in the global arena, environmental concerns in light of increased industrialisation, socio-economic issues. Will Chinese influence make a

---

① The fifth FOCAC inter-ministerial plan stipulated the following planned initiatives concerning infrastructure development: 4. 3 Infrastructure Construction. 4. 3. 1 The two sides agreed to prioritize infrastructure in China-Africa cooperation and strengthen cooperation in transport, telecommunications, radio and television, water conservancy, electricity, energy and other areas of infrastructure development. 4. 3. 2 To support Africa in achieving connectivity and integration and developing more integrated infrastructure, China and the African Union will establish a cooperative partnership in the design, inspection, financing and management of projects under the Program for Infrastructure Development in Africa and the Presidential Infrastructure Championing Initiative, strengthen relevant dialogue and exchanges, and provide support for the project planning and feasibility study. 4. 3. 3 The Chinese government will continue to encourage capable Chinese enterprises and financial institutions to participate in transnational and trans-regional infrastructure construction in Africa and provide preferential loans to support infrastructure building in Africa (see FOCAC website, http://www.focac.org/eng/).

momentous difference on this level as well? If Chinese foreign relations are built upon the cultural and philosophical ideas from the past then it I inevitable that a dialogue will have to take place between the ideas and traditions of Chinese and other cultures.

South Africa is part of the so-called BRICS-countries (Brazil, Russia, India, China, South-Africa) and the government is favouring intra-African trade, and trade with BRICS countries and the East. Traditionally Europe, the UK and USA were dominant trade partners. The People's Republic of China (PRC) is since 2010 South Africa's biggest trading partner. China's investment projects topped MYM200 billion in 2013. No one can doubt the seriousness of South Africa's commitment to strengthening ties with China Simultaneously the ANC is eager to strengthen ties with the other BRICS countries.①

The following initiatives between China and South Africa stands out:

6. The first visit by a government official after the first democratic election in 1994 was the visit of South African Deputy President Phumzile Mlambo-Ngcuka in September 2007. Since 2010 bi-lateral visits and agreements proliferated.

7. In late March 2010 CPPCC② Chairman Jia Qinglin visited South Africa and met with South Africa's President Jacob Zuma and signed contracts worth more than USMYM300 million.

8. In August 2010 President Jacob Zuma led a South African delegation of 17 cabinet members and 300 businesspeople to China where they signed the Beijing Declaration on the Establishment of a Comprehensive Strategic Partnership between the People's Republic of China and the Republic of South Africa.

9. The speaker of the National Assembly of South Africa Max Sisulu visited China in October 2010.

10. In November 2010 Chinese Vice President Xi Jinping travelled to South Africa to meet with South African Vice President Motlanthe and signed bilateral cooperation

---

① President Zuma met Russian president Putin at the end of August 2014 to discuss the implementation of the Intergovernmental Committee on Trade and Economic Cooperation (ITEC), trade and investment issues, and preparations for the 12th ITEC Session to be hosted by South Africa during the course of 2014. The situation in Syria, the Israel-Palestine matter, as well as developments in Ukraine were discussed as well. The South African government has backed Putin's stance on these matters up to now.

② The Chinese People's Political Consultative Conference (CPPCC), also known as "The PCC", is a political advisory body in the People's Republic of China.

agreements in energy, trade statistics, banking regulation and other areas.

11. China's top legislator Wu Bangguo visited South Africa in May 2011 as part of his Africa-Asia tour which included Namibia and Angola.

12. In September 2011 South African Vice President Motlanthe led a trade delegation to Beijing at the invitation of Chinese Vice President Xi. During the visit the China Development Bank and the Development Bank of South Africa signed a USMYM2.5 billion agreement. The two countries also signed a Memorandum of Understanding on geological exploration and mineral resources.

13. On 17 July 2012 President Zuma led a South African delegation that included International Relations Minister Maite Nkoana-Mashabane, Minister in the Presidency Collins Chabane and Trade and Industry Minister Rob Davies to attend the fifth Forum on China-Africa Co-operation (FOCAC) in Beijing (see http://en.wikipedia.org/wiki/China%E2%80%93South_Africa_relations. Accessed 10/08/2014).

14. On 4 March 2014 basic Education Minister, Mrs Angie Motshekga has overseen the signing of an implementation plan between the Ministry of Education in China and the Department of Basic Education in South Africa in Beijing this week. This follows the signing of a collaboration agreement between the two countries Presidents in March last year, when Chinese President Xi Jinping visited South Africa.

15. On 10 March 2014 South Africa's education minister announced the introduction of Mandarin into the school curriculum. An agreement this month between the two nations focuses on five areas of cooperation: curriculum development, math and science, teacher training, vocational education, and research and development in basic education. New partnership: Ministry of Basic Education Spokeswoman Troy Martens said "It is very exciting because it takes the relationship between South Africa and China beyond just trade relations and into the mutual development for both of our developing countries".

16. 2014 has also been declared the year of South Africa in China with the understanding that the two countries share excellent international relations and wish to extend their relationship beyond trade into areas of mutual development. Education is a priority imperative for both countries and this implementation plan is centred on strengthening education ties at an institutional and policy level.

17. Deputy minister of the Cultural Ministry Ding Wei met with the deputy minister of South African Ministry of Arts and Culture, Joyce Mabudafhasi during his state

visit to South Africa. Ding said that with the increasing mutual political trust and deepening pragmatic cooperation, the comprehensive strategic partnership between the two countries is facing great challenges. China attaches great importance to cultural exchange and cooperation, which is an important part of bilateral relations. And China is willing to take the opportunity of the reciprocal cultural year program to further promote the cultural exchange and cooperation between the two countries to improve the bilateral relations.

Mabudafhasi stressed that South Africa is ready to host the Chinese year and keep in touch with China to make a splash in South Africa with Chinese culture, and further promote the cultural exchange and cooperation between China and South Africa. Ding Wei and Mabudafhasi signed the Memorandum of Understanding of the Reciprocal Cultural Year Program in 2014 and 2015 (see http://www1.chinaculture.org/info/2014-08/21/content_558702.htm).

Sino-South-African relations received bad press when His Holiness the Dalai Lama who attended the Parliament of the World's Religions in 1999, was denied a visa when he was asked to attend an international peace conference in March 2009. A second visit was also cancelled when he was invited to South Africa for Archbishop Emeritus Desmond Tutu's 80th birthday party on 7 October 2011. The government's relation with China was the obvious reason that the VISA was denied.

**THE IMPACT OF CHINESE PRESENCE IN AFRICA**

Bilateral trade between China and African countries reached MYM210 billion in 2013 (see African Analysis May 4, 2014). The programmes China has launched and the cultural and other programmes launched are overwhelming. What is impressive are Chinese construction programmes undertaken and completed very efficiently over short periods of time with predominantly Chinese workers. China has huge investment interests in Angola, the DRC, Nigeria, Kenya, and South Africa to mention only some of the most significant deals.

Given the powerful entrenched Western interests it faced in Africa, Beijing had to offer a unique package of economic, political and security inducements to fast track its entry into key natural resource producing regions of the continent. These included: Targeted debt relief; Participation in peace-keeping operations in places such as Liberia, DRC and Sudan; Cheap loans linked to infrastructure development; Political junkets for African leaders to Beijing; Support for Africa in global forums such as the United Nations (UN), World Trade Organisation (WTO), International Monetary Fund (IMF) and World Bank; Competitive military deals; Collaborative projects on "traditional medicines"; Political "non-interference" in the internal policies of African countries; The promotion of "south-south" linkages; The establishment of parallel funding agencies to institutions such as the IMF and World Bank.

On a cultural level many initiatives were taken. In October 2000 the Forum on China-Africa Cooperation (FOCAC) was launched in Beijing. FOCAC was to meet every three years. The second FOCAC ministerial conference was held in Addis Ababa, Ethiopia, in 2003. FOCAC 5 was held in South Africa (see FOCAC website for updated initiatives: http://www.focac.org/eng/).

The first conference of the *China-Africa Think Tank Forum*① hosted by Zhejiang Normal University (in Hangzhou, Zhejiang Province) on 27 October 2011. As a high-level platform for China-Africa academic exchanges whose founding was approved by the Ministry of Foreign Affairs and Ministry of Commerce of China, the Forum offers a bridge for linking up important ideas of Chinese and African elites. The China-Africa Think Tank Forum is incorporated by the Foreign Ministry into the framework of the Forum on China-Africa Cooperation (FOCAC) as a regular mechanism for civil dialogues between China and Africa which will be held alternatively in China and Africa once a year (see http://www.focac.org/eng/xsjl/t894943.htm).

***Post-colonial lessons learnt***

In an interview with the Financial Times (3 March 2013) South Africa president Zuma warned western companies to change their old "colonial" approach to Africa or risk losing out even more to the accelerating competition from China and other developing powers. He said that Western businesses and governments have a "psychological problem" and are still prone to lecturing Africa. 'Instead of saying: "Let us help you", they come and they say: 'Change your economic structure. Don't do this. Do

---

① To put Chinese academic muscle in perspective one can refer to Mark Leonard Leave a comment Prospective Magazine, March 28, 2008 ) where he relates his first visit, in 2003, to the Chinese Academy of Social Sciences (CASS) in Beijing. He was welcomed by Wang Luolin, the academy's vice-president, who told him that his academy had 50 research centres covering 260 disciplines with 4,000 full-time researchers-and this was only one of many institutions.

that.' This has a colonial smell and Zuma warned 'If you want to treat Africa as a former colony ... then people will go to new partners who are going to treat them differently'. He advised them to resist warning against the embrace of China and rethink their own investment strategies. Zuma also stressed that Africa was aware of the risks of being bossed around by China. "Africa does not want to be dominated again." "China is doing business in a particular way and we think we can see the benefits, but we are very, very careful," he said, citing Africa's experience of colonialism. Such a relationship must "benefit both. And this is what we and China have been agreeing" (Financial Times, 3 March 2013).

This was underscored by Premier Li Keqiang before his May 2011 trip to Ethiopia, Nigeria, Angola and Kenya when he said that he wanted to assure China's African friends in all seriousness 'that China will never pursue a colonialist path like some countries did, or allow colonialism, which belongs to the past, to reappear in Africa'. He stressed that Chinese firms in Africa will keep local laws and regulations and protect the interests of local communities. Concerning the threat of a neo-colonialism of Africa, Qianru (2011: 153) reminds us that "China was in a leading position throughout the course of several thousand years of history. It is only the last hundred years or so that China became weak, following powerful invasions. At no time in the past or in the present has China made hegemony over the world the gaol of its development".

In 2009, China overtook the United States as Africa's biggest trading partner, and Xinhua said more than 2,500 Chinese firms operate on the continent. Beijing has been accused of holding back the continent's economic development by focussing on the pursuit of raw materials rather than the creation of local jobs and markets (African Analysis May 4, 2014).

Human rights groups and western officials have criticised China's readiness to strike deals with oppressive governments. But South Africa's ruling African National Congress, which admires China's state-led capitalism, has promoted the relationship arguing South Africa has the laws and diplomatic clout to defend its interests.

***China's success story a recipe for Africa?***

The easy answer behind the Chinese economic success story of the last 30 years is abundant and cheap labour. But this is also valid for India who cannot boast the same successes. Other factors like the emergence of economic globalisation, the electronic revolution, lower transaction costs, the role of well-trained Chinese students[①] etc. must be taken into account. Another important factor is the Chinese government that allocates resources and directly or indirectly commands a large proportion of national assets and income. The government is not subject to the same democratic pressures in making unpopular decisions, such as raising taxes. This may have facilitated China's rapid industrialisation (see Hayat 2011).

Is state control a model that for consideration in Africa? Is this not what the *de facto* situation is in South Africa where the ANC-government is almost in position of having two thirds parliamentary majority which boils down to a one- party state? Madeleine Bunting, for example, in her review of Dambisa Moyo 's book *Dead Aid* (criticising Western aid of MYM300bn to Africa since 1970) avers that the single important question to ask concerning African failed economies is why African states have failed to function. Why have there been so much civil war and so many corrupt dictators? She then says that the keys to success in many Asian countries were the role of a strong, interventionist state that nurtured industry and an elite who invested in their own country. These have been missing in many African countries, where elites have exported capital to western bank accounts and pursued ruinous policies. Moyo is not interested in the role of the state and stresses the private sector, free enterprise, and non-interference of the state in business. This is the Western model and may work within a Western context. Bunting views Moyo's proposal to phase out (Western) aid in five years as disastrously irresponsible: it would lead to the closure of thousands of schools and clinics across Africa, and an end to the HIV antiretroviral, malaria and TB programmes, along with emergency food supplies, on which millions of lives depend.

The question is whether a number of factors can be singled out to explain a nation's economic, military, aesthetic, or scientific success? Is the magic factor the kind of religion practiced, a specific philosophy, or is it perhaps the political, religious or intellectual leaders that are determinative or is it perhaps simply fortuitous factors? The link between economic, military, scientific, religious or any other suc-

① Since 1978 over one million Chinese students received training in foreign countries (especially America).

cesses and a specific pervasive influence whether it is ideological, philosophical, or religious or some influence ascribed to the charisma or fear of a specific leader remains relative.

It is part of the modernist legacy that we seek specific 'causes' for an historic event, be it war, economic misfortune or cultural success. But such unilateral causative factors very seldom exist. No direct link between a specific idea and material successes can be guaranteed. But neither can we simply deny any influence. The challenge is to specify the role of a diverse number of factors making up a specific complex situation.

***The link between the economic superstructure and the cultural substructure: Lessons from Weber?***

The important question is if Chinese involvement in Africa in the 21st century is possible on an exclusive economic level, without any cultural, ideological, political or philosophical influences? Can economic presence be isolated from cultural (ideological) factors? A specific economic model implies a specific take on the world. Chinese policies recognise this, therefore the importance of opening Confucian Institutes all over the world. But is any single underlying philosophy to be pin-pointed as reason for Chinese economic successes or is it simply factors of chance?

The sociologist Max Weber ascribed the success story of Western capitalism to a large extent to the Protestant (English Puritan) ethic. These principles would later be implicitly seen as applicable on Africa as well and if it did not work it must have been due to the mystery of God. It was precisely the power of religious asceticism (the notion of calling, duty, sobriety, conscientiousness, work as a life purpose willed by God) that gave man the "comforting assurance that the unequal distribution of the goods of this world was a special dispensation of Divine Providence, which in these differences, as in particular grace, pursued secret ends unknown to man" (Weber 1965:177).

The question is now whether the Chinese success story can be ascribed to the ethos of Confucianism. Weber also wrote *The Religion of China: Confucianism and Taoism*, in which he touched upon the difference in economic performance between China and the West. What Weber wanted to know was whether, at any point in their history, non-European civilizational traditions had within them the religious and cultural resources to give rise to a capitalist spirit as had happened with forms of Protestantism in Europe and North America. His studies of China, South Asia, and the Islamic world were a counterpart to his famous Protestant Ethic thesis in the European context (Gellner 2011:49).

Chinese culture did not develop capitalism to the same extent as was the case in the West and this he ascribed to Chinese urban development, Chinese patrimonialism and officialdom, and Chinese religion (Confucianism, Taoism). Chinese cities never received political autonomy and in fact sometimes had fewer rights than villages. The lack of city development was partially due to strengths of kinship ties, which stems from religious beliefs (in ancestral spirits) and maintaining strong ties to the villages in which one's ancestors lived. The guilds likewise competed against each other for the favour of the Emperor, never uniting in order to fight for more rights (see Gellner 2011: 48-62).

Unlike European dividedness, China was united under an imperial government with a centralized officialdom. Relatively peace in the first centuries of Chinese history meant that the military was not singled out when the power structures were formed.

Political power shifted from land to the distribution of offices, which with their fees and taxes were the most prominent source of income for the holder. The state depended on the services of those freely removable and non-hereditary officials, rather than on the service of military (knights), like in Europe. For the members of the officialdom, it was their rank, or status, which was of prime importance. The 'superior' man (literati) should stay away from the pursuit of wealth (though not from the wealth itself). Therefore, becoming a civil servant was preferred to becoming a businessman and granted a much higher status class.

The key condition lacking in China, according to Weber, was the 'spiritual' factor, some equivalent of the Protestant ethic capable of inducing entrepreneurs to live austerely, endlessly (and from one point of view irrationally) reinvesting their profits in further capitalistic activity, rather than turning themselves (or their progeny) into gentlemen (Gellner 2011: 50). Chinese civilization had no religious prophecy nor a powerful priesthood class. The emperor was the high priest of the state religion and the supreme ruler. Weber emphasized that Confucianism tolerated the simultaneous existence of many popular cults and made no effort to organize them as part of a religious doctrine, while nonetheless curtailing the political ambitions of their priests. Instead it taught adjustment to the world. This forms a sharp contrast with medieval Europe, where the Church was often able to superimpose its will over those of secular rulers, and where the same, singular religion was the religion of rulers, nobility and the common folk.

## THE USE OF PHILOSOPHICAL 'UNIVERSALS' TO REGULATE INTERNATIONAL RELATIONS: CONFUCIUS IN AFRICA

Confucius is the Socrates of the East. Confucianism dominated China's feudalistic society for thousands of years before the founding of the People's Republic of China in 1949. This is remarkable, taking into account that Confucius lived 2500 years ago. He is the oldest philosopher sage influencing millions of people today. Chai (1961:36) sees the Chinese people as "essentially Confucian in their outlook and mentality; and except for the Buddhist and Taoist trends in the arts and letters, Chinese culture and Confucianism are almost synonymous, if not completely so". Confucius as well as his students Mencius, Lao Tzŭ and Chang Tzŭ (399-295 B.C.) provided a philosophical basis for Chinese culture. Mencius (372-289 BC) popularised his thought, Chang Tzŭ was the romantic mystic and Lao Tzŭ[1] founder of Taoism (Chai 1961:69). Chinese culture may be built on the pillars of Confucianism, Taoism and Buddhism, but these traditions are so old, so wide and spread out over so many groups that it becomes very difficult to decide what is still relevant today. We may admire and wonder at the sagacity of ancient cultures but to what extent can ancient wisdom be normative in a global world where present day human rights and democratic accountabilities are widely accepted.[2]

---

① Although probably a legendary figure, he is reckoned a contemporary of Confucius

② The aim of Confucianist humanism is to protect the ruler, not the ordinary people. Though it says to love the people and pay attention to their needs, what it really cares about is how to use them to serve the ruler's own interests. Confucianism divides people into two kinds, the mental labourers and manual labourers. "Those who do mental labour rule and those who do manual labour are ruled. The Confucianist ideas of patriotism, world commonwealth and harmonious relationships have exerted great influence on modern human rights thought. In the past, they encouraged the Chinese people to safeguard their state independence and national sovereignty, to fight for freedom and human rights. At present, they are still of theoretical and practical importance in dealing with various relationships, in promoting world human rights dialogue and cooperation, as well as pushing forward Chinese and international human rights development (see Chunde, 2014; http://www. humanrights. cn/zt/magazine/200402004827111009. htm).

The Western analogy may be informative. We know that Western though has its basis in classical Greek culture. To pinpoint direct causal lines of thought is however difficult. Chai (1961:xxiii) refers to early Greek migration which eventually covered the limits of the then known world. It was linked to curiosity about the universe and man's role in it. This boosted the interaction between philosophy and science as expressed in the work of Pythagoras, Plato, Aristotle and the like. Developments in China were radically different because of geographical factors. China lies in the centre of the great land mass of Eastern Asia and no need was felt outside exploration. "It is not surprising to find the world of man more important to the ancient Chinese than the world of nature. Their thought was focused on social and political problems instead of scientific ones, with the result that where the Greeks were scientists and philosophers, the Chinese were political theoreticians and philosophers" (ibid). If this is analogously valid for African history as well it may favour a natural affinity between African and Chines philosophical ideas. In Africa, where great migrations similar to the Greek example are absent, the emphasis falls on community life. It is the people that determine the fate of the people, it is the community that determines the place of the individual and it is in the communal realm that the ideas that are to shape the fate of the community is born. This is the captured by the idea of African Ubuntu.

Nevertheless an important person like Yan Xuetong maintains "that any creation in China's international relations theory must be on the basis of our ancient, traditional culture and thought. On the basis of traditional cultural thought we should mirror the experience of foreign theories and in that way we can more quickly create a worthwhile theory" (Xin 2011:239-240). Taken the difference in worldviews, as well as differences in the political, culture and social worlds of ancient Chinese sages and present-day leaders one cannot but suspect that lessons taken from the past will be those that in one way or another suit what leaders wish to achieved today. The same hermeneutical questions confront all present-day religions that are based on ancient texts. But hermeneutical and other important preconditions are conceded by Qianru (2011:54-155). He mentions that research in pre-Qin interstate philosophy has tried to formulate abstract principles linked to a specific historical background, (historical background, trends and facts of importance) and then used these principles to understand texts of the pre-Qin masters. Analytical and other methods were used to find logical connections in these texts which were then compared with Western international political theory. The results were then applied to real politics (ibid. 155).

Because of the difficulty in verifying the truthfulness of historical events, the emphasis fell on the thoughts of pre-Qin masters, and Qianru correctly acknowledges that "no reading of history is able to free itself entirely from the subjective hermeneutical perspective of the research" (ibid. 156).

It is therefore thought-provoking to see what factors are single out by leading Chinese thinkers as the foundations of present-day Chinese culture. We select a few pivotal ideas.

***Heaven, earth and the human***

Chai (1961: 36-37) sees *jen* as hermeneutical key to Confucianism. It stresses good relations. It teaches one how to be a good ruler, citizen, parent, child, neighbour etc. "If modern civilization is to survive, human relations, instead of being based on domination, must be founded on the principle of *jen*" (Chai 1961:38). *Jen* is built on filial piety. Filial piety is feasibly the fundamental cornerstone of Chinese culture pre-dating Confucius by many years. It can be seen as the generic source of all virtue, serves as the basis of public morality, maintains the spiritual continuity between the living and the dead, and links together the creative powers of Heaven, Earth and Human order. It concerns authority and responsibility and represent the Confucian principle of reciprocity or mutual response (De Bary 1999: 325). What Heaven has endowed is called the nature. Following the nature is called the Way. Cultivating eth Way is called instruction (De Bary 2011:334).

According to Chun (2012: x) the integration of Heaven and Human involve all physical beings. Civilians were seen as heavenly citizens (tianmin), emperors as heavenly sons (tianzi), and every human being was seen as endowed with heavenly conscience (tianliang). Humans are born with heavenly benevolence, and Confucianism values human life greatly. Confucian social morals became the civilian norm and basis of the official societal ideology. The chief moral principles were filial piety, loyalty, and righteousness to family, country, and the world under heaven.

Chun (2012:36) names five meanings of heaven: sky; nature and natural law; the idea of

God[1]; moral principles; and fate as destined by the heavens ( See also De Bary 2011:335).

The Mandate of heaven grants the emperor the right to rule and is applicable to only one emperor at a time. It implies that the emperor is competent and virtuous. It also implies that no specific dynasty is guaranteed to rule for ever. The Mandate of Heaven is given to a just ruler who is called Son of Heaven. Heaven will not mandate a despotic ruler which will result in his fall. Once fallen, a ruler has lost the mandate of heaven. The fall of the emperor in a successful rebellion is a sign that he had lost the Mandate of Heaven and the rebel leader had gained it. The idea was first applied to the rule of the kings of the Zhou Dynasty (1046-256 BCE) as just rulers, and to legitimate their overthrow of the earlier Shang dynasty. Similarly the Qin Dynasty ended in 206 BCE, after the successful uprisings led by the peasant rebel leader Liu Bang, who founded the Han Dynasty. The same happened in1644 when the Ming Dynasty (1368-1644) lost the Mandate and was overthrown by Li Zicheng's rebel forces. Li Zicheng's was ousted by the Manchus, who founded the Qing Dynasty (1644-1911), China's final imperial dynasty.

***All under heaven and Possessing all under heaven***

Xunzi (313-238 BCE) was a philosopher from the Warring States Period. The idea of *all under heaven* is the basis of Xunzi's view of state power. He identifies three kinds of international power namely humane authority, hegemony, and tyranny (Xuetong 2011:70; de Bary & Bloom 1999:161-183). Xunzi, like Mencius believes that humaneness and rightness of the true king give him unassailable authority and an ability to compel the allegiance of others (de Bary & Bloom 1999:166).

All under heaven means world leadership and not simply heading a state. World leadership or *Possessing all under heaven* cannot be seized but is given to you (Xuetong 2011:86). Mencius is well known for his view that human nature is good (on the basis of which he defended the Confucian ideal and developed an account of the self-cultivation process). Xunzi challenged this view and defended the alternative view that human nature is bad. Xuetong (2011:87-88) explain Xunzi's idea that morality is the foundation for attaining leadership under heaven with the example of The Vatican

---

① Heaven was believed to be the origin of all beings in the universe. The Shang Dynasty developed a hierarchy of gods in their religion. On top was the highest being of heaven (god), followed by the natural world, and then human ancestry (see Chun 2012:42).

occupying a small space but exerting its authority right over the world. Only the sage could possess humane authority for Xunzi: "The sage is someone who possess the Way and is perfect all round and who is the standard for judging the authority under heaven" (Xueton 2011: 87). In contrast hegemony is interstate domination when the ruler's moral level falls short of that required for humane authority…" (ibid. 88). As can be expected tyranny is lower than hegemony and relises on military force and strategems to invade the territory of other states (ibid. 89).

As already mentioned Xunzi viewed human nature as evil. People strive for personal gain. This leads to competition and inevitably to violent conflict. This is the first point of note in political realism: "Political realism believes that politics, like society in general, is governed by objective laws, that have their roots in human nature …. Human nature, in which the laws of politics have their roots, have not changed since the classic philosophies of China, India, and Greece endeavoured to discover these laws" (Xuetong 2011:92).

**Yan Xuetong and the philosophical basis of Chinese foreign policy**

Yan Xuetong is a remarkable person. Born December 7, 1952 in Tianjin, China, is Dean of the Institute of Modern International Relations at Tsinghua University and the Chief Editor of The Chinese Journal of International Politics (Oxford University Press). He experienced the Cultural Revolution first hand as part of the construction corps, and persevered through much suffering (see Xin 2011:230-231). He received his Ph.D in political science from the University of California, Berkeley in 1992. In 2008 he was named as one of world's top 100 public intellectuals by the American journal Foreign Policy. His book Analysis of China's National Interests won 1998 China Book Price and his *Practical Methods of International Studies* was authorized as text book by Chinese Education Ministry in 2006. His views closely mirror those of Chinese leaders (see Xin 2011:229-237,239).

When he returned home after completing his Berkeley studies, he noticed that no one studied what the motives for Chinese foreign policies were, how Chinese foreign policies worked or the relation between domestic policies and foreign policies (Xin 2011:238). These were pivotal issues which he tended to.

Xuetong is frank about his vision for Chinese foreign relations. He views China's national interest as the starting point for foreign policy (ibid. 238); China's international relations theory must be built on basis of the ancient, traditional culture and thought (ibid. 239-240). This is worked out in more detail in chapter two of his book (Xuetong 2011:70-106) He mentions the dilemma that China lacks meaningful academic criticism because of the political setup in China. International relations cannot be severed from politics and that cannot be discussed freely (ibid. 240). He laments that foreign relations policy did not allow more freedom in development of foreign relations theory which is picking up now (ibid. 246).

The riddle is how present-day foreign relations theory can be built upon philosophy and 'historical' events that are thousands of years old. The pre-Qin period and its interstate political philosophy is selected as main source for present-day foreign policy (Qianru 2011:147).

The Zhou dynasty (c.1046-256 BC) followed the Shang dynasty and preceded the Qin dynasty. Although the Zhou dynasty lasted longer than any other dynasty in Chinese history, the actual political and military control of China by the dynasty lasted only until 771 BC, a period known as the Western Zhou. About 900 BC the feudal empire of Zhou began to decay as the princes of individual feudal states grew strong and weaker states were eliminated by warfare (see Chai 1961: xxiv; Qianru 2011: 148). In the spring and autumn periods (eight to third century BCE) several large princely states enjoyed sovereignty and territory, indispensible features of any modern state.

**CONFUCIANISM HUMANISM AND AFRICAN UBUNTU**

Mencius further developed the idea and put forward the concept of free conscience, which means the kindness, or goodness of a human being. Mencius considered free conscience as symbolic of a human being. He said, "One with no sympathy is not good; one who is not shy when doing wrong is not human; one who does not know how to politely decline is not human; and one who cannot distinct right from wrong is not human" (Chunde 2014).

Mencius usually converted political issues to moral ones. This emphasis makes him such an important thinker in a context were present day international relations are based on Chinese philosophy. Jin (200:178) stresses the importance of morals in this context: "The influence of morality and values cannot be discounted in international relations or in a state's foreign policy. Hence, Mencius's international political philosophy with its moral idealism still has something to contribute to the realization of China's foreign policy and to international relations theory" (ibid).

Chinese think that all human beings are born and brought up in the family, and the world is nothing but an enlarged family (Chun 2012:xi). Filiality is related to this and the is paradigm for all inter-personal relations. This is not foreign to the African idea of Ubuntu①, and fits in with the idea of the extended family as important pillar of social life.

Confucius emphasized a harmonious society based on respect and compassion, and self-improvement through education. Comparing African ideas with those of Confucius will probably as sterile as comparing it to Greek thinking or Egyptian thought. There will however always be similarities albeit on analogous level. We are dealing after all with the same human nature. What follows are some important concepts and ideas in African culture. It is put in juxtaposition to few ideas selected above from Chinese culture. The idea is that we keep this stereo-vision intact in thinking about any interaction between China and Africa.

African cultures, like European and Eastern cultures, have many commonalities. Just as the physical environment has the same effect on different peoples, cultural similarities, as well as interdependence, needs and threats can lead to similar cultural patterns. A much discussed example is ubuntu, which is said to typify African cultural unity. Africans are historically linked by the common experience of colonialism and a common history of oppression and suffering out of which Ubuntu was born. Ubuntu stresses the role of the community in shaping African life, identity and mode of living. Any individual's identity is determined by his or her place in the community. This is similar to the notion that the meaning of a word is determined by its place in the sentence. Sentences carry meaning and so is meaning on a social level carried by the community.②

It would be a mistake, however, to limit African society to ubuntu, or to restrict personal identity to communal identity. Identifying personhood with an individual's

---

① Ubuntu is the South African version of Tanzanian Ujaama which formed the basis of Julius Nyerere's social and economic development policies after it gained independence from Britain in 1961.

② Without elaboration the link to a communal ethic found in Japanese Shinto-religion can be mentioned.

interaction with other persons does not eliminate personal identity. It simply says that personal identity is manifested in one's interaction with, and place in, one's community. Ubuntu is an ethic that developed in a context of essential interdependence and dire need. It may well be discarded by urbanised, economically independent Africans. Ubuntu is easily romanticised by whites suffering from the isolation and fragmentation that comes with individualism.

Ubuntu functions as a tribal social security system. The much vaunted ubuntu system must be seen in the context of a specific tribe, clan and family. Traditionally members of the clan were dependent on each other for agricultural and general assistance (Wiredu 1992a: 201ff). Depending on the acuteness of the need or the severity of the threat, ubuntu caring and sharing principles are applied selectively. This is in line with acceptance of African diversity. In the words of Nyasani (quoted by Basu 1994:6), "The African's surrender to the 'we' is the result of an inveterate psychological disposition largely born out of a hostile environment in which he finds himself." Basu continues that it is equally illegitimate to assume that Africa has a collective philosophy. This assumption fails to recognise its diversity. He further distinguishes economically based European socialism from ethnically related African communitarianism (Basu 1994:8; see also Gyekye 1992b:111). The point is not that African society is predominantly collective, but that an African person should not be limited to collectiveness any more than a Western person can be restricted to individualism. One has a right to live beyond one's culture, on the border of cultures, to transcend one's own surroundings, one's native culture and one's milieu. This is no betrayal, because the confines of culture are often too narrow for the full range of human potential (see du Toit 2007:48-49).

African culture seems remarkably altruistic. Ubuntu, being the African version of humanism, displays an altruistic ethic. African altruism parallels the biological roots of altruism. Unlike other animals, humans are characterised by openness to the world, behavioural plasticity and imperfect biological equipment. Lacking a genetically controlled orientation system similar to animals' instincts, they have to rely exclusively on cultural inventions such as ubuntu. Both selfishness and altruism are part of human nature. Conflict and cooperation between human beings form the very core of human sociality, and both have an evolutionary basis. Altruistic behaviour is biologically explicable. If selfish genes program an organism in such a way that its altruistic acts are directed to conspecifics (your fellow tribesperson) whose genes it shares by descent, then natural selection can favour this behavioural trait. Although maximising 'inclusive fitness' by supporting one's kin has been the major solution to the puzzle of altruism, it fails to explain instances of mutually beneficial cooperation between non-kin. These are explained by the concept of reciprocal altruism, when a non-related recipient of a benefit reciprocates at a later stage. Altruistic impulses, once limited to one's kin and one's own group, might be extended to a wider circle when we realise that we and our kin are one group among others. The scope of moral principles cannot be confined to just one group, for two reasons. Firstly, everyone (presumably) will be a non-member of some group and, secondly, if conduct is regulated only within groups, we still face the possibility of unrestricted hostility and conflict between groups.

African culture and polyethnicity should not be limited to some essence. Ubuntu can be seen as a non-essentialist and open meaning of African ethnic identity. This means that it must be polysemous, vague and active in ethnic sagacity, oral history, rites, rituals and custom. African ethnic identity is a narrative identity which comes to the fore in people's life stories. Personal identity is embedded in the meaning-giving life stories that make up the history of the people. Ethnic tradition and practices have a narrative history which must be known in order to understand the tradition. Ethnotheology is recounted in different stories, whose multi-interpretability in different contexts contributes to the richness of the tradition. Stories unify the significance of a tradition in a meaningful way.

***Ubuntu and community life***

African spirituality hinges on belonging. People belong to the soil (in Shona belief and language vhu [soil] symbolises the ancestors; see Manley 1995). People belong to one another. People and ancestors belong together. Without this sense of belonging a human is more than half dead (Alt 1995:116).

Ubuntu means participating in a common humanity (see Shutte 1993:46-51). In Africa a person is identified by her interrelationships and not primarily by individual qualities. The community identifies the person, not the person the community. His identity is his place in the community. In Africa the axiom is, 'I participate, therefore I am'.

Although Africans are as individual as anyone else, they are rarely individualistic in the Western sense. The extended family, at any rate in rural parts, is still a very real force in most African communities. Human life exists only by being shared. This naturally incorporates the extended family, where life is shared with all for whom you have to take responsibility. Consequently the accent is on consensus and reconciliation. Talking till agreement is reached is the hallmark of African democracy-which explains the resistance to an adversarial style of multiparty government (Shutte 1993: 50). African religion reconciles opposites. It does not have a dualistic approach to life and the divine (Alt 1995:115).

*Forefathers*①

Veneration of forefathers is the best known and most powerful feature of African religion and spirituality. African ancestor cults have a remarkably uniform structure, and have been well assimilated into Christianity. Christ, by virtue of his incarnation, death, resurrection and ascension into the realm of spirit power, is seen as the Supreme Ancestor. An ancestor is not a nebulous being or personified mystical presence but has a name and an identity, encapsulated in the totem system.

People do not pray to their ancestors. The ancestor is invited to participate in a ceremony. A welcoming address is given, explaining the invitation, and then prayers are said to introduce the event for which the invitation was issued. The idea is that the ancestor participates in these prayers, directed to deities or the Supreme God (Bediako 1995:220-221).

***Life-force, the power that determines life***

Life-force is analogous to the Western concept of being, albeit not being in and for itself but as integrated with the totality of life. A relational ontology describes this force better than a substantialist ontology. The origin of all force, like the origin of the universe, is God. This force binds the universe and humans together in an inti-

---

① According to Confucianism, the worship of great deities was the affair of the state, ancestral worship is required of all, and a multitude of popular cults are tolerable. Confucianism tolerated magic and mysticism as long as they were useful tools for controlling the masses; it denounced them as heresy and suppressed them when they threatened the established order (hence the opposition to Buddhism). Another notable quality was the avoidance of irrational ecstasy and excitement, as well as mystic contemplation and metaphysical speculation.

mate ontological relationship. The force of everything, especially living things, is continually waxing or waning. Human beings constantly influence each other, directly or indirectly, by way of the ancestors. The dead play a very important role in the universe of forces, and continue to interact causally with the living (Shutte 1993:52-54).

This force is the power behind spirituality. Without it spirituality would be dead. When it integrates humans with their fellow humans, nature and God, then spirituality flourishes. African spirituality, unlike Western spirituality, depends entirely on the other to be realised. Any act of separating oneself from others (through prayer, meditation, fasting or silence) negates the spiritual force of Africa. Spirituality reaches fruition only when one is linked into the causal chain that binds the individual, community, ancestors, nature and God together in a holistic force field. Western spirituality is fractured, diversified, decentred and individual. Westerners experience this as alienation. They have lost their awareness, their feeling of belonging and integration. They have lost their self, have become estranged from their own life force and potentialities.

For Africans the aim of life is to experience and enhance life force and become part of it. Anything that diminishes this force is evil and anything that increases it is good. In these terms apartheid was not experienced as a discriminatory political ideology, but as the evil that snatched life force away from black Africans and killed their spirituality by breaking up their community life, dividing their families, ridiculing the ancestor cult and isolating individuals. Not that post-apartheid society is benevolent to African spirituality. Not only are many of the legacies of apartheid still intact, but socially atomising forces like technology and the free market system are gaining ground.

In primal cultures reality is a network of interrelated spiritual forces, which do not restrict themselves to some terrain of life. The forefathers' presence is experienced in everyday situations. Social, psychological, religious, political and cultural aspects are all interwoven with the religious and the secular. In the traditional African world nothing is profane.

***Land***

African spirituality is closely tied up with land. Land is the link to the fore-fathers, to tradition and life. Alienating people from their land causes spiritual, sometimes physical death. Violation of their space and place violates the very spiritual values that hold them together. African life force is rooted in the soil (The statement 1992). Land is thus a religious symbol designating belonging, community and identity. For the AICs the question 'Who owns Christianity?' recedes before the more immediate question 'Who owns Africa?'

Manley (1995:42-53) draws attention to the fact that the Western concept of title deeds is alien, if not blasphemous to the African concept of land. For the Shona in Zimbabwe, blood links human beings to the soil in an intimate identification. The soil cannot be owned. It belongs to the people; it is a free gift like life itself, bestowed by Musikavanhu, the creator God. After birth the umbilical cord is buried, thus literally 'rooting' the infant in the ancestral soil. The ancestors are the soil by virtue of their blood that sank into it. The chief is a guardian of the land, he does not own it. These values obviously oppose the Western view of land tenure, in which production and profit are the only prerequisites for successful ownership. Part of black land tenure is the system of traditional leadership. Although authoritarian, it serves the basic interests of those communities. Self-determination remains a key term and implies some degree of sustainability.

***Spirituality***

Spirituality is an exceptional super-sensory awareness of a presence. This presence can be designated the Whole, the Transcendent, the Other or God. It can also come from one's interpretation of one's life experience, the life world with all its co-determinants. Spirituality links awareness of this presence with one's lifestyle. It may take the form of a demand on one's energies, the risk of commitment or giving oneself for a cause. Spirituality is inauthentic if it is divorced from life-one's own and other people's.

The South African liberation struggle depended heavily on African spirituality, which provided a support system that unified and strengthened those who suffered and risked their lives. The struggle made it clear that spirituality impinges on every area of life. Edwards (1991:120) speaks of a thoroughly incarnational spirituality that penetrates the whole of life, so that its effect is experienced as a new creation.

Yet we cannot deny that African spirituality grew from poverty and deprivation. Conversely, affluence and the consumer society seemingly stifle the human propensity for spirituality. It does not make poverty a virtue. It still needs to be combated, as India and China are doing successfully. Africa has a long way to go. But in the process it must harness the spiritual life force that has characterised its culture over the ages.

**Chinese presence in South African context**

A 2013 Pew study found South Africans have mixed feelings about China. The survey showed 46 percent of South Africans did not like the spread of Chinese ideas and customs in their country, and 60 percent dislike Chinese music, movies and television. If this survey is reliable it is bound to change soon as the impact of Chinese investments become visible (see http://www.pewglobal.org/2013/07/18/chapter-3-attitudes-toward-china/).

***Confucius institutes in South Africa***

By the end of 2013, 440 Confucius Institutes and 646 Confucius Classrooms have been established worldwide. There are now 25 Confucian institutes across Africa, usually linked to universities. Confucian Institutes in Southern Africa countries are situated at the universities of Zimbabwe, Botswana, and Antananarivo in Madagascar. There are four Confucius institutes in South Africa situated at Rhodes University①, Tshwane University of Technology in Pretoria, Stellenbosch University② and the University of Cape Town③.

Confucian institutes seem to be the desired instrument to promote cultural links between the two countries. Confucian institutes may teach Mandarin (simplified traditional Chinese), like the institute at the University of Cape Town is doing; teach credit bearing courses (through a university's school of language and literature) and organise cultural events. The newest institute last month began offering free Chinese classes to University of Cape Town students through an agreement between the institution and the Chinese Hanban, the Chinese Language International Office. (see University world news, 05 September 2010 Issue No: 61, http://www.universityworldnews.com/article.php? story=20100905072629973).

---

① The Institute at Rhodes was launched in August 2008 with Marius Vermaak as director.

② The Confucius Institute of Stellenbosch University (CISU) is currently managed by co-directors, Professor Zuo Xu Xie of Hanban and Mr. Hennie Kotze of the Postgraduate and International Office of Stellenbosch University.

③ Professor Wu Qianlong is the deputy director of the Confucius Institute at the university of Cape Town. He foresees that courses in Mandarin and Chinese studies would eventually become available to the public.

***Buddhism in South Africa***

Buddhism was first introduced to South Africa on a very small scale by Indian indentured labourers who were drafted into the sugar industry around Durban in Natal after 1860 (Krüger 1991: 32). Around 1917 the Overport Sakya Buddhist Society was formed under inspiration Rajaram Dass, son of a Indian Buddhist revivalist. They later became the Natal Buddhist Association. Buddhism, however, never had a black following in South Africa and Buddhist activities are limited to the initiatives of some individuals in Natal and the Western Cape (see Krüger 1991:32-33).

Various Buddhist groups grew up in the major cities from the 1970s, and there has been a proliferation of distinct Buddhist traditions since the mid-1980s.[①] These include Theravada, Zen, Nichiren and Tibetan schools. The Fo Guang Shan Buddhist order has erected Nan Hua Temple, the largest Buddhist temple and monastery in Africa, in the town of Bronkhorstspruit near Pretoria.

The following persons has contributed significantly to the establishment of South African Buddhism: Rob Nairn (Buddhist teacher, author and populariser); Leela Verity ( Founder and Director of Sat Chit Anand); Heila and Rodney Downey (Students of Zen Master Seung Sahn); Jennifer Woodhull ( Student of Pema Chödrön); Kelsang Mila (Resident Teacher of the Vajrapani Centre in Johannesburg); Professors Michel Clasquin and Jacobus Krüger (both from the University of

---

① For Buddhist Centres and Groups in South Africa see Dharma centres in South Africa, http://buddhactivity. org/action. htm? -Response=buddhacountry. htm&ccountry=South Africa.

The following centres are operative.

Western Cape : Diamond Way Buddhist Centre, Cape Town; Kagyu Samye Dzong-Tibetan Buddhist Meditation Centre, Kenilworth, Cape Town; Sat Chit Anand Buddhist Centre, Plettenberg Bay, Home of Contemporary Zen in South Africa; Tushita Kadampa Buddhist Centre, Cape Town; Hout Bay Theravada Buddhist Centre; Shambala Training Centre, Cape Town; Tibetan Meditation Centre and Tea House, Simons Town; Bodhi Khaya Retreat Centre, Gansbaai (Overberg region); Vipassana Association of South Africa, Worcester.

KwaZulu-Natal: Dharmagiri Buddhist Hermitage; Buddhist Retreat Centre, Ixopo; Maitreya Kadampa Buddhist Centre, Hillcrest/Durban; Mahasiddha Kadampa Buddhist Centre, Durban; Nyingmapa Tradition Buddhist Center (Dzogchen teaching), Amanzimtoti.

Gauteng: Diamond Way Buddhist Centre, Johannesburg; Nan Hua Monastery; Johannesburg Meditation Centre (JMC); Lam Rim Buddhist Temple, Johannesburg; Vajrapani Kadampa Buddhist Centre, Johannesburg; Shantikula Buddhist Centre, Johannesburg.

Other centres countrywide: Kagyu Lineage of Tibetan Buddhism in South Africa; Soka Gakkai International-South Africa; Emoyeni Retreat Centre, North West.

South Africa). Because of some similarities between Christianity and Mahayana Buddhism (dedicating one's life to the well-being of the world as the bodhisattva ideal exemplifies) the latter has received quite some attention in South Africa (see Keown 2013:62ff; Krüger 1991, 1995).

A PEW-study estimates, the Buddhist adherents In South Africa in 2010 (may include Taoism and Chinese Folk Religion) between 0.2% and 0.3% of the South African population, or between 100 to 150 thousand people while the number of practicing Buddhists maybe low. (See Pew research Religion and public life project, December 18, 2012).

Buddhist traditions are represented in South Africa in many forms. Temples, centres and groups are common in the metropolitan areas and the country is thought to comprise the largest Buddhist community in Africa. The very impressive Buddhist temple, The Nan Hua Temple Complex, is situated at Bronkhorstspruit (near Johannesburg and 60 km from Pretoria).

Kruger (1995:14) mentions that Buddhism is exotic to South Africa even feared. Although this may be applicable to a small minority of Christians, Buddhism is not a religion in the normal sense of the word and not experienced as a threat. In 'secularised' form it is practiced in Yoga, mindful meditation, reiki healing etc. But this is practiced not for religious purposes but because of health, the feeling of well-being or vogue concerns. Ideas pertaining to reincarnation, karma, chakras and various practices having their origins in Buddhism and Hinduism are not uncommon (Singleton 2014:152).

**CONCLUSION**

Chai (1961:38) criticises Confucianism as perhaps too humanistic, too much focused on the ideal life and too little on the need for progress and change. "Thus the old systems are to be preserved but not reformed; the ideas of the past to be venerated but not criticized. The result has been an overbalanced conservatism that the modern Chinese are most emphatic in condemning" (ibid.). Chinese foreign policy could have focused on pure present-day pragmatic concerns without reverting back to the Chinese cultural legacy. But is exactly this respect for tradition and age old ideas that has a tremendous appeal and gives hope for the future. It remains to be seen to what extend age-old philosophical ideals will affect present-day Real-Politics where politics accommodate human need.

If one read this in light of the African principles discussed there are sufficient sources of wisdom to ponder on. The challenge would be to translate these in everyday pragmatics.

Sino-Afro history must still be made. The Chinese initiatives especially to introduce Confucianism to Africa may have a fruitful outcome with the proviso that a frank dialogue between Confucian and African ideas takes place. It can be expected that as Chinese economic activity become more conspicuous on the continent that cultural interaction will follow. If both parties put their cards on the table and if the interactions are mutually beneficial, one can expect a very fertile relationship for decades to come.

**BIBLIOGRAPHY**

African Analysis May 4, 2014, *China writes off African economic grievances with China as "growing pains"* (http://africajournalismtheworld.com/tag/china-africa).

Alt, J 1995. The divine call and the human response, in Makobane, M, Sithole, B & Shiya, M (eds), *The church and African culture*, 114-126. Conference papers Lumko, Germiston.

Basu, A 1994. The concept of person in African philosophy. *37th annual meeting of the African Studies Association*. Toronto.

Bediako, K 1995. *Christianity in Africa. The renewal of a non-Western religion*. Edinburgh: Orbis.

Bunting, Madeleine 2009. The road to ruin, in *The Guardian*, Saturday 14 February 2009 (http://www.theguardian.com/books/2009/feb/14/aid-africa-dambisa-moyo).

Chai Sh'u 1961. *The story of Chinese philosophy*, Connecticut: Greenwood Press.

Clasquin, Michel / Krüger, Jacobus S. (eds.) (1999): Buddhism and Africa. Pretoria: University of South Africa.

Clasquin, Michel 2002. Buddhism in South Africa, in Charles S. Prebish / Martin Baumann (eds.), *Westward dharma: Buddhism beyond Asia*, 152-162, Berkeley, Calif.: Univ. of California Press.

Chun, Shan 2012. Major Aspects of Chinese Religion and Philosophy. Dao of inner saint and outer king. Berlin, Heidelberg :Springer Verlag.

Chunde, Gu 2014. *Confucian Human Rights Ideas and Their Influence on Modern Human Rights Thought*, China Society For Human Rights Studies, http://www.humanrights.cn/zt/magazine/200402004827 111009.htm.

De Bary, Theodore & Bloom, Irene (Eds.) 1999. Sources of Chinese tradition, Vol. I, From earliest times to 1600. NY: Columbia University Press.

De Bary, Theodore 1999. Heaven, earth an eth human in the Classic of Filiality (Xiaojing), in De Bary, Theodore & Bloom, Irene (Eds.) Sources of Chinese tradition, 325-329, New Delhi; Singapore; Washington DC: Sage.

Dessein, Bart 2014. Faith and Politics: (New) Confucianism as Civil Religion, Asian Studies II (XVIII), 1 (2014), pp. 39-64.

Du Toit, CW 2007. *African challenges. Unfolding identities*. Pretoria: RITR.

Edwards, F 1991. Theology and love in crisis and struggle, in Worsnip, W & Van der Water, D (eds), *We shall overcome. A spirituality for liberation*, 117-131. Pietermaritzburg: Cluster.

Financial Times, 3 March 2013, Zuma warns west's 'colonial' corporates, http://www.ft.com/cms/s/0/7824cc28-83ed-11e2-b700-00144feabdc0.html#ixzz3BNwFNNZn. (Accessed 10 August 2014).

Gelner, David N 2011. The Uses of Max Weber: Legitimation and Amnesia in Buddhology, South Asian History, and Anthropological Practice Theory, in Peter Clarke (ed.), *The Oxford Handbook of the Sociology of Religion*, 48-62, Oxford: OUP.

Gyekye, K 1992. Person and community in African thought, in Wiredu, K & Gyekye, K (eds), *Person and community*, 101-122. Washington: CIPSH/Unesco.

Hayat, Usman, 6 December 2011. What Explains China's Economic Growth, And Is It Sustainable? , Enterprising investor, http://blogs.cfainstitute.org/investor/2011/12/06/what-explains-china% E2% 80% 99s-economic-growth-and-is-it-sustainable (Accessed 12 August 2014).

Kieschnick, John 2003. The impact of Buddhism on Chinese material culture, Princeton and Oxford: Princeton University Pres. Keown, Damien 2013. Buddhism, Oxford: Oxford University Press.

Krüger, Jacobus S 1991. Buddhism from the Buddha to Asoka, Pretoria: University of South Africa.

Krüger, Jacobus S 1995. *Along Edges: Religion in South Africa-Bushman, Christian, Buddhist*, Pretoria: National Book Printers.

Manley, M 1995. Land and soil: a European commodity in Shona traditional perspective. *Journal for the Study of Religion*, 8(1), 27-54.

Moyo, Dambisa 2009. *Dead Aid: Why Aid Makes Things Worse and How There Is Another Way for Africa*. New York: Farrar, Straus and Giroux.

Moyo, Dambisa 2012. *Winner Take All: China's Race for Resources and What It Means for the World*. New York: Basic Books.

Qianru, Yang 2011. An examination of the research theory of pre-Qin interstate political philosophy, in Yan Xuetong (Ed.) *Ancient Chinese thought, modern Chinese power*, 147-160, Princeton and Oxford: Princeton University Press.

Riegel, Jeffrey 2013. Confucius, in *The Stanford Encyclopedia of Philosophy* (Summer 2013 Edition), Edward N. Zalta (ed.), URL =http://plato.stanford.edu/archives/sum2013/entries/confucius/ .

Shutte, A 1993. *Philosophy for Africa*. Cape Town: University of Cape Town Press.

Singleton, A 2014. *Religion, culture, society. A global approach*, LA; London; New Delhi; Singapore; Washington DC: Sage.

The Pew Forum, 2013. *Global Religious Landscape*-Religious Composition by Country. Retrieved 28 July 2013.

Weber, Max 1965. *The Protestant ethic and the spirit of capitalism*, London: Unwin University Books.

Wiredu, K 1992. Problems in Africa's contemporary self-definition, in Wiredu, K & Gyekye, K (eds), *Person and community*, Washington: Council for Research in Values and Philosophy, 101-122.

World Christian Database 2010. *Religious Adherents*, 2010 - *South Africa*. Retrieved 28 July 2013.

Xin, Lu 2011. Yan Xuetong: A realist scholar clinging to scientific prediction, in Xuetong, Yan (Ed.) 2011. *Ancient Chinese thought, modern Chinese power*, 229-251, Princeton and Oxford: Princeton University Press.

Xin, Lu 2011. Yan Xueton: A realist scholar clinging to scientific prediction, in Xuetong, Yan (Ed.), Ancient *Chinese thought, modern Chinese power*, 229-251.

Princeton and Oxford: Princeton University Press.

Xuetong, Yan (Ed.) 2011. *Ancient Chinese thought, modern Chinese power*, Princeton and Oxford: Princeton University Press.

Xuetong, Yan 2011. Xunzi's interstate political philosophy and its message for today, in Xuetong, Yan (Ed.), *Ancient Chinese thought, modern Chinese power*, 70-106. Princeton and Oxford: Princeton University Press.

# How does Confucianism Resonate in China's International Relations with Latin America?

**Diana Gómez**[①]

## INTRODUCTION

In order to understand China's international relations, it requires to broaden the spectrum from where we conceive Political Sciences and International Relations (IR) in the West. Indeed, International Relations as a scientific discipline has taken shape very recently in the West and got strengthened in the United States after the 2nd World War alongside Political Sciences and Sociology, doing *tabula rasa* of History and specific conditions of other latitudes.

Almost every paradigmatic and theoretic-methodological debate has taken place first in the United Kingdom and later in the USA. There, the IR have been conceived with a markedly ethnocentric, American and western character, in direct relation with the own problematic of U.S. foreign policy and in connection with those same interests. This is how the scientific character IR is very much linked with the political Realism definitely established for a good part of the 20th Century.

In this context, we could not even affirm the existence of a genuine scientific community in the field of IR, since in the USA it is usually to ignore practically everything that has contributed to this field in other languages different from English-the *lingua franca* of IR -, and that would be part of other scientific and cultural referents.

---

① Diana Gomez is a PhD Candidate in Political Studies and International Relations, Associated Professor (副教授) at the Department of Political Sciences and Director of China's Lecture at the National University of Colombia. The author would like to thank her colleagues Joaquín Franco y Luz Marina Díaz for the final edition of this paper.

Then, IR have been developing in an exclusivist and closed context. We can affirm that for the most part Latin America has reproduced this theoretic-methodological perspective in its conception of IR.

In face to this theoretic-methodological gap of conceptions about IR, it is necessary to broaden the spectrum to approach China-Latin America's relations with a different view from the traditional one and re-embark on a new study of China in a straightforward manner, without intermediary.

China represents a great opportunity to widen Western thought to other historical, philosophical and cultural references. To open oneself to understand other systems of thought means relativizing one's own universe. In the words of Singaporean political scientist Kishore Mahbubani, "Asians and Westerners think differently about the same issues... The world will be a much richer place when Western minds cease to assume that Western civilization represents the only universal civilization. The only way for the Western mind to break with this mentality is first to conceive the possibility that it could be limited"①.

In order to break with such limitation, it is necessary to deepen the knowledge of Chinese thought and how China is threading its relations with the world.

The construction of the link between China and Latin America is a scenario that should be studied integrally and it represents a great opportunity for both regions to deepen their mutual knowledge.

For Latin America, the rapprochement with China means understanding the structural axes of Chinese thought. It is specifically about identifying and studying the most representative aspects of Confucian tradition, Taoism and Buddhism, among others.

Thus, this paper aims to point out how Confucian tradition expresses itself in China's relations towards Latin America through the study of International Politics news coming from Chinese state news agency Xinhua.

This document is based on the analysis of news published in Xinhua website in the period between 1st of July 2008 and 1st July 2012. This analysis arose from more than 40 interviews with Latin-American and Spanish scholars, diplomats and journalists ex-

---

① Kishore Mahbubani, Can Asian think? Understanding the divide between East and West, Steerforth Press, Canada, 2002, pág. 27.

perts on China that live or have lived in the Asian country for more than 8 years, and with Chinese scholars, diplomats and journalists that live or have lived in Latin America and Spain for more than 8 years.

Among the most important results of this research we can mention: the importance of hierarchy in relations and its linkage with rituality, the integral view in Chinese political discourse, the conception of time as a trait of Chinese worldview, the relevance given to social discipline, the value of trust and the capacity of learning not only one's own but also towards others.

We conclude that these traits are closely linked with Confucian tradition in the China's relations with Latin America.

**CONFUCIAN THOUGHT AS VITAL ELEMENT THAT TRANSCENDS TIME**

There are peoples in the world for who the past, not only the recent one but fundamentally the remote one, is so ruling, relevant, and significant that it is perceived as a living entity. This happens in the case of China. The Asian country throughout its history has experienced invasions, breaks, but the lines of continuity of Chinese thought have stood the test of time.

Renowned figures from Ancient China, such as Confucius, mentioned more than 2500 years ago the interstate order, governance, power, moral, authority, among other issues. However, the contributions made by thinkers such as Confucius remain a real black hole among Western knowledge.

Indeed, it is difficult for the West to recognize that the Confucian system has been the most long-lasting political order in human history. As Jacques Martin points out (2008, p.209), "to this day… the ability of China's political world, unlike other institutions, to survive relatively unchanged is remarkable, a testament to its own resilience and the place it occupies in Chinese psyche".

One of the reasons it has lasted is due to two factors in constant relation: space and time understood as a system. It is a dialectic relation that means that Chinese political system has been characterized for being traditionally monolithic in the spatial sense of the term -each one occupies its place within a rigid hierarchic system-, but not in the temporal sense of the term -underlying an enormous flexibility and adaptability to circumstances-, between the great global transformations.

The principles that inspired this form of government developed as pattern that was followed by Japanese, Korean, Vietnamese and other nations from South-East Asia.

The fact that Chinese live in and through their history allows us to present different approaches such as historian Wang Gungwu´s: "About what other country one can say that its writings about foreign relations from one thousand or even two thousand years ago are as convincing and alive as today?" According to the renowned Chinese academic Yan Xuetong, the pre-Qin era is more than two thousand years old and some of the views of that time may still be used to explain today's realities (Xuetong, Y., 2011, p. 201).

**THE ERA OF PRESIDENT HU JINTAO AND THE CONFUCIAN VALUES**

How does Confucianism resonate in Chinese society at large? As Daniel Bell argues, "Given that the Chinese Communist Party spent its first three decades in power trying to extirpate every root and branch of Confucianism that it regarded as a feudal and reactionary worldview hindering progress, it would seem to be a losing battle. It could be argued, however, that the parts of Marxism that really took hold in the population -the importance of material well-being and an aversion to otherworldly outlooks -did so because they resonated with deeper Confucian roots" (Bell, 2008, p. 10).

Already, Chinese culture -in form of food, painting, medicine, martial arts, and so on -has spread and enriched other societies. Centuries earlier, Chinese technology has spread and enriched other societies. But Chinese political values have not spread so successfully (Bell, op.cit. p. 20).

Echoing Confucian themes, Hu Jintao president said China should promote Confucian values, as well as forge a closer relationship between the people and the government. In March 2007, the Prime Minister, Wen Jiabao made even more explicit references to tradition: "From Confucius to Sun Yat-Sen, the traditional culture of the Chinese nation has numerous precious elements, many positive aspects regarding the nature of the people. For example, recovering Confucius heritage, the government is saying that growing economic power won't translate into military adventurism and that peaceful resolution of conflicts is the way to go (Bell, op.cit. p. 9). The way those arguments are translated to Chinese foreign policy practice generates debates in Western political and academic spheres.

So, which values China promote abroad? The contemporary Chinese intellectual Kang Xiaoguang has argued that Chinese soft power are based on Confucian culture, the most influential Chinese political tradition. But which Confucian values form the core of China's policy and its foreign policy?

**RELEVANCE OF THIS PAPER**

Based on the above thought, this paper focuses on the analysis of news cast by the official Chinese government agency Xinhua regarding international policy towards Latin America through its web portal in Spanish. The aim is to establish patterns of behaviour of the Chinese government towards Latin America①. As mentioned earlier, the research confronts the news analysis with more than 40 interviews with Latin-American academics, diplomats, and journalists with over 8 years experience in China, and with Chinese academics, diplomats, and journalists with over 8 years experience in Latin America.

The focal issue for this research has been: How does Confucianism resonate in China's international relations with Latin America?

The period examined goes from the 1st of July 2008 to the 1st of July 2012 for two good reasons:

First, Beijing being the host of the 29th Summer Olympic Games in 2008, it marked the entrance of China in the big leagues of world politics. This entrance was enhanced by the organization of Expo Shanghai in 2010. These two events were key for a great number of analysts allowing China to position itself in the international arena.

For the academic Xu Shicheng, these two events put forward before the world the great soft power of China: the combination of tradition with modernity, of culture with science and technology; the cohesive strength of this great nation and its deep traditional root, the great capacity of organization and mobilization of the Communist Party and the Chinese government. These two global events represented an excellent opportunity to promote the rebirth of Chinese culture (Xu, 2011).

The second significant reason is the outbreak of the global financial crisis in September 2008. It represents an unprecedented event in the last seven decades of the 20th

① This paper is a doctoral thesis abstract of the author, in which is included also economic and cultural issues in China-Latin America relation.

century. In this beginning of the $21^{st}$ century, it is the event with the major global repercussion -besides 9/11-. In the global order, such event unleashed a series of worldwide reactions. This allows us to study the behaviour of countries such as China, particularly in issues such as political implications of the crisis for all the countries, among them those from Latin America.

**XINHUA: MANDATORY SOURCE OF REFERENCE**

From Latin America, the geographic distance, the cultural difference, the linguistic barrier do not allow us to understand easily the motives that determine China's actions in both domestic and international contemporary context.

Meanwhile, a simple analysis of modern diplomacy let us observe a substantial change in the last decades regarding traditional diplomacy: the important role of the media and culture in IR. On the one hand, the media not only inform and contribute to shape public opinion, but also influence the international public agenda. On the other hand, in the context of globalization, culture turns to be a dynamic element of IR by creating networks that share the same cultural values and habits (Gomez, 2009)①.

In the case of China, the most important media companies are state-owned, both in television and in press and radio. China also has a gigantic news agency that distributes information not only in China but also around the globe: Xinhua. It is the official news agency of the Chinese government, which depends from the State Council. It is also the largest news agency in the world, with more than 10,000 employees and 170 offices around the world.② It owns 19 newspapers and a dozen magazines. It is also a publishing house that publishes in eight languages: Mandarin, English, Spanish, French, Russian, Portuguese, Arabic and Japanese. Any other Chinese media has as mandatory source Xinhua, from printed press like *China Daily*③, *through TV broad-*

---

① An actual global 'Chinese tribe', composed by overseas Chinese, has been an important factor for the process of economic growth of the People's Republic of China.

② Xinhua, "Xinhua News Agency celebrates 80th anniversary, Beijing, November 7, 2011. Available in http: http://spanish. news. cn/principales/2011-11/07/c_131232737. htm Viewed 27th January, 2012.

③ It was created in 1981 and has a daily circulation of 200,000 copies, a third of which is distributed in over 150 countries. It depends on supplements and other local publications in English like *China Daily Hong Kong Edition*, *Shanghai Star* and *Beijing Weekend*.

casting like CCTV[①], *radio like China Radio International*[②], *the People's Daily*, to other local media.

Recently the role of Xinhua has been redefined as a media for China to exert influence abroad. In 2012, the agency, which was established 82 years ago, launched a news station in English that broadcast 24 hours a day, took over a skyscraper in Times Square in New York City and announced plans to increase the number of its offices from 170 to 200.

The State-owned news agency has journalists spread across the American continent[③]. This contrasts with the scarce number of Latin-American news agencies in China.[④]

Xinhua's dimension and impact, and the fact that it is the mandatory source of reference for the large Chinese and foreign media, were decisive arguments to choose the news published by Xinhua as object of study.

**THE NEWS**

We analysed 10% of the news published about each of the seven countries that were selected in order to have a sample representative enough. About Colombia, we analysed 100% of the news since it is the country of origin of the author of the research. News where only Latin America appeared as referent of the facts were taken into account in their totality.

For the systematization and analysis of the news, the following classification was made:

Table 1

---

① Central Television, CCTV, has 24 hours international channels in 11 languages in addition to Simplified Chinese and Traditional Chinese.

② China Radio International, founded in 1941, broadcast daily programming in 61 foreign languages, four Chinese dialect variations and Putonghua (common language of China).

③ China Central Television CCTV is also expanding in the region-only in Brazil CCTV has 18 journalists -.

④ Currently in China, only 16 Latin American Spanish-speaking journalists are working there, 10 of whom are employed by Chinese media as Xinhua, CRI or CNTV, so remain only six, of which four belong to Latin American news agencies and are accredited by the Beijing government. The four Latin American journalists accredited by Beijing are two Cubans working in the Cuban news agency Prensa Latina and People's Daily Online, respectively, linked to "El Comercio" newspaper of Peru and the Colombian portal China Files.

NEWS PUBLISHED BY XINHUA REGARDING LATIN AMERICA

PERIOD 1ST OF JULY 2008 TO 1ST OF JULY 2012

| COUNTRY | Total Number of News | % of total of news | 10% of total of news |
|---|---|---|---|
| Latin America * | 255 | 4,88% | 255 |
| Brazil | 1656 | 31,74% | 166 |
| Mexico | 1093 | 20,95% | 109 |
| Chile | 814 | 15,60% | 81 |
| Peru | 520 | 9,96% | 52 |
| Costa Rica | 336 | 6,44% | 33 |
| Ecuador | 317 | 6,07% | 31 |
| Colombia * | 226 | 4,33% | 226 |
| TOTAL | 5217 | 100% | 953 (18,26%) |

Note: From Colombia and Latin America we considered 100% of the news

From a total of 5217 news referring to the seven Latin American countries, we studied 18,26% of the news. Why did we choose such countries? It was about carrying out a comparative study taking into account countries with different levels of relation with China.

The research shows firstly that 52,69% of the news refer to two countries: Brazil and Mexico.

Brazil grabs a bit more than 30% of the news. This highlights not only the level of relation between the two countries, but also the importance that China give to this regional power. Indeed, both have established strategies that strengthen the bilateral linkage. China and Brazil set a Joint Action Plan for the period 2010-2014, establishing a detailed road map to deepen the relation between both countries (Xinhua, 2010).

The case of Brazil, which is definitely the great protagonist of the relations with the region, shows the connection of both countries, not only regards to trade, it also reveals the enhancement of relations where political, scientific-technological and academic exchanges are relevant.

In addition, both countries show identical or similar points of view regarding to several international issues. We could point out common concepts such as advocating for multipolarization, as well as the common need to reform the international financial system and some multilateral organisations such as the United Nations (China Today, 2011).

It is worth mentioning that the reference to the BRICS (Brazil, Russia, India, China and South Africa) in the news about Brazil is very repeatedly brought up, to the point that in the 82 political news on this country during the period 2008-2012, the BRICS are mentioned 83 times, representing 101,21% of the total of political news.

In the case of Mexico, it is the first Latin-American country to have developed Asian studies at academic level, and this carries great importance for China. It is the country with the longest tradition in Latin America regarding education in Asian studies at master's degree and PhD level, and in the creation of research centres on the Asian country①. Mexico is also very active in teaching Mandarin, dynamic in the organization of symposiums, seminars, fairs (Expo China-México)② and in the production of publications about China-México and China-Latin America relations③.

Moreover, It is also a dynamic country in promoting twin cities and municipalities, building synergies in different areas such as Tapachula, Chiapas, in Mexico, and the municipality of Dongying, China, taking advantage of the important Chinese immigration in this area of the Latin American country.④

In the case of Mexico, we can observe an important cultural rapprochement carrying out itinerant archaeological exhibitions where it could be highlighted some common aspects such as the use of jade, common element to the Olmeca, Teotihuacan,

---

① Notably the China-Mexico Studies Center (Cechimex) at National Autonomous University of Mexico (UNAM) and El Colegio de Mexico, among others. The UNAM also created the Center for Mexican Studies (CEM), a joint project of UNAM and the University of Foreign Languages of Beijing.

② Xinhua. (2010, 11th November). "The Expo China-Mexico 2010 begins and hopes to overcome comercial trades", Mexico D. C., 11 November, 2010. Available in: http://spanish. news. cn/principales/2010-11/11/c_13601454. htm

③ This is the case, among others, the collection of books on the Latin America and the Caribbean with China relation about political, economic and cultural matters, elaborated after the First International Seminar on 'China, Latin America and the Caribbean: conditions and challenges in the XXI Century', Mexico, D. F., May 2012.

④ See more in Dussel Peters, Enrique "40 years of the Relation between Mexico and China. Agreements, Disagreements, Future". UNAM, Mexico, 2012.

Mayan and Mexican civilizations in Mexico with Chinese civilization①.

Chile is the third country in number of news, which are almost totally related to the economy. This is due to a large extent to the early development of Chile´s commercial relations with the Pacific and to the free trade agreement (FTA) signed with China and other countries: it was the 4th country in the world to have signed an agreement of this kind with the Asian power. The news regarding Chile represent 15,6% of the total of the news.

In descending order, Chile is followed by Peru, Ecuador, Costa Rica and Colombia. If we consider that the number of news reflects the level of relation of the different Latin-American countries with China -given that the news show dynamism of the relations- we can conclude that the countries with a high-level development of relations with China are Brazil and Mexico. Chile and Peru have a mid-level development. Then follow those with a low-level development of relations: Costa Rica, Ecuador y Colombia②.

A general postulate of Xinhua is that Latin American nations in 2010 go into a new stage of relations development with China, where the protagonist is the Economy.③. Here the financial crisis -declared in September 2008- was crucial to seek opportunities for rapprochement between China and Latin America. In that sense, Xinhua highlights recent initiatives to strengthen ties with China as is the case in Brazil with the "China Agenda", Chile with the "Policy Plan on China" and Mexico with the "Working Group on China".④

On the other hand, what draws the attention is the increase of the number of news proceeding from countries such as Peru and Costa Rica, due largely to the signing of the respective FTAs with China.

Furthermore, we could stress all the news related to Chinese immigration in the

---

① Available in http://spanish. china. org. cn/international/txt/2012-03/30/content_25024416_2. htm

② These trends correlate with the size of the Latin American embassies in Beijing. In 2012 the author accounted the number of officials at each Latin American embassy in Beijing, their academic level, and staff members who speak Chinese language. Colombia was the embassy with the lowest rates.

③ Xinhua, "Analysis relations between China and Latin America: trasforming the crisis in an opportunity for development", 5 January, 2010. Available in: http://spanish. china. org. cn/international/txt/2010-01/05/content_19180447. htm

④ Ibidem.

region and the existing Chinese neighbourhoods in our subcontinent, for instance in some suburban areas in Brazil and Peru, and including Costa Rica where it was starting the construction of a "Chinatown" in an area of 8,300 $m^2$ in the capital San Jose.①

The analysis of the news allows us to understand other issues than the development of the relations between China and the Latin-American region: a cultural logic fed by elements that come from the clearest Confucian tradition.

Below we will make reference to each of the elements of Confucianism found in the analysis of the mentioned news.

**HIGH-LEVEL VISITS AND THE NOTION OF HIERARCHY**

One aspect to point out in the news about political relations is the great importance given to the high-level visits. By fact, 40% of the political news are related to this kind of visit.

In addition, we noted a number of words with a particular meaning for Chinese diplomacy that structure the level of relation with each one of the Latin-American countries. In descendant order there are: integral partners, strategic partners, cooperation partners, friendship partners. This explains an own and hierarchical scheme of relations, according to the degree of antiquity, solidity and dimensions of the linkage.

The registry of the high-level visits is crucial in the analysis of the news, and is related with certain characteristics that unveil the way how the relations are understood in China: it must follow a strict hierarchical order, with face-to-face meetings according to the level in the political and social order, cultivated in the long term, and all of this keeps building trust, indeed, a very much appreciated value in Chinese culture. In the background of all of these characteristics underlies the clearest Confucian tradition in the handling of relations.

In fact, the very high frequency of news about this topic is related to the importance given in the Chinese cultural context to the notion of hierarchy. According to D. Bell, "One of the most puzzling features of East Asian societies is that they seem rigidly hierarchical" (Bell, 38).

---

① Xinhua, "Standing the first stone chinese neighborhood in San Jose", 19 October 2009. Available in: http://spanish. peopledaily. com. cn/31617/6786401. html

One factor concerning the hierarchy is the fact that the news broadcasts China on Latin America have in mind primarily governmental sources, which are not confronted with other sources, as happens in the West. Only when an event warranted, Xinhua takes in account some sources as multilateral or international organizations. In turn, Xinhua continuously refers to documentary sources, universities spokesmen and research centers. The absence of the voices of representatives from guilds, private companies, NGOs and federations is recorded. Only the Friendship Associations of Latin American Countries with China are taken into account.

Indeed, 77. 99% of the sources consulted by Xinhua correspond to official sources, 11.43% are academic sources and 10.46% from other sources.

This trend in the way Xinhua relates to the sources is coherent with the fact that this Asian country preserves the Confucian tradition that should give prominence to the official source on the others, following the political order.

Sources of high-level academic type -being knowledgeable of the issues and have a high degree of respectability in the Chinese context- are taken into account in some cases explaining and contextualizing news stories. This alludes to another aspect of the Confucian tradition: "In East Asian societies with a Confucian heritage, the teacher has Relatively high status" (Bell, op.cit. p. 48).

In China the idea that different sources of authority could and should coexist has been seen as ethically wrong. The only near exception were the great teachers and intellectuals: "who, though always marginal to the centre of power, could, under certain circumstances, be more influential than ministers, acting as the cultural transmitters and guardians of the civilizational tradition and the representatives of the people's well-being and conscience -even, in tumultuous times, as the emissaries and arbiters of the mandate of Heaven" (Jacques, M. ,2009, p.209).

Luis Roa is a Colombian official at the Colombian Embassy in Beijing. He lives in China since 28 years ago and about hierarchy in China he says: "The system is totally hierarchical, it continues to be a Confucian system taken to the new communist-socialist system. Everyone obeys to the hierarchical level. For instance, at official level when you go to a meeting and you have a job title, they relate to your job title, but if for example someone with a higher title like the ambassador goes to a meeting, then he is welcomed by his equal. The hierarchy goes up. The hierarchical concept is very important, because it is a cultural concept"[①].

Gina Caballero is a consultant of ECLAC and Executive President of the NGO Latin China Network for Development. After several years in China, she considers that "one believes that there is always a leader in every environment. It does not matter in which position he is, there is always a leader"[②].

**THE RITUALITY**

In different cultures, social behaviours with some degree of relevance are associated with rituals. Chinese culture is linked with a series of ritual conducts in the relationship between individuals that is reflected in foreign affairs. It is the case of high-level visits when delegations from China and other countries gather to give place to meetings, signing of agreements, opening of entities, etc. Chinese delegations happen to be numerous, always organized according to the hierarchical level of each member of the delegation. The access to the official with the highest rank is not allowed, unless the official who has the meeting with him holds the same level in the visited country. The way to dress is very similar between the members of the delegation (very classic clothes with dark colours and white shirt), as well as the individual behaviour: they usually have a great body inexpressiveness in Western perspective. In fact, in the Chinese case, the Confucian heritage unveils that "The moral level of a state is determined primarily by the quality of the state's leaders" (Bell, op.cit. p.10).

Daniel Bell explains that "Human beings can be "made good by conscious exertion". They can learn to contain their natural desires and enjoy the benefits of peaceful and cooperative social existence. The key to transformation is ritual. By learning and participating in rituals, people can learn to contain their desires, there will be a better fit between people's actual desires and the goods available in society, and social peace and material well-being will result. Rituals provide bonds not based solely on kinship that allow people to partake of the benefits of cooperative social existence" (Ibidem, p. 39-40).

The exemplary rulers of the past self-consciously implemented and promoted the rituals to limit human desires and establish social order: "The ancient rulers abhorred such chaos, so they established the regulations contained within rituals and moral

---

① Interview done by the author in Beijing, October 2011.

② Interview done by the author in Beijing, November 2011.

principles in order to civilize human desires and to supply the means for their satisfaction. This is the origin of rituals" (Ibidem, p. 40).

The method of analysis employed by Confucius and Mencius is the level of the individual person, specifically, the ruler. Confucius believes that the stability or instability of the world order is wholly determined by the moral cultivation of the political leader. Confucius maintains that the personal virtue of the leader is the foundation of social order (Xuetong, 2011, p. 28)

By fact, the rituals should be proportionate to the emotions involved. This characteristic expresses a reality in the ritual conduct promoted by Confucius, which is common in cultures in the Asian continent, according to the prominent anthropologist Clifford Gertz: "The more refined are one´s feelings, the deeper is our understanding, the more elevated is our moral character…. The handling of the emotional economy of the individual is for this reason his primary concern... A singular inner calm is the valued psychological state, what marks a truly noble character... One needs to try to overcome the emotions of daily life in order to reach the genuine feeling-sense that is within ourselves" (Gertz, 1990, p.125).

Thus, and according to Bell, "Rituals involve people with different power in common social practices that treat people differently… such practices are essential for generating a sense of community" (Bell, op.cit. p. 42).

Nonetheless, informal rituals still have an important role to play in securing a sense of community in China. For example, the ritual governing gift-giving, with gifts that vary in accordance with the social status of the recipient, are common in all East Asian societies. The greeting of guests and parting rituals are far more elaborate than those in most Western societies. (ibid., p. 46).

But the Confucian approach to promoting rituals would not rely first and foremost on the strong arm of punishment to promote rituals. One of the most famous passages in *The Analects* of Confucius is the following: "Lead the people by means of regulations and keep them orderly with punishments, and they will avoid punishments but will be without a sense of shame. Lead them with moral power and keep them orderly by means of rituals and they will develop a sense of shame as well as correct themselves" (ibid., p. 52).

Still, the defence of rituals is less likely to be taken seriously in contexts that do not have a Confucian heritage. For one thing, it is difficult to translate the key terms

-*li* and *rang*- in ways that sound appealing to, say, English speakers. Bell has translated *li* as "ritual", but the term often has negative connotations in English; one seems to be defending mechanical and uncreative practices from outdated eras. Other common translations such as "rites" and "ritual propriety" are hardly improvements. The typical translations of *rang* -defer, concede, yield, give in- also seem like outdated notions from aristocratic and hierarchical times. (ibid., p. 54).

In one of the interviews I did to some colleagues from Latin American countries and Spain, I found some references to rituals such as this one, from the most renowned Spanish expert on China, Xulio Rios: "I think that what is happening in China is a rebirth of tradition, for instance the rise of rituals. Today, you take the metro in Beijing and you see on the TV screens of the wagons the ceremonies that took place in the Temple of Heaven during imperial times. You are witnessing how all this tradition is being brought back today"①.

**THE HOLISM**

A common denominator in Xinhua news is the tendency to integral view in the Chinese political discourse. It is frequent that the news refer to terms such as:

18. "…the commitment of Beijing to go towards a *strategic interdependence*… to establish a *multifaceted cooperation* and in the long term with the Latin-American countries."②

19. "Both sides have strengthen their cooperation in political, economic and trade, scientific and technological matters, as well as in the field of humanities. In addition, China and Latin America are helping each other mutually in international issues".

This demonstrates the *integral and whole vision* of bilateral relations③.

A superficial analysis of this feature of political discourse which is reproduced in the news story would falsely affirm a demagogic approach of the Chinese Communist Party. However, this point of view fails to present a distinctive trait of Chinese cul-

---

① Interview done by the author in Beijing, October 2011.

② Xinhua, "Increases the Exchange between China and the Countries of Unasur", Quito, 10 August, 2009. Available in http://spanish.news.cn/chinaiber/2009-08/11/c_1324465.htm

③ Xinhua, Young Latin American political debate with Chinese officials on bilateral ties", Beijing, 13 April, 2010. Available in http://spanish.news.cn/chinaiber/2010-04/13/c_13249714.htm

ture that is the holistic view of reality, which at last se traduce in concrete strategies in foreign policy such as the Chinese omnidirectional diplomacy.

In that regard, an important Mexican scholar, Francisco Haro Navejas①, argues that: "Chinese interests in Latin America are multidimensionals, it is about trade but also about different topics and institutional levels".

Luis Roa states that: "Since the experience I have gained here, the Chinese government looks at every country as a complete package, they never look at a country just through a commercial, political, cultural, military or scientific lens. I think that for Chinese people every angle is important, just like the four legs of a table are equally important. Therefore they give the same priority to the cultural element than to the commercial, political, military or scientific element. This is what I have been able to understand here. They give the same importance to an art exhibition than to the Canton fair. Everything is important for them. I have been present different presidential visits, and I have seen that they welcome around 20 to 22 presidents per year and they give the same importance to every one of them, whether it is an African president or the president of the United States".

**THE LONG TERM**

Xinhua news usually addresses the context in which the facts take place and it means to refer to past history and implications for the future. However Chinese tradition does not simply refers to the immediate past or future. The long term is inherent to the conception of time, contrary to a large part of the Western countries.

Thus, Xinhua news are a reflection of the Chinese worldview of time. In this regard, Kung-Tsé knew better than anyone the history of his country, since he had studied it thoroughly. Confucius, therefore, when he was campaigning for the return to the past, he did it with basis, since he based his position in the fact that history is the master of life (Confucius, p 32).

Hence, China is a country with tradition of planning in the long run towards the future. This is reflected in the news when we read: "Considering the predominant presence of China in the global economy for the coming years and the rest of the 21st

① Proffesor at Colima University, Mexico, and author of the book 'History of relations Mexico-Asia'. Interview done by the author in Bogota, September, 2012.

century…"[①].

The first secretary of the Colombian embassy in China, Luis Roa, says in this regard: "the plans of the Chinese government are already set until 2050: they already have approximately calculated how much will the population grow, the GDP, the cities, etc., therefore it is a very planified country".

The Colombian anthropologist and movie director Andrés Mora has been living in China for the past 12 years. For him, to think in the long term is a very Chinese characteristic: "For example, many Chinese that are in Latin America have the objective of getting to the USA. They think in a 25 years plan to get to the US, they stay some years in Ecuador, then they go to Mexico and finally they get to educate their children in American universities. The distant goal is always very clear. This is something that we do not have in Latin America". And later on he adds: "From the Chinese government perspective for the relations between countries you need time and constancy... It is necessary for the countries to cultivate long term relations".

**THE SOCIAL DISCIPLINE**

After a detailed analysis of the news we perceive the importance of social discipline for Chinese people, another aspect that comes from ancient tradition, revalued and spread by Kung-Tsé.

In one of the news, as a result of the earthquake that took place in the province of Qinghai, we can read:

"Public entertainment also will be suspended on Wednesday, said in an announcement the State Council. After the announcement, the Ministry of Culture published an urgent circular ordering to the administrative departments to strengthen the supervision of entertainment places and that they will punish those who would not respect the rule. Other than the entertainment places such as theatres, karaoke bars, clubs and internet cafes, online groups also have to cease all the online services of music, games, comics, films and TV shows; including a great ceremony of a new touristic casino"[②]. This shows the strong social discipline, in comparison with countries such as the Latin American.

---

① Xinhua (2011, November 23) "Cumbre Empresarial China América Latina despierta expectativas", available in http://spa nish. mofcom. gov. cn/article/ferias/201111/20111107838695. shtml

② Xinhua, "China raises more donations for quake-hit area", Beijing, 21 April, 2010.

Luis Roa says that "I think that if there is something that distinguishes this country from others is its discipline. The discipline is a direct command; they come from a methodology of life of direct command, even if we do not get it. So, discipline is clearly military, traditional, strong. I think they are very disciplined… It is a country that makes you feel different but... what is the difference? It is a very strong system, very solid, in which there is a lot of security... there are problems like anywhere else, robbery, hold-ups, injuries, there is everything. But if they catch you doing the misdeed... you are done. It shows another kind of perspective. I have been doing a lot of work outside my area and you get to understand when you deal with government entities, judicial entities, the Supreme Court, anti-narcotics, the police, you understand that there is a very strong control in here. The one that is caught is caught, and if he is caught, he is done, not like in the West. It is a strong hand... because there are too many, we are talking about 1,3 billion people. So, it requires quite a strong system, rigid with clear policies. A simpler example: what the world saw in the 2008 Olympic Games, this gives you an insight about what is happening in this country. In Beijing, everything was working like a clockwork, everything worked the way it had to work. It is not that normally things do not work, but when the country relies on a system to run things, this is the way it works. So, everything is impeccable, everything is excellent: logistics, hotels, transports, security. There were some problems like everywhere, but China demonstrated to the world that this is its country, its people, its cities, that it is a country that is growing. Therefore, I think that it is a country with a strong hand, it has to be that way in order to work. The West can interpret it as being an authoritarian country, as they would like to interpret it, but China is not interested in this. China is interested in keeping things working. You can look at it the way you want. Because too many people live here".

Patricia Castro Obando, correspondent in China for the Peruvian daily journal *El Comercio* and analyst of Chinese politics (she has been living in the Asian country for more than 11 years) argues that: "While we're talking about a Latin American region full of resources where a seed falls and you get a tree full of fruits, however, come across the world where we have a third part of arid lands, where there have been several historical famines, where resources themselves are so hard to get, then we are talking about two different realities. Here the issue of enjoyment of life is not conceived that way it is done in Latin America, but there is something that goes beyond, the Chinese have a word to describe that, the importance of learning Chinese beyond just communicating -. For example when they say 努力 [nǔlì], on one hand, is an expression that has to do with what the effort, characterizes much of the way of life of the Chinese, and the other is a compliment after a work that has required a lot of effort. The effort does not have a negative connotation that it does in the Americas. The effort here is part of the component of life, is part of the normal life of the person and a necessary process to achieve total satisfaction. We are facing a different way of thinking and understanding life①.

**THE VALUE OF TRUST**

In the news regarding the speeches and interventions of high-level officials of the Chinese government in their visits in Latin America, we can observe a word that is very repetitive: "trust". A single example is represented by the case of Colombia since it is a country distant from China in comparison with other countries from the region, which implies an important work of trust building. In fact, president Hu Jintao in his meeting with Colombian president Juan Manuel Santos the 8th of May 2012 in Beijing recommended in the first place "to improve mutual trust in politics" and advocated that "high level officials from government, parliament and political parties from both countries should strengthen dialogue, with the objective to better understand and support each other in issues of mutual interest". These words, the same as meeting face-to-face, carries great value in the building of relations with China, since people-to-people dialogues strengthen the climate of trust (Gómez, *El Espectador*, 2012).

Trust "is more valuable than gold or any other currency", argues Ma Zhengang, director of China Institute of International Issues and ex ambassador in the UK.

The tours of the former president Hu Jintao in Africa, of the former prime minister Wen Jiabao in Europe, of the former vice-president at this time, Xi Jinping, in Latin America during the Hu presidency (2003-2013) and of other high representatives, were defined by the Chinese government as "trips of trust". This brings us to a key value in Chinese culture for the establishment of long-lasting relations.

Trust is not precisely a focal point of study in Political Sciences nor in IR in the West, where it is considered that its opposite, mistrust, is the centre of Realist and

---

① Interview done by the author in Beijin, November, 2011.

Neorealist IR theories, and it is at the base of interstate relations, related to interest and rational calculation. It is usually the starting point from where States and individuals relate to each other in the contemporary Western world.

Besides the resources of power that the West knows such as tax administration, the parliament, the judicial branch, police forces, the army and other institutions, in the Chinese conception there is a crucial aspect that gathers all the formers: trust. The following reference to Confucius is very eloquent in this respect: "A disciple asked about the art of governing, Confucius argued that "It is necessary to guarantee the subsistence, guarantee the defense and inspire trust to the people"①. If it would be necessary to renounce to one of these three elements: Which one would it be? Asked a disciple. Confucius replied: "The army". Again the disciple asks him which one it is better to renounce between the last two, and he replies: "Food. Men have always had to die, however, if the people lose its trust in those in charge, there would be no one who would defend the government". This is the reason why it is a system in which each and every one of its people march in unison. Trust explain why the people obey to a ruler or a ruling party with an almost reverential respect. It even carries more weight than the capacity of coercion of many Western laws.

Andres Mora states that "to lose face or to lose trust is something serious for them. In Colombia the mistakes are made since the first moment, for instance, in a meeting a Colombian delegation receives the business card of their Chinese counterparts and at the end of the meeting Colombian people leave it on the table or drop it on the floor. With Chinese people, it is necessary to build trust and it takes years. If there is not trust, you can't do anything, this is the base of the relationships".

It is such important trust in China that this country holds the presidency of the Conference on Interaction and Confidence-Building Measures in Asia (CICA). The CICA is composed by 24 member countries and 13 observing States and organizations. It was considered as the largest multilateral forum on security in Asia②.

**THE CAPACITY OF LEARNING FROM EACH OTHER**

The analysis of the news allows to envisage China's necessity of learning from

---

① Analects XII,7.

② The CICA was established in 1993 as a forum for dialogue and consultation, as well as for the promotion of measures to build confidence among its members. See more in http://espanol.cri.cn/741/2014/05/09/1s312685.htm

other realities. In some news, references are made about the fact that "China has to learn from other countries"[①].

Patricia Castro argues that "Chinese also learn from the mistakes of others, they have not been willing to repeat neither the American model, nor its model with Africa. Chinese have learned a lot from their ties with Africa to establish relations with other regions of the world".

**FINAL THOUGHTS**

The results of the research presented here gather substantial elements of Chinese culture for a better understanding by Latin America. This is where knowledge about China is even scarcer than in Europe or the United States.

In order to start to overcome the cultural abysm, a systematic work is needed that would take into account the following steps:

First, the translations from Mandarin to Spanish are less numerous than from Mandarin to English. It would be necessary to have more Latin-Americans speaking Mandarin and more Chinese speaking Spanish because it is mandatory the training of translators from Mandarin to Spanish and vice versa, that would serve the mutual understanding. This is the beginning of the road to cover.

Second, and in conjunction with the former, experts knowledgeable on both cultures are needed, as they would know how to interpret the codes from the other side of the ocean. This requires the universities and research centres to examine both cultures and the relations between China and Latin America. Therefore, this research draws attention to the necessity for Political Sciences and IR, with the aim to become more universal and whole as a field of study, to get closer to History and Cultural Studies if we want to acquire a more certain knowledge regarding what is happening in the Eastern hemisphere and in Latin America. On the contrary, any attempt to interpret would fall into mere speculation.

Specifically in the field of Political Sciences and IR, we ought to further our understanding on Chinese thought, its political system, their developments regarding IR theories and the legacy in terms of International Political Philosophy of ancient thinkers from the Asian giant. Renowned figures from ancient China, such as Confucius,

---

① Ibidem.

Guanzi, Laozi, Mencius, Mozi, Xunzi and Hanfeizi referred to the interstate order, governance, power, moral, authority among other issues. This knowledge is essential to strengthening the trans-Pacific relations. This way, it requires China to increase the study of Latin-American political thought.

The contribution of Confucius' political thought and his approach regarding international relations will need to be recognized by Western scholars and policy-makers at some point of the first half of the 21st Century.

**BIBLIOGRAPHY**

Bell, D. A. (2008). *China's New Confucianism. Politics and Everyday Life in a Changing Society*. New Jersey: Princeton University Press.

Caballero, G. (2011, Noviembre). Jerarquía. (D. A. Gómez, Interviewer)

Castro Obando, P. (2011, Noviembre). Esfuerzo. (D. A. Gómez, Interviewer) Beijing.

China Today. (2011, 04, 28). "Opportunities and challenges in the cooperation between China and Latin America and the Caribbean in the post-crisis era ", Beijing, April 28, 2011. Available in: http://www.chinatoday.com.cn/ctspanish/se/txt/2011-05/11/content_357063.htm

Confucio. (1974). *Los Cuatro Libros Clásicos*. Barcelona: Bruguera S.A.

Confucio. (1974). *Las Analectas* in *Los Cuatro Libros Clásicos*. Barcelona: Bruguera S.A.

Dussel Peters, E. (2012). *40 años de relación entre México y China. Acuerdos, desencuentros y futuro*. México, D.F.: Universidad Nacional Autónoma de México. http://dusselpeters.com/53.pdf

Embajada de la República Popular China en la República de Chile. (2011, Noviembre 24). Cumbre empresarial China América Latina despierta expectativas. *Embajada de la República Popular China en la República de Chile*. http://cl.china-embassy.org/esp/sbxw/t880736.htm

Geertz, C. (1990). *La interpretación de las culturas*. Barcelona: Gedisa S.A.

Gómez, Diana. A. (2009). La presencia china en Colombia. Revista *Amigos de China, Bogotá, p.* 36.

_______ (2012). Aproximación a las raíces del Ascenso de China en el siglo XXI. *2o simposio electrónico de política internacional sobre política china*. Available in http://sp. theorychina. org/view_ 2489/ politics /201209/W020120928635827432923. pdf

________(2012, Mayo 11). Es urgente una Política hacia China. *El Espectador* journal. Available in http://www. elespectador. com/noticias/politica/urgente-una-politica-china-articulo-345612

Jacques, M. (2009). *When China rules the World: The end of the Western World and the birth of a new global order*. New York: The Penguin Press.

Pueblo en Linea. (2009, Octubre 19). Colocan primera piedra de Barrio Chino en San José. *Xinhua*. Retrieved from http://spanish. peopledaily. com. cn/31617/6786401.html

Rios, X. (2011, Octubre). Ritos. (D. A. Gómez, Interviewer) Beijing.

spanish.china. org. (2010, Enero 5). Análisis de las relaciones entre China y América Latina: convertir la crisis en una oportunidad para el desarrollo. *spanish. china. org*. Retrieved from http://spanish. china. org. cn/international/txt/2010-01/05/content_19180447.htm

spanish.china.org. (2012, Marzo 30). Museo exhibirá más de 220 piezas de jade creadas en México y China. (R. Dong, Ed.) *Xinhua*. Retrieved Mayo 13, 2012, from http://spanish.china. org.cn/international/txt /2012-03/30/content_25024416.htm

spanish.people.cn. (2014, Mayo 24). China debe aprender de otros países, dice presidente Xi. *spanish. people. cn*. Retrieved Mayo 31, 2014, from http://spanish.peopledaily.com.cn/n/2014/0524/c31621-8732102.html

Xinhua, "Analysis relations between China and Latin America: trasform the crisis in an opportunity for development", 5 January, 2010. Available in: http://spanish.china.org.cn/international/txt/2010-01/05/content_ 19180447.htm

Xinhua. (2009, Agosto 11). Xinhua, "Increases the Exchange between China and the Countries of Unasur", Quito, 10 August, 2009. Available in http://spanish.news.cn/chinaiber/2009-08/11/c_1324465.htm

Xinhua. (2010, Abril 21). China recauda más donaciones para zona afectada por sismo. *Pueblo en Linea*. Retrieved from http://spanish. peopledaily. com. cn/31621/6957614.html

Xinhua. (2010, 11th November). "The Expo China-Mexico 2010 begins and hopes to overcome comercial trades", Mexico D.C., 11 November, 2010. Available in: http://spanish.news.cn/principales/2010-11/11/c_13601454.htm

Xinhua. (2010, February 12). "Chinese and Brazilian presidents talk about bilateral relations by phone", Beijing. Available in http://spanish.news.cn/chinaiber/2010-02/12/c_13173039.htm

Xinhua. (2010, 13th April). Young Latin American political debate with Chinese officials on bilateral ties", Beijing, 13 April, 2010. Available in http://spanish.news.cn/chinaiber/2010-04/13/c_13249714.htm

Xinhua, "Standing the first stone chinese neighborhood in San Jose", 19 October 2009. Available in: http://spanish.peopledaily.com.cn/31617/6786401.html

Xinhua. (2011, Noviembre 7). Agencia de Noticias Xinhua celebra 80a aniversario. *Xinhua*. Retrieved enero 27, 2012, from http://spanish.news.cn/principales/2011-11/07/c_131232737.htm

Xinhua (2011, November 23) "Cumbre Empresarial China América Latina despierta expectativas", available in http://spanish.mofcom.gov.cn/article/ferias/201111/20111107838695.shtml

Xuetong, Y. (2011). *Ancient Chinese Thought, modern chinese power*. New Jersey: Princeton University Press.

Xu, Shicheng (2011). El Surgimiento del Poder Blando de China. Revista *Amigos de China*, Bogotá, p.3-4.

# Confucius in the 21st Century and the Role Played by Confucianism Outside Mainland China in the New Millennia: The Case of Portugal

**Elisabetta Colla**

This paper will focus on the research, education, popularization of Confucianism in Portugal in the new millennia. *Kongzi* was one of the greatest thinkers of the Chinese History and Culture. His impact on the social structure, educational system, moral and ethical path is still present in today's China. His philosophy went to several transformations and was kept alive by the Chinese tradition along the centuries. The first great contact between Confucianism and the West occurred during the 16th Century from and in Macao Confucius and his classics were translated for the first time into Latin language causing a great impact in all over Europe. At present Portuguese is the sixth most widely spoken language in the world but Confucius and Confucianism is mainly studied on English, French or German sources available.

**SHORT BIO**: Elisabetta Colla is an Assistant Professor at the Faculty of Arts-Lisbon University (Portugal). She holds a PhD in Studies of Culture obtained from the Faculty of Human Sciences of the Portuguese Catholic University of Lisbon, and currently teaches Asian Art, Introduction to Asian Literatures and History of Ancient and Imperial China at the Faculty of Arts (Lisbon University), as well as Chinese Culture and Language and Asian Visual Culture at the Faculty of Human Sciences (Portuguese Catholic University of Lisbon). She has also collaborated with museums and other institutions and has given her own contribution to several catalogues of exhibitions on China held at such institutions. She is a member of the Centre of Communication and Culture (Portuguese Catholic University of Lisbon), of the Institute of Art History (LisbonUniversity) and associate researcher at the Macau Scientific and Cultural Centre (Lisbon). She has obtained a Master's degree in Asian Studies from the Faculty of Human Sciences of Oporto, a postgraduate degree in Modern Chinese Studies from the Technical University of Lisbon, a Master's degree (*Laurea*) in Oriental Languages and Literatures from "Ca'Foscari", University of Venice, and a diploma in Chinese Language from the former Beijing Languages Institute. Publications: http://ucp.academia.edu/ElisabettaColla

**Introduction**

Ten years after the first mo state ritual of the twentieth first century performed in honour of Confucius and the founding of the First Confucius Institute in 2004,[①]the academic international community is nearly to celebrate the 2565th Anniversary of Confucius' Birthday inaugurating the fifth academic meeting on Confucian studies. Scholarly attention inside and outside China had long been devoted to Confucian studies, but in Portugal the situation is quite different even if is changing very rapidly. This essay will present the impact of studies Sinology[②] and Chinese studies in Portugal today, more specifically what is available in terms of Confucius studies to the Portuguese audience through a cultural and historical analysis. The paper will be divided into three main parts: an introductory note on "tradition" and the "canon" as general cultural phenomena, repeated social phenomena with a specific psychological impact to a certain kind of audience; a brief introduction on Chinese studies in Portugal and finally the impact of Confucius studies in Portugal a presenting brief historical analysis of the extant Portuguese translations of the Confucian canon.

**The tradition and the canon**

The word tradition is a practice, an idea or an object associated to the past and somehow continuous. The fact of being linked to the past does not mean that it is necessarily a very ancient phenomenon. In fact, according to Eric Hobsbawm most of the "traditions" which claim to be old are often quite recent in origin and sometime invented (Hobsbawm and Ranger, 1983: 1). Tradition and canon are two interlinked terms; in both cases there is the aim to preserve selectively a particular intellectual heritage. As George Kennedy claims the "canon formation is a natural human instinct, an attempt to impose order on multiplicity, to judge what is best out of many

---

① The first Confucius Institute was established in Seoul (2004) opening a new China's thought management. (Brady, 2012)

② For a definition of this term see: Li Xueqin, 1997.

options, and to preserve traditional knowledge and values against the erosion of time and influences from outside the culture" (Gorak, 2001: 105). The case of rituals in honour of Confucius, defined by Anne Cheng as the "l'éternel retour" (eternal return) (2012), is somehow paradigmatic, not because they are invented but because recently reconstructed on the basis of a very ancient tradition. Confucius, supposedly lecturing from Xitan 杏坛①, he had dedicated his entire life to train a group of disciples in the art of governing a country and to govern themselves in the spirit of rituals and sense of humanity between the sixth and the fifth centuries B.C., is now considered emblem *par excellence* of the Chinese identity (Cheng, 2012; 1997).

Rituals (*li* 礼)② were central in the whole Confucian philosophy and provide a specific content to Confucian ethics and an essential mechanism in the Confucian culture. They were very important in the process of virtue cultivation. The practice of worshiping Confucius had started during the Han dynasty. According to traditional records it occurred for the first time when in 195 BC Emperor Gaozu performed *tailao* 太牢 (The Grand Sacrifice) to Kongzi (551-479 BC) in Queli (Qufu).③ Since then Confucius officially became an important part of the Chinese society and synonym of Chinese culture itself. During the Han dynasty the figure of Confucius was finally canonized becoming a *shen* 神,④ a sort of divinity (Nylan; Wilson, 2010: 69) and a "Preeminent Teacher" (Nylan, 2001: 3). Classical texts such as the *Odes*, the *Documents* and the *Changes*, all defined as *jing* 经, canons, were conceived in a form to be easily

---

① The idea that Confucius was lecturing to his disciples from the Apricot Terrace was perpetrated from the eleventh century onward (Wilson, 2002: 98).

② This term-according to Chan translation-was essentially used in the sense of religious sacrifice and gradually also meant ceremonial, etiquette, rituals-among others (Chan, 1967: 367). In the *Da Tang Kaiyuan li* 大唐开元礼 (Ritual of the Kaiyuan of the Great Tang), one of the most complete to have survived in China, we find detailed information on Confucian ritual performance divided according to a hierarchy of official ranks.

③ During the Northern Song dynasty, in 1008, after the emperor Zhao Heng 趙恆-Zhenzong 真宗 (r. 997-1022) paid visit in person and performed a sacrifice to Confucius in Zhengdian 正殿 (Qufu 曲阜), the temple become very important. For more on the formation of the cult of Confucius see Wilson, 2002.

④ This was also the impact that Confucius exerted over the European culture, in fact he was normally depicted as a saint and academician master of arts and ethic in Europeans works.

orally transmitted①, were rewritten in order to leave a reference model for good government and were the path to be followed in self cultivation. The passage from oral to written form was fundamental for the formation of the canon. In fact-as Martin Kern claims: "When the written text rose to its enduring status of being the highest expression of Chinese culture, or, to phrase it more succinctly, when the idea of Chinese culture (*wen* 文) collapsed into that of written text (*wen* 文)" (2001: 44). As Martin Kern states in his essay "Ritual, Text and the formation of the canon" (2001), there is a very strong connection between the scriptural tradition,② which also represents a strong symbolical idea of cultural unity, rituality and the consolidation of the Confucian canon(s).③

Between the third and tenth centuries Confucianism went into steep decline. During this period Buddhism and Daoism flourished and exerted a big influence on Chinese culture and to Confucianism. In this period Confucianism underwent a metamorphosis. New cosmological as well as metaphysical dimensions were metabolized by Confucianism giving a new shape to Confucius' thought. This discontinuity was also emphasized by European thinkers who divided the earlier and later Confucianism into what we still call *classical* and *neo*-Confucianism. This categorizations were-according to some authors④-*invented* by Jesuits and was originated from the latinization of the Chinese term *Kong fuzi* 孔夫子 into Confucius during the sixteenth century.⑤ In writings, the Confucian school was named *Rujiao* 儒教 therefore stressing the importance of the *Four Books* 四书 (Mugello, 2009: 104-105) and highlighting the key role played

---

① Martin Kern stresses that "Han historical texts are replete with remarques that in the early empire, the works of the traditional canon were orally 'discussed' (*lun* 论), 'expounded' (*yan* 言), 'practiced' (*xi* 习), 'explained' (*shuo* 说, *jiang* 讲) and, as expression of their 'mastery' (*zhi* 治), 'recited' (*song* 诵)." (Kern, 2005: 180)

② See Kern, 2001:49, note 19.

③ The Confucian canon is diverse in its origin and varies according the different epochs (Henderson, 1991: 21).

④ See also Standaert, 1999.

⑤ According to Jensen-quoted by Nicolas Standaert- *Kong fuzi*, "Confucius," and also "Confucianism" were Jesuit "inventions." (1999: 116). In his essay Nicolas Standaert proves how this common belief is originated by a superficial interpretation of the word *ru*. In fact, "there is an important difference between the Jesuits' translation of *ru* as 'law of the literati' and Jensen's translation of it as 'Confucianism'." Moreover, "Even if our term "Confucianism" is derived from "Confucius," *we* use "Confucianism" while *they* did not." (Standaert, 1999: 117) For more on this topic also read Rule, 1986.

by *Literaty Theachings* in Confucius' thought.[①]

Does Confucian correspond to the translation of *ru* 儒? It seems that there is a strong connection between the word *ru* 儒 and the sacrifice, in fact as far as we know, this word-found in the oracle bones in the form *ru* 濡-with the radical "water"-was in use before Confucius era and the Confucianism, it meant a sort of ritual washing done before the *tailao*. When *ru*[②] became the synonym of Confucian, they were transmitters of the Confucian tradition and consequently "professional mediator" between the microcosm (Man) and the macrocosm (Heaven) they were also seen as perpetuators of ancient rituals. The classicists mastered *wen*, what the *Shuowen jiezi* 説文解字 defined as the "criss-cross pattern"[③](*cuohua* 错画; Kern, 2001: 43). According to Michael Nylan *ru*, meant classicist[④] who consider Confucius as their "Ancestral Teacher" (2001: 2), they were experts in antique rituals and writings (namely in the Five Classics). It was beginning with Jesuit's work that supposedly the relation *ru-literatus* was spread in Europe "manufacturing" a new category (Jensen, 1997).[⑤]

Confucius was a Master, a Saint, a Sage, as Michael Nylan claims in one of her last works developed together with Thomas Wilson (2010) Confucius was actually characterized not by one, but by many lives. Since the Eastern Zhou dynasty he had been object of many reinterpretations becoming the representative thinker of the Chinese moral values, social relations and governmental attitude along the centuries up to day. The success of Confucian culture of learning and the establishment of civil service examinations was so strong that was emulated by neighbouring countries in East and Southeast Asia, becoming in a process that William T. De Bary has defined a "dialogue in five stages" (1988) and constituting the so called "Confucian cultural sphere". Confucianism was a system that depended upon examination, education and relied on family ties system which was emulated (at least theoretically) by the system of imperial government. The Confucian thought did not only influenced East Asia,

---

① Confucius was transmitting the *Dao* 道 of the ancients, therefore he was considered a transmitter and not a creator.

② Even if not all *ru* were follower of the Confucian Way (Nylan, 2001: 3).

③ Patterns of Heaven, Earth and Man. (Kern, 2001: 43)

④ See also with Kern's explanation, in Kern, 2001: 45, note 4.

⑤ On this topic see previous note.

but also Europe, in fact beginning from the Sixteenth century when Matteo Ricci S. J. [①]became the "pioneer of the Confucian Studies in the West" (Yao, 2000: 2; Rule, 1986), the Confucian thought was having a great impact on the European thinkers such as Voltaire, Leibniz, Quesnay, Wolff, Tindal, among others, contributing somehow to the constitution of what was considered a modern state.

Since the Han dynasty onward Confucius was worshiped as the *su wang* 素王 (Uncrowned King) and believed to be the moral founder of a specific phase in the Chinese history that, although not always steady, survived the collapse of Han dynasty (Yao, 2000: 206; Nylan; Wilson, 2010: 67; Fung, 1953: 71). If Confucian thought and social structure left an indelible imprint on Chinese society and culture, the worshipping of Confucius did not survive steadily and continuously along the dynasties. There is today a revival of rites performed in various *Kongmiao* 孔廟 (Yang; Tamney, 2012: 309-328). [②] Now that the Weberian thesis lost credibility (Bell, Chaibong, 2003: 2), Confucianism is no more seen as an obstacle to modernization, economic development and democratization reappeared in the political discourse.

Kongzi that was already praised by Han Wudi[③] and was transformed into the father of the Confucianism and the architect of a new ethical order based on the classics, a significant model for the learning of inner sagehood in modern society (Yu, 1996, 179; Jiang, 2004: 313-317; Lee, 2010: 243). As William de Bary noted the Confucian scholarship was most probably one of the main reasons for the "stability and bureaucratic continuity [of the survival of] the Chinese dynastic state" (1988: 110). The revival of Confucianism in China intensified during the Twenty-first century, and more specifically after President Hu Jingtao launched the political slogan

---

① Nevertheless the Chinese masterpieces were known before Matteo Ricci's arrival in China. In this sense we cannot forget the personal collection of works donated by Philip II to the famous library of El Escorial in the Monastery of San Lorenzo (Lach, 1970: 46).

② For a complete survey on the revival of Confucian rites today see the Anna Sun's survey conducted from 2000-2010 (Yang; Tamney, 2012: 309-328).

③ As stressed by Ban Gu 班固 (32-92) in the *Liang du fu* 两都赋 "Rhapsody on the two capitals": "When the Great Han was consolidate in its initial years, [the emperor], day after day, did not get enough leisure. Reaching the eras of [emperors] Wu and Xuan, they venerated the offices of ritual and examined the *wenzhang* 文章. Within [the palace] they set up the institutions of the Bronze Horse [Gate] and the Stone Canal [Pavillion]; outside [the palace] they initiated the task of harmonizing the pitch pipes in the Office of Music" (Kern, 2001: 49)

"*hexie shehui* 和[1]谐社会", harmonious society, in 2004.[2] The revival was evident also in many other cultural manifestations such as the founding of the first Confucius Institute in 2004, the popularization of Confucian culture through Yu Dan's famous TV serial in 2006 and in the Summer Olympics opening ceremony in 2008 and Zhang Yimou's suggestive choreography on Chinese characters and by an army of scribes quoting sections of the *Analects*.[3] Confucianism is part of the political agenda, present in education and general culture.[4] Yesterday as today, there are some aspects of the Confucian canon(s) and tradition(s), even if recycled, that reflect the enduring (*jiu* 久)[5] nature of the Confucius' thought in Chinese society and culture.

**Confucius and his impact on Portugal**

The impact of Confucius on Portuguese culture was not enduring indeed. The field of Chinese Studies and Sinology in general, and Confucius studies more specifically, in Portugal has been characterized by a paradox. In fact, although the Portuguese were the first European population that arrived and settled in China its interest toward China had decreased along the centuries (especially if compared with the trend of other European contexts) till recent time. De facto, in the last decades Portugal has tightened again his relationship with China,[6] and this revival coincided with the creation of new courses focused especially in the study of modern Chinese language and to train future translators and interpreters especially focused on current topic and less to the ancient or imperial culture.[7] The attraction of Portugal toward China is

---

① *He* 和, was also the Chinese characters displayed during the performances of the Opening ceremony of the Olympic games in Beijing.

② This was the year that marked the beginning of the first official modern state ritual to Confucius in Qufu.

③ See Bachner, 2014.

④ For a complete analysis on Confucianism in our contemporary era see Bell; Chaibong, 2003 and Bell, 2010.

⑤ This concept is central in many philosophers of the Chinese tradition such as Mozi, Laozi and Zhuangzi. For an analysis on this ideia see Carr and Zhang, 2004.

⑥ One example in this sense is the "Golden Visa Programme" launched by the Portuguese authorities in October 2012.

⑦ I. e. "Línguas e Culturas Orientais-Universidade do Minho", "Traduäo e Interpretaäo: Português/Chinês-Chinês/Português-Instituto Politécnico de Leiria-Escola Superior de Educaäo e Ciências Sociais" and "Estudos Asiáticos-Universidade de Lisboa-Faculdade de Letras," just to quote some.

very old, in fact was born with the age of discoveries and when Jorge Alvares first arrived in China in 1513. After the Portuguese settled in Macau (1553/1557)①many other European arrived in China and Macau became an open door on the European culture, economy and society.② This attraction was not enduring indeed and this discontinuity in interest did not affected only Chinese studies but also any other topic related to Asia in general (Neves, 2009). In Portugal, as far as the Confucius thought is concerned, one of the first, if not the first, Confucius biographies in Europe can be found in the Portuguese masterpiece by António de Gouveia S.J. (1592-1677) *Monarchia da China dividida por seis idades* [mss. 2919/Biblioteca Nacional de Espanha].③ This work which was probably written around 1656, is still in manuscript form④-according to Luís Filipe Barreto-is the first Western Confucius' biography. Barreto claims⑤ that this biography was inspired by Sima Qian's work and was printed for the first time in Latin language in the work *Sapientia Sinica*⑥ *by Próspero Intorcetta S. J. and Ignácio da Costa S. J. in Jianchang Prefecture (Jiangxi) in* 1662 *and reprinted in the famous work also by Próspero Introcetta S. J. Confucius Sinarum Philosophus, Sive Scientia Sinensis* (Paris, 1687). ⑦ Father António Gouveia *exploit* was somehow frozen in time and represented one of the few examples of the Portuguese contribution to this field. In fact, if we exclude the period between the seventeenth and the eighteenth centuries, we practically do not have Portuguese original production on Confucian thought and we seldom find translations of Confucian classics in Portuguese lan-

---

① The dates depend on the different sources, normally the local gazetteer of Xiangshan appoint for 1553 while Western sources appoint for 1557.

② There are many different monographs on the early Portuguese settlement in Macau. Authors such as Jin Guoping, Tang Kaijian, Wu Zhiliang, or Luís Filipe Barreto, Ptak Roderich, Rui Loureiro, Vasconcelos Saldanha are good references for this topic.

③ *Inventario general des manuscritos* (Madrid 1970) Tomo 9 (Mss. 2825-3026) [pdf]) p. 215-217. I am grateful to Luís Filipe Barreto for this information.

④ The manuscript can be accessed online *Biblioteca Nacional de Espaäa*: http://bdh-rd. bne. es/viewer. vm? pid=d-3475116 (accessed 23/06/2014).

⑤ Data exchange in personal correspondence.

⑥ Sapientia Sinica exponente P. Ignatio a Costa Lusitano Soc. Ies. *à* P. Prospero Intorcetta Siculo eiusd. soc. Orbiproposita (*Kién Chām in urbe Sinarū/Provinciae Kiām Sī*. 1662. *Suepriorum Permissu*).

⑦ The *Confucius Sinarum Philosophus*, *Sive Scientia Sinensis* can be accessed online: https://archive. org/details/ confuciussinarum00conf (accessed 23/06/2014).

guage but in our era. In the last few years we assist to a new wave of Chinese studies in Portugal, this have not affected the translation of Chinese literary works in Portuguese language, nor the production of monographs and studies on Confucius and his thought. This year Portugal hosted for the first time the conference organized by the European Association for the Chinese Studies (2014), the slogan of the chosen to advertise the event was very interesting because it stressed somehow a position that Portugal hold in the past and could play in the future, but not at present: "the Country where Europe Ends and Sinology began" and being the place of "bridging the past and future of Chinese Studies". ① The past is evidently framed into the glorious epoch of discoveries, while the future is still uncertain. ②

The time span existing between the suppression of the Society of Jesus in 1773 with the bull *Domininus ac Redemptor* and the nineteenth century, corresponded not only to a void in the Portuguese contribution to sinology but also to a change in the internal politics of Portugal toward overseas territories and the consolidation of other nations abroad namely Great Britain and Neetherlands. Moreover in Europe the Confucianism, that was welcomed during the first phase of East-West encounter, went into steep decline and finally rejected by Europeans throughout the eighteenth century after the Macartney embassy. ③As David Mugello pointed out "using another culture to support a cultural program④ is not the most objective way to understand the other culture and inevitably results in its distortion." (2009: 129) In fact, during the eighteenth century Chinese culture and Confucianism were perceived differently by *sinophiles* and *sinophobes* (Mugello, 2009: 128-130). Between 1760s and 1830s Europe was facing a new historical phase that gradually brought to the Industrial Revolution and

---

① The Conference of EACS was held in Portugal in Braga and Coimbra between the 22nd and the 26th July 2014.

② Less uncertain if compared to a decade ago, and I believe that the future of Sinology in Portugal is only a matter of time and can actually rely on the graduate students from the Faculty of Arts of Lisbon University.

③ Toward the end of the eighteenth century Europeans not only changed their attitudes not only toward China but toward all the other countries (Mugello, 2009: 113).

④ The interest in China was supported by some European thinkers as model for their philosophical programs and rejected by others. In the case of the Enlightenment China was seen as a model-even if admired differently-by philosophers such as Voltaire and Leibniz. On the other side China was criticized by others thinkers such as Montesquieu and Diderot, who considered the "Middle Kingdom" as despotic government (Mugello, 2009: 114).

China was no more appreciated as a model. This trend resulted into a generalized *lacuna in* Sinology *that lasted up to the nineteenth century when we finally assisted to the establishment of academic chairs connected to this field in* Europe. In Europe, Sinology *has been rooted in philology and as such was developed in France*①, Sweden, Netherlands, England, Germany, Czechoslovakia, and Italy among others.② Today the abovementioned countries have kept a steady sinological tradition.

In Portugal, this void in sinological studies started from Bento de Góes, Gaspar da Cruz, Tomás Pereira and practically persisted till Joaquim Guerra③, Benjamin Videira Pires and Manuel Texeira. At present Portugal have not a strong sinological tradition and in most of the cases editions related to the Chinese Studies are the result team works that involves cooperation between Chinese and European researchers. The classical Chinese philology is still not taught in Portugal and most of the courses are focused on the study of modern Chinese language (mandarin). Today, at least in the Faculty of Arts of Lisbon University the students are provided with rigorous training in both literature and linguistics, and to combine these disciplines in their approach to the analysis and interpretation of at least modern texts. This study is complemented by literary, linguistic, and cultural theory appropriate to the study of those texts. At the Faculty of Arts of Lisbon University give the possibility to students to have a first approach to Confucianism at least at three different academic units such as "East Asian religions"; "Ancient and Imperial China (up to $14^{th}$ century)"; "Chinese History: Ming-Qing";"Introduction to Asian literatures"; "Arts of Asia"; "Chinese Culture", "Japanese and Korean Cultures", among others. Since no classical Chinese (or Literary Chinese) is provided by any Portuguese faculty, students do not acquire enough linguistic experience to translate classical writings. Those who continue to study a-

① The first chair was instituted in Paris in 1814.

② There are different works on this topic: Shirokauer, 2013; Honey, 2001; Wilkinson, 2001; Thote, 1997; Zurndorfer, 1994; Demiéville, 1966; Duyvendak, 1950, among others.

③ In 2008 I was personally involved in the celebration for the centenary of Joaquim Guerra's birth promoted by the Macao Scientific and Cultural Centre. I presented a paper (never published) "Introductory note on the Chinese Classics: object of study by father Joaquim Guerra" (see: "Nota Introdutoria sobre os Clássicos Chineses: Objecto de Estudo do Padre Joaquim Guerra" no âmbito das celebracõoes do Centenaáio do Nascimento do Padre Joaquim Guerra, S.J. (1908-1993). I am personally grateful to father Henrique Rios dos Santos S.J. for providing me detailed information on father Joaquim Guerra's biography.

broad possibly can acquire enough knowledge to translate the Confucian classics. In this sense I positively believe that Portugal would have again a strong class of sinologist specialized in the study of the Confucian canon and the literary classics. Nevertheless one question remains open here: I was wondering whether Portugal is really the sole case in Europe or if there is actually a more generalized indifference toward the study of the Confucian canon and toward literary Chinese?

Among all the institution① involved in Chinese studies, which in most of the cases were-at least till recently-synonym of Macao studies or Sino-Portuguese Relations researches, very few works were specifically devoted to Chinese Studies and/or Sinology even less to Confucius Studies. Beginning with the new millennium we have assisted to a second wave of Chinese Studies and Sinological researches, in most cases inserted in broader programme on Asian studies. Graduate and postgraduates courses as well as university degrees were promoted in order to respond to an increasing demand of specialists in this area. Miguel Santos Neves believes that the reason why since 2000 there has been an awakening of interest toward Asian studies was due to the fact that China was rising as global power joining the WTO in 2001 and there was an increase in the number of Chinese immigrants in Portugal (2009). In fact very active centres such as the Asiania-Centro de Estudos Asiáticos (ISCTE), the CEsA-ásia (ISEG) and the IEEI, are focused on international relations programmes (eg. Eu-China relations) and Chinese economy related topics, but none of these centres developed specific sinological researches or more specific Confucius studies. But it will take some time to create a

① Only considering Lisbon we have institutions such as the Macao Scientific and Cultural Centre (CCCM, I. P.), tutored by the Portuguese Ministry Education and Science and directed by Luís Filipe Barreto, who is also the actual director of the BA Course in Asian Studies of the Faculty of Arts of Lisbon University; CCCM also host one of the most specialized libraries on Asian Studies in the Iberian Peninsula; the Consortium of Asian Studies a joint postgraduate programme of the Faculty of Arts of Lisbon University and the Faculty of Human Sciences of the Portuguese Catholic University offers a Master in Asian Studies; the Portuguese Institute of Sinology (former Centre of Chinese Studies hosted by the ISCSP-Technical University of Lisbon and now), directed by Ana Maria Amaro, whose activities are basically focused in the yearly organization of the so called "Forum of Sinology" whose papers are collected once per year in the *Zhongguo Yanjiu* 中国研究 (Review); the Orient Institute of ISCSP-Lisbon University, directed by Narana Coisoró; the Institute of Oriental Studies hosted by the Faculty of Human Sciences (Portuguese Catholic University) and the Asian Studies Consortium an association between the Faculty of Human Sciences of the Portuguese Catholic University and the Faculty of Arts of Lisbon University.

strong group of Portuguese sinologists that could be compared to those of the seventeenth and eighteenth centuries.

In Portugal there are two Confucius Institutes: the older was established in September 2005 at Minho University and second one in 2007 at the Lisbon University. Both the institute represent a decisive step to strengthen the cooperation between Portugal and China, promoting the spread of Chinese Language and Culture as well as the interchange of students between the two countries, but again none of the two institutes promote translations or studies linked to the classical tradition.

**Joaquim Guerra S. J. (1908-1993)[①] and Confucius**

Portugal that was pioneer in the sinological studies could hardly keep is fame in this field and his importance was slowly shadowing by the global cultural panorama. During the nineteenth century and before father Joaquim Guerra S.J. there were very few sinologists most of them settled in Macao and linked to religious orders.[②] Names such as the lazarist father Joaquim Afonso Gonçalves, who spent a life span to edit a Chinese-Portuguese dictionary, and Manuel da Silva Mendes, who mostly devoted himself to Daoist studies, emerge as sinologists in the Portuguese panorama. As already stressed before, Portugal and the Portuguese sinology are interwoven to the Macanese cultural environment and it is very difficult to determine the border between the Macanese and the Portuguese sinology that in most cases is practically the same thing. In Macao two great names are linked to sinology: Luís Gonzaga Gomes (1907-1976)[③] and Pedro Nolasco da Silva (1842-1912). Sinology, in most of the cases, is an umbrella concept that includes sinology itself but also sinophily and Macao studies and very few it was written on this regard.

Father Joaquim Angélico de Jesus Guerra S.J. is considered one of these modern Portuguese sinologists. He was born in 8 April 1908 in Lavacolhos, in a very small vil-

---

① Most of the biographical data are collected in Jorge Baptista Bruxo's master thesis published in 2004, from the sources preserved at the library of the CCCM, I. P. and from the PhD thesis by António Bezerra de Menezes Jr (2013).

② This was quite common also in other European countries with sinological tradition, during the nineteenth and beginning of the twentieth century.

③ Among his works we can remember a translation of the Daodejing into Portuguese language (*Livro da Via e da Virtude de Láucio*) and the translation of the Four Books (*As Quatro Obras: Discurso e Diálogos; Suprema Educação, Meio Constante*).

lage closed to the Serra da Estrela in the North of Portugal. He left traces of his own biography in his literary production and in the various prefaces to his translations of the classics (Bruxo, 2004: 16). Joaquim-as many others young male children-studied in a catholic seminar that granted to him a good education. Father Joaquim Guerra S. J. believed that the Chinese classics were the soul of China and a masterpiece of the heritage of humanity (Bruxo, 2004: 36). This is the reason why between 1970 and 1980 (Menezes, 2013: 16) he decided to translate the Four Books and the Five Classics. Beside he also translated the *Daodejing* 道德经. He began his work in translating the *Shijing* 诗经- *Livro dos Cantares* (1979), than the *Shangshu* 尚书- *Escrituras Selectas* (1980), after he translated The *Chunqiu* 春秋 with commentary of Zuozhuan-*Quadras de Lu e Relação Auxiliar* (1981-83), the *Four Books* 四书-*Quadrivolume de Confúcio* (1984); the *Mengzi* 孟子- *As Obras de Mancio* (1984); the *Yijing* 易经-*Livro das Mutações* (1984); the *Daodejing* 道德经- *A Prática da Perfeição* (1987); and finally the *Liji* 礼记- *O Cerimonial* (1987-88). All these editions were republished several time with the same title and considered revision of the previous works, among the revisited works also appeared *The Perfect Way* (original work written in English). ① Moreover he revised the translation of the classics by James Legge. ②

According to Joaquim Guerra himself, when he started the translation of the Confucian canon, there were only very few Portuguese translations, therefore he considered his work as a pioneer one (Menezes, 2013: 10)③. António Menezes claims that Guerra's *magnum opus* can be only compared to James Legge's translation of the Chinese Classics in completeness and magnificence (2013: 10). According to Menezes at that time Joaquim Guerra was the sole able to reinterpret the Chinese Classics and

---

① A deep analysis on this works is under progress to determine which sources Joaquim Guerra translated. The research is quite difficult because the kind of Romanization he used is the one he determined himself in a study that has never been published. Documentation on this topic is available at CCCM's library. These sources can eventually be considered as good starting point for new Portuguese translations.

② The work appeared with the title The Book of Songs, Sundry Texts from James Legge's translation, Revised. The relation between Guerra's and Legge's translations were recently analysed by António Jose Menezes Jr.

③ I believe that this affirmation relies only on the fact that he was comparing himself to his contemporaries and he was not taking in consideration the work done by the Jesuits between the fifteenth and the eighteenth centuries.

comparing them with the Legge's translation. The Portuguese sinologist-using the as principal method of argumentation the *disputatio*-was arguing that James Legge's translation was too much influenced by the neoconfucian thought (Menezes, 2013: 10). According to Guerra himself most of the translations proposed by him took inspiration from previous interpretation proposed by the Jesuits during the seventeenth and eighteenth centuries, Guerra explicitly took in consideration concepts such as *Shangdi* and *Tian* manifesting a theistic position and arguing that the original meaning of *Tian* is God, ascribing this position to Confucius and giving to Confucian thought an universalistic nature. He openly criticized other translations as being too much agnostic or deistic. It is not worth to comment Guerra's own position, my point here is just to stress that in any case Guerra's translations of the Confucian Classics are somehow obsolete and need to be further studied and revised. Today there are already good Western translations of the Confucian classics such as those proposed by D. C. Lau 劉殿爵, or by Marcel Granet, or by Bernard Kalgren, or by Arthur Waley, among others.

Joaquim Guerra did not devoted himself solely to the translation of the Confucian classics but also to linguistic and Chinese studies He produced works such as the *Structural Semantics* and Chinese-Portuguese Dictionary (*Dicionário Chinês-Português de Análise Semantica Universal*).[①] A third series of works are manuals written for the teaching of the Chinese Language. Beside he elaborated a sort of "alphabetic Chinese" that aimed to teach the Chinese language only using the phonetic a transcription of the Chinese characters. Among these works there was also an international paper presented in 1972 at the International Congress of Chinese Studies (Leiden).[②] I will not discuss the quality of these work here, nevertheless it is quite clear that the Portuguese experience with the Chinese classics was confined to the sixteenth[③] up to the seventeenth centuries and that later works have never been really considered as strong contributions in the history of International Sinology. So far we cannot argue if this void

① The thesis exposed in these last works is Joaquim Guerra's belief that the human language was only one and was created by God.

② So far I was not able to find any review or critical work related to this topic.

③ It is worth to remember that the first dictionary between an European language and the Chinese language was written in Portuguese language and was the result by a team work promoted by Matteo Ricci S. J. and Michele Ruggeri (see Witek, 2001). Copy of this dictionary is displayed at the Museum of the Macao Scientific and Cultural Centre in Lisbon.

was due philological questions or by the academic quality of these editions, serious study are needed in order to measure and qualify the scholar contribution of this works to Confucian studies.① To conclude and without declassifying the father Guerra's contribution to Chinese Studies, it is important to support the production of original works in Portuguese language not only related to Confucius and Confucian canon as well as about other masterpiece of the classical Chinese culture.

**Concluding remarks**

I am convinced that very soon there will be available good Portuguese language translations not only of Confucian classics but also of other literary works and this would happen most probably in cooperation with scholars from Macau/China. The state-of-the-art is that-even if there is the necessity to introduce more Chinese philological studies, Chinese palaeography and etymology studies-both the Macau Scientific and Cultural Centre② and the BA Course in Asian Studies promoted by the Faculty of Arts of Lisbon University, have done a lot and had created the necessary conditions for the training of future Portuguese translators not only for current matters related to China but also topics related to the past. The Sino-luso relation has a very long history. China has relied on Macau for its expansion in the Lusophone world. This relationship-even if reminiscent of the political scenario-has been a friendly cooperation that has lasted more than five hundred years. Both for historical and affective reasons, Macao/China has had a specific reason to foster and maintain its relation with Portugal and thanks to its geographical location it holds a key position and has continued to mediate bilateral relations between Portugal and China, but also has contributed to enhance the relations between China and the larger community of Portuguese-Speaking Countries. The Lusophone world is one of the linguistic and cultural spaces in constant expansion and Portugal together with Macao/China has again the opportunity to regain the time lost and create a Sinological centre for the Lusophony.

Moreover, Macao was the laboratory for an incipient globalization during the

---

① As far as Joaquim Guerra is concerned we only have one monograph published (Bruxo, 2004) and an unpublished work: Anónio Menezes' PhD thesis.

② Especially under the Luis Filipe Barreto's precidency and managent period (2006- up to date). The CCCM in this period also counted with the support of the FCT (The Foundation of Science and Technology) in Portugal and the Macau Foundation (澳门基金会) in China.

seventeenth and eighteenth centuries and due to the historical conjuncture we are living today, Macau is a privileged channel in the communication between Portugal/Europe and China. Intercultural communication to be effective goes far beyond a mechanical translation from one language to another is a process that involves cultural variables (i.e. beliefs, values, attitudes, self-perception, social organization, nonverbal gestures, concept of time etc.). There is a strong relation between the cultural variables, collective memory, one's culture, commemorative symbols and history. Study the past means to understand the present and the past of China is above all linked to the Confucian tradition which is also preserved in the classics.

BibliographyParte superior do formulário


Ames, R. &D. Hall. 1987. Thinking Through Confucius, Albany: State University of New York.

Bachner, Andrea. 2014. Beyond sinology: Chinese writing and the scripts of culture. New York: Columbia University Press.

Barreto, Luiís Filipe. 2006. *Macau: poder e saber: séculos XVI e XVII*. Queluz de Baixo: Presenc? a.

Bell, Daniel, and Chae-bong Ham. 2003. Confucianism for the modern world. Cambridge, UK: Cambridge University Press.

Bell, Daniel. 2008. *China's new Confucianism: politics and everyday life in a changing society*. Princeton, N.J.: Princeton University Press.

Biblioteca Nacional (Spain). 1970. *Inventario general de manuscritos de la Biblioteca Nacional*. 9, 9. Madrid: Ministerio de Educ. Nacional.

Brady, Anne-Marie. 2012. *China's thought management. Abingdon, Oxon: Routledge.*

*Bell, Daniel.* 2008. *China's new Confucianism: politics and everyday life in a changing society*. Princeton, N.J.: Princeton University Press.

Boyer, Pascal. 1990. *Tradition as truth and communication: a cognitive description of traditional discourse*. Cambridge [England]: Cambridge University Press.

Carr, David, and Canhui Zhang. 2004. Space, time, and culture. Dordrecht: Kluwer Academic.

Chan, Wing-tsit. 1967. *Chinese philosophy* 1949-1963: *an annotated bibliography of Mainland China Publications*. Honolulu, Hawaii: East-West Center Press.

Cheng, Anne. 2012. "Confucius ou l'éternel retour" in Bulard, Martine. 2012.

"Chine, pouvoir et puissance". *Le Monde Diplomatique*. 2012 (702): (http://www.monde-diplomatique.fr/2012/09/CHENG/ 48111, accessed 26/06/2014).

Cheng, Anne. 1997. *Histoire de la pensée chinoise*. Paris: Ed. du Seuil.

Confucio, and Joaquim A. de Jesus Guerra. 1990. *Quadrivolume de Confúcio*. Macau: Instituto Cultural de Macau.

Confucius, Prospero Intorcetta, Chrétien Herdtrich, François de Rougemont, and Philippe Couplet. 1687. *Confucius sinarum philosophus, sive Scientia sinensis latine exposita*. Parisiis: Apud Danielem Horthemels, viâ Jacobæâ, sub Mæcenate. (archive.org, accessed 24/06/2014).

De Bary, William Theodore. 1988. *East Asian civilizations: a dialogue in five stages*. Cambridge, Mass: Harvard University Press.

Demieéville, Paul. 1966. *Mélanges de sinologie offerts à Monsieur Paul Demieáville*. Paris: Presses universitaires de France.

Dubs, Homer H., 1946, "The Political Career of Confucius," *Journal of the American Oriental Society*, 66(4): 273-282.

Duyvendak, J. J. L. 1950. *Holland's contribution to Chinese studies*. London: China Society.

Durrant, S. 1995. *The Cloud Mirror: Tension and Conflict in the Writings of Sima Qian*. Albany: State University of New York.

Fan, Ruiping. 2010. *Reconstructionist Confucianism rethinking morality after the West*. Dordrecht: Springer.

Feng, Youlan, and Derk Bodde. 1952. *A history of Chinese philosophy*. Princeton: Princeton University Press.

Fingarette, H. 1972. *The Secular as Sacred*, New York: Harper.

Fuehrer, Bernhard. 2012. "S. J Thierry Meynard. (ed.): Confucius Sinarum Philosophus (1687). The First Translation of the Confucian Classics. viii, 449 pp. (Nova Series 6.) Rome: Monumenta Historica Societatis Iesu, 2011. ISBN 978 88 7041 206 2". *Bulletin of the School of Oriental and African Studies*. 75 (02): 420-422.

Gomes, Luis G. 1997. O claóssico trimeétrico: Veraão Portugesa, introducção e notes de Luiís Gonzaga Gomes. Macau: Direccção dos servicáos de educacção e juventude.

Gomes, Luiz Gonzaga. 1944. *A piedade filial*. Macau: [s.n.].

Gorak, Jan. 2001. *Canon vs. culture: reflections on the current debate*. New York: Garland.

Graham, A. C. 1989. *Disputers of the Tao*, La Salle: Open Court.

Guerra, Joaquim A. de Jesus, and James Legge. 1986. *The book of songs: sundry texts from James Legge's translation revised = Shi ching ping chu*. [Macao]: Aidan.

Guerra, Joaquim A. de Jesus, and Kvao Tjyntoq. 1981. *Dicionaário chineŝ-portugueŝs de anañlise sema? ntica universal = [Zhong Pu wan yu pou zi jiu yi zi dian]*. Macau: Jesuiítas Portugueses.

Guerra, Joaquim A. de Jesus, Confucius, and Ming Zuoqiu. 1981. *Quadras de Lu e relação auxiliar*. Macau: Jesuiítas Portugueses.

Guerra, Joaquim A. de Jesus. 1972. *An alphabetic standardization of the Chinese Names*. Lisboa: Instituto de Linguas Africanas e Orientais.①

Guerra, Joaquim A. de Jesus. 1979. *Livro dos cantares = She keng*. Macau: Jesuítas Portugueses.

Guerra, Joaquim A. de Jesus. 1979. *Livro dos cantares = She Keng*. Macau: Jesuítas Portugueses.

Guerra, Joaquim A. de Jesus. 1980. *Escrituras selectas: Zhyaw shu: introduçao, texto Chines em alfabeto e caracteres = shang shu*. Macau: Jesuitas Portugueses.

Guerra, Joaquim A. de Jesus. 1980. *Structural semantics*. Macau: Portuguese Jesuits.

Guerra, Joaquim A. de Jesus. 1983. *O livro das mutaçoes*. Macau: Jesuitas Portugueses.

Guerra, Joaquim A. de Jesus. 1984. *Quadrivolume de Confucio*. Macau: Jesuitas Portugueses.

Guerra, Joaquim A. de Jesus. 1987. *O cerimonial*: (Lei-ky). Macau: Jesuitas Portugueses.

Henderson, John B. 1991. *Scripture, canon, and commentary: a comparison of Confucian and western exegesis*. Princeton, N.J.: Princeton University Press.

Hobsbawm, E. J., and T. O. Ranger. 1983. *The Invention of tradition*. Cambridge [Cambridgeshire]: Cambridge University Press.

Honey, David B. 2001. *Incense at the altar: pioneering sinologists and the devel-*

① Actual Instituto Superior de Ciências Sociais e Políticas e Instituto de Relações Internacionais.

*opment of classical Chinese philology*. New Haven, Conn: American Oriental Society.

Idema, W. L. 2014. *Chinese studies in the Netherlands: past, present and future*. Leiden, Boston: Brill.

Jensen, Lionel M. 1997. *Manufacturing Confucianism: Chinese traditions and universal civilization*. Durham: Duke University Press.

Jiang, Qing 蔣慶. 2004. *Shengming xinyang yu wangdao zhengzhi: rujia wenhua de xiandai jiazhi* 生命信仰與王道政治 ：儒家文化的現代價值 (Life beliefs and the kingly way of governance: the modern values of Confucian culture). Taibei xian: Yangzhengtang wenhua.

Jin, Guoping, and Zhiliang Wu. 2000. *Correspondencia oficial trocada entre as autoridades de Cantaão eos procuradores do senado: fundo das chapas sínicas em portuguеŝ*. [Macau]: Fundão Macau.

Jin, Guoping. 2000. *Zhong-Pu guanxi shidi kaozheng* 中葡关系史地考证 (An Historical and geographic examination of Sino-Portuguese relations). Aomen: Aomen ji jin hui.

Kern, Martin. 2001. "Ritual, Text, and the Formation of the Canon: Historical Transitions of Wen in Early China". *T'oung Pao*. 87 (1): 43-91.

Kern, Martin. 2005. *Text and ritual in early China*. Seattle: University of Washington Press.

Kircher, Athanasius. 1966. *Athanasii Kircheri China monumentis, qua sacris qua profanis, nec non variis naturae et artis spectaculis, aliarumque rerum memorabilium argumentis illustrata*. Frankfurt a.M.: Minerva.

Kim, Terri. 2009. "Confucianism, modernities and knowledge : China, South Korea and Japan". *Comparative Education*. 55 (3): 857-872.

Lach, Donald F. 1970. *Asia in the making of Europe: volume II, a century of wonder*. Chicago: University of Chicago Press.

Lau, D. C. 1979. *Confucius: The Analects*, Harmondsworth: Penguin.

Li, Xueqin 李学勤. 1997. *Guoji Hanxue manbu* 国际汉学漫步 (A stroll through International sinology). Shijiazhuang Shi: Hebei jiaoyu chubanshe.

Lee, Ming-huei. 2010. "Confucian Traditions in Modern East Asia: Their Destinies and Prospects". *Oriens Extremus*. 49: 237.

Loureiro, Rui. 2009. *Nas partes da China: colectanea de estudos dispersos*. Lisboa: Centro Cientiífico e Cultural de Macau.

Makeham, J. 2003. *Transmitters and Creators: Chinese Commentators and Commentaries on the Analects*, Cambridge, MA: Harvard University Asia Center.

Mencius, and Joaquim A. de Jesus Guerra. 1990. *As obras de Man cio*. [Macau]: Instituto Cultural de Macau.

Menezes Jr, António Jose Bezerra de. 2013. *Joaquim Guerra S. J.* (1908-1993): *releitura universalizante dos clássicos chineses*. São Paulo (Phd Thesis).

Ming, Wilson. 1995. *Europe studies China: papers from an International conference on the history of European sinology* [held on April 17-22, 1992, Taipei, Taiwan]. London: Han-Shan Tang Books.

Mungello, D. E. 1989. *Curious land: Jesuit accommodation and the origins of Sinology*. Honolulu: University of Hawaii Press.

Neves, Miguel Santos. 2009. *Asian Studies in Portugal-the state of the art*, inhttp://www. eurasiane. eu/ contenu/magazine/research-panorama/upload/Portugal-1.pdf (acceded 22/05/2014).

Nivison, D. 1996. *The Ways of Confucianism*, La Salle: Open Court.

Nylan, Michael, and Thomas A. Wilson. 2010. *Lives of Confucius: civilization's greatest sage through the ages*. New York: Doubleday.

Nylan, Michael. 2001. *The five "confucian" classics*. New Haven: Yale University Press.

Rule, Paul. 1986. *K'ung-tzu or Confucius?: the Jesuit interpretation of Confucianism*. Sydney: Allen & Unwin.

Saldanha, Valconcelos. 2002. "Historiografia de justifição e justifikção da historiografia: a propósito da sinologia portuguesa dos séculos XIX e XX". *Daxiyangguo*: Revista Portuguesa de Estudos Asiáticos. 2: 3-9.

Santos, Henrique Rios dos. 2008. *Padre Joaquim Angélico Guerra, S. J.: Um globetrotter ao serviçQ de Deus e da China*. Macau: Instituto Internacional de Macau.

Schirokauer, Conrad. 2013. "Herbert Franke and the Postwar Transformation of Continental European Sinology: A Brief Appreciation". *Journal of Song-Yuan Studies*. 42 (1): 1-4.

Schwartz, B. 1985. *The World of Thought in Ancient China*, Cambridge, MA:

Harvard University Press.

Standaert, Nicolas. 1999. "The Jesuits Did NOT Manufacture 'Confucianism'". *East Asian science, technology and society*. 16: 115-32.

Sterckx, Roel. 2011. *Food, sacrifice, and sagehood in early China*. New York: Cambridge University Press.

Thote, Alain. 1997. "At the Source of Modern French Sinology: Edouard Chavannes". *Orientations*. 28 (6): 42.

Weber, Max. 1951. The religion of China: Confucianism and Taoism. Glencoe, Ill: Free Press.

Wilson, T. A., 2002, *On Sacred Grounds: Culture, Society, and the Formation of the Cult of Confucius*, Cambridge: Harvard University Asia Center.

Witek, John W. 2001. *Dicionário Português-Chinês =: Pu Han ci dian = Portuguese-Chinese dictionary*. San Francisco, CA: Ricci Institute for Chinese-Western Cultural History (University of San Francisco).

Yang, Fenggang and Joseph B. Tamney. 2012. *Confucianism and Spiritual Traditions in Modern China and Beyond*. Leiden, Boston: Brill.

Yao, Xinzhong. 2000. *An introduction to Confucianism*. New York: Cambridge University Press.

Yu, Yingshi 余英时. 1996. *Xiandai ruxue lun* 现代儒学论 (On Modern Confucianism). River Edge, NJ: Bafang wenhua qiye gongsi.

Wilson, Thomas A. 2002. *On sacred grounds: culture, society, politics, and the formation of the cult of Confucius*. Cambridge, Mass: Harvard University Asia Center.

Zurndorfer, Harriet S. 1995. "A Brief History of Chinese Studies and Sinology," in *China Bibliography*, Brill: 4-44.

# Footsteps of Confucius in Hungary-The Hungarian Interpretations of Lun Yu

**Klára Zombory**（克拉拉）

In order to get to know a country, a land and its nation, the thinking, the mentality, and the life of the people, one "path" leads through culture, philosophical and literary works, and art. In our hasty, globalized and profit-seeking world this is also one possible way to understand China, this fast-growing, huge country with its long-long history. Although from this small country with less than 10 million's population, sometimes it seems to be quite a great challenge.

Hungary, despite the fact that its population is less than that of a bigger Chinese city, started the recognition of China quite early, and contributed several internationally acknowledged sinologists and China-explorers to the world. So being aware of this fact it might not be too surprising that we have three different Hungarian interpretations of the most important classic of Confucianism, *Lun Yu*《论语》. All the three versions are rather different form each other in approaching the original text. Two of them are complete versions, and were translated from classical Chinese, and one consists of roughly half of the total volume and was translated from intermediate German language. In smaller or greater extent they differ in the usage of the main terminology.

Confucius is present in the everyday life of the Hungarians. Day by day one can meet the sayings and teachings of the great Master on different platforms. The "easy understandable" writing of Yu Dan, *Confucius from the Heart*《于丹<论语>心得》, and the rapid growth of the number of the Confucius Institutes in Hungary (Budapest 2006, Szeged 2012, Miskolc 2013) also contributed to the awareness of the wisdom of the great Chinese philosopher not only among the intellectual elite, but also the bigger circle of the masses.

Being engaged in literary translation of contemporary Chinese fiction for almost

20 years, of course, I do not intend and dare to hold a lecture on philosophy, philology or hermeneutics etc. I would only undertake the task of highlighting the fact that Confucius has a "noble place" in Hungary, the cultivated people and the ones who are receptive towards Eastern culture are well familiar with his name and oeuvre, and the majority have read *Lun Yu* as well-so Confucius, as it is indicated in the title, has left its footsteps on the land of my country. This is mainly due to the fact that the thoughts of the great Master has reached the Hungarian people in excellent interpretations of very great and influential Hungarian scholars, namely **Béla Hamvas**, the "rediscovered" philosopher and aesthete, who published his interpretation in the 40's; and **Ferenc Tökei**, the well known sinologist, whose reputation far overstepped the borders of Hungary, he published *Lun Yu* in Hungarian in the 60s. The fact that the Confucian classic was newly interpreted by a young sinologist, and he successfully managed to find a publisher for the book after the two well known and influential versions, also proves that there are still "place" for new interpretation(s), and the so called "Opening to the East" hints not only commercial, political and economic, but also cultural interactions and exchanges, and it also testifies that the Hungarians' interest towards "Eastern thinking" is living its renaissance.

My lecture starts with the short introduction to the Chinese-Hungarian relations, it is followed by a more detailed description of the three literary translators along with the three Hungarian versions of Lun Yu, and I close my presentation with a few insights about *Confucius from the Heart*, translated by myself from original Chinese.

**The history of the Chinese-Hungarian relations in a nutshell**

China and Hungary built up diplomatic relation in 4 October 1949, almost exactly 65 years ago, but the first intercourse between the two countries had started much earlier.

It is proved that as early as in the 14th century a few Hungarian missionaries reached China, but in the following decades since the Turkish (Ottoman) Empire controlled all the routes to the Far-East, the connection had broken for a long time, up till the 17th century, when again several Hungarian missionaries arrived to the Middle Kingdom. In the 18th-19th century quite a few adventurers and scientists visited China, just to mention the most acknowledged ones: **Sándor Kőrösi Csoma** (1784-1842), linguist and librarian, who in the 1820's spent a long time in different Tibetan monasteries, and although he could not find the traces of the Hungarians' roots, but with his Tibetan-English dictionary and grammar book, along with other scientific works he became the worldwide respected "founder" of tibetology; **Earl Béla Széchenyi** (1837-1908), the son of the "greatest Hungarian", Istvάn Széchenyi, with his expedition between 1877-81 visited several significant parts of China; Lajos Lóczy (1849-1920), the world-renowned geologist and geographer, member of the Széchenyi expedition; **Aurél Stein** (1862-1943), the Hungarian originated, British nationality archeologist and explorer, who arrived to Dunhuang in 1907, and whose activity in the Thousand Buddha Caves is rather condemned by the Chinese; Earl **Jenõ Zichy** (1837-1906), who arrived to Beijing in 1898 through the continent, only to mention the most famous ones.

To discuss in details the relation between China and the Austrian-Hungarian Monarchy, and the relation of the two countries between and under the two world wars would require a separate presentation-it was explored and published by my professor Sάndor Józsa (尤山度)-so I only would speak about the "reconnection" of the two countries in the 20th century that is said to be the milestone regarding to the establishment of the Hungarian sinology. As I have mentioned earlier, Hungary was among the first countries that only after a few days of the declaration of the People's Republic of China already established diplomatic relation with the New China, in 2014 we celebrate the 65th anniversary of this event. It was not only the starting point of political and economic cooperation between the two countries, but it also contributed to cultural, educational and scientific exchanges.

The first group of Hungarian scholarship students arrived to Beijing in 1950, and between 1950 and 1966 almost thirty Hungarian students studied in China, such as: **Endre Galla** (高恩德), **Vilma Mészάros**, **Sάndor Józsa**, **Géza Pajor**, **Pάl Miklós**(米白), **Barna Tάlas**, **Péter Polonyi** 鲍洛尼.彼得, **éva Kalmάr** (谷兰) etc. They were the ones basically who established sinology in Hungary along with a few philologists, philosophers and literary translators, who had gained their professional and Chinese knowledge in Hungary, such as Ferenc **Tökei** (杜克义) and **Barnabάs Csongor** (陈国). They have translated several classical and modern Chinese literary and philosophical works into Hungarian with the greatest competence, wild range of knowledge and stylistic sense, and the faculty of Chinese of the Eötvös Lorάnd University (ELTE), became the educational center of the following sinologist generations, and the base of the Chinese-Hungarian literary translation. Between the 1950's and 70's, or even in the 80's quite a great amount of Chinese works were published in Hungary. In those times the "great Chinese classics" such as the Tang-poets' anthologies (Li Bai, Bai Juyi, Du Fu), the famous romances (*Dream of the Red Chamber* /translated from Gernman/, *Water Margin* or *Outlaws of the Marsh*, *Jin Ping Mei* /translated from German/, *Pilgrim to the West*) or the *Dao De Jing* and of course *Lun Yu* could be found in almost every Hungarian intellectual family's bookshelf. Several great Chinese classics were reprinted in those decades.

**The Hungarian translations of *Lun Yu***

As I have mentioned, up till now, *Lun Yu* was published in Hungarian in three different high quality translations, these are the followings in chronological order of publishing (*Source*: *"Chinese bibliography" compiled by Attila Födi*)

**1. Béla HAMVAS (translator)**

***Kungfutse*: *Lun yü-Kung mester beszélgetései*. (*Gongfuzi*: *Lun Yu-The conversations of Master Gong*)**

Publishing details

• **KUNG Fu-tse**: *Lun Jü* : *Kung mester beszélgetései*. (Lun Yu: The dialogues of Master Gong) Translator: Hamvas Béla. Budapest : Bibliotheca Kiadó, 1943.

**2. Ferenc TÖKEI (translator)**

***Konfuciusz*: *Beszélgetések és mondások*. (*Confucius*: *Conversations and Sayings*)**

Publishing details:

20. In: *Kínai filozófia* : *ókor I-III*. (*Chinese Philosophy*: *Antiquity I.-III.*): Selection, translation, prologues and notes: Tökei Ferenc. Budapest : Akadémiai Kiadó, 1962-1967.

2.nd edition. Budapest : Akadémiai Kiadó, 1980.

3.rd edition. Budapest : Akadémiai Kiadó, 1986.

21. *KONFUCIUSZ*: *Beszélgetések és mondások*. (*Confucius*: *Conversations and Sayings*). Translation, prologues and notes: Tökei Ferenc. Szeged : Szukits Könyvkiadó, 1995.

1. 2nd edition. Szeged : Szukits Könyvkiadó, 1995.

22. *KONFUCIUSZ*: [*Lunyu*]: *Beszélgetések és mondások*. (*Confucius*: *Conversations and Sayings*). Translation and notes: Tökei Ferenc. Budapest: Argumentum

23. In: *Kínai filozófia : ókor I-III.* (*Chinese Philosophy: Antiquity I.-III.*): Selection, translation, prologues and notes: Tökei Ferenc. Budapest : Magiszter Társadalomtudományi Alapítvány : [Budapest : Kossuth Kiadó], 2005. Tökei Ferenc oeuvre series I-III.

**3. SándorÖRI (translator)**

***Konfuciusz bölcseletei-Lun jü.* (*The Analects of Confucius-Lun Yu*)**

Publishing details:

*Konfuciusz bölcseletei-Lun jü.* (*The Analects of Confucius-Lun Yu*). *Translation*: Öri Sándor. Budapest: Golden Goose Kiadó, 2012.

**Hamvas Béla /1897-1968/**

The legendary writer, philosopher, aesthete and social critic was born in 23 March 1897 at Eperjes (Prešov in Slovakian, city in Eastern Slovakia) into a Lutheran pastor family, and died in 7 November 1968 at Budapest. He played the piano form the age of ten, later he also composed music, and he did it with such a great devotion that his parent believed him for a long to become a musician.

In 1919 his father refused to take an oath of allegiance to Czechoslovakia, and because of this reason his family had to move to Hungary, they settled down in Budapest. Between 1919 and 1923 he attended the Pázmány Péter University, the faculty of Hungarian and German, but he still studied music theory, moreover medicine. 1919-20 his first writings were published in a literary periodical in Bratislava. From 1923 for three years he worked as a journalist in Budapest. For almost twenty years (1927-1948) he worked as a librarian in the Capital Library, but meanwhile he published studies, essays, critics and reviews, all together almost 300 pieces in about 25 periodicals.

During the Second World War he was drafted to military service three times. He continued his literary work while on the front lines-translating Laozi, Confucius and Heraclitus among others. He wrote novels and essays as well, and started his monumental work-*The Hall of Fame of the Ancestors*-, that was finished only in the 60's. This four volume work is the collection of the most influential sacred and philosophical books of the world along with his introductory notes. The second volume consists of Chinese Taoist, Chan, Tibetan and Japanese Zen Buddhist texts.

After the war he started to compile a series of books-*The Studies of the University Press*-, all together more than 20 volumes of it were published. 1948-1951 he was secluded to Szentendre, where he was farming, growing fruits and doing gardening. He published several great scale novels and essay collections during this time. Before retiring in 1964 he worked in different storehouses in the countryside, and worked as a janitor. Whenever he could, he read, translated, wrote, and studied languages (Sanskrit and Hebrew).

Béla Hamvas posthumous received Kossuth Prize (the highest state-sponsored award to acknowledge outstanding personal and group achievements in the fields of science, culture and the arts) in 1990, and was remunerated with Hungarian Heritage Award in 1996.

**Hamvas's interpretation of *Lun Yu***

Hamvas-the very influential philosopher, but not sinologist-published parts of Lun Yu in Hungarian in 1943 for the first time. This is not the total version, it consists of about half of the total volume, and does not follow the chapters and order of the original text. It is more like a collection of the most cited sayings of *Lun Yu*. Instead of using Roman and Arabic numerals, titles are inserted above every section, one keyword(s) of the following sayings or dialogue, such as: "Peace, happiness, wisdom", "The root of a man", "Moral", "Self-examination", "Advices" , "Poverty and wealth", "Pole-star", "Parents", only to mention a few. Hamvas's terminology is strange and also the Romanization he uses-a kind of mixture of the German and the Hungarian Romanization, sometimes makes it difficult for the ones who "grew up" on Tökei's Lun Yu to recognize the names. But the language is absolutely captivating, and his wording is very consequence and thorough.

Hamvas's great contribution above the interpretation itself that being an influential philosopher he "placed" Confucius among other philosophers and great masters, whom the Hungarian intellectuals were more familiar with. In his prologue, for example, he draws parallel between Confucius, Laozi, Buddha (India), Zarathustra (Iran), Heraclitus (Asia Minor), Pythagoras (Greek) who all lived around at the same time, although they lived in far away parts of the world, but all of them had the common feeling: they were living in a chaotic world, the biggest convulsion of mankind had started, the people lost their happiness, and there was no hope for order in terms of politics, clear life, peace of the families etc. They all desired to return to "ancient" times, they wished to bring back several "old" things in order to pacify and "straighten" the world and to avoid "darkness". Darkness of the world was inevitable, growing poverty, coarseness, immorality, disorder and confusion were around everywhere. There was not much hope, but they (philosophers, masters) at least needed to make a try, they could not give up. Of course they all went on different "paths". This topic is discussed in details in the prologue and also in several later essays of Hamvas.

Thanks to Hamvas's essays the name of Confucius and also the basic thoughts of Confucianism were introduced to the Hungarian intellectuals.

**Tökei Ferenc (1930-2000)**

FerencTökei 杜克义(1930-2000) sinologist, literary historian, literary translator, historian of philosophy, member of the Hungarian Academy of Sciences (MTA), one of the greatest personages of the 20th century Hungarian sinology. He was born in a Catholic family. After high school graduation he was admitted to the Eötvös Loránd University (ELTE) Budapest, the Faculty of Chinese and Tibetan studies. During his high school years he already became interested in Marxism, and he was greatly influenced by the works and thoughts of György Lukács, the renowned Marxist philosopher, so besides his sinology studies his interest gradually turned towards philosophy. He received his diploma in 1953, Ph.D. degree in 1965, and received doctorate of literary history in 1956. In 1956 he worked in the Hopp Ferenc East-Asian Art Museum, and later became the editor of Európa Publishing, where he initiated the publication of a great amount of Chinese and other Oriental books. He took part in the editing and translating process of these works, and also provided work to the best Hungarian poets of that time. Only to mention a few works to be published during his editorship: The Book of Songs, *The Temple of The Dragon King (tales)*, *The Heart of Beauty. Old Chinese essays* etc.

From 1967 he was the fellow member, 1969-1972 the director of the Philology Department of MTA. 1971-1990 he worked at ELTE as the professor of the Philosophy Department, from 1990 till his death as that of the Chinese Department. 1972-1994 the leader of the MTA Oriental Team, from 1973 corresponding member, from 1985 full member of MTA.

His academic achievements and papers were published mainly in *Acta Orientalia Hungarica*, and also in foreign journals. His study on the question of "The Asiatic Mode of Production" published in 1965-translated to six languages-raised significant international response.

Besides publishing Oriental subject papers, studies and essays Ferenc Tökei translated numerous classical Chinese literature and philosophical works into Hungarian, and being one of the most productive and talented translator he contributed with a great deal to the popularization and familiarization of the Chinese culture in Hungary. He has outstanding achievements in the interpretation of classical Chinese philosophical texts into Hungarian. In his three volumes *Chinese Philosophy: Antiquity, Vol. 1-3.* he published a collection of the most influential ancient philosophers' (Confucius, Mozi, Mencius, Laozi, Xunzi, Han Feizi etc.) works, either the full versions, or the most important parts, chapters of them. He did not only translate philosophical writings, but also great works of different genres. He was fascinated by the tales of Pu Songling, and besides he translated Chinese dramas, poems, novels, novellas and essays. It should be mentioned as well that he made a great amount of rough translations to the best Hungarian poets of the 20th century, and their "cooperation" resulted very high quality aesthetical "end products".

Ferenc Tökei is still highly respected and honored in Hungary and also abroad, the round anniversaries of his birth is celebrated with books, publications and conferences dedicated to him. In 2000, on his 70th birthday a book was published (*Stability in changing: To the 70th birthday of Ferenc Tökei*. Editor: Ildikó Puskás. Budapest: Politika+Kultúra Alapítvány, 2000). In 15 October 2005, on the 15th anniversary of his birth, a memorial meeting was held in Beijing at Beijing Foreign Studies University (Beijing Waiguoyu Daxue) the Vice Rector Yang Jianwei, the Hungarian Ambassador Sándor Mészáros and Gong Kunyu the famous hungarologist, the former Head of the European Languages Department at "Beiwai"-my first Chinese language teacher at the university-opened the session. At the same year one of the oldest and most prestigious publishing houses in Hungary, Kossuth Publishing, started a book series of his oeuvre, all together nine volumes were published up till know. In 2010, on the 80th anniversary the ELTE Confucius Institute together with the MTA Sociology Research Department organized a conference, where Tökei's colleagues, friend and students had attended and hold speeches on social sciences and sinology.

To share my personal insight towards him: it was my honor to be one of last students at the university. I have studied a lot from him, for example about being respective and "subservient" towards the long-standing Chinese culture, literature and language. He was not only a great scholar but also a real "teacher" whom one could study not only technique, style and language, but also the attitude of handling sinology and "treating" Chinese language and texts.

**Tökei's interpretation of *Lun Yu***

In my my opinion the "Hungarian Confucius" without doubt "belongs to" Tökei. This is the version usually used when Confucius is cited, and I am also using his translation whenever Confucius' sayings emerge in a modern literary work. First time his translation of *Lun Yu* was published in *Chinese Philosophy: Antiquity, Vol.* 1. in 1962, and it has several reprinted a revised versions (for publication details pl. see previous chapter). It might be an interesting fact that as a separate book it was published only in 1995, but since then it has two reprints.

This is a full version, all together twenty chapters, indicated by Roman numerals, and the separate sayings in a chapter with Arabic numerals. As we got used to from Tökei-being a philosopher, philologist and sinologist-the terminology he uses is very accurate and thorough, and the most important key words appear in the text in Chinese-in Romanization-as well, in the earlier versions using the so called Scientific Hungarian Romanization System, and in the later revised editions that of pinyin, and also Chinese characters.

This is the only version that has endnotes: all the important names, places are explained in detail, but also the keywords, objects, customs etc. that are difficult or impossible to understand to the average Hungarian readers deriving from cultural differences and the diverse educational background. In his endnotes he also forwards important commentaries and explanations in connection with the original source text. From the prologue the readers get to know the life of Confucius, the genesis of the text, and the different variations of Lun Yu.

**Öri's interpretation of Lun Yu**

This is quite a great challenge and "boldness" to translate *Lun Yu* again after such noble predecessors. Sándor Öri, the member of the "new" generation of sinologists was willing to take the risk, and after years of work and research he published "his version" of the text in 2012. This is also a full version, translated from original classical Chinese, and he uses the latest archeological findings at Dingzhou as well. He believes that despite the two previous interpretations there are still place for new approaches from other point of view that is testified in different style and terminology.

The publisher does not have a long history as Akadémiai or Szukits Publishing, but they definitely did a great job. This is the kind of book that "catches the eyes", the layout of this bilingual book (the Chinese is printed on the left side page and the Hungarian is on the right side one) is beautiful and easy to handle. One "golden saying" form the actual page is highlighted on every other pages. It is using the same numbering with Tökei (Roman and Arabic numbering), so one can easily make a comparison of the two versions. According to the translators prologue the main differences with that of Tökei is: 1. Differing in terminology, mainly in the usage of the philosophical terms; 2 Translated not in prose, but in rhymes; 3. Keeping the ambiguous wording of the original text; 4. Deliberate absence of notes, as he hints, he does not wish to "interfere" into the text's reception of the reader with inserting plus information, he believes that the text purely will infiltrate into the reader's mind in this way, and in his opinion it would be even more inspirational to the readers. He is planning to publish a separate book with all the notes, background knowledge and commentaries, but this one consists of only the "pure" text. .

**Yu Dan: *Confucius from the Heart* (Translated by Klára Zombory)**

When the Háttér Publishing assigned me to translate the book of Yu Dan, I have to admit that I started to read it with doubts and reservations in my heart, but the more I was involved in the translation process, the more I realized the positive intentions and the potential beneficial effects of the book. One can like or dislike the worldwide trend of making everything easier and faster to understand, this is a kind of "instant" way of consuming even literary, philosophical and art "products", using media tools instead of academic ones etc. It is a general phenomenon in my country as well: for example there is a fierce debate even these days whether the Hungarian classics, mainly the 19th century long novels (e.g. Mór Jókai's) and juvenile literature of the last century written in "old fashioned" language, those works that are definitely part of the Hungarian literary canon, should or should not be rewritten in easier, simpler style, and should or should not necessary to shorten their length. This is the same with the "very classical", well-known or even "cultic" translations of different literary pieces (e.g. Shakespeare's dramas by János Arany, one of the biggest poets of the 19th century) or opera librettos (e.g. *The Magic Flute*) are published in new translations by talented young writers and poets, despite the fact that very influential and famous writers did the first or previous interpretations. What is more important? To keep these literary pieces "alive", to be received by the young people as well, even if its "price" is the reconstruction, rewriting, reediting of the original texts, and making new more modern translations? Or should a nation reserve its old "qualities" in unchanged form? I do not intend and I am not able to answer this question with certainty, I could only assure that the "new trend" has resulted in several very excellent new interpretations.

And I have the same feeling with "Confucius form the Heart". There are several people in Hungary who would have never read Confucius sayings without it, because they were "afraid of" reading such a noble and sophisticated philosophical book, and from this point of view Yu Dan has completed a kind of mission. The other point is deriving from the feedbacks I received from the readers: they were just fascinated by the actuality of Confucius teachings. I know that this book has flaws and deficiencies as well, I do not wish to praise it to the sky, mainly not in a forum full with serious experts of Confucius from different academic circles, but it is indisputable that Yu Dan's book has fulfilled a task in spreading Confucius's thought to a wider circle of readers in China and also in the world.

It is only an additional remark: "Confucius from the Heart" was not only warmly welcome by the readers, but it has received a professional award by the Hungarian Publishers' and Booksellers' Association, the so called "Beautiful Book 2009" prize in Informative Education Category, that is for the typography, layout, and the harmony between the outlook and the content.

This is only a coincidence while writing these lines, 4 July 2014, the first Confucius sculpture was inaugurated in Hungary, at ELTE Confucius Institute. The two meter high bronze bust was the present of the Shandong People's Municipality. The leaders of the Shandong delegation, the dean of ELTE University and the Managing Director of the Hungarian Tourism Corporation have attended the ceremony.

The cultural exchanges are blooming, more and more Hungarian students study in China, and vice versa, last year Mo Yan's The Republic of Wine, this year Frog will be published, and this year due to the 65th anniversary of the beginning of the diplomatic relations between the two countries several cultural programs will be held throughout my country-I strongly believe that this positive trend will continue in the near and far future as well.

# François Noël (1651-1729) and Latin Translations of Confucian: Classical Books Published in Prague in 1711[①]

**Vladimír Liščák (李世佳),**
**(Oriental Institute, Czech Academy of Sciences, Prague)**
(捷克科学院东方研究所,布拉格)

**Introduction**

The first acquaintance of Europe with Confucianism is contributed to Jesuits working in China in the 16th to 18th centuries. The first contribution was the translation of the introduction to Da xue 大學 into Latin, published in Rome (Italy) in 1593. However, the first translation of the Confucian classic books, which attracted significant attention, was *Confucius Sinarum Philosophus* [Confucius, the Chinese philosopher], published in Paris in 1687. This publication has contained the annotated translation of three of Four *Books* of the Confucian canon.

The history of the Jesuits in China can be viewed as having been bounded by either of two different sets of dates:

1. from Francis Xavier's (1506-1552, 聖方濟·薩威 Shèng Fāngjì · Sàwēi) arrival in 1552 to the disbanding of the Jesuits in 1773 [②], or

2. from Matteo Ricci's (1552-1610; Chinese name: 利瑪竇 *Lì Mǎdòu*) reception in1600 at the Chinese court to the death of the last Jesuit in Peking (Father de Poirot)

---

① 衛方濟 (François Noël, 1651-1729): 1711 年在布拉格出版的拉丁文《中華帝國六經》(***Sinensis Imperii Libri Classici Sex***)

② Pope Clement XIV disbanded the Jesuits in 1773 through an encyclical entitled *Dominus et Redemptor*.

[1]in 1813.

In addition to setting up missionary activities among the people as had the Franciscans, the Jesuits also set about exploring classical Chinese thought. The Jesuits' main reason for studying the Chinese canonical works was to aid in their missionary activities. As a result, most of the Jesuits used and interpreted the Confucian classics as their catechetical supplements to Christian doctrines.

Francis Xavier, one of the ten founding fathers of the Jesuits, visited India and Japan. While preaching in Japan, he learned that China was the centre of Asian civilization. He then left Japan for China, but died on the island of Shangchuan (*Ilha Sanchoão*, *St. John's Island*, 上川島 *Shàngchuān Dǎo*), off the coast of China. Although he never reached mainland China, he is still honoured as the father of the China mission, as well as the father of Jesuit missions in general. As the pioneer of Jesuit missionary activities, his policies became the models for Jesuit missionary work.

Alessandro Valignano (1539-1606; Chinese name: 范禮安 Fàn Lǐ'ān), the second major Jesuit in the East Asian mission, successfully opened the China mission. In order to avoid Portuguese domination, he chose fellow Italian Jesuits, Michele Ruggieri (1543-1607; Chinese name: 羅明堅 *Luó Míngjiān*), Francisco Pasio (1551-1612), and Matteo Ricci, for the China mission. Like Xavier, he wanted his Italian Jesuits to learn the Chinese dialects and become adept in Chinese philosophy as well.

Following Valignano's directions, Ruggieri and Ricci garbed themselves in Buddhist habits. After they became more sensitive to the Chinese intellectuals' Confucian orientation, they adopted Confucian robes. In order to understand the Chinese, Ruggieri and Ricci both studied Confucian classics diligently. These studies would enable them to teach succeeding Jesuit missionaries the complexities of Chinese culture, and also to send accounts of Confucianism back to Europe.

Ruggieri was the first Jesuit to translate the Confucian *Four Books* into Latin; however, he was prohibited from publishing this work and his Chinese catechism 天主

---

① Louis Antoine de Poirot (1735-1813; Chinese name: 賀清泰 *Hè Qīngtài*) was a Jesuit painter and translator of the 18th and early 19th century, who worked in the service of the Chinese emperor Qianlong 乾隆. He was the last of the Western painters who worked for Qianlong, together with Father Giuseppe Panzi (1734-before 1812; Chinese name: 潘廷章 *Pān Tíngzhāng*). Poirot also made a translation of the Old Testament in the Manchu language, and a translation of the New *Testament* into the Chinese language.

實錄 (*Tiānzhǔshílù*) in Latin, because of the opposition of Valignano and Ricci. Ruggieri's Latin translation of the Confucian classics was only a by-product; his major concern was to make the Bible in some form available in Chinese. ①

Like Ruggieri, also Ricci prepared a rough translation of the Four Books, known as the *Tetrabiblion Sinense de moribus* [Chinese Four Books on morals], at some time prior to November, 1593. Unfortunately, there is no trace of this work in any European archives. (Mungello 1989, 250-251) Ricci maintained that the contemporary Chinese interpretations of Confucianism were too metaphysical, that emphasis should be placed on the pragmatic aspects of Chinese ethics and political organization.

Prior to the publication *of Confucius Sinarum Philosophus* in 1687, the Jesuit missionaries focused their efforts on formulating catechetical interpretations of Confucianism in Chinese. They studied the Confucian classics, and adopted Confucian sayings in their Christian publications. In addition to Ricci's and Ruggieri's two Chinese catechisms, Ricci wrote sixteen books in Chinese. Most of the other seventeenth century Jesuit missionaries in China were also competent in Chinese composition. (Chen Shouyi 1970, p. 81)

**The first Latin translation of the Confucian canon**

When the Jesuits faced difficulties in preaching to the Chinese, they retreated to their work on the translation of the Confucian classics. In 1662, the first Latin translation of the Confucian canon was published in China by Inácio da Costa (1603-1666; Chinese name: 郭納爵 *GuōNàjué*) and Prospero Intorcetta (1626-1696; Chinese name: 殷鐸澤 *Yīn Duózé*). This Latin translation only included part of the Lun yu 論語 [Annalects] and the Da xue 大學 [GreatLearning], two of the Confucian Four Books. ② In 1667, Intorcetta published, in Guangzhou 廣州, a part of one of the other Confucian canon, Zhong yong 中庸 [Doctrine of the Mean], under the title of Sinarum Scientia Politico-*Moralis*. ③ In 1669, an edition of this latter workwas published in

---

① He eventually published his 天主實錄 [True Record of the Lord of Heaven] in 1584. The Chinese term for God in the title of this book, 天主 (Lord of Heaven), has remained the name for God in China and also the Chinesename used for the Catholic religion.

② *Sapientia Sinica exponente P. Ignatio a Costa Lusitano Soc. Ies. à P. Prospero Intorcetta Siculo eiusd. soc. orbi proposita*. Kiam-cham in urbe Sinarum Provinci? Kiam-si, 1662.

③ *Sinarvm Scientia Politico-Moralis a P. Prospero Intorcetta Sicvlo Societatis Iesv, in lucem edita*. Quam-Cheu (= Canton), 1667.

Goa, to which was appended a preface and a "Life of Confucius" (*Confuciivita*).① After Intorcetta returned to Europe in 1668, his books were reprinted in Paris in 1672② and translated into French in 1676. The rarity of the works in European libraries demonstrates their limited circulation.

***Confucius Sinarum Philosophus*** ③

It was only with the publication of Confucius Sinarum Philosophus in 1687 that European scholars began noticing these works on China. This book represented the cumulative, collaborative result of the Jesuit interpretations of Chinese culture. In particular, it included translations of three of the Confucian canons: *Tá-Hiŏ*, Magna Scientia [Great Learning, 大學], *Chūm-yam*, *Medium sempiternum* [Doctrine of the Mean, 中庸] and *Lún Yú*, *Ratiocinantium Sermones* [Analects, 論語]. Since Ricci rejected Mencian interpretations of Confucian classics, the Mencius 孟子 was not included.④ Ricci also excluded all of the commentaries by later Chinese scholars, which Chinese traditionally study along with the original texts.

The European interpretations of the Confucian classics in the *Confucius SinarumPhilosophus* touched off the Chinese Rites Controversy in Europe. This controversy grew out of Ricci's policy that the Chinese should be allowed to continue to perform public and private Confucian rites. Some Jesuits, among them his successor Nicholas Longobardi (NicolòLongobardo, 1559-1654, or 1565-1655; Chinese name: 龍華民 Lóng Huámín), opposed Ricci's liberal policies. This controversy was further stirred by the general debates among European intellectuals resulting from the Latin translations just mentioned.

The *Confucius Sinarum Philosophus* is a magnificently printed folio, published from the manuscript in the Royal Library by orders of Louis the Great (Louis le

① Sinarvm Scientia Politico-Moralis a P. Prospero Intorcetta Sicvlo Societatis Iesv, in lucem edita. Goæ, 1669.

② Paris edition: *Sinarvm scientia politico-moralis*, *sive Scientiæ Sinicæ liber inter Confvcii libros secvndvs*, *a P. Prospero Intorcetta ... in latinam versa ...* Parisiis, 1672.

③ *Confucius Sinarum Philosophus*, *sive Scientia Sinensis latine exposita*: studio et opera Prosperi Intorcetta, Christiani Herdtrich, Francisci Rougemont, Philippi Couplet, Patrum Societatis Jesu. Parisiis, Apud Danielem Horthemels, via Jacobâ, sub Mâcenate, M. DC. LXXXVII. (1687).

④ Ricci criticized (天主實義, Vol. II, p. 67) a saying in *Mencius* "There are three kinds of unfilial persons; theworst is the one who has no offspring." Since the Jesuits did not marry, they could not agree with this opinion.

Grand, i.e. Louis XIV of France, 1638-1715, reign: 1643-1715). It contains translations of the first three of the *Four Books* and a life of Confucius (*Philosophorum Sinensium Principis Confucii Vita*, pp. cxvi-cxxiv) with a full-page, icon-like portrait of the sage (p. cxvi). There is a very long introduction, called Proëmialis Declaratio [Methodological Introduction] (pp. ix-cxiv), and Couplet's *Tabula Chronologica Monarchiæ Sinicæ*① appears at the end of the book.

Most of these texts must have been composed in Canton between 1665 and 1671, when twenty-two Jesuits, four Dominicans and one Franciscan, expelled from their mission stations, were living together in one of the Jesuit churches in that city. It may well be that it owes its birth to the relative leisure and the somewhat unsettled atmosphere of this exile, but the history of the composition of the various parts of the work and the details of the final editing in Paris have not been elucidated. (Lundbæk 1991, p. 38)

The four authors listed on the title page (i. e. Prospero Intorcetta, Christian Wolfgang Herdtrich, François de Rougemont, Philippe Couplet) were all in their early forties and had come to China between 1658 and 1660. As mentioned above, Intorcetta had already completed his Chinese-Latin edition of the *Great Learning* and the first part of the *Analects*. He had also translated or was about to translate the *Doctrine of the Mean*. Rougemont may have been the main translator of the rest of the *Analects*, perhaps with the help of Herdtrich, but this fine calligrapher may have been busy writing the many Chinese characters that were, according to the plan, to be printed alongside the Latin text. It is not known, whether Couplet took part in the translation work perhaps being wholly absorbed in composing his *Chronologia*.

Intorcetta came to Rome as procurator in 1671, bringing with him his two short works and perhaps also an introduction which came to be used-after many revisions-for the first part of the *Proëmialis Declaratio*. The remainder of the texts were sent after him, but he did not get to see them by the time he departed for China in March 1673. It was left to Philippe Couplet, who was in Europe between 1682 and 1693, to arrange for the edition of the work. Perhaps Couplet made the many revisions and de-

---

① *Tabula Chronologica Monarchiæ Sinicæ juxta cyclos annorum* LX. Ab anno ante Christum 2952. ad annum post Christum 1683. Auctore R. P. Philippo Couplet Belga, Soc. Jesu, Sinensis Missionis in Urbem Procuratore. Parisiis, M. DC. LXXXVI. (1686).

letions in the texts, and wrote the last part of the *Proëmialis Declaratio*-he signed it as if the whole of it was his work. (p. cxiv)

The translations are long-winded paraphrases, slightly "christianizing" in many cases the Chinese text. The *Proëmialis Declaratio* has two main points. Firstly, the adulation of ancient Confucian moral philosophy or natural theology, together with the denigration of the metaphysical comments appended to it by the Song philosophers, the Neo-Confucians. And secondly an apology for the special missionary technique initiated by Matteo Ricci, the socalled accommodation method, criticized by a few of the Jesuits and by most of the non-Jesuitmissionaries.

The *Confucius Sinarum Philosophus* is not a scholarly work but rather a grandiose piece of missionary propaganda, intended to promote the Jesuits' China mission. This was suspected by many at the time and now, of course, it is clear. These intelligent and highly educated men, building on the foundation of three generations of earlier China Jesuits, did precisely what they were supposed to do.

**François Noël-early years**

New translation of the mentioned books was published in Prague in 1711. The author was François Noël (1651-1729; Latin: Franciscus Noël; Chinese name: *Wei Fangji* 衛方濟), a Belgian poet, dramatist and Jesuit in China. His *Sinensis Imperii Libri Classici Sex* [SixClassics of Chinese Empire] has contained a new translation of the first three of the *Four Books and added the Mencius* (*Mengzi* 孟子). He also included in this book the *Classic of Filial Piety* (*Xiao jing* 孝經), one of the *Thirteen Classics*, as well as the *Small Learning* (*Xiao xue* 小學), a collection of texts put together for children by Zhu Xi 朱熹. (Mungello 1983, 515-541)

The late seventeenth/early eighteenth century Jesuit, Franëois Noël, came from Hestrud in the French part of the County of Hainaut (*Hainaut français*), which is today within theborders of France, just on the border between France and Belgium. As he was born in thehistoric Flemish territory, he sometimes calls himself a "Fleming". (Rule 2003, p. 137)

Noël joined the Society of Jesus (*Societas Iesu*, S. J.) on 30 September 1670 in Tournai(now in Belgium), in the Jesuit *Provincia Gallo-Belgica*, at nineteen years of age. He made the usual education of the Jesuits. He studies theology at Douai (in Romance Flanders, *Flandre romane*, now in France), he also studied mathematics and astronomy. Afterwards, he became professor of Latin and Rhetoric in Tournai.

Noël's career was extraordinary in many respects. He wanted to go to the Japan mission, but this was impossible, because Japan was closed for all Europeans and especially for priests. He left Lisbon for the East in January 1684, like his fellow Belgian Jesuit and immediate predecessor, Antoine Thomas (1644-1709; Chinese name: 安多 *Ān Duō*), under the patronage of Maria, Duchess of Aveiro (*D. Maria de Guadalupe de Lancastre Cardenas Manrique, Duquesa de Aveiro*, 1630-1715). He tried to go to Japan, but in vain. Therefore he went to Macao where he arrived on 9 August 1685. In Macao he made his four solemn vows on 2 February 1686.

**Noël in China**

After other attempts to get in Tokugawa Japan, which failed, Noël settled for the China Mission. After preparatory Chinese language studies in Macao, he crossed over into China proper in 1687. He continued his Chinese studies in Shanghai 上海 and began his mission work on Chongming Island 崇明島 at the beginning of October 1688. By August of the following year he was claiming spectacular success in his evangelisation of the Chongming district and Shanghai, which confirms the view of this period as a high point in Catholic conversion.

The mission activities of François Noël from 1687 to 1702 were mostly in South-central China, especially various cities in the modem Jiangxi 江西, Jiangsu 江蘇, and Anhui 安徽 provinces: Huai'an 淮安, Nanking 南京, Wuhe 五河, Nanchang 南昌, Ganzhou 輯州, Jianchang 建昌, Nanfeng 南豐, and Nan'an 南安. (Rule 2003, p. 139) However, in the beginning of 1702 he was sent as procurator for the Jesuit China Mission to Rome, together with his confrere, the Bavarian Caspar Castner (or *Caspar Kastner*, *Kaspar Castner*, 1665-1709), to act in favour for the Chinese Rites.

**Noël and the Chinese Rites controversy**

It is not certain why Noël, a missionary from the provinces who, so far as we know, had never been near the court, nor had much contact with Chinese scholars, was chosen as procurator, but it was probably due to the esteem in which he was held by his fellow Belgian, Antoine Thomas, then the Jesuit Vice-Provincial. Thomas had left Europe for China four years before Noël and was ten years his senior in the Society of Jesus, and they seem never to have been together in China, except for ten days in Macao in August 1685. However, besides being members of the same Jesuit province, they shared a common enthusiasm for the Japanese mission and Noël had collaborated with Thomas on a project to upgrade maps of Siam, Macao and Japan. Thomas may have known Noël's early reputation in Belgium for scholarship and eloquence.

In 1704, Noël and Castner submitted in the name of their brethren and of four Chinese bishops a collection of documents to the Holy Office, which was responsible for the decision in the Rites Controversy. These documents should support the accommodation policy of the Jesuits: besides *Tianzhu* 天主, Lord of the Heaven, also *Tian* 天 (Heaven) and *Shangdi* 上帝(Emperor on High) should be permitted as names for the Christian God, the Chinese Christians should be permitted to take part at the veneration of the Ancestors and of Confucius.

In 1706 Noël left Lisbon with Castner back for China, reaching Macao on 22 July 1707. The unusual feature of this voyage was that, on the insistence of Castner, the mathematician, the captain of the ship experimented with a new quicker route which henceforth became standard: via Timor and then directly to Macao, bypassing Goa and the Straits of Malacca.

But instead of returning to his mission, less than six months later Noël was aboard ship once more en route for Europe. Already in 1708, he was sent again to Rome, this time by the emperor Kangxi 康熙帝 (1662-1721). He was in company of the two Jesuits, António Francesco Giuseppe Provana (1662-1720; Chinese name: 艾若瑟 *ài Ruòsè*) and José Ramón Arxó (1663-1711), and of the Chinese Jesuit Louis Fan (1682-1753; 樊守義 *Fán Shŏuyì*)[①].

They should get a good solution of the controversy, namely that Confucianism and Christianity were compatible.

They left Macao on 14 January 1708 on the Portuguese ship *Bom Jesus de Mazagão dasBrotas* and sailed via Batavia and Bahía in Brazil to Lisbon where they arrived in September. Provana and Fan reached Rome in February 1709 after a consid-

---

① Louis Fan Shouyi was the first Chinese to live in the West who reported about his experiences after his return to China. He arrived in Lisbon in 1708 as an aide to Francesco Provana, S. J., who was ambassador of the Kangxi emperor to the pope. Fan entered the Jesuit Order in Rome in 1708 and was ordained priest in 1717. In 1719 he returned to China with Provana. He reported on Europe in at least one audience with the emperor. The eyewitness account, *Shenjianlu* 身見錄, was written at the request of Kangxi, who wanted first-hand information about Europe; and Fan took the opportunity to stress the achievements of Catholic civilization. (Chatterjee 2008, p. 88)

erable stay in Portugal, but it is possible that Noël preceded them.

**François Noël in Prague**

We do not know how long he remained in Rome, but in 1711 we find him in Prague, where he published his major works. In Prague Noël began lecturing mathematics at the Jesuit-run Charles-Ferdinand University (now Charles University) in Prague. ①He used his stays in Prague to publish several books on Chinese religion, philosophy, the rites and a translation of the *Sishu* 四書, the "Four Classics", namely as the first complete translation of the *Lunyu*, the *Zhongyong*, the *Daxue* and of *Mengzi*. He has also published a book on mathematical observations.

The first, a collection of astronomical observations taken in India and China reveals yet another talent of this multi-faceted man. ② The three major works, however, the *Chinese Philosophy*, the *Six Classical Books of the Chinese Empire*, and the *Historical Notice of theChinese Rites and Ceremonies*, are all about sinological matters and must be the fruit of his previous ten years of advocacy for the China Mission and its views. Perhaps those four years at sea had given him leisure for the task, and his work of collating and translating documents for the Roman congregations was clearly the foundation for these books about China. A draft exists for the introduction and first treatise of the *Chinese Philosophy* but unfortunately it bears no indication of date, and extant but incomplete manuscripts of the *Six Books* are dated 1700, demonstrating that the translations had been begun in China. ③

① On 23 February 1654 Emperor Ferdinand III (1608-1657) merged the former independent universities of Carolinum and Clementinum and created a single university with four faculties. Carolinum had at that time only the faculty of arts, as the only faculty surviving the period of the Hussite Wars. Starting at this time, the university designated itself Charles-Ferdinand University (Latin: *Universitatis Carolinœ Ferdinandeœ*). The dilapidated Carolinum was rebuilt in 1718 at the expense of the state.

② Observationes mathematicœet physicœ in India et China factœ *à* Patre Francisco Noël Societatis Jesu, abanno 1684 usque ad annum 1708. Pragæ, typis Universit. Carolo-Ferdinandeæ, in Collegio Soc. Jesu ad S. Clementem, per Joachimum Joannem Kamenicky factorem, 1710. [National Library in Prague, sign. 49 B 44, 49 B 105]

③ E. g. *Memcius ex sinico in latinum idioma traductus a P. Francisco Noël Societatis Iesu missionario Sinensi, Nancham in China*, 1700. *-Dudink, Ad C. M. Chinese Books and Documents (pre-*1900) *in the Royal Library of Belgium at Brussels*. Brussels, Archives et Bibliothèques de Belgique, Archief- en Bibliotheekwezen in Belgi?, 2006, pp. 45-47.

***Sinensis Imperii libri classici sex***

The *Philosophia Sinica*① is a quite sophisticated work, and in many ways an advance on its Jesuit predecessors. Nevertheless, from a sinological point of view, the translations of the "Six Classical Books" (*Sinensis Imperii libri classici sex*)②, that is the Confucian writings, theGreat Learning《大學》[*Adultorum Schola seu Doctrina*, Ta Hio]③, *Doctrine of the Mean*《中庸》[*Immutabile Medium*, Chum Yum]④, *Analects*《論語》[*Liber Sententiarum*, Lun Yu]⑤, *Mencius*《孟子》[*Memcius*, Mem Tsu] ⑥, *Classic of Filial Piety*《孝經》[*Filialis Observantia*, Hiao Kim] ⑦, and *Small Learning*《小學》[*Parvulorum Schola seu Doctrina*]⑧, is Noël's greatest contribution to Chinese studies. It was not based on the earlier Jesuit translations which culminated in the *Confucius Sinarum Philosophus*, but a completely fresh work, and contained the first published translations in European languages of the *Mencius*, *Filial Piety* and Zhu Xi's primer, the *Xiao xue*. The texts of the Four Books are preceded by Chu Hsi's prefaces from his annotated edition, the *Si shu jizhu* 四書集注 [Collected commen-

---

① 15 *Philosophia Sinica tribus tractatibus*, *Primo Cognitionem Primi Entis*, *Secundo Ceremonias erga Defunctos*, *Tertio Ethicam*, *Juxta Sinarum mentem complectens*, Authore P. Francisco Noël Societ. Jesu missionario. Pragae, typis Universit. Carolo-Ferdinandeae, in Collegio Soc. Jesu ad S. Clementem, per Joachimum JoannemKamenicky factorem, anno 1711. [National Library in Prague, sign. D IV 34, 49 E 18]

② *Sinensis Imperii libri classici sex*: *nimirum Adultorum Schola*, *Immutabile Medium*, *Liber Sententiarum*, *Memcius*, *Filialis Observantia*, *Parvulorum Schola*. E Sinico idiomate in latinum traducti, a P. Francisco Noël Societatis Jesu Missionario. Pragæ, Typis Universitatis Carolo-Ferdinandeæ, in Collegio Soc. Jesu ad S. Clementem, per Joachimum Joannem Kamenicky p. t. Factorem, Anno 1711. [National Library in Prague, sign. D IV 34, 49 E 19]; *the French translation*: *Les livres classiques de l'empire de la Chine*, recueillis par le Pere F. Noël, précédés d'*Observations sur l'origine*, *la nature & les effets de la philosophie morale & politique dans cet empire*. 7 vols. A Paris, Chez De Bure, Barrois aîné & Barrois jeune, 1784-1786.

③ *Sinensis Imperii liber primus classicus dictus* Adultorum Schola, *Sinicè* Ta Hio, pp. 1-29.

④ *Sinensis Imperii liber secundus classicus dictus* Immutabile Medium, *Sinicè* Chum Yum, pp. 31-73.

⑤ *Sinensis Imperii liber tertius classicus dictus* Liber Sententiarum, *Sinicè* Lun Yu, pp. 75-198.

⑥ *Sinensis Imperii liber quartus classicus dictus* Memcius, *Sinicè* Mem Tsu, pp. 199-472.

⑦ *Sinensis Imperii liber quintus classicus dictus* Filialis Observantia, *Sinicè* Hiao Kim, pp. 473-484.

⑧ *Sinensis Imperii liber sextus classicus dictus* Parvulorum Doctrina seu Schola, *Sinicè* Siao Hio, pp. 485-608.

taries to the *Four Books*][1], but Noël also used other sources. The translations are divided up in small, numbered sections like the Chinese original. When comments are given, often at the end of a section, they are usually accompanied by the name of the commentator. Many of the sentences are introduced by lengthy paraphrases and sometimes followed by brief, helpful explanations.

Unlike the translations of the *Confucius Sinarum Philosophus* there is no or very little Christian discourse interpolated in the text. Noel's work appears to be a serious attempt at a scholarly presentation of the ancient text, perhaps in deliberate contrast to the aims of the Jesuits who composed their *Confucius Sinarum Philosophus* half a century before. (Lundbæk 1991, p. 39)

Although Noël translated six Confucian classics into Latin in 1711, his translations were banned by the authorities both in Rome and in Germany. Because of Du Halde's laudatory acknowledgment of Noel's work in the *Description*[2], Noël exerted a great influence on German scholars such as Gottfried Wilhelm von Leibniz (1646-1716) and Christian Wolff (1679-1754) in the seventeenth and eighteenth century.[3] Du Halde not only adopted Noël's translations of the *Four Books*, but also gave a summary and a commentary for each of the Confucian Five Classics as representing the primary body of the Chinese classical canon (*livres canoniques du Premier ordre*).

*Sinensis Imperii libri classici sex* is a comparatively free translation. Noël explains in the preface that it represents "not, so to say, what the Chinese wrote, but, I hope, what they really meant."[4] Noël is clearly using the standard Zhu Xi edition, since he includes in each case Zhu Xi's preface. But his interpretation is European and scholastic, in a mode that has many precedents in the China Mission.

A good example is the opening line of his translation of the *Zhong yong* 中庸

---

① "Ad hunc libellum Sinicus Interpres *Chu hi* sequens præmittit proœmium."

② *Description géographique, historique, chronologique, politique, et physique de l'empire de la Chine et de la Tartarie chinoise, enrichie des cartes générales et particulieres de ces pays, de la carte générale et des cartes particulieres du Thibet, & de la Corée; & ornée d'un grand nombre de figures & de vignettes gravées en tailledouce*. A La Haye, Chez Henri Scheurleer, 1736, 4 vols. in folio.

③ Donald F. Lach, "The Sinophilism of Christian Wolff (1679-1754),", *Journal of the History of Ideas*, 14(1953), 561-574. See also his "Leibniz and China," *Journal of the History of Ideas*, 6 (1945), 436-455.

④ "non tantùm ut discas, quæ Sinæ scripserunt, sed & ut agas, quæ rectè senserunt"-Sinensis Imperii libriclassici sex, "Praefatio ad lectorem", p. 2.

("Doctrine of the Mean"). The original literally goes something like this: "the mandate of Heaven is called nature; to follow nature is called the way; to cultivate the way is called teaching."①Ninety years before, when called upon to comment upon this passage in a scholarly academy in Fuzhou 福州, Giulio Aleni, SJ (or Alenio, 1582-1649; Chinese name: 艾儒略 *ài Rúlüè*), had interpreted it as follows: "The Law of Heaven is called Nature. To follow its direction is called the way, or natural law. To particularize and order this natural law, is called positive law."② Noël's interpretation is far less tendentious, but still includes a distinctly scholastic flavour: "the law of Heaven is nature itself; the tendency of this nature is the way of acting correctly; the direction of this life is a right discipline of life, or the right precepts for living."③

***Historica notitia rituum***

The last of the trilogy published in 1711 in Prague is the *Historica notitia rituum acceremoniarum Sinicarum*.④ The *Historica notitia covers* much the same ground as the secondtreatise of the *Philosophia Sinica*⑤ but in somewhat greater detail, and with liberal citations from Chinese texts. The arguments of the Historica notitia are again standard, but backed up by liberal citation. He also displays considerable knowledge of the historical development of ancestor rituals, pointing, for example, to the late introduction of the wooden tablets to replace the form of ancestor ritual described in the *Shi jing* 詩經 where a small boy stands in for thedeceased.⑥

***Noël's final years***

After 1711 we almost lose sight of Noël until his death in 1729 in Lille. On 10 June 1715 Noël applies for a new authorization to return to China. This was three month after Clement XI had issued Papal bull Ex illa die which officially condemned

---

① 「天命之謂性;率性之謂道;修道之謂教。」(中庸 I. 1)

② Bartoli, Daniello, SJ, *Historia della Compagnia di Giesu del R. P. Daniello Bartoli della medesimaCompagnia*: la Cina, terza parte dell'Asia. Roma, de Lazzeri, 1663, p. 812.

③ "Cæli lex est ipsa natura; hujus naturæ ductus est recta agendi via; hujus viæ directio est recta vitæ disciplina, seu recta vivendi præcepta."-Sinensis Imperii libri classici, p. 41.

④ *Historica notitia Rituum ac Ceremoniarum Sinicarum In colendis Parentibus ac Benefactoribus Defunctis, Ex ipsis Sinensium Authorum libris desumpta*. A P. Francisco Noël, Societatis Jesu Missionario. Pragæ, typis Univers. Carolo-Ferdinand. in Collegio Soc. Jesu ad S. Clementem, per Joachimum Joannem KamenickyFactorem, Anno 1711. [National Library in Prague, sign. B IV 262]

⑤ *De Ceremoniis Sinarum erga Denunctos*.

⑥ "puer actor defunctorum"-*Sinensis Imperii libri classici*, p. 44; *Shi jing* II. 6. (209) 楚茨.

the Chinese rites. (Rule 2003, p. 161) In the end, Noël has returned to Lille (we don't know exactly the reasons-age,illness, or other circumstances) where he continued his research and writing in Sinology. His works demonstrate a thorough knowledge of the literature and Chinese thought. His "Poetical Works" published in 1717 in Latin include nine tragedies as well as devotional works. ①

**Conclusion**

Whereas the translations of the Confucian classics made by Fr. Intorcetta and other Jesuits which culminated in *Confucius Siriarum philosophus* (1687) were familiar to Voltaire (*François-Marie Arouet*, *dit Voltaire*, 1694-1778) and other French philosophers, JeanBaptiste Du Halde (1674-1743; Chinese name: 杜赫德 *Dù Hèdé*) helped to disseminate the less well-known translations published by François Noël in 1711. Du Halde states that he had drawn his understanding of the *Four Books* from Fr. Noël's translations and recommends them to readers interested in improving their understanding.

Although *Confucius Sinarum philosophus* and Noël's *Sinensis imperii libri classici sex* differ in many respects, they both emerged from the same long-term Jesuit translation project which is traceable to Ruggieri and Ricci's pioneering efforts in the closing years of the sixteenth century. Noël's translations represent a culmination of that project in the sense that they are more refined versions of the original translations. Furthermore, whereas *Confucius Sinarum philosophus* omitted Mencius, Noël included all of the *Four Books*.

François Noël thus ranks among the most important cultural intermediaries between China and Europe in the early 18th century. His translations have sustainably influenced the Enlightenment in Europe because they dropped a theological interpretation and thus displayed an image of a philosophy, which had given continuity and social stability of an ancient culture without God and the Church. ②Noël's work is full

---

① *Reverendi Patris Francisci Noel e Societate Jesu Opuscula poetica in quatuor partes distributa*. Francofurti,apud Thomam Fritsch, 1717: "Vita Jesu Christi sub nomine divini amoris"-"Epistolæ Marianæ-"Vita SanctiIgnatii de Loyola Societatis Jesu fundatoris"-"Tragœdiæ".

② "Aussi peut-on assurer que jamais les livres de Confucius et de ses disciples n'ont été aussi bien entendus, niaussi complètement expliqués qu'ils le sont dans l'ouvrage du P. Noël." [We can ensure as well, that he books of Confucius and his disciples were not as well understood or as completely explained as they are in the work of Father Noël]. -*Biographie universelle*, *ancienne et moderne*, *ou Histoire*, *par ordre alphabétique*, *de la vie publique et privée de tous les hommes qui se sont fait remarquer par leur écrits*, *leurs actions*, *leurs talents*, *leurs vertus ou leurs crimes*. Paris, Chez L. G. Michaud, 1822, tome 31, p. 336.

of protracted paraphrases of Medieval Latin, and this can be conceived as a product of cultural translation under the principle of domestication in early modern Europe. It is known that Noël attracted widespread criticism for his conscious effort to intermingle the text and the commentaries. However, as the Jesuits were evidently not able to translate separately the Four Books and the commentaries during the seventeenth century, it was necessary for them to add the commentaries to the text in order to make the translation more intelligible to the literati in the Western world at that time. For precisely the same reason, Noël's paraphrastic renderings did not only come from the original Chinese text and the commentaries, but also from his own elaboration. (Wong 2013, p. 171)

**Bibliography**

Chatterjee, Kumkum; Hawes, Clement (eds.), *Europe Observed: Multiple Gazes in Early Modern Encounters*. Lewisburg, PA, Associated University Presse, 2008.

Chen Shouyi 陳受頤，中歐文化交流史事論叢 [Discourses on the History of China-European Cultural Communication]. Taipei, Commercial Press 臺灣商務印書館, 1970.

Dai Wei-Yang 戴維揚, "Confucian and Christian Canons 論儒家經典西譯與基督教聖經中譯",《教學與研究》, No.3 (1981/05), pp. 247-278.

Lee, Thomas H. C. 李弘祺 (ed.), *China and Europe: images and influences in sixteenth to eighteenth centuries. Hong Kong*, The Chinese University Press, 1991.

Lundbæk, Knud, "The First European Translations of Chinese Historical and Philosophical Works," in Lee (1991), pp. 29-44.

Meynard, Thierry 梅谦立, "《论语》在西方的第一个版本 (1687) / The First Edition of the *Analects* of Confucius in the West (1687)," 神州交流 / *Chinese Cross Currents*, Vol. 7,No. 2, April 2010, pp. 98-111.

Mungello, David E., "Confucianism in the Enlightenment: Antagonism and Collaboration between the Jesuits and the Philosophes," in Lee (1991), pp. 99-128.

Mungello, David E., *Curious Land: Jesuit Accommodation and the Origins of Sinology*. Honolulu, University of Hawaii Press, 1989.

Mungello, David E., "The First Complete Translation of the Confucian Four Books in the West," in *International Symposium on Chinese-Western Cultural Interchange in Commemoration of the 400th Anniversary of the Arrival of Matteo Ricci*,

*S. J. in China* /紀念利瑪竇來華四百週年中西文化交流國際學術會議論文集. Taipei, Fu Jen University Press 輔仁大學出版社, 1983, pp. 515-541.

Pinch, William R., "The Corpse and Cult of St. Francis Xavier, 1552-1623," in Mathew N. Schmalz and Peter Gottschalk ed. *Engaging South Asian Religions: Boundaries, Appropriations, and Resistances*. New York, State University of New York Press, 2011. Po-Chia Hsia, Ronnie, "The Question of Who: Chinese in Europe," in Chatterjee (2008), pp.83-102.

Rule, Paule, "François Noël, SJ, and the Chinese Rites controversy," in Walle (2003), pp.135-166.

Walle, W. F. Vande, Noël Golvers (eds.), *The History of the Relations Between the Low Countries and China in the Qing Era* (1644-1911). Leuven/Louvain, Universitaire Pers Leuven / Leuven University Press / Presses Universitaires de Louvain, 2003.

Wong Ching Him, Felix 黃正謙, 論耶穌會士衛方濟的拉丁文《孟子》翻譯 [On the Latin Translation of *Mencius* of François Noël, SJ], *Journal of Chinese Studies*《中國文化研究所學報》, No. 57, July 2013, pp. 133-172.

# Confucianism and Its Relevance: Reinforcing South America and its International Relations.

**Milton Reyes**[①]

This paper will describe some of the most relevant issues derived from the Confucian tradition in the International Relations Discipline, and how these can reinforce national projects currently under construction. It will also consider how these efforts can improve new development paradigms (at national and regional integration levels) across South America, and gain a better understanding of relations between society - state and modern world order.

This paper will first review the characteristics of modern states and how these how they balance the complex relationships between their institutions and social forces, and the the limitations of these current approaches of *vis a vis* modernization efforts in South America.

We will then review the sphere of domestic politics, and how the struggles for power within a country can also generate empowerment or weaknesses affecting such countries' relative positions in the modern global system, considering the many economic and security challenges they may face.

Given that states and social forces are not isolated from the world order, we must also remember that population -at the level of concrete practices-reproduce long term ideas that can be understood as *habitus* or long terms intersubjective ideas.

The problem then is to analyze and resolve how development paradigms in South America aim to modernize the domestic economic and political realms, thereby attempting to make their societies and economies play a more strategic and intelligent

---

① Institute of Higher National Studies / Pontifical Catholic University of Ecuador/ Rio de Janeiro's Federal University, Brazil

role in the interstate relationships by overcoming dependency -and simultaneously-confronting problems stemming from different visions of progress and interpretations of justice. These visions are not limited to "civil society", but include various other social forces, including bureaucracy.

Therefore, this paper will analyze how Confucian thought and ideas can transform the mentality and South American view (also worldview) of social forces (ethics at educational and political level), and which lessons can be learned by bureaucrats and policy makers. By articulating the role and relationships between institutions and their own social forces, we can construct a more viable strategy for a deepening involvement in the $21^{st}$ century world order.

**Keywords**: Individual -State / Society -World Order Continuity. Ideas. Virtues. Values. Legitimacy. Confucianism and International Relations. Union of South American Nations. *New Integrationism*.

**World Order, state and society: a critical approach**

As a first step to link IIRR and Confucianism and then to the challenges South America faces, this paper begins by setting the theoretical framework of how it defines International Relations.

We will therefore propose a critical perspective of mainstream IIRR from the International Political Economy, trough the approach of Robert W. Cox, as one of the main thinkers of Critical Theory. From a structural and historical method (strongly influenced by Marxian thinking), the author[①] proposes the emancipation to achieve equitable and legit order, rather that legitimization within the prevailing order.

In that sense this paper will understand IIRR from a specific approach: the *World Order* in its relations with local and international *Social Forces* and the *States*. Where, each level crosses and is crossed by each other in a double way. Thus, first Cox uses the term World Order,

---

① His job has illuminist roots and "the influence from the Greek classical thought about autonomy, and for which democracy is considered as good as Nietzsche and Weber thought" (according to Devetak: 1996, p. 147). The influence from Frankfurt School is undeniable and provides a renewed strength "in which the term critical theory came to be used as the emblem of a philosophy which questions the prevailing order of social and political modernity through a method of immanent critique" (*Ibid*).

**in preference to "inter-state system" as it is relevant of all historical periods (and not only those in which states have been the component entities) and in preference "World System" as it is more indicative of structure having only a certain duration in time and avoiding the equilibrium connotation of "system". "World" designates the relevant totality, geographically limitations by the range of probably interactions (some past "worlds" being limited to the Mediterranean, to Europe, to China, etc.). "Order" is used in the sense of the way things usually happen (not the absence of turbulence); thus, disorder is included in the concept of order. An inter-state system is one historical form of world order. The term is used in the plural to indicate the particular patterns of power relationships, which have endured in time, can be contrasted in terms of their principal characteristics as distinctive world orders (Cox and Sinclair: 1996, pp. 116-117).**

At the same time we will understand "state is thought to be absolutely inseparable from civil society as together they constitute and reflect the hegemonic social order" ① . The state (here) plays a relatively intermediate autonomous role between, on the one hand, *Social Forces*, and the other hand, a *World Order* which embodies a particular configuration of power determined by the states-system and the global economy" (Devetak:1996, p. 160 ).

Here as much as a Confucian approach to IIRR, a continuity between State and Society exists (*Social Forces* meanwhile there is a "state-society complex" as Cox describes), and between the domestic and the foreign affairs. The latter has been denied within the main premises stemming from a classical perception, in most western policy makers -with backgrounds *in liberal economics*.

Meanwhile the modern State is portrayed here under a Weber´s perspective②(See Weber State and society), about his concrete form of materialization: institutions.

---

① According to Cox, this distinction made practical sense in the Eighteen and early Nineteenth centuries when it corresponded to two or more less distinct spheres of human activity or practice: to an emergent society of individuals based on contract and market relations which replaced a status-based society, on the one hand, and the state with functions limited to maintaining internal peace, external defense and the requisite conditions for market, on the other. Traditional IIRR theory maintains the distinctness of the two spheres, with foreign policy appearing as the pure expression of state interests. State and society are so interpenetrated that the concepts have become almost purely analytical (Cox: June, 1981, p. 126-7).

② See Max Weber, Economy and Society. (Referred here as "Economía y Sociedad". México, Fondo de Cultura Económica, 1era edición, 1942).

The state's institutions "are also the relation of the reflection of power in its origins, although they can have a life of their own, these can become contrary tendencies in a battle field. Even in the society it is possible to stimulate the creation of rival institutions that reflect different tendencies (Cox: 1981, p.150).

Additionally, this occurs due to a tight relationship between institutionalization and *hegemony*. Even more so, "the institutions can adopt the function of a hegemonic strategic anchor, because they can face the representation of diverse interests, as much as the universalization of politics", although it is impossible to limit hegemony to an institutional dimension. "The institutions could be a means for the regulation of conflicts (hegemonic function), but this is only one expression of hegemony, not a synonymous" (Op. Cit., Ibid. pp 158-159)

Hegemony "is represented as a fit between material power, ideology and institutions... It is a form of domination where a particular interest parades itself as universal" (Ibid, p.160); meanwhile, institutionalization has become as stabilization method for the perpetuation of a particular order.

As stated, modern institutions represent very peculiar amalgams of Ideology and Material Power, while exerting their influence in the development of *Ideas* and the *Material Capabilities*.

These three levels: *Institutions*, *Ideas* and *Material Capabilities* influence each other permanently. Because of this Cox will analyze the concept of "ideas" as part of the structure that can help us reach an understanding of hegemony. Thus he recognizes two classes of *Ideas*:

"a) ***Inter-subjective meanings***, the shared notions related to the nature of social relations that tend to perpetuate habits and behavioral expectations"

b) Those related to a historic structure, and are referred to as "world held by different groups within societies, such as the ***collective images*** of social order, justice, public good and a common development path of a social order held by different groups of people"①. Then the possibilities for "the clash of collective images and the sprouting of an alternative structure" (Op.Cit. Ibid.p.158)

For this author the *Material Capabilities* represent productive and destructive powers. These in their dynamic form, exist as technological and organizational capabilities, and in their accumulated forms -as natural resources susceptible to transformation trough technology-as concentrations of equipment (for example industries and weaponry), and the wealth that commands them all (Op.Cit., Ibid.).

Cox according to the *Marxian* perspective that recognizes the contributions of Realism at IIRR, is not concerned about reaching a final stage for the human history, contrary to certain liberals with backgrounds in economics. He does recognize the conformation of historical structures and within them, the complexity of *Social Forces*, and the competitions between *Blocs* of Power (alternative, hegemonic), in the domestic (intra-state) and the foreign scenarios (inter-state). Precisely beacause of this his job recognizes that utopia is necessary, but only one that can be viable, *a utopia recurbed by reality*②. Therefore alternative projects must take into account that is necessary to build strategic guides to action, as much as the articulation between forces (blocs). This is a perspective inherited from Gramsci's job, useful in order to gain a better understanding, as well as enabling one to propose processes to reinforce organizations as the Union of South American Nations (UNASUR in Spanish).

An effort such as UNASUR reminds us that the existing order can't be understood without taking account the historically changing interaction between ideas, consciousness, ideologies, and analytical concepts on one hand, and the concrete social, economic and political circumstances on the other③, as well as the need to pay strong attention to the relationship between knowledge and values.

Following this path, ideas, representations, images, knowledge and values, are in a level at where we can propose a first concrete contribution from the Confucian

---

① Collective images are not aggregations of fragmented opinions of individuals such as compiled trough surveys; they are coherent mental types expressive of the world views of specific groups such as may be reconstructed trough the work of historians and sociologists, *e.g.* Max Weber's reconstruction of forms of religious consciousness (Cox: june,1981, p. 153)

② Interpretation by Professor Alexei Paéz Cordero, at several interviews and congresses (Quito, 2004-2011).

③ Reason why Cox, (according to Devetak), "directs his attention to the domination and subordination relations, which cross the globe".

thinking to the attempts of constructing a viable and sustainable political community as UNASUR, as well as every member state.

Because -as we have seen-state institutions and social forces are also impacted by ideas, it is possible to suggest that the Confucian principles related to meritocracy, virtuosity and ethics can positively affect the development of mentalities of social actors, but also within the bureaucratic mechanisms within the states' institutional levels.

This first suggestion could already be a huge contribution if we are capable to accept that the strongest institutions and bureaucracy -by *legitimacy-* reinforce the State not only at the domestic sector, but also at the foreign policy sphere (external sector).

Thus the already stronger state members, plus the reinforced UNASUR institutions, could reinforce these two sectors in facing hegemonic actors in the World Order.

Once we have already established a theoretical relationship between the state, society and world order -and linked those levels to the importance of ideas, given we've also posed how IIRR from critical theory understands internal and external sectors as a continuum-, it is necessary to discuss the articulations between Confucianism to the debate of the specific IIRR disciplinary frame and the Critical Theory, in order to attempt to extract the contributions to South American countries members of UNASUR at the institutional level, and specially in their IIRR approach, to face the challenges of the present World Order.

Society, State and IIRR: The Confucian contribution approach.

Confucius did not live in a context of national states as conceived by modernity, but Confucian thinking can be related to IIRR reflections. Confucius' views on the nature of international relations stem from his conception of the virtuous individual (Doupe: 2003, p.2).

A first approach can be made if we understand the conceptions of international society of this great ancient Chinese philosopher and teacher, through an analysis of his conceptions of the nature of man and state (Ibid.). As an introduction we can point out that:

**Confucius' concept of the nature of the human being centers mainly on his theories**

**regarding virtues and human relations… Confucius places the ideas of "jen[①]" (goodness and virtue), the "harmony chain[②]", "tao" (the way[③]), the importance of the family (filial piety)[④], "i" (righteousness or justice)[⑤], "chung-shu" (loyalty and consideration[⑥]), and "li" (propriety or justice)[⑦]… (he) uses these concepts to identify the way he believes common people, public servants, and especially rulers should act. Virtues are of supreme importance to Confucius (Op. Cit., Ibid.).**

For the philosopher the main virtues are humaneness or benevolence (*ren*), dutifulness, wisdom, good faith, and observance of ritual (Herrlee: 1951)[⑧]; where he believes humaneness to be the most important of these virtues, as he says it plays an integral role in social relationships (Doupe, p. 2).

Because of the continuity of individual, society, state and the relation with other countries, *humaneness* or benevolence (*ren*) once again has great importance to construct leadership and legitimacy in a country's IIRR.

According to Confucius, humanness plays an integral role in social relationships. He defines humaneness in two parts: The first, an attitude of reverence in human re-

---

① The concept of "jen" is an integral part of Confucius' conception of international relations, as seen through the idea of the "harmony chain". Specifically, if the individual can put the "jen" way of life into practice, then this concept will spread to one's family, then state, then country, and eventually to the world (Doupe: 2003, p. 3)..

② According to the philosopher, this concept is applicable at the international level: If all people exemplify the aforementioned virtues, relations between humans, whether in government or civilians, would be peaceful and harmonious (Doupe: 2003, p. 3).

③ According to Confucius, the term means "the way", and applies to the nature of man, the state, and international relations, as it represents the manner in which he thought behavior should be conducted between individuals and states worldwide. Confucius explains that "if all under heaven have the way" or a particular state "has the way," moral principles prevail (Ibid.)

④ A high valued virtue, at present time in China.

⑤ Confucius defines this concept as something that is fitting, right, or seemly. (D. Howard Smith, *Confucius* (New York: Charles Scribner's Sons, 1973) 73 (at Doupe, p. 4).

⑥ Confucius feels that loyalty and consideration or "chung-shu" is of great importance for those individuals involved in public life. By loyalty, Howard D. Smith suggests that Confucius implies serving wholly with all one's heart, whereas, by consideration, the ancient Chinese philosopher refers to putting oneself in the place of others (Smith: 1973, p. 73). (At at Doupe, p. 4).

⑦ Translated, the term means propriety or the rules of good behavior. It is simply the interactions of polite society and the proper way to conduct oneself (Ibid.).

⑧ Herrlee Glessner Creel, *Confucius: The Man and the Myth* (London: Routledge & Kegan Paul Ltd, 1951) 45 (at Doupe: 2003).

lationships, and the observance of a respectful behavior at all times; the second is to show consideration to others by not carrying out actions one would not want done to oneself. (Ibid.).

Both premises can be understood in a social relationship (domestic), but also at IIRR level[①]; and even more, the last one looks to be clearly orienting Chinese foreign policy. This is why some analysis conceive *for example*, that one of the principles Chinese IIRR is based upon is to look at other countries as China is looked at by them (China treats other countries the way they treat China)[②].

As part of the afore mentioned continuity, a contribution to the relationship between domestic and external sectors will be gaining an understanding of Confucian background Chinese ethics -enriched with Mencius[③]' *The Great Learning*[④]-as a deontological system of a continuity spanning a range from personal to public concerns without differentiation: a good society is a good state, and a good world all have to rest upon the foundation of a good individual. (Hso, Cho-Yun: 1999, p.160).

We must point out that even though individual virtues, moral and ethics, tradition and ritual, play a main role in the orientation of society, Confucianism cannot lay the whole responsibility on governed individuals. If this were true, that Confucius found respect for institutions and order as indispensable, we couldn't consider his philosophy politically conservative, or his thinking as proposing the maintenance of the prevailing order at any cost. Rulers and governments also have responsibilities, and

---

① . This also can be observed because of the Confucius' ideas center upon the notion of *ren*: on the one hand, *ren* constitutes the basis upon which the maintenance of public order is founded. It is a set of norms, principles and rules that both the ruler and subjects are expected to follow, governing the way in which a policy maintains its legitimacy. On the other hand, the external dimension of *ren* presupposes a universality of morality transcending political boundaries, (Tamaki: 2007, p.285). A fact that being over-dimensioned by authors that find a realist matrix in Confucius thinking, but that can be understood trough historically comprehension of Confucius days (to see the limits of identified Confucianism and Realism, see the brief characterization that has been made in tis paper).

② Interview with Professor Shi Yinhong, Quito, October, 2010.

③ Mencius extended Confucianism in several aspects. One of his contributions was the integration of the concept of *i* with Confucian *jen* to create a new fundamental notion of the Confucian system (Op. Cit., Hso, Cho-Yun: 1999, p.157).

④ The entire Confucian system of ethics as refined and extended by Mencius is crystallized in *The Great Learning*, one of the four classics of the Confucian tradition. The Great Learning appears to have been a guidebook for Confucian students to gradually appreciate the connections between various items of virtues (Ibid. p.159).

should reach a state of virtue：

**Confucius believed that the government should benefit all people, not just the representatives, involved therein. Keeping in line with the themes of individuality and virtue, Confucius wanted a social order that was based on personal ethics where the political is the result of the personal. This is to say that, if people are virtuous and kind, then the state can be so as well. Furthermore, if harmony is to be present in the state, it must begin with the people①. Confucius was often asked how one could contribute to government. To this question, he offered the idea of personal contribution through actions. He is quoted in *The Analects* as having said, "only be dutiful towards your parents and friendly towards your brothers, and you will be contributing to government."②Confucius implies that the practice of social virtues, within the family, by those without political power, makes a significant contribution to government, by contributing to social harmony, which he believed to be the purpose of government. ③(Doupe: 2003, p. 5).**

Only such way rulers could reach *legitimacy*. This is because, according to Confucius, people under the ruler also play an important role. He also felt they should be loyal to their leader, if he is just and good to them. Conversely in cases of tyranny, Confucius advocated for rebellion (Ibid, p.6).

Once again we can deduce a deep relationship between the individual and society and their mutual influences and their impact on power related actors. This deduction grows stronger if we were to understand that *loyalty* within Confucianism would be possible between the people and their ruler, helping to create the ideal virtuous society④. We remember some of Mencius' contributions within the Confucian system of thought：

**Mencius repeatedly redefined *i* as an innate virtue, with which a human was born. He argued that *jen* and *i* were both aspects of human nature. However, his *i* did stand as a rather others-oriented virtue, in contrast of self-oriented virtue. Although he denied that he held *i* as different from *jen*, he related *jen* to a mentality of general compassion, and *i* to a consciousness of shame (Hso, Cho-Yun: 1999, p. 157).**

---

① Raymond Dawson, *Confucius* (Oxford: Oxford U. Press, 1981) 103. (At Doupe: 2003)

② Ibid.

③ Ibid.

④ Ibid.

Conversely as we've seen, there is a continuity between individuals, society, authorities and the state within Confucian thinking, it is important for the foreign sector to have a competent and able representative, because (following Confucius) a good and proper ruler is the individual who is the most directly involved in all aspects of inter-state and international relations. (Doupe: 2003, p. 6).

Although this paper does agree with the last statement, we also have to understand the historical and political context, and propose that on modernity, a leader-representative is only one actor within the inter-state relations, and that the political power is represented by the figure of *State*. Here the *State* is not only the head (ruler, prime minister, president, king, emperor), but also its institutions and bureaucracy. There once again, lays the importance of the Confucian virtuosity system, in order to enforce the capabilities of a country in the domestic and IIRR realms.

Those capacities based on virtue according to Confucianism, can be reached through *education*, not by punishment and law[①]. Thus, Confucius education policy was linked to political ideas. One of the foremost aims of Confucianism was to produce a constant supply of the right kind of people for government and administrative service[②]. Otherwise if a state is corrupt because it contains corrupt individuals, it will be unsuccessful in building positive and mutually beneficial relations with other states (Ibid.).

We have so far made a brief review of some articulations between Confucianism and relationships in and inter states. It necessary to understand that: 1) this philosophy has in its matrix some contributions that have directly or indirectly influenced western political theories; as well as, 2) these matrix of thought have made contributions to some IIRR theoretical approaches together with Confucian statements.

Thus, in the first level we can find that Confucius thinking has informed some a-

---

① Law controls merely through fear of punishment does not build moral character within a person "If you lead the people by means of regulations and keep order among them by means of punishment, they will be without conscience in trying to avoid them. If you lead them by virtue, and keep order among them by ritual, they will have a conscience and will reform themselves" (Dawson: 1981, 103). Law does not educate, rectify past deeds, or make any contribution towards the Confucian aims of transforming people, where the emulation of virtuous role models would (Ibid.). (Doupe: 2003, Obcit. p. 5-6)

② D. Howard Smith, *Confucius* (New York: Charles Scribner's Sons, 1973) 94. (at Doupe: 2003)

bout the political perception of liberalism:

**His ideas spread beyond the borders of ancient China to foreign lands. This can be seen in a more contemporary light, with Jesuit missionaries who entered China in the seventeenth and eighteenth centuries to become scholars and even court officials. They brushed aside the facades that had been built around Confucius' teachings over the millennia and worked to find the real Confucius through study of ancient literature. In several letters back to Europe, these individuals praised Virtue and the Individual: Confucius' Conception of International Society this "new" philosopher they had discovered. It was through these missionaries that Confucius' teachings were brought to Europe. At the time he became known to the West, it was the beginning of the great philosophical movement known as the Enlightenment. Many philosophers, such as Voltaire, Leibniz, and Wolff used Confucius' name to further their arguments, and they were themselves influenced in the process[①] (Doupe: 2003, p. 6-7)**

Additionally the Enlightenment -that directly nourished *Political Liberalism* and *Idealism* in IIRR-and its re-interpretations of Confucianism reinforced the existing perceptions of *historical change* as part of the matrix of *Realism*. During the Enlightenment, European scholars discovered that the Chinese had virtually abolished hereditary aristocracy[②]. In France and in Great Britain, anti-monarchists used this in their quest for abolition of hereditary privilege (Ibid. p. 7).

At a second level we can find articulations between the Confucianism, Realism, and Idealism (Liberalism) matrixes. In the first case -given the individual is the center of the possibilities of producing social change (by virtue in Confucianism)-, the State, seen as an individual in the Realism tradition, can also produce historical change in the inter-state relations.

This articulation can be made only in that level because Confucianism does not believe -as realism does-, that human beings and the states (in the continuity between individual and states) have an immanent selfish essence, and are moved just for selfish-interests within an anarchical world (anthropological pessimism).

---

① Herrlee Glessner Creel, *Confucius: The Man and the Myth* (London: Routledge & Kegan Paul Ltd, 1951) 151 (at Doupe: 2003).

② Virtual Abolishment clearly influenced by the virtues and the meritocratic values proposed and develop at practiced trough centuries by Confucianism thinking.

Another interesting aspect: both these thoughts articulate the possibilities of human and state actions within a historical frame, also the possibility of promoting change. Under this line of thought, both approaches reject conservative ideas of superior and ahistorical explanations -i.e. *the divinity* as in the religion, or *the system* (or a-historic structures) on the neorealism or on *problem solving theories*①-, explain how states and actors make decisions and perform within international scenarios.

We can meanwhile find articulation between Idealism in IIRR to Confucian thinking, especially at the level of cooperation,

**According to Herrlee Glessner Creel, if Confucius' major work, *The Analects*, and its historical setting are studied closely, the principle of a cooperative world is apparent②. Confucius is convinced that suspicion, strife, and suffering are largely unnecessary, while cooperation between people of the earth is possible, for war and injustice hurt everyone, even those who supposedly profit from them. Confucius notes that each person's way differs according to his or her interests and abilities (Doupe: 2003, p. 3).**

Cooperation under Confucian sphere is related to principles of mutual benefits emerging from the mutual links between virtues and continuity between individuals, the state and among states. This idea of cooperation outgrows the purely economist discourse from economic neoliberals, and does not meet the neoliberal premises for the construction of -neoliberal-institutions, following a strong need for the normative construction of these and international regimes, at least under the neoliberal perspective that IIRR that institutions and regimes could weaken states sovereignty and their independence.

We could be tempted to conclude as Tamaki (2007, p. 300) that we have much to gain from a Constructivist re-reading of The Analects. Not only does Confucius impel us to practice honesty and benevolence, he also teaches us that it is imperative for us to construct intersubjective structures conducive to good governance.

This could be interesting for the perspective of this paper because the historically structured *Ideas* and the domestic -IIRR continuity proposed by Confucius, and Criti-

---

① Problem-solving theory takes the present as given and reasons about how to deal with particular problems within the existing order of things… it focuses synchronically upon the immediate and reasons in terms of fixed relationships (Cox: 1992, p. 2)

② Herrlee Glessner Creel, *Confucius: The Man and the Myth* (London: Routledge & Kegan Paul Ltd, 1951) 152 (At Doupe:2003)

cal theory can be found in a Constructivist re-reading of The Analects, that sheds light on how *ren* can be re conceptualized as both an imperative and a norm of behavior conducive to the realization of good governance. Not only as a power -political relationship, but also an intersubjective, sociological process; and how it can be applied to international relations, both in theory and in practice (Ibid. p. 291).

Finally at this level, we find that Confucianism and Critical Theory can be complementary thoughts in the International Relations realm as proposed: both pay attention to the importance of the State-Society and the Domestic-External relationships, while making approaches to the importance of Ideas (such as *Virtue* and *Values*). Given that Confucianism focuses on the individual as one who can change his social and political environment, *i. e.* A virtuous person could transform anyone who did not practice Confucian ideals, simply by living amongst them for a period of time thereby exposing them to virtue (Doupe: 2003, p. 2). Cox identifies Ideas as part of a structural historical construction, and a conflict to maintain or transform the prevailing order. In the long run both thoughts believe more in the possibility of changing the social-state order with the participation of individuals, than over any *Divine Mandate*.

It is true that the IIRR field under an International Political Economy perspective in Cox's critical approach, is oriented to the transformation of the prevailing world order -it focuses strongly on materiality (economy)-, the level of *Ideas* and *Values* is an important component to be understood, but also to transform this very reality and the world order.

As Critical Theory recognizes the possibilities of historical change, this perspective proposes the emancipation from the status quo. An emancipation that aims to set an alternative and legit project, which at the same time must be viable, considering the power competition scenario against non-legit hegemonic forces, therefore requiring the construction of blocs.

In this context we will analyze the UNASUR Project, its perspectives and limits; and how can it be enriched by Confucianism at the intra-state level, and at the construction of the political community that represents the South American Region, also with its relation to the world order.

**UNASUR: perspectives, limits and probable Confucianism contributions**

UNASUR is integrated by 12 independent South American states: Argentina, Bolivia, Brazil, Chile, Colombia, Ecuador, Guyana, Paraguay, Peru, Surinam, Uruguay and Venezuela.

This integration process has developed many proposals at the political and economic levels, although their viability and limitations are not yet doubt free.

From a historical[①] context, UNASUR did substitute the South American Community (SAC), and we can date its birth at the presidential summit at Cuzco (Peru) in 2004; even though it was necessary to wait until 2008, when Brazil did approved the UNASUR Constitutive Agreement, when effectively this organization replaced SAC.

It is true that UNASUR's process has been critiqued and questioned, including previous initiatives constructed before its formal foundation. It is also fair to consider its importance to the region. It pursuits an integration process with horizontal characteristics. The issues are related to the normativity of inter-state relationships among members, and how UNASUR addresses important issues as the reduction of economic asymmetries between them. All these parameters have built a discourse and practice corpus that can be understood as the conception of the South American *new regionalism*.

UNASUR advances as process, beyond criticism. One that aims to become an alternative to different integration process -with vertical characteristics-, a political expression with a positive impact on the World Order[②]-specifically with regards to equitable efforts at the economic sphere in order to benefit a greater population-, governmental legitimacy, sovereignty, and the pursue of less asymmetric relationships between states in the World Order.

From the UNASUR perspective we find possibilities to generate a reality that takes account its members ideological differences, and could materialize in the construction of *Bloc* capable to reduce dependence and grow in sovereignty from *International Hegemonic Sectors and Actors*[③], and yield an alternative development model.

At the same time this initiative attempts to be a response to the region's historical

---

① This theme is based onthe article: América del Sur: Entre la Dependencia y Seguridad (Milton Reyes y Oscar Montero, 2013)

② Using the term from a Cox's perspective.

③ Which includes those who are part of the Local Hegemonic Social forces (HSF), and are totally articulated to the *liberal-economic* globalization conditions; meanwhile acting as an international HSF resonance megaphone.

demands. The economics are not the only important ones, there are also political, social issues, other regarding the identities and security ambits, all under a vision that consider integration as a strategic objective as the ability to respond to new scenarios posed by *World (dis) Order*①; *as well as maintaining the consolidation of South America as a Territory of Peace*②.

Thus when referring to UNASUR, we talk about a strategic process that focuses on the political-institutional integration, oriented to the strengthening of the whole region③; but we also need to recognize some limits for its institutional construction, and the aim for a deeper *legitimation*. These limits directly affect the UNASUR consolidation process, and also the consolidation of the current national projects; trough these, the integrationist effort. In the first case we can mention:

—*Local Hegemonic Actors* in member countries think from their particular self-interests. These are articulated to hemispheric and international hegemonic actors which, through their discourse and actions, promote the present status quo and the maintenance of the prevailing order at international scenarios; and also compete against governments and initiatives that -as UNASUR-propose alternative models of development (with more inclusive and equitable characteristics).

—Important official sectors at Foreign Ministries and in international policy forums still reproduce a matrix based on *Realism*, and specially keep shaping up the decision process to ideas. Because of this the perception of national selfish interests is

---

① The article 2 of the constitutive treaty of UNASUR sets an objective " to construct, trough participation and consensus, a space of cultural, social, economic, and political integration between its peoples members; to establish a priority on political dialogue on social policies, education, energy, infrastructure, funding and environment among others, aimed towards the elimination of social-economic inequities; to pursue social inclusion and citizen participation, strengthen democracy, and reduce the asymmetries in the frame of strengthening sovereignty and independence of member states".

② If we see the historical conflicts within the region, we can concluded that these have been very few in comparison with other regions; and even more, we can find in recent years that inter-state conflicts are almost inexistent, or have been resolved through pacific measures. Other example is the only conflict, as the civil war in Colombia, which has been resolved through peace dialogues, with the support of UNASUR and other countries in Latin America.

③ In spite of UNASUR's complexity and limitations, this political community has been reaching and increasing its efficiency and efficacy. A few examples are the *coup d'etat* attempts at Bolivia, Ecuador (2010), or recently at Venezuela, where governments with different ideological perspectives responded together as a bloc with the rest of UNASUR members.

still perceived as more important than integration (despite the mutual benefits proposed by *new integrationism*), and in the practice, some actions of cooperation between south America Countries are postposed or weakened.

Meanwhile at national level -and because of subsisting colonial mentalities-, the institutionalization projects (especially in countries involved in more equitable efforts), have not completely resolved and materialized, although governments have strongly set an objective the construction of a society under meritocratic values.

That fact can be explained because some of the new national projects include diverse factions that operate to maximize their own interests, minimize more "radical" visions (as equitable projects), and bias a reactive orientation of what is proposed as an alternative model. All within a scenario that could be characterized as conflict and competence between several *Interest Groups*①, and, or between discursive articulations② generated by images and *identitary* adscriptions.

We need to understand that the "mentality of a colonial heritage", as *Ideas part of intersubjective thoughts* (*remembering Cox*), are crossing to the different *Social Forces* (as hegemonic as well as actors that come from subaltern social forces), and because of this they reproduce the same kind of ideas and images in their political practice, within the field of various kinds of *power* (in the widest sense of the term *power*) as in the institutional field.

Thus we can claim this particular conformation of *intersubjective ideas* can be comprehended from the notion of *socially constructed habitus*, because

**That nutritious field, as unifier principle and generator of all practices… when is not as effects of "the raising of awareness"; is not other thing that the habitus, system of unconscious dispositions, which is the product of the internalization of the objective structures… (Habitus that is) a geometric place of the objectives determinisms and a determination of the objective futurity and the subjective hopes (Bourdieu, 2006: Opcit. 44).**

Because of the instability that does not permit better levels of efficiency and efficacy, oriented to end structural exclusions -a historical heritage of South American national states -against important sectors of national populations (and considering that national projects with more equitable visions aren't totally materialized), a possible

① See *domination* by virtue of a *constellation of interests* at Weber's "Economy and society".

② See Ernesto Laclau, y Chantal Mouffe, 2001.

scenario where traditional Hegemonic Social Forces operate to:

—Reconstruct their power inside the institutional instances and deconstruct the inclusive policies proposed by the present national projects.

—Sabotage the integration process as promoted by UNASUR.

—Make new attempts to articulate to extra-regional hegemonic interests, minimize gains related to independence and sovereignty reached by national states at South America, thanks to the actions and proposals made by the bloc of UNASUR.

Also, is necessary to consider that the disenchantment could generate an increasing displeasure within sectors-that although are not allies with the actors articulated to the old and illegitimate order-could being coopted or functionalized by attempts of a reactionary (dis)institutional reconstruction.

As observed, these problems can generate a scenario where the national projects (with all its limitations already exposed, but that still representing the possibility of an alternative development model), could become increasingly inviable.

Therefore, all these limits -at the level of Ideas-that still persist in the continuity and mutual relation of the individual -society -institution, and the negative impacts for the construction of a national project and a process of integration (mutually complementary and inter-dependent), is not only a need, but also makes it clearly legit to propose the exploration of Confucianism conceptions to strengthen this process.

Because of this we will review next some of the Confucian contributions related to the level of Ideas and Institutional procedures, with the objective to set proposal and actions oriented to avoid the risks for the security of the present South American national projects and his political community UNASUR.

**Confucianism: an approach to make a contribution to the South American Region**

This short paper believes that Confucianism can contribute to the South American Region in two different but complementary levels: At the level of Ideas, images, representations, and values, and in the level of practical procedures.

***At the level of Ideas***, Confucianism as system of values can strengthen the institutionalization (bureaucracy, technocracy, authorities, etc.) and social harmony (including individual and members of "civil society").

Confucian contributions at the level of ideas can be reached through educational efforts, mainly related to programs that consider Confucianism as alternative school thought within formation and capacitation programs. This could be offered not only to the public sector members, but also within the whole educational system, and especially in the themes referred to Ethics.

This objective can be reached as a first stage with the cooperation of countries such as China, and institutions that have the capabilities to construct and sustain educational and research programs based on Confucianism; it will mean a investment to generate local capacities, as trainers, teachers, researchers and thinkers that can teach and construct new approaches between Confucianism and local realities and thoughts.

This objective not only can improve the public service, but also to future bureaucrats and authorities and to the rest of society, which could impact:

—To compete and overcome the negative *intersubjective ideas* and *long term habitus* -inherited from some of the historical construction of power with colonial background. Promoting meritocracy trough virtuosity, deconstructing ideological perspectives and minimizing their actions based on lobbies, connections, corruption privileges. Thus, deconstructing an ideological perspective that has been assumed as part of a natural order, and as an essential reality impossible to be changed.

—To strengthen the thought process and the actions articulated to those collective images (materialized in new national projects) that are proposing more equitable and beneficial relations at domestic and international orders. Collective images that attempt to construct an alternative model of development and compete with discourses of illegitimated projects

These matters as seen, are not important only for states, and for South America's political community (UNASUR), but also to the world order because as part of the Confucian's continuity we can deduce that:

—If a state is corrupt because it contains corrupt individuals, it will be unsuccessful in building positive and mutually beneficial relations with other states. (Doupe: 2003, p. 6).

—If individuals and states minimize corruption, it is possible to arrive to mutually beneficial relations with other states, and trough virtuous states articulations and blocs, to promote a more equitable, legit, and sovereignty respectful World Order.

Another important contribution to the sphere of the Ideas are Confucian conceptions about the importance of *Tradition*, *Ritual*[①] and *Reciprocity*[②], and can be discussed and re-interpreted within South American countries and their thinking traditions. These values, and their own local particularities are also still important within South-American cultural construction. These are part of a discursive base of political projects that are promoting alternative models of development; and they -as part of the political proposal -have been part of the legitimation between subaltern social forces (values legit at society that at the same legitimate the political project).

Even though the last conceptions are referred to in very general terms in South American countries, we must specify that every society within the region has their own and particular interpretations, and that those values and practices are particularly intensely reproduced at societies that keep (in their own cultural constructions) strong influences of their native and ancestral populations (*e. g.* Andean region).

Therefore strengthening the discussion regarding these values can also strengthen the rescue of these virtuous concepts, as part of a tradition and linked to the wellbeing of a community over particular interests (the potentiation of the own values enforced by experience of other countries with Confucian matrix). Allowing the reproduction of the materialization of new alternative models of development, and their sovereign construction in front of the world order hegemonic powers, can become more legit and viable.

At this point we also describe the concrete ***Confucian contributions to institutional procedures***, focusing on ideas and practical levels (concepts and actions are related) are only separated for analytic approaches.

Most evidently, Confucianism can contribute to the construction of a stronger merit system to access and to make a professional career within the bureaucracy, and to integrate the decision planning and execution areas within the South American states and the institutional spaces of their political community (UNASUR). This ob-

① For Confucius, rituals were necessary in many facets of life such as etiquette, relations with people, and matters of government. He stressed the significance of rituals by stating: "if the ruler loves ritual, the people will be easy to employ." Raymond Dawson, *Confucius* (Oxford: Oxford U. Press, 1981) 60. (At Doupo: 2005, p. 5)

② Reciprocity that has being explained has relation with the idea of show consideration of others by not carrying out actions one would not want done to oneself; conception that can be consider a universal value.

jective is important for the current historical context, where alternative projects are facing threats from hegemonic actors, locally and internationally.

Trough the merits of bureaucracy and government officials -trough actions addressed to pursuing the communities' wellbeing-, mutual and equitable benefits, and the legitimation of public worker actions, there could be stronger legitimacy for the new national projects based on values.

Therefore the internal support will also strengthen the project articulation challenging the prevailing hegemonic world order, and supports the idea of an alternative model of development -in a bloc of countries.

This important for South America: This the first time that issues of great importance within an integration process are materializing from the own region's strategic interests, more than from the hemispheric powers' hegemonic interests.

Finally at this contributions level, but not less important, in a pragmatic way, Confucianism can nourish the acknowledgement in South America, oriented to achieve better negotiation processes, and to take advantage of the mutual benefits possibilities, especially with countries and societies where the Confucian matrix is still a central thought. Opportunity, very important for the consolidation of a different kind of relationships based on real and mutual benefits on the world order; an articulation that based on legit principles surpasses to the hiper-realistic practices of hegemonic powers and their self-justification rhetoric of "humanitarian" idealism.

With all that has been exposed in this short paper we can conclude that in order to strengthen the alternative model of development and the new integration process at South-America, the proposal of a rational and well-designed project is mandatory but not is enough. It is also necessary to recognize the possibilities and limits as well as, to comprehend that one of the main components of the political project viability is located in the *Ideas* level. It is here where a project can be legitimized (relation of virtuous relation between ideas-practices), and where we can find a strong vein of Confucian legacies and contributions.

Otherwise, if a project is still being perfected only on paper, but did not construct legitimacy and a virtuous relationship between authorities and society, we can identify three probable scenarios:

a) The State institutions and new projects can be at risk of not being executed as required,

b) These schemes could generate a dynamic that weakens new national projects, putting them at risk or even allowing an opening for the return of the old elite forces (seemingly interested in reproducing dependence), and

c) The worst-case scenario: could endanger national security and the national and integration process at South America.

**Bibliography**

Bourdieu, Pierre (2006). Intelectuales, Política y Poder. Buenos Aires. Editorial Universitaria de Buenos Aires.

Doupe, Aaron. Virtue and the Individual: Confucius' Conception of International Society, Glendon Papers, Glendon College, Ontario, Volume no. 3, 2003, pp. 1-8.

Cox, Robert & Sinclair Timothy (1996). Approach to the World Order, Cambridge University Press, Cambridge.

Cox, Robert.Social Forces, States and World Orders: Beyond International Relations Theory Millennium -Journal of International Studies, June 1981, vol. 10 no. 2, pp. 126-155.

Cox, Robert (1981), Fuerzas sociales, estados y órdenes mundiales: más allá de la teoría de las relaciones internacionales, en: John Vasquez, 1994 *Relaciones Internacionales. El pensamiento de los clásicos*. Editorial Limusa, Barcelona.

Cox, Robert W. (1992). Globalism, Democracy, Multilateralism, Academic Council on the United Nations Systemin Providence, RI.

Hsu, Cho-Yun. "Applying Confucian Ethics to International Relations," in Ethics and International Affairs. Edited by Joel Rosenthal. Washington: Georgetown University Press, 1999, 148-69.

Reyes, Milton & Montero, Oscar. "América del Sur: Entre la Dependencia y Seguridad y Seguridad", Revista Emprendodurismo y Estrategia Organizacional, n. 7, Escuela Politécnica del Ejercito, Quito, 2013, pp. 1-28

**Other Sources**

*Creel*, Herrlee *Glessner*, (1951). Confucius: The Man and the Myth (London: Routledge & Kegan Paul Ltd, (at Doupe: 2003)

Dawson, Raymond (1981). Confucius. Oxford: Oxford U. Press, (at Doupe: 2003)

Laclau, Ernesto & Mouffe, Chantal (2001). Hegemony and Socialist Strategy:

Towards a Radical Democratic Politics, Editorial Verso, London.

Smith, D. Howard, (1973), Confucius. New York: Charles Scribner's Sons, (at Doupe: 2003)

Tamaki, Taku. Confusing Confucius in Asian Values? A Constructivist Critique. International Relations, Sage, Published by http://www. sagepublications. com, 2007; pp. 285-304. Available on http://brianventura. files. wordpress. com/2010/02/confusing-confucius-in-asian-values. pdf, Reviewed on June 10th, 2014.

Weber, Max (1942): "Economía y Sociedad". México, Fondo de la Cultura Económica, 1era edición.

Constitutive Treaty of UNASUR, available on:

http://www. comunidadandina. org/unasur/tratado_constitutivo. htm, reviewed on June 12th, 2014.

**Interviews and notes:**

Interviews and notes with Professor Alexei Paéz Cordero, Quito, 2004-2011.

Interview with Professor Shi Yinhong, Quito, Octuber, 2010.

# Confucius and International Relations

**Mohamed Noman Galal (PHD)**

**Introduction:**

There are various philosophical concepts that explain inter-human relations throughout the march of human history. Prominent among them are two main concepts: the concept of Conflict and the concept of Harmony. One could trace these two concepts in the three main civilizations i.e. Western, Chinese and Muslim Civilizations. However I will limit the paper to the Chinese Civilization with the focus on the Confucius ideas.

Pondering upon the march of history, one can draw four main conclusions, as follows:

First: Selfishness, greed and bigotry are the core reasons for all conflicts among people and nations

Second: All religions and creeds call for peace and harmony as a matter of principle . Nevertheless, many politicians, businessmen or even clergy from all religions and cultures envisage conflicts and wars as a way to develop their nations particularly through military industry . Invasion and conquest of other nations became sometimes tools to gain spoils or to impose tributes or taxes on the conquered territories or to take-over their natural resources . The economic concept of "*cut-throat competition*", or the political concept of modernization or urbanization ,or the military concept of *invasion / conquest* or the religious concept of *missionary and converting* others to one's own religion, are but few of the nefarious concepts promoted by shortsighted politicians, clergy , businessmen and military people.

Third: Due to the huge devastation and destruction of many lives of people, their properties and many of the achievements of humanity through the ages, many philosophers and thinkers and even wise individuals called, over the years, for peace, harmony and cooperation

Fourth: The way out, of our current dilemma or the vicious cycle of violence, conflicts and wars, is through dialogue and reconciliation. This approach of dialogue, though it sometimes seems tedious and endless, is less perilous and could lead to reconciliation and harmony rather than mobilization of forces to settle differences through saber rattling. The paper concludes that the Confucius ideas particularly the concept of harmony could be relative to the $21^{st}$. century. this is whey former president H Jintao give more emphasis and priority for this concept during his tenure. The paper highlighted that the concept is an essential part of the Chinese culture.

**Main Political Concepts in Chinese culture:**

There are two main concepts, conflict and harmony, prevailed all over the Chinese political history. The legalist school, particularly "*Han Fei*," focused on the concept of conflict while "*Confucius*" paid great attention to promoting the concept of Harmony. The dichotomy between them is similar to that between *Thomas Hobbs and John Locke*. It is to be remembered that the Taoist school also advocated the concept of love and harmony in society

It is pertinent at this juncture to elaborate a little on the roots of the concept of Harmony in Chinese culture and in Chinese political philosophy.

One can trace these roots through three ideas:

First: The idea of the "*yin and yang*" the negative and positive or the female and male, or darkness and light. The "*yin and yang*" concept emphasizes the complementarities of life as well as its balanced status, thus harmony could be achieved.

Second: The idea of the "*Tao*". The Chinese philosopher, "*Lao Tzu*" (b. 600 d. 470), believed that human life, like everything else in the universe, is constantly influenced by external forces. He encouraged his followers to observe and seek to understand the laws of nature, to develop intuition and to build up personal power, and to use that power to lead life with love and without force.

The core of Taoism is the concept of "*Wù Weí*" that involves knowing when to act and when not to act. It is a natural reaction, as planets revolve around the sun but naturally doing it. It means doing things naturally without effort. One saying of "*Lao Tzu*," "*The truth is not always beautiful, nor beautiful words are the truth*". Lao

Tzu's main book is called "*Dao De Jing* (DDJ). It can be compared to *Confucius's* "*Analects*" or "*Sun Tzu*'s" "*Art of War*". It can also be compared with the *New Testament* as "*Lao Tzu*" has been compared with *Jesus Christ*. Some scholars even found that *Jesus* and "*Lao Tzu*" features astonishing have great resemblance. These two spiritual masters led their followers down the same path despite vast differences in era and geography.

Third: The legalist school (legalism: *Fă Jia* i.e. school of law). It was one of the main philosophic schools during the "*Spring and Autumn*" period and the "*Warring States*" period (770-221 BC). It was a period of great cultural and intellectual ferment in China and gave rise to the famous concept of let one thousand Schools of Thought to contend and one thousand flowers to blossom.

Under the political leadership of "*Li Si*", his form of legalism became predominant in China. Some scholars consider *Li Si's* form of legalism to have been one of the earliest known totalitarian ideologies. Legalism was a pragmatic political philosophy that did not address higher questions like the nature and the purpose of life. The school's most famous proponent and contributor, is "*Han Fei*". He believed that a ruler should govern his subjects using the following trinity:

7. *Fă*: Law or principle. All people under the ruler are equal before the law.

8. *Shù*: Method, tactic or art. These should not be publicized but used by the ruler and if successfully enforced, even a weak ruler will be strong.

9. *Shì*: (legitimacy or power). It is the position of the ruler, not the ruler himself, that holds the power. The early thoughts on legalism were first formed by "*Shang Yang*" and further developed by "*Han Feizi*" and "*Li Si*". It meant to strengthen the government and reinforce the adherence to the law. The legalism, fully emerged during the "*Warring States Period*" and preceding "*Spring and Autumn Period*", was marked by frequent violence and wars. This school believed that a lone individual had no legitimate civil rights or any personal freedom but to strengthen the ruler. It considered the people and their actions are evil and foolish. Nevertheless, it allowed even common people to gain noble rank on merit. The school played a very important role in *King Zhuang Xiang*, *of Qin's Dynasty*, *to* rise to power. It could be called a "*Realpolitik*" school. It was discredited, later on, as it focused on the use of force. It could be compared with philosophy of Machiavelli the "Ends Justify the Means". However, some of the ideas by the Legalist School were revived, now and

then, particularly when "*Mao Zedong*" approved some of its methods.

**Confucius and Chinese Culture:**

Confucius is the most influential Chinese philosopher. He left his permanent imprint all over the Chinese history and civilization. With the advent of the 21st century Confucius thoughts and ideas got a new momentum after a period of more than half a century of neglect and even defame. It came under severe criticism since the Chinese communist emerged in July 1921 and came under severe attack during the decade of the Cultural Revolution as it had been accused of supporting feudal system and conservative reactionary values of despotic rule. His thoughts were accused of humiliating human beings particularly through the so called Confucius concept of the four relationship i.e. relation between ruler and ruled, relation between husband and wife, relations between parents and siblings, relation between elder and younger. Nevertheless one has to emphasize that each philosophy reflects the society where it stemmed from and the era when it appeared as any philosophy or philosopher seeks to deal with issues of his / her own society at a certain period. Of course if the ideas of a philosopher address more general and universal issues, they will have more permanent imprint.

Confucius lived in a period of Chinese history that had five main Characteristics:

First : It was the spring of the Chinese civilization . Many philosophical schools of thought flourished. The main concept was to " let one thousand flowers to blossom and one thousand schools of thought to contend ".

Second: The concept of the Chinese unity was dormant. Chinese history was not yet mature to develop the civilization into a Chinese political system based on the concept of one state. China at that time was divided into Warring States where central power was weak. There was no central ruler with enough power to dominate or with charisma to represent a magnet to attract other states into one fold.

Third: The Chinese identity had not been materialized and sense of belonging to a particular culture in the period from (800-200 BC) was evolving. It was in 551 BC when Confucius was born in a milieu where culture was developing. The Chinese culture was to a great extent well established while Chinese political identity was still evolving. This led to the feeling of Chinese people, that they possess a civilization that has a continuity for more than five thousand years. It developed since nearly 2500

BC[i].

Fourth: The emperor of the Zhou dynasty in the Western region of China overthrew the Shang dynasty. He based his action upon one of the concepts that became dominant through the Chinese history that of the "Mandate of Heaven, or "*Tianming*". *The emperor propagated that* he was given the "Mandate of Heaven" due to his virtues. While the emperor of *Shang* (1766-1122 BC) was a tyrant oppressing his people and showing his disrespect and irreverence to the ancestors. Duke of Zhou dynasty assumed being the regent after the death of his brother the emperor of Zhou and delivered a speech[i]. In which he emphasized that getting the Mandate is without limitations of happiness" all over the state. There is no limitation for concerns also. Heaven strips its mandate from the unjust ruler who left his people in poverty, misery and who entrusted the unworthy corrupt people with authority over them. This situation led the poor to pray to heaven for mercy, thus the heaven outstrip the unjust ruler and bestows its mandate upon a virtuous ruler who should take care of his own people. These two concepts of "Heaven and Virtue" were introduced by Zhou dynasty into the Chinese culture since then. Confucius highly revered the Duke as a ruler due to his piety and virtuous character. He called upon all rulers to follow his example.

Fifth: with the fall of Western Zhou Dynasty in the year 771BC at the hands of nomadic tribes and the assassination of the king by one of his subordinated traitors, a new capital of Zhou was built in Eastern China called "*Luoyang*". The King of Eastern Zhou was dedicated only to perform rituals and rites while the nobles took over power and launched a devastating war against each other. China lived the era of the Warring States. The fall down of the political system became concomitant with the fall of morals and ethics. People looked at the Heaven (*Tian*) as god to bestow their mandate upon good rulers and punish bad ones . The "LI" ethics and morals or the gentlemen's characteristics were neglected by the nobles. Chaos as well as disorder and instability prevailed. Looting, killing, fear and insecurity and in-safety became widespread. The three main schools that presented a response to these challenges were: The Legalists in the Fourth Century BC who called for applying strict rule of law and order. The Daoism advocated morals and universal love. The most important school was Confucian that based its thinking on a combination of legalism and Daoism. The most famous advocate of the legalist school was "*Han fei*-280-233 BC" who emphasized that old ethics and morals lost its validity as they responded to a limited number of population and abundance of resources. As population greatly increased and goods became limited people start fighting . The way to rule is through law and force, thus order and peace could be restored. They advocate the ruler with absolute authority and central power.

While the *Daoism* advocated by *Laozi* in the Fourth Century who published his book for this school entitled "*Dao de Jing*", *Daoism* highlighted the concept of returning to nature before civilization which sowed greed and evil. The third school which came to build its concepts on the two previous schools in addition to the ancient traditions of China, its philosophy, customs regarding the good rulers. Confucianism which became, as time went on, the most dominant school and reemerged more than once in the form of neo-*Confucianism* and modern Confucianism. Sometimes it is called revivalist Confucianism in the beginning of the 21st century.

**Confucius and the concept of Harmony**

Confucian philosophy could be dubbed, in general, as the philosophy of harmony

Confucianism (*Rújiā*); This is the philosophy of ethics and morals developed by Confucius (*Kong Fuzi* or *Master Kong* 551-479 BC). It advocated totally opposite concepts to legalism. It stressed the importance of education for moral development of the individual so that the state could be governed by morals and virtues rather than by the use of coercive laws. *Mencius*, who was the second exponent of this philosophy, said that, "*Ever since Man came into this world, there has never been one greater than Confucius*". Confucius believed that people live their lives within the parameters firmly established by "*Heaven*" which means the "*Supreme Being*" as well as "*Nature*" which has fixed cycles and patterns, although he argued that men are responsible for their actions and especially for their treatment of others.

*Confucius's* social philosophy largely revolves around the concept of "*ren*", compassion or loving others. His political philosophy is rooted in his belief that a ruler should learn and practice self-discipline and govern his subjects by his own example, i. e. if the ruler is good the subject will be good. He advocated the conformity between names and deeds in his theory of "*Zhengming*" i.e. a proper use of language or rectifying the behavior of people so that it exactly corresponds to the language by which they identify and describe themselves. The "*de*" or virtue is the moral power that allows one to win followers without recourse to physical force.

World Order in the 21$^{st}$Century through Chinese Cultural Prism:

The expression world order has several meanings. Three of these meanings could be as follows:

10. A *state of affairs* of distribution of existing arrangements among some states and or/ non- state actors.

11. A *normative vision* prescribing preferred relations among these actions (normative ideals).

12. A *policy behavior* i. e. approaches of a country towards world order (conduct).

All the three meanings are interrelated. It is a promotion of certain vision, *Values*, based on a particular understanding of *Empirical Reality* and *Approach* to manage or alter it. China views on world order have been formulated on the base of its historical conditions, physical milieu and political fortune. However, these views are not often shared by all Chinese or have been consistent all the time; this is the case in each country especially with a long history, vast geographical area, and huge population, so diversity and flexibility are normal matters. Moreover, differences or rather discrepancies can exist between form and content, belief and rites, ideas and actual practices. Coexistence with practical acceptance of divergent beliefs has been a hallmark of traditional Chinese culture.

This is not hypocrisy or bad faith or deliberate deviation. It is a fact of life and politics[i]. It could be applied to many countries in various regions. Let alone any foreign policy is influenced by its domestic as well as its economic and social circumstances.

If one applies this general understanding on Chinese politics, one may state that its formation dates back to pre-modern China i.e. the three dynasties of Xiao, Shang and Zhou (Circa 2205-256 BC). During that period the core of the Chinese civilization developed. So its value system and its national identity which are mainly maintained until the mid of Nineteenth Century. The idea of Nation-state or nationalism comes late to China as a result of its encounters with the West. Westphalia system of sovereign state since 1648 gave a "*de facto*" recognition of European fragmentation and regulated the relations among its constituent states. These relations were marked by rivalry and even cut -throat competition[i] all these led to wars, arm race, destruction and loss of millions of souls in the First and Second World Wars. It led also to appearance of new terminologies and theories like balance of power, alliances as well as industrialization, inventions, arms industry and entrepreneurship and the emergence of new social economic and political systems.

China geography, population, history and natural resources gave it an edge over other countries in its region of East Asia contrary to the European Countries. Local authorities were given substantial autonomy in implementing the emperor decrees. Tolerance prevailed as far as there is conformity with the general Confucian precepts and popular rituals. Traditionally, Chinese emperor"*reigned rather than ruled*". This is contrary to European monarchs who often took direct role in politics. "*The Universal Pacification* "of the Chinese empire produced a concept of *world order based* on *culture rather than politics*.

Confucians tradition determined social classes that considered the lowest are the merchants and soldiers while the highest are the gentry and literal class. The distinction between civilized and barbarian is based on the knowledge and behavior according to the tenets of the Chinese culture and the acceptance of Confucian precepts. This could provide an explanation why China had not developed a concept of world order based on sovereign state.

This Chinese culture could be compared with the Islamic culture, which came later on, and based its concept of civilization on being a "Muslim Nation" believing in one god and giving up polytheism . A Muslim world order did not develop or elaborate the concept of equal sovereignty except at later stage of the Abbasside dynasty when some sort of recognition of other states appeared. One could say the same for European Catholic Empire. So, one has to look at political life as it was in these centuries i. e. within its historical context.

However the concept of universal pacification as highlighted by Steve Chan is not totally accurate so is the concept of universal community. These are new ideas or concepts developed by academia to explain the behavior of ancient countries. In my view the "Universal Pacification" is based upon self satisfaction of the Chinese people at that time within its old vital sphere, if one could use this term. Or rather to say it's "vital cultural and civilizational sphere". While the situation in Catholic Europe and Arab Muslim civilizations were totally different as natural resources were in scarcity, tribal system was dominating, contrary to agrarian societies like Egypt, Mesopotamia or other civilizations in West Asia. It is to be noticed that China's population stems from two ethnic groups: Ts'in and Han, the Chinese culture emanated mainly from "Huang He" (the Yellow River not the Yangtze River).

China's cultural traditions were the most effective source of its influence. The ideal of "*Da Tong*" or universal community would be realized when all people join a union of common norms and values. The imperial Chinese concept of world order rested on proclaimed moral virtues than compelling military power. Steve Chan urged that traditional Chinese concept could boost that it was based on the concept" "*Right*" *defines* "*Might*" not the other way round. The national power could be viewed as reflection of national virtue[i]. The Chinese world order was based on the emperor universal virtue "*Mandate of Heaven* "and the influence of Chinese culture. The norms and structure supposed to reflect universal and timeless ethical standards and moral principles. As China was the supreme power in its region with no rival. So the concept of world order on equal sovereignty was not an issue of concern to China at that time. The sense of complacency and superiority were shaken when China come into encounters with Western and Japanese imperialism in the mid of 19th century.

One could claim that there was a Chinese world order derived from the concept of "*Zhonggou*" which means the Central Kingdom. Thus China is the center of the civilized and the strong world. It is rather a predominant country while others are barbarians none civilized, and weak. The way the Chinese Emperor look at the envoys from other countries is vivid illustration of such thinking[i]. These envoys were admitted to audience with the Chinese Emperor as they do not represent countries equal to China. They are given valuable gifts not for them alone but also to their kings[i]. The claim of the Chinese Emperor is based on two counts:

First: He is the emperor of the Central Kingdom i.e the only super power.

Second: He has the "Mandate of Heaven" as he is the most virtuous person in China. So he rules by virtue rather than by power.

The result of these two counts is the formulation of the concept of harmony as the predominating concept that controls the relations within the country. Thus it is natural to control the relation among all countries.

To highlight the concept of harmony in the 21st century one has to recall that the concept of harmony propagated in world affairs by the (then) president of China "Hu Jintao". It is contrary to the concept of conflict or war or struggle and the power politics propagated by European politicians. Thus, they elaborated theories of right of conquest, right of invading uncivilized Africa, Asia …etc so imperialist phenomenon emerged and many countries, for nearly two centuries, were dominated by European states. Rivalry and scramble for invading Africa, Asia and the new world of the Americans became facts or events in the history of modern Europe.

**Conclusions**

To conclude the modern Confucianism could be relative to the international relations in the 21$^{st}$. Century. The concept of harmony developed by the Chinese political culture could be a panacea for today world problems and conflicting national interests. Today world that is full of extremism, terrorism, hatred, bigotry and greed may find practical prescription or solutions in the Chinese concept of harmony and of correction of names to make them reflect the actual meanings of terminologies and concepts to reflect the realities in today world and lead to similar understanding among nations. Thus, bridging the differences in the world related to understanding the core issues that create conflict. Chinese absorption of various philosophies, ideas and schools of thought could narrow the gap in the differences among people thus lessening the antagonistic tendencies and promoting harmony instead of clash of civilizations. The world needs Chinese wisdom developed through centuries particularly the neo- Confucianism that gets together the idealism and realism as the neo-Confucianism itself absorbed the principles and values of ancient Confucian ,Taoist, Buddhist and legalist philosophies. This could help in building a new world order that takes into account visions and policies as well as the interests of other nations. So world can live according to the famous concept "*Diversity in Unity and Unity in Diversity*'. This is not a utopian thinking but a practical policy adopted and implemented by China today with the concept of *one state two systems applied* in Hong Kong or Macao cases. It can also adopt the principle of one state three systems in Taiwan case. This practical and pragmatic policy is elaborated and adopted thanks to the ingeniousness of Deng Xiaoping. One can be sure that president Xi Jinping and his team could elaborate new concept to usher the world into a peaceful and cooperative one.

**End Notes**

1. See Konard Seitz (2001), "China ", Siendler verlog , Random House , Germany , Chapter 3 .

2. Ibid. Chapter 4.

3. See Steve Chan," Chinese perspective on World Order", in TV Paul & John A. Hall," International Order: and future of world politics ", 2000. Cambridge university press, UK, PP 197-198.

4. Ibid P. 199.

5. Toynbee volume L p. 184. And also: the author noticed the unification of China in the year 221 BC, this put an end to the warning states. Nevertheless, the conflicts between the two main ethnic groups are the Ts'in and Han but the war between the various states broke out once again see Toynbee Volume II P. 302 (In Arabic translation).

6. Ibid PP. 200-201.

7. Arnold Toynbee "A study of History "an Abridged Volume I (in Arabic translation), p.p. 65-75.

8. Ibid PP 92-94 . the author quoted a letter sent to the British embassy in china written by the Chinese emperor *Ch' ien Lung* in the year 1793 to the British king George Third . the main sentence that shows the Chinese says "I, the emperor of China, do not care about the strange and peculiar gift which you sent to me from the product of your country. However, I consider it a symbol of you humbleness so I will accept it for this reason".

# Confucian Geopolitics in the Age of Competitive Regionalism

**Rosita Dellios and R. James Ferguson (Faculty of Society & Design Bond University)**①

If Confucius was as celebrated in international relations as Sunzi has been in the study of strategy, the world would now enjoy greater peace and more equitable governance. Efforts by the People's Republic of China (PRC) to promote the concept and practice of a harmonious world, first articulated on the global stage by the then PRC president Hu Jintao at his United Nations speech of 2005, can be seen as compatible with Confucian ideals of good governance and balanced statecraft. The theme of harmonious and peaceful relations has been continued by current President Xi Jinping via numerous initiatives, which are discussed below. While it is easy to understand in a competitive world the need for tactical deceptions-or stratagems-as advocated by Sunzi's *Art of War*, it is not so readily appreciated that Confucian harmony can generate positive perspectives on state relations. The notion of Confucian-inspired international relations is no mere deception of the tactical Daoist variety toward Legalist (or state power) ends. Confucianism's scope is much greater as a political philosophy and practical guide to governance than it has been given credit for.

This should not be surprising when looking back at the lessons of Chinese history and philosophy. Confucius (551-479 BCE), in emphasising the link between government and morality, had set the tone for good administration for generations to come. His 'school of scholars' (*rujia*)-which we have come to know as 'Confucianism' or the Confucian school-was adopted under the reign of Emperor Han Wudi (141-86

---

① *Authors: Rosita Dellios, PhD, is Associate Professor of International Relations at Bond University. R. James Ferguson, PhD, is Director of Bond University's Centre for East-West Cultural and Economic Studies, and Assistant Professor of International Relations.*

BCE). It remained influential in imperial China, responding to changing circumstances and the introduction of Buddhist ideas. Confucius himself is still revered as the foremost figure in Chinese philosophy and an exemplar in his own right. His emphasis on harmony was revived by the Chinese Communist Party in an effort to 'humanise' a society stressed by rapid economic development (hence the policy of 'harmonious society') and also to contribute to global peace ('harmonious world').①

This shows that in the manner of a grand concept, the Confucian enterprise in Chinese philosophical thought finds contemporary policy relevance. It offers 'instrumental, conceptual and symbolic utilization', a framework well summarized by Johan Eriksson: '…instrumental utilization refers to recommendations for action (on an operational, tactical, or strategic level), conceptual utilization to how concepts and worldviews are formed, and symbolic utilization to legitimation or a critique of established positions.'②

In the first instance, Confucian thinking can be used *instrumentally* for formulating plans of action, not only the above-mentioned 'harmonious society' and 'harmonious world' with their accompanying action plans,③ but also China's 'peaceful rise', and its institutionalising of cooperative regional relations, most notably the Shanghai Cooperation Organisation (discussed below). Second, Confucian thought can be applied *conceptually* to analyse problems. One example is that of security. As also shown below, China has proposed a new security concept that is more inclusive and promotes a 'win-win' outcome. This matches its focus on cooperative regionalism and distinguishes itself from the Cold War security mindset. Finally, Confucian thought is used *symbolically* to provide legitimacy to China's ruling authorities. As Errikson states, 'All communication of ideas and policies entail "editing" and "translation" and grand concepts with disputed or multiple meanings easily lend themselves for competing symbolic utilization.'④ The political treatment of the Confucian school of thought in the PRC certainly reflects this. Unlike the past when Confucius was vili-

---

① See Rosita Dellios and R. James Ferguson, *China's Quest for Global Order: From Peaceful Rise to Harmonious World*, Lexington Books, Lanham Md., 2013.

② Johan Eriksson, 'On the Policy Relevance of Grand Theory', *International Studies Perspectives*, Vol. 15, No. 1, February 2014, pp. 102-3.

③ Dellios and Ferguson, *China's Quest for Global Order*, especially pp. 4, 145-7.

④ Eriksson, 'On the Policy Relevance of Grand Theory', p. 104.

fied as a class enemy, his reputation has been restored to fill a values vacuum as the pursuit of wealth becomes all-consuming, while internationally Confucius serves as a figurehead of Chinese identity. This is evident not only in the proliferation of Confucius Institutes around the world but in the singular event of the 2008 Beijing Olympics. It featured an opening ceremony with Confucian characteristics. The *Analects* of Confucius was quoted to welcome guests: 'Is it not delightful to have friends coming from distant quarters?' At this time of a peacefully rising China, the symbolic utilisation of Confucius clearly comes through. His teachings have become associated with a proud Chinese culture that upholds the value of harmony.

Essentially, Confucianism seeks harmony in the socio-political sphere. It emphasises the proper cultivation of relationships at all levels-within the family, among friends and between sovereign and subject-in order for society to function in a manner beneficial to its members. If this happens it is not necessary for a leader to rule with an iron fist, but through example. Those who did rule with an iron fist were known in ancient times as Legalists. They believed in a strong state with a powerful army. Legalism (*fajia*, school of law)[①] derives its name from the application of the law equally to all classes. Privilege provided no escape from the severity of punishments. The problem with Legalism was that it was not sustainable. The founding dynasty of imperial China, the Qin, was Legalist but lasted only 40 years after reunifying China in 221 BCE. This was blamed on the harshness of Emperor Qin Shihuangdi and the second emperor's failures in governance. Yet Legalism was not forgotten. It had its uses. The emperor who adopted Confucianism as the state ideology, Wudi, engaged in extensive military campaigns and territorial expansion, showing a Legalist bent and the empire's 'limits of harmony'.

It is evident that China has known the benefits of both ethical primacy and military strength. Finding an effective balance has been, and continues to be, an imperative for its longevity. Sharing in this quest are other philosophical traditions that have shaped Chinese political and strategic culture. Notable among them is Daoism, the school of the Way (the *dao*). It was critical of Confucian ritual and a tendency to

---

① The term first appeared in 90 BCE in *Records of the Grand Historian*. Yuk Wong, 'Legalism', in Antonio S. Cua (ed.), *Encyclopedia of Chinese Philosophy*, Routledge, New York, 2003, p. 361.

pomposity, preferring instead to learn from nature. Often considered a secondary philosophy to Confucianism it can be argued to be its equal but in a *yin-yang* mode. This fundamental principle in Chinese philosophy refers to the dynamic unity of complementary opposites-in other words, a dialectics of harmonisation. Daoism's *yin* of strategic yielding to transform and transcend a situation may be compared to a Confucian *yang* of social order and the transformative power of learning through norms. If the first represents survival, an understandable preoccupation in the Warring States Period (475-221 BCE), followed by strategically-induced change; the other concerns ideological change to a more humane order. Confucianism is associated primarily with the human world of public order and Daoism with the natural world which holds lessons for human action.

Principal among these is an attitude of *wu-wei*, which can be thought of as non-action, spontaneous action and non-interference. In other words, do not act unnaturally or try to over-manage things. According to the Daoist classic, the *Daodejing*: 'The way never acts [wu-wei] yet nothing is left undone.'① Daoism's orientation of prevailing by indirect means accorded with Sunzi's advice in planning stratagems to deceive the enemy, and to win without taking the fight to the battlefield. If viewed through the lens of the levels of strategy-levels that cascade down from grand strategy, to operations and tactics but which are mutually dynamic-it is possible to see how a Confucian grand strategy may have need of a Legalist operational art that enables 'winning local wars under conditions of informationisation', as China's defence slogan goes (of which more will be said below), and a Daoist tactical strategy of the 'three warfares'-that is, psychological, media, and legal warfare.② Out of such a consideration emerges the idea of a 'Confucian geopolitics'. Before embarking on an exploration of Confucian geopolitics, the geography upon which regional politics is being played out-often more competitively than cooperatively-needs to be considered. The following incident illustrates the state-of-play in 2014.

When a Chinese general departed from his prepared address at a regional security

① Lao Tzu (trans. D. C. Lau), *Tao Te Ching* [*Daodejing*]. Penguin, London, 1963), I. 37.

② In 2003, the CCP Central Committee and the Central Military Commission approved the concept of the 'Three Warfares'. These are discussed in Larry M. Wortzel, *The Dragon Extends Its Reach: Chinese Military Power Goes Global*, Potomac Books, Washington DC, 2013, Ch. 9.

summit in May 2014 he did so in response to what he saw as a blatant rift in regional security perceptions. Lieutenant General Wang Guanzhong, the deputy chief of the General Staff Department of the People's Liberation Army, criticized the speeches made by Japan's Prime Minister Shinzo Abe and US Defence Secretary Chuck Hagel as 'provocative actions against China'.① Abe had spoken of Japan assuming a 'more proactive role' in regional security and pledged Japan's 'utmost support for the efforts of the countries of ASEAN [Association of Southeast Asian Nations] as they work to ensure the security of the seas and the skies'.② Hagel, in turn, had said: 'China has undertaken destabilizing, unilateral actions asserting its claims in the South China Sea. It has restricted access to Scarborough Reef, put pressure on the long-standing Philippine presence at the Second Thomas Shoal, begun land reclamation activities at multiple locations, and moved an oil rig into disputed waters near the Paracel Islands.'③ General Wang had counteracted by saying that 'assertiveness has come from the joint actions of the United States and Japan, not China.'④

This polarisation of views occurred at the Shangri-La Dialogue, an annual meeting in Singapore of defense ministers, diplomats, and security specialists, organised by the London-based International Institute for Strategic Studies. The event took place shortly after the Conference on Interaction and Confidence-Building Measures in Asia (CICA), held in Shanghai, on 20-21 May 2914, and in which President Xi Jinping articulated a new security mechanism for the region. It was one which the United States and Japan would have limited roles as observers to the CICA group. President

---

① 'IISS Provisional Transcription of Translated Audio Feed: Unscripted Section of General Wang's Plenary Speech', in Andrew Erickson Updates (blog), 'PLA LtGen Wang Guanzhong's Remarks—Scripted & Unscripted—at Shangri-La Dialogue', 1 June 2014, http://www.andrewerickson.com/2014/06/pla-ltgen-wang-guanzhongs-remarks-scripted-unscripted-at-shangri-la-dialogue/ (accessed 5.6.14).

② The IISS Asia Security Summit, 'Shangri-La Dialogue 2014 Keynote Address Shinzo Abe, Prime Minister, Japan', 30 May 2014, https://www.iiss.org/en/events/shangri%20la%20dialogue/archive/2014-c20c/opening-remarks-and-keynote-address-b0b2/keynote-address-shinzo-abe-a787 (accessed 5.6.14).

③ 'The United States' Contribution to Regional Stability: Chuck Hagel', in Shangri-La Dialogue 2014: Links, Full Text of Speeches, and Q&A, *Andrew S. Erickson. China Analysis from Original Sources*, 31 May 2014.

④ 'PLA LtGen Wang Guanzhong's Remarks—Scripted & Unscripted—at Shangri-La Dialogue', 1 June 2014.

Xi had warned that common security was not being served by efforts to 'beef up an entrenched or military alliance targeted at a third party…'① Such divergent security views from Washington and Tokyo on the one side and Beijing on the other, are not an isolated phenomenon. They are part of a trend which can be termed the age of competitive regionalism.

**The Age of Competitive Regionalism**

From the 1990s onwards the Asia-Pacific saw a rapid expansion of the roles of regional organizations across a range of areas including trade, investment, diplomatic and security issues. Many of these were ASEAN-centred, for example, ASEAN-plus-three, ASEAN Regional Forum (ARF), or ASEAN initiatives such as the East Asia Summit (EAS). The People's Republic of China came to see these as useful for improved diplomatic engagement (compatible with its good-neighbour policy), for reducing threat perceptions through extended cooperation in non-traditional security areas, and for mutual economic growth, such as its free trade agreement with ASEAN (ACFTA).② For the following decade this was part of a wider 'charm offensive' whereby China came to be viewed as a partner in regional development, with maritime disputes either side-lined or downplayed in major ASEAN and ARF meetings.

However, this approach could not be sustained from 2009 when the United States stated that it was coming 'back' to Asia, becoming a full member of the East Asia Summit from 2011, as well as being more active in regional fora such as the ARF and the ASEAN Defense Ministers Meeting-Plus (ADMM-Plus). Followed by the military and strategic rebalance ('pivot') in the Indo-Pacific announced by the Obama administration, this set the tone for a change in regional diplomacy. ASEAN-related meetings through 2010 to 2014 were dominated by tensions over disputes in the South China Sea (with the Philippines and Vietnam) and the East China Sea (with Japan). The United States in particular insisted that it opposed the use of force or threats, and supported freedom of navigation, while the PRC replied that the South China Sea had e-

---

① Quoted in AFP, 'China to promote its security theory at Shangri-La Dialogue', *Channel NewsAsia*, 31 May 2014, http://www.channelnewsasia.com/news/asiapacific/china-to-promote-its/1129720.html (accessed 3.6.14).

② Lai Foon Wong, 'China-ASEAN and Japan-ASEAN Relations during the Post-Cold War Era', *Chinese Journal of International Politics*, Vol. 1, No. 3, 2007, pp. 373-404, http://cjip.oxfordjournals.org/content/1/3/373.full (accessed 8.9.10).

merged as a 'core interest' for China and warned against external meddling in these territorial disputes.[①] In effect, this largely split cooperation with the ASEAN groupings, with tensions peaking through 2012 (when the ASEAN Summit was unable to issue a joint communique) and only leading to fragile consensus in the May 2014 meeting, which agreed on refraining from taking actions that would 'escalate tensions'.[②] These meetings, once emblems of regional cooperation, seemed to become conduits for division and even confrontation, symbolised by the surprising confrontation between American, Japanese and Chinese positions in the Shangri-La Dialogue in May 2014.

Likewise, the Indian Ocean has also been seen as a region that needs increased regional cooperation to boost economic development and cope with a range of security issues ranging from shifting patterns of piracy to disaster relief operations. Cooperation has begun on these areas through the Indian Ocean Rim Association (formerly IOR-ARC, the Indian Ocean Rim Association for Regional Cooperation). China is a dialogue partner with this group, which is largely driven by Indian, South African and Australian interests. However, China's engagement with the Indian Ocean is increasing, partly because of deepening economic interests in Pakistan, Bangladesh, Sri Lanka, Egypt and Kenya, but also because of its investment in improving port facilities in several of these countries (leading to the 'string-of-pearls' concept whereby friendly ports reach from Hainan all the way to the Suez Canal).[③] Although driven largely by trade, energy and economic interests, this does provide some justification for an increased presence of the People's Liberation Army (PLA) Navy in the region. Alongside its role in anti-piracy activities with Task Force CTF 525, it has been reported that since 2008 China has deployed 25 warships (in 10 groups) into the Indian Ocean,

---

① Thomas J. Christensen, 'The Advantages of an Assertive China: Responding to Beijing's Abrasive Diplomacy', *Foreign Affairs*, Vol. 90, No. 2, March/April 2011, pp. 54-67

② Shannon Tiezzi, 'How China Won the ASEAN Summit', *The Diplomat*, 12 May 2014, http://thediplomat.com/2014/05/how-china-won-the-asean-summit (accessed 15. 6. 14)

③ Nina Lebedeva, 'Second Wind for China's String of Pearls Strategy: Part 2', *Neo: New Eastern Outlook*, 16 April 2014, http://journal-neo.org/2014/04/16/rus-vtoroe-dy-hanie-kitajskoj-strategii-nit-zhemchuga-chast-2/ (accessed 10. 5. 14); Christopher Pehrson, 'String of Pearls: Meeting the Challenge of China's Rising Power Across the Asian Littoral', *Strategic Studies Institute*, July 2006, http://www.strategicstudiesinstitute.army.mil/pdffiles/pub721.pdf (accessed 10. 10. 12).

demonstrating the ability to operate forces at long-range into the region. ①

This has sparked considerable concern in India, and has led to perceptions of a possible Indian Ocean arms race among major military powers including the PRC, India, and the United States, and to a lesser extent Australia and France. ② This competition has been moderated by the creation of the Indian Ocean Naval Symposium (IONS), active since 2008 with a goal of cooperative security among its 35 members to manage regional maritime problems. ③ However, the grouping has not accepted China as a member, in spite of requests by the PLA Navy to be involved. Likewise, increased cooperation by India with the United States, France, Japan and Australia in security affairs and military purchases could also be seen as part of balancing against rising Chinese influence. Thus the IONS group could be viewed as a way of balancing or containing Chinese influence in the Indian Ocean. ④

It is not surprising, then, that regional cooperation seems to be marred by an increasing pattern of competitive regionalism, based on a changing balance of power within these organisations. Different visions for China of the centrality of an East Asian core as the basis of development are juxtaposed with tensions found in the wider Indo-Pacific, leading to some recalibration of Beijing's engagement. More effort has

---

① Vijay Sakhuja, 'Increasing Maritime Competition: IORA, IONS, Milan and Indian Ocean Networks', *Institute of Peace and Conflict Studies*, 3 March 2014, http://www.ipcs.org/article/india-the-world/increasing-maritime-competition-iora-ions-milan-and-the-indian-ocean-4320.html (5.5.14).

② For the French engagement in the wider region, Bruno De Paiva, 'France: National Involvement in the Indian Ocean Region', Strategic Analysis Paper, 5 December 2011, http://www.futuredirections.org.au/files/FDI%20Strategic%20Analysis%20Paper%20-%2005%20December%202011.pdf (accessed 12.8.12); Arnaud Bielecki, 'France and Australia Intensify Strategic Cooperation', *Defence Today*, June 2013, http://www.ambafrance-au.org/spip.php?page=mobile_art&art=5516, (accessed1.3.14).

③ Vinay Kumar, 'India, Australia Raise the Pitch on Maritime Cooperation', *The Hindu*, 5 June 2013, http://www.thehindu.com/news/national/india-australia-raise-the-pitch-on-maritime-cooperation/article4783997.ece (accessed 10.6.13); P. K. Ghosh, 'Indian Ocean Naval Symposium: Uniting the Maritime Indian Ocean Region', *Strategic Analysis*, Vol. 36, No. 3, 2012, pp. 352-35; Joshy M. Paul, 'Cooperative Security in the Indian Ocean Region: The IONS Way', *RSIS Commentaries*, 55/2010, 27 May 2010.

④ Minghao Zhao, 'The Emerging Strategic Triangle in Indo-Pacific', *China Power: A New World Order*, 4 June 2013, http://thediplomat.com/china-power/the-emerging-strategic-triangle-in-indo-pacific-asia/ (accessed 7.7.13); Kumar, 'India, Australia Raise the Pitch on Maritime Cooperation'.

been placed into cooperation with the SCO (Shanghai Cooperation Organization, embracing Russia, PRC and most of Central Asia) via Xi Jinping's New Silk Road projects.① However, despite increased economic and naval cooperation with Russia through 2014, Beijing remains cautious over too strong an engagement with Russian anti-western ambitions.② In turn, Xi Jinping proposed a New Security Concept for Asia at the CICA meeting in May 2014. The concept features 'common, comprehensive, cooperative and sustainable security'.③ If developed, this effort to build comprehensive security would involve some 26 member nations across East Asia, Central Asia and Eurasia.④ As noted above, Japan and the United States are observers, but not full members. Combined with major economic initiatives (including the New Silk Road projects, the China-Pakistan Economic Corridor and the Bangladesh-China-India-Myanmar Economic Corridor), this suggests that China is searching for fresh cooperative mechanisms to offset existing competitive tensions. These trends are part of a wider 'Confucian geopolitics' that seeks a balance between cooperation and deterrence.

**Confucian Geopolitics**

In the book, *China's Quest for Global Order: From Peaceful Rise to Harmonious World*, we ask the reader to consider two psychological profiles of China: the 'Gentle Giant' and the 'God of War'. We also note that these can be regarded as metanarra-

---

① See CCTV, 'President Xi proposes to carry forward Silk Road Spirit', 5 June 2014, http://english.cntv.cn/2014/06/05/VIDE1401940321781431.shtml (accessed 9.6.14)

② David Gordon and Jordan Schneider, 'Treacherous Triangle: China, Russia, the United States and the New Superpower Showdown', *Foreign Affairs*, 22 May 2014, http://www.foreignaffairs.com/articles/141450/david-gordon-and-jordan-schneider/treacherous-triangle (1.6.14); Jutyna Szczudlik-Tatar, *China's New Silk Road Diplomacy*, PISM Policy Paper No 34 (82), December 2013, https://www.pism.pl/files/? id_plik=15818 (accessed 15.6.14).

③ This is a common description. See, for instance, Xinhua, 'Chinese vice FM says new security concept needed to solve Asia's security problems', *China-US Focus Digest*, 10 June 2014, http://www.chinausfocus.com/china-news/chinese-vice-fm-says-new-security-concept-needed-to-solve-asias-security-problems/ (accessed 13.6.14).

④ Bloomberg, 'China Proposes Security Alliance to Counter U.S. influence', *Japan Times*, 21 May 2014, http://www.japantimes.co.jp/news/2014/05/21/asia-pacific/politics-diplomacy-asia-pacific/china-proposes-security-alliance-counter-u-s-influence/#.U4vHffmSwQp (accessed 15.6.14); Mu Chunsun, 'What is CICA (and Why Does China Care About It)?', *The Diplomat*, 17 May 2014, http://thediplomat.com/2014/05/what-is-cica-and-why-does-china-care-about-it/ (accessed 15.6.14).

tives that go beyond the popular dichotomies of 'dragon-slayer' versus 'panda-hugger' which are also simplifications that stereotype China as either a source of threat or opportunity. 'Gentle Giant' is an Occidental referent that provides a bridge to the Oriental other: Confucian China. Confucius serves this image well as he was not only the giant of Chinese philosophy but was also of reputedly tall physical stature. Another gentle giant may be found in the imposing figure of the Ming Admiral Zheng He with his 'treasure ships' on diplomatic missions abroad. The 'God of War', in turn, is no ordinary war deity. He represents a complex character that shows a love of learning from the past: he is often depicted as a soldier holding the historical *Spring and Autumn Annals*.

The Gentle Giant assumes China's peaceful rise-cum-development with a New Security Concept of 'win-win' cooperation rather than 'the old era of Cold War and zero-sum mentality'.① More specifically, in terms of the region, the New Security Concept for Asia that was introduced by President Xi Jinping at CICA focuses on development as the best form of security. His desire for a New Silk Road, which goes hand-in-hand with the New Security Concept for Asia, underscores the economically-based security concept that China is promoting. Moreover, the energy-rich Eurasian landmass allows for China to promote overland energy routes. This was seen in the case of the Pakistan-China Economic Corridor between Western China and Gwadar port near the mouth of the Persian Gulf. Another major project out of the Central Asian region is Russia's new gas pipeline to China. In May 2014, the two countries signed a 30-year, MYM400bn agreement for gas to be delivered to China. Russia's President Vladimir Putin described the agreement as 'the largest in the gas sphere during the era of the USSR and Russia'.②Paralleling these developments is Xi Jinping's launch of the Maritime Silk Road (MSR) from 2013, designed to engage Southeast Asia, India (invited into the MSR dialogue from 2014) and the Indian Ocean rim economies

① This is a common refrain with regard to perceived US security thinking and was used, for example, by PRC President Xi Jinping in a speech at the Conference on Interactions and Confidence-Building in Asia (CICA) in May 2014.

② Alec Luhn and Terry Macalister, 'Russia signs 30-year deal worth MYM400bn to deliver gas to China', *The Guardian*, 22 May 2014, http://www.theguardian.com/world/2014/may/21/russia-30-year-400bn-gas-deal-china (accessed 9.6.14)

through extended trade, cooperation and connectivity. [1]

China's cultivation of cooperative regionalism is understandably more successful in Central Asia where it enjoys full membership, notably in the SCO, than maritime Asia where others lead, as exemplified by the ASEAN arrangements or China's limited engagement in the Indian Ocean regional bodies such as the Indian Ocean Rim Association (IORA, where China is a dialogue partner) and China's absence from the Indian Ocean Naval Symposium. Here is where the God of War finds a role to play. But first, who is he?

The God of War assumes China must fight the good fight. The Confucian 'charm offensive' changes under China's more assertive behaviour to what seems like a 'harm offensive' in regard to maritime territorial disputes with Japan, Vietnam and the Philippines. However, such 'harm' becomes 'protection' from the Chinese perspective of *active defence* which is the official defence strategy of proactive defence. It is captured in the slogan, hailed in China's defence white papers, [2] of 'winning local wars under conditions of informationisation'. This refers to warfare in the Information Age that is short, intensive and regionally-based. The threatening face of Chinese military power thereby becomes the brave, even if frightening, face of Guandi. This Chinese god of war is meant to guard against all manner of foes, both external and internal. The historical figure upon whom Guandi is modelled is general Guan Yu (162-220 CE). He was immortalised in *The Romance of the Three Kingdoms*, a historical novel whose dominant theme was the arduous but determined effort to reunify China. The God of War represents a China that is militarily gifted in asymmetric strategies as well as developing stronger capabilities. While the People's Liberation Army cannot afford to be mistaken for the Gentle Giant when it comes to issues of sovereignty, including any temptation on Taiwan's part to declare formal independence, it does permit the Gentle Giant aspect of China to implement its grand strategy

---

① Ankit Panda, 'China Invites India To the "Maritime Silk Road"', *The Diplomat*, 15 February 2014, http://thediplomat.com/2014/02/china-invites-india-to-the-maritime-silk-road/ (accessed 3. 3. 14); Yukon Huang, 'Courting Asia: China's Maritime Silk Route vs America's Pivot', *Carnegie Op Ed*, 25 April 2014, http://carnegieendowment.org/2014/04/25/courting-asia-china-s-maritime-silk-route-vs-america-s-pivot/h93c (accessed 27. 4. 14)

② See, for example, State Council Information Office, PRC, *The Diversified Employment of China's Armed Forces* (White Paper), Beijing, April 2013. http://news.xinhuanet.com/english/china/2013-04/16/c_132312681.htm

of 'peaceful development' from a position of comprehensive strength. Such comprehensive power is designed to deter actions harmful to China's security.

The interactive possibilities of the Gentle Giant and the God of War bring out their dialectic qualities of *yin* and *yang*. Seen spatially, one may identify *yang*-oriented *strategic theatres of cooperation* (STOC) and *yin*-oriented *strategic theatres of protection* (STOP). STOC apply to resource-rich and development-driven frontiers, especially Central Asia and beyond to the Middle East on the New Silk Road. STOP, by comparison, are essentially buffer zones. They include the internal territories of Tibet and Xinjiang. Externally, an effort is being made to create maritime protective buffers against competitors and territorial claimants. In Western strategic literature, this is known as a strategy of 'anti-access, area denial' (A2/AD).

Under this *yin-yang* schema, the Gentle Giant represents China's win-win rhetoric via the New Security Concept for Asia in STOC; while in STOP the God of War shows the angry face of China. His rhetoric is sovereignty-laden and accusatory, well reflected in General Wang's remarks at the 2014 Shangri-La meeting. Thus the counterpoint to multilateral dialogue and development in Central Asia is the bilateral approach, in which China is the stronger party, when dealing with maritime disputes. Threat-based hard power shows itself to be more pronounced in STOP than STOC with its soft power posture of mutual opportunity. Where the military finds a role in STOC, it turns away its angry face of deterrence and takes on one of the many identities and roles of Guandi, God of War. This is underlined by China's title to its 2013 defence white paper: *The Diversified Employment of China's Armed Forces*.① The Gentle Giant element of the PLA is represented in 'military operations other than war' (MOOTW), as a specified role for the PLA in the $21^{st}$ century. China's 2008 defence white paper states that through MOOTW 'China participates in international security cooperation, conducts various forms of military exchanges and promotes the establishment of military confidence - building mechanisms in accordance with this guideline'.②A US report speaks of China's 'military investments for a range of mis-

① The State Council Information Office, PRC, *The Diversified Employment of China's Armed Forces* (White Paper), Beijing, April 2013.

② The State Council Information Office, PRC, *China's National Defense in* 2008 (White Paper), Beijing, January 2009.

sions beyond China's coast, including sea lane security, counterpiracy, peacekeeping, and humanitarian assistance/disaster relief (HA/DR)'.①

As we have noted in our book, the geopolitics of cooperation (STOC) and protection (STOP) interact so that an *active defence* strategy that sees the deployment of armed forces abroad cannot be viewed as mere power projection. Rather, it demonstrates a Confucian interpretation of geopolitics which finds historical precedent in the Ming dynasty diplomatic voyages of Zheng He to Southeast Asia, Africa and the Middle East; the same as found in today's MOOTW.②

It may be concluded that China is producing a new model whereby military capabilities can be a productive, rather than divisive, element in regional order-building with Confucian characteristics. That which needs to be considered is whether Confucian thought as both grand theory and grand strategy can be adopted with the same level of enthusiasm as its Chinese sponsors? After all, Sunzi's *Art of War* is taught in the West as well as the East, and in both military academies and business schools. The ubiquitous *yin-yang* or Taiji symbol, commonly identified with Daoism, is now a globalised emblem of harmony in personal life, such as self-development, the martial arts and health. Could Confucianism get beyond the confines of the Confucian Institutes of language learning and culture? The answer would largely depend on its value for other actors in international relations, that is, does it have instrumental, conceptual and symbolic use when applied to global governance? Certainly when formulating action plans, analyzing problems and their causes, or interpreting Confucian thought in relation to its contemporary relevance, there is hope of bringing Confucius more prominently into international relations discourse. As the famous Chinese adage goes, 'A journey of a thousand li starts beneath one's feet'.

**BIBLIOGRAPHY**

AFP. 'China to promote its security theory at Shangri-La Dialogue'. *Channel NewsAsia*, 31 May 2014.

Bielecki, Arnaud. 'France and Australia Intensify Strategic Cooperation'. *Defence Today*, June 2013.

---

① Office of the Secretary of Defence, US DoD, *Military and Security Developments Involving the People's Republic of China*, Annual Report to Congress, Washington, D.C., 2014, p. i.

② Dellios and Ferguson, *China's Quest for Global Order*, p. 130.

Bloomberg. 'China Proposes Security Alliance to Counter U.S. influence'. *Japan Times*, 21 May 2014.

Christensen, Thomas J. 'The Advantages of an Assertive China: Responding to Beijing's Abrasive Diplomacy'. *Foreign Affairs*. Vol. 90 no. 2, March/April 2011: 54-67.

Chunsun, Mu. 'What is CICA (and Why Does China Care About It)?'. *The Diplomat*, 17 May 2014

Confucius (trans. D. C. Lau). *Analects*. Penguin, Harmondsworth, 1979.

De Paiva, Bruno. 'France: National Involvement in the Indian Ocean Region'. Strategic Analysis Paper, 5 December 2011.

Dellios, Rosita and R. James Ferguson. *China's Quest for Global Order: From Peaceful Rise to Harmonious World*. Lexington Books, Lanham Md, 2013.

Eriksson, Johan. 'On the Policy Relevance of Grand Theory'. *International Studies Perspectives*. Vol. 15, No. 1, February 2014: 94-108.

Ghosh, P.K. 'Indian Ocean Naval Symposium: Uniting the Maritime Indian Ocean Region'. *Strategic Analysis*. Vol. 36, No. 3, 2012: 352-35; Paul, Joshy M. 'Cooperative Security in the Indian Ocean Region: The IONS Way'. *RSIS Commentaries*. 55/2010, 27 May 2010.

Gordon, David and Jordan Schneider. 'Treacherous Triangle: China, Russia, the United States and the New Superpower Showdown'. *Foreign Affairs*, 22 May 2014.

Huang, Yukon. 'Courting Asia: China's Maritime Silk Route vs America's Pivot'. *Carnegie Op Ed*, 25 April 2014.

IISS Provisional Transcription of Translated Audio Feed: Unscripted Section of General Wang's Plenary Speech. In Andrew Erickson Updates (blog). 'PLA LtGen Wang Guanzhong's Remarks—Scripted & Unscripted—at Shangri-La Dialogue', 1 June 2014.

International Institute for Strategic Studies (IISS). 'The United States' Contribution to Regional Stability: Chuck Hagel'. In Shangri-La Dialogue 2014: Links, Full Text of Speeches, and Q&A. *Andrew S. Erickson. China Analysis from Original Sources*. 31 May 2014.

International Institute for Strategic Studies (IISS). *Asia Security Summit*. 'Shangri-La Dialogue 2014 Keynote Address Shinzo Abe, Prime Minister, Japan', 30

May 2014.

Kumar, Vinay. 'India, Australia Raise the Pitch on Maritime Cooperation'. *The Hindu*, 5 June 2013.

Lao Tzu (trans. D. C. Lau). *Tao Te Ching* [*Daodejing*]. Penguin, London, 1963.

Lebedeva, Nina. 'Second Wind for China's String of Pearls Strategy: Part 2. *Neo: New Eastern Outlook*, 16 April 2014.

Luhn, Alec and Terry Macalister. 'Russia signs 30-year deal worth MYM400bn to deliver gas to China'. *The Guardian*, 22 May 2014.

Office of the Secretary of Defence, US DoD. *Military and Security Developments Involving the People's Republic of China*, Annual Report to Congress. Washington, D.C., 2014.

Panda, Ankit. 'China Invites India to the "Maritime Silk Road"'. *The Diplomat*, 15 February 2014.

Pehrson, Christopher. 'String of Pearls: Meeting the Challenge of China's Rising Power across the Asian Littoral'. *Strategic Studies Institute*, July 2006.

Sakhuja, Vijay. 'Increasing Maritime Competition: IORA, IONS, Milan and Indian Ocean Networks'. *Institute of Peace and Conflict Studies*, 3 March 2014.

Sun Tzu (trans. Samuel B. Griffith). *The Art of War*. Oxford University Press, London, 1963.

Szczudlik-Tatar, Jutyna. *China's New Silk Road Diplomacy*. PISM Policy Paper No 34 (82), December 2013.

The State Council Information Office, PRC. *The Diversified Employment of China's Armed Forces* (White Paper). Beijing, April 2013.

The State Council Information Office, PRC. *China's National Defense in* 2008 (White Paper). Beijing, January 2009.

Tiezzi, Shannon. 'How China Won the ASEAN Summit'. *The Diplomat*, 12 May 2014.

Wong, Lai Foon. China-ASEAN and Japan-ASEAN Relations during the Post-Cold War Era'. *Chinese Journal of International Politics*. Vol. 1, No. 3, 2007: 373-404.

Wong, Yuk. 'Legalism'. In Antonio S. Cua (ed.). *Encyclopedia of Chinese Philopsophy*. Routledge, New York, 2003.

Wortzel, Larry M. *The Dragon Extends Its Reach: Chinese Military Power Goes Global*. Potomac Books, Washington DC, 2013.

Zhao, Minghao. 'The Emerging Strategic Triangle in Indo-Pacific'. *China Power: A New World Order*, 4 June 2013.

# Rote Learning Chinese Classics Outside Asia

Reg Little

The advance of communities with a strong Confucian ethos has been achieved by out-strategizing the Anglo-American powers. This has highlighted failings in the universal values of an Anglo American genius that has transformed the world.

The 21st Century seems likely to see power move from the English language, financial might and scientific innovation. Chinese language and culture seems likely to command political authority and a rediscovery of the natural dynamics of living beings that are threatened by feral corporate and scientific ambitions.

As wealth and power become inseparable from but subject to the values, wisdom and thought culture of the Chinese classics and their history, their research, education and popularization will shape the future of all peoples. Equally, failings in the universal values promoted by Anglo American powers are likely to be identified and discredited.

But Chinese language and culture are much more difficult to master than English language and culture. Globally, Confucian popularization will come from China's wealth and power. Confucian education will only come for those who make an heroic and resolute effort. Confucian research will have difficulty managing the uncertainties created by the interaction of popularization and education.

My experience of the Confucian tradition and its revival under the ICA suggests that it has many subtleties and riches that escape the Western mind. Perhaps, understanding outside Asia will come only from a bi-cultural education, including very early rote learning of the Chinese classics.

**Confucian Renaissance Over the Past Fifty and Twenty Years**

I am an Australian who has explored the Confucian tradition and the Chinese classics for half a century and who has been a member of the International Confucian Association (ICA) for the two decades of its existence. I began as a diplomatic language student in Tokyo in 1964, who was determined to understand how Japan could disregard many of the economic principles I had studied at university and have an annual growth of ten percent or more.

I could only conclude that its success was grounded in its culture and that this was probably most effectively identified as Confucian. From this it followed that others with a similar cultural tradition would be likely to emulate Japan. Gradually, the four dragons, Korea, Taiwan, Hong Kong and Singapore started to provide evidence that my thinking was not far off the mark. Even so, at that time few were willing to openly admit such a relationship between economic growth and culture.

After Tokyo, I passed two years in Vientiane, Laos, during the Indo-China war and could not but be struck by the strategies employed by the Vietnamese in defying the might of the United States and its allies, including Australia. It was not difficult to suspect that both Japan and Vietnam drew on a body of strategic wisdom, which could shape both economic and political contests, that was not readily accessible by the West.

After brief detours through Bangladesh, the United Nations New York and Ireland, I passed fifteen months in Hong Kong in 1974 and 1975 studying Chinese. As these were in the final years of the Cultural Revolution many of the articles I studied were seemingly dismissive of the value of Confucianism and related traditions. I was impressed, however, by the fact that the same articles often provided me with a valuable introduction to and education in many qualities of the tradition.

I arrived in Beijing in 1976, Chairman Mao Zedong's last year, as Deputy to the Ambassador, It was immediately after Premier Zhou Enlai's death and Tiananmen was soon covered with a forest of wreaths, tributes and classical quotations. This reinforced my sense that China and Asia could only be understood in the context of tradition and history. It seemed obvious to me that Western influence after a troubled period of little more than one hundred years could not be that deep.

Consequently, I soon declared to Embassy colleagues my conviction that China would follow Japan's example of annual growth of ten percent. I won no friends, as my colleagues were more interested in their understanding of modern Western ideology than my perceptions of traditional Chinese culture.

I was stubborn, however, and the Ambassador wrote a despatch reflecting on the implications for Australia of possible rapid Chinese economic growth. According to a public lecture in 2007 organised by the Department of Foreign Affairs and Trade, Prime Minister Fraser welcomed and approved what apparently became an influential despatch. Other sources of information suggest that senior Departmental officers were less than happy with such a departure from conventional wisdom.

In a sense, that was the high point of my life as a diplomat, although I continued to have interesting and challenging responsibilities, including overseeing international economic organisations, policy planning and the Australia China Council while in Canberra and covering over 20 separate political entities in the Caribbean, Central and South America as Australian High Commissioner in Jamaica.

Before I chose to leave diplomacy and my position in charge of the Australia China Council in 1988, a Chinese friend in Australia had me invited to the First International Conference on Confucian Studies in Qufu in 1987. His father had a distinguished revolutionary history and a key role in organising this occasion, which proved to be a seminal event in terms of my life separated from diplomatic responsibilities. It was the first of more than fifty conferences related to Confucian tradition that I have attended in China and other parts of Asia since then.

It also encouraged me to write, together with a friend who had been a member of the Australian Secret Intelligence Service and had a deep knowledge of Japan, a short book entitled *The Confucian Renaissance*. This has been published several times in both Japanese and Chinese.

A number of leading Australian officials and academics participated in a seminar organised at the Australian National University to explore the relevance of the book and its general thesis. I had long been familiar with the English speaking world's conventional wisdom that dismisses the possible competitiveness of non-Western cultural traditions. Nevertheless, I was disappointed by the lack of any genuine openness or readiness to examine whether Australia needed to explore and evaluate a culture that was already challenging many conventional views.

My casual discussions with my friend had provided an introduction to the world of Chinese Confucian study. Fundamentally, these discussions were driven by my dissatisfaction with the standard English language explanations of Japanese and other Asian growth and striking contrasts between Western and Eastern behaviour. Essential to my process of discovery and personal development was a determination to evaluate my lived experience against established orthodox thought as I understood it in Australia.

I was assisted and reinforced in this by a strong conviction, nurtured by my growing Asian experience. This was that Australian orthodoxies left it vulnerable to traditional Asian wisdom and energy that was being revitalised as Japan led the way in demonstrating American and other Western vulnerabilities. My interest in nascent Anglo American decline did not immediately impress my colleagues and friends but did continue to intrigue and challenge me. I could think of no more important issue arising from my work as an Australian diplomat.

This background and perception is fundamental to all my exploration and evaluation of the Confucian tradition, which I increasingly identified in contemporary behaviour. Moreover, I came to use the word Confucian almost as a label for the whole Chinese classical tradition, incorporating Daoist, strategic and other dimensions. In this sense the Confucian tradition is multi-faceted. Yet it is maintained by a central ethos attributed to the recorded teachings of the Sage and illuminated over several millennia by the attempts of many generations to respect that ethos.

On many occasions I found judgements, which were based on my instincts but initially rejected by others who accepted mainstream sentiments, were proven correct. None was perhaps more fundamental than the sense that despite the Cultural Revolution China remained profoundly Confucian. Equally important and fundamental was the sense that this equipped China to more than emulate Japan in economic growth and, in the process, transform the global community.

Most of the above experience and related evaluations predated the establishment of the International Confucian Association in 1994. Again my friend, who had introduced me through his father to Chinese Confucian studies in Qufu in 1987, played a critical role. Without a full explanation, he energetically persuaded me of the importance of this forthcoming meeting and insisted that I make the effort to be present. At the time, for personal reasons, I was a little reluctant to make this effort but felt I owed it to my friend to accept his guidance.

Again, I have had reason to be most grateful. For the following twenty years I have been consistently involved in the progress of the Confucian renaissance in China and elsewhere in Asia. Moreover, I have made many friends and have been able to trial my ideas in Eastern and Western contexts, without the intrusive and compromising responsibilities that might accompany a professional diplomatic role. In addition, I have been able to experience directly the discreet regeneration of Chinese cultural identity, confidence and assertiveness.

Further, on one occasion early in the $21^{st}$ Century, in my own living room in Brisbane, I heard directly from uniquely connected Chinese visitors, about the deep rooted character of the Chinese Confucian commitment. I was told that in 1976, soon after the arrest of the Gang of Four, the new responsible leaders met and discussed how to revive traditional Confucian values. This was only months after the death of Mao Zedong and the end of the Cultural Revolution when most Western observers would have thought such a meeting highly unlikely. There was apparently agreement on direction and commitment. Discussion was needed only in respect of determining the responsible leader, as the most obvious candidate ruled herself out as a woman who had been active in the 1919 May Fourth Movement that had been critical of traditional values.

The fact that I attended the First International Conference on Confucian Studies in Qufu eleven years after 1976 offers evidence of the cautious and discreet, if deliberate, way this decision was implemented. Moreover, I had previously heard nothing of this early decision made while I was actually working in the Australian Embassy in Beijing. However, the 1976 decision set the course for China's future and the passing years have both confirmed its wisdom and witnessed its implementation.

Today, the importance of the Confucian tradition is evident in the economic and political success of all parts of Asia shaped by the tradition and in the overt commitment China has now made to educating others about its qualities. I feel privileged to have been involved with the International Confucian Association for the full length of its existence. Further, I feel it is possible to draw many lessons from that experience that are now of substantial value as China emerges in a position of global economic and political leadership.

The first six years of the existence of the International Confucian Association, were clouded by the aftermath of Western interpretations of the 1989 Tiananmen Square Incident and by misguided Western celebrations over the 1997 Asian Financial Crisis (AFC). In contrasting ways, each reflected Western uncertainties and apprehensions about the rise of Asia.

This is clear evidence of American and Western failure to comprehend the combined cultural and economic forces at work in transforming global order. For example, American unwillingness to trust Japan to play a proactive role in mitigating the severe impact of the AFC in various parts of Asia worked unintentionally to thrust China into an Asian leadership role for the first time. China's stability and steady progress provided the major reassurance at a time when Western comment was much focused on the failure of Asian values.

**21st Century Rise of Chinese Civilisation**

China continued to grow steadily but rapidly in the early 21st Century, guided by the leadership of Hu Jintao and his emphasis on a peaceful rise. Most Western political and economic leaders were drawn into China's orbit and under Chinese influence by the quality of its Confucian diplomacy.

There was a total inability in the West to recognise the genius of Chinese civilisation at work in an increasingly interconnected global community. The blind commitment to defending Western claims to universal authority and values crippled any capacity Western communities may have had to identify challenges and opportunities that appeared with China's rise. Of course, the American inspired "War on Terror" played a fortuitous, if subsidiary, role in distracting attention from the importance China's rise.

Moreover, the West has been blind to a most daunting reality. This is that Chinese civilisation is so rich, diverse and energetic that it is likely to raise questions about most aspects of the Anglo-American certainties that have defined recent centuries. Already, it is apparent that China's rise has raised fundamental and transformative questions about administrative competence, educational excellence, financial authority and political influence.

More profound civilisational changes have yet to become so obvious. Yet for those with eyes to look it is evident that Chinese traditional values in health, food, energy, science and technology have much to offer a global community struggling with systemic harm done in these areas by Anglo American progress and innovation.

The reality that China suffers as much as, or more than, others from progress and innovation in these areas is likely to ensure that it will soon give priority attention to such issues. Besides having paid the highest price for its rapid conquest of Western commercial, industrial and technological cultures, it has the unique tradition of highly educated and virtuous administrative authority that is essential to begin seriously the task of pervasive systemic reform.

This systemic reform will pose profound problems for Anglo American communities. They have not only reaped great benefits from the world they have shaped over recent centuries but have fallen into the trap of assuming this represented some form of innate and eternal superiority. In reality, history is likely to judge Anglo American reverence for indiscriminate economic growth, scientific progress and technological innovation harshly. It may come to be seen as an unfortunate example of one of those areas of cultural curiosity that characterise particular political regimes.

Consequently, it seems likely that, after a period of cultural reform under Chinese leadership, many

features of the period of Anglo American leadership will have been subject to severe review and re-evaluation. This will largely be conducted in the context of China' s traditional classical wisdom and long historical experience.

Anglo American leaders and scholars have totally failed to remark on the rapidly growing challenge posed by a revitalised Confucian tradition over the past half century. During this period they have had unrivalled resources and opportunities to examine and evaluate this emerging alternative leadership culture. Yet, not only have they done nothing but they have been determined to defend their privileges with complacency, ignorance and blindness. This does not augur well for their prospects of adjusting to and prospering within an emerging order defined by Confucian wisdom and discipline.

Some passages that follow from a book I wrote in 2006, *A Confucian Daoist Millennium?* will show that it has not been impossible to explore and outline major qualities in Chinese civilisation that are reasserting their authority in the early 21$^{st}$ Century. There has, however, been little or no interest or capacity in the West to pursue such exploration. Rather, there seems to have been a mindless plethora of self-destructive initiatives to bolster the crumbling ramparts of Anglo American mythology and its universal values.

Perhaps none of these universal values has been more pervasive or more corrosive in its appeal than Anglo American democracy, which is often used for disruptive and intrusive political adventures. A brief review of some background to modern democratic processes may help explain both the pervasive ineptness of Western responses to the emergence of a renascent and revitalised Confucian Asia and the fact that it remains almost an heretical offense to outline these failings.

The famous statement of Mayer Amschel Rothschild (1744-1812), "Let me issue and control a nation's money and I care not who writes the laws", illustrates much of the genius of Western commerce. Together with Adam Smith's seminal *An Inquiry into the Nature and Causes of the Wealth of Nations* in 1776, much of the character of modern Western progress was determined by the second half of the 18th Century. Its political character was also settled.

Rothschild and Smith consolidated the earlier work of the British East India Company in using the limited liability corporation to mobilise finance and under-employed labour to lay the foundations of a global British Empire. Together, their influence shaped the financial mechanisms and intellectual frameworks that have consolidated a dynamic and transformative, but often unfair and destructive, process of economic progress. Monetary systems were managed discreetly by privately controlled, money issuing Central Banks. Economic and political activity was guided by reverence towards widely believed marketplace mythologies. Together, these forces were ideally placed to take control of global economies and evolving democratic processes.

These forces continued essentially unchallenged until after 1945. Despite defeat and occupation, Japan's Confucian administrators did not surrender control of their Central Bank policies nor observe the same unqualified reverence towards the mythologies of the marketplace. Their behaviour was most discreet and poorly understood in the West. Yet, they were soon emulated by other Confucian administrators elsewhere in Asia, including ultimately in Communist China.

Since 1945, Asian communities guided by Confucian elites have discreetly but relentlessly abandoned those working in models dictated by Rothschild and Smith. The 1997 Asian Financial Crisis, driven by activities originating in the financial world of New York, was a last, counter-productive attempt to halt this advance. Claims of widespread crony capitalism only strengthened the resolve and resilience of Confucian Asia. They set most Western economies up for the mounting crisis and decline that has followed the Global Financial Crisis of 2008.

One of the key characteristics of the Rothschild Smith model was the use of financial and theoretical mechanisms to allow Western communities to consume much of the wealth of the rest of the world. Confucian Asia has put an end to this and Western communities have failed to understand the strategies that have brought this about. As a result, earlier customs of living off the resources, labour and wealth of distant politically or financially colonised peoples have come to an end. This has driven Western financial and corporate elites to seek quasi-colonial privileges in their own communities in a form of economic cannibalism.

As a result, financial and corporate power has sought to institutionalise and legitimise ever more predatory practices in Western communities that are already experiencing economic decline. Protests against this trend are growing in number and articulateness but remain far from mainstream recognition.

The awkward example of China's success, achieved without paying serious deference to Western Capitalist ideals, is rarely treated as a matter for considered exploration and evaluation. Rather the simple use of the descriptor Communist China can imply lazily that this issue has somehow been resolved by the failure of the Communist Soviet Union and has little value.

In fact, however, it is becoming ever more likely that China is shaping standards that many will seek to follow, although this will not be an easy model to emulate. China's success is not rooted not in any familiar ideology. Chinese and much Asian success is nourished by ancient classics that are difficult to understand and absorb without a type of lived experience of their meaning and application. Those Asian communities that seem to observe democratic processes and values mislead most observers. They are best understood by their preservation of Confucian values like administrative excellence, rigorous education, soft strategy, social hierarchy and discreet humility.

Moreover, an educated Confucian elite is not an intellectual class as some in the West might assume. Rather it is a highly learned class of practical administrators who often disdain Western style analysis that seeks the truth. They can be much happier living in the Dao.

Consequently, it is common for Western and other outside minds to totally misunderstand polite exchanges that pay deference to widely asserted Western priorities. The values of tradition, culture, stability, order, family, community, education and productive fulfilment will all be discreetly guarded. They are likely to be valued much more highly than the West's concern for progress, growth, and innovation, although these will be embraced if necessary to protect Eastern priorities.

This reserve about democracy and other Western universal values makes it very easy for outsiders to go astray in a Confucian environment. Failings and hypocrisies in their practice of democracy and universal values can be obvious. Equally, they can be quickly evaluated and managed as appropriate by highly educated Confucians.

First amongst these failings is the way discreet and not so discreet financial and corporate interests have taken effective control of democratic processes. They monopolise political funding, vet all candidates for office and manipulate information flows. The aggressive promotion of democracy in other political systems often reflects a determination to place those communities under more complete outside financial and corporate control. Confucian Asian communities have reversed this practice and formed a variety of financial and corporate alliances that assist them to penetrate and shape Anglo American perceptions, evaluations and policies.

A second example of the inefficiency and vulnerability of democratic communities is to be found in their frequent changes of government personalities, development policies and strategic thought. Even without external influence the democratic process often leads to several fundamental changes of government and direction within a single decade. The character of democratic contest then leads to the new government setting out to establish its authority and character by abandoning many aspects of the previous government' s work. The decade long authority of Chinese leadership groups, all selected after establishing confidence amongst powerful colleagues over three decades or more is unthinkable. Consequently, long term development strategies are unthinkable.

A third example of democratic competitive failure is to be found in the lack of relevant knowledge and experience among both voters and candidates. The contemporary voter with a demanding family and work life has no opportunity to be adequately informed about the complex and obscure implications of casting a vote one way or the other. Even worse, successful candidates often have little relevant knowledge or experience when they take on ministerial responsibilities.

These three areas of democratic weakness leave Confucian Asian communities, which have highly educated, experienced, stable, strategic and authoritative administrative classes, with major competitive advantages. Internal failings of democratic systems not only leave their processes ineffective and poorly informed but also ensure that they are easily penetrated and influenced by corporate and financial outsiders.

Moreover, democratic systems tend to be based on an unquestioning faith in their universal values and to be poorly equipped to exercise self criticism and reform.

These weaknesses have grown more acute as democratic governments have been influenced to move education away from classics, history and literature and towards functional disciplines that prepare almost exclusively for a role in the work force. There are simply fewer and fewer opportunities to gain a sound education in the forces that have shaped human struggle, fortune, behaviour and wisdom throughout the ages.

Moreover, there is mounting evidence that even those who assume discreet background financial and corporate authority are simply not educated to understand the forces reshaping the global community and its interactions. They also are not educated to exercise the responsibilities that they have inherited or gained by other non-democratic means.

In other words, the globalisation of Chinese civilisation is already well advanced and consolidated. This goes unremarked, however, either because of Confucian strategy and discretion or because of Western complacency and ignorance.

**The Globalisation of Chinese Civilisation**

The advance of China and its Confucian civilisation has many diverse characteristics. These include the grand ceremonial receptions in Beijing, the disarming generosity of China's tributary traditions, the sheer competence of Chinese officials, the advanced physical development of Chinese cities and the remarkable reach of Chinese economic activity. Exploring the streets of a major Chinese city can often overshadow the evidence of its economic statistics. Exploring the character and thought of Chinese public and private leaders can impress even more. Yet Hu Jintao's decade of China's peaceful rise seemed almost over before Western commentators started to recognise that China was overtaking the United States in many areas of global leadership. And even now the West sees the economic advance but is blind to the civilisational renaissance.

I was so impressed with China's progress that in 2006 I followed up two books I had co-authored titled *The Confucian Renaissance* (1989) and *The Tyranny of Fortune: Australia's Asian Destiny* (1997) with a third, of which I was the sole author, titled *A Confucian Daoism Millennium*?

I wanted to raise a bold question in the title. Is it probable that the world might be entering a period like the last two millennia when for all but a period of around 150 years after the mid 19th Century Opium Wars the world was effectively led politically, economically and technologically by societies shaped by Confucian and Daoist thought?

Of course, apart from Asian peoples, few had close, regular contact with Confucian and Daoist influence until the 19th Century. Moreover, my experience suggests that there is little understanding today in most contemporary societies outside East and South East Asia of the way in which Chinese classics have shaped a unique and highly advanced thought and behavioural culture. Even China's decade of peaceful rise and the startled realisation that it now challenged the best in the West has not provoked a serious exploration of China's unique qualities. Rather, those who should be most interested in understanding China's unique qualities and strengths usually fall back lazily on references to Communist China.

In seeking to assert the primacy of their claims to global authority, first Britain and then America have cultivated a form of intellectual apartheid. This effectively condemns thought and value cultures as inferior if they do not conform with the ideas of the European Enlightenment. These Enlightenment values might be most readily identified as the so-called universal values of democracy, equality, freedom, rule of law and market economics.

Given the competitive decline of Western economies and the often hypocritical use of universal values to serve narrow political goals, the practice of intellectual apartheid seems to me to no longer be serving its purpose. Rather it encourages inferior education standards, incomprehension of other cultures, ignorant policy officers, and a breakdown of communication in a global community. For America, it also seems to lead to repeated failures in small wars, to a hollowed out economy and to disastrous financial practices.

Accordingly, I started to write my new book in an attempt to identify those qualities that were unique in the Confucian worlds of East and South East Asia and that could be traced back to one area or another of the Chinese classics.

I found myself writing two chapters on what I identified as Confucian features, two on Daoist features, two on Book of Changes features, two on strategic features and two on food and health features. In each of these areas the Chinese classical tradition displayed qualities that seemed to lead to unique strengths in the 21st Century. Moreover, these seemed to be lacking or deficient in the Western world of universal values. Since completing the book I have become much more aware of other classics that may have been featured in my writing and to the important role played by knowledge of Chinese history in illustrating and enriching classical wisdom.

I have to admit to relying for much of my historical sense on the belated discovery of a variety of long (often 30 hours or more) television series on major Chinese historical figures and events. Although my Chinese friends may be critical of the historical accuracy of some of these series, I always find myself marvelling at the way in which they can give contemporary immediacy and relevance to events that happened as much as thousands of years ago while sitting cramped before a video player. It is hard to envisage any possible rival for these historical videos in creating a sense of shared community across the people of the world's most populous nation. Moreover, the visual immediacy of a video recreation crosses all possible barriers of education and literacy.

A quick outline of the major chapters in my latest book may serve to illustrate the weight and relevance of the classical tradition as I had unravelled it before my discovery of many of these historical videos. Initially, however, I should note that the Chinese tradition not only seems much less based on abstract concepts on which rational and theoretical structures are built than it is based on practical behaviour guided by a cultivatedawareness of the rewards, challenges and riddles that characterise life. This awareness is often founded on the words of the classics but these are more inspirational and nurturing than they are prescriptive.

Accordingly, it seems to me that it can be very difficult for a Western reader of these classics, especially when they are in translation, to comprehend how they pervade and shape life in Confucian Asia. This happens in the most subtle of ways but the most relentless of ways. One example is the number of phrases in Chinese that are taken from the classics or as an historical illustration of an idea from the classics. Those foreigners whose Chinese language advances to the level where this is easily understood are likely to be completely absorbed in Chinese life. However, they are likely to find it very difficult to explain their experience and understanding to a foreigner with less mastery of the language.

A major challenge confronts anyone of Western background and responsibility who tries to link up the various relevant factors that dictate Asian behaviour in today' s world. Elements that must be considered and evaluated include the pace of contemporary Chinese and Asian economic advance, the continuing definitive influence of Chinese classics, the sense of a continuing historical experience where Western influence can seem but a passing phase and the ongoing contest between Western presumption and Asian soft strategies. One can then be left with the feeling that this hardly begins to lift the veil on much that is being conducted with the most disciplined and careful discretion.

Compounding such a challenge is the reality that the West's favoured analytical and evaluative tools often seem excessively simplistic and stereotypical and lacking in any cultural knowledge or interest. One must then add to this a sense of superiority and complacency that characterises what passes for policy and strategic evaluation.

Accordingly, my writing about a possible Confucian Daoist millennium could only minimally utilise classical texts. Rather it has sought to trace my thoughts back to evidence I have encountered in practical situations where Asian behaviour suggested forces unfamiliar to a Western sensibility were shaping behaviour. Passages from the beginning of each of the ten main sections of the book may serve to illustrate the diversity and range of areas where Chinese civilisation is likely to be reflected increasingly in the future course of globalisation.

Under the general heading of "Qualities of a Confucian-Daoist Millennium", I addressed initially the distinctive character of Confucian "Community" and focussed on "The Power of Administrative Excellence" with these words.

The central quality informing the Confucian-Daoist civilizations of East Asia is a unique and unrivalled millennia long tradition of highly educated administrative excellence. This tradition is rich in examples of both success and failure and is familiar with the problems of imperial excess and indulgence and the various forms of corruption, and associated vulnerabilities, that are nurtured by great imperial power.

The ideological stereotypes of the post-Enlightenment West, which in the second half of the $20^{th}$ Century dictated an excessively simplistic division between capitalist and communist, blinded most observers to reality. Such distinctions make little sense in East Asia, except as slogans for subtle manipulation by master administrators.

Anglo-American ignorance also ensured that few, if any, commentators remarked on the fact that the Confucian-Daoist governments of East Asia have been informed by ideals of virtuous and benign administration, severe legalistic authority and liberal notions of *wu wei* or non action-translated by the French physiocrats as *laissez faire* - that dictate minimal interference in the affairs of the people. This tradition has nurtured communities where people have been both trusting and obedient towards governments, which in turn have tried to guide but not interfere unnecessarily in the commercial lives of the people.

Second, under the heading of Confucian "Learning", I wrote of "The Power of Early Ritual Learning".

The high priority placed by Chinese tradition and culture on early and continuing learning ensures that each new generation masters quickly as much as possible of the wisdom of its predecessors and identifies as deeply as possible with the community. This priority on learning assumes a timeless quality that protects against passing fads and fashions and ensures strong community reinforcement of educational effort and standards. It instils in each generation of youth habits of obedience, learning and aspiration largely through ritual and repetition. This is a time proven means of equipping future administrators and leaders with the knowledge, discipline, stamina, understanding and wisdom essential to address the world's cultural, political, economic and scientific complexities. This produces strong antibodies that protect communities against yielding authority to those unprepared by the socializing disciplines of rigorous education.

Third, under the heading of Daoist "Spirituality" I wrote of "The Power of Non-Religious Spirituality in this World".

The Chinese spiritual tradition contrasts with Christianity in being essentially unencumbered by monotheism and faith. In addition, it has not been institutionalised and politicised in a manner comparable with the history of Christianity, does not comfortably fit the description of a religion as this is understood in the West and has prospered largely free of the dogma that has been used to organize and mobilize people in the Christian tradition through the centuries. Moreover, it emphasises a holistic and naturalistic exploration of the paradoxes and contradictions to be found in all aspects of human experience and organic life. It has a profound commitment to mastering the realities of daily life in a way that is highly sensitive to physical and human nature and that enhances spiritual robustness and fulfilment. This produces spiritual qualities that are resilient and creative and can flourish independent of faith.

Fourth, under the heading of Daoist "Consciousness" I wrote of "The Power of

Consciousness"

Both Confucian and Daoist influences in Chinese spiritual tradition also place a strong emphasis on the personal, disciplined cultivation of self-understanding and conscious insight, nurturing reflection, intuition, calm and judgment. This has all been undertaken within a broad sense of nature, or of a demanding cosmos. In does not seek to understand the Truth but rather to explore and follow the Way or the Dao. With the emphasis on practical action, community accord and natural harmonies, there is a capacity to develop qualities that are comparatively neglected in the West.

In one sense the consciousness tradition is the essence of the spiritual tradition, but in another it is a separate and robust virtue in itself, complementing the spiritual tradition in the same way the learning tradition complements the community tradition. It ensures that rote learning, whether physical or cerebral, comes alive in the most vital and mature way possible. Indeed, the endless, disciplined repetition that is necessary to advance in the art of *qigong* provides a profound insight into a fundamental reality. This is that much understanding, insight and consciousness will be denied those who refuse to accept the guidance and discipline of a trusted master, teacher or guru. This is necessary to undertake obscure processes of learning that pass on the wisdom of earlier generations, but only after long, disciplined and painstaking effort.

Fifth, under the heading of "Change", I wrote of "The Power of Mature Judgement in Managing Change".

There is no more seminal influence in Chinese culture than a book that has a history of over three thousand years, the *Yi Jing*, or *Book of Changes*, the authority of which is likely to increase with the age and experience of the reader or interpreter. Anything with related aspirations in the West-perhaps astrology or the Tarot-was marginalized either by the Christian Church or by the tradition of Greek rational thought. Consequently, despite its growing popularity in alternative circles, it is difficult for mainstream Western thought to accommodate or relate to the correlative disciplines of the *Yi Jing*. Yet, the *Yi Jing* has made the mature management of inevitable and irresistible change one of the great art forms of the East Asian ruler, or administrator.

The use of the *Yi Jing* as a book of divination has worked to spread its influence through all levels of society, even while true mastery of it is perceived to be the preserve of those who are learned, experienced and wise in the ways of the world. Its capacity to unify the spirit of both Confucianism and Daoism, often wrongly perceived to be rivals for influence, strengthens its role as the major seminal foundation of Chinese culture.

Sixth, under the heading of "Science", I wrote of "The Power of Organic Life".

The inspiration of the *Yi Jing* is at the heart of Chinese civilization-ancient, present and future. While these is little question that the *Yi Jing* has been a fundamental and central source of thought throughout Chinese history, there are many like Joseph Needham who question its contemporary relevance. This can be found with a little reflection, however, in the discreet role it plays in inspiring the contemporary rejuvenation of East Asian industry and technology and in protecting East Asian thought from the mechanical and reductionist fallacies that are the source of the devastation caused by so much Western medicine and science. In the future, it seems likely that scientific thought that is informed by the *Yi Jing* will have a major role to play in healing the human, ecological and environmental damage of the part two hundred years of the West's aggressive mechanistic science.

Seventh, under the heading of "Service", I wrote of "The Power of Service".

One of China's greatest, if not the most widely known, strategic legacies is associated with Jiang Taigong, the leading military and strategic figure in the founding of the Zhou Dynasty. A work attributed to him and titled in translation *Six Secret Teachings* contains *Twelve Civil Offensives* that outline a distinctive Chinese path to conquest through service. It is noteworthy that the wisdom of Jiang Taigong and of the *Yi Jing* are both commonly associated with the imperial founders of the Zhou Dynasty (1045BC-256BC).

It may be that the essence of this strategy, as captured by the *Twelve Civil Offensives*, seems little more than common sense when clearly stated. However, this succinct statement of ways to overcome an adversary without violence, outlined thousands of years ago, also serves to emphasise the fundamental importance of human virtue and moral strength, and the vulnerability of those who lack these qualities. This remains poorly understood in the West, particularly in the corporate world. The *Twelve Civil Offensives* make it clear that any moral weakness in a leader is an invitation to exploitation by a thoughtful and resourceful rival. Ultimately the only true strength is virtue.

Eighth, under the heading of "Knowledge", I wrote of "The Power of Knowledge of Self and Others".

One of the best known passages of the Chinese strategist, Sunzi, declares that victory and success depends on a complete knowledge of oneself and of one's rival. Moreover, this is fundamental to his approach to warfare, which emphasizes that the successful strategist achieves victory without fighting. This strategic understanding seems to widely inform the behavior of East Asian communities, but to be generally neglected by Anglo-American peoples. In the early 21st Century, the latter are invariably misled by their own Enlightenment creation of universal values and the narrow priorities of corporate lobbies.

Ninth, under the heading of "Health", I wrote of "The Power of Health in a Community".

As in administration, China has the longest and most comprehensive recorded history of what works and what does not work in health practices. This history is not lacking in cautionary tales and includes stories of an all-powerful emperor tempted and poisoned by a reputed elixir of life that promised immortality. Importantly, it contains extensive records of the medicinal values of foods and of the mastery of the body's energies. Moreover, the spiritual elements of the tradition are integrated with health disciplines and teach the importance of self-empowerment in maintaining personal well-being, essentially through cultivated calm, relaxation, reflection and consciousness.

Tenth, under the heading of "Energy", I wrote of "The Power of the Body's Energies".

The Chinese emphasis on balance, resonances and correspondences in nature has accompanied an extensive exploration of *qi*, or energy, in relation to human internal and external environments. Principles, which are deeply rooted in Confucian, Daoist and Buddhist traditions, have guided this exploration. Other traditions, most notably the Indian with its concepts of *prana*, *charkas* and the like and its utilization of homeopathy, have identified and utilized related qualities.

Energy, as identified by *qi* or *prana*, has been fundamental to Chinese and Indian medical therapy for at least several millennia. Energy medicine, however, only began to be marginally recognized in the modern West in the latter part of the 20th Century. As ancient Chinese and Indian medical wisdom has gained greater authority as the source of popular alternative therapies and as the insights of quantum physics have been recognized as relevant in health therapies the dogmas of Western medicine have lost their credibility with some intrepid thinkers.

**The Decline of Anglo-American Order**

The above exerts from a book written in 2006 can, I believe, illustrate how backward and reluctant the West has been to address the riches that Chinese civilisation brings to an increasingly interconnected global community. While this unquestionably reflected a determination to defend Western claims to universal authority and values, it has in reality prevented Western communities from identifying challenges and opportunities that have appeared with China's rise.

Further reflection and interactions with others engaged with the Confucian tradition have helped to further expose serious limitations in Western culture. These have been hidden as it has transformed the whole global community over the past several centuries and has awed and dominated societies everywhere. The thought culture can be traced back to the Greek Plato and his transcendent forms, which subsequently shaped much of the doctrine and dogma of the Roman Church and later much of the European Enlightenment thought that gave the world universal values like democracy, equality, freedom, human rights, rational economics and innovative science. When examined against the background of the Chinese classics this tradition seems excessively abstract, rational, theoretical and faith based. Nevertheless, the British use of the Limited Liability Corporation to mobilise under-employed labour to venture forth and bring back the wealth of distant societies, reinforced by moving first to exploit the energy of fossil fuels like coal and oil, helped enshrine the Enlightenment's universal values. These proved invaluable in cloaking aggressive expansion in apparently high minded, civilising principles.

It has taken several centuries for peoples of the Confucian tradition to draw on the fluid, intuitive, holistic and practical thought nurtured by classics like the Analects, Daodejing, Book of Changes and some strategic works to identify and master failings inherent in this Western tradition and its recent global expansion.

It is only now becoming apparent that the imaginative and innovative science, which is still seen by many as capable of reversing Western decline, is fundamentally flawed. True, when conducted within the framework of Western abstractions, rationalities and theories, reinforced with faith, it has frequently proven irresistible in solving problems and delivering desired results. Unfortunately, however, the abstract, rational and theoretical definition of problems and goals has fostered a culture that systemically neglects and ignores unintended consequences. Today's problems with polluted environments, disappearing ecologies, poisonous processed foods, lethal medicines and much else are all a systemic product of an innovative culture that has little inclination to explore issues with fluid imagination, intuitive thought, holistic sensibility or practical reflection about consequences.

These failings in Western physical sciences are also evident in Western social sciences where the past half century has provided voluminous evidence of the failure of Western economic, political and strategic thought culture. When confronted with the fluid and subtle strategies of Confucian communities, which now commonly understand the West better than it understands itself, Western nations has proven inept, first in recognising the processes at work and even more in devising possible strategies to defend accustomed privileges.

Another fundamental aspect of Western cultural, organisational and political failing relates both to Anglo American dependence on the Limited Liability Corporation and to a seemingly deeply rooted Western financial tradition of allowing private bankers to control community or national monetary issuance and policy. The latter tradition is evident in today's Western central banking practice and might be traced back through practices in Medieval Venice, Biblical Rome and Ancient Babylon. In contrast, Central Bank authority appears to be used much more strategically for the benefit of community development throughout Confucian Asia. Corporate and financial power, often exercised inter-generationally, has become so pervasive and dominant in a number of leading Western nations that formal political leadership seems almost irrelevant.

As a result, the processes of Western government increasingly produce a series of strategically incoherent policies and actions. Corporate and financial powerbrokers have simply failed to understand the need to nurture the discipline, knowledge and experience which is necessary for large scale national purpose and which has been the traditional goal of a Confucian education and up-bringingand

The fact that the above perceptions are rarely if ever explored by Western authorities and universities is explained both the culture of intellectual apartheid and by the powerful vested interests of corporations and financiers. This highlights the seriousness of Western problems. It also goes far to explain the irreversible character of the decline of Anglo American order. There is simply a lack of the intellectual independence, integrity and purpose necessary to identify and address these deep rooted problems.

As the following section will indicate, the situation is made more daunting for Western communities by the character of the challenges posed by Confucian civilisation. As will be suggested, the language, culture, classics and history of the Confucian tradition are almost impossible for a Westerner to master unless such a carefully focused education begins at a much earlier age than is at all fashionable in the West. The cultural divide might even be symbolised by many Chinese parents' concern to use the best learning years between three and six to maximum advantage in learning the classics and the scorn widely shared for any such early learning in the West.

**Challenges posed by Chinese Civilisation**

Preceding passages leave little or no room for debate about the decline of Anglo American global order. They do, however, imply that there is an increasingly urgent need to address the implications of this decline in a practical manner. The capacity to respond to this challenge seems to exist almost exclusively in the Confucian and not in the Anglo American world.

Chinese language and culture are much more difficult to master than almost any other language and culture. Moreover, outside research into Confucian achievements will have difficulty comprehending the spread of Chinese commercial cultural successes when educators have little or no understanding of the culture, values and history that have inspired that success. Globally, a type of Confucian popularization will come from China's wealth and power. Yet Confucian education will only come for those who make an heroic and resolute effort.

Experience to date suggests that the West and other non Asian societies are neither equipped nor inclined to tackle the task of both acknowledging and accepting the growing authority of what is a totally alien culture of thought and behaviour. In particular, the West now faces a challenge not unlike that it has posed for other cultural traditions with its aggressive financial and corporate strategies. The Confucian challenge is, however, an even deeper, more subtle and more demanding challenge than that posed by Western financial and corporate practices.

Of course, there is a high probability, even if it is by no means certain, that Confucian economic power will be more benign and less predatory that that of the Anglo

American communities. Throughout its history and even in contemporary times China has been prepared to make economic sacrifices to achieve forms of political stability and cooperation. Problems are, however, likely to arise when some declining powers fail to understand the need for environmental, ecological, health or related reforms and choose to persist with poorly understood and destructive forms of commercial activity.

Simply put, it is impossible to emerge in a position of pervasive global authority without being encumbered with a wide range of global responsibilities, desired or undesired. This is certainly true in the contemporary interconnected global community regardless of whether authority has been achieved in the schoolroom or marketplace or on the battlefield.

Consequently, China confronts a challenge that the West has only addressed in the most cursory, offhand and disinterested manner. That challenge is one of identifying and communicating a culture of global community activity that escapes the naiveties of democracy, the destructiveness of the marketplace and the neglected side-effects of scientific innovation.

The American fantasy that innovation can rescue it from financial excess and mounting debt has become a threat to humankind. The marketplace cannot be allowed to bolster harmful practices like genetic modification and energy fracking well after serious problems have been identified in such practices. Otherwise the human genius will become its greatest liability.

The global community is largely the creation of an Anglo-American genius that has utilised energies mobilized by the limited liability corporation, ambitions inspired by market profit and opportunities invented by innovation. This genius has liberated the human spirit and reshaped cultural traditions everywhere. Only communities with a strong Confucian ethos have succeeded in out-strategizing the Anglo-American powers. Their success will, however, bring the less popular and more onerous need to restore a type of human self-awareness and self-discipline that was abandoned in the Anglo American celebration of growth, progress and scientific innovation.

Recent decades of steady and transparent decline in the major Anglo American powers have moved some inspired parties to highlight widespread failings. These communities have, however, shown little capacity to systemically reform themselves, whether in terms of political behaviour, financial discipline or environmental management. Rather, powerful corporate and financial lobbies have become even more active and influential in demanding narrow and self serving policies that leave their larger communities increasingly weakened and vulnerable.

These declining Anglo American communities have been readily outplayed in terms of economic and financial strategy and many are now in a serious condition of disarray, even disintegration. In many ways, they could not be more poorly prepared to respond to the challenges and opportunities posed by Chinese civilisation. Previously disadvantaged peoples in Africa, Latin America and elsewhere, who are not burdened and misled by a misjudged sense of superiority, may be better prepared to evaluate and actively embrace a world that is being shaped by Chinese civilisation.

The twenty years of the existence of the International Confucian Association has witnessed many changes in the global community but none greater than the emergence of a powerful China. China's rise has been inspired by the genius of a Confucian civilisation that had seemed dormant but that is deep, pervasive and active. Administrative meetings of the ICA explore ways to reinforce the wisdom of the tradition in China and to share it more widely outside China. To my regret, at this time few people outside Asia recognise the urgency to educate themselves in what to most seems to remain no more than an exotic remnant from a distant past.

The above is a tragic comment on the way international education and culture have evolved under Anglo American influence over recent centuries. It has been possible to provoke controversy over a clash of civilisations but not to promote serious understanding of a renascent alternative civilisation. It is also an indication of the challenge that lies ahead of the ICA. The Confucian tradition is one of immense richness, power and subtlety but it is also one that can only begin to be understood through extensive and rigorous education and experience. Modern life offers few people born outside the tradition any real opportunity to access the necessary education and experience.

Being of Australian and thereby more or less of Anglo American identity, I have long pondered how the Australian community can break free of the bonds of a declining world mythology and respond to a more subtle, complex and demanding ethos. This is an ethos that prepares children from the earliest possible age in the most ordered and attentive way possible by using youthful energies and expectations to become intimate with the accumulated experience and wisdom of many millennia. I identified this educational ethos and the answer to my questions about Australia's future at the Four Seas Confucius Academy. Sadly, I can find few Australians who agree with me but that has not shaken my conviction. The final part of this paper will address my exploration of that ethos.

**Early Childhood Education**

My experience and exploration of the Confucian tradition and its revival leaves me convinced that it has many subtleties and riches that continue to escape the Western mind. Given the conviction that it is likely to carry the responsibility for the future of the global community I have continued to explore ways to better understand it. In particular, I have become interested in forms of bi-cultural education, including early rote learning of the Chinese classics, that might be developed to address the global challenges that can be predicted in the future.

As with my introduction to the Chinese Confucian revival and the establishment of the ICA, a Chinese friend appeared to lend a helping hand. I had only met the Principal of the Four Seas Confucius Academy, Feng Zhe, several times. I acted on an intuition that experiencing such early learning practice would teach me important qualities about a tradition that has survived and prospered over several millennia.

First, it would give me personal experience of this learning culture and equip me better to evaluate the relentless, hostile criticism of it by Western education authorities. These often seem to have buried themselves in learned and arcane theories as they have overseen a steady deterioration in the quality of much Western education. Most importantly, they have failed to produce a generation who could match wits and wills with their Confucian counterparts in Asia.

Second, my own experience had largely persuaded me that the Chinese classics can be unsatisfactory when read (particularly in translation) but can be a powerful influence on behaviour when committed to memory.

Third, I was intrigued by the fact that schools such as the Four Seas Confucius Academy are reappearing in China as private enterprises despite all the lock-step Western comment on Communist China as a cultural desert after the Cultural Revolution.

While I had initially thought I might sit at the back of classrooms and simply join in the singing and chanting of the children, my hosts knew better. They treated me even more generously. The Principal allocated his twenty year old nephew to be my dedicated teacher and daily take me through my own reading and rehearsal of the classics I choose to study. I was, nevertheless, still in intimate contact with the children passing them on their way to classes, hearing them in adjacent rooms joyfully singing and chanting, joining them in taiji exercises or examining their memory of texts they had learnt.

It should be apparent that I am experienced in surrendering myself to various Asian thoughts, habits and practices that capture my imagination. Yet no previous experience gave me such a gentle but overwhelmingly persuasive introduction to a way of approaching life that seems almost incomprehensible in Western terms. Moreover, I had no true idea when I started my three months at the Academy that I would leave with the conviction that the West would never begin to comprehend seriously the Confucian civilisations of Asia until it ensured that a significant quota of children undertake each a rote learning education in the Chinese classics.

Of course, it took me a lifetime (or half a century), a uniquely privileged series of opportunities, a stubborn character and a growing awareness of the inadequacy of the West's standard responses to successive Asian economic miracles to bring me this far. It also required me to understand that simply reading the major classics does not produce the same behaviour and thought I found in Asian societies. Something more was needed.

That was what I found at the Four Seas Confucius Academy. Here it quickly became apparent that children who at a very early age learnt ancient classics that could be recited word perfectly in a spontaneous manner gained

1. an immediate sense of pride and fulfilment,

2. a natural acceptance of disciplined and purposeful activity,

3. a lifetime confidence and eagerness in undertaking further learning challenges,

4. an intuitive understanding of the rewards to be gained from an understanding of China's past, and

5. much more.

Of course, some people recount tales of rote learning inflicted on young children in a brutish and bullying manner. The Four Seas Confucius Academy made it clear that this could only be seen as an aberration of the type that occurs in all human activity. When properly conducted, as at the Academy, rote learning of the Chinese classics had none of these fabled failings. On the contrary, it gave children an immediate sense of maturity, responsibility and purpose in their daily activities. When I reflected on the qualities of a child educated in this manner from the age of three to twelve with comparative qualities of a child educated in Australia from five or six to twelve, I could only struggle with a sense of loss and waste.

Academies like the one I attended are still private enterprises in China but I could only conclude that they represent the way in which China will move forward. This will intensify the challenges facing those outside

the tradition who will need to interact in matters of finance, commerce, technology and education.

The comparative achievements of Chinese and other Asian children in Western universities is no accident. Rather they are a product of an education tradition and culture that has survived the confusions and disruptions of the past century and a half and that is now going through a process of renaissance, regeneration and reinvention. It is not easy to see how other communities beyond Asia are going to inspire similar activity.

Many remark on the fact that there are also a large number of schools being established in China that teach children from an early age in English, seemingly downgrading the value of Chinese language and culture. To a degree, this is true but it is difficult to see this practice producing China's future leaders. It may prove useful in training a cadre to manage China's exploding interactions with the rest of the world and this type of work will have many personal rewards. Yet, it is likely to be marginal to the major activities taking place in Zhongnanhai, or the centre of Chinese government activity, that will reverberate to all parts of the world.

Perhaps something of the true character of the Four Seas Confucius Academy is best explained by saying more about the Principal. Not only has he founded the Academy but he seems to be at the heart of many activities that are generating a profound sense of pride in the Chinese identity. After studying economics at university, he went to work in the publishing business. While still in his twenties and against the advice of many, he took the initiative of making contact with and recruiting a number of what the Japanese would call China's living treasures. These were men in their seventies and eighties, who had been educated in the manner that is being revived at Four Seas Confucius Academy and who had skills that had been neglected by following generations.

In other words, these men were in their later years. Before the natural course of events could take them from this world, however, their talents were recognised in an unexpected way and they were recruited to begin building what has become the Library of Chinese Classics, published in bi-lingual Chinese and English texts, and, for major texts, in other language combinations. The Library has now gained such recognition that it has been taken over by the Chinese government. Moreover, the Library, which now encompasses more than a hundred works, is often presented by China's leaders to visiting dignitaries. It provides an endless source of both inspiration and frustration for interested foreigners, who are unlikely to ever find time to read all the classics, even in translation.

The Library serves as a powerful and striking reminder to foreigners browsing Chinese bookshops that Chinese classical literature has an inexhaustible body of riches. The Library also serves as a reminder of talents that later generations had little opportunity to cultivate. The Principal loses few opportunities, however, to remind his friends that the generation being educated today at the Academy will revive those skills. My sense is that they will go far beyond just reviving literary skills and will inspire future generations to reinvigorate much that has been forgotten in China under pressure to match Western challenges.

Having shown the way with the Library of Chinese Classics and the Four Seas Academy, the Principal, who is still a young man with a young family, seems likely to undertake new cultural enterprises and explore other areas of China's traditional culture that have been allowed to lie dormant. He now also has two vegetarian restaurants, one well located near the centre of Beijing and one within a few minutes walk of the Four Seas Confucius Academy. The vegetarian food served to the children at the Academy and the recent establishment of a garden to grow the Academy's food are further expressions of his attention to a wide range of issues that many consider themselves too pressured by economic imperatives to worry about.

The Principal's wide range of friends and associates reflects all his various interests and represents his capacity to inspire related activities all over China and in many areas of culture. It is possible to conclude that he has understood and captured many of the aspirations of the Chinese people, which until very recently could not find expression in their lives. Whether with the Library of Chinese Classics, the Four Seas Academy or his vegetarian restaurants, he has demonstrated that there is a widespread demand for opportunities in these previously neglected areas. Just as important in today's financially preoccupied world, he has shown that these opportunities can be developed in a commercially viable manner.

Daily living experience in China reveals a broad knowledge of and affection for its classics. Chinese leaders all seem to have a discreet but profound education in these classics. This includes Mao Zedong, whose writings display an intimate knowledge of them.

Classical rote learning from three will increasingly shape the future of China and much of the rest of the world but the character of this influence is almost incomprehensible from a Western perspective. One must see a five year old stand erect and proud and recite classic chapters word perfect. One must also be familiar with these chapters and reflect on their lifetime influence. With this classic wisdom as the foundation of consciousness, it filters all later experience. But these classics are not constructed on abstract theories and reinforced with faith. Rather they are invitations to reflect on the eternal patterns, challenges and riddles of life.

The *Analects*, *Daodejing* and *Book of Changes* all do this in unique and complementary ways. There are many other classic texts that complement and reinforce this teaching. There are no comparable classical texts in the Western tradition. The first three lines of the *Analects* celebrate lifetime learning, collegiality and humility. The first two lines of the *Daodejing* celebrate the Dao and the absence of any unchanging "truth". Readings of the *Book of Changes* offer constant invitations to review oneself and one's life.

This classical learning begins with three year olds chanting and singing the classics in unison. They are forming a community with other three year olds and millennia of earlier Chinese. The community exists in space and time and a place is earned through effort and study. The community rewards and privileges those who study and understand this.

Contemporary Western progress and innovation is of interest but in some ways is alien. It is learning discipline and community duty that enables the West's best to be outplayed. The foundation in classical Chinese makes all known Chinese history accessible. This enriches an understanding of the classics as it shows their practical successes and failures. There is progress from early knowledge of the classics through history to the modern world. This has the capacity to engage and win commitment to ongoing disciplined study. This is often mistaken for mindless memorisation in the West but it is much more.

Chinese history is full of tales that educate in the value of social form and discretion. This contrasts with the political and technological adventurism that informs the West's "progress". 2,500 years of Eastern learning and 250 years of Western progress offer stark contrasts which lead to contesting thought cultures, behavioural customs, basic certainties and strategic resources.

The West is now trapped by an inability to comprehend a Confucian consensus that informs and shapes East and South East Asia. In the mid $19^{th}$ Century China's leaders could not comprehend the Western challenge. It is not clear that the West has the cultural wisdom to reinvent itself as China has done. The refusal to explore the education that shapes the Confucian tradition is a key obstacle.

Western leaders need to visit schools like the Four Seas Confucius Academy. The physical joy and enthusiasm of teachers and pupils illustrates a profound life energy. This energy can shape a whole lifetime but with increasing discretion with increasing years.

The education that shapes the Confucian trading is already shaping the $21^{st}$ Century. Phrases like "Contesting Thought Cultures" and "A Crisis in Western Thought" can only be understood in this context, a challenge that few in the West seem willing to address.

Sadly, there remain many obstacles to developing effective communication and understanding between East and West. Yet work in this area outside Asia has hardly commenced even though it is inevitable that these obstacles will demand and consume much attention in coming decades. In conclusion, one could suggest that some of the most daunting are:

6. Fundamentally contrasting classic traditions and thought cultures

7. Cultivated Western intellectual apartheid that closes minds to the unfamiliar

8. The unique character of the Chinese classics and the thought they nourish

9. The daunting richness of recorded Chinese historical experience

10. The need for Chinese language mastery to access Chinese classics and history

11. The difficulties inherent in mastering Chinese language unless begun in infancy

12. The assertive character of Western certainties and universal (transcendent) values

13. The narrow fragmented financial and corporate interests that dictate Western policy

# Confucius and Education of Taku City

**Yokoo Toshihiko (Mayor of Taku City, Japan)**

The Confucius view of human itself is so important for not only in our daily lives but also for successful management in business or public administration.

His idea and vision appeared in the Book of "Rongo", for example, the famous records of his dialogue and talk with his disciples.

For instance he answered when the Duke of She asked about government.

The Master (Confucius) said, "Make those nearly pleased and those far off folk to you". This is the essence of governmental management.

His answer about government was "Do not crave for speed; do not covet petty gains. If you crave for speed, you will not reach your destination; if you covet petty gains, great undertakings will not be accomplished."

Like these words he is still giving us both answers for life and good inspirations for action.

Since I became the Mayor of Taku city in September 1997, I have experienced a public governmental position for about 16 years, of course I am still now the mayor at present. Through my real experience as a mayor of the city where the Confucius Temple was founded in 1708 AD, I am sure that Confucius teaching is even now a very significant guideline and advice for all public officers. I also strongly I feel that we should call Confucius the master of management.

Generally speaking the so-called top leader of various social organizations has to be alone in mental aspects. This must be the destiny of the leader.

As you may know, already the leader must have the responsibility for all final decisions. So he should create a new vision, setup a new plan, startup a new action, manage to complete a new purpose and share the result with other people. This kind of leader's role cannot be replaced with other person.

Confucius has taught us in his words. He says that as far as one spends one's life with virtual efforts day by day, the person would be blessed with spiritual confidence and fellows or comrades.

Living in such a changing society like these days, we need concrete or an everlasting view or idea of human. Every leader should be right always, be gentle for people and be hard on oneself at every moment every day.

Because only leader can guide and influence people to complete a prosperous future, and have responsibility for all, he or she should be a really good person before becoming a leader.

Due to reasons like these, Confucius teachings are so important for us.

In this paper I would like to be grateful for readers to simply understand our tiny efforts in Taku city, my home city, to improve our era and society.

**1: Confucius and Successful Management**

Recently people of the world have a strong enthusiastic interest to find a way for making real prosperity. Because there are a lot of problems and difficulties in the all aspects of society and human life; people of the business community want to succeed in their business; people of educational or academic fields need to have confidence to teach, guide, encourage and lead the young generation; and people of politics and public administration demand successfully strategic ways for their glory.

All persons of all fields of human societies really want to be successful, even if in their difficult conditions. They might ask: "what should I do?"

There will be answers for every person. And then we wonder if where is such a common essence to reply for various problem. Yes we can find the so called common answer for now and the future. Then we want to know "where is an answer ? " or want to know " who is the master to answer all questions ? ".

Yes, the answer must be "Confucius". He created a new vision of philosophy for mankind. Of course, Confucius himself had lived so long ago. We should call him as an ancient teacher for people and human life. He put strong respect upon the values of personality and self-confidence to follow the right way of life. He respected more "how to be" than "how to do". Also Confucius created the walkway of life even for the top leader of a country as well as a generally ordinal person.

As mentioned above, we should call Confucius the master of management.

Talking about the master of management, let me introduce one person who has been called the master of management.

In the year of 1980, in April, I joined the Matsushita Institute of Government and Management, as one of the first entered-fellows, newly founded by the so called master of management, Mr. Konosuke Matsushita. He graduated elementary school when he was about 10 years old, and started his business when he was 20 years old. After some social and business experience he became the founder of Panasonic Corporation, and has been called as one of the successful leaders in business management.

Through his life experience as a management leader, Mr. Konosuke Matsushita realized the importance of human education. Education itself has a power to cultivate the capability of mankind. He always tried to educate his members of his company. Nevertheless he only graduate from elementary school, he utilized those who graduated from higher educational institutions or schools, and he himself became the master of management in Japan.

He has respected the importance of tiny actions of daily life or tiny ways of thinking of everyday. He has

got to know that as long as we take the right action the so-called existence like the heaven helps us always. The very simple and frank teaching essence will bring the successful management, if that teaching would be

realized by real action.

In order to educate the next generation leaders, he founded the Matsushita Institute in 1980. I have learned directly from him and self-studied there for five years. One of the important lectures was related to Confucius. He invited the teaching master, Mr. Masahiro Yasuoka, who has directly guided and advised the Prime Ministers of Japan for some decades in the 20th century. Mr. Yasuoka explained that the most important book for us was the Confucius Rongo (論語), The Analects of Confucius. It was so impressive.

**2: Way to be Mayor of "Confucius city"**

After learning at Matsushita Institute of Government and Management as well as other various activities, I decided to run election to become the mayor of my home town when I was 41 years old.

In the election of September 1997, the citizens of Taku finally chose me as the

Mayor of Taku city. It was a rather hard and hot election. For the preparation to win the election, I made a policy agenda to innovate the city administration. "Innovation" itself is the key to reform and progress the municipal administration for the future.

Especially I put emphasis upon the key word: "management". Personally I prefer for using "management" rather than "administration" for public governmental work.

So as soon as I became the mayor of my city, we started a management meeting every month. At the first office day of every month we usually have a special meeting to share our information among all sections of the Taku City government office. About the importance of the management meeting, I was taught by the mayor of New York City, Mr. Rudolph William Louis Giuliani, through reading his book about the terrorism of 9.11 and his city management, when the world trade center buildings were attacked by two high-jacked airplanes.

For improving management there are unlimited ways to change and progress all aspects of management. For example, how to use one's name card/tag, how to greet citizens who come over to the city office, how to listen to voices among people for improvement and so on. Even in these small matters there must be big hints and seeds to change administrative management.

It was a starting point of my public office carrier, now already the time has been passed for me 16 years as a mayor of the city of Confucius Temple history.

Taku city, my home country-land, is located at the center part of Saga Prefecture, in Kyushu, the most southern-located or one of the four main islands of Japan.

Taku is surrounded with not only by mountains but also green leaves, woods, forest and flowers of our nature and agricultural fields. You can easily find beautiful cherry blossom flowers in spring and also wonderful red and yellow leaves among trees in autumn. In the morning a lot of birds sing here and there. Taku city is just like a garden in forests.

Those who recently visited Taku city prefer to call it "the clean and green city". For example, in this spring the representative college students from India have home-stayed in the city area. They evaluated and talked "Taku city is clean and green". They were surprised by the cleanness of the downtown in the city, the condition of no-trash on streets, the brightness of green fields and forests.

Also they asked "the secret" or reason for those surprising matters. The secret is the teaching essence of Confucius and his followers. There are many teachings and lessons for us in their words.

For example, the importance of clean or sweep was written in the textbook of Confucius and follower's lessons. The action to sweep and clean itself is regarded as one of daily routine works, and is looked down upon as an easy dust job. But is it true? I would like to emphasize the essence of sweep and clean work.

Mr. Konosuke Matsushita respects its importance and significance. He said that "If you would be successful to sweep and clean, you can also have success in all human activity". You also can find many lessons through real action to sweep and clean. When you do so, you will find a small stain sometimes in front of you. Then after you clean up, you also find the pleasure after cleaning up that stain and making comfortable condition. In addition to those, you will also find the understanding of people who dedicate to you. It is necessary for a leader of management to understand his staffs and their effort, to develop his virtue, and get their trust. Trust itself is one of the most indispensable virtue for humans, Confucius mentioned.

**3: Taku and Confucius Temple : "Taku Seibyo"**

From the old time of our country history, the area of Taku city has been called as the "Tankyu-no-sato"(丹邱の里) place or the "Bunkyo-no-sato"(文教の里)place.

The word "Tankyu" itself literally means the utopia where the "Sennin"(仙人) lives. This "Sennin" (仙人)means such definition as ① one not bound by earthly desires or the thoughts of normal men, ② immortal mountain wizard (in Taoism), ③ mountain man (esp. a hermit). And the word "Bunkyo" means "culture and education". Because of the existence of the Taku Confucius Temple and its history, many people have called Taku in such an expression.

The plenty of natural treasures and the scene of the Taku Confucius Temple produce an unique atmosphere for all generations.

The Confucius Temple itself brought a new relationship with the birthplace of Confucius, Qufu in China. It is important not only to innovate within our area and among people here but also to expand our capability and friendship with other cities of foreign countries. Over two decades both cities have experienced friendly exchange activities as the twin friendly sister cities between Qufu city and Taku city. Qufu is the very historically memorial place where Confucius was born. We send delegation of citizen of Taku to Qufu almost every year and visit the Confucius historical points.

Through these activities we share mutual understanding with each other.

In addition to such activities in Taku we also have been developing our educational activities with using Confucius teachings and his philosophy as a theme, especially for the younger generation. The "Rongo-Karuta" activity is one of them.

Within these twenty years, we also have introduced the "Confucius Festival Dances"(释菜之舞) from Qufu(曲阜). The teachers of this special dance in China were invited to Taku, they have taught the moving of hands and feet in detail to senior and young citizens in Taku. Now at the Seikei junior high school, the students have been mastering how to dance, and in the elementary school the students have been learning the "Yoko-dance"(腰鼓), they have made a well-trained performance in front of the Taku Confucius Temple at the time of formal festival, both in spring and autumn.

At the heart of the land of Taku city, you can find the Confucius Temple.

We call this sacred building "Taku Seibyo" (多久聖廟), literally means the holy temple of Confucius in Taku.

More than 300 years ago, in 1699, the Lord governing Taku area, whose name was the Lord Shigehumi Taku, started the local school "Togenshosha"(東原庠舍). This Togenshosha school opened its door for not only the samurai children but also common younger people who had strong enthusiasm to learn and study at this school. At that time of the Edo period era in the Japanese history, it must be said that such school attitude and guidelines were very rare, probably no example existed in other area in those days. This means the Lord Shigefumi Taku had such a very strong sense of mission to educate common people for vitalizing the Taku community and economy.

For the purpose of respect-mind for study or even academism, he decided to build the Confucius Temple, "the Taku Seibyo" (多久聖廟), and completed its construction in 1708.

The Lord of Shigehumi Taku has left his words: "Although my governing land is very small and local, as the lord of this land, I am supposed to be a leader with responsibility to keep excellent management of this area. I would like to emphasis the importance of public administration and education". In addition, he respected the significance of humbleness and sincerity as a human. "At first sight of the Confucius Temple, people should be encouraged to be respected and self-motivated by themselves", he had expected.

According to developing and realizing his vision, he and his government had needed construction materials. Materials such as woods had been collected from all over Taku area. That enabled the Building of Confucius Temple to be reserved and utilized over the three centuries. The carpenters at that time had no experience to see such a Confucius Temple before, so they have had to study and picture the structure and design of a New Temple. That means it was necessary to be creative always.

The building itself is colored and painted with yellow-red, which symbolize the divine color of the holly buildings. The same pattern of the color arrangement is found at any shrines of Japanese history.

When you walk forward, and step by step try to enter into the "Taku-Seibyo", you must walk under the Gyoko-mon (高仰門) Gate, then progress your steps towards to the temple. When you reach to the steps of the temple you will step up with five steps to the holly temple. Then you can see a numerous variety of scriptures such as dragons, carps, qilin(麒麟: giraffe), bamboo-trees and divine power spot of holly force and so forth.

Especially you will be able to see the "Taotie"(饕餮) just under the entrance gate of this Taku Seibyo. The taotie itself is thought, in ancient Chinese history, as a sacred existence which eat all vicious or evil things. In the era of Chinese Yin dynasty and Zhou dynasty, the taotie was built in as the holly design on the surface of bronze ware at the Bronze Age. And the Zhou dynasty is the era that Confucius had been eager to follow and realize as the excellent governance model. This Taku taotie is made from a wooden scripture not a bronze one.

Then you can enter the building, you must carefully follows the historical formal rule of manner.

Just after entering the Taku-Seibyo, above your head there is the holly picture of the sacred dragon on the ceiling. According to the old saying, this dragon originally has been lacked of one piece of his scales, so he cannot fly in the air. If someone can add that one peace scale he would fly up to the sky. It is an interesting story, isn't it? However, don't worry so far, nobody could find or see such a dragon's action.

Just under the dragon ceiling, when you stand and look forward in front of you, you can find the Confucius Stature of the Taku Seibyo. This holly Stature was designed and created in the year of 1708 AD by one of the sophisticated Confucianism teacher in the Edo period, whose name was Tekisai Nakamura, he lived in Kyoto and has been became well-known as the Confucius philosopher.

On both side of the Taku Confucius Stature surrounding space in the temple, there are the 4 sacred image statures of the well-known followers of Confucius, such as Gansi(颜子), Soushi(曹子), Shishishi(子思子) and Moushi(孟子).

In Taku, we have continued cerebrating the special festival "Sekisai" (釈菜) for more than 300 years, to express our worship and respect to Confucius in spring and autumn since 1708. At present every April $18^{th}$ and the forth Sunday of October the festival is hold in the Taku Seibyo area. For over the three centuries this ceremonial event has been continued with no delay and cancellation.

In the ceremony, all officials to take care of the important roll with Ming Dynasty's Costumes for the Confucian Scholar. The mayor of Taku city has a roll as the chief leader of the Confucius Ceremony.

At the very beginning and during of this Sekisai (釈菜) ceremony, the Japanese traditional court music"Gagaku" (雅楽) is performed by "Reijin" (伶人), court musician for Gagaku orchestra. It is seemed just like an oriental orchestra.

One of musical instruments of Gagaku is "Sho"(笙), a traditional Japanese wind instrument resembling panpipes. Its sound has been believed as a sound of the universe. This unique instrument is made by seventeen bamboo tree tubes, cut and connected in a special method. If you were in the real universe, you might be able to listen to such sounds from cosmos.

There is another instrument "dragon flute", "Ryuteki" (龍笛), that literally means "the sound of dragon".

Another unique instrument is "Hichiriki"(篳篥), a small double-reed wind instrument used in Gagaku (made of bamboo, with 7 holes on top and 2 below).

Anyhow these special sounds are played and created sacred atmosphere by those musical instruments from the old days.

Then the masters and servants for the Sekisai festival are coming toward the Confucius Temple. Of course, there are rules and customs from the very first time. It must be called a kind of tradition or grammar of the festival. This very important rule is also edited and compiled by Tekisai Nakamura.

At the time of the first Sekisai, the Lord Shigefumi Taku directed as the top of the newly started festival. So people of Taku area naturally appreciated that the administrative top leader should take a role of the director of Sekisai, just like the maestro or conductor of orchestra. So now the mayor of the Taku city takes such an important role on the Sekisai festival-day.

As far as the acting movements of the formal Sekisai concerned, there are more than 100 movements. All members who attend the festival must memorize in his or her body and spirit. Every movement has each meaning, and is acted especially to celebrate the virtue of Confucius life and his teaching.

**4: Confucius and Education**

According to these history and tradition, we have been developing an educational effort to expand Confucius teachings.

In Japan during junior high or high school, in the class of studying classics, students learn some of Confucius teaching, from Rongo and other books.

14. Rongo-Karuta（論語かるた）: power of word

We have continued the Rongo-Karuta study drill in our elementary schools and junior high schools in Taku city. Almost all students memorized about 100 teaching words from "Rongo", one of the typical Confucius teaching-books.

Students learn in their class room at the first time. They receive the study book of Rongo Karuta prepared and published by the public foundation Koshino-sato, that the mayor of Taku is the president. They take it to their homes and make efforts to memorize those words through home-drill. Many times at each school in Taku city, students quite often participate in such activities to compete in their ranking among friends of the class-room or school. After some training they will join the Rongo-Karta competition conference.

Of course the teachers teach in their classrooms. Furthermore, every school has some original efforts to guide students in memorizing Confucius words and Rongo teachings. For example, one school has a unique master-stage-ranking system. Every student can admit the valuation drill examination in front of the school master. When he or she can pass it he or she get a special calling name, master ( meijin 名人), expert ( tatsujin 達人) and so forth. One school made the Rongo study stairs as the memorizing tools, where every step you can find Rongo teaching words. In all schools, as you can easily find, there are the Rongo-Karuta memorizing kits. You will be able to see the enlarged size Rongo Karuta on corridor walls. By using these kits and tools, students learn daily in their usual school days. Indeed these are some efforts for realizing "practice makes perfect"

There is a special reason to progress these efforts in every school. I would like to respect the significance of "word". Maybe I should say "the power of word".

Just think when we are in trouble, you must encourage ourself to overcome such trouble. At that moment, how can we encourage ourselves? There should be "word". For example, "Try our (my) best", "Fight", "Hang on" and so on, we use these words to encourage ourselves and our team-mates in sports and so forth. We need words to express our mind and feelings.

So when we have knowledge of good words, we can encourage ourselves or others effectively. In this sentence, the Confucius words have special power to empower people.

15. Sodoku(素読) : reading with concentration for progress

At elementary kindergartens or nursery schools in Taku city, there are some another trials to inspire children. For example, to guide and teach the Rongo words and to encourage kids to memorize some important sentences of Rongo book there are some special study programs. Through simply reading the classics such as 論語、大学、小学、中庸、孝経, they memorize those sentences. Young students train his/her mental or spiritual power for life. Of course every subject of all kinds is so important but the most important subject is how to be a good person. These classics always guide and show us the right way for life. So every day reading classics makes our mind and brain the very fundamental basics to live.

This simple training "Sodoku" empowered the young at an innovation age of Japan. Those who participate in the historical innovation have read such basic classics. For instance just before the Meiji Restoration many young students in each local school have trained themselves every day. That experience brought wisdom and courage even virtue to those young fellows. Some of them visited The United States of America and European countries. In spite of the first visit to foreign countries they could meet and communicate with those nations important. Maybe the virtue helped a lot. For their study the text books the most important writer or teacher is Confucius.

16. Lifelong Education : never-ending effort

Lifelong education is one of the most important matters today. Compared to the past, we are blessed with a more healthy life by medical care progress. To develop self-realization in our lives we need correct and appropriate knowledge in each generation age.

In Taku city we put importance upon lifelong study or learning. It is necessary for people to receive an educational chance to learn what they need to study or know.

To do so we started "Citizen's College" for lifelong study with many various programs for people. The city government support financially, the members and students of its college plan and operate well. This program includes such as culture, sports, gardening, musical and social activities.

Also the Taku club of the aged started the program of "the age-favor graduate school". It is not a real graduate school but the name of the school has been made to empower the aged. Among its program there is Rongo Study every year. They study some sentences or quotations of Rongo.

**5: The Foundation for Confucius**

Taku city founded the public interest incorporated foundation "Koshinosato" (孔子の里), literally means "the village of Confucius", which originally started in 1990. This foundation board of trustees consists of socially active people from various fields. The president of the foundation is the mayor of Taku city, so I am now the president, and the vice president is the superintendent of education of Taku city. Which means Taku city put strong interest and assistance upon this foundation.

This "Koshinosato" foundation has taken care of all aspects to maintain the Taku Confucius Temple and direct its events such as the original education activities for the young and adults as some courses of lifelong study. Of course this foundation also takes part in a committee to manage the Rongo-Karuta Competition Conference.

It also introduced the traditional Chinese dances like a Lion dance (狮子舞), a waist dram (腰鼓) and a special praising Confucius dance (积菜舞) to educate the younger generation.

The reason for its name "the village of Confucius" is rooted in the city's history. More than 300 years ago the people of Taku have had a chance to worship Confucius teaching through looking at the Confucius temple and studying his lessons from the classics at the local school.

So there has been a saying that many people surrounding Taku area regarded Taku as "the village of Confucius". We thank our predecessors, ancestors and pioneers. They had an inspiration about the significance of education. Maybe such idea created the local school and our Confucius Temple in this countryside.

Education itself is vital and inevitable items for us as human beings. Only wisdom and positive attitude can explore the brighter future.

In order to do so, we need education. It depends on the atmosphere and environment of education. We also need the excellent teachers for study. Even though Confucius passed away 2565 years ago, his significant teaching contents are still living in this modern era. We can meet him in his books. We can talk in the Rongo book. His words and actions written in those old textbooks of Confucianism always bring a new inspiration for us.

The foundation members would always like to try and think of a new activity to promote Confucius spirit in our society for the future.

In 2005 the foundation has started up the junior guide system. In this system young students from elementary and junior high schools learn the history and explanation of Taku Confucius Temple, and they sometimes guide visitors to the Taku-seibyo Temple. It is a kind of lessen and practice to study Confucius. Members of the junior guide completely memorize explanation and realize the meaning of Confucius teachings. Visitors so far are pleased with their cute and friendly guide.

**6: Confucius and Future**

Today we are in changing world. These changes sometimes cause confusion in our mind and society. To overcome such matters we should create a better condition toward the future. To do so, we should focus on the vision and philosophy of Confucius as a teacher, guide and advisor for innovation.

Confucius left his words and records of his idea and activity. Of course those are in the acient time. Some says it is too old. It must be true to some extent.

However even though his words are so old his advices must be a meaningful one for us today. Each time we read his words we will be bestowed with inspiration, and it guides us to a better future for each of us.

In order to use or utilize Confucius vison, we need to hold our sense of mission. As Confucius mentioned about the age of 50 was the time of mission to set our lifelong purpose or target. At the edge of a half century we should focus and dig into our mind deeply to find our real mission. It must be different man by man through religious conditions between one another. But we can point out common value of life as human beings.

To think in such a way, we may sympathize with every person whom we meet everywhere. Even if we are different from each other in various ways for various reasons, we can look at the same feeling of truth.

In my country just before the Meiji era there was an unique person who loved Confucius so much. After the Meiji era started as a new age of the country he took the role of incubation. Especially he managed to start many important companies, and those companies are still take roles of Japanese economic vitality. His related companies are those of manufactures, national-bank and local-banks, gas industry, insurance company, paper industry, train-company, hotel, stock-exchange, beer brewery, textile industry and so on. So now he is said as the father of Japanese capitalism.

His name is Mr. Eiichi Shibusawa (1840-1931), the multi-talented person. He has such a strong enthusiasm on Confucius vision and sense of value that he left a famous saying "the Confucius Rongo on right hand, the Japanese abacus on left hand". He always tried to follow which was right rather than which was profitable. Through his trial he devoted himself for society development. Confucius teaching has encouraged always him.

As he did, we can do so. His custom watching the meaning of Confucius Rongo message inspired a lot.

We should follow such custom to explore our future personally and socially. Through such efforts, maybe someday each of us will be a father or mother of a new activity field of humans in the future. Of course like many people say this sounds like a vague dream, but as long as we are confident in ourselves and our efforts, we can make a new creation of society.

In order to accomplish our life fruitful with meaning, we need to cultivate our mind plant. It needs water, sunlight, minerals and so on. The most important item must be self-confidence. How can we grow it? Whenever we meet a good day or bad day, we have to follow just one righteous way. Such efforts bring us a peaceful mind and a strong spirit.

Confucius taught such important lesson. His word inspires us about our mission.

We should carry on realizing our mission day by day.

# 卷　三

# 儒学研究、教育、传播与普及

一、儒学思想与人物研究

二、儒学与当代教育

三、儒学传播与普及

# 目 录

## 卷三 儒学研究、教育、传播与普及

### 一、儒学思想与人物研究

## 二、儒学与当代教育

## 三、儒学传播与普及

## 一、儒学思想与人物研究

# 周易与中国哲学

北京师范大学 郑万耕

《周易》是中国文化的源头活水之一。《汉书·艺文志》以《周易》为“五经之首”、“大道之源”。用现代的观念来看，我们也可为说，中国哲学正是从《周易》这片沃土上成长起来的。不研究易学及其发展的历史，就很难深入了解中国哲学。著名哲学史家朱伯崑先生曾经说过：“中国人的理论思维水平，在同西方的哲学接触以前，主要是通过对《周易》的研究，得到锻炼和提高的。”《周易》的影响并不限于儒学的领域，其他系统的哲学也不同程度上从《周易》的研究中吸取对自己有用的东西。如魏晋玄学和道教哲学同易学的发展有着密切的联系。不懂得易学，对玄学的形成和演变，对道教的炼丹理论都难以做出正确的评论。而宋明道学作为中国古代哲学的一种形态，从周敦颐到朱熹，再到王夫之，其哲学体系和理论思维形式，是通过其易学而形成和发展起来的。周易文化对中国古代哲学的深刻影响和巨大贡献，是其他任何流派或系统都不可比拟的。现不揣浅陋，择其要者作一简略说明，以就教于各位专家、学者。

### 一、太极观

“太极”是周易文化最重要的范畴之一。通过对此范畴的研究和阐释，形成并不断完善了中国哲学的宇宙论和本体论体系。

战国时期的《易传》论述易卦形成的程序说：“易有太极，是生两仪，两仪生四象，四象生八卦。”此所谓“太极”并非实体性范畴，而是指蓍草数目的最高极限，属于筮法范畴。可是，此种解说包含着一种理论思维，即认为从太极到八卦是一个从单一到多元、从简单到复杂的不断分化的过程。正是在这种思维的启发下，后来的易学家和哲学家，才由此衍生出一套关于宇宙形成的理论。

到了汉代，《周易》被尊为五经之首，对《周易》的解说也成了一种专门的学问。《易纬·乾凿度》解释“易有太极”章，以探讨乾坤两卦和八卦是怎样形成的，从而提出了宇宙形成的四阶段说。认为“太极”乃浑而未分的元气，元气分化便产生了阴阳二气，阳气清轻，上升形成天，阴气重浊，下降形成地。天地之气相交合，就产生了宇宙万物。到宋代，道学鼻祖周敦颐作《太极图说》，又在此基础上提出了一个系统而精致的宇宙论体系，成为中国哲学中宇宙形成论的典型代表。

魏晋以降，中国易学和哲学都发生了巨大变化。作为易学和哲学重要范畴的太极，也赋予了新的涵义。在晋人韩康伯的《系辞注》中，保存了王弼对“大衍义”的解释，其中提出了玄学派的太极观。认为“不用之一”即是太极，此“一”并非数，故又可称为“无”。就哲学意义说，太极为无，天地万物为有。有生于无，有依赖于无。以此宣扬“以无为本”的世界观。王弼派以虚无实体为太极，既否定了《易纬》的神秘主义（以太极为北极神），又反对了汉易以太极为原初物质的学说。

从哲学史上看，玄学家不再讲太极生天地，太极生阴阳，而是认为天地没有开端，天地是太极的体现。太极是本是体，天地是末是用，太极乃天地赖以存在的根据。天地万物与太极的关系不再是彼生此的关系，也没有一个时间上的先后顺序，而是体用、本末的关系。这样，就由讨论太极生两仪，气（元气）生天地的宇宙形成论，走上了讲“天地万物皆以无为本”的宇宙本体论的道路。

南宋朱熹继承并发挥了程氏易学的太极观，认为“太极者，其理也”（《周易本义》），阴阳变易之理就是太极。太极之理没有行迹，所以又称为“无极”。无极表示太极之理是最高范畴，没有极限，并不是说在太极之先还有一个“无极”的阶段。所以他对周敦颐《太极图说》做了订正，改第一句为“无极而太极”。他不赞成宇宙发生论的观点，而认为太极生阴阳本无先后之可言，太极与万物也不是先有此而后有彼，“但统是一个大源，由体而达用，从微而至著耳”（《朱子语类》卷94）。太极之理为体，万物为用，体微而用显，万物乃太极之理的显现。依据此种理论解释周敦颐由“太极动而生阳”到“万物化生”的过程，阴阳五行以至万物都是太极之理自身的展开和显现，没有一个时间上的先后顺序；展开之后，太极又在阴阳、五行和万物之中，“人人有一太极，物物有一太极”（同上），一物各具一太极。太极与万物不即不离，只是一种本体与现象的关系。这样，就以程颐的“体用一源，显微无间”说改造了周敦颐的《太极图说》，从而将其宇宙发生论转变成为宇宙本体论的体系

明清之际，王夫之集宋明易学之大成，继承张载的“一物两体”说，又吸收朱熹的“物物有一太极”说和方以智的太极为理气统一体的观念，则以“太和絪缊之气”，解释太极本体的内涵，称其为“太和絪缊之本体”，“太和絪缊之实体”（《张子正蒙注·太和》）。这一方面表示，阴阳二气作为世界之本体，其特性在于合一，即相成相济，融为一体；有此太和絪缊之实体，阴阳二气方能发挥其动静、聚散、清浊等性能功效。另一方面又表示，阴阳合一之实体具有运动变化的性能。在王夫之看来，所谓“絪

缊”，就是“二气交相入而包孕以运动之貌”（《周易内传·系辞下》），阴阳二气相互渗透，其中包含有运动的本性。因此，王夫之认为，“太极”作为世界的本体，其自身具有运动的本性，此乃生化万物的根本。此种太极观，扬弃了张载以“清虚一大”言太极或本体的论点，将气本论从道家思想的影响下解脱出来，实现了张载及其后学没有完成的任务；同时，也打击了朱熹的“太极不动”说，解决了理学派长期未能解决的，即现象世界为什么流转不已、生生不息的问题。他深刻论证了太极作为阴阳合一之实体，既为万象的共同本源，又寓于天地万象之中，始终不脱离具体器物而存在，克服了脱离现象而言本体的种种弊病，将宋明以来本体论思潮的发展，推向了高峰，从而建立起了较为完善的气学本体论体系。

## 二、道器之辨

围绕道器关系所展开的辩论，是中国古代易学哲学长期讨论的重要问题，对中国哲学本体论的形成和发展产生了极为深刻的影响。

道器这对范畴也是《易传》提出来的。其中说：“形而上者谓之道，形而下者谓之器”（《系辞上》）。道指乾坤和阴阳变易的法则，法则是无形的，称为形而上。器指卦画和有形之物，称为形而下。但在易学史上，真正展开道器之辨，是从晋人韩康伯开始的。此后，围绕道器（形上形下）关系问题，便展开了长期的争论。

在韩康伯看来，一切有形有象的事物都是器，无形无象的东西即为道。而无形的东西总是有形事物的宗主。阴阳和万象作为有形象的形器，只有依靠形而上的道，才能存在。以此宣扬“天地万物皆以无为本”的玄学理论。

唐朝初年，孔颖达作《周易正义》，以体用范畴说明道器关系，进一步阐发并改造了韩康伯的道器观。关于道器关系，孔疏同韩康伯一样，区分了形而上和形而下，认为先有形而上的“道”，后有形而下的“器”，“先道而后形”；器依赖于道而存在，有道方有器，此即“凡有从无而生，形由道而立”（《系辞》疏）。但是，他以道为“体”，以器为“用”，认为体用是相联系的，不能脱离器用，孤立地空言道体。这是对玄学派的贵道贱器、贵无贱有倾向的一种纠正。同时，又将“道”归结为阴阳二气自生自化，无所营为的属性，从而扬弃了玄学派以“道”为虚无实体的内容，重新肯定了阴阳二气的永恒性，将玄学中的贵无论引向了崇有论。

两宋时期，易学空前兴盛，易学家们围绕着道器问题，更展开了长期的辩论。程朱理学以区分形而上和形而下两个世界为其学说的根本前提。程颐易学以此解释道和阴阳的关系，认为道和阴阳是有区别的，阴阳属于气的领域，气是有形的，不能称为“道”。“有形总是气，无形只是道”（《程氏遗书》六），只有所以为阴为阳者才是道。

二者虽有区别，道并非阴阳，但又不脱离阴阳，它们只是形上和形下的不同。他以道为理，理无形，属于形而上，即阴阳之所以然，以阴阳二气为形而下，认为阴阳二气作为器类，乃其所以然之理的显现，二者为体用一源，所以道不是阴阳，但又不离于阴阳。这就以本体论的观点解释了道和阴阳的关系，从而将道器有无之争引向了道器理气之争，揭开了宋明哲学中理气之辨的序幕。

南宋著名易学家和理学大师朱熹继承了程颐的说法，亦区别阴阳和道，以“所以阴阳者”为道，但更加明确地指道为“理”，即其所说：“此理即道也”（《朱子语类》卷74）。一阴一阳循环往复之理即是道。并进一步把道器之辨引向了理事之辨。他说：“一物便有阴阳，寒暑生杀皆见得是形而下者。事物虽大，皆形而下者，尧舜之事业是也。理虽小，皆形而上者。”（《朱子语类》卷75）这是区别阴阳变易之事和阴阳变易之理。事属于形而下的世界，道或理属于形而上的世界。朱熹认为：道器、理事两个世界既有区别，又有联系。就其联系说，阴阳之理通过阴阳之事表现自己，此即“道非器不形”；阴阳之事靠阴阳之理方能成立，此即“器非道不立”。就理事关系说，朱熹认为，有其理方有其事，理乃事之所以然，构成事物的本质，以此论证理为事的本原。并通过理事之辨，建立起其理本论的易学哲学体系。

与程朱理学派相反，心学派的易学则不区分形上形下，主道器合一说。比如程颢，以为道器虽有形上形下之分，但就本质说，道器并无区别，此即其所说：“器亦道，道亦器”（《程氏遗书》一）。又如王宗传作《童溪易传》，亦主此说。讲“道外无器，器外无道，其本一也。故形而上者与形而下者皆谓之形，则易之形见，盖有不可掩也。”认为道与器，二者不容分割。

功利学派薛季宣的易说，就哲学而言，主要讨论道器关系问题，又将心学派的道器不二说引向了“道不离器”说，断言道在器中，并非离器而独立自存的实体，器用乃无形之道体存在的依据。据此，他批评离事言理，离器求道的学说是异端之见，空无之学，不能以道为本，器为末。这又是对程朱学派道本器末说的一种打击。

元明易学中的气学和象学派，皆主道器合一说或道不离器说。如明初薛瑄认为道器是体用一源，显微无间的关系。所谓：“显者器也，微者道也。器不离道，道不离器，故曰无间。”（《读书续录》卷3）蔡清著《周易蒙引》，来知德著《周易集注》，也都讲道不离器，而方以智则明确地阐发为“道寓于器”说。

王夫之作为古代易学的集大成者，对易学史上的道器之辨也作了一次总结，比较正确地解决了道与器的关系问题。首先，他区分了形上和形下的关系，但否认有一个形而上的世界。认为形而上的道不能离开具体的形器而单独存在，形上即在形下之中，“道”的内容是由“器”决定的，“有形而后有形而上”（《周易外传》卷五）。其次，针对程朱道本器末的道器观，明确指出，充满天下的实体只是“器”，“天下惟器而已矣”，而“道”不能作为独立的实体存在。所以，“道”只能是“器”的道，不能说“器”是“道”的器，此即“道者器之道，器者不可谓之道之器也”（同上）。由此，王夫之又提出了一个十分重要命题，即“无其器则无其道”。“道”作为法则或一物之所以然，不能独立存在，只能以“器”作为自己存在的实体。从而阐发了没有个体便没有规律，没有个别便没有一般，没有现象便没有本质的理论思维。这样，就正确地解决了“道器”或“理事”谁依赖于谁的问题，从而在易学和哲学史上做出了重要贡献。

## 三、天人之学

天人关系问题是中国传统哲学的核心问题。《易传》综合早期儒道关于天人关系的学说，提出一个较为系统的天人谐调论，成为古代天人之学的主流。

作为战国时期第一部儒道融合的著述，《易传》接受老子“域中有四大”思想，提出“三才”说，肯定了人在自然界中的地位。它既承认天人相通，强调“天地设位，圣人成能”，“圣人则天”，“顺天休命”，又承认天道与人道的区别，开启了荀子、刘禹锡“天人相分”的先河。其所谓“制而用之谓之法”的观念成为荀子“制天命而用之”的先导。尤其值得重视的是，它提出“裁成天地之道，辅相天地之宜”的学说，强调人与自然的协调和统一，“与天地合其德”，“先天而天弗违，后天而奉天时”，主张在遵循自然规律的基础上，对自然加以辅助、节制或调整，使其更加符合人类的要求。人类在自然面前，既要有所作为，改变自然的现状，又要顺应自然，又不破坏自然。这是一种典型的天人谐调论，实乃“辅万物之自然而有所为”，克服了道家“蔽于天而不知人”的理论缺憾，较为正确地解决了自然与人为的关系，对中国古代天人之学的发展做出了重要贡献。在中国思想史上，此种学说一直受到易学家和哲学家们的重视和推崇，并不断加以阐扬和完善，建立起具有中国特色的天人之学的理论体系。

宋代易学家都追求天道与性命的贯通，着眼于探讨天与人、主与客、自然与社会的相互关系，企图通过这些探讨，找到某些规律性的东西，以指导人事。因此，他们都主张天人合一，认为天道与人道具有共同性，但其具体观点差异相当悬殊，并不完全一致。

心学派的先驱程颢不区分天和人，认为天人本无差别，于人之外别立一天，是讲天人二本，提出了“天人一本”说。南宋心学派易学的代表人物杨简，进一步发挥程颢的“天人一本”说，提出“天人本一”、“天人一致”等命题。而理学派易学的创立者程颐，同样主张合天人，一内外，提出了“天人一道”或“天人一理”说。但又认为天道与人道各有自己的本分，不能混同，要求人合于天道或天理。从而为儒家的名教理想提供了一个形上学的依据。

气学派易学的奠基人的张载，则提出了“天人合一”的命题，反对将天人加以割裂。因此，张载易学并不脱离天道而孤立地探索人道，也不脱离人道而孤立地探索天道，而是言天必及于人，言人必上溯于天，企图建立一个贯通天人，体用不二的思想体系。但又强调“人不可以混天”，反对把人的思虑忧患和仁德强加于天。天无心无为，无所主宰，而人则有思虑谋划，经营万事万物，以成就天地化育之功。这是对《易传》“与天地合其德”的天人谐调论的进一步发展，也为气学派建构一个天人之学的思想体系，奠定了理论基础。

明代末年，方孔炤、方以智父子著《周易时论合编》，继承张载的“圣人主天地”说，进一步发挥“圣人成能”的思想，提出了“圣人宰天”说。认为圣人作《易》，是教人依《周易》的法则，极深研几，认识世界的本质，掌握事物变易的规律，从而支配自然，治理好人类社会生活，做世界的主宰者。人类依据所认识的造化之理，发挥其能动性，“因造化之薪，传造化之火，热造化之水，制造化之器，熟造化之物”（《时论合编·系辞上》），即可以对自然物加以损益，创造出新的东西。这就将古老的天人之辨引向了改造自然的方向，是方氏易学对中国哲学的一大贡献。

著名易学大师王夫之则对宋明以来的天人之辨作了总结，又提出了“天人合用”的命题，主张“延天以祐人”（《周易外传·系辞上》）。他继承张载气学派易学的天人观，认为人是自然的产物，不能违背自然法则，此即其所说“以人合天”（《外传·系辞下》）；但人类又不同于一切自然物，“天道无择，而人道有辨”（《内传·系辞上》），具有高度的智慧，是天地万物的主导者，能自觉地为改善自己的生存条件而斗争。所以，人类不屈服于自然，此即“与天争权”，“天之所死，犹将生之”。也就是说，人类应该而且能够发挥自己的聪明才智，即主观能动性，延长自然的功能，使其更加适合于人类的需要，此即“延天以祐人”。然而，改变自然，不是破坏自然物和自然界的秩序，而是按照自然的基本法则，即阴阳变易之理，调整人与自然不谐调的关系。所以称其说为“延天”或“相天”。“延”或“相”，都表示不破坏自然。此种学说，主张人与自然并存，而且相资相济，共同发展，所谓“天人之合用”，辩证地处理了人与自然的关系，是王夫之天人之辨对易学哲学的一大贡献。

## 四、阴阳变易学说

阴阳变易学说乃《周易》知识系统的核心，经过历代易学家的阐发，成为中国哲学所特有的一种辩证思维方式。长期以来，这种思维方式成为中国知识界和文化人用来观察和解释世界的工具，对中国古代哲学、宗教、科学、文学、艺术以及政治、伦理生活，风俗习惯，都起了深刻的影响。

《易传》以阴阳变易法则解释和阐扬《周易》的基本原理，初步提出了阴阳变易学说的体系，大致包括四个方面的内容："一阴一阳之谓道"；"阴阳不测之谓神"；"日新之谓盛德，生生之谓易"；"刚柔相推而生变化"。历代易学家都在不断地阐发这些古老而又常新的命题，使之成为贯通整个中国哲学的理论思维，渗透到中华民族的思想意识之中。

汉代京房阐发"一阴一阳之谓道"说：《周易》是讲变化的，所谓变化，无非是阴阳变易。阴阳二气千变万化，新新不停，生生相续，永无止境，这就叫作"易"。而事物及其卦爻象的变易，总是又阴又阳，不能拘于一个方面，比如离卦象为二阳一阴，这是"本于纯阳，阴气贯中"（《京氏易传》）。如果只专于一面，有阳而无阴，或有阴而无阳，或者只能长不能消，其结果必然失败。所以《系辞传》说"一阴一阳之谓道"。他还阐发了阴阳相互转化的观念，提出"阴阳相荡，至极则反"的"物极则反"说。中国哲学中"物极必反"这一命题。就易学系统说，始于京房的"物极则反"说。扬雄模仿《周易》而作《太玄》，又将阴阳变易学说发展为"阴阳消息"说，并对事物发生、发展和消亡的过程，作了较为细致的分析，提出"九天"、"九事"说。同时又认为，事物在发展过程中总是有继承（因循），又有变革（革化），阐发了"因革相成"说，成为两汉时期辩证法思想的主要代表。

张载作为宋代著名的易学家和哲学家，更集中阐发了阴阳变易学说。他提出"阴阳兼体"说和"一故神，两故化"（《横渠易说·说卦》）说，以阴阳对立面相互渗透和相互推移说明一切事物的运动变化，认为其根源即存在于作为物质实体的、阴阳兼有的太极之气中。并对事物变化的两种形式即"著变"和"渐化"作了区分，所谓"变言其著，化言其渐"（《易说·系辞上》），认为显著的变化也必须经过逐渐积累的过程。这就说明了气为什么能够运动变化的问题，又将中国哲学中的内因论观点提高到了一个新的水平。这是张载易学的一大贡献。

南宋朱熹作为宋易中义理学派的集大成者，又提出"易只是一阴一阳"的命题，强调阴阳变易是《周易》的基本法则，认为一切事物的存在及其变化，归根到底，无非是一阴一阳。他更将阴阳变易的法则阐发为"阴阳流行"和"阴阳对待"说，流行指相互推移、相互转化；对待即相互交错，相互渗透，又意味着阳中有阴，阴中含阳。所以朱氏又提出了"阴阳各生阴阳"说，以说明卦象和事物的对立是错综复杂的，对立面是由许多层次构成的，不能将《周易》所说的"分阴分阳"简单化。从而进一步丰富和发展了《易传》以来的阴阳变易学说。

至明末清初，王夫之又对宋明易学及其哲学进行总结，提出了"阴阳实体"说，即以阴阳二气为天地万物的本体，以气的性能及其变化规律解释事物的变化法则，并将"一阴一阳之谓道"这一古老的命题纳入了气本论的体系。他以为，作为天地万物之本体的阴阳二气是“实有”的客观存在，人物之生死只表示阴阳二气互相屈伸往来，其本身并无损益增减。阴阳二气虽有差异，但总是相资相济，絪缊交会，谐和为一，从而构成万物的本体，推动事物的变化。阴阳相资互补，和谐一致是一切事物存在和发展的基本规律。王夫之还着重讨论了“神”作为阴阳二气生化万物的动因，为什么神妙莫测的问题。认为阴阳变易没有一成不变的格式，总是变动不居，“不主故常”。阴阳二气交合而生化万物，既有定又无定，既有序又无序，即既有必然性，又有其偶然性，反对以某种既定的格式或公式规范世界的变化过程。这又在承认确定性的基础上，提出了非确定性的原则，“虽有大成之序而实无序”（《周易内传·系辞下》），认为人类所认识到的原则、规律和模式，不可能概括和穷尽世界变化的全部过程，特别是对世界未来的变化，不可能做出确切不移的结论。此种学说，闪烁着辩证思维的光芒，其对世界变易性的论述，无论从深度和广度说，都超过了前辈学者的水平，从而对中国哲学思维的发展做出了重要贡献。

除上述几点之外，《周易》所提出的“保合太和”的价值理想，“仰观俯察”、“彰往察来”、“穷理尽性以至于命”的认知方法，“自强不息，厚德载物”的人生总原则，“与时偕行”、“革故鼎新”的创新精神，都对中国哲学产生了深远影响。总起来说，在长期的历史过程中，《周易》文化对中国哲学的发展做出不可磨灭的巨大贡献。在大力发展中国文化的现时代，对《易经》哲学探讨、对易学理论思维的研究，更应该引起各有关方面的高度重视，加大力度，以创造中国文化新的辉煌。

# 周易之中和思想

香港城市大学 郑滋斌

## 一、緒言

“中和”思想向來視為儒家一項重要思想，它的發生來自何處，並不容易追溯，在《周易》中，它沒有一起出現，但“中”與“和”，尤其是“中”字，卻常出現，如果十翼是孔子的作品，這樣《周易》的“中”與“和”思想，恐怕就是儒學“中”、“和”說的部分源頭，至少儒家的“中”、“和”說，可以在《周易》中尋得。

在《周易》六十四卦中，有四十八個卦，在其〈彖辭〉、〈象辭〉中，出現“中”這字詞，它們是：坤、蒙、需、訟、師、比、小畜、履、泰、同人、大有、豫、隨、蠱、臨、觀、噬嗑、復、无妄、大過、坎、離、咸、恆、大壯、晉、睽、蹇、解、損、益、夬、姤、萃、升、困、井、鼎、震、艮、漸、歸妹、旅、巽、兌、節、既濟、未濟。至於提及“和”的，則只有乾、咸、夬三個卦而已，但沒有“中和”合成詞。可見在《周易》裏，沒有把“中”、“和”合在一起說的思想，兩者分別出現，而“中”又較“和”為常說到的概念。同樣地，《論語》也沒有把“中”、“和”合在一起說，記錄孔子對“中”與“和”意見的文字，分別只有兩條，細讀其文字，可見孔子較重視“中”。

對於《周易》〈彖辭〉和〈象辭〉的作者，至今仍未有定說，而向來謂孔子撰寫十翼，而包括上述二者。這兩部分表現對“中”與“和”的意涵，而重在“中”的主張，與孔子在《論語》中的表現不謀而合，然則整理《周易》對“中”“和”的思想旨歸，有助於認識孔子在這兩個課題方面的思想，甚至於思量《周易》與孔子的關係。既然《周易》與《論語》沒有把“中和”合在一起說，則日後儒者把“中和”並說，恐怕不是孔子的原意。

在討論《周易》的“中”與“和”的思想旨歸前，先看《論語》中孔子的“中”、“和”意思。

《論語·雍也篇》“子曰：“中庸之為德也，其至矣乎！民鮮能久矣。”魏何晏認為“庸，常也。中和，可常行之德也。世亂先王之道廢，民鮮能行此道久矣，非適今也。”[①] 梁皇侃說：“中，中和也；庸，常也。鮮，少也。言中和可常行之德，是先王之道，其理甚至善，而民少有行此者也。已久，言可歎之深也。”[②] 把“中”解釋為“中和”，並不合理。宋邢昺有相類似的意見，說：“此章言世亂人不能行中庸之德也。中，謂中和；庸，常也；鮮，罕也。言中和可常行之德也。其至極矣乎？以世亂先王之道廢，故民罕能行此道久多時矣，非適而今也。”[③]

朱熹也許覺察到把“中”解為“中和”，並不妥當，所以他的《論語集注》作了以下解釋：“中者，無過無不及之名也。庸，平常也。至，極也。鮮，少也。言民少此德，今已久矣。”這解釋恐怕啟自程頤，朱熹引程子說：“不偏之謂中，不易之謂庸。中者，天下之正道；庸者，天下之定理。自世教衰，民不興於行，少有此德久矣。”[④] 認為“中”就是不偏不倚，無過無不及，這在孔子學說中的，是有它的獨特性和重要性的，人能夠秉持這種精神去處事待人，才顯現不凡的智慧與情操；然而孔子認為“民鮮能久矣”，可見得“中”、處“中”、行“中”，是極不容易的事，這不但在實際的空間位置上如是，在人的心理素質也如是。

不能得中時，孔子認為可能有兩個表現。《論語·子路篇》子曰：“不得中行而與之，必也狂狷乎！狂者進取，狷者有所不為也。”皇侃引東漢包咸說：“中行，行能得其中者也。言不得中行，則欲得狂狷者也。”[⑤] 朱熹則別有會心，說：“行，道也。狂者志極高而行不掩，狷者知未及而守有餘。蓋聖人本欲得中道之人而教之，然既不可得，而徒得謹厚之人，則未必能自振拔而有為也，故不若得此狂狷之人，猶可因其志節而激厲裁抑之，以進於道，非與其終於此而已也。”[⑥] 朱熹把“行”解為“道”，大概受到孟子的啟發。《孟子·盡心下》引《論語》此章時，便作：“孔子‘不得中道而與之，必也狂狷乎！狂者進取，狷者有所不為也。’”孟子接著說：“孔子豈不欲中道哉？不可必得，故思其次也。”分明孟子把“中行”視為“中道”，朱熹解釋這章時，便徵引《孟子》的文字。“中道”在《周易》中是普遍的概念，孟子是否因此而作了結合，不得而知，但朱熹把“中行”解釋為“中道”，較包咸“行能得其中者也”的解釋，卻無

① （梁）皇侃：《論語集解義疏》卷三，載魏何晏《論語集解》語，《四庫全書》第 195 冊，上海：上海古籍出版社，1987 年，第 394 頁。

② 同上注。

③ 邢昺：《論語注疏》卷六，《四庫全書》第 195 冊，第 585 頁。

④ 朱熹：《四書章句集注·論語集注》卷三，中華書局，1983，第 91 頁。

⑤ 皇侃：《論語集解疏證》卷七，第 462 頁。

⑥ 朱熹：《四書章句集注·論語集注》卷七，第 147 頁。

意間貼近《周易》的概念。如果承認《周易》與孔子的關係，則這樣的結合，無疑更有會心之言。

在《論語》中，孔子談到“和”的，只有兩條。一在《子路篇》。孔子說：“君子和而不同，小人同而不和。”何晏認為：“君子心和，然其所見各異，故曰不同。小人所嗜好者同，然各爭其利，故曰不和也。”① 皇侃說：“和謂心不爭也，不同謂立志各異也。君子之人，千萬千萬，其心和如一，而所習立之志業不同也。云小人同而不和者，小人為惡如一，故云同也。好鬭爭，故云不和也。”② 何晏和皇侃從心志出發，認為“和”就是不與人計短論長，而“同”則從原則上說。朱熹雖然也從心志出發，但加入義利之辨這元素，用來說明“和”與“同”的特性。《論語集注》說：“和者無乖戾之心，同者有阿比之意。”又引尹焞之言，曰：“君子尚義，故有不同；小人尚利，安得而和。”③ 由於孔子的話，到此為止，沒有其他信息可供思考，以故孔子的“和”、“同”思想，並不能夠清楚地說明他所討論的題材內容，這樣，不論從心志立論，或者增加義利這元素，都是可以的，但如果結合下文《論語·季氏篇》孔子對“和”的意思，則義利這元素，可能較適合。

孔子因季氏將伐顓臾的事，再次提及“和”這觀念。他對冉有說：“丘也聞有國有家者，不患貧而患不均，不患寡而患不安。蓋均無貧，和無寡，安無傾。”從政治穩定性來思考“和”。包咸認為“政教均平則不貧矣，上下和同不患寡矣，小大安寧不傾危矣。”④ 在“和”之上加入“同”，沒有把握“和”與“同”的不同性質，他的解釋，徒然令“和而不同”這觀念變得含混起來，以為“和同”是相同的價值觀，而邢昺仍包咸之說，殊不足取，故不予引述。⑤ 朱熹從季氏在魯國的位置，與魯君的情勢作比較，並思量冉有為季氏侵略顓臾的藉口，做出較合理的解釋。《論語集注》云：“寡謂民少，貧謂財乏。均謂各得其分，安謂上下相安。季氏之欲取顓臾，患寡與貧耳。然是時季氏據國，而魯公無民，則不均矣。君弱臣強，互生嫌隙，則不安矣。均則不患於貧而和，和則不患於寡而安，安則不相疑忌，而無傾覆之患。”⑥ 朱熹認為孔子在這章的“和”，是一種“和衷共濟”的心，是一種協調性的處理，而基於勢力、利益相若的情

---

① 皇侃：《論語集解疏證》卷七，載何晏《論語集解》，第463頁。

② 皇侃：《論語集解義疏》卷七，第463頁。邢昺《論語注疏》合襲何晏之說，云：“此章別君子小人志行不同之事也。君子心和，然其所見各異，故曰不同；小人所嗜好者則同，然各爭利，故曰不和。”卷十三，第650頁。無甚發明，故不予討論。

③ 朱熹：《四書章句集注·論語集注》卷七，第147頁。

④ 皇侃：《論語集解疏證》卷八，第489頁。

⑤ 邢昺：《論語注疏》卷十六：“蓋均無貧，和無寡，安無傾者，孔子既陳其所聞，更為言其理。蓋言政教均平則不貧矣，上下和同不患寡矣，小大安寧不傾危矣。”第680頁。

⑥ 朱熹：《四書章句集注·論語集注》卷七，第170頁。

況產生的，但這需要季氏能夠有明辨義利的心志，才可以達到“均無貧，和無寡，安無傾”的結果。

從《論語》所載孔子的“中”、“和”主張，雖然可以肯定兩者都是治國者需要思量的課題，可是既然說“中庸之為德也，其至矣乎！民鮮能久矣”，顯然孔子把“中”看得較“和”為重要，而這同樣屢見於《周易》多個〈象辭〉和〈彖辭〉中，細讀其中“中”“和”的文字，固然可以了解《周易》在這方面的思想主張，同時可以藉此以思量《周易》十翼與孔子的關係，孔子撰寫〈象辭〉和〈彖辭〉的可能性。一旦〈象辭〉與〈彖辭〉與孔子的關係明朗化起來，甚至由此而容許推斷孔子撰寫〈象辭〉與〈彖辭〉，則孔子以至儒家思想的研究範圍和內蘊，才可以因《周易》得到擴闊和縱深。

## 二、《周易》的“中”說二義

《周易》的“中”包括三個內容：“中”是處事方式和態度；“中”是個人修養；“剛”是“中”的本質。一和二，只是一體兩面，既用於修身，又施於行事，然則三個內容，可總結為兩個義項。這兩義又基於兩個重要性質，一是本身要“中正”或“正中”，二是能夠“中正”或“正中”，端在於它是以陽爻居陽位，而陽為剛，故述說“中”時，便又出現“剛”這概念，而是“中”的本質。無論是“中正/正中”還是“剛而中”，都需要“得中”才成。以下分述這兩個意旨。

### (一)“中正”或“正中”

《周易》在六十四個卦中，有十個卦都在卦的二、五爻位置，用上“正中”或“中正”這詞語，它們是〈乾卦〉的九二〈文言〉、〈需卦〉的九五〈象辭〉、〈訟卦〉的九五〈象辭〉、〈豫卦〉的六二〈象辭〉、〈晉卦〉的六二〈象辭〉、〈姤卦〉的九五〈象辭〉、〈艮卦〉的六五〈象辭〉、〈比卦〉的九五〈象辭〉、〈隨卦〉的九五〈象辭〉、〈巽卦〉的九五〈象辭〉。此外，散見於其他各卦的“中”、“中正”、“正中”或者“剛中”等詞語，仔細檢察，或多或少與二、五爻有關。《周易·繫辭下傳》第九章已作了歸維：“二多譽……五多功。”所以兩者較少問題，多受讚賞，與它們位於卦的“正中”或“中正”位置有關。

“中正”、“正中”等概念，對於任何人，尤其是執政者，在修身、行為、處事等都有極重要和正面、積極的指導作用。

能夠秉持中正的心態，心理質素良好，平日處事，便不會遲疑不決。〈豫卦〉六二爻辭說：“介于石，不終日，貞吉。”〈象辭〉說：“不終日，貞吉；以中正也。”〈豫卦〉的二三四爻為艮為石，伏兌為附決，為剛貞，所以說：“介于石。”二爻為離，為日，既已居於是而得正，不變，則二三四爻成不了離卦，以故說“不終日”。這樣沒有不好，因為二爻得中得位，所以說“貞吉”。《易經·繫辭上傳》對這爻又作了發揮，說：

子曰：“知幾其神乎！君子上交不諂，下交不瀆，其知幾乎！幾者，動之微，吉凶之先見者也。君子見幾而作，不俟終日。《易》曰：‘介于石，不終日，貞吉。’介如石焉，寧用終日，斷可識矣。”

《易·繫辭》的“子”，一般認為就是“孔子”。他認為君子要抱持中正之心與人交接，能夠對上不諂、對下不瀆，這思想在〈中庸〉也有類近說明：“在上位，不陵下；在下位，不援上。”又說：“是故居上不驕，為下不倍。國有道，其言足以興；國無道，其默足以容。”① 漢揚雄在《法言·修身》也說：“君子之所慎：言、禮、書，上交不諂，下交不驕，則可以有為矣。”② 因為一旦放棄自己的做人原則，與人相交而無準則，可能與人結怨，或者取笑於人，均足以令自己名聲有損，甚或釀成禍災，鑑諸歷史，不乏其例。在禍事未成，端倪難見時，一般人不會相信，唯有智者才能洞微識深，免於禍害。〈中庸〉說：“知遠之近，知風之自，知微之顯，可與入德矣。”③ 也就是這意思。然則秉中而立，不偏不倚，如石之堅剛，無猶豫，不疑惑，才明白交際之道，知為人之方，〈豫卦〉六二重視中位之道理，也就豁然起來。

能以“中正”或“正中”之心待民，則可以與民同樂。〈需卦〉九五〈象辭〉說：“酒食貞吉，以中正也。”〈需卦·彖辭〉說：“需，須也。”須者，待也。〈需卦〉的九五爻，王弼認為“需之所須，以待達也。已得天位，暢其中正，无所復須，故酒食而已，獲貞吉也。”④ 這解釋是可以的，但不夠清晰。要知道〈需卦〉的坎卦為酒，居於在乾上，而乾卦二爻得位之中，五為坎卦之中位，亦為乾之君位，所以說：“酒食貞吉”，全由於能在中正之位。本來，〈需卦〉的〈象辭〉說：“雲上於天，需，君子以飲食宴樂。”但要到第五爻時，才出現“飲食宴樂”的情形，因為發展到這爻，君子居中得位。宋朝耿南仲的《周易新講義》對這爻的意蘊，有不錯的發揮，說：

雲上於天，則所需方在上而未下也，故言飲食宴樂者，所需方及朋友故舊，兄弟甥舅，忠臣嘉賓，而未及民也。需於酒食，則及民矣。蓋凡民莫不有酒食之養，但不得與人君宴樂耳。今九五獨言酒食，而不言宴樂，是以知其及民也。蓋中正盛德，九五尊位，故能需於天下之求，无不厭足其分。⑤

儒家思想的終極關懷，在於開物成務，而民受其澤，之所以能臻達是境，則君臣

① 朱熹：《四書章句集注·中庸章句》，第24頁。

② 揚雄：《法言·修身》，韓敬注本，北京：中華書局，1992年，第52頁。

③ 朱熹：《四書章句集注·中庸章句》，第36頁。

④ 魏王弼：《周易注》卷一，《四庫全書》第七冊，上海：上海古籍出版社，1987年，第209頁。

⑤ （宋）耿南仲：《周易新講義》卷二，《四庫全書》第九冊，第605頁。

須合德同志，上下和諧，可以一起分享成果，飲宴歡樂，這精神從朝廷開始，以至於民間。《詩經・小雅・鹿鳴》，《毛詩》〈小序〉解釋為“燕群臣嘉賓也。既飲食之，又實幣帛筐篚，以將其厚意，然後忠臣嘉賓得盡其心矣。”這是朝廷的君臣燕樂，〈需卦〉的九五爻辭，則是遍惠廣施，及於民的表現。要達成這功效，由於君主能居中得位，而且其心能持中。

為君者，固然要惠澤於民，而仁心也可用於禽獸。〈比卦〉九五〈爻辭〉說：“顯比，王用三驅，失前禽。邑人不誡，吉。”〈象辭〉解釋道：“顯比之吉，位正中也。舍逆取順，失前禽也。邑人不誡，上使中也。”〈比卦〉上坎下坤，五陰一陽，而陽在五爻。所謂“王用三驅，失前禽”，張載《橫渠易說》：

失前禽，謂三面而驅，意在緩逸之，不務殺，惟順奔，然后取之，故被傷者少也。以剛居中，而顯明比道，伐止有罪，不為濫刑，故邑人不誡，為上用中，此之謂也。[①]

張載所說的，大抵就是天子田獵時去其三面的精神，它可能始於商湯。《史記・殷本紀》載：

湯出，見野張網四面，祝曰：“自天下四方皆入吾網。”湯曰：“嘻，盡之矣！”乃去其三面，祝曰：“欲左，左。欲右，右。不用命，乃入吾網。”諸侯聞之，曰：“湯德至矣，及禽獸。”[②]

《禮記・王制》云：“天子不合圍，諸侯不掩羣。”大抵周代沿商湯這一措施，而目的一如鄭玄注稱“為盡物也”,[③] 在網開一面。

這種仁恩愛心，由於能得中正之位，這個“位”，既是可見之位置，也是無形的心理狀態，在處理訟訴時，兩者同樣重要。〈訟卦〉九五〈爻辭〉說：“訟元吉。”〈象〉辭說：“訟元吉，以中正也。”〈訟卦〉由上乾下坎兩卦組成。乾為天，坎為水，〈訟卦・象辭〉說：“君子以作事謀始。”儒家不希望有紛爭，孔子便曾說：“聽訟，吾猶人也，必也使無訟乎！”（《論語・顏淵》）這是一種持中的心理狀態。王弼解釋〈訟卦・象辭〉說：“無訟在於謀始，謀始在於作制。契之不明，訟之所以生也。物有其分職，不相濫，爭何由興？訟之所以起，契之過也。故有德司契而不責於人。”[④] 訴訟的出現，原因很多，王弼找到其中一個，在於為政者如何制定法律條文，制定的原則是否合乎中道。條文不清楚，不合乎中道，的確會導致訴訟，而訴訟的過程、發展會令當事人備受困擾，蠱惑者得以乘間鼓舌舞文，這一切都由於不由乎中，不發乎誠。為政者如

---

① 宋張載：《橫渠易說》卷一，《四庫全書》第 8 冊，第 675 頁。

② （漢）司馬遷：《史記》卷三，北京：中華書局，1972 年，第 95 頁。

③ 《禮記》卷三〈王制〉，鄭玄注，《四庫全書》第 115 冊，第 263 頁。

④ 王弼：《周易注》卷一，總 210 頁。

果明白這點，便要重視自己的位置和身份，重視自己的心理質素，以中正之心制定條文法規，這樣即使有訴訟，也可使爭論的過程、結果得到合理的解決。或者在處理訴訟時，秉持中正之心，以判斷案件的是非曲直，然後可以得到合理的裁決。明乎此，〈訟卦〉的九五〈爻辭〉和〈象辭〉所說的，意思便豁然起來。王弼說："處得尊位為訟之主，用其中正以斷枉直，中則不過，正則不邪，剛无所溺，公无所偏，故訟元吉。"①

《周易》的陰陽哲學，極具啟發性，陽爻雖然居陽位，而不得中位，仍未能發揮其優勢，〈訟卦〉的九五爻，正好符合陽爻居中的條件，主政者居是，便要善於運用其性質和位勢，能夠以中正之心臨民處事，才可以避免或者減少訟事的出現。

能夠秉持中正之心，居中正之位，領導者自然有賢能之臣追隨。〈隨卦〉九五爻辭說："孚于嘉，吉。"〈象辭〉曰："孚于嘉吉，位正中也。"〈隨卦〉上兑下震，卦辭說："元亨利貞，无咎。"〈彖辭〉解釋說："隨，剛來而下柔，動而說隨，大亨貞，无咎，而天下隨時。隨時之義大矣哉!"隨的性質既然如此，現在九五之位，在乾為君位，在兑則陽處陰，〈隨卦〉內藏坎卦，而坎為孚，故有誠信之意蘊藏於內。為政者處高位而得中，以誠信待人，且收陰柔之德性，所以陰陽合德，於是既嘉且吉。

與〈隨卦〉九五爻辭之義相近的，是〈臨卦〉六五爻辭，說："知臨，大君之宜，吉。"〈象辭〉說："大君之宜，行中之謂也。"〈臨卦·象辭〉說："澤上有地，臨。君子以教思无窮，容保民无疆。"本來就指示作為領袖的，要有包容的氣度，如地之畜水而為澤，顯示無疆之坤德，這樣可以容受一切，才可以保民。有這氣度和智慧，一旦為天下之領導人，便可以成就大事業，所以六五爻辭要給有意於為領袖者指導〈臨卦〉的意思，誠如張浚所開示的例子："周成任周公為知臨，政事一出，恃為心腹，周公聰明智力，成王之聰明智力也，成王知臨矣。"② 此爻居坤之二，以陽行陰之性質，捨去五陽之尊，而甘於與二陰相配，就是一種過人智慧和胸襟，而全由於能夠明白"行中"之道。"中"者不偏，恰如其分，這就是一種良好的心理質素的表現。

與"中正"或"正中"概念相近的，是"中道"，而它出現於〈蠱〉、〈離〉、〈夬〉和〈既濟〉的二爻位置上。

〈蠱卦〉九二〈爻辭〉說："幹母之蠱，不可貞。"〈象辭〉說："幹母之蠱，得中道也。"張浚說："事繼世主，而事適墮壞，求以治之，其道貴中，不可過，過則失中，且强所難能，卒不可行，何益於治，周公相成王，善用其中，終能大文武之業，不可貞，謂不可過貞，非直謂貞道不可行也，故夫子明為之訓曰，得中道云，二以剛居巽

---

① 王弼：《周易注》卷一，總210頁。

② 張浚：《紫巖易傳》卷二，第66頁。

中，是謂得中道。”[①]

〈離卦〉六二〈爻辭〉說：“黃離，元吉。”〈象辭〉說：“黃離元吉，得中道也。”二是坤卦主位，而坤為臣，乾坤生六子，離卦六二之位，仍然因它是坤的主位而受到重視，故〈離卦〉六二〈爻辭〉和〈象辭〉有以上的表示。朱震再解釋說：“黃者，地之中，萬物必有所麗，六二坤柔在下，麗乎中，而與五合一，得中道也。夫中者，天地萬物之所共，由天地之長久，日月維斗之不息，聖人之道亘古今而无弊者也。六二得之，故能守正而不遷，乘剛而不懼，抱明德而獨照，是以元吉。”[②]

〈夬卦〉九二爻辭說：“惕號，莫夜有戎，勿恤。”〈象辭〉說：“有戎勿恤，得中道也。”〈夬卦〉上兑下乾，乾卦〈象辭〉說：“天行健，君子以自強不息”，〈乾卦文言〉於九三〈爻辭〉說：“君子終日乾乾，夕惕若，厲，无咎。”〈夬卦〉二爻如果有所動作，變而為陰，便出現離、巽兩卦。離為目，巽為風，又為多白眼，張浚說：“二居乾中，乾健不息為惕乾，九三亦曰，夕惕若厲，號先事戒備也，教化素行，禮法刑政素修，皆惕號事，惕號，君子之恭也，戎烏恤乎，莫夜莫夜有戎，變皆倉卒，浮言胥起，未易明也，斯蓋眾人所甚懼，君子得中，先事備具，尚奚恤乎？”[③] 其分析值得參考。

〈既濟卦〉六二〈爻辭〉說：“婦喪其茀，勿逐，七日得。”〈象辭〉說：“七日得，以中道也。”〈既濟卦〉的下卦為離，為中女，為文。二爻為坤位，為輿；三爻為坎位，為輪。二爻與五爻相呼應，往而之五，則成震，震為竹，竹在車前，與離文之象相結合，以故有婦人、茀之象。本來五爻居陽位，宜不動，但為了要成就茀之象，以故二之五，一旦如此，則離卦不存，而文明不復，所以說“婦喪其茀”了。既然如此，二爻宜不動，這樣才正確，以故有“勿逐”之意。從二爻開始計算，至上爻為五，然後從初爻計算，至二爻為止，其數為七。故有“七日得”之意。簡單說來，〈既濟卦〉六二爻辭強調能秉執中道，便有所獲。

（二）“中”與“剛”的關係

“中”既然如此重要，但它一定要有“剛”的性質，才可以在任何環境中巋然屹立。

〈蒙卦・象辭〉說：“初筮告，以剛中也。再三瀆，瀆則不告，瀆蒙也。蒙以養正，聖功也。”這裏說的“剛中”，一般認為跟〈蒙卦〉第二爻有關係，而它是這卦的精神所在。〈蒙卦〉九二〈爻辭〉說：“包蒙，吉。納婦，吉。子克家。”〈蒙卦〉上艮下坎，山在水上，二爻陽居陽位，五爻陰居陽位，雖然得中，而均未得位，一旦二與

① 張浚：《紫巖易傳》卷二，第 62 頁。
② 朱震：《漢上易傳》卷三，第 110 頁。
③ 張浚：《紫巖易傳》卷五，第 137 頁。

五呼應，二爻陽剛而能接受五爻陰柔，情況便起變化。從卦的結構和內容看，上艮為少男為蒙，現在二爻能夠包容接受艮卦五爻，陰陽相濟，所以說“吉”。二爻一旦與五爻相應，而〈巽卦〉成，巽為長女，所以說“納婦”，艮巽相配合，故曰“吉”。原來下卦為坎，為中子，由乾卦而來，所以說“子克家”。由此可見，不論在任何情況下，“中”與“正”的關係極其密切，而二爻在這卦能夠秉持中而且堅毅剛健的性質，便可以成就家道。家與國的關係至為密切，把持家之道用之於國，則何所往而不利?

由人而成家，家是構成社會的最基本單位，合群而成眾，其力量絕對不可容忽視。〈師卦·卦辭〉說：“師，貞，丈人，吉，无咎。”〈彖辭〉解釋說：“師，眾也。貞，正也。能以眾正，可以王矣。剛中而應，行險而順，以此毒天下，而民從之，吉，又何咎矣。”從“師，眾也”，到“可以王矣”。意思很清楚，“剛中而應”以下，解釋〈卦辭〉所以說“吉，无咎”的原因，而“剛中而應”一句，則發揮九二、六五爻辭的意思。〈師卦〉是上坤下坎，五陰一陽，這陽爻在二位，用來指揮師眾，可見〈師卦〉的精神在二爻。二爻是陽剛居中位，與六五陰爻相呼應，所以說“剛中而應”，坤為順，而坎為陰，二三四爻為震，為行，所以說“行險而順”。秉持正心驅使民眾，即使需要戰爭，而民莫不從。正如朱震所稱：“聖人不得已而用之，以去民之害，猶用毒藥以攻疾，雖曰毒之，其實生之，以此毒天下，而民安有不從者哉!”[①]（卷一）所謂“以生道殺民，雖死不怨殺者。”這種帶領百姓不畏艱難、勇敢前往的精神，需要領導者有“剛”的本質，才有機會成就非常之功。

師為眾，能夠得到羣眾的幫助，果效當然大，故此〈師卦〉之後是〈比卦〉。〈比卦·彖辭〉曰：“比，吉也，比，輔也，下順從也。原筮元永貞，无咎，以剛中也。不寧方來，上下應也。”緊接於〈師卦〉的是〈比卦〉，〈序卦傳〉說：“師者眾也。眾必有所比，故受之以比。比者，比也。”師是眾，而比是相輔相助，人數眾多，自然出現互相依靠的情形。以故〈彖辭〉說：“比，吉也。比，輔也。”之所以說“下順從也”，因為坤下坎上，全卦只有九五是陽爻，其餘為陰爻，五爻居中得位，得眾力依輔，而坤為順，故云。“原筮”以下，朱震說：“原，再也，如原蠶、原廟之原。〈比〉自〈復〉來，一變〈師〉，二變〈謙〉，三變〈豫〉。自〈謙〉至〈豫〉，有〈艮〉，手持〈震〉草，占筮之象，故曰原筮。原筮，則其慎至矣。”[②] 按：《周禮》：“禁原蠶者。”鄭玄注：“原，再也。”是朱震所依據的理由，如其說無訛，則“原筮”就是“再筮”，本來在〈蒙卦〉說：“初噬告，以剛中也。再三瀆，瀆則不告，瀆蒙也。”然而慎於處事，並無不妥，故朱震的意見是合理的。能夠筮而“元永貞无咎”，〈彖辭〉作者認為是由

---

① 朱震：《漢上易傳》卷一，第31頁。

② 朱震：《漢上易傳》卷一，第37頁。

於九五爻有“剛中”的本質。

〈小畜·彖辭〉說：“小畜，柔得位而上下應之，曰小畜。巽剛中而志行，乃亨。”虞翻認為〈小畜卦〉與〈需卦〉和〈豫卦〉、〈復卦〉有關。[①]〈需卦〉六爻變，遂成〈小畜卦〉。〈豫卦〉是震上坤下，四爻陽，其餘都是陰，與〈小畜卦〉四爻陰，其餘是陽，恰好成對比。〈豫卦〉上卦與下卦互換，便成〈復卦〉，從另一角度言，把〈豫卦〉的四爻與初爻相換，也成〈復卦〉，可見四爻在〈小畜卦〉、〈豫卦〉和〈復卦〉的微妙性質。〈復卦〉是十二消息卦中的第一卦，春雷萌動，大地蘊藏生氣，開始有所蓄積，虞翻以故說：“復小陽潛，所畜者少，故曰小畜。”〈小畜卦〉既然只有第四爻是陰爻，其餘是陽爻，以陰柔性質居於是，四與初應，而又與五相鄰，所以說“柔得位而上下應之。”此外，二爻是陽爻居陰位，不得其位，唯有第五爻以陽爻居陽位，得中得位，所以說“巽剛中而志行，乃亨。”這啟示了甚麼？張浚說：“小畜何以尚往？曰：臣事君，勉盡吾道而已，不以未孚而怠其愛君之心，畜道斯成。孟子曰：‘畜君何尤？畜君者，好君也。’小畜貴往。〈序卦〉曰：‘物畜然後有禮。’小畜其必自禮始乎？”[②]其意見是可取的。

〈履卦·彖辭〉說：“履，柔履剛也。說而應乎乾，是以履虎尾，不咥人亨。剛中正。履帝位而不疚，光明也。”〈履卦〉上乾下兌，兌為少女，為陰；乾為父，為陽，以陰隨陽，所以說“柔履剛也。”兌為口，為悅懌，所以說“說而應乎乾”。全卦只有第三爻是陰爻，其餘是陽爻，王弼認為這就是〈履卦〉的主爻。[③]兌是西方，是虎，既然它跟隨乾卦，以說“履虎尾”，這樣本來很危險，不過，它以陰柔性質自處，以故沒有被虎所咥，故曰“不咥人亨”。〈履卦〉上為乾，為君，五爻是乾卦主位，陽爻處陽位，得中得正，故曰“剛中正，履帝位而不疚，光明也。”從這〈彖辭〉得到的消息，張浚認為可從堯舜之事來說明，他說：“堯安安允恭克讓，光被四表，舜溫恭允塞，重華協帝，奚其疚？”[④]

〈大過·彖辭〉說：“大過，大者過也。棟橈，本末弱也。剛過而中，巽而說行，利有攸往，乃亨。大過之時義大矣哉！”〈序卦傳〉說：“不養得不可動，故受之以〈大過〉。”〈大過卦〉緊隨〈頤卦〉之後，〈頤卦〉與〈大過卦〉剛好完全相反，比較起來，〈大過卦〉顯得動作極大，所以〈大過·彖辭〉說：“大者過也。”〈大過卦〉初與上爻都是陰爻，形成頭尾柔而中間剛的情形。〈大過·卦辭〉有“棟橈”二字，〈彖辭〉解

---

① 李鼎祚：《周易集解》引虞翻說，《四庫全書》第七冊，第33頁。

② 張浚：《紫巖易傳》卷一，第32頁。

③ 魏王弼：《周易注》卷一：“凡彖者，言乎一卦之所以為主也。成卦之體在六三也。”，第213頁。

④ 張浚：《紫巖易傳》卷一，第35頁。

釋這“棟橈”現象，是由於“本末弱也。”這樣看來，〈大過卦〉要啟示的，是本與末的對比關係，棟橈當然不好，但正由於知道它的可能性，便要善於處理。這卦的二、五爻都是陽爻，特別是第五爻，是陽爻居陽位。既然知道本末柔弱，而能夠讓中四爻剛強，是一種處事智慧，所以說“剛過而中，巽而說行，利有攸往，乃亨。”最後讚歎說：“〈大過〉之時義大矣哉!”然則二五爻在本卦，即使有危險潛伏，卻因有“剛”的本質，仍會安然無恙，“剛”的好處實在不言而喻。

〈井卦·卦辭〉說：“井，改邑不改井，无喪无得，往來井井。”〈彖辭〉解釋道：“改邑不改井，乃以剛中也。”這裏所說的，仍然是指第二爻的性質，不是整個卦都如是。〈井卦〉是上巽下坎。一般地說，聚居成邑，不易遷徙，不過，真的要遷徙時，邑可以有改變，而井水始終仍在那裏，故謂“改邑不改井。”井水在一固定地方，沒有問題出現時，汲取其水，不覺得水量減少，不汲取它，也不覺得水量增加，所以說“无喪无得。”水是生命之源，居住於邑中之人，熙往攘來，都使用這井，故謂“往來井井。”〈彖辭〉對以上的〈卦辭〉又作了補充，認為能夠出現“改邑不改井”，是由於“剛中”。是指井水能夠恆常地存在，就由於它有居中的道理，而〈井卦〉九二爻辭，以陽爻居陽位，是以陽剛之性質而居中得位。井的重要性，本來已很明白，因這爻的性質，更加清楚作為井在邑的角色，就是不論邑存在不存在，有任何改變，井始終仍是井，表現其恆常的德性，這種堅持，正是“剛”本質，是〈彖辭〉撰寫者所捕捉到的信息，顯然賦予道德精神，朱震說：“君子窮居不損，大行不加，窮亦樂，通亦樂，非剛中不變能之乎？故曰‘改邑不改井，乃以剛中也’。”[①] 能體會到〈彖辭〉撰寫者可能要透露的道德信息，而這種道德信息，與孔子的思想是配合的，也許由此推論，〈彖辭〉與孔子，恐怕有關係。

〈漸卦·彖辭〉說：“漸之進也，女歸吉也。進得位，往有功也。進以正，可以正邦也。其位剛，得中也。止而巽，動不窮也。”〈漸卦〉上巽下艮，〈卦辭〉很簡單，只是說：“漸，女歸吉，利貞。”根據〈序卦傳〉所說：“物不可以終止，故受之以漸；漸者進也。”〈漸卦〉要說的是，萬物不會永遠停止不動，停止後，需要前行，所以〈艮卦〉之後有〈漸卦〉。〈漸卦〉之後，是〈歸妹卦〉，巽為長女，艮為少男。〈漸卦〉和〈否卦〉有關係，〈否卦〉下卦是〈坤〉，上卦為〈乾〉，四爻在乾位而與三爻在坤位的互換，則是男下女之象，然則女歸於男，一旦四下三，便成〈漸卦〉，所以說“女歸吉，利貞。”〈彖辭〉解釋〈卦辭〉時，也從這角度說。〈否卦〉三爻與四爻互換成〈漸卦〉，由三至四，是漸進之象，一旦前進，便發生作用，所以說“進得位，往有功也。”〈漸卦〉的六二與九五爻，都是居中得正，在國家立場言，是端正不過的事，所以說

---

① 朱震：《漢上易傳》卷五，第166頁。

“進以正，可以正邦也。”“其位剛，得中也”，再次強調五爻的位置及其“剛”的本質；“止而巽，動不窮也”，則再解釋巽與艮合成〈漸卦〉的信息。

(三)《周易》中的“和”

《周易》只有〈乾卦〉、〈夬卦〉和〈兌卦〉說到“和”這概念，其重視程度，明顯地遠不及“中”，而所謂“和”，就在於配合、協調。這首先見於〈乾卦〉。〈乾卦·彖辭〉曰；“乾道變化，各正性命。保合大和，乃利貞。”《周易》很重視〈乾〉、〈坤〉二卦，認為是天地的門戶，〈繫辭上傳〉第十二章所謂：“〈乾〉、〈坤〉，其《易》之門邪?〈乾〉、〈坤〉成列，而《易》立乎其中矣。”在〈乾〉、〈坤〉二卦中，又特別重視〈乾卦〉，在這裏，認為〈乾卦〉所顯示的，是能夠“保合大和”，如是則“利貞”。要了解其義，不妨結合〈乾卦·文言〉來看，說：“利者，義之和也。”則所謂“利”，其實是“義之和”，即與“義”和諧共處，不與“義”分裂，然則“保合大和乃利貞”，也就是與“義”保持結合在一起，產生大和，才是利貞。

〈夬卦·彖辭〉說：“夬，決也，剛決柔也。健而說，決而和，揚于王庭，柔乘五剛也。”〈夬卦〉上兌下乾，兌為柔、為悅，乾為剛、為健，所以說“剛決柔”“健而說，決而和。”既然能“和”，便可以“揚于王庭”，而全因一陰在上，五陽在下，“柔乘五剛”，可見〈夬卦〉要顯示的，就是雖陽而不凌陰，反而讓柔居上爻，這就是一種“和”的表現，能如是，則朝庭便沒有了爭執。然則從〈夬卦〉顯示一信息，“和”在於取得協調性。

〈兌卦〉初九〈爻辭〉說：“和兌，吉。”〈象辭〉說：“和兌之吉，行未疑也。”三畫的〈兌卦〉是八純卦之一，由上下三畫的〈兌卦〉組成的六畫〈兌卦〉。〈兌卦·卦辭〉說：“麗澤，兌，君子以朋友講習。”已說出了這卦的主要精神，在於能與朋友講習，而講習由於“和”。初九為陽，與四陽應，雖然不能以陽見陰，反而沒有黨附情形，所以“和”。《論語》孔子謂“君子和而不同。”借此以言〈兌卦〉，則初與四均是陽爻，如君子之行，果然能和而不同。王弼說：“居兌之初，應不在一，无所黨係，和兌之謂也。說不在諂，履斯而行，未見有疑之者，吉其宜矣。”[1] 其言是適當的，然則〈兌卦〉所說的“和”，仍然從協調性言。

總上所述，《周易》中的“和”，講究的是協調、配合，這與《論語》所說的“和”，在本質上沒有甚麼分別，然則，《周易》和《論語》在這方面的思想主張，表達不同，而旨趣則一。

① 王弼：《周易注》卷六，第251頁。

## 三、總結

《周易》“中”與“和”的義蘊，跟孔子的主張極其相近。《論語·陽貨》載孔子向子路說明“六言六蔽”，其中“好勇不好學，其蔽也亂。好剛不好學，其蔽也狂”兩項，乍看似乎對於“剛”，沒有給予完全的肯定，這是未能認識清楚孔子的思想哲學所致。孔子說：“剛毅木訥近仁。”（《論語·子路》）分明肯定“剛”。朱熹解釋“好剛不好學，其蔽也狂”說：“勇者剛之發，剛者勇之體。狂，躁率也。”又引范氏曰：“子路勇於為善，其失之者未能好學以明之也，故告之以此。曰勇、曰剛、曰信、曰直，又皆所以救其偏也。”① 朱熹體察孔子對子路的要求和希望，所以指陳子路的蔽，目的在“救其偏”，也就是不讓子路失去“中道”。跟“不得中行而與之，必也狂狷乎”一章相呼應。以故當孔子喟然而歎“吾未見剛者”，而有人提出申棖時，孔子便說；“棖也慾，焉得剛!”可見孔子認為“剛”是一種可貴的精神氣質，剛者無慾，才可以近於“仁”；一旦有慾，則有所蔽，不能持中，“剛”遂不成。這種對“剛”的執持和肯定，與上文所引《周易》的文字，其精神是一致的。孔子認為“不仁者不可久處約，不可以長處樂。”又說：“唯仁者能好仁，能惡不仁。”（《論語·里仁》）說明持“中”的態度和修養。中、剛，與仁的關係密切，《周易》把中與剛合在一起說，《論語》則把兩者分別而言，而都是儒家的重要價值觀念，在《論語》是近乎仁以至於為仁的要項，在《周易》是為君者宜有的修養和需要的位置。儒家希望仁在高位，因著中、剛、仁、君四者，《周易》、《論語》兩書得到契合。至於“和”，則是為人為君所處事的態度和智慧，較之於“中”、“剛”的性質與身分位置，顯然是不及的，研究儒家思想時，需要注意。

總而言之，《周易》重視“中”，較少說到“和”，《論語》所載孔子對兩者的意見也如是。《周易》雖然肯定“中”的重要性，但必需有“剛”的本質，才可以成就事情；孔子在《論語》中也說到“剛”與“中道”、“仁”的關係，性質大致相同。從這“中”“和”內容義蘊看，在《周易》，它們存在於〈彖辭〉和〈象辭〉中，而向來認為孔子撰寫〈彖辭〉和〈象辭〉，因這“中”“和”思想，也許可以由此得到其中的信息，一旦這意見能確立下來，探尋、發掘儒家思想，《周易》自當成為重要的學術資源。

---

① 朱熹：《四書章句集注·論語集注》卷七，第178頁。

# 孔子“孝”论的三个向度

中国人民大学 罗安宪

《孝经》是否为孔子所作，尚有争议。今讨论孔子关于“孝”的理论，主要以《论语》一书为主。“孝”一字在《论语》中，凡19见，然有些章节虽无“孝”字，而其意旨，却是“孝”之重要理论。《论语》关于“孝”的理论，分布于22章之中。其中有子所言1章，曾子所言3章，子夏所言1章，其余17章，为孔子之言。《里仁》篇“三年无改于父之道”一章，是对《学而》篇的重复，实际所言，共16章。

考察孔子关于“孝”的理论，就会发现，其所论所议，并非只是随时所发、因事而议，实是系统的理论。孔子关于“孝”的理论，主要包括两个方面的内容：一是何为“孝”，二是“孝”与仁以及其他德行之间的关系。今只就《论语》有关章节，论述第一个方面的问题。

何为“孝”?《说文解字》曰：“善事父母者也。”怎样才算“善事父母”? 孔子从三个方面、也可以说从三个层次、三个向度对“孝”作了解释和说明。

第一个层次，亦即第一个向度，是养父母。子女对于父母，首先要做到赡养和养护。

子游问孝，子曰：“今之孝者，是谓能养。”(《论语·为政》)

子夏问孝，子曰：“色难。有事弟子服其劳，有酒食先生馔，曾是以为孝乎?”(《论语·为政》)

“能养”，首先是能从饮食上供养父母，这是“孝”最基本、最基础的表现，也是当时人们最为普遍的看法。所以才有所谓“今之孝者，是谓能养”这样的说法。中国人的基本价值观念即是“老有所养”以及“养儿防老”。但“孝”并不只体现在父母“老”之后，未“老”之前难道不存在“孝”的问题? 孔子思考问题的深度正表现于此。从饮食上供养父母，在“孝”的义理中是最基本的、但也是最为低级的层次。

虽然父母身体健康，他们还正当年，物质生活方面也有可靠的保障。但仍有“孝”的问题，因为他们也需要关心爱护，作为儿女也有责任和义务关心和爱护父母，所以才有了所谓：“有事弟子服其劳，有酒食先生馔。”先生即父兄。家有劳烦之事，应代父兄而为之；有好的饮食，亦应先请父兄享用之。这里不存在饮食供养不足的问题，但其所要标明的却是：物质享用上应当先父母，劳烦之事则要为父母承担。所以，“能养”并不只是饮食上的供养，还包括“养护”的含义。“养护”之“护”包含有爱护、守护、保护的含义。[①]

第二个层次，亦即第二个向度，是继承父志，完成父业，并使父之事业发扬光大。《礼记》云：“子也者，亲之后也。”（《礼记·哀公问》）董仲舒云：“子者，父之合也。”（《春秋繁露·基义》）《汉书》云：“子者，父之阴也。”（《汉书·杜钦传》）《白虎通》云：“子者，孳孳无已也。”（《白虎通·三纲六纪》）在中国传统社会，子首先是个家庭成员，其历史责任是使家族的事业兴旺发达。加之，在中国古代，社会产业并不发达，职业部门相对有限。所以，“子承父业”是基本的职业习惯。在这种条件下，社会要求一个人继承父志、完成父业，成为理所当然。并且，继承父志、完成父业，不仅是人子的职责，也是“孝”的重要内容。

子曰：“父在，观其志；父没，观其行；三年无改于父之道，可谓孝矣。”（《论语·学而》）

孔安国曰：“父在，子不得自专，故观其志而已。父没乃观其行。孝子在丧，哀慕犹若存，无所改变父之道。”[②] 宋人范祖禹不同意此说，认为：“为人子者，父在则能观其父之志而承顺之，父没则能观其父之行而继述之。”[③] 朱熹、张栻、钱大昕、李光地等人均肯定范氏之说。查后文关于“三年无改于父之道”，范氏之说是矣。

然“三年无改于父之道”又何谓也？《礼记·坊记》曰：“子云：君子驰其亲之过，而敬其美。”“三年无改于父之道”非于普通人言之，而是于继位之君言之。皇侃曰：“所以是孝者，其义有二也：一则哀毁之深，岂复识政之是非，故君薨，世子听冢宰三年也。二则三年之内哀慕心事亡如存，则所不忍改也。或问曰：若父政善，则不改为可。若父政恶，恶教伤民，宁可不改乎？答曰：本不论父政之善恶，自论孝子之心耳。

---

① 子游问孝，孔子之所言者，突出“敬”；子夏问孝，孔子之所言者，突出“色难”。“能养”、“服劳”、“先生馔”等，于此二章并非重点或关键。历代注家为突出此两章之重点或关键，或多或少都对“能养”与“服劳”有所轻视，甚至予以否认。马融曰：“孔子喻子夏，服劳先食，汝谓此为孝乎？未孝也。”（参见：何晏、邢昺：《论语注疏》，北京大学出版社，2000年，第197页。）邢昺曰：“言若家有劳辱之事，或弟或子服其勤劳，有酒有食，进与父兄饮食，汝则谓是以为孝乎？言此未孝也。”（同上书，同页。）常人以为“能养”、“服劳”、“先食”等即是孝，孔子非认为此不是孝，而是认为此并非孝的全部。马融与邢昺的解释均是错误的。以此为孝之全部是错，以此不为孝也是错。朱熹曰：“服劳奉养未足为孝也”。（朱熹：《四书章句集注》，北京：中华书局，1983年，第56页。）朱子之说是矣。“能养”、“服劳”、“先食”等事无疑是孝的重要的内容，是需要大加肯定的。

② 参见何晏、邢昺：《论语注疏》，北京大学出版社，2000年，第11页。

③ 参见程树德：《论语集释》，北京：中华书局，1990年，第44页。

若人君风政之恶，则冢宰自行政；若卿大夫之心恶，则其家相邑宰自行事，无关于孝子也。”[①]“三年无改于父之道”，重点所言是孝子三年居丧之内敬慕、爱戴其父之心。

曾子曰：“吾闻诸夫子：孟庄子之孝也，其他可能也；其不改父之臣，与父之政，是难能也。”（《论语·子张》）

虽是曾子之言，所述则是孔子之意。孟庄子之孝虽有数项可举，然“其不改父之臣与父之政”，却是最为难能可贵的。所以如此，胡寅曰：“庄子之继世也，必其先臣先政有不利于己者，他人不能不改而庄子能之，是以称难。”[②]孔子所以称孟庄子“不改父之臣与父之政”为“难能”，定然有其道理与事实根据，其事实之根据现已不明，想必当如胡寅之所说。儿子的基本职责是继承父志，完成父业，这才是孔子所要表达的基本思想。

在孔子看来，孝子之所事者，即是使父亲所开创的事业发扬光大。[③]使父亲开创的事业发扬光大，这是儿子的本分，所以也是身为人子最基本的“礼”。

孟懿子问孝，子曰：“无违。”樊迟御，子告之曰：“孟孙问孝于我，我对曰‘无违’。”樊迟曰：“何谓也?”子曰：“生，事之以礼；死，葬之以礼，祭之以礼。”（《论语·为政》）

“无违”即是无违于“礼”。具体而言，即是生之时、死之事、祭之制，严格依礼而事。依礼而事亲，就是按照社会规范而事亲。社会规范虽是外在的，但对于孝子而言，则要求其必须是自觉地依照规范行事。朱熹曰：“人之事亲，自始至终，一于礼而不苟，其尊亲也至矣。”[④]依于礼而行事，依于礼而尽“孝”，其所要求与突出的是作为人子的本分，是社会对于人子的要求。不管一个人内心如何，不管一个人内心里是否爱戴父母，他必须依照“礼”、依照当时的社会规范来待父母，否则，必将受到谴责。社会如此要求个人，个人亦须如此要求自己，这就是孔子所说的：“出则事公卿，入则事父兄，丧事不敢不勉，不为酒困，何有于我哉?”（《论语·子罕》）上述四者即是个人对于自己的要求。

第三个层次，亦即第三个向度，是要从内心里对父母充满爱意。“孝”不单单是尽到子女对于父母的职责上的本分。本分是外在的，是人所共睹的，但子女对于父母的

---

① 程树德:《论语集释》，第 44 页。

② 程树德:《论语集释》，第 1330 页。

③ 《孝经》所言：“立身行道，扬名于后世，以显父母，孝之终也。”宣扬光宗耀祖，孔子之“孝”论尚不至于此。孟子说:“不孝有三，无后为大。”（《孟子·离娄上》）赵岐注曰:“于礼有不孝者三事，谓阿意曲从，陷亲不义，一不孝也。家穷亲老，不为禄仕，二不孝也。不娶无子，绝先祖祀，三不孝也。三者之中，无后为大。”（赵岐、孙奭:《论语注疏》，北京大学出版社，2000 年，第 245 页。）孔子之“孝”论尚不至于此。

④ 朱熹:《四书章句集注》，北京：中华书局，1983 年，第 56 页。

“孝”应当是发自内心的真诚，而不是做出来给他人看的。孔子“孝”论的第一层含义与第二层含义，即“能养”与继承父志、完成父业，可以说是对当时社会普遍观念的认可，是对当时世俗观念的概括与总结。但这些只是作为人子的本分，是社会对于人子的基本要求。

在孔子看来，一个人只是尽到自己作为人子的本分还不够，更为重要的是要具有发自内心的对于父母真诚的爱意。作为人子的本分、职责还是外在的，对于父母真诚的爱意才是内在的。孔子“孝”论的最大理论意义正在于强调这种对于父母真诚的爱，这也是孔子对于传统“孝”论思想最大的发挥。

子游问孝，子曰：“今之孝者，是谓能养。至于犬马，皆能有养；不敬，何以别乎?”（《论语·为政》）

“能养”，这是传统的观点，也是世俗的观念。但只是“能养”，还远远不够，如果没有对于父母的“敬”，“养父母”与“养犬马”又有什么区别?对于“至于犬马，皆能有养；不敬，何以别乎?”以往之解释，略有四种不同。（一）谓犬马养人。包咸曰：“犬以守御，马以代劳，皆养人者。”[①] 皇侃曰：“犬能为人守御，马能为人负重载人，皆是能养而不能行敬者。”[②] 邢昺曰：“犬以守御，马以代劳，皆能有以养人者，但畜兽无知，不能生敬于人，若人唯能供养于父母而不敬，则何以别于犬马乎?”[③]（二）谓人养犬马。朱熹曰：“犬马待人而食，亦若养然。言人畜犬马，皆能有以养之，若能养其亲而敬不至，则与养犬马者何异。”[④]（三）谓养父母之犬马。包慎曰：“犬马二句，盖极言养之事。虽父母之犬马，今亦能养之。”[⑤]（四）谓犬马之相养。程友菊曰：“言犬马之子皆有以养其亲，但养以敬为本，不敬，何以别于犬马之子养其亲乎?”[⑥]

然于此四种解释之外，尚有别解。邢昺于上述解释之外，还有一说：“人之所养，乃至于犬马，同其饥渴，饮之食之，皆能有以养之也。但人养犬马，资其为人用耳，而不敬此犬马也，人若养其父母而不敬，则何以别于犬马乎?”[⑦] 邢昺此说，言人养犬马，“资其为人用耳”，是因为犬马对人而有用，此意定当细说。今人之所以养父母，如果出于父母对自己尚有用，比如可以给自己做饭、做家务、带小孩，或者父母有存款、有可观的遗产，或者现在父母还有较为可观的收入，等等，如果出于此方面的考

---

① 参见何晏、邢昺：《论语注疏》，第 18 页。

② 参见程树德：《论语集释》，第 86 页。

③ 何晏、邢昺：《论语注疏》，第 18 页。

④ 朱熹：《四书章句集注》，第 56 页。

⑤ 参见程树德：《论语集释》，第 87 页。

⑥ 参见程树德：《论语集释》，第 87 页。

⑦ 何晏、邢昺：《论语注疏》，第 19 页。

虑而善待父母，可否理解为“孝”呢？答案一定是否定的。因为出于此方面原因而善待父母，并非出于对于父母的爱，而是出于自私的考虑。现在这种情况还少吗？现在出于这种原因而善待父母的人还少吗？现在因为父母年老无用而置父母于不顾的人还少吗？孔子认为只是“能养”父母还不够，更为重要的是“敬”。“敬”既有尊敬的含义，也有敬爱的含义。无论尊敬还是敬爱，其根本是对于父母真诚的爱。不管父母现在有用还是无用，不管父母有知还是无知，甚至不管父母有德还是无德，对于父母的爱一点也不减少，对于父母的爱一点都不改变。如此，才是“孝”的根本。所以，简单地“孝”还不够，还必须是“孝敬”父母。“孝”必须和“敬”、“爱”紧紧地联结在一起，方才是真正意义上的“孝”。

“孝”的根本是对于父母真诚无私的爱。正因为如此，所以，如果只做到“能养”，只做到“服劳”、“先食”等事，还是远远不够的。孔子在回答“子夏问孝”时，答曰“色难”。何为“色难”？包咸曰：“色难者，谓承顺父母颜色为难。”[①] 其意以为不使父母有不悦之色为难。朱熹的解释则是：“色难，谓事亲之际，惟色为难也。……盖孝子之有深爱者，必有和气；有和气者，必有愉色；有愉色者，必有婉容；故事亲之际，惟色为难耳，服劳奉养未足为孝也。”[②] 谓总是和颜悦色地对待父母，是难为也。如此两说，虽有不同，而其对于父母真切深刻的爱则是必须的。

因为有对于父母真诚深刻的爱，所以凡事会替父母着想，会设身处地地为父母着想。

孟武伯问孝，子曰：“父母唯其疾之忧。”（《为政》）

子曰：“父母在，不远游，游必有方。”（《里仁》）

“父母唯其疾之忧”，是言除疾病之事外，不使父母因为自己而有任何担忧。马融曰：“言孝子不妄为非，唯疾病然后使父母忧。”[③] 不妄为非，是因为惧怕父母为自己担忧。“父母在，不远游，游必有方。”其意也是不使父母为自己担忧。《礼记·祭义》记载乐正子春之事曰：

乐正子春下堂而伤其足，数月不出，犹有忧色。门弟子曰：“夫子之足瘳矣，数月不出，犹有忧色，何也？”乐正子春曰：“善如尔之问也，善如尔之问也！吾闻诸曾子，曾子闻诸夫子曰：天之所生，地之所养，无人为大。父母全而生之，子全而归之，可谓孝矣。不亏其体，不辱其身，可谓全矣。故君子顷步而弗敢忘孝也。今予忘孝之道，予是以有忧色也。壹举足而不敢忘父母，壹出言而不敢忘父母。壹举足而不敢忘父母，

① 参见何晏、邢昺：《论语注疏》，第 19 页。

② 朱熹：《四书章句集注》，第 56 页。

③ 参见何晏、邢昺：《论语注疏》，第 18 页。

是故道而不径，舟而不游，不敢以先父母之遗体行殆。壹出言而不敢忘父母，是故恶言不出于口，忿言不反于身。不辱其身，不羞其亲，可谓孝矣。”

乐正子春乃曾子弟子，其所行所言，不敢忘父母，“不辱其身，不羞其亲”，亦出于对于父母深深的爱意。曾子本人亦是如此。

曾子有疾，召门弟子曰：“启予足！启予手！诗云‘战战兢兢，如临深渊，如履薄冰。’而今而后，吾知免夫！小子！”（《论语·泰伯》）

曾子一生小心谨慎，唯恐伤害到自己的身体，唯恐做出不法之事而伤及自己的身体。[①] 只是到临死之时，他那一直提着的心才终于放了下来。《孝经》所谓：“身体发肤，受之父母，不敢毁伤，孝至始也。”爱护自己的身体其实也是出于对于父母的爱。“父母全而生之，子全而归之。”我的身体本不归我所有，而是归我的父母所有，我必须为我的父母照看好我的身体。这种“受全归完”的思想观念很有中国文化的特色。

因为有对于父母真诚深刻的爱，所以父母的任何变化，以至于年龄的变化，总是牵动着孝子的心。

子曰：“父母之年，不可不知也。一则以喜，一则以惧。”（《论语·里仁》）

邢昺曰：“言孝子当知父母之年也。其意有二：一则以父母年多，见其寿考则喜也；一则以父母年老，形必衰弱，见其衰老则忧惧也。”[②] 一年过去了，父母仍然健康，这是多么值得高兴的事。由此体会孟子所谓君子之三乐，其第一乐即是：“父母俱存，兄弟无故。”（《孟子·尽心上》）盖父母身体无故，真是孝子最大的幸福。但另一方面，父母的身体又明显不如从前了，这又是多么令人忧伤的事。

因为有对于父母真诚深刻的爱，所以，父母的事，就是自己的事；父母的安危，就是自己的安危；父母的错误，就是自己的错误；父母受过，就是自己受过。孝子对于父母，不仅要有“爱”，还要有“护”。“护”不仅是维护，更重要的是爱护，是保护。

子曰：“事父母几谏。见志不从，又敬不违，劳而不怨。”（《论语·里仁》）

知父母有过，出于爱护、保护父母，所以要“谏”，但却要是“几谏”，亦即以委婉的方式指出。父母也许不听，但却不因父母不听从自己的意见而丝毫减损对于父母的爱意与尊敬。然而其结果证明自己真的是正确的，父母是错误的，并且因为父母的错误而带来一定的损失甚至灾难。面对如此情境，自己所要做的，不是对于父母的怨，而是为父母承担责任，而是自觉地并且无怨无悔地承担一切后果，并且因此而丝毫不减损对于父母的爱意与尊敬。这就是所谓的“劳而无怨”，“劳”意味着为父母代劳，“无怨”意味着不因为父母的过失、不因为父母不听从自己的“几谏”而有任何怨气。

---

① 因为曾子时代尚普遍实行肉刑，做出不法之事，可能会遭到肉刑而伤及身体。

② 何晏、邢昺：《论语注疏》，第57页。

这就是孝子之行，这也才是孔子“孝”论中最深刻的内容。

理解了“劳而不怨”，才有可能理解孔子所谓的“父为子隐，子为父隐”。

叶公语孔子曰：“吾党有直躬者，其父攘羊，而子证之。”孔子曰：“吾党之直者异于是。父为子隐，子为父隐，直在其中矣。”（《论语·子路》）

父子关系是儒家最为强调的一种关系。《郭店楚墓竹简》有《六德》一篇，指出：“为父绝君，不为君绝父。”在孔子以至稍后的时代，父子关系远远高于君臣关系。君臣关系、夫妻关系、朋友关系、邻里关系，都是可以改变的，唯有父子关系，一旦发生，就是不可改变的。父子关系不是利益关系，甚至不是情义关系，而是一种最为亲密的血缘关系。此人是你的父亲，无论如何，这是永远无法改变的事实。处理父子关系的根本是“慈”与“孝”，亦即“父慈子孝”。“慈孝”之中，儒家更强调“孝”。认为：“孝弟也者，其为仁之本与!”（《论语·学而》）孝是为人之子的根本，[①] 如果离开这一根本，不仅不能谓为人之子，甚至简直就不可谓为人。《礼记》曰：“孝弟忠顺之行立，而后可以为人。”（《礼记·冠义》）子之爱父，父之爱子，是自然而然的，是无须任何外力使然的。如王阳明所言：“见父自然知孝，见兄自然知弟。”（《传习录》上）如果一个人连自己的父亲都不爱，连自己的儿子都不爱，而置自己的父亲、自己的儿子于不义，那么这个人还有什么事情干不出来呢？我们对于这样的人还能有什么期待呢？“父慈子孝”，就其无须任何外力使然而言，是父子关系的常态。

“其父攘羊，而子证之。”子何以要证父之攘羊？[②] 是因为在子的心目中有一个更为强大的东西压倒了对于父的“爱”，对于父的“孝”。那么这一可以压倒对于父的“爱”、对于父的“孝”的东西是什么呢？只能是对于自己的爱，只能是狭隘的私利。为己之私利而陷父于不义，这难道是人子可为之事吗？相反，“父为子隐，子为父隐”，所体现的正是“父慈子孝”，所体现的正是父子关系的常态，所体现的正是父子之“直”。所以，孔子说：“父为子隐，子为父隐，直在其中矣。”

“父为子隐，子为父隐”，何谓“隐”？有解释为隐瞒之“隐”。郑玄曰：“隐谓不称扬其过失也”。刘宝楠说：“盖子之事亲，当时微谏，谕父母于道，不致有过失。若不

---

① 有子言“孝弟也者，其为仁之本与!”“仁”当作“人”，言孝弟乃为人之本。陈善曰：“古人多假借用字，《论语》中如‘孝弟也者，其为仁之本与’，又曰‘观过，斯知仁矣’，又曰‘井有仁焉’，窃谓此‘仁’字皆当作‘人’。”王恕曰：“‘为仁’之‘仁’当作‘人’，盖承上文‘其为人也孝弟’而言。孝弟乃是为人之本。”其说是矣。（其二人之言参见程树德：《论语集释》，第13页。）二程亦反对“孝弟为仁之本”，以为：“谓行仁自孝弟始，孝弟是仁之一事。谓之行仁之本则可，谓是仁之本则不可。”（参见朱熹：《四书章句集注》，第48页。）

② 邢昺曰：“有因而盗曰攘。言因羊来入己家，父即取之，而子言于失羊之主，证父之盗。”（何晏、邢昺：《论语注疏》，第201页。）

幸而亲陷不义，亦当为讳匿。”① 此说所有一定道理，其道理在于若亲陷不义，子亦须有担当。但“隐”不仅是隐瞒之“隐”，亦是恻隐之“隐”。恻隐即是不忍，即是痛楚。孟子说：“恻隐之心，人皆有之。”（《孟子·告子上》）“隐”即是恻隐之“隐”，先秦文献里不乏例证。《诗经·邶风·柏舟》：“耿耿不寐，如有隐忧。”《孟子·梁惠王上》：“王若隐其无罪而就死地。”《荀子·儒效》：“隐隐兮其恐人之不当也。”由“其父攘羊，而子证之”，而引出“父子相隐”，其“隐”有“讳匿”之义，但子不隐忍父之受苦，亦为人之常情。《春秋公羊传·文公十五年》曰：“父母之于子，虽有罪，犹若其不欲服罪然。”所以，“父子相隐”既有“讳匿”之义，也有不忍、痛楚之义。

“父子相隐”表现出的是人之常情。而这一人情之常维护的是人伦关系中最为重要的一层关系。如果父子关系遭受破坏，所破坏的不仅仅是父子关系，而是整个社会赖以维系的根基。《韩非子》书中记载有一则故事：“楚之有直躬，其父窃羊而谒之吏，令尹曰：‘杀之’，以为直于君而曲于父，报而罪之。”（《韩非子·五蠹》）窃羊一事固然对社会有危害性，但由此而引发的子证父之窃羊，则破坏了正常的父子关系，破坏了整个社会赖以维系的根基，此一危害远远超过了窃羊这一事件本身。所以，“父子相隐”，不仅反映了父子关系的常态，而且有助于维护人伦关系的根本，故此孔子对其持肯定态度。

子不可证父，不仅出于人伦之常，而且子从来不具有证父的资格。在子看来，攘羊者为己之父而非己。而问题在于，攘羊者为尔父而非他人之父。在尔看来，攘羊者为尔父而非尔自己，而在他人看来，这里的差别其实并不很大。《白虎通》曰：“君不为臣隐，父独为子隐为何？以为父子一体，荣耻相及。”（《白虎通·谏诤篇》）父子关系是永远不可改变的，是荣辱与共的。“其父攘羊，而子证之。”在子看来，父为父，己为己；而在他人看来，尔父为尔父而非他人之父。尔可以举报他人之父攘羊越货，却不能举报自己的父亲越货攘羊。一个人，作为独立存在的实体，作为一个自然人，有很多权利和义务，但是，并不具有指证自己父亲的权利和义务。因为一个人天生不具有、后天亦永远不可取得这样一种指证父亲的资格。

子不证父，父不证子，“父子相隐”，乃人情之常。儒家对于父子人情世故的关注，并非只停留于人之常情的层面。父子关系的本质是“父子一体，荣耻相及”，“一体”意味着永不分离；“相及”意味着相互担当。如前所述，“孝”并非一意曲从，并非不分是非，而是要替父母着想，而是在父母未为不善时，力谏；父母已为不善时，勇于自己承担。用现代的观点讲，一个儿子或父亲所能做的，不是当自己的父亲或儿子违法犯罪以后取指证他，也不是千方百计去包庇他，而是劝告其投案自首，而是勇于担

① 刘宝楠：《论语正义》，北京：中华书局，1990年，第537页。

当由此所产生的一切责任。

孔子“孝”论的三个向度，是依次展开的，亦是逐次上升而升华的。第一个向度之所谓“能养”，是最基础的；第二个向度之所谓继承父志、完成父业，是社会对于人子的基本要求；第三个向度，从内心里对父母充满爱意，才是问题的根本所在。第一个向度与第二个向度的理论是孔子对于世俗理论的总结和概括，第三个向度的理论，才是孔子“孝”论的根本与核心。就第二向度，亦即继承父志、完成父业而言，其带有很大的历史局限性，带有强烈的时代痕迹。第一个向度，亦即“能养”，是最基本的，亦是最基础的，现今并不是毫无意义，因为此方面确实也还存在问题。而第三个向度，亦即从内心里对父母充满爱意，不仅是孝的根本，而且现今最为缺乏的正是这一根本。我们能像父母惦记我们一样地惦记父母吗？我们能像父母想念我们一样地想念父母吗？我们能像父母关心我们一样关心父母吗？即使如此，也不能说我们尽到了孝，况且，我们真的没有做到，况且，又有几个人自信自己已经做到？从内心里爱父母，真诚无伪地爱父母，不仅是关心，不仅是敬爱，还有爱护，还有保护，这既是孔子“孝”论的核心，也正是我们如今所要深刻反省的。

**参考文献：**

[1] 何晏、邢昺. 论语注疏. 北京：北京大学出版社，2000.

[2] 朱熹. 四书章句集注. 北京：中华书局，1983.

[3] 程树德. 论语集释. 北京：中华书局，1990.

# 孔子的生活体验、德福观及道德自律

## ——从郭店简《穷达以时》及其相关文献来考察

北京大学 王中江

## 引 言

20世纪特别是70年代以来，中国许多地下文献的出土为重新审视古代早期中国思想尤其是儒家和道家思想提供了新的机遇。我这里使用的新文献《穷达以时》就是这种机遇之一。这篇文献出土于中国南方湖北荆门郭店一座公元前300年左右的楚国墓葬中，它是这座墓中陪葬的许多竹简文献中的一种。自从1995年它被公布以来，[①] 我们对之已进行了各种各样的研究，[②] 它同传世文献保留的记忆之间的关联就是其中之一。这些传世文献有《论语·卫灵公》、《孔子家语·在厄》、《孔子家语·困誓》、《庄子·让王》、《荀子·宥坐》、《吕氏春秋·慎人》、《韩诗外传》卷七、《史记·孔子世家》、《说苑·杂言》和《风俗通义·穷通》等。

通过比较，我们可以看出《穷达以时》同这些文献留下的记忆在什么地方是类似的，在什么地方又是不同的。[③]《穷达以时》同传世记忆明显的不同，一是它提出了"天人关系"的新说，二是它没有呈现出它的背景，也没有呈现出背景中的人物和对

① 参见《郭店楚墓竹简》，文物出版社，1995年。这篇佚文共有16枚简组成，简长26.4厘米，共300字左右。这篇佚文的年代下限大约在公元前300年左右，作品的实际年代要早一些，一般被认为是孔子弟子的作品，但我们尚不能确定具体是出自孔子的哪位弟子之手。

② 参阅庞朴的《孔孟之间——郭店楚简中的儒家心性说》（见姜广辉主编的《中国哲学》第二十辑"郭店楚简研究"，沈阳：辽宁教育出版社，1999年）、张立文的《〈穷达以时〉的时与遇》（见同上）、李学勤的《天人之分》（见郑万耕主编的《中国传统哲学新论》，北京：九州图书出版社，1999年）梁涛：《竹简〈穷达以时〉与早期儒家天人观》（见《哲学研究》，2003年第4期）、池田知久的《郭店竹简〈穷达以时〉研究》（见池田知久的《池田知久简帛研究论集》，曹峰译，北京：中华书局，2004年）、林启屏的《限制与自由：从〈穷达以时〉论起》（见林启屏的《从古典到正典：中国古代儒学意识之形成》，台北：台湾大学出版中心，2007年）、王中江的《〈穷达以时〉与孔子的境遇观和道德自主论》（见《浙东学术》第一辑，浙江大学出版社，2009年）等。

③ 有关这一方面请参阅池田知久的《郭店竹简〈穷达以时〉研究》（见池田知久的《池田知久简帛研究论集》，曹峰译，北京：中华书局，2004年）、王中江的《〈穷达以时〉与孔子的境遇观和道德自主论》（见《浙东学术》第一辑，浙江大学出版社，2009年）。

话，它是一种议论体。要说为什么它同传世记忆具有可比性，这主要是因为，它们留下的都是这样一种记忆，即孔子和他的弟子们对他们经历的一次生死考验的反思。这种反思涉及了人类生活中人追求美德和幸福这两者的关系问题，也涉及什么是人的真正幸福、什么才是人生的挫折与亨通等问题。有关德福关系，我们知道西方传统的早期亚里士多德的看法，也知道西方近代以来康德、功利主义和德性伦理学等的看法。[①]在中国，不说墨家、道家以及后来佛教的说法，单就儒家的立场而论，它就是多元的，《穷达以时》及其相关传世记忆就是一个最好的例证。

但围绕这方面我们的关注显然是不够的。在这篇论文中，首先我想呈现一下孔子和他的弟子们遭遇的一次特殊境遇和体验，虽然说起来它只是孔子和他的弟子们周游列国时的许多境遇和体验之一，但这是孔子和他的弟子们面对的一次最严峻的（生死的）考验。正是这样，它引发了孔子和他的弟子们对他们的人生选择和行为的深刻反思，并在这种反思中孔子对德福关系、对幸福和穷达提出了复杂的、多重主张，与此同时孔子也更坚定了他在伦理道德上的偏好和自主选择。

## 一、事件和境遇：生活体验、反思和真理

在生活与哲学的关系被重新唤醒的当代，[②]我们不仅需要直面当前的生活世界去从事哲学的思考，而且也需要回过头去追寻在以往的哲学传统中哲学家是如何在哲学与生活之间保持统一性的。西方的苏格拉底，中国的孔子，他们都是直面生活、在亲身感受和体验中去思考人和社会问题的典范性人物。现代中国哲学家金岳霖对东西方哲学的这一传统情有独钟，并为现代哲学越来越失去这一传统 感到惋惜。[③]

具体到孔子，他的哲学和思想始终是同他一生的经历息息相关的，或者正像金岳霖所说的那样，他的哲学就是他的“自传”。思想的语境，同时就是孔子的生活的境遇。我们可以举出很多这方面的例子，如他说的“吾未见好德如好色者也”这句著名的话。《论语·子罕》只记载了这句话而没有记载孔子说这句话的实际境遇。按照《史记·孔子世家》的记载，这句话是孔子对卫灵公和他的名叫南子的夫人同坐一辆马车出游、招摇过市而发出的感叹。孔子陪同了他们，他的马车跟随在后面，他目睹了卫灵公的一举一动。又如，孔子观察了他的弟子宰我的实际表现之后，他得出了一个结

---

① 有关这方面，参阅迈克尔·桑德尔（Michael J. Sandel）的《公正：该如何做是好?》，朱慧玲译，北京：中信出版社，2012 年。

② 有关这方面，参阅哈道特（Pierre Hadot）的《作为生活方式的哲学》（见《世界哲学》，2007 年第 1 期）。

③ 参阅金岳霖的《中国哲学》（见《金岳霖集》，北京：中国社会科学出版社，2000 年）、《哲学与生活》（同上）。

论，说判断一个人不仅要听他承诺了什么，还要看他实际上做得如何。[①] 我们这里讨论的孔子对美德和幸福等问题的思考更是如此。它相应于一个真实的背景和历史事件，是孔子和他的弟子们对他们的实际生存境遇和境况的一种反应，而不是单纯理论沉思的产物。这一事件和境遇就是一般所称的“厄于陈蔡”（“陈蔡之厄”。出于便利，后面的讨论仍沿用这种称谓，虽然它不一定确切），这是孔子在周游列国时遭遇到的一次最严峻的考验。根据讨论问题的需要，我们对孔子和他的弟子们所处的这一境遇作一简略说明。

按照上述传世文献等的记载，公元前489年（鲁哀公六年），吴国伐陈国，楚国援助陈国。当楚国得知孔子在陈察之间（实际上应该是在蔡国），[②] 楚昭王就邀请孔子到楚国去。孔子接受了楚昭王的邀请，这一年他63岁。他和他的弟子们前往楚国。由于楚国援助陈国，实际上应该是蔡国的大夫而不是陈、蔡大夫认为，孔子对当时社会和诸侯国的批评都言中时弊，并担心孔子到楚国被任用后，会对蔡国构成威胁，于是蔡国的大夫就动用党徒和劳役之人阻拦孔子和他的弟子们前往楚国，并将它们围困在野外长达七日之久。在七天的被围困中，孔子和他的弟子们断绝了粮食和食物，连最粗劣的食物都没有了，虽然中间子贡潜逃出去用带的财货向乡人换了些米，最后孔子的弟子们都因饥饿而病倒了，几乎到了被饿死的境地。后楚昭王派兵解除了蔡人对他们的围困并保护他们到了楚国的负函（今河南信阳）。

可以想象，孔子和他的弟子们要渡过这漫长的七天是多么困难，期间在被围困的地方肯定也发生了各种各样的事情。[③] 面对严峻的困境，孔子仍向他的弟子们讲诵《诗》、《书》，他还演奏音乐、唱歌。但孔子的这种精神并不能完全安慰和平抚他的弟

---

① 《论语·公冶长》记载：“宰予昼寝。子曰：朽木不可雕也，粪土之墙不可杇也；於予与何诛？子曰：始吾于人也，听其言而信其行；今吾于人也，听其言而观其行。於予与改是。”《礼记·檀弓上》记载“有子问于曾子曰：‘问丧于夫子乎？’曰：‘闻之矣，丧欲速贫，死欲速朽。’有子曰：‘是非君子之言也。’曾子曰：‘参也闻诸夫子也。’有子又曰：‘是非君子之言也。’曾子曰：‘参也与子游闻之。’有子曰：‘然，然则夫子有为言之也。’曾子以斯言告于子游。子游曰：‘甚哉，有子之言似夫子也。昔者夫子居于宋，见桓司马自为石椁，三年而不成，夫子曰：‘若是其靡也，死不如速朽之愈也。’死之欲速朽，为桓司马言之也。南宫敬叔反，必载宝而朝。夫子曰：‘若是其货也，丧不如速贫之愈也。丧之欲速贫，为敬叔言之也。’曾子以子游之言告于有子，有子曰：‘然，吾固曰，非夫子之言也。’曾子曰：‘子何以知之？’有子曰：‘夫子制于中都，四寸之棺，五寸椁，以斯知不欲速朽也。昔者夫子失鲁司寇，将之荆，盖先之以子夏，又申以冉有，以斯知不欲速贫也。’”

② 虽然传世文献大都说孔子是“厄于陈蔡”，但由于当时吴国攻打陈国，楚国援助陈国，并邀请孔子到楚国，陈国参与围困孔子的可能性不大。当时蔡国还没有灭亡并入楚国（前531年，楚一度灭蔡。前506年蔡国曾随吴国伐楚，并攻入郢都。前493年，楚国逼迫蔡昭侯迁都州来，即今安徽凤台县）。直到前447年，蔡国才完全灭亡，并入了楚国。

③ 如做饭的颜回被怀疑偷吃了东西等。参阅《孔子家语·在厄》。

子们身心两方面的焦虑和痛苦。我们也可以相像，孔子对他们的境遇也不可能无动于衷，他在力求保持坦然和达观的同时，内心自然也要承受巨大的压力，不免忧虑和痛苦。在这一过程中，孔子的弟子特别是子贡、子路对“德命”一致论提出了质疑，甚至对孔子演奏音乐也表示了不满。他们觉得追随孔子，追随美德，不应该受到这种不公正的待遇。

面对弟子特别是子路、子贡等的困惑和疑问，孔子对德福关系、对什么是穷达进行了深度的思考和反思。按照克尔凯戈尔的看法，尼采也表达了类似的立场，一个人对真理的认识和把握的程度总是同他们对生活的感受和所遭受的痛苦程度相对应。[①] 我们也知道，孔子精神的光大者孟子，曾以神圣的使命感表达了类似的立场，这是大家都非常熟悉的《孟子·告子下》中的一段著名的话：

舜发于畎亩之中，傅说举于版筑之间，膠鬲举于鱼盐之中，管夷吾举于士，孙叔敖举于海，百里奚举于市。故天将降大任于斯人也，必先苦其心志，劳其筋骨，饿其体肤，空乏其身，行拂乱其所为，所以动心忍性，曾益其所不能。人恒过，然后能改；困于心，衡于虑，而后作；徵于色，发于声，而后喻。入则无法家拂士，出则无敌国外患者，国恒亡。然后知生于忧患而死于安乐也。

中国古代伟大的史学家司马迁更以自己不幸的人生遭遇诠释了痛苦的生命情调与追求真理的相应性，他在《太史公自序》（又见《报任安书》）中的一段话对中国人来说同样十分著名，同样十分熟悉：

昔西伯拘羑里，演《周易》；孔子戹陈蔡，作《春秋》；屈原放逐，著《离骚》；左丘失明，厥有《国语》；孙子膑脚，而论兵法；不韦迁蜀，世传《吕览》；韩非囚秦，《说难》、《孤愤》；《诗》三百篇，大抵贤圣发愤之所为作也。此人皆意有所郁结，不得通其道也，故述往事，思来者。（司马迁：《史记》）

孔子的经历特别是“陈蔡之厄”具有震撼性，他以亲身的体验诠释了痛苦的生活体验、生命情调同追求真理的关系。

传世文献除简明记载孔子和他的弟子们所处的境遇之外，主要记载的是孔子和他的弟子们对他们生死遭遇的反思。《穷达以时》没有记载孔子和他的弟子在蔡国被围困的事件及其境遇，但事实上它也同孔子和他的弟子“厄于陈蔡”有关。其主要根据是，这一文献对人的德福和穷达关系的思考，与传世的其中一类文献留下的记忆具有很高程度的类似性。这一类文献是《荀子·宥坐》、《孔子家语·在厄》、《韩诗外传》卷七和《说苑·杂言》等。相比之下，《穷达以时》等文献同《吕氏春秋·慎人》和《史记

---

① 参阅 L. J. 宾克莱（Luther J. Binkley）：《理想的冲突——西方社会中变化着的价值观念》，马元德、陈白澄等译，北京：商务印书馆，1988 年，第 176、196 页。

·孔子世家》等留下的记忆差别较大，同《庄子·让王》、《风俗通义·穷通》的差别更大，它呈现出的是孔子对德福、对穷达明显不同的另外的视角。

## 二、德福的一致与不一致

“德福关系”在更广的意义上是人的理性行为同他所期待的良好结果的关系。依照韦伯的概括，理性行为包括了工具（目的）理性和价值（伦理、审美和宗教的）理性，此外人的社会行为还有情感式的和传统式的、习惯性的等。中国人的理性行为概念，可划分为“合理的”、“合法的”、“合情的”。如果采取二分法的话，它可分为合乎道理的行为和合乎道德的行为。一般来说，人作为理性的存在，作为一种期望性的存在，他的好的行为，不管是哪一方面的，他希望都有一个良好的结果。这十分合情合理。但事实上，大量的过去的例子和经验，不管是公共的理性选择和行为，还是个体的理性选择和行为，并不都能如愿以偿，有不少是得非所愿的坏结果。这样的情形不仅容易让我们心情沮丧，也常常让我们困惑不解。

同样，对于以道德和自我完善为目标的人来说，他也希望他的努力能得到社会的肯定性评价和获得相应的福祉，即所谓“好人好报”。有什么理由让一个好人得不到相应的回报，更有什么理由让好人遭受厄运。但事实上，具有美德或追求美德的人，他不一定就能得到相应的好的社会回报，他甚至还有可能遭到不幸。《穷达以时》（整理者选择文中的一句话来题名）篇名的意思就是，一个人的事业是穷困还是通达最终取决于个人所无法左右的运气。这里说的事业是指儒家道德上的追求和淑世主义；所说的“困”、“穷”与“通”、“达”主要是指有德的人是否会有社会政治上的机会、身份和与之相应的俸禄（孟子称之为“人爵”），或者是否幸运、幸福和快乐；所说的运气主要是指机遇、时运、“世道”和“天”。

《穷达以时》中的穷与达，或者说儒家甚至中国文化中一般所说的穷与达，一般都以贤能的人是否有社会政治机遇、地位等来衡量，换言之是以人是否得志、幸福和快乐判断。儒家坚持认为，“贤人”、“君子”和真正的“儒者”，都应该是社会政治地位的拥有者。孟子和荀子的思想在某些方面差别很大，但在主张德能和社会地位的统一上他们的看法是一致的。如孟子说：

贤者在位，能者在职。（《孟子·公孙丑上》）

尊贤使能，俊杰在位，则天下之士皆悦而愿立于其朝矣。（同上）

惟仁者宜在高位。（《孟子·离娄上》）

按照孟子的说法，贤能和仁者，不仅应该有社会政治职位，而且应该有很高的职位。在荀子那里，我们同样能够看到社会政治地位要根据德能来分配的主张：

图德而定次，量能而授官，皆使民载其事而各得其宜。（《荀子·正论》）

上贤禄天下，次贤禄一国，下贤禄田邑，愿惠之民完衣食。（《荀子·正论》）

如同孟子和荀子的这种理性期望，如同黑格尔相信“凡是现实的都是合理的，凡是合理的都是现实的”，[①] 孔子曾期望“德福一致”。但信念、期望与现实并不都能一致。[②]《穷达以时》和其他文献列举了这方面的许多例子就是为了说明这一点：

“梅伯（简14）初醢醢，[③] 后名扬，非其德加［也］；[④] 子胥前多功，后戮死，非其智（简9）衰也。”

《说苑·杂言》记载：

“昔者汤困于吕，文王困于羑里，秦穆公困于殽，齐桓困于长勺，句践困于会稽，晋文困于骊氏。夫困之为道，从寒之及暖，暖之及寒也，唯贤者独知而难言之也。易曰：‘困亨贞，大人吉，无咎。有言不信。’圣人所与人难言，信也。”

按照《穷达以时》等文献的立场，美德与幸福之间并没有“内在一致性”或确定性的对称关系。这是因为幸福受着“时运”和“天命”的制约：

有天有人，天人有分。察天人之分，而知所行矣。有其人，无其世，虽贤弗行矣。[⑤]

遇不遇，天也。

穷达以时，德行一也。[⑥]

---

① 参阅见黑格尔（Georg Wilhelm Friedrich Hegel）：《法哲学原理·序言》，范扬、张企泰译，北京：商务印书馆，1961年。

② 康德（Immanuel Kant）曾探讨过理论的正确、实践上为什么行不通的问题。参阅康德：《历史理性批判文集》，何兆武译，北京：商务印书馆，1996年，第164—210页。

③ 原释文此句同“子胥”句相连。原释文“初韬晦”句缺少主语。但将第9支简同第14支简编连，可以恰当地解决问题。“醢醢”的读法，取赵平安说。（参阅赵的《〈穷达以时〉第九号简考论——兼及先秦两汉文献中比干故事的衍变》，载《古籍整理研究学刊》，2002年第2期）“梅伯”的读法，取陈剑说（参阅同上文）。

④ 据后句“衰也”，当补“也”字。

⑤ 《淮南子·缪称训》对“人为”与“天”之界限有更为具体的说明：“人无能作也，有能为也；有能为也，而无能成也。人之为，天成之。终身为善，非天不行；终身为不善，非天不亡。故善否，我也；祸福，非我也。故君子顺其在己者而已矣。性者，所受于天也；命者，所遭于时也。有其材，不遇其世，天也。太公何力，比干何罪，循性而行指，或害或利。求之有道，得之在命。故君子能为善，而不能必其得福；不忍为非，而未能避免其祸。”

⑥ 《庄子·秋水》篇记载孔子被围困于匡地时表达的也是这种穷达时命观：“孔子游于匡，宋人围之数匝，而弦歌不辍。子路入见，曰：‘何夫子之娱也？’孔子曰：‘来，吾语女。我讳穷久矣，而不免，命也；求通久矣，而不得，时也。当尧、舜而天下无穷人，非知得也；当桀、纣而天下无通人，非知失也：时势适然。夫水行不避蛟龙者，渔父之勇也；陆行不避兕虎者，猎夫之勇也；白刃交于前，视死若生者，烈士之勇也；知穷之有命，知通之有时，临大难而不惧者，圣人之勇也。由，处矣！吾命有所制矣！’无几何，将甲者进，辞曰：‘以为阳虎也，故围之；今非也，请辞而退。’”

可以看出，这里的“天人之分”是人事与命运的区分。① 其“命运之天”与时、世道、遇等都是相近的用法。依据这种二分的逻辑，有美德的人只有同时也有时遇、运气，他才能通达、幸福和快乐；否则他就会遭遇穷困和不幸。“陈蔡之厄”就是孔子和他的弟子没有时遇和运气的结果。孔子甚至干脆认为，追求美德的人，他原本就不能期望通和达。《论语・卫灵公》记载说，子路对他们的境遇即陈蔡之厄感到不满，他生气地问孔子：“君子亦有穷乎?”。对此，孔子回答说：“君子固穷。小人斯滥矣。”

《穷达以时》这种“德福未必一致”（甚至“有德无福”）的立场并不孤立。上述《荀子・宥坐》、《孔子家语・在厄》、《韩诗外传》卷七和《说苑・杂言》与《穷达以时》的类似性主要就表现在这里。如这四个文献中都有“遇不遇者，时也”的说法。

由《穷达以时》等文献表现出的这种“德福未必一致”的立场，同儒家“德福一致论”的立场明显不同。按照这种立场，具有美德或追求美德的人一定能获得通达、幸福和快乐。《荀子・宥坐》、《孔子家语・在厄》、《韩诗外传》卷七和《说苑・杂言》等这四个文献，都有“为善者，天报之以福；为不善者，天报之以祸”这种“福善祸淫论”的立场。这是子路在陈蔡之厄中向孔子“进谏”时说出的话。在《荀子・宥坐》中，他说这个话是他听来的，在《孔子家语・在厄》中，他说这是他老师之前讲过的话。

在“厄于陈蔡”这一境遇之前，孔子是不是讲过这样的话，或者在此之前孔子是不是有“德福一致论”的立场，这是一个问题。按照子路所说，他在“陈蔡之厄”之前相信的是“福善祸淫论”，而这种立场非常有可能是孔子提出的。主要根据之一，是《礼记・中庸》保存有孔子的“大德必受命”的思想：

子曰：“舜其大孝也与！德为圣人，尊为天子，富有四海之内。宗庙飨之，子孙保之。故大德必得其位，必得其禄，必得其名，必得其寿。……故大德者必受命。”②

照此说来，孔子曾具有“德位”、“德命”和“德禄”因果必然性和一致性的信念。③《周易・文言》说的“积善之家，必有余庆；积不善之家，必有余殃”、帛书

---

① 它同荀子的“天人相分”不同。其所说的“天”，也不同于孔孟一般“天人合一”的“天”。

② 《说苑・敬慎》也认为善恶报应有必然性：“老子曰：得其所利，必虑其所害；乐其所成，必顾其所败。人为善者，天报以福；人为不善者，天报以祸也。故曰：祸兮福所倚；福兮祸所伏；戒之，慎之！君子不务，何以备之？夫上知天、则不失时；下知地、则不。日夜慎之，则无灾害。”

③ 孔子这里说的“受命”的“命”，同上述的“天人相分”的“天”、“生死由命”的“命”类似，它不同于“天佑正义”的“天命”。孔子的“德命一致性”，不是建立在这种正义性的“天”和“天命”之上的。这种天命是天赋予人的使命。孔子在匡地被误认为是阳虎而受到围攻时，他就以“天”之“斯文”担当者而自信地说：“文王既没，文不在兹乎？天之将丧斯文也，后死者不得与于斯文也；天之未丧斯文也，匡人其如予何！”（《论语・子罕》）在从曹国去往宋国的路上，孔子受到了宋国司马桓魋的威胁。脱险之际，孔子也自信“天”赋予了他追求“德”的使命，桓魋不能奈何他。确实，在不少场合，孔子多次明言他“受命于天”，显示出对“天”的信赖。按说有这种命，就应该有穷达的命，但在孔子那里这两者有非一致性。

《要》说的“君子德行焉求福，故祭祀而寡也；仁义焉求吉，故卜筮而希也”等，都是类似的思想。

在“陈蔡之厄”中，子路正是从这种立场出发，疑惑他们受困是不是因为孔子的积德和信誉还不够。面对眼前的生死境遇，孔子重新反思了“德福”、“德命”关系，他改变了之前的立场，并列出了许多贤、人君子不得志的例子，得出了“德福未必一致”的新论断。这样说来，孔子本身前后就具有“德福一致”和“德福未必一致”的两种立场。思想和逻辑上的这种不一贯，源于孔子生活感受和体验的复杂性和矛盾性。

## 三、什么是真正的幸福和快乐？

如果说希腊语的幸福（eudaimonia，由 eu 的“好”和 daimon 的“神灵”构成，字面意义为吉星高照）不能简单地同英文的幸福（happiness）画等号，后者常常被等同于快乐和人的情感上的满足，而前者更有人的本性满足的意义，就像亚里士多德的用法，它是指人生活的完满目的和符合德性并值得人去过的最好生活状态，因而人对幸福的追求与对美德的追求是同一的、一致的，[①] 那么，上述孔子和他的弟子对幸福和快乐的看法，就同功利主义有某种类似性，因为这种意义上的幸福和快乐是期望美德能够给个人带来世俗利益的回报。也正是在这种意义上，孔子认为德福有一致性（当然也有不一致性）。与此不同，在陈蔡的特殊境遇中，孔子还对幸福和快乐提出了类似于亚里士多德立场的看法。

根据上面的讨论，“陈蔡之厄”使孔子改变了德福、德命一致论的乐观主义思维。同样，在“陈蔡之厄”中，在七天漫长的生死考验中，孔子也重新反思了“穷达”，反思了什么是真正的幸福，什么才是不幸。如上所述，“陈蔡之厄”不仅让孔子得出了“君子固穷”的论断，而且他也不敢再期待世俗意义上的幸福和快乐了。如果说一个人只要追求道德和人格完善，做一个正人君子，他原本就会“穷困”（“君子固穷”），那么，他就只能以道德和人格来衡量自己的价值并同他人竞争。不能期待世俗意义上的显赫和发达，孔子转而对“穷达”提出了新的解释。

这种新的解释之一，是将不幸意义下的“穷困”转化为积极的意义，即将它们看成是考验人、锤炼人和造就人的机会。这是保留在《孔子家语·困誓》和《说苑·杂言》中的孔子对“陈蔡之厄”的另一种反思。按照这两个文献的记载，孔子和他的弟

---

① 参阅尼古拉斯·布宁（Nicholas Bunnin）、余纪元编著：《西方哲学英汉对照辞典》，王柯平、江怡等译，北京：人民出版社，2001 年，第 335—336 页。此外，有关亚里士多德和功利主义者对幸福和快乐的看法，参阅阿拉斯代尔·麦金太尔（Alasdair MacIntyre）：《伦理学简史》，龚群译，北京：商务印书馆，2003 年，第 93—125、253—263、297—322 页。

子们最后摆脱了困境。这时，子贡挽着缰绳感叹说，这次他们跟着他们的老师遭受了一次生死的考验，对此他们是不会忘记的。但孔子不同意子贡的“坏事”说，他认为“陈蔡之厄”对他们来说不仅不是不幸，相反它是锻炼他们的难得机会。《说苑·杂言》记载说：

明日免于厄，子贡执辔曰：“二三子从夫子而遇此难也，其不可忘已”。孔子曰：“恶，是何言也！……夫陈、蔡之间，丘之幸也。二三子从丘，皆幸人也”。[①]

孔子为什么说陈蔡之地的生死考验是幸运的呢？在《说苑·杂言》的记载中，孔子给出的理由是：

“故居不幽则思不远，身不约则智不广。……语不云乎？三折肱而成良医。……吾闻人君不困不成王，列士不困不成行。……夫困之为道，从寒之及暖，暖之及寒也，唯贤者独知而难言之也。”

《孔子家语·困誓》也记载说：

“吾闻之：君不困不成王，烈士不困行不彰。庸知其非激愤厉志之始于是乎在？”

照此说来，此前孔子和他的弟子们的一系列遭遇对他们来说都是幸运的。在生活的世界中，一般看来是坏和恶的东西，它也有带来好的和善的结果的可能。所谓“愤怒出诗人”、“环境锻炼人”、“坏事变好事”等，就是说不幸和恶劣的状态、环境，也有“化腐朽为神奇”的可能性。前引《孟子·告子下》和司马迁的《报任安书》中的话，说的就是一些反作用的东西能对人产生积极的意义。《孟子·尽心上》也有一段话说：“人之有德慧术知者，恒存乎疢疾独孤臣孽子，其操心也危，其虑患也深，故达。”孔子说穷困是幸运的有些类似。但就其原来的意义说，穷困、“疢疾”本身仍不是好事。人间固然没有免费午餐，但以不幸的代价获得积极的东西，仍然不合乎人类的一般理性。

孔子对“穷达”新的解释之二是，他改变了“穷达”的意义，不再将穷达看成是是否获得了相应的社会回报，而是将它们视之为人是否具有美德和追求美德本身，即一个人追求美德和自我完善本身就是幸福和快乐的，否则他就是不幸（穷困）和痛苦的。这种“穷达观”，在儒家那里虽然罕见，但确实又是一种类型。在陈祭之厄的境遇中，孔子依然不断地弹琴唱歌，超然不以为“穷”，这让他的弟子们感到困惑，他们私下议论他们的老师是不是“不知耻辱”。正是面对他的弟子“如此者可谓穷矣”的怨言，孔子回答说：

是何言也？君子达于道之谓达，穷于道之谓穷。今丘也拘仁义之道，以遭乱世之

---

① 《孔子家语·困誓》此处的记载略有不同：“善，恶何也？”。

患，其所也，何穷之谓？（《吕氏春秋·慎人》）①

对于以道德为最高价值的儒家来说，将“有德”本身作为是否“穷达”的标准，这也是情理之中的事。子张就有以“德行”而不是以政治上的地位论贵贱的看法。《庄子·盗跖》篇记载：

子张曰：“昔者桀、纣贵为天子，富有天下。今谓臧聚曰，汝行如桀、纣，则有怍色，有不服之心者，小人所贱也。仲尼、墨翟，穷为匹夫，今谓宰相曰，子行如仲尼、墨翟，则变容易色，称不足者，士诚贵也。故势为天子，未必贵也；穷为匹夫，未必贱也。贵贱之分，在行之美恶。”

对于津津乐道“仁者不忧，智者不惑，勇者不惧”的孔子来说，他是“无忧”的。子路询问“君子亦有忧乎？”孔子断然回答说：“无也。君子之修行也，其未得之，则乐其意；既得之，又乐其治，是以有终身之乐，无一日之忧。”（《孔子家语·在厄》）孔子的“无忧”是基于他对道德和人格的自信。如果说孔子也有忧虑的话，他忧虑的是“德之不修，学之不讲，闻义不能从，不善不能改。”（《论语·述而》）孔子认为贤人是“无怨”的。如冉有问伯夷和叔齐是什么样的人，孔子说是古代的贤人，冉有问他们是否抱怨，孔子回答说：“求仁而得仁，又何怨？”（《论语·述而》）按照世俗的立场，伯夷和叔齐都是结局悲惨的人，但在孔子看来，他们成就了自己的人格，他们不会有什么怨言。对儒家来说，一个人只要成就了他的道德自我，他就拥有了一切，正如荀子所说：

故君子无爵而贵，无禄而富，不言而信，不怒而威，穷处而荣，独居而乐！岂不至尊、至富、至重、至严之情举积此哉！（《荀子·儒效》）

概括起来，孔子的“穷达观”除了以是否“有机遇”或“有位”而论外，还有以“困境”（或磨难）造就人格、以是否“有德”来表现的两种表现。由此，幸福和快乐的意义也发生了变化。这三种不同的表现，既是孔子对其处境和境遇给予的不同解释和说明，也是他们为同一事件和处境赋予不同意义的方式。

## 四、追求美德：自主、自足和自律

从文本和整理者的题名来看，《穷达以时》好像主要是讨论“人”的“时遇”的，但事实上不是。它关注的主要是人作为道德主体对道德选择的自主性和自足性。按照境遇伦理学的观点，人的行为的正当性取决于他当下所处的境遇，在不同的境遇下我

---

① 《吕氏春秋·慎人》用的是“穷达”（“君子达于道之谓达，穷于道之谓穷”），《庄子·让王》和《风俗通义·穷通》用的都是“穷通”（“君子通于道之谓通，穷于道之谓穷”）。

们往往会有不同的伦理、道德判断尺度。[①] 在儒家那里，不仅伦理和道德的尺度、判断人的行为的标准（“经”），不能因境遇而轻易改变（只有在特殊的情况下，才能使用“权变”的策略），而且人们追求美德的信念、志向和精神更是不能改变的。

《穷达以时》虽然说人的命运是个人无法左右的，但他并没有悲叹人生命运的捉摸不定和抒发人生如梦的情调，而且更没有因此而改变自己的道德志愿和追求：

善否，己也。穷达以时，德行一也；誉毁在旁，听之弋之。[②] ……动非为达也，故穷而不（简 11）[怨；隐非] 为名也，故莫之智而不吝。芷 [兰生于林中]，（简 12）[不为无人] 嗅而不芳；璑璐瑾瑜包山石，不为 [无人识而]（简 13）不理。穷达以时，幽明不再。故君子敦于反己。（简 15）

在此，我们看到的是：第一，一个人是求善还是作恶这是由他自己决定的，而不是由外在的时运决定的。为此《穷达以时》区分了天与人、遇与不遇、穷与达。还有，郭店竹简《语丛一》说：“知天所为，知人所为”；《孔子家语·在厄》说：“为之者人也，生死者命也”；《荀子·宥坐》说：“为不为者，人也；遇不遇者，时也；死生者，命也”；《说苑·杂言》说：“为不为者，人也；遇不遇者，时也”。凡此等等，这些文本在说明现实世界中人的道德偏好、行为与社会回报具有不确定性的同时，更重要的是要昭示人，不要因这种不确定性而放弃我们的追求。

人们会说，我们要改变命运。但正如中国人喜欢说谋事在人、成事在天那样，儒家追求美德的立足点是谋事在人，[③] 而不是去关心“成事在天”的命运。如果“贤不贤”、“德不德”的“人”是静态性的“人”，那么“为不为”的“人”则是动态性的“人”。正是这种动态性的始终的“人为”，则充分体现了儒家不懈追求道德的精神。从这一主旨来说，将《穷达以时》的篇名命名为《天人有分》或《德行一也》则更为恰当，它不容易引起误解。儒家强调“人为不为”，就是认为道德实践取决于自身。孔子说的“为仁由己，由乎人哉”（《论语·颜渊》）、“人能弘道，非道弘人”（《论语·卫灵

---

① 参阅约瑟夫·弗莱彻的（Joseph Fletcher）《境遇伦理学》，程立显译，北京：中国社会科学出版社，1989 年。

② 有关此句的校读，参阅王中江的《〈穷达以时〉与孔子的境遇观和道德自主论》，见《浙东学术》第一辑，浙江大学出版社，2009 年，第 14 页。

③ 孔子和孟子都相信追求道德和自我完善是人的能力，他是人完全能够做得到的事情。孔子认为，古代礼仪性的射击不要求都穿过皮制的靶心，这是因为人的力量有大有小。（见《论语·八佾》）但人求仁、求道，只要坚持他都可以做到，他没有看到过有谁力量不够。冉有说他喜欢老师的道，但他的力量不够。孔子告诉他说，力量不够的话是走到中途而不能再走了，但你还没有走就停下来了。（见《论语·里仁》和《论语·雍也》）孟子向齐宣王区分了不能与不为的不同，他告诉齐宣王说，让你背负泰山到北海这是不能，但做一个明王这如同请你折一个树枝，这是非常容易的。如果这都不做，那是不为而不是不能。（见《孟子·梁惠王上》）

公》)、“仁远乎哉？我欲仁，斯仁至矣”（《论语·述而》）“三军可夺帅也，匹夫不可夺志也”（《论语·子罕》）等，都很能说明这一点。

第二，在孔子看来，不管你是穷、是达，你都应该前后一贯地追求和保持自己的“德行”。虽然《穷达以时》同陈蔡之厄部分文献的记载有不小的差别，但在展示儒家以道德本身为目的的自主性、自足性上它们是一致的。《庄子·让王》和《吕氏春秋·慎人》两处的记载几乎一样，都是认为一个人不管遭遇如何，他始终都要保持道德自觉和操守：

故内省而不穷于道，临难而不失其德。天寒既至，霜雪既降，吾是以知松柏之茂也。……古之得道者，穷亦乐，通亦乐。所乐非穷通也。道得于此，则穷通为寒暑风雨之序矣。

故内省而不疚于道，临难而不失其德。大寒既至，霜雪既降，吾是以知松柏之茂也。……古之得道者，穷亦乐，达亦乐。所乐非穷达也，道得于此，则穷达一也，为寒暑风雨之序矣。

《风俗通义·穷通》（卷七）的记载，其意旨也类似：

故内省不疚于道，临难而不失其德，大寒既至，霜雪既降，吾是以知松柏之茂也。[①]

第三，人追求美德本身就是目的，它原本不是为了其他的东西和目标。《穷达以时》说的“动非为达也”，同孔子说的“君子谋道不谋食”、“君子忧道不忧贫”、“君子喻于义”等一样，都是强调政治地位和待遇的获得对儒家来说不是目的。在这一点上，韦伯对儒家的评论是恰当的：

“君子不器”这个根本的原理告诉我们，君子是目的本身，而不只是作为某一特殊有用之目的的手段。……儒家高尚的等级理想，与禁欲的耶稣教会的职业概念形成更加强烈的对立，因为前者主张培养出具有通才的绅士（Gentmet）或译为“德沃夏克”（Dvorvak）的“贵人”（君子）。这种建立在全才基础上的“美德”，即自我完善，比起通过片面化知识（Vereinseitigung）所获得的财富，要来得崇高。即使是处于最有影响地位的人，若不具备来源于教育的这种美德，在世上便会一事无成。因此，“高等”的人所追求的是这种美德，而非营利。[②]

从孔子到孟子再到荀子，虽然他们都强烈地试图参与政治，但他们不能在政治上

---

① 《荀子·大略》也说：“君子隘穷而不失，劳倦而不苟，临患难而不忘细席之言。岁不寒无以知松柏，事不难无以知君子无日不在是。”

② 马克思·韦伯（Max Weber）：《儒教与道教》，洪天富译，南京：江苏人民出版社，1993年，第187页。

发挥出他们所期待的作用，部分原因在于外在的社会实际的复杂性，部分原因在于他们自身的道德理想主义。儒家的道德和伦理越是理想化，它同现实之间的鸿沟就越大；儒家越是想把信念伦理和个人道德“公共化”，它同现实世界的冲突就激烈。但在儒家信徒看来，现实不能接受他们的道德理想那是现实的问题，而不是他们的问题。颜渊说：

夫子之道至大，故天下莫能容。虽然，夫子推而行之，不容何病，不容然后见君子！夫道之不修也，是吾丑也。夫道既已大修而不用，是有国者之丑也。不容何病，不容然后见君子！（《史记·孔子世家》）

在“个人道德”的优越感与“有国者之丑”的这种对比中，儒家超越了道德理想同现实冲突的焦虑。虽然孔子有时也感到无奈，说“道之不行也，我知之矣”（《礼记·中庸》），甚至产生了“乘桴浮于海”（《论语·公冶长》）的念头。[①]

但从孔子一生的经历来看，他说的“用之则行，舍之则藏”，不能从一般意义上的善于变通来理解。孔子的超凡精神和魅力在于，他虽然不断遇到挫折和打击，但他始终不放弃他的信念。罗素在《社会改造原理》（Principles of Social Reconstruction）一书的最后提出一个问题“什么是我们能够做的”，开头他说：“当我们活着的时候我们能为这个世界做些什么？有许多男女要想为人类服务，但是他们迷惑不解，而且他们的力量似乎非常渺小。他们为失望所控制；热情最高的人，因为感觉到自己的无力，痛苦最深，而且因为缺乏希望的缘故，最容易造成精神的衰败。”[②] 但孔子没有为他的热情“造成精神的衰败”。他确实是一位“知其不可而为之者”（《论语·宪问》），而不是庄子所说的“知其不可奈何而安之若命”那样的人。在罗素看来，有四个人比任何人都更有力量，他们是释迦牟尼、耶稣、毕达哥拉斯和伽利略，其实至少应该加上孔子。他们生前都没有获得特别的权力，但他们对人类一直产生着巨大和深远的影响。

令人敬仰的是，孔子“不怨天，不尤人”（《论语·宪问》）。按照孔子的看法，一个人真正应该忧虑的是自己是否有进步，而不是忧虑别人不知道自己。《穷达以时》说的“君子敦于反己”，同儒家一般所说的“反己”、“反求诸己”一样，是以道德主体和道德自觉为基础要求人对自己的言行进行道德上的检查，它一方面表现为道德上的以身作则，先正己而不是先正人；另一面表现为寻找自己在道德上的缺失，促使自己不断完善。即使自己不被人知或得不到他人肯定性的道德评价，也不责备他人而是继续

---

① 孔子的精神痛苦显然是巨大的。《论语·子罕》记载：“子曰：凤鸟不至，河不出图，吾已矣乎！”《孔丛子·记问》的记载更具体：“天子布德，将致太平，则麟、凤、龟、龙先为之祥，今宗周将灭，天下无主，孰为来哉？遂泣曰：‘予之于人，犹麟之于兽也，麟出而死，吾道穷矣。’乃歌曰：‘唐虞世兮，麟凤游，今非其时来何求？麟兮麟兮我心忧。’”孔子人生的悲剧性就在这里。

② 罗素（Russell）：《社会改造原理》，张师竹译，上海：上海人民出版社，1959年，第132页。

查找自己做得如何。在这一点上，荀子的说法也很有代表性。“自知者不怨人，知命者不怨天，怨人者穷，怨天者无志。失之己，反之人，岂不迂乎哉！”（《荀子·荣辱》）

## 结　语

总而言之，本文依据《穷达以时》及其相关文献，从孔子和他的弟子们对陈蔡之厄境遇的体验出发，考察了孔子和他的弟子们在生活世界中体认和洞察真理的方式。我们看到，正是在陈蔡之厄的特殊体验中，孔子和他的弟子们一起追问和探讨了德福了关系。结果，孔子不仅得出了与已有的他的德福一致主张不同的“德福未必一致”的新主张，而且对什么是真正的幸福和快乐、什么才是不幸提出了新看法；不仅为穷困赋予了不同于世俗的积极的意义，而且认为追求美德和自我完善本身就是幸福和快乐的，否则那才是人生的不幸。《穷达以时》看似是关心人生的穷达和时遇的关系，但它真正要向人们昭示的是，不管他追求美德和自我完善多么困难，他都要坚持不懈。他应该不断地进行自我反思，过一种心安理得的生活，用《周易·说卦》的话说就是过一种“和顺道德而理于义，穷理尽性以至于命”的生活。

# 孔夫子

## ——诗人、圣贤、哲学家

俄罗斯科学院 A.E.卢基扬诺夫 著 黄立良 译

孔夫子（公元前551—479）代表着人类教育思想中全部的中华传统文化，大多数的人认为孔夫子不仅是一位圣贤，而且是位哲学家，但很少有人称他为诗人。

孔夫子其实是一位真正明了终极人性的诗人、圣贤、哲学家。《论语》指出：“不知言，无以知人也。”在《易经》中，也有类似的说法。《系辞下》：“夫《易》，彰往而察来，而微显阐幽，开而当名，辨物正言断辞，则备矣。”这一段，是孔夫子根据卦爻辞而阐发的“道”，和正言与断辞一样体现了诗意、哲理、天才的“道”。如果我们更深入的渗透到“道”，那我们将越来越接近孔夫子诗人、哲学家和圣人的精髓。

诗人孔夫子的理念体现在天地之间。天行有常，天地自然有自己的符号图案文字、螺旋运动形态和有序的运行规律。这三位一体的字母符号、运动形态和有序节奏，让“道”脱离了人的自然本性而成为一种超越自然的存在，原始人类脱离自然界的过程就是如此。作为社会生活总体的一部分，“道”在人类活动中，表现为舞蹈和音乐。后来，人与自然的和谐统一被打破，天生诸子而济世救民，而孔子为其一。

孔夫子呕心沥血、竭尽全力地恢复自然与天命，但最终仍未如愿以偿。子贡曰：“夫子之文章，可得而闻也；夫子之言性与天道，不可得而闻也。”夫子罕言性与天道，连及门高弟也没有听到过。《论语·公冶长》虽然通过诸多方式探讨了孔子的“道”——仁，但后世仍难以把握其义理精髓，我们更容易看到的是，真正的夫子其实是一个诗人。

孔夫子述而不作，遗留给我们更多的是他教授学生的语录。他删诗书，定礼乐，保留了古代的优秀文化。经他编定的《诗经》，是唯一真正地反映上古文明的圣歌。孔夫子以自己的“道”为标准，整理了古代广泛流传的民歌，按照孔子理念编著的史诗般的文学集——《诗经》，亦由此而诞生。

《诗经》与传统的文集相比有几个明显特点。首先，《诗经》选取那些诗句最能体现“五常”——仁、义、礼、智、信精神实质的原型；其次，《诗经》的音乐和舞蹈，通过空间与时态，体现了孔子的“道”。在他的诗词中，仪式和音乐进行过程里，再现了“道”的本来面目。子曰：“兴于诗，立于礼，成于乐。”（《论语·泰伯》）意思是始于诗歌，按照仪式，大成于音乐。

因此，作为中国的精神象征——《诗经》是“道”的天然表达，孔子是一位天才的诗人。尽管孔子没有自己直接动笔作诗，但他编定的《诗经》丝毫不亚于李白的诗作，因为《诗经》所体现的孔子的“道”，是中华文明的源泉。在追寻古代印记和领悟灿烂《诗经》的过程中，李白有着刻骨铭心的感悟：“好道心不歇”（《天台晓望》）——尊崇“道”的灵感精神不止歇。

贤者孔子，以人道与天道、地道相会通，其思想无所不包。“圣”（聖）从象形文字表示为神圣、智慧，圣人就是“智慧”的载体，那就是“自然的人”、“聪明智慧的人”，天下由聪明智慧的人来管理。因此，他俯瞰着天下的一切开始与结束，以和谐的理念引导着万物。（子曰：“为政以德，譬如北辰，居其所而众星共之。”）智慧的本质在于智者自己顺应自然规律，人与自然和谐共存，天人合一。如此，社会空间、大自然与智者在这种三位一体完善的中达到了一定程度的完美统一，那就是至圣。用智者的话来讲，就是自然规律、道德理念与天地自然完美地结合。（夫大人者，与天地合其德，与日月合其明，与四时合其序，与鬼神合其吉凶。先天下而天弗违，后天而奉天时。天且弗违，而况于人乎？况于鬼神乎？）《礼记·中庸》中如此描述孔夫子：“仲尼祖述尧舜，宪章文武；上律天时，下袭水土。辟如天地之无不持载，无不覆帱，辟如四时之错行，如日月之代明。萬物并育而不相害，道并行而不相悖，小德川流，大德敦化，此天地之所以为大也。”就是说，孔子继承尧舜，以文王、武王为典范，上遵循天时，下符合地理。就像天地那样没有什么不承载，没有什么不覆盖。又好像四季的交错运行，日月的交替光明。刀物一起生长而互不妨害，道路同时并行而互不冲突。小的德行如河水一样长流不息，大的德行使万物敦厚纯朴。这就是天地的伟大之处啊！

此处所指的古代文明的顶点是尧、舜，下至文王和武王。孔子学究天人，合乎天地自然的意志，踏着日月轮回的节奏，契合春夏秋冬的秩序，顺应神鬼的吉凶，用以唤醒人们“道”与“德”的和谐，成就其伟大的人格。

所以，作为一个诗人和圣人，孔子天人合一之道，更适合以诗歌和音律的形式来传播。处在中国精神文明中心的孔子，依赖于朝气勃勃、富有青春气息的古风，以设定规范自己的教学风格：“述而不作，信而好古，窃比于我老彭”。（《论语·述而》）

作为哲学家的孔子主张“修身”，以成君子。君子是社会之子，也就是社会维度的代表。“修身”和谐有机地结合了内在品格和精神文化：“质胜文则野，文胜质则史。文质彬彬，然后君子。”（《论语·雍也》）

结合“质”与“文”获得的能力，就能够找到进入天地的途径。君子之道，就是天地人三者的和谐统一。在这里，孔子表现为一个哲学家，“道”表现为哲学。

在儒家的经典论文《中庸》就是描述这种类型的理念：“天命之谓性，率性之谓道，脩道之谓教。道也者，不可须臾离也，可离非道也。是故君子戒慎乎其所不睹，恐惧乎其所不闻。莫见乎隐，莫显乎微，故君子慎其独也。喜怒哀乐之未发，谓之中；发而皆中节，谓之和。中也者，天下之大本也；和也者，天下之达道也。致中和，天地位焉，万物育焉。”

“教”即改善之道，实际上也是一种哲学。不仅儒家，诸子百家均在其理论中提到了“教”的说法。教是一种自我教育，自我完善，它涵盖儒家学说中所有的哲学概念和宗教教义，是最重要的儒家理论。《中庸》里说，人们自觉地进行自我修养、自我监督、自我教育、自我完善，把自己培养成为具有理想人格，达到至善、至仁、至诚、至道、至德、至圣、合外内之道的理想境界，这是诗歌一样的语句。钟爱“道”必将产生对学习的热爱和对智慧的追求——这就是“好学”。

“好学”之人以提高自己的道德修养和才能学问才是我们求学的目的。随时完善自己的德性和才能的好学之人，被称作“子”，类似古代希腊的毕达哥拉斯。孔子首先称自己是一位好学的人：“十室之邑，必有忠信如丘者焉，不如丘之好学也。”（《论语·公冶长》）要成为孔子所说的哲学家，就要在生活中随时修行：“君子食无求饱，居无求安，敏于事而慎于言，就有道而正焉，可谓好学也已。”（《论语·学而》）

哲学强调的特定内涵就是喜爱——“好”。孔子找到了学习的最高境界，制定了“好”的特定内涵：“知之者不如好之者，好之者不如乐之者。”（《论语·雍也》）——懂得它的人，不如爱好它的人；爱好它的人，又不如以它为乐的人，这就是“好”的最高境界。哲学证实“好学”的概念，无论是古希腊的观念还是中国的“好学”——哲学理念都表达了哲学世界里非凡的法定意义的事实。因此，孔子的哲学是必然诚心遵循“道”与专心追求学问——好学，进而自然而然的诞生了哲学家。因此，沿着孔子的“好”—“好道”，在诗句中就是“就有道”，显示出孔子对“道”的追求，对智慧圣贤的敬畏，由此开创塑造了自己的哲学。

下面就个人的认识阐述中华文明在俄罗斯的传播弘扬：

第一：最近十年里，中国文化在俄罗斯得到越来越大的发展。

中国文化以丰富多彩的艺术形式走进俄罗斯，像武术、风水、太极拳等等。典型、严肃的文学作品翻译和历史的题材作品等影片，在俄罗斯产生了越来越大的影响。儒学和道家都在俄罗斯广泛地传播。可是，在肯定积极因素的同时，还要看到在俄罗斯弘扬中国文化的过程中产生的消极因素。首先，书店柜台充满水平低劣、毫无顾忌、肤浅的伪科学，一味追求商业利润的介绍中国文学的著作。其次，中国文化实际上甚至被某些专家难于理解，原因在于没有相同的术语在使用。例如，俄罗斯的文化

（культура）和文明（цивилизация）这两个概念，与中国文化和文明这两个概念有不同的意思。还有别的概念和语句：和而不同，协和，大同，小康……要准确无误地翻译是很困难的事情。为了克服这些传播中国文化中的困难，俄罗斯科学院远东研究所在2008年创建了“孔子之家”中心，领导人是俄罗斯科学院院士M. Л. 季塔连科所长。近些年来中心的工作人员出版了一些儒学专著的俄语译本，如周敦颐《太极图说》、《通书》，《论语》、《易经》、《中庸》、《正蒙》、《尚书》、《三字经》等等。我们和我们的领导M. Л. 季塔连科院士准备了充分的材料，已经出版发行了《中国精神文化百科大典》1—6卷，新的译本介绍了孔子理论继承者张载、程颐、程颢和朱熹的思想脉络。这部书耗时多年，可称得上是在欧洲独一无二的开创性巨著，它不仅对学者专家有重大意义，而且惠及广大俄罗斯民众。希望《中国精神文化百科大典》的出版，能对推动中国文化在俄罗斯的传播。2011年6月，时任总统的梅德伟杰夫在莫斯科克里姆林宫亲自为M. Л. 季塔连科院士等三位参与此巨著的科学家授予国家奖章。

第二，世界上有不少汉学家说，“中国哲学”还没有自己的概念，认为“哲学”这个词，从历史上说来自20世纪初期的日本。但是，哲学史中“好学”一词就是儒家理论中“哲学”的原本称谓，这同古代希腊哲学理念中的完全相同。正如《论语》所示：“十室之邑，必有忠信如丘者焉，不如丘之好学也。”季康子问：“弟子孰为好学?”孔子对曰：“有颜回者好学……不幸短命死矣！今也则亡。”

第三，研究《白虎通》后，我成功地揭示了五行与儒学的线性变化。这就是我研制的图表方程式和说明。

木王火相土死金囚水休

土王金相水死木囚火休

水王木相火死土囚金休

火王土相金死水囚木休

金王水相木死火囚土休

五行是有规律性相互转化、不可替代的。

а б в г д

1 木土水火金王

2 火金木土水相

3 土水火金木死

4 金木土水火囚

5 水火金木土休

它们有水平线和垂直线的示意图，他们相互交叉，作为五行成分的线型与环绕形的交错，在其内部有必然的水平线型联系，于是就出现了下列示意图：

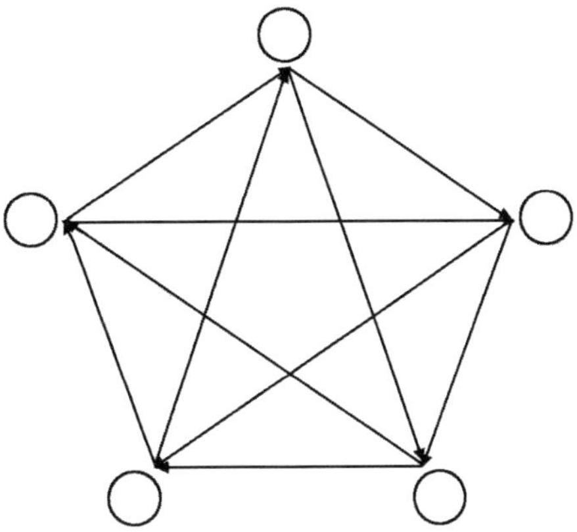

五行就像《白虎通》中那样的这种说法，存在于天地之间和日常生活之中，体现在国家和宇宙运行的自然规律之中。

第四，现在要追寻俄罗斯文化的渊源。俄罗斯既不是发源于东正教的文化，亦非斯拉夫民族的文化，而是独特的、有着自己源头的俄罗斯文化，它的名字就是“Глагол”。研究证明，关于俄罗斯自己独特的文化，表现在18—19世纪初的普希金、果戈理、秋切夫、费特等大师的著作里，用俄罗斯语言表述的共同的俄罗斯文化总轮廓已经被揭示。今后我们的主要工作就是找出俄罗斯文化的内在联系，这样，俄罗斯文化与中国儒家文化之间就可以相辅相成、相互理解了。

为此，我连续法办了一系列关于中国文化的讲座，并出版了相关文化教材，该教材面向俄罗斯大学生及研究生，适用于学习汉语的学校高年级学员，中专及学院的学生，也同样适用于非汉语教学课堂。

第一节讲座是《中国古代哲学》，包括五个部分：第一部分为中国哲学的形成，第二部分为道家学派，第三部分为儒学，第四部分为各个流派的哲学，第五部分为中国哲学在俄罗斯。按照年代次序循序渐进，囊括了中国哲学从公元前3000年到公元前3世纪的发展进程，有二十多讲。每一讲必包含四个部分：讲义（研究结果）、图书目录、术语词典、带有相关图表的文选读本。讲座内容全部来源于汉语原始资料，文选部分包括全部俄文译文。不仅汉语学习者会对该讲座感兴趣，所有喜欢古代中国哲学的爱好者都会从中受益。

第二节讲座是《神话与神话学》，讲述中国古代神话中关于宇宙的观念及中国哲学的起源。开始分析了基本的宇宙概念，特别注意了空间系统的存在、类别、变化和静态条件的认识论——原本论的哲学思维结构，最后用详尽文字和并引述中国古代神话的主要来源之一——《山海经》，提供了一个术语列表、资源列表和相关科学文献，关注了读者的问题，使本次讲座成为有益于自我研讨的交流机会。

第三节讲座是《道文化的原型》，专门破译了道文化原型，揭示了印度和古希腊奥姆文化标志的原型，并将这些原型放在一起相比较而发掘其中的内在关系。道文化原型代表是植根于普遍的、充满活力的神话时代，最终成型于充满哲辨思想的上古社会。当神话中的人变成可感可知的圣人，恢复了天地人的本来面目，哲学开始了。

神话时代是所有文明都拥有的特别形式的民族文化，比较这些文化，可以感受到不同文明在同一个时空的交汇，进而通过比较道文化和奥姆文化而更容易理地理解两种不同的文化。分阶段对道文化和奥姆文化进行详尽地分析，而揭示“道”螺旋式辩证发展的自然规律。

讲座第一次在结构上形成了明确的“道”理论，系统地从框架和细节方面揭示其本质，运用诗人、圣人、哲人的语言，在人类文化中和谐的传播。通过三个名词：五行、五常、五术的运用，扫除语言障碍，赋予其明确意义，告知日常生活背后“百姓日用而不知”的真理以及天人合一的修行方法，“道”文化对于当今文明的深刻影响。

第四节讲座是《中国传统哲学的理念》。在这一节中，我论述了中国的经典哲学及其著作，关注中国古代早期哲学思想的形成、完善，概括把握其现象本质属性，详细讲述中国哲学产生、形成、发展的不同阶段，分析不同哲学之间的区别及其内在联系。“道文化”是中国哲学在相当长的历史阶段而形成的独特的思想形式，从研究它的基本原理出发，高屋建瓴地阐明中国哲学的特殊性，再对照、比较古印度、古希腊的哲学体系，系统地研究中国哲学，确定了中国哲学体系与其他哲学体系一样，有着自己独有的思想方法和认识论。用数据从理论和实践两个方面，分析了中国哲学中思想、理论相一致的三个分支学派。孔子的哲学思想代表“好学”；道家思想代表“绝学”；《周易》概括象征世间万物皆为“阴阳”、黑白标志组成的“太极”。毫无疑问，中国的哲学在理论上具有独一无二的独创性，同印度和希腊的哲学思想并驾齐驱，缔造、完善了世界哲学。中国哲学原始的三位一体概念，符合哲学历史发展的需要，任何人发现都可能视其为它是全球的哲学观，中国哲学在全球化的同时保留了属于自己的独特定位。

第五节讲座是《诗经与哲学的起源》，从世界观的观点来研究文学与古代中国哲学。《诗经》带有上古神话时代人类文明的遗迹，通过诗词、舞蹈与音乐来表现民族时候的生产力和生产关系，表现当时的人生观和宇宙观，从而具有了玄学的意义和哲学思维的特征。

《诗经》的诠释者是孔子及其弟，体现了中国早期历史、宗教与社会。《诗经》宗旨为“无邪”，体现了原始精神情感的五常原形——仁、义、礼、智、信，使诗与宇宙融合起来。《中庸》里多次引用《诗经》的诗句，用以阐释孔子的儒家思想，从天文学、历史学、政治文化、本体论等等中阐发其“乐与怒，忧与喜”的情感哲学性质。（《中庸》第1节）

《诗经》的诗词、舞蹈与诗歌音乐形成孔子的哲学信念。子曰："兴于诗，立于礼，成于乐。"（《论语·泰伯》）如此而来，孔子提出了他从事教育的三方面内容：诗、礼、乐，而且指出了这三者的不同作用。它要求学生不仅要讲个人的修养，而且要有全面、广泛的知识和技能。孔子个人在这里明确其世界观并提出了儒学教学的总纲领。

第六节讲座中分析了《易传》的起源、作者、方法、结构和内容。创作《易传》的目的乃是按照"道"的文化原型来复归它。创作《易传》的方法即模仿宇宙的变化，并以图形和数字体系来记录这些变化。讲座从图形和文字两个子系统中分析了《易经》，指出图形部分由八种基本卦和六十四卦组成，文字部分由卦名、系辞传、说卦传和卦辞、爻辞组成。《系辞传》是对卦的整体说明，《说卦传》是对六十四卦的特点的说明，还有解释八卦和六十四卦的卦辞和爻辞。讲座的"结语"部分，展开了对《易经》的描述。《易经》不仅仅是一部哲学作品，而且《易经》的图形部分描述的哲理是永恒的，对人类生活的所有领域都具有指导作用。文字部分是《易经》的百科全书，囊括了天地人三才之道。《易经》是"大道之源"，是自然哲学与人文实践的理论根源。

第七节讲座讨论两个主题：长诗《天问》，作者屈原（前339—278）；作为人格规范的《三字经》，作者是王伯厚（1223—1296），这是中国作为教育和培养正统人格的一部蒙书。

《天问》的主要特点是对宇宙自然、人类社会总体认识的总结与升华的一种艺术再现，阐述和表达了对宇宙和人生的理性探索（《天问》即为《对天的提问》），从而达到人性的自我完善提高，从而成为忠君爱国的君子。《天问》全文内容分为宇宙起源、神话和历史，对天、对地、对自然、对社会、对历史、对人生提出了系列问题，大家可以通过这部作品了解中国传统文化的脉络。

《三字经》相对《天问》而言，讲得更多的是如何培养和教育年轻人成为一个合格的公民。在《三字经》诗一般的模式合乎"天—人—地"相统一的规范。《三字经》是一部在儒家思想指导下编成的读物，教育年轻人积极的人生观，并引导其后天正确成长。

《天问》和《三字经》在哲学思维的深度和广度的进程上虽有天壤之别，但它们都有其自身特点，分别展现了其艺术、教育与文化的本质。

除此之外，经过多年的研究，我以俄语向俄罗斯的读者介绍了中国古代文化经典《山海经》，并且勾画了五行、五常、五数的原本模式体现。（在前面介绍《白虎通》中已经详细表述）它的三个明显特色：儿子，父亲和母亲。在"主导"方面永远是儿子，属于"中朝"、"乾化"；谁能"休整"呢——由此引发的是父亲，即在"衰老"（"死神"）的近邻；母亲伤害儿子的原因使得转到另一序列"伤害到父亲那里去"。在中国道家哲学的玄天原型和"道"的实施方案中，也有一个螺旋形的五常模式。

在中国哲学宝库中有原本的“道”，当然具有创建性的螺旋形态。这些思想记录在《淮南子》中：

木胜土，土胜水，水胜火，火胜金。故禾春生秋死，菽夏生冬死，麦秋生夏死，荠冬生中夏死。

以水和土，以土和火，以火化金，以金治木，木复返土。五行相治，所以成器用。

因此，从孔子的儒学看，儒学在五行的模式即为：“五常”来自于“仁”——“仁者人也”，而孝弟为“仁”之根本——“君子务本，本立而道生。孝弟也者，其為仁之本與”。

热忱欢迎各国各位专家学者对本人的研究与分析论断提出宝贵意见。

# 孔子的朋友之道

中国社会科学院研究生院　栾贵川

“朋友”，自从它“产生”的那天起，就注定要在人类社会担当起重要的角色，正所谓“自天子至于庶人，未有不须友而成者”，[①] 朋友对于任何人都是十分重要的社会关系，要做成一件事，一定要有朋友的帮助。然而，根据现有材料，在孔子之前，对于朋友，并没有过多的记载。也就是说，是孔子较早并且较为全面系统地对于“朋友”进行了论述。《论语》等书所记载的有关孔子择友、处友的原则，至今仍具重要的理论价值和借鉴意义。

孔子是闻名遐迩的博学之士，又在鲁国作过大夫，周游列国十几年，他与鲁国、卫国以及不少其他诸侯国各阶层的人士有过广泛的交集，但是，孔子并不滥交朋友，在同时代的人物中，值得他所敬重的不过寥寥数人而已。[②] 孔子之所以较多地述及“朋友”，是由于他弟子众多，他视弟子为朋友。《孔丛子》卷1《论书》记载：“周文王有胥附、奔辏、先后、御侮，谓之四邻。以免乎牖里之害。（孟）懿子曰：‘夫子亦有四邻乎？’孔子曰：‘吾有四友焉。自吾得回（颜回）也，门人加亲，是非胥附乎？自吾得赐（端木赐）也，远方之士日至，是非奔辏乎？自吾得师（颛孙师）也，前有光，后有辉，是非先后乎？自吾得由（仲由）也，恶言不至于门，是非御侮乎？’”[③]

---

① 《诗经·小雅·伐木》序。

② 《史记》卷67《仲尼弟子列传》记载：“孔子之所严事：于周则老子；于卫，蘧伯玉；于齐，晏平仲；于楚，老莱子；于郑，子产；于鲁，孟公绰。”孟公绰是鲁国的大夫，对于他的生卒年代，典籍失载，司马迁认为孟公绰应是与孔子同时代的人，因下文记载：“数称臧文仲、柳下惠、铜鞮伯华、介山子然，孔子皆后之，不并世。”唐代司马贞《索隐》也认为：“自臧文仲已下，孔子皆后之，不并代。”（见《史记》修订本，中华书局，2013年，第7册，第2644、2645页。）

③ 傅亚庶：《孔丛子校释》，中华书局，2011年，第20、21页。但是，后人的理解总是别出心裁，东汉班固《白虎通》卷8《辟雍》把孔子与其弟子分作朋友、父子、君臣三种关系，他认为：“师弟子之道有三：《论语》‘朋友自远方来’，朋友之道也。又曰‘回也视予犹父也’，父子之道也。以君臣之义教之，君臣之道也。”（见吴则虞点校，陈立：《白虎通疏证》，中华书局，1994年，第258页。）

孔子待人真诚，对其弟子一无所隐，[①] 在很多场合，孔子是以自己的交友心得教诲其弟子，所以，孔子有关朋友的论述，与其甄别人物、识人之法紧紧联系在一起。孔子的“朋友之道”，不仅表现出他的生活智慧、政治智慧，更体现了他的仁者情怀。

## 一、孔子的择友原则

1. 反对滥交朋友

由于经历、生活环境等因素的影响，致使每个人的品性、才具也各有不同。朋友长期相处，相互间势必相互熏染，孔子告诫其弟子，交友时必须有所选择。

《论语·季氏第十六》记载，孔子曰：“益者三友，损者三友。友直、友谅、友多闻，益矣。友便辟、友善柔、友便佞，损矣。”孔子认为，有益的朋友有三种，有害的朋友也有三种。结交正直的人、讲诚信的人、见闻广博的人，对自己有益。相反，如果结交谄媚取宠的人、阳奉阴违的人、夸夸其谈的人，对自己有害。

“直”之所以可贵，在于自己有了过错的时候，友人自会及时直言劝诫。《论语》记孔子主张“朋友切切偲偲”，是说朋友在相处时，要诚恳而严肃地互相督责。《孟子》也强调“责善，朋友之道也；父子责善，贼恩之大者”，责善就是劝勉从善，以善相责。朋友是父子兄弟这种血亲关系的重要补充，而以善相责，是父子、兄弟所无法做到的。《荀子·修身》认为：“是我而当者，吾友也。”自己做得正确，能够及时给予肯定的，才是真正的朋友。由此可见，朋友间对于对方的所作所为，只有正直的人，才可以给予确当的反馈。自己犯错时，也能够及时得到朋友的纠正；自己做得对，也能得到朋友的鼓励和认可。所以，朋友的“直”，的确是一种好的品质。“谅”指诚信。“信”在《论语》中多有述及，孔子及其弟子认为，诚信是保持朋友间友谊的必要前提和基石。“多闻”的朋友，可以直接提供知识，有助于增广异闻、开阔视野，这在知识、信息不大普及、发达的古代，是尤为难得的。所以“多闻”也被孔子视作一种“益友”。有的注释家认为，这一章是孔子说与国君的，孔子提醒国君，臣下有优有劣，在任用时务必有所留意。其实，这句话具有广泛的适用性，也未尝不是对其弟子的忠告，足可视作是孔子识人、交友的重要原则。

对于本章中所列举的三类损友，清代经学家刘宝楠分别作了解释，他认为：“盖‘便辟’是体柔，即所谓‘足恭’也。‘善柔’是面柔，即所谓‘令色’也。‘便佞’是

---

① 《论语·述而第七》记：“子曰：‘二三子以我为隐乎？吾无隐乎尔。吾无行而不与二三子者，是丘也。’”

口柔，即所谓‘巧言’也。”① 孔子对于其弟子的培养目标是“君子”，而“君子”理应自重、自爱，致力于进德修业，所以，在结交朋友时，必须有所选择。

2. 无友不如己者

《论语·学而第一》记载：“子曰：‘君子不重则不威，学则不固。主忠信，无友不如己者。过，则勿惮改。’”孔子是说，作为君子，如果自己为人不持重，就不会有威严，即便读书，学业也不会牢固。在品德上，要讲忠、信。在交友时，不要结交那些在品德上不如自己的人。有了过错，就不要怕改正。

“无友不如己者”，是孔子择友的一项重要原则，但是，现今很多人已经不能准确地理解认知它真正的含义，所以有必要对这句话稍加分析。要注意孔子是在说“主忠信”，“主”就是守持、坚守的意思。“无友不如己者”是历代注释家歧义较多的一句话，主要有以下几种意见：

一是，把“如”字理解为“如同”，“如己”就是“和自己同类”，意思就是说，不和不同类的人交友，认为这就与孔子“道不同不相为谋”暗合了。事实上，在孔子所处的时代，即使是政治、学术主张完全不同的人，也能够相互尊重、相互包容，不像后世各学派之间的门户森严、势如冰炭。②

二是，没有哪个朋友不如自己，即人人都有可取之处。这种观点的主要依据是，孔子曾经说过“三人行，必有我师焉。择其善者而从之，其不善者而改之”（《论语·述而》）。其实，这是指孔子“学无常师”、“好学”虚心学习的态度，并不是择友的原则。假如孔子真的以为人人都胜过自己，他还有什么必要择友、友贤呢？还有什么必要“里仁”呢？其次，孔子注重仁德，他对他的弟子的培养目标，正是造就君子品格，《论语·述而第七》记载：“子以四教：文、行、忠、信。”北宋邢昺解释道：“文为先王之遗文；行为德行，在心为德，施之为行；中心无隐，谓之忠；人言不欺，谓之信。”“文”属于文献知识等教育内容，“行”、“忠”、“信”三项则全是道德教育内容。完全可以说，孔子站在道德、仁德的制高点上，试想，在忠信等道德操守方面，他怎么可能认为人人都胜过自己呢？

第三种观点是笔者所赞同的：不要结交不如自己的人。我认为，孔子“无友不如

---

① 见高流水点校，刘宝楠《论语正义》卷16，中华书局，1990年，第658页。《论语·学而第一》：“子曰：‘巧言令色，鲜矣仁！’”又，《公冶长第五》篇记：“子曰：‘巧言、令色、足恭，左丘明耻之，丘亦耻之。匿怨而友其人，左丘明耻之，丘亦耻之。’”

② 《庄子·天下篇》记：“天下之治方术者多矣，皆以其有为不可加矣。……天下大乱，圣贤不明、道德不一，天下多得一察焉以自好。譬如耳鼻口，皆有所明，不能相通。”（郭庆藩：《庄子集释》卷10下，第1065—1069页。）《史记》卷63《老子韩非列传》记载了司马迁对后世不同学术流派相互攻讦现象的批评，他写道：“世之学老子则绌儒学，儒学亦绌老子。‘道不同不相为谋’，其谓是邪？”

己者”这句话，是直接引用周公的话。《大戴礼记·曾子制言中》记曾子说：“吾不仁其人，虽独也，吾弗亲也。”意思是说，假如我认为某人没有仁德，即使我独学无友，也不会亲近他。卢辩注解说：“人而不仁，不足友也。故周公曰‘不如我者，我不与处，损我者也。与吾等，吾不与处，无益我者也。吾所以处者，必贤于我。’”[①] 南朝梁代皇侃也认为：“凡结交取友，必令胜己。胜己，则己有日所益之义；不得友不如己，友不如己，则己有日损。故云‘无友不如己者’。或问曰：‘若人皆慕胜己为友，则胜己者岂友我耶？’或通云：择友必以忠信者为主，不取忠信不如己者耳，不论余才也。或通云：敌则为友，不取不敌者也。”[②]

这样理解，在《论语》中也能找到“内证”，《子张第十九》记载，子张不同意子夏“可者与之，其不可者拒之”的做法，说“我之大贤与，于人何所不容？我之不贤与？人将拒我，如之何其拒人也？”我不如对方“贤”，对方自会拒绝我。这岂不正是“无友不如己者”么？

需要特别指出的一点是，前引皇侃的注释中所涉及一个问题，这也是现今人们深感困惑的一个问题：假如人人都按照这个“无友不如己者”的交友原则，那么，人人都不会找到朋友。这就陷入了一个“死循环”。

其实，“如”还是“不如”，是每个人心中的主观的“标准”，而不是一个可以量化的客观的“标准”。这样理解，才可以知晓孔子“三人行，必有我师焉。择其善者而从之，其不善者而改之”的本来含义。反过来说，假如这个标准是“客观”的，如同人的身高、体重，那就真的是人人都找不到朋友了。

3. 交友必须择优

孔子告诫其弟子，在交朋友时，一定要选择最优秀的人。《论语·子路第十三》记载：“子曰：‘不得中行而与之，必也狂狷乎！狂者进取，狷者有所不为也。’”孔子是说，假如找不到合乎中庸之德的人和他交往，也一定要和狂、狷的人相处，因为他们是仅次于“中行”的人，狂者言行有些“过”，如子张；狷者言行则“不及”，如子夏。即使“过犹不及”，两者都不完美，但是，孔子认为，狂者肯于进德修业，狷者不至于做坏事。

“中行”是指合乎中庸之德的人。曹魏时人何晏《论语集解》卷七引包咸的解释是：“狂者进取于善道，狷者守节无为。”朱熹《论语集注》卷七也认为：“狂者，志极

---

① 王文锦点校，王聘珍：《大戴礼记解诂》，中华书局，1983年，第92页。其实，周公的这段话，始见于《吕氏春秋·观世篇》，孔子有很多话并未言明出自何处，在研读《论语》时尤其需要予以重视。

② 皇侃：《论语义疏》卷1，见《论语》上册，中华书局“四部要籍注疏丛刊”本，1998年，第162页下栏。

高而行不掩。狷者，知未及而守有余。”“狂者”有些过分，为人做事往往不够完美，而“狷者”的能力或许有些“不及”，谨小慎微、比较保守，但他绝不至于胡作非为。这两种人，都是最为接近于中庸之德的人。

今人蔡尚思认为孔子在很多方面都合乎中庸的标准：“‘人而不仁，疾之已甚，乱也’（《论语·泰伯第八》），是他对物的中庸；‘季文子三思而后行，子闻之，曰：“再，斯可矣”’（《论语·公冶长第五》）是他做事的中庸；‘见危授命’与‘危邦不入’（《论语·宪问第十四》、《论语·泰伯第八》），是他处理生死的中庸；‘师也过，商也不及’（《论语·先进第十一》），是他评价人物的中庸；‘乐而不淫，哀而不伤’（《论语·八佾第三》），是他审美的中庸；‘敬鬼神而远之’（《论语·雍也第六》），是他对待鬼神的中庸；‘周而不比’、‘和而不同’（《论语·为政第二》、《论语·子路第十三》），是他交友之道的中庸；既要‘亲亲’，又想‘尚贤’，是他善用人才的中庸；‘礼之用，和为贵’（《论语·学而第一》），是他治国之道的中庸。”①

4. 不可结交“乡愿”

《论语·阳货第十七》记：“子曰：‘乡愿，德之贼也。’”乡指乡党、乡亲。愿，又作“原”、善。“乡愿”即乡里间人们所称道的“善人”，此指不讲原则、不辨是非，凡事一味地取悦于人的“老好人”。孔子告诫其弟子：乡里间的这些好好先生，正是败坏道德的人。“乡愿”通常很具欺骗性，孔子特别提及这种人，以引起弟子们的注意。汉代徐干的理解是准确的，他说：“乡愿亦无杀人之罪也，而仲尼恶之，何也？以其乱德也。”②

《孟子》对于孔子这句话的背景材料有较为详细的记述，足可参考。孟子曾为其弟子万章解释“乡愿”，他说：“孔子曰：‘过我门而不入我室，我不憾焉者，其惟乡原乎！乡原，德之贼也！’（万章问）曰：‘何如斯可谓之乡原矣？’曰：‘何以是嘐嘐（赵岐注：“嘐嘐，志大言大者也。”）也？言不顾行，行不顾言，则曰，古之人，古之人行何为踽踽凉凉（朱熹注：“踽踽，独行不进之貌”），生斯世也，为斯世也善，斯可矣。阉然媚于世也者，是乡原也。’万子曰：‘一乡皆称原人焉，无所往而不为原人。孔子以为德之贼，何哉？’曰：‘非之无举也，刺之无刺也，同乎流俗，合乎污世，居之似忠信，行之似廉洁，众皆悦之，自以为是，而不可与入尧、舜之道，故曰“德之贼也”。’”③

孔子一向主张明辨是非，反对人云亦云、似是而非。《论语》中另有两章可以与这

① 蔡尚思：《孔子思想体系》，上海人民出版社，1982年，第115、116页。
② 徐干：《中论·考伪》，见孙启治《中论解诂》，中华书局，2014年，第201、202页。
③ 焦循：《孟子正义》，中华书局，1987年，第1029—1031页。

句话互参，《子路第十三》记载："子贡问曰：'乡人皆好之，何如？'子曰：'未可也。''乡人皆恶之，何如？'子曰：'未可也。不如乡人善者好之，其不善者恶之。'"《卫灵公第十五》又记："子曰：'众恶之，必察焉；众好之，必察焉。'"

5. 不交虚荣之人

孔子的弟子，大都出身贫寒，如《荀子·大略篇》记载："子夏家贫，衣若悬鹑。"弟子们的学习生涯过得十分不易。孔子很同情他们的艰辛处境，《论语·泰伯第八》记载："子曰：'三年学，不至于谷，不易得也。'"孔子是说，三年读书期间，并不想出仕为官以脱贫，这已是很难得了。为了帮助学生渡过难关，孔子曾把鲁国执政季氏馈赠给他的大量粮食分发给其数百名弟子。[①] 但是，孔子还认为，作为"士"，就应该一心向学，心无旁骛。他告诫他的弟子说，讲求虚荣的读书人是不值得交往的。《论语·里仁第四》记载："子曰：'士志于道，而耻恶衣恶食者，未足与议也。'"孔子认为，作为读书人，理应有志于探究学业和真理，可是，有人却把吃得不好、穿得不好看作一种耻辱，对于这种人，不值得和他商讨学问。

"士"在春秋时期，是一个介于平民与官吏的过渡身份，孔子的很多弟子后来都出仕为官，成了有位的"君子"。如何使他们成为一个有德的当政者，是孔子十分关注的一个问题。

孔子认为，"士"应"有志于道"，在学习期间，应该致力于学业。他的弟子端木赐（即子贡）因"倦于学"[②] 而去"货殖"，孔子就严厉地批评他"不受命"。[③] 冉求因贪恋禄位而为季孙氏聚敛财富，由此招致了孔子的严厉训斥。孔子批评这种"未足与议"的"士"，目的在于使弟子们有所遵循。《论语》中孔子的很多话都是对其弟子的训诫。

6. 决不违心交友

孔子反对违心地结交朋友。《论语·学而第一》记载孔子说："巧言、令色，鲜矣仁！"《论语·公冶长第五》又记"子曰：'巧言、令色、足恭，左丘明耻之，丘亦耻之。匿怨而友其人，左丘明耻之，丘亦耻之。'"孔子是说，对于花言巧语、伪装容貌、过分谦恭的现象，左丘明认为是可耻的，我也认为是可耻的。掩饰自己内心的怨恨，仍像好朋友那样与对方交往，左丘明认为是可耻的，我也认为是可耻的。

孔子一贯强调"主忠信"，就是要表里如一、恪守忠诚与信实，他认为这是君子品

---

① 《孔子家语》卷2《致思》，杨朝明：《孔子家语通解》第79、80页。又见《孔丛子》卷上《记义》，见傅亚庶《孔丛子校释》第50页。

② 王先谦：《荀子集解》卷19《大略篇》，中华书局，1988年，第509页。

③ 《论语·先进第十一》。

格的最低要求。他说过“刚、毅、木、讷，近仁”。[①] 而“巧言”、“令色”、“足恭”以及“匿怨而友其人”的共性就是虚假、丑恶，孔子认为这都是可耻的。

《礼记·表记》还记孔子说：“君子不失足于人，不失色于人，不失口于人。是故君子貌足畏也，色足惮也，言足信也。《甫刑》：‘敬、忌而罔有择言在躬。’”[②] 这就是说，“巧言”就是指失口、失信；“令色”就是指失色；“足恭”就是指失足。南宋人洪迈的分析十分确当，他说：“刚毅者，必不能令色；木讷者，必不为巧言。此近仁鲜仁之辨也。”[③]

7. 决不勉强交友

孔子认为，在与人交往时，要认识到，人各有志，不可勉强，交友更须慎重。《论语·卫灵公第十五》记：“子曰：‘道不同，不相为谋。’”孔子是说，因为价值观不同，就不可能在一起共同商讨学问，也不可能结交为朋友。皇侃在他的《论语义疏》中解释说：“人之为事，必须先谋。若道同者共谋，则精审不误，若道不同而与共谋，则方圆凿枘（又叫枘凿，是指榫眼、榫头。方枘圆凿，比喻两不相合），事不成也。”

孔子所处的春秋末期，诸家思想已隐然成形。但是，儒、道、农、墨、兵等家异流而同源，这个总的源头，就是先代传承下来的“有形”和“无形”的文化资源：“有形”的是指“六经”等先代文化典籍[④]“无形的”是指历史传说、习俗、器物等等。所以，诸家思想并非全然对立，而有许多相通之处。对此，《庄子·天下篇》的记述十分精当，其云：“天下之治方术者多矣，皆以其有为不可加矣。……其明而在数度者，旧法世传之史尚多有之。其在于《诗》、《书》、《礼》、《乐》者，邹鲁之士缙绅先生多能明之。《诗》以道志，《书》以道事，《礼》以道行，《乐》以道和，《易》以道阴阳，《春秋》以道名分。其数散于天下而设于中国者，百家之学时或称而道之。天下大乱，圣贤不明道德不一，天下多得一察焉以自好。譬如耳鼻口，皆有所明，不能相通。……悲夫，百家往而不反（返），必不合矣！后世之学者，不幸不见天地之纯，古人之大体，道术将为天下裂。”[⑤]

道，在这里是指价值观念，也可以指政治主张、学术观点。价值观念不同的人，不可能成为真正的朋友。正如《孟子·尽心下》记载孟子所说的那样：“好名之人，能

---

① 《论语·子路第十三》。

② 孙希旦《礼记集解》卷51，第1298页。

③ 孔凡礼点校，洪迈：《容斋随笔》第2卷，中华书局，2005年，第25页。

④ 除“六经”外，尚有“志”、“军志”、逸诗、古语等，《周礼·春官·小史》：“小史掌邦国之志。”见《十三经注疏》，第818页中栏。汉代贾谊《新书》卷九《修政语》上、下，专记皇帝、颛顼、帝喾、帝尧、帝舜、大禹、商汤、周文王、周武王遗训，当不无根据。

⑤ 郭庆藩：《庄子集释》卷10下，中华书局，1961年，第1065、1067、1069页。

让千乘之国，苟非其人，箪食豆羹见于色。”喜好名誉的人，可以把君位拱手让给别人；如果不是这样的人，吃他一碗粗茶淡饭也不高兴的。价值取向差异如此之大，是绝不可能结交为朋友的，即使勉强交友，也绝不会持久。

8. 不要遗弃故旧

《论语·宪问第十四》记载：“原壤夷俟。子曰：‘幼而不孙（逊）弟（悌），长而无述焉，老而不死，是为贼。’以杖叩其胫。”原壤很有可能与孔子年龄相仿，且是儿时的伙伴，当属“故旧”，所以，即使十分反感原壤的无礼，但仍然要维持这个关系，原壤的母亲去世以后，孔子仍然前往料理后事。据《礼记·檀弓》记载，原壤在其母亲死后的表现十分怪异：“孔子之故人曰原壤，其母死，夫子助之沐（郑注：沐，治也）椁。原壤登木（郑注：木，椁材也）曰：‘久矣予之不讬于音也。’歌曰：‘狸首之斑然，执女手之卷然。’夫子为弗闻也者而过之。从者曰：‘子未可以已乎？’夫子曰：‘丘闻之：亲者毋失其为亲也，故者毋失其为故也。’”① 据清人孙希旦推测，原壤很可能是道家学派的人：“原壤母死而歌，与子桑户死，孟之反、琴张临丧而歌相类，盖当时为老氏之学者多如此”。②

《大戴礼记》卷四《曾子立事》记载曾子说：“其少不讽诵，其壮不论议，其老不教诲，亦可谓无业之人矣。少称不弟（悌）焉，耻也；壮称无德焉，辱也；老称无礼焉，罪也。”③ 曾子所谴责的正是原壤这样的人。

《孔子家语·屈节篇》还记载：“孔子之旧曰原壤，其母死，夫子将助之以沐椁（沐椁，即治棺）。子路曰：‘由也昔者闻诸夫子曰：“无友不如己者，过则勿惮改。”夫子惮矣，姑已若何？’孔子曰：‘“凡民有丧，匍匐救之。”况故旧乎？非友也。吾其往。’”④ 孔子认为，无论是谁家有了丧事，大家都要竭尽全力相助。更何况原壤是我的旧相识呢？我不是在结交他，而是去帮助他。

在今本《论语》中，有一些章节记载的是历史文化知识，可能是孔子弟子的听课笔记。如《微子篇》记载这样一段话：“周公谓鲁公曰：‘君子不施（弛）其亲，不使大臣怨乎不以（不被任用）。故旧无大故，则不弃也。无求备于一人。’”西周初年，由于周武王刚刚去世，成王还年幼，鲁国始封君周公姬旦受命留在朝里辅佐周成王。周公不得亲临鲁国，他的儿子伯禽代为前往鲁国进行治理。周公叮嘱他说，对待亲人不要怠慢，不要使大臣觉得不被信任，老朋友只要没有大的过错，就不要断绝关系。

---

① 孙希旦：《礼记集解》卷 11《檀弓下》，中华书局，1989 年，第 302 页。

② 孙希旦：《礼记集解》卷 11《檀弓下》，第 303 页。

③ 见方向东：《大戴礼记汇校集解》，第 455、457 页。

④ 杨朝明等：《孔子家语通解》，齐鲁书社，2009 年，第 428 页。

其实，《诗经·小雅·伐木》序也记载说："亲亲以睦友，友贤不弃，不遗故旧，则民德归厚矣。"孔颖达《疏》解释说："既能内亲其亲以使和睦，又能外友其贤而不弃，不遗忘久故之恩旧而燕乐之。"也就是说，不遗弃老朋友，是前代流传下来的美德之一。孔子珍视这种美德，他也对弟子说："君子笃于亲，则民兴于仁；故旧不遗，则民不偷（冷漠）"。[①] 他的这两句话，是对前述周公之语的注释。因为上行下效，"孝弟也者，其为仁之本欤"，[②] 当政者笃行孝亲，民众才有可能养成仁德；当政者不轻易抛弃老朋友，民众才有可能热情相待。

通过孔子对原壤的态度，可见他的交友原则：对于故旧，也绝不轻易遗弃。

## 二、孔子的处友之道

1. 取信于友

诚信是友谊的基石。孔子主张真诚待人，他即使对弟子也无不恪守这一原则，《论语》记载，孔子曾经先后两次对他的弟子承认自己说错了话。[③]《论语·述而第七》记载孔子直接向其弟子表白，自己对他们一无所隐，其记："子曰：'二三子以我为隐乎？吾无隐乎尔。吾无行而不与二三子者，是丘也。'"[④]

从现有的文献资料看，孔子和他众多弟子的关系是很融洽的。但从其弟子对他的形象的描述中，仍可以反映出其师徒间的距离感，《论语·述而第七》记载，他的弟子对他的印象是"温而厉，威而不猛，恭而安"。就是说，他给人的感觉是温和而又严厉，有威严而不凶猛，庄严却又安详。

一个人的学问，可以随年岁而递增，而其习惯、性情，也会由于外界的影响而改变。从《史记》所记录的两条材料，可以反映出，孔子在年轻时的壮志豪情。《史记》记载孔子见老子时，老子忠告孔子说："吾闻之，良贾深藏若虚，君子盛德，容貌若愚。去子之骄气与多欲，态色与淫志，是皆无益于子之身。"[⑤]"聪明深察而近于死者，好讥人者也。博辩广大危其身者，发人之恶者也。为人子者毋以有己，为人臣者毋以有己。孔子自周反于鲁，弟子稍益进焉。"[⑥]

孔子见老子，是在鲁昭公二十四、二十五年（公元前518－517年），当时，孔子年方三十四五岁，血气方刚、踌躇满志。老子的话，正中要害，从此以后，他便潜心

① 《论语·泰伯第八》。

② 《论语·学而第一》记有子之言。

③ 分别见于《述而第七》"陈司败问昭公知礼乎章"和《阳货第十七》"子之武城章"。

④ 何晏《论语集解》卷四引包咸曰："二三子，谓诸弟子。"

⑤ 《史记》卷63《老子韩非列传》。

⑥ 《史记》卷47《孔子世家》。

学问，养成不多言的习惯。孔子认为这是养成仁德所必需的，他说："仁者，其言也讱(即迟缓)"。[①] "刚、毅、木、讷近仁"，[②] 他尤其讨厌花言巧语，认为"巧言乱德"。[③]

孔子学识高深，又不喜爱多说话，弟子们便认为他逢事故意有所隐瞒。孔子当是针对这样的疑惑作的解释。孔子何以如此重视弟子的疑虑呢？因为，能否赢得弟子的信任，不仅是私人感情的问题，更是攸关教育成败的大问题，正如《礼记·学记》所说的那样，"安其学而亲其师，乐其友而信其道，是以虽离师辅而不反（返）也"。

2. 切切偲偲

孔子认为，朋友和兄弟不同，兄弟之间，最重要的是保持亲密无间的关系，而真正的益友之间，则必须诚恳而严肃地以善相责。《论语·子路第十三》记，子路问曰："何如斯可谓之士矣？"子曰："切切偲偲，怡怡如也，可谓士矣。朋友切切偲偲，兄弟怡怡。"子路向孔子问道，怎样做才可以称得上是士？孔子回答说，诚挚地相互督责、切磋，并能友好相处，就可以称为士了。朋友相处应该这样地督责切磋，兄弟相处则应和睦快乐。

孔子为子路的解答，具有明显的针对性，朱熹在《论语集注》卷七引胡氏曰："切切，恳到也。偲偲，详勉也。怡怡，和悦也。皆子路所不足，故告之。又恐其混于所施，则兄弟有贼恩之祸，朋友有善柔之损，故又别而言之。"。[④] 胡氏所谓"贼恩"，就是贼害恩情、伤感情的意思。

《孟子正义》卷 17《离娄下》："责善，朋友之道也；父子责善，贼恩之大者。"[⑤] 父子之间，理应父慈子孝；兄弟之间，理应兄友弟恭，至亲至近的血缘关系，决定了他们必须和睦相处，天伦之"恩"便成为主题词。假如父子兄弟之间也像对待朋友那样地相互"责善"，便是"贼恩"了。

《大戴礼记》卷 4《曾子立事》记载曾子说："君子之于子也，爱而勿面也（《集解》引卢辩曰："不形于面"），使而勿貌也（卢辩注："不以貌劳来之"），导之以道而勿强也。宫中雍雍，外焉肃肃，兄弟嬉嬉，朋友切切。远者以貌，近者以情。友以立其所能，而远其所不能，苟无失其所守，亦可与终身矣。"[⑥]

而作为朋友，在对方做错事时，理应成为"争友"，责成其改正。《荀子·子道篇》

---

① 《论语·颜渊第十二》。

② 《论语·子路第十三》。

③ 《论语·卫灵公第十五》。

④ 朱熹：《论语集注》卷 7，见《四书章句集注》，第 148 页。

⑤ 焦循：《孟子正义》卷 17《离娄下》，第 599 页。

⑥ 方向东：《大戴礼记汇校集解》第 473 页。

记载孔子的话说："士有争友，不为不义。"[①] 这里的"争"，指的就是"切切偲偲"。

同志为"友"，朋友相处，是因为志同道合，为着一个共同的价值理念走到一起，"义"便是他们的"固着剂"，如果有人言行不合乎这个"义"，对方必会提出批评，敦促他改正，这是一项重要的义务。若是不履行这种义务，便是对朋友不负责任，称之"善柔"，他也不再是真正意义的"友"了。

《诗经・小雅・常棣》："虽有兄弟，不如友生。"唐代孔颖达《疏》曰："兄弟之多则尚恩，其聚集则熙熙然，不能相励以道；朋友之交则以义，其聚集切切、节节然，相劝竞以道德，相勉励以立身，使其日有所得，故兄弟不如友生也。"[②] 切切、节节是指相互切磋勉励。

这是朋友、父子、兄弟相处的区别所在。

3. 责善有度

前述《孟子》主张"责善，朋友之道也"，以善相责是朋友间的责任。但是，孔子提醒他的弟子，对朋友，责善也要适度。《论语・颜渊第十二》记："子贡问友。子曰：'忠告而善道（导）之，不可则止，毋自辱焉。'"朋友如有过失，本应如实告诉他并耐心地引导他改正，如果对方知错不改，就不要再规劝他了，不然就要自取其辱了。

子贡（姓端木，名赐）是孔子最为亲近的弟子之一，有口才，善于经商。《史记》卷67《仲尼弟子列传》记载："子贡好废举，与时转货赀（意即囤积货物，逐时贸易）。喜扬人之美，不能匿人之过。常（尝）相鲁卫，家累千金。"子贡常年活跃在各国的商界、政界，为人热心肠，有很多朋友，但不知道怎么与他们相处，所以他向孔子请教朋友之道。孔子则告诫他，朋友间相处要留有余地，不能过分亲密或过严督责，否则就会自寻烦恼。朱熹在其《论语集注》卷6解释道："友所以辅仁，故尽其心以告之，善其说以道之。然以义合者也，故不可则止。若以数而见疏，则自辱矣。"[③]

《后汉书》卷43《朱穆传》唐代李贤注引东汉蔡邕《正交论》记载说："盖朋友之道，有义则合，无义则离。善则久要不忘平生之言，恶则忠告善诲之，否则止，无自辱焉。"[④] 这里所讲的也是这个道理。

处友还要宽缓和善。刘向《说苑》卷10《敬慎篇》记载："桓公曰：'金刚则折，革刚则裂，人君刚则国家灭，人臣刚则交友绝。'夫刚则不和，不合则不可用。是故四马不和，取道不长；父子不和，其世败亡；兄弟不和，不能久同；夫妻不和，室家大

① 沈啸寰、王星贤点校，王先谦：《荀子集解》下册，第530页。
② 孔颖达：《毛诗正义》卷9，见《十三经注疏》，第408页下栏。
③ 朱熹：《论语集注》卷6，见《四书章句集注》第140页。
④ 范晔：《后汉书》卷43《朱穆传》，第1475页。

凶。《易》曰：'二人同心，其利断金。'由不刚也。"[①] 朋友间的责善，同样需要耐心，规劝时也要讲求方式方法，不得太过急于求成，兼顾和气，只有这样，友情才能持久。

4. 相互接济

生活在世间，难免会遇到困难，朋友间本应相互帮助、接济。《管子·牧民篇》记载说："吝于财者失所亲。"帮助朋友不要吝惜财物，否则，就有可能失去亲朋好友。

在财物上，孔子对朋友十分慷慨大方。《礼记集解》卷8《檀弓上》记载说："孔子之卫，遇旧馆人之丧，入而哭之哀，出，使子贡说（脱）骖而赙之。子贡曰：'于门人之丧，未有所说（脱）骖，说（脱）骖于旧馆，无乃已重乎？'夫子曰：'予乡者入而哭之，遇于一哀而出涕。予恶夫涕之无从也，小子行之！'"[②]

《韩诗外传》卷2还记载："孔子遭齐程木子于郯之间，倾盖而语终日。有间，顾子路曰：'束帛十匹以赠先生。'子路不对。有间，又顾曰：'束帛十匹以赠先生。'子路率尔而对曰：'昔者由也闻之于夫子：士不中道相见，女无媒而嫁者，君子不行也。'孔子曰：'夫诗不云乎："野有蔓草，零露漙兮。有美一人，清扬婉兮。邂逅相遇，适我愿兮。"且夫齐程木子，天下之贤士也，吾于是而不赠，终身不之见也。大德不逾闲，小德出入可也。'"[③]

但是，孔子的原则是，对待朋友要雪中送炭，不要锦上添花。《论语·雍也第六》记载："子华使于齐，冉子为其母请粟。子曰：'与之釜。'请益。曰：'与之庾。'冉子与之粟五秉。子曰：'赤之适齐也，乘肥马，衣轻裘。吾闻之也：君子周急不继富。'"

公西赤此次出使齐国时，正在孔门求学，所以冉子为其母"请粟"。孔子以自己的粮食接济弟子亲属，在《论语》中仅此一例，估计不应是特例，而是常有的事。孔子在鲁国广招门徒，虽说他与当政者的政治思想并不全然合拍，但他与国君、执政交往密切，经济上应不致过于贫困。执政大夫季桓子曾经一次赐予他粮食千锺（约合今40万斤）之多，孔子就把粮食分给了他几百名贫困的弟子。[④]

朋友间在财物上可以互通有无，在当时称作"通财"。孔子的处事原则是"朋友之馈，虽车马，非祭肉，不拜"。[⑤] 凡是朋友所馈赠的，哪怕像车马这么贵重的东西，只要不是祭肉，孔子一概不拜谢对方。祭肉，是指朋友馈赠给孔子用以祭祀先人的肉。朱熹《论语集注》卷6："祭肉则拜者，敬其祖考，同于己亲也。"孔子接济朋友时十分

---

① 向宗鲁：《说苑校证》，中华书局，1987年，第245页。

② 孙希旦：《礼记集解》卷8《檀弓上》，第193页。

③ 见许维遹：《韩诗外传集释》，中华书局，1980年，第50、51、52页。

④ 《孔子家语》卷2《致思》，杨朝明：《孔子家语通解》第79、80页。《孔丛子》卷上《记义》亦载，见傅亚庶：《孔丛子校释》第50页。

⑤ 《论语·乡党第十》。何晏《论语集解》卷5引孔安国曰："不拜者，有通财之义。"

慷慨，在接受朋友的馈赠时也很坦然。反映出孔子对待朋友时的真诚率直。

5. 宽以待人

《论语·卫灵公第十五》记载："子曰：'躬自厚而薄责于人，则远怨矣。'"朋友相处，难免会出现误解、矛盾，孔子认为，这时就要深刻反省自己、改正错误，对于别人不作过多的指责，这就可以消解怨恨，化解矛盾。皇侃《论语集解义疏》引孔安国注："自责己厚，责人薄，所以远怨咎也。"孔子"君子求诸己，小人求诸人"是完全一致的。

孟子继承了孔子思想，他说："爱人不亲，反其仁。"朋友疏远了自己，就要多从自己身上寻找原因。

《论语·公冶长第五》记载："子曰：'伯夷、叔齐不念旧恶，怨是用希（稀）。'"

伯夷、叔齐兄弟因为不记过去的仇怨，所以别人很少怨恨他们。

伯夷、叔齐分别是西周初年孤竹国君的两个儿子。他们弃国逃奔周朝，但又认为周武王未葬文王即兴兵伐商是不孝、不仁，不食周粟，饿死在首阳山上[①]

在孔子看来，伯夷既是一位贤人，又是一位求仁得仁的人、有风节志操的人。但是《论语》对伯夷记述甚少，《孟子》《公孙丑上》、《离娄上》、《万章下》、《尽心下》等篇记载较多。通过这些记述，伯夷的形象大为丰满和生动了，可见他是一位爱憎分明、疾恶如仇的仁者，知时务、远祸患的智者，领袖人伦、风仪天下的贤者。

《论语·述而第七》记："互乡难与言，童子见，门人惑。子曰：'与其进也，不与其退也，唯何甚？人洁己以进，与其洁也，不保其往也。'"据后世注家推测，这名互乡的童子大概是曾经冒犯过孔子，现在又穿戴一新前来见孔子，弟子们感到不解，孔子则认为，对方有长进，就应肯定他的进步，而不应过分地记恨他，纠缠于他既往的过错。

孔子主张，与人交往，要胸襟宽广。对待朋友更应讲宽容，忌苛刻。因为宽容可以消除怨恨。

孔子还认为，真正值得敬重的好朋友应该经得住时间考验，所以，在结交时，要耐心观察，对人不要急于下结论。

《论语·公冶长第五》记载："子曰：'晏平仲善与人交，久而敬之。'"孔子说："晏平仲善于和人交往，交往越久，别人越发敬重他。"

晏平仲，名婴，谥平，字平仲。齐景公时任国相。晏婴生活在春秋末期，年龄长于孔子，两人有过交往。晏婴历仕齐国灵公、庄公、景公，是老牌政治家、思想家，以善于进谏、崇尚节俭闻名。关于晏子的思想，民国时人张纯一在其《晏子春秋校注

---

① 《史记》卷61《伯夷列传》。

叙》中说："综核晏子之行，合儒者十三四，合墨者十六七。如曰'先民而后身，薄身而厚民'，是其俭也、勤也、兼爱也，固晏子之主旨也。夫儒非不尚俭，未若墨以俭为极；儒非不尚勤，未若墨勤生之亟；儒非不兼爱，未若墨兼爱之力。此儒、墨之辩也。然儒家囊括万理，允执厥中，与墨异趣也。晏子儒而墨。"有关晏婴的资料，集中于《晏子春秋》一书，司马迁写《史记》时，说其书"世多有之"，流传已很广，所以，在《史记》卷六十二《管晏列传》中只是很简略地记载了晏子的几则"轶事"。司马迁十分钦佩晏婴，说："假令晏子而在，余虽为之执鞭，所忻慕焉。"①

《晏子春秋·内篇》记晏婴的交友之道："其交友也，谕身（信）行义，不为苟戚（亲），不同则疏而不诽，不毁进于君。"②

6. 敬其所终

《左传》襄公二十五年有"慎始而敬终，终以不困"。借来表述对朋友的善始善终，确也是比较恰切的。孔子认为，朋友在生死之际，更应该注重友情。

《论语·乡党第十》记载："朋友死，无所归，曰：'于我殡。'"朋友死了，没有人为他安葬，孔子说："在我那里停丧吧（我来为他安葬）。"无所归是指无人为其安葬。殡，停丧待葬。此指安葬。孔子对自己的朋友，慷慨大方，善始善终。《礼记·檀弓》："宾客至，无所馆。夫子曰：'生于我乎馆，死于我乎殡。'"③ 这条材料，与本章当是一事两记，可以互参。由此可见孔子的仁者情怀。

对于这一章，如果没有其他材料，就不容易理解。现有两条材料，和今本《论语》不同。

《白虎通·三纲六纪》引《论语》："朋友无所归，生于乎馆，死于我乎殡。"《孔子家语》卷10《曲礼子夏问》的记载比较详细："子夏问于孔子曰：'客至无所舍，而夫子曰："生，于我乎馆。"客死无所殡矣，夫子曰："于我乎殡。"敢问礼与？仁者之心与？'孔子曰：'吾闻诸老聃曰："馆人，是人若有之（客人如同在自己家里一样）。"恶有有之而不得殡乎？夫仁者，制礼者也。故礼者不可不省也。礼不同不异，不丰不杀，称其义以为之宜。'"④

其实，朋友得到安葬以后，事情并没有结束，在一年之内，只要路过朋友的坟墓，都要哭丧。《礼记·檀弓上》记曾子说："朋友之墓，有宿草而不哭焉。"⑤ 可见，孔子

---

① 《史记》卷62《管晏列传》。

② 张纯一：《晏子春秋校注》卷4《内篇问下第四》，见《诸子集成》第6册，河北人民出版社，1992年，第113页。

③ 孙希旦：《礼记集解》卷9《檀弓上》，第227页。

④ 杨朝明、宋立林：《孔子家语通解》，齐鲁书社，2009年，第547页。

⑤ 孙希旦：《礼记集解》，中华书局，1989年，第170页。

处友之道是合乎礼的要求的。

## 三、孔子朋友之道的特点及影响

1. 孔子的朋友之道是他施教内容的一部分，他对于择友、处友的论述，往往与人物评价、识人之道紧密联系在一起。《论语·卫灵公篇》记载："子曰：'众恶之，必察焉；众好之，必察焉。'"《子路篇》也有类似的表述："子贡问曰：'乡人皆好之，何如?'子曰：'未可也。''乡人皆恶之，何如?'子曰：'未可也。不如乡人之善者好之，其不善者恶之。'"结交朋友必须识人。所谓识人，就不能人云亦云。

2. 孔子的朋友之道，是他培养弟子仁德的一个组成部分。如何选择朋友、处好朋友？这就要求弟子切实提高自身修养。《论语·颜渊篇》记载，司马牛忧曰："人皆有兄弟，我独亡。"子夏曰："商闻之矣：死生有命，富贵在天。君子敬而无失，与人恭而有礼。四海之内，皆兄弟也。——君子何患乎无兄弟也?"子夏认为，只要自己对人做到"敬而无失"、"恭而有礼"，到哪里都能结交到像兄弟那样的好朋友。子夏的话，可以说完全遵从了孔子的思想。《子路篇》记："樊迟问仁。子曰：'居处恭，执事敬，与人忠，虽之夷狄，不可弃也。'"

曾子也有类似的表述，《大戴礼记》卷5《曾子制言上》："曾子门弟子或将之晋，曰：'吾无知焉。'曾子曰：'何必然？往矣。有知焉谓之友，无知焉谓之主（卢辩曰：且客之而已）。且夫君子执仁立志，先行后言，千里之外，皆为兄弟。苟是之不为，则虽汝亲，庸孰能亲汝乎?"[①] 曾子所说的"知"，即契合，指朋友。能否结交到好朋友，提高自身修养、具备仁德是必要的前提条件。

3. 孔子的朋友之道体现了他的仁爱思想。《论语·宪问第十四》记载："或曰：'以德报怨，何如?'子曰：'何以报德？以直报怨，以德报德。'"用正义回报仇恨，用恩惠回报恩惠。怎样"报怨"，孔子主张以"直"。

但是，孔子更主张"以德报怨"。《礼记·表记》记："子曰：'以德报德，则民有所劝。以怨报怨，则民有所惩。《诗》曰："无言不雠，无德不报。"《太甲》曰："民非后，无能胥以宁；后非民，无以辟四方。"'子曰：'以德报怨，则宽身之仁也。以怨报德，则刑戮之民也。'"孙希旦在《集解》中解释说："劝者，勉于施德。惩者，戒于树怨。引《太甲》言君能安其民，则民能戴其君，以德报德之义也。吕氏大临曰：'以德报怨，虽过于宽而本于厚，未害其为仁也。以怨报德，则反易天常，天下之乱民，法所当诛者也。'愚谓宽犹容也。以德报怨，则天下无不释之怨矣。虽非中道，而可以宽

---

① 见方向东：《大戴礼记汇校集解》，第547、548页。

容其身，亦仁之一偏也。若以怨报德，则为人情之所共忿，而刑戮必及之矣。”①

《韩诗外传》卷9也记载：“子路曰：‘人善我，我亦善之；人不善我，我不善之。’子贡曰：‘人善我，我亦善之；人不善我，我则引之进退而已耳。’颜回曰：‘人善我，我亦善之；人不善我，我亦善之。’三子所持各异，问于夫子。夫子曰：‘由之所言，蛮貊之言也；赐之所言，朋友之言也；回之所言，亲属之言也。《诗》曰：“人之无良，我以为兄。”’”②

在孔子所处的春秋末年，同态复仇还有存在的社会基础，孔子的“以德报怨”，体现了他的仁爱思想。至于何谓“直”，则指公平正义、不挟私、不过分，笔者将撰写专文进行讨论。

4. 孔子的朋友之道体现了他的中庸思想。《论语·泰伯第八》也记载：“子曰：‘人而不仁，疾之已甚，乱也’。”孔子主张，对于不仁不义的人，尤其是对于朋友，最要不得的是反应过激、用极端的方式来回应。

5. 孔子的朋友论所规范的人际关系，无疑突破了宗法伦理，是一种能够推及全社会的理想的人际关系。他所奠定的朋友之间的平等、相知相爱、道义等原则，对后世影响深远，是奠定君子人格的重要理论基础。

---

① 孙希旦：《礼记集解》卷51《表记》，第1300、1301页。

② 许维遹：《韩诗外传集解》第312页。

# 从圣、俗的观点看孔子的礼

韩国中央大学 卢仁淑

## 一、前言

神圣性与世俗性可以说是人类历史发展过程中所固有的两种存在方式。这同现实与理想，自然与超自然，合理与神秘如此的二元对立也有着密切的关系。

按传统观点，西洋强调的是圣与俗，东洋强调的是天与人，自然与人为之间相互对立，紧张、调和的历史。基督教圣经里出现的该隐与亚伯，善与恶，天使与恶魔，天国与地上，教会与世俗，信仰与理性的对立体现了在西欧的思维方式的焦点存在着圣与俗的对立。法自然的道家，出世的佛家，天人合一的儒家思想体现了东方思想的核心亦为天・人结构。在西欧往往出现试图调和圣与俗对立的努力，从本质上讲与西方的将此视为对立与矛盾关系相反，东方则主张自然与人两者之间的调和，坚持超越对立的立场。冯友兰把这种立场称为“极高明而道中庸”，“即世间而出世间”，并把这种立场视为中国哲学所追求的精神穷极的理念。儒家所追求的这种“即世间而出世间”的价值结构我们可以将此与现代宗教学者提出的圣化与世俗的模式进行一下对比。

过去我们对作为孔子思想的核心的“礼”主要是从天理与人事，自然与人为的观点来进行了考察。往往局限于将礼规定为“天理之节文 人事之仪则”的《礼记》与宋代性理学者的影响范围之内。笔者在本文则试图将此还原到西欧圣、俗的概念来进行考察。《论语》中不存在圣、俗的概念，后代学者的解释与註释也从未从圣、俗的观点对其进行过分析。因为圣、俗的概念从本质上来讲是属于西欧的概念。

笔者之所以要试图从表面上看来与《论语》似乎无关的圣、俗的概念对礼进行考察，其原因可以总结为如下几点。首先，孔子所处的时代与如今我们所处的时代相同，圣域崩溃，俗圈泛滥，同时是其领域不断扩大的过程。如此的时代背景下出现的孔子的教诲的本质不能断言与圣、俗无关。当然这里所说的圣域与俗圈与和传统的权威与革新的挑战有着相关性。传统的权威的崩溃即可看作为圣域的崩溃。第二，圣、俗矛盾异常尖锐的今天，处于被歪曲的世俗化的漩涡之中的人，如何才能实现高贵的生命历程，完成共同体神圣的旅程，对此期待着从我们所继承的孔子的教诲来找到答案。第三，与过去儒学常用的天理与人事如此古典的概念相比较圣、俗的概念在今天更加一般化，大众化。为活着的学术概念。Herbert Fingarette 则曾将孔子称为“神圣的世俗人”，笔者由此得到了许多启示。

## 二、孔子礼思想的形成背景与动机

孔子所处的时代为政治与社会极为混乱的时代。所谓混乱的时代意味着具有神圣权威的传统秩序崩溃，新的改革的气运升腾而起的时代。即可称为俗圈泛滥的时代。在如此混乱的时代隐遁避世，努力躲避世俗的避世之士往往大量出现。这一点我们可以从《论语》中找到例证。

楚狂接舆歌而过孔子，曰：“凤兮凤兮，何德之衰！往者不可谏，来者不可追。已而已而！今之从政者殆而！”（《微子》）

长沮、桀溺耦而耕。孔子过之，使子路问津焉。长沮曰：“夫执舆者为谁？”子路曰：“为孔丘。”曰：“是鲁孔丘与，”曰：“是也。”曰：“是知津矣。”问于桀溺。桀溺曰：“子为谁？”曰：“为仲由。”曰：“是鲁孔丘之徒与？”对曰：“然。”曰：“滔滔者天下皆是也，而谁以易之？且而与其从辟人之士也，岂若从辟世之士哉？”（《微子》）

孔子听到这些以后深深地叹息道：

“鸟兽不可与同群！吾非斯人之徒与，而谁与？天下有道，丘不与易也。”

引用部分所出现的长沮、桀溺、楚狂接舆等都是洁身自好，为了保持自身的圣洁而躲避世俗的人物。但与这些人物相对比孔子却没有放弃对现实，即世俗的爱。孔子将道视为“处于乱世与俗世间的道”。

春秋时代的混乱是由小规模的腐旧分裂，原始的地方文化向新的大规模统合成为更伟大的单一文化移行过程所产生的必然的现象。由此孔子的教诲所体现的实际的内容可以称为为克服当时无秩序的状态对新的普遍秩序的一种探索。孔子把当时的混乱视为古代完美的礼随着时间的推移道德与政治堕落带来的结果。由此认为必须将其复原。这意味着回归到周公所制定的礼乐。

但我们不能简单将孔子视为陷入对过去的乡愁的尚古主义者或者复古主义者，而应视为伟大的文化变革家。孔子最大的梦想在于他所追求的中国真实实在的未来蓝图（Vision）。即对建立在统一的政治组织之上的庞大而强有力的统一文化的幻想。这是孔子所提出的如果能够被所有士人接受的话，就会实现统合和平，一种人类实践与理想的宏图。孔子曾经试图在自己的祖国鲁国通过文化改革实践自身的这种新的社会秩序建构的设想。

孔子如此试图从文化改革出发建立新的社会秩序与其出身于鲁国不无关系。作为相对国土面积较小国力衰微的鲁国国民，孔子清醒地认识到无法将恢复中国天下秩序，实现政治统一的梦想付诸军事的征服。同时与其他邻近地域相比较鲁国相对更加完好地发展并保存了古代的文化，由此孔子拥有了试图依靠以鲁国为中心的卓越的文化来恢复天下秩序的想法，这对孔子是非常自然的事情。

孔子如此新的理想以渊源于传统的礼及仪式的形式体现出来。孔子为什么要强力主张如三年丧，八佾舞等当时并不普遍施行的礼仪之说呢？这是因为与实际的现实相比较孔子更加重视自己所理想的合理井然的社会秩序。而建立如此合理井然的社会则离不开理想，对于孔子理想则为遵照周公制定的礼乐秩序的社会。可孔子所面对的课题不是只单纯地再现袭承以前的礼乐，而是如何统一仪式与全体相连结的实现，有机地发挥其功能，即如何在传统的基础上重新树立。“述而不作”“信而好古”“温故而知新”等集中体现了孔子重视传统的立场。这里的“故”与“古”除去时间的意义以外还蕴含着我们该学习并实践的理想。

人们普遍的对传统往往会持有否定的偏见。实现社会调和，稳妥的统合单纯只依赖于政治的力量是远远不足的。而得到社会普遍认可的传统才能更加有效地完成这一使命。同时与动物相区别人不只是单纯地按照本能来行动，而是按照理性传统来行动以期保全自身的力量与尊严性。如此抛弃传统则意味着与自身过去的割离，也会疏离人与人之间的关系。由此孔子认为深切领会传统不仅对于社会共同体秩序的建构，同时对维持我们自身生存的方向性，统合性及人与人之间真正美好的关系的建立都极为重要。

孔子的这种观点我们从《论语》中可以得到确认：

> 道之以政，齐之以刑，民免而无耻；道之以德，齐之以礼，有耻且格。（《为政》）

这段文章在讲述的是如何鼓励教化人的自发性，赋予其尊严性，使人成为真正意味的人。在相似的时代背景下法家的立场则与儒家形成了最为鲜明的对比。儒法两家都标榜着实现治国平天下的理念，孔子在以建立在传统之上的礼与德作为治道手段，法家则以与传统无关的刑罚作为治道的手段。但孔子的礼与德以人性的高扬，人格的完成为目标，法家的目标则在于社会秩序的构建，政治的安定，统一国家的形成。由此可见两者主张的治国平天下内涵的差异。即儒家所主张的礼与法家主张的刑不仅意味着秩序建构方法的差异，也是目标本身的差异。儒家将目标设定于自身的理想，法家则将目标设定于现实，其结果法家的方式对政治的天下统一做出了贡献，实现了其目标，儒家则实现了高扬人性的文化建构的目标。

## 三、作为人性完成的仁与仪式的礼

仁与礼为《论语》两个意味深长的用语。与礼比较起来仁被言及的频度更高，由此大部分学者均认为孔子更强调的是仁。但也有学者认为礼才是孔子思想的核心，仁是通过论及礼来加以说明的，由此更应该关注礼这一概念。

普遍来讲，在亚洲的思想中存在着将个人与自我视为妄想与苦痛，挫折与束缚的根源的倾向。因此人该努力的部分是由如此的束缚之中解脱出来。孔子的思想则与此形成了鲜明对比。孔子强调人为了达成目标该竭尽全力不断地付出努力。孔子认为人应该不断增进自身的学识与能力，启发有品位的态度，把行动确立在正确的原则之上来进行努力。努力，决断，忍耐，勤勉则被视为为了成为真正高贵的人即君子必需的道德。对于孔子伟大的课业并不是表现为丧失自我解脱的自我超越，而是自我启发。

由此孔子在《论语》中比起对个人及社会的论及更多谈到的是该成为一个怎样的人。自由的人，完美的人的理想在《论语》中则表现为仁。

孔子认为人是由礼派生出来，融入于礼的独特的具有尊严性与力量的特殊的存在。成为文化人则意味着对身体、生理、本能的阶段的克服。如此礼与仁到底有怎样的关系呢？这里在两者的关系中首先考察一下礼的特性。

1. 礼关注的是传统社会行为与关系的形态。

2. 礼为不变的规范。并随着个人地位体现为相应的特定的行为。

3. 礼属于公共范畴是持续不断的，体现为鲜明的行动方式的行为。

再来看一下仁的特性。

1. 仁关注的是追求人行为方式的人与维持如此的关系的人。

2. 与成人的行为相关联，与礼所规定的行为态度所体现的相关联。

由此仁与礼可视为同一问题的两个侧面。

“仁者人也”意味着人可能成为社会人的可能根据。除此仁如“仁相人偶”中阐释的则意味着与社会的相关性中存在的意义。这里社会的意味不仅单纯指人聚居之处所，同时还是启发弘扬人性，展示尊严性与价值的处所。

但要从《论语》中捕捉孔子对仁真正鲜明的见解并不是容易的事情。因我们无法找到对仁具体的言及。下面引用的两段或许对我们理解仁的本质会有一些帮助：

> 己欲立而立人，己欲达而达人。能近取譬，可谓仁之方也已。（《雍也》）
>
> 克己复礼为仁。（《颜渊》）

由上文我们可以知道仁与人及人与人之间的关系有着紧密的联系。引用文 1 阐明了这种关系为一般的互惠的信赖，被描述为忠，恕。引用文2赋予了互惠的信赖特定的内容。即为礼所详细描述的特定的社会关系。简而言之，互惠的善的信赖与尊敬（忠、恕）表现为礼的形式的地方则为通向仁的路。如果说礼的本质在于为了维持秩序的社会认同，这种社会认同的基础则为构成人的德性的仁。“克己复礼为仁”也可以理解为作为社会认同的传统应在主体的实践中得到确认。

“先难而后获”强调的是仁要通过艰难的过程才可能达成。人如果不进行后天的修养的努力，自然状态的人按照粗野的冲动与本能来行动，但通过修养则有可能改变成为拥有高贵的思想与行动的存在。即有修养的高尚的态度是依靠后天的刻苦努力形成的。为了获得这些比起超自然的力量更需要人自身的努力训练与忍耐。

仁形成于礼之内，无法超越礼所发展的范畴。言而总之，对他人的态度不进入一系列的状况是得不到发展与丰富的。即仁是通过礼实现的。人离开他人是无法成熟的。人为了自身的成熟他人是绝对的必要条件。因为礼对于同一情况也存在着不同的过程。从这种意义上讲仁与礼可视为同一问题的两个侧面。实现了礼则达成了仁。

孔子除了如此将礼的概念视为过去的祭式仪式以外还将其扩展到包括所有文明社会的惯习，加深了礼的含义。孔子认为人通过礼可以形成真正的共同体，为了习得礼需要不断的努力与学习，但一旦习得了其结果则会成为一种‘自然’的生存形态，并非束缚而是自由。复礼的人一切都极为自然。孔子70岁所自述的境界“从心所欲不踰矩”与“克己复礼为仁”可以说与此同出一辙。换而言之，礼并不是依赖于形式主义对人性的压制，是人的欲望受到教化的表现，即相互尊重与诚实的人与人之间关系的表现。即调节所有人的行为，确立作为人的完美状态，升华人的存在。孔子教导其子伯鱼“不学礼，无以立”，强调学礼的重要性也出于同一脉络。

## 四、作为世俗社会圣化的礼

孔子试图通过礼（仪式）的实践来完成人性（仁的实现）。对孔子礼具有着如下两种作用。第一，使社会更加美好调和，人与人交际的过程中体现出尊严性。第二，充分认识参与礼仪式的他人与自身同样为具有同一尊严性的存在来相互对待，以完成德性。

礼原本意味着“神圣的仪式”，但孔子试图将礼扩展到社会惯习的总体，即有根基的传统与文化，合理的习俗的用语。孔子不仅是教育家，政治家同时作为富有哲学性的人的学者比起形而上学的思辨或与世俗无关的精神安慰（安心立命）更加深切地关注着现世人的生存状态。孔子所最为关心的并非个人的自我实现，而在于“作为神圣仪式的人的共同体的实现”。这是可以与基督教“兄弟爱（brotherhood）”作对比的儒教的概念，也是孔子通过礼所要强调的部分。即对于孔子礼不仅表现为仪式的义务，而是人与人的关系中我们应该履行的规范性的行动。孔子追求的并不是超自然的奇迹，而是如“如切如磋，如琢如磨”所描述的可以美好调和地参与社会的实际修行。孔子平素不谈论怪力乱神（子不语怪力乱神）也向我们证明了这一点。

如此看来人能够自我实现的场所即为如此拥有权威，无论何人都可以参与的开放的礼之中。从这一观点出发孔子认为人离开了礼也就无法存在，同时人为拥有礼所蕴含的尊严性与独特的力量的特殊存在。由此在《论语》中不将个人与社会分开来论及，只谈论人在社会之中该成为怎样的人。人的尊严性并不是从个体的，生物学的存在来寻找而是通过参与共同体的仪式而赋予人尊严性。

对于孔子比起个人的完成礼更意味着人的共同体的完成或共同体中形成的交际的完成。礼为了发挥其作用必须具备以下的几个条件：

1. 拥有被社会成员学习或容纳的习惯。

2. 适当的情况下可以号召惯习的力量。

3. 礼仪仪式郑重举行。

4. 担当仪式修行任务的人被赋予恰当的权限。

不具备上述条件的礼不管其形式如何华丽但均可规定为非本质的而丧失礼原有的意味。

礼要通过不断的学习才能够习得。“如切如磋 如琢如磨”所描述的自我修养是为了参与共同体所必须具备的素养。但只有自我修养对确保人的尊严性是不够的。更加重要的是在仪式的行为过程中来完成人性。

《论语》中有将君子比喻为“器”的一段话，“君子不器”。“器”意味着制约性与局限性。这一段强调的是君子应为完美无缺的人。孔子与弟子子贡间的对话也曾用过关于“器”的比喻。

> 子谓子贱：“君子哉若人！鲁无君子者，斯焉取斯！”子贡问曰：“赐也何如?”子曰：“女器也。”曰：“何器也?”曰：“瑚琏也。”(《公冶长》)

这里值得我们注意的是孔子与子贡之间的对话中登场的对于瑚琏的比喻。朱子对这一部分解释道，孔子之所以对子贡提及瑚琏是因为虽然子贡没有达到“不器”的君子境地，但并非普通的“器”，而是贵重的祭器，孔子试图以此来安慰子贡。但正如“君子不器”的比喻是关于器的用途的比喻，并不是关于其价值的比喻一样，“瑚琏”的比喻是在说明价值并非用途。原本瑚琏是指为了祈祷丰收而举行祭祀时盛粮食的用玉制成的珍贵的器皿。这一器皿圣洁而神圣，用来盛成熟的粮食，象征着丰饶。这种器皿的神圣并不在于青铜或玉如此材料的珍贵性与稀少性，或是装饰的精美及用来盛粮食的用途。这里瑚琏之所以神圣是因为瑚琏为构成仪式的要素之一。除却祭祀仪式时的作用瑚琏只不过是普通的用来盛粮食的贵重坛子而已。正如瑚琏之所以珍贵不在于装饰精美的价值，而是因其参与仪式的作用而被赋予了作为祭器的神圣性。同样，个人的存在也是因其参与宗教仪式、社会仪式如此的共同体并在那里起到作用时才能获得最高的尊严性与神圣的权威。

这里我们可以看到，原本意味着宗教仪式的礼的意味被加入了社会的意味，成为了根植社会远景的方式，其意味因孔子得到了扩展。即人通过与他人参与公共的仪式得到意味与价值的变化。如没有变化则不能称为真正意义的人，只是一种潜在的人，如婴儿、狼孩儿、野人。作为共同体仪式参与者的人，如同祭器一般被赋予了新的神圣美好存在的意味。换而言之，作为个体的人由此确保了其自身的神圣性。

如同父子，兄弟，君臣，夫妇这样的社会规范因为在礼之中的位置与作用也显得极为神圣。换而言之，社会依靠惯习与道德性的义务来适当地调节，而形成一个巨大的修行仪式的场所，从而具有了如同宗教仪式一般的神圣性。人穷极的尊严性并非来源于个人存在本身，也并非来自于集团的存在，而是通过生命历程中仪式修行而被赋予。也就是说人的生命历程其历史、道德、文化、政治的形式是世俗的。但由于全面参与如此生命历程的形式而使得生命获得了历史、道德、文化、政治的意义，同时变得神圣。

将人说成是仪式的存在（ceremonial beings）如此孔子的思想里面，除了阐明了人是合理、经验、现世的如此的认识以外，同时在强调人所具有的超经验、超合理、神秘的一面。引用 M. Eliade 的话来讲就是“人虽然是世俗的存在，但在这世俗里面已经包含了神圣的一面。”人虽然生活在世俗之中，但却以神圣为原型，努力在世俗之中实现神圣，只有这样才能够成为真正的人。儒家之所以重视丧礼、祭礼并非是想通过迷信的祈愿以期达到这样的效果，而是对仪式过程本身赋予了极为重要的意义。孔子对与死者共同下葬的明器的使用意义谈道“之死而致死之，不仁而不可为也，之死而致生之，不知而不可为也。”这表明其意义正在于理智与情感的兼备。我们也能够由此确认试图调节圣（仁）与俗（智）的礼的真正意义所在。

## 五、结语

古代人通过祭祀仪式来再现宇宙开辟的时代，由自身来重新发现生命的奥秘。孔子则通过礼的形式将祭祀仪式内面化、日常化，确立世俗的人与人之间的关系，再现恢復神圣的传统。如果不只是从狭义的制度化的角度来看待宗教，而是（将其意义扩展）理解为人类仪式的现象，那么涵盖着日常性中的非日常性的所有人类生命的形态均可以规定为宗教性的。对出生与冠、婚、丧、祭等通过仪礼赋予深刻的意义，“吾一日三省吾身”所强调的反省中体现的敬虔，随时穿梭于天地境界的天人合一的境地，如此确立于儒教理念的对生命的理解可以说是一种宗教性质的。从这一点来看对儒教宗教性质的论争也可以说是毫无意义的。唯独儒教仪式中对神圣的恢复与其他宗教不同，其差异在于并非集团的而是个人的，同时并非通过周期的仪式，而是贯穿于人的一生不断在进行着。孔子强调：克己复礼为仁（《论语·颜渊》）；为仁由己（《论语·颜渊》）；任重而道远，仁以为己任，不亦重乎？死而后已，不亦远乎？（《论语·泰伯》）如此不间断的内在的努力。孔子危笃之际，子路请求进行祈祷，但孔子道：“丘之祷，久矣（《论语·述而》）。”从如此的告白中我们可以知道孔子一生即为从未间断过的祭式。由此我们看到了一生既为俗亦为圣的作为普通人的孔子。

为了成为真正意味的人，我们必须超越自然的层次，将生命上升到既为宗教的同时为文化的更高层次。表现为人伦日用的世俗的领域蕴含着神圣，即神圣与世俗合一的生命历程才是孔子所追求的理想，亦为真正意义上的礼。

# 《论语》中“礼”、“仁”属性的重新审视

天津师范大学 方 勇 方 达

“仁”的概念发轫于孔子，阐释于思孟鼎盛于宋明，早已被严格固定于道德观念之范畴。然而细细思索，这一系列理解发生发展的过程实际上都是建立在一个默认的前提之下：“仁”发自于人内心的某种情感取向，具有主观自主性。① 究其根源，孔子虽于《论语》中反复论及“仁”、“仁者”，但几乎全部都从正面积极肯定“仁”并阐述其效用，而未曾明确定义“仁”的属性。如此便遗留给后人上述这种主观的积极的情感接受倾向，并被儒门后学不断利用和阐释，最终呈现出现有的默认状态。为探求《论语》中“仁”的真实属性，本文从反面之“不仁者”的相关章句入手，首先发明其内在矛盾点，并引入“克己复礼为仁”，梳理“仁”的理论前提“克己复礼”后，重新审视“仁”、“礼”的基本属性。

## 一、于“不仁者”中探求“仁”命题的两种理解取向

子曰：“不仁者不可以久处约，不可以长处乐。仁者安仁，智者利仁。”（《论语·里仁》）此句以“不仁者”论“仁者”的话颇给人一些古怪的感觉，不像《论语》他处直言“仁者”时让人接受起来十分自然顺畅。究其原因，首先是因为此处采用“仁”之否定式，需要将其对应为正面的“仁者”进行理解；其次便是在这种对应理解的过程中，如何理解“不仁者不可以久处约”的含义。依照逻辑推导此句，“仁者”既可“久处约”也可“不久处约”，既可“长处乐”也可“不长处乐”。虽然看似拗口，但若按后世将“仁”之概念对应为道德观念范畴，理解此句也毫无问题，因为《论语》中的颜回形象正好是此句最佳注脚，“一箪食，一瓢饮，在陋巷，人不堪其忧，回也不改其乐”（《雍也》），即“仁者”无论现实处境如何都可以得到心境上的莫大快乐。但仔细想来，这种理解实际上是建立在一种默认的逻辑前提之上：“仁者”无论现实情况如

---

① 即可理解为孟子所持“性善论”，人内心有趋善因子。

何都是“乐于”置身其中的，即这种“仁”的内涵属性根源是一种自发的、乐观的情感取向。这种理解取向的根源在于：《论语》中几乎所有篇章都是从“仁者”的正面角度阐释其功用、效用，而这种积极主观的方式便很容易给人造成上述的这种理解倾向。也正因此，后人在理解孔子“仁”的思想内涵时长期忽略了一个事实：孔子在《论语》中从未曾给“仁”下过一个严格的属性定义，他所有的论述仅仅在说明“仁者”所应具备的外在表现行为和社会群体对此的积极反馈。

基于此，“不仁者不可以久处约”实际上还有另外一种理解取向：即“仁”与“仁者”本身不具备主观情感因素，仅仅是一种客观状态，一种既不可能长期处于“达”的境界，也不可能长期处于“约”的“中庸”和谐的社会关系。[①] 实际上，这种理解对于此章后半句的解读是有辅助作用的：如若“仁”果真是这种长期被阐释为道德观念的载体，那何谓“智者利仁”呢？因为此处无论将“利”理解为“有利”或是“利用”，都与“仁者”所代表的道德观念是不相匹配的——道德是脱离社会实际功用的一种意识形态，为人们共同遵守的正面价值取向，不能成为利用、役使的客观对象。

界定这两种理解取向的关键点还是在于《论语》中对“仁”内涵属性的定位。如上文所述，正是由于孔子未对“仁”进行过直接明晰的内涵界定，才会导致这种理解上的歧义存在。因此我们没有必要也不可能在“仁”的内部对其内涵属性进行反复探讨和界定，这种做法只会陷入结论与论证过程互为前提的论证死循环。因此此处不妨引入孔子的另一句话，从“仁”之为“仁”的前提来推导出“仁”的内涵属性。子曰：“克己复礼为仁。一日克己复礼，天下归仁焉。”（《颜渊》）“归仁”前提有二，一为“克己”，一为“复礼”。“克己”所表达的“克制约束自己（欲望）”的表面意思十分清楚，但实际上也存在着一种潜在方式和目的的问题，即“如何克己”和“克己何为”。而这种方式和目的的根本指向在于“复礼”时“礼”的实际属性。因此，孔子思想中“礼”的属性界定成为了论证所有问题的基本出发点。

## 二、《论语》中“礼”的属性界定

对孔子志在恢复的“周礼”，历代学者通过不断地阐释，将其固定描述为一种带有儒家倾向的社会政治、经济、意识形态综合体，而这种理解的根源则在于对《三礼》的综合认知。[②]“夏道尊命，事鬼敬神而远之，近人而忠焉，先禄而后威，先赏而后罚，

---

① 按照传统理解，“达”与“约”（“穷”）实际上都是现实社会中的两极，是人类理想中所亟欲达到或摆脱的现实处境。

② 综合认知：忽略文本产生的时间和思想发展脉络，将其界定为儒家经典思想的有机统一体加以综合阐释、论证。

亲而不尊；其民之敝：蠢而愚，乔而野，朴而不文。殷人尊神，率民以事神，先鬼而后礼，先罚而后赏，尊而不亲；其民之蔽：荡而不静，胜而无耻。周人尊礼尚施，事鬼敬神而远之，近人而忠焉，其赏罚用爵列，亲而不尊；其民之敝：利而巧，文而不惭，贼而蔽。”（《礼记·表记》）这段话往往被用来理解孔子对待夏礼、殷礼、周礼时的不同态度，并进而说明“周礼”是儒家思想的根源。但正如上文所述，这段话本身就是“综合认知”的产物：子曰：“夏礼，吾能言之，杞不足征也；殷礼，吾能言之，宋不足征也。文献不足故也。足，吾能征之矣。”又，子曰：“周监于二代，郁郁乎文哉！吾从周。”（《八佾》）孔子自己明确说过，由于缺乏可征的“文献”，他对“夏礼”、“殷礼”的认知是不全面的，而这也是他遵从“鉴于二代”而又“郁郁乎文哉”的“周礼”主要原因之一。既然如此，《礼记》里这段言之凿凿的，带有强烈儒学理论倾向的论述又是从何而来的呢。仔细考量《三礼》：《周礼》成书年代至今两说且多认为其中内容与实际情况不符，《礼记》又多为儒门后学阐释申发，唯独《仪礼》被普遍接受为战国末期时对实际社会通行礼仪的反映。[①] 又，定公问：“君使臣，臣事君，如之何?”孔子对曰：“君使臣以礼，臣事君以忠。”（《八佾》）此章与上文所引两章共同表明：孔子不仅对“夏礼”、“殷礼”的认知没有那么全面，“周礼”的统摄作用也并非十分强大，因为对不同阶层的效用不尽相同，故而也不能代表当时最高的意识形态。而这一特点与普遍认为的“周礼”中以周公统治术为代表的，具有强烈“儒家人治”倾向的观点明显不符。为了真实了解孔子所谓“周礼”的实质，最为现实的方法便是对孔子思想自有的材料进行独立分析。[②]

《八佾》是《论语》中最为集中讨论“礼”的篇目，开篇便是孔子谓季氏，“八佾舞于庭，是可忍也，孰不可忍也?”对于“忍”的主体，历代有两说：一为孔子，意谓孔子不能容忍季氏僭礼的行为；一为季氏本人，认为其人不遵行礼制，没有不忍心而为之事。表面观之似是两可，但实际上关注点不同：前者主要说明季氏这种行为对人在情感道德上的冲击，而后者则是侧重说明不遵守“礼制”的现实后果，即扰乱纲常。通过对此篇其他章的对比，理解上偏向后者的权重愈发倾斜。三家者以《雍》彻，子曰：“‘相维辟公，天子穆穆’，奚取于三家之堂?”季氏旅于泰山，子谓冉有曰：“女弗能救与?”对曰：“不能。”子曰：“呜呼！曾谓泰山不如林放乎?”子曰：“禘自既灌而往者，吾不欲观之矣。”子贡欲去告朔之饩羊。子曰：“赐也！尔爱其羊，我爱其礼。”孔子在这些章节中更多的是在愤怒鲁国三家大夫不遵守规定的祭祀仪式而越制使用天子之祭祀，而非谈及这种行为对于个人情感上的冲击。此外，林放问礼之本。子曰：

---

① 《荀子·大略》中多有与《仪礼》相同之处。

② 最大限度上直接体现孔子本人思想而未经后世过多阐发的文本唯有《论语》。

"大哉问！礼，与其奢也，宁俭。丧，与其易也，宁戚。"以及对于管仲不知礼[①]的批判更是说明，孔子真正重视的是"周礼"这种规范的行为方式，而非其中"仁治"的意识形态。另一方面，孔子对于祭祀形式的高度重视还说明"周礼"的来源正是来自于此。

近代甲骨卜辞的出土验证了"国之大事，在祀与戎"（《左传·成公十三年》）的确切：在已得到释读的甲骨字形中，确定为祭祀名称的字形就达100余种，远远超出其他类别的字词，此外尚有诸多未能释读但确定与祭祀相关字形。由此说明，"殷礼"的实质多为繁复的祭祀活动。虽然孔子未曾知晓，但上述的论证以及"周监于二代"都印证了他所谓的"周礼"主体仍是以祭祀活动为主的这一事实。如果继而能确定上古三代祭祀仪式的内在属性是强调一种既成的行为规范而非主要体现"王"的意志，那《论语》中"礼"和"仁"的内在属性也便可得到确定。

"绝地天通"的概念在《尚书》和《国语》中都有提及，并且成为探讨古代社会思想、意识形态发展的重要节点之一。不同学者对于这一概念的使用不尽相同，结论指向性的偏差自然也是南辕北辙。此处先引入一个假设对此进行解说，尔后再辅以文献论据。以历史唯物观看，这一举动实际上就是部落中祭祀和统治权力上下分层时的一个过程，意味着对于部落内部宽泛自由的自然崇拜一次统一规范过程，而这恰恰决定了原始祭祀活动的内在属性。根据西方人类学家的普遍共识，在原始部落中，一切活动都旨在利于部落的繁衍和延续。由此衍化出的祭祀活动无论是有意识或是无意识的自然崇拜，其目的都在于此。又弗朗兹·博厄斯[②]在论及原始部落文化时说："文化进步取决于是否有机会吸取邻近社会群体经验。"这就表明，以祭祀活动为代表的远古部落意识形态的产生和发展关键点在于部落与部落，部落中人与人之间的交流作用。因此，祭祀活动实际上是由族群中的成员在长久的日常生活中通过交流而建立起来的一种有利于群体发展目的的纯朴举措，同时这种举措高于个人情感意向，因而具备了其本身以共识状态为第一性，强制规范为第二性的社会属性。

相应的，"绝地天通"产生的历史背景便可解释为：与天沟通（自然崇拜）这一行为本身是族群内部的普遍行为，旨在获得个人更好的生命延续，但是在不断的交流沟通中，这些普遍的个人行为逐渐形成了一种对群体整体具有共同益处的共识状态，并最终演变成了后世所谓的祭祀活动，而随着群体（方国）社会属性的不断加强，这种

---

① 子曰："管仲之器小哉！"或曰："管仲俭乎？"曰："管氏有三归，官事不摄，焉得俭？""然则管仲知礼乎？"曰："邦君树塞门，管氏亦树塞门。邦君为两君之好，有反坫，管氏亦有反坫。管氏而知礼，孰不知礼？"（《八佾》）

② "文化相对主义"（cultural relativism）的代表人物，他认为文化形态无高低之分。

共识状态渐渐具备了强制规范的效用，并需要一小部分人（巫祝、史）对此进行引导统摄，并最终形成了“绝地天通”后的祭司阶层（王和贵族）。这种假设下的推断与后人所认为孔子倡导的“周礼”是由周文、武王以及周公创立的一系列具有深层意识形态指向和高尚道德取向，即“仁治”内涵的情况明显不相符合。

实际上，以上对于以祭祀活动为主要内容的“周礼”之内在属性的推断并非只是一种假设，这种认知的意识倾向在东汉许慎所著《说文解字》中也有现实体现。许慎作为东汉时融合今古经文经学之争的一位通儒，势必比后人更为接近、了解先秦儒家典籍思想的原始面貌。同时，他基于对儒家思想认知而具备的思想方法主线必定贯穿于其《说文解字》一书。《说文》前六个部首分别为“一”、“丄”、“示”、“三”、“王”、“玉”，这六个部首实际代表了意识形态中的四个部分：“一”、“丄”代表至高自然界上天（上帝），“示”代表祭祀活动，“三”、“王”代表人间帝王、“玉”代表人、神在祭祀活动中沟通时所需要的媒介。因而，这四个部分不仅主宰、统领后文以534部文字为代表的人世间一切现实之物；其内部次序排列也表明，“礼”的地位是介于“天帝”和“人王”之间的，而并非灌注有“人王”的主观意识。这就和上文的假设以及孔子在《论语》中对于三家大夫僭礼的态度共同验证了，儒家原始倡导的“周礼”并非一套融合了复杂“仁治”内涵倾向的意识形态载体；而只是一套体现了共识状态第一性，强制规范第二性的行为标准。既然界定了“复礼”的根本属性，便可继而确定“克己”的方式与“仁”的内涵。

## 三、《论语》中“仁”的属性以及与“克己”的关系

“礼”的内在属性决定了其本身的两个特点：一是高于个人情感取向而存在的一种共识状态，二是这种共识状态虽然具备一定的强制约束力，但仍未上升到“理性法”的层面。而这两个特点对本文第一段论及的“克己”的潜在方式和目的产生了指向作用：这种“克己”的行为的目的是抑制内心中有违群体共识状态和行为规范标准的个人情感取向，其方式是一种对外在规则的遵守而非对内在心理进行道德上的修养和制约。因此在这两个前提下推导出“仁”的内涵和属性便应是，其本身不具备主观情感因素，仅仅是一种客观状态，一种维护社会正常运转，具有基本共识的和谐的基础社会关系。如此定义，不仅使“不仁者不可以久处约，不可以长处乐”变得易于接受，“仁者安仁，智者利仁”也与前者有内在情感逻辑的顺承性。“仁者”是普遍意义上社会规范中的人，经过不断同化而将这种规范与个人情感融合为一，因此自然安于这种共识状态之中。而“智者”则仍旧保留着对共识状态与个人情感的对立统一的认知，所以不仅使“仁”具有客观对象性，且可以在保证恰当安排两者关系的基础上达成更

为有利的现实状况。

诚然，这种对“仁”重新审视的角度不仅仅适用于此章，对《论语》中其他章句和儒门后学的发展关系同样具备内在逻辑关联。子曰：“巧言令色，鲜矣仁!”（《学而》）子曰：“人而不仁，如礼何？人而不仁，如乐何?”（《里仁》）孔子认为，抑制自己情感上的“巧言令色”是遵守“仁”的基本条件，而“仁”又是践行其时社会最高规范“礼”、“乐”的基本出发点。有子曰：“其为人也孝弟，而好犯上者，鲜矣；不好犯上，而好作乱者，未之有也。君子务本，本立而道生。孝弟也者，其为仁之本与!”（《学而》）虽然孔子此处说“孝弟”为“仁之本”，但这不但不能说明这两者具备同样的道德属性，反而更有助于将“仁”从普遍认为的道德范畴中提升一个层次，成为个人情感道德和社会规范的有效媒介。同时，先秦儒门后学发展脉络的实际情况更能为此论断提供有力依据。思孟发展孔子“仁”学说而自成心性之学一派的客观背景正是未能进一步认清孔子学说中“仁”与“道德”的实质关系。他们不仅将“仁”作为道德范畴中的概念和现实不断发生关联，从而提出“仁政”、“圣王”的政治理想。而且还将孔子达成“复礼为仁”的“克己”方式申发为一种不断向内的自我精神探索方式，并在一般社会民众之上预设一个“圣人”形象作为最高道德行为载体，以此成为“人皆可以成尧舜”（《孟子·告子下》）的“性善论”基本出发点。而儒学另一支的代表荀子却对此大为鞭挞。荀子首先认为孔子的“礼”是现实社会中的强制行为规范，并意欲将此进一步提升到理性法治的高度而成为普通民众和帝王共同遵守的法则。其次，荀子极力反对孟子“性善”和“涂之人可以为禹”（《荀子·性恶》）的观点，认为在具备共识状态特性的社会行为规范下，一切个人的欲望都不利于这种状态存在，是天生“恶”的由来。在此基础上，他进一步否定孔孟认为有“君子”、“小人”之分，认为一切现实中的人都只统摄于“群”的概念之下，只有通过“礼”（理性法）的教化才能实现“群分”。

最后，引用荀子在《非十二子》中对于思孟的具体批判，进一步说明本文所论，孔子学说中“仁”、“礼”概念的另一种理解取向的现实性。“略法先王而不知其统，犹然而材剧志大，闻见杂博。案往旧造说，谓之五行，甚僻违而无类，幽隐而无说，闭约而无解，案饰其辞而祇敬之曰：此真先君子之言也。子思唱之，孟轲和之，世俗之沟犹瞀儒，嚾嚾然不知其所非也，遂受而传之，以为仲尼、子游为兹厚于后世，是则子思、孟轲之罪也。”荀子三为“稷下学宫祭酒”，对其时流行于世的各种学说都有了解，因此批判子思孟子假借孔子学说而发端的“五行之说”为“往旧造说”、“僻违无类”、“幽隐无说”必有所根据。即使不论思孟的“心性之学”与孔子之说到底有多少关联和偏差，荀子的这种说法也为从另外角度理解孔子“仁”、“礼”属性和关系提供了最为可靠的依据，使得一直从思孟学派角度看待孔子的方式得以自我反思。其次，

“弟陀其冠，神禫其辞，禹行而舜趋，是子张氏之贱儒也。正其衣冠，齐其颜色，嗛然而终日不言，是子夏氏之贱儒也。偷儒惮事，无廉耻而耆饮食，必曰君子固不用力，是子游氏之贱儒也”更是表明，儒学在孔子荀子之间由于过于注重个人内外的修养而逐渐导致流于表面的状况，而这种状况必然不是孔子论及“仁”、“礼”的初衷所在。

综上所述，虽然《论语》“仁”、“礼”概念中客观、理性的成分比重占据有待进一步论证，但至少其所涉及的个人情感和道德范畴远未达到后人普遍意义上对此的认知。对于先秦儒家的认知，也以将孔子、思孟、荀子三分为宜，而不应该武断认为思孟顺承孔子，荀子为儒家异端。

# 《論語》“聽訟”章與《大學》篇的誤讀

清华大学 廖名春

《論語·颜渊》篇有載:

子曰:“片言可以折獄者,其由也與!”

子路無宿諾。

子曰:“聽訟,吾猶人也。必也使無訟乎!”

這三段話,何晏(193—249)《集解》以第一、第二段為一章,第三段為一章;皇侃(488—545)《義疏》本之;① 邢昺(932—1010)《疏》、② 朱熹(1130—1200)《集注》③ 同。我們今天的分章,基本遵循了這一傳統的做法。

其“聽訟”一章,雖然常為我們所津津樂道,但其詮釋卻頗成問題。

楊伯峻(1909—1992)將此章“子曰”的内容譯為:“審理訴訟,我同别人差不多。一定要使訴訟的事件完全消滅才好。”④ 這是說孔子講的是兩件事,一是說自己治獄的能力,“吾猶人也”,不過爾爾,“同别人差不多”;一是說自己的心願,“必也使無訟乎”,希望“一定要使訴訟的事件完全消滅才好”。如此說來,此章夫子自道,是說自己雖然有良好的願望,但治獄水平卻欠佳,孔子是在作檢討。這一理解於史無證,明顯不能成立。⑤

黄懷信則認為:“‘必也’:指必使聽訟,舊連下為句,非。”因而譯作:“審理訴訟,我和别人差不多。如果一定(讓我去做),(我會)使沒有訴訟吧!”⑥ 這是說,孔子雖然自認為治訟能力一般,但如果執掌治訟大權,就能做到“無訟”。如此說來,孔

---

① 文淵閣《四庫全書》(電子版,武漢大學出版社,1997年,下同)經部四書類《論語集解義疏》卷六。

② 文淵閣《四庫全書》經部四書類《論語注疏》卷十二。

③ 朱熹:《四書章句集注》,北京:中華書局,1983年,第136—137頁。

④ 楊伯峻:《論語譯注》,北京:中華書局,1980年,第136頁。

⑤ 案:孔子曾為魯中都宰,又任魯司寇三年,現存史籍並無其治獄不當的記載。

⑥ 黄懷信:《論語新校釋》,西安:三秦出版社,2006年,第294頁。

子是一個缺乏自知之明的人，明明知道自己治訟能力不行，卻還奢望執掌治訟大權能做到“無訟”。就好比百米跑水平一般的運動員，說如果一定要我參加奧運會，我就會贏他一塊奧運會百米跑金牌回來。這樣的釋讀，這樣的理解孔子，殊不足取也。

南懷瑾（1918—2012）的分析是：“孔子說：‘聽訟，吾猶人也。’這句話要注意了，真正的意思是不要有主觀，聽原告的話時，自己就站在原告的立場。聽被告的話時，自己就站在被告的立場。以現在哲學的觀念，這才是絕對的客觀。然後再來判斷是非。但是我們往往最容易犯的錯誤，是自己先有成見，所以要為任何一個人設身處地。‘必也，使無訟乎！’為什麼要做到那麼客觀，因為我們判斷是非的人，最主要的目的，是使大家沒有紛爭，都能心氣平和，心安理得，合理的得到解決。”① 這是說，“聽訟”要以己度人，替人著想，做到客觀公正，因為目的都是爲了息訟。“聽訟”客觀公正，就能息訟，這是有道理的。但“吾猶人也”，怎麼就變成了“絕對的客觀”？這樣的訓詁，實在是不靠譜。

孫欽善的譯文是：“聽訟判案，我跟別人的本事差不多。能不能一定讓人們沒有訴訟呢？”其解釋是：“孔子提倡禮治，但又排斥刑罰，他主張禮治為主，刑罰為輔。”② 案：這一譯文有訓詁上的錯誤，不能說是忠實於原文。因為以此句的“乎”為疑問語氣詞，以“必也使無訟乎”為疑問句，表達的只能是否定的意思。因此，決不能將“必也使無訟乎”譯為“能不能一定讓人們沒有訴訟呢”，只能譯為：“能一定讓人們沒有訴訟嗎？”但這樣，意思也就反了。變成了孔子是說，他“聽訟”，跟別人的本事差不多，一定做不到“無訟”。可見，將“必也使無訟乎”理解成疑問句的確是捍格不通。

但孫氏以為此章孔子是主張禮治為主，刑罰為輔，卻也淵源有自，值得注意。朱熹《集注》引范氏曰：“聽訟者，治其末，塞其流也。正其本，清其源，則無訟矣。”③ 這是說孔子做“治其末，塞其流”的“聽訟”之事，是“吾猶人也”，跟別人的本事差不多。但“正其本，清其源，則無訟矣”之事，就“必也”，就只有他了。這實質是說，孔子不以治末的“聽訟”見長，而是以治本的禮治見長。

朱熹《集注》又引楊氏曰：“子路片言可以折獄，而不知以禮遜為國，則未能使民無訟者也。故又記孔子之言，以見聖人不以聽訟為難，而以使民無訟為貴。”④ 這將上文“片言可以折獄者，其由也與”章與此章聯繫了起來，認為“聖人不以聽訟為難”，

① 南懷瑾：《論語別裁》，上海：大學復旦出版社，1990年，第576頁。

② 孫欽善：《論語本解》，北京：生活·讀書·新知三聯書店，2009年，第152頁。

③ 朱熹：《四書章句集注》，第137頁。

④ 朱熹：《四書章句集注》，第137頁。

這一點子路一類的人都可以做到;“而以使民無訟”,也就是禮治“為貴”,這是孔子所追求的,也是子路一類的人做不到的。爲什麼?因為“聽訟”為治末,而“無訟”為治本。

范氏、楊氏的禮本刑末說其實也源於古注。“必也使無訟乎”,何晏(193—249)《注》引王肅(195—256)曰:“化之在前也。”皇侃(488—545)《義疏》:“言我所以異於人者,當訟未起而化之使不訟耳。”① 是說孔子說他與別人不同的地方,只不過是在獄訟未發生時就將獄訟化解了,從而使獄訟不產生罷了。所謂“化之”,就是以禮化訟,以禮息訟。皇侃進一步引孫綽(314—371)說以證之:“夫訟之所生,先明其契,而後訟不起耳;若訟至後察,則不異於凡人也。此言防其本也。”② 是說獄訟還沒有發生時,在事前就化解了其產生的契機,這樣獄訟就不會發生了;如果獄訟發生後才來處理,就跟一般人沒有什麼不同了。③ 這是說治獄聽訟要把功夫放在獄訟產生的根本,也就是禮治上。

這一解釋若要再往前追溯,我們就不能不提到影響巨大的《禮記·大學》篇。其云:

子曰:“聽訟,吾猶人也,必也使無訟乎!”無情者不得盡其辭,大畏民志,此謂知本。④

這一段話的理解也有問題。鄭玄(127—200)注云:“‘情’猶實也。無實者多虛誕之辭,聖人之‘聽訟’與人同耳。必使民無實者不敢‘盡其辭’,大畏其心志,使誠其意,不敢訟。”“‘本’,謂誠其意也。”⑤ 這是說,“無情者不得盡其辭,大畏民志”這一段話也是“子曰”的內容,都是孔子所說。這樣,就當標點為:

子曰:“聽訟,吾猶人也。必也使無訟乎!無情者不得盡其辭,大畏民志。”⑥此謂知本。

如此,孔子就是說:聽訟,我跟平常人差不多。但我一定要使人們不發生獄訟!使沒有事實依據的人不敢放肆地誣陷他人,使民心大大地畏服。這就是懂得治獄的根本。

---

① 文淵閣《四庫全書》經部四書類《論語集解義疏》卷六。

② 文淵閣《四庫全書》經部四書類《論語集解義疏》卷六。

③ 案:從文義看,“夫訟之所生”當作“夫訟之所未生”,“生”前疑脫一“未”字。故譯文加上了“還沒有”3字。新安鮑氏知不足齋本(見中華書局四部要籍注疏叢刊本《論語》,1998年,第246頁)同文淵閣四庫本,“生”前皆沒有“未”字。

④ 龔抗云整理:《禮記正義》繁體點校本,北京大學出版社,2000年,第1866頁。

⑤ 文淵閣《四庫全書》經部禮類禮記之屬《禮記注疏》卷六十。

⑥ 案:高流水點校本劉寶楠《論語正義》(北京:中華書局,1990年,第503頁)就是這樣標點的。

與《論語·顔淵》篇“聽訟”章比較，鄭玄注的斷句顯然有問題。儘管有“疏不破注”的傳統，但孔穎達（574—648）還是指出：“‘大畏民志’者，大能畏脅民人之志，言人有虚誕之志者，皆畏懼不敢訟，言民亦誠實其意也。‘聽訟吾猶人也，必也使無訟乎’，是夫子之辭。‘無情者不得盡其辭，大畏民志’，是記者釋夫子‘無訟’之事。然能‘使無訟’，則是異於人也，而云‘吾猶人’者，謂聽訟之時，備兩造，吾聽與人無殊，故云‘吾猶人也’。”[①]《論語》邢昺《疏》也説：“‘聽訟，吾猶人也，必也，使無訟乎’，是夫子辭。‘無情者不得盡其辭，大畏民志’，是記者釋夫子‘無訟’之事，意與此注及王弼不同，未知誰是，故具載之。”[②] 後來言《大學》者，皆取孔穎達説，以“‘無情者不得盡其辭，大畏民志’，是記者釋夫子‘無訟’之事”，這與“此謂知本”一樣，都是《大學》的作者對孔子“聽訟，吾猶人也，必也使無訟乎”的解説，是非常正確的。

從《大學》篇的解釋看，“聽訟”是末，所以孔子説“吾猶人也”，他與眾人一樣。但孔子爲什麽説他“必也使無訟乎”，就因為他知道治本，在誠信上下功夫。這樣，沒有事實依據的人就不敢放肆地誣陷他人了，民心畏服了。做到了禮治，獄訟自然就無從發生了。從禮主刑輔的本末説來解説《論語》此章的思想，突出孔子司法觀的哲學高度，《大學》篇應該説是開了先河。

《大學》篇的這種解釋在先秦兩漢文獻中能得到普遍的支持。

《大戴禮記·禮察》篇云：“凡人之知，能見已然，不能見將然。禮者，禁于將然之前；而法者，禁于已然之後。是故法之用易見，而禮之所為至難知也。若夫慶賞以勸善，刑罰以懲惡，先王執此之正，堅如金石，行此之信，順如四時；處此之功，無私如天地，爾豈顧不用哉？然而曰‘禮云禮云’，貴絕惡于未萌、而起信于微眇，使民日從善遠罪而不自知也。孔子曰：‘聽訟，吾猶人也，必也使無訟乎。’此之謂也。”[③]《新書》卷十[④]、《漢書·賈誼傳》[⑤] 所載同。這是説《論語·陽貨》篇孔子説的“禮云禮云，玉帛云乎哉？樂云樂云，鐘鼓云乎哉”，是説禮樂的重要不僅僅在於“玉帛”這些形式、“鐘鼓”這些器物，而在於罪惡還沒有萌發時就先消滅了它，從極微小處培養起誠信來，使百姓一天天接近善良遠離罪惡而自己並不知道。也就是説，行禮如儀是末，而通過禮樂來規範民眾、教育民眾才是本。而云《論語》“聽訟”章孔子曰為“此

---

① 龔抗云整理：《禮記正義》繁體點校本，第1873頁。

② 文淵閣《四庫全書》經部四書類《論語注疏》卷十二。

③ 文淵閣《四庫全書》經部禮類禮記之屬《大戴禮記》卷二。

④ 文淵閣《四庫全書》子部儒家類《新書》卷十。

⑤ 文淵閣《四庫全書》史部正史類《前漢書》卷四十八。案：顔師古有注：“《論語》載孔子之言也。言使吾‘聽訟’，與眾人齊等，然能先以德義化之，使其‘無訟’。”

之謂也”，也正是這一意思。

《史記·酷吏列傳》太史公曰：“法令者治之具，而非制治清濁之源也。昔天下之網嘗密矣，然姦偽萌起，其極也，上下相遁，至於不振。當是之時，吏治若救火揚沸，非武健嚴酷，惡能勝其任而愉快乎！言道德者，溺其職矣。故曰‘聽訟，吾猶人也，必也使無訟乎’。”[①]《漢書·酷吏傳》[②] 同。這是說刑罰為末，德治為本，所以孔子稱“使我‘聽訟’，猶凡人耳，然而立政施德，則能使其絕於爭訟”，[③] 認為孔子強調自己所長並不是“聽訟”治獄，而是以德化訟、以德息訟。

《鹽鐵論·大論第五十九》載“文學”辯駁“大夫”之言曰：“孔子曰：‘聽訟吾猶人也，必也使無訟乎！’無訟者難，訟而聽之易。夫不治其本而事其末，古之所謂愚，今之所謂智。以棰楚正亂，以刀筆正文，古之所謂賊，今之所謂賢也。”[④] 也認為孔子是說自己之功不在“事其末”的“聽訟”，而在於“治其本”的“無訟”。

王符（85？－163？）《潛夫論·德化第三十三》：“是故上聖不務治民事而務治民心，故曰：‘聽訟，吾猶人也。必也使無訟乎！’導之以德，齊之以禮，務厚其情而明則務義，民親愛則無相害傷之意，動思義則無姦邪之心。夫若此者，非法律之所使也，非威刑之所彊也，此乃教化之所致也。”[⑤] 此是說“上聖不務治民事”，所以孔子說“聽訟，吾猶人也”；“務治民心”，“導之以德，齊之以禮”，所以孔子說“必也使無訟乎”。“教化之所致”，“民親愛則無相害傷之意，動思義則無姦邪之心”，所以孔子之“務治”，真正抓住了根本。

從《大戴禮記》到《史記》到《漢書》，從《新書》到《鹽鐵論》到《潛夫論》，它們解說《論語》“聽訟”章的基本精神與《禮記·大學》篇完全相同，都是以孔子重本輕末來詮釋《論語》“聽訟”章的思想。這一解釋既維護了孔子作為“聖人”的神聖化，又照顧到了孔子思想的系統性，突出了孔子思想的核心價值和區別性特徵：重德教而輕刑罰。因此，自然會被後來的注家所繼承，成為眾口一詞的見解。所以，追根溯源，我們今天關於《論語》“聽訟”章的代表性詮釋，其始就出於《禮記·大學》篇。從戰國到兩漢，從禮家諸子到史家班馬，大家的口徑與《禮記·大學》篇的解釋都是一致的。

不過，最早的解說、最權威的解說、眾口一詞的解說未必是最正確的解說。從《論語·颜渊》篇“聽訟”章的本文看，以《禮記·大學》篇為代表的孔子重本輕末說

---

① 文淵閣《四庫全書》史部正史類《史記》卷一百二十二。

② 文淵閣《四庫全書》史部正史類《前漢書》卷九十。

③ 《漢書》顏師古《注》，見文淵閣《四庫全書》史部正史類《前漢書》卷九十。

④ 王利器：《鹽鐵論校注》，北京：中華書局，1992 年，第 604 頁。

⑤ （漢）王符著、（清）汪繼培箋：《潛夫論箋校正》，北京：中華書局，1985 年，第 376 頁。

顯然有誤讀原文、增字為訓、過度發揮的問題。

大家知道，“聽訟”的解釋，從邢昺《疏》的“聽斷獄訟”，[①] 到楊伯峻的《譯注》的“審理訴訟”，[②] 當無異議。

“吾猶人也”，除南懷瑾說外，從何晏《注》引包咸曰到皇侃《義疏》，再到邢昺《疏》、楊伯峻《譯注》，都是“我同別人差不多”的意思，解釋也沒有什麼大的不同。

但是，承認“子曰：‘聽訟，吾猶人也’”是孔子自認其“聽訟”能力“同別人差不多”，就帶來了兩個問題。

一是貶低了孔子的治國能力。孔子一生，孜孜以求的是將自己仁政理想付之於治國的實踐，而“聽訟”，再怎麼說，也是治國最重要的內容。一個“聽訟”能力平常的人，又有什麼資格要求去治國平天下呢？所以，孔子如果自認其“聽訟”能力平平，實際就否定了自己從政的可能。因此，毫無疑問，孔子是決不會這麼說的。

二是有違歷史的事實。《史記·孔子世家》云：“定公以孔子為中都宰，一年，四方皆則之。由中都宰為司空，由司空為大司寇。……定公十年春，孔子攝相事。”[③] 孔子做了一年的中都宰，其治理達到了“四方皆則之”的程度。又做了三年的魯國大司寇，是專門負責治獄的，甚至由此攝行魯國相事。說其“聽訟”能力平平，可能嗎？

文獻關於孔子“聽訟”的具體內容有如下一些記載：

《荀子·宥坐》篇：“孔子為魯攝相，朝七日而誅少正卯。門人進問曰：‘夫少正卯，魯之聞人也，夫子為政而始誅之，得無失乎？’孔子曰：“……此小人之桀雄也，不可不誅也。是以湯誅尹諧，文王誅潘止，周公誅管叔，太公誅華仕，管仲誅付里乙，子產誅鄧析、史付；此七子者，皆異世同心，不可不誅也。”[④] 孔子誅少正卯事，又見於《新語·輔政》篇[⑤]、《說苑·指武》篇[⑥]、《孔子家語·始誅》篇[⑦]、《史記·孔子世家》[⑧]、《漢書·王尊傳》[⑨]、《後漢書·李膺傳》[⑩] 等。人或不信，暫且不論。但如其可信的話，孔子將其誅少正卯與“湯誅尹諧，文工誅潘止，周公誅管叔，太公誅華仕，管仲誅付里乙，子產誅鄧析、史付”相比，是不可能自認“聽訟，吾猶人也”的。

---

① 文淵閣《四庫全書》經部四書類《論語注疏》卷十二。
② 楊伯峻：《論語譯注》第137頁。
③ 文淵閣《四庫全書》史部正史類《史記》卷四十七。
④ 文淵閣《四庫全書》子部儒家類《荀子》卷二十。
⑤ 文淵閣《四庫全書》子部儒家類《新語》卷上。
⑥ 文淵閣《四庫全書》子部儒家類《說苑》卷十五。
⑦ 文淵閣《四庫全書》子部儒家類《孔子家語》卷一。
⑧ 文淵閣《四庫全書》史部正史類《史記》卷四十七。
⑨ 文淵閣《四庫全書》史部正史類《前漢書》卷七十六。
⑩ 文淵閣《四庫全書》史部正史類《後漢書》卷九十七。

《荀子·宥坐》篇又載:“孔子為魯司寇,有父子訟者,孔子拘之,三月不別。其父請止,孔子舍之。季孫聞之,不說,曰:‘是老也欺予。語予曰:“為國家必以孝”,今殺一人以戮不孝,又舍之。’冉子以告。孔子慨然歎曰:‘嗚呼!上失之,下殺之,其可乎!不教其民而聽其獄,殺不辜也。三軍大敗,不可斬也;獄犴不治,不可刑也,罪不在民故也。嫚令謹誅,賊也;今生也有時,斂也無時,暴也;不教而責成功,虐也。已此三者,然後刑可即也。’”[1] 這一記載又見於《韓詩外傳》卷三[2]、《說苑·政理》篇[3]、《孔子家語·始誅》篇。[4] 此是說孔子為魯司寇處理父子之間的官司,久拖不判,至息訟乃止。魯國的執政季孫氏因而對他有誤解。孔子告訴他的學生冉有他這樣做的原因是不能“不教其民而聽其獄,殺不辜也”,要先教而後刑,只有制止了“嫚令謹誅”之“賊”、“生也有時,斂也無時”之“暴”、“不教而責成功”之“虐”,然後刑罰才可以施加到人們身上。從這一處置來看,孔子“聽訟”的水平是相當高超的,不可能說是能力平平。

《說苑·至公》篇:“孔子為魯司寇,聽獄必師斷,敦敦然皆立,然後君子進曰:‘某子以為何若?’某子以為云云。又曰:‘某子以為何若?’某子曰云云。辯矣,然後君子[曰]:‘幾當從某子云云乎?’以君子之知,豈必待某子之云云然後知所以斷獄哉!君子之敬讓也。文辭有可與人共之者,君子不獨有也。”[5]《春秋繁露·五行相生》篇也載:“司寇尚禮……至清廉平,賂遺不受,請謁不聽,據法聽訟,無有所阿,孔子是也。為魯司寇,斷獄屯屯,與眾共之,不敢自專。是死者不恨,生者不怨。”[6]《孔子家語·好生》篇[7]、《淮南子·主術》[8] 也有相近的說法。這些記載一是說孔子“聽獄”有民主集中制之風,不專制武斷;二是說孔子為司寇清廉自律,“據法聽訟,無有所阿”,以致于斷獄達到了“死者不恨,生者不怨”的地步。從這些記載看,孔子“聽獄”不但不可能是水平一般,而且應當是相當傑出。

所以,無論是從事理上分析,還是從歷史記載出發,說“聽訟,吾猶人也”,是孔子自認其“聽訟”能力“同別人差不多”都是不能成立的。

在承認“聽訟,吾猶人也”,是孔子自認其“聽訟”能力“同別人差不多”的前提下,《禮記·大學》篇為了維護孔子的權威,引入禮本刑末說,將“聽訟”與“無訟”

---

① 文淵閣《四庫全書》子部儒家類《荀子》卷二十。
② 文淵閣《四庫全書》經部詩類《韓詩外傳》卷三。
③ 文淵閣《四庫全書》子部儒家類《說苑》卷七。
④ 文淵閣《四庫全書》子部儒家類《孔子家語》卷一。
⑤ 文淵閣《四庫全書》子部儒家類《說苑》卷十四。
⑥ 文淵閣《四庫全書》經部春秋類《春秋繁露》卷十三。
⑦ 文淵閣《四庫全書》子部儒家類《孔子家語》卷二。
⑧ 文淵閣《四庫全書》子部儒家類《孔子家語》卷一。

對立起來，以“聽訟”為末，以“無訟”為本。這樣，孔子雖然在末節上表現平平，但在根本上卻遠遠高出於衆人。表面上看，孔子自認其“聽訟”能力不突出的問題得到了解決，但實質上既從事理上卻陷入了歸謬法，否定了孔子出仕的必要性；又有悖於歷史的記載，得不到文獻的支持。所以，《禮記·大學》篇這種禮本刑末說的詮釋，看似高明，其實卻經不起分析。

筆者認為，長期以來以“聽訟，吾猶人也”，是孔子自認其“聽訟”能力“同別人差不多”的解釋純粹是一種誤讀。“聽訟，吾猶人也，必也使無訟乎”，其實當讀作“吾猶人也，聽訟，必也使無訟乎”。爲了突出“聽訟”，孔子特意將其前置，放到了“吾猶人也”之前。這種前置或者說倒裝，其實是一種修辭的方法，上古文獻習見。比如說《論語·憲問》篇載“子曰”：“君子哉若人！尚德哉若人！”即“若人君子哉！若人尚德哉！”[①] 是謂語前置。又《顏淵》篇：“何哉，爾所謂達者？”[②] 即“爾所謂達者，何哉？”是賓語前置。《左傳·閔公元年》：“不如逃之，無使罪至，為吳大伯，不亦可乎？猶有令名，與其及也。”[③] 即：“與其及也，不如逃之，無使罪至。為吳大伯，猶有令名，不亦可乎？”是說與其遭殃，不如逃走，不讓罪名臨頭。出走後做個吳國太伯那樣的人，還有美名，難道不好嗎？這種倒裝則更為複雜。

許世瑛對《論語》此章做過句法分析，他說：引號中的第一句（案：指“聽訟，吾猶人也”）是判斷繁句。主語“聽訟”是詞結，謂語“吾猶人”也是詞結（準判斷簡句）。第二句是致使繁句。“必”是修飾致使述詞“使”的限制詞，爲了要加強它的重要性，所以在“必”字底下，加了一個停頓語氣詞“也”字，使語氣可以在此一頓。“使”字之下省去了一個止詞兼起詞的“之”字，是泛指“人”的。“無”等於“不”，修飾述詞“訟”。“乎”是句末表測度的語氣詞，相當於白話的“吧”字。至於這兩句之間的關係，可以說是補充關係。[④]

這一句法分析注重表面，但並沒有吃透孔子語義的精神。“聽訟，吾猶人也，必也使無訟乎”，其實是兩個句子，一個是“吾猶人也”，一個是“聽訟必也使無訟乎”。“吾猶人也”可以說是因，“聽訟必也使無訟乎”可以說是果。因此這可以說是一個因果複句。而作為結果分句的“聽訟必也使無訟乎”，可以有兩種理解：一種是假設語氣，即“若吾聽訟，必也使無訟乎”。“聽訟”是條件，“必也使無訟乎”是結果。這樣的話，此時孔子尚未“聽訟”，尚未成為司寇，是在向魯君或執政的季氏求職。另一種

---

① 文淵閣《四庫全書》經部四書類《論語注疏》卷十四。

② 文淵閣《四庫全書》經部四書類《論語注疏》卷十二。

③ 文淵閣《四庫全書》經部春秋類《春秋左傳注疏》卷十。

④ 許世瑛：《論語二十篇句法研究》，臺北：臺灣開明書店，1978年，第229頁。

是陳述語氣，即“吾聽訟，必也使無訟乎”。是說我“聽訟”，追求的、致力的是“使”人“無訟”。這樣，孔子則是在解釋自己正在進行的行為，說明孔子正在“聽訟”。楊伯峻分析：“孔子這話或許是剛作司寇時所說。”[①] 其實可修正為：孔子這話當是其作司寇時所說。上述《荀子·宥坐》篇所載“孔子為魯司寇”處理“父子訟者”一事就是證明。孔子“聽訟”追求“無訟”，所以“有父子訟者，孔子拘之，三月不別”。直至“其父請止”，“孔子”才“舍之”，做到了“息訟”。執政的季氏“不說”，以為孔子是瀆職。其學生“冉子以告”，孔子於是對他的“息訟”之舉，也就是“聽訟”的問題做了一番解釋。其說與《論語》此章所載雖有出入，但也可互相印證發明。說《論語》此章所載是孔子“為魯司寇”處理了“父子訟者”之事後，向人解釋自己的“聽訟”行為，應該是信而有徵的。比較起來，假設和陳述這兩種理解，當以後者為是。正因為此章語義的重點是孔子向人解釋自己“聽訟”的特色，所以，孔子特將“聽訟”兩字前置以醒目。

從形式邏輯的角度看，這一段話其實是省略了大前提的三段論推理。“人皆欲‘使無訟’”可以說是大前提，在此省略了。“吾猶人也”是小前提。結論是“吾”“聽訟”“必也使無訟乎”。

由此可知，此章孔子的本意是說：我跟大家一樣，聽訟斷獄，一定要致力於使訴訟不再發生。“吾猶人也”，是說人同此心，心同此理，我自不能例外；“聽訟，必也使無訟乎”，是說我“聽訟”是為了息訟，是為了止訟。這裡的夫子自道，是強調其治訟的目的和特色，並非檢討自己治獄水平一般。完全用不著來貶低孔子的治獄水平，也完全用不著引進與禮本刑末說，製造“聽訟”與“無訟”的矛盾。因此，可以說，《禮記·大學》篇是在誤讀“聽訟，必也使無訟乎”句基礎上增字解經，從而對《論語》“聽訟”章做出了錯誤的詮釋。

《大學》篇的作者，《禮記》鄭玄《注》沒有明言，程顥（1032—1085）以為“《大學》乃孔氏遺書”。[②] 朱熹認為其“《經》一章，蓋孔子之言，而曾子述之”，“其《傳》十章，則曾子之意而門人記之也”。[③] 影響至深，幾成定論。但後人亦有不信者，如馮友蘭（1895—1990）認為《大學》“出於荀子後學”，[④] 徐複觀（1903—1982）以為其成

---

① 楊伯峻：《論語譯注》，第 137 頁。

② 文淵閣《四庫全書》子部儒家類《二程遺書》卷二上。

③ 朱熹：《四書章句集注》，第 1、4 頁。

④ 馮友蘭：《中國哲學史》，北京：中華書局，1963 年，第 437 頁。

書於秦漢之際，[1] 日人武内義雄（1886－1966）更認為《大學》是漢武帝以後的作品。[2] 現在看來，《大學》當爲秦火前、戰國時代的作品，其出於曾子後學的可能性最大。其對《論語》“聽訟”章的解說並非“孔子之言，而曾子述之”，也不一定是“門人記之”“曾子之意”。其時距孔子已遠，曾子後學誤讀了孔子之說，百密一疏，千慮一失，亦屬當然。

比如《大學》篇下文：“《詩》云：‘穆穆文王，於緝熙敬止！’為人君，止於仁；為人臣，止於敬；為人子，止於孝；為人父，止于慈；與國人交，止於信。”鄭玄《注》：“此美文王之德光明，敬其所以自止處。”[3] 從“為人君，止於仁；為人臣，止於敬；為人子，止於孝；為人父，止于慈；與國人交，止於信”來看，《大學》的作者是把《詩・大雅・文王》篇“於緝熙敬止”的“止”看成了實詞“居止”之“止”。但孔穎達《疏》卻云：“止，辭也。《詩》之本意，云文王見此光明之人，則恭敬之。此《記》之意，‘於緝熙’，言嗚呼文王之德緝熙光明，又能敬其所止以自居處也。”[4] 孔穎達這是說，“止”在《詩經》本文裡，本來是虛詞，“敬止”是“恭敬之”的意思。但在《禮記・大學》篇，卻被理解為“居止”之“止”。這實質是說《大學》篇斷章取義，曲解了《詩》意。朱熹雖然在《大學章句》說：“《詩・文王》之篇。穆穆，深遠之意。於，歎美辭。緝，繼續也。熙，光明也。敬止，言其無不敬而安所止也。引此而言聖人之止，無非至善。五者乃其目之大者也。學者于此，究其精微之蘊，而又推類以盡其餘，則於天下之事，皆有以知其所止而無疑矣。”[5] 將“止”解為“居止”之“止”。但其《詩集傳》卻云：“止，語辭。……言穆穆然文王之德，不已其敬如此。”[6] 現代學者多接受孔《疏》，認定是《禮記・大學》篇誤讀了《詩・大雅・文王》篇之文。如勞思光就說：“但‘於緝熙敬止’一語，引於此處，分明將原詩中之‘止’字視作與《大學》所論之‘止’相同者。此顯與《詩經》原句之意不符。原句之‘止’字，當是一虛字，不似有‘歸宿’之意。”[7] 新出的清華簡第三冊《周公之琴舞》篇，其中

---

① 徐複觀：《中國人性論史・先秦篇》，武漢：湖北人民出版社，2001年，第233－240頁。

② 武内義雄：《兩戴記考》，江俠庵編譯：《先秦經籍考》上冊，上海：商務印書館，1933年第183頁。

③ 文淵閣《四庫全書》經部禮類禮記之屬《禮記註疏》卷六十。

④ 文淵閣《四庫全書》經部禮類禮記之屬《禮記註疏》卷六十。

⑤ 朱熹：《四書章句集注》，第5頁。

⑥ 文淵閣《四庫全書》經部詩類《詩經集傳》卷六。案：戴震有云：“‘敬止’者，言敬慎其止居不慢也。故《禮記・大學》篇引之，以明‘止於至善’；《緇衣》篇引之，以明慎言行。說《詩》者以‘止’字為辭助而已，於引捍格則歸之於斷章取義。考古人賦詩斷章，必依於義可交通，未有盡失其義、誤讀其字者。使斷章取一句而並其字不顧，是亂經也。”見氏著：《毛鄭詩考正》卷三，張岱年主編：《戴震全集》第1冊第634頁（合肥：黃山書社，1995年）。

⑦ 勞思光：《新編中國哲學史》第2卷，桂林：廣西師範大學出版社，2005年，第41頁。

有今本《詩・周頌・敬之》篇全文。今本的“維予小子，不聰敬止”之“敬止”，清華簡本就寫作“敬之”。[①] 這説明“敬止”就是“敬之”，《禮記・大學》篇不明《詩・大雅・文王》篇“敬止”之“止”是借字，以“假借之字而強為之”説，確實是犯了文不對題的錯誤。

由此看，《禮記・大學》篇誤讀了《論語》“聽訟”章之義，也並非偶然。在重視先秦孔門後學經説的同時，對其解經的錯誤，對其誤讀孔子思想的問題，我們也應該有足夠的警惕。

① 清華大學出土文獻研究與保護中心編、李學勤主編：《清華大學藏戰國竹簡（叁）》，上海：中西書局，2012年，第133頁。

# 四種對《論語·學而篇》首章的詮釋

## ——古注與朱熹·王守仁·荻生徂徠的詮釋比較

日本北海道大学文学院 佐藤錬太郎 著 趙熠瑋 譯

### 序

對於《論語·學而篇》首章“學而時習之，不亦說乎。有朋自遠方來，不亦樂乎。人不知而不慍，不亦君子乎”，漢代以來一直有各種詮釋。從這三句可以聯想到如“學習之餘時而溫習之，豈不是件愉快之事？友人自遠方而來，豈不是件值得高興之事？不被人理解卻不動氣，豈不是堪稱君子？”這樣的意思。不過，“學”是向誰學習什麼；“時”是指何時；為何喜悅；“朋”是何意；“人”又是指誰，諸如此類疑問就會浮現出來，但從三句之中無法找出具體答案。而三句互相之間又是何種關係；三句是緊密相關，還是彼此獨立；是孔子自身的回顧，抑或是向其弟子闡述學習的三個階段（初步階段、成長階段、完成階段）之辭。看似平實的表述，仔細斟酌卻會滿腹疑問。歷代的注釋家對這些疑問點是如何闡述的。對這簡潔的三句中蘊含的意味，自古以來就有諸多解釋。本稿將舉出作為古注代表的魏代何晏《論語集解》及梁代皇侃對其注釋之書《論語義疏》（四庫全書本）、北宋邢昺的《論語正義》（四庫全書本）；作為新注代表的南宋朱熹《論語集注》及明代王守仁《傳習錄》相關內容，另舉出日本古學派注釋，荻生徂徠之《論語征》加以對比考察。

### 第一　古注

何晏（？—294年）《論語集解》中引用了王肅（195年—256年）的如下注釋：

時者學者以時誦習也。誦習以時，學無廢業，所以為悅懌也。

據王肅所言，“時習”者，能“時”而背誦學習，持續自身學業即為喜悅之理由。但是，他並未明言“學”是學什麼，“時”是指何時。

在皇侃（488年—545年）《論語義疏》中，以“學而時習之，不亦說乎”為第一段，疏曰：“明學者少時法也。”，並對“時”進一步追述道：“明學者幼少之時也。學從幼起，故以幼為先也。”他認為“時”是指幼少之時。

皇侃又以“有朋自遠方來，不亦樂乎”為第二段，疏曰：“明學業稍成，能招朋聚友之由也。既學已經時，故能招友為次也。”即以學業有成，能招待友人為第二階段。皇疏作為典據而舉出《禮記》學記篇中一句：

一年視離經辨志，三年視敬業樂群，五年視博習親師，七年視論學取友，謂之小成。

據皇侃所言，第二階段即為闡述初等乃至中等教育的學習方法。

皇疏又以“人不知而不慍，不亦君子乎”為第三段而疏曰：“明學業已成，能為師為君之法也。先能招友，故後乃學成，為師君也。”即學業已成，能為人師為第三階段。作為依據，他舉出《禮記·學記篇》中“九年，知類通達，強立而不反，謂之大成”與“能博喻，然後能為師。能為師，然後能為長。能為長，然後能為君”兩句。也即九年之中學有所成而能為人師；為人師後才能為人長；能為人長後才能為人君。

然而，對於“學”一字，皇疏根據《白虎通》中“學，覺也，悟也”疏曰：“用先王之道，導人情性，使自覺悟而去非取是，積成君子之德也。”即以先王之道導人性情為善，自覺積累善行而成君子之德。以人自覺領悟之物為善惡判斷的基準，也即六經中先王之道所示之道德規範。

對於“時”，皇疏列舉出“三時”。一是“身中時”，二是“年中時”，三是“日中時”。

第一“身中時”者，據《禮記·學記篇》云“時過然後學，則勤苦而難成”；內則篇雲“六年教之數與方名，七年男女不同席，八年始教之讓，九年教之數日，十年學書計，十三年學樂誦詩舞勺，十五年成童舞象。”即言童年時期應施以符合其成長年齡階段的學習內容。因此，“身中時”即指年歲。六歲開始學習數字與名稱，七歲時男女有別，八歲學習禮儀，九歲學習曆法，十歲學習書寫與計算，十三歲以後學習音樂詩歌與舞蹈。

第二“年中時”者，據《禮記·王制篇》云“春夏學《詩》《樂》，秋冬學《書》《禮》”，皇侃曰：

夫學隨時氣，則受業易入。春夏是陽，陽體輕清。《詩》《樂》是聲，聲亦輕清。所以輕清時，學輕清之業，則為易入也。秋冬是陰，陰體重濁。《書》《禮》是事，事亦重濁，所以重濁時。學重濁之業，亦易入也。

可知此處所言“年中時”指季節。即選擇應時的經書來學習是基於自然現象和人類活動緊密聯繫的時令思想，從天人感應的角度做出的解釋。春夏兩季心情閒適，宜學詩歌（《詩經》）和音樂（《樂記》），秋冬兩季則適宜以嚴肅的心態學習歷史（《書經》）和禮儀（《禮記》）。

第三"日中時"者，是指朝夕而言。據皇侃所言，對學習相應的成長階段和時令季節相應所學內容，要日日複習而不荒廢。

皇侃詮釋"學而時習之，不亦說乎"道：

"而"猶因仍也。"時"為日中之時也。"習"是修故之稱也。言人不學則已。既學，必因仍而修習，日夜無替也。"之"之於所學之業也。云"不亦說乎"，"亦"猶重也。"說"者懷抱欣暢之謂也。言知學已為可欣，又能修習不廢，是日知其所亡，月無忘其所能，彌重為可悅。

皇侃詮釋為"學習因仍學習，日夜無替，繼續學習而去於所學之業，重懷抱欣暢"。不把"之"看作賓語，而把其作為動詞，是非常有特色。其含義說的是能朝夕學習一事固然非常愉快，若能進一步堅持溫習，則每日都能注意到自己所忘之物。如能不遺忘每月所習內容的話就會愉悅愈增了。總而言之，皇侃的詮釋就是說，學習積累並能日日溫習，學業就能有所長進，由此愈加能感受到內心的喜悅。

北宋的邢昺（932年－1010年）《論語注疏》大體上沿襲皇疏之說做出如下的解釋：

此章勸人學為君子也。……學者，覺也。（學之為言，覺也。）覺悟所未知也。孔子曰，"學者而能以時誦習其經業，使無廢落，不亦說懌乎。學業稍成，能招朋友。有同門之朋從遠方而來，與己講習，不亦樂乎。既有成德，凡人不知而不慍之，不亦君子乎。"

以上內容概而言之，宋代成立的《論語注疏》的解釋是說常常誦讀學習經書，持續學習，則能自覺學業的進步，此即為無與倫比之愉悅。這是針對官吏錄用考試（科舉）應試而做出的解釋。

## 第二　新注

朱子學在中國歷經元明清三個王朝，大約八百餘年，一直是科舉（官吏錄用考試）的基準，成為官員必需的教養。李氏朝鮮亦然。在日本江戶時代，亦作為官學被視為武士的修養。下文將闡述新注的代表——朱子的《論語集注》與王陽明《傳習錄》中對"學而時習之"一章的解釋。

朱子的解釋：

認為學問的目的在於"學而至聖"的朱子（1130年—1200年），對"學而時習之"做出了如下注釋：

說、悅同。學之為言效也。人性皆善，而覺有先後，後覺者必效先覺之所為，乃可以明善而複其初也。習，鳥數飛也。學之不已，如鳥數飛也。說，喜意也。

既學而又時時習之，則所學者熟，而中心喜說，其進自不能已矣。程子曰："習，重習也。時複思繹，浹洽於中，則說也。"又曰："學者，將以行之也。時習之，則所學者在我，故說。"謝氏曰："時習者，無時而不習。坐如屍，坐時習也；立如齊，立時習也。"

也即是說，持續學習先覺者的事蹟的話，就能恢復與生俱來的本來善性（本然之性）。而繼續學習以達純熟後，學業就會進步，心靈亦得喜悅。

對於接下來的"有朋自遠方來，不亦樂乎"，朱子作了如下解釋：

朋，同類也。自遠方來，則近者可知。程子曰："以善及人，而信從者眾，故可樂。"又曰："說在心，樂主發散在外。"

這個解釋說的是，交友之樂在於因慕德而從遠方來訪眾多同類之友。

而對於"人不知而不慍，不亦君子乎"，朱子做了如下說明：

慍，含怒意。君子，成德之名。尹氏曰："學在己，知不知在人，何慍之有。"程子曰："雖樂於及人，不見是而無悶，乃所謂君子。"愚謂及人而樂者順而易，不知而不慍者逆而難，故惟成德者能之。然德之所以成，亦曰學之正、習之熟、說之深，而不已焉耳。程子曰："樂由說而後得，非樂不足以語君子。"

朱子解釋說，因以德感化別人為樂，即使不為人認可也不發怒，這就是完成"德"的君子。朱子的解釋可以歸納如下：

模仿學習道德先覺者的事蹟而努力習取善德的話，就會由心喜不自禁而取得進步。同類的朋友也會因仰慕其善德而遠道而來。將善德播及信從者則是非常喜悅之事。即便他人不認可自己也不發怒，這就是獲取了完德之人。

朱子把學習的對象解釋為"先覺之所為"，並解釋說，常學習道德上的先覺者的事蹟而回復自己的善性，從而得到喜悅。朱熹把人性分為兩種，即善惡渾濁的現實中的"氣質之性（肉體固有之性）"和純粹至善的理想的"本然之性（本該如此之性）"。他所提倡的複初說是說，必須通過學問陶冶"氣質之性"而回復"本然之性"。朱子在此處所言"複其初"，就是回復自身本有的純粹至善的道德性，即"本然之性"。朱子重視"先覺之所為"這一外在規範。

王陽明的解釋：

王陽明（1472年—1528年）於正德十三年（1518年）七月出版《古本大學》，批判了朱子的《大學章句》。同時，為了調和自己的學問與朱子學，從《朱子文集》中摘錄了朱子晚年的學說，著《朱子晚年定論》。他在序文中批判朱子的《四書章句集注》與《四書或問》的內容是朱子"中年未定之見解"。

正德十五年六月，南京吏部右侍郎羅欽順（1465年－1547年）致信王陽明，批評王陽明的"大學"解釋背叛了朱子學，並指出《朱子晚年定論》的年代考證是杜撰的。

時年49歲的王陽明在給羅欽順的回信中，再次批評朱熹把“大學”分為經文和傳文的行為。他說，“夫學貴得之心，求之於心而非也。雖其言之出於孔子，不敢以為是也。而況其未及孔子者乎。……夫道，天下之公道也。學，天下之公學也。非朱子可得而私也。非孔子可得而私也。”（《傳習錄》卷中“答羅整庵少宰書”）。作為儒者，這種措辭極為不妥，然而王陽明對孔子並無否定之言。

在和羅欽順論爭的翌年即正德十六年，王陽明宣言道，“聖人之學是心學”（“象山文集序”），表彰陸九淵的心學為儒學正傳，同時開始提倡致良知說。王陽明在與朱子學決別，提倡致良知說之前，苦心於對自己的學問和朱子學間的調和。他背逆了朱子學全盛這一時代潮流，提倡了致良知說。王陽明把自己比擬為“狂”，達到了擺脫朱子學常識束縛的境地。王陽明似乎是以與羅欽順的論爭作為契機，放棄了與朱子學間的調和，堅定了對抗的覺悟。

王陽明在解釋《論語》時，從未批判孔子及其學問。然而，對於以孔子為天生完人的朱子“集注”中的解釋，他逐一加以了批判。王陽明認為，孔子立志努力，一生持續學習、不斷向上。王陽明認為問之於己心，如不正，則雖言之出於孔子，也不敢以為是。這並非是欲言孔子言行有誤，而是表明自己無法信服“而況其未及孔子者”，即朱子的學說。

弟子問王陽明，“先儒（朱子）以學為效先覺之所為，如何?”。王陽明對朱子的解釋做了如下批判：

> 學是學去人欲，存天理。從事于去人欲存天理，則自正諸先覺。考諸古訓，自下許多間辨思索存省克治工夫。然不過欲去此心之人欲，存吾心之天理耳。若曰效先覺之所為，則只說得學中一件事。事亦似專求諸外了。“時習”者，“坐如屍”（朱子在《論語集注》中所引謝上蔡之言），非專習坐也。坐時習此心也。“立如齋”（朱子在《論語集注》中所引謝上蔡之言），非專習立也。立時習此心也。“說”是“理義之說我心”（《孟子·告子上》）之“說”。人心本自說理義。如目本說色，耳本說聲。惟為人欲所蔽所累，始有不說。今人欲日去今人欲日去，則理義日洽浹。安得不悅。”（《傳習錄》卷上·112條）

即王陽明批判道，朱子關於學習先覺者事蹟的解釋，只是在說學問中一事，把學習的對象置於心外。王陽明所謂的“學習”就是“去人欲存天理”。學習的對象並非在心外，而是在自己的心中。如孟子所說，人心本來就為悅理義而生，所以學習正心必然喜悅。關於學習正心的解釋，是從“心即理”即心中本來存理，不應在心外求理這一立場做出的。

## 第三　日本古學派的解釋

荻生徂徠（1666年－1728年）是日本江戶時代中期的儒學者。號徂徠。因其先祖為物部氏而自稱物徂徠。其父為五代幕府將軍德川綱吉的御醫，因得罪將軍而被趕出江戶（今日本東京都）。時年十四歲的徂徠隨父親一同被流放到上總國長柄郡二宮莊本能村（今千葉縣茂原市）。元祿九年（1696年）徂徠三十一歲時開始仕於將軍寵臣柳澤吉保，十四年間作為儒學者得到柳澤吉保的信任，並在著名的赤穗義士的處置問題上，其意見被採用。

徂徠三十餘歲初期因讀古學派伊藤仁齋《大學定本》、《語孟字義》後深受觸動，致信仁齋。但未獲得年事已高的仁齋的回信，不久仁齋過世。其後，徂徠怒於其私信被無端收入於仁齋傳記資料集《古學先生碣銘行狀》中，而於正德四年（1714年）著《蘐園隨筆》批判了仁齋。但正如大阪（今大阪）懷德堂中井竹山（1730年－1804年）所言，"徂徠晚年之見臭味於仁齋"（《非徵篇》），徂徠的思想與仁齋頗有諸多共通之處。徂徠受明代李攀龍、王世貞的影響而致力古文辭的研究，並提倡古文辭學。

寶永六年（1709年），將軍綱吉去世，柳澤吉保也因此失勢。徂徠搬出柳澤氏宅邸遷居于日本橋茅場町（今東京都中央區）。從公務中解放出來的徂徠更加熱衷於古文辭研究，其門下太宰春台、服部南郭等人才輩出。享保元年（1716年），五十一歲時確立了基於古文辭學的獨創儒學，開始執筆《論語徵》。

以下淺析荻生徂徠《論語徵》中對"學而時習之"一章的解釋。

首先，對於"學"、"習"，其做出如下闡述：

> 單言"學"者、學先王之道也。學先王之道、自有先王之教。傳曰、"樂正崇四術、立四教、順先王詩書禮樂以造士。"（《禮記》王制）是也。"習"者、肄其業也。"時習之"、王肅曰、"以時誦習之。"（古注）傳曰、"春誦、夏弦、秋學禮、冬讀書。"（《禮記》文王世子）其習之亦如之。以身處先王之教也。

徂徠定義"學"為學"先王之道"，"習"則是隨季節變換，春誦詩、夏習樂、秋學《禮記》、冬讀《書經》，以修得先王之教。

對於"說"一字其解釋為，仰慕先王之道，喜於德之提高。其陳述如下：

> "說"者、心深受而有所愛慕也。蓋先王之道，善美所會萃，天下莫尚焉。而其教法。順陰陽之宜以將息之，假以歲月而長養之。學者優遊于其中，久與之化，德日以進。

第二句之"朋"字則解釋為仰慕孔子之德而師事孔子之人。"樂"則被看作是不拘泥於貧富，得英才以教育之的喜悅。其做出了如下說明：

“朋”、黨類。謂從我遊者也。“樂”、謂樂其在我者而不復它求也。學成而孚於人，遠方士亦有來從我遊者。我教而育之，亦以在我者已，是其可樂之至。豈複有所慊而它求乎。凡天下之樂，皆在富貴。而貧賤之樂，其大而可能者，唯是已。故“自西自東，自南自北，無思不服。”（《詩經・大雅》〈文王有聲〉）文王之詩，而孔子廼足當之矣。

進而對第三句，其解釋為即便不得任用也不悶悶不樂者，這才是立于民上治理民眾的武士，還以為這是讚賞“知命安分”之君子。其解釋道：

“人不知”，謂不見用於世也。“慍”，謂心有所怫鬱也。蓋慍鬱一音之轉，不必訓“怒”。“君子”，治民者之稱，包大夫以上。雖在下，其德足以長民，亦謂之君子也。士學先王之道，以成德，將以用於世。然人不知而不我用也。其心豈莫所怫鬱乎。為下者之情為然。然亦有命焉。行先王之道於世，命也。傳先王之道於人，命也。唯命不同。於是時教學以為事，藉以忘憂。其心莫有所怫鬱。豈不以為君子之人乎。（中略）“不亦乎”者，贊辭。贊學習之道可悅可樂亦可以為君子也。蓋先王之道，敬天為本，禮樂刑政，皆奉天命以行之。故知命安分，為君子之事矣。

徂徠做出以上解釋後，對於朱子將“學”訓作“效”做出了激烈的批評：

朱子以“效”訓“學”，是字學家釋名之說。謂聲音之道，輾轉相因，“效”轉為“學”。故“學”亦有效意耳。然“效”“學”一分，“效”自“效”，“學”自“學”。豈可混乎。且“學”字，本不須訓詁，其義自明。朱子所以引“效”字纏繞立說者，坐誤讀《中庸》《孟子》，妄求為聖人故耳。夫聖人聰明睿知之德受諸天，豈可學而至諸。何況效乎。先王四術，詩書禮樂。辟如化工生花。學以成德，德以性殊。立言制行，亦人人殊。何必效為。宋儒非剪綵之花則裡婦效顰西施，可謂陋矣。

徂徠進一步指出，訓“學”為“覺”的解釋並非儒學聖人之道，而是道教佛教的修錬法，亦是窮物之理的“格物窮理說”的彌縫補救之策，其批評道：

又如訓“覺”，是其“一旦豁然貫通”（〈大學章句〉）之說，聖人之道所無。（中略）宋儒主理貴知，欲先明理而後踐之。故有其格物之說。今日格一物，明日格一物。有何窮盡。

徂徠又進而對朱子“後覺者必效先覺之所為”的解釋持否定態度，他批評其性善說是源自孟子，與佛教學說相近，並非孔子所言。還批評其“複初說”、“性即理說”也顯然都是臆測。這是史上罕見的對朱子學的嚴酷批評：

《論語》“先覺”（〈憲問篇〉），謂覺人之詐偽耳。豈語“學”哉。“人性本善”（程子），亦原於孟子，而孔子所不言。孟子亦有所為而言之。且其所謂性，廼宋

> 儒氣質。“善”亦大槩言之。宋儒性，如佛氏“性相”之性。大失古言。其所謂“善”，亦以至者言之。遂加一“本”字而有“復初”之說。然赤子無聖人之德。其可言者理耳。故又曰，“性即理也”（《中庸章句》）。是宋儒取諸其臆妄作者，昭昭乎明矣哉。

徂徠又嚴厲批評古學派前輩伊藤仁齋（1627 年－1705 年）的《論語古義》中的解釋是源自其誤讀，對朱子的解釋他做出了全面的否定。

又如仁齋以“稽古補偏”為“學問之功”者，亦誤讀《中庸》，而謂道不竢聖人而有之故也。果其說之是邪。孔子奚學為。“習”訓“重習”（《論語集注》程子之說），亦為纏繞。（中略）朱子解經，可謂無特操者已。（中略）“說”訓“喜”意，殊為不知字義。（中略）“悅”固在心，然何必求諸心也。“樂主發散在外”，緣朋友來造是無用之解，其謬昉於皇侃。殊不知凡言樂者。皆樂在我而不須它求之義。“悅”“樂”之分，“悅”者道尚在彼而我學之，“樂”者道已在我而我教人。豈不明白乎。“慍”訓“含怒意”，亦至於“南風”“解慍”而窮矣。且“人不知而怒”，雖非君子，亦無是事。至於樂與不慍為所遇境有順逆者，則其謬甚矣。

徂徠以“悅”者為學道之悅，“樂”者為持道育人之樂，進而對朱子學做出如下批評：

> “人不知”，本謂在上之人不知有長民之德治邦之才耳。如“莫我知也夫”（〈憲問篇〉）。豈為七十子不知夫子乎。故朋來之樂，亦“人不知”之事。廼以教育英才自樂。而雖人不知亦不慍耳。是儒者之事，足以當君子之德。故曰“不亦君子乎”。朱子以講道授徒為大小大事。以朋來為順境，以生徒零落為“人不知”，為逆境。所見之陋，宜其生鵞湖之爭也。

徂徠認為如孔子般學習用以安民之先王之道，即便不受重用，不得仕官也能樂於詩書而忘卻憂愁者才是儒者、君子。徂徠展示了這一獨特的見解：

> 蓋先王之道，安民之道也。“學”者學之也。“學優則仕”（〈子張篇〉）。以行其道。子路曰：“不仕無義，君臣之義，如之何其廢之。”（〈微子篇〉）孔子時議論如此。故人不知而不仕，其心有所怫鬱，士子之常也。樂詩書以忘憂，儒者之事也。孔子以此自處，亦以勸人。此章之義也。

總而言之，徂徠解釋“學而時習之”一章的主旨為江戶時代的武士階層應向孔子學習，即便不得出仕為官也應安于本分勤勉於學問教育。

朱子學不僅在中國，即便在李氏朝鮮也被視為官僚的必備修養。但是在日本，這一情況有所不同。或許因為日本沒有科舉制度，武士的身份也是世襲制的，所以朱子學並沒有絕對的權威。徂徠對朱子學的批評肆無忌憚。王陽明雖然也對朱子學有批評，但並沒有如徂徠般貶低。徂徠認為朱子學深受釋道兩教的影響，而標榜自身是古學的回歸。但其實質上濃厚反映了其生於江戶時代的武士階層的政治觀，具備了時代的特殊性。因此並沒有如古注和新注那樣成為帶有普遍性的公認解釋。大阪懷德堂的朱子學者五井蘭州著《非物篇》，其弟子中井竹山著《非徵篇》都批評了徂徠的學說。

## 小　結

本稿將魏代何晏《論語集解》、皇侃《論語義疏》、北宋邢昺《論語正義》的古注，南宋朱熹《論語集注》，明代王陽明《傳習錄》的新注，以及日本古學派荻生徂徠的《論語征》中“學而時習之”章相關內容摘選出來，對其實態加以比較考察。其注釋的要旨分別要約如下。

首先，古注認為，“學習六經禮樂，幼少時選擇與其時期相應的內容（春夏時為《詩經》、《樂記》，秋冬時《書經》、《禮記》）並暗誦複習不殆，（學業就會日日有所進步）是由衷喜悅之事。（因學業長進）而同門的友人自遠方而來，是非常愉快的事情。（因為即便學先王之道而內心之德有所成也無法從外表分辨）不被他人理解也不生氣則是君子。（另解，教育常人，即便不被對方理解也不發怒則實為君子）。”

朱熹沿襲古注之解，認為“努力模仿道德先覺者的事蹟，習得善德的話，就有由衷喜悅不絕。同類的友人也會因仰慕其善德而自遠方而來。將善德播及信從之人則是非常愉快之事。即便他人不認可自己，也不發怒，則是完成德業之人。”朱熹認為這是孔子自身的述懷。對此相對，王陽明批評朱熹“模仿先覺者事蹟”的解釋是“只說得學中一件事。事亦似專求諸心外了”，並解釋說，“學是學去人欲，存天理。從事于去人欲存天理，則自正諸先覺。考諸古訓，自下許多問辨思索存省克治工夫。然不過欲去此心之人欲，則僅存吾心之天理。”喜悅的理由則是，“人心本自悅理義。僅僅因為人欲所蔽所累，故有不悅。如每日去人欲，則理義日盈其心。安得不悅。”

荻生徂徠解釋道：“學習旨于安民的先王之道，隨四季變化而習《詩經》、《書經》、《禮記》、《樂記》四術，即受其感銘而仰慕不止。向因得知自己學者之名而從遠方遊學而來之士傳播自己的學問，則無關對方地位、貧富，都是至高的樂趣。不被為政者賞識重用，而從事教育事業、心中不存鬱悶委屈之意的話，即便在野，也足以被稱為立於民眾之上的君子。”

綜上所述，對於“學而時習之”一章，歷代的注釋都據儒學經典而展開。但其解釋多種多樣，並隨時代背景以及注釋者自身思想的不同而大異其趣。尤其是朱熹、王陽明和荻生徂徠的解釋非常濃厚的反映了他們自身的思想。

# “蜀學”三事：成都文翁石室叢考

四川大学 舒大刚 任利荣

猶之乎佛有“佛、法、僧”，儒有“六經、仁義、圣人”一樣，[1] 吾蜀學術亦有“三事”焉，即“文翁石室、周公禮殿、孟蜀石經”是也。北宋吕陶曰：“蜀學之盛，冠天下而垂無窮者，其具有三：一曰文翁之石室，二曰高公之禮殿，三曰石壁之《九經》。”[2] 文翁石室、周公禮殿、石壁九經皆為蜀學至寶，其對蜀學的發展、興盛所起的作用無可估量，若從首創性言之，其對天下學術文化的啟發亦為不淺，故得“冠天下”、“垂無窮”之譽。南宋名臣席益亦在《府學石經堂圖籍記》中言：“蜀儒文章冠天下，其學校之盛，漢稱石室、禮殿，近世則石壁《九經》。”[3] 亦將石室、禮殿、石經作為“蜀學”影響天下後世的三大法寶，足可見其在歷史上自有其不同凡響的貢獻和領先全國的意義。

## 一、知识殿堂：天下倡始之文翁石室

蜀學之盛，始于漢文翁石室。“文翁石室”是漢景帝、武帝時期，廬江人文黨守蜀時在成都所開學宫，文翁石室即“文翁化蜀”最為重要的舉措，更是天下儒學大興之倡始！

（一）文翁化蜀

西南自古為夷人所居，而以巴國、蜀國為君長。《戰國策·秦策一》張儀曰：“今夫蜀，西辟之國而戎狄之長也。”巴蜀後為秦所滅，遂成為秦國經略天下的重要基地，

---

① 《漢書·藝文志·諸子略儒家序》：“儒家者流……游文於六經之中，留意于仁義之際，祖述堯舜，憲章文武，宗師仲尼”云云。

② 吕陶《經史閣記》，《成都文類》卷三〇。又《靖德集》卷一四亦載是篇，題作《府學經史閣落成記》，首句作“蜀學之盈”云云。

③ 宋扈仲榮、楊汝明：《成都文類》卷三十，影印文淵閣《四庫全書》本，臺北：商務印書館，1986 年。

風俗迅速“染秦化”。[①] 直到西漢初年，其蠻夷之風猶然未改。漢景帝末年，文翁守蜀，設學校以教化之，巴蜀學術文化乃勃然興起。

《漢書·循吏傳》載：

文翁，廬江舒人也。少好學，通《春秋》。以郡縣吏察舉，景帝末，為蜀郡守。仁愛好教化，見蜀地辟陋，有蠻夷風，文翁欲誘進之。乃選郡縣小吏開敏有材者張叔等十餘人，親自飭厲，遣詣京師，受業博士，或學律令。減省少府用度，買刀布、蜀物，齎計吏以遺博士。數歲，蜀生皆成就還歸，文翁以為右職，用次察舉官，有至郡守、刺史者。

又修起學官於成都市中，招下縣子弟以為學官弟子，為除更繇。高者以補郡縣吏，次為孝弟力田。常選學官僮子，使在便坐受事。每出行縣，益從學官諸生明經飭行者與俱，使傳教令，出入閨閤，縣邑吏民見而榮之。數年，爭欲為學官弟子，富人至出錢以求之。繇是大化，蜀地學於京師者比齊魯焉。

至武帝時，乃令天下郡國，皆立學校官，自文翁為之始云。文翁終於蜀，吏民為立祠堂，歲時祭祀不絶。至今巴蜀好文雅，文翁之化也。

文翁通《春秋》，“仁愛好教化”，是純然儒吏；派弟子到長安從博士主習儒家《七經》，兼習漢家法令；在成都“修起學宮”，選下縣子弟“以為學官弟子”就學，是最早在地方政府辦學，並為之設置官學生的開始；選拔學習成績“高者，以補郡縣吏，次為孝弟力田”，是最早採用儒術來選撥官員的發端；又“從學官諸生明經飭行者”與他一道行縣，“使傳教令”，讓人民產生羡慕，從而激起整個社會向學之風，巴蜀地區前往京師遊學的人與齊魯相當。所有這些，都在董仲舒建議“罷黜百家，表章六經”和公孫弘建議設立“五經博士”、“置弟子員五十人”之前若干年。

宋時傳有一方《漢文翁學生題名》：“凡一百有八人。文學、祭酒、典學從事各一人，司儀、主事各二人；左生七十三人，右生三十人。”歐陽修曰：“文翁在蜀，教學之盛，為漢稱首，其弟子著籍者，何止於此？蓋其磨滅之餘，所存者此爾。”[②] 當時石室的辦學規模，遠大於中央太學。宋人李石《左右生題名》詩有曰：“蜀地雖遠天之涯，蜀人只隔一水巴。自從文翁建此學，此俗化為齊魯家。頖林春風桑椹熟，集鼓坎坎聞晨撾。諸生堂奥分左右，相比以立如排衙。”[③] 遠在天涯的巴蜀由於有文翁建學立教，乃使“此俗化為齊魯家”，蠻夷之風迅速地儒化。

---

① 常璩撰，劉琳校注：《華陽國志校注》，成都：巴蜀書社，1984年。

② 歐陽修《集古錄》卷二。按，洪适《隸釋》卷一辨曰：“成都又有左右生題名一巨碑，蓋左學、右學諸生也。其間江陽、寧蜀、晉原、遂寧乃蜀晉所置郡，歐陽公以爲‘漢文翁學生題名’，非也。”存疑。

③ 《成都文類》卷四。

《漢書·地理志下》述巴、蜀、廣漢風俗情形時說："景、武間，文翁為蜀守，教民讀書、法令，未能篤信道德，反以好文刺譏，貴慕權埶。及司馬相如游宦京師、諸侯，以文辭顯於世，鄉黨慕循其迹。後有王褒、嚴遵、揚雄之徒，文章冠天下，繇文翁倡其教，相如為之師。"此即"文翁化蜀"之史實及其重大的影響。文翁教民讀書，習法令，一改蠻夷之風的狀態，從此巴蜀仕女乃愛好文雅，追迹中夏，成為出人才、出文學，甚至"文章冠天下"的地區。《三國志》（蜀書·秦宓傳）、《華陽國志》（蜀志）都說文翁立學後，出現"蜀學比於齊魯"的局面；唐盧照隣《文翁講堂詩》："錦里淹中館，岷山稷下亭。……良哉二千石，江漢表遺靈。"岑參有詩："文公不可見，空使蜀人傳。講席何時散，高臺豈復全。"① 裴鉶有詩："文翁石室有儀刑，庠序千秋播德馨。"② 北宋田況《進士題名記》也說："蜀自西漢教化流而文雅盛，相如追肩屈、宋，揚雄參駕孟、荀，其辭其道，皆為天下之所宗式。故學者相繼，謂與齊魯同俗。"③ 喻汝礪《過府學遂謁文公堂》："我行魯侯宮，獨謁文翁堂。若人骨已朽，道在斯不亡。遂令蜀文章，照耀日月傍。世事俱腐臭，斯文真久長。"④

倡始斯為難，繼志易為功。文翁之功，意義不僅僅在化蜀，重要的是開啟了漢家"重視儒術""經學入仕"的先河，史載漢武帝"令天下郡國，皆立學校官"，開啟"儒化中國"之新篇章！清吳省欽《重修錦江書院講堂碑記》："以景帝之不任儒，又郡國向未立學，（文）翁振厲絕業，所舉向風，固宜為循吏首。"⑤ 楊慎《全蜀藝文志·序》稱："昔漢代文治，興之者文翁。……文之有關於道若此，文翁之功不可誣也。"

（二）文翁石室代有傳承

文翁創立石室教化蜀人，其後即成為成都經久不衰的最高教育機構，在二千餘年的歷史長河中，不斷得到修繕擴建，代有傳承，史料所載有繕修事跡可考者有近五十次之多，使得巴蜀之學薪火相傳，遂為天下學術大宗！

東漢建武十年（甲午，公元 34 年），梓潼文君又增造"吏舍二百餘間"⑥；漢獻帝初平五年（興平元年，公元 194），高眹"重修石室講學及禮殿，繪開闢以來歷代君臣、孔子及其弟子像"。⑦ 整個漢代從創立文翁石室，到東漢兩次增修，使得儒學在巴蜀延綿不斷地傳播發展，尤其是東漢末年，戰亂不斷，高公恢復石室，特別是重修周公禮

① 岑參：《文公講堂》，《全唐詩》卷一九八，北京：中華書局，2012 年。
② 裴鉶：《題文翁石室》，《全唐詩》卷五九七，北京：中華書局，2012 年。
③ 《成都文類》卷三十。
④ 《成都文類》卷四八。
⑤ 李承熙：《錦江書院志略》（《儒藏》史部第 246 册，成都：四川大學出版社，2011 年）卷上。
⑥ 《殿柱記》，《金石録》一八，趙明誠考其為《華陽國志》之文參，或疑其為文翁後人。
⑦ 趙明誠撰，金文明校證：《金石錄校證》，桂林：廣西師範大學出版社，2005 年，卷一八《殿柱記》。

殿，使得文翁石室成為名副其實的“廟學合一”之所，具有重要的歷史意義。

至晉南北朝，對文翁石室的修繕擴建有五次。晉太康中（公元280—289），刺史張收“增繪後賢像於壁間”[①]；南朝宋武帝（公元454—464），宋武帝代王“檄文于石壁之室，以丹青增飾古畫，仍加豆盧辨、蘇綽之像”[②]；齊永明十年（公元483—493），刺史劉悛[③]“益以禮家器服制度，弟瑱更為圖”[④]；梁天監九年（公元510）蕭憺“興學校，祭漢蜀郡太守文翁，由是人多向方”[⑤]；北周大象二年（公元580）辛昂“益州平，昂行成都令，到縣即與諸生祭文翁學堂”。[⑥] 這五次中有對石室中供奉先賢進行完善者，有增加其器服制度者，亦有作為表率參拜文翁，使得人多向學者。晉至南北朝，為歷史上較為混亂時期，朝代更替之快，亦為史上少有，然儘管如此，不少有識之士仍對文翁石室尊崇不減，對文翁石室的發展做出重要的貢獻，對儒學的傳播起到了積極作用。

唐宋時期，文化發達，儒學大興，文翁石室受到極高的推崇，得到了進一步地完善。史料所載唐代有七次，五代社會戰亂不已，政治分裂形同南北朝，然孟蜀仍對石室有所修繕。至宋代達十二次之多。唐宋時期乃中國文化，尤其是儒學發展的黃金時期，對文翁的尊崇亦足可彰顯其時文教儒學的勃然之勢。

唐永徽元年（公元650），《輿地碑記目》載佚名者“修學館廟堂，賀公亮撰《碑記》，刻石”；唐武則天時期，益州刺史齊國公宇文憲於石室“立《總管太學碑》，刻石”[⑦]；唐神龍二年（公元706），史熹“修州學廟堂，撰《益州州學廟堂頌》刻石”[⑧]；唐開元二十七年（公元739），唐玄宗“追謚孔子冊文”，[⑨] 後至宋代太平興國五年由尹辛仲甫立石；開元中（公元713—741），周灝“撰《益州孔子廟堂碑》，刻石”[⑩]；唐大曆十年（公元775），維州刺史鄭藏休“撰《石室贊》”，由殿中侍御史李樞篆書；[⑪] 唐會昌五年（公元845），裴儋[⑫]“修文宣王廟，撰《益州文宣王廟碣》，刻石”[⑬]；另有顏有意書、陳玉等撰立《唐益州學館廟堂記》，時顏為成都縣令，陳為法曹。又有闕名“文

① 席益《成都府學石經堂圖籍記》，《成都文類》三十。
② 李膺《益州记》，《元和郡县图志》卷三二引。
③ 或作“錢悛”，不確。
④ 席益《成都府學石經堂圖籍記》，《成都文類》卷三十。
⑤ 李延壽：《南史》卷五二，北京：中華書局，1975年。
⑥ 令狐德棻：《周書》卷三九，北京：中華書局，1971年。
⑦ 宋王象之：《輿地碑記目》，北京：中華書局，1985年。
⑧ 同上。
⑨ 同上。
⑩ 同上。
⑪ 同上。
⑫ 或作裴坦。
⑬ 宋王象之：《輿地碑記目》，北京：中華書局，1985年。

學太子詹事待詔弘文館陵州長史”某。[1]

總體而言，唐代對文翁石室的完善，有進一步確立孔子的地位者，即唐玄宗之舉；有修葺文宣王廟者，如裴儋之舉；其他皆撰寫記文，刻石立碑以誌紀念，而以此類為最多。唐代對儒學的推行是漢後的一大高潮，對孔子、文廟的尊崇亦遠勝前代。唐代而後的五代十國時期，孟蜀廣政七年（942），毋昭裔“仿太和石經，摹刻廟堂石壁”。[2]此外，還於此中雕版印刷《九經》在內的各類文獻，詳見下文。

宋代，儒學的發展呈現新的態勢，老干新姿，欣欣向榮。對文化的重視，對儒學發展的大力推行，使得文翁石室得到了前所未有的完善和發展。太宗太平興國五年（公元980），府尹辛仲甫刻石立唐明皇玄宗所撰之《追諡孔子冊文》[3]；仁宗慶曆中（公元1042—1048），知府蔣堂“漢文翁石室在孔子廟中，堂因廣其舍為學宮，選屬官以教諸生，士人翕然稱之”，然學宮成，而蔣堂去，“繼任轉運使毀之以增廨舍”[4]；蔣堂擴學興教，實為大善，然繼之者却悍然毀之，以增廨舍，這是宋代成都父母官中唯一一例不和諧的舉措，看來漠視教育、熱衷官衙者古今有之。宋皇祐中（公元1049—1054），知府田況“增刻石經，呂陶撰《經史閣記》”，[5] 此舉為後世考證石室沿革有着極其重要的史料價值，尤其是前述呂陶所作之《經史閣記》，總结了“蜀學”的沿革和三大特徵，影響至遠。宋嘉祐中（公元1056—1063），知府宋祁“就西學廢址建文翁祠，撰《記》”，[6] 又有知府王素“摹禮殿壁圖像為七卷，凡一百五十五人”[7]；宋治平中（公元1064—1067），知府韓絳“修講堂，張俞作《頌》”[8]；紹興六年（1136），蜀帥胡宗愈“作石經堂以貯圖籍”，知府席益“作《記》”，[9] 且“摹禮殿人物图像於石經堂，凡一百六十八人”[10]；同年，宋高宗從教授范仲殳之請，“御書‘大成殿’，榜成都府學”，對孔子紀念建築的高度重視與尊崇，足可證石室之重大影響力；宋紹興二十八年（公元1158），制置使王剛中“修殿廡齋舍四百楹，深廠精邃，馮時行撰《記》”[11] 擴充石室規模，此舉為功甚巨；另有蜀帥陳某“就崇甯故址修四齋二十八楹，李燾撰

---

① 《集古錄》卷二、《金石錄》卷二四。
② 宋曾宏父：《石刻鋪叙》，文淵閣《四庫全書》本卷上。
③ 宋王象之：《輿地碑記目》，北京：中華書局，1985年。
④ 元脫脫等：《宋史》卷二九八本傳，北京：中華書局，2012年。
⑤ 《成都文類》三十。
⑥ 《成都文類》三十。
⑦ 李石：《方舟集》，影印文淵閣《四庫全書》本卷二，臺北：商務印書館，1986年。
⑧ 《成都文類》四八。
⑨ 《成都文類》三十。
⑩ 《成都文類》三十。
⑪ 《成都文類》三十。

《記》”[1]；宋淳熙二年（公元1175），蜀帥范成大“修禮殿石室、學官講堂、齋舍，楊甲撰《記》”，[2] 等等。

宋代對石室的尊崇與修繕遠超前代，不論是皇帝崇敬膜拜孔子、高度評價文翁；還是知府、太守、蜀帥對石室的增建，都形成一時高潮，王剛中、范成大、陳某擴建石室之舉，為功甚高。蜀學在宋代大盛，影響全國，遂有“蜀學之盛垂位窮”之史實，“蜀儒文章冠天下”之美譽！蜀學之興始於漢之文翁，蜀學之盛成於宋之諸帥，宋代的成都守臣對文翁石室的高度重視和維護為蜀學發展達到頂峰起到了關鍵性作用。

宋末戰亂紛繁，元代建立，石室經歷兵火，仍然是儒者心中的聖殿。元元貞初（公元1295），教授解瑨“修廟學門，撰《記》”；元泰定中（公元1324－1328），節使趙世延“置贍學田，羅壽撰《記》”[3]；元至正五年（公元1345），王守誠巡四川省，“儒學提舉謝晉賢請復文翁石室為書院，從之”。[4] 元初壓制漢人，尤其對抵抗最堅的四川人痛入骨髓，對此地儒學的踐踏，也為歷來最甚，故元代九十七年間僅對石室有三次修繕。三次修繕中，尤以王守誠巡四川時為功頗高，不僅恢復石室，且將其作為書院，使其具備了自由講習書院的功能。

明代，經歷元代的戰火肆虐，不得不對其進行重修恢復，史料所載有五次。明洪武間（公元1368－1398）重修；[5] 明弘治十三年（公元1500），修學，有碑記；[6] 明嘉靖中（公元1522－1566），御書程子《四箴》；[7] 明萬曆六年（公元1578），提學耿定力“重修殿廡門堂階垣齋舍如制，樓鑰撰《記》”[8]；提學郭子章“刻唐吳道子所繪聖像于石，撰《記》”。[9] 至明末張獻忠入蜀，“焚毀書院，古制盡毀”。[10] 歷代石室雖歷經戰火，仍有遺存，張獻忠之舉使書院焚毀，古制盡毀，為歷代最為惡劣者，何其慘痛！

清代，同元代一樣為少數民族入主中原，但是不同之處為清代崇儒修文，大力發展文化，對儒學進行推廣。有清一代，近三百年間有史料所載有九次對石室進行完善。相較于唐代的七次、宋代的十二次，亦屬值得稱道者。

清順治十八年（公元1661），巡撫佟鳳彩“捐修大成殿、東西廡、戟門、靈星門、

---

① 《成都文類》三十。
② 《成都文類》三十。
③ 明楊慎撰，劉琳。王曉波點校：《全蜀藝文志》卷三六，北京：線裝書局，2003年。
④ 明宋濂等撰：《元史》《王守誠傳》，北京：中華書局，1976年。
⑤ 《錦江書院紀略》卷上。
⑥ 《錦江書院紀略》卷上。
⑦ 《錦江書院紀略》卷上。
⑧ 《錦江書院紀略》卷上。
⑨ 《錦江書院紀略》卷上。
⑩ 《錦江書院紀略》卷上。

啟聖宮、明倫堂、敬一亭、左右學舍、坊垣悉具，撰記"，司事張明彩亦有《記》；[①] 此舉甚的人心，明末張獻忠將書院盡毀，清代立國初即予以恢復，足可見對石室書院的高度重視，同時也說明石室的重大影響力，是新征服者不得不重視的。清康熙八年（公元 1669），巡撫張德地增修學宮；[②] 四十三年按察使劉德芳即石室故址重建錦江書院；[③] 四十九年（公元 1710），知府殷道正重修書院；[④] 六十年（公元 1712）提學使方覲"增修講堂、學舍三十餘間；拔通省士之尤者，延師教之，一時文物稱盛"。[⑤] 清初對石室的五次恢復和修建，是其重視地方教育和興儒措施的表現。到了康熙末年即出現了儒學繁榮局面，"一時文物稱盛"。乾隆三十九年（公元 1771），總督文綬與布政使錢鋆、署按察使顧光旭重修石室書院，提學吳省欽撰《記》；[⑥] 嘉慶十九年（1814），李堯棟"仿古制，建石室於講堂後"[⑦]；嘉慶二十二年（1817），蔣攸銛"查書院自雍正、乾隆、嘉慶年間歷經培修，舊制狹隘，次處倡捐重修，改修門路，規模宏厰、增修房舍"[⑧]；在清中期，乾隆間僅修建一次，嘉慶間兩次，此時蜀中學問與宋代時"冠天下"的盛況相較，顯得頗為單薄，蜀學在清代的發展也遠遜於宋代，但石室仍然是當時四川最高教育機構，具有較高學術地位。清代末年光緒二十八年（1903），總督岑秦煊將"錦江書院併入四川通省大學堂（1902 年尊經書院與中西學堂合併所建），改稱四川省城高等學堂"[⑨]；是即四川大學的前身。

文翁石室一路風雨，累廢累興。五代以後，不僅書院未息，而且在宋代還得到更大發展。宋末曾經毀於兵火，元代又予修起。明代繼續，明末復毀于張獻忠之亂，清代再起，並於其地建錦江書院，成為有清一代四川最高學府。

（三）文翁石室影響深遠

文翁石室在長達兩千餘年的辦學活動一直在延續著，儘管名稱有變，甚至同時有書院、孔廟和府學（或州學）並存的狀況，但是地點和功能卻一直未變。文翁石室為巴蜀培養了一批批影響天下後世的學者，成為建設巴蜀乃至影響全國的中堅力量和學術干城，蜀學之發端，發展，鼎盛皆賴文翁石室之教化，無愧於人類歷史上最早的地方學府！文翁的石室學宮，自漢而下，直到明清，一直是四川成都最高學府，除了少

---

① 《錦江書院紀略》卷上。
② 《錦江書院紀略》卷上。
③ 《錦江書院紀略》卷上。
④ 《錦江書院紀略》卷上。
⑤ 清黃廷桂、張晉生：雍正《四川通志》，《文淵閣四庫全書》影印本，卷二四。
⑥ 《錦江書院紀略》卷上。
⑦ 《錦江書院紀略》卷上。
⑧ 《錦江書院紀略》卷上。
⑨ 四川大學校史編纂組：《四川大學史稿》第一冊第三章，成都：四川大學出版社，2006 年。

數幾個短暫時段遭到破壞而有所沉寂外，其他時期都承擔了傳播儒學、作育人才的歷史使命。它不僅是歷代“蜀學”教育中心和思想振起的策源地，也是中國儒學的重要傳播和發展基地。其重大的歷史文化價值不言而喻！

宋代張俞《華陽縣學舘記》説：“三代之學繇秦廢，蜀郡之學由漢興，而天下之學由蜀起。歷漢至宋，殿室畫像古制盡在，蜀之學，其盛遠矣哉！”① 並有《頌》稱讚：“維蜀學宫，肇於漢初。用倡庠學，盛於八區。八區洋洋，絃誦復興。周法孔經，是纘是承。”又在《成都府學講堂頌》序中曰：“蜀之學遠矣，肇興於漢，歷晉、唐至於五代，世世傳誦不衰。所謂周公禮殿、文翁石室，越千餘載而巋然猶存。”② 説“天下之學由蜀起”，説它率先“倡學”，“盛於八區”，“絃誦”“纘承”“周法孔經”，就其歷史（特別是宋代及其以前）而言，一點也不誇張。

北宋吕陶《經史閣記》也説：“始漢景末，距今凡十六代、千二百四十餘年，崩離變革，理勢不常，而三事（即學宫、禮殿 、石經）之盛，莫易其故。然則冠天下而垂無窮，非夸説也。”③ 要之，文翁石室於蜀地文教，與蜀學大興，於天下學術，為功至偉！

## 二、精神家園：“廟學合一”之周公禮殿

石室學宫所創造的文化奇跡，最值得稱道的就是前引吕陶、席益所舉“冠天下而垂無窮”的“周公禮殿”和“石壁九經”。“周公禮殿”建於東漢，是當時在曲阜之外最早開設祭祀周公、孔子以及歷代聖賢的專門建築。“石壁九經”又稱“石室十三經”，始刻於五代孟蜀，是儒家《十三經》的最早結集。都對中國儒學發展史產生過重要影響！下文試述其概。

文翁石室化蜀之功為巨，千年以來薪火相傳，至東漢蜀太守高眹重修周公禮殿，使得石室與禮殿相融合，“廟學合一”之制正式形成，彪炳千秋！

“周公禮殿”，是祭祀以周公、孔子為主的歷代聖賢及儒林人物的廟祀場所，重建於東漢後期興平元年（公元194年），比北魏和平十三年（489）在京師建立的孔子廟早295年，是當時蜀學對先聖先賢進行緬懷和祭祀的場地，内中陳列有歷代聖君賢臣畫像，也繪有孔子及其弟子等儒家著名人物，並且歲時祭祀，供人景仰。既是歷代賢君名臣（政統）的薈萃，也是歷代學術文化精英（道統、學統）以及地方文化之代表人物的遴選，無異於蜀學的精神家園，也是中國古代學校廟學合一的最早標本。這一

---

① 《成都文類》卷三一。

② 《成都文類》卷四八。

③ 吕陶《經史閣記》，《成都文類》卷三十。

體系的建立，較之唐代貞觀二十一年（647）形成的陪祀制度及人選，要早453年。

（一）周公禮殿之建立及沿革

石室周公禮殿的建置和沿革，清雍正《四川通志》（下稱“通志”）卷二四《古跡（成都府》“文翁石室”有詳盡記載，可謂文翁石室周公禮殿“興廢簡史”：

一、禮殿是東漢獻帝興平初（194）蜀郡太守高眹重建，其功能是祭祀以周公為代表的歷代聖賢和孔子為首的儒林人物。

二、在禮殿中“畫三皇五帝、七十二子，及三代、兩漢君臣像於壁”，以供憑弔。

三、這些圖像和文字，曾歷經高眹、蔡邕、鍾會、劉瑱、張收、丘文播、黃筌、王素、席益等人維護和增飾，直到明末才為張獻忠所毀，康熙時又得劉德芳恢復重建。

高眹其人名字，或作朕，或作勝，[①] 或作眹、联、肞，[②] 或又疑为高躬，[③] 俱不确，[④] 當以作眹者為得。其重建禮殿之事，不見正史，最早記錄見殘存于宋代的《殿柱記》：

漢初平五年，倉龍甲戌，旻天[⑤]季月，修舊（《隸釋》無此二字）築周公禮殿。始自文翁，應期鑿度，開建頖宮，立堂布觀，廟門相鉤。閎司幔延，[⑥] 公辟相承。至於甲午，故府梓潼文君，增造吏寺二百餘間。四百年之際，變異蠭起（《隸釋》作“啟”），旋機離常，玉衡失統，強桀並兼，人懷僥幸，戰兵雷合，民散失命。烈火飛炎，一都之舍，官民寺室，同日一朝合為灰炭，獨留文翁石室廟門之兩觀。禮樂崩塌（《隸釋》作“坦”），風俗混亂，誦讀已絶，倚席離散。夫禮興則民壽，樂興則國化，[⑦] 郡將陳留高君，節符典（《隸釋》作“典”）境，迄斯十有三載。會直[⑧]撥亂，（闕）慮匡救，濟民塗炭。閔斯丘虛，（闕三字）冠，學者表儀，（闕四

① 董逌《廣川書跋》卷五《周公禮殿記》：“昔人嘗疑‘朕’非制名可稱於臣下者。自秦漢天子所為稱，豈復可存耶？流俗謂為‘高勝’，至宋璋洗視，知為‘高朕’，范蜀公嘗為人道之甚詳。余嘗至其處，求字畫得之，實為‘眹’字。知在漢猶未有嫌，不必曲辨‘朕’為‘勝’也。《蜀書》有‘高勝’，為郪縣人，昔人疑其為守，非也。魏文帝時夏侯霸為右將軍，霸父朕嘗仕於漢，可信也。”清吳省欽《重建錦江書院講堂碑記》：“翁之後，唯眹最賢，眹，董逌作朕，記述遼曠，名有顯晦，跡有興廢，惟其德長以不毀耳。”（李承熙《錦江書院紀略》卷中）

② 范鎮《東齋記事》卷四：“其西有文翁石室，其南有高肞石室，比文翁石室差大，皆有石像。肞，或以為勝，宋溫之璋洗石以辨之，乃肞字也（音持禀反）。”

③ 李承熙《錦江書院紀略》卷上：“陳壽《魏志（高柔傳》注：高幹父躬，蜀郡太守，陳留圉人。疑即此人，而字訛作眹也。”並無證據，難以取信。

④ 洪适《隸釋》卷一按：“又云‘郡將陳留高君者’，高眹也。諸書多有誤以眹爲‘朕’者。”

⑤ 天，原阙，據洪适《隸釋》卷一補。

⑥ 閎，原阙，据《隸釋》補。後“幔”，《隸釋》作“幬”。

⑦ 玆二句，原文作“夫禮興則國化”，玆據《隸釋》補。

⑧ 直，原闕，據《隸釋》補。

字）。大小推誠，興復第館。八音克諧，鬼方來觀。為後昌基，（闕）神不（闕）。[①]

這段文字，分別著録于歐陽修《集古錄》、趙明誠《金石録》、洪适《隸釋》等金石文獻。石刻首句稱“漢初平五年，倉龍甲戌，旻（闕）季月，修舊築周公禮殿”云云，歐書卷二“據顔有意[②]《益州學館廟堂記》云：‘……獻帝無初平五年，當是興平元年，蓋時天下喪亂，西蜀僻遠，年號不通，故仍稱舊號也。’今檢范曄《漢書》本紀，初平五年正月改為興平。顔説是也。”[③] 當時正處於三國前夜，軍閥力政，各方力量正為擴大或固守勢力範圍而大肆較量，天下戰亂，即碑文所言自漢初文翁首開石室學宮，四百年後，突遭“烈火飛炎”，“一都之舍”，包括學宮“同日一朝、合為灰炭”，只剩下“文翁石室廟門之兩觀”。

太守高公處“變異蠭起，旋機離常，玉衡失統，強桀並兼，人懷僥幸”之時，面對“烈火飛炎，一都之舍，官民寺室，同日一朝、合為灰炭”之景，痛心“禮樂崩塌，風俗混亂，誦讀已絶，倚席離散”之狀，獨懷文翁“仁愛好教化”之盛德，仍然以“禮興則民壽，樂興則國化”為治國理念。追古吊今，繼絕存亡，鄙棄干戈，崇尚禮樂，修起石室，重建禮殿。希望通過“八音克諧，鬼方來觀”的途徑，實現孔子當年“遠人不服，則修文德以來之”的遠大理想。終使文翁仁化之教得以延續，蜀人尚文之風因之奠定。

（二）周公禮殿之聖賢圖祀

文翁石室的周公禮殿，除了作為學校祭祀先聖先師的專門場所外，還選定了所祀先聖先師的基本人物，並繪製了這些先聖先師的圖像。

禮殿所繪人物，唐李吉甫《元和郡縣志》卷三二引李膺《益州記》云：“壁上悉圖古之聖賢，梁上則刻文宣及七十弟子。齊永明中，劉填更圖焉，朱齡、石平、譙縱勒。宋武帝檄文于石壁之室，代王更以丹青增飾古畫，仍加豆盧辨、蘇綽之像。”宋樂史《太平寰宇記》卷七二引任豫《益州記》：“厦屋三間，皆圖畫古人之像及禮器瑞物。”北宋蜀人黃休復專門記錄唐五代蜀中名畫的名著《益州名畫記》卷下“無畫有名”，清

① 缺名《殿柱記》，《成都文類》卷三十。

② 按，此記乃顔有意所書，並非顔氏所撰。趙明誠《金石録》卷二四《唐益州學館廟堂記》跋：“成都縣令顔有意書，撰人題‘法曹陳玉，文學太子詹事待詔弘文館陵州長史”，而姓名殘缺不可辨。《集古録》直以為有意撰，非也。碑陰載當時官僚姓名，後人題云‘此記賀遂亮撰’，未知果否。”又作“贺公亮”。

③ 按《後漢書（劉焉傳》：“初平二年，犍為太守任岐及賈龍並反，攻焉，焉擊破，皆殺之。……焉四子：范為左中郎將，誕治書禦史，璋奉車都尉，並從獻帝在長安。……興平元年，征西將軍馬騰與范謀誅李傕，焉遣叟兵五千助之，戰敗，範及誕並見殺。焉既痛二子，又遇天火燒其城府車，重延及民家，館邑無餘，於是徙居成都。遂疽發背卒。”是時益州劉焉父子與李傕把持的朝廷有仇，故不奉其主政時正朔，非因道路阻滯致政令不通也。

晰的記載："壁上圖畫上古盤古、李老等神，及歷代帝王之像。梁上又畫仲尼七十二弟子，三皇以來名臣。"所繪人物有三類：一是"上古盤古、李老等神及歷代帝王"，二是"仲尼七十二弟子"，三是"三皇以來名臣"。名君、名臣、名儒皆具。

席益《成都府學石經堂圖籍記》亦言高公於石室東作禮殿，圖畫邃古以來之君臣，聖賢，其間亦有魏晉人物，故有以為是刺史張收所畫。然實則圖畫始自高公，後歷代又有增益，故壁間又有東晉人物。王應麟《玉海》載《益部耆舊傳》刺史董榮增譙周像，令李通頌之。又因李業高節，亦增入。至南宋朝，據李膺《記》，增"豆盧辨、蘇綽"。《益州名畫記》卷下，南朝齊永明中，刺史劉悛弟劉瑱繪"仲尼四科十哲像"暨"車服禮器"于其中，完善祀典制度。北宋宋祁《文翁祠碑》言嘉佑二年宋祁增蔣堂像於殿中。

南宋李石《禮殿聖賢圖》序言①載北宋嘉佑間王素曾摹寫壁間人物，七卷155人，南宋紹興間，席益摹可辨可考者168人，重繪于石經堂。王象之《輿地碑記目》所載之圖像當即席益所摹刻。摹寫石室人物並拓印者，代有其人，自《隋書》以來藝文志多有著錄。然多亡佚，宋代已無此類。故才有王素等摹寫重繪之舉。

與王素摹繪同時者，尚有知成都的趙抃。抃另輯有《成都古今集記》三十卷；又摹繪"周公禮殿圖像"八軸。紹興十七年（1147），向子諲（薌林）于臨江府刻禮殿圖于石，樓鑰得之，因與先人所藏圖不侔，借趙抃摹本《禮殿圖》對勘，發現趙本"丹青煥然，自盤古而下位次，向背不同者十八九"；特別是"第七軸畫文翁……豆盧，第八軸畫漢武帝……兒寬，丹青愈工，皆石刻所無"。② 紹興三十年（1160），王剛中帥蜀，作《續成都古今集記》二十二卷，其中亦有禮殿人物圖記，成為元人考知禮殿風貌的主要依據。

宋末戰火肆虐，元代僅存圖冊，故劉申之有"況衣冠禮樂之盛乎？"③ 之歎。蜀人費著撰《成都志》時，據南宋王剛中《續成都古今記》，考其"可辨識姓名者一百七十三人，今貌像宛然者一百四十九人，僅存仿佛者三十二人，姓名存者六十五人"。④《成都志》已佚，其所考姓名尚載于明人曹學佺《蜀中廣記》，大體如下：

---

① 李石：《禮殿聖賢圖》序，《方舟集》，影印文淵閣《四庫全書》本，臺北：商務印書館，1986年，第1149册，卷二。"嘉祐中，王素命摹寫為七卷，總一百五十五人，為《成都禮殿聖賢圖》。蜀守席益又嘗摹其容貌名位可別識者一百六十八人于石經堂。"

② 樓鈅：《跋周公禮殿圖》，《攻媿集》，影印文淵閣《四庫全書》本，臺北：商務印書館，1986年，第1152册，卷七十二。

③ 劉岳申：《送蒲學正序》，《申齋集》，影印文淵閣《四庫全書》本，臺北：商務印書館，1986年，第1204册，卷二。

④ 費著：《成都周公禮殿聖賢圖考》，曹學佺：《蜀中廣記》，影印文淵閣《四庫全書》本，臺北：商務印書館，1986年，第591册，卷一百五"畫苑記第一"。

第一類是上古至周代聖君賢臣，若盤古、伏羲、神農、堯、舜等；

第二類是孔子及其弟子，若孔子、顏回、閔損、漆雕徒父、公孫龍等；

第三類是秦以來名君賢臣及名儒，若李冰、蕭何、張良、杜預等。

這個本來是祭祀遂古以來歷代聖君賢相和學術人物的禮殿，因漢代崇尚周公、孔子，周公又為孔子所推尊，故稱為“周公禮殿”。唐代取消周公之祀，禮殿成為孔廟專祠，是為成都孔廟最早起源。

（三）周公禮殿之垂芳千古

楊慎《全蜀藝文志·序》稱讚漢代“蜀學”影響曰：“昔漢代文治，興之者文翁：禮殿之圖，後世建學倣焉；七十子之名，馬遷之立傳徵焉。當時號為‘西南齊魯，岷峨洙泗’。文之有關於道若此，文翁之功不可誣也。”文翁石室除了開漢代郡國之學外，還在立殿祭祀周孔、圖繪七十子上，為後世學校樹立了榜樣和規範。

首先，周公禮殿是曲阜之外中國所建最早祭祀周公孔子的機構。

中國古代學校具有祭祀先聖、先師、先賢的功能，而孔廟（或稱文廟）是實現這一功能的主要設施。春秋末年，魯人據孔子故宅及弟子內，收藏孔子琴車書，歲時致祭，初步形成“孔廟”雛形。然至漢末，此建制僅限於曲阜，且是私家性質，若皇帝祭孔，皆需至曲阜方可實現。北魏暨唐代才改變此狀況。北魏孝文帝始于京師設“孔子廟”，唐代承之，因令地方學校亦得建孔廟，然以上舉措皆晚。相對中央而言，遠在西南的成都，漢文翁所建講堂石室，立學之初即有祭祀先賢的功能；至東漢後期高眹守蜀，重建周公禮殿，正式形成“廟學合一”之制。專門祭祀周公、孔子為代表的歷代聖賢和儒林人物，即使以恢復的時間算也比太和所建整整早了296年。禮殿在周、孔並重的漢晉南北朝時，稱“周公禮殿”，隨著唐代專尊孔氏，遂成為祭孔專門場所，但其包容各家的圖像以及殿宇建築仍得到保留。王象之《輿地碑記目》載：“《益州孔子廟堂碑》，開元中周灝撰；《益州文宣王廟碣》，會昌五年裴儋撰。”時人已徑稱周公禮殿為“孔子廟堂”、“文宣王廟”了。周公禮殿的建立，在規範周孔祭祀、完善學祭禮儀方面，具有重要推動作用。

其次，周公禮殿確立了廟學中系統的祭祀體系。

周公禮殿確立了固定的學校祭祀。《禮記》雖說學生四季都要“釋奠於先師”，又說始立學者“必釋奠於先聖先師”，這些“先聖先師”都不固定。到了漢朝“表章六經”，宗崇儒術，學校祭祀已經逐漸形成以周公、孔子為先聖先師的認識，但朝廷仍未以固化的方式將其確立。晉人感慨：“《禮》：‘始立學，必先釋奠於先聖先師，及行事必用幣。’漢世雖立學，斯禮無聞。”[1] 祀典不正，學禮也就難以真正興起。

---

① 《晉書》卷一九《禮志上》。

周公禮殿形成了系統的陪祀人物體系。《後漢書（章帝紀》載元和二年（85）三月曾經帝“進幸魯，祠孔子及七十二弟子”；《孔僖傳》也載元和二年春，“帝還過魯，幸闕裡，乙太牢祠孔子及七十二人，作六代樂”云云，[①] 雖然以七十二弟子陪祭，但是只是臨時舉措，沒有固定制度，在前引文獻中，從漢代到南北朝祭祀孔子時只“以顏淵配”。中央王朝直到貞觀末年才确定“陪祀”人选。[②] 此後尚递有增損，乃成定制。成都周公禮殿早在东汉後期（194）即將祭祀人员基本固定下來，並且使孔子弟子整體得到呈現，其祭祀對象和建制得到系統化和正規化。若細分，共有六類：一是盤古、伏羲、神農等傳說中神聖，二是堯、舜、禹等歷代聖君，三是咎繇、伊尹、傅說等歷代名臣，四是蒼頡、沮誦、老子等學術人物，五是孔子及弟子等儒林人物，六是與巴蜀有關特別是巴蜀名宦，如李冰、文翁、高公等。自上古，迄于魏晉。這種遴選，體現了當時人們的宇宙觀、正統觀、文化觀、鄉土觀和價值觀，中國歷史上的“道統”、“政統”、“學統”以及價值體系，都在其中得到反映。

其三是創造了以畫像祭祀的方式。

漢人曾說：“廟者，貌也，以其貌言之也。”（《尚書大傳》）廟是代表神的，那麼神又如何在廟中被代表呢？古之祭祀，有立尸，有设主，有遺物，[③] 有塑像，有繪畫，文翁石室的周公禮殿，就是採取的畫像方式。相較而言，主和物皆無貌可言，尸又不易備，塑像較笨重且後起，只有畫像最為方便易行，且不乏藝術性。文翁石室周公禮殿的聖賢畫像，即是如此，受到歷代文士贊譽！

東晉書法家王羲之就稱贊其“畫文精妙”，託益州守“欲因摹取，得廣異聞”。隋、唐之間，《文翁石室圖》成了藏家的心愛之物；五代末、北宋初，黃休復在《益州名畫錄》中專門記錄了禮殿圖像。[④] 王素、趙抃、王剛中等人，則不厭其煩地描摹其像。南宋李石在看了這些圖像之後，有詩贊其堪稱“神品”：“視之若有見，日月星象空中垂耿光。聽之如有聞，衝牙玉佩鳴以鏘。三古以降歷今世，視聽所感猶一堂。乃知此畫自神品，碌碌餘子非所望。”[⑤] 直到圖像被兵火銷毀 500 年後，乾隆皇帝還向當時四川守臣提及“古禮殿畫像，垂問存否”。[⑥] 可見其影響之深遠。

---

① 王應麟《玉海》卷一一三“漢祠七十二弟子孔子弟子籍”。

② 王應麟《玉海》卷一一三“孔子庙”：“古者惟功臣與祭大烝，未聞弟子從祀于師也。自建武祠七十二子于孔廟，然亦不出闕里也。貞觀末，加以左、卜諸儒，從祀太學，而武成王之祠亦倣而為之。總章開元以來，又加諸儒以三等之爵，而州縣學官咸有從祀矣。”

③ 司馬貞《史記索隱》：“孔子沒後，後代因廟藏夫子平生衣冠、琴、書於壽堂中。”

④ 黃休復《益州名畫記》卷下“無畫有名”：“古有《益州學堂圖》，今已別重粧，無舊迹矣。”

⑤ 李石《禮殿聖賢圖》，《方舟集》卷二。

⑥ 吳省欽《重修成都府學大成殿碑記》，李承熙《錦江書院志略》（《儒藏》史部第 246 冊，四川大學出版社，2011 年）卷上，第 270—271 頁。

其四是形成了左廟右學的廟學合一制度。

中國上古的學校同時具有祭祀功能不假，“凡祭及養老於東序”，但是東序還不是“廟”。孔子故里曾經在魯哀公十七年就以孔子故居和弟子內形成了祭孔場所，但曲阜孔廟還不是“學”。東漢“郡縣學校祀聖師周公孔子”，[①] 但畢竟學校沒有專門固定的祭孔場所。有之，亦學亦廟，有堂有殿，則自文翁石室始。

東漢高公“漢初平五年，倉龍甲戌，旻天[②]季月，修舊築周公禮殿。始自文翁，應期鑿度，開建頖宮，立堂布觀，廟門相勾。”周公禮殿與頖宮講堂都是文翁石室的組成部分。禮殿是專門用來祭祀以周公、孔子為首的歷代先聖、先賢和先師的場所。顏有意書《益州學館廟堂記》：文翁“石室，一名玉堂。安帝永初間，烈火為災，堂及寺舍並皆焚燎，惟石室獨存。至獻帝興平元年，太守高朕（眹）於玉堂東，復造一石室，為周公禮殿。”[③] 將“學館”與“廟堂”並提，禮殿在石室東邊，正是後來“左廟右學”雛型。樂史《太平寰宇記》卷七二：“文翁學堂，一名周公禮殿。”學堂與禮殿在一處，故可互稱。這一體制，雖歷經變遷，都得到基本保持或修復。

## 三、經典盛宴：“十三經”結集之“蜀石經”

“蜀石經”為文翁石室、周公禮殿外第三大蜀中至寶，始刻于孟蜀廣政初（938），其主體工程卒刻於北宋皇佑元年（1049），前後延續112年。至徽宗宣和五年（1123），席貢補刻《孟子》入石，最終形成“十三經”的典範。

（一）“蜀石經”之真貌

蜀石經，或稱“孟蜀石經”，又稱“石壁九經”、“石本九經”、“蜀刻十經”、“蜀刻十一經”、“蜀刻十二經”和“石室十三經”等。據此可見歷代學人對“蜀石經”的面貌特別是刻經數有不同認識，也反映出學界對“蜀石經”認識的模糊程度。

北宋盛行“九經”說，當是繼承唐代概念，為“群經”之泛稱。若宋趙抃《成都記》：“偽蜀相毋昭裔捐俸金，取《九經》琢石于學宮。”及張俞《華陽縣學館記》、席益《成都府學石經堂圖籍記》、呂陶《經史閣記》都有“石壁九經”之說。洪邁《容齋隨筆》卷四亦有“蜀石本九經”，“皆孟昶時所刻”之說。曹學佺《蜀中廣記》卷九一亦有“石本九經”一目，亦與此同。

“蜀石經”在“九經”說外又有“十經”之稱。晁公武《石經考異序》列“偽蜀相

① 《後漢書（禮儀志》明帝永平二年（59）三月：“上始帥羣臣，躬養三老五更于辟雍，行大射之禮。郡縣道行鄉飲酒于學校，皆祀聖師周公、孔子，牲以犬。”

② 天，原闕，據洪适《隸釋》卷一補。

③ 洪适《隸釋》卷二一引。

毋昭裔”所鐫“石經”曰：“《孝經》、《論語》、《爾雅》，廣政甲辰歲張德釗書；《周易》，辛亥歲陽鈞孫逢吉書；《尚書》，周德正書；《周禮》，孫朋吉書；《毛詩》、《禮記》、《儀禮》，張紹文書；《左氏傳》不志何人書，而‘詳’字闕其畫，亦必為蜀人所書。然則蜀之立石蓋十經。”然晁序所言“十經”僅指孟蜀時期八年之中所刻，未包括北宋後續所刻數種，因此“十經”說不代表“蜀石經”全部。

明代以來有“十一經”之說。明顧起元有稱：“蜀（永）〔廣政〕年之‘十一經’。”[①] 對此近人學者有一些觀點，或以為蜀刻只有十一經，或以為《三傳》、《孟子》都是孟蜀時所刻，[②] 或將《孝經》和《爾雅》從“蜀石經”中排出，[③] 都是想當然之辭，羌非事實。

另有“蜀石經”七種說，吳任臣《十國春秋·後蜀主本紀》便是如此：“廣政十四年，詔勒諸經于石。秘書郎張紹文寫《毛詩》、《儀禮》、《禮記》，秘書省校書郎孫明古寫《周禮》，國子博士孫逢吉寫《周易》，校書郎周德政寫《尚書》，簡州平泉令張德昭寫《爾雅》。”

凡此種種，可謂歧說紛呈，莫衷一是。通過對宋代以來各類文獻的考察，我們發現以上種種記載都不準確，有的顯然失考（如“十一經”說），有的則出於誤記（如“十經”、“七經”說），有的則將孟蜀石經與北宋補刻石經互相混淆（如“十一經”說）。

我們認為，“蜀石經”一名而含二義，一是五代孟蜀所刻石經；二是始于孟蜀成於北宋在蜀地所刻石經。“蜀”字既代表時代又代表地域，前後二義所指皆同，即在同一地區發生並延續進行的同一個工程，不能只取前而不取後。故“蜀石經”不僅有孟蜀石經，而且也包括北宋後續在成都所刻的石經。“蜀石經”一共刻了十三部，比同時代或前朝任何一種石經或儒學叢書納入的經典都要多（今存于西安碑林的“開成石經”雖有《孟子》，系清代補刻），因此我們認為：“蜀石經”是儒家“十三經”最早結集的典範，它開創或奠定了儒學文獻最穩定的規範和模式。

“蜀石經”之真貌，晁公武《石經考異序》有較為信實記載：“按趙清獻公（抃）《成都記》：‘偽蜀相毋昭裔捐俸金，取《九經》琢石于學宮。’而或又云：毋立裔依太和舊本，令張德釗書。國朝皇祐中田元均補刻公羊高、穀梁赤二《傳》，然後十二經始

---

① 顧起元：《說略》，文淵閣《四庫全書》本，卷一二。

② “五代時，後蜀皇帝孟昶命宰相毋昭裔楷書《易》、《詩》、《書》、三《禮》、三《傳》、《論》、《孟》等十一經，刻石列于成都學宮”。

③ 蔣伯潛先生說：“五代時蜀主孟昶《石刻十一經》，不列《孝經》、《爾雅》而加入《孟子》。”

全。至宣和間，席升獻（貢）又刻孟軻書參焉。"[①] 外此，曾宏父《石刻鋪敘》也有詳盡描述：

"益郡石經，肇于孟蜀廣政，悉選士大夫善書者，模丹入石。七年甲辰，《孝經》、《論語》、《爾雅》先成，時晉出帝改元開運。至十四年辛亥，《周易》繼之，實周太祖廣順元年。《詩》、《書》、《三禮》不書歲月。逮《春秋三傳》，則皇祐元年九月訖工。時我宋有天下已九十九年矣，通蜀廣政元年肇始之日，凡一百一十二祀，成之若是其艱。又七十五年，宣和五年癸卯，益帥席貢始湊鐫《孟子》，運判彭慥繼其成。乾道六年庚寅，晁公武又鐫《古文尚書》暨諸經《考異》。"[②]

據曾氏所言，"蜀石經"從孟蜀廣政初（938）開始刻，到七年刻成《孝經》、《論語》、《爾雅》、《周易》、《詩經》、《尚書》、《三禮》及《左傳》，共用了八年時間。至北宋皇祐元年（1049年）刻成《公》《穀》二傳，又過去了112年。再經過75年在宣和五年，才將《孟子》入石。如果要算乾道六年（1170年）晁公武作《考異》和刻《古文尚書》的時間，則前後經歷了230餘年！

"蜀石經"所刻經數，晁公武《石經考異敘》是十三部，而《讀書志》著錄時卻只有十部。曾宏父《鋪敘》則備列"十三經"之名，亦即今所奉行的"十三經"。

"蜀刻十三經"形成後，從南宋至明代曾以拓本形式廣為流傳。晁公武用通行"監本""十三經"與"蜀石經"對校，撰有《石經考異》，記載："《周易》經文不同者五科，《尚書》十科，《毛詩》四十七科，《周禮》四十二科，《儀禮》一十一科，《禮記》三十二科，《春秋左氏傳》四十六科，《公羊傳》二十一科，《穀梁傳》一十三科，《孝經》四科，《論語》八科，《爾雅》五科，《孟子》二十七科。"[③] 十三部石刻經典的名稱及其與"監本"之異同，皆章章在目，毫無含混。曾宏父《石刻鋪敘》也據拓本對每一經的文字都有詳盡記錄。知其為十三部書毫無問題，前述諸人稱之為"九經"、"十經"、"十一經"、"十二經"，都是不準確的。

（二）"蜀石經"之意義和價值

"蜀石經"共計十三部，其中不僅有《孟子》，而且也有《孝經》、《爾雅》。這十三部石經刻成于成都府學文翁石室之中，故又號稱"石室十三經"。它是儒家"十三經"的首次結集，對儒學"十三經"的正式定型，特別是對儒家經典"文獻典範"的形成，都起到過重要的推動作用。

---

① 晁公武：《石經考異序》，見范成大《石經始末記》引，《全蜀藝文志》卷三六，北京：線裝書局，2005年。

② 曾宏父：《石刻鋪敘》，文淵閣《四庫全書》本。

③ 晁公武.《石經考異序》，見范成大《石經始末記》引，《全蜀藝文志》卷三六，線裝書局，2005年。

首先，“蜀石經”是最早的“儒學十三經”。儒家經典的結集和傳播，在大型儒學叢書產生之前，主要是靠石經的刊刻來實現的。在歷代石經中，“蜀石經”最早形成了“十三經”的規模。“熹平石經”只有《周易》、《尚書》、《春秋》、《公羊傳》、《儀禮》、《禮記》、《論語》七經；“正始石經”只有《古文尚書》、《春秋左傳》二種；唐“開成石經”有十二種卻無《孟子》；北宋熙寧“二體石經”雖有《孟子》卻只有九經；南宋高宗“紹興石經”，即趙構所書《易》、《書》、《詩》、《左氏傳》、《論語》、《孟子》及《禮記》五篇，也只有七種而不完整。唯獨“蜀石經”刻成了包含《孟子》在內的儒家十三部經典。承此風者，有清朝乾隆時所刻之《清十三經》。“蜀石經”具有儒學文獻規模初具、典範粗成的承上啟下的作用。近時有學人指出：“在石經系統，《十三經》成為一部配套的叢書，是在北宋末徽宗宣和年間”的《蜀石經》，而且“十三經”之稱也以此最早，① 極有見地。蜀石經規模宏大，“其石千數”②，有經有注，遠較其他石經完備。在歷代所刻石經中，只有蜀石經是經注一起刻（唐玄宗時所立《石台孝經》有注，但規模太小），故其立石亦為歷代石經之最，③ 所耗時日也最長。

其次，“蜀石經”曾以拓印本形式影響學界。“蜀石經”不是簡單地刻石儲藏而已，而且公開展示，任人校閱，對儒家“十三經”的廣泛傳播和規範起到了促進作用。此外，“蜀石經”還廣泛拓印流行，形成了規格統一、規模宏大的印本“十三經”，拓本“蜀石經”是歷史上最早的“十三經”叢書。對以拓本形式流傳的“蜀石經”，趙希弁《郡齋讀書附志》和曾宏父《石刻鋪敘》都有詳盡著錄：

《石經周易》，右《周易》十卷，經、注六萬六千八百四十四字，將仕郎守國子助教、臣楊鈞、朝議郎守國子《毛詩》博士柱國、臣孫逢吉書。

《石經尚書》，右《尚書》十三卷，經、注並序八萬一千九百四十四字，將仕郎、試秘書省校書郎、臣周德貞書，鐫王冊官陳德超鐫。

《石經毛詩》，右《毛詩》二十卷，經、注一十四萬六千七百四十字，將仕郎、試秘書省校書郎張紹文書。

《石經周禮》，右《周禮》十二卷，經、注一十六萬三千一百單三字，將仕郎、試秘書省校書郎孫明吉書。

---

① 杜澤遜：《〈孟子〉入經和〈十三經〉彙刊》，《文獻學研究的回顧與展望——第二屆中國文獻學學術研討會論文集》，臺北：學生書店，2002 年。

② 晁公武《石經考異序》：“偽蜀相毋昭裔捐俸金，取《九經》琢石于學宮……凡曆八年，其石千數，昭裔獨辦之，尤偉然也。”范成大《石經始末記》引，載《全蜀藝文志》卷三六，線裝書局，2005 年。

③ 開成十二經，刻於 114 塊碑上，雙面共刻，才 228 面。乾隆十三經，刻於 190 塊碑上，雙面，亦才 380 碑。

《石經儀禮》，右《儀禮》十七卷，經、注一十六萬五百七十三字，將仕郎、試秘書省校書郎張紹文書。

《石經禮記》，右《禮記》二十卷，經、注十九萬六千七百五十一字，卷首題曰‘御刪定禮記月令第一集，賢院學士、尚書左僕射兼右相吏部尚書修國史、上柱國、晉國公、臣林甫奉勑注’，《曲禮》為第二，蓋唐明皇刪定之本也，將仕郎、試秘書省校書郎張紹文書。

《石經春秋》，右《春秋經傳集解》二十卷，經、注並序三十四萬五千一百四十四字，不題所書人姓氏。

《石經公羊》，右《公羊》十二卷，經、注一十三萬一千五百一十四字，不題所書人姓氏。

《石經穀梁》，右《穀梁》十二卷，經、注八萬一千六百二十字，不題所書人姓氏。

《石經論語》，右《論語》十卷，經、注並序三萬五千三百六十八字，將仕郎、前守簡州平泉縣令、兼殿中侍御史、賜緋魚袋張德釗書，潁川郡陳德謙鐫字。

《石經孝經》，右《孝經》一卷，經、注並序四千九百八十五字，不題所書人姓氏，但題‘潁川郡陳德謙鐫字’。

《石經孟子》，右《孟子》十四卷，不題經注字數若干，亦不題所書人姓氏。

《石經爾雅》，右《爾雅》三卷，將仕郎、前守簡州平泉縣令、賜緋魚袋張德釗書，武令升鐫。不題經注字數若干。

以上《石室十三經》，蓋孟昶時所鐫，故《周易》後書‘廣政十四年歲次辛亥五月二十日’，唯《三傳》至皇祐初方畢，故《公羊傳》後書：‘大宋皇祐元年歲次己醜九月辛卯朔十五日乙巳工畢’”①

這裡著錄的既有總目（《石室十三經》），又有子目（自《周易》至《爾雅》13種），儼然一部叢書目錄。我們若視“蜀石經”為“以石質為印板的經學叢書”亦不為過。

其三，“蜀石經”最早擁有“十三經”之名。如上所揭，趙希弁已有《石室十三經》之稱，而且不把十三部書分別隸屬於各經分目下，說明諸本原來即匯儲一處；趙氏徑稱之“石室十三經”，說明這十三部拓本原有一個總名，已經具有“叢書”性質。除此之外，尤袤《遂初堂書目》於“總類”經部開卷之首即著錄《成都石刻九經》；王應麟《玉海》卷四三也徑稱之為《石室十三經》。明任浚有謂：“若夫《石室十三經》，始自孟蜀。”② 清閻若璩《古文尚書疏正》卷二亦稱“《石室十三經》”③ 認定“十三經”

① 趙希弁《讀書附志》附《郡齋讀書志》卷五，文淵閣《四庫全書》本。
② 任浚《十三經注疏序》，雍正《山東通志》卷三五之六，文淵閣《四庫全書》本。
③ 閻若璩：《潛丘劄記》，文淵閣《四庫全書》本，卷五。

形成于蜀之石經，皆深有見地之言。是故沈廷芳說："'十三經'始蜀毋昭裔、孫逢吉諸人。"[①] 葉德輝《書林餘話》卷下說："石經為經本之祖。（略）唐開成立十二經石經，孟蜀廣政立十三經石經"云云，[②] 也都繼承了這一習慣稱呼。

其四，"蜀石經"將《孟子》刻入石經，是儒家"尊經"、"崇傳"向"重子"過程轉變的標誌。隨著"蜀石經"影響的日益擴大，《孟子》在經部的地位也更加鞏固和穩定。漢代雖設《孟子》博士，但是後來以其為諸子而取消了，故《漢志》仍列其于"諸子略"，說明漢人心目中《孟子》並不是經，只是諸子百家之一。唐代學人曾有立《孟子》為經的建議，但未成功。始列《孟子》經者自"蜀石經"和"嘉祐二體石經"始。據學人考訂，"《孟子》正式被官方列為經書，並做為科舉考試的內容之一，是始于熙寧四年。"[③] 但是，對《孟子》的尊崇和推重，似乎還要早些。仁宗嘉祐時，已經將《孟子》刻入"二體石經"了，遠在熙寧之前。宣和時，席貢再次將《孟子》刻入"經"時，曾有序說："偽蜀時刻《六經》于石，獨無《孟子》，經為未備。"說明在席氏心裡，早有《孟子》是"經"的信念。自"蜀石經"刻《孟子》入石，其在經部的地位遂更加鞏固，南宋高宗書石便直接將《孟子》寫入了。

其五，"蜀石經"決定了後來中國儒學經典體系的基本格局。自從"蜀石經"被稱為"石室十三經"後，"十三經"之名遂固定下來，成為儒家原典的權威稱號，成為儒家經典文獻的總稱和典範，宋代甚至於還有以"十三經"為基礎，再加入《大戴禮記》形成"十四經"的動議，如蜀人史繩祖即有"《大戴記》一書雖列之十四經云云"。[④] 儒生博通群經，從前只謂之"身通六藝"，現在謂之"博通十三經"了；從前群經通論謂之"六藝論"、"五經說"，現在謂之"十三經云云"。以"十三經"命名的各類著述也日益增多，若《明史》卷九六"陳深《十三經解詁》六十卷"；《池北偶談》卷一一載李因篤"博學強記，《十三經注疏》尤極貫穿"；《江南通志》卷一九〇之著錄顧夢麟之《十三經通考》二十卷；《續通志》卷一六一著錄羅萬藻《十三經類語》十四卷等。明清時期，"十三經"已經取代"六經"或"五經"之稱，與"二十一史"（或"二十四史"）成為傳統文獻中經部、史部的總代表。此變化的實現，"蜀石經"起到了開風氣之先、典範粗具的作用。

## 結　語

西漢景帝末年（約前141）文翁所建石室玉堂，是中國地方最早設學傳播儒學的創

① 沈庭芳：《經解》，《皇清文穎》，文淵閣《四庫全書》本，卷一二。
② 葉德輝：《書林餘話》卷下，《書林清話》附，北京：中華書局，1999。
③ 董洪利：《孟子研究》，南京：江蘇古籍出版社，1997年。
④ 史繩祖：《學齋佔畢》，文淵閣《四庫全書》本，卷四。

舉，是中國統一時期郡國學的鼻祖。東漢獻帝初平五年（興平元年，194）高公重修文翁石室和周公禮殿，是當時專門用來祭祀以周公、孔子為代表的歷代先聖、先師和先賢的專門場所，是中國古代最早“廟學合一”的雛型。長期收藏于文翁石室之中的“蜀石經”，始刻于孟蜀廣政初（938），其主體工程卒刻於北宋皇祐元年（1049），前後延續 112 年。至徽宗宣和五年（1123），席貢補刻《孟子》入石，最終形成“十三經”。這是最早匯刻於一處的十三部儒家經典，也是最早獲得“十三經”稱號的儒學叢書。[①] 標誌著儒學《十三經》正式確立，中國儒學從尊經、崇傳，到重子書時代的轉移，正式從“經學時代”進入了“理學時代”。

文翁化蜀創石室，高公尊孔建禮殿，孟蜀重儒刻“石經”，形成知識殿堂、精神家園、經典展陳三位一體的教育中心和文化中心，是乃蜀學之至寶也。斯三事者，在歷史上皆具有“為天下倡始，為往聖繼絕，為當代致太平，為後世垂典範”的功能，故宋人稱讚其“冠天下而垂無窮”，非虛譽也！在兩千餘年的歷史長河中，石室學宮一直是成都的最高學府，繼絕存亡，死而復蘇，延續教化，重興禮樂，弦誦之聲不絕，大雅文章屢見，培養了成百上千、一代又一代的優秀人物，成就了歷代“蜀學”之學術大宗地位，若視其為“西南齊魯，岷峨洙泗”、“寰宇經久學府”、“天下第一學宮”都不為過！

**參考文獻：**

[1] 司馬遷．史記·孔子世家．北京：中華書局，1982.

[2] 班固．漢書·循吏傳．北京：中華書局，1982.

[3] 宋扈仲榮，楊汝明．成都文類．影印文淵閣《四庫全書》本．臺北：商務印書館，1986.

[4] 常璩撰，劉琳校注．華陽國志校注．成都：巴蜀書社，1984.

[5] 洪適．隸釋．北京：中華書局，1986

[6] 趙明誠撰，金文明校證．金石錄校證．桂林：廣西師範大學出版社，2005.

[7] 呂祖謙編．“宋文鑒”卷七六，影印文淵閣《四庫全書》．臺北：商務印書館，1986.

[8] 李石．“禮殿聖賢圖”序．方舟集．影印文淵閣《四庫全書》本．臺北：商務印書館，1986.

[9] 朱長文．墨池編．影印文淵閣《四庫全書》本．臺北：商務印書館，1986.

[10] 樓鑰．跋周公禮殿圖．攻媿集．影印《文淵閣四庫全書》本．臺北：商務印

① 史繩祖：《學齋佔畢》，文淵閣《四庫全書》本，卷四。

書館，1986.

[11] 劉岳申．送蒲學正序．申齋集．影印文淵閣《四庫全書》本．臺北：商務印書館，1986.

[12] 費著．成都周公禮殿聖賢圖考．曹學佺：蜀中廣記．影印《文淵閣四庫全書》本．臺北：商務印書館，1986.

[13] 魏收．魏書．北京：中華書局，2003.

[14] 吳兢．貞觀政要．濟南：齊魯書社，2010.

[15] 王應麟．玉海．影印文淵閣《四庫全書》本．臺北：商務印書館，1986.

[16] 房玄齡．晉書．北京：中華書局，1974.

[17] 吳省欽．重修成都府學大成殿碑記．李承熙：錦江書院志略．《儒藏》史部第246冊．四川大學出版社，2011.

[18] 範曄．後漢書．北京：中華書局，2012.

[19] 舒大剛．從"蜀石經"的刊刻看《十三經》的結集．林慶彰主編．經學研究論叢．臺北：學生書局，2009（5）第16期.

[20]"蜀石經"與《十三經》的結集．周易研究．2007（6），第68—75頁.

[21] 周九香．周公禮殿——歷史名人紀念堂．文史雜誌，2003年第2期.

[22] 沈庭芳．經解．"皇清文穎"卷一二．影印文淵閣《四庫全書》本.

[23] 張俞．華陽縣學館記．"成都文類"卷上三一．影印文淵閣《四庫全書》本.

[24] 席益．成都府學石經堂圖籍記．"萬氏石經考"卷下，影印文淵閣《四庫全書》本.

[25] 呂陶．經史閣記．"成都文類"卷上三〇．影印文淵閣《四庫全書》本.

[26] 顧起元．"說略"卷一二．影印文淵閣《四庫全書》本.

[27] 晁公武．石經考異序．見范成大《石經始末記》引．《全蜀藝文志》卷三六．線裝書局，2005.

[28] 曾宏父．石刻鋪敘．影印文淵閣《四庫全書》本.

[29] 楊士奇．文淵閣書目．卷三"辰字型大小"．影印文淵閣《四庫全書》本.

[30] 張萱．"疑耀"卷一．影印文淵閣《四庫全書》本.

[31] 杜澤遜．《孟子》入經和《十三經》彙刊．文獻學研究的回顧與展望——第二屆中國文獻學學術研討會論文集．臺北：學生書店，2002.

[32] 趙希弁．讀書附志．附《郡齋讀書志》卷五．影印文淵閣《四庫全書》本.

[33] 任浚．十三經注疏序．雍正《山東通志》卷三五之六．影印文淵閣《四庫全書》本.

[34] 閻若璩．"潛丘劄記"卷五．影印文淵閣《四庫全書》本.

［35］葉德輝.“書林餘話”卷下.《書林清話》附. 中華書局，1999.

［36］董洪利. 孟子研究. 南京：江蘇古籍出版社，1997.

［37］史繩祖.“學齋佔畢”卷四. 影印文淵閣《四庫全書》本.

基金项目：国家社科基金重大委托项目（102ZH005）《巴蜀全书》，四川省社科基金重点基地儒学研究中心项目（SC12E001）《中国儒学文献通史》，中央高校基金业务费资助项目《儒学文献发展史》。

# 王夫之的格物知性与由性生知

北京大学哲学系 张学智

王夫之在他中年以后的重要著作《读四书大全说》中对心性问题有集中的阐发。尤其在对《孟子》的疏解中，心的含蕴，格物与致知的关系，性体与心体的区分与缩结，德行与知识的界限与关联等，都有深入论究。这些方面表明他受明亡惨祸烈毒的刺激，对中国哲学基本精神所做的反思，表现出深切的忧患意识和强烈的人文关怀。

## （一）

王夫之发挥格物致知论，注重从心的含蕴方面加以阐说，以彰明格物的首要目的在尽心知性，所以王夫之十分重视心统性情这一宋明哲学的根本概念，他说：

盖曰“心统性情”者，自其所含之原而言之也，乃性之凝也。其形见则身也，其密藏则心也。是心虽统性，而其自为体也。则性之所生，与五官百骸并生而为之君主，常在人胸臆之中，而有为者则据之以为志。故欲知此所正之心，则孟子所谓志者近之矣。①

在王夫之这里，人就其本质说，乃一性、形、心的浑合体。人禀天命以为性，故人即天诸种性质的凝聚体。但此凝聚是一抽象的设定，必有形体为之承负、显现。故身为性承托之地，心为性密藏之所，其现其隐皆在心中。故性为体，常在人心而为身之主宰。这与心为主宰的通常见解不同。王夫之要凸显的是：人之为人的根本在于人之性，心则只是知觉灵明和性密藏显发之地。心为主宰突出的是心对意志趋向、思虑营为的统御、选择、范导作用，而性为主宰突出的是，性是天之所命，是人的全部价值的凝聚，是至善的理想；人应以性做主，去规范、导正灵妙驰骛之心。这个意思王夫之说得十分明白：

夫此心之原，固统乎性而为性之所凝，乃此心所取正之则。而此心既立，则

① 王夫之：《读四书大全说》，北京：中华书局，1975年，第8页。

一触即知，效用无穷，百为千意而不迷其所持。故大学之道，必于此授之以正，既防闲之使不向于邪，又辅相之使必于正，而无或倚靡，无托于无正无不正之交。当其发为意而恒为之主，则以其正者为诚之则。（自注：《中庸》所谓“无恶于志”）。当其意之未发，则不必有不诚之好恶用吾慎焉，亦不必有可好可恶之现前验吾从焉；而恒存恒持，使好善恶恶之理，隐然立不可犯之壁垒，帅吾气以待物之方来，则不睹不闻之中，而修齐治平之理皆具足矣。此则身意之交，心之本体也；此则修诚之际，正之实功也。故曰“心者身之所主”，主乎视听言动者也，则惟志而已矣。①

性在显发于心中时，贞定为志。志为心理活动的引领者，未发时恒存恒持，好善恶恶之理严阵以待；已发时帅气正志，诚意正心之实功俨然可行。这就是性的全体大用。王夫之反复申明、着意提揭的，就是此性。心为身之主宰，而性又为心的主宰。所以，在王夫之这里，性实心虚，心是性的灵处。

此性既凛然具于心，但它是一种形而上的潜存。性显发于心至为重要。使性显发的功夫就是格物。所以格物不仅是穷事物之物理，更重要的是穷体现在事物上的性理，二者实际上是对同一个理的不同观照与理解。归根结底，格物是为了知性。王夫之非常强调这一点，在《读四书大全说》中反复申说，如：

朱子以格物言知性，语甚奇特。非实有得于中而洞然见性，不能作此语也。孟子曰“万物皆备于我矣”，此孟子知性之验也。若不从此做去，则性更无从知。其或舍此而别求知焉，则只是胡乱推测卜度得去，到山穷水尽时，更没下落，则只得以此神明为性。故释氏用尽九年面壁之功，也只守定此神明做主，反将天所与我之理看作虚妄。是所谓“放其心而不知求”，不亦哀乎！②

此处说朱熹以格物言知性，是就格物的最终目的及最后归宿说。朱熹的格物有许多功夫节次，并且各处对格物的解说有不同的侧重，但最终目的不外乎此。所以王夫之对朱熹这一点是赞许的。“万物皆备于我”者，为性。知性是人格修养的重要一环和必经之地，舍此别有路径，舍性别有所求，皆非正路。佛教与儒家的最大差别即在对性的理解不同，儒家对佛道二氏的批评，多指其“作用是性”。所以二程屡屡申说：“吾儒本天（性），释氏本心（灵明）。”以此为判释二者的根本界限。

知性在格物，对格物致知的不同层次，不同方面，王夫之也有分疏，他说：

大抵格物之功，心官与耳目均用，学问为主，而思辨辅之，所思所辨者皆其所学问之事。致知之功则唯在心官，思辨为主，而学问辅之，所学问者乃以决其

① 王夫之：《读四书大全说》，北京：中华书局，1975年，第9页。

② 王夫之：《读四书大全说》，北京：中华书局，1975年，第714页。

思辨之疑。“致知在格物”，以耳目资心之用而使有所循也，非耳目全操心之权而心可废也。[1]

这是说，格物阶段以耳目感官所获得的事物的感性材料为主，心对这些材料的分析论断为辅，而致知阶段以心对耳目获得的初步知识进行考辨、解析、论证等为主，而以耳目感官的活动为辅。这里实际上强调的是，在格物、致知二个阶段，心都起决定作用，耳目应受心的主导而有所持循，不能以耳目当权而废心的思维作用。而在格物致知与知性的关系上，王夫之特别强调一以贯之的作用，而对达到一以贯之的途径及得到这种状态之后的心理境界，王夫之也有特别的理解，他说：

格物者知性之功，而非即能知其性；物格者则于既格之后，性无不知也。故朱子以曾子之唯一贯者为征。“一以贯之”，物之既格也，而非多学而识之即能统于一以贯也。穷理格物只是功夫，理穷物格亦格物穷理之效，乃至于表里精粗无不豁然贯通之日，则岂特于物见理哉！吾心之皆备夫万物者固现前矣。[2]

这里有格物、理穷、物格、一贯、豁然贯通、见物理、现性理诸层次。格物是一活动，即就物而穷究其理。格物的目的是知性，但格物是知性的手段、媒介。格物是活动，知性是结果，格物非即能知性，而知性必在物既格之后。王夫之对于格物与致知二者的不同功用辨之甚详，但在格物致知与知性的关系上，王夫之把格物与致知作为一个范畴来看，他们合起来作为知性的媒介。格物是研究具体物理，而知性是一精神的，内省的活动，所以须有一“一以贯之”的步骤，把格物所得之具体的、杂多的物理转换为一个统一的性理。一以贯之是一种识度，一种修养，一种境界。故非多学而识即能达到一贯。须对儒家的道德形上学实有解悟，体之身心，然后真积力久，下学而上达，才能获得这种识度和境界。而一旦获得此种识度而豁然贯通，不惟物理见得明彻，心中本具之性理亦彰焉大显。此处王夫之对朱熹《补大学格物传》中所说步骤，皆本其对性理的强调一一点明，一一收归于性，使之紧紧围绕形体展开而不致游走离散。

王夫之对知性与体验未发的关系，也本其以上理解而有深入阐发，他说：

到此方识得喜怒哀乐未发之中。盖吾之性本天地之理也，而天下之物理亦同此理也。天下之理无不穷，则吾心之理无不现矣。吾心之理无不现，则虽喜怒哀乐之未发而中自立焉。万物之皆备于我者，诚有之而无妄也。此非格物未至者所可知之境界。故难一一为众人道耳。[3]

---

① 王夫之：《读四书大全说》，北京：中华书局，1975 年，第 12 页。
② 王夫之：《读四书大全说》，北京：中华书局，1975 年，第 714 页。
③ 王夫之：《读四书大全说》，北京：中华书局，1975 年，第 714 页。

这里的阐发涉及两个问题，一个是格得物理与心中性理显现的关系。一个是性理显现与未发之中的关系。前一个问题，王夫之实际上继承了程颐朱熹的“性即理”。在他看来，天所命于人之性与体现在事物上的理归根结底是同一的。人之性，其内容无非是四德，而物理经过“伦理的投射”，亦无不可认其为性理，如“物之生理”，在儒家学者对特别是宋明理学中，即是仁，即是生意。王夫之这里认为，宇宙根本之理，人之性理，具体事物之理，从根本上说是同一的。因为是同一的，具体的物理可以诱发心中的性理。王夫之同朱熹一样，认为性理是浑全的、形而上的，物理是具体的、形而下的；物理获于心，可以激发性理显于心。物理积累既多豁然贯通之时，就是性理“桶底子脱”，顿然全体显现于心中之时。这就是王夫之说的“天下之理无不穷，则吾心之理无不现矣。”而实际上性理物理只是一心指向之转换，并非有两个实体。但从形而上的潜存到形而下的实存，从人之为人的根本之预设，到实然的物理之穷格，这二者间的关系的理论假定却是人这一“最高的存在”从本体到功夫，从初始到知性知天这个现实流动过程所需要的。理学对人的这种看法虽在某种意义上说有虚玄之处，但在天人合一、知行合一的框架中观照人、解释人，这是理学的特出之处，其功夫途径在理学的意义脉络中也是切实可行的。

就后一个问题看，王夫之实际上同意朱熹中和新说的看法：喜怒哀乐未发之时为静，此时心的状态是中，中指心的不滞不系，不偏不倚，所谓“鉴空衡平”。而据“天命之谓性”这一前提和预设，心的鉴空衡平是性理显现的先决条件。这也就是朱熹《中和说三》所谓：“方其静也，事物未至，思虑未萌，而一性浑然，道义全具，其所谓中，乃心之所以为体，而寂然不动者也。”[①] 王夫之此处以“万物皆备于我者”代性体，故喜怒哀乐未发之中就是性体全具，“诚有之而无妄”。王夫之并特别点明，性体之显现，未发之中之获得，是格物后事，而且是从事儒学修养，实地做功夫的人才能体验到的境界，所以难为众人道。

此处需要分疏的是，朱熹和王夫之对二者关系的理解有所不同。在朱熹，未发之中是心体，天命是性体，未发之中只是性体显现于心的条件，还不就是性体直接转换为心体 。性体在心体中的显露，还需格物功夫，并非只要中无私欲，达到未发状态，性体自然显露。所以在朱熹，既讲涵养用敬，又讲格物致知。尤其是对初学者，格物致知是全部功夫的第一义。格物致知的功用不仅在“进学”，也是显发性理的媒介。而王夫之这里十分明确的是，格物后性理显现，此时即未发之中。在朱熹，未发之中是性理显现的前提，而在王夫之，获得性理是未发之中的前提。此处的分别虽亦可成立，但统观二人的思想，未发之中和理性显现实际上是一而二，二而一的。都是对理论预

---

① 黄宗羲：《宋元学案》，北京：中华书局，1986年，第1506页。

设中的关联关系的说明，不是有两个东西实然对应。

王夫之对格物中性体与心体的关系，特别是尽心之后心体的状态与内容也有深切的说明：

物理虽未尝不在物，而于吾心实自实；吾心之神明虽己所固有，而本变动不居。若不穷理以知性，则变动不居者不能极其神明之用也固矣。心原是不恒底，有恒性而后有恒心。有恒性以恒其心，而后吾之神明皆致之于所知之性，乃以极夫全体大用，具众理而应万事之才无不致矣。故曰“尽心则知至之谓也”，言于吾心之知无所吝留而尽其才也。此圣贤之学所以尽人道之极，而非异端之所得与也。呜呼！严矣。[①]

在物之理与心中的性理本一，这里上面的论述中多已涉及。性体是王夫之最为着重的方面，是一切论说的出发点。需要特别注意的是这一段话中王夫之对心的说明。心是个体的，心的本性是变动不居，无一时不运，无一息或停。心之功能如不运用，心之大用如不发挥，则天予人之神明将枯涸僵滞，人本有之生气将消逝殆尽。格物获得性理，对心来说是一大改变：在性的能动作用的驱迫下，变动不居的心将趋赴有意义有价值的目标，这就是“有恒性以恒其心”。性本恒，它本是一价值目标，一意义结构。它可以占据心、范导心、带动心趋赴价值目标。获得性理之后，此时理智的最高统御者是性，理智依恃性的范导作用以应对具体事物，故就价值层面说它才可以有最大限度的发挥。也就是说，在价值理性的统领下充分发挥知识理性的作用。这才是穷尽心之大用，穷尽心之含蕴，这才是知之至。反之，如果没有价值理性的范导，知识理性即使极其才，也不能说充分发挥了心的功能。心的知至是知道德理性，在道德理性统领下知识理性充其极，这才是儒家的“尽人道之极”。这与释道及功利主义者完全不同。后者因无价值理性的范导，其知识理性充其极，反较一般人更泛滥决裂，王夫之指斥此类人说：

如公孙衍、张仪、刘穆之、刘宴一流人，他这知觉运动之心何尝不玲珑剔透，一倍精采？只他邪向权谋上去，便是“心不若人”。又如释氏之徒，至有闻蚁拽虫尸如人拽大木者，亦有三十年胁不粘席者，亦有一日三唤主人翁者，又岂不精细灵警，丝毫不走作；只他邪向虚寂上去，便是“心不若人”。（自注：此正为“即心即仁”之毒所中。）若一向醉生梦死，悠悠之徒，则与沈疴恶疾在身，不知恶之以求医者等，圣贤从无心情与此辈较量。[②]

从这里可以看出王夫之之重视性体、指斥纯用心而无性体范导之非的意指所在。

---

① 王夫之：《读四书大全说》，北京：中华书局，1975年，第715页。

② 王夫之：《读四书大全说》，北京：中华书局，1975年，第693页。

## （二）

王夫之重视性体，以此为人之为人的根本，性体是他的一切论说的出发点和基础，在性体上可以推导出人的精神活动的一切含蕴，一切内容。由此在性体和知体的关系上，王夫之有一个深刻的命体："由性生知"。这是他对性体的特别重视在德知关系上的鲜明表现。他说：

> 太虚者，阴阳之藏，健顺之德存焉。气化者，一阴一阳，动静之几、品汇之节具焉。秉太虚和气健顺相涵之实，而合五行之秀以成乎人之秉彝，此人之所以有性也。原于天而顺乎道，凝于形气，而五常百行之理无不可知，无不可能，于此言之则谓之性。人之有性，函之于心而感物以通，象著而数陈，名立而义起，习其故而心喻之。形也，神也，物也，三相遇而知觉乃发。故由性生知，以知知性，交涵于聚而有间于中，统于一心，由此言之则谓之心。顺而言之，则惟天有道，以道成性，性发知道；逆而推之，则以心尽性，以性合道，以道事天。惟其理本一原，故人心即天；而尽心知性，则存顺没宁，死而全归于太虚之本体。不以客感杂滞遗造化以疵纇，圣学所以天人合一，而非异端之所可溷也。①

这是对张载"由太虚，有天之名；由气化，有道之名；合虚于气，有性之名；合性与知觉，有心之名"一句的解释。这段话完整地表达了王夫之对天、道、性、心这几个理学根本范畴的理解，可以看作他的哲学纲领。

首先，王夫之继承了张载，认为天就是太虚。本来天可有主宰之天、命运之天、义理之天、自然之天、积气之天等不同解释。"太虚"语出《庄子》，本指虚无飘渺之辽远的太古阶段，在张载，主要指气之无形无象，遍满均平于一切之本体状态，故说"太虚无形，气之本体"。王夫之认为，太虚即气之本体，它本身潜藏着阴阳之性，有阴阳就有健顺之德，有健顺就有气运动的潜能。所谓道，指一阴一阳之气的变化过程，气受健顺之德的驱动，升降往来于天中，此运动潜能的最初发动，就是几；气在运动中形成各种度量规定，这就是具体事物的节度。人禀受天之和谐健顺之德以为性，禀受五行之秀气以为形，所以人性是"原于天而顺乎道，凝于形气"。此性的内容是五行百常之理。性函于心中，心又能感物以通，据积淀于心中的具体事物的标准而对各种现象加以识别、表象。王夫之论天、道、性、心，皆以气为基础，在气的各种形态和功能中，觉解到各种价值性规定。王夫之是把人放在宇宙这个大背景下来观照的，在他的眼中，人不是政治和社会动物，也不是会制造工具获得生活资料的动物，人是宇

① 王夫之：《张子正蒙注》，上海：上海古籍出版社，2000年，第94页。

宙中的一个生物族类，它的性、它的形获之于天并且最后能自觉地类同于天，消释于天。它有来源、有归宿；有本体，有功夫。王夫之不把人在实现自己最终目的的过程中不得已假借的东西作为人的本质性规定。这是王夫之对人的观察、人的规定，这个眼光是卓越的。

这里合理的推论便是，政治、社会是人在实现自己的进化过程中不得不假借的，因为族类的个体差别必然构成不同的强弱群体。为了保证这个族类的总体和谐必须有等级、有契约、有规则。所以中国古代文化的最高形态—理学固然把某些政治信条作为天经地义，在政治运作层面，在人不能摆脱政治的束缚这个阶段，把这些信条强调为人的第一等大事。但人最后的归宿，应该是摆脱一切束缚，回复到“原始的天性”，即冯友兰《新原人》中所谓“天地境界”。在后者的比照下，政治、社会都是人回复到自己的归宿不得不假借的工具。社会是人类必须采取的一种存在形式，人必须群居。由群居派生出的一些不得不有的特性，如家庭、财产、生活保障机构等，是人不能离开的。但这些东西不能作为人这个生物族类的本质特征。理学家常比照“虎狼之父子，蜂蚁之君臣”，以区别人的社会组织的独特性、道德在社会组织中的决定作用等。但人同时是个体存在。群体只是个人的存在形式。人是个体的，有自由意志的，它最后的境界升华不取决于他是否群体中的一员，而在于他对上述人与天的关系的独特理解。所以，人是可以“内在超越”的，—超越一切形式的束缚而“上下与天地同流”。这种觉解并不神秘，也并不虚玄。在不具有这种觉解的人眼中的神秘和虚玄，正是具有这种觉解的人自我超越的依凭。人的群体性的思维是实证的、共通的、物质性的，而属于个人的天地才是空灵的、独特的、玄想的、有归宿感的。这就是“独与天地精神相往来”所昭示的人的宇宙本体论意义。从这个意义上说，理学对天地万物的觉解，对超然世外的归向具有浓烈的宗教精神。

人是会制造工具并以此获得生活资料的动物，这个说法最难于辩驳，因为人的进化史，人的科技文明，还有最直接、最有说服力的，人必须获得生活资料才能生存，都在证明这一点。所以，最低层次的“生存哲学”最容易获得同调。在“生存哲学”的信奉者看来，人对精神世界的寻求，人的永恒感、崇高感，极而言之，“胸次悠然，上下与天地同流”的境界是虚伪的、多余的、“高处不胜寒”的，人不能追问捞摸不着的形而上问题，追问这些是庸人自扰。但是王夫之以上这一大段话映照出，他所思所想的，是精神世界的问题。通篇并无生存哲学的物质性思考。他并非不知道物质的重要性，他的哲学的出发点是气，由气构成的血肉之躯，不能脱离形而下的物质生活而存在。但他谆谆恳恳向我们反复论证反复叮咛的，是人的精神世界。在他眼里，人的物质生活，人满足血肉之躯的一切欲望是为了达到某种最后的纯净，这种纯净并不是不要物质生活，而是物质生活必须在价值目标的指导下。价值目标连带下的合理的物质生活本身即是纯净。人之为人，人的特质不在物质方面，物质方面是人与动物共通的。人超出动物之处在于其精神性。生产工具的发达，物质生活的进步，只是促使人在精神生活的驿站上走得更疾更顺。他痛心疾首的是道之不修，学之不讲。他最不能容忍的是自暴自弃。他最鄙视的是孟子所谓“饮食之人”。在他眼里，人还有更重大的使命，更重要的担负，这就是对价值目标的趋赴和对最后归宿、最终境界的寻求。

在这一框架下看，王夫之的“由性生知”是顺理成章的。他所谓性，是人的全副存在、人的各种性质的统合体，是人的肉体、精神的全部功能，全部获得，全部性质的浓缩。这里“性”是个沉重而丰富的字眼。它可以伸展出、拓殖出人的精神生活的各个方面。从这里说：“性善”、“性恶”等辩论中的“性”字都不能和它并列，都在它的比照下显得局促和偏狭。所以王夫之并不抽象地说性善性恶，而是把性说成“诚”、“万物皆备于我”、“太极”等有本体意味的字眼。“由性生知”的思维方式、命题方式，是把人的各个方面特别是精神生活的各个方面，各种性质，各种获得统合、凝聚、概括为一个字，由这个字做统率，做主宰，从它紬绎出、延展出、推论出各种具体蕴含内容。这些从中紬绎、推论出的内容又受这个总的性质的统御和范导。它不是一般和个别的关系：一般和个别有太强的知性的、逻辑的色彩；它也不是局部和整体的关系：局部和整体有同质的东西的叠加、增减的意味。它是一种观照、投射、象征、顿悟等具有美学和宗教意味的东西，它表示本体和现象、主宰者和从属者、价值目的和具体实在等等关系。

在这种理解下，“由性生知”的“性”字是复合的，它所包含的“知”也有不同的类别。照王夫之对《孟子》的阐释，“知”至少有两种：理智的知和直观的知。理智的知在知具体物理，直观的智在知性理，理智的知在知具体事物，直观的知在知道、知性、知天。知与性的关系是，性包括知，性可以紬绎出知、推论出知。这里的“生”不是母生子那样的实体的生、经验的生，而是逻辑的生、象征的生。由性生出的知可以反观性、成遂性。性与知是同一个框架中的组成成分。所以“交涵于聚”。二者又不可混一看，所以“有间于中”。性与知是心的主要内容。心是性理之灵处。所以王夫之反对心是神明之舍的说法。神明之舍容易使人想象心是一空的框壳，里面可以驻着性，驻着情。这样的比喻、想象容易把心这一活泼无方、应用不穷的灵物视为一僵死的被动的框壳。所以心统性情比“心如郛郭，性如王，王驻于郛郭之中”更能描述心的能动义。心最主要的功能是知性而不是知物，这表示王夫之是把以理智知物作为以直观知性的媒介、手段。媒介、手段包含在目的中。故只说“以知知性”。知不仅是成遂具体事物的前提条件，也是成就理想人格的前提条件。同时“以知知性”表明，王夫之为人树立的最终目的是尽心知性知天，是以朱子的功夫完成孟子的理想。

此外，这段话中王夫之提出了天与人的关系的两个序列：顺的序列是“唯天有道，以道成性，性发知道”，这就是前所论承认天即宇宙大化之道，道有理有气，有本体有流行。代表这宇宙大化的价值物就是性，性天赋于人，人是不同于动物的存在，人有自己独特的性质，性可以生发出知。逆的序列是，人可以通过修养功夫穷尽心的含蕴而知性，由知性而上知天道，由行道而尽事天之责。从逆的序列，可以说王夫之有一重要思想：“心生性”。心生性是说，性虽天赋于人，但它并非时时朗现，时时明觉于心，心会由物欲的牵引、熏染而昏昧，性由此不显。只有在性的范导下，去除心的昏昧，才能“心含性而效动”。心虽统性，而性自为体，性是在人的修养中通过尽心知性而显发的。从这个意义上可以说“心生性”。“心生性”实际上是王夫之的重要命题“性日生日成”的理论基础。

## (三)

“由性生知”、“心生性”是同一的功夫论的双向活动。是王夫之心性论的二个重要层面。也是王夫之针对王门后学“虚玄而荡”、“情识而肆”两种流弊提出的救治之方，是王夫之在身受明亡的惨祸烈毒刺激之下对宋明理学提出的反省。

刘宗周曾说：“今天下争言良知矣，及其弊也，猖狂者参之以情识，而一是皆良；超洁者荡之以玄虚，而夷良于贼，亦用知者之过也。”[①]“虚玄而荡”指斥的是王门后学中抹杀良知，以心为无善无恶，功夫流于禅悟一派人。“情识而肆”指斥的是以为良知人人现成，只遵从良心所认为是者去行，即无不是道，故情识肆行无忌而自以为良知一派人。明清之际一批主张由虚反实，提倡重新确定朱子学的宗主地位的学者对阳明及阳明后学多有指摘，甚至将明亡的罪责归于王学“束书不观、游谈无根”的学风。如顾炎武说：

> 盖自弘治、正德之际，天下之士厌常喜新，风气之变，已有所自来。而文成以绝世之资，倡其新说，鼓动海内。嘉靖以后，从王氏而诋朱子者始接踵于人间。而王尚书（世贞）发策谓：今日学者，偶有所窥，则欲尽废先儒之说而出其上。不学，则借一贯之言以文其陋；无行，则逃之性命之乡以使人不可诘。此三言者，尽当日之情事矣。故王门高弟为泰州（王艮）、龙溪（王畿）二人。泰州之学一传而为颜山农（钧），再传而为罗近溪（汝芳）、赵大洲（贞吉）。龙溪之学，一传而为何心隐（本名梁汝元），再传而为李卓吾（贽）、陶石篑（望龄）。昔范武子论王弼、何晏二人之罪深于桀纣，以为一世之患轻，历代之害重；自丧之恶小，迷众之罪大。而苏子瞻谓李斯乱天下，盛于焚书坑儒，皆出于其师荀卿高谈异论而不

① 黄宗羲：《明儒学案》，北京：中华书局，1986年，第1572页。

顾者也。《困知》之论，《学蔀》之编，固今日中流之砥柱矣。[①]

他甚至认为阳明学说对于世道之祸犹如王衍之导清谈，王安石之倡功利："以一人而易天下，其流风至于百有余年之久者，古有之矣。王夷甫之清谈，王介甫之新说，其在于今，则王伯安之良知是也。"[②] 王夫之本其朱子学，对阳明及阳明后学特别是王畿、李贽、何心隐诸人抨击尤甚，如：

姚江之学出，更横拈圣言之近似者，摘一字一句以为要妙，窜入其禅宗，尤为无忌惮之至。[③]

阳明抚赣以前，举动俊伟，文字谨密，又岂人所易及！后为龙溪、心斋、绪山、萝石辈推高，便尽失其故吾。故田州之役，一无足观。使阳明而早如此，则劾刘谨、讨宸濠事亦不成矣。[④]

其中对李贽批评尤苛，认为是取法于王龙溪四无说，究至废理欲之大防：

贽为郡守，恣其贪暴，凌轹士民，故滇人切齿恨之。贽受法于龙溪。龙溪之告唐应德曰：他人以戒定慧治贪嗔痴，公当以贪嗔痴治戒定慧。宜其心印之若此。[⑤]

自龙溪窃释中峰（明本）之说，以贪嗔痴治戒定慧，惑世诬民。李贽益其邪焰，奖谯周、冯道而诋毁方正之士。时局中邪佞之尤者，依为安身之计。[⑥]

若近世李贽、钟惺之流，导天下于邪淫，以酿中夏衣冠之祸，岂非逾于洪水烈于猛兽者乎？[⑦]

王夫之与顾炎武都受明亡的刺激，有纠正学术偏弊，使之归于笃实的担承，故对王门后学中鄙弃实地功夫，径任先天本体的泰州、龙溪批评甚为严厉。王夫之认为，王门后学的弊病皆由心中无有性的规约、范导所致。故须倡导"由性生知"。性之挺立，可以摧破"虚玄而荡"、"情识而肆"种种弊病。"由性生知"一语是纠治阳明后学的良方。

而性的显发、畅达于心，完全靠实地功夫而得。性在功夫着到之前，只是一潜在的、抽象的、预设的有。实地功夫使其由潜在到实在，由抽象到具体，由预设到实现。功夫着到一分，则性实现一分。故"性日生日成"。在这个意义上，可以说"心生性"。

---

① 顾炎武著，黄汝成集释：《日知录》，石家庄：花山文艺出版社，1990年，第829页。
② 顾炎武著，黄汝成集释：《日知录》，石家庄：花山文艺出版社，1990年，第832页。
③ 王夫之：《俟解》，北京：中华书局，1956年，第14页。
④ 王夫之：《俟解》，北京：中华书局，1956年，第13页。
⑤ 王夫之：《船山全书》第十二册，长沙：岳麓书社，1996年，第625页。
⑥ 王夫之：《船山全书》第十二册，长沙：岳麓书社，1996年，第648页。
⑦ 王夫之：《读通鉴论》，《船山全书》第十册，长沙：岳麓书社，1996年，第1178页。

王夫之曾说："愚于《周易》、《尚书》传义中，说生初有天命，向后日日皆有天命。天命之谓性，则亦日日成之为性，其说似与先儒不合。"[①] 而这正是王夫之为纠治时代风习而提出的有针对性的思想。可以说，"生初有天命"、"天命之谓性"是"由性生知"之"性"。"向后日日皆有天命"、"日日成之谓性"，是"心生性"之"性"。二者是统一的修养过程之一来一往两个回环。由以上对阳明及阳明后学的批评看，王夫之确实是在身受明亡的惨祸烈毒的刺激而对宋明理学乃至整个中国思想进行反省的。他崇尚健动有为的精神，他提倡致广大而尽精微的治学方法，他提出"六经责我开生面"的以经学带动理学的学问方向，他对经学、理学的一系列有力阐发，都是他的这一根本思想富有创造力的实践。

---

① 王夫之：《读四书大全说》，北京：中华书局，1975 年，第 13 页。

# 朱熹《四書章句集注》中的“湖湘學脈”

台湾政治大学 陈逢源

## 一、前言

朱熹（1130－1200）形構四書義理體系，《四書章句集注》是朱熹一生追尋聖人的成果，[①] 朝鮮韓元震（1682－1751）直言“孔子（前551－前479）天地間一人而已矣！朱子孔子後一人而已矣！有孔子則不可無朱子，而尊朱子者乃所以尊孔子也。”[②] 由朱熹上承孔子，乃是極為正確的觀察。近人何佑森先生檢討近代學術發展：“朱子學博大精深，前後經歷了四個世紀，每當時代動亂，思想的發展有了偏差，唯一能補偏救弊的，則只有朱子一脈相傳的儒學。”[③] 風氣時移世異，翩其反矣，但朱熹學術具有“中軸”地位，原因所在，清程逢儀提出觀察，〈四書朱子大全序〉云：

> 朱子之書，廣大悉備，其學無所不通，而一生精力尤在四書。……余嘗博考朱子之書，見近世所詆朱子者，朱子早已解之；疑朱子者，朱子早已定之；辨駁朱子，自以為獨得之解者，朱子早已窮其弊而唾棄之。未嘗見朱子之全書，而肆其胸臆，攘臂叫囂，以狎侮程、朱。如是而曰吾以明聖人之道，吾不信也。[④]

救弊補偏，廣大悉備，原因出於朱熹融鑄前賢的努力。朱熹從學李侗，接續道南“靜中看喜怒哀樂未發之謂中，未發時作何氣象”的修養法門，終於從摻雜佛道而歸於

① 參見拙撰〈從體證到建構：朱熹《四書章句集注》的撰作過程〉，《朱熹與四書章句集注》（臺北：里仁書局，2006年9月），頁131。

② （韓）韓元震撰〈朱子言論同異考序〉，《朱子言論同異考》（首爾：奎章閣藏朝鮮木刻本），頁2。

③ 何佑森撰〈朱子學與近世思想〉，收入《儒學與思想——何佑森先生學術論文集（上冊）》（臺北：臺大出版中心，2009年4月），頁126。

④ 程逢儀撰〈四書朱子大全序〉，朱傑人等人主編《朱子全書》（上海：上海古籍出版社，合肥：安徽教育出版社，2002年12月）第27冊“序跋”，頁687－688。

純粹，在儒學當中獲致生命依歸，只可惜從學日短，無法了解默坐澄心之效，[1] 窮無所歸之際，旁求張栻所傳湖湘之學，開展匯聚眾流的階段，此一思想轉折，稱為“丙戌之悟”。[2] 參悟“中和”問題，既是個人學術的躍升，也是朱熹思以承繼南宋兩大伊洛學脈，進而成就個人思索的結果。[3] 朱熹日後續有發展，但道學脈絡已經具備，體證工夫已有雛形，朱熹從師與求友進程，確認北宋儒學樣態，建構聖人學術的了解，筆者梳理《延平答問》，撰成〈“聞之師曰”——朱熹與李侗〉一文，[4] 了解承襲“道南”一系的細節，又撰成〈“道南”與“湖湘”——朱熹義理進程之檢討〉，[5] 對於朱熹學術遂有大要的觀察，為求深入，推究朱熹與張栻交誼，一探“湖湘”家法，乃是了解朱熹學術進程極為重要的問題，從兩人斟酌所在，考察去取之間，《四書章句集注》徵引“湖湘”諸儒意見，也就有分判的依據。

## 二、朱熹與張栻

朱熹於隆興元年（1163）與張栻（1133—1180）初識相見，《朱子語類》云：“張魏公被召入相，議北征。某時被召，辭歸，嘗見欽夫與說……”，[6] 張栻為張浚（1097—1164）之子，將門之後，名重朝廷，兩人商議，充滿熱情，朱熹申其主戰立場，似乎尚未及於學術。隔年張浚病逝，朱熹前往弔唁，兩人得以再見，與談更為深入，〈答羅參議書〉云：

> 九月廿日至豫章，及魏公之舟而哭之，云亡之歎，豈特吾人共之，海內有識之所同也。自豫章送之豐城，舟中與欽夫得三日之款，其名質甚敏，學問甚正，若充養不置，何可量也。[7]

相聚雖短，然而張栻學問以及人品，讓朱熹無比欣賞，此時是否談及“中和”之

---

① 朱熹撰 陳俊民校編《朱子文集》（臺北：德富文教基金會，2000 年 2 月）第 8 冊 卷 75〈中和舊說序〉，頁 3786。

② 陳來撰《朱熹哲學研究》（臺北：文津出版社，1990 年 12 月），頁 110。

③ 劉述先撰《朱子哲學思想的發展與完成》（臺北：臺灣學生書局，1995 年 8 月），頁 79—90。

④ 參見拙撰〈“聞之師曰”——朱熹與李侗〉，《孔孟月刊》第 52 卷第 5、6 期（2012 年 6 月），頁 29—37。

⑤ 參見拙撰〈“道南”與“湖湘”——朱熹義理進程之檢討〉，《“融鑄”與“進程”：朱熹《四書章句集注》之歷史思維》（臺北：政大出版社，2013 年 10 月），頁 179—220。

⑥ 黎靖德編《朱子語類》（臺北：文津出版社，1986 年 12 月）第 8 冊，卷 131，頁 3152。又第 7 冊，卷 103，同載一事云：“上初召魏公，先召南軒來。某亦赴召至行在，語南軒云：‘湯進之不去，事不可為。莫擔負了他底，至於敗事!’某待得見魏公時，親與之說。度住不得，一二日去矣。”頁 2608。朱熹與張栻相聚時短，關心議題，顯然是孝宗北伐的布局，尚未及於學術。

⑦ 朱熹撰 陳俊民校編《朱子文集》第 10 冊 續集卷 5〈答羅參議〉，頁 4999。

說，似乎尚有爭議，[1] 但由張栻以求湖湘學術，明顯是於此開始，〈答羅參議書〉云：

龜山〈論語序〉本為世學膠固，學者類多以分文析字、執辭泥跡為務，故有“視其所視，遺其所不視”之說，但所引用之事，從《莊》、《列》中說作太過，遂致微失本意，卻似精粗本末真有二致，所以中間竊以為疑，非疑其意，特疑其語耳。後見張欽夫、吳晦叔，乃知文定亦嘗疑之，不審尊意以為如何，幸有以見教。胡仁仲所著《知言》一冊內呈，其語道極精切，有實用處，暇日試熟看，有會心處，卻望垂諭。……欽夫嘗收安問，警益甚多，大抵衡山之學，只就日用處操存辨察，本末一致，尤易見功。某近乃覺知如此，非面未易究也。……某塊坐窮山，絕無師友之助，惟時得欽夫書問往來，講究此道，近方覺有脫然處，……[2]

朱熹循李侗（1093－1163）“道南”一脈，顯然還有諸多疑問，無可參酌之際，張栻無疑是最重要的人物，胡安國（1074－1138）的學術判斷、胡宏（1106－1162）《知言》的工夫，乃至於“操存辨察，本末一致”的法門，朱熹如數家珍，對於湖湘學術並不陌生，顯然關注已久，《朱子文集》當中〈與張欽夫三〉、〈與張欽夫四〉、〈答張敬夫三〉、〈答張敬夫四〉，往復討論，關乎中和境界的討論，[3] 乃是朱熹斟酌儒學義理所在，試行體驗湖湘學術的成果，云：

人自有生，即有知識，事物交來，應接不暇，念念遷革，以至於死，其間初無頃刻停息，舉世皆然也。則有所謂“未發之中，寂然不動”者，夫豈以日用流行者為已發，而指夫暫而休息，不與事接之際為未發時耶？嘗試以此求之，則泯然無覺之中，邪暗鬱塞，似非虛明應物之體，而幾微之際一有覺焉，則又便為已發，而非寂然之謂。蓋愈求而愈不可見，於是退而驗之於日用之間，則凡感之而通，觸之而覺，蓋有渾然全體、應物不窮者，是乃天命流行，生生不已之機，雖一日之間萬起萬滅，而其寂然之本體則未嘗不寂然也。[4]

前書所稟寂然未發之旨，良心發現之端，自以為有小異於疇昔偏滯之見，但其間語病尚多，未為精切。比遣書後，累日潛玩，其於實體，似益精明，因復取凡聖賢之

---

① 劉述先撰《朱子哲學思想的發展與完成》認為此時場合不對，不可能有深度的學術討論。頁79。然而束景南撰《朱熹年譜長編》（上海：華東師範大學出版社，2001年9月）於隆興二年（1164年）載“九月，赴豫章哭祭張浚，與張栻面論湖湘學中和之說，得胡宏《知言》，結識胡宏弟子吳翌。”頁330。似乎更能反映朱熹於李侗過世之後，求學若渴，急於求解的心情。

② 朱熹撰 陳俊民校編《朱子文集》第10冊 續集卷5〈答羅參議〉，頁5000－5001。

③ 朱熹撰 陳俊民校編《朱子文集》第3冊 卷30〈答張欽夫三〉、〈答張欽夫四〉，頁1157－1159。及卷32〈答張敬夫三〉、〈答張敬夫四〉，頁1241－1244。此四書即論中和舊說四劄，束景南撰《朱熹年譜長編》繫於乾道二年（1166年），頁355－358。陳來撰《朱熹哲學研究》（北京：中國社會科學出版社，1993年3月）考其語脈順序，應是第一書、第四書、第二書、第三書。頁103－104。

④ 朱熹撰 陳俊民校編《朱子文集》第3冊 卷30〈與張欽夫三〉，頁1157－1158。

書，以及近世諸老先生之遺語，讀而驗之，則又無一不合。蓋平日所疑而未白者，今皆不待安排，往往自見灑落處。始竊自信以為天下之理，其果在是，而致知格物、居敬精義之功，自是其有所施之矣，聖賢方策，豈欺我哉！蓋通天下只是一箇天機活物，流行發用，無間容息。據其已發者而指其未發者，則已發者人心，而凡未發者皆其性也，亦無一物而不備矣。夫豈別有一物拘於一時、限於一處而名之哉？即夫日用之間，渾然全體，如川流之不息，天運之不窮耳。此所以體用精粗、動靜本末，洞然無一毫之間，而鳶飛魚躍，觸處朗然也。存者，存此而已；養者，養此而已。必有事焉而勿正，心勿忘，勿助長也，從前是做多少安排，沒頓著處，今覺得如水到船浮，解維正柂，而沿洄上下，惟意所適矣，豈不易哉？始信明道所謂未嘗致纖毫之力者，真不浪語。而此一段事，程門先達惟上蔡謝公所見透徹無隔礙處，自餘雖不敢妄有指議，然味其言亦可見矣。[①]

朱熹於下自注"此書非是，但存之以見議論本末耳。下篇同此。"[②] 日後續有體悟，又有新進程，然而依循張栻引導，在心念當中，印證經典內容，原本求於未發之際，愈求愈不可得的困境，在此指引之下，終於有所突破。朱熹嘗試在日用之間，追求"天命流行，生生不已之機"的本體經驗，人生於世，應對進退之間，皆為已發，在萬起萬滅當中，進行操存辨察的工夫，所謂"累日潛玩，其於實體，似益精明，……。蓋平日所疑而未白者，今皆不待安排，往往自見灑落處。""灑落"正是李侗指引的境界，竟然於"湖湘"一系心法中得見，明道的"未嘗致纖毫之力"，朱熹試之有驗，欣喜之情，甚至發為歌詠，〈觀書有感〉二首：

半畝方塘一鑑開，天光雲影共徘徊。問渠那得清如許，為有源頭活水來。

昨夜江邊春水生，蒙衝巨艦一毛輕。向來枉費推移力，此日中流自在行。[③]

"方塘"是映照萬物的"心體"，"源頭活水"則是省察的工夫，"如水到船浮，解維正柂，而沿洄上下，惟意所適矣"，正是反映"中流自在"的心理感受，方法輕鬆自然，容易操作，因此遂有自信，認為天地之間，流行發用，渾然一體，並不是於一時、一處之地用力，而是體用粗精，動靜本末無絲毫間隙，觸處朗然，言之有驗，超脫自在，讓朱熹對於謝良佐深致推崇，認定辨察於已發之際、居敬於日用之間的"湖湘"心法乃是儒學正傳，張栻為朱熹解開糾結的學術難題，欣喜與愉悅，衷心稱賞，〈答何叔京十一〉云："欽夫之學，所以超脫自在，見得分明，不為言句所桎梏，只為合下入處親切。今日說話雖未能絕無滲漏，終是本領是當，非吾輩所及，但詳觀所論，自可

① 朱熹撰 陳俊民校編《朱子文集》第 3 冊 卷 32〈答張敬夫四〉，頁 1243。

② 朱熹撰 陳俊民校編《朱子文集》第 3 冊 卷 30〈與張欽夫三〉，頁 1157。

③ 朱熹撰 陳俊民校編《朱子文集》第 1 冊 卷 2〈觀書有感〉二首，頁 73。

見矣。"[1] 甚至朱熹於〈劉共甫二〉中向劉珙（1122—1178）舉薦人才，認為朝堂不可無君子，直言"敬夫尤不可後"，[2] 兩人學術相契，推崇之心，於此可見，朱熹欣慕嚮往，贊歎不已，於是在乾道三年（1167年）九月再度往訪張栻，停留兩個月的時間，分享心得，澄清疑義，以往多以為是討論已發未發中和之說，不過依束景南《朱熹年譜長編》所考，朱熹與張栻長沙之會，既無意氣，又無立場，乃是一次全面性的學術講論，討論內容，包括：討論"主敬"、討論"仁說"、討論"中庸"學、討論撰寫〈張浚行狀〉、與湖湘學者論論，批評湖湘學之禪氣、對各自經學、史學著作之討論，[3] 兩人充分討論，纖介不遺，束景南指出〈行狀〉中張浚訓諸子門人"學以禮為本，禮以敬為先"，標舉"敬"的工夫；強調"學者當清明其心，默存聖賢氣象"，以"默"來體現心體清明，[4] 朱熹與張栻乃是結合謝良佐所傳湖湘一脈"主敬"法門，以及楊時所傳道南一脈"主靜"心法，對於一代名將，深致詠嘆，呈現張浚人格全面樣態，[5] 兩人一方面交換學術心得，另一方面也開展"道南"與"湖湘"兩大學脈化異求同的思考。李侗過世之後，朱熹得到張栻之助，於迷惘當中，得到方向，欣賞當中，更有相互扶持，志同道合的愉悅，兩人暢遊同歡，酬酢唱和，張栻〈詩送朱元晦尊兄〉云："君侯起南服，豪氣蓋九州。……盡收湖海氣，仰希朱泗游。"[6] 直指朱熹學術豪情與氣魄，朱熹〈二詩奉酬敬夫贈言并以為別〉之二云："昔我抱冰炭，從君識乾坤。……萬化自此流，千聖同滋源。"[7] 交代自己往會的心情與體會，兩人真情爽朗，心平而公，至誠論交，以聖賢相期，既是儒者雅事，也成就南宋學術一段佳話。不過比較而言，朱熹不僅承張栻以繼湖湘心法，試行檢驗；另外，也特別留意一方風土，了解湖湘之教的成果，因此對於張栻與其他學人之間，也有諸多觀察，朱熹〈與曹晉叔書〉云：

> 熹此月八日抵長沙，今半月矣。荷敬夫愛予甚篤，相與講明其所未聞，日有問學之益，至幸！至幸！敬夫學問愈高，所見卓然，議論出人意表。近讀其《語》說，不覺胸中洒然。誠可歎服。嶽麓學者漸多，其間亦有氣質醇粹、志趣確實者，只是未知方向，往往騁空言而遠實理，告語之責，敬夫不可辭也。長沙使君豪爽

---

① 朱熹撰 陳俊民校編《朱子文集》第4冊 卷40〈答何叔京十一〉，頁1722。

② 朱熹撰 陳俊民校編《朱子文集》第10冊 別集卷1〈劉共甫二〉，頁5096。

③ 束景南撰《朱熹年譜長編》乾道三年"九月八日，至潭州，與張栻嶽麓講學兩月"，下文之討論，頁373—375。

④ 朱熹撰 陳俊民校編《朱子文集》第9冊 卷95下〈少師保信軍節度使魏國公致仕贈太保張公行狀下〉，頁4672—4673。

⑤ 束景南撰《朱熹年譜長編》，頁374。

⑥ 張栻撰《南軒集》（臺北：廣學社印書館，1975年6月）卷一〈詩送朱元晦尊兄〉，頁25。

⑦ 朱熹撰 陳俊民校編《朱子文集》第1冊 卷5〈二詩奉酬敬夫贈言并以為別〉之二，頁172。

俊邁，今之奇士，但喜於立異，不肯入於道德，可惜！……①

所謂“未聞”正是湖湘學術精彩之處，此書距離與會僅半個月，切近當時心情，對於張栻學術的稱賞，人品的推崇，言語之中，充滿佩服，講論之益，讓朱熹印象深刻，不過對於湖湘一地學人，朱熹顯然尚有期待，蹈空立異，皆非正學，朱熹甚至認為張栻應有告語之責，期勉張栻為湖湘領袖，朱熹顯然有更深的思考，此一觀察於日後更為明顯，朱熹〈答石子重書五〉云：

熹自去秋之中走長沙，閱月而後至，留兩月而後歸，……欽夫見處，卓然不可及，從游之久，反復開益為多。但其天姿明敏，從初不歷階級而得之，故今日語人，亦多失之太高。湘中學子從之游者，遂一例學為虛談，其流弊亦將有害。比來頗覺此病矣，別後當有以救之。然從游之士，亦自絕難得朴實頭理會者，可見此道之難明也。胡氏子弟及他門人，亦有語此者，然皆無實得，拈槌豎拂，幾如說禪矣。與文定合下門庭，大段相反，更無商量處。惟欽夫見得表裡通徹，舊來習見微有所偏，今此相見，盡覺釋去，儘好之商量也。②

觀察更廣，思索更深，時隔一年，觀察稍有不同，對於張栻所傳的湖湘心法，推崇依舊，但對於湖湘學者蹈虛入禪，缺乏篤實為學的進程，學有偏差，頗為憂慮，胡氏門人既已違失其教，其他更不殆言，朱熹甚至認為張栻言語“失之太高”，也有“不歷階級”的缺失，可惜眾人守之甚固，無法溝通，朱熹驗之於己與察之於人，明顯存在落差，不免心生疑慮，懷疑後人已失門徑，體認既深，已啟進一步的思考。所幸兩人情誼深厚，溝通無礙，給予朱熹支持的力量，朱熹承教試行，張栻也調整偏失，兩人互相提攜，張栻不僅是湖湘學術的引路人，也是朱熹融鑄而進，可以激勵，可以商量的學術同道，朱熹於乾道四年（1168 年）再修訂《謝上蔡語錄》，並編訂《程氏遺書》，刻版於泉州，取徑湖湘學術，已有明顯的成果，朱熹〈有懷南軒老兄呈伯崇擇之二友二首〉：

憶昔秋風裡，尋盟湘水傍；勝遊朝挽袂，妙語夜連床。別去多遺恨，歸來識大方。惟應微密處，猶欲細商量。

積雨芳菲暗，新晴始豁然。園林媚幽獨，窗户愜清妍。晤語心何遠，書題意未宣。懸知今夜月，同夢舞雩邊。③

朱熹於“晤語心何遠”下注“謂日與擇之講論”，所指為林用中；於“書題意未宣”下注“謂數收伯崇近書”，所言為范念德，朱熹學術參酌更多，然而對於張栻論交之情，從“積雨”至“新晴”，終於得見方向，欣喜心情始終一致，不過其中“微密

① 朱熹撰 陳俊民校編《朱子文集》第 3 冊 卷 24〈與曹晉叔書〉，頁 910。
② 朱熹撰 陳俊民校編《朱子文集》第 4 冊 卷 42〈答石子重五〉，頁 1835。
③ 朱熹撰 陳俊民校編《朱子文集》第 1 冊 卷 5〈有懷南軒老兄呈伯崇擇之二友二首〉，頁 196。

處”的不安，反映朱熹後續的思考，乾道五年（1169年）春與蔡元定（1135－1198）講論，頓悟中和之旨，確立一生學問宗旨，“已發”、“未發”只是狀態不同，不應視為本體與日用之別，此為“己丑之悟”，即是所謂的“中和新說”。朱熹匯聚體驗，歸之於己，在“道南”與“湖湘”學脈之中，從李侗至張栻，又從張栻而出，悠遊思考，轉折而進，無疑是蓄積已久的結果，朱熹將此體會寫成〈已發未發說〉一文，[①] 並將心得寄給張栻與湖湘學者：

> 《中庸》未發已發之義，前此認得此心流行之體，又因程子“凡言心者，皆指已發而言”，遂目心為已發，性為未發。然觀程子之書，多所不合，因復思之，乃知前日之說，非惟心性之名，命之不當，而日用功夫，全無本領，蓋所失者，不但文義之間而已。按《文集》、《遺書》諸說，似皆以思慮未萌、事物未至之時，為喜怒哀樂之未發，當此之時，即是此心寂然不動之體，而天命之性，當體具焉，以其無過不及，不偏不倚，故謂之“中”；及其感而遂通天下之故，則喜怒哀樂之性發焉，而心之用可見，以其無不中節，無所乖戾，故謂之“和”，此則人心之正，而情性之德然也。然未發之前，不可尋覓，已覺之後，不容安排，但平日莊敬涵養之功至，而無人欲之私以亂之，則其未發也鏡明水止，而其發也無不中節矣，此是日用本領工夫，至於隨事省察，即物推明，亦必以是為本，而於已發之際觀之，則其具於未發之前者，固可嘿識。故程子之答蘇季明，反復論辨，極於詳密，而卒之不過以“敬”為言。又曰：“敬而無失，即所以中。”又曰：“人道莫如敬，未有致知而不在敬者。”又曰：“涵養須是敬，進學則在致知。”蓋為此也。向來講論思索，直以心為已發，而日用工夫，亦止以察識端倪為最初下手處，以故闕卻平日涵養一段工夫，使人胸中擾擾，無深潛純一之味，而其發之言語事為之間，亦常急迫浮露，無復雍容深厚之風，蓋所見一差，其害乃至於此，不可以不審也。[②]

“未發”是指思慮未萌、事物未至，心體寂然不動之時；“已發”是思慮已萌，感而遂通的階段，心體言其“中”，心用求其“和”。“已發”、“未發”不是“心”、“性”之別，而是“情”、“性”之分，“心”具眾理，貫通其中，兼有“已發”、“未發”，湖湘學者主張“先察識後涵養”，強調於已發時下工夫，但對於思慮未萌的“未發”階段，欠缺“平日涵養一段工夫”，臨事之際，無可掌握，不免“胸中擾擾”、“急迫浮露”，缺乏雍容深厚氣度，朱熹釐清層次，深化修養進程，更臻於密，乃是數年之間反省湖湘學術的結果。湖湘學者守住樊籬，無法接受朱熹說法，但往復之間，朱熹與張

---

① 朱熹撰 陳俊民校編《朱子文集》第7冊 卷67〈已發未發說〉，頁3375－3378。

② 朱熹撰 陳俊民校編《朱子文集》第7冊 卷64〈與湖南諸公論中和第一書〉，頁3229－3230。

栻已逐步取得默契，意見漸趨一致，朱熹納湖湘學派“察識”於“致知”之中，特別揭櫫程頤“涵養須是敬，進學則在致知”的主張，“敬”既具道德意涵，又兼攝“靜”的工夫“主敬”、“窮理”兼融並至，道南與湖湘學脈因而匯流，此乃南宋伊洛學術的一大進展，也是朱熹與張栻共同成就的學術事業。[①] 日後朱熹撰〈記謝上蔡論語疑義〉、〈《知言》疑義〉，針對湖湘學術的核心要義，總結觀察，[②] 與張栻討論〈觀心說〉、〈仁說〉，深化儒學義理的體會，[③] 朱熹串貫其中，從入而出，遂能於分歧之中，確定方向，朱熹學術的進程於此可見。

## 三、湖湘學脈

湖湘學派由胡安國，上溯謝良佐（1050－1103）而及於二程之學，學術具有淵源；胡安國以《春秋》名家，胡寅關注又及於《論語》，[④] 學術饒有根柢；胡宏《知言》延續明道（1032－1085）〈定性書〉、〈識仁篇〉，強調“心性兩分”、“先察識後涵養”，學術具有操持的法門，人材為盛，名儒輩出，成為南宋重要的學術門派，[⑤] 以聲勢而言，實盛於羅從彥（1072－1135）、李侗“道南”一脈，朱熹藉張栻引入，釐清“已發”、

---

① 朱熹撰 陳俊民校編《朱子文集》第 3 冊 卷 32〈答張欽夫十八〉云：“來教又謂熹言以靜為本，不若遂言以敬為本，此固然也。然‘敬’字工夫，通貫動靜，而必以靜為本，故熹向來輒有是語，今若遂易為敬，雖若完全，然卻不見敬之所施有先有後，則亦未得為諦當也。”頁 1275。參見拙撰參見拙撰〈從“理一分殊”到“格物窮理”：朱熹《四書章句集注》之義理思惟〉，《朱熹與四書章句集注》，頁 331－409。

② 朱熹撰 陳俊民校編《朱子文集》卷 70〈記謝上蔡論語疑義〉，張栻撰《南軒集》卷 24〈答朱元晦祕書〉云：“《上蔡語解》偏處甚多，大有害事處，益知求道難也。”頁 590。又《朱子文集》第 4 冊 卷 35〈答劉子澄四〉云：“《知言》之書，用意精切，但其氣象急迫，終少和平。又數大節目亦皆差誤，如‘性無善惡’、‘心為已發’、‘先知後敬’之類，皆失聖賢本旨。頃與欽夫、伯恭論之甚詳，亦皆有反復，雖有小小未合，然其大概亦略同矣。”頁 1407。對於湖湘學術的檢討，朱熹、張栻顯然已有默契。

③ 朱熹撰 陳俊民校編《朱子文集》第 7 冊 卷 67〈觀心說〉、〈仁說〉，頁 3389－3392。〈仁說〉云：“專言‘知覺’者，使人張皇迫躁，而無沉潛之味，其弊或至於認欲為理有之矣。”頁 3392。朱熹憂慮所在，也就清楚明白矣。

④ 胡寅撰《斐然集》（影印文淵閣《四庫全書》第 1137 冊，臺北：臺灣商務印書館，1986 年 3 月）卷十九〈上蔡論語解後序〉云：“《論語》一書蓋先聖與門弟子問答之微言，學者求道之要也。”頁 540。

⑤ 按：全祖望認為胡安國出於私淑，不應列於謝氏門下，黃宗羲原著 全祖望補修《宋元學案》（臺北：華世出版社，1987 年 9 月）卷 34“武夷學案”，頁 1170。然而牟宗三先生卻以五峰開出湖湘學統，乃是承明道、上蔡而來，實義是承明道圓教模型而開出。《心體與性體》，頁 46。進一步按覈黎靖德編《朱子語類》卷 101“程子門人”朱熹論其淵源云：“他資質好，在太學中也多聞先生師友之訓，所以能然。……文定卻從龜山求書見上蔡，……畢竟文定之學，後來得於上蔡者為多。他所以尊上蔡而不甚滿於游、楊二公……”頁 2586－2587。湖湘學術可以上溯於謝良佐，應無可疑。

“未發”，推究“中和”問題，與湖湘學者的論辨當中，朱熹心體的掌握已經具備，不管是“失之太高”、“學為虛談”，抑或“闕卻平日涵養一段工夫”，湖湘學術未能通貫銜接，顯然是朱熹心有未愜的關鍵所在，於是反復思索，綜合過往，期以建構靜養動察，敬貫內外，全幅飽滿的儒學義理，儒學規模以及工夫進程有了全然的安排，細節或有調整，但心統性情的主調，大體已經定型，《四書章句集注》也於後逐步完成，束景南《朱熹年譜長編》推斷乾道八年（1172年）年底朱熹完成《大學章句》、《中庸章句》草稿，[①] 持續商討修訂到淳熙二年（1175年），相關討論見於朱熹與呂祖謙、張栻的往返書信中，一方面可見朱熹持續思索儒學內涵，另一方面，也將建構思想體系的心力，進一步落實於經典詮釋當中。事實上，湖湘學者對於朱熹不僅是激化義理的思考而已，講論成果更涓滴匯流，成為朱熹重構經典事業的重要材料，朱熹從學李侗之前，早已留意謝良佐，《朱子語錄》自述少年為學情況，載云：

> 某少時為學，十六歲便好理學，十七歲便有如今學者見識。後得謝顯道《論語》，甚喜，乃熟讀。先將朱筆抹出語意好處；又熟讀得趣，覺見朱抹太煩，再用墨抹出；又熟讀得趣，別用青筆抹出；又熟讀得要領，乃用黃筆抹出。至此，自見所得處甚約，只是一兩句上。卻日夜就此一兩句上用意玩味，胸中自是洒落。[②]

朱熹毫不鬆懈，一字一句反覆咀嚼，得其激發，用心如此，成為上溯二程的津梁，束景南懷疑上蔡《論語解》其實是胡寅所予，[③] 可見朱熹接觸湖湘學術早有淵源，由“道南”入於“湖湘”，轉折並無不自然。《宋元學案》載“明道扶溝事，先生往從之。明道謂人曰：‘此秀才展拓得開，將來可望。’”黃宗羲按語云：

> 程門高弟，予竊以上蔡為第一，《語錄》嘗累手錄之。語者謂“道南”一派，三傳而出朱子，集諸儒之大成，當等龜山于上蔡之上。不知一堂功力，豈因後人為軒輊！且朱子之言曰：“某少時妄志于學，頗藉先生之言以發其趣。”則上蔡固朱子之先河也。[④]

---

① 束景南撰《朱熹年譜長編》據《張南軒先生文集》中答朱熹書信考云：“按書十三言及魏掞之疾危，魏卒於乾道九年閏正月。……可見朱熹先約在十月寄《中庸章句》首章，然後約在十二月寄去全本《中庸章句》。朱熹之草成《中庸章句》約在十一二月間。”頁480。按：《朱子文集》卷31〈答張敬夫十〉標為“壬辰冬”，內容討論“在中之義”，而〈答張敬夫十一〉則已舉出《中庸章句》。頁1186－1188。

② 黎靖德編《朱子語類》卷115“訓門人三”，頁2783。

③ 束景南《朱熹年譜長編》於紹興十九年“得上蔡謝良佐《論語解》，刻苦研讀”下注云：“二程洛學，一脈由楊時至羅從彥、李侗，發展而為東南閩學，以《中庸》為入道之要；一脈由謝良佐至胡安國父子，發展而為湖湘學，以《論語》為入道之要。……亦可知胡寅於紹興十九年來崇安省覲本生母，當與其來哭祭劉勉之同時，朱熹必能見到胡寅。疑朱熹之有上蔡《論語解》即其時胡寅所予，並面告其‘看謝氏《論語》，以文字上多有發越處’，朱熹遂苦讀上蔡《論語解》也。”頁127。

④ 黃宗羲原著 全祖望補修《宋元學案》卷24“上蔡學案”，頁917。

謝良佐乃是程門高弟，踔厲風發，具有激昂朱熹之作用，地位不容忽視，檢覈語錄，頗有相近的議題：

謝子曰："道，須是下學而上達，始得。不見古人就灑掃應對上做起?"曰："洒掃應對上學，卻是太瑣屑，不展拓。"曰："凡事不必須高遠，且從小處看。只如將一金與人，與將天下與人，雖大小不同，其實一也。……又若行千尺臺邊，心便恐懼；行平地上，心卻安穩。我若去得恐懼底心，雖履千仞之險，亦只與行平地上一般。只如灑掃，不著此心，怎灑掃得?應對不著此心，怎應對得?故曾子欲'動容貌，正顔色，出辭氣'，為此。古人須要就灑掃應對上養取誠意出來。"

學者且須窮理。物物皆有理，窮理則能知天之所為，知天之所為，則與天為一。與天為一，無往而非理也。窮理則是尋箇是處。有我不能窮理，人誰識我?何者為我?理便是我。窮理之至，自然"不勉而中，不思而得，從容中道"。曰："理必物物而窮之乎?"曰："必窮其大者。理一而已，一處理窮，觸處皆通。恕，其窮理之本歟?"[①]

以心著性，心性對揚，日用間即可著力，有觸處皆通的感受，隱約之中，使朱熹有"分殊"見"理一"的自信，也有回應灑掃應對的思考，"灑掃應對"與"理一而已"，正是"道南"一脈的核心議題，觀點可以銜接，甚至"須要就洒掃應對上養取誠意出來"以及"一處理窮，觸處皆通"的主張，訴求更為清楚，立場更為激昂，自然吸引朱熹注意，用以解決無法於"未發"處體驗的窘境，就思想發展而言，其實是自然而然的結果。然而從以往觀其發越處，朱熹與張栻論交之後，進而及於工夫法門的思考，[②] 謝良佐論仁以覺；論敬以常惺惺；論窮理以求是，英明果決，生機活潑，極富魅力，朱熹嘗試超越，在高明之處，推究細節，激昂也就有歸於醇厚的發展。以朱熹《四書章句集注》徵引"湖湘"一脈言論分析，《大學章句》、《中庸章句》未見引用；《論語集注》引謝良佐六十三次、胡安國二次、胡寅四十一次、張栻八次；《孟子集注》引謝良佐三次、胡安國一次、張栻二次，[③]《四書章句集注》徵引湖湘一系詮釋成果以

① 謝良佐撰、朱熹輯錄《上蔡語錄》收入朱傑人、嚴佐之、劉永翔主編《朱子全書》外編本（上海：華東師範大學出版社，2010 年 9 月）第 3 冊，卷上，頁 14、卷中，頁 21。

② 詳見陳谷嘉撰《張栻與湖湘學派研究》（湖南省：湖南教育出版社，1991 年 8 月）第九章〈張栻湖湘學與朱熹閩學〉，頁 139－157。

③ 數目依大槻信良撰《四書章句集註典據考》（臺北：臺灣學生書局，1976 年 4 月）判定結果，除朱熹標示為謝氏之外，大槻信良也覈以《論孟精義》，抉之而出，遂有更為豐富的觀察。其中《論語集注》卷八〈衛靈公〉朱注引程子曰："義以為質，如質榦然。禮行此，孫出此，信成此。此四句只是一事，以義為本。"又曰："'敬以直內，則義以方外。''義以為質，則禮以行之，孫以出之，信以成之。'"頁 165。乃程明道之說。然《精義》載謝顯道亦述此師說，所以也列入統計之中，頁 248。此外，《論語集注》卷五〈鄉黨篇〉"食不語，寢不言"章引"范氏曰：'聖人存心不他，當食而食，當寢而寢，言語非其時也。'"，按覈《論孟精義》為謝良佐之語，朱熹誤記，故仍列入計算。頁 164。

謝良佐最多，主要集中於《論語》，至於胡氏，乃是胡寅而非胡宏，《朱子語類》云：

問："《語解》胡氏為誰?"曰："胡明仲也。向見張欽夫殊不取其說，某以為不然。他雖有未至處，若是說得是者，豈可廢!"①

朱熹並不因為張栻意見而偏廢，以胡寅為主，原因恐怕與胡寅撰《論語詳說》，朱熹取材較為方便。朱熹撰《論孟精義》收有程顥、程頤（1033－1107）、張載（1020－1077）、范祖禹（1041－1098）、吕希哲（1036－1114）、吕大臨（1044－1091）、謝良佐、游酢（1053－1123）、楊時（1053－1135）、侯仲良、尹焞（1071－1142）等諸家之說，② 至撰《四書或問》討論範圍擴及周敦頤（1017－1073）、蘇軾（1037－1101）、蘇轍（1039－1112）、周孚先、晁說之（1059－1129）、曾幾（1084－1166）、胡寅、洪興祖（1090－1155）、吳棫（約1100－1154）、張栻、林之奇（1112－1176）、陳暘（1064－1128）、李郁、徐度等諸家之說，胡寅、張栻乃是後期附入內容，正是朱熹取徑湖湘學術的結果。

一、討論聖人氣象

聖人氣象是北宋儒學核心議題，朱熹《四書章句集注》徵引湖湘一系，特別留意聖人氣象的討論，《論語·述而篇》"子不語"一章，朱注引謝良佐云：

聖人語常而不語怪，語德而不語力，語治而不語亂，語人而不語神。③

與"怪"、"力"、"亂"、"神"相較，聖人更重視的"常"、"德"、"治"、"人"，補充極為適切，聖人精神因茲而顯。《論語·衛靈公篇》"予一以貫之"章，朱注引謝良佐云：

聖人之道大矣，人不能徧觀而盡識，宜其以為多學而識之也。然聖人豈務博者哉？如天之於衆形，匪物物刻而雕之也。故曰："予一貫之。""德輶如毛，毛猶有倫。上天之載，無聲無臭。"至矣！④

聖人之化，如天之德，"一以貫之"也就有深刻的想像。《論語·學而篇》"夫子溫、良、恭、儉、讓"一章，朱注引謝良佐、張栻之言：

---

① 黎靖德編《朱子語類》卷十九"語孟綱領"，頁438。

② 朱熹撰 陳俊民校編《朱子文集》第8冊 卷75"序"〈語孟集義序〉云："宋興百年，河、洛之間，有二程先生者出，然後斯道之傳有繼，其於孔子、孟子之心，蓋異世而同符也，故其所以發明二書之說，言雖近而索之無窮，指雖遠而操之有要，使夫讀者，非徒可以得其言；非徒可以得其意，而又可以并其所以進於此者而得之，其所以興起斯文，開悟後學，可謂至矣。間嘗蒐輯條疏，以附本章之次，既又取夫學之有同於先生者，若橫渠張公、范氏、二吕氏、謝氏、游氏、楊氏、侯氏、尹氏，凡九家之說，以附益之，名曰《論孟精義》，以備觀省。"頁3781－3782。

③ 朱熹撰《論語集注》卷四〈述而篇〉，《四書章句集注》（臺北：長安出版社，1991年2月），頁98。

④ 朱熹撰《論語集注》卷八〈衛靈公篇〉，《四書章句集注》，頁161。

謝氏曰："學者觀於聖人威儀之間，亦可以進德矣。若子貢亦可謂善觀聖人矣，亦可謂善言德行矣。今去聖人千五百年，以此五者想見其形容，尚能使人興起，而況於親炙之者乎?"張敬夫曰："夫子至是邦必聞其政，而未有能委國而授之以政者。蓋見聖人之儀刑而樂告之者，秉彝好德之良心也，而私欲害之，是以終不能用耳。"①

聖人一動一靜，皆是門人關注的焦點，"溫、良、恭、儉、讓"不僅可以讓人想見孔子形象，也有助於修養進德，子貢所言之效，孔門弟子親炙之功，謝良佐激昂其事，言之成理，極富闡釋作用，然而孔子德既可以感動千五百年後之人，卻終究不為時君所用，張栻言其理由，乃是"良心"雖萌，而"私欲"害之，於此補充，導入人心之辨，更為周全完整。

二、辨析經文來源

朱熹特別留意胡寅對於《論語》辨析成果，如《論語·里仁篇》"三年無改於父之道"章，引胡氏曰："已見首篇，此蓋複出而逸其半也。"②《論語·里仁篇》"君子欲訥於言而敏於行"章，引胡氏曰："自吾道一貫至此十章，疑皆曾子門人所記也。"③《論語·公冶長篇》篇題朱注"胡氏以為疑多子貢之徒所記云。"④《論語·子罕篇》"末由也已"一章，朱注引胡氏曰："抑斯歎也，其在請事斯語之後，三月不違之時乎?"⑤《論語·先進篇》朱注引胡氏曰："此篇記閔子騫言行者四，而其一直稱閔子，疑閔氏門人所記也。"⑥《論語·憲問篇》朱注引胡氏曰："此篇疑原憲所記。"⑦《論語·衛靈公篇》"吾猶及史之闕文也"章，朱注引胡氏曰："此章義疑，不可強解。"⑧《論語·季氏篇》"齊景公有馬千駟"章，朱注引胡氏曰："程子以為第十二篇錯簡'誠不以富，亦祇以異'，當在此章之首。今詳文勢，似當在此句之上。言人之所稱，不在於富，而在於異也。"⑨ 章，《論語·陽貨篇》"君子尚勇乎"章，朱注引胡氏曰："疑此子路初見孔子時問答也。"⑩《論語·微子篇》"柳下惠為士師"章，朱注引胡氏曰："此必有孔子斷

---

① 朱熹撰《論語集注》卷一〈學而篇〉，《四書章句集注》，頁 51。
② 朱熹撰《論語集注》卷 2〈里仁篇〉，《四書章句集注》，頁 73。
③ 朱熹撰《論語集注》卷 2〈里仁篇〉，《四書章句集注》，頁 74。
④ 朱熹撰《論語集注》卷 3〈公冶長篇〉，《四書章句集注》，頁 75。
⑤ 朱熹撰《論語集注》卷 5〈子罕篇〉，《四書章句集注》，頁 112。
⑥ 朱熹撰《論語集注》卷 6〈先進篇〉，《四書章句集注》，頁 123。
⑦ 朱熹撰《論語集注》卷 7〈原憲篇〉，《四書章句集注》，頁 148。
⑧ 朱熹撰《論語集注》卷 8〈衛靈公篇〉，《四書章句集注》，頁 166。
⑨ 朱熹撰《論語集注》卷 8〈季氏篇〉，《四書章句集注》，頁 173。
⑩ 朱熹撰《論語集注》卷 9〈陽貨篇〉，《四書章句集注》，頁 182。

之之言而亡之矣。"[①]《論語・微子篇》"周公謂魯公"章，朱注引胡氏曰："此伯禽受封之國，周公訓戒之辭。魯人傳誦，久而不忘也。其或夫子嘗與門弟子言之歟?"[②] 等，凡經文辨析，推究來源，往往以胡寅意見為主，湖湘學者由《春秋》入《論語》，從經教而及於言語之間，切近聖人氣象，對於經典文字也就更加留意，自然成為朱熹援據依據。

三、推究學術進程

湖湘學脈有其宗旨，《論語・學而篇》"道千乘之國：敬事而信，節用而愛人，使民以時。"朱注引胡寅云：

> 凡此數者，又皆以敬為主。[③]

"敬"之一端，正是湖湘一系心法，然朱熹於下云："愚謂五者反復相因，各有次第，讀者宜細推之。"顯然有更廣泛的思考，相同之處，《論語・顏淵篇》"樊遲從遊於舞雩之下"章，朱注引胡寅云：

> 慝之字從心從匿，蓋惡之匿於心者。脩者，治而去之。[④]

由治心而成工夫，無疑正是"察識"的最佳說明，湖湘學術成為朱熹詮釋的材料。只是朱熹認為湖湘學者往往有過高之弊，對於學術進程的主張，也就特別留意，《論語・為政篇》"七十而從心所欲，不踰矩"一章，朱注引胡寅云：

> 胡氏曰："聖人之教亦多術，然其要使人不失其本心而已。欲得此心者，惟志乎聖人所示之學，循其序而進焉。至於一疵不存、萬理明盡之後，則其日用之間，本心瑩然，隨所意欲，莫非至理。蓋心即體，欲即用，體即道，用即義，聲為律而身為度矣。"又曰："聖人言此，一以示學者當優游涵泳，不可躐等而進；二以示學者當日就月將，不可半途而廢也。"[⑤]

不失本心，成為彰顯聖人境界的最佳說明，以心就理，落實於日用之間，達致本心瑩然，隨所意欲，莫非至理的境界，修養工夫為"心即體，欲即用，體即道，用即義"，於此乃湖湘一系之精彩所在，朱熹取以證明聖人終極進程，朱熹並非不明白道體朗現的直捷趣味，只是"聖"、"凡"有別，朱熹必須於詮釋之中，區別進程。《論語・雍也篇》"中人以上"章，朱注引張栻云：

> 聖人之道，精粗雖無二致，但其施教，則必因其材而篤焉。蓋中人以下之質，驟而語之太高，非惟不能以入，且將妄意躐等，而有不切於身之弊，亦終於下而

---

① 朱熹撰《論語集注》卷9〈微子篇〉，《四書章句集注》，頁183。
② 朱熹撰《論語集注》卷9〈微子篇〉，《四書章句集注》，頁187。
③ 朱熹撰《論語集注》卷1〈學而篇〉，《四書章句集注》，頁49。
④ 朱熹撰《論語集注》卷6〈顏淵篇〉，《四書章句集注》，頁139。
⑤ 朱熹撰《論語集注》卷1〈為政篇〉，《四書章句集注》，頁55。

已矣。故就其所及而語之，是乃所以使之切問近思，而漸進於高遠也。①

強調學有次第，觀點已與朱熹一致。

另外，《論語・子路篇》“必也正名乎”，《論語・陽貨篇》“苟患失之”，以及《孟子・滕文公下》“孔子懼，作《春秋》”等三章，朱注引“胡氏曰”，所謂“胡氏”並非胡寅而是胡安國，以《孟子・滕文公下》朱注引：

胡氏曰：“仲尼作春秋以寓王法。惇典、庸禮、命德、討罪，其大要皆天子之事也。知孔子者，謂此書之作，遏人欲於横流，存天理於既滅，為後世慮，至深遠也。罪孔子者，以謂無其位而託二百四十二年南面之權，使亂臣賊子禁其欲而不得肆，則戚矣。”②

胡安國《春秋傳》乃湖湘學術基礎，也是承繼二程最重要的成果，朱熹徵引胡安國經學研究成果，可見朱熹固然從湖湘一系得其辨析心性的思考，卻也同樣留意經典研究的進程。③

## 四、結論

“道南”與“湖湘”學術分流，所傳有異，全祖望（1705－1755）以謝良佐“氣剛”、楊時“氣柔”，說明兩人氣質不同，各有體會。④ 朱熹思索心體動靜問題，究察日用功效，張栻引介啟發，居功厥偉，假設無兩人的努力，化除歧見，二程學術分而不合，日失其緒，終難有今日面貌，⑤ 朱熹〈祭張敬夫殿撰文〉言其交誼：

我昔求道，未獲其友，蔽莫予開，吝莫予剖。蓋自從公，而觀於大業之規模，察彼群言之紛糾，於是相與切磋以究之，而又相厲以死守也。⑥

在同中有異，異中有同之中，兩人獲得共識，求道之公，心念之平，朱熹言其過往，情懷令人感動。只是針對張栻，前人卻有不同看法，牟宗三先生云：

南軒雖師之，然“受教之日淺”，固不能發其師之精蘊。又其天資明敏，心思活潑，看似通達柔和，而實稟性清弱，故其與朱子往復辯難，率多以朱子為主動，

---

① 朱熹撰《論語集注》卷3〈雍也篇〉，《四書章句集注》，頁89。

② 朱熹撰《孟子集注》卷6〈滕文公下〉，《四書章句集注》，頁272。

③ 參見拙撰〈集注與章句：朱熹四書詮釋的體例與方向〉，《朱熹與四書章句集注》，頁193－194。

④ 黄宗羲原著 全祖望補修《宋元學案》卷24“上蔡學案”，頁917。

⑤ 陳谷嘉撰《張栻與湖湘學派研究》（湖南教育出版社，1991年8月）云：“朱熹和張栻……繼承、綜合北宋理學各派創立的思想成果，將理學思想發展推向一個新的階段——理學集大成階段。”頁141。

⑥ 朱熹撰 陳俊民校編《朱子文集》第9冊 卷87〈祭張敬夫殿撰文〉，頁4293。

順從朱子之格局，其所言說大都尾隨其後而彌縫之。……此見其力弱才短，故軟塌而被吞沒也。其學無傳，亦非偶然。朱子樂與之談，而又深致贊佩之辭，亦只喜其明敏而隨和耳。①

對於張栻未能守住師法，深致批評，“力弱才短”與“軟塌”的形容，實在是極為嚴苛的批評，然而“天資明敏”與“稟性清弱”乃是矛盾陳述，與朱熹契合是否即屬陷落，對於張栻缺乏好感，恐怕出於朱熹為別子的預設立場。② 然而與此相反，黃宗羲《宋元學案》有較為平實的看法，按語云：

南軒之學，得之五峯。論其所造，大要比五峯更純粹，蓋由其見處高，踐履又實也。朱子生平相與切磋得力者，東萊、象山、南軒數人而已。東萊則言其雜，象山則言其禪，惟于南軒，為所佩服。一則曰：“敬夫見識，卓然不可及。從遊之久，反復開益為多。”一則曰：“敬夫學問愈高，所見卓然，議論出人表。近讀其說，不覺胸中灑然，誠可嘆服。”然南軒非與朱子反復辯難，亦焉取斯哉！③

黃氏於後言：“五峯之門，得南軒而有耀。”④ 肯定張栻於湖湘學的地位，⑤ 也留意朱熹與張栻的交誼。朱熹學既嚴謹，與張栻同輩論交，一生相互欣賞，識見可以推知，張栻受教胡宏雖淺，然而一聞其說，即能體驗實踐，深造有得，聰穎於此可見。朱熹即云張栻“欽夫最不可得，聽人說話，便肯改”⑥、“南軒從善之亟”，⑦ 以其識見，以其聰穎，身為湖湘學術領袖人物，卻能無嫌隙，無偏狹，以聖學為究竟，持平而公的態度，整合歧異，論其意義，恐怕比鵝湖朱、陸之會更為重要，朱熹《四書章句集注》融鑄前賢意見，並未徵引陸九淵說法，然而張栻說法，卻是諸多援引，彼此商討。朱熹確立一生思想旨趣，二程歧異得以釐清，湖湘學術在朱熹與張栻努力當中，得以轉折存續，此乃前人未及觀察之處，卻是真實存在，是以列舉分析，撮舉觀察如下：

一、朱熹從學李侗，從摻雜佛道而歸於純粹，在儒學當中獲致生命依歸，可惜從學日短，無法真切了解默坐澄心之教，窮無所歸之際，旁求張栻所傳湖湘之學，開展匯聚眾流的階段。

二、朱熹依循張栻引導，原本求於未發之際，體察泯然無覺的狀態，愈求愈不可得，在此指引之下，終於有所突破，“灑落”正是李侗所指引境界，竟然於“湖湘”一

---

① 牟宗三撰《心體與性體》（二）（臺北：正中書局，1968年10月），頁432。

② 牟宗三撰《心體與性體》（一）第一部“綜論”，頁45。

③ 黃宗羲原著 全祖望補修《宋元學案》第3冊 卷50“南軒學案”，頁1635。

④ 黃宗羲原著 全祖望補修《宋元學案》第3冊 卷50“南軒學案”，頁1635。

⑤ 朱熹言之更明，黎靖德編《朱子語類》第7冊，卷103，云：“敬夫說本出胡氏。胡氏之說，惟敬夫獨得之，其餘門人皆不曉，但云當守師之說。”頁2606。

⑥ 朱熹言之更明，黎靖德編《朱子語類》第7冊，卷103，頁2606。

⑦ 朱熹言之更明，黎靖德編《朱子語類》第7冊，卷103，頁2610。

系的心法中得見。

三、然而湖湘學者蹈虛入禪，缺乏篤實進程，朱熹心生疑慮，頓悟“中和”之旨，於是納湖湘學派“察識”於“致知”之中，揭櫫程頤“涵養須是敬，進學則在致知”主張，以“主敬”、“窮理”交相為用，確立一生學術方向。

四、朱熹《四書章句集注》徵引“湖湘”一脈言論，謝良佐六十六次、胡安國三次、胡寅四十一次、張栻十次，有關聖人氣象、經文來源、學術進程等思考成果，成為朱熹詮釋取用的重要來源。

五、朱熹與張栻同輩論交，化解動靜紛擾，究察日用之效，一生相互欣賞，二程歧異得以釐清，南宋儒學得以開展，張栻引介啟發，居功厥偉，湖湘學脈也在朱熹與張栻的努力之下，得以留存於經典詮釋當中。

南宋“道南”與“湖湘”兩系各走一端，於儒學各自經營，朱熹與張栻兩人相互交流，彼此支持，由本體以見工夫，又由工夫以見本體，兩位領袖人物，整合歧異，以聖學為究竟，無嫌隙，無偏狹，持平而公的態度，正是南宋儒學得以開拓的關鍵，也是《四書章句集注》重要的義理來源，只是線索既雜，數量龐大，本文提供初步觀察，所論不敢自是，尚祈學界先進有以教之。

# 简论宋儒“一体之仁”的思想及其现代意义

## ——以张载、二程、朱子的“一体之仁”思想为例

武汉大学 吴根友

仁学思想是儒家思想的核心，但在儒家思想的发展历史过程中，并非所有的儒家学者都是围绕“仁”这一核心观念来建构自己的思想体系的。虽然如此，但作为儒家思想阵营的思想家或学者，都或多或少地对仁学思想有新的阐发，进而自然而然地形成了一个自在的仁学发展的历史。值得欣慰的是，当代中国儒学的发展出现了一些可喜的现象，出现了两本自觉以仁为核心观念的新著作，① 体现了当代中国儒学在继承前人的基础上有所发展，有所深化的新趋势。笔者至今还清楚地记得，1999年在哈佛燕京学社做访问研究的时候，时任哈燕社社长的杜维明教授在接见我的一次面谈中曾经问到（原话的大意是）：你认为儒学是在传统社会，还是在现代民主社会得到更好的发展？我当时不假思索地回答道：在今天民主社会会得到更好的发展。现在看来，这一回答未必那么确定，但今天民主社会里更需要儒家的仁学智慧，或者如陈来所说的，更需要儒家“爱的智慧”，我想这一点应该是没有问题的。本文试图以断代思想史的方式，仅择取张载、二程、朱熹四位思想家为例，扼要阐明两宋儒学中“一体之仁”的思想，并试图揭示这一新仁学思想对于当今社会所具有的启迪意义。本文所说的“一体之仁”，是对宋儒“儒者以天地万物为一体”的新仁学命题的一种缩写版表达，此一表达在阳明的《传习录》已有先例，② 特此说明。

### 一、张载的“一体之仁”思想

一般哲学史及哲学论著的叙述，多将张载看作是北宋时代的气论思想家，对其

---

① 其一是牟钟鉴的《新仁学构想——爱的追寻》（人民出版社，2013年），其二陈来的新著《新原仁——仁学本体论》，生活·读书·新知三联书店，2013年。笔者本人也曾经撰写过《儒家仁爱思想论纲》，载孙熙国、李翔海主编《北大中国文化研究》（第1辑），社会科学文献出版社，2012年。

② 王阳明：“圣人有忧之，是以推其天地万物一体之仁以教天下”。“盖其心学纯明，而有以全其万物一体之仁”。《答顾东桥书》，《传习录》下，中州古籍出版社，2008年，第192，193页。

“知太虚即气则无无”的哲学命题更为重视。这也没有错。但张载在儒家思想史的另一个重要贡献则是对“一体之仁”的系统阐发。这一点，思想史的重视似乎不够。在《正蒙·天道》篇，张载说：“天道四时行，百物生，无非至教；圣人之动，无非至德，夫何言哉！天体物不遗，犹仁体事无不在也。‘礼仪三百，威仪三千’，无一物而非仁也。‘昊天曰明，及尔出王，昊天曰旦，及尔游衍’，无一物之不体也。”[①]

张载仁与天作对比性的论述，着重揭示“仁”所具有的普遍性之爱的特征：“天体物不遗，仁体事无不在。”而一切制度及其具体信轨，都是仁爱的根本体现。这当然不一定是事实层面的叙述，而仅是一种理想性的要求，希望一切规范及其具体仪轨都能体现仁爱的性质。

张载还从“天道”的高度来规定人、物之性的，他说：“由太虚，有天之名；由气化，有道之名；合虚与气，有性之名；合性与知觉，有心之名。”[②] 这样，“性”是人物所有的一种基本属性，而人与物的区别恐怕更在于“心”，因为“心”是性与知觉融合的更高级的一物，而人与物的根本性区分正在于“知觉”。

不过，张载此处所讲的“性”，主要是从“性之源”的角度来讲的，而非从“性之成”的角度来讲的。也正是从“性之源”的角度，张载提出了“一体之仁”的思想。他说：“性者万物之一源，非有我之得私也。惟大人为能尽共道，是故立必俱立，知必周知，爱必兼爱，成不独成。彼自蔽塞而不知顺吾理者，则亦未如之何矣。”[③]

如果从“性之成”的角度讲，只有做到仁至义尽，永不间断地求善，才能实现人性之成，可见宋儒以天道广大，天德广普为参照系，为人性在道德方面的至善追求提供了一个实际上是无限广阔的领域。在这一无限广阔的领域里，同时也是在一无限追求的过程之中，个人的德性成就与社会生活领域里对他人的关怀、照料密切相关，因此，仁、义之德，作为一种社会教化的手段，就不完全是用人为的力量去强力推行，也有顺应天道自然的意义。此一层的天道自然更多表现为社会生活习俗中自发形成的自然而然。也即是“百姓日用而不知”的意思。不过，儒家的顺应天道，不是放任不管，而是在人的理性不能完全把握、控制的情况下，有意地“存”之，因而也是一种主动的“让”万事万物在自然而然的活动过程中实现各自的成长，因此，张载将“久存”与“至德”，“顺物”与“时中”联系起来，进而称这种颇为克制的人为活动——“进德”的行为为“仁至义尽”，将“知微知彰”的理智活动与进德行为结合在一起，才可以称之为“成性”。张载的原文这样说道：“神不可致思，存焉可也；化不可助长，

① 张载著：《张载集》，章琛点校，中华书局，1978年第2版，2012年第6次印刷，第13页。
② 张载著：《张载集》，章琛点校，第9页。
③ 张载著：《张载集》，章琛点校，第21页。

顺焉可也。存虚明，久至德，顺变化，达时中，仁之至，义之尽也。知微知彰，不舍而继其善，然后可以成（之）［人］性矣。”①

就个体的能动性而言，“成性”的主要途径就是“大心”。张载说：“大其心则能体天下之物，物有未体，则心为有外。世人之心，止于闻见之狭。圣人尽性，不以见闻梏其心，其视天下无一物非我，孟子谓尽心则知性知天以此。天大无我，故有外之心不足以合天心，见闻之知，乃物交而知，非德性所知；德性所知，不萌于见闻。”②

此一层面的“一体之仁”的确有如后来朱子所说的是“仁之后果”与“仁之量”的意思，但张载在《乾称》篇所阐述的“一体之仁”的思想，则是一种本体论或曰宇宙论意义上的“一体之仁”。

《乾称》篇就社会政治生活、制度安排、人际关系的整体性而言，提出了“仁者与天地万物为一体”的思想，张说：

“乾称父，坤称母；予兹藐焉，乃混然中处。故天地之塞，吾其体，天地之帅（注——神也），吾其性。民吾同胞；物吾与也。大君者，吾父母宗子；其大臣，宗子之家相也。尊高年，所以长其长；慈孤弱，所以幼其幼。圣其合德，贤其秀也。凡天下疲癃残疾、惸独鳏寡，皆吾兄弟之颠连而无告者也。”③

有关这段“仁学”思想性质的讨论，历史上有多种说法，其诸种说法中最为关键之处在于，张载所阐发的儒家“仁爱”思想与墨家的“兼爱”思想有何异同。就笔者的观点来看，张载的新“仁爱”思想包含着“爱所有的人”这一思想要求，与墨子并无不同。但以什么方式去实现这种爱，则是有差异的。即张载在这里还是强调儒家的“由近及远”，有亲疏之别的差等之爱，而墨家的“兼爱”是没有差等的爱。墨家的“兼爱”理论不是说不好，而是太好了，好到了现实生活中的人们绝大多数都做不到。除上述这一根本性区别之外，张载在此处所表现出的博爱思想，还涉及对宇宙万物的爱，这是对孟子“亲亲、仁民、爱物”思想的系统化表达。这一思想应该是墨子思想中所没有明确表述过的，尽管墨家声称“兼爱”是天志的表现，但并没有说要兼爱万物。

要而言之，“一体之仁”的思想在先秦儒家孔子、孟子那里都有零星的表述，但没有像张载这样给予系统化的论证。宋儒所发明的一套学说既可以称之为宋明道学，也可以称之为宋明理学，但就其学说体系中的仁学思想而言，其思想的核心还是先秦儒家的，但有所深化、系统化。张载的仁学思想体系其实很丰富，如就仁、义的各自功

① 张载著：《张载集》，章琛点校，第17页。
② 张载著：《张载集》，章琛点校，第24页。
③ 张载著：《张载集》，章琛点校，第62页。

能而言，张载提出了“仁义各有动静”有观点：“义以反经为本，经正则精；仁以敦化为深，化则行显。义入神，动一静也；仁敦化，静一动也。仁敦化则无体，义入神则无方。”[①] 在此段文献中，张载将“易无方而神无体”的易学思想，向着儒家的仁义道德方向作进一步的融通，强调儒家道德教化的渐进性与灵活性的特点。

在“成性”的问题上，张载通过性与道、命之间的关系的阐述，融合孟子与荀子的思想，一方面承认“天所性”与道、命之相通（这是孟子的思想）。另一方面强调“学”的重要性，认为如果“天所性”在具体的个人身上没有实现或体现出来，问题不是出在“天所性”层面，而是人后天没有认真地学习的结果，而这正是荀子《劝学》篇反复阐明的“学不可以已”，“积学成圣”的道理。张载说：“天所性者通极于道，气之昏明不足以蔽之；天所命者通极于性，遇之吉凶不足以戕之，不免乎蔽之戕之者，未之学也。”[②] 张载的这一说法，从学术发展史的角度看，实开戴震融合孟、荀之先河。而张载专门作《大心》篇，恰恰就是要求人们通过后天的学习，然后领悟人与天地万物为一体的本然状态，进而提高人的道德境界。

## 二、二程论仁与“一体之仁”思想

1. 程颢的“识仁”说。程颢伦理学的最重要特点强调“识仁”。而“识仁”之所以重要，是因为“仁”对于个人的修养及其在社会活动中的指导作用具有根本性，如他说：

> “学者须先识仁。仁者，浑然与物同体。义、礼、知、信皆仁也。识得此理，以诚敬存之而已，不须防检，不须穷索。若心懈则有防，心苟不懈，何防之有？理有未得，故须穷索。存久自明，安待穷索？此道与物无对，大不足以名之，天地之用皆我之用。孟子言‘万物皆备于我’，须反身而诚，乃为大乐。若反身未诚，则犹是二物有对，以己合彼，终未有之，又安得乐？《订顽》意思，乃备言此体。以此意存之，更有何事？‘必有事焉而勿正，心勿忘，勿助长’，未尝致纤毫之力，此其存之之道。若存得，便合有得。盖良知良能元不丧失，以昔日习心未除，却须存习此心，久则可夺旧习。此理至约，惟患不能守。既能体之而乐，亦不患不能守也。”[③]

对于“仁者，浑然与物同体”的命题，程颢还有另外的表述，其意思是一样的，

---

① 张载著：《张载集》，章琛点校，第 18 页。

② 张载著：《张载集》，章琛点校，第 21 页。

③ 《遗书》卷第二上，二先生语上，《二程集》（上），王孝鱼点校，中华书局，1981 年版，第 16—17 页。

如他说："医书言手足痿痹为不仁，此言最善名状。仁者，以天地万物为一体，莫非己也。认得为己，何所不至？若不有诸己，自不与己相干。如手足不仁，气已不贯，皆不属己。"①

与此段文献类似，《宋元学案·明道学案》又有另一则材料，可以作为补充："刚毅木讷，质之近乎仁也；力行，学之近乎仁也。若夫至仁，则天地为一身，而天地之间，品物万形，为四肢百体。夫人岂有视四肢百体而不爱者哉？圣人，仁之至也，独能体是心而已，曷尝支离多端而求之自外乎？故能近取譬者仲尼所以示子贡求仁之方也。医书以手足风顽，谓之四体不仁，为其疾痛不以累其心故也。夫手足在我，而疾痛不与知也，非不仁而何！世之忍心无恩者，其自弃亦若是而已。"②

要而言之，大程子论"仁"，重在人与人之间的道德上的"感通"之情。这与张载的"大心"有类似之处。而在日常的生活中如何践行仁德，使人从普通的人逐步向圣贤靠拢，程颢的观点非常简约。这与孟子所讲的"存其大体"的方法在精神上是相通的。不过种简易的方法有点类似禅宗的修行方式，主要强调修行者对一种绝对价值的精神觉解。

2. 程颐论仁。相对于大程的"识仁"说，小程论仁的思想非常丰富，他仔细地辨析了仁与博爱，仁与圣，仁与孝、仁与心的异同，体现了小程子哲学思想的分析精神。③ 就其"仁学"思想的主要特征而言，他论"仁"比较侧重于"公"的伦理取向，对于"一体之仁"的问题，他似未有明确的论述，但他所说的"物我兼照，故仁"，实际上也有"一体之仁"的意思，如他说："仁之道，要之只消一公字。公只是仁之理，不可将公便唤做仁。公而以人体之，故为仁。只为公，则物我兼照，故仁，所以能恕，所以能爱，恕则仁之施，爱则仁之用也。"④

在《河南程氏粹言》中，有一段论及"仁者以天地万物为一体"的文献："子曰：'仁者以天地万物为一体，莫非我也。知其皆我，何所不尽！不能有诸己，则其与天地万物，岂物相去千万而已哉？'"⑤《粹言》为杨时所记，主要语录是程颐的，但其中也有程颢的。依其语气，当是程颢的。即使程颐没有十分明确的"仁者与物一体"的思

① 《二程遗书》卷二上，《二程集》(上)，王孝鱼点校，第15页。

② 沈善洪主编，吴光执行主编：《黄宗羲全集》(三)，浙江古籍出版社，2005年，第671—672页。

③ 《二程遗书·伊川先生语四》，《二程集》(上)，王孝鱼点校，第182—183页。

④ 《二程遗书·伊川先生语一》，《二程集》(上)，王孝鱼点校，第153页。有关仁与公的联系，程颐还有类似的论述："仁者，天下之公，善之本也。""仁者，天下之正理，失正理则无序而不和。"分别见《伊川易传》卷二《复传》，《二程集》(下)，王孝鱼点校，第820页，《伊川经说》卷六，《二程集》(下)，王孝鱼点校，第1136页。

⑤ 《二程集》(下)，王孝鱼点校，第1179页。

想，但他肯定不反对这一思想。他曾经对自己的弟子说，他死后，就把他当年为其兄所写的行状来写他自己，可见他在主要思想方面与其兄是相通的。

程颐比较谨慎，他对仁与万物关系的论述，在《经说》《论语解》中的一段话可能更能反映他的真实想法，他对有子论“其为人也孝弟”一段解释道：“孝弟于其家，而后仁爱及于物，所谓亲亲而仁民也，故为仁以孝弟为本。”[①] 程颐不反对“一体之仁”，但必须有个次第关系：亲亲、仁民、爱物。

伊川论“仁”在理论上最有创发处在于：将爱与仁分开。他说：“孟子曰：‘恻隐之心，仁也。’后人遂以爱为仁。爱自是情，仁自是性，岂可专以爱为仁？孟子曰：‘恻隐之心，仁之端也。’既曰仁之端，则不可便谓之仁。退之言‘博爱之谓仁’，非也。仁者固博爱，然便以博爱为仁，则不可。”[②]

后来朱熹将此思想凝练为“仁者心之德爱之理”的命题，写入《论语集注》之中，成为理学关于“仁”的重新表述的经典命题。

## 三、朱熹论仁

朱子在两宋理学史上的地位，既具有承前启后的性质，也具有集大成的性质，对于理学中的许多问题都有度越前人的论述。在“一体之仁”的问题上，朱子亦有独到的见解。首先，他匠心独具，以“生意释仁”，并以春夏秋冬为喻，说道：“春为仁，有具生意；在夏，则见其有个亨通意；在秋，则见其有个诚实意；在冬，则见其有个贞固意。在夏秋冬，生意何尝息！本虽凋零，生意则常存。（大雅）”[③] 并又说：“得此生意以有生，然后有礼义智信。以先后言，之，则仁为先；以小大言之，则仁为大。（闳祖）”[④]“仁，浑沦言，则浑沦都是一个生意，义礼智都是仁；对言，则仁与义礼智一般。（淳）”[⑤]

其次，他接受程颐的说法，将仁看作“爱之理，心之德”，认为“爱是恻隐，恻隐是情，其理则谓之仁。心之德，德又只是爱。谓之心之德，却是爱之本柄。人之所以为人，其理则天地之理，其气则天地之气。理无迹，不可见，故于气观之。要识仁之意思，是一个浑然温和之气，其气则天地阳春之气，其是则天地生物之心。”[⑥]

在理气关系论的框架下，朱子进一步来讨论“就人身上看这意思是如何”的问题

① 《二程集》（下），王孝鱼点校，第1133页。
② 《二程遗书·伊川先生语四》，《二程集》（上），王孝鱼点校，第182页。
③ （清）黎靖德编：《朱子语类》卷六，王星贤点校，中华书局，1994年，第105页。
④ （清）黎靖德编：《朱子语类》卷六，王星贤点校，第105页。
⑤ （清）黎靖德编：《朱子语类》卷六，王星贤点校，第107页。
⑥ （清）黎靖德编：《朱子语类》卷六，王星贤点校，第111页。

时，涉及“一体之仁”的问题，他认为，“克去己私以复于礼，自然都是这意思。这不是待人旋安排，自是合下都有这个浑全流行物事。此意思才无私意间隔，便自见得人与己一，物与己一公道自流行。须是如此看。”[①]

上文说到的“这意思”，即是指“仁是生意”，这一股生意落实在个人身上，只要不被一己私意间隔，则人己、人物之间就会是一自然而然生意流行的世界，因而也就自然而然是“万物一体”的。因此，我们可以说，朱子并不反对“一体之仁”的说法，而是更进一步地讨论了“一体之仁”何以可能的问题。

在“求仁”的问题上，朱子不反对致知、格物、博学、审问、慎思、明辩、力行等多种途径，但关键处还是要“存得此心”：“且要存得此心，不为私欲所胜，遇事每每着精神照管，不中随物流去，须要紧紧守着。若常存得此心，应事接物，虽不中不远。”[②] 而且，他特别强调“仁是温和之物”的特征，说道：“仁虽似有刚直意，毕竟本是个温和之物。但出来发用时有许多般，须得是非、辞逊、断制三者，方成仁之事。及至事定，三者各退，仁仍旧温和，缘是他本性如此。人但见有非、节文、断制，却谓都是仁之本意，则非也。春本温和，故能生物，所以说仁为春。”[③]

其三，他对于前贤的“一体之仁”与“仁者无私欲”的两种说法都有仔细的辨证。他说：“谓之无私欲然后仁，则可；谓无私便是仁，则不可。盖惟无私欲而后仁始见，如无所壅底而水方行。”[④] 当方叔说“与天地万物一体是仁”时，朱子说道：“无私，是仁之前事；与天地万物为一体，是仁之后。惟无私，然后仁；惟仁，然后与天地万物为一体。要在二者之间识得毕竟仁是甚模样。欲晓得仁名义，须并‘义、礼、智’三字看。欲真个见得仁底模样，须是从‘克己复礼’做工夫去。今人说仁，如糖，皆道是甜；不曾吃着，不知甜是甚滋味。圣人都不说破，在学者以身体之而已矣。（闳祖）”[⑤]

上段文献表明，朱子并没有简单地接受“仁者以天地万物为一体”的说法，并不表明他反对这一说法，而只是认为这一说法不足尽“仁”之意思，仁还有“公而无私”的特性，亦即是说，“仁”还有前置的条件，如果人不能做到公而无私，就无法实现“仁者与天地万物为一体”的结果。只要人有私欲横隔在人我、物我之间，就无法实现“一体之仁”的结果。朱子在反对杨时的“万物与我为一”为仁的命题时还说道：“此不是仁之体，却是仁之量。仁者固能觉，谓觉为仁，不可；仁者固能与万物为一，谓

---

① （清）黎靖德编：《朱子语类》卷六，王星贤点校，第111页。

② （清）黎靖德编：《朱子语类》卷六，王星贤点校，第114页。

③ （清）黎靖德编：《朱子语类》卷六，王星贤点校，第114页。

④ （清）黎靖德编：《朱子语类》卷六，王星贤点校，第117页。

⑤ （清）黎靖德编：《朱子语类》卷六，王星贤点校，第117页。

万物为一为仁，亦不可。譬如说屋，不论屋是木做柱，竹做壁，却只是说屋如此大，容得许多物。如万物为一，只是说得仁之量。（因举禅语是说得量边事云云。德明）"[①]

朱子就"仁"的问题，还有很多的讨论，如仁与知觉的关系，认为"仁固有知觉，唤知觉做仁，却不得。"[②] 但在根本上，他强调"仁是根"的道理，亦即强调"仁是生意"的这一意思，他说："仁是根，恻隐是萌芽。亲亲、仁民、爱物，便是推广到枝叶处。（夔孙）"[③]

他甚至认为，"仁：鸡雏初生可怜意与之同。意思鲜嫩。天理著见，一段意思可爱，发出即皆是。"[④] 这些说法，对于儒家仁爱思想的深化与发展都具有积极的意思。不过，他对"一体之仁"的理解仍然有问题的。就张载、程颢的"一体之仁"的观念来说，并不能理解成公而无私之后的"仁"之结果，而应该是一种万物本然状态。这种天地的本然状态即是天道至诚无息的状态。人由于小我、私体之隔，忘记了自己与天地自诚无息，生生之仁的内在联系，故通过"大心"、"识仁"的"反身而诚"的认识活动，真切地体认到"仁者与天地万物为一体"的本然状态。而这一真切的体认过程，即是自明而诚的过程。所以，朱子将"一体之仁"看作是人们求仁的结果是可以，但浑沦地将"一体之仁"命题看作是仁之结果，或者看作是"仁之量"，则并不恰当。

## 余　论

"一体之仁"的说法，在明代儒学之中，数王阳明的说法最为极端，他引进禅宗的思想，以更加夸张的形式，多复阐述万物之间皆有情性的思想观念。他将"一体之仁"上升到一种心本体的高度，说道："大人者 ，以天地万物为一体者也，其视天下犹一家，中国犹一人焉。……大人之能以天地万物为一体也，非意（后天的主观意识所为，引者注）之也，其心之仁本若是，其与天地万物而为一也。岂唯大人，虽小人之心亦莫不然，彼顾自小之耳。是故见孺子之入井，而必有怵惕恻隐之心焉，是其仁之与孺子而为一体也……故夫为大人之学者，亦惟去其私欲之蔽，以自明其明德，复其天地万物一体之本然而已耳；非能于本体之外而有所增益之也。"[⑤]

而王阳明所说的这种心本体，实即是他说的"良知"。阳明学经过后学的发展，特别是晚明市民阶层代表人物如王艮的进一步发展，逐步变成了儒学的"异端"，出现了

---

① （清）黎靖德编：《朱子语类》卷六，王星贤点校，第 118 页。

② （清）黎靖德编：《朱子语类》卷六，王星贤点校，第 118 页。

③ （清）黎靖德编：《朱子语类》卷六，王星贤点校，第 118 页。

④ （清）黎靖德编：《朱子语类》卷六，王星贤点校，第 119 页。

⑤ 王阳明：《大学或问》，《王阳明全集》（下），吴光、钱明、董平、姚延福编校，上海古籍出版社，1992 年，第 968 页。

李贽这样的新思想家，而到了清代，这种新思想经过文学家、艺术家的重新解释，发展成为一种新人文思想，像郑板桥、袁枚等人同情下层民众的遭遇，特别是同情受压迫最深的女性、妓女等，逐渐发展出了中国式的近代人道主义思想。到近代之初，谭谭嗣同在西方现代文化的强大力量冲击下，提出“仁以通为第一义”的新仁学思想，已经将古老的儒家“仁学”思想与近现代的人道主义思想结合在一起了，与其他戊戌维新之士一道，开启了中国现代思想运动。

在当代中国的社会主义现代文化建设过程中，“一体之仁”的说法，经过现代人道主义的洗礼，即是普遍的爱人思想。而且不仅仅停留于爱人的层次上，可以与生态文明的爱物、惜物思想发生内在的关联。亲亲、仁人、爱物的“一体之仁”的次第，仍然具有普遍的可接受性与经验上的可行性。当然，在亲亲、仁人的问题上，更要重视亲人、他人的自由意志，对于亲人、他人以一种礼敬的态度对待之，而对自己当然亦当以自尊为前提。则儒家的“一体之仁”不仅在中国的现代文化建设中焕发出新的青春活力，而且也可以成为当今全球伦理的最为重要的思想资源之一。（2014年8月27日星期三，第一稿）

# 张载经典阅读的方法论

长安大学马克思主义学院 李 刚

阅读经典与消遣读物、专业书籍不同，是“仰望星空、反观道德”的活动，最为持久，也最为切身。中国古代的许多思想家潜心于经典的研读，创立自己的思想体系，也形成了独特的经典阅读方法论。北宋著名的哲学家、思想家张载，一生潜心攻读经典，创立关学学派，树立关中勤奋向学、勇于创新的学风，知行合一，在中国思想、阅读史上留下了光辉的一页。大力呼唤经典阅读的时代，剖析张载的经典阅读方法和观点，有一定的启发意义。

## 一、张载是苦读、精思、力行的思想家

张载“勇于造道”，本着“为天地立心，为生民立命，为往圣继绝学，为万世开太平”的伟大理想，形成了别具一格的哲学思想体系，是宋明理学的重要创始人之一，更是一位善于读书的学者。

张载（1020－1077），姓张名载，字子厚。张载之名，出自《周易》的“厚德载物”。张载祖籍大梁，父亲张迪于真宗初携妻陆氏上任于陕西长安。天禧四年（1020年）张载生。天圣元年（1023年）年任涪州知州。张迪在涪州任上病故，十五岁的张载和五岁的张戬与母亲，护送父亲的灵柩越归葬大梁，至郿县横渠，无力返归故里，遂将父安葬于横渠，定居于此，人称张载为横渠先生。

张载“少孤自立，无所不学”，[①] 喜欢读书思考，关心国家大事。当时西夏常对西部边境侵扰，朝廷向西夏“赐”绢、银和茶叶等大量物资。年仅二十一岁的张载就向当时任陕西经略安抚副使、主持西北防务的范仲淹上书《边议九条》，并打算组织民团夺回被西夏侵占的洮西失地。范仲淹在延州军府召见了张载，认为张载可成大器，劝他道：“儒家自有名教，何事于兵。”[②] 勉励他读《中庸》。张载听从劝告，苦攻《中

① 张载：《张载集》，中华书局，1978年，第381页。

② 张载：《张载集》，中华书局，1978年，第381页。

庸》，遍读佛学、道家经典十多年，最后回到儒学，创立起关学思想体系。

张载仕途坎坷，能守志而行。仁宗嘉祐二年（1057年）张载赴汴京应考，时值欧阳修主考，张载与苏轼、苏辙兄弟同登进士。先后任祁州司法参军，云岩县令著作佐郎，签书渭州军事判官等职，实行德教。神宗熙宁二年（1069年），御史中丞吕公著向神宗推荐张载，张载对王安石变法持保留态度，不久被派往浙东明州（今浙江省宁波）审理苗振贪污案。张载之弟监察御史张戬因反对王安石变法，被贬知公安县，张载辞官回到横渠。熙宁十年（1077年）秦凤路守帅吕大防上奏神宗召张载回京任职。张载带病而行，担任同知太常职务，与礼官不合，加之病重，便辞职西归，行至临潼病逝。

张载虚心向学、勤奋著述。中进士后，张载受宰相文彦博支持，在开封相国寺设虎皮椅讲《易》。遇表侄洛阳程颢、程颐兄弟，虚心听取二程对《易经》的见解，第二天就对听讲的人说："比见二程深明《易》道，吾所弗及，汝辈可师之。"① 撤座缀讲，发奋钻研，写成《横渠易说》。

张载勤于著述，也能学以致用。张载辞官回到横渠后，依靠薄田度日，"终日危坐一室，左右简编，俯而读，仰而思。有得则识之，或中夜起坐，取烛以书，其志道精思，未始须臾息，亦未尝须臾忘也。"② 张载作《砭愚》、《订顽》训辞即《东铭》、《西铭》，书于大门两侧，训诫学者，完成代表性著作《正蒙》，并与弟子进行恢复古礼和井田制两项试验，至今这一带还流传着"横渠八水验井田"的故事。

张载青少年时便喜欢读书，勇于思考，也勤于读书，达到废寝忘食的地步。他终日端坐一室，左右置书，俯而读，仰而思，随想随记，有时半夜披衣而起，及时记下心得。张载一生，读书治学，未尝有个停歇；无论何时何地，都不忘读书，读书读到了"朝思暮想"的地步。有的经典著作，张载一读就是几十年。张载得到范仲淹的规劝和指点，读《中庸》二十年，用功之深，可以想象。张载强调读书要靠只争朝夕："学者不可谓少年，自缓便是四十五十。二程从十四岁时便锐然欲学圣人，今尽及四十未能及颜闵之徒。"③ 不可有片刻停歇："勿使有俄顷闲度，逐日似此，三年庶几有进。"④ 他恨不得将全天都用于学习："学者又且须以自朝及昼至夜为三节，积累功夫，更有勤学，则于时又以为恨（限）。"⑤ 遇到困难，要果敢而进，勇闯难关："今人为学如登山麓，方其迤逦之时，莫不阔步大走，及到峭峻之处便止，须是要刚决果敢以

① 张载：《张载集》，中华书局，1978年，第386页。
② 张载：《张载集》，中华书局，1978年，第383页。
③ 张载：《张载集》，中华书局，1978年，第280页。
④ 张载：《张载集》，中华书局，1978年，第376页。
⑤ 张载：《张载集》，中华书局，1978年，第321页。

进。”[①] 张载苦心力索，学者少有能如横渠用功者。

读书为学，不是一件容易的事情，须不断提高。张载自谦地说，我三十年来读书写作，如果还有所得的话，那不过是碰巧了。他打比方说，读书治学，就像一个小偷想偷窃财物却不明底里，或者向外人打听，或者夜里在墙外偷听，或者在墙上凿一小孔窥视，所见要么不可靠，要么非常有限，必须自己亲自进入屋内，才能探得实情。进了室内，又不能点蜡烛，还须在暗中不断摸索。没有耐心，不下功夫找寻，是得不到有价值的东西的。就是有所得，也不过是一件宝贝而已，更好的东西还有很多，而不能止步不前：“慕学之始，犹闻都会纷华盛丽，未见其美而知其有美不疑，步步进则渐到，画则自弃也。”[②] 只有不断努力，才能真正有收获。他谈自己的体会说，他满以为自己学有所成了，但仔细回味，只不过得到了读书治学的一个具体途径而已，才知道要进一步下功夫读书。所以，张载说：“学者恶其自足，足则不复进。”[③] 浅尝辄止，小有收获就自以为是，是谈不上读书的。读书为学如此不易，张载就将自己的读书体会总结的非常仔细致，希望嘉惠后学。

## 二、张载形成了系统的经典阅读方法论

经典的阅读，重在提高人生境界，树立人生更高的理想。清代学者张伯行说总结张载之学说：“道以居正为大，学以尽心为要，此古今不易之理也。”[④] 读书而没有心性品德的提高，终归是不会有大的收获的。用张载的话说，“德薄者终学不成也”。[⑤] 他以音乐为例，说明读书和人的德性修养是相关的：“律吕有可求之理，德性深厚者必能知之。”[⑥] 经典作家有相当高的人生境界，没有一定的修养，是无法理解经典作家的精神境界的。“为学大益在自求变化气质，不尔皆为人之弊，卒无所发明，不得见圣人之奥。”[⑦] 张载认为读经典的目的，在于变化人的气质：“学者先须变化气质，变化气质与虚心相表里。”[⑧] 换句话说，读经典重要读如何成为一个理想中的人：“学者当须立人之性。仁者人也，当辨其人之所谓人。学者学所以为人。”[⑨]

---

① 张载：《张载集》，中华书局，1978 年，第 283 页。
② 张载：《张载集》，中华书局，1978 年，第 283 页。
③ 张载：《张载集》，中华书局，1978 年，第 270 页。
④ 张载：《张载集》，中华书局，1978 年，第 394 页。
⑤ 张载：《张载集》，中华书局，1978 年，第 273 页。
⑥ 张载：《张载集》，中华书局，1978 年，第 263 页。
⑦ 张载：《张载集》，中华书局，1978 年，第 274 页。
⑧ 张载：《张载集》，中华书局，1978 年，第 274 页。
⑨ 张载：《张载集》，中华书局，1978 年，第 321 页。

经典的阅读，要养成良好的读书志趣。陶冶了性情，变化了心性气质，才能虚心读书，养成读书的志趣。读书不在人聪明与愚笨，勤奋不勤奋，最主要的还是在人的志趣。有了志趣，就会坚持下去，否则会学而无成。如果只为功名利禄而读经典，是缘木求鱼。抱着急功近利的心理去读书，就像刚一上手就想像鲁班一样做木工活，没有不伤手的，读之无益。经典的阅读，不能只求实用，要求的低，得到的肯定少；只有高要求，才能有大的收获。立志读书，天长日久，就会养成学习的兴趣。兴趣是学习的动力："'乐则生矣'，学至于乐则自不已，故进也。"① 养成良好的读书习惯和兴趣，就会以读书为乐，并主动去读书。

经典的阅读，入门最难。张载强调初学不可不记："经籍亦须记得，虽有舜禹之智，吟而不言，不如聋盲之指麾。故记得便说得，说得便行得，故始学亦不可无诵记。"② 虽不可死读硬背，但对初学者来说，记下一些基本的知识，却是不可少的。他谈自己的学习《中庸》的体会说："答问者命字为难，己则讲习惯，听者往往致惑。学者用心未熟，以中庸文字辈，直须句句理会过，使其言互相发明，纵其间有命字未安处，亦不足为学者之病。"③因此，"在始学者，得一义须固执，从杂入精也。如孝事亲，忠事君，一种是义，然其中有多少义理也。"④ 读书入门，须关键段句须读之成诵，明确基本意义，经过积累，就会由杂入精，融会贯通，且容易记住："书须成诵精思，多在夜中或静坐得之，不记则思不起，但通贯得大原后，书亦易记。"⑤

经典的阅读，博而后能精。博与精是成正比的，二者并进而有功："故只是要博学，学愈博则义愈精微，舜好问，好察迩言，皆所以尽精微也。舜与仲尼心则同，至于密察处料得未如孔子。"⑥ 由博方可入专，由杂方能为精。博与专的道理，张载讲得非常具体。当然，由博入精，由杂入专门，有一个过程，不可操之过急："大率玩心未熟，可求之平易，勿迂也。若始求太深，恐自兹愈远。"⑦ 但是，"多闻不足以尽天下之故"，⑧ 只有博览群书，由浅入深，并持之以恒，不断思考，既获得了义理，陶冶了性情，才是读书有得："读书少则无由考校得义理，盖书以维持此心，一时放下则一时德性有懈，读书则此心常在，不读书则终看义理不见。"⑨

---

① 张载：《张载集》，中华书局，1978年，第282页。
② 张载：《张载集》，中华书局，1978年，第277页。
③ 张载：《张载集》，中华书局，1978年，第284页。
④ 张载：《张载集》，中华书局，1978年，第287页。
⑤ 张载：《张载集》，中华书局，1978年，第275页。
⑥ 张载：《张载集》，中华书局，1978年，第270页。
⑦ 张载：《张载集》，中华书局，1978年，第274页。
⑧ 张载：《张载集》，中华书局，1978年，第376页。
⑨ 张载：《张载集》，中华书局，1978年，第275页。

经典的阅读贵在贯通，得其大体。如果只从字面阅读，只能误解、怪罪作者："若只泥文而不求大体则失之，是小儿视指之类也。常引小儿以手指物示之，而不能求物以视焉，只视于手，及无物则加怒耳。"[①] 幼儿视野有限，理解力弱，只看人的手指，而不看手指所指的东西。望文生义，断章取义，就像幼儿一样短视。因此，张载强调读书"须是大体上求之"，"观书必总其言而求作者之意。"[②] 多闻阙疑也是必要的："疑则阙之，更多识前言往行以养其德，多闻阙疑，多见阙殆。"[③] 只有得其大义，才能融会贯通。张载说："大抵人能弘道，举一字无不透彻。如义者，谓合宜也，以合宜推之，仁、礼、信皆合宜之事。"[④] 如何才能贯通？张载强调要放开眼界："博大之心未明，观书见一言大，一言小，不从博大中来，皆未识尽。"[⑤] 从大处着眼，以开阔的眼界读书，就能"博文以集义"："博文以集义，集义以正经，正经然后一以贯天下之道。"[⑥] 经过泛观博览，获得了经义，也能触类旁通，也能多读书而不忘："书多阅而好忘者，只为理未精耳，理精则须记了无去处也。仲尼一以贯之，盖只着一义理都贯却。学者但养心识明静，自然可见，死生存亡皆知所从来，胸中莹然无疑，止此理尔。"[⑦] 读书易忘，还是义理不精，精则不忘。

经典的阅读贵在熟读精思而有心得。张载批评孔子的学生子贡说："道听途说不可为读书。耳不可以闻道。'夫子之言性与天道'，子贡以为不闻，是耳之闻未可以为闻也。"[⑧] 读书只以耳目见闻为限，不进入深入思考，是难以见得义理的。张载批评孔子的高足颜渊说："学不能推究事理，只是心粗。至如颜子未至于圣人处，犹是心粗。"[⑨] 不能"推究事理"，就是未进入经典的奥妙处，未能体会到圣人的用心处。如果能熟读精思，"闻之知之，得之有之。"[⑩] 有闻有知，进而变成自己的体会，读书才有效果。重要的书须反复阅读："某观中庸义二十年，每观每有义，已长得一格。六经循环，年欲一观。"[⑪] 一篇文章一读二十年，堪为熟读精思的典范了。张载强调读书以"心解"为主，不必字字相较："心解则求义自明，不必字字相校。譬之目明者，万物纷错于前，

---

① 张载：《张载集》，中华书局，1978 年，第 276 页

② 张载：《张载集》，中华书局，1978 年，第 275 页。

③ 张载：《张载集》，中华书局，1978 年，第 270 页。

④ 张载：《张载集》，中华书局，1978 年，第 287 页。

⑤ 张载：《张载集》，中华书局，1978 年，第 277 页。

⑥ 张载：《张载集》，中华书局，1978 年，第 29 页。

⑦ 张载：《张载集》，中华书局，1978 年，第 279 页。

⑧ 张载：《张载集》，中华书局，1978 年，第 281 页。

⑨ 张载：《张载集》，中华书局，1978 年，第 274 页。

⑩ 张载：《张载集》，中华书局，1978 年，第 276 页。

⑪ 张载：《张载集》，中华书局，1978 年，第 277 页。

不足为害，若目昏者，虽枯木朽株皆足为梗。”[①] 只有反复“涵泳”，仔细体会，才会有心悟。作好读书笔记，及时记下心得体会，就能巩固“心悟”：“学者潜心略有所得，即且志之纸笔，以其易忘，失其良心。若所得是，充大之以养其心，立数千题，旋注释，常改之，改得一字即是进得一字。始作文字，须当多其词以包罗意思。”[②] 书要熟读，思考须简省：“思虑要简省，烦则所存都昏惑，中夜因思虑不寐则惊魇不安。”[③] 思考问题不能钻牛角尖，而须得其大义，理解经典的基本精神：“古之能知诗者，惟孟子为以意逆志也。夫诗之志至平易，不必为艰险求之，今以艰险求诗，则已丧其本心，何由见诗人之志!”[④] 如何精思？张载提出了“下学上达”之法：“下学而上达者两得之，人谋又得，天道又尽。”[⑤] “下学”是见闻知识，“上达”是德性义理。由见闻而获得义理，才算读书的真正收获。因此，张载明确地说：“学贵心悟，守旧无功。”[⑥] 旧的道理不通，当求新意：“义理有碍，则濯去旧见以来新意。”[⑦] 这是一种新的读书态度。

经典的阅读，贵在有疑，于不疑处有疑，才是真正的进步。“可疑而不疑者不曾学，学则须疑。”[⑧] 读书提不出问题，是未能深入书中：“所以观书者，释已之疑，明己之未达，每见每知所益，则学进矣，于不疑处有疑，方是进矣。”[⑨] 疑从何来？“譬之行道者，将之南山，须问道路之自出，若安坐则何尝有疑。”[⑩] 当然，如果毫无根据地怀疑，则会为书所迷而不能有得。关键在于读书要有自己的观点和看法，而不为别人或他书所轻易动摇：“人之迷经者，盖己所守未明，故常为语言可以移动。己守既定，虽孔孟之言有纷错，亦须不思而改之，复锄去其繁，使词简而意备。”[⑪] 融会贯通，有了主心骨，就不会为书所迷惑。如果疑而未通，须重新思考：“凡致思到说不得处始复审思明辨，乃为善学也。若告子则到说不得处遂已，更不复求。”[⑫]

经典的阅读，贵在心静。有了读书志趣，虚心向学，还要心静。张载谈自己的经典研读体会说：“近来思虑大率少不中处，今则利在闲，闲得数日，便意思长远，观书

① 张载：《张载集》，中华书局，1978年，第276页。
② 张载：《张载集》，中华书局，1978年，第275页。
③ 张载：《张载集》，中华书局，1978年，第289页。
④ 张载：《张载集》，中华书局，1978年，第256页。
⑤ 张载：《张载集》，中华书局，1978年，第279页。
⑥ 张载：《张载集》，中华书局，1978年，第274页。
⑦ 张载：《张载集》，中华书局，1978年，第321页。
⑧ 张载：《张载集》，中华书局，1978年，第321页。
⑨ 张载：《张载集》，中华书局，1978年，第275页。
⑩ 张载：《张载集》，中华书局，1978年，第286页。
⑪ 张载：《张载集》，中华书局，1978年，第277页。
⑫ 张载：《张载集》，中华书局，1978年，第377页。

到无可推考处。”① 闲暇心静，仔细品味，容易进入读书佳境。但是，闲暇得之不易，须不断克服困难，争取时间读书：“古人耕且学则能之，后人耕且学则为奔迫，反动其心。何者？古人安分，至一箪食，一豆羹，易衣而出，只如此其分也；后人则多欲，故难能。然此事均是人情之难，故以为贵。”② 受外界诱惑太多，心不能静，是当代人读书之大忌。张载强调“安分”“少欲”，有现实意义。其实，一旦心静下来，读书的收获是明显的：“处得安且久，自然文章出，解义明。”③ 一目十行地读书，于消遣读物可以，但阅读经典或重要的书，这种急迫的态度，是不会有得的：“观书且不宜急迫了，意思则都不见。”④ 因此，读书须闲暇，当然，更重要的是心境闲暇：“有急求义理复不得，于闲暇有时得。盖意乐则易见，急而不乐则失之矣。”⑤

经典的阅读更要不耻下问，与师学友不断切磋。张载说：“从不肯问遂生百端欺妄人。我宁终身不知。”⑥ 不自欺欺人，就要不耻下问：“人多是耻于问人，假使今日问于人，明日胜于人，有何不可！如是则孔子问于老聃、苌弘、郯子、宾牟贾，有甚不得！聚天下众人之善者是圣人也，岂有得其一端而便胜于圣人也。”⑦ 只有不耻下问，才能得众人之善。张载把这一精神叫“无我”：“人私意以求是未必是，虚心以求是方为是，责己者当知天下国家无皆非之理，人之耻于就问，便谓我胜于人，只是病在不知求是为心。故学者当无我。”⑧ 又说：“无我而后大，大成性而后圣。”⑨ 毋意、毋必、毋固、毋我，去掉自己的主观偏见和自满，不但向老师请教，学友之间，更须相互学习，才有益于经典的阅读，也就是说：“惟圣人知朋友之取益为多，故乐得朋友之来。”⑩ 或者说：“人相聚得言，皆有益也，则此甚善。”⑪ 朋友相聚，互相讨论学术，是最为有益的：“学不长者无他术，惟是与朋友讲治，多识前言往行以畜其德，非礼勿言，非礼勿动，即是养心之术也。”⑫ 学友之间，互相切磋琢磨，品德与学问自会长进，否则就是自暴自弃了：“义理有疑，则濯去旧见以来新意。心中苟有所开，即便札记，不思则还塞之矣。更须得朋友之助，日间朋友论着，则一日间意思差别，须日日如此讲论，久

① 张载：《张载集》，中华书局，1978 年，第 281 页。
② 张载：《张载集》，中华书局，1978 年，第 266 页。
③ 张载：《张载集》，中华书局，1978 年，第 283 页。
④ 张载：《张载集》，中华书局，1978 年，第 276 页。
⑤ 张载：《张载集》，中华书局，1978 年，第 276 页。
⑥ 张载：《张载集》，中华书局，1978 年，第 276 页。
⑦ 张载：《张载集》，中华书局，1978 年，第 283 页。
⑧ 张载：《张载集》，中华书局，1978 年，第 283 页。
⑨ 张载：《张载集》，中华书局，1978 年，第 17 页。
⑩ 张载：《张载集》，中华书局，1978 年，第 377 页。
⑪ 张载：《张载集》，中华书局，1978 年，第 284 页。
⑫ 张载：《张载集》，中华书局，1978 年，第 284 页。

则自觉进也。”[①] 当今社会，缺乏奇文共欣赏、疑义相与析的传统。张载强调师友之间相互切磋，在今天是非常有现实意义的。

经典的阅读，贵在能知能行。知之不若信而行之，知而不行，反不如不知：“知之而不信而行之，愈于不知矣，学者须得中道乃可守。”[②] 知而不行，终究是未落到实处：“尊其所闻则高明，行其所知则光大，凡未理会至实处，如空中立，终不曾踏着实地。”[③] 明代学者吕楠评价张载的著作说，“诸书言简意赅，皆出于精思力行之后”。[④] 张载“仰望星空”，又“踏着实地”，是读书的典范。

## 三、全面看待张载的经典阅读方法论

当然，张载是正统的经学家，板起面孔谈读书，许多读书观点也难免偏颇。如他对史书的偏见：“观书且勿观史，学理会急处，亦无暇观也。然观史又胜于游，山水林石之趣，始似可爱，终无益，不如游心经籍义理之间。”[⑤] 张载是体会不到“读万卷书，行万里路”之妙的。又如他主张不讲而学：“圣人于文章不讲而学，盖讲者有可否之疑，须问辨而后明，学者有所不知，问而知之，则可否自决，不待讲论。”[⑥] 这一观点是自相矛盾的。时过境迁，好在这些观点大家都不会认真计较了。

张载“学古力行”，似乎在读书态度上有些矛盾。张载所读的经典，主要是儒家的经典，以及道家与佛教的经典。比起当时的读书人，张载广泛地学习了当时的自然科学，在《正蒙》中还有科学知识来为自己的哲学思想论证。另外，从青年时期张载就对军事和边防有浓厚兴趣，并进行过井田制的试验。一方面学习古典知识，另一方面勇于实行。这二者是如何统一的？原来，古代经典给了张载以“民胞物与”的“星空”，社会问题让他不断地回到“现实”关怀中来。正是对现实社会民生的关怀，使张载的经典阅读具有了深厚的现实情怀。总的来看，张载的阅读经典的思路是清晰的。但是，受各方面条件制约，张载的经典阅读理想与现实社会的结合毕竟是非常有限的。古典是伟大的，从古典审视现实，难免有保守主义情节。特别是他对史书的偏见，或多或少地限制了他的视野。让张载从现实超越经典，这已超出了张载的预期。在同时代人中，张载的经典阅读，已经是非常卓越了。

从当代哲学史家冯友兰的“抽象继承法”来看，张载的经典阅读方法论并没有拘

---

① 张载：《张载集》，中华书局，1978年，第286页。

② 张载：《张载集》，中华书局，1978年，第271页。

③ 张载：《张载集》，中华书局，1978年，第272页。

④ 张载：《张载集》，中华书局，1978年，第389页。

⑤ 张载：《张载集》，中华书局，1978年，第276页。

⑥ 张载：《张载集》，中华书局，1978年，第280页。

泥于古典，而是有自己的立场和理想。张载对古典进行了创造性阐释和创新，形成了别开生面的哲学思想和理论命题，成为宋代“勇于造道”的人。如果要对张载进行较严格批评的话，我们只能说他的“抽象”还并不是那么充分。儒家的情怀、乡土的立场、固执的个性等，使他的理论思考与现实关切交织渗透，正统意识自觉不自觉地干扰着他的理性判断。从二程、朱熹来看张载，张载的经典阅读是有特点的，但也是一个未完成的阅读。天假之以年，张载的思想从内容到体系，当会呈现出新的面貌。

总的来看，张载的经典阅读方法论，“仰望星空，脚踏实地”，亲切深刻，起而可行，对当代的经典阅读有一定的启发意义。

# 由氣之進路論王安石的性情說

中国文化大学　王俊彦

## 一、前言

孔子首言“性相近，習相遠”之言，開始儒學對人性問題之探討。孟子主性善、荀子主性惡、董仲舒主人貪二性、楊雄主性善惡混、韓愈分性為三品。主張亦夥矣。秦漢時期多由氣化論性，儒學故如是，而道教更視為主流。為隋棠佛學興起，佛性本體亦成為學術主軸，而氣化之論勢衰。及至宗明初其周敦頤、張載等為重振儒學反佛老，便多言重實然之氣以言天到性命。而王安石亦此時之重鎮，及朱子理氣論，陽明致良知，重本體之論又顯於世，氣論之勢似又衰，唯明中葉及清重實之風又起，由氣論道言性之風又起，而所以能上接秦漢以來之氣論而不墜者，王安石之功不可滅也。

## 二、道通一氣

人之精神與天地同流，通萬物一氣也。易曰：“乾道變化，各正性命，保合太和，乃利貞。”故占夢掌其歲時，觀天地之會，辨陰陽之氣，以日月星辰占六夢之吉凶。[①]

孟子由性善論的主軸，通過盡心知性知天的架構，強調上下與天地同流的終極目標。在朱子推尊孟子為四書之前的王安石，自未必以性善作為貫通天人的主軸，而是以秦漢以來，儒道二家多言的“生之謂性”的傳統，作為貫通天人的本體。而“生”者便是佛、理學、心學強調形上本體外，另主張上下一體的路數，即由“氣”來作為通貫萬物之本體。安石有云：“道有體有用，體者元氣之不動，用者冲氣運行於天地之間。”（容肇祖：《王安石老子注輯本・道德經・道沖章注》：中華書局，1979年）。道之體是陰陽尚未分立之氣，道之用是本體之氣分為陰陽二氣，而有相生相成之作用。道之體與用皆以氣為體為用，則氣便非只有形氣義，亦具有本體義。同為北宋初期的濂

---

① 程元敏：《三經新義輯考匯評［三］——周禮（上）》，“國立編譯館”，1987年，第357頁。

溪，亦由陰陽五行之氣論太極。横渠亦主張太虚即氣。可知在朱學主張理氣二分，理為本體，氣為形下的學風前，安石順“生之謂性”傳統，將氣提升為通萬物為一的本體是合理的。

> 蓋一陰一陽之謂道，道之在天，日月以運之，星辰以紀之；其施于人，仁莫尚焉，無為而仁者，山也。仁而不可知者，龍也。仁藏于不可知，而顯于可知者，禮也。①

由氣説本體説道，則道之本體義、生生義、價值義便自然由氣來説。道在天所顯現的日月星辰的生生義，施於人而有的仁、禮之價值義，因道之上下為用而使生生義與價值義真實呈現，而顯其本有之本體義。日月交運因陰陽二氣相生而有。無為而仁之山，仁而不可知之龍，藏諸仁顯諸用之禮。種種由元氣流行而有的本體與價值皆在陰陽相生之道中得以各正性命而為實有。道即在氣化中是上下一體，而非道屬形上，物屬實然而二分。

> 五行也 者，成變化而行鬼神，往來乎天地之間而不窮者，是故謂之行。天一生水，其于物為精，精者，一之所生。地二生火，其于物為神，神者，有精而後從之者。天三生木，其于物為魂，魂從神者。地四生金，其于物為魄，魄者，有魂而後從之者。天五生土，其于物為意。精、神、魂、魄具而後有意。自天一自天五，五行之生數也。以奇生者成而耦，以耦生者成而奇，其成之者皆五。②

若道屬無形本體，則“成變化而行鬼神”之行，只能是無形之生生作用，無法具體成化真實的萬物。若道由初生之本體，透過陰陽之氣之生生作用，並漸凝漸滯而化成形物之實體。如此由無形之作用，凝為有形之實體，則使生生之氣既有無形之生生作用也有具體成化有形氣物之質性。此時“行”不只是無形作用，而是通貫上下兩間的“行”。天地間既指形體之天地，也指無形之統體性的價值秩序義。因氣化流行不已，故統括有無兩間之天地，自亦生化無窮。此時由本體之無限義，也確定天地是無窮的真實存在於兩間之中。

秦漢以來即對有形無形兩層中的中介段落，多所討論。如以道為本體層，萬物為形氣層，而道由無而有之過程，道將其作用降為神魂不測之作用，神魂再具體化便是精魄，精魄的形氣化便是形物，是由無而有、由上而下的描敘。安石此處由五行在同一横剖面，即同在形氣層上説生生無窮，此亦重實然人道之特色，又因天一至地十，仍有上下縱横之意。意即安石是將上下貫通與同層相生，並構成一上下内外感通無隔之整體。以此真實對治佛老之虚空及為變法之理據。如天一生水是精，地二生火是神，

---

① 程元敏:《三經新義輯考匯評(三)——周禮(上)》,“國立編譯館”,1987年,第317頁。
② 王安石:《王文公文集》(上册),第25卷,上海人民出版社,1974年,頁281。

天三生木是魂，地四生金是魄，天五生土是意。如此陰陽天地固可概“耦”而生偶數，亦因天五為奇，而生亦相“耦”而生奇數，奇偶皆具，滿數自足。另將近於形質的精魄分為北之水與西之金，將近於作用的神魂分為南之火與木之東。亦即精魄屬水、金屬北、西近陰，神魂屬火、木屬南、東近陽，同時精神魂魄具而後有意。亦即二氣可分為五行，五行由二氣而來，但最終歸於一“意”。如此既說明以氣為道之體，二氣又分為五行，而五行則內化為形氣之精神魂魄意，使萬物因之而生化無窮。又強調了由一而二而五而萬物成化的宇宙生成圖式，是能通萬物為一的“氣”所完成。確立安石以氣為本體論與宇宙論之主軸，才能討論其性情說，而不致擺盪於諸說間。

> 北方陰極而生寒，寒生水，南方陽極而生熱，熱生火，故水潤而火炎，水下而火上。東方陽動以散而生風，風生木，木者，陽中也，能變，能變，故曲直。西方陰止以放而生燥，燥生金，金者，陰中也，故能化，能化故從革。中央陰陽交而生濕，濕生土，土者，陰陽冲氣之所生。①

安石將陰陽的偶數配入東南西北中，再將四個方位合為中土，於是奇數的五行便可產生。如同董仲舒一年12個月分為四時，每時3個月，但為配合五行，於是將每3個月各去18天，而每時剩72天，而五行便可成立。此為以氣說天地而有的理性的推論。天地是無限而不可描敘的。如此機械式的推論，只是虛擬比附的一種方式，若執此方式為真實，易流為迷信。若以“得意忘言”工夫，領略其宇宙氣化的過程與關係，知執之則非道，不執之而所體悟者才是道。則二五圖式的描敘，只是進入無限之道的必要前提，仍需做一番陳述。

安石以陰陽之極配北水與南火，是以陰陽入五行的第一步，水下火土確立方位，以陽中陰中配東、木與西、金，再將陽動加入東，陰止加入西，凸顯陰陽動靜的作用，最後再將方位與動靜統一於中土。“土者，陰陽冲氣之所生”即指屬無形作用的動靜與實然的水火木金等素質皆融會在實然層的土中，但土非蠢然的實然，而是內蘊有陰陽相生無窮的實然，亦即本體便在宇宙生化中，非超越在宇宙生化之上。

> 蓋五行之為物，其時、其位、其材、其氣、其性、其形、其事、其色、其聲、其臭、其味，皆各有耦，推而散之，無所不通。一柔一剛，一晦一明，故有正有邪，有善有惡，有丑有好，有兇有吉。性命之理，道德之意皆在是。耦之中又有耦，而萬物之變遂至于無窮。其相生也，所以相繼也。其相剋也，所以相治也。②（洪範傳）

五行為萬物的基本作用與性質，舉凡時、位、材、氣、性、形、事、色、聲、臭、

---

① 王安石：《王文公文集》(上冊)，第25卷，上海人民出版社，1974年，第282頁。

② 王安石：《王文公文集》(上冊)，第25卷，上海人民出版社，1974年，第281頁。

味等，皆由五行組成。而且“皆告有耦”，每一時、位、材中皆有陰陽二氣，故時、位、材中又分陰之時、位、材與陽之時、位、材。此強調陰陽與五行相合成物，為萬物普遍性的基礎。剛、柔、晦、明既可為實然層的特性，亦可說是人事、倫理的原則，於是時、位有陰陽之別，而價值上也有正、邪、美、惡之分。命運上也有吉凶之分。故偏向實然的性命與偏向價值道德二者，皆蘊化于陰陽五行生成的場域，而生克無窮。

## 三、太極與性

> 夫太極者，五行之所由生，而五行非太極也。性者，五常之太極也，而五常不可謂性。夫太極生五行，然後利害生焉，而太極不可以利害言。性生乎情，有情然後善惡形焉，而性不可以善惡言。①

安石以有體有用者為道，道之本體義明確。此又言運化與成就萬相的五行為太極所生。則能生之太極即道即本體，而所生之五行，即為太極的生生作用，五行已落入第二義。但此第二義非即實然層者，而是太極本體趨向形氣的第一個階段。五行的形質義顯而作用義微時。五行才成為形物層的材質？五行一有材質義，便落於相對有限界，而有利害的產生。故太極雖生五行，但太極仍是絕對之體，五行則是相對之用，不可將絕對之太極，降為相對之五行。如此，則太極賦於人而有的性，應是絕對的體，不可與性所生的相對的情等同。亦即性如太極是體無相對者，故不可以善惡言。如五行是用而有相對者，有善惡之分別，此由太極說明性具本體義，故不可說有善惡之別。如安石云：“道有本有末。本者，萬物之所以生；末者，萬物之所以成。本者，出之自然，故不假乎人之力而萬物以生也；末者，涉乎形器，故待人力而後萬物以成也。”②可知不假乎人力之體之性，自應無人為干擾而不分善惡。在有人力干擾的形器層之情，自會有善惡之分。

> 變化之應，天人之極致。是以《書》言天人之道，莫大於《洪範》，《洪範》之言天人之道，莫大于貌、言、視、聽、思。故孟子曰：“我善養吾浩然之氣，充塞乎天地之間。”楊子曰：“貌、言、視、聽、思、性所有，潛天而天，潛地而地。③

安石由太極此性，使性有本體位階外，亦重視性在人事的作用，如“天人之極致”，在能感應萬物之變化。氣化無窮，感應自亦無已，而使感應具體完成，且合於天人之道標準的重點，便在於性。性之具體成化禮樂刑政的實現，便是通過形氣的貌、

---

① 王安石:《王文公文集》(上冊)，第27卷，上海人民出版社，1974年，第316頁。
② 《王安石全集》，卷27，雜著，第231頁。
③ 《王安石全集》，第29卷，染著，第251頁。

言、視、聽、思等感官的表現。感官可由中性說，但若感官是由本體之氣化說，則貌、言、視、聽、思便非是無價值義的作用，而是以天人之極致為目標，具道德義的呈現。安石即由孟子善養浩然之氣，作為貞定言行合價值的論證。且唯有言行合德，才是天人之道的實現。故性既是天與人之道。亦是言行所以合道的本質作用。故楊子將貌、言、視、聽、思皆歸於性之表現。且因一氣相通之故，天地亦在性的生化作用之內。

> 神生于性，性生于誠，誠生于心，心生于氣，氣生于形。形者，有生之本。故養生在于保形，充形在于育氣，養氣在于寧心，寧心在于致誠，養誠在于盡性，不盡性不足以養生。能盡性者，至誠者也。能至誠者，寧心者也。能寧心者，養氣者也。能養氣者，保形者也。能保形者，養生者也。不養生不足以盡性。生與性之相因循，志之與氣相為表裏也。生渾則蔽性，性渾則蔽生，猶志一則動氣，氣一則動志也。[①]

安石以為生與性相因循，猶志與氣相表裏。而生者以形為本。形中有氣，氣中有心，心中有誠，誠中有性，性中有神。生者之形中有依次上提化為無形不測之神用。故要掌握養生之原則，便要由可見之保形，進而養氣、寧心、至誠、盡性，以至於神，才能保其形。此與由價值本體論性者，主張由本而末致之之法異趣。主張由可見之形向內修養而至于不可見之神。見其重性之實然面的特色。另“不盡性不足以養生”、“不養生不足以盡性”，則指出形氣層保形養生的完成，要由能在形氣層起創生化育作用的性來發動與主導。順著“生之謂性”的傳統，而以氣論性的安石，不將性視為純粹形上之本體與氣有一間之隔，而是視性除具本體義外，亦與形氣層諸段落，皆有緊密關係與秩序。而為一架構完整，無上下內外間隔，而實然義又明顯的性。

## 四、對孟、荀、楊、韓性之批評

> 性生乎情，有情然后善惡形焉，而性不可以善惡言也。孟子以惻隱之心，人皆有之，因以謂人之性無不仁。就所謂性者如是說，必也怨毒忿戾之心人皆無之，然後可以言人之性無不善，而人果皆無之乎？孟子以惻隱之心為性者，以其在內也。夫惻隱之心與怨毒忿戾之心，其有感于外而后出乎中者有不同乎？

荀子曰：“其為善者偽也”。就所謂性者如其說，必也惻隱之心，人皆無之，然後可以言善者偽也，為人果皆無之乎？荀子曰：“陶人化土而為埴者，埴豈土之性也哉？”夫陶人不以木為埴者，惟土有埴之性焉，烏在其為偽也？且諸子之所言，皆吾所謂情也、習也，非性也。

---

① 《王安石全集》，第29卷，雜著，第249頁。

楊子之言為似矣。猶未出乎以習言性也。喜、怒、愛、惡、欲而善，然後從而命之曰仁也，義也；喜、怒、愛、惡、欲而不善，然後從而命之曰不仁也、不義也。故曰有情，然後善惡形焉。然則善者。情之成名而已矣。[1]

安石主元氣為道之體，冲氣運行為道之用，則性即是有體有用之氣於人的本質。故對孟子性善說，質疑其不能解釋怨毒忿戾之心人亦有之的現象。孟子由道德之天下貫於人說人之性善。並於父子、君臣與仁義的關係上，自覺的主張父子之仁為性，但有命限于擾時，仍以自覺之行仁為主，不為命所限。此在安石看來，順氣化生生而有之性，自然亦有各種方向與速度生化的可能性，則隱惻之心固有性發，而怨毒之心自亦由性所發出。安石以孟子天性上下貫通之說為不足，故又強調性在形氣層有各種方向與速度不同之可能性。

安石以為荀子"為善者偽"之說能成立，應植基於性無惻隱之心，須靠後天教化才為善之觀點。惟安石以為氣性生化不已且無方所限制，故性不能有絕無惻隱之心發生的可能性，只要有一點惻隱作用之發動，則荀子性中無善之說便不能成立。故又舉埴由土而成，是因埴中有土之性才成，無土之性則不成。反過來說，安石應主張性中必有為善之能，能否成為善行，則待情之合理否。對孟子之評說，則知安石又認為性中亦有為惡之可能。純由價值本體說，安石之性，難以理解。若由氣化不已說性，則安石之說可成立。

安石又認楊子的。性善惡混為似。但仍是以已發後有善惡之情，且情已成習來說"性善惡混"，然性實非"善惡混"的。因喜怒之情需發而後且成習後，才能說是仁義之善。此時所謂善，已是既發且成習之情所為，而非性之所為。故楊子之說當為"情善惡混"非"性善惡混"。亦即從外在所見之善惡，是情所為，不能據之即判斷外在之善惡即性所為。可知安石以為善惡不能言性，是因性有太極本體義，太極會生五行，但五行非太極；故性生情，情有善惡，但情非性，故性不能說有善惡。可見安石將氣性安置於不可分說的本體位置。

且韓子之言弗顧矣，曰："性之品三，而其所以為性五。"夫仁、義、禮、智、信，孰而可謂不善也？又曰："上焉者之于五，主于一而行之四；下焉者之于五，反于一而悖于四。"是其于性也，不一失焉，而后謂之上焉者。不一得焉，而后謂之下焉者。是果性善，而不善者，習也。[2]

韓子有上智、下愚、中人三品之說。以為於仁義禮智信者五常能主於一而不一失是上智，但於五常是反于一而悖于四則是下愚，於是作為價值主體的仁義禮智信，本

① 《王安石全集》，第 27 卷，雜著，原性，第 235－236 頁。
② 《王安石全集》，第 27 卷，雜著、性說，第 237 頁。

應是性的本質，亦即韓子之性應是善的。唯韓子卻將應具無限本體義，不能分解說的性，卻落於相對界而說性可分解說為五，且此外五者又失其為必然的存有，而分解為無必然性的偶然存在。而無必然性的有限存在，對安石來說是情而非性。由反對韓子對性的分解說，可見安石對性是無限與整體性的主張。

> 夫人之生，莫不有羞惡之性，且以羞惡之一端以明之。有人于此，羞善行之不修，惡善名之不立，盡力乎善，以充其羞惡之性，則其為賢也孰御哉？此得乎性之正者，而孟子之所謂性。有人于此，羞利之不厚，惡利之不多，盡力乎利，以充羞惡之性，則其為不肖也孰御哉？此得乎性之不正，而楊子之兼所謂性者也。今學者是孟子則非陽子，是楊子則非孟子，蓋知讀其文而不知求其指耳。①

安石由陰陽五行相生不已之太極喻性，故性除本體義外，亦有沛然不已的生生運動義，與順生生秩序而有之價值義。羞惡之性為人生所本有，即指性之二五生化作用沛然莫之能禦，亦即羞善之不修，羞利之不厚，皆氣性流動不已的自然作用。唯安石於此又以羞善不修者為性之正。以羞利不厚者為不正之性。於是性由自然狀態被賦予了價值意義，而成為有趨向價值義的性。一般由氣論性者，多由理性論道德，非由道德主體論道德。故學者多以他律視之。然其實未必可全由他律，自律二分掌握。因由氣論性者，性之自然義固然明顯，唯其氣化生生之必然秩序，即蘊涵了價值的應然義，如天行健，君子以自強不息，即是乾道之流行。則在自然義中自蘊有飽滿之價值義。安石之由氣說性，亦不免要強調外在學習之重要。再將外在之學習內化於氣性中，引發氣性中本蘊涵的價值之常，使內外一體，貫通上下而為真實的道德世界。

> 道有君子有小人，德有吉有兇，則命有逆有順，性有善有惡，固其理也。夫古之人，以為無君子道為無道，無吉德為無德，則去善就惡謂之性亡，亦不可也。②

在朱子性即理與陽明心即理，由絕對善論性風潮前，濂溪、橫渠等皆主由自然之氣論性，惟不廢儒學仁義道德之旨，故有義理之性，氣質之性的分解說。安石未明白分性為義理，氣質二者，但亦距此義不遠。如道應為形上，卻有君子小人之分，則知是由道在形氣層之表現說。人得道之表現為德，則德亦由形下相對界言而有吉凶之分。安石由太極元氣說性，故性有本體義外，亦有氣化流行義。故順此段主由形氣層之語氣說性，性在相對形氣層之生化實現，自亦有相對界善惡不同之分判。亦即性有趨善趨惡的各種可能性，就性有為善為惡之各種可能性的本體位階言，性難以用善、惡來界定限制住。若就有各種生化可能的性在形氣層上的表現言，各種可能性已落入相對

---

① 《王安石全集》，第27卷，雜注、楊孟，第234頁。

② 《王安石全集》，第7卷，答王深甫書。

界而被限定為是善或是惡的表現。故安石以為現實上的去善就惡，只是現實上性之善被掩蓋，而性之惡則呈現出來，故只可說現實上不見善，但不能因之說有為善為惡各種可能性不存在。安石之意實指氣性合無形、有形兩間而統論，非可只以有形或無形單一層面來討論。

然則孔子所謂“中人以上可以語上，中人以下不可以語上，惟上智與下愚不移”何說也？曰：“習于善而已，所謂上智者。習于惡而已，所謂下愚者。”一習于善，一習于惡，所謂中人者。上智、下愚、中人，其卒也命之而已。有人于此，未始為不善，謂之上智可也。其卒也去而為不善，然后謂之中人可也。有人於此，未始為善，謂之下愚可也。其卒也去而為善，然後謂之中人可也。惟其不移，然後謂之下愚，皆于其卒也命之，夫非生而不可移。[1]

安石以為性本為自然而有，人皆相同，而且謂上智與下愚，非指本性有智愚之別。智愚者後天學習而成的。故智愚不可移，非指其性不可移，是指後天學習後所得的結果不可移。明清之際，由氣說作者或有以為性為氣質所蔽，而有智愚之別。但安石處於宗明學的前期，尚屬統括說性時期，尚未進到理學中後期，受朱子、陽明影響，而對性有更細緻的討論。故安石以性皆以氣化之自然言，故可說“性相近”，使性不被限定為只是本體或只是形氣的一偏，而可以是通貫上下，日進有功，可創造禮樂社會的本質。氣化之性習于善為上智，習于惡則為下愚，其為氣性不因後天之習而有改變。而一習善一習惡者為中人，亦指氣性有往善惡不同方向發展的可能性。又後天境域改變，使未為不善之上智，淪為中人。或未為善之下愚，使之上升為中人的兩種情形，皆有可能。此固強調後天之習的重要。也彰顯了性無分智愚，不習者才會不移。習者則性可移也。

## 五、性情一也

性情一也。喜、怒、哀、樂、好、惡、欲發于外而存于心，性也。喜、怒、哀、樂、好、惡、欲未發于外而見於行，情也。性者情之本，惰者性之用。

彼曰性善無它，是嘗讀孟子之書，未嘗求孟子之意耳。彼曰情惡無它，是有見于天下之以此七者而入于惡，而不知七者之出于性耳。故此七者，人生而有之，接于物而後動焉。彼徒有見于情之發于外者為外物之所累，而遂入于惡，因曰情惡也，害性者情也。是曾不察于情之發于外而為外物之所感，而遂入于善者乎？蓋君子養性之善，故情亦善。小人養性之惡，故情亦惡。故君子之所以為君子，

① 《王安石全集》，第 27 卷，雜注、性說，第 237 頁。

莫非情也。小人之所以為小人，莫非情也。

> 自其所謂情者，莫非喜、怒、哀、樂、好、惡、欲也。舜之聖也，象喜亦喜，使舜當喜而不喜，則豈足以為舜乎？如其廢情，則性雖善，何以自明哉？誠如今論者之說，無情者善，則是若木石者尚矣。是以知性情之相須，猶弓與矢之相待而用，若夫善惡，則猶中與不中也。曰："然則性有惡乎？"曰："孟子曰：'養其大體為大人，養其小體為小人。'楊子曰：'人之性善惡混。'是知性可以惡也。"①

安石由氣言性，則氣質之喜、怒、哀、樂、好、惡、欲等，自為氣化生生各種可能之向度。故"未發於外而存于心"為性。及氣化各種向度，化為可見於行的作用，此即為情。唯氣質之各種向度與作用，仍屬無行層次。故性為情本，情為性用，此種體用關西在作用層的意義，是使性之生化得以向現實面推進一步而仍維持性的本質。如此情既以性為體，情又是性接近實然的作用。故曰："性情一"也。唯喜怒是性的各種生生向度，而情則是形質層之有限制的，可被感知的某一種向度與能力。亦即性是客觀潛存的，依情之可被知覺才能被體會到。故性有喜怒之不同表現向度，故情即有喜怒不同之表現。若性不可以善惡言，則情亦不可以善惡言，唯情見于行一則即受形之限制而為有限，而有相對之善惡可說。

由情見於形，使情之發有所限制，遂在價值上判為惡。此固有之，但情之發之所限若不當於理則固為惡。若情發而當於理則為善，且限制正是善之具體實踐。故性本有各種生生向度，情則受境域之限制而有善惡不同之表現，不可說情必為惡，為害性者也，情意有為善之表現能力。

"君子養性之善，故情亦善。小人養性之惡，故情亦惡。"此言性有善惡，或有異議。唯說君子養性之善，既已為行善之君子，則所養必為性有趨向善之向度，見于行之情自為善。既已說為惡之小人，則小人所養必為性有趨向惡之可能之向度。見于行之情自為惡。安石既要性有趨向任何向度之可能，故重視情為性之用。又要性為任何情用之本質，使任何情之發，都有性來貞定，故重視性為情之體價值判斷言，性之自然義較顯，情則價值判斷亦較顯。

"君子之所以為君子，莫非情"現實層言，非無限之道，而是道在人間，有限而如理的表現。如是能承載有限而如理表現者便是情而非性。而非道之小人，除本即有限，只不能如理承載性，則其性之表現亦惡。此中除善惡之判斷外，情則是承載與完成善惡不可缺之作用亦即世界因情之發用而為真實。"如其廢情，則性雖善，何以自明哉？"知情除落入相對界而有善惡之分外，相對界之實然亦因情之發用而成為真實。如此由氣論性言情，使價值層與實然層相通為一。可避免價值超越實然之上，而有蹈空之蔽，

① 《王安石全集》，第27卷，雜注、性情，第235頁。

反因重情之實然之公用，而有加深儒學重實之功。

## 六、結論

本文對由氣所論之道、性、情討論後，以為安石身為政治家及理學前期者，自然有重實然之趨向，故其道由氣化言，重貫通形上形下兩間的特色。依道而言之性，保有道之生生、價值、本體諸義。同時由氣言性，此性亦有貫通上下之特色。而為性之用的情，既有貫通形氣層內外之功用，亦使有情世界成為真實。

# 王阳明对儒家仁学的诠释与深化

首都师范大学 白 奚

儒家学说的基本特征和最高境界可以用“天人合一”来概括，宋明理学更是致力于对“天人合一”的论证和探求。宋明儒者对“天人合一”的道德理想进行了细致、具体的展开和论证，他们更多地是从形而上的本体论和心性论层面上探究天与人的关系，这种探求主要就落实和表现为对“心”和“理”的关系的探讨。探讨“心”和“理”的关系，可以说就是宋明理学的主题。宋明时期的儒者对“心”和“理”的关系虽然有不同的解决方式，表现为不同的特点和理论形式，但他们的结论却都是一致的，那就是都主张“心理合一”。以程、朱为代表的理学派，其最高范畴是“理”，但同时也十分重视“心”，他们从客体之“理”出发寻求“心理合一”，提出了“理与心一”①的命题。以陆、王为代表的心学派，其最高范畴是“心”，但也十分重视“理”，他们采取从主体之“心”出发寻求“心理合一”的途径，提出了“心即理”②、“心外无理”③的命题。“心理合一”是宋明儒学的最高境界，达此境界，就完成了理想的人格，实现了人生的理想。这个境界就是“圣人”境界，也就是“仁”的境界，诚如朱熹所言：“仁者理即是心，心即是理。”④

虽然都是以“心理合一”为最高境界，但程、朱与陆、王毕竟是有所不同，这种不同就具体表现为：是否承认心外有理，要不要向外求理。朱熹承认心外有理，主张格物穷理。王阳明则认为心外无理，反对向外求理。他认为，如果承认心外有理并求此心外之理，就不是“心理合一”而是“心理为二”⑤了。王阳明的这一观点，集中地表现为其“致良知”的学说，他认为，“天理”就是“良知”，人人皆有“良知”，人人心中亦皆有“天理”。因而，为学毋须外求，只须“致”此心中本有之“良知”即可；

① 《河南程氏遗书》卷第五《二先生语五》。

② 《陆九渊集》卷十一《与李宰》之二。

③ 《王阳明全集》卷一《语录一》。

④ 《朱子语类》卷三十七。

⑤ 《王阳明全集》卷二《语录二》。

道德修养也毋须外求，只须在自己心上下功夫，“致吾心之良知”，即可达至“仁者”境界。王阳明的“仁者”境界，具体来说，就落实和表现为其“万物一体之仁”的思想。

## 一、“万物一体之仁”与儒家的心性论传统

“万物一体”的思想是儒家的一个重要传统，也是儒家“仁”学和心性论的重要内容，这个传统可以上溯到战国时期的思孟学派。《孟子·尽心上》提出了“上下与天地同流”、“尽其心者，知其性也。知其性，则知天矣”和“万物皆备于我矣，反身而诚，乐莫大焉。强恕而行，求仁莫近焉”的思想。《中庸》提出了“赞天地之化育”的思想，其言曰：“惟天下至诚为能尽其性。能尽其性，则能尽人之性。能尽人之性，则能尽物之性。能尽物之性，则可以赞天地之化育。可以赞天地之化育，则可以与天地参矣。”《中庸》还提出“成己成物”的思想，其言曰：“君子诚之为贵。诚者，非自成己而已也，所以成物也。成己，仁也。成物，知也。性之德也，合外内之道也。”这些论述都把“仁”、“心”、“性”、“诚”、“天地”、“万物”这几个重要的概念联系起来，都主张将人的道德关怀扩大到天地万物，都认为人的主观精神可以与天地万物的大化流行浑然一体，人的道德行为可以参赞天地之化生和培育万物。思孟学派的这些思想是宋儒“万物一体之仁”思想的渊源，为后者的深入开展奠定了理论基础、思想特征和致思路向。

宋儒沿着思孟学派的这一思想路线继续发展，“万物一体之仁”的思想逐渐开显、丰富和深化，成为宋明理学的核心思想。张载《西铭》曰：“天地之塞，吾其体；天地之帅，吾其性”，并提出了“民吾同胞，物吾与也”的著名思想，发挥了“万物一体”之义。程颢对“万物一体之仁”有重要的阐发，他说：“学者须先识仁。仁者，浑然与物同体。义、礼、知、信皆仁也。”[①]又曰：“仁者，以天地万物为一体，莫非己也。”[②]王阳明将这一理论发挥到极致，他说：

> 大人者，以天地万物为一体者也。其视天下犹一家，中国犹一人焉。若夫间形骸而分尔我者，小人矣。大人之能以天地万物为一体也，非意之也，其心之仁本若是，其与天地万物而为一也。”[③]

在王阳明看来，人与天地万物是一个血肉相连、休戚与共的整体，而不应该“间形骸”、“分尔我”。能达此思想境界者是为“大人”，而“大人”之所以能达此境界，

---

① 《河南程氏遗书》卷第二上。

② 同上。

③ 《王阳明全集》卷二十六《大学问》。

乃是由于“其心之仁本若是”，即心中本有之“仁”所决定的。

儒家的经典著作《大学》中提出了所谓的“三纲领”之说，即“大学之道，在明明德，在亲民，在止于至善。”王阳明作《大学问》，用“天地万物一体”的仁学思想对《大学》的“三纲领”进行了全新的解释。他指出，“大学”之名，即指“大人之学”，而“大人”的标志就是“以天地万物为一体”，达此境界者即为“大人”。

具体来讲，所谓“明德”，他认为就是“根于天命之性，而自然灵昭不昧者”，即人人生而具有之“仁”心“仁”性。他特别指出，这个“万物一体之仁”不仅是“大人”所具有，而且是“小人之心亦必有之”，是人所共有的普遍的人性。他认为，此“明德”往往被私欲所蔽而晦暗不明，“大人”与“小人”之分别，不在于有无此“明德”，而在于能否“明”此“明德”，在于此“明德”是否受私欲的蒙蔽，“故夫为大人之学者，亦惟去其私欲之蔽”。因而，所谓“明明德”就是“自明其明德”，通过去除“私欲之蔽”的方法以“明”此心中本有之“明德”，确认、彰显和恢复这一人所共有的“万物一体之仁”，这是成为“大人”的唯一途径。

所谓“亲民”，王阳明认为乃是“达其天地万物一体之用也”，即将此“一体之仁”广泛地施用于大众乃至万物。具体来说就是：

> 亲吾之父，以及人之父，以及天下人之父，而后吾之仁实与吾之父、人之父与天下人之父而为一体矣；实与之为一体，而后孝之明德始明矣！亲吾之兄，以及人之兄，以及天下人之兄，而后吾之仁实与吾之兄、人之兄与天下人之兄而为一体矣；实与之为一体，而后弟之明德始明矣！①

同样道理，君臣、夫妇、朋友以至于山川鬼神鸟兽草木，莫不亲之爱之，“以达吾一体之仁”：

> 君臣也，夫妇也，朋友也，以至于山川鬼神鸟兽草木也，莫不实有以亲之，以达吾一体之仁，然后吾之明德始无不明，而真能以天地万物为一体矣。②

所谓“止于至善”，是对“至善”的强调和追求。王阳明认为“至善”是“明明德”和“亲民”的“极则”，即最高原则，也就是人心中本有的“明德”和“良知”，明此“明德”致此“良知”止于此“至善”，是“明明德”和“亲民”所能达到和所应达到的最高境界。《大学》本是系统阐述人生理想和实现此理想之途径的儒家经典，是儒家为学与问政的实施纲领，经过王阳明的这样一番诠释，遂将《大学》的“三纲领”完全纳入到了他的“致良知”和“万物一体之仁”的思想体系中来，“致良知”和“万物一体之仁”也就被他提升为儒家学说的理想目标和最高境界。

---

① 《王阳明全集》卷二十六《大学问》。

② 同上。

## 二、“仁民爱物”与“天地之心”：人在天地间的道德定位

王阳明的“天地万物一体之仁”，也是对孟子“亲亲而仁民，仁民而爱物”思想的继承、发挥和发展。“亲亲”是儒家的一个基本原则，强调血缘亲情的重要性和优先性，儒家向来把“亲亲”作为仁爱的自然心理基础和出发点，主张“立爱自亲始”，并以此原则而与主张“爱无差等”的墨家相区别。“亲亲而仁民”则是主张在满足了血缘亲情之后，还必须将仁爱之心向外扩展，施于大众，这是儒家仁爱观念之所以能够成为人类道德生活的普遍原则的根本原因。“亲亲而仁民”是儒家仁爱学说的基础部分，它是由儒家的创始人孔子所奠定的。“仁民而爱物”则把仁爱的原则继续贯彻推广，将此人类特有的道德观念和原则超出了人类社会的畛域，扩展到对待万物，这是孟子对孔子仁爱观念的一个重大推进，并为儒学在宋明时期的巨大发展开辟了广阔的空间。王阳明的“天地万物一体之仁”，则将孟子“仁民而爱物”的思想诠释和发挥到了极致。

“仁民而爱物”的命题突出了人的主体意识，它要求用人类的道德情感对待万物。不过，到此为止，仍然是将万物看成是外在于自己的“他物”而爱之，如此，则不爱万物对人亦并无损害，因而尚不能确保“爱物”落在实处。宋明时期的儒者显然看到了这一点，于是他们对此作了理论上的重要推进，提出了“万物一体”的观念，以确保“爱物”不至于落空。程颢曰：

> 医书言手足痿痹为不仁，此言最善名状。仁者，以天地万物为一体，莫非己也。认得为己，何所不至？若不有诸己，自不与己相干，如手足不仁，气已不贯，皆不属己。故博施济众，乃圣之功用。仁至难言，故止曰“己欲立而立人，己欲达而达人，能近取譬，可谓仁之方也已。”欲令如是观仁，可以得仁之体。①
>
> 若夫至仁，则天地为一身，而天地之间，品物万形为四肢百体。夫人岂有视四肢百体而不爱者哉？……医书有以手足风顽谓之四体不仁，为其疾痛不以累其心故也。夫手足在我，而疾痛不与知焉，非不仁而何？世之忍心无恩者，其自弃亦若是而已。②

程颢在这里借用了医书中将四肢麻木称为不仁的说法，以说明天地间的品形万物并非与人无关痛痒的外在之物，而是与人同为一体，血肉相连，休戚相关，因而人必须如爱护自己的手足般地爱护万物。这样一来，“爱物”便落在了实处。

根据程颢的说法，天地间的万物共为一体，人为万物之一，则亦为此一体中的一

---

① 《河南程氏遗书》卷第二上。

② 《河南程氏遗书》卷第四。

部分，在这一点上，人与万物就没有什么不同。但人在天地之间显然居于一特殊的地位，否则便不能对人提出特殊的道德要求。那么，人在天地这“一身”中居于何等的地位呢？从程颢的论述看，他实际上已经把人定位为天地之“心”了，因为唯有“心”能“知”手足之疾痛。人既为“天地之心”，万物为“四肢百体”，其疾痛则无不通达于心，没有这样的感受便是“不仁”。不过，这只是我们的逻辑推论，程颢毕竟没有明确地提出人在天地这“一身”“一体”中居于“心”的地位的思想。王阳明引入了早期儒家关于“人者，天地之心”的思想资源，明确地解答了这个问题。

“天地之心”的提法，首见于《易·彖传·复》：“复，其见天地之心乎”，但尚未同“人”直接联系起来。《礼记·礼运》第一次提出“人”是“天地之心”的观念：“人者，天地之心也，五行之端也，食味别声被色而生者也。”“人者，天地之心”的命题，是儒家对人在宇宙间的哲学定位，标志着儒家对人之为人的一种高度的自觉。这一命题中蕴含着的另一层意思，是认定人具有不同于万物的特质。人之所以有这样的特质，按照《礼运》的说法，在于人是“五行之秀气”，万物皆禀五行之气而生，惟人独得其“秀气”，故能为“天地之心”。人独得天地间“五行之秀气”，因而人就是“万物之灵”。人为万物之灵，也是中国先民由来已久的观念，最早出现在儒家早期典籍《尚书·泰誓》中：“惟天地万物父母，惟人万物之灵。”人既是“万物之灵”，则为万物中之最贵者，故孔子有“天地之性人为贵”①的说法。人为“天地之心”、“万物之灵”以及“人为贵”，都是先民自我意识的精粹，都是非常重要的思想。

王阳明明确指出：“夫人者，天地之心。天地万物，本吾一体者也，生民之困苦荼毒，孰非疾痛之切于吾身者乎？”②

人既是“天地之心”，则天地间万物之危难痛苦无不通达于此“心”，此“心”则必然做出反应而怜恤爱护之：

是故见孺子之入井，而必有怵惕恻隐之心焉，是其仁之与孺子而为一体也；孺子犹同类者也，见鸟兽之哀鸣觳觫，而必有不忍之心焉，是其仁之与鸟兽而为一体也；鸟兽犹有知觉者也，见草木之摧折而必有悯恤之心焉，是其仁之与草木而为一体也；草木犹有生意者也，见瓦石之毁坏而必有顾惜之心焉，是其仁之与瓦石而为一体也。”③

显然，如果没有作为“天地之心”的人，万物之疾痛又有谁来关切呢？万物的危难又有谁来解救呢？如果人在天地之间不是居于“心”这样的特殊地位，而是同万物

---

① 《孝经·圣治章第九》。

② 《王阳明全集·卷二·语录二》。

③ 《王阳明全集·卷二十六·续编一》。

没有区别，又如何能对人提出特殊的道德要求呢？这就是王阳明引进“人为天地之心”观念所要回答和解决的问题。见孺子之入井而有怵惕恻隐之心，是吾心本有之“仁”的必然反应，说明吾心之“仁”与同胞同类合为一体。同样道理，见非同类的鸟兽之哀鸣，见有生命的草木之摧折，见无生命的瓦石之毁坏，吾心本有之“仁”都会做出反应，而有不忍之心、悯恤之心、顾惜之心，这是吾心之“仁”与万物合为一体。这里我们看到，孟子的“爱物”还只是一个道德原则，到了王阳明这里，“爱物”已经被落到实处，具有了可操作性；孟子的“爱物”还是笼统言之，到了王阳明这里，仁爱的对象已被扩大到真正的“万物”，甚至到了没有生命的“瓦石”；孟子的“爱物”还是讲的应当如此，而在王阳明这里，“爱物”已经是非如此不可了。

“天地之心”是儒家对人在天地之间的道德定位，是实现“仁民爱物”的内在道德动力。宋明儒者对确认识人在宇宙中的地位，摆正人与自然万物的关系的问题十分强调。邵雍对“以我观物”的认识立场提出了批评，认为这种以人的利益和意志为中心的立场是一种偏见，是导致“任我”从而宰制万物的认识根源。他认为，正确的认识立场是“以物观物”和“因物”。张载《西铭》曰：“乾称父，坤称母，予兹藐焉，乃混然中处。”认为人与万物一样，都是天地所生，人在无限广大的天地中是微不足道的。这无疑是一种谦逊的态度。二程亦曰：“人在天地之间，与万物同流，天几时分别出是人是物？”①然而，天虽然不分别是人是物，人却不能仅如此为自己定位，否则便是把自己看小了，故二程又曰：“人与天地一物也，而人特自小之，何耶？”②在宋明理学家看来，人于天地之间，虽藐然七尺之躯，却担当着全部的道义。人必须“赞天地之化育”而“与天地参”，③ 承担起爱养万物的责任，方不愧于“天地之心”、“万物之灵”的称号。

## 三、“尽心”与“万物一体之仁”：“仁者”的最高境界

将“仁”提升为“万物一体之仁”，是宋明理学对儒学的一个重要发展。其意义不仅在于通过“仁”使人心与万物相感通而连为一体，也不仅在于为“仁”提供了宇宙论和本体论方面的根据和论证，更重要的还在于使人对万物负有了一种不可推卸的道德上的义务和责任。人非但不能凌驾于万物之上，而且还必须担负起维护万物之生养的责任，用自己的爱心行动使万物各得其所，否则便是没有尽到责任。作为“天地之心”的人，必须明确地意识到自己所担当的责任之重大。王阳明对此有高度的自觉，

① 《河南程氏遗书》卷第二上。
② 《河南程氏遗书》卷第十一。
③ 《中庸》第二十二章。

他把孟子的“尽心”同“天地万物一体之仁”联系了起来，用“尽心”来发挥“一体之仁”。他反复强调说：

“仁者以天地万物为一体，有一物失所，便是吾仁有未尽处。[①]

“人者，天地万物之心也；心者，天地万物之主也。[②]

“夫圣人之心，以天地万物为一体，其视天下之人，无外内远近，凡有血气，皆其昆弟赤子之亲，莫不欲安全而教养之，以遂其万物一体之念。[③]

“圣人之求尽其心也，以天地万物为一体也。吾之父子亲矣，而天下有未亲者焉，吾心未尽也；吾之君臣义矣，而天下有未义者焉，吾心未尽也；吾之夫妇别矣，长幼序矣，朋友信矣，而天下有未别、未序、未信者焉，吾心未尽也。吾之一家饱暖逸乐矣，而天下有未饱暖逸乐者焉，其能以亲乎？义乎？别、序、信乎？吾心未尽也；故于是有纪纲政事之设焉，有礼乐教化之施焉，凡以裁成辅相、成己成物，而求尽吾心焉耳。心尽而家以齐，国以治，天下以平。故圣人之学不出乎尽心。”[④]

所谓“天地万物之主”，绝不是要做天地万物的主人，绝不是要控制、主宰天地万物，而是以“昆弟赤子之亲”待之，要让人担当起参赞天地之化育、照管万物之生长的道德义务。这一思想向来被宋明儒者所强调，如张载所说，天地本无心，是人“为天地立心”；朱熹也说“人者，天地之心。没这人时，天地便没人管。”[⑤] 这个“管”字，绝不是“管束”、“管理”和“管制”，而是“管顾”、“照管”，是一种道德义务的担当；王夫之亦曰：“自然者天地，主持者人。人者，天地之心。”[⑥] 人在从宇宙观的高度为自己确立了“天地之心”的价值定位的同时，不是拥有了主宰、控制万物的权力，而是主动承担起了自然万物的“主持者”、照管者的责任和义务。从人与天地万物的关系的角度来看，王阳明的“尽心”，就是“尽”人心中本有之“仁”，对万物“尽”其道德责任和义务，实现“天地万物为一体”，使万物各得其生、其养、其所；与此同时，人作为天地间唯一的道德主体，也就实现了道德的完善，达到了人生的最高境界。

在上引王阳明对“尽心”的论述中，王阳明把“圣人之学”的全部内容都归结为“尽心”，而“尽心”所要实现的最高目标就是“以天地万物为一体”，其中既包含对自然万物“尽”其道德义务，也包含对父子、君臣、夫妇、长幼、朋友等人伦秩序以及

---

① 《王阳明全集》卷一《语录一》。

② 《王阳明全集》卷六《文录三》。

③ 《王阳明全集》卷二《语录二》。

④ 《王阳明全集》卷七《语录四》。

⑤ 《朱子语类·卷四十五·论语二十七》。

⑥ 王夫之《张子正蒙注》。

“纪纲政事”、“礼乐教化”、“齐家治国平天下”等政治生活“尽”其社会责任，故曰“圣人之学不出乎尽心”。孟子的“尽心”学说在王阳明这里可谓得到了淋漓尽致的发挥和最大程度的扩展。

“万物一体之仁”的思想，集中了自孔子和孟子以来的儒家仁学的思想成果。从战国时期的思孟学派到宋明时期的理学和心学，儒家学者对“仁”所进行的心性论和宇宙论、本体论的论证，至王阳明乃粲然大备。“以天地万物为一体”是儒家仁爱思想的最终目标，是“仁者”的最高境界，是儒家道德关怀的最高体现，也是儒家“仁”学发展的最高阶段。王阳明“万物一体之仁”思想的提出，使得“仁”学获得了最完备的理论体系，终于发展到中国古代哲学所能达到的最高的理论形态。

## 四、“万物一体之仁”的生态伦理意义

王阳明不仅集“心学”之大成，而且集此前儒学思想发展的大成，中国古代儒学发展的思想成果在王阳明这里成功地得到了融汇和贯通。“万物一体之仁”可以说是王阳明的一个创新性、综合性极强的思想，其中汇集了先秦以来重要的儒学思想资源，从心学的角度加以融会贯通，解答了历代儒学所关心的重要理论问题。如前所论，“万物一体之仁”是用仁爱精神将人与万物联为一体，把人类的道德关怀扩大到人类之外的天地万物，使人类担当起自然万物的照管者、主持者的道德角色，以今观之，“万物一体之仁”的思想就包含有重要的生态伦理意义。

从哲学的角度看，生态学的基本问题是人与自然的关系问题，亦即人应该如何对待自然万物的问题，这个问题的关键，又在于人如何看待自己、为自己定位的问题。关于这个问题，我们在中国古老的文化传统中可以举出三种不同的、有代表性的观念：道家的万物平等观念，以荀子、董仲舒为代表的人类中心主义观念，以孔子、孟子、宋明儒家为代表的生态伦理观念。

根据老子提出的“道”的理念和“道法自然”的原则，万物在大道面前都是平等的，人不过是万物中的普通成员，因而人与万物也是平等的，人类并不优于万物。“道法自然”的原则落实在人与万物的关系上，要求人应该以自然的态度对待万物，“辅万物之自然而不敢为”，[①] 尊重万物的自然状态而不妄加干预。庄子认为人优于万物的观念是人类的一种偏见，足以导致对万物的戕害，他提出“以道观之，物无贵贱”的思想，将老子的万物平等观落实在尊重万物的“天性”之上，对人类的自我优越观念和“以人助天”、“以人灭天”的行为进行了深刻的反思和批评，提出了人类的标准并不适

---

① 《老子》第六十四章。

合于万物的鲜明主张，旨在消解和纠正以儒家为代表的人贵于万物的世俗观念。根据现代生态伦理学的标准，道家的万物平等观无疑可以归入非人类中心论的范畴。道家的万物平等观对于当前保护生态环境和合理利用自然资源，实现人类社会的可持续发展，无疑具有独特的价值和意义。由于本文主题所限，兹不多言表。

以荀子和董仲舒为代表的一派儒家认为，万物存在的价值就在于能够为人类所利用。荀子把万物看成是人类的财富，虽然他也主张在取用自然资源时要有所节制，然而在他看来，万物最大限度地、可持续地为人类所用，这便是万物之“宜”了。正是基于这样的认识，荀子提出了“人定胜天”的思想，主张对自然界（“天”）“物畜而制之”。董仲舒则从神学目的论出发，阐述了天创造万物是为了人类所用的观点。他说：“天地之生万物也，以养人，故其可食者以养身体，其可威者以为容服。”[①] “生五谷以食之，桑麻以衣之，六畜以养之，服牛乘马，圈豹槛虎，是其得天之灵，贵于物也。”[②]在荀子和董仲舒看来，人贵于万物，人类的利益高于一切，因而人类为了自己的利益而自由取用自然资源，这是天经地义的事，即使是有所爱惜和保护，也只是为了人类的长远利益。以现代生态伦理学的标准来看，这是一种典型的人类中心论。

从思、孟到程、朱、王阳明的一派儒家则主张把道德情感扩大到人类社会之外，把自然万物纳入到人类的道德关怀之范围，这一理论路向和价值取向在王阳明的“万物一体之仁”思想中得到了最深刻、最完整的表达。如本文所论，这一派儒家认为人是“天地之心”、“万物之灵”，是万物中之最贵者，这是这一派儒家对人在宇宙之间的自我定位。但是人在对自己做出如此定位的同时所获得的不是控制、主宰万物的权利，而是对万物的生养所承担起的道德责任和义务。这种观念可能达致的实践效果同现代生态伦理学的基本诉求是一致的，我们可以将其称为中国传统的生态伦理思想。

通过以上比较我们可以看到，同样是从人贵于万物的观念出发，荀子和董仲舒一派儒家的理论路向所导致的实践效果是对自然万物的主宰，思、孟和宋明理学一派儒家的理论路向之实践效果却是对自然万物承担道德责任。有趣的是，这两派儒家认为人贵于万物的理由是相同的，那就是万物中唯独人具有道德属性。荀子认为：“人有气有生有知亦且有义，故最为天下贵。”[③]董仲舒也认为，万物莫贵于人，是因为“惟人独能为仁义”[④] 那么，为什么同样是这个人贵于万物的观念，在荀子和董仲舒那里成为了索用、控制、征服自然万物的理由，而在思、孟和宋明理学家那里却成为了保护、关

① 《春秋繁露·服制像》。
② 《汉书·董仲舒传》。
③ 《荀子·王制》。
④ 《春秋繁露·人副天数》。

爱自然万物的理由了呢？笔者认为，导致这一重大差异的原因就在于，在前者那里，道德观念的适用范围限定在人类社会的领域，而后者则把道德关怀扩大到宇宙万物，并把通过对万物承担道德责任的方式来参赞万物之化育视为人类道德完善的最高标志。

下面需要讨论的是，我们把荀子和董仲舒一派儒家的思想认定为人类中心论，那么我们应该如何认定思、孟和宋儒的生态伦理思想的性质呢？他们的观念是否属于人类中心论呢？

近几十年来，随着全球性的生态危机的日益严重，人们开始对以往人类对待自然的态度和方式进行反思，曾长期作为西方社会主流思想的人类中心论受到越来越多的质疑，并被认为应当对当前的生态危机负责，与此同时，各种各样的非人类中心论也不断涌现。这些非人类中心论承认非人类存在物也具有自身的内在价值，也拥有生存和发展的权利，人类必须尊重此种价值和权利，对它们予以道德关怀。这些主张同思、孟和宋儒的生态伦理思想有一致或相通之处，但是我们也必须看到两者在是否以人为中心这一关键问题上持有相反的立场。两者都肯定人与其他生命形式同处于一个生命共同体中，但在人与万物在此共同体中拥有何等地位这一问题上却存在着明显的差异。以西方非人类中心论的重要派别生物中心论为例，该学派反对人类优等论，认为一切生物都是平等的，人类与其他物种一起构成了一个互相依赖的生态系统，在这个系统中，人类只是一个普通的成员。儒家学说则明显不同，他们在人是宇宙的中心这一点上从来都是坚定不移的，有着极强的自觉意识。儒家始终坚持“人最为天下贵”的立场，对儒家来说，肯定人贵于万物，是对人提出仁爱万物的高标准道德要求的前提。儒家主张“万物一体”，但这个“一体”不同于生态系统的是，它有一个特殊身份的成员，那就是作为“天地之心”的人，相对于人这个“天地之心”，万物都是“四肢百体”。在儒家那里，此“心”与“四肢百体”是血肉相连的，万物的危难和痛苦无不通达此“心”，此“心”则必然做出反应而怜恤爱护之。如前引朱熹所说：“‘人者，天地之心。’没这人时，天地便没人管。”人之于万物就如同一位充满爱心、高度负责、无私的“家长”，或如王夫之所说的“主持者”，就是人在宇宙中的特殊地位。人作为“万物之灵”和“最贵者”，理应对万物以爱心相待，参赞天地之化育，否则就是没有尽到责任，就是道德尚未完成。在儒家看来，如果没有作为“天地之心”的人，万物之疾痛又有谁来关切呢？万物的危难又有谁来解救呢？如果人在天地之间不是居于“心”这样的特殊地位，而是同万物没有区别，又如何能对人提出特殊的道德要求呢？这就是“人为天地之心”的伦理学意义，也是我们把儒家的生态伦理思想定位为人类中心论的主要理由。赅而言之，思、孟和宋儒的生态伦理思想显然不能划归非人类中心论的范畴，而只能视为人类中心论的一种。

然而，思、孟和宋儒的人类中心论同当今大受诟病的西方传统的人类中心论又是不可同日而语的。西方的人类中心论，说到底是以人类的利益为中心的，而思、孟和宋儒的人类中心论，则是以人类的道义为中心。因而我们应该承认，人类中心论不应一概而论，而是可以分为不同的类型，古代中国特有的历史文化传统孕育出儒家以道义为中心的人类中心论，它是对以利益为中心的狭隘的人类中心论的超越，其实践效果也是有利于环境保护和可持续发展的。我们不必因为西方的人类中心论正在受到广泛的质疑而有意地回避儒家生态伦理思想的人类中心性质，而是应该大张旗鼓地宣扬儒家式的人类中心论的理论价值。儒家以道义为中心的人类中心论对人与自然的关系做出了独特的理解和阐释，包含着深刻的生态伦理意义，可以为我们突破和超越西方的人类中心主义提供一种不可多得的传统思想资源，应该得到足够的重视和大力的提倡。

荀子和董仲舒一派儒家对待自然万物的态度也是以人类的利益为中心的，这同西方式的人类中心论显然没有什么两样，这一派儒家的立场并没有成为儒家处理人与万物关系的主流。构成儒家的主流和深厚传统的，是从孔子、孟子到宋明理学的以道义为中心的立场，因而中国儒学基本上可以归属为道义型的人类中心论。儒家道义型的人类中心论和道家以万物平等为核心思想的非人类中心论，都是中国古代哲学对人类社会可持续发展的重要思想贡献，儒道两家对待人与自然万物关系的思想如双峰并峙，交相辉映，道家闪耀的是理性的光辉，儒家展现的则是博大的道德情怀。

# 儒家博爱观念的起源及其蕴含[①]

中国人民大学 向世陵 辛晓霞

一百多年前，梁启超在概括康有为哲学的特色时，将其以“仁”字为唯一宗旨的哲学概括为“博爱派哲学”。[②] 的确，康有为以为，“仁者，在天为生生之理，在人为博爱之德”，[③] 故阐发了他自己“博爱之谓仁”和“仁莫大于博爱”[④] 的博爱论说。康有为论仁和博爱，虽然有西学平等博爱的背景，但他以生之理、爱之德言仁，走的明显是宋明理学的理路；而“博爱之谓仁”的哲学，更是承接传统儒学的博爱论而来。尽管今天的人们更为熟悉的，是源自西方的博爱观念，事实却是博爱的观念本来孕育生长于中国文化的土壤。[⑤] “博爱”的观念和境界，从一开始就深深地浸润在中华民族精神及其生命智慧的源头活水中，并使中国社会在根本上保持了和谐的凝聚力，“和”为一个中华的群体且绵延不衰。

## 一、博爱观念的萌发

儒家文化的博爱情怀，渊源于商周时期形成的仁的观念。仁是博爱的母体，但在文本的层面，此时之仁尚未与爱关联起来。[⑥] 作为一种厚重的情感，爱的生发有“类”

---

① 基金项目：本文为国家社科基金重点项目《儒家博爱论研究》阶段性成果（项目批准号：13ZX011）。

② 梁启超：《南海康先生传》，《饮冰室合集》第1册《饮冰室文集之六》，北京：中华书局，1989年，第71页。

③ 康有为：《孟子微·中庸注·礼运注》，北京：中华书局，1987年，第208页。

④ 康有为：《颜渊》、《宪问》，《论语注》，北京：中华书局，1984年，第187、213页。

⑤ 其实，人们所以能用中文“博爱”概括基督教的“爱人如己”和翻译西语普遍的“兄弟”之爱（universal fraternity /fraternité）——“民胞物与”便是其例，正说明博爱的观念深深植根于中华仁爱精神的沃土，张载之“以爱己之心爱人则尽仁，所谓‘施诸己而不愿，亦勿施于人’者也”（《正蒙·中正》，《张载集》第32页）的对儒家仁爱的界定便是一例。

⑥ 譬如，《尚书》诸篇已有仁的观念，但主要在人性和德政的意义上使用，尚未与“爱人”的情感相关联。

或血缘的生理基础："凡生天地之间者，有血气之属必有知，有知之属莫不知爱其类。"（《礼记·三年问》）落实于人身，爱引出的是人内在的高级心理需要。[①] 需要本身基于生理的驱力，属于"类"的行为，进入到价值领域，是与仁德的直接联系。到春秋时期，仁与爱开始互为训解，并从根本上呼应了普遍的人道关爱与和谐群体的中国社会发展需要。

春秋后期，晋公子孙周（后为悼公）在周侍奉周王卿士单襄公，其时他"言仁必及人"，而单襄公评价他亦是"爱人能仁"，并预言孙周以其近乎完美的品行必然成为晋的新君。[②] 这一在孔子出生前二十多年的史实，披露了仁爱的规范在其孕育的雏形中，就是以一般性的爱人即博爱为特质而昭显于世的。后来，韦昭注《国语》的解释便是："博爱于人为仁"，"言爱人乃为仁也"。[③] 以博爱释仁，以爱人为仁，将博爱与仁德相关联，说明爱在满足心理需要的同时，也在根本上滋润着人的德性培育。《国语》及《注》的这些说法，表明孔子创建自己具有普遍意义的仁爱思想体系，是有深厚的历史底蕴的。

与博爱观念的产生相呼应，"博爱"语词可能也在这一时期出现。汉刘向《说苑》记载说：

> 晋平公问于师旷曰："人君之道如何?"对曰："人君之道，清净无为，务在博爱，趋在任贤，广开耳目，以察万方。不固溺于流俗，不拘系于左右，廓然远见，踔然独立，屡省考绩，以临臣下，此人君之操也。"平公曰："善。"[④]

师旷答晋平公之问，使用了"务在博爱"的表述。倘若刘向的记载属实，则"博爱"一词在春秋后期便已产生。当然，在历史上，《说苑》的史料价值并不那么确定。从这一整段话的语气和词汇表达来说，有可能受到了汉初语言环境的影响，譬如"清净无为，务在博爱，趋在任贤"这一类话，放在儒、道、墨各家交融的汉初，不会感到很唐突。然而，刘向作为西汉中后期最有盛名的学者，他之捡拾陈说、"录遗闻佚

---

① 按照马斯洛的需要层次论，爱是人的基本需要且属于高级需要。见《动机与人格》，许金声等译，北京：中国人民大学出版社，2012年，参见该书第2章和第5章的论述。

② 《国语》卷三《周语下》，上海：上海古籍出版社，1988年，第94、96页。

③ 见《国语》卷三《周语下》，第95、97页。陈荣捷先生认为："'博爱'一词首见于《国语·周语下注》，《注》云：'博爱于人为仁。'《孝经》亦用之。"（见《仁的概念之展开与欧美之诠释》，《王阳明与禅》，台北：台湾学生书局，1984年，第10页）陈先生虽未明言《国语注》的作者和时间，但所引"博爱于人为仁"正是今存最早的《国语注》——韦昭《注》之语。即便韦昭《注》可能保留了汉以前先贤的旧说，但却陷于无法验证的境地。据此，"《孝经》亦用之"意味《孝经》成书在"首见"博爱的韦昭之后，与学术界主流观点不同，故本文不取。《孝经》的成书，本文采较为通行的战国后期之说。

④ 刘向：《君道》，《说苑》卷一，文渊阁《四库全书》本，台北：商务印书馆，1986年（影印）版，第696册，第4页。

事”，的确保存了不少散佚的史料，况且，此条记载作为《说苑》全书之开篇，说明刘向对此十分重视，不应当是虚构无据之言。“虽间有传闻异词，固不以微瑕累全璧矣”，[①]《四库总目提要》的评价还是比较公允的。同时，清净无为虽是汉初政治的特点，但其思想本身在孔、老已经提倡，孔子便以“无为而治”去概括舜的政绩，舜所以能“恭己正南面而已”（《论语·卫灵公》），乃是因他孝顺和博爱的德行影响和感染了天下的臣民。因此，舜之治天下如果可用“无为”来评价的话，师旷所答的务在博爱、趋在任贤、屡省考绩、以临臣下等对策，又都是可以理解的。

事实上，参考本文随后的分析，如果立足于普遍地爱人和对仁的价值的集中揭示来说，认同博爱的观念产生于春秋时期是可以成立的。同时，博爱观念的萌发，虽然源自对特定人士品行的评价和对善的治道的真诚期待，但它的出现和被提倡本身，却无疑具有一般性的普遍意义。在此基础上，儒家博爱论在其孕育和成形的过程中，生成了适应中国社会特点的丰富蕴含并在社会国家管理及人与人关系的调节中，发挥了十分重要的意义和作用，从而需要进一步来予以探讨。

## 二、爱的先人后己

博爱观念的产生具有重要的意义，但更重要的还在于它的实施即爱人的实践。在实践中首先会碰到的问题，就是同作为爱的对象，己身与他人之间应当如何去选择，即其中谁处于优先的地位。这在情感、动机和道德选择上都具有重要意义，并由此披露了后来儒家博爱观的基本走向。

《国语》记载，晋公子重耳谋臣赵衰劝重耳娶怀嬴，并引《礼志》之言曰：

> 将有请于人，必先有入焉。欲人之爱己也，必先爱人。欲人之从己也，必先从人。无德于人，而求用人，罪也。[②]

《国语》所引《礼志》乃已逸古礼书，礼学文献由于孔子对礼的重视——“不学礼，无以立”（《论语·季氏》），后来都收归于儒学并成为其基本典籍，加之前述的“爱人”又的确是与仁德相关联，所以儒家博爱论的起源与整个中国传统博爱论的起源在义涵上是等值的。《礼志》所言之“有请于人，必先有入”，可以说是中华最初形态的推己及人观。在这里，人与己虽然同样需要爱，但在实际操作中却有先后之分——“爱人”先于“爱己”。《礼志》所考虑的人己先后，是作为一般性的原则和礼的要求而呈现的，应当已具有一定的社会影响力，赵衰也才能以此来劝导重耳。固然，爱己在

① 纪昀等：《子部一·儒家类一·说苑二十卷》解题，《四库全书总目提要》，石家庄：河北人民出版社，2000 年，第 749 页。

② 见《国语》卷十《晋语四》，第 358 页。

这里可以说是目的，爱人是实现目的的手段，但手段一经使用，也会产生脱离具体目的的一般性意义，并成为社会评价人的德行的一个基本标准。

那么，博爱观念出现于中国社会，首要的标志就是爱人先于爱己的先人后己说。在如此的博爱观念浸润和影响之下，中华文化系统中更为普遍的“先人后己”意识也随之孕育和诞生。《礼记·坊记》便引孔子之言曰：“君子贵人而贱己，先人而后己，则民作让。”从上层社会到普通民众，在他们的日常生活实践之中，都是认同“先人后己”的美德的并给予了普遍性的赞扬。即先人后己之爱在君子的示范作用下，开始具有了“心之所同然”的意义，“爱己”的目的性考量实际上已经淡化。

相较于中华的情况，西方基督教的博爱论同样也在人己关系上打下了自己的烙印。但在那里，不是讲先后，而是说同一，即强调“爱人如己”。[①] “爱人如己”在中国社会，首见于墨子的学说，所谓“视人之国若视其国，视人之家若视其家，视人之身若视其身”（《墨子·兼爱中》）。后来的儒家则吸取了墨子的这一思想。《毛诗》有论“大王居豳”之义，郑玄注《礼记·哀公问》时发挥其爱民说，以为“是言百姓之身犹吾身也，百姓之妻、子犹吾妻、子也”。由此，“爱人如己”可以在中西得到共同的呼应。当然不应忽视其中的差异。儒家在传统上更为推崇“先人后己”之爱，注重“人”对于“己”的优先性；基督教则更为看重人与己的一致性。在一定程度上，这体现了中国文化更重“人”、西方文化更重“己（我）”的区别。

回到文献的层面，在战国诸子出现和孟子游说诸侯的时代，应当还保存有不少春秋时期传下的典籍，从而影响到《郭店楚墓竹简》作者和孟子等思想家博爱观念的形成。譬如前述《礼志》的思想便在郭店竹简中得到继续，其曰：

> 反诸己而可以知人。是故欲人之爱己也，则必先爱人；欲人之敬己也，则必先敬人。[②]

“爱人”先于“爱己”是《礼志》博爱观念非常有特色的表述，但郭店简所述显然又有扩展，它将自我反省而知人作为了爱人敬人的前提，即“知己”而能“知人”，“知人”则能“爱人”，博爱的情感已处于理性认知的指导之下，是意识自觉的产物。

---

① 《马太福音·最大的诫命》（22.34—40）记载：当法利赛人问耶稣“摩西法典当中那一条诫命是最重要的”时，耶稣回答说：“‘你要全心、全情、全意爱主——你的上帝。’这是第一条最重要的诫命。第二条也一样重要：‘你要爱邻人，像爱自己一样。’摩西全部的法律和先知的教训都是以这两条诫命为根据的。”（参见中国基督教三自爱国运动委员会、中国基督教协会2006年印行《圣经（双语并排版）》）在“爱上帝”这一条上中西没有可比性；其“一样重要”的第二条就是集中体现基督教博爱精神的“爱人如己”说。就此而论，与产生于中国本土的爱之“先人后己”说有相似也有不同。

② 荆门市博物馆：《成之闻之》，《郭店楚墓竹简》，北京：文物出版社，1998年，第167页。其中首字因不能辨认暂缺。

而就“敬人”来说，不论是《国语》还是《论语》，甚至包括《墨子》，都只有具体的敬君上、敬父母、敬鬼神以及敬事等，到郭店简则从“爱人”推进到一般性的“敬人”，并在随后的《孟子》中得到呼应，博爱带上了更多的德性的色彩。

在理论上，爱己必先爱人的成立，依赖于将心比心的推度和自我心态的调适，[①] 属于内在性的范畴；但“先人后己”之爱落实于实践，却是需要由外在的客观尺度来确认的，故也带有外在性的意义。博爱的主体或施予者，在这里亦不限于上层社会的贤达或君子，而是已下移到普通的百姓，其所期待的，是我爱人、人爱我的善的社会效果的呼应。

## 三、爱的互惠性

爱己必先爱人和我爱人、人爱我的社会良性互动，实际引出的是儒家博爱的第二层蕴含，即爱的互惠性，它在博爱的实践中，表现为利他性、目的性与自觉性的统合。

郑声公五年（前496），郑相子产过世，“郑人皆哭泣，悲之如忘亲戚”。所以如此，司马迁的说法，是因子产“仁爱人”和“侍君忠厚”的缘故。按他的记载，孔子先前路过郑国时，曾与子产相交“如兄弟云”；闻知子产去世，孔子哭之曰：“古之遗爱也。”[②] 孔子与子产相交的“如兄弟”，可以用后来郑玄注《礼记·中庸》“仁者人也”的“以人意相存问”来解释。至于“遗爱”，裴骃《史记集解》引贾奎语曰：“爱，惠也”；杜预《左传正义》则解释为：“子产见爱，有古人遗风也”。[③] 显然，在孔子与子产二人心中，仁爱或博爱的观念实际上已扎下根来。“爱人”在这里，已经转化为目的本身。子产被郑人所爱戴，乃是他之治国能够施惠于郑国民众，博爱表现为惠民的实践。

“惠”之一词，在《论语》中多指在物质利益上施惠于民之意，孔子曾数次使用，“惠则足以使人”是仁人五种德行的归结（见《论语》之《公冶长》、《宪问》、《阳货》等篇），“博施于民而能济众”（《论语·雍也》）可谓其最高境界。孔子多次称赞子产，在于子产正是“养民也惠”的“惠人”。所以，《说文》释“爱”为惠，释“惠”为仁。

---

① “将心比心”，亦即《礼记·大学》所说的“絜矩之道”，参见《朱子语类》中的相关讨论，王星贤点校，北京：中华书局，1986年，第362—363页。

② 《史记》卷四十二《郑世家》。

③ 《史记》卷四十二《郑世家》，并参《左传·昭公二十年》。

同时，爱惠在孔子，并不只是单方面的惠人养民，而应当是互惠的。[①] 弟子宰予因为幼时享有父母的慈爱，成年后就当孝敬和感恩于父母，为逝去的父母服丧三年作为回报。但他不愿如此，故被孔子斥之为“不仁”。

“仁”与“人”之际，弟子“樊迟问仁”，孔子答之曰“爱人”；又自述“泛爱众而亲仁”（《论语·学而》），等等。在孔子，凡涉及“人”的概念，事实上都是泛指，即所有的人，否则，便是如“成人”、“小人”、“善人”、“乡人”一样的有具体的限定。那么，“爱人”自应当是泛爱众人，“博爱，泛爱众也”。[②]《论语》中另外还有两处“爱人”——“节用而爱人”（《论语·学而》）和“（君子）学道则爱人”（《论语·阳货》），也都是在这一意义上立言的。子夏所谓“四海之内皆兄弟也”（《论语·颜渊》），将孔子与子产相交“如兄弟”的君子间的个别实践扩展到全天下之人，这样的推广只有在博爱的普遍情怀背景之下才可能成立。[③]

进入到词汇的分解，孔子“泛爱众而亲仁”这句话实际涉及爱、亲、仁三个语词，但孔子并未解释这三个语词的具体含义。战国初中期，郭店竹简中的儒家文献第一次对它们有了具体的解说，并联系人性的概念进行了探讨。在郭店简，对爱与亲的细致分辨是一大特点。所谓“爱生于性，亲生于爱”，[④] 排出了性—爱—亲的前后序列：爱由性生，性内含而爱外现，亲近的情感则生成于爱的实践。至于仁，则首先与人的本性相关：“仁，性之方也，性或生之，……唯性爱为近仁。”[⑤]仁揭示了性之方所，[⑥] 即性朝向爱（这一方向处所）的自然展开，所谓性生爱也。在此意义上，性生成的爱自然最靠近仁，仁所要发明的，正是由本性生发的爱。

从而，仁、爱、亲这些概念实际是互为训释的。但结合对象，可以对它们进行区

---

① 互惠（Reciprocity）是当代社会学的一个重要概念。美国社会学家阿尔文·古尔德纳（Alvin W. Gouldner）认为：“互惠规范，就其普遍的形式来说，有两种相互关联的最低要求：⑴人们应该帮助那些帮助过他们的人，而且⑵人们不应该伤害那些帮助过他们的人。一般来说，互惠的规范可以被视作一种可以在所有价值体系中找到的尺度，而且，特别是作为普遍地出现在道德标准中的多种‘首要成分’（Principal Components）之一。”见《互惠规范：一个初步的陈述》，冯钢编选：《社会学基础文献选读》，杭州：浙江大学出版社，2008年，第355页。

② 孔安国：《古文孝经孔氏传》云：“博爱，泛爱众也。”文渊阁《四库全书》本，第182册，第11页。

③ 以上三段文字所引文献及阐释，笔者在已发表文章《仁爱与博爱》中有过简约的表述。见《哲学动态》2013年第9期。

④ 荆门市博物馆：《语丛二》，《郭店楚墓竹简》，第203页。

⑤ 荆门市博物馆：《性自命出》，《郭店楚墓竹简》，第180页。

⑥ 在郭店简如《性自命出》中，有不少“……之方”的表达句式，这里解作“方所”，系参考《周易正义·系辞下》“井以辩义”句，孔颖达疏韩康伯“施而无私，义之方也”为：“井能施而无私，则是义之方所，故辨明于义也。”

分，譬如“亲而笃之，爱也；爱父，其攸爱人，仁也”，等等。[①] 在这里，亲近笃实的情感标示出爱的品性，而由爱父而推广到普遍的爱人就是仁。爱作为亲与仁的中介，体现出兼备特殊性与普遍性的双重角色，特殊性以爱父为标识，普遍性则通过爱人来体现，这既包容了仁者爱人的思想意识，也将爱之普遍性视作了仁的根本特色，故可泛言之曰：“爱，仁也”。[②]

不过，爱父与爱人作为仁，其实是有善的道德预设在其中的，即所谓“爱善之谓仁”[③] 也。性善的基调在这里已经发生作用，换句话说，仁者爱人，乃是性善的结果。事实上，正是郭店简提出了中国最早的性善观念，所谓“未教而民恒，性善者也”。[④] 当然，其思想较稍后的孟子性善说简单。孟子认为民情是有恒产者有恒心，在此基础上，“然后趋而之善”以“治礼义”（《孟子·梁惠王上》）。由于这一工夫实际上也就是教化的过程，故与郭店简“恒”在“教”之先的思想可以相吻合，民因恒有善德，故而有爱。

在孟子，关于亲、爱、仁的关系，有一个影响深远的说法，即：“君子之于物也，爱之而弗仁；于民也，仁之而弗亲。亲亲而仁民，仁民而爱物。”（《孟子·尽心上》）孟子将仁爱的实施按对象的亲疏远近进行了划分：一是爱物。相对于“泛爱众”而言，爱之对象已更为扩大，爱具有最大的普遍性，天地万物无所不爱，这扩展了孔子仁爱的范围。二是仁民。与“物”相对的“民”，实际就是“人”或孔子所说的“众”，对他们应当普遍地关爱，施以恩惠，但却不必亲近。三是亲亲。亲亲是家庭成员之间的情感交流实践，相对于亲之“近”来说，仁与爱在对象的层面可以说都是“远”，突出了人与人之间普遍性的爱或互惠。

孟子又说：

> “仁者爱人，有礼者敬人。爱人者，人恒爱之；敬人者，人恒敬之。有人于此，其待我以横逆，则君子必自反也：我必不仁也，必无礼也，此物奚宜至哉？”（《孟子·离娄下》）

从《礼志》到郭店简，“爱人”与“爱己”可以解释为手段与目的的关系，带有一定利益考量的色彩，故爱人是应当；到孟子则转型为前提与结果的关系，爱的互惠性品格，已成为确定的心理预期，从此出发，爱人就是必然。他的这段话，对儒家仁爱—博爱的基本面及其实现机制做了较为恰当的揭示，实际上将仁、爱人、敬人、自反

① 荆门市博物馆：《五行》，《郭店楚墓竹简》，第 150 页。其中的“攸”字，按整理者意见当读为“迪（进）”或“继”。

② 荆门市博物馆：《语丛三》，《郭店楚墓竹简》，第 211 页。

③ 荆门市博物馆：《语丛一》，《郭店楚墓竹简》，第 198 页。

④ 荆门市博物馆：《性自命出》，《郭店楚墓竹简》，第 181 页。

和互惠整合了起来：仁表现为爱人的落实；礼则表现为敬人的实践；仁礼施与人，人必以仁礼回报之，如果不然，只能是自己的爱敬不够诚恳笃实。从郭店简的“反诸己”到孟子的“自反”，为爱人的行为是否普遍真切地实施，提供了内在的自省和自纠机制。

## 四、爱的两大内涵与儒墨之合

孟子无疑反对墨家互惠性的兼爱主张，但是，孟子反躬自省的德性权衡与墨家的主张又不是不可以调和。① 作为仁爱的发生学基点，它们可以在孔子答仲弓问仁的“己所不欲，勿施于人”（《论语·颜渊》）处找到源头，即自己不想要他人不爱我，就不能不爱他人；或者，自己想要他人爱我，就要把自己的爱施与他人。当然，从孔子“泛爱众而亲仁”到孟子的“仁者爱人”（《孟子·离娄下》），其间也存在细微的差别。孔子较为单纯地倡导人与人之间的泛爱或博爱，孟子则除了弘扬博爱之外，更多注意到亲与民之间的爱的差别。所以如此，在于孟子的时代，现实政治的需要具有更大的紧迫性，所谓“仁者无不爱也，急亲贤之为务”（《孟子·尽心上》）。

孟子此说，实际已将仁爱的两大内涵和盘托出。一是普遍之爱的一般原则在具体落实时，需要考量时政的急需，因而需要以亲亲尊贤为先，这与《礼记·中庸》中孔子所讲“仁者人也，亲亲为大（先）”② 的宗旨是相呼应的。二是“仁者无不爱”——或者说仁者博爱，毕竟是大前提，所以《礼记·哀公问》中孔子答哀公问政，所提出的便是“古之为政，爱人为大（先）”的治国原则。事实上，孟子对时政和君王的批评正是从此原则出发。他指责梁惠王说：“不仁哉，梁惠王也！仁者以其所爱及其所不爱，不仁者以其所不爱及其所爱。”（《孟子·尽心下》）“所爱”与“所不爱”按其文意是指子弟与民众，“仁者”由爱亲到爱民，亦即前面郭店简所说的“爱父，其攸爱人，仁也”；“不仁者”却相反，由不爱民走向不爱亲。这说明，爱人与爱亲、“爱人为大”与“亲亲为大”看似冲突，但又不是不可以调和。博爱与差等双方，本来是同一个仁

---

① 譬如墨子说“夫爱人者，人必从而爱之；利人者，人必从而利之”（《墨子·兼爱中》）便与孟子之言颇相似。况且，利的概念，孔子并非不谈，孔子言仁惠亦讲利：“因民之所利而利之，斯不亦惠而不费乎?”（《论语·尧曰》）。

② 孔颖达疏解《中庸》“仁者人也，亲亲为大”之意说：“‘仁者人也，亲亲为大’者，仁谓仁爱，相亲偶也。言行仁之法，在于亲偶。欲亲偶疏人，先亲己亲，然后比亲及疏，故云‘亲亲为大’。……‘亲亲之杀，尊贤之等，礼所生也’者，五服之节，降杀不同，是亲亲之衰杀。……礼者所以辨明此上诸事，故云‘礼所生也’。”见阮元校刻：《十三经注疏》，北京：中华书局，1980 年（影印），第 1629 页。孔氏要说明的，是仁爱在实施中表现出来由近及远的先后次序，或者丧服、丧期在礼制上由亲及疏的依次递减问题。简言之，“亲亲为大”即亲亲为先；“亲亲之杀”即由亲及疏，服丧渐轻。

爱在普遍原则和具体实践的不同层面的表现。实际上，“亲亲为大”往往只通行于有限的人际关系，且要受相应法律条文的制约。对于统治者来说，社会国家的安稳是第一位的，而这便与和谐民众、疏通民心的“爱人为大”关联了起来。相应地，儒家博爱论的重点，亦由博爱初起时关注的人己先后，转向亲亲与爱人的适当折中和一定条件下的侧重。

同时，还需要考虑的，是亲亲、爱父还是爱人，并不是当然如此，而是教化的结果。大致成于战国晚期的《孝经》，明确宣扬了博爱教化的理念。其称：“先王见教之可以化民也，是故先之以博爱，而民莫遗其亲。”（《孝经·三才章》）儒家先王立教化民，首先践行博爱，民众就不会遗弃自己的双亲。这说明在儒家先王眼中，父子之间虽有血缘维系，但子女并不必然产生对父母的爱敬，换句话说，爱有差等亦不是当然如此。爱敬孝顺之心是在先王博爱德行的感召下彰显出来的。那么，由教化而生起仁爱之心，与孟子立足仁义内在和善心弘扬的模式讲爱人便存在着矛盾，但这可以在荀子“化性起伪”的框架下予以化解。《孝经》的这一理路，在郭店简中已有迹可寻，《唐虞之道》便称“孝之方，爱天下之民”，[①] 以爱天下之民来阐扬孝道，说明孝是可以在普遍之爱的层面上被理解的。

《孝经》提出和阐发的“博爱”观，无疑是孔子“泛爱众”观念的恰当引申和发展，但同时也与对墨家兼爱、尚同等思想的吸取有关。班固《汉书·艺文志》总结墨家的思想说：“（墨家）养三老五更，是以兼爱；……以孝视（示）天下，是以尚同。”墨家的这两大“所长”主张，不但被儒家的后来人所继承，更被汉以后的国家所采纳。那么，孟子声称兼爱则无父（不孝）的论断，在作为东汉儒家正统代表的班固这里，事实上已经被否定。

融合儒墨的典型文本是《礼记·礼运》。[②] 在文中，其所提出的“人不独亲其亲，不独子其子；使老有所终，壮有所用，幼有所长，鳏寡孤独废疾者皆有所养”的倡导普遍之爱的“大同”之道，与随后所提及的“天下为家，各亲其亲，各子其子”的“未有不谨于礼”的维护等差的“小康”礼制社会，在形式上表现为退化和替补的关系，博爱与差等之爱也相应成为划分大同与小康两个社会发展阶段的基本参照。然而，

---

① 荆门市博物馆：《唐虞之道》，《郭店楚墓竹简》，第 157 页。

② 《礼记·礼运》是儒墨融合的作品。肯定儒家吸收了墨家思想，在前辈学者已有充分的论述。如伍非百：《礼运》“大同”之说“实则墨子之说而子游弟子援之以入儒耳”；“‘不独亲其亲，不独子其子’则兼爱也”（见蔡尚思主编：《十家论墨》，上海：上海人民出版社，2008 年，第 84 页）；蒙文通：“究之《礼运》一书，取之墨而义又有进于墨者”，“夫儒墨同为鲁人之学，通《诗》、《书》，道仁义，则《六经》固儒墨之所共也”（见《先秦诸子与理学》，桂林：广西师范大学出版社，2006 年，第 92、94 页）；张岱年：“所谓大同，实即以兼爱为原则之社会”，“大同实乃儒家吸取墨家思想后创立之社会理想”（见《中国哲学大纲》，北京：中国社会科学出版社，1982 年，第 279、280 页）。

这一划分在《礼运》本身便是受限定的："选贤与能，讲信修睦"的天下为公在礼制社会同样是遵循的准则；而"养生送死"的"人之大端"既是礼制社会、也是博爱"大道"的基本内涵。所以，匡正"强者胁弱，众者暴寡，知者诈愚，勇者苦怯，疾病不养，老幼孤独不得其所"的社会弊病而推行礼义，与博爱的大道之行在质上是同一的。后来历代儒家思想代表的博爱情怀，事实上正是建立在这一基础之上。①

更重要的是，"使老有所终，壮有所用，幼有所长，鳏寡孤独废疾者皆有所养"的大同理想，在历代的先进分子那里是一直都在发出的呼声。《礼运》所描述的"以天下为一家，中国为一人"的礼制社会，实际上预告了秦汉以后"大一统"的中国社会现实。张岱年先生说："'以天下为一家'，即兼爱全人类；'以中国为一人'，可谓即通国一体之说。此通国一体之思想，可谓较墨家兼爱说为进一步。由兼爱而发展，可得到一群一体，或通国一体之概念。"②"通国一体"固然离不开有强制力的国家政权，但同样也离不开由于兼爱或博爱思想浸润而积淀起来的华夏心理认同。就思想资源来说，到汉董仲舒时，孔子的"泛爱众"、"博施济众"与墨子的"尚同"、"兼爱"已经被整合起来。孔子之道就是圣人之道，就是先王之道，"其道如一而所上同也"。③"尚（上）同"在董仲舒就是"大一统"。如果能行"博爱"而"尚同"，则一统可至，太平可达。

## 五、结语："博爱之谓仁"的命题与实践

汉末三国时，韦昭注《国语》以"博爱于人为仁"释"仁"，将"仁"之要义落实到博爱的践行上，恰当地揭示了仁爱的普遍之爱内涵。在此之后，儒家仁爱的理论概括，大都不离这一特点和轴心。东晋袁宏撰《后汉纪》，他对两汉之际名士李业不愿在公孙述治下为官而甘愿饮毒酒自尽的事迹，做出了中肯的评论，并概括出了"博爱之谓仁"的典型命题，认为"博爱之谓仁，辨惑之谓智，犯难之谓勇，因实立名，未有殊其本者也"。④

袁宏概括的根基，可以追溯到孔子的"知者不惑，仁者不忧，勇者不惧"（《论语·子罕》）。在这里，"辨惑之谓智"、"犯难之谓勇"直接继承了孔子；但"博爱之谓仁"与"仁者不忧"在形式上则有距离，二者如何关联需要斟酌。汉孔安国和苞咸于

---

① 整合博爱、仁义和礼乐来治理国家，在儒家官吏那里被认为是理所当然的。如唐朱敬则在总结秦以来的国家政治所著的《五等论》中便认为："盖明王之理天下也，先之以博爱，本之以仁义，张四维，尊五美，悬礼乐于庭宇，置轨范于中衢。然后……使天下之人，心醉而神足。"见《旧唐书》卷94《朱敬则传》。

② 张岱年：《中国哲学大纲》，第280页。

③ 见《汉书》卷五十六《董仲舒传》。

④ 参见《后汉纪》卷三《光武皇帝纪》。

“仁者不忧”分别有“无忧患也”和“不惑乱也”之解，[①] 参考孔子由“季氏之忧”引出的“有国有家者，不患寡而患不均（安），不患贫而患不安（均），盖均无贫，和无寡，安无倾”（《论语·季氏》）的言说，可以联系到物质上的贫乏与救济的观念。博爱并不仅仅是一种精神慰藉，它包括了精神和物质的双重蕴含。从孔子的“泛爱众”可以推出给人民以恩惠，达致在邦、在家无怨。事实上，当子张向孔子问仁时，孔子明确以“惠则足以使人”（《论语·阳货》）为“天下为仁”的内涵之一，因为它直接体现着“爱人”的物质层面的关怀，而“博施济众”便是典型的表现。博施济众不是高于仁，而是仁在“王”的层面的实现，亦可说是孟子所称颂的饱食、暖衣、逸居的王道仁政。

可能正是基于如此的考虑，梁皇侃疏解“仁者不忧”为：“仁人常救济为务，不尝侵物，故不忧物之见侵患也。”他处又说：“仁者，周穷济急之谓也。”[②]在皇侃，忧患、惑乱都与“物”相关，因为有救济作为常务，以爱物为己任，所以就不担心人物有灾患。那么，当物质的救济和关爱成为“仁人”的基本考量之时，仁德的博爱内涵就得到了突出的彰显。所以，皇侃以“广爱一切”释“泛爱众”，以“人有博爱之德谓之仁”释仁，[③] 从正统儒家经学的立场推进了袁宏的典型概括。

到唐代，唐玄宗注《孝经·天子章》“子曰‘爱亲者，不敢恶于人’”为：“博爱也。”唐玄宗将爱亲与博爱统一起来，以倡导人人相爱的“泛爱众”思想，接续了经学的博爱理路，是抓住了传统博爱观的脉络和孔子思想的实质的。在这一时期，随着佛道众生平等和慈悲等观念的渗入，博爱为三教所共同倡导和推行。欣赏佛教的柳宗元，在为其叔父柳氏所作的墓版文中，称赞他是“用柔和博爱之道以视遇孤弱，仁著于内焉，此公修己之大经也”。[④] 柔和博爱之道就是内在的仁德和大经，能否躬行博爱，其时已成为社会评价人的修身水准的基本标识。反抗佛教而坚守儒家道统的韩愈，在博爱观上与佛教的融通儒墨却保持了一致性。韩愈进一步确认了“博爱之谓仁”的命题，以为大爱体现的正是儒家的仁德，这在后来产生了深远的影响。他并直接以“泛爱亲仁”和“博施济众”释“兼爱”，肯定儒墨“同是尧舜，同非桀纣”，而不应当强化二者的差别。这不是说差别不需要考虑，但那是次一位的——“行而宜之之谓义”，义可

---

① 参见何晏：《论语集解》，孙钦善校点，《儒藏精华辨》，北京：北京大学出版社，2007 年，第 104 册，第 143 页。

② 皇侃：《论语义疏》之《子罕》、《卫灵公》，陈苏镇等校点，《儒藏精华辨》第 104 册，第 372、496 页。

③ 参见皇侃：《论语义疏》之《学而》、《为政》的相关注疏，《儒藏精华辨》第 104 册，第 221、243 页。

④ 柳宗元：《故叔父殿中侍御史府君墓版文》，《柳河东全集》，北京：中国书店，1991 年（影印），第 133 页。

以在行仁而适宜上去体现，它不应妨碍普遍之爱这一最高的准则。[1]

而从国家政治和统治者的层面说，推行博爱也是一个基本的考量。唐高宗永徽年间完成并颁行、后被誉为中国古代法典楷模和中华法系代表作的《唐律疏义》，便有“惩其未犯而防其未然，平其徽纆而存乎博爱”的条款，按其《疏义》的解释，此条“言国家制刑，惩一而诫百，使之畏于未犯之先。不幸而丽于法，则宽平其徽纆，而心则主于博爱之仁也”。[2] 在唐代的立法者这里，制定刑法固然是为了惩戒犯罪，但最后的目的并不在惩戒本身，而是在未犯之先的预防和已犯之后的宽宥，其中贯穿的是博爱仁德的精神指导。

可以说，从汉到唐，倡导普遍性的仁和博爱，已成为包括统治者和思想家在内君臣上下的共识，并形成一种普遍化的社会情怀。这当然不是说汉唐时期没有了等级观念和阶级冲突的情势，而是表明要成功维护大一统的中华国家，不可能只从差等的观念来强化等级和职分。董仲舒之“圣人之道，不能独以威势成政，必有教化。故曰：‘先之以博爱，教以仁也’”[3] 的观点，便是对此做出的深刻阐发。国家的长治久安需要内在的凝聚力，博爱观念的灌输和相应政策的施行是最有利于国家的安定和民心的疏通的。博爱从情感的层面抚慰人心，和谐国家，也最终与诸多因素一起，合力造就了至今值得中国人骄傲的汉唐盛世。当然，从先秦到汉唐的博爱论在理论水准上还主要限于经验的层面，将博爱论与宇宙观结合起来，从形而上的角度阐释和论证博爱的精神和价值，是后来宋明理学才承担起的任务。

---

① 参见韩愈：《原道》、《读墨子》，《韩昌黎全集》，北京：中国书店，1991年（影印）版，第172、184页。

② 长孙无忌等撰：《唐律疏义》卷一《名例一》，文渊阁《四库全书》本，第672册，第21—22页。

③ 董仲舒：《为人者天》《春秋繁露》，上海：上海古籍出版社，1989年（影印）版，第65页。

# 《大学》与孙中山的儒学思想

中国人民大学　韩　星

## 一、《大学》的思想结构

《大学》言简意赅，纲目明晰，教义深刻。就全书的文字结构，可以归纳为两大部分：

（1）三纲领：明明德、亲民、止于至善，是从大纲讲大学之道。

（2）八条目：格物、致知、诚意、正心、修身、齐家、治国、平天下，是从细目讲大学之道。

这两大部分的关系是——“明明德”与格物、致知、诚意、正心四者相对应，修养途径是知、止、定、静、安、虑、得七证，都是“修身”分内的事，是属于内圣方面的；“亲民”与齐家、治国、平天下相对应，都是“修身”分外的事，是属于外王方面的。“止于至善”是总体目标，“明明德于天下”是最终理想，二者为内圣外王一体两面的统一，而实现目标、达致理想的根本环节是“修身”，所以说“自天子以至于庶人，壹是皆以修身为本”。

“八条目”以“修身”为界，又可以分为前后两个部分：格物、致知、诚意、正心所要达到的结果是修身，离开修身的格、致、诚、正都失去了意义；修身又是齐家、治国、平天下的前提，齐、治、平是修身的主体推衍。两方面合起来可以与孟子所说的“穷则独善其身，达则兼善天下”相互发明（《孟子·尽心下》）。“八条目”从逻辑上展示了双向互逆的思路：一是从“明明德于天下”到“格物”，即“明明德于天下”→治国→齐家→修身→正心→诚意→致知→格物；二是始于“格物”终于“平天下”，即格物→致知→诚意→正心→修身→齐家→治国→平天下。这两条思路正好相反，第一条思路是逆向的，是由终极理想向起点的逆推，前一项是后一项的发展，后一项是前一项的基础；第二条思路是顺向的，是由始基向终极的顺推，前一项是后一项的基础，后一项是前一项的发展。第一条思路表述前一项必须依后一项为先始，故二项的连接总用一个“先”字；第二条思路表述在有前一项而后才有后一项，故二项的连接总用一个“后”字。因此，在《大学》那里，实际形成了这样一种循环往复的道德实践过程，一方面由修身出发，达到“家齐、国治、天下平”，而“家齐、国治、天下平”则在更大范围内使明明德成为可能，使社会的每一个人都能够去修其身、齐其家、治其国、平天下，使社会每一个人的道德生命都得到充分实现，而社会每一个人道德生命的实现，反过来又促使“家齐、国治、天下平”，如此延续，不断循环。①

总之，《大学》典型地体现了儒家“内圣外王”的基本思想。三纲领和八条目是儒家实现“内圣外王”的根本途径和方法。在三纲中，明明德是内圣，亲民是外王。“内圣”意即“内求于己”，也就是“八条目”所说的“格物、致知、诚意、正心、修身”；“外王”表示“外用于世”，指的是“八条目”中的“齐家、治国、平天下”。由内圣达于外王，外王以内圣为依据。儒家内圣外王的意蕴在这里表达得十分圆融。所以，熊十力《读经示要》认为：“八条目虽似乎说，其实，以修身为本。君子尊其身，而内外交修。格致诚正，内修之目也，齐治平，外修之目也。家国天下，皆吾一身。故齐治平，皆修身之本。”②

## 二、中西古今文化冲突下孙中山的文化观

1923年孙中山在《中国革命史》一文中说：“余之谋中国革命，其所持主义，有因袭吾国固有之思想者，有规抚欧洲之学说事迹者，有吾独见而创获者。”③ 这里“因袭”是沿袭、继承的意思，“规抚”是仿效、依循的意思。这句话表明“因袭”是“创获”之源，“创获”又是“因袭”经与“规抚”相连接的飞跃，深刻地阐明了在继承传统和吸收外来文化的基础上才能实现创新。

在近代中西古今文化冲突的背景下，孙中山对源远流长的中华文化表示了极大的热情，他尽可能地把握儒家的中道思想，在当时多元复杂的文化思潮中提出自己的观点：一方面他主张在学习西方新文化的过程中坚决反对那种完全抛弃中国传统文化的做法：“吾人采取外国良法，对于本国优点亦殊不可抛弃”，④ 即不能只吸收西方文化而否认本土文化的精华，不要走到全盘西化的道路上去；另一方面中国要进步，要对旧文化需要改造，变成中国的新文化，则离不开从外国的新文化中引进新养分，即不能

---

① 梁涛：《〈大学〉新解——兼论〈大学〉在思想史上的地位》，《中国哲学》第23辑，辽宁教育出版社，2001年。

② 熊十力：《读经示要》，北京：中国人民大学出版社，2009年，第83页。

③ 《孙中山全集》第7卷，北京：中华书局，1986年，第60页。

④ 《孙中山全集》第3卷，北京：中华书局，1985年，第332页。

只承认本土文化，而不加区别地反对一切外来文化，不要狭隘的国粹主义道路上去。概括地说，在弘扬中国传统文化，让中国传统文化在新时代重放异彩的时候还要学习外国的长处，这是建构中国新文化的可行之路。为此，孙中山提出了“易旧为新”的文化观。他指出：“中国的文明已有数千年，西人不过数百年，中国人又不能由过代之文明变而为近世的文明；所以人皆说中国最守旧，其积弱的缘由也在于此。殊不知不然。不过我们中国现在的人物皆无用，将来取法西人的文明而用之，亦不难转弱为强，易旧为新”。[①] 这种“易旧为新”不同于文化激进主义者的弃旧图新，也不同于顽固守旧派的“祖宗之法不能变”，而是要在继承中国传统文化的优秀成分前提下吸收西方文化的长处，在新旧嬗变中更新发展中国的传统文化，创造一种以中国文化为主体，中西合璧的新文化，实现中国人自立于世界民族之林，与欧美并驾齐驱的文化理想。

孙中山这种文化观是在比较中西文化之后得出的结论。孙中山认为：“持中国近代文明以比欧美，在物质方面不逮固甚远，其在心性方面，虽不如彼者亦多，而能与彼颉颃者正不少，即胜彼者亦间有之。”[②] 在他看来，中国是有数千年悠久历史的文明古国，道德文明远高于外国，不及外国的只是物质文明。今天我们看到的外国物质文明发展，只用了二三百年功夫，“我们采来就用，诸君看看，便宜不便宜？由此看来，我们物质上文明，只须三五年即可与外国并驾齐驱。我们道德上文明，外国人是万万赶不及我们大。结果岂不比东西各国更加倍文明？彼时我中华民国在地球上，不特要在列强中占一席，驾乎列强之上，亦意中事”。[③] 通过比较中西文化，他提出了弘扬中国的道德文明，引进西方的物质文明，调和中西文化，借以超越西方文明的具体方案。1923 年 1 月 1 日孙中山在《中国国民党宣言》中用精炼的文字表述了他的文化观：“内审中国之情势，外察世界之潮流，兼收众长，益以新创。”他晚年看到民国成立后，虽然建立了共和制度，但出现“军阀专擅，道德坠地，政治日腐，四分五裂”的局面。[④] 同时，经过第一次世界大战，西方也暴露了本身靠科学和物质进步无法解决的社会问题，与此同时，在世界范围则兴起了东方文化思潮，所以，他主张用中国的道德文明、王道文化去补救西方的物质文明、霸道文化。他指出：“东方的文化是王道，西方的文化是霸道；讲王道是主张仁义道德，讲霸道是主张功利强权；讲仁义道德，是由正义公理来感化人，讲功利强权，是用洋枪大炮来压迫人。”（注：《大亚洲主义》，《国父全集》第 2 册（8），台北 1973 年版，第 306 页。）孙中山在 20 世纪中国积弱积贫的背景

---

① 《孙中山全集》第 1 卷，北京：中华书局，1981 年，第 278 页。
② 《孙中山全集》第 6 卷，北京：中华书局，1986 年，第 180 页。
③ 《孙中山全集》第 2 卷，北京：中华书局，1982 年，第 533 页。
④ 《孙中山全集》第 5 卷，北京：中华书局，1985 年，第 531 页。

下重提王道政治，与孔孟在春秋战国时期复兴王道政治有着极大的相似性。孔孟主张行王道仁政，实际上是正统儒家的一种政治哲学，他们相信道义的力量胜过军事武力，民心的向背乃是得天下失天下的关键。孙中山对儒家的这一政治哲学加以现代诠释，并且以此作为处理国与国之间关系的最高准则，力求在世界范围内形成和谐、平等、合作的新格局与新秩序，有以王道来实现世界大同的理想追求。孙中山说："孔子周游列国，是为什么事呢？是注重当时宣传尧、舜、禹、汤、文、武、周公之道。他删诗书，作礼乐，是为什么呢？是注重后世宣传尧、舜、禹、汤、文、武、周公之道。所以传播到全国，以至于现在，便有文化。今日中国的旧文化，能移和欧美的新文化并驾齐驱的原因，都是由于孔子在二千多年以前所做的宣传工作。"这就证明了孔子奠定中国道统。

## 三、孙中山的儒学思想

（一）民族精神——孙中山儒学思想的现实起点

孙中山有感于近代以来中国积弱积贫，中华民族处于历史的最低点，满怀忧患意识，遂提倡民族主义，寻找一种民族精神来凝聚四万万人，拯救古老的中国：

我们这种民族，处现在世界上是什么地位呢？用世界上各民族的人数比较起来，我们人数最多，民族最大，文明教化有四千多年，也应该和欧美各国并驾齐驱，但是中国的人只有家族和宗教的团体，没有民族的精神，所以虽有四万万人结合成一个中国，实在是一片散沙，弄到今日，是世界上最贫弱的国家，外国际中最低下的地位。人为刀俎，我为鱼肉，我们的地位在此时最为危险。如果再不留心提倡民族主义，结合四万万人成一个坚固的民族，中国便有亡国灭种之忧。我们要挽救这种危亡，便要提倡民族主义，用民族精神来救国。[①]

孙中山对民族精神特别重视，他拿中国人与西方列强，甚至与东方的日本进行比较，说明"因为他们有民族主义的精神，所以便能发奋为雄，当中经过不及五十年，便由衰微的国家变成强盛的国家。我们要中国强盛，日本便是一个好模范。"[②] 所以他竭力提倡通过弘扬民族精神来挽救中华民族的危亡，使有数千年文明教化的中国真正强大起来，自立于世界民族之林。那么民族精神从何而来？当然必须从中华民族的历史中来，特别是从中国传统文化中来。孙中山非常重视对中国传统政治哲学、传统道德的继承。

在讨论民族主义与世界主义的关系时，孙中山虽然主张民族主义，却并不否认世

---

① 《孙中山全集》第9卷，北京：中华书局，1986年，第188—189页。

② 《孙中山全集》第9卷，北京：中华书局，1986年，第190页。

界主义，他将世界主义视为人类社会发展的目标，而民族主义则是实现这一目标的工具。孙中山是从中国当时的实际情况出发，认为满清的民族压迫造成了汉族民族主义思想的灭亡，而近代以来受到国外世界主义的影响，反对民族主义，他指出："世界主义，就是中国二千多年以前所讲的天下主义。……世界上的国家，拿帝国主义把人征服了，要想保全他特殊地位，做全世界的主人翁，总想站在万国之上，故主张世界主义。"[①] 而今天的中国不同，今天的中国需要民族主义而不是世界主义，"我们受屈民族，必先要把我们民族自由平等的地位恢复起来之后，才配得来了讲世界主义。"就是说，通过讲民族主义先把我们的民族凝聚起来，把我们的国家强大起来，有能力参与到世界的事务当中去，才能发挥我们传统政治哲学中固有的道德文明，"所以我们以后要讲世界主义，一定要先讲民族主义，所谓欲平天下先治其国。把从前失去了的民族主义从新恢复起来，更要从而发扬光大之，然后再去谈世界主义，乃有实际。"[②] 这里，他引用了《大学》中欲平天下者先治其国来说明这个道理。因此，可以看出，孙中山提倡民族主义，但他自己并不是一个狭隘的民族主义者，他是在民族主义和世界主义之间寻找一个中道，在复兴中华民族的同时又追求天下大同的理想。1924 年 1 月 27 日，孙中山开始在广州国立高等学堂演讲三民主义，每在《民族主义》第 6 讲的结尾，孙中山总结到："我们要将来能够治国平天下，便先要恢复民族主义和民族地位。用固有的道德和平做基础，去统一世界，成一个大同之治，这便是我们四万万人的大责任。诸君都是四万万人的一分子，都应该担负这个责任，便是我们民族的精神。"（注：《三民主义·民族主义》，《孙中山选集》，人民出版社 1981 年版，第 691 页。）这就坚持了儒家的中道精神。

（二）《大学》是"最有系统的政治哲学"

《三民主义》作为孙中山晚年思想的主要代表作，认为中国古时有很好的政治哲学，"欧洲之所以驾乎我们中国之上的，不是政治哲学，完全是物质文明。……我们现在要学欧洲，是要学中国没有的东西。中国没有的东西是科学，不是政治哲学。至于政治哲学的真谛，欧洲人还要求之于中国。"[③] 强调中国要向西方学习中国没有的东西，中国政治哲学高于西方，西方人还要向中国学习。能够代表中国政治哲学精髓的就是儒家，而儒家政治哲学的代表作则是《大学》。孙中山说：

我国历史本素注意政治，所谓正心、修身、齐家、治国、平天下，屡言于数千年

---

① 《孙中山全集》第 9 卷，北京：中华书局，1986 年，第 216 页。
② 《孙中山全集》第 9 卷，北京：中华书局，1986 年，第 231 页。
③ 《孙中山全集》第 9 卷，北京：中华书局，1986 年，第 230—231 页。

前，是吾人政治经验，应算宏且富矣。[1]

中国有一段最有系统的政治哲学，在外国的大政治家还没有见到，还没有说到那样清楚的，就是《大学》中所说的“格物、致知、诚意、正心、修身、齐家、治国、平天下”那一段话。把一个从内发扬到外，由一个人的内部做起，推到平天下止。像这样精微开展的理论，无论外国什么政治哲学家都没有见到，都没有说出，这就是我们政治哲学的知识独有的宝贝，是应该要保存的。[2]

孙中山把《大学》的“八条目”看作我国传统的“最有系统的政治哲学”，认为这种由“内”到“外”，由“小”到“大”、由思想意识到具体行动的过程，抓住了中国政治哲学也即儒家政治哲学的特色，是需要我们继承和传扬的珍宝。可以看出，孙中山不像传统儒者那样首先从心性之学角度来讲《大学》中的这种正心、诚意、修身、齐家的道理。这种道理在传统上属于道德修养范围，是讲功夫论的。而他首先把这些道理放在知识论的范围内来讲，原因便在于“自失了民族精神之后，这些知识的精神当然也失去了，所以普通人读书，虽然常用那一段话做口头禅，但是多是习而不察，不求甚解，莫名其妙的。”所以，他认为要首先把这一套精密的道理从知识论的角度弄明白，然后在这个基础上才能落实到生活实践中。为此，他继承传统《大学》以修身为本的观念，结合中国人的实际生存状态，就“修身”问题进行了集中讨论。他指出，我们中国人对于修身一方面的功夫是很缺乏的，中国人一举一动都欠检点，象吐痰、放屁、留长指甲、不洗牙齿等这些都是修身上寻常的功夫，中国人都不检点，所以外国人一遇见中国人便以为很野蛮，不能得到他们的尊重。现在各国的政治都进步了，只有中国是退步，一个重要原因便在于没有很好地继承古代的政治哲学，特别是近几百年以来修身、齐家、治国中国人都做不到，所以对于本国便不能自治。外国人看见中国人不能治国，便要来共管。那么为什么中国会退步呢？表面看是因为受外国政治经济的压迫，但推究其根本的原因，还是由于中国人不修身。所以，他最后强调“我们现在要能够齐家、治国，不受外国的压迫，根本上便要从修身起，把中国固有知识一贯的道理先恢复起来，然后我们民族的精神和民族的地位才都可以恢复。”[3] 这样就把修身提高到国家民族落后挨打，培育民族精神，提高民族地位的高度来认识，可以说是对《大学》修身、齐家、治国的一种现代发挥。

孙中山的这些思想与当时的新文化运动倡导者激进的反传统主义格格不入，可以看作是对新文化运动倡导者的批评，所以后来也遭到了新文化阵营的反批评。胡适后

---

① 《孙中山全集》第4卷，北京：中华书局，1986年，第332页。
② 《孙中山全集》第9卷，北京：中华书局，1986年，第247页。
③ 《孙中山全集》第9卷，北京：中华书局，1986年，第249—250页。

来在《新文化运动与国民党》一文中对孙中山及其继承者这样批评到："这些话都可以表示中山先生实在不能了解当时的新文化运动态度。新文化运动的大贡献在于指出欧洲新文明不但是物质文明比我们中国高明，连思想学术，文学美术，风俗道德都比我们高明的多。陈独秀先生曾指出新文化只是拥护两位先生，一位是赛先生（科学），一位是德先生（民治）。吴稚晖先生后来加上一位穆拉尔姑娘（道德）。中山先生既欢迎科学，又分明推崇民治政治，却不幸在这里极力用夸大的口气，抬高中国的旧政治思想和旧道德，说话之间稍有轻重，便使读者真以为中山先生相信'欧洲的新文化都是我们中国几千年以前的旧东西了'。这种附会的见解，在三四十年前的老新党的言论里毫不足奇怪，但在中山先生的讲演里便是很可诧异，更可惋惜的了。"[①] 胡适的批评显然是站在自由主义西化派的立场，认为"我们自己百事不如人，不但物质上不如人，不但机械上不如人，并且政治社会道德都不如人。""要肯认错，要大彻大悟地承认我们自己百不如人。"他说，一部分西洋学者崇拜东方文明的议论，只是"一时病态的心理"，助长了东方旧势力的气焰。[②] 后来，胡适甚至发展到了完全否认中国文化而主张全盘西化。

（三）《大学》内圣外王之道与社会政治

孙中山总结中国的历史，认同儒家所推崇的尧、舜、禹、汤、文、武、周公这些古代圣王。这些古代圣王"能够负政治责任，上无愧于天，下无怍于民，他们所以能够达到这种目的，令我们在几千年之后都来歌功颂德的原因，是因为他们有两种特别的长处：第一种长处是他们的本领很好，能够做成一个良政府，为人民谋幸福；第二种长处是他们的道德是很好，所谓'仁民爱物'，'视民如伤'，'爱民若子'，有这种仁慈的好道德。因为他们有这两种长处，所以对于政治能够完全负责，完全达到目的。"[③] 这里讲的"很好的本领、很好的道德"其实就是儒家的内圣外王之道。他认同传统儒家的看法，认为中国几千年来只有这些古代圣王令后人崇拜，秦汉以后的皇帝不知道有多少，他们虽然没有本领、没有道德，但是很有权力，这就形成了漫长的专制主义，同时形成了人民对于皇权的崇拜与畏惧心理。

《大学》的"八目"集中体现了儒家的"内圣外王"思想，"内圣"必然表现为"外王"，而"外王"也必然以"内圣"为基础，表明理想人格与理想政治之间的逻辑关系：即理想的人格才能造就理想的政治，反之亦然。孙中山正是遵循这一思路，强调国人都应该将《大学》"八目"作为人生目标，从修身做起，磨炼意志，砥砺品德，

---

① 《胡适文集》第6册，北京：北京大学出版社，1998年，第583—584页。

② 胡适：《我们对于西洋近代文明的态度》，《现代评论》1926年1月10日4卷83期。

③ 《孙中山全集》第9卷，北京：中华书局，1986年，第325页。

增进知识，以达治国平天下，即振兴中华，建成民国之目的。他认为每个人都应努力去修身，但在当时修身对于革命党人、军人、学生尤为重要，并为他们提出了一些不尽相同的修身要求。1923年11月他在中国国民党恳亲大会上发表了《国民党员不可存心做官发财》的演说，强调对于革命党员来说，修身首先必“正心”，以树立起高尚的人格：“要存心做大事，不可存心做大官，然后本党才可望蒸蒸日上，不致失败。”孙中山先生进一步提出怎样克服“国民党员不可存心做官发财”的措施，主要是要“得人心”，而“人心就是立国的大根本，……得人心的方法很多，第一是要本党现在的党员，人格高尚，行为正大，不可居心发财，想做大官，要立志牺牲，想做大事，使全国佩服，全国人民都信仰。”① 他要求革命党员要有“民胞物与”、“天下为公”的胸怀，他本人也以“天下为公”的新圣王自期。对军人，孙中山认为修身的关键是要修成“智、仁、勇”三达得的军人精神，要使自己能“别是非，明利害”，“识时势”、“舍生以救国”。② 对于学生，孙中山认为，最重要的是要树立救国大志，要求学生要“学问志愿两者并行”，以修成大器，服务于国家。因为学生求取学问应该是为了“拿学问来救国”，“图国家之富强”，如果大志不立，那么“十年窗下任你读书几许卷，终亦无补于国家，只一书锥而已”。③

（四）《大学》与人格、国格

《大学》以修身为本，最终要落实在人格建树上。孙中山把人格建树与提升道德，改良社会联系起来，认为有了好的人格，就可以形成良好的社会道德风尚，促进社会的发展进步。他说：

国家是人类凑合而成，人人都有机会，可以造成一个好国家。我们要造成一个好国家，便要人人有好人格。④

最重要的，就是要令人群社会，天天进步。要人类天天进步的方法，当然是在合大家力量，用一种宗旨，互相劝勉，彼此身体力行，造成顶好的人格。人类的人格既好，社会当然进步。⑤

想中国改良成一个好国家，便是想得有一个机会，令四万万人都变成好人格。这个方法是在什么地方呢？要正本清源，自根本上做工夫，便是在改良人格来救中国。⑥

孙中山所说的人格是指道德人格。以儒家为主的中国文化非常重视道德人格的建

---

① 《孙中山选集》下卷，北京：人民出版社1981年，第463页。
② 《孙中山全集》第6卷，北京：中华书局，1983年，第16—23页。
③ 《孙中山全集》第5卷，北京：中华书局，1983年，第557页。
④ 《孙中山全集》第8卷，北京：中华书局，1985年，第319页。
⑤ 《孙中山全集》第8卷，北京：中华书局，1985年，第315—316页。
⑥ 《孙中山全集》第8卷，北京：中华书局，1985年，第319页。

树，一方面强调人所具有的独特品格，使人与禽兽区别开来；另一方面强调人的品性所呈现的价值层级，即小人、君子、贤人、圣人自下而上的层级，它使人与人区别开来。孙中山的人格更具有针对性，更具体：一是提倡互助道德。“物竞争存之义，已成旧说，今则人类进化，非相匡相助，无以自存。”① 二是提倡服务人格，特别是所谓先知先觉者，优势群体更应如此。孙中山认为以先知先觉自居的人，应该“勉求学问，琢磨道德，以引进人群，愚者明之，弱者强之，苦者乐之而已”。② 三是要立大志，做大事。孙中山经常教导人们要立大志，做大事。所谓大志、大事，这就是不专为一己发达，要为国为民立志，救贫救弱，不为做大官，要“抱持救国救民为天职”。③

以《大学》为主的儒家强调通过修身造就一种独立的“人格”，把它推到“治国平天下”就是一种“国格”。在儒家传统里，先秦儒家注重人格培养，到了秦汉以后建立了大一统的国家，逐渐由形成了国格观念。由人格建树到国格形成，实践人格与国格的并建，是以苏武为标志的。苏武以大汉使者出使匈奴，被匈奴拘留，放逐到天寒地冻、荒无人烟的漠北，但仍然“杖汉节牧羊，卧起操持，节旄尽落”（《汉书·苏武传》），宁死不屈，19 年后老态龙钟，才终得回归汉朝。苏武用自己的生命一方面塑造了宁死不屈，坚守气节的个体人格，同时也彰显了大汉王朝的国格。后来，在中国历史上又出现了许多苏武一样的志士仁人、民族英雄，他们有一种对国家安危、天下兴亡的责任感，将完善的人格转化为改造社会的动力，追求“立德、立功、立言”的三不朽人生境界，以“国治天下平”为最高目标，往往都是以自己的身家性命树立了“人格”，成就了“国格”，并由此产生出民族的凝聚力和向心力。孙中山对儒家这种“人格”与“国格”的传统观念十分重视，他曾经说：“人格与国格乃民族之魂。”④ 在 20 世纪的新时代，他把“人格”观念升华为人的价值观念的同时又把“国格”发展为一种崇高的爱国主义精神，试图在传统的“人格”与“国格”的思想基础上，铸造出具有时代精神的民族之魂，为中华民族的伟大复兴提供精神动力。

（五）孙中山对儒家传统道德的现代转换

儒家讲形而上之谓道，形而下之谓器。总体来看，孙中山的政治思想主张在“器”的层面更多地学习西方，而在“道”的层面更多趋向于传统，所以他对中国传统道德非常肯许，相信传统道德实现国治天下平的基本精神力量源泉。面对近代以来中华民族亡国灭种的危机，他说：“要维持民族和国家的长久地位，还有道德问题，有了很好

① 《孙中山全集》第 2 卷，北京：中华书局，1982 年，第 360 页。
② 《孙中山全集》第 2 卷，北京：中华书局，1982 年，第 360 页。
③ 《孙中山全集》第 4 卷，北京：中华书局，1985 年，第 38 页。
④ 《孙中山全集》第 2 卷，北京：中华书局，1986 年，第 152 页。

的道德，国家才能长治久安。”[①] 他总结历史上蒙元、满清虽然使国家灭亡，却没有使民族灭亡，根本原因就是我们有道德：“因为我们民族的道德高尚，故国家虽亡，民族还能够存在；不但是自己的民族能够存在，并且有力量能够同化外业的民族。所以穷本极源，我们现在要恢复民族的地位，除了大家联合起来做一个国族团体以外，就要把固有的旧道德恢复起来。有了固有的道德，然后固有的民族地位才可以图恢复。”[②]

所谓“固有的道德”即指儒家伦理中的忠孝、仁爱、信义、和平。他不像五四新文化运动那些新派人物那样提倡新文化，打倒旧道德。他说：“讲到中国固有的道德，中国人至今不能忘记的，首中忠孝，次是仁爱，其次是信义，其次是和平。这些旧道德，中国人至今还是常讲的。但是现在受外来民族的压迫，侵入了新文化，那些新文化的人，便排斥旧道德，以为有了新文化，便可以不要旧道德。不知道我们固有的东西，如果是好的，当然是要保存，不好的才可以放弃。”[③] 这就批评了新派人物把旧道德与新道德截然对立起来的做法，与“易旧为新”的文化观相应，他要与时俱进，进行传统道德的现代转换。

在所谓“旧道德”中，被当时人们批判最多的是“忠”。“忠”在先秦主要是忠诚无私，尽心竭力地对待别人，做好本分事情的意思，《大学》里虽然没有直接出现“忠”字，但所讲的“诚意”与“忠”有关，“絜矩之道”与忠恕之道有关；秦汉以后“忠”狭隘化为“忠君”。孙中山对“忠”字作了新解释，剔除传统的忠君内容，注入新的民主观念。他说：“以为从前讲忠字是对于君的，所谓忠君；现在民国没有君主，忠字便可以不用，……实在是误解。……我们做一件事，总要始终不渝，做到成功，如果做不成功，就是把性命去牺牲，亦所不惜，这便是忠。……我们在民国之内，照道理上说，还是要尽忠，不忠于君，要忠于国，要忠于民，要为四万万人去效忠。为四万万人效忠，比较为一人效忠，自然是高尚得多。故忠字的好道德还要保存。”[④] 孙中山对“忠”的观念加以改造，对“忠”的内涵加以新的阐释，是具有时代意义的，是他的独创。《大学》所讲的齐家之道主要是指孝悌之道。孙中山对孝道也特别推崇。他曾说：“讲到孝字，我们中国尤为特长，尤其比各国进步得多”。“《孝经》所讲孝字，几乎无所不包，无所不至。现在世界中最文明的国家，讲到‘孝’字还没有像中国讲到这么完全。所以‘孝’字更是不能不要的。”[⑤] “讲伦理道德，国家才能长治久安。孝

---

① 《孙中山全集》第9卷，北京：中华书局，1986年，第242页。

② 《孙中山全集》第9卷，北京：中华书局，1986年，第243页。

③ 《孙中山全集》第9卷，北京：中华书局，1986年，第243页。

④ 《孙中山全集》第9卷，北京：中华书局，1986年，第244页。

⑤ 《孙中山全集》第9卷，北京：中华书局，1986年，第244页。

是无所不适的道德，不能没有孝。”[①]

“仁爱”是儒家思想的核心内容，《大学》讲“唯仁人为能爱人，能恶人”，“一家仁，一国兴仁；……尧、舜帅天下以仁，而民从之。”“仁者以财发身，不仁者以身发财”。孙中山说：“仁爱也是中国的好道德”，中国“古时在政治一方面所讲爱的道理，有所谓‘爱民如子’，有所谓‘仁民爱物’，无论对于什么事，都是用爱字去包括。”“仁爱的好道德，中国现在似乎远不如外国。中国所以不如的缘故，不过是中国人对于仁爱没有外国人那样实行，但是仁爱还是中国的旧道德。我们要学外国，只要学他们那样实行，把仁爱恢复起来，再去发扬光大，便是中国固有的精神。”[②] 他极为赞赏韩愈对“博爱之谓仁”的解释，认为“博爱云者，为公爱而非私爱。即如天下有饥者，由己饥之；天下有溺者，有己溺之意。与夫爱父母妻子者有别，以其所爱在大，非妇人之仁可比，故谓之博爱，能博爱，即可谓之仁。”[③]

讲信修睦是《礼记·礼运》篇中提出的大同社会的道德境界之一。孙中山指出：“中国古时对于邻国和对于朋友，都是讲信的。依我看来，就信字一方面的道德，中国人实在比外国人好得多。”[④] “至于讲到义字，中国在很强盛的时代也没有完全去灭人国家。”因此，“中国所讲的信义，比外国要进步得多。”[⑤] 显然，孙中山所讲的“信”、“义”已经剔除了不符合时代的内涵，发挥出具有时代性和普世价值的意义。

中华民族自古以来就是爱好和平的民族。孙中山说：“中国人几千年酷爱和平，都是出于天性。”“爱和平就是中国人的一个大道德，中国人才是世界上最爱和平的人”。[⑥] 显然，他对儒家道德的借鉴是有选择的，是辩证的，他吸收和弘扬了儒家道德中符合近代民主精神的，能为反帝反封建的民主革命事业服务的积极因素，而对于其中落后的、不适应时代发展要求的因素则予以剔除。经过孙中山的重新诠释，忠孝、仁爱、信义、和平等儒家道德观念被赋予了民主主义的革命内容，成为教育和启迪人民群众的革命意识、民主意识和爱国意识的重要思想武器。所以戴季陶说：“我确信中山先生的主义最崇高的一点是在他说明忠孝、仁爱、信义、和平的道德精神是民族自信力的基础。”[⑦]

孙中山强调中国现代政制设计也邀建立在道德基础上。他说：“以人言之，则有三

① 《孙中山选集》，北京：人民出版社，1981 年，第 679 页。

② 《孙中山全集》第 9 卷，北京：中华书局，1986 年，第 244—245 页。

③ 《孙中山全集》第 6 卷，北京：中华书局，1985 年，第 22 页。

④ 《孙中山全集》第 9 卷，北京：中华书局，1986 年，第 245 页。

⑤ 《孙中山全集》第 9 卷，北京：中华书局，1986 年，第 245—246 页。

⑥ 《孙中山全集》第 9 卷，北京：中华书局，1986 年，第 246 页、230 页。

⑦ 中国人民大学中共党史系编：《戴季陶主义资料选编》，北京：中国人民大学出版社，1983 年，第 22、14 页。

系焉：其一先知先觉，为创造发明；其二后知后觉者，为仿效推行；其三不知不觉者，为竭力乐成。有此三系人相需为用，则大禹之九河可疏，秦皇之长城能筑也。”[①] 他将人群分为先知先觉、后知后觉、不知不觉，认为中国目前的政治基本状况是“民智未开”，无法直接实行宪政，即使制度设计也不能克服这一缺陷，而应当把重点放在先进者对后进者的引导上，而且强调先知先觉者要担负起教育民众的责任，“以先知觉后知，以先觉觉后觉”，“以引导人群，引导社会，决不可随波逐流，毫无振作”,[②] 这就是他所谓的革命党人对公众的引导上，这显示了儒家德治主义对于孙中山的深刻影响。

## 结　语

对孙中山的思想的怎么进行定位和评价？孙中山多大程度上受到中国传统文化的影响？儒家思想在孙中山思想学说中究竟占多少分量？处于什么样的地位？对此，半个多世纪以来学界多有歧义，人们众说纷纭。1925 年，戴季陶写成《三民主义之哲学的基础》，指出：“中山先生的思想，完全是中国的正统思想。就是继承尧舜以至孔孟而中绝的仁义道德的思想。在这一点，我们可以承认中山先生是二千年以来中绝的中国道德文化的复活”,[③] 这与 1921 年年底，孙中山在桂林军次对共产国际代表马林讲话时曾说的“中国有一个道统，尧、舜、禹、汤、文、武、周公、孔子相继不绝。我的思想基础，就是这个道统，我的革命，就是继承这个正统思想，来发扬光大”[④] 符合。大陆有些学者则否认孙中山先生是尧舜禹汤文武周公孔子以来道统的继承者，否认传统文化是孙中山先生思想学说的核心，这其中包含了过多的政治因素和意识形态分歧，此不深论。应该说，孙中山的思想既有中国儒家思想的精华，其核心是道统，又吸收了西方的先进思想，形成了以中（儒）为体，以西为用的中体西用，中西合璧的思想模式。

---

① 《孙中山全集》第 6 卷，北京：中华书局，1985 年，第 201 页。

② 《孙中山选集》上卷，北京：人民出版社，1956 年，第 156 页。

③ 戴季陶：《孙文主义之哲学的基础》，上海：上海三民书店，1925 年，第 33－34 页。

④ 《与马林的谈话（一九二一年十二月）》，《马林在中国的资料》，北京：人民出版社，1984 年；另据《马林档案》第 3111 号。

# 利瑪竇與1589年的進士

国立东方语言文化学院（法国巴黎） 王论跃（Frédéric WANG）[①]

對利瑪竇的研究無論在西方還是在中國，都已經很深入。人們對現有的中西文材料進行了各種不同角度的探討。面臨這一困難，我將選取一小段時間，即十六世紀末（1599年2月到1600年6月）利瑪竇在南京逗留的那段期間作爲討論對象。1595年，在廣東已經呆了12年之久的利瑪竇決定北上，前去南京與北京。謝和耐教授對這一年發生的事情這樣描述：

從1595年起發生的一個根本變化將對耶穌會傳教史以及中國與歐洲的關係史具有至關重要的後果，這就是利瑪竇與其他耶穌會士放棄憎袍改穿儒服，並以“道人”自居。[②]

利瑪竇總共在南京逗留了三次。第一次是在兵部侍郎石星（利瑪竇書中稱之爲將軍）的幫助下來到南京。石星想讓利瑪竇照顧他那因爲科場失意而得病的兒子。不過，利瑪竇這一次在南京只呆了15天，他那自以爲是朋友，並且在廣東就認識的徐大任侍郎叫他立即離開南京，並答應“隨便去哪裏，都可以幫他”。[③] 因爲當時中國正支持朝鮮打擊進犯的日本人，任何在兩京的外國人都容易引起嫌疑。利瑪竇不得不重新南下，來到南昌。在那裏，他受到了皇親貴族以及士人的大力歡迎。

利瑪竇第二次來到南京是在1598年。根據其《中國傳教史》記載，南京禮部尚書王弘誨（1542—1615，字 忠銘），曾經答應帶他去北京參加修曆工作。[④] 當王尚書得知

---

① 本文主要依據本人的法文文章《Mattéo Ricci et les lettrés de Nankin》（利瑪竇與南京士子）翻譯改寫而成，原文載 Isabelle Landry-Deron, éd., La Chine des Ming et de Mattéo Ricci（明代與利瑪竇時期的中國），Paris, Cerf, 2013, p. 29—42。

② Jacques Gernet,《La politique de conversion de Matteo Ricci en Chine》（利瑪竇在中國的歸化策略），Archives des sciences sociales des religions, vol. 36 (1973), p. 75.

③ Bernard Henri, Le père Mathieu Ricci et la société chinoise de son temps (1552—1610) [利瑪竇神父與他那時候的中國 (1552—1610)], Tianjin, 1939, p. 222.

④ Matthieu Ricci et Nicolas Trigault, Histoire de l' expédition chrétienne au royaume de la Chine (1582—1610)(1582—1610年中國傳教史), Paris, 1978, p. 376.

利瑪竇以及他的同事希望“帶著給皇帝的禮物”去南京時：

［他］回答很樂意與他們同行去南京，甚至去北京。尚書到南京一個月之後必須抵達北京向皇帝祝壽（農曆8月17日，在西曆9月）。對他來說，這個時候向皇帝進獻這個國家還沒有見過的禮物非常合適。[①]

然而，南京還是對外國人封閉著。利瑪竇並沒有真正在那裏住下來。他只是租了一條船並在船上住了一段時間，拜訪了一些南都名流，然後就沿著運河北上北京。他與他的同事們在1598年9月份抵達北京。因爲沒有獲准在北京的居留權，他在北京只呆了幾天，不得不再回南方。利瑪竇先在他的朋友，1589年在廣東韶州認識的瞿太素（瞿汝夔）的老家蘇州城住了一段時間，于1599年2月6日再一次來到南京。如果說他的前兩次的南京之行都毫無結果，這第三次南京之行卻很有收穫。[②]

利瑪竇第三次也是最後一次在南京的居住了一年零三個月。這期間，他結交了很多儒者。可以說這段經歷對他後來能夠在北京呆下來極爲關鍵：

如果沒有在南都建立的人際關係，如果沒有在官場周旋的應對經驗，如果沒有在學界樹起的西儒形像，如果沒有在士林結識的名流的揄揚，如果沒有對他在南京官紳社會初獲成功而驚喜不已的澳門葡商倍力支援，那麽利瑪竇要在北京立足，必定困難得多。[③]

必須説明的是利瑪竇最後一次到南京的時候，朝鮮與日本的戰爭已經結束，在南京的官僚不需要再迴避他。我在這裡想探討的問題是：他在南京結識了哪一些名流？這些儒者對他的態度如何？跟他們的接觸對後來的魏忠賢（1568－1627）[④]與 東林鬥爭是否有什麽影響？

林金水先生在其著作《利瑪竇與中國》一書中曾經作了一個統計，計算出他在中國一共結交了142位權貴以及士林名流。在這142位名人中，林金水的表中羅列了在南京結交的31位名人，佔總數的四分之一。[⑤] 這一數字當然還需要作進一步的核實，

---

① Ibid.

② Vincent Cronin, Matteo Ricci, Le sage venu de l' Occident（西賢利瑪竇）, Albin Michel, 2010, p. 175. 利瑪竇在《中國傳教史》中說：“主要的是，同伴們發現利瑪竇神父現在受到衆人的尊重，被視爲這座城裏的奇才。可是，他第一次從這裡被驅逐，第二次不得不隱藏起來。”頁429。

③ 朱維錚主編：《利瑪竇中文著譯集·導論》，上海：復旦大學出版社，2007年，頁5。

④ 關於明代太監，參見丁易《明代的特務政治》，北京：群衆出版社，1983年。Robert B. Crawford,《Eunuch Power in the Ming Dynasty》, T' oung pao 49, No. 3, p. 115－148 et Shih-shan Henry Tsai, The eunuchs in the Ming dynasty, New York, 1996.

⑤ 林金水：《利瑪竇與中國》，北京：中國社會科學出版社，1996年，頁286－316。有關林金水資料的局限性，參見 Nicolas Standaert (ed.), Handbook of Christianity in China: Volume One (635－1800), Leiden, 2000, p. 475, note 2.

它不包括那些在利氏來南京以前認識並繼續交往的朋友，當然他在劄記中也承認並非“所有的朋友都是值得信賴的”。[①] 在利瑪竇來南京以前，有一些官僚因爲收到他的禮物，或者閱讀他的中文著作，已經知道其大名。我這裡主要討論在西方利瑪竇研究中不太被注意到的幾個官僚文人。

對於利瑪竇能夠于1599年在南京站住腳起了重要作用的人物中，首先應該提到的便是南京吏部尚書王弘誨。王弘誨原籍廣東海南，是海瑞（1514—1587）的同鄉和崇拜者，還為海瑞寫過傳：《海忠介公傳》。[②] 這一點值得一提，因爲利氏認識的朋友中有不少曾經為海瑞立傳。如李贄（1527—1602）在《續藏書》就撰有《太子少保海忠介公傳》。跟東林黨人具有良好關系的鄒元標（1551—1624）曾經爲1618（萬曆四十六年）年刻的《海忠介公文集》作序。利瑪竇將在北京结识鄒元標。鄒元標在序中強調海瑞對陸九淵的推崇。[③] 這一點可以让我們推斷出利瑪竇試圖接觸那些享有美譽的學者。王弘誨應該說比較接近陽明弟子王艮（1483—1541）創立的泰州學派。他死後是焦竑（1540—1620）为他寫了墓志銘。在1599年致仕並從此彻底離開南京的王弘誨爲利瑪竇接觸在南都的官僚名士提供了種種可能性。这里首先涉及他的部下，南京吏部侍郎葉向高（1559—1627）、楊道賓（1552—1609）和南京國子監祭酒郭正域（1554—1612）。等到這些要人晉升到北京擔任尚書的時候，他們繼續在北京保護利瑪竇及其同伴。也是得益于王弘誨，應天府巡撫趙可懷（利氏《中國傳教史》中稱之爲南京總督）在利瑪竇第二次來到南京的時候接見了他。利氏在廣東的時候就結識的王應麟（1545—1620）曾經把他的《坤輿萬國全圖》的一張複制品轉送給趙可懷。1599年利瑪竇正是在時任鎮江巡撫的王應麟家裏過的春節。王應麟後來到北京擔任同样的职务，是他在1615年爲利瑪竇寫了墓碑。

關于利瑪竇與焦竑尤其是與李贽的交往，已經有不少文獻與研究提及。焦竑是1597年北京鄉試的主考官，曾經錄取了後來成爲利瑪竇弟子的徐光啓（1562—1633）。李贽曾經送給利瑪竇一首詩，這首將利氏比作莊子的詩用毛筆寫在一面扇子上。[④]不過，李贽在另一封寫給一個朋友的信中也宣稱並不明白利瑪竇來中國的真正原因。[⑤] 利瑪

---

① élisabeth Rochat de la Vallée 寫道：“歸化者並不多。況且，一旦神父遠離，歸化者很少繼續信教。很難曉得他們是皈依基督還是皈依利瑪竇。所有的中國朋友，甚至是最好的朋友，並不都是靠得住的。諒解、理解到哪一程度？甚至連他的一些西方同僚都批評他。”Matteo Ricci，Le sage venu de l’ Occident（西賢利瑪竇），《引言》，頁 13。

② 其文參見《海瑞集》，北京：中華書局，1962年，頁530—533。

③ 《海瑞集》，頁606—607。

④ 利瑪竇在劄記中把中國士大夫的扇子與西方貴族的手套類比。

⑤ J. Gernet 在 Chine et christianisme. La première confrontation（中國與基督教：首次衝擊）一書中曾經將李贄的詩譯成法文，Paris，1991，頁29—30。

竇自己對于與三槐法師就人性的爭論津津樂道。[①]這裏，我把討論的重點放到他在南京認識的另兩個文人：王肯堂（1549－1613）與祝世禄（1539－1610）。

王肯堂是在最早傳播利瑪竇作品的文人之一，甚至早于馮應京（1555－1606）與李之藻（1565－1630）。王肯堂是南京刑部侍郎王樵（1521－1599）之子。他是1589年的進士。這一年的進士中有狀元焦竑，鄒元標的朋友、思想家馮從吾（1556－1627?）、東林領袖之一高攀龍（1562－1626）以及著名書畫家董其昌（1555－1636）。王肯堂曾經擔任庶吉士、檢討、南京行人司副、福建參政等職。[②] 著有《論語義府》、《尚書要旨》、《律例箋釋》。最後一本書是對其父親所著《讀律私箋》的發揮。在歷史上，王肯堂尤其因為名醫而著名，其著作《證治準繩》至今還被認為是醫學名著。王肯堂同時也是一個書法家兼書法收藏家。利瑪竇去世的那一年，即1610年，王肯堂編撰了明代最優秀的書法作品集之一：《鬱岡齋集帖》。他的四卷本《鬱岡齋筆塵》類似一種筆記文集，收錄了他閱讀各種經典、醫學、《易經》象數解釋等的心得。他把利瑪竇的《交友論》以及《二十五言》也收錄在其中。著名思想家王夫之（1619－1692）在《詩經裨疏》、方以智（1611－1671）在《物理小識》中都曾經提到王肯堂的《鬱岡齋筆塵》。利瑪竇說王肯堂曾經派弟子到他那裏學習數學。[③]

在收入《鬱岡齋筆塵》的《交友論》序中。王肯堂這樣說明：

利君遺余《交友論》一編，有味哉！其言之也，病懷為之爽然，勝枚生《七發》遠矣。使其素熟于中土語言文字，當不止是。乃稍删潤，著于編。[④]

《四庫全書總目》也基本上如此介紹《交友論》，說此書曾經“為肯堂所點竄矣”。[⑤]所有的材料都認為此書是利瑪竇1595年在南昌為建安王而寫的。王肯堂將《交友論》與枚乘的《七發》做對比有一定的道理。首先，兩個文本都是為王公大人而寫，主張斯多葛斯式的倫理思想。深明醫術的王肯堂也沒有忽略利瑪竇《交友論》在語言上與哲理上的療效。我們知道在枚乘《七發》的最後提到，楚太子在聽了客人引了多個哲人（孔子、老子、莊子、孟子、墨子等）之後說“涣乎若一聽聖人辯士之言”。“涊然

---

① 《中國傳教史》第六卷第七章的題目就為《利瑪竇神父與一個名和尚就我們的信仰論爭》，Ricci et Trigault, op. cit., p. 421－427.

② 《明史》，卷221，北京：中華書局，1974年，頁5818。

③ “他是他的老師派來的。老師是一個著名的哲學家，北京翰林的士大夫。他們被認作帝國文人的精華，受人敬重，享有盛譽。”Matthieu Ricci et Nicolas Trigault, op. cit., p. 411.

④ 王肯堂：《鬱岡齋筆塵》卷三，《北京圖書館古籍珍本叢刊》，No. 64，子部—雜家類，北京：書目文獻出版社（萬曆影印本），頁548。關於枚乘，參看《漢書》卷51（北京：中華書局，1962，頁2359－2365）。

⑤ 《四庫全書總目》，子部，雜家類存目，北京：中華書局，1965，頁1080。

汗出，霍然病已”。[1] 王肯堂提到的《交友論》的醫療效應跟石星把科場失意的兒子托付給利瑪竇照應是不矛盾的。

收入王肯堂《鬱岡齋筆麈》的《二十五言》的節錄用的是另一個書名：《近言》：

利君又貽余《近言》一編，若淺近，而旨深遠矣。亦錄數條，置之座右。[2]

有的評論者認為王肯堂給《二十五言》另取了一個名字。不過，也有可能《近言》是利瑪竇在南京寫作該書時所時用的第一個書名，1604 年馮應京在北京刻書時，則采用《二十五言》之名。[3] 也有可能在南京的時候，書名還沒有定下來。《鬱岡齋筆麈》也提及利瑪竇在南京的科學活動。其劄記的第五、第六卷的題目就為《得益於數學，我們在南京的權威得到了有力的加強》。

現在我們來談祝世祿。祝世祿字延之，號無功，曾經在南京給利瑪竇提供了各種方便。利瑪竇說他“深受眾人尊重”，“被認為不光是一個道德科學方面的好哲學家，而且還寫得一手好字”。[4] 利瑪竇在《中國傳教史》中不止一次提到祝世祿的大名，而有關他的中文文獻相對匱乏。利瑪竇到南京的時候，把準備帶到北京的禮物做了幾次陳列，但是來觀看的人實在太多，管理上困難很大。後來利瑪竇就把所有的禮物交給祝世祿，委托他保管。利瑪竇最後一次離開南京的時候，也是祝世祿負責辦理其所有的手續，包括租船、辦理通行證等等。

祝世祿原籍江西德興，1589 年與焦竑、王肯堂等人一起考取進士。這一年的會試的主持是許國（1527—1596）和王弘誨。我們知道 1587 年曾經成為黃仁宇先生的一本書的題目。1589 年可能也值得在科舉史上特別一提。我們甚至可以將之與 1057 年的科舉做一個對照。那一年，主考官歐陽修（1007—1072）錄取了蘇軾（1037—1101）、蘇轍（1039—1112）、曾鞏（1019—1083）以及其他文學名家。與焦竑、王樵（王肯堂父親）一樣，祝世祿也註解過《老子》。祝世祿聽過王門浙中弟子錢德洪（1496—1574）、王畿（1498—1583）在江西時的講學。與焦竑一樣，祝世祿後來成為耿定向（1524—1596）的弟子，耿定向曾經是李贄的朋友，只是後來他們斷了交。《四庫全書總目》的存目部分收錄了《環碧齋詩集》三卷，《尺牘》三卷、《環碧齋小言》一卷。黃虞稷（1629—1691）的《千頃堂書目》中收錄《祝無功集》八卷。彭元瑞（1731—1803）在

---

① 《交友論》中有類似的句子：“友也，為貧之財，為弱之力，為病之葯焉”。《利瑪竇中文著譯集》，頁 113。

② 王肯堂，同上引，頁 550。

③ 1601 年馮應京爲利瑪竇的《天主實義》以及《交友論》作序。不太可能像謝赫奈在《 La politique de conversion de Matteo Ricci en Chine 》（利瑪竇在中國的歸化策略）一文中說的那樣：馮在南京已經是利瑪竇的朋友。這位在河北的時候與李贄爲難的正直的士大夫不太可能與利瑪竇同時在南京。

④ Matthieu Ricci et Nicolas Trigault, op. cit., p. 406.

《天祿琳瑯書目》中指出祝世祿曾經為焦竑的《養正圖解》作過序。《養正圖解》是焦竑擔任東宮講讀官的時候使用的“教材”。當利瑪竇結識祝世祿的時候，他任南京吏部的給事中。

黃宗羲（1610－1695）《明儒學案》第35卷中錄有下面這一段《環碧齋小言》。不過黃宗羲用的是《環碧齋小言》的別名：《祝子小言》：

> 謬見流傳，心在身中，身中直一團心耳。原來身在心中，天包地外。身，地也；心，天也。海起伏漚。身，漚也；心，海也。未有此身，先有此心。幻身滅後，妙明不滅。所以孔子許朝聞而夕可；莊生標薪盡而火傳。①

黃宗羲非常贊賞祝世祿“身在心中”的觀點，說那“實發先儒之未發”。不容置疑，這種身心觀屬於孟子的傳統，孟子視“心”為大體，身體的其他部位為小體，因此“身”從屬于“心”。王陽明對祝世祿的影響在下面這一段更為明顯：

> 王新建在事業有佐命之功，在學問有革命之功。蓋支離之說浸灌入人心髓久矣。非有開天闢地大神力、大光明，必不能為吾道轉此法輪。②

“支離之說”大概指的是朱熹的學說。這裏，祝世祿用了佛教用語“法輪”一詞來稱贊王陽明（新建伯）。因此，黃宗羲認為祝世祿的有些話“非儒者氣象，乃釋氏作用，見性之說也”。《四庫全書》的編者也註意到祝世祿對王陽明以及弟子王畿的追隨。跟大多數接觸過耶穌會士的學者一樣，祝世祿在自己的著作中很少提及利瑪竇。不過，他在他的文集中保留了下面這首題爲《贈利瑪竇》的詩作：

> 十年一葦地天長，百國來從西海洋；應是吾君文告遠，梯航無處不來王。
> 于腮黃卷深瞳碧，鈡巧自鳴分百刻；宣尼牟尼了不聞，晝夜一心天咫尺。
> 一齋一榻入無窮，別學偏於象緯工；道在何之非我土，老聃西去達磨東。
> 華言華服欲華顛，漢制都從九譯傳；一自變夷歸聖軌，至今分給大官錢。③

這首詩對利瑪窦的外表、能力以及宗教信仰作了很好的描繪。同時，作者本人對自己本文化的優越感絲毫不加掩飾。詩中所說的“鍾”屬于利瑪窦准備帶給朝廷的禮物。最後兩詩句可能影射詩人爲利瑪窦能夠順利從南京赴北京，不得不向大官行賄。“歸”字隱含歸化、信仰改變之意，不排除寫詩的祝世祿設想或者夢想著利瑪窦的徹底“漢化”，不僅是外表、語言、穿著，還有信仰。這一假設還可以從“變夷”的這一詞組的使用得到佐證。我們可以做這樣的假設：如果說利瑪窦成功地讓某些儒者信仰天主教，有一些文人也試圖讓利瑪窦儒化。這麽說來，“泰西儒士”這一稱法具有相當的

---

① 《祝子小言》，載黃宗羲：《明儒學案》，卷35，北京：中國書店，1990，頁407－408。

② 《明儒學案》，頁408。

③ 《贈利瑪竇》，載《環碧齋詩》卷一，《四庫全書存目叢書》，集部，第94集，濟南：齊魯出版社，1997年，頁220。

合理性。

除了上面提到的文人、官員，利瑪竇在南京還結識了其他要人，如開國將領徐達（1332－1385）後人徐弘基。在明廷很有權勢的太監與正直的士大夫之間，利瑪竇基本上站在士大夫一邊。當然，爲了達到靠近朝廷的目的，他有時候爲形勢所迫，也拉攏、利用一些太監。

從上我們不難發現，盡管利瑪竇的著作中沒有提及王陽明的名字，他實際上受到了跟王學相關的士人、官員的禮遇。應該指出的是利瑪竇抵達澳門的那一年正是張居正（1525－1582）去世的那一年。後者曾經下令關閉傳播王陽明心學思想的相關書院，並逮殺爲李贽稱頌的何心隱（1517－1579）。張居正一去世，萬曆皇帝就把他那嚴厲過度的老師一家幾乎滿門抄宰。因此，利瑪竇到澳門的時候正是泰州學派開禁的時候。王陽明的後學實際上並不一定認同利瑪竇的教義，更不認爲天主教可以替代儒學。但是，他們的非正統的思維方式使得他們能夠容忍基督教，並對利瑪竇本人更爲寬容。當然，利氏本人爲了使得天主教接近原儒思想，也做了最大的努力。在他來南京以前，利瑪竇曾經在南昌接觸了大量受陽明學影響的文人，如1546年考取進士的郭應聘、王泮、彰潢等。另外，這些士大夫對佛教也比較寬容，而利瑪竇對佛教的批評之嚴厲往往超過王門後學。可以這樣認爲，利瑪竇到北京以前結交的士大夫主要是王學的支持者。在南京的時候，他結交的人多了，圈子似乎也擴大了，但是我們也注意到這一圈子可以緊縮到同一個源頭，那就是葉向高的上司王弘誨。王弘誨是焦竑的老師，焦竑則是利瑪竇將在1600年認識的徐光啓的老師。並且，作爲李贽的朋友的焦竑與王肯堂、祝世禄都同年，都在1589年爲王弘誨錄取。這樣一來，同年關系在利瑪竇在南京的交往中起了至關重要的作用。

1602年之後的狀況似乎有了不同。首先，1604年開始東林黨人對朝政有了更大影響。他們反對佛教、主張廉政。李贽被逮捕了。利瑪竇非常敏感、注意適應。也許是出于機會主義的動機，他與他的傳教士同伴很快與泰州學派的敵人，如吏部尚書馮琦（1558－？）等結盟 。這一態度改變跟政局的變化有關，但是也跟利瑪竇需要找到新的联盟有關。況且，利瑪竇早就對泰州後學的三教合一傾向做出過批評。1602年之後的狀況似乎有了不同。首先，1604年開始東林黨人對朝政有了更大影響。他們反對佛教、主張廉政。李贽被逮捕了。利瑪竇非常敏感、注意適應。也許是出于機會主義的動機，他與他的傳教士同伴很快與泰州學派的敵人，如吏部尚書馮琦（1558－？），結盟。[①] 這種態度改變跟政局的變化有關，但是也跟利瑪竇需要找到新的依靠有關。況且，利瑪竇早就對泰州後學表現出的三教合一傾向做出過批評。不難理解，利瑪竇對部分精英

---

① 參看 Jacques Gernet, op. cit., p. 81－82。

希望“重整道德、回歸正統、反對屈從佛教影響，或者采取袖手旁觀的態度”。[①]同時也應該說明的是東林學者並不摒棄所有的王學內涵，因爲他們與江右學派的聯系頗爲密切。江右派主靜、重視道德踐履，這一點足以說明鄒元標與同爲1577年進士的馮琦之間的良好關係。然而，曆史的滄桑將促使重道德的東林學者進入另一鬥爭，即與以魏忠賢爲首的閹黨之間的鬥爭。這一屬于政治層面而不屬于思想領域的衝突將以閹黨的臨時取勝而告終。這一結果是明廷衰弱的又一信號，也預告了其不可避免的滅亡。

**參考書目：**

[1] 班固. 漢書. 北京：中華書局，1962.

[2] Bernard，Henri. Le père Mathieu Ricci et la société chinoise de son temps (1552—1610). Tientsin，Hautes études，1939.

[3] Cartier，Michel. Une réforme locale en Chine au XVIe siècle : Hai Rui à Chun' ai 1558—1562，Paris / La Haye. Mouton & Co，1973.

[4] Cheng，Anne (trad.)，Entretiens de Confucius，Paris，Seuil，1981.

[5] Cheng，Anne，Histoire de la pensée chinoise，Paris，Seuil，1997.

[6] 邱澎生. 有資用世或福祚子孫：晚明有關法律知識的兩種價值觀. 清華學報，33. 1 (2004) 頁1—43.

[7] Crawford，Robert B.，Eunuch Power in the Ming Dynasty. T' oung pao 49，No. 3，p115—148.

[8] 丁易. 明代的特務政治. 北京：群衆出版社，1983.

[9] Dunne，George H.，Generation of Giants：The Story of the Jesuits in China in the Last Decades of the Ming Dynasty，Notre Dame，1962.

[10] Gernet，Jaques，Chine et christianisme. La première confrontation，Paris : Gallimard，1992.

[11] Gernet，Jaques. La politique de conversion de Matteo Ricci en Chine. Archives des sciences sociales des religions，vol. 36 (1973)，p. 71—89.

[12] 海瑞. 海瑞集. 北京：中華書局，1962.

[13] Hsia，P. Po-Chia (ed.)，The Cambridge History of Christianity，Volume 6，Reform and Expansion 1500—1600，Cambridge，Cambridge University Press，2006.

[14] Huang，Ray，1587，A Year of No Significance，New Haven & London，Yale University Press，1981 (Le déclin de la dynastie des Ming，Paris : Presses Universitaires de France (《Histoires》)，1985).

---

① Anne Cheng，Histoire de la pensée chinoise (中國思想史)，Paris，1997，p. 530。

[15] 黄宗羲. 明儒學案. 北京：中國書店，1990.

[16] Levi，Jean（trad.），Les《uvres de Ma》tre Tchouang，Paris，éditions de l'Encyclopédie des nuisances，2006.

[17] 林金水. 利瑪竇與中國. 北京，中國社會科學出版社，1996.

[18] Ricci，Matthieu，Trigault，Nicolas，Histoire de l'expédition chrétienne au royaume de la Chine（1582－1610），Paris，Desclée de Brouwer / Bellarmin，1978.

[19] Masson，Michel（éd.），Mattéo Ricci，un jésuite en Chine. Les savoirs en partage au XVIIe siècle，Paris，éditions Facultés jésuites de Paris，2010.

[20] Rochat de la Vallée，élisabeth，《 Préface》à Vincent Cronin，Matteo Ricci，Le sage venu de l'Occident，trad. par Jane Fillon，Albin Michel，édition au format de poche，2010，p. 9－18.

[21] Sapriel，Marc et Stoltz，Patrick，Une introduction à la médecine chinoise，Paris，Springer France，2006.

[22] Standaert，Nicolas，Yang Tingyun，Confucian and Christian in Late Ming China：His Life and Thought，(Sinica Leidensia 19)，Leiden / New York / Kobenhavn / Köln，Brill，1988.

[23] Standaert，Nicolas（ed.），Handbook of Christianity in China：Volume One（635－1800），Leiden，Brill，2000.

[24] 孫尚揚. 利瑪竇與徐光啓. 北京：中國國際廣播出版社，2009.

[25] 談遷. 國榷. 北京：中華書局，1958.

[26] Tsai，Shih-shan Henry，The Eunuchs in the Ming dynasty. New York，State University of New York Press，1996.

[27] 王力平. 海隅明臣——晚明王弘誨研究. 海口：海南出版社，2008.

[28] 吳晗，論海瑞. 海瑞集（Œuvres de Hai Rui）. Pékin，Zhonghua shuju，1962.

[29] 吳莉葦. 從利瑪竇和艾儒略的傳教策略看晚明基督宗教與儒學對話機制的缺失. 復旦學報（社會科學版），No. 4，2009，頁 63－71.

[30] 吳青、陳文源. 明代士宦祝世祿與利瑪竇交遊述略. 廣西民族學院學報（哲學社會科學版），vol. 27，No. 4，2005，p. 99－101.

[31] 永瑢等. 四庫全書總目. 北京：中華書局，1965.

[32] 張學智. 明代哲學史. 北京：北京大學出版社，2000.

[33] 張曉林. 天主實義與中國學統. 上海：學林出版社，2005.

[34] 張廷玉等. 明史. 北京：中華書局，1974.

[35] 朱維錚. 走出中世紀. 上海：復旦大學出版社，2007.

[36] 朱維錚 主編. 利瑪竇中文著譯集. 上海：復旦大學出版社，2007.

# 近代东亚的《阳明先生肖像》

韩国岭南大学　崔在穆

## 一、序言

在越来越受西方思想影响的近代东亚，王阳明（名守仁，1472—1528）思想重新被评价为不仅可以对抗西方思想，也可以衔接近代思想并改革当时社会风气的具有“近代”意义的传统东方思想。[①]

在明治维新时期的日本，起源于中国的王阳明思想被重新评价，并与朱子学、古学一样产生了一种新概念——“阳明学”。与中国和日本相比，阳明学在韩国的发展虽然在时间上有一定距离，但也渐渐发展成一门学科。在东亚内部，帝国主义在扩张的同时，通过留学生及知识分子的互动交流，近代知识的传播与交流也越来越频繁。其中，《阳明先生肖像》被表现为代表近代精神的重要标志之一，起着一种传媒作用。即，它虽然从中国传入，但韩国和日本从另一个新角度来进行复制或再生产，刊登在刊物或著作中。

以中国为代表的东方肖像画被称为传其精神的一种画法，它不单纯描绘人的表情，而关键在于表现其精神，这是一种创造。因此，肖像画是通过创造，把所画对象的精神深入人心，以提高人的思想觉悟的一种比较容易的途径。我们可以想象耶稣、孔子、毛泽东、退溪、金日成的肖像挂在大街上的情景。就像这种情况一样，著作里若有一

① 参见崔在穆：《关于崔南善〈少年〉志的“新大韩少年”规划》，《日本文化研究》第11辑（东亚细亚日本学会，2006年）；《崔南善　出现在〈少年〉志的阳明学及近代日本阳明学》，《日本语文学》第32辑（日本语文学会，2006）；《在郑寅普阳明学演论中的黄宗羲与明儒学案理解》，《从本民到民主——黄宗羲民本思想国际学术研讨会论文集》（浙江古籍出版社，2006年）；《郑寅普〈阳明学演论〉的王龙溪之理解》，《阳明学》第16号（韩国阳明学会，2006年）。

幅再现王阳明人格和思想的肖像，就说明编者有某种意图或传达一种信息。[①] 本人认为，在这里可以找到近代韩国和日本“近代思想”里隐藏着的另一种战略。目前，此类研究并不多，一般认为这是美术或艺术领域的研究，但它又的确属于思想史的范畴。

在王阳明生前及逝后有多种肖像，其中一部分流入韩国和日本，并被复制或模仿。而一部分在中国已失传只存在于日本，这也符合近代东亚的复杂情况。在朱子学为主流的当时的韩国，阳明学的发展受到诸多阻碍，因此基本不存在《阳明先生肖像》，《少年》终刊号刊登的《阳明先生肖像》可以说是唯一的一幅。作为特刊，此刊大幅刊登了谦谷朴殷植（1859－1925）的《王阳明先生实记》。而在日本，包括东敬治（号正堂，名敬治，1860—1935）主管之《阳明学会》发行的《阳明学》在内的多种刊物[②]和著作里，都有大量的《阳明先生肖像》。在这里只对影响朴殷植的《阳明学》进行探讨。[③] 仅《阳明学》就刊载过多幅《阳明先生肖像》，而这些肖像在中国几乎都已失传。

总之，在近代东亚，《阳明先生肖像》在一般群众特别是青少年中起了传播“实践精神”的传媒作用，肖像的选取各有其意义。也可以说，肖像为传播近代思想起了助推作用。本文首先考察王阳明生前至逝后出现的肖像，再通过崔南善《少年》和东敬治《阳明学》的《阳明先生肖像》探讨其思想战略的近代意义。

## 二、王阳明去世前后出现的肖像画

王阳明的肖像是在他生前或逝后出现并流传的，主要目的是为了纪念作为思想家的王阳明的道德和思想。在佛教里，佛分为代表其肉体的色身和代表真理的法身，佛

---

① 比如，楠本正继的《宋明时代儒学思想之研究》（千叶：广池学圆出版部，昭和六十年）在所刊登的新建伯王文成公像（明代，黄节氏所藏）后做了如下解说：“早在昭和四年秋至第二年春，作者停留在北京。此照片是朋友桥川时雄氏借黄节氏所藏的一捆书画里的一幅明代肖像画。谢廷桀的《王文成公全书》卷首中画像并不是在流传的唯一的一幅阳明肖像，但作者相信这幅是最好的一幅表现哲人面貌的画像。特别感谢两位的好意。”（下划线）就像这样选取肖像也会介入一种观点。那么，比如《阳明学》第49号刊登的⑹阳明先生肖像与日本陆军乃木希典将军有关意味着什么？

② 主要有：①《阳明学》（吉本襄编，铁华书院刊，明治二十九年（1896）7月—明治三十三年（1900），5月），②《王学杂志》（东敬治编，明善学舍刊，明治三十九年（1906），3月—明治四十一年（1908），11月）（继承吉本襄的阳明学运动，三年发行31期）③《阳明学》（东敬治编，阳明学会刊，明治四十一年（1908），11月—大正七年（1918），8月）（②的续刊。即，《王学杂志》改为《阳明学》，明善学舍改为阳明学会）④《阳明学》（石崎东国编，大阪阳明学会刊，大正六年（1917），1月——大正七年（1918），8月）⑤《阳明主义》（石崎东国等编，大阪阳明学会刊，大正八年（1919），1月）

③ 朴殷植曾写两封信《给日本阳明学会主干》《再与日本哲学士阳明学会主干东敬治书》，其中后一封信的部分内容刊载于《阳明学》16号（明治四十三年（1910）2月1日）第36页的《文苑》一栏。它可能是朴殷植通过《阳明学》了解近代日本阳明学及当时在日本讨论的阳明学知识并进行交流的一种形式。

像代替其色身。在儒学里，肖像代替其身体向人们传达其心意。

研究王阳明肖像的同时考察铜像、石像可能更有意义。比如，王阳明降职赴任的贵州省修文县阳明洞“阳明园”内新立的王阳明像，以及贵州省贵阳市阳明祠、六广河边、余姚王阳明故居等地的多种多样的王阳明像，都是理解王阳明的重要资料。但本文则因版面问题，对此不作探讨。本文只是简略地说明目前本人收集的王阳明肖像的出处及有关事项。每幅画像都表现出王阳明的人格与思想。这些肖像可以为后面所提的韩国、日本的肖像进行比较做一种标准。

对上面肖像附简单说明如下：

①

②

③

④

⑤

⑥

⑦

⑧

⑨

⑩

⑪

王氏遵鏡三世祖士元公忘王文成(陽明)公七代遺像

⑫

⑬

⑭

①王阳明晏服肖像（贵阳阳明祠）①

②新建侯文成王公小像②

③王阳明像（余姚市文物管委会，为纪念封为新建伯）③

④王文成公像（不明，与江西某地方立功有关之肖像）

⑤王阳明像（中国历史博物馆藏）④

⑥新建伯王文成公像（明代，黄节氏所藏，与⑦⑪相似）⑤

⑦王阳明像（与王圻编《三才圆会》里的新建伯王文成公守仁像相似。面露病容）⑥

---

① 贵阳市文物保护委员会、贵阳市文化局编：《贵阳阳明祠阳明洞碑刻拓片集》，贵阳：贵州人民出版社，2002年，第56页。

② 山本正一：《王阳明》，中文馆书店，昭和十八年。

③ 王守仁：《王阳明全集》（卷1），上海古籍出版社，1992年。

④ 计文渊编：《王阳明法书集》，西冷印社出版社，1996年。

⑤ 楠本正继：《宋明时代儒学思想之研究》，（千叶：广池学圆出版部，昭和六十年。楠本正继氏在该书前言里有如下评价："谢廷桀的《王文成公全书》卷首中画像并不是在流传的唯一的一幅阳明肖像，但作者相信这幅是最好的一幅表现哲人面貌的画像。"

⑥ 间野潜龙：《朱子和王阳明—新儒学和大学的理念》，东京：清水书院，昭和63年。

⑧王阳明像（孙天人提供）[①]

⑨王阳明先生朝服大像（光绪七年仲春月贵筑杜瑞微捐刊，贵阳阳明祠）[②]

⑩先儒王子像[③]

⑪新建伯王文成公守仁像（王圻编《三才圆会》）[④]

⑫王氏3世祖士元公迁移余姚后王阳明为止7代人物画[⑤]

⑬新建伯[⑥]牌坊[⑦]

⑭王阳明的山水画（正德元年1月7日后的作品，故宫博物院藏）[⑧]

以上肖像经常出现在中国、韩国、日本的近代及现代著作中。

## 三、韩国、日本的“阳明先生肖像”

1. 崔南善《少年》中的“阳明先生肖像”

从朝鲜时代到近代韩国，朱子学一直是主流学科，虽有杂志或报纸介绍了一些王阳明思想但其肖像并未流传，《少年》终刊号的“阳明先生肖像”可以说是仅有的一幅，是在大幅介绍谦谷朴殷植（1859—1925）的《王阳明先生实记》[⑨] 中刊登的。《少年》于1908年11月1日（第1年第1卷）创刊，因日本帝国主义严格的检阅措施，1911年5月15日（第4年第2卷）停刊。从阳明学角度来考察此特刊，可以说它把重点放在阳明学上，整刊基本上介绍阳明学。首先，崔南善写的前言《关于提倡王学》[⑩]一文刊载了下面很长一篇文章。

---

① 张祥浩：《王守仁评传》，南京：南京大学出版社，1996年。

② 贵阳市文物保护委员会、贵阳市文化局编：《贵阳阳明祠阳明洞碑刻拓片集》，贵阳：贵州人民出版社，2002年，第1页。

③ （明）吕维琪编：《圣贤像赞》，孔子文化大全编辑部，1989年。

④ 《三才圆会》是部百科全书，由明代王圻编著。

⑤ 计文渊编：《王阳明法书集》，西冷印社出版社，1996年。

⑥ 正德十六年（1521）12月被封为“新建土地之伯爵”意义的“新建伯”，后来在余姚设立“新建伯”牌坊。

⑦ 计文渊编：《王阳明法书集》，西冷印社出版社，1996年。

⑧ 因刘瑾被弹劾而上诉，正德元年（阳明35岁，1506）2月王阳明被捕，此山水画是1月7日被捕之前画的。

⑨ 参见崔在穆：《朴殷植的阳明学和近代日本阳明学的关系》，《日本文化研究》第13辑，东亚细亚日本学会，2005年。

⑩ 高大亚细亚问题研究所编：《六堂崔南善全集》卷10（汉城：玄岩社，1974）（以下再收入于《六堂全集》第145—148页。《少年》志有上、下两卷影印本（崔南善，《少年》上、下，汉城：文阳社，1969年）（以下《少年》页码与原页码相同），另有高丽大学亚细亚问题研究所编纂的全集（高大亚细亚问题研究所编：《六堂崔南善全集》（汉城：玄岩社，1974年）（以下《六堂全集》是按分类收入，最近发行的影印本全集《六堂崔南善全集》1—14卷，汉城：亦乐，2003年）也按分类收入。

现在我们一切之痛苦就掌握在我们少年之手中，省悟也好，施舍也罢，闪光也好，抹黑也罢，都取决于我们之行为。（中略）打破他人之物，勉强压制自己欲望之火者［斯文乱贼射毒箭者，斥邪植正挂盾牌者］其意尽到，终不得不将自己之物而延命，故自己周围不存在他人的身影。这些人首先咬住的是阳明先生和他的良知学。（中略）故［某些人］连根拔掉提倡心即理与主张知即行的阳明学也是其中之一，（中略）揭穿其谎言者是其复活之救世主，揭开其面纱者是其再造之恩人。我们深信，王子之学是对其唯一的良斧好锯。（中略）少年们，不要犹豫，与我们共同接受王学（阳明学）之洗礼。你已得病为何不求良药，你已虚弱为何不用珍世之补药，你将远行，为何不备坚硬的拐杖。还顾虑什么？大道是笔直的，还忌讳什么？混王的头颅已挂在市上，无拦截之者。让社会栋梁之少年铭记此理，成为真正的儒家（事业家、活动家）。只希望教会他们道义和策略，（中略）认为王学就是途径，因此我们提倡王学，我们宣传王学。①

在这篇文章中，崔南善敦促人们重视知行合一的王学。朴殷植的《兴韦庵书》认为王学是活学，王阳明是事业家，阳明学对振兴青年事业心有贡献。② 因此，崔南善用“儒家（表示事业家、活动家）”一词也有类似的意思。《关于提倡王学》一文以“阳明先生王守仁之像”→明治维新前后致力于王学的著名人士：佐久间象山、吉田松阴、西乡隆盛→朴殷植的《王阳明先生实记序》→凡例→《王阳明先生实记》的顺序整理刊载了资料。即，中国哲学思想家王阳明像后面刊登继承其精神的日本三名志士之像，最后才是《王阳明传记》。

以下四张复印件的内容分别是：

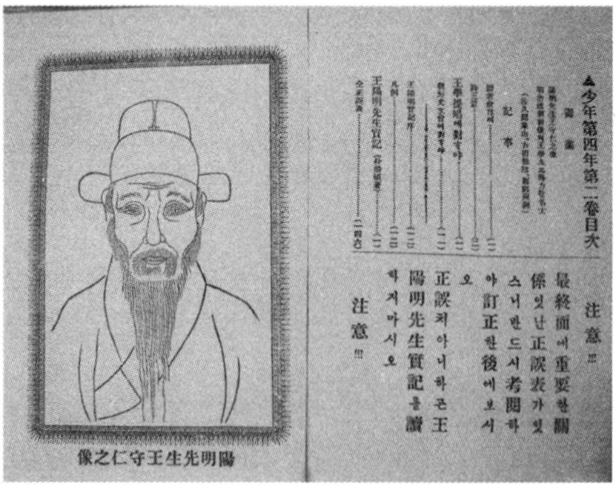


①

②

---

① 参见《六堂全集》卷 10，第 145、146、148 页。

② “王学活学也，事业家也，学不明，则士气不活，青年之事业心，亦无由以振兴也。”（《白岩朴殷植全集》第 v 卷，第 126 页）

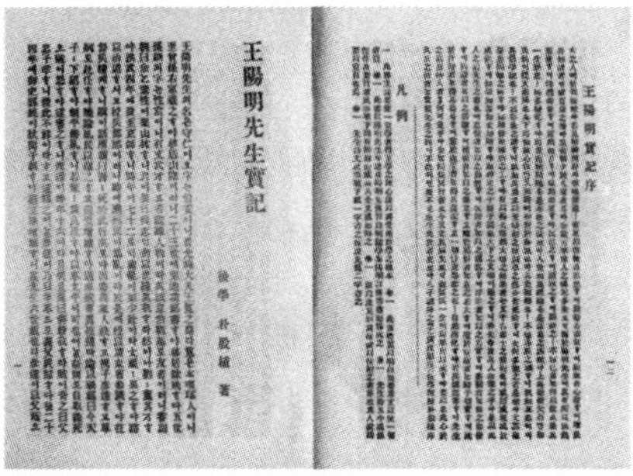


③

④

①目录及会话“阳明先生王守仁之像”部分

②“阳明先生王守仁之像”

③朴殷植《王阳明先生实记》部分

④明治维新前后致力于王学之士：佐久间象山、吉田松阴、西乡隆盛

《少年》刊登的“阳明先生王守仁之像”与前面加以说明的《三才圆会》刊登的肖像很相似，[①] 也许是影印画，也许是摹仿中国原画或《三才圆会》肖像的作品。不过不清楚该画像是由朴殷植提供的还是崔南善本人收集的，可以确认的只是此画的选取是由崔南善决定的。有趣的是，当时在日本流传很多带有武士风格的庄重的阳明肖像，而这幅更像韩国的儒学学者或元老学者，富有文人风采，不同于武士风貌的其他阳明肖像。

2. 东敬治《阳明学》中的“阳明先生肖像”

在近代东亚产生“阳明学”一词与日本明治、大正、昭和时期阳明学研究潮流有关。明治时期开始日本使用“阳明学”一词，其后，日本、（并与其有渊源的）中国、韩国也广泛使用。[②] 从名称的变化来看，明治以前的江户时期（即中国明代末期至清代中期）曾称作“姚江学”、“良知学”，[③] 幕末维新时期（即中国清代末期）则称作“王学”，[④] 明治后期才称作“阳明学”。[⑤] 因此，明治以后出版的有关王阳明、阳明学的著

---

① 中国部分参考⑦。

② 参见吉田公平：《阳明学在日本》，东京：淘河社，1999年，第5—24页，下面有关日本阳明学内容也参考了此书。

③ 比如明末清初黄宗羲《明儒学案》中的《姚江学案》，清朝中期彭定求的《姚江释毁录》和罗泽南的《姚江学辨》等。

④ 张武承《王学质疑》，丰田信贞《王学辨集》，野田冈齐《王学论谈》，吉田秋阳《王学提纲》，山口菅山《王学驳议》，东敬治编《王学杂志》等。

⑤ 吉本襄编《阳明学》，东敬治编《阳明学》，石崎东国编《阳明》、《阳明主义》以及大阪阳明学会等阳明学会的建立，井上哲次郎《日本阳明学派之哲学》，井上哲次郎、蟹江义丸编《日本伦理汇编》第一部分的《阳明学派》，三岛复《王阳明的哲学》，高濑武次郎《日本之阳明学》、《阳明学阶梯》、《王阳明详传》等。中国有梁启超的《阳明学》、钱穆 的《阳明学要》，韩国有朴殷植的《阳明先生实记》、郑寅普的《阳明学演论》、李能和的《朝鲜儒界之阳明学派》等。

作及论文、《传习录》等翻译作品非常多，这也说明当时研究王阳明及阳明学是一个热门，也许还是日本知识分子的必修课程。

从明治至昭和10年止，日本阳明学研究具有以下几个特点：一是深受时代影响的阳明学信徒们以启蒙、宣传为目的而进行的研究；二是因为大部分著作是信仰王阳明及阳明学并为其倾倒的信徒们所倾力而出的大作，所以直到现在很多书都仍有参考价值；三是大胆地与西欧及印度思想进行比较研究。明治、大正时期推进阳明学研究的动力，主要来自于以阳明学为基本纲领的民间社团以及由它们发行的普及宣传阳明学的刊物。

对上述肖像（略）附简单说明如下：

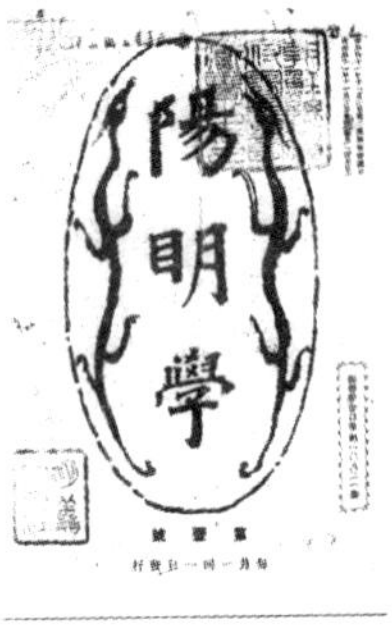


①

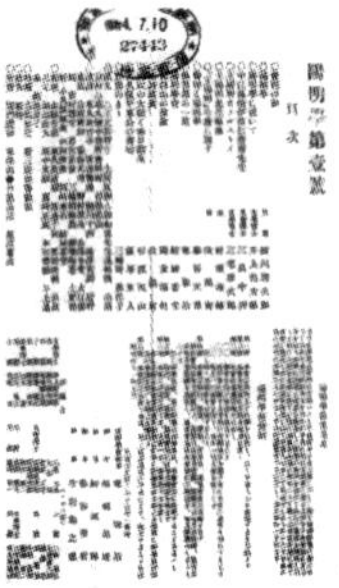

②

③

④

⑤

⑥

⑦

⑧

⑨

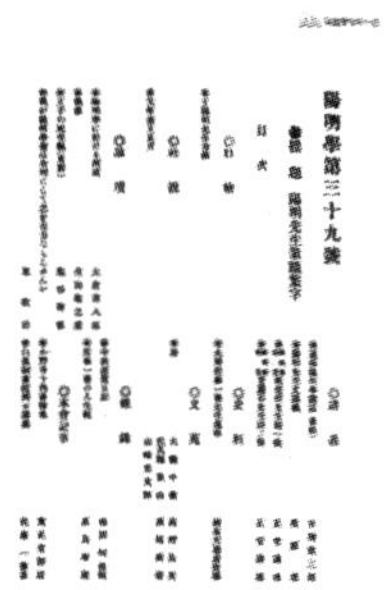

⑩

⑪

⑫

⑬

①《阳明学》第1号（明治四十一年（1908），11月3日）封面

②《阳明学》第1号目录

③王文成公遗像（《阳明学》第1号（明治四十一年（1908），11月3日）。椿恒吉摹仿三轮执斋所藏的明代曾鲸（波臣）之画）[1]

④阳明先生肖像（《阳明学》第15号（明治四十三年1月1日），大桥讷庵所藏，椿椿山书写。天保14年阴历11月30日大桥周道邀请佐藤坦（一斋）摹仿清代彭定求颂词的《王文成公画像》）[2]

⑤王阳明先生肖像（《阳明学》39号（明治四十五年1月1日）三轮执斋所赠，纪念中江藤树的《藤树书院》所藏）

⑥阳明先生肖像（《阳明学》第49号（大正一年11月1日），乃木将军题词，阳明学会会员中目尚广氏所藏。题词是“破山中贼易，破山中贼难”[3]）

⑦阳明先生肖像（《阳明学》第51号（大正二年1月1日）。写有故楠本端山先生

① 东敬治说明了该肖像的复杂由来。简要地说：三轮执斋藏有明代普京（波臣）的画，宫川侯手抚把它赠送给佐藤一齐，大桥讷翁得到此画后让椿山摹仿（等于副本）。椿山因另有想法让自己儿子椿恒吉再摹仿副本，就是此幅画。（右文成公肖像，先君子云，获之路卿，其幅出于三轮执齐，传于佐藤一齐先生而大桥讷翁使椿山摹之，而此其副本，然今既疑曰，纪正民写，而又曰，宫川侯手抚见赠，曰椿恒吉摹，其言既叠见错出，而又皆与先君子所识不合，然其实恒吉作之，恒吉名彰，号华合，椿山长子，亦有画名而早没云，先君子以之为椿山所作之副本者，盖误以恒吉为椿山，抑亦路卿当时告之先君子亦漫信之耳，予以谓，宫川侯手抚云云，及纪正民等字，亦皆恒吉识之，（中略）总而言之，最初明曾波臣真迹原画，则三轮执齐所藏，而宫川侯手抚其圆以赠一齐先生，大桥讷翁又就其一齐所藏，命椿山写之，椿山别有所见，一齐藏副别使其子恒吉摹之，即此副是也。（后略）

② 据《阳明学》第15号刊载之肖像说明，肖像上部前面有《王文成公画像清彭定求颂》，后面有《天保十四年仲冬晦为大桥周道属、江都佐藤坦书》。

③ 阳明47岁的正德十三年（1518）正月，他从江西与广东临界山区大帽出发征讨三利。此话是当时写给原在湛甘泉门下读过书的弟子杨仕德（和弟弟杨仕鸣一起当弟子）、薛尚谦的信（《阳明全书》卷4《与杨仕德薛尚谦》）中内容。

所藏，邹东廓先生赞，佐藤一斋先生题词，鹅溪画）

⑧在余姚的阳明先生亲笔题字的“第一山”石碑照片（《阳明学》第 81 号（大正四年 7 月 1 日），高濑武次郎（石碑左侧之人）所藏[①]）此照片与王阳明肖像并未有直接关系，但却是与近代日本主要阳明学研究者之一高濑武次郎有关联的贵重资料。[②]

⑨阳明像（安冈正笃所藏，画家桥本关雪在余姚龙山观参观阳明像后，于大正九年夏天模仿此画并附题阳明诗《啾啾吟》）[③]

⑩《阳明学》第 39 号目录

⑪阳明先生笔迹集（《阳明学》39 号（明治四十五年 1 月 1 日）封面）

⑫王阳明像（冈田武彦氏藏，日本文化九年摹仿明代末期画家曾鲸（波臣）的原画，画家不明，原画有三轮氏藏字样，像似三轮执斋）。[④] 与《阳明学》无直接关系

⑬王阳明像（似前九州大学教授故冈田武彦氏所藏，可推定为最近作品）。[⑤] 与《阳明学》无直接关系

综上可以看出，这些肖像的基本特点是阳明先生肖像基本上由继承了日本阳明学始祖中江藤树→熊泽藩山的主要阳明学者三轮执斋和佐藤一斋，以及与近代阳明学关联的人物楠本端山、现代日本阳明学者安冈正笃、冈田武彦收藏的中国原画或赝品。贵重的王阳明肖像大部分流入日本的原因并不明，但通过阳明先生肖像可以看出，日本阳明学不仅是一种抽象的理论，而且通过表现其心理的肖像的传播更趋完整。另外，中国的肖像大多是半身像，而日本全身像为多。

在王阳明肖像上题词《破山中贼易，破心中贼难》的木乃将军是指把 1904—1905 俄日战争引向胜利的乃木希典（1949－1912）。非常信任他的明治天皇去世后，出殡那天，乃木和夫人一起在家自杀。他是当时自杀的日军中的最高指挥官，后与东乡平八郎一起被神化为“海军的东乡、陆军的乃木”。和东乡一样，乃木也对阳明学有浓厚的兴趣，这与日本的武士道——军国主义不无关联。[⑥] 近代日本的阳明学以日本近代帝国

---

① 底部有“本会评议员高濑博士寄赠”，两侧有“支那余姚石碑阳明先生亲笔题字（右侧）蹲踞碑下者即高濑博士也（左侧）”。

② 高濑武次郎及其对韩国近代阳明学的影响参考崔在穆《关于高濑武次郎的〈王阳明详传〉》，《日本语文学》第 34 辑，日本语文学会，2006 年。

③ 后被越后长冈的野本互尊翁所藏，重新赠送给安冈正笃。参见安冈正笃的《阳明学十讲》，（东京：二松学舍大学阳明学研究所，平成四年）说明文。

④ 荒木见悟责任编辑：《朱子·王阳明》，东京：中央公论社，1974 年。

⑤ 题词下方有“丁卯之秋”，参见冈田武彦：《王阳明大传（一）》，（东京：明德出版社，2002），无特别说明。

⑥ 最近，小岛毅教授的《近代日本的阳明学》（东京：讲谈社，2006）详细叙述了近代日本的“阳明学——武士道——国学”是如何与西欧学术相结合，而在日本帝国主义掌握国民国家的权力方面所做出的贡献。

主义为背景，这一点也说明日本再生产并传播阳明先生肖像的意义和目的。

## 四、结束语—“阳明先生肖像”的近代思想战略

可以看出，阳明肖像及题词明显表达了一种信息。被评价为具有实践性、实际性、行动性学说的阳明学，是一个宣传近代思想的战略工具。阳明学具有近代思想的东方思想，它可以与近代西方思想相对抗。当然，不可否认的是，这一点同时也为帝国主义理论的形成起到了一定作用。

在近代东亚，特别是日本《阳明学》刊登的“阳明先生肖像”，曾起到过很重要的传播近代思想的传媒作用。那么，日本的近代思想与阳明学有何联系呢？荻生茂博氏说：近代阳明学的显著特点之一，就是不仅仅把王阳明当成是著作或讲坛里讲的学者，而在政界他被认为伦理的实践者，从而重视其曲折的传记。在日本近代，“知行合一”、“事上磨练”为中心的阳明哲学认识论体系被理解为实践第一。井上哲次郎在《日本阳明学派之哲学》（1900年）一文中提出的“朱子重视学理，阳明崇尚实行”遂成为定论。继承井上阳明学说的高濑武次郎著《王阳明详传》（1904年）的理由，是“王阳明传记具有鼓舞读者精神，特别是鼓舞青少年精神的力量 ”。这里应注意的是重视王阳明传记的背景为当时西方流行伟人传，特别流行为近代国家建设做出贡献的“国民英雄”传记。日本在幕末维新时期，已开始流传拿破仑、彼得大帝的诗歌，只是那是一种浪漫的憧憬，但到明治中期对世界政治形势情报方面有质的变化，日本在世界上的地位也开始上升，传记类书籍因不失连贯性的同时有其特点而受到宠爱。尤其是传记类书籍的主要读者群是青少年，从而使“青年/少年”一词在日本产生“国民国家”的明治20年代前期是具有非常重要意义的历史用词。德富苏峰写了《新日本之青年》（明治二十年，当时德富25岁）一文后，便一跃登上了当时最高学者的地位。在此论文中，他规定明治维新至自由民权运动期的一代为“天保老人”（旧世代），而他们自己的那一代则被称为“我们明治青年”（新世代），认为“旧日本几乎灭亡”“明治青年的命运就是明治世界的命运”，并大力鼓吹青年应站在“知识世界第二次革命”之社会运动的前沿。“青年/少年”是他们所指望的新日本（国民国家）“国民”的代名词，而传记则成了培养他们的主要形式。[①] 按照荻生茂博氏的理论，“阳明先生肖像”属于培养“新日本（国民国家）国民”的传记（伟人传）范畴，是启蒙青少年的一种武器。和中国、韩国的半身像不同，日本喜欢全身像的理由会不会就隐藏着从全身角度能更加直观地理解王阳明的意图呢？

---

① 荻生茂博：《近代阳明学在日本的成立》，《季刊日本思想史》第59号，东京：淘河社，2001年，第13页。

对于在近代与朱子学或其他学说相比被更加广泛流传的阳明肖像及其含义，无疑应从新的角度来进行研究。近代意义上的阳明学并不局限于单纯地读阳明著作，写一些论文或著作等来提高修养。不能不看到，“阳明先生肖像”具有某种让青少年亲身感受阳明精神、并把他们引向具体行动和实践的奇特效果。仔细调查并比较当时韩国、日本的刊物及著作里的“阳明先生肖像”，可以从新的角度更加明确地看到其近代思想战略。

# 经典诠释的治疗意涵

## ——论李二曲对儒家经典的治疗诠释

韩国岭南大学 郑炳硕

实际上，类似孔子或苏格拉底一样的古代哲学家，与其说埋头于探求哲学理论，倒不如说是作为共同思考、诊断和助言别人的孤独或痛苦的，并与大众沟通的哲学家而活动。但是，随着这种与大众沟通哲学传统的逐渐消失，陷入经典章句或复杂理论的游戏，每天只是“口头圣贤”或“纸上道学”被认为是哲学家当然的任务，哲学与一般人的距离就更远了。这里有必要倾听所谓经典与其说起到连接和疏通哲学家与大众的作用，反而说阻碍了哲学家与大众疏通的通路，只起到制造压迫机制的批判作用。

应该把经典重新归还给普通人的观点，不是从根本上全面否定或抛弃经典具有的经典性（canonicity），而是意味着其现代的扩张或突破（breakthrough）。也就是说，其目的不在于试图片面否定现有的对哲学古典的解释或观点，而在于试图开启现在和未来的新视域的扩大和融合。

有关这点，与孙奇逢、黄宗羲一起被称为清初三大儒家的二曲李颙（1627－1705）强烈批判了关起房门，每天谈论道德和性名义理的口头圣贤和纸上道学。① 这种“口头圣贤”或“纸上道学”可以说正是学者具有的最大病痛。如果做学问的目的单纯地止于背诵句子或做文章，那就说明不了解做学问的最终目的和效用。在这里，二曲从诊断、处方和治疗现实问题的治疗学观点上看哲学，从所谓“治疗”的实用的、实践的观点来谈论儒家经典和儒家哲学。特别是，这里最重要的正是儒家经典。这是因为，尽管曾经作为最优秀哲学医生的圣贤们都已经离世，但是他们的著作或语录中分明留下了治疗的记录。本文试图以可称为其代表作的《四书反身录》和《悔过自新说》中体现的经典治疗问题和可以称为自疗的修己问题为中心，来分析二曲所主张的儒学的治疗性质，

---

① 李颙撰，陈俊民点校，《二曲集》卷19，《杂著·急务》，北京：中华书局，1996年，第230页，“作口头圣贤，纸上道学。”

## 一、李二曲对儒学本质的批判和明体适用

李二曲是明清交替之际重要的思想家，一生拒绝做官，过着清贫生活，是只集中于讲学的、具有独特经历的学者。他明确主张儒学的本质或最终目标在于实用和实践，而不在于思辨和理论。他的这种见解可以说明确指出了现有的儒学回避现实问题，只局限于书本，每天只谈论高尚的道德或义理的“口头圣贤”或“纸上道学”弊端。这可以说是强调了儒学或哲学的性质要从对人与现实所具有的痛苦和问题进行诊断和开处方的观点上寻找的事实。

在这点上，他用所谓“口头圣贤”或“纸上道学”批判了现有的儒家或儒学：

> 虽日日讲道德，谈性命，不过口头圣贤，纸上道学。[1]
>
> 人生契紧要务，全在明己心，见己性，了切己大事。……如其未也，何贵著述！口头圣贤，纸上道学，乃学人通病。[2]

李二曲不是从追求概念知识或思辨真理的抽象学问，而是从所谓解决现实与生活具体问题的现实和实践学问的观点中去寻找儒学本质。李二曲从儒学的这种本质或学问本性的观点上，批判了当时流行的儒学风气。他批判“口头圣贤”或“纸上道学”属于“无用的言说阶段”，认为“无用的言说阶段”只是代表知识或理论的理解，必须进入“实践活动阶段”的实践躬行，才算实现真正的儒学精神。[3] 李二曲在这里批判了当时的知识人只是空谈心性的态度，在作为儒学本质的经世致用观点上，强调了重新恢复儒学的基本精神和适应时代需要是当务之急。他所强调的经世致用的主要内容正是“明体适用”：

> 儒者之学，明体适用之学也。秦汉以来，此学不明，醇朴者梏于章句，俊爽者流于浮词。……儒学晦，则士之所攻者，辞章记诵之末技，处也无守，出也无为，生民毫无所赖，而世运宁有不否。[4]

在此，李二曲不仅把“明体适用”看作其经世致用观的哲学根据，而且看作是儒学的核心内容。他主张所谓“明体适用”核心命题的理由是为了批判宋明以后的儒学致力于章句解释和空谈心性的风气，恢复传统儒学的“经世致用”和“康济群生”的

---

① 《二曲集》卷十，《南行述》，第 76 页。

② 《二曲集》卷十六，《答徐斗一第二书》，第 158 页。

③ 李二曲对儒学本质的观点，参照郑炳硕《对李二曲儒学本质的反省的论议和明体适用》第 406 页。

④ 《二曲集》卷十四，《周至问答》，第 120 页。

优秀传统和基本宗旨。[①] 李二曲从明道救世的政治目的出发，继承了张载“学贵有用”的关学学风，主张明体适用之学。为了纠正道学的无用，他认为应该从两个观点出发。第一，改革宋儒的学风，主张经济实学，为使之成为可能，提出应该广泛地阅读多种书籍。为此，他将之分为“明体”和“适用”的两种书目，并以这种方式自己率先垂范，加以实践。第二，认为应该实修实证，达到开物成务、康济群生。

李颙在这里把当时学者共同具有的病痛批判为“口头圣贤”或“纸上道学”，主张“明体适用”的观点。他提出，“儒者之学，明体适用之学也。”[②] “六经四书，儒者明体适用之学也。”[③] 对何谓“明体适用”，他叙述如下：

> 穷理致知，反之于内，则识心悟性；实修实证，达之于外，则开物成务，康济群生，夫是之谓明体适用。明体适用，乃人生性分之所不容已，学而不如此，则失其所以为学，便失其所以为人矣。……不明体，于不适用，徒汩没于辞章记诵之末，便是俗儒。[④]

“明体适用”志向于内圣外王之道，使传统儒学的命脉复归到孔孟的根本儒学要旨。李二曲把宋明以来理学的空疏心性论看作不良学风，认为其制造了传统儒学的危机。其目标在于唤醒天下人心，显露学术，康济群生，他提出了“明体适用”，将之看作是“经世致用”的实质意义。这里的“明体”正是以顾炎武所谓“明道”，在“穷理致知，反之于内，则识心悟性。”的观点上而言的。“适用”是指“救世”和“救人”，属于传统儒学中常说的“经世致用”。

## 二、悔过自新的治疗思维和作为医书的经典

二曲所强调的“明体适用”的核心和基础出自“悔过自新”的观点。二曲在“悔过自新”的基础上展开了“明体适用”的观点。“古今名儒倡导救世者非一，……虽各家宗旨不同，要之总不出‘悔过自新’四字。”[⑤] 在二曲看来，有了“悔过自新”四个字，才能概括六经和四书的深奥含义。“经书垂训，实具修齐治平之理，岂专为一身一心，悔过自新而已乎?”[⑥] 李颙指出，“悔过自新”说是古今名儒所谓“明道救世”的宗旨，是六经和四书的核心。他强调学问或做人的问题，甚至于就连社会问题也都要从

---

① 郑炳硕，《李颙的悔过自新说与治疗思维》，《哲学》第98集，韩国哲学会，2009年，第4—5页。

② 参照注释6。

③ 《二曲集》卷十五，《富平答问》，第104页。

④ 《二曲集》卷十四，《周至问答》，第120页。

⑤ 《二曲集》卷一，《悔过自新说》，第3页。

⑥ 《二曲集》卷一，《悔过自新说》，第4页。

“悔过自新”的观点上来看。

李二曲所提出的“悔过自新”说最终要达到的目标不是止于单纯的个人修身问题，而是要纠正时代和社会所处的弊端或问题。只是为了实现这一目标，他强调在方法上要从纠正人心出发。对此，他叙述如下：

> 大丈夫无心于斯世则已，苟有心斯世，须从大根本、大肯綮处下手，则事半而功倍，不劳而易举。夫天下之大根本，莫过于人心；天下之大肯綮，莫过于提醒天下之人心。然欲醒人心，惟在明学术，此在今日为匡时第一要务。①

李二曲认为，由于人心的错误和道德的衰退正是国家灭亡和社会腐败的根本原因，如果要想治愈社会的病痛，最首要的就是要纠正人心。从纠正学术中寻找这种纠正人心的方法，即纠正当时现实的第一个核心任务。如何能阐明学术和纠正人心？这里二曲首先对作为学术内容的经典工夫提出了自己独特的观点。他对把经典只用于科举或借用经典的权威做尽坏事的伪儒学者进行了尖锐的批判：

> 诵经读书，见闻渊博，而暗于政事，短于辞令，此章句腐儒之常，犹无足怪，惟是藉经书以行私，假圣言以文奸，政事明敏，辞令泉涌，适足以助恶而遂非，其为害有甚于腐儒，乃经学之贼，世道之蠹也。②

李二曲把诸多不可取类型的儒者如何对待经典的问题非常痛快地联系起来谈论。他提出，儒家中存在只知经典的章句而对世事闭塞的腐儒，即便他们的学问既广又深，但存在一个严重的弊端或病痛，可以说那是没有具备外王的表现。在这里，他对没有把握经典所具有的本质的腐儒、霸儒和俗儒分别加以批判。③ 应该用克服社会现实的方法唤醒人心，并用这种方法纠正学术，其关键可以归结于如何看待经典所具有的性质的问题。

李二曲从“悔过自新”的观点上考察了当时产生社会病痛的根源是什么，发挥儒学真正的精神，探索如何解决这类问题。“悔过自新”观点的提出不是直接的救世，而是可以看作转换为救心的方向，这既是救世的间接方式，同时也是最根源的方式。

通过二曲这种“悔过自新”说的解决方式大部分是治疗性的。他指出，“先觉倡道，皆随时补救，正如人之患病，受症不同，故投药亦异。”④ 在他看来，圣贤所说的内容都是为了纠正那个时代所处的痛苦和人心问题，即为了治疗的恰当投药。在这一点上，李二曲把儒家的圣贤大儒看作是杰出的名医，把儒家的经典看作是治疗患者的

---

① 《二曲集》卷十二，《匡时要务》，第104页。

② 《二曲集》卷三十八，《四书反身录》，《论语》下，子路。

③ 《二曲集》卷二十九，《四书反身录·大学》，第401页。

④ 《二曲集》卷十，《南行述》，第76页。

医书。二曲认为，由于各时代有各自不同的时代问题，所以解决时代问题的内容会根据条件而有所不同。因此，儒家根据各时代产生的病而投药，都是为了治疗时代之病和人心之错误。由于二曲把代表儒家的经典，例如四书五经都看作是救世良方，所以他认为儒家的四书五经等经典应该具有类似医书一样的机能：

> 孔、颜、思、孟，及宋之濂、洛、关、闽，明之河、会、姚、泾，俱是医人的名医；《五经》、《四书》及诸儒语录，俱是医人的良方。[①]

二曲把四书五经和宋明时期的语录看作医方，把诸子百家和圣贤大儒看作名医，强调儒学所具有的治疗功能和价值。这种观点从根本上把读者与经典以及哲学家设定为患者与医学书籍以及医生等的治疗关系。二曲有关哲学家和经典具有治疗个人和社会病痛的功能的观点是非常值得探讨的问题。

他利用中医学中使用的医术、医方、医书、自疗、疾病等用语来比喻纠正身心的错误，以及使之朝向成圣阶段的过程。即把“主体”、“经典”、“哲学家”（原典作者）比作“患者”、“医书”、“医生”的治疗关系。在这种关系中所进行的治疗方法或治疗目的，区别于通过一般性药物治疗或手术等解除病因的方式。[②] 所谓治疗的词典意义是用来指“治疗病或伤处，使之痊愈”。然而，这里所谓作为治疗对象的病可以说是不属于任何一般意义的喉炎或癌等身体症状、抑郁症或偏执症等精神性疾病的第三疾病。由于该病与患者的自我认同性、世界观、价值观、伦理等有关，所以并不是通过药物等自然科学态度所能治疗的。为了治疗这种病，要求通过不是自然科学的医学或神经科学层面的哲学来治疗。即，不是立足于说明方式的自然科学态度，而是要求立足于理解方式的人文学态度。二曲所谓的治疗意义或思维，可以说属于哲学治疗或治疗思维。

二曲把经典的创作者和经典设定为医师和医师的处方，认为经典本身具有治疗性质。阅读经典是指读经者从经典出发，把握经典的创作者体现的意义脉络，对之加以理解并化为自己的，回顾自己，治疗错误或疾病。在这点上，他强调读书的重要性。二曲把经典看作类似医书一样，认为对人的疾病具有治疗和自疗的机能，这就是他对儒家经典“通经致用”的新的运用和诠释。

## 三、李二曲哲学中经典治疗的成立可能性及其意义

李二曲关注儒家经典所具有的治疗功能。他认为四书五经和宋明语录等是医方，把先秦和宋明时期的圣贤大儒看作名医。其意义在于，从治疗观点上重新诠释儒家经

① 《二曲集》卷三，《常州府武进县两庠汇语》，第 28 页。

② 郑炳硕，《周易的治疗含义》，《哲学论丛》第 48 辑，新韩哲学会，2007 年，第 357 页。

典所具有的历史功能和价值，在今天的观点上看，也是非常有创意的和新鲜的。当然，由于二曲的这种观点与作为其主要哲学主张的悔过自新说有关联，可以缩小来看，但同样重要的是，他的这种观点可以为今天儒家经典具有的存在意义提供重新阐明的契机。

因此，这里存在应该首先从方法上整理和越过的先决问题。这就是二曲所谓的有关对“治疗”问题的概念设定、内容及范围等。即考察二曲所谓的治疗所包含的意义是什么，以及其目的何在的问题，看起来有必要首先分析和整理这种治疗思维与现代所说的治疗概念有多么一致，以及具有多大连贯性的问题。把这类问题压缩为两个，具体如下。第一，二曲通过“悔过自新”的概念，从“治疗”视角谈论儒家哲学的修己问题和社会的经世问题，这里所谓的“治疗”与今天所说的“哲学治疗（Philosophical therapy)”概念有多少是相符的呢？第二，“经典治疗”观念是否有成立的可能。

现代所谓“哲学谘商”或“哲学治疗”最为关注的，首先是以对人的理解和诠释为中心的治疗。这种治疗的关键在于，并不是让外部的某种药物或疗法介入，而是对有心病的人所处情况的本质给予主体的、主动的理解，同时使之能把握自己的本质。这种诠释活动正是哲学的治疗。在世界观或价值观的矫正问题上，尤其需要这种哲学治疗。找出因错误的认识、错误的逻辑、错误的价值观或世界观所导致的疾病，开出适当的处方，这是哲学治疗。在这点上，作为哲学治疗对象的哲学疾病，与肉体的疾病或心理的乃至于神经精神科的疾病相比，可以说更志向于价值。又一个重要问题是，由于所谓什么是哲学疾病没有完整的客观基准，所以哲学疾病的概念是有可能同时具有暧昧性和模糊性的概念。在这点上，所谓“哲学疾病”用“哲学障碍”来代替也应该没有问题。①

李二曲在《二曲集》中多次指出，把治疗作为必要的部分，也是与价值观或世界观问题相关而产生的“心病”。通过哲学治愈痛苦的治疗，不像心理治疗或精神治疗那样偏重于把所有人都“疾病化”，而是关注于为了正常人的治疗法。二曲也没有把治疗的对象放在上根人（二曲将之称为上士）或下愚，而是提出以普通的中材人为中心。这是由于根器高的上士和具有普通根器的中材人在犯错误时，其反应是各不相同的。上士的情况是，知道错误的原因在于自己，从根源处改正错误，就会容易行道，而中材人通过静坐、观心等知道错误后加以改正的话，会变得稍微吃力。② 当然，尽管哲学

① 金荣振，《对哲学病的诊断和处方一临床哲学》，哲学与现实社，2004 年，第 36—37 页。

② 《二曲集》附录二，第 611 页，“上士之于过，知其皆由于吾心，则直向其根源匀铲除之，故其为力易。中材稍难矣，然要之以静坐观心为入手，静坐乃能知过，知过乃能悔过，悔过乃能改过以自新。”

治疗的目标在于使正常人恢复到正常人，但是二曲所说的这种治疗目标，不仅仅止于良知本心的体验或恢复到正常人，而是更进一步，其最终目标在于“成圣”，这点有所不同。这种差异在治疗的限界或范围上也有区别。即，如果说现代的哲学治疗对于治疗个人所具有的心灵痛苦和疾病方面设定其范围的话，二曲在这里则更进了一步。二曲在《四书反身录》中，不是指单纯的个人治疗，即“修己”或“悔过自新”，而是扩张和深化到社会的自我治疗范围。他所谓的“修己”没有止于个人的“己”，而是连社会的“己”也包括在内。这里所谓社会之“己”的治疗所说的实质内容，即属于“经世”或“安百姓”。上述内容用图表可以整理如下。

李二曲的观点与现代哲学治疗的比较

| | 治疗的对象 | 接受治疗的人 | 治疗的方法和工具 | 治疗的目标 |
|---|---|---|---|---|
| 李二曲的观点 | 心病，追求名利的人 | 中材人（普通资质的人） | 自我修养，阅读经典或语录等 | 良知本心的体验、成圣和经世 |
| 哲学治疗的观点 | 心病，不正常的世界观或价值观 | 正常人 | 对话，咨询，读书治疗等 | 恢复正常 |

接下来将考察“经典治疗”的概念。经典治疗基本上属于读书治疗（Biblio-therapy）的治疗法。在读书治疗中，特别是把通过经典治疗为主的方法用“经典治疗”来指称，将对其成立可能性进行考察。所谓读书治疗是指，通过书治疗人的情感、社会和精神副作用问题的临床咨询的一个领域。实际上，书对无以计数的很多人起到了安静的咨询者的作用。读者可以通过书越过自己偏狭的观点，接触到各样的世界观、价值观和生活方式。例如，诗或小说等在处理读者面临的问题方面，可以提供直接帮助的模型。有关读书治疗的知名研究者 John T. Pardeck 和 Jean A. Pardeck 等提出，除了诗或小说之外优质的非小说，特别是“自助书籍（self-help books）”可以说能够提供解决读者面临问题的具体提案和助言。这里所谓“自助书籍”是指包含人们能自己治疗自己的内容的书。这里主要被广泛阅读的书中，哲学古典或经典被提及很多。[①] 因此，所谓“经典治疗”的名称看起来具有充分的说服力来使用。适用于经典治疗的，具体可以举出东洋的诸多儒家、道家和佛家的经典。除了著名的荣格（Jung）之外，还有西洋哲学治疗领域最有名的学者之一马利诺夫（Lou Marinoff）在《拍拉图灵丹（Plato not Prozac）》一书中，谈论了在哲学治疗上对《周易》的具体适用，甚至达到

① John T. Pardeck & Jean A. Pardeck, Bibliotherapy : A Clinical Approach for Helping Children, Gordon and Breach, 1993, 参照第 1—2 页。

了干脆在该书后面以追加资料形式添加有关《参考周易的方法》附录的程度。[①]

实际上，经典的治疗可能性在朱子那里也有明确体现。朱子在《读书法》中正式提出了有关经典和身心治疗的问题：

读书，不可知传就纸上求义理，须反来就自家身上（以手自指）推究。[②]

看书非止看一处便见道理。如服药相似，一服岂能得病便好！须服了又服，服多后，药力自行。[③]

朱子在谈到读书时，经常使用“用药治病”的比喻。事实上，这种比喻可以说是朱子自己明确地表明了读书本身是一种身心修炼活动，即具有治疗身心的意义。把读书本身看作用药治疗，是指把读书看作一种身心修炼的工夫。通过这种治疗过程，根本目标是体会和实践儒家经典中的道理，改变气质，最终成就圣贤的人格。在这点上，二曲对通过阅读经典的治疗或自疗问题也提过多次。他在《悔过自新说》中对儒学经典所具有的治疗效能曾明确地说过，五经、四书和诸多儒家的语录，没有不是医师的良方的。

## 四、作为治疗的修己和自疗

从治疗思维的观点上，二曲把现有的儒学风气看作因吃太多食物而患消化不良的食积状态，将之比喻为所谓“骨董积”的疾病：

一友患食积，王教以服消积保中丸，先生因言，凡痰积、食积，丸散易疗，唯骨董积，非药石可攻。王询其故，先生曰：诗文盛世，无关身心，声闻远播，甚妨静坐。二者之累，廓清未尽，则此便是积。……功业冠绝一世，而胸中功业之见，一毫消镕未尽，则此便是积。道德冠绝一世，而胸中道德之见，一毫消镕未尽，则此便是积。以上诸积，虽浅深不同，其为心害则一，总之皆骨董积也。[④]

李二曲认为，当时的儒家大部分为了自己荣达而患上了因积攒陈旧思想或知识而产生的“骨董积”之病。他说，尽管在中医学的病理学，对于痰滞、食滞等病症根据症状投药可以较容易地使之消化和治愈积滞，但如果是特殊的骨董积的话，则通过适合症状的投药来治愈是很困难的。在这里，二曲认为，见闻的骨董堵住了心灵的本来面目，妨碍真正的心灵活动。对于该病而言，本心的自觉和体会的治疗是必须的。其治疗过程，即工夫的进路在于领悟根本和树立根本的心性体认和工夫修养，这是治疗

---

① Lou Marinoff, Plato not Prozac, New York, Harper Perennial, 1999, Appendix。

② 《朱子语类》卷11，《学五》。

③ 《朱子语类》卷10，《读书法上》。

④ 《二曲集》卷四十五，《历年纪略》，第566页。

的真正意义。相对而言，如果主体的有限生命偏重于博闻强记或著书立说等，就会陷入所谓玩物丧志的大病。换句话说，对于主体而言，博闻强记或著书立说不仅不是治疗，而且作为反治疗，是使疾病更加严重的主犯。[①]该治疗通过投药的方法是很难实现的。这里必要的治疗方法可以说是用所谓“自家治疗”，即“自疗”恢复本性，或主体自身的反省是核心，其目的是“没有瑕疵阶段”的“成圣”。因此，他说，“学问的要体在于自己治疗自身的病痛”，[②] 从治疗的观点看作学问本身。二曲的这种观点与我们今天所谓的哲学治疗，尽管在内容或方向上不是完全一致的，但在诸多层面上还是有很多值得关注的。

在二曲看来，心灵的过误和道德堕落现象正是国家灭亡和社会腐败的根本原因。因此，为了真正发挥儒家的学说，治愈当时社会的病痛，仍然无法脱离“悔过自新”的治疗或实践工夫。他认为，心灵之对错和学术之明暗等与天下治乱具有内在的必然关系。在这里，李二曲认为矫正社会的方式首先要从矫正人心出发。所谓矫正就是治疗。二曲多次指出，把治疗作为必要的部分也是与价值观或世界观的问题相关而产生的“心病”。二曲认为，导致这种“心病”最恶性的病根是贪求名誉的“名心”。疾病表现为欲望体系的紊乱和无秩序，其中最严重的病根在于好名的名心。因此，他认为好名之心不仅是疾病的根源性素材，而且是诸多疾病的根源：

> 吾人诸病，犹易拔除，惟葛藤好名之病，病在膏肓，卒未易除。……浅之为富贵利达之名，深之为圣贤君子之名，浅深不同，总之为大病。[③]

他认为这种追求名誉欲的病不容易治愈。结果，为了治疗这种病，不得不要求所谓根本的世界观或价值观的矫正问题。那么，问题是谁能治疗这种心病。二曲认为“须是自克自治”，提出“自疗”。[④] 这个层面与现代哲学治疗中“解除分析地对待患者(被咨询者)，推翻其诊断方式，帮助患者，使之自己解决问题”、“帮助患者，使之找到最终的自己”方式几乎一致。首先李二曲对根本的治疗叙说如下：

> 然治病于标，可谓得学之骨，非学之髓也。……先生欣然告以安身立命之旨，脱去支离，直探原本，言约而道大，词显而理精，……学者诚敛华就实，惟髓是急，得其髓则骨自健，肤自丰，无所往而不可，否则肤骨虽或无恙，而元髓不允，庐扁将望而却走矣，恐未见其能济也。[⑤]

---

① 叶守桓，《从治疗学观点论李二曲的成圣之道》，《兴大人文学报》第35期，2005(6)，第206－207页。

② 《二曲集》卷三，《常州府武进县两庠汇语》，第28页，“学问之要，在于自治其病。”

③ 《二曲集》卷三，《常州府武进县两庠汇语》，第28页。

④ 《二曲集》卷三，《常州府武进县两庠汇语》，第28页。

⑤ 《二曲集》卷二，《学髓序》，第16页。

李二曲在说学习的深浅和阶段时，将之分成所谓学皮肤、学骨架、学精髓三个阶段，这是从病理观点上考察学习者接触学习的核心课题的问题。是否明确掌握了学习的重点？从中医学的病理层面上说，为了治病应该治疗根本，如果治疗表皮，由于只能暂时缓和疾病状况，所以只能获得一时的效果而已。如果所患的病根依然存在的话，唯有治疗根本，才能彻底完治疾病。身体的健康是指，只有使内在的根本结实，体现在外面的骨骼才自然健康，容貌或皮肤也自然柔润光泽。即只有到达学习精髓的理致，才能直接进入本源，确立和实现根本，自然地学习表皮直至到达学习骨架。这里重要的是自己治疗自己的治疗过程：

> 我这里论学，本无定法，本无一定下手之要，惟要各人自求入门，自图下手耳。……我这里论学，却不欲人闲讲法论，只要各人恢广返照，自觉各人受病之所在，知有某病，即思自医某病，即此便是入门，便是下手。[①]
>
> 著里之学，当如何下手？……别无他法，各从自己病痛上着工夫。务今病去，则本体自全。自古圣贤，未尝于本体外有所增益也。如所病不除，虽终日讲究，总是闲图度，终日祗修，总是不贴切。[②]

学问的要旨正在于自己治愈自己的病患，没有其他方法。对自己的病痛加以工夫的话，就更实际了。如果患病的话，不是仅仅好好治病，从本体上添加什么或使之变化。如果整天只是用嘴说要解除病痛，这并不能改善疾病的状况。治疗和治疗的最终目标在于，其身体自然恢复和治疗疾病。这种恢复的过程除了通过经典的自己治疗以外，更重要的一个就是对自己本心的体验。二曲把主体自疗，即良知本心的体验好像看作是“知道本心的善良（立本）”的实践过程。

## 五、结语

从李二曲的立场上看，强调儒家的经典不是单纯的认知对象，而是使身体完整无损、使心灵醒悟的医书，读书本身不是目的，目的在于改变气质，最终成就圣贤的人格。就改变气质和成就圣贤人格而言，读书本身是必经之路。即二曲把经典的诠释活动本身看作身心修炼的工夫，把经典诠释看作是与圣人之心相连接的实践法门。作为身心修炼的经典诠释活动，不仅有悔过自新的功能，而且具有身心治疗的意义和效果。正因如此，在二曲看来，经典不仅具有认识论意义上的诠释学意义，而且更具有价值实践的宗教含义。因此，在二曲哲学中，通过经典治疗是使良知本心的体验成为可能的最重要阶段。

---

① 《二曲集》卷三，《常州府武进县两庠汇语》，第 27 页。

② 《二曲集》卷六，《传心录》，第 45 页。

最能明确表明二曲哲学性质的就是“悔过自新”的观点。二曲所强调的治疗的核心内容正是“悔过自新”，换句话说，就是“修己”。如此，有现实之过失的自己通过回顾反省的方式自己治疗自己并加以重塑的这种过程，不是要求立足于说明方式的自然科学态度，而是要求立足于诠释学理解方式的人文学态度。这不是指医师的药物治疗，而是指通过自己的反省把握疾病的原因所在，并寻找相应的治疗方法。从这种角度上，属于医师的哲学家或属于医书的原典的功能，并不是单方面的指示或介入疗法，而只是起到引导（Orientative）的作用而已。

所谓“引导治疗”作为没有对象化的治疗，更强调主体参与的方法，意味着一种自己治疗。这是因为，尽管经典用多样的形式引导患者寻找疗法，但更重要的是患者本身的自觉和意志。因此，二曲所谓经典治疗的几个阶段中，最先要确立患者本身的自觉和意志。其后，从方法上首先诊断疾病的原因或病根是什么，在经典里发现和治疗适合其症状的处方。如此，经典所具有的最重要的治疗机能是引导性的。试图通过自我的转换使世界的转换成为可能。即狭义的“悔过自新”（自我的转换或变化）变化为广义的或深义的“悔过自新”（世界的转换或变化）。

# 项穆《书法雅言》尽善尽美的书法美学思想

韩国成均馆大学 曹玟焕

## 一、序言

孔子曾用“尽善尽美”来评价舜乐的“韶”，用“尽美未尽善”来评价武乐的“武”。[①]在艺术中，尽善指的是内容，尽美指的是形式。朱熹把尽美的“美”看作是“盛容之盛”，把尽善的“善”看作是“美之实”。[②]尽美意思是美的旋律蕴涵着舜的德性和圣人气象。《礼记·乐记》中把“乐”与德性和功业联系起来理解。[③]“乐”中蕴涵着圣人的德性和气象，而德性和气象构成尽善的内容。在孔子看来，“尽善”是符合仁之要求的内容。孔子的尽善尽美，在表现上区分为善和美，而且蕴涵着善比美更根本、更优越的思想。但孔子并非仅仅强调尽善。尽善尽美是追求文质彬彬与中和的儒家美学所向往的另一种审美理想。如若适用文质彬彬的思维，那么尽善尽美的表现就蕴涵着要求善美统一的思维。

孔子在“乐”中所说的尽善尽美的思想对书法产生了巨大影响。扬雄在《法言·问神》中曾说过“书，心画也”。项穆也在《书法雅言·神化》中说：“书之为言，散也，舒也，意也，如也。”刘熙载在《书概》中说：“书，如也，如其学，如其才，如其志。总之，曰如其人而已。”苏轼也在《书唐氏六家书后》中说过“古人论书者，兼

---

① 《论语·八佾》，“子谓韶尽美矣，又尽善也。谓武尽美矣，未尽善也。”

② 《论语·八佾》，“子谓韶尽美矣，又尽善也。谓武尽美矣，未尽善也”에 대한朱熹 註释，“韶，舜乐。武，武王乐。美者，声容之盛。善者，美之实也。舜绍尧致治，武王伐纣救民，其功一也，故其乐皆尽美。然舜之德，性之也，又以揖逊而有天下。武王之德，反之也，又以征诛而得天下，故其实有不同者。”

③ 《礼記·乐记》，“乐者，所以象德也”，“天下大定，然后正六律，和五声，弦歌诗颂，此之谓德音，德音之谓乐”，“乐章德”；“德者，性之端也。乐者，德之华也”；“夫乐者，象成者也”，“然则先王之为乐也，以法治也，善则行象德矣”。“王者功成作乐，治定制礼。是以五帝殊时，不相沿乐，三王异世，不相袭礼。”

论其平生，苟非其人，虽工不贵也”这样的话。以上所举都是说书法是表现心的艺术。把一个作家的书体和他的生平联系起来讨论，意味着它与“如其人（尽善的要素）”有关。如果“非如其人”，不管它“技巧的一面（尽美的要素）”如何突出，也不能看作是优秀的作品。这里说的是，书法不仅是作家的学识、人品和资质的反映，同时也是表现公共性和伦理性的艺术。这是一种“书如其人”的思想。因此与其他艺术体裁相比，强调“书如其人”的书法与孔子的尽善尽美思想有着密切的联系。书法在强调“心画”和“书如其人”时，很难明确区分尽善和尽美的界限。也就是说，就笔迹自身所能讨论的尽善尽美只是书法的特征。

书法的尽善尽美可分为内容和形式两方面。从项穆的《书法雅言》来看，它在内容上包括书法创作前作家的学识、人品、修养与否以及心的状态等。例如，面对创作前的“无自欺、思无邪、诚意正心、意在笔先”等。从形式上上看，运笔的结果就是符合中和、中行。但这两个方面不能分裂开来，这是书法的特征。与其他艺术体裁相比，作为心画的书法与尽善尽美有更密切的关系。其具体内容我们将通过项穆的《书法雅言》来了解。

## 二、项穆之前书法的尽善尽美

之前虽然没有尽善尽美之类的表达来讨论书法，但是早在东汉时代就已出现与此相似的思维。东汉的蔡邕在《笔论》中谈及书法创作时说过“先散怀抱，任情恣性”和“默坐静思，随意所适，言不出口，气不盈息，沉密神采，如对至尊，则无不善矣”这样的话。“先散怀抱”和“默坐静思”发展成了尽善的内容，同时也成了尽美的前提条件。从尽善尽美角度讨论书法的文字始于王羲之的《记白云先生书诀》。这篇文章中，他讨论尽善尽美时强调“书之气，必达乎道，同混元之理”和“把笔抵锋，肇乎本性”。[①]从尽善尽美的侧面来讨论书法的代表作是唐太宗李世民论述王羲之书法的《王

---

① 王羲之：《记白云先生书诀》，“天台紫真谓予曰，子虽至矣，而未善也。书之气，必达乎道，同混元之理。七宝齐贵，万古能名。阳气明则华壁立，阴气太则风神生。把笔抵锋，肇乎本性。刀圆则润，势疾则涩，紧则劲，险则峻，内贵盈，外贵虚，起不孤，伏不寡。回仰非近，背接非远，望之惟逸，发之惟静。敬兹法也，书妙尽矣。”

羲之传赞》。[①]唐太宗首先用“尽善”的标准评价了张伯英、师宜官，钟繇、王献之、萧子云等历代书法家的长处和短处，并且把王羲之作为实现尽善尽美的事例。他用尽善尽美评价王羲之书法的核心是“心摹手追”。[②]

这里应引起注意的是，评价一个作家的艺术世界时，把其心与手联系起来进行了讨论。因为如果仅讨论技巧的优越和美感，就不必联系“心的状况”来理解。唐太宗所说的“心摹手追”首先与运笔的超然与书体的形态之美有关。也就是说，唐太宗评价王羲之书法尽善尽美时所说的“点画形态的精巧、分间布白的绝妙、体势的自然变化”等，接近孔子所说的尽美。但考察“心摹手追”之“心”所蕴含的王羲之的学识和人品，就会发现尽美之中包含着尽善。也就是说，如果列举王羲之以外的其他书法家的弊病，诸如不能“会通古今”、运笔中缺乏“生动感”和“新意奇巧”、缺乏大丈夫之气势等，就不能单纯从尽美的要素来分析。从这一点来看，唐太宗认为王羲之的书法没有弊病，称得上是尽善尽美。孙过庭在《书谱》中也提起过王羲之书法的优点。当时，孙过庭所说的仔细观察作品中人物的性格和特征，与此不无关系。[③]

与唐太宗的观点一致，孙过庭讨论了书法达到尽善尽美的艺术家王羲之。他在《书谱》中一方面称达到尽善很难，一方面通过王羲之的作品具体谈论尽善的要素。孙

---

① 唐太宗：《王羲之传赞》，“伯英英临池之妙，无复馀踪，师宜悬帐之奇，罕有遗迹。逮乎钟王以降，略可言焉。钟虽擅美一时，亦为迥绝，论其尽善，或有所疑。至于布纤浓，分疏密，霞舒云卷，无所间然。但其体则古而不今，字则长而逾制，语其大量，以此为瑕。献之虽有父风，殊非新巧。观其字势疏瘦，如隆冬之枯树，览其笔踪拘束，若严家之饿隶。其枯树也，虽槎枿而无屈伸，其饿隶也，则羁羸而不放纵。兼斯二者，固翰墨之病欤。子云近出，擅名江表，然仅得成书，无丈夫之气。行行若萦春蚓，字字如绾秋蛇，卧王濛于纸中，坐徐偃于笔下，虽秃千兔之翰，聚无一毫之筋，穷万谷之皮，敛无半分之骨，以兹播美，非其滥名耶。此数子者，皆誉过其实。”

② 唐太宗：《王羲之传赞》，“所以详察古今，研精篆素，尽善尽美，其惟王逸少乎。观其点曳之工，裁成之妙，烟霏露结，状若断而还连，凤翥龙蟠，势如斜而反直。玩之不觉为倦，览之莫识其端。心摹手追，此人而已。”

③ 孙过庭：《书谱》，“但右军之书，代多称习，良可据为宗匠，取立指归。岂惟会古通今，亦乃情深调合。致使摹蹋日广，研习岁滋，先后著名，多从散落。历代孤绍，非其效与。试言其由，略陈数意。止如《乐毅论》《黄庭经》《东方朔画赞》《太史箴》《兰亭集序》《告誓文》，斯并代俗所传，真行绝致者也。写《乐毅》则情多佛郁，书《画赞》则意涉瑰奇，《黄庭经》则怡怿虚无，《太史箴》又纵横争折，暨乎《兰亭》兴集，思逸神超，私门诫誓，情拘志惨。所谓涉乐方笑，言哀已叹。岂惟驻想流波，将贻啴暖之奏，驰神睢涣，方思藻绘之文。虽其目击道存，尚或心迷议舛，莫不强名为体，共习分区。岂知情动形言，取会风骚之意，阳舒阴惨，本乎天地之心。既失其情，理乖其实，原夫所致，安有体哉。”

过庭认为要在性情不一中理解书法，而如若不是“心闲手敏”，那就很难做到兼通。[①]

他所说的“兼通”其实是尽善尽美的另一种表述。即，“心闲”可看作尽善的要素，“手敏”可看作尽美的要素。“心闲”和“手敏”兼而有之的“兼通”的另一个意思便是中和。从这一点来看，孙过庭指出了脱离“中和”的偏工问题，并称遒丽和骨气同时具备时才能达到“尽善”的书法。[②]“非偏工”和“兼通”正是追求中和的孙过庭书法美学的核心。孙过庭所说的类似书法尽善尽美的思想对项穆产生了影响。

除此之外，唐代的张怀瓘在《书断》中谈到王献之和王羲之的作品时，认为王献之的书法是“尽美未尽善”，而王羲之的书法则是“尽善尽美”。[③]他还在《书议》中曾说过“智则无涯，法固不定，且以风神骨气者居上，妍美功用者居下”这样的话。妍美功用是尽美的要素，风神骨气是尽善的要素。宋代姜夔在《续书谱》中说：“所贵熟习精通，心手相应，斯为美矣。”意思是重视技巧熟习精通角度的“心手相应”之美。“心手相应”之美的重心是放在尽善之心还是尽美之手二者之间有差别。清代康有为在《广艺舟双楫》中说：“书若人然，须备筋骨血肉，血浓骨老，筋藏肉莹，加之姿态奇逆，可谓美矣。”意思是相对于尽善而言，更应侧重尽美。康有为通过书迹形势强调“盖书，形学也”。[④]“书法乃形学”与尽美的要素有关。

人们对书法的传统理解有两种，一种是把书法与作家的人品、学识联系起来的“书如其人”。这种理解与用心学、传心来理解书法有密切关系。另一种是从与运笔形式有关的形学角度来理解。根据这种差异，可以把对尽善尽美的理解分为强调尽善的一面，还是强调尽美的一面两个部分。从心学角度来看，相对于尽美而言，在强调尽善的同时，更倾向于追求尽善与尽美二者的结合。项穆的《书法雅言》就让我们更好地看到这一点

---

① 孙过庭：《书谱》，“然消息多方，性情不一，乍刚柔以合体，忽劳逸而分驱。或恬憺雍容，内涵筋骨，或折挫槎枿，外曜锋芒。察之者尚精，拟之者贵似。况拟不能似，察不能精，分布犹疏，形骸未捡，跃泉之态，未睹其妍，窥井之谈，已闻其丑。纵欲唐突羲献，诬罔钟张，安能掩当年之目，杜将来之口。慕习之辈，尤宜慎诸。至有未悟淹留，偏追劲疾，不能迅速，翻效迟重。夫劲速者，超逸之机，迟留者，赏会之致。将反其速，行臻会美之方，专溺于迟，终爽绝伦之妙。能速不速，所谓淹留，因迟就迟，讵名赏会。非其心闲手敏，难以兼通者焉。”

② 孙过庭：《书谱》，“假令众妙攸归，务存骨气，骨既存矣，而遒润加之。亦犹枝干扶疏，凌霜雪而弥劲，花叶鲜茂，与云日而相晖。如其骨力偏多，遒丽盖少，则若枯槎架险，巨石当路，虽妍媚云阙，而体质存焉。若遒丽居优，骨气将劣，譬夫芳林落蕊，空照灼而无依，兰沼漂萍，徒青翠而奚托。是知偏工易就，尽善难求。”

③ 张怀瓘：《书断》，“然子敬可谓武，尽美矣，未尽善也。逸少可谓韶，尽美矣，又尽善也。”

④ 康有为：《广艺舟双楫》《缀法》，“古人论书以势为先。中郎曰九势，卫恒曰书势，羲之曰笔势。盖书，形学也。有形则有势，兵家重形势，拳法亦重扑势，义固相同。得势便则已操胜算。”

## 三、项穆《书法雅言》尽善尽美的书法美学

1. 作为心相的书法和尽善尽美

项穆在《书法雅言·心相》中用传心的艺术和“书如其人”的思想来理解书法。[①]首先，《书法雅言·心相》中谈到书法创作前的“书之心”的状态和书法创作后的“书之相”的状态。“书之心”中的“心”是尽善的内容。“书之相”中的“相”是尽美的形式。项穆还通过“德性根心”提出“得新应手”这个概念，其意是表现心和技巧合二为一的“得心应手”是尽善和尽美的另一种表述。得心是尽善的要素，应手是尽美的要素。[②]书法艺术追求的终极目标就是得心与应手二者的合一。从这一点来看，书法虽有尽善和尽美两个方面，但它的特征只有一个。若就先后来说，想要表现“心”的内容是先，而与笔运有关的技巧是后。项穆联系人品来论述这一点，基本上为“有诸中必形诸外”的思维做了铺垫。“中”就是创作心或心的状态，“外”是通过运笔和技巧表现的书法作品。同时“观相”可以说是识心。[③]相同的思维基本上以《大学》第六章的“诚于中形于外”为根基。

项穆在《书法雅言·心相》中扩充了柳公权所说的“心正则笔正”，提出了“人正则书正”的观点。心正和人正是尽善，笔正和书正是尽美。项穆说心正的内容与《诗经》的“思无邪”和《礼记》中的“毋不敬”有关。[④]从尽善尽美的角度理解书法时，就尽善而言，书法所蕴涵的心的状态很重要。从这点来讲，“思无邪”和“毋不敬”与尽善有关。在这个认识的基础上，项穆认为正心之后才能正笔，正笔之后才能正书，而正心、正笔、正书之中最重要的是正心。项穆通过“诚心正意”和“格物致知”来具体说明正心。他说，诚意就是以此心“端己澄神”和“勿虚勿贰”、致知就是以此心“审其得失”、格物就是以此心“博习精察”。而诚意、致知、格物都是尽善尽美的前提

---

① 《书法雅言·心相》，“夫经卦皆心画也，书法乃传心也。如罪斯言为迂，予固甘焉勿避矣。”

② 《书法雅言·心相》，“盖闻德性根心，睟盎生色，得心应手，书亦云然。人品既殊，性情各异，笔势所运，邪正自形。书之心，主张布算，想像化裁，意在笔端，未形之相也。书之相，旋折进退，威仪神采，笔随意发，既形之心也。”

③ 《書法雅言·心相》，“试以人品喻之。宰辅则贵有爱君容贤之心，正直忠厚之相。将帅则贵有尽忠立节之心，智勇万全之相。谏议则贵有正道格君之心，謇谔不阿之相。隐士则贵有乐善无闷之心，遗世仙举之相。由此例推，儒行也，才子也，佳人也，僧道也，莫不有本来之心，合宜之相者。所谓有诸中，必形诸外，观其相，可识其心。”

④ 《书法雅言·心相》，“柳公权曰，心正则笔正。余今曰，人正则书正。心为人之帅，心正则人正矣。笔为书之充，笔正则书正矣。人由心正，书由笔正，即诗云思无邪，礼云毋不敬。书法大旨，一语括之矣。”

条件。[①]

《书法雅言·辨体》中说到“书法乃由心生”。[②]如由心而生，就与天赋的性情有特别的联系。在这里，项穆指出了天赋性情刚柔之不同、手之运用的乖合、性之所偏形成的资质表现以及书体问题等。他认为这些都背离了中庸之道。性情刚柔之不同于尽善有关，手之运用的乖合与尽美有关。随后，项穆强调施教者的“贵因材”和自学者的“先克己”。[③]这里的“贵因材”是尽美的起点，而“先克己”则是尽善的起点。《书法雅言·资学》认为虽然性情各异，但实现了“资学兼长”且做到了“神融笔畅”的话，便可达到“从心所欲不逾矩”的境界。他特别指出，实现了“资学兼长”且做到了“神融笔畅”的人物正是王羲之。[④]

孔子所说的“从心所欲不踰矩”中，“从心”就是尽善，“不踰矩”就是尽美。“从心”和“不踰矩”不能分开，“从心所欲不踰矩”的境界就是尽善尽美。《书法雅言·神化》中提到“能变”和“能化”时，从“手不从心，发而不中”出发要求其“至诚”，而“至诚”正是尽善的要素。同时也提到“不息其功”，而这正是尽美的要素。

---

① 《书法雅言·心相》，“故欲正其书者，先正其笔。欲正其笔者，先正其心。若所谓诚意者，即以此心端已澄神，勿虚勿贰也。致知者，即以此心审其得失，明乎取舍也。格物者，即以此心博习精察，不自专用也。正心之外，岂更有说哉。由此笃行，至于深造，自然秉笔思生，临池志逸，新中更新，妙之益妙，非惟不奇而自奇，抑亦己正而物正矣。”

② 《书法雅言·辨体》，“夫人灵于万物，心主于百骸。故心之所发，蕴之为道德，显之为经纶，树之为勋猷，立之为节操，宣之为文章，运之为字迹。爰作书契，政代结绳，删述侔功，神仙等妙，苟非达人上智，孰能玄鉴入神。但人心不同，诚如其面，由中发外，书亦云然。”

③ 《书法雅言·辨体》，“夫人之性情，刚柔殊禀，手之运用，乖合互形。谨守者拘敛杂怀，纵逸者度越典则，速劲者惊急无蕴，迟重者怯郁不飞，简峻者挺倔鲜遒，严密者紧实寡逸，温润者妍媚少节，标险者雕绘太苛，雄伟者固愧容夷，婉畅者又惭端厚，庄质者盖嫌鲁朴，流丽者复过浮华，驶动者似欠精深，纤茂者尚多散缓，爽健者涉兹剽勇，稳熟者缺彼新奇。此皆因夫性之所偏，而成其资之所近也。他若偏泥古体者，蹇钝之迂儒，自用为家者，庸僻之俗吏，任笔骤驰者，轻率而逾律，临池犹豫者，矜持而伤神，专尚清劲者，枯峭而罕姿，独工丰艳者，浓鲜而乏骨。此又偏好任情，甘于暴弃者也。第施教者贵因材，自学者先克己。审斯二语，厌倦两忘。与世推移，量人进退，何虑书体之不中和哉。”

④ 《书法雅言·资学·附评》，“夫自周以后，由汉以前，篆隶居多，楷式犹罕。真章行草，趋吏适时，姑略上古，且详今焉。夫道之统绪，始自三代而定于东周。书之源流，肇自六爻而盛于两晋。宣尼称圣时中，逸少永宝为训。盖谓通今会古，集彼大成，万亿斯年，不可改易者也。第自晋以来，染翰诸家，史牒彰名，缥缃著姓，代不乏人，论之难殚。若品格居下，真迹无传，予之所列，无复议焉。盖闻张，锺，义，献，书家四绝，良可据为轨躅，爰作指南。彼之四贤，资学兼至者也。然细详其品，亦有互差。张之学，锺之资可尚已。逸少资敏乎张，而学则稍谦。学笃乎钟，而资则微逊。伯英学进十矣，资居七焉。元常则反乎张，逸少皆得其九。”

除此而外，还要求“澄心定志”和“博习专研”。①“澄心定志”是尽善，“博习专研”是尽美。项穆还要求在写字之前先定志、统率其气，写字时要养气，要让目标充实起来。②

项穆在《书法雅言·心相》中用书法的尽善尽美来比喻人体的外在之美。例如，美男子以端厚之威仪和高逸之词气为美，而美女子则崇尚贞静之德性和秀丽之容颜。③还提到有关人品所蕴含的“爱君容贤之心”和“正直忠厚之相”，“尽忠立节之心”和“智勇万全之相”，“正道格君之心”和“謇谔不阿之相”，“乐善无闷之心”和“游世仙举之相”。④这段话中，前面与“心”有关的是尽善的要素，后面与“相”有关的是尽美的要素。

项穆在《书法雅言·正奇》中指出了鉴赏者不能理解书法所蕴含的这样内容，即偏重于尽美的形式和技巧问题点。例如，他认为鉴赏者仅指出“毫端努奋之巧”，体会不到“规矩法度之踰”、临池之士每次在“形势猛诞之微”中过度运用技巧以及不能在“性情骨气之妙”中追求工巧等都是问题。这些恰恰反倒是“轻道德而重功利”、“退忠直而进奸雄”的问题。项穆指出这一点，反过来说就是要‘重道德’、‘轻功利’，要‘进忠直’、‘退奸雄’。而‘重道德’和‘轻功利’，‘进忠直’和‘退奸雄’正属于尽善的范畴。⑤

---

① 《书法雅言·神化》，“手不从心，发而不中矣。然不动则不变，能变即能化，苟非至诚，焉有能动者乎。澄心定志，博习专研，字之全形，宛尔在目，笔之妙用，悠焉忘思，自然腕能从臂，指能从心，潇洒神飞，徘徊翰逸，如庖丁之解牛，掌上之弄丸。执笔者自难揣摩，抚卷者岂能测量哉。中庸之为物不贰，生物不测。孟子曰深造自得，左右逢源。生也逢也，皆由不贰深造得之。是知书之欲变化也，至诚其志，不息其功，将形著名，动一以贯万，变而化焉，圣且神矣。”

② 《书法雅言·神化》，“未书之前，定志以帅其气。将书之际，养气以充其志。勿忘勿助，由勉入安，斯于书也，无间然矣。夫雨粟鬼哭，感格神明，徵往俟来，有为若是。法书仙手，致中极和，可以发天地之玄微，宣道义之蕴奥，继往圣之绝学，开后觉之良心，功将礼乐同休，名与日月并曜。岂惟明窗净几，神怡务闲，笔砚精良，人生清福而已哉。”

③ 《书法雅言·心相》，“试以人之形体论之。美丈夫贵有端厚之威仪，高逸之辞气。美女子尚有贞静之德性，秀丽之容颜。岂有头目手足粗邪瘢瘇，而可以称美好者乎。”

④ 《书法雅言·心相》，“试以人品喻之，宰辅则贵有爱君容贤之心，正直忠厚之相。将帅则贵有尽忠立节之心，智勇万全之相。谏议则贵有正道格君之心，謇谔不阿之相。隐士则贵有乐善无闷之心，遗世仙举之相。”

⑤ 《书法雅言·正奇》，“书法要旨，有正与奇。所谓正者，偃仰顿挫，揭按照应，筋骨威仪，确有节制是也。所谓奇者，参差起复，腾凌射空，风情姿态，巧妙多端是也。奇即连于正之内，正即列于奇之中。正而无奇，虽庄严沉实，恒朴厚而少文。奇而弗正，虽雄爽飞妍，多谲厉而乏雅。奈夫赏鉴之家，每指毫端努奋之巧，不悟规矩法度之逾。临池之士，每炫技于形势猛诞之微，不求工于性情骨气之妙，不犹轻道德而重功利，退忠直而进奸雄也。好奇之说，伊谁始哉。伯英急就，元常楷迹，去古未远，犹有分隶馀风。逸少一出，揖让礼乐，森严有法，神彩攸焕，正奇混成也。”

《书法雅言·知识》中谈论了“善书”和“善鉴”。[①]这种思想能很好地说明什么是尽善尽美。“善书”、“善鉴”讨论的是“温而厉、威而不猛、恭而安”。“温而厉、威而不猛、恭而安”出自《论语·述而》,[②] 指的是孔子德性之完备及中和之气。这样,书法所追求的理想人物涉及书体就与“书如其人”有关。具体而言,《书法雅言·神化》中与“神化”境界有关的说法,即“形质法度、端厚和平、参互错综、玲珑飞逸”,就是尽善尽美的另一种表述。紧接着,项穆以王羲之书法的“心手交畅”为例来具体说明尽善尽美。[③]而“心手交畅”也是尽善尽美的另一种表达。

从同样的思维出发,项穆在《书法雅言·知识》中总结到,“论书”和“观书”就如同“论相”和“观人”。[④]这种思维与把书法看作是“心画”有关,同时与书法追求的尽善尽美也有更深一层的关系。就是说,强调“论相”和“观人”并非单纯从形态美的角度来讨论笔迹。书法作为一种“心画”,是一种追求表现作家人生和内心世界的艺术。这样,从“心画”、“传心”和“书如其人”的角度来理解书法的思维,就更让人明白书法是追求尽善尽美的艺术。

2. 中和与尽善尽美

项穆用儒家的道统观和异端观来阐述王羲之中心主义的书统观。他把集儒学大成的孔子和集书法大成正鹄的王羲之放在同一脉络中进行理解。[⑤]项穆立足于王羲之书法的“中和美学”,强调尽善尽美的书法精神与其写作《书法雅言》有关。[⑥]特别通过“辟

---

① 《书法雅言·知识》,“评鉴书迹,要诀何存。温而厉,威而不猛,恭而安。宣尼德性,气质浑然,中和气象也。执此以观人,味此以自学,善书善鉴,具得之矣。”

② 《论语·述而》朱熹 注释,“人之德性,本无不备,而气质所赋,鲜有不偏。惟圣人全体浑然,阴阳合德,故其中和之气,见于容貌之间者如此。”参照。

③ 《书法雅言·神化》,“人之于书,形质法度,端厚和平,参互错综,玲珑飞逸,诚能如是,可以语神矣。世之论神化者,徒指体势之异常,毫端之奋笔,同声而赞赏之,所识何浅陋者哉。约本其由,深探其旨,不过曰相时而动,从心所欲云尔。宣尼,逸少,道统,书源,匪不相通也。乡党之恂恂,在朝之侃侃,执圭之踧踧,私觌之怡怡,于鲁而章甫,适宋而逢掖。至夫汉方朔赞,意涉瑰奇,燕乐毅论,情多抑郁,修禊集叙,兴逸神怡,私门誓文,情拘气塞。此皆相时而动,根乎阴阳舒惨之机,从心所欲,溢然关雎哀乐之意。非夫心手交畅,焉能美善兼通若是哉。”

④ 《书法雅言·知识》,“故论书如论相,观书如观人,赏鉴能事大概在斯矣。”

⑤ 《书法雅言·古今》,“是以尧,舜,禹,周,皆圣人也,独孔子为圣之大成。史,李,蔡,杜,皆书祖也,惟右军为书之正鹄。”

⑥ 《书法雅言·书统》,“其间豪杰奋起,不无超越寻常。概观习俗风声,大都互有优劣。明初肇运,尚袭元规,丰,祝,文,姚,窃追唐躅,上宗逸少,大都畏难。夫尧舜人皆可为,翰墨何畏于彼。逸少我师也,所愿学是焉。”《书法雅言·古今》,“奈何泥古之徒,不悟时中之妙,专以一画偏长,一波故壮,妄夸崇质之风,岂知三代后贤,两晋前哲,尚多太朴之意。宣圣曰,文质彬彬,然后君子。孙过庭云,古不乖时,今不同弊。审斯二语,与世推移,规矩从心,中和为的。谓之曰天之未丧斯文,逸少于今复起,苟微若人,吾谁与归。”参照。

异端意识”指出，正书法就是正人心。他还通过正人心来讨论“闲圣道”。[①]由此看来，“正人心”和“闲圣道”与追求尽善在内容上是一致的。

项穆把王羲之看作是尽善尽美的典型。他说王羲之“会通古今”、集书法之大成。这是用另一种方式来表述王羲之的书法已经达到了尽善尽美。项穆在《书法雅言·书统》中用尽善尽美的标准评价了汉、唐、宋和明初的书法风格。对这几个时代进行评价时他用了一个“过”字，意思是他们偏离了中和美学。[②]随后又具体评价了不少卓越的书法家。他用“少”来评价智永和虞世南，用“乏”来评价欧阳询，用“鲜”来评价褚遂良，用“失”来评价李邕、颜真卿、柳公权、张旭、怀素、陆柬之、徐浩和孙过庭等，用“过”来评价蔡阳、用“专”来评价赵孟頫。项穆认为这些书法家已经偏离了“中和”的书法境界。[③]他的评价与尽善尽美有关。“尽善”首先与写字前的状态有关，它基本上没有偏离形式上的规矩。对这一点，他通过《书法雅言·神化》中的“欲书必舒散怀抱，至于如意所愿”来讨论。[④]

《书法雅言·功序》中谈论了书法的“三戒”和“三要”。可以联系尽善尽美的思维来理解“三戒”和“三要”。[⑤]“三戒”中的“不均与欹、不活与滞、狂怪与俗”和“三要”中的“混杂与偏邪、骄怒与枯涩、矜持与恣肆”都偏离了中和，连尽美都够不上。与此相比，“三要”中的“清整、温润、闲雅”都属“温柔敦厚”，因此也属尽美

---

① 《书法雅言·书统》，“攻乎异端，害则滋甚。况学术经纶，皆由心起，其心不正，所动悉邪。宣圣作春秋，子舆距杨，墨，惧道将日衰也，其言岂得已哉。柳公权曰，心正则笔正。余则曰，人正则书正。取舍诸篇，不无商，韩之刻，心相等论，实同孔，孟之思。六经非心学乎。传经非六书乎。正书法，所以正人心也。正人心，所以闲圣道也。子舆距杨，墨于昔，予则放苏，米于今。垂之千秋，识者复起，必有知正书之功，不愧为圣人之徒矣。”

② 《书法雅言·书统》，“宰我称仲尼贤于尧，舜，余则谓逸少兼乎锺，张。大统斯垂，万世不易。第唐贤求之筋力轨度，其过也严而谨矣。宋贤求之意气精神，其过也纵而肆矣。元贤求性情体态，其过也温而柔矣。”

③ 《书法雅言·取舍》，“逸少一出，会通古今，书法集成，模楷大定。自是而下，优劣互差。试举显名今世，遗迹仅存者，拔其美善，指其瑕疵，庶取舍既明，则趋向可定矣。智永，世南，得其宽和之量，而少俊迈之奇。欧阳询，得其秀劲之骨，而乏温润之容。褚遂良得其郁壮之筋，而鲜安闲之度。李邕得其豪挺之气，而失之竦窘。颜，柳得其庄毅之操，而失之鲁犷。旭，素得其超逸之兴，而失之惊怪。陆，徐得其恭俭之体，而失之颓拘。过庭得其逍遥之趣，而失之俭散。蔡襄得其密厚之貌，庭坚得其提衄之法，赵孟得其温雅之态，然蔡过乎模重，赵专乎妍媚，鲁直虽知执笔，而伸脚挂手，体格扫地矣。苏轼独宗颜，李，米芾复兼褚，张。苏似肥艳美婢，抬作夫人，举止邪陋而大足，当令掩口。米若风流公子，染患痈疣，驰马试剑而叫笑，旁若无人。”

④ 《书法雅言·神化》，“书之为言，散也，舒也，意也，如也。欲书必舒散怀抱，至于如意所愿，斯可称神。书不变化，匪足语神也。所谓神化者，岂复有外于规矩哉。”

⑤ 《书法雅言·功序》，“大率书有三戒，初学分布，戒不均与欹，继知规矩，戒不活与滞，终能纯熟，戒狂怪与俗。若不均且欹，如耳目口鼻，窄阔长促，邪立偏坐，不端正矣。不活与滞，如土塑木雕，不说不笑，板定固窒，无生气矣。狂怪与俗，如醉酒巫风，丐儿村汉，胡行乱语，颠仆丑陋矣。”

的范畴。[①]

紧接着《功序》又谈论了实现尽善尽美的方法。实现尽善尽美与实现中和是一致的。书法不是一蹴而就的艺术，要经过“下学而上达”的过程。同时，虽然浮华的外在形式很重要，但是应该了解其内在的实理。外在的浮华是形式美，而内在的实理是内容美。[②]随后，项穆谈论了“尽美”形式框架的完成过程。首先是建构大体，追求“均齐方正”。其次是确定筋骨，追求雄健贯通。再次是尊重威仪，追求端庄温雅。最后才是审其神情。[③]

与此同时，项穆具体指出实现尽美的过程与临摹有关。临摹首先要“专宗一家”。其次要“博研众体”、“融天机于自得”和“会群妙于一心”，最后是集大成。[④]与之前所见相同，集大成便是实现尽善尽美。这一点，项穆将其归纳为从“平整”到“秀拔”、从“险绝”到“中和”，最后使心与笔俱传等不同阶段。心与笔之俱传是达到尽善尽美的状态。与此对比，如果“分布少明即思纵巧、运用不熟便欲标奇”的话，就会与尽善尽美拉开距离。而追求“纵巧”与“标奇”则是对外在形式美的追求。[⑤]

在《书法雅言》《形质》中，项穆认为“天地之气”就是所谓“节宣阴阳而调和元气”中的“中和”。因为天赋的品性和习气之间有差异，因此“得心应手”的结果只能是“天形万状”、中行或者肥瘦中的一个。[⑥]随后，他把“中行之书”称之为“修短合

① 《书法雅言·功序》，“又书有三要，第一要清整，清则点画不混杂，整则形体不偏邪。第二要温润，温则性情不骄怒，润则折挫不枯涩。第三要闲雅，闲则运用不矜持，雅则起伏不恣肆。以斯数语，慎思笃行，未必能超入上乘，定可为卓焉名家矣。”

② 《书法雅言·功序》，“临池赏鉴，代不虚人，评论体势，悉非真谛。拟形于云雨，譬象于龙蛇，外状其浮华，内迷其实理。至若无知率易之辈，妄认功无百日之谈。岂知王道本无近功，成书亦非岁月哉。”

③ 《书法雅言·功序》，“初学之士，先立大体，横直安置，对待布白，务求其均齐方正矣。然后定其筋，向背往还，开合连络，务求雄健贯通也。次又尊其威仪，疾徐进退，俯仰屈伸，务求端庄温雅也。然后审其神情，战蹙单叠，回带翻藏，机轴圆融，风度洒落，或字馀而势尽，或笔断而意连，平顺而凛锋芒，健劲而融圭角，引伸而触类，书之能事毕矣。”

④ 《书法雅言·功序》，“第世之学者，不得其门，从何进手，必先临摹，方有定趋。始也专宗一家，次则博研众体，融天机于自得，会群妙于一心。斯于书也，集大成矣。”

⑤ 《书法雅言·功序》，“第昔贤遗范，优劣纷纭，仿之贵似，审之尚精。仿之不似，来续尾之讥，审之弗精，启叩头之诮。舍其所短，取其所长，始自平整而追秀拔，终自险绝而归中和。心与笔俱专，月继年不厌。譬之抚弦在琴，妙音随指而发，省括在弩，逸矢应鹄而飞。意在笔前，翰从毫转。后圣再起，吾言弗更矣。若分布少明，即思纵巧，运用不熟，便欲标奇，是未学走而先学趋也。书何容易哉。”

⑥ 《书法雅言·形质》，“穹壤之间，齿角爪翼，物不俱全，气禀使然也。书之体状多端，人之造诣各异，必欲众妙兼备，古今恐无全书矣。然天地之气，雨旸燠寒，风雷霜雪，来备时叙，万物荣滋，极少过多，化工皆覆。故至圣有参赞之功，君相有燮理之任，皆所以节宣阴阳而调和元气也。是以人之所禀，上下不齐，性赋相同，气习多异，不过曰中行，曰狂，曰狷而已。所以人之于书，得心应手，千形万状，不过曰中和，曰肥，曰瘦而已。”

度、轻重协衡、阴阳得宜、刚柔互济”。[①]同时要求临池之士从“肥”“瘦”向“中行”迈进。项穆把“肥”“瘦”视为“狂狷”，结果是“自狂狷而进中行”。[②]

《书法雅言·品格》中，项穆把与技巧有关的“擅长殊技”正式分为“正宗、大家、名家、正源和傍流”五个部分，并指出了尽善尽美是什么。他从书体角度指出尽善尽美就是正宗。总而言之，正宗就是集大成，就是“会古通今，不激不厉，规矩谙练，骨态清和，众体兼能，天然逸出，巍然端雅，奕矣奇解”。而达到正宗这一境界的人物正是集书法大成的王羲之。[③]“会通古今”、“不激不厉”的孙过庭在《书谱》中推崇王羲之，理由与项穆相同。项穆同时推崇孔子和王羲之，在《书法雅言·规矩》中称“岂有舍仲尼而可以言正道，异逸少而可以为法书者哉”，还讨论了正道和书法的关系。规矩是形式，属于尽美的要素。规矩所蕴含的“明彝伦而淑人心”、“昭荡平正直之道”是尽善的要素。若大学之旨的“先务修齐正平、皇极之畴的”首戒偏侧反陂属于尽善的要素，“规矩方圆之至”则属于尽美的要素。[④]《书法雅言·中和》中谈到关于“方圆”和“正奇”的尽善尽美。至“礼乐”止，他讨论了扩张外延使书法具备“中和”的意义。[⑤]与中和有关，还讨论了“方圆互成”、“正奇相济”、“称物平施”等，这些都是尽美的核心。[⑥] 同时他还把“偏有所著”看作问题，因为它不“中和”。

除此而外，项穆还从其他角度讨论了有关尽善尽美的内容。《书法雅言·正奇》中谈到“正”和“奇”的意义，指出二者之间的混合。他认为所谓的“正”就是“偃仰

---

① 《书法雅言·形质》，“若而书也，修短合度，轻重协衡，阴阳得宜，刚柔互济，犹世之论相者，不肥不瘦，不长不短，为端美也。此中行之书也。”

② 《书法雅言·形质》，“临池之士，进退于肥瘦之间，深造于中和之妙，是犹自狂狷而进中行也。慎毋自暴且弃哉。”

③ 《书法雅言·品格》，“夫质分高下，未必群妙攸归，功有浅深，讵能美善咸尽。因人而各造其成，就书而分论其等，擅长殊技，略有五焉。一曰正宗，二曰大家，三曰名家，四曰正源，五曰傍流。并列精鉴，优劣定矣。会古通今，不激不厉，规矩谙练，骨态清和，众体兼能，天然逸出，巍然端雅，奕矣奇解。此谓大成已集，妙入时中，继往开来，永垂模轨，一之正宗也。”

④ 《书法雅言·规矩》，“天圆地方，群类象形，圣人作则，制为规矩。故曰规矩方圆之至，范围不过，曲成不遗者也。大学之旨，先务修齐正平，皇极之畴，首戒偏侧反陂。且帝王之典谟训诰，圣贤之性道文章，皆托书传，垂教万载，所以明彝伦而淑人心也。岂有放辟邪侈，而可以昭荡平正直之道者乎。”

⑤ 《书法雅言·中和》，“圆而且方，方而复圆，正能含奇，奇不失正，会于中和，斯为美善。中也者，无过不及是也。和也者，无乖无戾是也。然中固不可废和，和亦不可离中，如礼节乐和，本然之体也。礼过于节则严矣，乐纯乎和则淫矣。所以礼尚从容而不迫，乐戒夺伦而皦如。中和一致，位育可期，况翰墨者哉。”

⑥ 《书法雅言·中和》，“方圆互成，正奇相济，偏有所着，即非中和。使楷与行真而偏，不拘钝即棱峭矣。行草与草而偏，不寒俗即放诞矣。不知正奇参用，斯可与权，权之谓者，称物平施，即中和也。”

顿挫、揭按照应、筋骨威仪、确有节制”，而“奇”则是“参差起复、腾凌射空、风情姿态、巧妙多端”。实现了尽善尽美的王羲之正是混合了“正”和“奇”。①《书法雅言·老少》中谈论了书法的“老”和“少”。“老”就是“结构精密、体裁高古、岩岫耸峰、旌旗列阵”，而“少”则是“气体充和、标格雅秀、百般滋味、千种风流”。随后，他还讨论了“老”、“少”通融的“中和”与“尽美”，谈到了玄鉴之士在典则之间寻求“老”—尽美的要素，也谈到了在神情之内探索“妙”—尽美的要素等问题。②他认为若实现了“规模宏远，意思窈窕，抑仰旋折，恬旷雍容”，达到了“无老无少”状态，就是达到了尽善尽美。③但“任笔成形，聚墨为势，漫作偏欹之相，妄呈险放之姿”等却是问题。④这些偏离“中和”及“温柔敦厚”的“任笔、聚墨、漫作、妄呈”等行为及其结果“偏欹之相”和“险放之姿”等，与达到尽善尽美相差甚远。

项穆在书法中强调的“中和”与“中行”是尽善尽美的实质内容。他所说的“中和”要求肥与瘦的合一，正与奇的合一，方与圆的合一，老与少的合一。他否定了纵巧、标奇等“偏”的美学，要求其从狂狷前进到中行。通过“中和”与“中行”实现尽善尽美是项穆书法美学的目标。

## 四、结语

自孙过庭始，诸多书法家用“心画”来理解书法。这对用尽善尽美来理解书法产生了很大影响。项穆把书法看作是“传心”和“心相”的艺术，认为“心相”思维要

---

① 《书法雅言·正奇》，“书法要旨，有正与奇。所谓正者，偃仰顿挫，揭按照应，筋骨威仪，确有节制是也。所谓奇者，参差起复，腾凌射空，风情姿态，巧妙多端是也。奇即连于正之内，正即列于奇之中。正而无奇，虽庄严沉实，恒朴厚而少文，奇而弗正，虽雄爽飞妍，多谲厉而乏雅。奈夫赏鉴之家，每指毫端努奋之巧，不悟规矩法度之逾。临池之士，每炫技于形势猛诞之微，不求工于性情骨气之妙，不犹轻道德而重功利，退忠直而进奸雄也。好奇之说，伊谁始哉。伯英急就，元常楷迹，去古未远，犹有分隶馀风。逸少一出，揖让礼乐，森严有法，神彩攸焕，正奇混成也。”

② 《书法雅言·老少》，“书有老少，区别浅深。势虽异形，理则同体。所谓老者，结构精密，体裁高古，岩岫耸峰，旌旗列阵是也。所谓少者，气体充和，标格雅秀，百般滋味，千种风流是也。老而不少，虽古拙峻伟，而鲜丰茂秀丽之容。少而不老，虽婉畅纤妍，而乏沉重典实之意。二者混为一致，相待而成者也。”

③ 《书法雅言·老少》，“玄鉴之士，求老于典则之间，探少于神情之内。若其规模宏远，意思窈窕，抑扬旋折，恬旷雍容，无老无少，难乎名状，如天仙玉女，不能辨其春秋，此乘之上也。”

④ 《书法雅言·老少》，“初观虽少，细观实老，丰采秀润，结束巍峨，引拂轻扬，气度凛毅，世所谓少年老成，乘之次也。鳞羽参差，峦峰掩映，提拨飞健，萦纡委婉，众体异势，各字成形，乃如一堂之中，老少群聚，则又次焉。筋力雄壮，骨气峻洁，剑拔弩张，熊蹲虎踞，只见其老，不见其少，有若师儒寿耇，正色难犯，又其次焉。灿烂似锦，艳丽如花，初视彩焕，详观散怯，正如平时夸伐，自称弘济，一遇艰大，节义遂亏，抑又其次矣。夫任笔成形，聚墨为势，漫作偏欹之相，妄呈险放之姿，疏纵无归，轻浮鲜著，风斯下矣，复何齿哉。”

跟“有诸中必形诸外”联系起来理解。而把书法理解为“心画”和“传心”的艺术并不意味着单纯从技巧上探讨书法。项穆强调了书法创作之前的“心的状态”和“修养程度”等问题。他还强调“思无邪”和“毋不敬”，“诚意正心”和“意在笔先”、“得心应手”等都与尽善有关。

中和适用于尽善和尽美。在内容上，中和不仅意味着人类内心的“中节”，也适用于“端整、均齐、优雅”等书体的形式美。项穆认为立足于“中和”美学，实现了尽善尽美的人物是王羲之，同时也把他视为技巧方面的正宗。他认为王羲之也是书法界从狂狷迈向中行的中心人物。中行是中和的另一种表达。他还强调“中行”并非仅限于讨论书体具备的外在形式，也应讨论中行所蕴含的、有节制的“心性”。这种思维意味着书法应该是内容与形式统一的、尽善尽美的艺术。

尽美未尽善思想蕴涵着对尽善的重视。重视尽善的弊端在于促使其消灭尽美所具有的美的特质。尽管如此，东方国家在传统上仍然强调尽善。在强调书法本身就是心灵修养之艺术的同时，也为书法重视伦理性和公众性的思维做了铺垫。对于这一点，项穆在《书法雅言》中通过重视“书如其人论”和传心、中和与中行展开了讨论。

# 关于朝鲜儒者巍岩与南塘的未发论辨之考察

上海复旦大学　邢丽菊

## 一、从朱熹的未发论谈起

如我们所知，未发与已发问题最初见于《中庸》的“喜怒哀乐之未发，谓之中。发而皆中节，谓之和。中也者，天下之大本也。和也者，天下之达道也”。此处将心的作用按照现实中的发显与否依次定义为“和”与“中”。即心感于外部事物之前的本然之面貌是未发的状态，即“中”；思考的作用已经开始，并能根据情况进行适当调节，从而达到不偏不倚，这是已发的状态，即“和”。因此，未发与已发的问题可以通过中和论来考察。这种中和的思维是儒学中研究心论的原型，是制约儒学思想体系以及引导其方向的先验性思维。作为人性论的核心，中和论也是阐明中国儒学乃至韩国儒学本质的原点。[①]

朱熹对中和论的认识经过了多次变化，由最初的不理解引发排斥，再到逐渐接受，后来在各种学说间彷徨，最后再到自己定论。[②] 他的认识变化我们通过“中和旧说”以及“中和新说”可以很明显地看出来。

在中和旧说中，朱熹认为，只要人生存着，心的作用就从不停止，故心在任何时候都处于已发状态。既然心任何时候都是已发，那么未发指的就是心体，即性。性才是寂然不动的未发。[③]这可以概括为“心为已发，性为未发”。他认为，所谓的“未发”作为“浑然全体”，它是“应物”而“寂然之本体”（《晦庵集》卷32，《与张敬夫》）。换言之，未发是内在的心体，而已发是外在的作用，性体心用。未发只有通过已发才能显现，并不是通过某物、某个时间或场所就可以规定的，即性体只有通过心体的作用才能显现，这就是“即用见体”。

---

① 崔英辰：《中和思想的哲学探究》，成均馆大学硕士学位论文，1977年，第68页。

② 李天承：《湖洛论辨中未发的意义》，载于《韩国哲学论集》第5辑，1998年，第176页。

③ 陈来：《宋明理学》华东师范大学出版社，2004年，第133页。

几年后，他又认为“于心性之实未始有差，而未发已发命名不当”(《朱子文集》卷67，《已发未发说》)，“未发已发字顿放得未甚稳当”（《朱子文集》卷43，《答林泽之六》)，[①]并指出中和旧说的错误在于将一切心的作用（心体之流行）都看作已发。而这与《中庸》的原意相差甚远。他在总结了程颐的各种观点后认为，心并不总是已发，也存在未发。换言之，心体的流行存在两种状态，即思虑未萌时的未发和思虑已萌时的已发。在他看来，思虑未萌是心体流行的寂然不动的阶段或状态，思虑已萌是心体流行的感而遂通的阶段或状态。未发和已发是心理活动的不同阶段或状态。未发为心之体，即性；而已发为心之用，即情。所以心就具有统摄未发之性与已发之情的两面性，这就是“心统性情”。[②]

可见，未发具有两种含义：一种是它是置于已发基础之上的，具有时间上的先在性；另一种是它作为性的具现体，是一切善的根源。因为未发既是在已发之前，又是大本、中。朝鲜后期代表儒者南塘韩元震（1682－1751）和巍岩李柬（1677－1727）二人各自以朱熹的未发论为依据，围绕未发问题产生了激烈的论争，在朝鲜儒学史上影响深远。其中，巍岩认为未发心体纯善，而南塘则认为有善恶，二人对朱熹的理论有各自的理解和阐释。本文将以二人的未发论为重点来探讨他们各自的主张，并归纳出二者理论的差异。

## 二、巍岩的未发论

巍岩首先把朱熹对未发的说明划分为三个层次：“浅言”、“深言”与“备言”。“浅言”指的是心没有应接事物的状态，此时凡人的气质是昏浊的，巍岩将其称为“不中底未发”;[③]“深言”指的是追寻源头而求其本质的状态，此时圣凡人是相同，故“未发之时，至虚至静，所谓鉴空衡平之体，虽鬼神有不得窥其际者”（《巍岩遗稿》卷12，《未发辨》)，巍岩将其称为“大本底未发”;[④]“备言”指的是统合心的存失、浅深而言的。[⑤]巍岩在《未发辨》中指出“然未发二字，煞自有浅深界分”，强调要严格区分。若

---

① 《朱子文集》卷43，《答林泽之六》。

② 陈来:《朱子哲学研究》，华东师范大学出版社，2000年，第175页。

③ 《巍岩遗稿》卷12，《未发辨》：据其不接事物故粗谓之未发，不属情用，故亦谓之性。而实则其性粗，在靠不得，故君子有不性焉。自孔子相近之性以下，至退栗性亦有善恶者，皆指此也。故朱子曰：“恶者，固为非正；而善者，亦未必中也。”此不中底未发，自是一界分也。

④ 《巍岩遗稿》卷12，《未发辨》：朱子曰：“以此心而应万物之变，无往而非中矣。”此大本底未发，真个是筑底处也。

⑤ 同上：此心存，则寂然时皆未发之中。感通时，皆中节之和。心有不存，则寂然木石而已，大本有所不立也。感通驰骛而已，达道有所不行也。

只是从“浅言”阶段认为未发是“思虑未萌，事物未至”，则这只是“不中底未发”。只有“深言”指的才是真正意义上的未发，即“大本底未发”。那么，他所理解的未发的概念究竟为何呢？

“求于未发之旨，则无论圣凡，必此心全体，寂然不动，方寸之间，如水之止，如镜之明，则夫所谓清浊粹驳之有万不齐者，至是一齐于纯清至粹（此气之本然也）。而其不偏不倚四亭八当之体，亦于是乎立。则所谓天下之大本也。”（《巍岩遗稿》卷7，《答韩德绍别纸》）

所谓真正的“未发”就如同明镜止水般，是心的寂然之状态，这种状态纯清至粹，是为“天下之大本”。这是对明德本体的“深言”，是“大本底未发”。即未发不单指的是事物未接的状态（不中底未发），同时也具有是心的“湛然虚明”之本体（大本底未发）的意义。在谈论未发时，这两种状态即不中底未发与大本底未发必须都考虑到才算周全，这就是“备言”。如果说“不中底未发”指的是接触外部事物以前的感情的未分化状态，属于物理性（时间性）的层次，而“大本底未发”指的就是本质层次上的未发。①

以这种未发论为基础，他进一步将心区分如下：

“夫气一也，而语其粗则血气也，语其精则神明也。统精粗而谓之气，而所谓心则非血气也。统粗精而谓之气，而所谓心则非血气也，乃神明也。心体也至精，而气质也至粗，心体也至大，而气质也至小。（中略）若如此都无辨别而混谓之一物，则安得为识心之论也？”（《巍岩遗稿》卷13，《未发辨后说》）

如上，他将心区分为神明至精的心体与至粗的血气之心。而作为心体的心是他未发论的重点。前者是本然之心，而后者是气质之心。巍岩还据此提出了“未发心体纯善论”。心虽然为一，但未发时“虚灵洞彻”和“神明不测”的心体起主宰作用，所以只能是纯善的，没有恶的可能性。这也是“大本底未发”时的心。这种本然的心体在圣凡人身上体现出来也是相同的。他指出：

“未发之体，小子谨就《大学》明德而言之，夫气禀所拘之明德，则其昏明有万不齐矣。其所谓本体之明德，则圣凡当是无别矣。”（《巍岩遗稿》卷4，《上遂庵先生》）

可见，他在论未发的过程中始终认为心体的纯善与圣凡人所具有的明德之心体是没有区别的。这一观点是以朱熹的“未发之时，自尧舜至于途人，一也”以及栗谷的“众人幸于一瞬之间，有未发之时，则即此全体湛然，与圣人不异矣”为依据的。

上述他将心区分为本然之心与气质之心的依据在于本然之性与气质之性的区分。

---

① 崔英辰著，邢丽菊译：《韩国儒学思想研究》，东方出版社，2008年，第249－250页。

不仅如此，他还进一步将本然之心对应于本然之性，气质之心对应于气质之性。[①] 巍岩借用朱熹之言指出，本然之心就是虚灵不昧之明德，气质之心就是受气禀所拘之明德。同是一明德，因受气禀之拘与否而区分为两种不同的心。就善恶来讲，气质之心是在未发状态下也有的刚柔善恶之心，而本然之心是“虚灵洞澈，神妙万物，操存舍亡，元无不善之心体者”。[②]气质之心的未发是浅层的未发，是不中底未发；而本然之心的未发是深层的未发，是大本底未发。[③]

而且，他还从修养论的角度如下解释本然之心与气质之心。

> “故天君主宰，则血气退厅，而方寸虚明。此即本然之心，而其理即本然之性也。天君不宰，则血气用事，而昏明不齐，此即气质之心，而其理即气质之性也。”（《巍岩遗稿》卷13，《未发辨后说》）

本然之心是“天君主宰，血气退厅，方寸虚明”之状态，等同于“虚灵不昧，以具众理应万事者（明德）”。气质之心是“天君不宰，血气用事，昏明不齐”之状态，等同于“为气禀所拘者”。从“所得乎天”来看，本然之心是先天性的存在，而它同时又是血气受天君统制的产物，这就证明了其后天性。这一理论是基于儒家思想通过后天修养来回归原始状态的基础之上。[④]所以人应该通过“戒惧慎独”的修养工夫来驱除浊驳的血气之影响，恢复湛然纯一的本然之气，从而使本然之心成为一身的主体性、主宰性存在，实现心性一致。

“理气同实，心性一致”是巍岩的独创理论。原文如下：

> “噫！未发是何等精义，何等境界！此实理气之大原，心性之筑底处，而谓之大原筑底处者，无他，正以其理气同实，心性一致而言也。圣人则合下以理为心，故心即性，性即心，体即中，用即和，无容可议矣。”（《巍岩遗稿》卷13，《未发辨后说》）

他理解的未发是理与气、心与性的根源处，这就是理气共存、心性一致的地方。当然，此时的心是本然之心，是与本然之性相一致的心。而且从“圣人则合下以理为心”也可以看出，巍岩试图阐明的是心与性在价值论上的一致性。尧舜般的圣人之心能够实现善的本性而成为实质上的圣人，是因为他们的纯善之心与纯善之性是一致的。

---

① 《巍岩遗稿》卷13，《未发辨后说》：故天君主宰，则血气退厅，而方寸虚名。此即本然之心，而其理即本然之性也。天君不宰，则血气用事，而昏明不齐，此即气质之心，而其理即气质之性也。

② 同上：然则德昭所认之心，不过是气质之善恶，而夫所谓虚灵洞澈，神妙万物，操存舍亡，元无不善之心体者，则不啻隔重关复岭矣。

③ 同崔英辰上书，第256页。

④ 崔英辰：《从“心是气”到“心性一致”》，18世纪韩国儒学思想会议论文集，2007年，第78页。

心的道德性价值取决于不受气的影响的理究竟能够发显多少的问题。① 即，巍岩通过心性一致来试图将心牵引到本然纯善的层次上，并从性的角度来考虑。形而上之性在现实中的实现需要形而下之气的媒介作用，而形而下之气同样需要形而上之性来确保其善性。他的这一心性论观点是以理气不离和理气同实的理气论为基础展开的。

巍岩的“理气同实”具有两层含义：一是从理气不离的角度来主张心性一致；二是重视理气的相互依存性。巍岩曾说过，“所谓实事，则必待夫理气同实，心性一致，然后方可谓实事”（《巍岩遗稿》卷12，《未发有善恶辨》）。理与气必须在实质上相同，心与性一致，这才是实在的事情。具体而言，“理气同实”是“气之正通，理亦正通；气之偏塞，理亦偏塞”（同上），“心性一致”是“本心存，则天理明；本心亡，则天理灭”（同上）。关于理气的相互依存性，朱熹曾指出，“理非别为一物，即存乎是气之中。无是气，则是理亦无挂搭处”（《朱子语类》卷1），“如阴阳五行错综不失条绪，便是理。若气不结聚时，理亦无所附著”（同上）。理无为至通，因无形而无法在现实中实现，于是就需要有气这一现实性的载体。巍岩继承了这一观点，认为如同理在现实中存在必须要有气的存在般，性为了在现实中具现，也需要心。“所谓理气，以心性而言也。心之不正而性能独中者，天下有是乎？性故本善，虽则不本于心，而其善之存亡，实孙于心之善否”（《巍岩遗稿》卷12，《未发辨》）。即，巍岩不能接受脱离心的性善。只有心性一致，则善才得以在现实中存在。他在心的方面不仅仅强调气的本然性，而且通过本然之心而使得本然之性的纯善性得以现实存在，同时也能发现未发的真正含义。可见，巍岩通过本然之性和本然之心的一致来努力确保善的现实性，并阐明不受气质约束的纯粹的善在现实中存在的可能性。

但是，巍岩的心性一致论被南塘及其他异论派学者批判为类同于阳明学的“心即理”，而有违于正统朱子学的“性即理”。应如何来理解这一理论性冲突呢？在朱子学中，“性即理”的“性”是本然之性，也就是“天命之谓性”的性。而在阳明学中，“心即理”的“心”是本来的心，即良知。因此，“心即理”指的就是“良知即天理”。此处，若将朱熹的心看作是知觉主体的意义，则阳明的心则具有道德主体的含义。而另一方面，巍岩所主张的“心性一致”是将本然之性的性与本然之心的心一致化，即赋予了心本然的含义。这与朱熹在“性是心之理，情是心之用”（《朱子语类》卷5）中强调心的本然的层面是一脉相承的。我们可以将巍岩“心性一致”中的“心”看作是强调心的本然性，而阳明的“心即理”不仅将心所具有的理的方面视为其本质，更将其等同于天理。巍岩虽然承认并强调心的本然性，但并没有将此心直接看作天理。也可以这样认为，巍岩的“心性一致”是朱子学向阳明学发展的一个逻辑过程，它在哲

① 郑渊友：《巍岩李柬的性理学说研究》，成均馆大学硕士学位论文，2007年，第60－65页。

学性和思想性上起着连接朱子学和阳明学的作用，也体现了朝鲜中后期朱子学的“心学式”发展趋向，这在思想史上具有非常重要的意义。

然而，巍岩的未发论被南塘批判为是“二心二性论”。对此巍岩回应说，实际上并不是二心，而是根据气禀的拘与不拘而有心存与心不存之区别而已。即，大本底未发与不中底未发、本然之心与气质之心、本然之性与气质之性并不是独立存在的概念，而是根据气禀的影响而有的逻辑性区分而已。但他的这一主张并不为南塘所接受。南塘认为巍岩的未发论违背了人只有一心一性的朱子性理学之大前提。

## 三、南塘的未发论

首先值得注意的是，南塘在展开自己理论的过程中提出了“心即气”[①] 这一观点，并将其与“性即理”相对应。此时的气同时包含着湛然虚明与气禀之两方面。他将前者理解为气质的纯善的方面，将后者看作有善恶的方面。所以他将心与气联系起来理解就意味着将心与气质中所存在的善恶问题相关联来解释的意图。[②] 换言之，在南塘的理论中，气质的善恶问题就转换为心的善恶问题。所以，南塘将湛然虚明之气与气禀之气都看作存在于未发状态下的气。这就意味着，在他的学说中，湛然虚明与气禀实质上就是未发心的问题。

关于未发的概念，南塘如下指出：

> “盖未发当做如何求？以冥然无觉为未发，则冥然无觉是昏气用事，不可谓未发也。以有所知觉谓未发，则有所知觉已涉思虑，亦不可谓未发也。然则至虚至静之中，但有能知能觉者在，而无所知所觉之事。此一悉时节，正为未发也。”[③]

如上，南塘认为，未发时虽然冥然无觉，但实际上昏气已经开始起作用，所以这不是未发。而有知觉也是心已经与外部事物发生关系，思虑已萌，这就是已发，而非未发。因此，他把虽然看似极为虚静但实际上潜在着能知觉能力的状态视为未发。进一步来讲，南塘认为未发就是寂然不动、不昏不昧的“气不用事”的状态。

既然未发是心的一个状态，肯定会受到气的影响。其实未发论辨最初的争论点便是未发状态下有无气质之性。巍岩一派认为“未发之前只有本然之性，而不可谓有气质之性”（《南塘集》卷30，《本然之性气质之性说》），而南塘则认为未发状态下存在气质之性。他认为：

---

① 《南塘集》卷11，《附未发气质辨后说》：心即气也，性即理也。

② 洪正根：《湖洛论争的成立与南塘、巍岩的心性论》，载崔英辰等编《韩国哲学史》，首尔：新文社，2009年，第186－212页。

③ 《经义记闻录》卷2。

“专言理则曰本然之性，专言气则曰气质之性。而心有未发已发，故未发是性之体，而已发是性之用也，但未发之前，气不用事，故但见其理之至善，而不见其气之善恶。及其发而后，方见其气之善恶。故愚又曰：“未发之前，气质之性不可见，而已发之后方可见也。”（同上）

性之概念是在气的前提下成立的，未发中也存在气，所以兼指气时就是气质之性，单指理时就是本然之性。尽管如此，未发状态下心是“至虚至明”的，“无以掩蔽天命之本体”（《南塘集》卷11），原因就是“气不用事”。南塘指出，未发状态下的气虽有“清浊粹驳”和“刚柔善恶”的多样性之本色，但是由于不发挥作用，所以不会妨害心的虚明本体。

但巍岩的理解是不同的。他认为：

“然则所谓未发，正是气不用事时也。夫所谓清浊粹驳者，此时无情意无造作，湛然纯一，亦善而已矣。此处正好单指其不偏不倚，四亭八当底本然之理也，何必兼指其不用事之气而为言乎?”（《巍岩遗稿》卷7，《与崔成仲》）

他也认可未发是“气不用事”，不仅仅是不接触外物，更重要的是只有本然之气，没有血气的作用，故“湛然纯一，亦善而已”。比较而言，在巍岩那里，真正的未发是不受血气的影响，所以本然之性如实展现，纯粹至善；而南塘认为未发是未接触事物的状态，此时兼具善恶的气质虽然存在，但不用发挥作用，所以不会影响理的善，但仍具有恶的可能性。[①] 所以他指出“未发虚明，明德本体；美恶不齐，气禀本色”。可见，与巍岩一直强调未发之气湛然清虚不同，南塘则非常关注人所禀赋的气质的差异，由此可以推导出其未发心体有善恶的观点。

相比之下，巍岩将未发分为大本底未发（本然之心）和不中底未发（气质之心），并指出只有寂然不动和湛然虚明才是未发。但是所谓的不中底未发指的是寂然不动，所以巍岩的不中底未发就是南塘理解的未发。南塘所说的未发意味着寂然不动，所以未发时湛然虚明和气禀不齐同时存在。他所说的“大本惟湛然虚明方可见本体”与巍岩所认为的“中有中底之未发是才可以确保本性的纯善”是相同的；而巍岩所认为的“不中底未发是由于血气的作用，故善恶兼在”与南塘的“未发气质有善恶”也是一脉相通的。可见二者的本来意图是相同的，但是对未发的定义不同导致了立场的差异。所以，巍岩的大本底未发相当于南塘的“心之本体”，而不中底未发相当于南塘的“心之气禀”。

关于中底之未发与不中底未发的关系，巍岩的观点可以认为是“异位异时论”（也

---

① 全仁植：《李柬与韩元震的未发、五常论辨研究》，韩国精神文化研究院博士学位论文，1998年，第126页。

称为“二位二时论”)，而南塘的则是“同位同时论”（也称为“一位一时论”)。“位”指的是一元（同位）或二元（异位），“时”指的是同时存在（同时）或不同时存在（异时）。更具体来讲，巍岩将心二元化理解，所以说“本然之心”与“气质之心”；而南塘将一心从两个层面来理解，所以说“心之本体”与“心之气禀”。这种用语的差异也体现了这一点。[1] 所以，南塘批判巍岩的“异时异位论”是“二心二性”，主张自己则是在“一心一性”的观点上展开逻辑的。依照南塘的观点，未发之心可以分为湛然虚明的心之本体和禀气不齐的心之气禀两个方面，而且只有这样才可以阐明心的善恶。湛然虚明的心的本体是“气的精爽”，体现在人身上也称为“虚灵”，是心善的层面，这一点上所有人都是相同的。相反，气禀说的是清浊粹驳的不齐的气质，也就是心有善恶的层面，这一点上每个人都不同。

注意的是，南塘区分“心之本然”与“心之气禀”的做法仅仅只是理论上的区分。就具体现实来讲，还是只存在一心，他借用铁镜与潭水的比喻如下指出：

> “盖镜水则心也，镜水之明止，即心之未发虚明也。潭之大小，铁之精粗，即心之气禀不齐也。镜水之明止与铁潭，决非二物。（中略）心之虚明与气禀，亦犹是耳。”（《南塘集》卷 11，《附未发五常辨》）

正如镜子的明亮与铁的精粗都是镜子的两方面，水的静止与潭的大小都是潭水的两方面一般，湛然虚明的心之本体与万端不齐的心之气禀也是同时存在的心的两个方面而已。所以他说“虚灵则气禀之虚灵，气禀则虚灵之气禀，非有二物也”（《南塘集》卷 15)，“虚明气禀，又非二物，则此所以性无二性，而心无二心也”（同上，卷 11)。他也据此主张“圣凡心异论”。圣人之心禀赋清气，心的虚灵之本体不受遮掩；凡人之心禀赋浊气，所以心之本体被遮蔽。故圣凡心有异。这就与巍岩所认为的圣凡心都共同体现了湛然虚明的心之本体的主张是不同的。

综上再来分析一下南塘对巍岩的批判。在南塘看来，巍岩在未发心性论中犯错误的根本原因是以心为中心来论性。在心中试图论性善，则只能将与性善相对应的心设定为本然之心，那么其余不是纯善的心就是气质之心，而且在这种气质之心基础上很自然就联系到了有善恶的气质之性。南塘意识到这一点，所以没有采取在本然之心框架下论性善的方式，而是像孟子一样以性善为主来论本然之心。换言之，他认为在自己的理论结构中论性善与心善完全没有问题。[2] 虽然心中存在兼具善恶的气禀与纯善的湛然虚明之本体，但在寂然不动的未发状态下，气不用事，故不妨害心善，所以性的

---

① 韩国哲学史研究会编：《韩国哲学思想史》，首尔：心山出版社，2005 年，第 284—285 页。

② 洪正根：《任圣周对湖洛论争的批判性止扬研究》，成均馆大学博士学位论文，2002 年，第 70—81 页。

纯善也会如实显现。而且他还举出朱熹对《孟子》所作的注解“气质所禀，虽有不善，不害性之本善”为依据。

但是，南塘在未发中论“一心一性”时，会遇到一个难题。如同朱熹在中和新说中所指，未发状态下心性具有不二的关系，而南塘的未发心不仅包括心纯善的层面，还包括有善恶的气禀。而且未发状态下同时存在本然之性与气质之性，如此，在未发状态下就很难确保性善。因为南塘的未发之心是心之本体与气禀同时存在的一心，而受气禀影响很容易被认为是气质之心；南塘的未发之性是本然与气质同时存在的一性，性由于气质的影响具有被认为是气质之性的危险性。基于这一点，巍岩认为南塘的未发心性论不过是在未发心基础上论未发性的不中底未发。所以巍岩认为，预想主张完全的性善，就必须在南塘的性论中去除有善恶的气禀的层面。

所以，巍岩认为南塘未发心性论的根本问题在于无法确保人的纯善本性。

## 四、二者的比较及差异

南塘和巍岩都以朱子性理学为依据构筑并展开自己的理论，但是彼此的着重点不同导致了他们互相坚持自己观点的正当性而展开了激烈的论争。巍岩将未发心性界分为二心与二性，而南塘则坚持一心一性。如前所述，巍岩是在“异位异时论”的基础上将未发分为两个层面来论本然之性与气质之性，而南塘则是以“同位同时论”为依据来论本然之性与气质之性。他们共同的目标都是如何来究明性善（本然之性）的问题。因为若对本然之性的规定不同，则性善也就随之不同。对性善的规定是决定学问为正学还是异端的重要因素。[①] 在朱子学一尊的朝鲜时代，他们的论争无疑从侧面反映了当时社会的思想面貌。对巍岩来讲，性善是只有在本然之心的状态下才能确保的本然之性；而南塘的性善是因气质的本然之性，是在未发状态下性的一个层面，而心没有必要根据气禀的拘与不拘而界分，就是一心。视角的不同终究导致了观点的差异。下面比较分析一下二者的主要分歧：

1）未发的概念问题。未发是心的理想状态，它既具有不接外物的“思虑未萌，知觉不昧”、“寂然不动”的含义，又具有“不偏不倚之中”、“湛然虚明”的含义。南塘强调的是前者，而巍岩注重的是后者。就南塘来讲，未发具有时间上的先在性，是未接事物之前的寂然不动的状态；而巍岩的虽然将未发分为只有湛然清虚的本然之气存在而“血气退厅”的大本底未发与血气用事、昏明不齐的不中底未发，但他强调指出，只有大本底未发才是真正意义上的未发，它是一切善的根源。所以南塘的未发相当于

---

① 洪正根：《〈中庸〉与〈孟子〉的性概念冲突》，载于《齐鲁文化研究》第7辑，2008年6月。

巍岩的不中底未发。

2）未发心体的善恶问题。巍岩认为，真正未发状态下清浊粹驳的血气是不发挥任何作用的，只有湛然清虚的本然之气，故气是纯善的，因而纯善的心体就不受遮蔽，性的本善也能如实具现。而南塘则指出，清浊粹驳的多样性是气的本色，只有阐明气的多样性才能解释心发以后性的善恶之来源。所以未发之气中既有湛然虚明的心之本体，又有万端不齐的心之气禀。由于会受到气禀的影响，所以未发心体不会如实呈现，会有兼具善恶的可能性。只有在“气不用事”的条件下，纯善的心体才会呈现，性也会如此。据此，二者虽然都使用“气”这一用语，但其意义和层次确实不同的。但巍岩的气作为纯粹的本然之气是本源性的存在，是在未发状态下才可以确认的特殊之气；相反，南塘的气则是一般意义上有清浊粹驳的气质之气。

3）心是否为一的问题。巍岩在论争的过程中提出了本然之心与气质之心，并将其分别对应于本然之性与气质之性，被南塘批判为“二心二性论”。但巍岩反驳指出并不是有二心，而是根据气禀的拘与不拘而有心存与心不存的逻辑性区别而已。而南塘则坚持“一心一性论”，认为未发之心可以分为湛然虚明的“心之本体”和禀气不齐的“心之气禀”两个方面，而且只有这样才可以阐明心的善恶。湛然虚明的心的本体是“气的精爽”，体现在人身上也称为“虚灵”，是心善的层面；相比之下，气禀说的是清浊粹驳的不齐的气质，也就是心有善恶的层面。巍岩一直喜好使用“本然之心”与“气质之心”，而南塘则使用“心之本体”与“心之气禀”，从用语差异中也可以窥探出这点。

**参考文献：**

[1]《朱子文集》、《朱子语类》、《栗谷全书》、《巍岩遗稿》.

[2] 陈来．朱子哲学研究．华东师范大学出版社，2000.

[3] 陈来．宋明理学．华东师范大学出版社，2004.

[4] 崔英辰．中和思想的哲学探究．成均馆大学硕士学位论文，1977.

[5] 崔英辰．从“心是气”到“心性一致”．18 世纪韩国儒学思想会议论文集，2007.

[6] 崔英辰著，邢丽菊译．韩国儒学思想研究．东方出版社，2008.

[7] 崔英辰等编．韩国哲学史．新文社，2009.

[8] 洪正根．任圣周对湖洛论争的批判性止扬研究．成均馆大学博士学位论文，2002.

[9] 洪正根．《中庸》与《孟子》的性概念冲突．齐鲁文化研究第 7 辑．2008 年 6 月.

[10] 李天承. 湖洛论辨中未发的意义. 韩国哲学论集第5辑，1998.

[11] 郑渊友. 巍岩李柬的性理学说研究. 成均馆大学硕士学位论文，2005.

[12] 全仁植. 李柬与韩元震的未发、五常论辨研究. 韩国精神文化研究院博士学位论文，1998.

[13] 韩国哲学史研究会编. 韩国哲学思想史. 首尔：心山出版社，2005.

# 本质论与发展观的误区：性善论新解

清华大学　方朝晖

多年来我一直在教学中摸索如何讲解孟子的性善论，发现要让学生们理解性善论很难，关键是要有一套可以把孟子思想真义说清楚的语言。很多人认为，人性本质上是善还是恶，这其实是说不清的；如果人性本善，如何解释人间那么多的恶；况且，善恶本来就是人类社会道德的产物，先天的人性也许无所谓善恶。按照这样理解，就会觉得孟子太肤浅。然而，细读《孟子》可以发现，性善论根本就不是在上述意义上展开的，有关误解需要得到进一步澄清。数年前，我曾在《中华读书报》发表过一篇文章讨论这个问题，[①] 当然限于篇幅没有说清楚。本文顺着当时同样的思路，作进一步的阐释。

在历史上，关于孟子的性善论有太多的批评与争论。从荀子、董仲舒、王充到司马光、王安石、苏轼等人，从宋明理学家的气质天命之分到王夫之、戴震等人性不离气之说，有过很大争论。现当代学者康有为、唐君毅、徐复观、牟宗三、胡适、冯友兰、钱穆、张岱年等人对之均有所论述。在西方汉学界，有关性善论的研究也很热烈，特别是自从 20 世纪 60 年代末葛瑞汉发表那篇关于孟子的有名文章以来（见下），孟子的人性论引起了西方汉学界持久的讨论。夏威夷大学《东西方哲学》杂志 1997 年推出了一个儒家人性论的专辑；[②] 信广来（Kwong-Loi Shun）于 1997 年出版《孟子及早期中国思想》（Mencius and Early Chinese Thought，Standford））一书；[③] 2002 年出版、陈金樑（Alan K. L. Chan）主编的《孟子：背景及解释》（Mencius：Contexts and Interpretations，Honolulu）一书所集结的 13 篇论文中，有 9 篇直接或间接地论及孟子的

---

① 方朝晖，“重新认识强大的性善论”，《中华读书报》2011 年 3 月 9 日。

② Human “Nature” in Chinese Philosophy：A Panel of the 1995 Annual Meeting of the Association for Asian Studies (Special Issue)，Philosophy East & West，vol. 47，no. 1，January 1997，pp. 1－74.

③ Kwong-Loi Shun，Mencius and Early Chinese Thought，Standford，Calif.：Stanford University Press，1997.

人性论。[1] 顾立雅（Herrlee Glessner Creel）、史华慈（Benjamin I. Schwartz）、倪德卫（David Nivison）、孟旦（Donald J. Munro）、林毓生、张灏、安乐哲（Roger Ames）、柯雄文（Antonio S. Cua）、华霭云（Irene Bloom）、艾文贺（Philip J. Ivanhoe）等不少学者都曾对孟子或其人性论有研究或论述。本文试图以前人的成果为基础，进一步分析孟子性善论的理解与意义。

## 本质论

所谓本质论，我指认为人性有某种先验的本质，于是性善论就变成"人性本质是善的"，性恶论变成了"人性本质上是恶的"。对此，我想指出，孟子从未使用过"性本善"这一表达方式，他所使用的表述只是"性善"而不是"性本善"。"性善"与"性本善"的差别在于，"性善"就如同我们今天说"某某是个好人"一样，并不等于说这个人"本质上"好，更不意味着此人没缺点。

我们知道，把"性善"解释为"性本善"在历史上是后来的事；即便如此，"性本善"在中国古代也不是指"人性本质上是善的"。古汉语中的"本"是指个事字，原指树的根部，有两个基本含义：一指原初（本来），二指基本或根本。这两个意思都与现代汉语中的"本质"相距甚远。比如《三字经》中的"性本善"，其"本"字就是指"原初"，故前有"人之初"三字。

现代汉语中的"本质"一词来源于希腊哲学。希腊哲学中的"本质"（如柏拉图的 ousia，亚里士多德的 to ti en einai 等）针对现象而言，指在变动不居的现象背后永恒不变、确保事物自身同一性的属性（比如苏格拉底的体貌特征天天在变，但却不妨碍他仍然是苏格拉底，那个在变化之中确保苏格拉底为苏格拉底的东西就是他的本质）。这种隐藏在背后且永恒不变的"本质"概念在古汉语中未见，不过深受西方自然科学影响的现代汉语已经接受它，并在解释孟子性善论的时候不自觉地被引入：先把"性善"理解成"性本善"，再把"性本善"解释成人性"本质上"是善的。这是一系列误解的根源。

然而，"本质"一词虽来源于西方，并不等于古代中国人没有本质论的思维。严格说来，宋儒"天命之性"与"气质之性"之别，就是一种本质论。以天命之性为性之本质，以气质之性为性之载体。气质类似于表象，可以千变万化；天命之性类似于本质，保持永恒不变。气质类似于质料，形色露于外；天命类似于实质，特点藏于内。戴震有力地批评了这种本质论思维。他指出，宋儒以"气质之性"与"天命之性"分

---

① Alan K. L. Chan, ed., Mencius: Contexts and Interpretations, Honolulu: University of Hawaii Press, 2002.

释“性”，并不符合孟子本意。孟子说过“形色，天性也。惟圣人然后可以践形”（《尽心下》），“乃若其情，则可以为善矣，乃所谓善也。若夫为不善，非才之罪也”（《告子上》），因此“舍才质安睹所谓性哉”，所谓气质与天命之别本不存在。[①]

因此，假如我们放弃把“性善”解释为“性本善”、并进一步解释为“人性本质上是善的”，那么“性善论”丝毫也不否认人性之中存在着与生俱来的坏成分，而只是说人性从整体上看仍然是个好东西。如此，“性善”作为个判断句就不能理解为：

（1）人性本质上是善的（本质判断）

（2）人性全部是善的（全称判断）

（3）人性生来是善的（先天判断）

而只能理解为：

（4）人性总体上是善的（总体判断）

所谓“人性总体上是善的”，就是“总体上是好的”，但并不否定它也有不好的方面（就象我们说虽有许多缺点，但总的来说还是好人），类似于戴震所说的“材质良”。[②] 所谓“全部是善的”，是指对人性的好坏不加辨别，显然过于简单，难人让人信服。所谓“人性生来就是善的”，问题是有人认为人生来就有不善的成分（荀子的性恶说即是此意），而现代学者多倾向于认为人性在进入社会之前无所谓善恶（告子亦如此）。不难发现，这里的（1）（2）（3）三个判断都直接或间接地包含着某种本质论预设，甚至可以说判断（1）正是以判断（2）或（3）为基础推导出来的；如果判断（2）或（3）成立的话，那么就可以得出判断（1），即人性本质上是善的；而当人们说判断（1）的时候，他们心里想的往往是判断（2）或（3）。[③]

由此我们也可以理解，后世很多学者正是因为认识到判断（1）（2）（3）不成立，有人猛烈批判孟子的人性论（如历史上的告子、荀子、董仲舒、王安石、苏轼、司马光、胡仲仁、黄东发、张岱年等人）；有人为了替孟子辩护，提出各种新的解读，比如把性善论解释为有善论（戴震、陈澧、冯友兰），心善论（徐复观、唐君毅、杨泽波），向善论（焦循、陈大齐、傅佩荣），或善端论（杨泽波等），善性论（即以善性/人异于

---

① 戴震：《孟子字义疏证》，何文光整理，北京：中华书局，1982年第2版，第39页。

② 戴震以心、材质、理义三者合而言性，即所谓血气心知之性，谓此性之材质得天理之全，故谓“人之材质良”（《孟子字义疏证》，第183页）。不过，我这里只是借用，戴震对性善的论述倾向于“有善论”，与本人有所不同。

③ 本质论还有另外一种表现方式，即认为人性部分是善的，但由于这部分善的内容代表了人性的本质，即人之所以为人（或人异于禽兽）之处，所以可以说人性善。这一观点认为孟子的“性”与通常本能意义上的“性”不同，是他自己重新界定了“性”。这一观点非常有影响，戴震、冯友兰、张岱年、余纪元、梁涛等人主此说。对这种本质论，我计划另撰文详细批判，本文囿于篇幅，不专门讨论，但在下文中有涉及。

禽兽者为人性，冯友兰、张岱年、余纪元、梁涛等），天命论（张程朱子）等等。甚至可以说，宋代理学家张载、二程和朱熹等天命之性与气质之性的提出，也是为了走出孟子“性善”这一判断所带来的上述三个判断的困境。这些解释诚然各有一定道理，然而，如果性善论本来的表述只是指“从总体上是善的”，那么这些辩护的必要性是否有可能要另加考虑？

## 发展观

早在1967年，英国学者葛瑞汉（A. C. Graham）就曾撰文指出，孟子的性善论不能完全从西文 human nature 的角度来理解，西方哲学中的有关概念把人性固化，不适用于先秦人性论。① 安乐哲（Roger T. Ames）在后来的一系列论文中进一步阐述葛瑞汉的观点，强调孟子的“性”不是一个固定的、死的先天本质，而是指在特定的历史、文化情境不断自我创造、自我实现的过程；因此“性”是在后天修身中为实现自我而建立的，而非从初生时就被给定的抽象理念。安乐哲之所以反对把汉语“人性”翻译成 human nature，正是因为来自希腊哲学传统的西方人性论把人当作孤立的实体个体，把人性当作由外在法则（principle，archē，eidos 等）所支配的现象，其背后的宇宙论（cosmogonic cosmolgy）与中国先秦时期的宇宙论（non-cosmogonic cosmolgy）迥然不同。②

不难发现，安乐哲所反对的正是本质论思维。他的观点虽有道理，但如果完全把人性当成发展的过程，也有重要问题。孟子所讲的“性”严格说来不是在历史、文化情境中建构出来的产物；从孟子“仁义礼智根于心”、“先得我心之所同然”、“我固有之”、“皆备于我”到“知性知天”等论断，可以看出他强调人性的某些道德特征是先天的。他虽然重视修身和存养，但这些行为有一个共同的目标，即“尽其才”。所谓“尽其才”，实际上是完成上天所赋予我的天性要求，所以也即《中庸》的“尽其性”。我把“尽性”理解为“让生命得到健全、完整的成长或发展”（在孟子这儿是道德意义上的），葛瑞汉指出这是在不受伤害、营养充足的条件下实现的繁荣和发展。人怎样才

---

① A. C. Graham, “The Background of the Mencian Theory of Human Nature,” Studies in Chinese Philosophy and Philosophical Literature, Singapore: Institute of East Asian Philosophies, 1986, pp. 7－66.

② Roger T. Ames, “Mencius and a Process Notion of Human Nature,” in: Alan K. L. Chan, ed., Mencius: Contexts and Interpretations, Honolulu: University of Hawaii Press, 2002, pp. 72－90; Roger T. Ames, “The Mencian Conception of Ren xing 人性: Does it Mean ‘Human Nature’?” in: Henry Rosement, Jr., Chinese Texts and Philosophical Contexts: Essays Dedicated to Angus C. Graham, La Salle, Illinois: Open Court, 1991, pp. 143－175.

能获得健全、完整的成长或发展呢？这正需要我们下一步探讨的大问题，也涉及性善论能否成立的关键所在。这里先强调一下：人性的健全、完整发展肯定有自己的规则——本文称为“成长法则”，而成长法则可能是一生下来就已被赋予的；如果人的所作所为违背了这套法则，就会导致“逆性”、“伤性”、“害性”或“失性”，在孟子那儿就是“戕贼”、不能“尽其才”（当然主要是道德意义上）。

人们一般都承认，人的成长、发展有自己的规律，有自己的法则，包括生命周期、成长方式、营养条件、理想特征等在内。这些当然也是与生俱来或天生的，所以也属于“性”的范畴。以桃树为例，春天来了，我们看到园子里一棵棵桃树茁壮成长后枝繁叶茂，开放出鲜艳的花朵。这样的桃树可以看成已经在“尽其性”，即最大限度地挖掘了自身潜能、充分地实现了自身。而这棵树之所以“尽其性”，正是由于能够按照其成长法则的要求来培育它。设想另一棵桃树发育不充分、开花不鲜艳，枝条萎缩、躯干短小、树叶发黄，那么我们可以说这棵桃树没有“尽其性”，不符合其“天性”。这是由于外部伤害或营养不良所致，即孟子所谓“戕贼杞柳”。“戕贼杞柳”就是其柳之性受到了扭曲而不健康的意思，也就是违背了其成长法则的要求。

从孟子的“性”所代表的成长法则是先天而不是后天发生的这一重要事实看，安乐哲等人坚持孟子的“人性”是一动态过程的说法忽视了性的先天特征，恐怕与孟子本义有背离之处。孟子所说的人的发展过程，绝不是自然而然的发展（与自然事物不同），而是有目的、有方向的刻意努力；人的生命不可能漫无边际、没有极限的发展，不管历史－文化环境如何塑造它。换言之，修身、尽心、存养皆须遵循某种先天的规则，才能达到“尽其性（才）”的成效。从这个角度说，生命的全面发展乃是为了成全其原有的天性，其中包括充分实现其潜能，真正成全其自我。安乐哲认为亚里士多德所谓“潜能/现实”的二分不适合于孟子的人性论，[①] 恐未必正确。这也正是他受到华霭云（Irene Bloom）批评的主要原因吧。[②]

现在我们可以得出初步结论，“性”（人性）作为与生俱来或天生的特性，其实可以有两种完全不同的理解，一是指本能属性，二是指成长法则。从本能属性的视角看，人性是指人们生而具有的一些特点如食、色之类，这是性恶论的典型理解方式。但是其实还可以从成长法则的角度看，每种生命都有自己的成长法则或规律，这些法则或规律能决定一个生命能否健全、完整的成长、发展。这两个层面的“性”，孟子同样给

① Roger T. Ames, “The Mencian Conception of Ren xing 人性: Does it Mean ‘Human Nature’?” Henry Rosement, Jr., Chinese Texts and Philosophical Contexts: Essays Dedicated to Angus C. Graham, La Salle, Illinois: Open Court, 1991, pp. 159 。

② 华霭云：《孟子的人性论》，载（美）江文思、安乐哲编，《孟子心性之学》（Mencius' Learning of Mental-Nature），梁溪译，北京：社会科学出版社，2005 年，第 125－173 页。

予了重视；但是恰恰后面这个意义上的“性”，才是导致孟子得出人性善的主要原因，这一点下面论述。

孟子的“性”主要是从成长法则的角度来理解的，前人也指出过。例如，清儒戴震曾提出，孟子所谓的“性”，包括人先天地获得的一切特性；其中有些特性是可见的，如食色之类；有些特性是不可见的，如成长周期、成熟样式等。这些不可见的特征需要长时段观察才能发现，但不能否认它也是人性的一部分，它接近于本文所谓成长法则。他说，“其禀受之全，则性也；……如桃杏之性，全于核中之白，形色臭味，无一弗具，而无可见，及萌芽甲坼，根干枝叶，桃与杏各殊；由是为华为实，形色臭味无不区以别者，虽性则然，皆据才见之耳。成是性，斯为是才。”① 按照上述戴震的理解，性代表先天具有的潜能，才代表后天表现的形质。

葛瑞汉也注意到了孟子人性概念作为成长法则的上述含义。他指出，孟子的人性概念更加接近于《庄子》、《吕氏春秋》、《淮南子》等之中的人性概念。比如他引用《庄子·达生》“吾生于陵而安于陵，故也；长于水而安于水，性也；不知吾所以然而然，命也”等来说明，先秦中国学者的“性”还包括在成长中充分实现其潜能的特征，孟子的“性”概念也正是在此意义展现的。② 所以他反对局限于与生俱来的特征来理解孟子的“性”，因为“性”还包括人在成长过程所展现出来的特征（接近于本文所谓“成长法则”）。

## 成长法则

从成长法则的角度所说的“性”或“人性”，是指每一个生命要想得到了健全、完整的成长所要遵循的法则或规律。比如它的生命周期、健康状态、营养条件、成长方式等等。成长法则也代表生命健全、完整成长发展的根本需要，一旦违背生命就会走向枯萎，生机、活力受到压抑，我们称其伤性、逆性、害性或失性。这些需要或规律是生命刚出生或在种子阶段时就已经被决定了的。成长法则代表“性”的另一个重要方面，即生命生而具有的特征。成长法则决定了一个生命能否健康的成长，包括让它天生的潜能得到充分实现，即所谓“尽其性”（即孟子“尽其才”）。该长高时长不高，该开花不开花，该鲜嫩时却枯黄，皆是不能“尽其性”的表现。

---

① 戴震：《孟子字义疏证》，第39—40页。

② Graham, A. C., “The Background of the Mencian Theory of Human Nature,” Studies in Chinese Philosophy and Philosophical Literature, Singapore: Institute of East Asian Philosophies, 1986, p. 8. 中译参葛瑞汉：《孟子人性理论的背景》，载（美）江文思、安乐哲编，《孟子心性之学》(Mencius' Learning of Mental-Nature)，第13—14页。

事实上，在日常生活中，现代人也常常从成长法则的角度来使用“人性”一词。例如，当我们说某件事“没有人性”、“违反人性”或“没有人味”时，所谓违反人性或没有人性，意味着对生命的伤害或毁灭；而之所以会伤害或毁灭生命，正由于背离了生命成长的根本需要，也即是对其成长法则的违背或蔑视。这里的“人性”一词并不限于人的本能需要，更是指符合生命健全生长的根本需要，也即生命成长的法则。

应当认识到，人的本能需要、本能属性有时与生命的根本需要或成长法则是相冲突的。比如好逸恶劳是人的本能需要，但它可能使变得懒惰而失去活力，并不符合人的根本需要，因而我们也说它是反人性的。比如纵欲过度符合人的本能需要，但可能毁掉我们的健康，摧残我们的心理，因而也是不符合人性的，这是因为这类行为违背生命成长的法则，不符合健全成长的根本需要。

试以下表描述两种不同的“性”概念：

| | 性恶论 | 性善论 |
|---|---|---|
| 理解角度 | 本能属性 | 成长法则 |
| 作为需要 | 本能需要 | 根本需要 |
| 典型说法 | 人生来就是自私的 | 这种做法不符合人性 |

现在我要说的是，孟子所用的“性”正是从成长法则的角度说的。具体说来，我认为孟子的“性”或“人性”是指充分、健全、完整地生长、发展所遵循的规律，也可以说指向生命“充分地实现自身”的根本需要或条件。这是孟子“知其性”、“尽其才”等言语所蕴含的意思。如果我们忽略了孟子的“性”（人性）与荀子的“性”存在含义上的这一重要区别，就为理解孟子性善论设置了巨大障碍，从而无法理解孟子思想的深刻意义。荀子的人性概念更接近于本能属性，而孟子的人性概念包含成长法则。为了更好地理解这一问题，我提出下面几个问题供大家讨论：

其一，人们通常容易用“性”指食、色之类“与生俱来的属性”，但是顺着此性发展下却不合乎“人性”，这说明了什么？可见，“性”的含义本来就不应当限于指食、色、味、臭、安佚之类与生俱来的属性，而应当包括生命成长的规律或法则。这就表明，人们以本能属性来理解人性，是太过于肤浅了。孟子正是在这个意义上超越了告子、也超越了后来的荀子。孟子曰：“饥者甘食，渴者甘饮，是未得饮食之正也，饥渴害之也。岂惟口腹有饥渴之害？人心亦皆有害。”（《尽心上》）所谓“非饮食之正”，就是指害性，也即“戕贼杞柳”之义。

其二，当我们说“这个没有人性的畜生”时，这里的“人性”一词是指什么？显然不是指食、色等本性属性吧？那么它是什么意思呢？直观的含义当然是指一种价值立场，即我们所认可的最基本价值，也是指衡量人之为人的基本价值标准。那么，作为衡量人之为人的价值标准的“人性”概念究竟是如何得出的？我想“没有人性”在这里是指某种行为违反了人类生命成长的根本需要，或者说与人性健全成长、完全发展的法则相对立。所以，这里的“人性”概念照样与通常限于食色等本能需要来理解的“人性”概念有所不同，主要指成长法则，尽管这两种人性都指某种与生俱来的特性。

其三，孟子“睟面盎背”，“乐莫大焉”，“手蹈足舞”，“尽心知性”等一系列表述，主要是为了说明为善合乎人性，而不是为了确立所谓良心/本心之本体。为善不是由于善本身，而是为了“尽其性”、“尽其才”，善本身不是自在的价值或终极目标。“尽性”、“成己”，才是为善的根本目标（借《中庸》术语）。这正是孔子的“为己”传统。“率性”（《中庸》）与“尧舜性之”（《孟子·尽心下》）含义是一样的，无论是“率性”还是“性之”，都代表一种精神：“性”是比道德更高的标准。所以，道德的基础才能真正奠基于人性之内，而不是在其外。这才触及了孟子性善论的核心，才能证明仁义皆内而不在外。

戴震①、冯友兰②、张岱年③、余纪元④、梁涛⑤等人认为，孟子把人性定义为善性/人异于禽兽者。如果真是这样的话，则容易把修身、存养变成一个为了求善而求善的过程，忽视了人性本身才是孟子性善论的最高准则，反而可能走到与人性的对立面（扼杀人性）。我认为这一理解并不完全符合孟子性善论的精神。

其五，孟子强调自反、回到良心、不失本心，需要搞清的是：为何“自反”会有无比强大的力量？所谓“自反而缩”，所谓“舍生取义”，所谓“浩然之气”，所谓“大丈夫”，代表的是“自反”所带来的无比巨大的精神力量。这种精神力量从何而来？杨

---

① 戴震说，“人以有礼义，异于禽兽，实人之知觉大远乎物则然，此孟子所谓性善。”（戴震：《孟子字义疏证》，第 35 页），“性虽不同，大致以类为之区别……言同类之相似，则异类之不相似明矣。……人物之性，咸分于道，成其各殊者而已矣。”（同上书，第 25 页）又说：“人物之生，类至殊也；类也者，性之大别也。……盖孟子道性善，非言性于同也；人之性相近，胥善也。”（戴震：《读孟子论性》，见《孟子字义疏证》，第 182 页）

② 冯友兰：《中国哲学史》（上册），中华书局，1961 年，第 153－162 页。

③ 张岱年：《中国哲学大纲》，载刘鄂培（主编）《张岱年文集》（第二卷），北京：清华大学出版社，1990 年，第 222－229 页；张岱年：《中国伦理思想研究》，载刘鄂培（主编）《张岱年文集》（第六卷），北京：清华大学出版社，1995 年版，第 552、553、567、675 页。

④ Yu Yiyuan, “Human nature and virtue in Mencius and Xunzi: an Aristotelian interpretation,” in: Dao: A Journal of Comparative Philosophy, Vol. 5, No. 1, Winter 2005, pp. 11－30.

⑤ 梁涛：《“以生言性”的传统与孟子性善论》，《哲学研究》2007 年第 7 期；梁涛：《孟子“道性善”的内在理路及其思想意义》，《哲学研究》2009 年第 7 期。

泽波[1]谓性善的基础是良心本心，故要自反；然未解决为何良心本心有如此强大的力量？你可以说因为回到了人之所以为人的尊严与价值。但后者毕竟是后发的人为价值判断，我们在讨论性善论时要避免先入为主地从道德价值出发。从价值判断出发，我们确实可以说，善性/人高于禽兽者代表了人的高贵、尊严与价值；但是从事实判断出发，人的高贵、尊严与价值感是怎么建立起来的？原因在于：为善因为符合人性成长的法则，所以才使人变得生机勃勃、有无限活力。这也是“四体不言而喻”、“足之蹈之手之舞之”、“反身而诚乐莫大焉”、“先得我心之所同然”、“若决江河莫之能御”的根本原因。

其五，许多学者均已认识到，孟子“仁义礼智根于心”，将道德植根于人性而不是社会需要或环境，这是孟子性善论的强大意义所在。但是为什么这一观点成立？这一观点真的成立吗？前述“善性说”（或以人禽之别为人性）就回答不了这一点。为什么仁义礼智根于心呢？有人提出“人性的自然生长倾向”一说。[2] 但此说还是会面临何以有向善的“自然倾向”，难道不可以说人性中也有向恶的自然倾向吗？更多的人还是接受人性在纯粹自然状态（即生物学意义上）是无所谓善恶的。所谓“根于心”、“我固有之”、“心之同然”，我认为其真实含义是：当我们行善时，会发自内心地感到幸福，发现这才是真正符合自己人性的做法；也就是，由于仁义礼智从根本上有利于生命健全完整发展，让人觉得仿佛它们是发自人的内心一样；正因为当我们行善时，会有一种发生内心的舒适，会感到生命的繁荣灿烂，所以我们感觉这些善并不是出于外部的需要而行，而是从我内心流出来；而在相反的情形下，孺子入井而不救，自己会受到良心的责备，这也同时意味着自己的人性扭曲，所以不利于生命健全完整发展。这一思想，千百年来很少人为人所知。

## 性善何义

有了上述理解，我们就可以更好地理解孟子的性善论。既然孟子所谓的“性”是指生命充分实现自身的特征，“性善”的意思不过是指生命充分地实现自身——即得到充分完整的发育和健全的生长——是一件好事。如果我们认同“桃树得到充分的发育和成长比得不到充分的发育和成长要好”这一判断，那就等于承认“桃树之性善”。相反，假如我们不认同上述判断，那就等于认为“桃树之性不善”。这里衡量某一生命“性善”还是“性恶”的标准不在于其先天的本能需要，而在于它的充分、全面发展

① 杨泽波：《孟子性善论研究》（修订本），北京：中国人民大学出版社，2010 年，第 33、165 页，等。

② 杨泽波：《孟子性善论研究》（修订本），第 77－85 页。

(尽其性）好不好。

比如，我们有时认为，苍蝇这种东西越是得到充分的成长、发育，越是给我们的生活带来危害。这种态度如果上升为一种哲学立场，也可以说认为“苍蝇之性不善”。然而，我们不能仅仅从人、特别是特定人群的态度来下结论。从现代生态学立场看，苍蝇的健康、茁壮生长是也符合自然界发展的整体需要的。所以从这个角度说，苍蝇之性也可以说是善的。这也符合儒家的观点。儒家从上天有好生之德（“天地之大德曰生”，《周易·系辞》）的角度看，也会认为苍蝇的健康、茁壮成长（尽苍蝇之性）符合天道。(但是世界上是不是有什么生物，它的充分生长、发育是一件坏事呢？这个问题值得思考）

综合上面两条，我们可以得出，孟子所谓的“性善”只是指人如果能充分地实现他的性/天性，是好事一件。这就是孟子“性善”的本义。然而认识到这里还不是最重要的，最重要的是，为什么人的生命的健全、完整成长是一件好事呢？我认为这里有两个基本的前提假定，也可以说是性善论的两个前提假定：

(1）每个人都希望最大限度地成全自己的性/天性，即所谓“尽其性”（《中庸》）或“尽其才”（《孟子·告子上》）。

(2）人要成全自己的性/天性，就不能作恶，因为作恶会戕害自己的性/天性，即所谓“戕贼杞柳以为杯棬”（《孟子·告子上》）。

现在我们可以说：性善论是否成立，取决于前面1、2两条是否成立。那么这两条是否成立呢？第1条成立似乎没有问题，因为它符合我们的生活常识。第2条也应该没有问题，因为没有人认为一个为非作歹的人其人格是健康的。我们大概都承认，坏人的人性是扭曲的。

由此，“人性”或“天性”一词就获得了一种价值，即它是好东西，值得追求，故曰“性善”。设想吸血鬼（当然世间并无此物）为了生存必须以害人为前提；而人为了生存得好，就不能伤害他人。相比之下，可以说人比吸血鬼的“材质”好，即人性比鬼性好。所以性善也是相对而言的，并不涉及本质问题。

回到开头，当我们说“那个人没有人性”时，显然已经假定了“人性”是好的。换言之，这一说法已经预设了“性善论”。否则，如果人性不是好的，“没有人性”就不能成为一句骂人的话。那也就是说，人们在日常生活中也已经坚持了孟子的“性善论”了。尽管许多人在批评性善论时凿凿有词，但事实上他们也都是性善论者。关键在于：人们在内心深处都知道，生命的健全、完整成长是我们在有意无意之中追求的理想，也是我们衡量事物的最高价值之一；而与此对立的状态就是逆性、伤性、害性或失性，也就是违反了人性。尽管我们并不是总是明确地意识到这一点，但我们确实是从此预设出发来判断的，并最典型地体现在说某人是“没有人性的畜生”时。

再看性善说与性恶说的关系。性恶说抓住的是与生俱来的那些自私的欲望等特征，但是这一事实并不妨碍性善论。因为，顺着这些与生俱来的自私欲望，最终可能导致人性的扭曲。也就是说，这些私欲有时也是反人性的，因为不符合生命健全、完整成长的根本需要，也即违反了生命的成长法则。所以性善论、性恶论（甚至性无善无恶论）可以并存，并一定相互矛盾。

## 意义所在

经过上述解读，孟子的性善论具有强大的现实意义：

（1）性善论揭示了道德的真正基础不在于外部的社会需要或总体目标，而内在于每个人的天性之中；一个世纪以来，人们已经习惯于把道德的基础归之于外在社会需要（比如社会秩序和集体安宁之类），是一种典型的环境决定论，也正是孟子所反对的“以其外之也”、“行仁义”（非“由仁义行”）。孟子的高明之处在于从人性自身需要的角度来理解道德的基础。

（2）性善论主张人性的尊严和价值是比其他一切外在的社会需要或总体目标重要得多的东西，因为只有每一个人的人性都得到充分尊重和实现，才谈得上理想社会。这不仅是一切现代人本主义/人道主义的基础，也是支持了现代社会的最高价值之一，即以人为目标而不是手段（康德名言）。

（3）性善论包含一种全新的政治理论（王道），即统治者只需引导人民自觉追求自身天性/人性的完满实现即可天下太平，而丝毫不必害怕人民为非作歹。因为只要人民知道如何实现自身的天性/人性，自然就不会为非作歹。因此我们不必担心人们会不背叛，会不服从。这是一个革命性的结论，是刺向一切不尊重人性尊严的专制统治的一把匕首，这也是孟子性善论比荀子性恶论在历史上更受青睐的原因所在。

（4）性善论对于我们正确认识道德教育方式和人类社会的构成法则有巨大的启发。即道德教育和社会管理主要应着眼于引导人们走向人性的自我健全，而不是引导人们听话、服从或为整体利益献身。也即是说，性善论自然主张道德教育甚至一切教育都要立足于人性的自我挖掘。这样自然会反对一切形式的教条说教了。

# 日課：清道咸時期程朱理學的修養工夫

台湾铭传大学 田富美

## 一、前言

博究清代儒學思想，乾嘉學術往往是論者的關注所在，至於作為宋學主脈的程朱理學，受到的關注相對減少，即使多數學者認為此時程朱理學已僵化為官方統治思想而失去生命力，如章太炎（1844－1919）曾論清代理學是“竭而無餘華”[①]；錢穆（1895－1900）則言“清代理學既無主峯可指，如明儒之有姚江；亦無大脈絡大條理可尋，如誦如之有程朱與朱陸”，[②] 二位先生從學術思想的原創性與新穎性為考察視角，焦點集中於促成此一典範創新的精英學者身上，並按此對各種思想文獻進行取捨或剪裁，用以建構學術發展的詮釋方式。然而，這並不意味著清代的程朱理學發展沒有獨到之處。事實上，清代尊崇程朱的學者在面對各學派的挑戰、外在環境的衝擊下，試圖在肆應各時期的議題上，對程朱理學的內涵做出了相當的調整，甚至轉化；在晚清時期復興的程朱理學，[③] 亦應視為這種調整和轉化的一環，且理學在清代始終存在著影

① 章太炎：〈清儒〉，《訄書重訂本》，收入《訄書 初刻本 重訂本》，北京：生活·讀書·新知三聯書店，1998年，頁158。

② 錢穆：〈清儒學案序目·例言〉，收於氏著：《中國學術思想史論叢（八）》，臺北：臺灣商務印書館，2000年，頁484。

③ 本論題所言之“理學”，係指程朱理學而言，並不包括陸王心學；至於文後所言“宋學”，則是乾嘉漢學家作為與漢學相對應的宋學而言。學者認為，清代理學先後出現過兩次發展的興盛時期，一次是在康熙朝的振興，另一次是在晚清咸、同時期的振興。請參史革新：〈理學與晚清社會〉，收入氏著：《清代以來的學術與思想論集》（北京：社會科學文獻出版社，2011年），頁117－128；張永儁：〈清代朱子學的歷史處境及其發展〉，《哲學與文化》第28卷第7期（2001年7月），頁606－628。案：必須進一步說明的是，晚清所謂的理學復興，應是相較於清中葉之理學與晚清時期的漢學而論的。至於清代理學的分期，可參見龔書鐸主編：《清代理學史·緒論》（廣州：廣東教育出版社，2007年），上册，頁1－29。另有史革新將晚清理學分成嘉道、咸同、光宣三期，是以，本論題所言的晚清，即指清道光年至宣統時期。參見史革新：《晚清理學研究》（臺北：文津出版社，1994年），頁5－45。

響力，[①] 直至晚期仍持續發揮一定的社會教化作用，同時更是近代經世思想的淵源。[②]此外，何佑森先生分析近世朱子學，曾指出朱子學術在時代鉅變中所扮演的功能：

朱子學博大精深，前後經歷了四個世紀，每當時代動亂，思想的發展有了偏差，惟一能補偏救弊的，則只有朱子一脈相傳的儒學。[③]

透過理學汲取匡時濟世、個人修養的思想資源，成為後世儒者用以作為因應政治社會等情勢的方式之一，尤其近世儒者關注人倫日用，總聯繫著朱子持守誦習的思想範疇。道咸時期宦遊於精師的理學家們所興起的“日課”活動，即是鮮明的代表。

所謂“日課”，是一種自律的讀書方式，即每日訂定閱讀分量，限期計功，以求日有所得；並時時自我省察，以收及時踐履之效。這種“日課”的讀書方式，雖可溯源於《論語》“日知其所亡，月無忘其所能”[④] 之精神，然大量出現於儒者進德修業工夫的論述中，則是在程朱理學盛行之際。[⑤]

朱子所提揭“理一分殊”的架構中，典籍是反映先聖先賢言行在世界的展開與實踐，代表著各種具體、獨立的分殊之理（所謂“物物一太極”），治學者應透過平實的格究工夫以窮得各個分殊之理，才能豁然貫通的達到“眾物之表裏精粗無不到，吾心

---

① 如梁啟超（1873－1929）《清代學術概論》即述及程朱之學在清代受抨擊與因襲的情形，《中國近三百年學術史》中則專立一章〈程朱學派及其依附者〉；錢穆著《中國近三百年學術史》首章更明言清代學術乃淵源於宋學，且“漢學諸家之高下淺深，亦往往視其所得於宋學之高下淺深以為判”；陸寶千《清代思想史》中則有〈康熙時代之朱學〉、〈晚清理學〉二章闡述程朱之學在清代的發展，足見程朱理學在清代仍具有一定的影響力而不應被忽視。參見梁啟超：《清代學術概論》（臺北：臺灣商務印書館，1993 年），頁 6－8、《中國近三百年學術史》（北京：東方出版社，1996 年），頁 119－129；錢穆：《中國近三百年學術史》（臺北：臺灣商務印書館，1995 年二版），上册，頁 1；陸寶千：《清代思想史》（臺北：廣文書局，2006 年三版），頁 119－162：323－438。

② 清政府以理學為官方學術，士大夫藉理學晉階，民間則以理學為道德法則、文化宗仰。參見張昭軍：〈程朱理學與晚清社會〉，《雲南大學學報（社會科學版）》第 10 卷第 5 期（2011 年 5 月），頁 16－26；〈聖賢學問與世俗教化—晚清時期程朱理學與綱常名教關係辨析〉，《孔子研究》2008 年第 4 期，頁 82－94。此外，黃克武藉由《切問齋文鈔》之分析指出，過去學者解釋近代經世思想興起原因時多強調清今文經學復興的重要性，但事實上，清代理學內部演變的經世精神或許更具關鍵地位。參見氏著：〈理學與經世—清初“切問齋文鈔”學術立場之分析〉，《中央研究院近代史研究所集刊》第 16 期，頁 37－65。另可參李細珠：〈試論嘉道以來經世思潮勃興的傳統思想資源〉，《廣東社會科學》2005 年第 3 期，頁 110－117。

③ 何佑森：〈朱子學與近世思想〉，收於氏著：《儒學與思想—何佑森先生學術論文集》，臺北：臺大出版中心，2009 年，上册，頁 126。

④ 朱熹：《論語集注》，《四書章句集注》，北京：中華書局，2003 年，卷 10，〈子張第十九〉，頁 189。

⑤ 有關宋代儒者日課之序述，請參韓立平：〈日課：宋代流行的讀書法〉，《博覽群書》2012 年第 12 期，頁 86－89。

之全體大用無不明",[①] 即"理一"(所謂"統體一太極")的境界;其中,由於分殊之理遍及一切事物,勢必要經過長期積累的過程,方能透顯至理,故而即有學者以朱子臨終之言"積累日久,心與理一"為朱子一生堅持的信念,稱朱子解經方式為"積累之經學"。[②] 這種"積累"的概念,透過"日課"的工夫具體呈現,在朱子論述讀書方法時,便一再出現:

讀書不可不先立程限。政如農功,如農之有畔。為學亦然,今之始學者不知此理,初時甚鋭,漸漸懶去,終至都不理會了。此只是當初不立程限之故。

學者當以聖賢之言反求諸身,一一體察。須是曉然無疑,積日既久,當自有見。

先看《語》、《孟》、《中庸》,更看一經,却看史,方易看。先讀《史記》,《史記》與《左傳》相包;次看《左傳》,次看《通鑑》,有餘力則看全史。[③]

上述與"日課"相關的內容,說明了朱子不僅重視"日課"在學習上的成效,同時亦規範了研讀典籍的先後次序,並要求讀書所得必須反求諸己的體證。此一讀書方法對後世產生了深遠的影響:元代程端禮(1271－1345)便以朱子讀書法為基礎撰寫《程氏家塾讀書分年日程》,在當時成為官方頒布詔示天下學子的讀書準繩;[④] 至清代,該書被納入書院章程,大量刊刻頒行,或以此為準則進行增删,提供學子自我評判的標準,[⑤] 這都是朱子讀書法的延續,透過各種書院學規的制定,自有一明確的軌跡可循。除此一讀書法的規範傳承之外,考察"日課"工夫對於程朱理學的傳衍情形,以及當時理學家藉由會課活動所建構的群體關係,應有更為明確的釐析。本文即以道咸時期唐鑑(1778－1861)、吳廷棟(1793－1873)、倭仁(1804－1871)、曾國藩(1811－1872)等人為中心的京師理學群體為考察對象,梳理他們在"日課"工夫的徹底發揚情形,探求其對於此一時期理學復興的影響,以及對程朱理學的承繼與轉化。

---

① 朱熹:《大學章句》,《四書章句集注》,頁7。

② 楊儒賓:〈"積累"與"當下"—時間隱喻下的經典詮釋〉,收於氏著:《從〈五經〉到〈新五經〉》,臺北:臺大出版中心,2013年,頁59－97。案:朱熹之言,見蔡沈:〈夢奠記〉,《蔡氏九儒書》,收於《四庫全書存目叢書》(臺南:莊嚴文化事業公司,1997年),集部46,總集類存目三,頁793。

③ 黎靖德編,王星賢點校:《朱子語類》,北京:中華書局,2004年,卷10,〈讀書法上〉,頁174;卷11,〈讀書法下〉,頁181、195。

④ 參見宋濂等撰:《新校本元史并附編二種》(臺北:鼎文書局,1977年),卷190,列傳第七十七,頁4343;黃宗羲撰,全祖望補訂,王梓材增補:《增補宋元學案》(臺北:臺灣中華書局,1965年重印),卷87,〈靜清學案〉,頁3左－17右;張偉、刑書緒:〈程端禮及其《讀書分年日程》〉,《寧波大學學報(教育科學版)》第26卷第6期(2004年12月),頁39－43。

⑤ 徐雁平:〈《讀書分年日程》與清代的書院〉,《南京曉庄學院學報》2006年第3期,頁113－119。

## 二、道咸時期理學的復興及其思想特徵

道咸年間，接踵而至的西方軍事入侵與太平天國禍事使得清廷內外混亂之勢更甚於前，以唐鑑、吳廷棟、倭仁、曾國藩為首的理學士人受到朝廷拔擢，促使講求程朱理學的風氣藉由政治權力而受強化與推動；[①] 加上師友弟子如方宗誠（1818－1888）、方潛（1809－1868）、何桂珍（1817－1855）等人推波助瀾，於是受乾嘉漢學壓抑的宋學重新活躍起來，其中影響最鉅者，首推道光20年（1840）“學宗朱子”[②] 的唐鑑自金陵至北京任太常寺卿期間講學所攏聚的京城士子，方宗誠載言：

> 嘉道間，海內重熙累洽，文教昌明，而闇然為己之學，兢兢焉謹守程朱之正軌，體之於心，修之於身，用則著之為事功，變則見之於節義，窮則發之於著述，踐之於內行，純一不雜，有守先待後之功者，聞見所及約有數人：長白倭文端公、霍山吳竹如先生，官京師時與宗師何文貞公、湘鄉曾文正公、羅平竇蘭泉侍卿，日從善化唐恪慎公講道問業，不逐時趨；其時在下位者，則有湘鄉羅羅山先生，桐城方植之先生、永城劉虞卿先生，俱無所師承，而砥節礪行，為窮理精義之學。[③]

上述記載蒙受唐鑑“講道問業”者，包括誨誡京師名臣倭仁“學以居敬窮理為宗，此外皆邪徑也”[④]；提揭“懲忿窒慾，遷善改過”以臻“不遷怒、不貳過”予吳廷棟效法；[⑤] 囑何桂珍編修《續理學正宗》；勸勉曾國藩應以《朱子全集》為檢身之要、讀書之法，並言“經濟之學，即在義理之內”[⑥]；以及士子羅澤南（1807－1856）、方東樹

---

① 有關晚清咸、同年間程朱理學復興與政治的關係，請參史革新：〈程朱理學與晚清“同治中興”〉，收入氏著《晚清學術文化新論》（北京：北京師範大學出版社，2010年），頁1－30；車冬梅：《晚清理學學術研究》（西安：西北大學中國思想文化研究所博士論文，2005年），頁17－25。

② 不著編纂，王鍾翰點校：《清史列傳·儒林傳》，北京：中華書局，1987年，卷67，頁5400。

③ 方宗誠：〈校勘何文貞公遺言書敘〉，《柏堂集·餘編》，收入《清代詩文集彙編》，上海：上海古籍出版社，2010年，清光緒六年至十二年刻本，卷3，頁582。案：有關追隨唐鑑問學的相關記載，亦可參曾國藩：〈皇清誥授通奉大夫二品銜太常寺卿謚確慎唐公墓誌銘〉，收於唐鑑：《唐確慎公集》，收入《清代詩文集彙編》（上海：上海古籍出版社，2010年，清光緒元年刻本），頁475；徐世昌等編纂，沈芝盈、梁運華點校：《清儒學案·鏡海學案》（北京：中華書局，2008年），卷140，頁5512。

④ 倭仁：《倭文端公遺書·日記》，臺北：華文書局，1968年，清光緒元年求我齋刊本，卷4，頁215；亦見於《清史列傳·儒林傳》，卷67，頁5400－5401。

⑤ 吳廷棟〈劄記〉，《拙修集》，收於《清代詩文集彙編》上海：上海古籍出版社，2010年，清同治十六年六安求我齋刻本，卷2，頁329。

⑥ 曾國藩：《曾國藩全集·日記》（臺北：漢苑出版社，1976年），〈問學〉，辛丑7月，頁353。案文中言：“又至唐鏡海先生處，問檢身之要，讀書之法。先生言當以《朱子全集》為宗。時余新買此書，問及，因道此書最易熟讀，即以為課程，身體力行，不宜視為瀏覽之書。”

(1772－1851)、撰寫《理學宗傳辯正》的劉廷詔等人，均成為日後道咸時期理學復興的重要代表人物。

此時理學家致力於將程朱理學與躬行實踐、現實致用的工夫結合起來，[①] 成為經世濟民的致用之學，尤其強調體用兼備的觀點，如賀熙齡（1788－1846）曾載唐鑑為學：

奉程朱為的：主敬以立其體，忠恕以致其用，非有裨於身心意知之理者，不以關其慮也；非有關於天下國家之故者，不以用其功也。[②]

再如吳廷棟回應咸豐（1851－1861）質疑“學程朱者多迂拘不通”時，言：

> 此正不善學程朱之故。程朱以明德為體，新民為用，乃由體達用之學；天下斷無有體而無用者，其用不足，必其體尚多缺陷，凡臨事迂拘不通，正由平日不能如程朱之格物窮理，而徒資記誦，非學程朱之過也。[③]

方宗誠亦言：

> 夫道之大原出於天，聖人之書無非明天理也；而人之所以希天之功，則全在乎即人事以窮其天理之當然，即天理以見諸人事之實際，所謂精義入神以致用也，利用安身以崇德也。若不能致用崇德，雖使精義入神，見於文字之閒者，可以取名於後世，而究無當於身心國家之實用。[④]

上述諸說論者皆強調“致用”、“致其用”才是窮究經典、程朱之學的極致目的，一切以契合“天下國家之故”、“身心國家之實用”為學術價值的標準；是故，唐鑑以主敬、忠恕為程朱之學的體用關係，吳廷棟言“由體達用”之學，方宗誠亦屢言：“明體達用，非研窮宋儒之書，其道末由。”又言：“學者窮經，所以明體達用也。”“窮理者當由本及末，由麤入精，然後可以明體達用。”[⑤] 均以體、用關係來論述理學內涵，且緊扣著現實致用。基本上，宋明理學家常以“體”、“用”的概念來闡發對外王的關懷，他們所謂的“明體達用”之論亦可屢見於各理學家的論述中。但宋明儒者是以“體”、“用”來說明性命之學與其他學問的關係：性命之學是“體”，其他學問是“用”，體用不可分，因此，一切學問原則上都是體之展現，換言之，程朱的體用論是

① 王汎森：《中國近代思想與學術的系譜》，臺北：聯經出版公司，2003年，頁23－38；車冬梅：〈析晚清理學學術特徵〉，《西北大學學報（哲學社會科學版）》第39卷第4期（2009年7月），頁48－51；朱淑君：〈系譜重建與經世復歸：咸同時代理學復興的學術特徵考察〉，《文藝評論》，2011年第2期，頁158－161。

② 賀熙齡：〈唐確慎公集序〉，收於《唐確慎公集》，頁473。

③ 吳廷棟：〈召見恭紀〉，《拙修集》，卷1，頁322。

④ 方宗誠：〈答莊中白書〉，《柏堂集・續編》，卷7，頁277。

⑤ 方宗誠：〈上吳竹如先生〉，《柏堂集・外編》，卷2，頁679；〈春秋傳正誼敘〉、〈與汪仲伊書〉，《柏堂集・續編》，卷2，頁211；卷7，頁277。

一種“超越性本體及其展現”意義的學問。[①] 至於晚清儒者所論析體用之意涵，吳廷棟言：

幼讀程朱之書，知君臣、朋友之倫皆關吾性分，故不敢寄情物外，且深知性分至實，故信性之為體，不容參以虛無，而辨之極嚴；亦深知體立而後用行，故於日用酬應之際，凡稍涉干求、稍近名利，不敢開枉尺直尋之漸……。蓋欲以明德為體，而不矜語靈明；以新民為用，而不馳騖管商。[②]

方宗誠言：

夫學問之道非炫多鬬靡之謂也，所以求明體達用而已。體者何？吾心仁、義、禮、智之性是也；用者何？即吾心仁義禮智之性發而為惻隱、羞惡、辭讓、是非之情，見之於父子、君臣、夫婦、昆弟、朋友之倫與夫日用事物之微而已，非有他也，是其體也、用也，人心之所同然也。[③]

方宗誠在此論惻隱、羞惡、辭讓、是非之情為仁、義、禮、智之性所發的觀點，實是依朱子之詮釋。[④] 然而，無論是吳廷棟言明德為體、新民為用；或方宗誠所論仁、義、禮、智為“體”，視惻隱、羞惡、辭讓、是非之情體現於人倫事物為“用”，進而形構出一體用關係的詮解，都是晚清儒者在當時社會講求致用思潮下對程朱理學的新觀點。同時，並依此體用架構貫徹於理學的內涵，且突出躬行踐履的重要性，如曾國藩曾勸勉士子於義理、考據、辭章、經濟似刻中以義理為先，然必須體現於現世生活之中：

凡人身所自具者，有耳目口體心思。日接於吾前者，有父子兄弟夫婦；稍遠者有君臣，有朋友。為義理之學者，蓋將使耳目口體心思，各敬其職，而吾倫各敬其分，又將推以及物，使凡民皆有以善其身，而無憾於倫紀。[⑤]

足見，曾國藩所論的義理之學，實已涵括了踐履，在他看來，唯有致用才能呈現其價值。晚清諸理學家透過體用關係的闡述，強化了理學中致用的傾向；在重視踐履的前提下，除了希冀能以理學匡救當時衰敗的政治社會情勢外，另一方面對於切身的修養工夫，則是闡揚理學循序漸進、恆心持守的日課方式為最大特色。

---

① 參見楊儒賓：〈作為性命之學的經學—理學的經典詮釋〉，《長庚人文社會學報》第 2 卷第 2 期（2009 年），頁 201－245；尤其 214－218。

② 吳廷棟：〈與方存之學博書（辛酉）〉，《拙修集》，卷 9，頁 466－467。

③ 方宗誠：〈讀書說〉，《柏堂集・次編》，卷 4，頁 153－154。

④ 朱子：“惻隱、羞惡、辭讓、是非，情也；仁、義、禮、智，性也。心統性情者也。端，緒也。因其情之發，而性之本然可得而見，猶有物在中而緒見於外也。”《孟子集注》，《四書章句集注》，卷 3，〈公孫丑章句上〉，頁 238。

⑤ 曾國藩：〈勸學篇示直隸士子〉，《曾國藩全集・雜著》，頁 348－349。

## 三、日課的內容及意義

以載錄每日讀書所得、省察言行等一切修悟之事作為切身進德修業的工夫，是晚清理學家修養工夫的特色。方宗誠曾將自身問學、存養日記編錄成《志學錄》一書，於序文中說明受其師許鼎（1782－1842）囑咐："先生命每日讀書、應事、窮理、省身，有疑悟即隨筆以記，因為《志學錄》數卷就正先生，先生時為剖其是非，辨其疑似。"① 唐鑑立書院學規中有"勸學"條，要求學子"每日溫經幾卷，讀史幾卷，於所讀書得新知幾處、於所不知者從先生問得幾條，自立課程登記。②"可見，撰寫日課不僅需持續不斷，同時也交由師長剖辨得失，以收窮理、克治之效，這是屬於基本的模式；另外，亦有同儕士人定期會聚，相互批閱日課、談論所學，進一步砥礪勸勉的會課活動，如倭仁在師從唐鑑之前，便與河南同鄉李棠階（1798－1865）、王鈐（1801－1841）、高欽中（1815－1869）等人以陽明心學為主軸"立社為課，互相勉勵"③；後問學於唐鑑，轉向崇奉程朱理學，在當時攏聚的大臣士子中，結識吳廷棟、曾國藩等人，並持續會課活動。吳廷棟致弟家書中載言：

> 兄幸近日得三四朋友，皆好學深思，知恥立品者，大得其益，始信朋友列於五倫，為人生不可缺者，誠足樂也。其中尤足畏敬者二人：一為河南駐防蒙古人名倭仁，號艮峯，己丑科翰林，現任翰林侍讀學士，其人篤實力行，專以慎獨為工夫，有日記，一念之發必時檢點，是私則克去，是善則擴充；有過則內自訟而必改，一念不整肅則以為放心；自朝至暮，內而念慮，外而言動，及應事接物，並夜而考之，夢寐皆不放過，而一一記出以自責，其嚴密如此。一為雲南人竇垿，號蘭泉……。兄幸得事賢友仁之益，故益不敢自棄，日於身心下工夫，痛自洗剔，竊願以朱子為法，而一息尚存，此志不容稍懈。④

吳廷棟推崇倭仁克治自省自訟之功，"敬畏"倭仁撰日課的修養之道，促使自身倍加致力於理學心性涵養工夫。事實上，吳廷棟"生平篤信朱子"，⑤ 曾於咸豐 7 年

① 方宗誠：〈治學錄敘〉，收入《柏堂遺書・志學錄》，《原刻影印叢書集成三編》，臺北：藝文印書館，1971 年景印光緒中桐城方氏志學堂刊本，頁 1 左。

② 唐鑑：〈道鄉書院學規四則〉，《唐確慎公集》，卷 5，頁 578。

③ 李時燦：《中州先哲傳》，收入《清代地方人物傳記叢刊》（臺北：廣陵書社，2007 年），卷 7，〈李棠階〉，頁 534。案：有關倭仁學術思想演變及交游事跡，請參李細珠：〈倭仁交游述略〉，《近代中國》1999 年，頁 96－116；〈倭仁與吳廷棟交誼略論〉，《安徽史學》1999 年第 2 期，頁 42－47；〈晚清頑固派的典型—大學士倭仁〉，《百年潮》2000 年第 1 期，頁 67－71，75。

④ 吳廷棟：〈庚子都中與執夫子垣兩弟書〉，《拙修集》，卷 10，頁 480－481。

⑤ 吳廷棟：〈與方存之學博書（辛酉）〉，《拙修集》，卷 9，頁 463。

(1857)至咸豐9年(1859)多次與原本學主陸王心學的方潛會見、書信往返論學，促使方潛轉宗程朱之學，[①] 展現吳廷棟維護程朱理學之志；因此，便不難理解吳氏〈書倭艮峯先生日記後〉批閱倭仁日課大量評述之言，以及針對倭仁思想的糾舉，這種亦師亦友的切磋，對於倭仁思想的轉向產生了一定的影響。如對倭仁日記中載“看未發氣象，姚江有一段說得緊切。云此時教人用戒謹恐懼工夫，正目而視惟此，傾耳而聽惟此，洞洞屬屬不知其他，即程子敬而無失，即所以中之意。[②]”吳廷棟言：

> 取其語以證敬而無失則可，謂即程子敬而無失即所以中之意則未可。昔朱子初有取於延平體驗未發氣象，而終謂有偏者，誠慮人於此誤認氣為理耳，其防弊之意深矣。蓋理無形，而氣有迹，未發時氣未用事，初無端緒可尋。……姚江之誤實在於此，故其言則是，而其旨則非，要亦戒懼其所戒懼，而認心為性而已。[③]

由於倭仁學術“始由王學入手”，[④] 故不免以王學比附程朱理學，或有意綰合二者差異，此種相似的詮解方式，在晚清儒者的論述中頗多；然在嚴判程朱、陸王之別[⑤]的吳廷棟看來，則是必須詳加釐清，維護程朱道統地位的重要工作。當然，吳氏的本意不在理氣心性諸說上另創新說，故而此類批駁王學的相關論述，對於程朱理學系統的拓深或開新並無太大裨益，其意義乃在於透過此類會課活動，逐步建立一程朱理學群體的過程。倭仁日記中載錄吳廷棟“來極論致知為急，存心不致知，恐所存之心只是箇儱侗底影子，遇事依舊差錯。又言陸王之弊，謹守者含胡摸稜，高明者猖狂縱恣，所造愈深，受害愈甚，可謂深切之言”。[⑥] 恰恰說明了吳廷棟衛道的積極態度，以及對倭仁產生的影響；當倭仁確立尊朱黜王的學派立場後，吳氏表示：“倭艮峯先生之學亦從王學入手，惟致功於朱子格物之訓，故久而悟其非。……誠豪傑之士也。”“其能洗淨王學，一歸程朱，可謂大勇矣”。[⑦] 能夠服膺程朱理學，即是“豪傑之士”、“大勇”，顯然對於參與會課活動成就的高度肯定，同時，亦可看出此一學術群體在晚清程朱理學復興過程中的推動力。

---

① 相關記載，請參方宗誠：《吳竹如先生年譜》，收入《柏堂遺書》，頁39—42；方婉麗：〈晚清吳廷棟與方潛之辨學〉，《安慶師範學院學報(社會科學版)》第29卷第8期(2010年8月)，頁61—65。

② 吳廷棟：〈書倭艮峯先生日記後〉，《拙修集》，卷6，頁402。

③ 吳廷棟：〈書倭艮峯先生日記後〉，《拙修集》，卷6，頁403。

④ 方宗誠：《吳竹如先生年譜》，收入《柏堂遺書》，頁54右。

⑤ 吳廷棟〈與蘇菊邨學博書(辛酉)〉：“鄙見以為良知之精蘊實禪宗也，以視程朱，即鄭之亂雅，紫之奪朱之類，必闢之而後宗旨可以歸一。”《拙修集》，卷9，頁464。

⑥ 倭仁：《倭文端公遺書·日記》，卷5，頁341。

⑦ 吳廷棟：〈與蘇菊邨學博書(辛酉)〉、〈與方存之學博書(辛酉)〉，《拙修集》，卷9，頁464、頁466。

晚清理學家的會課活動，對於曾國藩的影響亦十分深遠。曾國藩在道光20年(1840)入京後，曾受邵懿辰(1810—1861)引領研治理學；[①] 至道光21年(1841)問學於唐鑑，結識倭仁，於日記中載倭仁日課情形："每日自朝至寢，一言一動作、飯食皆有劄記，或心有私欲不克，外有不及檢，皆記出"，且對於倭仁教戒"閑邪存誠"、"整齊嚴肅"、"主一無適"等言，曾氏"聽之昭然若發矇也"，至此，"遂以朱子之書為日課"[②]、以宋學為宗。後吳廷棟更建議曾國藩牽居至城內，以求會課方便，曾國藩於家書中言：

> 竹如必要予搬進城住，蓋城內鏡海先生可以師事，倭艮峯先生、竇蘭泉可以友事，師友夾持，雖懦夫亦有立志。予思朱子言："為學譬如熬肉，先須猛火煮，然後用漫火溫"，予生平工夫全未用猛火煮過，雖略有見識，乃是從悟境得來，偶用功，亦不過優游玩索已耳，如未沸之湯，遽用漫火溫之，將愈煮愈不熟矣。以是急思搬進城內，屏除一切，從事於克己之學。[③]

曾氏這段自述可看出進入以唐鑑為中心的理學群體，得以與倭仁、竇垿等人"師友夾持"，對於曾氏個人進德修業層次的拓深發揮了極大的作用，即如余英時以宗教經驗為喻，是"由苦修到皈依的過程"。[④] 透過這個理學群體的會課活動，正如其自言的"猛火煮"，自此有了另一番新氣象。距上封家書一個多月後，曾氏致書予兄弟言：

> 吾友竹如，格物工夫頗深，一事一物皆求其理；倭艮峯先生則誠意工夫極嚴，每日有日課冊，一日之中，一念之差、一事之失、一言一默，皆筆之於書，書皆楷字，三月則訂一本。自己未年起，今三十本矣。蓋其慎獨之嚴，雖妄念偶動，必及時克治，而著之於書，故所讀之書，句句皆切身之要藥，茲將艮峯先生日課鈔三頁付歸予諸弟看。余自十月初一日起，亦照艮峯樣，每日一念一事，皆寫之於冊，以便觸目克治，亦寫楷書。……余向來有無恆之弊，自此次寫日課本子起，可保終身有恆矣。[⑤]

曾國藩盛讚倭仁日課工夫，並仿傚此一錘煉方式著手撰寫日課，督責自身培養"終身有恆"的態度，明確地遵從理學循序漸進的修養之途。此後在曾國藩日記中，便

---

① 參見余英時：〈曾國藩與"士大夫之學"〉，《故宮學術季刊》第11卷2期(1993年冬季號)，頁79—95。

② 曾國藩：《曾國藩全集·日記》，〈問學〉，辛丑7月，頁353；黎庶昌：《曾國藩年譜》，道光21年條，長沙：岳麓書社，1986年，頁7。

③ 曾國藩著，李翰章編撰，李鴻章校刊：《曾文正公家書：附家訓》，卷1，道光22年9月18日致兄弟，北京：中國書店，2011年，頁22—23。

④ 余英時：〈曾國藩與"士大夫之學"〉，《故宮學術季刊》第11卷2期，頁85。

⑤ 曾國藩著，李翰章編撰，李鴻章校刊：《曾文正公家書：附家訓》，卷1，道光22年10月26日致兄弟，頁26。

不時可見其自勉“日日向上”、“日新又新”；自省言“日來自治愈疏矣，絕無瑟僩之意，何貴有此日課之冊？看來只是好名、好作詩、名心也；寫此冊而不日日改過，則此冊真盜名之具也。”“所以須日課冊者，以時時省過，立即克去耳。今五日一記，則所謂省察者安在？所為自新者安在？”① 透露撰寫日課務求省察自勵的期許。此外，又在家書中記載了自訂的日課內容：“每日楷書寫日記，每日讀史十頁，每日記‘茶餘偶談’一則”、“每日臨帖百字，鈔書百字，看書少亦須滿二十頁”；同時也勸勉兄弟：“雖極忙，亦須了本日功課，不以昨日耽擱而今日補做，不以明日有是而今日預做。”② 充分展現出日課的恆定與堅守特色。

## 四、結語

基本上，程朱理學所建構的體系中，透過“格物”工夫以窮盡事理，加上“主敬”工夫後方能透顯至理，學者對於相關過程已有豐碩的討論，自不待言。值得觀察的是，此一思想體系在傳衍過程中，由於時、空變化等因素而難以避免出現斷裂，故而有不同的擇取，於是呈顯出獨具該時代特質的理學圖象。嘉道時期，反乾嘉漢學大將方東樹再三強調格物致知以窮理在尋求孔門聖道中的重要性，同時展現自身在訓詁文字、考據典籍的工夫，對清考據學家的詰難發揮了一定的抗衡力量。③ 時至道咸，唐鑑、吳廷棟、倭仁、曾國藩等人面對時勢鉅變，一方面企圖由傳統理學中尋繹經世致用的論據；另一方面在自身修養的層面上，突顯日積月累，時時自我批判、自省的工夫，並透過會課活動，藉由學術交游而擴大理學影響範圍，以收“人心之興起，而天心之來復”的“世運轉移”④ 之功。這樣的日課特色，在晚清理學短暫興起之際，既有承繼的一面，亦含括了轉化的一面。

在承繼方面，道咸時期的理學家延續了朱子“積累日久，心與理一”的修養工夫，在晚清理學家文獻中屢屢出現相近詞語，如倭仁言：“積習既久，則恍然自有該貫

---

① 曾國藩：《曾國藩全集·日記》，〈問學〉，辛亥 8 月，頁 360、辛酉 12 月，頁 370；〈省克〉，壬寅，頁 378、癸卯正月，頁 381。

② 曾國藩著，李翰章編撰，李鴻章校刊：《曾文正公家書：附家訓》，卷 1，道光 22 年 12 月 20 日致兄弟，頁 30；道光 24 年 11 月 21 日致兄弟，頁 63。

③ 請參拙著：〈乾嘉學風下的尊朱視域—方東樹儒學思想研究〉，《彰師大國文學誌》，第 25 期（2012 年 12 月），頁 205－235。

④ 吳廷棟〈復洪琴西孝廉書（壬戌）〉：“竊謂世運之轉移在人材，而人材之奮興關乎風俗，風俗之盛衰係乎人心，人心之邪正由於學術，此學不明固無望人心之興起，而天心之來復也。”《拙修集》，卷 9，頁 473。

處”[①]；吳廷棟“惟窮理克己，銖積累寸以終吾身而已”[②]；曾國藩言：“吾人只有進德、修業兩事靠得住。進德，則孝弟仁義是也；修業，則詩文作字是也。此二者由我做主，得尺則我之尺也，得寸則我之寸也。今日進一分德，便算積了一升穀；明日修一分業，又算餘了一文錢。”[③] 這些強調循序漸進的積累工夫，輔以晚清講求躬行踐履的觀點，於是便轉化為強調日用之間進德之效的呈顯，載錄於日課之中，吳廷棟言：

凡日用間，聞一言之是非，見一事之得失，遇一人之賢否，皆一一反己內勘，而自責自修，必毋使一念放過，推之讀書尚論之際莫不然。[④]

倭仁言：

一日十二時中，密密推勘：思慮無邪否？言行無差忒否？有則改之，無則加勉，方不負此一日。

忠信所以進德。一日之中，自早至晚；一事之中，自始至終，一皆實心貫注，私偽不存，此進德實地工夫，勉之勿懈。

仁，人心也，不仁便非人，須體認仁是如何，一日中離者幾時，合者幾時，虛心靜慮，自證自考，庶有日新之機。[⑤]

這種將讀書窮理落實於生活體驗之中，並輔以時時刻刻的省察，無疑是朱學格物說的具體踐履及深化的表現。但從另一個角度來說，朱子論格物窮理的最終目標在於“豁然貫通”的境界，在道咸時期的理學家討論中則是相對缺乏的。換言之，自清代嘉道以來的理學家對程朱學術的傳繼上，乃在於格物窮理的修身工夫，並由此延伸到日用生活的實踐中，實頗具時代意義；同時，定期聚會論學、相互監督勸勉，都仍是值得現代學子借鑑的。

---

① 倭仁：《倭文端公遺書·日記》，卷 4，頁 300。

② 吳廷棟：〈與方存之茂才書〉，《拙修集》，卷 9，頁 463。

③ 曾國藩著，李翰章編撰，李鴻章校刊：《曾文正公家書：附家訓》，卷 2，道光 24 年 8 月 29 日致兄弟，頁 59。

④ 吳廷棟：〈劄記〉，《拙修集》，卷 2，頁 329。

⑤ 倭仁：《倭文端公遺書·日記》，卷 4，頁 240、253。

# 黎貴惇對宋朝朱熹論《書經》思想的評價

## ——通過研究《書經衍義》分析

越南河内国家大学 阮金山

## 一、作家、作品和《書經衍義》簡介

《書經衍義》作者黎貴惇(1726—1784),又名黎名方,字允厚,號桂堂。沿河縣沿河社(今太平省興河縣獨立社)人,乃黎朝進士黎富恕(後改名黎仲恕)之子。

黎顯宗景興十三年,黎貴惇時年 27 歲,進士及第第二名(榜眼)。黎貴惇歷任:翰林院承旨、秘書閣學士等職,爵穎成伯。為官不久,便辭官回鄉(1764),專於著書考辯。景興二十八年(1767),再度出仕,曆升入侍陪訟、戶部左侍郎,爵穎成候。黎景興三十一年(1770),左除侍副都禦史,後升工部右侍郎。1773 年,授任陪訟。1773 年至 1775 年,黎貴惇受命至山南地區進行查簿和測量、統計土地工作。1775 年,升吏部左侍郎兼國史館總裁,又於是年底被降職為禮部侍郎。1776 年,被派往順化任協鎮參贊軍機。次年,又被召回京授為戶部左侍郎、行都禦史。戊戌年(1778)轉任武職,授左校點、權撫事,爵義派候。1783 年,改任義安協鎮,不久又被召回京任都禦史,卒於 1784 年。

在十八世紀越南的儒學家當中,黎貴惇著述種類甚多,內容涉及經學、史學、文學、地理、考證學等諸多領域,越南人稱之為博學家。①

黎貴惇於 1772 年完成《書經衍義》及序,是在《尚書》58 篇正文的基礎上進行論經。他沒有過多注意文字問題、今文或古文問題,而是側重印證經書義理,尤其是各種政治思想。這是一本記錄黎貴惇解讀《尚書》的個人心得體會和獨特見解之書,還可視此書為黎貴惇撰寫的一本適用於對儒家經典以及《書經》瞭解到高層次的知識階

---

① 黎貴惇著作有:《桂堂詩集》、《桂堂文集》、《全越詩錄》、《皇越文海》、《撫邊雜錄》、《大越通史》、《見聞小錄》、《書經衍義》、《芸台類語》、《群書考辯》、《聖謨賢範錄》、《北使通錄》等。另外還有一些作品目前仍無法確定是否為黎貴惇所著作的。

層的講義，以此深入瞭解該領域，或應用於實際生活和發揚其思想。在書序中，作者希望本書對當時的君王亦有用，用它來學習和實現統治："亦可備人君經幄之覧，為迪德施治之一助"。向帝王進獻書的意圖體現在每卷首皆自"署臣黎貴惇"。十八世紀的越南社會發生多起政治動亂，黎貴惇闡述《尚書》有經世之意，政治意義很明顯。

《書經衍義》含三卷，卷之一包括自《堯典》至《微子》篇，卷之二自《泰誓上》至《無逸》篇，卷之三包括其餘各篇。如今僅有唯一一版《書經衍義》在越南流傳，這是一木刻版，包括序和跋在内總共 284 頁。刻本上無何時刊刻的記載，有作者于 1772 年自作之序，末有其門人李陳（王貫）于成書後 1778 年作跋一篇，此跋也未提及關於刻本的信息。該刻本缺序首頁，我們已經根據其他資料把這重要一頁補全，此頁打印加在刻本卷首。跋中亦有多字模糊或缺失，無法閱讀。此跋尚未在其他書籍中發現，因此缺失之字只能暫時留空。書中黎貴惇有引用《尚書》正文進行討論，但作者簡略引用，有刪減文字。這是一種概括引用，我們尊重作者的引用方法，所以不恢復原文。

## 二、《書經衍義》中黎貴惇的論經方法

札記成書

正如書名所示，黎貴惇為《書經》進行衍義，即論述《書經》的義理。《書經衍義》是分一段段論述《書經》内容的集合體，為全部 342 段評論、考究和辨正經文的集合。這不是一個注釋工作，也不是訓詁式地逐句解釋、逐字定義。作者深入討論，把那些濃縮的或難懂的地方解釋更清楚。作者已在序中把此工作性質說明："臣實愚陋，涵泳有年，粗窺大義。每讀古文，只覺意味溢出，理趣無窮，有所觸發，隨意書之。徵引傳記，討論古今，無非欲為聖經之印證也。"①

全書 342 段評論可以分成兩類，一類討論義理，一類考證典章制度、地理沿革、諸史群書、訓詁名物……然而，本書對問題進行考證是為了進一步弄清義理或者以之為立論的根據和領會經文思想的方法。因此，可以總體評價這是一本論述經書義理的著作。黎貴惇記錄讀書或給學生授課的心得，或者是對書中義理的理解和想法，這些記錄按照《尚書》58 篇的順序集合起來。因此在作品中，我們沒有發現作者抄錄經文。多處引文乃用於討論，引用也是相對的，不一定完全一致，但對《尚書》有所瞭解的人讀到這些論述是完全可以理解作者在論述何問題。黎貴惇面向的論述對象並非《尚書》初學者或剛入門者，而是有學問的儒士和儒學政治家。

① 《書經衍義》序。

閱讀黎貴惇所論述的內容，我們可以發現作者緊緊圍繞、直接閱讀和講解《尚書》正文。其他先儒、傳注只是用於比照討論，非論述對象。

黎貴惇對《尚書》各篇、每篇各部分的討論程度也不完全一樣。有的地方作者心得深刻就討論詳細，有的地方只是略略幾句帶過。《堯典》、《舜典》和《洪範》等篇討論非常詳細。很多地方，作者把《尚書》中的幾句、幾個意思合併起來一起討論。也有某些部分作者是就篇中主旨來討論而不是就字句。由此可見，此書的總體傾向是作者治《尚書》的心得體會，而不是《尚書》的傳注。它也顯示出此書相對于《尚書》來說，是具有獨立存在性的，而不是與原文同行的一本注解書，即它沒有依附性。這點對於加強對黎貴惇以及越南儒學家論述儒家經典思想研究這項工作的意義來說很有說服力，因此，黎貴惇此作品也帶有讀《尚書》札記之性質。

既然是讀書和講授之涵泳、心得的集合，就可以肯定它們是在不同時段創作的。它也因各篇內容而談論不同的問題，這點清楚顯示作者的關注點和不同心得。然而，它也有不足之處，缺少以學術研究為目的所需要的系統性、一貫性和高度集中性。

《書經衍義》提到的內容，包括經文、朱熹的注解、蔡沈的《書集傳》，我們可以斷定黎貴惇是在 15 世紀以後廣泛流傳於東亞學界的“書經大全”基礎上進行閱讀和衍義《書經》。

黎貴惇讀《書經》方法

——黎貴惇閱讀了一系列有關《書經》的整體群書，包括其他他能聯想到和覺得有關係的各種書籍。其他書籍幫助黎貴惇更好地理解《書經》中的問題，同時有助於他考校、對比對照或弄清哪個合理，或者哪個不合理、不足……

——用跨越空間和時間的思維來閱讀。

——在尋找和體驗政治路線及摸索經驗（後面將詳細介紹）中閱讀，讀《書經》與政治實際相結合。他認同越南與其他受儒家思想影響的國家之間的政治模式、方法和實際。

——用個人經歷讀《書經》，以親身經歷的政治實踐來體驗，即以本人親歷政治實踐的資格來讀《書經》。

——以唯理、判斷和批判的態度讀《書經》，又崇拜極致，但也視為可批判的物件而不盲目全信。以求是的精神來閱讀《書經》。

——以新思維閱讀看似陳舊的思想，以摸索和創作的資格來閱讀，引導其他人領會、領悟經文。因此該書還有為他人引論、導讀的性質。

——注意重點和帶有關鍵性的問題。

——根據現代研究者的觀點，黎貴惇的讀書方式是一種“文化解毒”法，對於《書經》，政治文化是軸心，貫穿全書。這種閱讀方法需要用到全部歷史、地理、風俗文化，文本學、政治、典章制度和儀式等等知識和經驗。

辨正性質、批判精神

我們可以看到批判、辨疑精神和對話性質貫穿《書經衍義》全書。他以個人獨特的邏輯和道理來讀書，不被任何條件拘束限制。當然他也大力歌頌和贊成一些先儒和注解，但這不等於他被動、盲目地聽從。

在《大禹謨》篇，黎貴惇表示不贊同宋朝《太史集》作者范祖禹的意見，認為："范祖禹"五刑之事，舜不與也"，不可以訓"，即有不贊成、批評范祖禹意。在黎貴惇看來，舜時已經制定明確的五刑並實施，又畫刑、明刑弼教怎能說舜與此無關。"似不是"（《畢命》）：這樣說似乎不對；"不敢信"（《畢命》）；"其失尤遠矣"；"君陳分陝三十五年"（《畢命》），而不是 二十五年……。

黎貴惇對很多論述直接進行評價，態度明確，例如："蔡《傳》以為"別立條教"，恐狹"；"此誠淺淺之見也"；"此說非也"；"周公先稱王命，下述已言，亦似牽強"；"亦是臆說"；"二句為說不通"（《康王之誥》）。

《洛誥》有一段關於某些句子和意見的駁斥很有趣，有些他評論說"殊不可曉"，有幾小段批評呂氏，認為理解錯誤，歪曲經典的旨意："語典端續與公自任天下挽留召公之意，大相違異"，"總因呂氏誤解"明農"二字，敷演至此"……

黎貴惇在《書經衍義》中批評最強烈的乃是針對宋朝蔡沈的《書集傳》。15 世紀以後廣為流傳，並在東亞各國儒學教育和科舉中做為正式學習教材的"書經大全"中，蔡沈的《書集傳》具有絕對權威，因此，黎貴惇對此書的批判在學術和思想上更值得注意。

他的批判精神體現在讀書方法、理解方法上，敢於質疑、辯正和相信自己的意見，批判精神貫穿於每一段討論和論述。關鍵問題是，黎貴惇論述經文的批判精神和態度有何值得引起注意?

回顧越南接受和衍義儒家經典的歷程，我們發現敢於對先秦儒家和宋儒以及整個儒家經典中某些問題提出質疑和批判的第一人應該算 14 世紀末 15 世紀初的胡季犛。然而胡季犛的批判主要是表達褒貶態度，指責駁斥，而不是帶有理性色彩的辯解，胡季犛的意見也未能建立在具體證據的基礎之上。到了 18 世紀的黎貴惇，批判精神達到一個全新境界。這種精神是在考證學基礎上形成的，在理和勢的邏輯（中古史學達到的最系統和客觀的思維方法）判斷證據上進行分析，這點可見越南儒家的儒學水平和能力達到了一個新層次。它也是 18 世紀特殊的學術環境和政治背景下，越南儒家經典論述活動興盛的標誌。更遠一些則反映了黎貴惇所接受的清朝儒學對其之影響，關於這點，本文作者將在後面繼續談及。

以史證經

黎先生對歷史事件及問題、典章制度和義理等進行討論、愚按最多。討論講解經典與討論史學書籍一致，體現出黎貴惇使用的史學研究方法。《六經佳史》認為，在六經裏，《秋經》是古代歷史資料完整的集合。在史書中，教育帝王是教其政治。所以討論《尚書》，我們可以看到考證經文方法、論史方法，看到哲學思想和政治思想。有考證學知識，也有論史知識，亦有政治思想。這是一種通經致用和史學經世的方法，為黎貴惇經世目的服務的論史考史方法與其《書經衍義》中的引史證經是彼此相通的，在這方面黎貴惇具有史學家的性質。

## 三、黎貴惇對朱熹論《尚書》的評價

本文作者的研究方向是受黎貴惇衍義經典和操作方法的啟發。黎貴惇論述《尚書》，而且在釋義過程，為了給讀者提供一個他認為最準確的意義，他採取逐段討論和批判的方法。他對已經研究討論和注解、论述过《尚書》的蔡沈、陳氏、胡氏和朱氏等儒學家們都有论及。書中很多地方，黎貴惇還擴大與其他史學家、未曾注解《尚書》的學者们進行辯論。然而，对于朱熹，他却是怀着一种特殊的态度。

《書經衍義》中有 12 處提及朱熹，其中有 10 處摘引朱熹論經書或義理的观点，或與《尚書》有關問題的看法。其餘 2 處论及朱熹思想不與任何具體摘引有關。分析上述 12 處，我們發現只有 2 處黎貴惇评论还有所保留，表示中立的態度或者犹豫，因為朱熹沒評價更具體。這 2 處分别是：

第一處是《舜典》篇，引用孔子《孔叢子》中的言论，黎貴惇论及朱熹論“舜入山林川泽”句意义的解釋：

“朱子謂：‘納於大麓’之說，當從《史記》為據。若‘主祭’之說，所不敢信。不見辨《孔叢子》所載，是否如何”。[①]

第二處是《禹貢》篇，討論簡河和潔河段：

“九河之說曰‘簡’，曰‘潔’。朱文公《孟子集注》與《爾雅》同，《蔡傳》以‘簡’、‘潔’為一。謂其一，則河之經流，不知何據”。[②]

除了上述 2 處，其餘各處黎貴惇皆詳細摘引和對其進行評論評價，直接表明態度。

黎貴惇引用朱子的解釋、考究和論證為根據，做為本人辨疑的支撐點。在《胤征》篇，論及“太康失河北”段，他摘引朱熹的觀點如下：

朱子曰：“太康失河北，至相方失河南”。是仲康之時，羿分河北以自帝也。禹德在人，人思仰之故。太康雖不復冀都，居於陽夏，兗、豫、青、徐之國猶相

① 《書經衍義卷之一 舜典 2》第 10 項。

② 《書經衍義卷之一 禹貢 5》第 48 項。

扶翊為之捍衛。仲康繼立稍振威令。帝相遷居帝丘，國勢日削。寒足已殺，後羿遂渡河滅夏，弒帝相。觀《左傳》稱“帝夷羿”，是羿非立仲康，而執國政之驗。①

在《酒誥》篇，論及此篇作者時，蔡沈認為是武王所作，黎貴惇認為是周公。他摘引朱子的觀點論證如下：

《酒誥》一篇，《蔡傳》以為武王作。朱子以為必是武庚與頑民將酒灌醉，管、蔡以語言離間之。周公所以做《酒誥》丁寧如此。想來朱子說當從。②

值得一提的是他對朱熹觀點明確肯定的態度，認為：“朱子說當從”。

以如此肯定的態度摘引還出現在《洛誥》篇中的一段，關於“胤保”兩字解釋的摘引：

“予乃胤保大相東土”。《蔡傳》謂：“繼太保而往”。臣對君言，不應稱保。朱子謂：“嗣攝政事，保佑王躬”。當從之。③

朱子觀點得到黎貴惇的高度評價，大力歌頌和讚揚，例如下段：

成王稱公勤施之德，又稱公棐迪之功。蓋推美尊敬之至。《蔡傳》因呂氏說，乃謂：“示所以留之之意”。又謂：“未可以言去”，頗為添贅。以平心看《書》中語脈自見。王曰：“公功肅將祇歡，公毋困哉，我惟無斁其康事”。朱子謂：“言公無以事自困”，如漢所謂：“閔勞公以官職之事也”，王則當無厭倦於安國安民之事”。此說最明。《蔡傳》謂：“毋求去以困我”亦非。總因呂氏誤解“明農”二字敷演至此。④

在《書經衍義》中，黎貴惇辨疑和批判很多，而與此同時朱熹的觀點卻始終得到作者肯定和推崇。他甚至還用朱熹的觀點去批判其他人，例如《酒誥》篇中：

《酒誥》一篇，《蔡傳》以為武王作。朱子以為必是武庚與頑民將酒灌醉，管、蔡以語言離間之。周公所以做《酒誥》丁寧如此。想來朱子說當從。⑤

黎貴惇尤其推崇朱熹“道問學”精神，批判陸九淵和王守仁“尊德性”精神，《說命下》篇中“學”字的討論就很值得注意，該段如下：

千古論學，始自傅說一篇：“人求多聞，時惟建事，學于古訓，乃有獲”。此道問學之工夫也。“惟學遜志，務時敏，厥脩乃來，道積厥躬”。此尊德性之工夫也。朱子窮理以致其知，反躬以踐其實，蓋兼體用，該內外，實得先聖賢之正傳。

① 《書經衍義卷之一 胤征 1》第 58 項。
② 《書經衍義卷之二 酒誥 1》第 168－169 項。
③ 《書經衍義卷之二 洛誥 1》第 189 項。
④ 《書經衍義卷之二 洛誥 12》第 194－195 項。
⑤ 《書經衍義卷之二 酒誥 1》第 168－169 項。

陸九淵、王守仁單提尊德性以教學者，而以讀書窮理為禁，皆傳說之罪人也。[①]

黎貴惇通過分析並贊成顧炎武關於理和心觀點，間接提高朱熹的理學思想，顧炎武視此為絕對真理，“流行天地間，貫徹古今”，理和心為一體，但也不是“即心是道”，而是理具於心，指揮心的運行，以理為心。該段文如下：

近世喜言心學，舍全章本旨，而獨論人心、道心，甚至單接“道心”二字，而直謂即心是道。蓋陷於禪學而不自知。其去堯、舜、禹授受天下之本旨遠矣。蔡氏《書傳》雖亦以是明帝王之心，而心者治國平天下之本，其說固理之正也。其後進此《書傳》於朝者，乃因以三聖傳心為說，世之學者遂指此書十六字為傳心之要，而禪學者，藉以為據依矣。

顧氏炎武曰：“心不待傳也，流行天地間，貫徹古今，而無不同者，理也。理具於吾心，而驗於事物；心者所以統宗此理，而別白其是非、人之賢否、事之得失、天下之治亂，皆於此乎判。此聖人所仕致察於危微精一之間，而相傳以執中之道，使無一事之不合於理，而無有過不及之偏者也。禪學以理為障，而獨指其心，曰：“不立文字，單傳心印”。聖賢之學自一心而達之天下國家之用，無非至理之流行，明白洞達，人人所同，歷千載而無間者，何傳之雲此。二說平正，最得聖人之旨。[②]

顧炎武基本上繼承朱熹理和心關係的理學思想，但兩人的觀點亦有區別。朱熹以理為心；心學以心為理。顧炎武以相互作用的雙向關係視之，兩者統一不可分割，他認為：“心不待傳也，流行天地間，貫徹古今，而無不同者，理也。理具於吾心，而驗於事物；心者所以統宗此理，而別白其是非”。確實已經對此兩範疇關係在觀念上有調整，這就是中和傾向。既批評心學，但又以心學可借鑒的觀點來調整和發展理學中的理觀點，黎貴惇贊成顧炎武的這種調整。他尊崇朱熹，但亦不因此而拒絕發揚或調整後世對發展朱熹思想所進行的調整或擴展。

黎貴惇接受清朝儒學思想的影響這點是很明顯的。他批判陸、王思想在某種程度上就是受了18世紀時期清朝儒學思想的影響。除了接受和贊成顧炎武關於理和心思想的調整外，黎貴惇還高度讚揚顧氏的考證學成就。

我們可以看一段論及顧炎武關於《顧命》篇見解的討論，黎貴惇稱讚道：“其辨論証據爰出千古”。該段文如下：

康王始即位，君臣皆吉服。先儒疑之，亦有曲為之說。惟顧氏《日知錄》斷以《顧命》中有脫簡，自“狄設黼衣綴衣”以下，當屬《康王之誥》。自此以上，記成王顧命登遐之事。自此以下，記明年正月上日，康王即位，朝諸侯之事。其

① 《書經衍義卷之一 說命下 2》第89－90項。

② 《書經衍義卷之一 大禹謨 13》第37－39項。

辨論証據爰出千古。[①]

從《書經衍義》對朱熹的評價來看，我們可以發現黎貴惇繼承了理學傳統，但他的理學思想具有時代精神，融入並接受東亞國家18世紀考證學和實學精神方面的影響。

## 結論

朱熹並非專門研究和討論《尚書》，他最出名的治學成果是著作《四書集注》和注釋《詩經》、《易傳》。朱熹只有幾段關於《尚書》的討論散佈在其門人輯錄的《朱子語類》書中。他關注《尚書》體現在他命門徒蔡沈著《書集傳》。[②] 也有意見認為朱熹關於《尚書》的討論意見均已集中到蔡沈的著作中 。這點可以證明黎貴惇已經仔細研究了《性理大全》。[③]《性理大全》通過在教育和科舉中使用對越南產生了巨大影響。

朱熹關於《尚書》很少的幾處討論意見受到黎貴惇特別的關注。朱子被摘引最多和最受推崇。這點證明朱熹思想對黎貴惇產生了具有權威性的影響，以及整個理學對越南儒家們也都有深遠影響。

朱熹的重要觀點、理學思想和“道問學”精神備受推崇。黎氏也將朱熹與陸、王對立來討論。從這點，再加上接受顧炎武的考證成就及對理觀念或多或少的調整，我們可以發現黎貴惇是受了清朝學術影響的儒學家。他是屬於站出來保衛和維護儒學正統脈絡的群體。這是證明越南儒學經過調整並融入18世紀東亞國家儒學思想轉變的標誌。這些新影響使得越南儒學家有必要重新審視以強調自古以來所接受的帶有精髓性和基礎性的思想，同時調整這些思想使之與時代發展需求相符。

---

① 《書經衍義卷之三 顧命 3 》第 248－249 項。

② 关于《书集传》是蔡沈受朱熹之托而著一事在该书序中有说明。

③ 《朱子性理语类》作为明朝胡广组织编撰的《性理大全》一部分的资格广泛流传。

# 以“行”释义

## ——儒家诠释文本的一种特殊方式

南京大学　李承贵

孔子曾经感叹：“天何言哉？四时行焉，百物生焉，天何言哉？”（《论语·阳货》）这句圣人之言一度引来无数英雄竞折腰，被作多种诠释。但无论作怎样的诠释，我倾向于认为：孔子所强调的是理解一种对象行为比语言更为可靠和重要。因而这句话所表达的是孔子对于文本诠释的一种方式，即“以行释义”的方式。值得注意的是，这种诠释方式普遍存在于儒家文本诠释实践中，成为儒家诠释经典文本的一种特殊形态。为了叙述、分析的方便，我们将“以行释义”的“行”姑分为“效行”、“身行”与“事行”展开讨论。

### 一、“效行”释义

所谓“效行”，是指当下的并已发生效果的实际行为。所谓“效行释义”，就是以“当下的并已发生效果的实际行为”对文本进行诠释从而使其意涵呈现。孔子曾说：“我欲载之空言，不如见之于行事之深切著明也。”（《史记·太史公自序》）那么，儒家文本诠释实践中是否存在这种情形呢？请看文献：

颜渊问仁，子曰：“克己复礼为仁。一日克己复礼，天下归仁焉。为仁由己，而由人乎哉？”颜渊曰：“请问其目。”子曰：“非礼勿视，非礼勿听，非礼勿言，非礼勿动。”颜渊曰：“回虽不敏，请事斯语矣。”（《论语·颜渊》）

“克己复礼”通常的诠释是约束自己的言行使之合乎礼，也就是说，“仁”的意涵绝不在概念自身，而在“克己复礼”，而“克己复礼”就是约束、规范自己的言行使之符合礼，所以是一种“行”。这种诠释已清晰明白，但颜渊笨拙，要求老师孔子说得更具体些。孔子继续解释说，凡是不符合礼的现象都不理不睬。换言之，就是用“礼”来规范、约束自己的视、听、言、动，以“礼”作为最高准则。可见，所谓“仁”，是指规范、约束自己言行使之符合礼的实践，即言“仁”的意涵就在具体的遵循“礼”的实践中。而颜渊说“请事斯言”，则进一步将“仁即在实际行为中”之义坐实了。在这里，孔子没有从文字构造、概念分析、逻辑推演等讲说“仁”，而是以“行为”呈现“仁”的意涵。以“行”诠释“仁”的现象在《论语》中非常普遍。比如，“仁者，己欲立而立人，己欲达而达人。”（《论语·雍也》）什么是“仁”？孔子的答案是：自己想站立起来也必须要他人站立起来，自己想发达起来也必须要他人发达起来。显然，这是以“己欲立而立人，己欲达而达人”这个“行”诠释“仁”。这再次说明，孔子对于“仁”涵义的诠释是通过实践行为完成的，而不是理论的阐述、概念的推演。换言之，如果没有实施“己欲立而立人，己欲达而达人”的行为，就不能理解“仁”了。正如朱熹所说：“圣人教人，多是于动处说，如云‘出门如见大宾，使民如承大祭。’”

又如“告颜子‘克己复礼为仁’，正是于视听言动处理会。”（《论语十二》，《朱子语类》卷第三十）

“知”也是孔子思想中的一个基本概念，那么，孔子是怎样诠释“知”的呢？请看文献：

> 樊迟问“知”。子曰：“知人。”樊迟未达。子曰：“举直错诸枉，能使枉者直。”樊迟退，见子夏曰：“乡也，吾见于夫子而问‘知’；子曰：‘举直错诸枉，能使枉者直。’何谓也?”子夏曰：“富哉言乎！舜有天下，选于众，举皋陶，不仁者远矣；汤有天下，选于众，举伊尹，不仁者远矣。”（《论语·颜渊》）

什么叫着“知”？樊迟把这个疑问抛给了老师。孔子的答案是“知人”，而“知人”就是“举直错诸枉，能使枉者直”。对于“举直错诸枉，能使枉者直”，学生子夏还给予了补充，将历史中的案例置于其中，使“知”的意涵具体化。“知”就是“知人”，虽然我们无法断定“知人”的性质与内涵，但“知人”肯定是对人的了解，也就是“行”，这没有问题。作为对“知”进一步诠释的“举直错诸枉，能使枉者直”，即“将正直的人放在邪恶的人之上，从而使邪恶的人转变为正直的人”，这无疑也是“行”。而子夏为孔子的答案提供的注脚——“舜有天下，选于众，举皋陶，不仁者远矣；汤有天下，选于众，举伊尹，不仁者远矣”，就是“舜有了天下之后，选贤举能，将优秀的皋陶推举出来，使那些坏人远离；汤有了天下之后，选贤举能，将优秀的伊尹推举上去，使那些坏人远离”，无疑也是“行”，是具体的“行”，也是更为复杂的“行”。不难看出，孔子对于“知”的诠释也是通过“行”完成的，即通过具体的实际行为对“知”的意涵做出规定。换言之，对儒家而言，“知”不是观念，而是实际的行为，只有实际的行为才有资格表述“知”的意涵。

我们再考察一下“孝”。对儒家而言，“孝”绝不是语言上的概念，更不是哲学上的思辨，而是实实在在的“行”，可以说“非行不孝”。先看《论语》释“孝”——“子游问孝，子曰：‘今之孝者，是谓能养。至于犬马，皆能有养；不敬，何以别乎?’”（《论语·为政》）在这里，“孝”被定义为“养”，无疑是一种行为。不过在孔子看来，光“养”还不够，犹需“敬”，而“敬”也是“行”，正所谓“莅官不敬，非孝也!”（《大戴礼记·曾子大孝》）“敬”表现为对父母、长辈在举手投足上的尊重与爱护，与父母聊天，照顾父母起居，满足父母喜好，尊重父母言行，等等，这就是“敬”，所以“敬”也是“行”。质言之，《论语》释“孝”，“行”为其归。再看《中庸》释“孝”：“践其位，行其礼，奏其乐；敬其所尊，爱其所亲；事死如事生，事亡如事存，孝之至也。”（《中庸》第19章）就是说，如果能做到“供奉好先王的牌位、举行先王留下的祭礼、演奏先王时代的音乐、敬重先王所尊敬的人、爱护先王所爱的子孙臣民、侍奉死者如同他在世时一样”等几条，便是“孝”的极致。而“供奉牌位”、“举行祭礼”、“演奏音乐”、“敬重先人”、“爱护臣民”、“侍死如生”等，哪一样不是“行”？因此，《中庸》中的“孝”也是由实践行为来定义的。再看《孝经》释“孝”：“夫孝，始于事亲，中于事君，终于立身。”（《孝经·开宗明义章》）无疑，所谓“事亲”、“事君”、“立身”也都是“行”，质言之，“孝”自始至终都是实践的，它的意涵就在“事亲”、“事君”、“立身”诸行为中。正如朱熹所说：“圣人只使得人孝足矣，使得人弟足矣，却无缘又上门逐个与他解说所以当孝者是如何，所以当弟者是如何，自是无缘得如此。”（《论语十七》，《朱子语类》卷二十五）在朱熹看来，“孝”的意涵不在言辞中，不在辩论中，而在具体的实际作为中。

不难看出，所谓“效行释义”，强调的是以“当下的并已发生效果的实际行为”对文本进行诠释。在这种诠释方式中，文本的意涵即在“当下的并已发生效果的实际行为”中。

## 二、“身行”释义

所谓“身行”，就是指身体或其他物的演示性、实际性的行为。所谓“身行释义”，就是以“身体或其他物的演示性、实际性的行为”对文本进行诠释并呈现其意涵。朱熹曾说：“读书不可只专就纸上求义理，须反来就自家身上推究，秦、汉以后，无人说到此，亦只是一向去书册上求，不就自家身上理会。自家见未到，圣人先说在那里，自家只借他言语来，就身上推究始得。”（《学五》，《朱子语类》卷十一）就是说，寻找文本之意涵围绕书册转悠是难以达到目的的，只有从身行中寻找才能如愿以偿。那么，儒家文本诠释实践中是否存在这种情形呢？请看文献：

樊迟问仁。子曰：“居处恭，执事敬，与人忠。”（《论语·子路篇》）

在回答樊迟什么是“仁”的提问中，孔子给出了这样的答案：“居处表现出谦恭之态，办事表现出崇敬之态，跟人交往表现出忠诚之态”。这里的“谦恭”、“崇敬”、“忠诚”都是面对不同的人或事时所表现的一种行为状态，即是说，“仁”的意涵就是“谦恭”之状、“崇敬”之状、“忠诚”之状。因此，孔子在这段文献中对“仁”的诠释，是典型的“身行释义”模式。清人阮元对以实践诠释“仁”的方式亦是非常肯定与推崇。他说：“凡仁，必于身所行者验之而始见，亦必有二人而仁乃见。若一人闭户斋居，瞑目静坐，虽有德理在心，终不得指为圣门所谓之仁矣。盖士庶人之仁，见于宗族乡党，天子诸侯卿大夫之仁，见于国家臣民，同一相人偶之道，是必人与人相偶而仁乃见也。”（《论语·论仁论》，《揅经室集·一集》卷八）质言之，只有实际行为才能彻底地呈现“仁”的内涵。

“舍生取义”是孟子提出的观念，那么，孟子是怎样诠释这个命题的呢？孟子说：“鱼，我所欲也，熊掌，亦我所欲也；二者不可得兼，舍鱼而取熊掌者也。生，亦我所欲也，义，亦我所欲也；二者不可得兼，舍生而取义者也。”（《孟子·告子上》）就是说，在生命与道义之间需要做出选择的时候，应该选择“道义”而非“生命”。可是，怎样才算“舍生取义”呢？孟子说：“一箪食，一豆羹，得之则生，弗得则死，呼尔而与之，行道之人弗受；蹴尔而与之，乞人不屑也。万钟则不辩礼义而受之，万钟于我何加焉？为宫室之美、妻妾之奉、所识穷乏者得我与？乡为身死而不受，今为宫室之美为之；乡为身死而不受，今为妻妾之奉为之；乡为身死而不受，今为所识穷乏者得我而为之，是亦不可以已乎？此之谓失其本心。”（《孟子·告子上》）如此看来，“舍生取义”就是宁愿放弃生命，也不吃那些让人格受辱的食物；就是放弃优厚的俸禄、富丽的宫室、成群的妻妾，也要坚守礼义。这就是说，“舍生取义”的意涵寓于“舍身”实践中。换言之，就是用“身体的亏损或牺牲换取道义”这一行为诠释“舍生取义”。

“咸”是《周易》中一卦，张载做了这样的诠释：“咸之道不一：或以同而感，圣人感人心以道，此是以同也；或以异而应，男女是也，二女同居则无感也；或以相悦而感，或以相畏而感，如虎先见犬，犬自不能去，犬若见虎则能避之；又如磁石引针，相应而感也。若以爱心而来者自相亲，以害心而来者相见容色自别。”（《横渠易说》，《张载集》）“咸卦”的意涵是什么？张载用了多种“行”进行说明：圣凡相感、男女相感、虎犬相感、磁石引针相感等等，都是人身或物实际的相感行为，但由于相感的原因不同，因而这种相感行为又表现出多样性。换言之，“咸”之为“相感义”及其丰富性可由圣凡、男女、虎犬、磁石引针等的“相感实践”以呈现。

“絜矩”是《大学》中的概念，向来诠释者络绎不绝，而朱熹的诠释别具一格：“且如自家有一丈地，左家有一丈地，右家有一丈地。左家侵著我五尺地，是不矩，我必去讼他取我五尺。我若侵著右家五尺地，亦是不矩，合当还右家。只是我也方，上也方，下也方，左也方，右也方，前也方，后也方，不相侵越。”（《大学三》，《朱子语类》卷第十六）朱熹说，我自家有一丈地，左家有一丈地，右家有一丈地，可是有一天左家侵占我家五尺地，这就是不守絜矩了，我必须去投诉讼他，将我那五尺地夺回来。但如果我侵占右家五尺地，也是不守絜矩，应该还给右家。因此，所谓“絜矩”，就是让自家、左家、右家各自拥有自己本来的方地而不相侵占。如此，“絜矩”的意涵便呼之而出了。

这里有一段陆九渊回答学生詹阜民什么是“礼”的记载——“某方侍坐，先生遽起，某亦起。先生曰：‘还有安排否?’”（《语录下》，《陆九渊集》）这段描述虽然简略，但非常传神、非常精彩。詹阜民曾问陆九渊什么是“礼”，陆九渊反问他怎么理解，詹阜民回答“安排”，陆九渊当时不置可否。一次詹阜民来到九渊处侍坐，又问什么是“礼”。陆九渊闭目养神，不予回答。詹阜民只好一直陪着，两人都默不作声。突然间，陆九渊起身往外走，詹阜民随即起身，紧跟其后并搀扶陆九渊。此时陆九渊回头冲着詹阜民神秘一笑：“还用安排否?”詹阜民顿时醒悟：“礼”就在心中，就在日常行为中！在这里，陆九渊没有对“礼”进行理论的分析、逻辑的推演、烦琐的讲说，而是用亲身的行为演示“礼”的意涵。也就是说，陆九渊诠释“礼”，是用“老师陆九渊起身，学生詹阜民随起”这一具体的行为加以呈现的。

不难看出，所谓“身行释义”，强调的是以“身体或其他物的演示性、示范性行为”对文本进行诠释。在这种诠释方式中，文本的意涵即在“身体或其他物的演示性、示范性行为”中。

### 三、“事行”释义

所谓“事行”，就是指发生过的事件或过往的行为；所谓“事行释义”，就是以“发生过的事件或过往的行为”对文本进行诠释并呈现其意涵。王阳明曾说：“以事言谓之史，以道言之谓之经，事即道，道即事。”（《传习录上》，《王阳明全集》上）正是强调由“事行”觉悟文本的道理。那么，儒家文本诠释实践中是否存在这种情形呢?请看文献：

> 子路曰：“桓公杀公子纠，召忽死之，管仲不死。”曰：“未仁乎!”子曰：“桓公九合诸侯，不以兵车，管仲之力也。如其仁！如其仁!”（《论语·宪问》）

子路问孔子，齐桓公杀了兄长公子纠，公子纠的师傅召忽因为公子纠而自杀，但他的另一位师傅管仲却活得滋润惬意，这样的管仲算得上仁吗?孔子的回答出乎子路意外：齐桓公多次成功地主持诸侯间的盟会，并阻止了战争爆发，防止了杀戮，使天下太平、社会稳定，人民得以安居乐业，都是管仲的力量与功劳，这还不足以让管仲配得上“仁”这个称号吗?就是说，对孔子而言，管仲“仁”还是“不仁”，要看他实际做了什么。孔子认为管仲辅佐齐桓公主持盟会，阻止了战争，防止了杀戮，使天下太平，这就是“仁”。可见，孔子在这里是用“发生过的事件或过往的行为”诠释

“仁”。

《礼记》中有关于孔子是否主张“丧欲速贫，死欲速朽”的讨论——“有子问于曾子曰：‘问丧于夫子乎’？曰：‘闻之矣，丧欲速贫·死欲速朽。’有子曰：‘是非君子之言也。’曾子曰：‘参也闻诸夫子也。’有子又曰：‘是非君子之言也。’曾子曰：‘参也与子游闻之。’有子曰‘然。然则夫子有为言之也。’曾子以斯言告于子游。子游曰：‘甚哉，有子之言似夫子也！昔者夫子居于宋，见桓司马自为石椁，三年而不成。夫子曰：若是其靡也，死不如速朽之愈也。死之欲速朽，为桓司马言之也。南宫敬叔反，必载宝而朝。夫子曰：若是其货也，丧不如速贫之愈也。丧之欲速贫，为敬叔言之也。’曾子以子游之言告于有子，有子曰：‘然。吾固曰，非夫子之言也。’曾子曰：‘子何以知之?’有子曰：‘夫子制于中都，四寸之棺，五寸之椁，以斯知不欲速朽也；昔者夫子失鲁司寇，将之荆，盖先之以子夏，又申之以冉有，以斯知不欲速贫也。”（《礼记·檀弓上》）在这段文献中，需要证明和解释的核心问题是：孔子是否有“人死了希望快速腐烂、失去官职希望快速贫穷”的观念。这个问题在有子与曾子之间展开。有子向曾子提出这个问题，曾子不加思索地做了肯定回答，并强调不仅自己亲自听说过，并与同学子游一起听说过，孔子是希望“人死了就快速腐烂、失去官职就快速贫穷”的。但有子否定了曾子的答案。有子认为即便孔子说过这样的话，也是有针对性的。至此，一方面曾子“听说”的答案不算数，另一方面即便孔子说过这样的话也不能代表他真正的想法。那么，孔子真正的想法或主张是什么呢？这个时候有子不紧不慢地亮出了他的证据——孔子任职中都宰时曾制定棺厚四寸、椁厚五寸的制度以及失去鲁国司寇职位后仍想方设法谋取官职。有了这种实际行为，还能说孔子是主张“死之欲速朽，丧之欲速贫”吗？显然不能。就是说，相对于曾子、子游的听说，相对于“夫子有为言之”，还是“四寸之棺，五寸之椁”和“先之以子夏，又申之以冉有”的实际行为更具有诠释力量，更具有权威性。这也许就是所谓“学至于行之而止”（《荀子·儒效》）的原因吧？因此，这段文献所表现出来的诠释方式，当是“以行释义”方式。

“知几”概念最早出自《周易》，所谓“知几，其神乎！君子上交不谄，下交不渎，其知几乎?”（《周易·系辞下》）这句话通常的解释是：能够预知几微的事理应该算是达到神的境界吧？君子与地位在自己之上的人交往不谄媚，与地位在自己之下的人交往不渎谩，这应该是预知几微的事理吧？可见，孔子本来就将“知几”的意涵落实在“君子上交不谄，下交不渎”的实践行为上。二程的诠释正是传承了这一精神：“知几者，君子之独见，非众人所能及也。穆生为酒醴而去，免于胥靡之辱。姜肱为土室之隐，免于党锢之祸。薛方守箕山之节，免于新室之污。其知几矣。”（《圣贤篇》，（《河南程氏粹言》卷第二）二程的诠释涉及三个典故：一个是“穆生为酒醴而去”，说是汉代楚元王与穆生交情很好，穆生不喜欢喝酒，元王每次设宴就为他准备甜酒，然而，后来楚王孙戊继位，不再准备甜酒，穆生便说："可以离去了。"然正是因为离去，穆生才免于劳役或腐刑。一个是"姜肱为土室之隐"，姜肱是东汉时公认的贤士，曹节打算任命他做太守。但当姜肱见到曹节派人送来委任状时却说，因为我有好的名声和威望，所以曹节等人邀我做官，但我不想违背我的节操，何况现在掌权的是曹节那帮阉竖小人，我怎么能遂他们的心愿呢？随即隐姓埋名，逃至海滨。正是因为这个选择使他免于党锢之祸。还一个是"薛方守箕山之节"，西汉末年，外戚王莽把持朝政大权，他一方面排斥异己，残酷打击忠于汉室、不归附他的大臣，另一方面笼络人心，加官晋爵，邀请清明方正之士进朝为官。薛方就是其中被征者之一。但薛方看破王莽虚假伪善的面目，拒绝了王莽的一再征请，免于与王莽同流合污，保全了清白声誉。所谓"箕山之节"，是指古代唐尧时的隐士许由、巢父隐居在箕山这个地方，从而使归隐箕山成了保全节操的象征。无论是"穆生为酒醴而去"，还是"姜肱为土室之隐"，抑或"薛方守箕山之节"，都是具体行为，由于是发生在过去，所以是"事行"。而二程告诉读者，所谓"知几"，就在"穆生为酒醴而去"、"姜肱为土室之隐"、"薛方守箕山之节"的实践中。换言之，二程对"知几"意涵的诠释是通过实际的行为完成的，即属于"事行释义"方式。将这种诠释用文字表达就是："知几"即能预见事物发生变化的隐微征兆，从而做出有利于自己的选择。不难看出，所谓"事行释义"，强调的是以"发生过的事件或过往的行为"对文本进行诠释。在这种诠释方式中，文本的意涵即在"发生过的事件或过往的行为"中。

## 四、结语

如上由"效行"、"身行"、"事行"三个向度对儒家"以行释义"诠释方式或形态进行了简要梳理，这种梳理足以说明"以行释义"方式或形态的客观性质。然而更为重要的是，我们在梳理过程中所发现的问题、所获得的启示。

1．"以行释义"的根据。环顾诠释学大家庭，似乎很难找到"以行释义"这个面孔，它无名无分。那么，为什么在儒家诠释学辞典中会产生这种非典型的诠释方式呢？或许如下几点可供我们参考：一是儒学"经世致用"的特质。对儒家而言，其学说的目标就是修身、齐家、治国、平天下。《周易》追求的是"开物成务"（《周易·系辞上》），《尚书》追求的是"正德，利用，厚生"（《尚书·大禹谟》），孔子追求的是"博施于民而济众"（《论语·雍也》），孟子的"仁政"不过是"制民之产"（《孟子·梁惠王上》），既然儒家思想的特质是经世致用，那么其对学说的要求必然是能够影响生活、改变生活、提升生活。而这种实用的价值取向表现在文本诠释上，就必然要落实到生活实践中。二是儒学“知行合一”的知行关系论。儒家对知行关系的基本态度是以“行”为基础的“知行合一”。孔子曾说“听其言而观其行”(《论语·公冶长》),荀子认为闻、见、知都不如“行”:“学至于行之而止矣”(《荀子·儒效》),程颐说“君子之学,贵乎行,行则明,明则有功。”(《周易程氏传》卷第四)朱熹认为行优先于知,所以说“知之之要,未若行之之实”(《学七》,《朱子语类》卷十三),王阳明的“知之真切笃实处便是行”(《答友人问》,《王阳明全书》卷六)说得太深邃、太精彩。这样的“知行合一”观,强调实践对于知识的优先地位,知识的来源、落实与验证都必须诉诸实践,那么表现在文本诠释上,对文本意涵的把握自然也是要求落实到实践。三是儒家“道器不离”的道器关系观。儒家有“形而上者谓之道,形而下者谓之器”之说,但从来不把二者割裂开来。孔子说“道不远人。人之为道而远人,不可以为道。”(《中庸》第十三章)程颐说:“离阴阳则无道。”(《论道篇》,《河南程氏粹言》卷第一)朱熹说:“道器一也,示人以器,则道在器中。”(《杂学辨·苏黄门老子解》,《晦庵先生朱文公文集》卷七十二)王夫之说:“道行于乾坤之全,而其用必以人为依。不依乎人者,人不得而用之,则耳目所穷,功效亦废,其道可知而不必知。”(《周易外传》卷一)既然“道”离不开洒扫应对,既然“道”表现于日用庸常,那么,如要理解和把握“道”的含义,只有从“器”中去寻找。这种道器关系观表现在文本诠释上,就是用实际的行为表示文本的意涵。综合言之,“经世致用”的特质、“知行合一”的主张、“道器不离”的观念,分别从价值旨趣上、知识路线上、思维方法上预制了儒家“以行释义”诠释方式或形态的形成。因此,儒家“以行释义”诠释方式或形态,绝不是无根之木,无源之水,它有着深厚的儒家精神气质和儒家思想方法基础,而这正是中国哲学的特质:“中国哲人心目中的哲学,决不在思想系统上,不在文字语言上,而在身体力行上。以思想系统或文字语言为哲学,乃西洋哲人之见解,而此土哲人则异是。”(谢幼伟,《现代哲学名著述评》,第8页)

2.“以行释义”的特点。尽管上述讨论让“以行释义”获得了根源上与存在上双重证明,但由于在诠释学大家庭中找不到长得像“以行释义”的成员,所以我们称之为“非典型性诠释方式”。那么,这种“非典型性诠释方式”具有哪些特点呢?第一,形式与内容的统一。考之上述案例,作为对文本进行诠释的“行”都有一个共同性,即形式与内容的统一。比如,诠释“孝”的“行”,不能是空手走路,也不能是游泳,而是“养”、“敬”等,但又不能是养山羊、敬老虎,所以说,诠释“孝”的“行”必然是“行”与“行什么”的统一。诠释“仁”也是一样,你不能说爬山是“仁”、打架是“仁”,只有“克己复礼”才能为“仁”,只有“己欲立而立人、己欲达而达人”才能为“仁”,这再次说明,“以行释义”必须是形式与内容的统一。换言之,只有“行”这个形式与“行什么”、“如何行”等内容结合起来,才构成“以行释义”诠释方式。

第二，一与多的统一。在“以行释义”实践中，被诠释的概念或命题的核心意涵是不变的，但表述这种意涵的“行”却是多姿多彩的。比如，“仁”基本内涵是“爱”，这是“一”，但表达“爱”的“行”是多样的，可以是“克己复礼”，可以是“己欲立而立人，己欲达而达人”，可以是“居处恭，执事敬，与人忠”，这就是多样性。再如，“孝”的基本内涵是养老敬老，这是“一”，但表达“孝”的“行”也是多样的，可以是“养育父母”，可以是“传宗接代”，可以是“毛发不伤”，可以是“事死如事生”，这就是多样性。可见，“以行释义”也是“一”与“多”的统一 。第三，确定性与不确定性的统一。没有疑问，“以行释义”只能在特定的时空条件下发生，而且每个“以行释义”的“行”都寓含特定的内容，这就是所谓确定性。但“以行释义”的时空条件又是变化的，而“以行释义”的“行”也具有动态性，这就是所谓的不确定性。比如，孔子对“知”的诠释，是“知人”，更进一步，是“举直错诸枉”，而所谓“举直错诸枉”，就是“舜有天下，选于众，举皋陶，不仁者远矣；汤有天下，选于众，举伊尹，不仁者远矣”，这是确定的。但孔子又说过“不患人之不知己，患不知人也”（《论语·学而》）、“知人固不易矣”（《论语·八佾》）、“不知言，无以知人也”（《论语·尧曰》）等话，这说明，“知”的意涵并不仅是“举直错诸枉”，“举直错诸枉”只是“知”的多个意涵之一。因而又表现出不确定性。第四，生动性与真实性统一。“以行释义”的“行”，不管是“效行”、“身行”，还是“事行”，都具有生动、可感性特点。比如，孔子以“居处恭，执事敬，与人忠”诠释“仁”，可以说栩栩如生。陆九渊对“礼”的诠释，尤为生动形象！他用“自己身起则阜民身起”告诉读者什么是“礼”，活灵活现，令人印象深刻。所以说，“以行释义”具有生动性特点。由于“以行释义”要求将文本（概念、命题等）意涵落实到“行”处，是否“孝”，是否“仁”，不是嘴巴说的；如何才算“知几”，孔子是否“丧欲速穷，死欲速朽”，全都以实际行为作为答案；质言之，“以行释义”是当下的、具体的、有目共睹的，因而具有真实性、可靠性。

3、“以行释义”的价值。作为一种诠释文本的方式或形态，“以行释义”究竟有什么特别的地方？之于诠释学、之于儒学究竟有什么特别贡献？这也许是写作本文应该关心的另一个重要问题。第一，“以行释义”是儒家诠释思想成立的基础。为什么可以做这么重要的判断？因为“以行释义”是创造文本、改变文本、丰富文本的基本途径。我们知道，观念意义上的文本并不是先天于人心的，而是后天的，是人类对自我实践的总结、概括和提升，也就是说，“文本”来自“行”。而“以行释义”基本内容之一就是由“行”（实践行为）表现文本的意涵，而“行”（实践行为）又是动态的、开放的，从而使文本不断得到调整和更新，并逐渐多样和丰富起来。比如，世界上本来没有所谓“仁”、“孝”、“礼”等概念，正是因为“以行释义”，即“孝”、“仁”、“礼”分别有了特定的“行”，才被概括转换成一种可供诠释的文本。而“以行释义”之“行”

又是动态的、开放的，从而为“孝”、“仁”、“礼”内涵的更新与丰富创造了条件。因此说，“以行释义”是儒家诠释思想得以成立的基础。夸张点说，没有“以行释义”，就没有儒家诠释学。关于这点，伽达默尔的话可以认为是极佳呼应：“在我看来，在所谓人文科学的自我理解方面，实践理性问题不仅是其中的一个问题，而且比所有其他问题更首要地被提了出来，……正式亚理士多德的实践哲学——而不是近代的方法概念和科学概念——才为人文科学正确的理解提供了唯一有承载力的模式。”（《理解与解释——诠学经典文选》，第25页）第二，“以行释义”是丰富、发展儒家思想的重要途径。如上所述，“以行释义”是动态的、开放的，一个文本可由多种“行”呈现它的意涵，从而使文本的意涵随着“行”的变化而得到更新、丰富与发展。儒家思想体系中的概念、命题等，都因“以行释义”而得到丰富和发展。比如，“仁”，在孔子那里，是“爱人”，而“爱人”可有许多不同的呈现；到了孟子，“仁”主要表现为“仁政”，表现为实际的物质生活的改善，表现为对人的生命的尊重；到了朱熹，“仁”有了新的发展，成为本体性范畴，是朱熹理学思想体系的根源之一；而到了现代，有学者提出，“仁”不应仅有横向的爱，还应有纵的向爱，应该关怀世世代代的人。而之所以有如此持续的、积极性变化，就在于对“仁”的诠释基于“行”（实践行为）而展开。因此，“以行释义”诠释方式对于儒家思想的传承、改造、更新与丰富等，是一条基本途径。第三，“以行释义”是迅捷且可靠的传达文本信息的方式。诠释的基本任务之一是将文本意涵阐发清楚、传递给读者，因而快捷与真实是两个基本要素。“以行释义”基本技巧是将文本对应于一种实践行为，或用一种实践行为将文本意涵进行叙述与呈现。比如，用“事死如事生，事亡如事存”诠释“孝”，用“男女相悦、犬畏虎、磁石引针”等诠释“咸”，用“某方侍坐，先生遽起，某亦起”诠释“礼”，用“我也方，上也方，下也方，左也方，右也方，前也方，后也方，不相侵越”诠释“絜矩”，等等，这不仅省去了烦琐的推演与论证，而且让读者直接领悟到“孝”、“咸”、“礼”、“絜矩”等概念的意涵，并因此获得一种理解上的安全感。这正是朱熹所谓：“盖是天下道理寻讨将去，哪里不可体验？只是就自家身上体验，一性之内，便是道之全体。”（《朱子十三》，《语类》卷一百一十六）由于“以行释义”的生动性、直接性，并因此成为一种快捷且可靠的传递文本信息的方式，从而具有了伽达默尔所指出的诠释学应有的特征：“这看起来毋宁是诠释学问题出现的一般特征，即必须把一些远离我们的东西拉进，克服疏远性，在过去和现在之间建造一座桥梁。”（伽达默尔，《哲学解释学》，第23页）第四，“以行释义”是一种洋溢着生命气息的诠释方式。“以行释义”作为文本诠释的一种形态或方式，最根本的特点是它的“生命性”，就是说，“以行释义”是一种生命的诠释方式。为什么做这样的断语？我们知道，“以行释义”基本工作之一是用“行”（实践行为）诠释文本，而文本（经典、概念、命题、观念等）形式是文字符号，这种符号只有落实到“行”（实践行为）才能使其内含的生命信息与能量表现出来，比如，“孝”，没有敬养父母的行为，“孝”永远只是枯瘪的概念，而有了敬养父母的行为，“孝”的生命便体现出来。其次，“以行释义”的精髓在“行”，而这个“行”是调皮的、好动的，从而在时空上表现出多个面向。这种特点意味着某个文本可能由多个“行”呈现，从而使文本的意涵表现为多样性，并且得到更新、丰富与发展。质言之，动态的、开放的“行”之诠释文本实践即是文本被淘汰与优化的过程。比如，“仁”，从孔子到孟子，从程颢到朱熹，再到熊十力，为什么内涵不断被更新、被丰富？就是因为不同时代主体对“仁”意义的诉求立足于不同时代的“行”。可见，“以行释义”在更新、丰富与发展儒家思想路径上亦是一种生命的成长。一般情形下，被诠释文本（作者）、诠释主体、诠释方式与读者构成诠释活动的四个基本要件。在“以行释义”诠释实践中，假如诠释文本是（礼），诠释主体是（陆九渊），诠释方式是（以行释义），读者是（詹阜民），那么，诠释文本（礼）因为诠释方式（师身起弟子起）而呈现其意涵（尊敬师长），读者（詹阜民）因为这种诠释明白了什么是（礼）。在这里，文本（礼）因为“以行释义”而呈现其意涵，读者（詹阜民）因为“以行释义”而明白其意涵，诠释主体（陆九渊）因为“以行释义”而与文本（礼）和读者（詹阜民）发生互动关系，可见，“以行释义”是一种整体的、有机的实践活动。更为重要的是，“以行释义”诠释方式的核心是“行”，而这个“行”是既受时空限制又超越时空限制的，即具有动态性、多样性、无限性特质，这就使“以行释义”诠释系统中的所有元素时刻处于紧张与松懈、激动与冷静、绝望与希望交织之中，即处于生命的新陈代谢之中。因此之故，我们说“以行释义”是一种生命诠释形态。

**参考文献：**

［1］古籍：

《史记》、《论语》、《朱子语类》、《礼记》、《孝经》、《孟子》、《陆九渊集》、《王阳明全集》、《荀子》、《周易》、《尚书·大禹谟》、《晦庵先生朱文公文集》、《周易外传》、《揅经室集一集》、《张载集》、《二程集》.

［2］谢幼伟．现代哲学名著述评．济南：山东人民出版社，1997.

［3］施莱尔马赫等著，洪汉鼎译．理解与解释——诠学经典文选．东方出版社，2001.

［4］伽达默尔著，夏镇平等译．哲学解释学．上海译文出版社，1994.

# 试论《中庸》的体用

## ——兼比较中西叙事文学“中庸”观念的运用

新加坡国立大学 辜美高

## 一、导言

《中庸》的探索，中西学者的研究成果累累，笔者只能择要看一些，而且觉得历来《中庸》的研究，宏观、微观的考察、验证都颇全面，但因为各家重点不同，对于“中庸”本体的分析，略有偏颇。本人不谫固陋，在本文把主要的研究成果加以梳理、补充。而《中庸》一书的确也谈到“应用”方面：“执其两端，用其‘中’于民”。[①] “用”即“应用”，所以“执中”有其应用的一面。这个“执中”在应用层面也颇为广泛，单就叙事文学而言，便可以找到相当的例证；而异质传统的西方叙事文学，也都有类似的题旨。从这个层面来说，“中庸观”有其普遍性的一面，这或许是汇通中西文化的一个切入点。

## 二、轴心时代的《中庸》本体的原貌及其精神层面

《中庸》为《礼记》的一篇，是汉代的产物。孔子（前551—479）的“中庸”思想传给子思，子思传给孟子（前372—289），孟子的思想在民间流传，为汉代的儒家所继承。毋庸讳言，“中庸观”到了西汉，才有比较系统的记录，理论也比较彰显。孔子述而不作，而且他对“中庸”的阐述，语焉不详，在《论语》中，只有“中庸至德”这么一句，使我们在了解早期儒家“中庸观”时有诸多困难。

我们如果参照轴心时代希腊的伦理思想，发现它跟早期中国儒家思想有很大程度上相似之处。尽管耶氏皮尔斯 Jaspers 的《轴心时代》文化理论受到雷爱泽 Heiner Ro-

① 《中庸》第六章。

etz 等人的质疑[①]但雷爱泽也承认，两套类似的伦理思想可以在不同的文化体系中同时发生。由于《中庸》跟阿里斯多德的《伦理学》的体系有很多类似的地方，所使用的关键词颇为一致，这对我们比较两个系统的逻辑推理是很有利的。孔子的时代，与柏拉图（前428—348）比较接近，孔子去世之后52年柏拉图才诞生，柏拉图的《理想国》中的伦理思想，传诸亚里士多德（前384—322），亚氏著有《伦理学》[②]、《政治学》等等，对于《理想国》的伦理等思想加以发扬光大。而亚氏的时代与孟子的时代很接近，[③] 其伦理思想跟《孟子》所承受孔子的伦理思想，也很近似；《孟子》的伦理思想，为西汉《中庸》所继承，并适度地发挥《荀子》的感知、理性调节与虚、一、静等等的思维。[④]《中庸》的宗教、伦理思想能自成体系，是很难能可贵的。如果将《中庸》跟亚里士多德的《尼可马科伦理学》对比，我们可以发现在精神层面上，两书很接近，这不是偶然的巧合，而是有一定的逻辑联系与根据的。由于年代湮渺、地域阻隔、语言移译的困难，以及语言工具本身的局限，造成我们对汉代流传下来的《中庸》思想全面的了解有很多困难。所幸自印欧文化系统的佛教传入中土之后，经过历代，尤其宋明理学家，援佛入儒，进行逻辑性的推论，益以现代学术的进步，汉代《中庸》的真谛才为我们所认识，而《中庸》思想的原始全貌，才得以更清晰地呈现出来。

研究《中庸》学者多从“中和”立论，这是无可厚非的。但《论语》提到“中庸”（“中庸至德”），[⑤] 只有1次；[⑥] 而西汉《礼记》中的《中庸》篇，“中庸”一词的出现，竟有9次之多，[⑦] 这是值得我们注意的现象。换句话说，对“中庸”观的重视与认识，在西汉更加全面，这部书也随着《礼记》被尊为儒学经典而得到更大的重视。“中庸”“未发”与“已发”那种均衡、和谐的物理状态——“中”，早为人们所理解。[⑧] “中”是喜怒哀乐在未发时看起来似静实际上是动的状态；而这种状态在发出时，则能中节，且不偏不倚，呈现“和”的状态。人们很少注意到，“喜怒”、“哀乐”两极情感的对立动态，[⑨] 把动态“喜怒”、“哀乐”的对立当成平面、静态看待。实际上“喜怒”、“哀

---

① 见 Robert N. Bellah 跟 Hans Joas 合编的英文专著《轴心时代及其影响》页248—273。

② 以《尼可马科伦理学》广为人知。

③ 亚氏比孟子大12岁。

④ 见燕国材《先秦心理思想》，著者没有指出《荀子》的认知论跟《中庸》认知论的联系，没有点到宗教的语境，很可惜！

⑤ 见雍也篇。

⑥ “中行”则见子路篇。

⑦ 见李申《四书全集译注》的统计。

⑧ 见《中庸》第一章：天命之谓性，率性之谓道。喜怒哀乐未发谓之中，发而中节谓之道。

⑨ 现代学者燕国材等例外。

乐”为两极的情感，其张力是势均力敌，看起来似静而实是动的均衡。情感是一种动力[①]也体会到这一点，可见在他们族群的传统文化认知中，情感是能量。现代学者唐君毅也体认到《中庸》的动态跟变化的力量。[②]

现在先让我们看看主要“情感”及几个重要概念在先秦儒家典籍中出现的情况。情感活动在希腊文为 energeia，是一种能量 energy，活跃、充沛 dynamic。但是英文没有对应的词语，而一般人也未加以注意。移译成华文时，更是隔了一层。加以在华人文化中，虽然有阴阳两元的思想，但两级对立的思维并不发达，因此容易被忽略。“喜”在《论语》只出现一次，[③] 而且它的古义是完成任务后的轻松心情，是属于比较崇高的情感。《论语·阳货》记载孔子见到他的学生治下的地方，弦歌不辍，莞尔而笑，跟他的学生开玩笑说：“割鸡焉用牛刀?”此处“笑”这个词，显然是会心的微笑、高兴的心态，虽然《论语》很少出现“喜”这个字眼，这里孔子的高兴心境，没有用“喜”这个词来表述，但也应该算进去。所以《论语》“喜”的词义，虽然不很多，应该重新加以统计。《孟子》“喜”这个词出现则多达 12 次，[④]“喜”的词义当然包括正面跟负面，负面的“不喜”也应该包括在内。“不喜”《论语》有时也用“不说（悦）”代替，如《阳货篇》：子路不“说”（悦）。

“怒”这个词在《论语》没有出现，令人惊奇，类似“怒”的情感，在《论语》出现多次，如“忿”，同“怒”；[⑤]“怨”在《论语》出现 20 次之多，毕竟“怨”跟“怒”的情感有距离，但次级情感的流动性比较大。“怒”在《孟子》则出现 10 次。[⑥] 我们退一步说，《论语》没有“怒”这个词，但《论语》“小不忍则乱大谋”中的“不忍”，[⑦]不正是说明主体抑制“怒气”么？又有“是可忍，孰不可忍!”[⑧] 这里的“忍”，也是忍怒的意思，则“怒”这种情感词义也见于《论语》。明代哲人所说的“忿懥”早见《礼记》，应该是“愤怒”的情感，所以真正统计起来，这类的词的数目，在早期的中国(early China)，可能会增加几个到十几个百分点。《论语》出现“怒”这个词义，在西方的文化中经常出现，且被列为七恶不赦的大罪，这一点中西方又似乎很一致！

其实，《论语》也有以“喜”与“惧”对举的情况：父母之年，不可不知也，一则

---

① 现代美国希腊裔作家的《中性》台版页 358。

② 见《中西哲学思想比较论文集》页 385－389。

③ 杨伯峻《论语语译》索引。

④ 杨伯峻《孟子译注》。

⑤ 先进篇。

⑥ 杨伯俊《孟子译注》。

⑦ 卫灵公篇。

⑧ 同篇。

以喜，一则以惧。[①] 这种两极的对立的情感，也未得到应有的注意。此外，正面的抽象情感如“忠”与“孝”，“孝”与“游”在不同的社会场域中，有时也会呈现相反的张力。这种伦理矛盾，虽然早为人们所熟悉，但其两极的思维的意义，并未发展起来。

中国早期所认识，或记录的情感，有什么七情六欲，一般人都不甚了了，说法也不一致。早期文献如《荀子》有所谓六情：喜怒、哀乐、好恶，[②] 发展到了后来如明代，也只举出好恶、恐惧、忧患、忿懥六？七种。[③] 王阳明所强调的“恻怛”。[④] “喜”、“怒”对举甚少，“哀”“乐”对举也罕见。孔子曾说：父母之年，不可不知，一则以喜，一则以惧，[⑤] 约略可见他列举两极感情的一斑。《论语》“哀”（出现 6 次），“惧”出现 7 次。顺此一提的是，“乐”多指感官的快乐（偶尔也有例外）。反观亚里士多德，在《伦理学》中胪列多种相对的“情感”（feelings）：欲望 lust、愤怒 anger、恐惧 fear、自信 confidence、忌妒 envy、喜悦 joy、友爱 friendship、憎恨 hatred、期望 longing、骄傲 emulation、怜悯 compassion——苗力田译作，页 31，英文夹住见 Dover Publications，Inc.，1998，页 25。必须说明的西方八十年代心理学界曾把情感分类及其对立图表如下：[⑥]

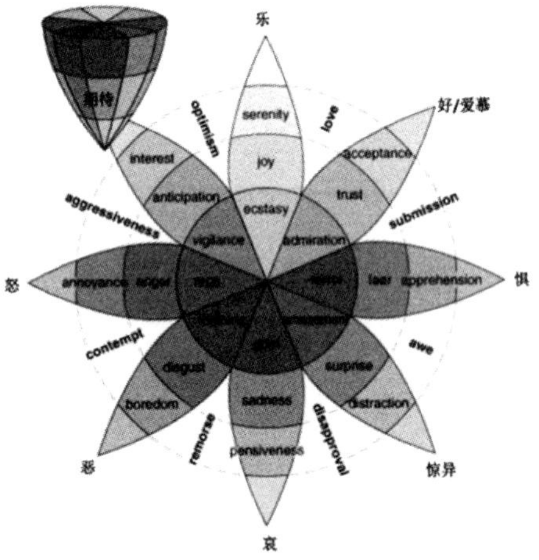


---

① 里仁篇。

② 见《先秦心理思想研究》页 132。

③ 张学智《明代的哲学》，北京大学出版社，2000。

④ 悲哀的意思，见诸《礼记》，也未见正式列入早期文献的“七情”中。六欲一般认为是耳目鼻口身意，说法则比较固定。燕国材认为中国先秦两汉“情”与“欲”的界限不很清楚，这是事实。也即是说，对于情感、欲望的认识，七情之说法不一致，且模糊了情感对立的实际。这种对立，虽然孔子已经有相当的认识：他的“好”“恶”论述，频频出现，或单独论述“好”或“恶”，或“好”“恶”对举（在《论语》）。约有 7、8 次之多，至少说明孔子洞悉到这类情感的对立性。顺此一提，《中庸》“好恶”并举，单举“恶”1 次，含有“恶义”的词“射”有 2 次。

⑤ 里仁篇。

⑥ 主要分为 8 个极类，各极类各有情感子目若干，其对立的状态，读者一目了然。

因此，体认“喜怒”、“哀乐”[①] 两极的情感张力，在理解《中庸》是很重要的。我们相信，在排除文字魔障之后，把先秦文献中有关情感词义的词儿，一一罗列出来，加以分类，相信能找出类似亚氏在《伦理学》中所罗列出来对立情感词汇。

至于“诚”，《中庸》说，中庸的本体是“诚”。这个“诚”字的意思，应该用它“诚恳”的本义！翻译成英文一般是 sincerity。这个《中庸》的道德本体，应该是一个动态的有机体（上面说，希腊原文“情感活动”的“活动 activity”含有“能”energy 的意思）。由“诚”可以派生很多正面的道德品质，如“敬”、“善”、“信”，乃至于“创作力”creativity，明代的王阳明认为这个道德主体是“良心”，这种种都有可能、可以接受的延伸义。因此，“诚”翻译成英文时，如果上下文需要，当然可以灵活地翻成 creativity。

由“诚”可以派生出“敬”respect 的品质或态度，在理解《中庸》也是很关键的。“诚”这个词，在《论语》出现 9 次。“诚”跟其他品质，在《论语》都统属于“仁”这个大概念之下。

“诚”和“敬”可以结合、联系起来，构建《中庸》的宗教精神，突显生命的意义！《中庸》“敬”出现 6 次，（这是一个关键词，未见李申统计）其实，《中庸》中的“尊”，如第 20 章“尊贤，礼之所生”、第 18 章“尊为天子”以及第 16 章祭祀时“齐明盛服，以承祭祀”等等，都含尊敬的意蕴；这些“尊敬的词义”，跟核心的“诚”在建构《中庸》敬业、敬人的崇高人生观和宗教精神，意义重大。

另外一个重要概念是“天”。“天”在《中庸》出现 11 次，[②]《中庸》的“天”是神。在《论语》，孔子对“天”、对“神”的态度不很明朗。早期的农业社会，宗教气氛十分浓烈，尽管孔子类似其他文化中的改革者 reformer，限于篇幅，不再申述。[③] 凯伦安斯特朗 KarenArmstrong 所列举在轴心时期的几个主要文化，都有宗教改革者出现，孔子便是其中的一位。孔子虽然说，“敬神鬼而远之”，[④] 但他不是无神论者，至少也是个 Agnotheist。笔者认为虽然这样，孔子还是对神明非常恭敬：“祭如在，祭神如神在。”。[⑤] 根据卡伦的描述，世界几大文化都跟重视祭祀 sacrifice，这跟他们的神话、信仰有关。祭祀的牺牲是生命的复始，生命从尸身重新诞生出来。[⑥]

《中庸》记载，（武王、周公）郊社之礼所以事上帝（第 19 章），当然可以用来证

---

① 包括后面提到“好恶”。

② 包括“天命、天命之性”——李申的统计。

③ 读者可以参考朱伯昆《先秦的儒家伦理》。

④ 雍也篇。

⑤ 《论语》八佾篇。

⑥ 用 sacrifice“牺牲”的本义，人们甚至于能产生自我牺牲 self-sacrifice 的崇高精神也渊源于此。

明《中庸》是有神论，《中庸》也很重视祭祀。确定《中庸》的宗教要素，并从这个语境来谈《中庸》的精神层面，才有可能。在这一点，中西（希腊）的看法不谋而合！《中庸》本体的性质是诚、是善，而圣人的性质跟“天”一样。[①]“诚”是《中庸》的本体，也是宇宙本体，因此道德主体的思维活动，能跟活跃的宇宙本体联系起来。君子平日的修养、格物，都储存于“诚”的本体“记忆库”中，表面上《中庸》没有“择”、“择善”的字眼，可是君子在修持的过程中是有所选择的，而所选择的点点滴滴都进入“诚”的记忆库里。所以《中庸》的主体，具有自动的选择本能，具有择善、化解负面的能力，这虽然是我们的推理，实际上，《中庸》第二十章便这样说，“诚者不勉而中，不思而得，从容中道。”《中庸》叙述君子平时修养，谨慎[②]审问、思辨，毕恭毕敬，一点都不马虎。如果圣人、君子在思辨的过程中，没有机制的自动调节、化解负面价值的能力，怎样能“不思而得”呢？怎能“从容中道”呢！“诚”是天道，“诚之者”是人，[③]“择善而固执之，……博学、审思、明辨、笃行，[④]”（同章）这是平日修养的功夫，择善而从，这些功夫，积淀于心（诚）的本体，所以道德主体也能跟圣人一样不思而得。“择善”有两种，一种是机制外的修养，一种是主体自动调节功能，早在《中庸》年代100年前的《荀子》，已经认识到这种思维功能，《中庸》继承《荀子》思路，不只是可能，而且是既然的事实！

上古人们似乎对于心官的思维功能认识不很够，不大谈这些，[⑤] 从形神的配合，整个思维过程比较完整地叙述出来，《荀子》的叙述则更为全面。《中庸》很可能继承《荀子》这种思维。文本中的“择”，“择善而从”的“择”，是一个关键词。在这里，他跟《论语》中多数的“择”语境有点不一样。《论语》中的“择”。多数是孔子教导他的学生在学习、修养时所作的“选择”，是外在修养的功夫。《中庸》此处的“择”，是思维过程的一种自动自发的行为，当然这种“择”跟外在修养的“择善”所沉淀于潜意识的自动调节功能是有联系的。《中庸》此处的“择”，除了显示主体的选择、调节的功能外，也暗示主体“择善”的自觉性。

英国浪漫诗人济慈（1795－1821）作诗，在美化丑恶的现实时更体会到脑海的negativecapability。[⑥] 当诗人全神贯注于创作 creativity，这种化解负面的 negativeca-

---

① 普通人很难达到圣人的境界；《中庸》一书中常常把“圣人”与“人”对举！普通人当然可以通过后天的修养，达到同样的境界。

② 有择善的意蕴。

③ 普通人。

④ 得做修养的功夫。

⑤ 只有墨家—见《先秦心理思想》页59－74。

⑥ 化解负面、对立面的能力。

pability是一种不自觉的本能。《中庸》虽然没有这样论证，但是它“择善”的自动、自觉的功能，似乎能达至同样的逻辑性的结果。

当道德主体在祭祀时对“天”、“神”诚惶诚恐、虔诚的态度，能达到忘我的境界ékstasis（ecstasies），注意这个词在希腊语只能作“忘我”解释，[①] 但不能诠释为“紧张、刺激”，这种ecstasies跟庄周梦蝶“忘我”的境界一样。在“忘我”那一刹那，精神超越到更高的境界（transcends）。《中庸》虽然没有用到这两个或对应的术语，可是在思维的过程中，逻辑上必定经过这两个步骤，人才能跟天地参合，参与天地的“教化”跟“创作”和“创造”transformation and creativity！

希腊人相信神—上帝God，上帝是善的Goodness，正和亚里士多德《尼克马斯伦理学》处处所强调的神性divine、divinity相通。亚里士多德的《政治学》，主张“公正”，“公正”也即是“善”！传统的中国也相信“天”是善良的，《窦娥冤》例外地诅咒天：“您错堪贤愚枉做天”！“天”，本来是公正、无私的，可是因为政治黑暗，“天”也变得不公正、不善良了！这样的思维，中西是比较一致的。

总之，本论文注重中庸的“中”和状态，对于《中庸》重点揭示“诚”的重要性，未加详细论述，有兴趣的读者，可以找专著来看，我们不乏这样的专著。至于为什么儒学从孔孟的仁学、仁政，发展到西汉，会变成“诚学”呢？“仁”可以统摄所有德目，上面已经点到，而且是尽人皆知的事。“诚”为仁的德目之一，见于《论语》上面已经说过了，一共9次，“敬”则出现21次。“诚”这个德目，由于时代不同，社会发生激烈的变动，从封建礼制的崩溃，发展到战国时期道德沦丧的尔虞我诈，突显“诚”品质，正是对症下药，补弊救偏。汉代提出“诚”作为儒家思想核心的核心，便是这个意思。中国历代虽然实行儒家思想，时代不同，重点常常移位、调整，是可以理解的。这个推论，是笔者对中唐白居易的道德观初步的观察，联想到秦汉时期的具体情况，初步这样蠡测。

上述我们强调《中庸》或亚氏的《伦理学》，必须在浓郁的宗教语境讨论“中庸”，golden mean，才能达到那样高超的思想境界，道德主体才能体悟到生命的意义！我们从诸多的关键词的联系、对比，看到中西哲理思路的一致性与逻辑性：“喜怒”、“哀乐”的两级对立以及中庸本体的“择善”自动调节的功能。由于中庸本体是诚、敬、善（goodness），道德主体在修持的过程中，持着虔诚、敬畏的心态，所以能进入忘我trance式地超越，达到更高的境界，参与天地化育万物的不朽事功。

---

① 《中性》的作者优金奈德斯也这样解释，见《中性》台译页414－415。

## 三、中庸应用的层面

中庸深深地植根于中西文化传统的源头里，影响长远。在现实生活里，处处可以找到中庸观应用的例子。西方的 moderation，广泛地应用于日常生活中。就拿中文的叙事文学而论，很多喜剧都有中庸观念。生活于明末的剧作家李渔，主张创作时先立主脑，他在《风筝误》中，主张婚姻美女配俊男、美美相配的理想，而任何违背这个理想的人，都会遭到笑声温和地谴责。《风筝误》叙述一个寄居戚补臣篱下的文人韩琦仲，羡慕才女詹淑娟的诗才，题诗风筝寄意。哪知风筝误落才女同父异母的姐姐丑女詹爱娟的手中。作者通过错误、误会、巧合，让美丑错位，丑女幽会戚补臣白丁的儿子“戚友先”。[①]“戚友先”（韩琦仲）见丑女，胸无半点墨汁，而且急色无礼，觉得好像碰到“魑魅、怪物”一样，借机溜之大吉。[②] 俗语说“知子莫若父”友先父亲的戚补臣倒也有自知之明，自家的儿子友先不求上进，终日吃喝嫖赌，怎样能匹配才女佳人呢？他不敢有奢望，[③] 还是比较踏实。虽然友先不喜欢丑女詹爱娟，但是婚姻由父母主持，最后他们也没奈何！这是作者通过情节手段，成功调和第一个“过分”的例子。作者又通过戚补臣为世交韩世勋的儿子主婚，撮合才女詹淑娟与新科状元韩琦仲的婚姻。本来男才女貌，天造地合！是中庸、理想的模式。可是由于种种的误会，这段理想的姻缘顿起波澜，在所有的疑虑冰释之后，才子配佳人的理想，才得以实现。全剧以婚姻为主线，平西川大败蛮兵为副线，副线制造机会让才子发挥他的文武才华，在剧本中占有重要的位置。主副两条线交织在一起，使剧情复杂多变化。内容方面，其中庸思想可以接受，其他的则由作者的人格关系，思想水平不很高尚。

明末清初吴炳的《绿牡丹》的题材也跟《风筝误》类似。主题除父为女择婿，注重才貌的匹配、不重门户的婚姻观外，更重要的是，作者借才子佳人的本事，反映及揭露明季学风的腐败、科场的舞弊，时代意义比《风筝误》更大。作者为避免被视为批评时政，把背景设在南宋。[④] 作者对于翰林沈重、才子顾生的描述比较含蓄，[⑤] 这可能是事实的。笔者以为，这个剧本的另外一个重要的主题是“鉴真”，[⑥] 实际上是 16、

---

① 其实是戚友生的同窗才子韩琦仲。

② 这都是双方的误会：“戚友先”为才子，而詹爱娟为“佳人”，丑妇拟嫁“俊男”“太过”的奢望！，引起观众、读者哄堂的笑声！。

③ “不过分”，中庸。

④ 第二十九出：假报：“今年大比，谢生、顾生入京赴举，此去临安（杭州）甚近，回家听榜”，明代首都不在临安，可证。

⑤ 见现代版第 20 出的眉批。

⑥ 第 25 出中会考的题目。

17世纪以来中西戏剧所常常探索的主题：假象与真相 appearanceand reality 的中文版。作者严肃地指出，假象[①]是欺诈，是犯法的![②]

这个剧本情节中的中庸观是很突出的。沈翰林一面为了自己的诗歌嗜好，一面为了奖掖人才，更为了择婿，退休后回乡组织文社，定期会考。他考试规则：坐必依号，动必执签。[③] 但他信任社员，“认为夹带、传递，非贤者所为”（同出），所以不加防范，考试规则比较松弛。反观其他文会，像顾粲的，会规非常严格：窃抄旧文者罚，传递者罚……。[④] 必须说明的是，沈翰林的社规很宽松，顾生文会的规则严格，互为对比。而所谓的“严”，是相对而言，而且这种“严”，不是“过分”的“严”，是恰到好处、正常的 norm，所以作者所要摆正的，不是从一个局端到另一个极端，而是从一个极端的不足（宽松）到正常 norm。沈翰林的“宽”造成种种弊病发生：柳五柳社考时请才子谢英代笔，博取第一名；车尚公请妹妹代笔，取了第二名，真材实料的顾生，只能屈居第三。假名士得逞之后，甚是嚣张，咄咄逼人。经过不断的揭发后，沈翰林才决定举行复试，他的态度也改变，从犹豫变得更坚定。他严格监考，禁止传递，[⑤] 考场所需的“供给”全由主考负责，考场备也有“净桶”，考生考试期间不许外出出恭。会长还亲自监考，“端然全注眼，时时背地偷看”[⑥] 真才才得以甄拔出来。

吴炳的中庸观，也体现在这个剧本的婚姻理想上。他认为才子应该匹配佳人，但不注重门阀，是比较进步的观点。作者描写冬烘的纨绔弟子，徒有其表，才学“不足”，却利用所获得的虚名，用不道德的手段奢望娶得美媳妇。作者以中和思想来遏制这种偏颇，通过符合生活逻辑的情节，先让纨绔子弟柳五柳、车尚公作假得逞，让他们拥有虚名之后，又逐步让他们出丑，处处嘲弄，让他们知道以假乱真的艰难，[⑦] 而对真才实学的士子，则让他们出人头地，社会秩序回复“中正”normal。基于同为文社同仁的情谊，作者又不做得太过分，他没让白丁太难堪，作者提供他们一个中间场所 middle place，温柔敦厚地让他们移位，从追求者变成证婚人，见证才子谢英、顾粲跟佳人车小姐、沈小姐成为眷属。

最近林芷莹的研究显示，这个剧本原是温体仁批评复社社员夤缘攀附，[⑧] 流传的粲花斋本《绿牡丹》为吴炳改写的传奇，是吴炳为复社社员辩护，情节、题旨的矛头则指

---

① 包括婚姻。
② 第28出：争婚：“骗婚，有犯科条!”。
③ 第5出：社集。
④ 第二出，强吟。
⑤ 很重要的一个关键词，不断地在剧本中出现。
⑥ 第25出：严试。
⑦ 面对难度高的考题，搜索枯肠，感到头痛、想呕吐。
⑧ 剧本已经失传。

向温体仁族人。但无论剧本批评的对象是谁，这个剧本批评明季的学风腐败则是事实。这个剧本，以美女喻复社，丑人比况喻温体仁的族人，力倡杜绝科场歪风，主试严防舞弊。这样的解读，应该是可以接受的。

上述连个剧本，似乎没有联系到宗教，实际上，儒家重视修身，修身多少具有恭敬诚信的情怀，在此不赘述。

现代丁西林的白话短剧《三块钱国币》也很重视中庸观。丁西林是物理学家出身，更懂得平衡这个道理。在他的这个剧作中，也贯穿了这种思想。剧本情节是这样：1940年代抗战时期，避难西南后方的有钱太太，家里雇了佣人，女佣不慎打烂她心爱的花瓶，理论上应该赔偿女主人，但从人情角度来看，房东不应该让女佣赔偿，因为女佣穷无立锥之地，因为贫穷，不得已才出来当女佣。在这样的情况下，情与理怎样取舍、调节，取得平衡？房客男大学生很有正义感，同情女佣，坚持女佣不应该赔偿。女房东则太过分，坚执己意，大学生与女房东争执相持不下，房东太太只好诉诸法律，把警察找来。最后还是富有同情心的路人看不过去，代女佣出了三块钱国币了事。矛盾似乎解决，但法理、人情没有得到平衡。作者为了让大学生泄愤，让他砸烂另外一个花瓶，掏出三块钱国币，掷给房东，让房东没脸，并发出协助弱势者的呼吁。因而全剧的主旨，情感、金钱、正义的处理，获得了平衡。

华人很讲究中庸，甚至于以“中庸”做座右铭，给孩子取名为“执中”，新加坡也有一位名人名字为“执中”，便是一例。《儒林外史》也有一位姓杨名执中的，可惜这位杨执中，不是不偏不倚的儒林楷模，而是吴敬梓批判的对象，说他名实不符！这样的例子可能还有，得更深入地发掘。我记得旧社会的市场，有中人的制度，碰到雇主与顾客有所争执，双方同意找中人调解，中人主持公道后，双方各付中人若干佣金。本地的考试，如果遇到主试人员意见不一，常常找第三者调协 moderate，协调者 moderator，尽管怎样客观，甚至于不让他看到分数，协调之后的平均分数跟两个极端分数加起来的平均分数往往差不多，大家也就无话说了。这跟市场制度中的中人没有什么不同。这是日常生活运用中庸观的实例，至于政经、宗教方面的争执、修正，持中庸态度与方法的例子恐怕不可胜数，不是这篇小文及笔者学力所能独立完成的科研。

在希腊罗马时代，亚里士多德的《伦理学》影响很大，奠定西方的伦理传统。希腊的文化，在罗马基督教化后，有一些仍残留在主流文化中。文艺复兴之后，西方各大学将亚氏的伦理学列为大学教科书，亚氏的伦理思想的地位，更加根深蒂固。大文豪莎士比亚，是一个闻名于世的中庸折中分子。学者们怀疑他的中庸思想是来自中古的道德剧，再早一点的源头好像还没有学者找出来。莎翁的剧作《一报还一报》Measure for Measure 是一个很出名的中庸案例。故事情节是有所本，是意大利及英国的剧作的改编，论者以为其立意、构思、人物塑造远在原作之上。故事描写维也纳（影射文艺复兴期的英国）的法纪在公爵文森修 Duke Vincentio 治理下越来越松弛，① 尤其是男女风化问题很严重。国王有鉴于此，采取强烈②的措施，委任一位严明的廷臣安哲鲁③摄政，负责执法的重任！这个铁面无私的安哲鲁，手段强硬到太不近人情。结果维也纳的法纪，从一个极端走向另外某一个极端！不公正，也不平衡！当安哲鲁抓到一对恩爱的青年男女克劳狄跟朱丽叶未婚先有关系、违反法纪时，拟控以奸淫罪，借以杀一儆百。不幸安哲鲁为前来为弟弟求情的伊莎贝拉的美色、贞洁所动，一时糊涂，威逼她与他幽会，竟然知法犯法！剧本中的人物狱吏给予安格鲁很多机会改变他的过激的想法，而他自己的亲信埃斯卡勒斯 Escalus 也频频示以处事中庸之道，但是安哲鲁却把它当耳边风。实际上，那对青年男女已经有婚约，因为聘金问题，迟迟未能举行结婚仪式，他们的关系，不算淫乱，不应该处以极刑！而安哲鲁的人格高尚，却在那特殊的情况下犯下错误，照常情来讲，也应该予以宽恕!。这个法理与人情的调协，只好落在公爵自己身上。他扮成教士，微行私访，并调动安哲鲁的旧爱人玛丽安娜，让她代替伊莎贝拉，跟安哲鲁幽会；而克劳狄也在善良的狱吏的协助下，逃过死亡的劫数，最后与朱丽叶完婚。公爵没有惩治安哲鲁，而让他向神忏悔，让上帝宽恕他，让他知道法外还有人情。④ 维也纳的法纪，从一个极端腐败，走到另外一个极端无情，摆回中正，只好靠公爵自己。司法兼顾人情，公爵的调整法纪，深得民心。

接下来要分析的是另外一部应用中庸观化解纠纷的小说《南与北》。这部长篇小说是维多利亚中期盖斯凯尔夫人所著的工业化小说，主要是分析当时英国工业社会劳资的矛盾以及化解的方法，很有借镜的价值和现代意义。当时在报纸连载，编者狄更生看到稿子的一部分，初步认为小说应该定名为《南与北》。如果按照这种思路，小说主要是在对比当时英格兰南方跟北的不同、优劣。从这个层面来看，作者通过两个主要人物马格烈跟年轻的企业家桑顿不同的视角表述出来。这是属于认识 perception 的问题。马格烈起先认为南方风景旖旎，空气清新，生活悠闲安逸，南方人有教养，有见识；而北方空气污浊，人们衣着不整洁，重视金钱而轻视教育。这种对南北不尽然的片面性主观的认识，当马格烈在北方的工业城弥尔顿⑤居住两年后，与工人来往，也跟企业家如桑顿过从，大大地改变过来。她发现北方人民的勤劳刻苦、进取、敬业乐业的优点，也认识到工人应有的权益；反观伦敦闹市哈利街，生活甚是舒适，却是很呆滞、灰暗、懒洋洋的，而且穷人没有得到应得的照顾，生活单调，缺乏想象；僻处于

---

① 不足。

② 过分严厉。

③ 性格过分。

④ To err is human，To forgive is divine！

⑤ 实际上是曼彻斯特。

海角的赫尔斯顿，当她重访故居时，发现那里表面上是景色宜人，可是基础设施原始、落后，她不想再待下去。马格烈经过这样的长期居住、观察及比较，对南北认识的偏差，才得以矫正过来！才能发现南方与北方，各有各的优缺点，才能持平与中庸！

作者的原意，该小说的另一个理想的书名为《死亡与改变》，这当然更能反映出作者本身的创作意图：劳资关系必须改变，应该避免暴力的阶级斗争！在这个层面，作者通过黑尔一家在变革的时代所面对的困难：信仰基督教义的唯一神教新诠释，使黑尔失去牧师的圣职，在南方待不下去，只好移居北方弥尔顿（曼彻斯特）。他靠替企业家桑顿补习，一家几口的生活才获得解决。那里的生活艰苦，空气污浊，生活压力大。家庭的变故、工厂的风波、工人的失业、女工的死亡、母亲的亡故等等的改变对他的女儿马格烈的生活、思想有着强烈的冲击，让她深刻反思。她因为在弥尔顿教会做慈善工作，有机会跟普通工人接触，了解他们的困苦，了解纺织工人对劳资关系的认识，以及洞悉他们对自己权益捍卫的决心。马格烈的父亲黑尔是桑顿的老师，有机会告诉桑顿从工人、市民处听来的故事，有时全家也出席桑顿的宴席，有机会跟桑顿家人交流。

由于马格烈对劳资双方的了解，作者设计她成为劳资冲突的调解的关键功能人物。工人总认为，资方剥削、压榨。当工人诉诸工业行动而老板想请爱尔兰工人来解决工潮时，饥饿、冲动的工人，在这种极端认识的激动下，包围资方，局势紧张，弩拔弓张，暴力一触即发。作者设计基督唯一神教教徒马格勇敢地烈挺身而出，用她的爱，劝工人回家，并且警告说，军队马上就赶到。当她看到工人俯身捡石头时，她意识到即将发生什么，连忙用她的身体掩桑顿。群众更愤怒，石头开始抛掷过来，不幸打中无辜的马格烈！马格烈应声倒地。群众见状，万分错愕，感到内疚，于是犹豫，退却。一场暴力的冲突，暂时平息来。工潮过后，工人找不到工作，带头围攻的鲍彻，自溺身亡，留下嗷嗷待哺的儿女。这次工潮，工会承认估计失误，也不够理性。所以事件过后，工人对资方极端的偏见逐渐摆平。这一切，都是通过马格烈的活动、穿梭，描述出来。作者也通过马格烈的活动，反映工潮也改变资本家极端的态度。鲍彻的自杀，也使桑顿进行反思：工人不是蛮不讲理，他们罢工，反对爱尔兰工人夺走他们的饭碗，是他们的基本权益；而他自己对罢工工人强硬不体恤的态度，也得检讨一下！怎样避免这种不愉快的局面呢？他不断地寻求答案。当时纺织业面临国际的压力，靠贩卖奴隶换取美国南方庄园园主的棉花供应的不光彩手段出了问题，[①] 而资本家面对难言的经济困境，工人完全不了解，双方各执偏激的见解，是造成劳资关系空前紧张的原因。这主要是是劳资双方缺少沟通所造成的。怎样追求劳资共同的利益，是后工潮双方反

---

① 这一点，连桑顿本身也不知道，小说第 41 章写他还在探索这个问题。

思的主要课题。桑顿着手改善管理方法，建立餐厅，提供劳资对话、交流的平台，主张劳资互访、沟通、互相尊重，成为调协劳资关系的不二法门。作者通过人物思想、行为的改变、调适，认为这样地消弭极端，即使不能绝对根除罢工，至少也可以缓和紧张气氛。维多利亚人的从折中、协商中追求进步，迈向盛世、和谐的心态，在这部小说中充分展现出来。盖斯凯尔夫人的中庸观，不亚于老前辈、戏剧泰斗的莎士比亚！

最后让我们管窥后现代的一部名著美国尤金纳德斯英文长篇小说《中性》，该小说2002年出版，主要是以美国的希腊移民史为背景，讲述一个中性人从女变男的过程和感受。笔者在此所关注的是作品中的关于希腊移民的民族感情这个课题，并用它来分析作者的中庸观，是小说的副题。这个课题，叙述者的表述一般很含蓄、点到为止。叙述者在处理土耳其跟希腊间的民族感情时，采用中庸的观点，小说也不乏他的老祖宗亚里士多德伦理思想的影子。叙述者基本是按照时间的顺序讲述祖孙三代的希腊情结，不时用回顾、倒叙 flashback 的手法，情节闪烁、跳跃，但是故事的发展基本上是线性的，不很凌乱，这是后现代作家故意刺激读者，让读者主动进行思考惯用的手法。叙述者的祖父母是希腊山村的蚕农，不幸的是，希腊、土耳其为领土的纠纷再度爆发战争。1922 年，土耳其挥军占领俾斯麦拿，进行大屠杀。叙述者祖父母的双亲在这场冲突中牺牲了，祖父母的友人费罗波先医生则全家被屠杀。他们仓皇逃命，乞求法国军舰的协助，逃离灾区，然后移居美国。这样毁家灭族的血海深仇，叙述者的祖母戴斯蒙德娜都一一记载在她的 6 个扇面上：多少人命伤亡，多少财物损失，多少房屋被焚毁。叙述者颇费篇幅讲述，他的意图、态度，这一点是毫不含糊的。叙述者单方面记载土、希民族的恩怨的不平衡情绪。他的祖父母抵达美国，从纽约入境后他们前往汽车制造中心底特律希腊移民社区生活。从叙述者的点滴描述，我们可以推测他们常上希腊正教的教堂礼拜，过着典型的希腊人的生活，希腊的情结，浓得化不开；希腊的民族仇恨，尤其是祖母，耿耿于怀。

但是叙述者的祖父到了美国，思想却有点变化。为了生活，他在福特汽车厂打工，接受厂家对他们生活的指导，工余学习英语，接受熔炉文化的洗礼，对希腊的情感逐渐有所淡化。1974 年，土、西的军事冲突再度爆发，希腊的移民在电视屏幕前观看新闻片，议论纷纷。美国总统尼克松，为了美国国家的利益，① 支持土耳其入侵希腊，希腊的移民哗然反对。只有叙述者的祖父，认同尼克松总统的外交政策，也因此遭到族人的疏离。作者用时间，将作者祖父的世仇记忆，在时间长河中冲刷，了无痕迹。

希腊移民的第二代，即叙述者的父亲弥尔顿，希腊文书写起来已经不很流利，对于希腊文化的认同，勉强还算可以。在母亲（叙述者的祖母）的影响下，为了感激烈

① 在地中海东部保留西方的影响力。

士圣徒克里斯多夫护佑儿子避免在朝鲜战场中充当炮灰，想举家回希腊旅行，乘机粉刷庙宇，答谢神恩！哪知土、希战争又爆发了，行程取消了，孩子们包括叙述者卡尔，都很高兴，他们很繁忙，有很多事情要做，取消行程，可以有时间留下来处理杂事。希腊对他们来说，实在没有什么，不过为了好奇，偶然注意一下！移民的第三代对希腊的认同，几乎消失殆尽，哪里有希腊土耳其间的深仇大恨存在的空间？叙述者卡尔在成长过程中，从性别的混淆、尴尬的边缘挣扎过来。叙述者幸好没有行为不良的记录，变性[①]的事实，不足构成他当公务员的阻力。他成功地当起外交官，派驻柏林，从事文化协调的工作。在柏林他跟土耳其人密切来往，而祖母所念念不忘的土、希的民族仇恨，压根儿已经不存在。这是作者用时间、距离，环境的转换，使土希的民族的仇恨在移民中稀释、淡忘 forgetting，实际上是提供第三场所 third place——美国，乃至于提供第四场所——德国的首都柏林！第一代人的仇恨，随着第一代人的消逝，深埋坟墓。叙述者派驻柏林，跟土耳其的移民或居民毫无猜忌地往返，土希民族的关系，成为一种新的常态 norm。基督的宽恕，再度成为和解的手段！土希民族的后裔，才能在第三场所和谐相处。

我们的比较，虽然不全面，但是粗略可以看出在叙事文学的领域，中西各种类型的中庸，而且都是呈现比较持久（permanent）的均衡状态。西方叙事文学描述的中庸的生活面似乎比较广泛，从法理人情到平息工潮，到种族仇恨的消弭跟种族的和谐相处，波澜壮阔。

## 四、极端的时代

中庸是庸俗的？尤其是在后现代，后现代排斥中庸思想？这是后现代知识界的焦虑。丽莎马尔斯雅诺 Lisa Marciano 在分析《莎士比亚戏剧中庸金科玉律》Shakespeare’s Comedic “Golden Mean ”，曾引用姚思华思科德尔 Joshua Scodel 的专 Excessin Early English Literature，早期英国文学中的“过分”题材，文学的权威理论家如赛依德 said，认为中庸的处事艺术在后现代还是管用，但在艺术美学方面则不适合。我翻开柏拉图的《理想国》最后一册，赫然发现他反对史诗、悲剧的论调。柏拉图反对模拟的诗歌，认为诗人被次级的感情所俘虏，从一个极端走到另外一个极端，不受理性所控制；[②] 而模拟方面模拟又不到精髓，而且又用夸饰、渲染，误导读者。[③] 柏拉图把诗人放逐，虽然后来很后悔，但是柏拉图对诗人大起大落描写极端的情绪始终没有

---

① 从女变男。

② 不够中庸、平允。

③ 柏拉图这一点，论者以为是片面的。

好感。

当新的极端时代来临，评论家认为中庸仍然有其相关性，但不适合美学·亚里士多德认为美学作品如悲剧追求强烈（极端）的情感，以引起读者怜悯、恐惧，达到净化作用；布莱希特则认为，艺术可以引起读者对不平的注意，然后加以改善。[①] 如果照布莱希特的说法，则中庸作品所达至的“中和”，是在事后，而不在作品本身或创作时的那一刹那。我们还需注意的是，后现代的文类区分已经很模糊，文类的发展，已经山穷水尽，作品文类掺杂混用，文类界线已经越来越模糊。针对文类的差异的理论，似乎有点风马牛不相及。

这样看来，极端时代所面对的美学问题，是老课题，我们得乞灵于历史，从文化源头探讨起。至于处事，在极端时代，采用中庸手法，寻求均衡、公正，是颠扑不破的真理，一般似乎没有异议。的确，我们此刻所处的是极端分化的时代，在历史的长河中，后现代未尝不是处于一种寻求平衡的过程。霍布斯鲍姆在他的著作《极端的时代》描述1914—1990这个极端的时期，从一战到冷战的结束，长长80年，中间不是有一段著者自称的黄金时代么？那个阶段是继续一战二战激烈的极端动荡时代之后，所获得的平衡。但几十年的黄金时代之后，我们又步入动荡、反恐反暴的极端时代，尤其是911之后。后现代的不稳定更加显著，人心惶惶。但是世界的领导不是坐视不顾，他们不停地争取和平，不断地再寻求新均衡。让时间来证明吧！十年，二十年，或许再久一点，尘埃落定之后，新的均衡迟早会出现的！

**参考书目：**

[1] 燕国材．先秦心理思想研究．长沙：湖南人民出版社，1981.

[2] 燕国材．汉魏六朝心理思想研究．长沙：湖南人民出版社，1981.

[3] 燕国材．中国心理学史．台北：东华书局，1996.

[4] 董根洪．儒家中和哲学通论．济南：齐鲁书社，2001.

[5] 唐君毅．中西哲学文化体系比较．台北：学生书店，1998.

[6] 霍布斯鲍姆著，郑明萱译．极端的时代（Age of Extremes）．南京：江苏人民出版社，1999.

[7] 亚里斯多德．尼各马科伦理学．北京：中国社会科学出版社，1982.

[8] 刘殿爵，陈方正．礼记逐字索引、大戴礼记逐字索引．香港：中文大学出版社．

[9] 李学勤．“孔子的天道观”早期文化的可能．北京：商务印书馆，2008.

① 理论家认为，这跟文类有关系：戏剧家要教导观众，必须夸大说明，观众才能明白。

［10］陈来．郭店楚简与儒学的人性论．（10 页，网络文章）

［11］李申译注．四书导读译注．成都：巴蜀书社，2002.

［12］杨伯峻．论语译注．香港：中华书局分店，1984.

［13］杨伯峻．孟子译注．北京：中华书局，1981.

［14］姚文放．中国戏剧美学的文化阐释．北京：中国人民大学出版社，1997.

［15］丁元植．郭店楚简．台湾古籍出版有限公司，2000.

［16］朱伯昆．“中庸为有神论者”中国伦理学．北京：北京大学出版社，1984.

［17］张学智．明代的哲学．北京：北京大学出版社，2000.

［18］王季思主编．中国十大古典喜剧选．济南：齐鲁书社，1991.

［19］丁西林．三块钱国币．新加坡：胜利出版社，1970.

［20］林芷莹．以剧为戈—传奇绿牡丹的写作与吴炳的改编．清华学报．（台）42 卷第 2 期．

［21］李隆献．荀子天道概说——台大开放式课程．（附录一：先秦两汉诸子对天的看法概说）

［22］司俊琴．试论戏剧传奇《绿牡丹》的戏剧性．社科纵横．2002（6）．

［23］优金奈德斯．中性．台北：时报出版事业股份有限公司，2006.

［24］柏拉图著，刘勉、郭永刚译．理想国．北京：华龄出版社，1996.

［25］钟彩钧主编．明清文学与思想中情、理、欲与学术思想篇．台北：中研院中国文哲研究所，2009.

［26］林顺夫．试论董说《西游补》“情梦”的理论基础及其寓意．同上．

［27］刘宗贤．阳明道学革新与良知说的情、理、欲机制．见上引钟彩钧编．

［28］盖斯凯尔夫人著，主万译．南与北．北京：人民文学出版社，1994.

［29］吴祖镏．关于《南方与北方》的一点看法．南通师专学报．1994（12）．

［30］William Shakespeare，Measure For Measure，USA：Wadsworth，2012.

［31］G. A Nedozchiwin，Marxism and Art：Writingsin Aesthetics and Criticism，Philadelphia：David Mckay Company，Inc.，1972.

［32］Weiming Du Centrality and commonality，Albany，NY：The State University of New YorkPress，1989.

［33］Robert N. Bellahand Hans Joas，The Axial Age and Its Consequences，MA：The Belknap Press of the Harvard University，2012.

［34］Aristotle，Nicomachean Ethics，Mineola，New York：Dover Publications，Inc.，1998.

［35］Tom Griffith（tr.），Plato The Republic，The Cambridge University

Press, 2000.

[36] KarenArmstrong, The Great Transformation, The World in the Time of Buddha, Socrates , Confuciusand Jeremiah, London: Atlantic Books, 2006.

[37] Golden Mean in Early English Literaturein Ben Jonson Journal supplied by EUP Kanaya.

[38] Oasamu," The Mean in the Original Confucianism " inPhilip J Ivanhoe (ed.) , Chinese Language , Thought , and Culture, Nivison and his Critics , Chicago and Illinois: Open Court, 1996.

[39] David Hall andRoger T. Ames, The Meantranslation with Annotations , Hawaii, 2002.

[40] Kate Flint (ed.) The Victorian Novelist: Social Problems and Social Change, London. New York . Sydney: Croom Helm, 1987.

[41] Yang MingAn, The Idea of Cheng (Sincerity/ Reality in the History of Chinese Philosophy, New York : Global Scholarly Publications , 2008.

[42] Julius MoravcsikandPhilip Temko (eds), Plato On Beauty, Wisdom and the Arts, Totowaand New Jersey: Rowman and Allanheld, 1982.

[43] G. R. F. Ferarri (ed) and Tom Griffith (tr.), Plato, The Republic, Cambridge: Cambridge University Press, 2000.

Joshua Scodel, Excess and the Mean In Early Modern English literature , Princeton and Oxford: Princeton University Press , 2002.

[44] Kate M. Loewenthal, The Psychology of Religion, a Short Introduction, Oxford : One World, 2000.

# 论黄以周的《子罕言说》

横滨市立大学　小幡敏行

## 一、引言

正如“江东称经师者，必曰黄氏”[①] 所称许的那样，黄式三、黄以周父子以代表晚清浙东学者的学术世家而闻名学界。[②] 因为既不是在官场上晋升高位、政治上大有作为，也不是在学术界居于主导地位，黄氏父子未必可以说是非常引人注目的存在，然而他们以不慕荣利的坚实学风受到了人们的尊崇。无用赘言，作为浙东学术的传统，史学最为著名，而黄氏家学的特长则尤长于三礼。黄氏父子广治群经，著作颇丰，质与量都非常杰出。就黄氏父子丰富的学术成果而论，本文所论只不过是其中的一端。本文拟就黄以周学问的特色和倾向，以他的义利观为中心，试作考察。众所周知，黄式三的《论语后案》是一部在《论语》的解释史上大放异彩的著作。黄以周在继承其父亲的学术成果的基础上，对《论语》子罕篇开头的“子罕言利与命与仁”八字做出了令人信服的解释。本文特别以此为例，追索一位以实事求是的学术精神、不拘泥于门户之见、努力弄清真正的经义的学者的足迹。

## 二、黄以周的生平

黄式三（1789－1862），字薇香，号儆居，七十二岁始以知非子为号。籍贯浙江定海，鸦片战争爆发后移居镇海。赴乡试之际，母亲骤逝，从此不再应试，以岁贡生而终。如黄以周《敕封徵仕郎内阁中书先考明经公言行略》（《儆季杂著》文抄五）、施补

① 参见谭廷献《黄先生传》（《续碑传集》卷七十三）及《清史列传》卷六十九儒林传下二 黄式三。

② 张舜徽《清儒学记》浙东学记第六（齐鲁书社，1991 年，278 页）：“两浙人士，闻风兴起，从事训诂考订的学者，逐渐增多。而定海黄式三和他儿子黄以周，并以学问精博著称于世，成为浙东学派的后劲。”

华《定海黄先生别传》(《续碑传集》卷七十三)所记载的那样,黄式三是一位将一生都奉献给学问的笃学至孝之人。他的著作收录于《儆居遗书》,其中《论语后案》是他的代表作,有“汉宋持平之著”之称。传承式三之学的儿子黄以周,字元同,号儆季,晚号哉生。① 据说本来名元同,字经籑,后来改名为以周,字元同。但是,根据黄氏家族按辈分以“式某”、“以某”、“家某”的排行进行命名这一点考虑,从以周之兄或者堂兄之名来看,“以同”应该是最初的名字。

下面依据黄以周的几个传记资料对他的生平作一个简单概述。以周生于道光八年戊子(1828),道光十一年辛卯(1831)四岁时,母亲亡故,以后对母亲一直追怀不已,无论是对继母还是生母都是同样尽孝。② 幼时开始同兄一起随父而学,经常与受到父亲注目的堂兄以恭(字质庭,光绪元年举人)切磋砥砺。③ 由学政瞿鸿禨的保荐,赐内阁中书衔。又由学政潘衍桐的保荐,奉旨升用为教授,旋补处州府学教授,以高龄而未就任。④ 在此之前,受江苏学政黄体芳(字漱兰)在江阴建立的南菁讲舍之聘,成主讲,基于“博文约礼”、“实事求是”进行教育,不立门户之见。其间,从光绪九年至十五年一直执教于南菁书院。光绪五年知府宗源瀚(字湘文)在宁波创建办志精舍之际,以周受请,为制定书院的名义规制,专门讲授经学。据说成就者甚众,“著录弟子千余人”。光绪二十四年戊戌(1898)移居归隐仁和半山之下,翌年光绪二十五年己亥(1899)十月十七日卒,葬于海晏乡黄家桥东。行年七十二岁。子息六人中,祖父式三特别寄予厚望的第二子家岱(字镇青)能传以周之学,然而三十八岁就离开了人世,没有大成。

黄以周的著作极多,如《儆季杂著》、《子思子辑解》等不胜枚举,代表作是历时

---

① 缪荃孙《中书衔处州府学教授黄先生墓志铭》(《续碑传集》卷七十五)云:“暮年多疾,因曰:‘加我数年,子思子辑解成,斯无憾。’既书成而疾瘥。更号哉生。”记事也见于《清史稿》卷四百八十二儒林传三,《清史列传》作六十九岁。

② 以恭是黄式颖(字穉生)之子,光绪八年五十四岁卒。黄以周有《先兄质庭志传》(《儆季杂著》文钞六)云:“以恭幼慧,从伯父读经,能知大义。伯父钟爱之如其子。”前引《清史列传》关于以周记载云:“少传父式三学,与从兄以恭作经课,互相质。”再有,以恭的生卒年推定为1829—1882,据此,以周比以恭大一岁。

③ 关于以周的任职,《清史列传》等记载“由大挑教职,历署遂昌、海盐、于潜训导,补分水训导。”支伟成《清代朴学大师列传》浙粤派汉宋兼采经学家列传第九记载:“同治庚午优贡。旋举于乡。会试选誊录,期满,当得知县,不就。又十年,大挑,用教职,补分水县学训导。”

④ 《清史列传》等多种资料作光绪十四年或十六年。但是,前引缪氏的《墓志铭》作“辛卯”(光绪十七年,1891),并记云:“而年已七十,礼宜致仕,遂不就。”缪氏受以周长子家辰之委托,为撰墓志铭,从光绪十四年戊子(1888)在南菁书院与以周共事过二年,而发生这样的记载上的差异令人不解。田云汉著《中国近代经学史》(三秦出版社,1996年,193页)记载“一八九一年升任处州府教授,因年届六十,未到任。”这或许是比较合理的。

十九年而成的名著《礼书通故》一百卷。这是专注于礼学的毕生成果，对汉唐至清代诸家旧说的错误加以订正，在古代的礼仪、名物、制度等方面大有发明。关于此书的执笔动机，以周自述“初予读秦氏五礼通考，病其吉礼之好难郑，军礼之太阿郑”（《儆季杂著》礼说一），对秦蕙田（字树峰，1702—1764）的《五礼通考》表明了他的不满，认为《五礼通考》对郑玄（字康成，127—200）之注缺乏一贯性。俞樾（字荫甫，1821—1906）就该书的意义作了如下评论。

惟礼家聚讼自古难之。君为此书，不墨守一家之学，综贯群经，博采众论，实事求是，惟善是从。（中略）洵足究天人之奥，通古今之宜。视秦氏五礼通考，博或不及，精则过之。（《礼书通故》序）

可知俞樾对其不拘泥于汉学宋学的门户之见，以实事求是的精神阐明礼学奥义作了高度评价。不用说，三礼之学虽以东汉郑玄之注为宗，但是对郑注不固执，不盲从，驳正之处颇多。如后面所述，这种是就是是，非就是非，排斥门户之见、汉宋兼采的立场，也是黄氏的家学传统。据说黄以周三十多岁的时候，屡次想向比他大七岁的诂经精舍主讲俞樾请教，而俞樾不以师弟而以对等的关系与之交往，四十岁前后，以周以《礼书通故》就正于俞樾，并想师事俞樾，而俞樾依然坚决没有同意。[①] 由此我们也能窥知俞樾对黄以周的尊重态度。顺便提一下，后来两者同在浙江书局共事。俞樾的弟子并听闻黄以周謦咳的章炳麟（1869—1936）也对《礼书通故》大加赞赏说：“盖与杜氏通典比隆，其校覈异义过之。诸先儒不溲之义，尽明之矣。”（《黄先生传》）[②]

还有作为裨益于学界的工作，值得一提的是在浙江书局时对《续资治通鉴长编》作了校补，在完成《续资治通鉴长编拾遗》六十卷的过程中，以周发挥了决定性的作用。

以上对“晚清一代经师”黄以周的生平和主要业绩作了概述，关于他的初名、补为处州府学教授时的年龄等问题，由于记载不明确，多种资料间存在着互为矛盾的地

---

① 唐蔚之《黄元同先生学案》（原书未见。据马文大、陈坚编著《清代经学图鉴》，国际文化出版公司，1998 年，268 页所引）。据梁启超《中国近三百年学术史》十三清代学者整理旧学之总成绩，《礼书通故》的成书是光绪戊寅，即一八七八年，当是五十一岁。徐世昌编《清儒学案》卷一百八十三曲园学案“曲园弟子”条举了黄以周，而同书卷一百五十四儆居学案下“儆季交游”条举了俞樾。另外，《清儒学案》中收录了以周给俞樾的书翰《答俞荫甫先生书》。

② 章炳麟《黄先生传》云：“其说经，陈事象物闳肃，超出钱大昕、阮元诸儒上远甚。（中略）久之，提督江苏学政黄体芳就南菁书院，延先生讲，主书院十五年，江南诸高材皆出其门。（中略）赞曰：余少时从本师德清俞君游，亦数谒先生。先师任自然，而先生严重经术。亦各从其性也。”再有，前引梁氏书中关于《礼书通故》也说“传其家学，博而能精。又成书最晚，先辈所搜辑所考证，供给他以较丰富的资料。所以这部书可谓为集清代礼学之大成”，又把《礼书通故》与孙诒让的《周礼正义》并称说：“《周礼正义》八十六卷。此书和黄儆季的《礼书通故》，真算得清代经师殿后的两部名著了。”

方。这里特别提一下以周究竟是黄式三的第几个儿子的问题。诸桥辙次的《大汉和辞典》(大修馆书店、1960年)卷十二之九八二页，将黄以周作为“式之第三子”，其依据是臧励和《中国人名大辞典》(商务印书馆、1921年)所记载的“式三子”，即把“式三之子”误读成“黄式的三子”。这完全是基于误读而偶然得到的结论，不值一提。就管见而言，主要有下面第三子和第四子两种说法。

作为第四子记载的资料有：

徐世昌编《清儒学案》卷一百五十四儆居学案下

支伟成《清代朴学大师列传》浙粤派汉宋兼采经学家列传第九

严文郁编《清儒传略》(台湾商务印书馆、1990年)

作为第三子记载的资料有：

张舜徽《清儒学记》浙东学记第六(齐鲁书社、1991年)

最为重要的《清史稿》儒林传、《清史列传》儒林传、缪荃孙《中书衔处州府学教授黄先生墓志铭》(《续碑传集》卷七十五)等传记中恰恰没有明确记载以周是式三的第几子。缪氏的《墓志铭》中仅提到“少承家学，与兄儆孟、儆仲相砥砺”，而没有确证。从上面所列文献资料的数量而论，作为第四子的记载要多一些。像最近刊行的马文大、陈坚编著的《清代经学图鉴》(国际文化出版公司、1998年)中也有照原样影印《清儒学案》的情况，可见《清儒学案》的影响力不会太少。但是，根据前面提到的黄以周自己撰写的《明经公言行略》，式三的原配袁孺人(1789－1874)生有长子以愚、二子以巽、三子以周以及女儿三人，而继配应孺人(1802－1874)没有孩子，所以认为以周是黄式三的第三子应该是不错的吧。如果更为慎重一点的话，那就必须彻底查明第四子说的根据。至于《大汉和辞典》把以周作为式三的第三子，完全是偶然的一致。

## 三、《子罕言说》

众所周知，围绕《论语》子罕篇开头的八个字“子罕言利与命与仁”的解释，一直存在着各种各样的争论。[①] 关于命暂且不提，而如果说孔子“罕言”仁，这完全是不符合实际的。这是引起各种争论的出发点。换句话说，作为思想上的问题，这关系到能不能把利与命、仁并列为同样范畴的问题。历代注释家为了解决这种矛盾而作的种种尝试固然颇有意思，然而笔者以为从通史的角度追溯一下“利”是如何被把握的，被认识的，这不是可以成为我们理解古代中国义利观的发展变化的一条线索吗？不过，

---

① 参照松川健二《关于〈论语〉子罕言利章》,《二松》第十三集，二松学舍大学大学院文学研究科，1999年，第27－283页。

细看历代关于义利的论说，有包摄利的义，与义一致的利，各种各样的概念定义中发生细微差别的情况很多，所以我们对利的判断应该避免一概肯定或者一概否定的武断做法。

利、命、仁三者概而括之，都作为“罕言”的对象，在《论语》的解释史上对利作肯定解释的，首先就古注而言，是魏时何晏（？—249）的《论语集解》。其云：

罕者，希也。利者，义之和也。命者，天之命也。仁者，行之盛也。寡能及之，故希言也。

何晏基于《周易》乾之文言传的吉利解释利，认为能达到其水平的人很少，所以说“罕言”。由于先行的诸家注释都已亡佚，我们虽然不能肯定何晏那样的解释是不是标准的，不过正如我们在皇疏、邢疏中看到的那样，可以肯定这种解释表示了后代理解中的一个方向。附带说一下，根据新出的郑玄注中“利有货之殖否。（中略）孔子希言利者，为其伤行也”（敦煌本伯希和文书二五一〇号）这种用货殖来解释利的话，那么利绝不是深奥莫测的吧。

其次，就新注而言，是南宋朱熹（1130—1200）的《论语集注》。其云：

罕，少也。程子曰，计利则害义。命之理微，仁之道大。皆夫子所罕言也。

朱熹之说基本上引用了程颐（1032—1107）的言辞。在此，明确将利与义相对，与命、仁画了一条界线。程朱将“计利”视作问题，所以并不能说他们对利本身作了全面否定，不过由此可以窥知程朱反功利主义的立场。作为这种立场的背景，我们可以指出的是，就像我们通过“义利之辨”所知道的那样，当时学者们对围绕义与利的关系问题怀有极大的关心。[①] 不管怎么说，与义水火不容的利，在朱子学中是受到排斥的。

从《论语》里仁篇的“放于利而行，多怨”、“君子喻于义，小人喻于利”等语句看，用利欲、货利来解释利倒是更为自然。古注将利、命、仁三者并列而论，难道对它与这些实例的不统一性视而不见吗？不用说，我们不能不考虑到“三玄”流行下《易》的地位之高的背景、利字多义用法等因素。另一方面，即使我们信从新注引用的程伊川之说，将利从命、仁那里分离出来，依然不能解消我们的疑问，因为《论语》中言及仁的地方是非常多的。正因为如此，朱熹的集注风靡一世之后依然没有定论，围绕“子罕言利章”的解释的问题火种依然存在如故。

围绕利的解释实在太多，不可能涉及各种说法，简洁言之，其他还有基于断句的

---

① 参照拙稿《关于“义利之辨”根据的考察》，《横滨市立大学论丛》第五十卷人文科学系列第二、三合并号，1999年，第111—136页。

解决法，[①] 或者像焦循（1763—1820）《论语补疏》中“谓古所谓利，今所谓义也”所解释的那样，试图用一种义利统一观来解消矛盾。但是总体来看，义利统一观、义之内外之利这种新概念的提出，对打破严格区别义利的传统的义利观并没有足够的力量。

在这样的情况下，稍晚于乾嘉之学隆兴而登场的黄式三的《论语后案》则是一种全新的尝试。他驱使其独特的文字学知识，做出了一种奇拔而出人意表的解释。[②] 而式三之子以周继承其父之学问，也有题为《子罕言说》（《儆季杂著》群经说三）之文章。以下就让我们来根据其行文看看其主要论点。所用版本以光绪二十年南菁讲舍刊本为底本。

> 夫子于礼曰极言，曰纵言，于诗书执礼曰雅言，于利命仁曰罕言。皆阐发滞义以通晓斯人也。

这里引用了《礼记》礼运篇的“言偃复问曰：‘夫子之极言礼也，可得而闻与’”、同上仲尼燕居篇的“仲尼燕居，子张、子贡、言游侍。纵言至于礼”，还有《论语》述而篇的“子所雅言，诗书执礼，皆雅言也”三条资料。将“极言”、“纵言”、“雅言”并列起来是为了把“罕言”作为一个固定用语，使它重新具有积极的意义，从而找出其中所隐含的孔子所想说的意思。尤其是从《礼记》的例子我们可以联想到在子游的提问中所看到的那种孔子对弟子们的启发场面。

《说文》罕训网，本无稀少义。训稀少者，字之借也。

这才是式三《论语后案》的重要之处，试图返回东汉许慎的《说文解字》，追求其本义。这绝不是有什么特别之处，不用说，许慎之学对于汉学家来说，其重要程度犹如人之背脊那么重要。《说文解字》的引用，不但重新确认了稀少不是罕之本义，而且根据罕在《说文解字》的网部，以及网和干的构字要素，重新确认了罕字的字形。

> 先儒以命仁非夫子所少言，多作别解。或训为微言，或解为难言之，或读子罕言利句绝，与命与仁，许命许仁也。或于子罕言利下，又作转语，子少言利，若言利，必合命与仁并言之义。皆迂回鲜有定解。

式三认为先儒们对前述矛盾的种种解释牵强附会，难于信从。然而《论语后案》对所批评的学术观点，不明言具体的人名，只是列举具有代表性的解释。不用说，皇侃、公羊学者的宋翔凤（1779—1860）《论语说义》是其批评的心中标的。

考古人罕轩子多通用。左传昭公元年郑罕虎，公羊经作轩虎。定十五年郑罕达，公羊经作轩达。昭四年郑浑罕，韩子外储说作浑轩。故先君子论语后案读罕为轩，训

---

① 参照杨希枚《〈论语·子罕〉章句问题评断》及《再论〈论语·子罕〉章句问题》，《先秦文化史论集》，中国神会科学出版社，1995年，第433—468页。

② 参照松川氏前引论文282页及拙稿《黄式三〈论语后案〉——汉宋兼学的成果》，松川健二编《论语的思想史》，汲古书院，1994年，第412—426页。

为表显言之。

在确认未有定说之后，式三想从古代罕与轩字的通借关系中找到解决问题的活路。他从经书等文献中搜求其佐证，以《春秋左氏传》、《春秋公羊传》，还有《韩非子》外储说左下用字的相异为根据，证明罕与轩两字的通用。因此，《论语后案》将“罕”读为“轩”，进而用表显来解释其义。

> 表显言之者，推广其义言之也。罕轩有明显义，亦有宽广自喜义。郑浑罕，字子宽。郑公子喜、宋乐喜，皆字子罕。庄子天地释文云，轩，宽悦之皃。此其证也。

这里比《论语后案》更进一步，从“表显”推广开去，从“明显”到“宽广自喜”，摸索字义的引申。同样再以《春秋左氏传》为根据，从名与字的意思上的相关关系证明字义的关联。还引证陆德明《经典释文》庄子音义云：

> 夫子于利与命与仁，皆喜推广言之。如言利必及义，言命必及性，言仁必及四德。皆阐发前圣未尽之意。

其解释即是言利推广而及义，言命推广而及性，言仁推广而及四德。这样，利、命、仁三者都作为罕言对象的矛盾就解消了。

> 文言传曰，利者，义之和也。说卦传曰，穷理尽性以至于命。子贡曰，夫子之言性与天道，不可得而闻也。天道，即命。合义以言利，合性以言命，此前圣未尽之义，蕴而阐发诸夫子者。故曰，不可得而闻。闻，谓闻之于古。仁，包四德言之。亦前古所未闻。

与上文同样，再以易传为旁证，对相互的关系作了补充说明。利用易传或许是与向古注的回归是一脉相承的。引《论语》公冶长篇“子贡曰：‘夫子之文章，可得而闻也；夫子之言性与天道，不可得而闻也。’”，认为“合义以言利，合性以言命”是孔子以前听不到的，是孔子的发明。仁包括四德也是孔子之前所不可听闻的。

> 大凡圣人之道，利普物我而无害。命通理数而无间。仁兼礼义而有节制。异端之学，往往执吾道之一端以自域，遂有偏而不举之弊。故言利而为我，言命而任运，言仁而兼爱天下。执一废百，语必贼道。

这里再一次从圣人之道强调利、命、仁表显而言的必要性。还从反面，陈述了异端之学的弊害，[①] 还言及了宿命论、杨朱的为我主义和墨翟的兼爱说。

> 夫子喜推广言之，所以救当世之末失而阐前圣之微恉。溯性于天道，即有物有则之遗言。利者义之和也，克己复礼仁也，又古训之传诵于时人者。述而不作，

---

① 前引缪氏《墓志铭》云：“至其道德性命之学，则在辨虚无辨绝欲。以执一端立宗旨为贼道。”前引《清史列传》云：“生平以明经传道为己任，辨虚无，辨绝欲，而以执一端立宗旨为贼道。”

此夫子自道意也。而狂澜既倒非夫子推广古意而表显言之，谁为中流砥柱。故学者有罕言之记。

以周认为《孟子》告子上中所引用的《毛诗》大雅・烝民的“有物有则”、《春秋左氏传》襄公九年的“利者，义之和也”、同上昭公十二年的“克己复礼，仁也”，是当时所传的古训。《论语》述而篇中有“子曰，述而不作”，这虽是孔子的自述，然而身在乱世，孔子不得不推广表显古义而言之。

以上解释上的结论以及基本资料的操作所依据的基本上都是黄式三的《论语后案》。就训诂方面而论，我们虽然不得不承认《论语后案》的旁征博引之精，然而“子罕言说”的简明扼要、条理分明的论述中有着一种新鲜的独特性，可以说别是一家言。

## 四、黄以周的义利观

为了更进一步理解支持《子罕言说》的理论，当然必须对黄以周的义利观进行考察。从传记中我们也能看到他关于“义利之辨”的态度，[①] 就义利问题进行论述的则有《对义利问》（《儆季杂著》文抄四）一文。有人以古典为依据，抓住“义利之辨”的矛盾，提出了两个责难。这篇文章就是对这两个责难的回答。还是以光绪二十年南菁讲舍刊本为底本，顺着行文对其论述试作概观。

或有疑于义利之辨，因举陆象山策以问曰，凡圣人之所为无非以利天下也。二典载尧舜之事而命羲和授民时，禹平水土，稷降播种。为当时首政急务。梁惠王问何以利吾国，未有它过而孟子何遽辟之峻、辨之力。夫子亦曰，君子喻于义，小人喻于利。樊迟欲学圃，亦斥以为小人，何也。

第一个责难：征引《尚书》中尧舜的治绩，说明利天下正是圣人的责任。然而当梁惠王请问国家之利益时，孟子立即进行了严厉的批判，孔子也有里仁篇君子喻于义章中那样的发言，子路篇中“樊迟请学稼。子曰：‘吾不如老农。’请学为圃。曰：‘吾不如老圃。’樊迟出。子曰：‘小人哉，樊须也’”，把想学习农业的樊迟看作是小人。这是为什么呢？就是说，孔孟否定利，这与尧舜为天下万民兴利不是矛盾的吗？这位提出责难的人究竟是谁不得而知，或许与不喜陆王之学的以周下面这个传说有关。《清史列传》中记载“镇海胡洪安悦象山之言，与以周纵言义礼，以周曰：‘经外之学，非

---

① 前引缪氏《墓志铭》“先生以孟子学孔子，由博反约，而未尝亲炙孔圣。其间有子思子，综七十子之前闻，承孔圣以启孟子，乃著子思子辑解七卷。而举子思所述夫子之教，必始于礼乐，及所明仁义为利之说，谓其传授之大恉，是深信博文约礼之经学，为行义之正轨，而求孟子学孔圣之师承，以子思为枢轴”云云，举示了在孔子与孟子之间发挥承继作用的子思的“仁义为利之说”，几乎同样的行文在《清史稿》、《清史列传》中也能看到。再有，式三对义利也有如下规定：“义所以利物通行咸宜，是谓义。利彼害此，是谓利。故圣训辨义利。”（《明经公言行略》）

所知也。'”

> 对曰，古之言利者，普其利于天下合义言之也。后之言利者，专其利于一己舍义言之也。利物合义，于古有明训。以利为利，于今有炯戒。梁惠王问利国，其合义言之，抑亦以利为利也。孟子于此苟非辟之峻、辨之力，何以为孟子。

以周的回答首先指出古代的利是以天下全体为对象，与义一致；后世之利专为个人，与义相悖。以周把古今之利二分为“利物和义”和“以利为利”。在此基础上，以周指出唯其能将梁惠王之义利作严格区别，这才不愧为孟子。

> 在上之君子，当普其利于天下。故曰，喻义。在下之小人，或专其利于一己。故曰，喻利。樊迟居夫子之门，当喻在上君子之所喻者而请学若彼。自与老农老圃为伍，何怪乎以小人斥之也。

这一段对孔子批评樊迟是小人的真实意图作了解释。上面所说的古今之公利与私利的区别同样适用于君子与小人的区别，樊迟学于孔门，应当以成为君子为目标，然而他仅希望学习农事，所以孔子才批评他是小人。

> 昔者禹平水土，稷降播种，教稼穑于举世不知之日，手胼足胝。君子谓之义，以其利物之功大也。若后世老农知稼、老圃知圃而区区学此，其利不亦细乎。

这里以禹、后稷为例，指出与他们对天下万民所做的巨大功绩，被后人称颂的义相比，学习农事之利其是何等的细小！

> 又问曰，辟土地、充府库、约与国、战必克，此其为国之利，固亦不细，而孟子顾以为民贼，何也。岂儒者之道，将坐视土地之荒芜、府库之空竭、邻国之侵陵而不为之计，徒以仁义自解如徐偃王、宋襄公者为然邪。世以儒者为无用、仁义为空言。不深究其实，则无用之讥、空言之诮，殆未可以苟逃也。

第二个责难：孟子把为富国强兵而谋取国家利益看作是民之贼，这是为什么？这个责难的依据是《孟子》告子下中的这段文字：“孟子曰：今之事君者皆曰，我能为君辟土地，充府库。今之所谓良臣，古之所谓民贼也。君不乡道，不志于仁，而求富之，是富桀也。我能为君约与国，战必克。今之所谓良臣，古之所谓民贼也。君不乡道，不志于仁，而求为之强战，是辅桀也。”再有，如果像徐之偃王、宋之襄公那样，在仁义的名下坐视国家的衰亡，那么就无怪乎世人要说儒者无用、仁义空言。这个责难基于现实的功利主义尺度，把重义轻利的理想论看作是不切实际的、虚伪的谎言。

> 对曰，土地其必贼民，乃辟乎。府库其必贼民，乃充乎。与国其必贼民，乃约乎。战必贼民，乃克乎。其相率而为之者，非徒无利而又害之。是以苏秦、商鞅、孙膑、吴起之徒，小足以灭其身，而诸侯之用之者，大足以亡其国。

这对这个责难，以周的回答是，如果为了谋图富强而必定伤害人民，那么就不应该这样做，因为这样做有百害而无一利。像纵横家、法家、兵家诸子，他们自己就不必说，给国家也带来了灭亡的结果。

惟儒者之道，以仁义为本，本立而效自见。是岂等于无用之空言哉。夫子曰，上下相亲谓之仁，除去天下之害谓之义。以是行之，利孰有大于此乎。传曰，仁人之言，其利溥。又曰，义以生利。又曰，言仁必及人，言义必及利。又曰，义所以生利也。仁所以保民也。不义则利不阜，不仁则民不生。是则外仁义以言利，利必参害。有利无害者，仁义也。

另一方面，以周认为儒家之道仁义是根本，只要根本的仁义得以确立，效用就会自然相随。首先作为孔子的言辞，引用《礼记》经解篇的“上下相亲，谓之仁，民不求其所欲而得之，谓之信，除去天地之害，谓之义”，举示仁义的效用，认为没有比这更大的利。其次引用《春秋左氏传》昭公三年、成公二年，还有《国语》周语①中的文句，以证明仁义与利的相关性。以周认为如果脱离仁义之利就伴随着害，只管追求仁义就只有利而没有害。就是说，作为仁义之结果的兴利除害是被积极肯定的。与先义后利或者唯义弃利相比，这是一种稍稍带有仁义至上倾向的义利统一观。

彼夫徐偃王、宋襄公其人者，平日未闻行一仁、施一义，临事仓猝反借仁义之名，徼幸于万一。是何足论哉。后之人不得援此败国丧师之人而疑儒者坐视其弊不为之计也。

更进一步说，徐之偃王、宋之襄公平时完全不实践仁义，只不过是发生问题之后托于仁义，这并不是仁义的失败。把所谓的“宋襄之仁”与仁义等同起来是不正确的，所以并不能以他们为根据而说儒者无用。

虽然，疑者之妄为疑，正由说仁义者之妄为说耳。其说曰，仁义中之功利，君子不计，必使冥情处事无所为而为之。若预参立功兴利之见于其中，即为小人。由是言之，则其受无用之讥、空言之诮也，亦宜。

以周分析招致那种责难的原因之一，是因为有人主张极端的反功利主义——甚至排斥对动机或效用的预见。以周认为对于那种对功利不屑一顾，将效用置之度外的过激主张，世间的“无用空言”的批判是最合适不过的。作为这种议论的背景，我们不难想起陆九渊（1139－1193）的“当辨其志”（《白鹿洞书院讲义》）、陈淳（1159－1223）《北溪字义》义利条对比天理与人情，认为“天理所宜者，即是当然而然，无所为而然也。人情所欲者，只是不当然而然，有所为而然也”等言说来。

正如上面概述的那样，针对第一个责难，以周把古今之利区分为“利物和义”和“以利为利”加以论驳。把利分为公利和私利，肯定前者而否定后者，这是典型的围绕义利之辨的一种议论。针对第二个责难认为儒者毫无对策、拱手坐视国家衰亡的批判，以周以一种义利统一观应对，主张只要是真正的仁义就不是无用的，而是功利相随的，

---

① 《国语》周语中“不仁则民不生”作“不仁则民不至”。

“宋襄之仁”等并不是因仁义而失败的先例。以周巧妙地避开了要么仁义要么功利的单纯的二选一，主张以仁义为根本，同时对功利也作积极的肯定。由此可见，我们可以认为黄以周排斥宋学中那种极端的反功利主义，而基于重视仁义的重义轻利的立场则是他的基本立场。他反对将义利作割裂的区别，反对对一切利的萌芽都不容忍的极端主义，积极肯定由仁义带来的兴利除害。再有，针对基于经书的责难，以周从正面根据对经义的解释进行反证则是其特色。

## 五、结语

“先生恪守父训，以传经明道为宗旨”① 的黄以周的《子罕言说》，乍看起来会有一种祖述其父《论语后案》的印象，实际上有着他自己明晰的论理逻辑。以周在《子罕言说》中把利、命、仁三者统括起来都作为“罕言”的对象，对利不作全面否定，对由仁义带来的利加以肯定。与宋学中明显的反功利主义的严格立场不同，黄以周把功利作为仁义的效用对利作了定位。但是，仅根据这一个事例说他有向汉学回归的倾向是不妥当的。不拘泥于汉学宋学的门户之见，② 阐明真正的经义才是其唯一的目的。以周并不是盲从古注，以易传为依据进行重新解释，在《对义利问》中对无用空言之批判进行反驳的义利统一观才是他的根据所在。

有一种观点认为，考据学只是埋头于文字音韵训诂的研究，做一些枝叶末节的琐屑小事。然而黄氏父子的研究绝不止于此，在他们的研究中我们可以感觉到他们想通过弄清经义而阐明圣人之道的崇高目的和为达此目的的一片热诚。结果如何，另当别论，我们至少不能同样把它归之于离奇古怪之说吧。从清代学术来看，正处在衰退时期的晚清，黄式三、黄以周父子的业绩肯定是闪亮的一道光束。再有，黄氏家学尤长于三礼，基于“欲挽汉宋学之流弊，其惟礼学乎”③ 这种信念的业绩，对于形成与理学相抗衡的礼学隆盛的时代风尚④发挥了巨大的作用。

---

① 据前引缪氏的《墓志铭》。关于孝行有如下记载：“其事父三十余年，未尝去左右。父卒前数月，大厥而苏，成偏枯疾，手不能作书。一日自叙黄氏塾课，字形蜿蜒难读。先生适自外返见而大惊，请口授为书之。父卒，先生装绝笔一纸，不忍毁弃，且曰：示我子孙知吾父拳拳，是书所以佑启后人者深且远也。居丧尽礼，不徇时俗。”

② 前引缪氏《墓志铭》有云：“先生以为三代下经学，汉郑君宋朱子为最。而汉学宋学流弊，乖离圣经，尚不合于郑朱，何论孔孟？”《清史稿》所记相同。《清史列传》“汉学宋学流弊，乖离圣经”作“汉学家破碎大道，宋学家乖经臆说”。

③ 前引缪氏《墓志铭》中语。

④ 参照张寿安《以礼代理——凌延堪与清中叶儒学思想之转变》（中研院近代史研究所，1994年）；王茂《凌延堪的“以礼代理”说》（王茂等著《清代哲学》、安徽人民出版社，1992年）所；拙译《凌延堪的“以礼代理”说》（北海道中国哲学会《中国哲学》第二十三号，1994年）。

# 民主视野的比较

## ——梁漱溟与牟宗三相关思想的一个对比

上海复旦大学 杨泽波

近代以来，在如何看待民主问题上，学界大致有两种不同的态度：激进主义者崇拜西方的文化，不相信自己的文化，认为只有把中国原有的东西统统扔掉，一切向西方学习，中国才有希望；保守主义者则对中国文化有强烈的认同感，特别强调中国文化有自己的特殊性，有着很高的内在价值，这些是西方有所欠缺，需要向我们学习的。梁漱溟和牟宗三虽然均属于保守主义阵营，但其具体看法又有所区别。将这二人的相关思想进行一个比较，在今天显得尤为重要。

当20世纪一些人主张全盘西化的同时，梁漱溟不畏压力，旗帜鲜明地站出来反对，坚持认为中国文化的特点不适合推行民主制度，成为一番独特的景象。梁漱溟提出这种主张主要基于这样一些理由：

其一，中国人在生活上奉行安分不争的态度，政治上崇尚消极无为，缺乏西洋人主动积极争取的精神。西方政治制度是建立在大家各自爱护其自由，争取其权利，关心其切身利害的基础之上的。在这种态度之下，法律不过是社会政治制度的表象而已。与此不同，中国人习惯于对政治不闻不问，对个人权利绝不要求，这种不争的态度与西洋民主制度格格不入。中国的问题不是争权夺利而是太不争权夺利，完全没有权利意识。中西文化在这方面的态度极其不合，决定中国不能发展民主。

其二，中国人崇尚谦德，尊敬他人，佩服他人，缺乏西洋人的竞争精神。西洋人好动，选举时政治家到处演讲，发表文章，不断表现自己。这是他们的可爱之处。中国人则喜静，推崇谦德。如中国推行选举，众人必有尊敬之心，佩服之心，而相率敬请于其人之门而愿受教益。被选举人则避谢不敢当，辞之不可，或且逃之。这种犹抑歉然若不足的崇尚谦谦君子的精神怎么可能发展出西方的选举之制呢？怎么可能发展出西洋的民主制度呢？

其三，中国人性善论发达，信任人，对人至诚无二，尊尚贤智，西洋人则以性恶为依据，人与人之间不存在信任。欧洲人的政治制度以性恶论为基础，人与人之间时时提防，所以政治上采取三权分立，主张制约与平衡，相互监督，推崇“有对精神”。

正是在这种精神下，西洋人能够在政治上运转灵活，推陈出新，又能在个人权利上有所保障。中国讲求至诚无二之心，首先是信，彼此相互信任，相互尊重；其次是礼，崇敬对方，信托对方，有极高期望于对方人。这种情况在西方人那里是没有的，他们的精神要粗些，彼此之间不信任，而中国人讲求礼，唯敬无二，崇尚“无对精神”。

其四，中国的态度不在欲望的满足，而在积极追求人生之理（亦是人生的价值意义），西洋民主政治是欲望本位的政治，在于保障人权，拥护个人的欲望。西洋人将人生放在欲望上，生活就是欲望的满足。西洋人受基督教的影响，强调罪的观念，人生即是一个赎罪的过程。出于对中世纪追求未来天国的反对而要求现世幸福，近代以来他们来了一个政教分离，从而发展出民主政治来。中国的人生价值在于理。中国人从不轻易抛弃人生向上的追求，认为人生与人生道理不能分家，中国的政教是不能分离的。①

正确看待中国社会的性质，对其有一个准确的感觉和描述，是一门高深的学问，极见悟性与学力。梁漱溟根据自己的体认和观察，认识到中国是一个伦理社会，与西方的阶级社会完全不同。这个伦理社会有着自己非常独特的精神特质，并不适合西方民主制度的发展。如果不充分尊重中国社会的特质，盲目推行民主，一定会造成极大的不适应，政治永无清明之希望，中国也永无前途之可言。梁漱溟的这些论述在当时多被视为食古不化，成为被讥讽的对象，但今天重温起来，却给人振聋发聩之感。不妨设想一下，如果在数十年前，中国真的大规模广泛推行西方的民主制度的话，中国会是一个什么样子？一定是天下大乱，永无宁日。从这个意义上说，历史无疑已经证明了梁漱溟的正确，证明他是一个胜利者，一个胜出者，无愧为20世纪中国政治的先知。当然梁漱溟的看法也有可以再推进之处。他对社会的观察多偏重于文化和精神方面，缺少历史的观点，没有能够看到民主其实是一种基于经济和文化而形成的独特的生活方式。经济和文化是可以改变的，民主也是可以改变的。虽然经济和文化的改变不能一蹴而就，民主的引进和开出，是一件极为艰苦工作，是一个漫长甚至极为漫长的过程，但随着社会的发展，人们在经济上有了独立的地位之后，有了独立的人权之后，一定会提出自己的要求，维护自己的权益。在民主思想已成为政治常识的情况下更是如此。近代以来，中国社会在经济制度和政治制度方面都已经发生了翻天覆地的变化，已不再是先前那个典型的伦理社会，不可能再固守着自己先前的传统一成不变了。一方面保持自己的传统，另一方面汲取民主的优势，已是大势所趋。

牟宗三与梁漱溟的致思方向有同也有异。一方面，牟宗三对中国政治传统同样有

---

① 参见梁漱溟《我们政治上的第一个不通的路》，《梁漱溟全集》第五卷，济南：山东人民出版社，2005年，第133—173页。

深入的分析，认为中国传统政治走的是道德一途，核心是“仁者德治”。中国传统政治这一特点，自然有其所长，即使将来中国政治进行改革，有了新的变化，也一定不能丢掉自己传统中好的东西。在这一点上，牟宗三与梁漱溟的立场非常接近。另一方面，牟宗三与梁漱溟又有所不同。梁漱溟认为，中国传统政治有自己的特点，在这个基础上没有办法发展民主。牟宗三则认为，中国传统政治将希望完全寄托在圣君贤相上，未能开出“对列之局”，一旦矛盾无法化解，最后只能想革命的办法。革命虽能解决一时的问题，但革命成功之后，好上一阵，随着新皇上的能力下降，达不到圣君贤相的程度，又会重新引发民众的不满，招致新的革命。中国数千年的政治历史，就是这样一治一乱，不断循环。要从根本上解决这些问题，一个有效的办法就是通过坎陷，“让开一步”，“下降凝聚”，开出民主。我在其他文章中已经说明，牟宗三论坎陷开出民主确实有其理论上的不足。如他只看到发展民主必须“让开一步”、“下降凝聚”，由仁的系统，变为智的系统，没有将精力更多地放在经济的层面，严格说来，解说并不到位，很容易给人一个错误印象，好像只要发展道德之下的认知层面，就足以完成开出民主的任务似的。可能正因为如此，尽管他反复讲坎陷，但坎陷如何开出民主的问题，不仅学界能够真正了解者甚少，而且在现实层面上也很难真正落实。但牟宗三认为，中国应该而且可以开出民主，走民主的道路，则是非常明确，没有疑问的。[①]

更为重要的是，牟宗三不仅不否认在中国发展民主制度的可能，甚至还对民主制度有很高的评价。在晚年《中国文化大动脉的现实关心问题》的讲演中，牟宗三对人类政治历史的发展有一个基本概括，认为人类政治的进步过程可分三个阶段：“初是贵族政治，再是君主专制，终是民主政治。只有这三个形态，再没有其他别的了。就政治形态来说，民主政治是最后的（final）形态。”“假定在人类集体生活中还需要政治，这种宪政民主式的政治形态便是最后的（final）形态了：如果说我们根本不需要政治，那自然另当别论。”[②] 明眼人一望即知，在这个问题上，牟宗三与梁漱溟有着重大的差异。梁漱溟从中国社会的特点出发，强调中国不适合发展民主制度。牟宗三则认为，中国下一步若要有所发展，必须走民主的道路，甚至强调民主制度是人类政治的“最后形态”。

---

① 关于牟宗三坎陷论的主要内容和具体分析，作者另文已有详尽分析，此处不再重复。有兴趣的读者可参见杨泽波相关的数篇论文，主要包括：《“坎陷”概念的三个基本要素》，《华东师范大学学报》，2011年第5期；《三分方法视域下的坎陷概念》，《复旦学报》，2012年第3期；《坎陷与民主——牟宗三坎陷开出民主论的启迪、补充与前瞻》，《中国哲学史》，2012年第3期；《坎陷开出民主不同理解九种——关于坎陷开出民主若干评论的评论》，《天府新论》，2014年第1期。

② 牟宗三：《时代与感觉》，《牟宗三先生全集》，台北：台湾联合报系文化基金会、联经出版公司，2003年，第23卷，第408页。

将梁漱溟和牟宗三相关的思想放在一起比较，以我个人的标准来衡量，牟宗三的立场似乎不如梁漱溟高远，态度也不如梁漱溟坚决。这个问题值得深思。尽管坎陷论始终包含“摄智归仁”的内容，由这个内容逻辑地可以引出我们的理想应是建立一种既不同中国传统政治，又与西方现行民主制度有异的更为合理的制度这样的结论，但至少牟宗三晚年并没有将思想的重点放在这里。牟宗三建构坎陷论的时候，反复重申坎陷开出民主必须借鉴中国传统政治的优点，泛道德主义不正确，泛政治主义同样不可取，但细细分析其相关论述又不难发现，他对西方的民主制度还是缺乏深刻的反思。坎陷“摄智归仁”这一重要思想只具有理论的意义，而缺乏实质的考量和建构。在其后期的一些文字中，这种思想倾向表现得尤为明显。认定民主制度是人类政治文明的“最后形态”是一个典型的例子。这一类说法大大地减损了坎陷论的理论价值，造成的影响不可小视。我之所以特别关注这个问题，是因为如果把我们的任务只规定为开出民主，那么“摄智归仁”的内容如何体现呢？如果“摄智归仁”的内容无法体现，那么这种新开出的民主与西方现行的民主又有什么不同的呢？如果新开出的民主与西方现行的民主没有区别，那么如何谈得上继承儒家道德理想主义的传统呢？这些问题不解决，将民主视为人类政治文明的“最后形态”，不仅降低了儒学的高度，而且在一定程度上从“外王三书”坎陷开出民主一定要“摄智归仁”的立场游离了出来。这一现象应该引起我们的足够重视，而这也是我对坎陷论最不满意的地方，认为是其最不应该有的一个短板。

当然，我们看问题需要有历史的眼光，不能苛责于前人。牟宗三有其特定的时代背景。从他后期的许多讲演可以看得非常清楚，他当时的精力主要集中在台湾与大陆政治局势的对比方面。比如在《文化建设的道路——现时代文化建设的意义》的讲演中，他这样说道：“有段时期我们考虑到以往二千年没有现代化的问题，现代才有，这二者的分别究竟何在呢？我曾以两个字来表示。就社会、政治、经济等等各部分的工作而言，若采取对列 co-ordination 的原则就是现代化，若采取隶属 sub-ordination 的原则就是非现代化。近代的精神是 co-ordination，非近代的精神是 sub-ordination，差别就在于此。co-ordination 是理性的，sub-ordination 是非理性的。”① “大陆上共产党统治之下没有私，也没有公，没有个人的生活、没有教养，一切都套在人民公社中……正好是 sub-ordination，而不是 co-ordination。”② 正是在这种强烈的对比中，牟宗三对台湾民主建设寄予了很高的希望。在《中国文化大动脉中的现实关心问题》的讲演中又说：“中华民国这个政治形态，在孙中山先生的理想中，就是一个 consitutional de-

① 牟宗三：《时代与感觉》，《牟宗三先生全集》，第 23 卷，第 390 页。
② 牟宗三：《时代与感觉》，《牟宗三先生全集》，第 23 卷，第 391 页。

mocracy，即是一个应以宪法为基础的民主政治。这就叫作‘民主建国’。辛亥革命的政治意义即在此。孙中山先生的政治理想，对以往中国二千多年的君主专制来说，是一种划时代的突破性‘进步’。”① “这个问题的唯一解决之道，就是‘民主建国’，就是依 consitutional democracy 的方式来建设国家。这是我们现时代中国人自己的事情，不能梦想几千年前的尧、舜，也不能交托给未来不可知的‘大圣人’。”② 这些材料充分说明，对大陆政治局势的不满，很自然地使牟宗三将希望寄托在台湾的民主制度方面。这种情况虽然是可以理解的，但从另一个方面看，也影响了他对民主政治本身的深入观察乃至理性批判，从而或多或少淡忘了他早年反复强调的坎陷必须“摄智归仁”的主张。在近些年来台湾政治的发展过程中，儒学很少能够发挥实际的作用，这或许是一个内在的原因。

当然，现在情况已经发生了根本性的变化。我们今天重新研究坎陷论，不应再将思想的重点放在这里，而应当特别注意对西方民主政治加以反省，将隐含在坎陷论中“摄智归仁”的重要内容凸显出来，让人们充分认识其意义，发挥其作用。由此说来，在新的历史条件下，我们讲坎陷必须同时在三条战线上作战。第一，必须坚持“让开一步”，不再固守“仁者德治”的政治模式，从道德层面退出身来，对过去的传统进行一个大的变革。第二，必须“下降凝聚”，不仅大力发展认知的层面，重视制度建设，不再将政治的希望完全寄托在道德上，而且进一步扩大视野，大力重视经济问题，重视恶在历史发展中的作用。第三，必须坚持在“让开一步”、“下降凝聚”的同时，努力“摄智归仁”。这一点在当前情况下尤为重要。只有这样我们才能保持中国政治传统之所长，才能保持儒家的道德传统，打破西方近代以来将道德与政治分离的做法，将民主置于道德的制约之下；而不是像一些短视者那样，一味向西方看齐，唯西方马首是瞻；最终形成一种既不同于传统中的中国政治，又与现行的西方民主政治有原则差异的独特政治模式。尽管这种独特的模式我们现在还没有完全找到，但这种努力一定不能放弃，这个方向始终要坚持。这是经过诠释后的坎陷论告诉我们最重要的道理。这样的视野才是全面的，足够的，才能达到预期目的。果真如此，中华文明复兴一定大有希望，那将是国家之幸，民族之幸，文化之幸。

理论界近些年的一些新进展，带给我们些许新的希望。随着中国国力的日渐强盛，重新认识中国政治传统的特点，反省20世纪以来盲目追求西方民主做法的失当，已成为不少学者的共同努力方向。这方面蒋庆无疑走在了前列。蒋庆一段时间以来对学界过分强调心性儒学的倾向十分敏感，持有批评态度，认为这种做法没有抓住儒学的本

---

① 牟宗三：《时代与感觉》，《牟宗三先生全集》，第23卷，第408页。

② 牟宗三：《时代与感觉》，《牟宗三先生全集》，第23卷，第412页。

质。在他看来，从根本上说儒学是一种政治之学，从而大力提倡政治儒学，引起很大的反响。在研究过程中，蒋庆花了很大气力分析儒家政治传统的合理因素。他认为，中国传统政治是一种王道政治，有着自身正当性，分别表现在“天”、“地”、“人”三个方面。“天”代表超越神圣的正当性，“地”代表历史文化的正当性，“人”代表人心民意的正当性。在新的历史条件下，这些正当性不能弃之不顾，必须保留下来，继续发挥作用。为此他还设计了三院制的方案，以通儒院代表超越神圣的正当性，庶民院代表人心民意的正当性，国体院代表历史延续的正当性。[①] 白彤东的进路略有不同。白彤东在美国留学时间较长，系统研究过西方政治理论，对西方民主制度的缺失有一定的体会。他认为，罗尔斯《政治自由主义》中所列举的民主社会的五个事实尚不全面，还需要补充第六个（组）事实。这一组事实主要包括三项内容：第一，人类有滑向私利的倾向，而一人一票鼓励了这个倾向的发展。第二，公民中总有人对政治事务采取冷漠的态度，不愿意参加投票。第三，绝大多数现代社会都太大了，不论政府付出多少努力，多数公民都很难充分了解相关政治事务和政治人员的内情。这就意味着，罗尔斯所理解的自由民主制度，或审慎思考与讨论的民主制度，要求绝大多数的公民都以平等的、一人一票的方式参与政治，在现实上是不可能的。为了弥补这一不足，白彤东在儒家智慧中寻找资源，“试图抵制当代民主社会里过度民粹化的倾向，并在民主制与精英制之间找到一条中庸之道”。[②] 贝淡宁则从一个西方人的视角，对这个问题进行了新的探索。贝淡宁早年研究伦理学，赞同社群主义，对西方的自由主义有所批评。这一立场直接影响到他对在东亚国家建立民主制度的看法。他认为，“要想在东亚塑造民主，就不能依赖那种抽象而且非历史（unhistorical）的普遍主义，西方的自由民主主义者就经常在这个问题上栽跟头。相反，东亚的民主只能从内部建成，经由东亚人民自身在日常道德与政治争论中使用的特定事例与论争策略加以实现。”[③] 当然，这并不意味着完全排斥民主，理想的情况是找到一个既保留东亚政治传统，又吸取民主制度合理因素的办法。经过不断探索，他找到了一个折中的办法：这就是一个新的两院制，即包括一个通过民主选出来的下议院，以及一个由竞争性考试为基础选出来的代表所组成的上议院。在尝试了多种方案之后，他最终听从妻子宋冰的建议，“将这种上议院称为‘贤士院’”，[④] 并对其进行了颇为详细的规定。蒋庆、白彤东、贝淡宁从各个

---

① 蒋庆：《生命信仰与王道政治：儒家文化的现代价值》，贵阳：贵州人民出版社，2004 年，第 156—170 页。

② 白彤东：《旧邦新命——古今中西参照下的古典儒家政治哲学》，北京：北京大学出版社，2009 年，第 65 页。

③ 贝淡宁：《东方遭遇西方》，上海：三联书店，2011 年，第 12 页。

④ 贝淡宁：《东方遭遇西方》，第 164 页。

不同方向所做的研究令人欣喜。不管这些具体结论是否过于理想化，有多少不够完善和有待讨论的地方，但至少有一点是看得非常清楚的：当今之世，再像五四之后那样，指望全盘引进西方民主模式以解决中国自己问题的做法，已是明白黄花，没有了任何价值。经过一个世纪的痛苦消化，人们不应再以那种陈旧的方式思考问题了，这一页已经彻底翻过去了。时隔半个世纪之后，我们今天重新探讨这个问题，其意义正在这里。如果牟宗三九泉有知，看到后人能够这样理解他的坎陷论，这样重视后来连他自己也或多或少有所放松、至少没有强力坚持的开出民主必须“摄智归仁”的思想，相信一定会由衷认同的。

# 析論謝幼偉的孝道論

中國文化大學　曾春海

## 前　言

謝幼偉先生早年以研究西方哲學為主，卻特別關注中國儒家的孝道問題長達三十年左右。他認為“孝道”似乎是中國文化與社會特殊思想，為其他文化和社會所缺少或較不受重視。他在1990年代首先發表過一篇〈孝與中國文化〉的文章,[①] 文中論述了中國文化乃是以孝為主，以孝為根本的文化。該文發表後，頗得一些人士的同情相感，特別是熊十力先生在其所著《讀經示要》一書中，一再提及謝先生對“孝”的提倡和研究。雖然謝先生已去逝近三十年，但是孝道與家庭的精神生活價值問題仍是我們當代社會所值得關注的問題，本人擬以先哲對這一問題的卓見扼要評述，期待再引發各界人士的關注和共同研究。本文從簡介謝幼偉的學思、他所發表過的〈孝與中國社會〉、〈孝治與民主〉二篇具主題性的鴻文、培養孝道的實踐工夫等面向來呈現謝先生對孝道的論述及值得我們繼續研究的若干相關性問題。

## 一、簡介謝幼偉先生的學思

謝幼偉先生（字佐禹，1904－1976）畢業於東吳大學，赴美入哈佛大學，師事舉世馳名的英國哲學家懷黑德（A. N. Whitehead，1861－1947)，獲碩士學位。返國執教於浙江大學兼哲學系主任，當時張鏡湖先生（台灣・中國文化大學創辦人）任文學院院長，謝幼偉在抗日戰爭期間以深邃的哲學新知，常投稿於當時極具影響力的《思想

---

① 該文發表於《思想與時代》月刊，第十三期。該月刊乃我國在抗戰期間極具影響力之刊物，編輯部設於貴州遵義的國立浙江大學，付印則在貴陽。

與時代》月刊。[①] 謝幼偉思想縝密、落筆敏捷、思路清晰、論證細緻，早年以《現代哲學名著評述》一書見重士林。其他哲學專著，尚有《西洋哲學史》（上古）、《西洋哲學史稿》（中世及近世）、《中西哲學論文集》、《伯烈德來的哲學》、《中國哲學論文集》、《懷黑德哲學》、《倫理學大綱》等，其譯著有《思想之方式》（Modes of thought，懷黑德原著）、《忠之哲學》（Philosophy of loyalty），美國哲學家魯一士（Josiah Royce，1885—1916）原著，《現代科學與現代人（柯南特原著）》等。其中以《中西哲學論文集》一書最足代表其一生哲學觀點，本文文本以此書為據，《懷黑德哲學》是首本被紹述於中國學界的專書。

先生於1949年南赴印尼，出任雅加達八華中學校長，1953年返台任中央日報總主筆，僑生大學先修班主任兼華僑中學校長，1963年任中國文化大學首位哲學系系主任，此後應聘赴港，執教新亞書院且任研究所教務長，1969年退休後再度返台繼任中國文化大學哲學研究所所長，1976年10月病逝於台北。他在台期間主授懷黑德哲學、羅素哲學、倫理學等課程，將哲學種子播種於中國文化大學、輔仁大學、台灣大學。他曾二度赴美國夏威夷出席世界哲學家會議，對中國倫理、孝道之闡揚特為盡力，在教育青年、宣揚文化方面貢獻深遠。他雖浸潤於西方哲學數十年，卻歸宗於儒家的仁道與孝道，他確信中國文化是以孝為主，以孝為根本的文化。他在其《中西哲學論文集》一書的序文中自述其哲學的主張說："以中國儒家思想為根據，視哲學為成人之學，而成人之道，主要在保存及發展人人天生的一點仁心仁性。此則非提倡孝道不可。作者有意寫《孝之哲學》一書，以表達這一哲學主張。今《孝之哲學》一書雖未成，而《孝之哲學》一書的雛形已具於這些論文中。[②] 今觀其論文集論孝的主要論文為〈孝與中國哲學〉和〈孝治與民主〉相關涉之論文有〈論人的價值〉、〈論道德自覺〉、〈論價值意識的培養〉、〈論感通與解蔽〉、〈論儒家變化氣質的方法〉等。

## 二、對英哲羅素（Betrand Russell，1872—1970）誤解儒家孝道之批評

羅素原是畢業於英國劍橋大學三一學院數學系的數學家，後來轉為數理邏輯家，之後又轉為著作等身的哲學家。他在1921年滿五十歲時訪學中國一年，返國後出版《中國問題》（The problem of China）一書，對中國人的生活智慧，特別是《老子》哲

① 《思想與時代》月刊於1941年8月創刊，張曉峯（鏡湖）先生總其事，連續四十期未間斷，後因日軍壓境，貴陽物價飛漲而一度中輟，1947年又再度複刊，該刊物集當時的知識精英，導思想於正軌，期能振興中華文化，復興民族生機，善盡時代使命，謝幼偉在前四十期中，共發表論文32篇之多。

② 謝幼偉著，《中西哲學論文集》，香港九龍，新亞研究所印行，1969年。

學中“生而不有，為而不恃，長而不宰”的玄德頗為讚賞，斷言：“許多世紀以來，中國人的生活方式，如能為全世界的人所採取，將可使他們蒙受幸福。”（原著 12 頁）他也正反俱立的點評了孔子，他認為中國的知識分子以孔子的倫理生活代替宗教的精神生活。因此，若從孔子的社會影響而言，實在可以和宗教的教宗般來看待。他認為孔子對人類制度及思想的影響力，其範圍之廣，乃與基督、釋迦或謨罕默德無異，性質卻迥然不同。孔子是歷史人物（不是神），垂訓了嚴格的倫理規則，永為後人崇拜，卻極少與宗教教條相關聯。儘管他如此高度評價孔子，但是他對儒家所倡導的孝道，卻有不正確之批評。他認為儒家所主張的孝道和一般的家庭力量，可能是孔子倫理中最弱之處，也是孔子倫理嚴重和常識脫節的僅有之點。對羅素而言，家庭情感是和公共精神是衝突的，老人的權威曾強化了古代風俗的專橫。顯然，羅素對儒家的孝道之理解仍是片面的、表層性的。

羅素在 1950 年，也就是他 79 歲時，榮獲諾貝爾文學獎，他獲獎的評語是：“一位人道主義與自由思想的勇猛鬥士。”他享壽 98 歲，於 1970 年 2 月 2 日逝世。謝幼偉曾撰〈羅素的思想與為人〉一文追悼他，刊登於是年 3 月 16 日在台北出版的“文藝復興”月刊（第一卷第三期）。文中追述了他和羅素的一面之緣，他親自聽過羅素在哈佛大學的公開性演講，且持一本書請羅素簽名，謝先生在這篇追悼文中說：“遠在 1923 年，我在蘇州東吳大學讀書的時候，我即對哲學有興趣，而首先讀的一本英文哲學原著，就是羅素著的《哲學問題》（The problem of philosophy）這一本書。……這本書的優點，一在文字流利，二在思想清晰，三在分析精細，差不多羅素著的書，都有這些優點。所以儘管作者不贊成羅素的思想，但對羅素所著的書，卻很喜歡讀，特別是這一本《哲學問題》。”謝先生批判羅素的思想“始終在變化、在衝突、在搖擺不定”，直至 1959 年他的《我的哲學發展》一書出版後，才算是晚年定論。他批判羅素在知識構成上只承認感性（sensibility）而不承認悟性（understanding）和理性（reson），同時，羅素的方法論過於著重分析法而不提綜合法，這些是偏見。

謝先生更是批判羅素的倫理觀，未能深層了解人性，昧於人之所以為人的道理，他在文中指出：“羅素是從物以論人的，他視人為一束的欲求，情感或情緒，而與禽獸沒有多大的區別。”這種昧於人禽之辨的說法是羅素最大的錯誤。因此，羅素對儒家孝道的批評也立基於這一錯誤的觀點所衍生。雖然，羅素曾論及良善生活乃是為愛所感動以及為知識所指導的生活，可是對“愛”應如何培養與發展的實踐工夫，未置一言，謝先生認為西方倫理學者的通病就在於不講究存養省察的工夫。謝先生認為羅素哲學立基於個人的偏見，他自己就始終侷限於偏見，且言行不相顧而不一致，他在《中國問題》一書中，就批儒家的孝道，卻又讚美中國人的道德生活，肯認中國文明的顯著優點乃在人生目的之正當概念，就如同羅素排斥人倫道德，但是羅素在個人生活及文化觀點上仍是重視道德的。謝先生評羅素說：“但他一生究無大過，而其晚年，九十高齡，猶為反戰而遊行而入獄的精神，更是可佩的道德精神”儘管羅素的言行具有前後不一致的缺點。我們透過謝幼偉駁斥羅素對儒家孝道的誤解，可探索出謝先生論孝道的兩條進路，一是歷史文化和社會的進路，為羅素所謂孝道會導致家庭情感與公共精神的衝突做澄清，二是以儒家的人禽之辨及自覺性的道德實踐工夫來釐清羅素的昧於人禽之辨所導致對中國孝道的誤判，謝先生的主要論證集中在其所著〈孝與中國社會〉、〈孝治與民主〉以及幾篇論人的價值、論儒家變化氣質的方法……等文章上。

## 三、論〈孝與中國社會〉

謝先生在這篇論文中主要以“孝”的倫理來解釋中國社會的特質，且進一步解釋孝道與中國人的實際生活關係及其所衍生的影響。首先他肯認中國哲學，包括哲學和倫理是注重成聖成賢的身體力行之實踐性，就其本質和目的而言，志在成就人之所以為人的倫理性或道德性的生命價值。他舉證〈大學〉首章：“大學之道，在明明德，在親民，在止於至善”為經典依據，指認這幾句話實在就是中國哲人傳統的中心思想。[①]若就中國哲學的基源問題在探討宇宙與人生的終極性意義和人生終極性價值的安頓而言，確是如此，然而就先生所舉〈大學〉文本及孝道的價值意識而言，當指儒家的精神傳統較為適切，事實上，謝先生對中國哲學的主要關注在儒家未推展至其他學派的哲學。

謝先生以〈大學〉標舉的三綱來界說中國哲學（更精確言之乃是儒家哲學）的目的在由修己，安人而成就完美的人格。他很讚同明儒許敬菴所言：“學不貴談說，而貴躬行，不尚知解，而尚體驗。”[②] 表示這幾句話最足表現中國傳統倫理學反躬實踐的精神，他說：“中國哲人不重思想系統的創造，不重文字語言的解說，而重身心之躬行與體驗。沒有躬行與體驗的實踐生活，則所有言說都是靠不住的，都是空言廢話，無益身心。”[③] 儒家以人之先驗道德本性“仁”為人禽之辨的形上根據，是人之所以為人的實存性之本真，由人性內在之“仁”德首先萌發出來的道德行為是子女對父母親所自發性呈現的孝愛，他說：

中國儒者言仁必言孝，這絕不是偶然的，這殆有重大的理由。這理由有二：一是

---

① 請參見謝幼偉著《中西哲學論文集》首篇論文〈孝與中國社會〉頁 1，這篇論文是謝先生於 1959 年在夏威夷舉行東西哲人會議上，用英文發表的萬餘字論文，曾引發東西學著們的熱烈討論。

② 重編《明儒學案》台北正中書局版，卷三十二，頁 354。

③ 《中西哲學論文集》，頁 4，他在〈孝與中國社會〉一文中也引錢穆〈中國思想通俗講話〉所言“一切思索言辨，本從人生實際來，而人生實際，則並不從思索語言辨來。”（香港民四四版，53 頁）來佐證謝先生同樣的觀點。

仁必須有仁的根據，二是仁必須謀仁的實踐。仁的根據何在呢？我們何處見人類之有仁呢？孟子曰："惻隱之心，人皆有之"又曰："惻隱之心，仁之端也"人皆有惻隱之心，就是人皆有仁的證據。但人類的惻隱之心，又從何而來呢？或從何處首先見人類之有惻隱之心呢？孟子的回答是，惻隱之心，隨人類的天性而來，是人類的良知良能，而其最初的發現，即發現在人類的愛親敬長上。所以他說："人之所不學而能者，其良能也，所不慮而知者，其良知也。"孩提之童，無不知愛其親也，及其長也，無不知敬其兄也。"……這人類天生的一點敬愛其父母，即人有孝心。這種孝心的存在，便是仁的根源，便是仁的萌芽或開端。[①]

對謝先生而言，人類愛敬父母的心，由純真無邪的兒童不自覺的呈顯出來，足證明孝愛是天生的非後天外鑠性學習而成的，這是就人性道德心靈在實存的生活世界中，當下就是的開顯，這是開顯本體的真、存有的真，得透過道德主體實存性的體驗，非知識理性抽象的思辨之知，概念分析性的解說。然而，孝愛的體驗之知是否對每一個人而言皆有必然性及普遍性呢？我們實在很難就實證性的個別性案例來證成一普遍性命題，筆者認為這是就正常的親子互動關係而言，可呈現為普遍性實情，當然不排除有個別性的特例除外，同時在父不父的非人倫之常的狀態中，子不子亦有較高的可能性。雖然，我們也可舉在父不父前題下，仍有人子盡善孝道的舜為例子。《孟子·盡心上》曰："仁義禮智根於心"、〈中庸〉二十二章云："仁者，人也，親親為大。""孝"之觀念的顯豁處可追溯至《詩經》的大小雅及周頌，計有十六"孝"字。《論語·學而》載有子之言："孝弟也者，其為仁之本歟?"子女對父母親所自發性地開顯出來的，是人性最原始的"愛"之現象，《孟子·離婁上》針對這一天生流露的"愛"親事實，做一事實陳述說："仁之實，事親是也。義之實，從兄是也。"儒家針對這一普世性的孝愛事實，證成了道德形上信念，奠立孝愛父母是本於人之道德天性的道德形上命題。謝幼偉雖認為人類道德的良知良能最初係發露在兒童的愛親敬長上，孝心雖有仁心仁性為其根荄，但是若不加啟發、培養，則仁心仁性亦有萎縮，甚至消失的可能。因此，謝先生認為"仁"既然是人道德生命的本根，則對"仁"能存在的存養以及發展成完美的德性人格，亦即對"仁"這一道德心源的體證以及對仁心最初所萌發的孝道予以自覺性的培養有其必要性。儒家論證言仁必孝的主要理由，扼要言之，"孝"是仁德或人倫道德實踐的起始點，因此，謝先生以此為理據來理解《孝經》首章所云："夫孝，德之本也，教之所由生也。夫孝始於事親，中於事君，終於立身。"以及《孟子·盡心

① 《中西哲學論文集》，頁 5，他在〈孝與中國社會〉一文中也引錢穆〈中國思想通俗講話〉所言"一切思索言辨，本從人生實際來，而人生實際，則並不從思索語言辨來。"（香港民四四版，53頁）來佐證謝先生同樣的觀點。

上》所言："親親而仁民，仁民而愛物"、〈梁惠王上〉曰："老吾老以及人之老，幼吾幼以及人之幼。"他對孝道有一創建性的論斷："一切品德有孝出，一切品德亦包括於孝德的完成中。中國經典上，無仁經而獨有孝經，孝在中國倫理上的重要性可見。蓋中國倫理實視孝為道德的根源，道德的起點，亦是道德的完成。"①

謝先生在〈孝與中國社會〉中論及孝道及家庭生活、社會生活、政治生活以及以孝代替宗教的孝的宗教生活。由於篇幅有限，無法盡述，茲僅就其所謂中國社會的倫理立基於孝道予以扼要論述。他認為中國人的倫理社會係以家庭為基礎而層層推擴出各種社群生活。首先由家庭推擴出去的是由婚姻關係所連結的親戚生活圈，再由縱向横攝關係推擴出宗族生活圈，再次就是由自己及父母祖宗生命生長地所連屬的同鄉情誼，再推擴出去就是師友了。他指出中國倫理特別注重尊師，每一家庭供奉神位的排序為"天、地、君、親、師"教師的地位僅次於雙親。他追究其中的原因在於中國人具有不忘本的孝心，他說：

蓋我的肉體生命，雖是由父母而得，我的精神生命或文化生命，則多半由師而得。我知自生命來源上孝父母，自然應知從精神或文化的來源上尊敬老師。至朋友的關係，一樣是由精神或文化的關係而產生。……如友道為師道的擴大，則中國人的師友關係，一樣是導源於孝道。親戚、同宗、同鄉及師友，這些關係構成中國人的主要社會關係。他們的社會生活，亦多半是這些關係中的生活。我們看今日海外華僑的集會結社，差不多不是以同姓同宗為基礎，就是以同鄉同邑為基礎，便知孝的精神，仍洋溢於今日華僑的社會。中國人對於親戚師友，同鄉同宗，常表現極濃的情誼，解衣推食，毫無吝嗇。②

謝先生所描述的當屬傳統的農業社會所重視之倫理親情，蓋周代社會順夏、商、周三代以氏族型態之社群所形塑成的宗法社會。宗法社會係有血有緣的宗法社會，由親疏遠近的血緣關係構成等差有序的倫理親情之社會，講究的是由親及疏，由近及遠的仁愛，仁愛源於人倫親情的天倫摯性，孝親之愛是人情真意切的道德本性之流露，如同梁漱溟在其《東西文化及其哲學》所分判的中國社會有別於西方工業化以來以個人為本位以法律權益為訴求之社會。中國社會以家庭倫理為本位，倫理情誼的感通為訴求。換言之，中國傳統社會是倫理本位，職業分途，是道德理性早熟的倫理社會。孝道及敬愛親長的家庭倫理是宗法社會的倫理基礎，孝道不是單一的美德，而是有横

① 《中西哲學論文集》，頁8，他在〈孝與中國社會〉一文中也引錢穆〈中國思想通俗講話〉所言"一切思索言辨，本從人生實際來，而人生實際，則並不從思索語言辨來。"（香港民四四版，53頁）來佐證謝先生同樣的觀點。

② 同上，頁16－17。

縱互聯的親屬關係網絡，透過孝道親子之間、兄弟姊妹之間有相依互賴的歸屬感和共同的根源意識，凝聚成共同的生命意識之價值感，孝愛是家庭精神生活的意義源泉，使整個家庭生活獲得充實、豐富和深刻的人文意義。

家庭是組成社會的最大基本社群，社會是統攝所有家庭的大社群。孝愛洋溢著對生命的感恩與珍惜，對家庭生活之溫暖與幸福滿懷著無限的願景。謝先生論述孝與中國社會之密切關係說："孝肯定人生，肯定生命的價值，同時也肯定了社會，肯定了社會的價值。"① 孝道不但肯定社會的存在，同時也是團結社會的根本力量，因為社會既然是家庭的擴大，則可由人人愛家庭的新擴展遷移於對社會的愛，謝先生指出孟子所謂"老吾老以及人之老，幼吾幼以及人之幼"乃是社會成立的條件，社會愛是團結社會和人類的根基和動力，孝愛是人性中所流露出來最真摯純潔的愛，這是可資培養社會大愛的根苗。

## 三、孝治與民主

謝先生繼〈孝與中國社會〉之後，過幾年又再香港"人生"雜誌發表〈孝治與民主〉一文，闡明其所提倡的孝道和當代普世所肯定的民主政治並無衝突。他所以要研究這一問題源於二因素，其一是熊十力在《原儒》一書中反對孝與政治的結合，理據是"但以父道配君道，無端加上政治意義，定為名教。由此有王者以孝治天下，與移孝作忠等教條，使孝道成為大盜盜國之工具，則為害不淺矣。"② 若我們回顧歷史，魏晉時代豪門士族以道德禮法的名教之治為標榜，將孝置於顯要德目，且以不孝羅織罪名陷害政治敵對者，確有其事。此外，民初五四時代的陳獨秀在"新青年"月刊上曾發表宣言說："要擁護那德先生（民治），便不得不反對禮教、貞節、舊儒理、舊倫治；要擁護賽先生，便不得不反對國粹和舊文學。"謝先生的質疑是為何可言孝道而不可言孝治呢？先生也質疑是否談民主和科學的人都是無禮、無義、無廉、無恥的人呢？針對第一個孝治天下的問題，他釐清"孝道"應該具備（一）親親；（二）敬長；（三）返本；（四）感恩四項涵義，"親親"旨在培養愛根以保存和發展人性中所蘊含的天倫摯愛，他引用名儒羅近溪所言："如言孝，必老吾老以及人之老，天下皆孝，而其孝始成，有一人不孝，即不得謂之孝也。"為孝治之極義，始說立意頗佳，但是實踐的過程和孝治的機制為何？筆者認為有仁智互見的不同意見，就終極目的而言，始難達成人

---

① 《中西哲學論文集》，頁 21，他在〈孝與中國社會〉一文中也引錢穆〈中國思想通俗講話〉所言"一切思索言辨，本從人生實際來，而人生實際，則並不從思索語言辨來。"（香港民四四版，53 頁）來佐證謝先生同樣的觀點。

② 熊十力：《原儒》，28 頁。

人皆孝的高度理想，只能說“苟志於仁，無惡也。”[①] 原則與方向有意義，至於能做到何種程度也只能以義立命，無法強求。雖然如此，孝治仍有立乎其上，取於其中的意義，“敬長”有知識上的意義以及精神上或道德上的意義。前者意指尊敬長者的學識經驗，後者所謂精神上的意義，意指長者縱使在學識經驗上比我豐富，但是我若認同他的價值理想則我應採取精神性的尊敬態度。謝先生自承這一論點乃資取於唐君毅的觀點。[②]“返本”指返乎生命之本，意指人子對父母的愛敬之情源發於人子愛一己的生命，進而愛國家民族，甚至愛上帝、愛全人類等人文教育即可得而施行。若不實施這種反本報恩的教孝教育，則愛社會、愛民族、愛國家、愛上帝、愛全人類的教育很難成功。“感恩”指感念父母生、養、教的恩情之重，教孝旨在知恩、感恩及報恩，由感念父之母恩進而感念社會與國家之恩，甚至感念上帝之恩。謝先生指出民主政治若只知究明義務和權利而不談感恩的意義和價值，則民主化的社會將倫為刻薄寡恩的無情社會。他所謂的“以孝治天下”旨在以德治國，尤其重視以孝德普及化的改教治理方針。[③]

他的孝治天下並不侷限在政府的一項教育理念和政策而已，他認為民主政治雖然有其優點，卻也有不少流弊存在，他舉出四種由孝治可整治的流弊：（一）民主國家中存在著層出不窮的人與人和國與國之間的爭端，若能彰顯親親之義，推展人類本有的仁心仁性，則可減少一些鬥爭；（二）青少年犯罪率高的社會若政府提倡敬長之義的教育，使青少年們能受教於長者老者，則至低限度人們能知敬長，則青少年犯罪率或可下降；（三）今日民主國家崇尚自由開放的政策，人們常濫用自由而殺人風氣盛行、自殺率也逐漸上升，若提倡孝道以自覺性的珍愛生命及返本報恩的孝道，將可稍戢輕視生命價值的不良風氣；（四）民主國家偏重權利主體，人與人的關係首重利害關係，輕忽人與人之間的道義情義，如此，則人淪為利益主體，社會淪為無人情味的個人主義社會。謝先生認為孝治是倡導人與人之間的感恩教育，教導人們能知感父母之恩、他人之恩、社會之恩、國家之恩，若社會充滿人與人之間的感恩之情，則不但可降低人與人間的敵意，也可增進人與人之間的人情味。[④] 謝先生這些真知高見對今日個人主義掛帥的民主化社會而言，針對人際間的冷漠疏離和異化確有其深刻的啟發性意義，問題在於我們應該如何去做（Knowing how）？這一實踐性的公共議題。

## 四、論孝道的實踐

謝先生在論孝道的實踐這一問題上也發表過一些相關涉性的論文，諸如：〈論人的

① 《論語·里仁》。

② 見唐君毅：《文化意識與道德理性》上冊，第二章。

③ 《中西哲學論文集》，頁30－34。

④ 同前，頁36－37。

價值〉、〈論道德的自覺〉、〈論價值意識的培養〉、〈論感通與解蔽〉、〈論儒家變化氣質的方法〉……等，本人認為所列舉之最後二篇論文頗為切要，他在〈論感通與解蔽〉一文中指出“蔽”是人類的通病，不論人在思想上或行為上的錯誤，乃至歷史上人類的一切禍患，主要原因就在於“蔽”之病。人類由於蔽於名、色、權、利而身陷罪惡而不自覺。解蔽端在於人德性自覺與理性自覺，獲得感而遂通之“通”字上，人心若無不通即無障礙障蔽，自然能融會貫通人情事理而無所不暢通，他認為人的解蔽之道在求“通”，其要訣在儒家所倡言的智、仁、勇三達德。儒家所言的“感而遂通”(〈易傳〉)，主要以仁為主體，人若能自覺性的培養仁的道德意識，至於精純的狀態，則不會麻木不仁。然而仁心仁性，卻常因識理不明，而不能無所蔽。他指出好人有時也會為惡（做錯事）就是“智”德不足。因此，任何美德，包括孝道，必須仁智雙攝互補，同時還須有“勇”德。蓋一切品德的實現，除兼備仁智之外，仍非有勇德不可，“見義不為無勇也”就在於缺乏道德的勇氣，乃致道德意志力不能貫徹到真切之實踐。他總結出儒家的全部學問，以及存養省察的工夫就在於以仁為體，以智為用，以勇行之，如此居仁由義才能“感而遂通”而無所蔽。[①]

此外，他在所發表的〈談儒家變化氣質的方法〉一文[②]強調他極力提倡孝道，志在自覺、保存、培養和發展人類天賦的一點仁心仁性。他認為仁心仁性之不能彰顯常蔽於人的氣質之性或非理性的獸性。因此，儒家在超化獸性方面提出變化氣質的方法，旨在減少人類的惡行，增進人類的善行，尤其是孝道。他歸納出儒家在變化氣質上有(一)自省；(二)慎獨；(三)研幾；(四)主敬等四種核心方法。“自省”旨在每天都要自動自發的“自我批評”檢驗自己所做過的行為是否有過失。“慎獨”本於〈大學〉所言：“所謂誠其意者，毋自欺也，如惡惡臭，如好好色，此之謂自謙。故君子必慎其獨。”他認為這是儒家預防惡行的德性修養法，他也更進一步地採四要點來說明，所謂：“(一)這是關乎己所獨知的，非若行為之可已公開的；(二)這是關乎行為前的內心活動，一切可以引起行為的動機；(三)這也是每日必須實行的工作，而不能間斷的；(四)這是以‘毋自欺’為主要的工夫的。”[③] 至於“研幾”工夫他也是從四點來說明，大致上是對“慎獨”工夫的延伸性的解釋，重點它是人之意念初起時的自覺性省察工夫，也是淨化動機的工夫。“自省”、“慎獨”、“研幾”是一層深於一層的方法。“主敬”是對道德主體的仁心仁性能自覺自重的一種莊嚴肅穆的精神狀態，謝先生也以四點來解說：“(一)在用敬以引起我們對內心之善的注意；(二)在用敬以加強我們內

---

① 請參閱謝幼偉〈論感通與解蔽〉一文，出處見前揭書頁 79－82。

② 見前揭書 83－89。

③ 同上，頁 85。

心之善的力量；（三）在用敬以加強我們對惡念的厭惡；（四）謀在敬的狀態中把惡念加以超化。”[①] 謝先生所提的孝道實踐方法，其要旨在於他所推崇的明儒許敬菴強調的“貴躬行”、“尚體驗”而不再深奧隱晦的理論之構作。

## 五、餘論

謝先生最後一篇論孝道的文章刊於台灣·中國文化大學中華學術院印行的“哲學論集”中，題目是〈孝之性質及其需要〉，文中較引人注意的論點有二：其一為“講孝乃關人類的命運與前途的事件”、其二為“講兼愛或博愛，必先講孝，則其愛為有根之愛；不講孝而光講兼愛或博愛，則其愛為無根之愛。無根之愛，會有甚麽好結果呢?”謝先生長於英美哲學的概念分析，命題論證及理論的系統化，文字清晰易懂，哲理深微富啟發之性靈生命的作用，相信一般人讀其著作能有“深人不覺其淺，淺人不覺其深”的普遍受益處。

① 請參閱謝幼偉〈論感通與解蔽〉一文，出處見前揭書頁86。

# 胡适《说儒》疏说

上海同济大学　季　蒙　上海集贤书院　程　汉

儒的问题是近代中国的大问题，各家屡有讨论，而以胡适的《说儒》最为典型。但是胡适的意见人们似乎重视不够，其实他对儒的考察，以《说儒》一文最为精审，该论无疑是胡适关于儒家问题的代表作。客观地说，20世纪文科学者一般都绕不开儒的问题。胡适作为20世纪中国的代表学人、中哲史研究的开山人物，他对儒的态度就更有一种参考的意义。而我们对“儒”这一问题的讨论也从历史事实（胡适《说儒》）开始。

## 林同济的观察

林同济曾经这样评价说：“胡适之先生的《中国哲学史大纲》，可算是开山之作。以今日的眼光与标准看去，这本书的内容，许多地方难免草率，全部结构也嫌散漫，可说聪明有余，深入不足。开山之作从来都是如此的。”“大家都怪着，为什么胡先生大纲的第二卷（大纲只出了上卷）到今日还不出来。我揣测他并不是材料缺乏，根本问题，恐怕是他已经不能再继续第一卷的作风而写出第二卷，要写的话，他必要从头写起!”“然而《中国哲学史大纲》终不失它在中国现代学术史上的真价值、真作用——它划出一个新时代。”（《第三期的中国学术思潮》）我们说，林同济的这一观察是细致的。胡适确实很早就推翻了他原来的认识，林同济说：“六年前胡先生自家就坦率告诉我说，他对他从前关于中国思想史的见解，已经全部推翻了。他那时候正在缮写《说儒》一文。”（《第三期的中国学术思潮》）照林同济的说法，胡适的《说儒》其实是他思想史研究的变法。

## 章太炎的《原儒》

从渊源上说，胡适明确以章太炎的研究为前导，而章太炎的方法乃是名学方法与历史方法的结合。《原儒》说：“儒有三科，关达、类、私之名。达名为儒。儒者，术士也……类名为儒。儒者知礼、乐、射、御、书、数……私名为儒……”胡适在肯定章太炎成就的同时又感到不满足，《说儒》就是胡适所做的补充。而论文的观点总以这一条为最关键：“（二）论儒是殷民族的教士；他们的衣服是殷服，他们的宗教是殷礼，他们的人生观是亡国遗民的柔逊的人生观。”胡适没有放过儒的两个基本古义，即《说文》和周易需卦所讲的柔与迟滞之义。“而需是密云未雨，故为迟待疑滞之象……需，事之贼也。”“所以儒的第一义是一种穿戴古衣冠，外貌表示文弱迂缓的人。”胡适详细考论了服制方面的问题，就是为了说明儒为殷人之后这样一个核心意思。“从儒服是殷服的线索上，我们可以大胆地推想：最初的儒都是殷人，都是殷的遗民，他们穿戴殷的古衣冠，习行殷的古礼。这是儒的第二个古义。”

## 儒与殷周民族

在胡适的论证中，有这样一个意思是非常关键的。即殷、周民族混居了六、七百年，两者的原始差异渐渐消磨，不容易为后世察觉。实际上，单就礼俗而言，殷、周便有明显的不同，比如三年丧的问题。胡适认为，孔子讲三年丧原是殷人的礼俗，至于周人则是既葬除服。因此三年丧并不具有普泛的意义，尽管孔子为他的主张和理论找了种种的理由，像三年去父母之怀一类，但当时即遭到孔门弟子（如宰我）的质疑。周人对殷人的统治是恩威并用的，所以殷人的礼俗周人没有过多地干预。这种情况有点像满人对汉人的态度，汉人是缠足的；但满人不缠足，也不干预汉人的习惯。虽然是考史，但是我们能够清楚看到胡适不同意什么。比如孔子所拟定的价值系统就不能夸大为人类之一般，它并不具有经义性。关于三年丧的问题，实际上有两点值得考虑：一是三年丧为殷人的礼俗，殷灭亡后，在周人的统治下很痛苦，本身有浓厚的丧的情绪；而维持自己的礼俗便有一种标示意味，这些胡适论述得很清楚。另外儒是以为人助葬相礼为职业的，尤其是所谓小人儒；孔子便多次为人助葬，所以丧的思想发达在儒者并不奇怪。像僧道在丧事中后来就扮演了很要紧的角色。胡适的考证工作本身说明，儒的价值体系、道德系统是不能反历史地夸大的。比如说，“到了孟子，他竟说三年丧是‘自天子达于庶人，三代共之’的了。到《礼记·三年问》的作者，他竟说三年丧‘是百王之所同，古今之所一也，未有知其所由来者也!’”而事实却是，“三年之丧是儒的丧礼，但不是他们的创制，只是殷民族的丧礼——正如儒衣儒冠不是他们的创制，只是殷民族的乡服。”所以《说儒》首先是一篇文化论文，它的技术细节还在其次，胡适写这篇论文隐含地表达了他对很多文化主义的回应。

## 商之名起于殷贾　儒之名起于殷士

任何一种人文，其普泛价值的建立，原本都是因承于某个具体的原始，就像儒服乃是因于殷民族的乡服那样。根据胡适的说法，儒之名在文化史上原来是与“殷”关联在一起的。“商之名起于殷贾，正如儒之名起于殷士。”但是到了周朝统治的时候，儒却成了亡国忍辱的一个特殊阶层。“他们不是那新朝的士；”“他们只是儒。”而且儒的位置好像处在一个上下交际的地段，“大概周士是统治阶级的最下层，而殷士是受治遗民的最上层。”这里明显有一个需要细心分别的节目，就是殷士与周士的轻重差别。儒在周朝已经不再是真正的士了，至少是有一个地位退化的情况。关于殷周民族的不同差异，后人已不容易有感性的了解。胡适说：“我们现在还不明白殷周民族在语言文字上有多大的区别”，就反映了这一点。但是，“几百年之中，殷商民族文化终久逐渐征服了那人数较少的西土民族。”这里面的同化过程也是显而易见的。“殷周两民族的逐渐同化，其中自然有自觉的方式，也有不自觉的方式。”如果说不自觉的同化是历史不得不然的综合情势所决定的，那么，“那自觉的同化，依我们看来，与儒的一个阶级或职业很有重大的关系。”“这就是去做臣仆。”所以，我们必须要予以关注的，便是儒的历史品质之形成这一问题。在这方面，胡适的论述详细而当理，本身已构成一个系统的义理定位。

## 儒的流品

胡适指出，孔子以前，儒的流品很杂，有君子儒，也有小人儒。而儒首先是要放到殷这个限定内去讨论的。首先是儒的职业问题，即作为殷的亡国遗民，他们是靠什么存活的，怎样生存。胡适是从依附关系上来解释的，“这就是去做臣仆。”他特别引周易需卦给以说明，“儒在酒食，是有饭吃了，是他最适宜的地位。”“需卦所说似是指一个受压迫的智识阶级，处在忧患险难的环境，待时而动，谋一个饮食之道。这就是儒。”儒在酒食，是需卦九五爻的内容。正是这样的生存样态，造成了儒（或者说加固了儒）“术士”的特点。“儒的职业需要博学多能，故广义的儒为术士的通称。”“天久不雨，国君也得请教于儒者。这可见当时的儒者是各种方面的教师与顾问。”“他们真得要无所不知无所不能的了。”这些显然都属于小人儒的方面，是由柔逊的寄生性所决定的；即殷亡以后确立起来的一种根深蒂固的从属性。从小人儒的生活里胡适总结说：“第一，他们是很贫穷的，”“这是因为他们不务农，不作务，是一种不耕而食的寄生阶级。第二，他们颇受人轻视与嘲笑，因为他们的衣食须靠别人供给；然而他们自己倒还有一种居傲的遗风，”第三，“他们熟悉礼乐，人家有丧祭大事，都得请教他们。”“第四，他们自己是实行久丧之制的，而他们最重要的谋生技能是替人家治丧。他们正是那殷民族的祖先教的教士，这是儒的本业。”所以，“儒是殷民族的教士，靠他们的宗教知识为衣食之端。”胡适把儒（至少是早期的儒）描述得寒伧是显而易见的，他自己也十分清楚这一点，所以特别解释说："如果还有人觉得我在上文描写儒的生活有点近于有心毁谤孔门圣贤，那么，我只好请他平心静气想想孔子自己说他的生活……"

## 君子儒

关于君子儒，尤其是孔子所代表的经过变革和提升的中兴的儒，其历史品质又是怎样的呢？胡适有一个总括的意思，说得相当清楚。"但这个广义的，来源甚古的儒，怎样变成了孔门学者的私名呢？这固然是孔子个人的伟大成绩，其中也有很重要的历史的原因。孔子是儒的中兴领袖，而不是儒教的创始者。儒教的伸展是殷亡以后五六百年的一个伟大的历史趋势；孔子只是这个历史趋势的最伟大的代表者，他的成绩也只是这个五六百年的历史运动的一个庄严灿烂的成功。"而"这个历史运动是殷遗民的民族运动。"历史原因方面，胡适谈到了一个关键的问题点，就是"五百年必有圣者兴"的"悬记"；这件事是与宋襄公的事迹对照着说的。胡适提到宋襄公用鄫子祭次睢之社，是因为他迷信五百年必有王者兴的预言，"这样恢复一个野蛮的旧俗，都有取悦于民众的意思。"因为宋本来是殷的遗留，最能够代表殷，所以宋襄公便抱有一个成为复兴殷商的王者的念头。虽然悬记"引起了宋襄公复兴殷商的野心"，但他最终还是失败了。而这一次民族复兴的运动失败以后，希望便落在一个将兴的圣王身上。这个人就是孔子。从"天之弃商久矣"到五百年的悬记，"所以我们可以假定，在那多数的东方殷民族之中，早已有一个将有达者的大预言。"所以说，孔子的业绩，很明显与儒的既成历史境况和各种时代条件有关。"在那殷周民族杂居已六七百年，文化的隔离已渐渐泯灭的时期，他们（指儒）不仅仅是殷民族的教士，竟渐渐成了殷周民族共同需要的教师了。""在他们自己民族的眼里，他们是殷礼（殷的宗教文化）的保存者与宣教师。在西周民族的眼里，他们是社会上多材艺的人，是贵族阶级的有用的清客顾问，是多数民众的安慰者。""向他们问礼的，不但有各国的权臣，还有齐、鲁、卫的国君了。"儒既然有了这种种的历史地位与条件的变化，当然就为孔子的最后提升（对儒的）作了准备。

## 孔子"吾从周"使儒中兴

胡适认为，孔子所以能够中兴"儒"，首先是因为他认清了文化逐渐混合的趋势。统治中国既久的周文化既然已无法拒绝，就只能冲破那民族的界限。由于后起的文化湮没了老文化，所以就连老文化的中心"都不能继续保存他们的文献了。"既然孔子有这样透辟的"历史的看法"、历史见解，他自然能放弃传统的保守主义。所以才有"吾从周"的口号，把殷民族的"祝人儒"变成了全国人的师儒。胡适这样评价说："从一个亡国民族的教士阶级，变到调和三代文化的师儒；用吾从周的博大精神，担起了仁以为己任的绝大使命——这是孔子的新儒教。”“仁以为己任，就是把整个人类看作自己的责任。”所以说，“儒的中兴，其实是儒的放大。”“孔子的伟大贡献正在这种博大的择善的新精神，他是没有那狭义的畛域观念的。”“这才是那个广义的儒。”胡适的这些说法，很有一些文化自况的味道。实际上，与同时代的所有学者一样，胡适也不能不在论文中透出透进东西文化交合的消息，这是那一代学人都会有的宿命；有很多说法显然都是 20 世纪的某种自道。比如胡适说孔子的自信，实际上就反映了他自己的自信。“到了孔子，他对自己有绝大信心，对他领导的文化教育运动也有绝大信心，”“所以他自己没有那种亡国遗民的柔逊取容的心理。”“有教无类，这四个字在今日好像很平常，但在二千五百年前，这样平等的教育观必定是很震动社会的一个革命学说。”所以胡适说：“以上述孔子改造的新儒行……这真是振衰而起懦的大事业。”虽然这些只是胡适对孔子的评价，但却处处使人觉得像是新文化运动的自况。因此，对历史研究与时代自道我们如何分别清楚，也是一个问题。

## 孔门弟子

其实在讲孔子以外，胡适对孔门的议论并不好。这种反差也透射出：一方面胡适所处的时代仍然有尊孔的臭味，迫使胡适不得不做出种种的协调，或者说圆通处理；而另一方面，胡适对历史中的儒又确实有很多看法，他的理智不允许自己表现出尊儒的俗态，这样自然会造成一个心理上的拉扯与紧张。加之对钱穆、冯友兰等学者定孔子的年代在前、大有立教主的意思的反对，都使得胡适在保持对孔子的客气之外，再也无法克制。尽管这些都是隐晦的。他说：“《檀弓》所记，已够使人厌倦，使人失望，使人感觉孔子的门风真是及身而绝了。”因为孔门弟子绝大多数还是只在小节上讨营生，孔子的风范并没有流行多远。“孔子和这班大弟子本来都是殷儒商祝，孔子只是那个职业里出来的一个有远见的领袖，而他的弟子仍多是那个治丧相礼的职业中人，”这才是孔子与门弟子的根本区别。孔子并不是没有职业痕迹，帮助原壤治丧就能说明孔子的职业痕迹，虽然“这一个不守礼法的朋友好像不很欢迎孔二先生的帮忙。”所以孔子只是能见其大而已，“不是拘泥仪文小节的。”当然从另一方面、相对于孔门弟子说，胡适还是承认了孔子的教主色彩。他说：“孔子有博学、知礼的名誉，又有学而不厌、诲人不倦的精神，故相传他的弟子有三千之多，这就是他的职业了。”这里所说的职业，与治丧相礼那种职业显然又有了不同，倒不如说更像是弘教的事业。“这都可表示他是殷民族的宗教的辩护者，正是儒的本色。”“他不但自己临死还自认是殷人，并且还有天下宗予的教主思想。”从《檀弓》记孔子将死的一段，“还可以听见一位自信为应运而生的圣者的最后绝望的叹声。”“这就是一个无冠帝王的气象。”这些话语，很有所谓“素王”的味道。

## 孔子将柔逊的儒发展为弘毅的儒

胡适总结说，孔子把柔逊的儒改造发展为弘毅的儒，“也就是《中庸》说的君子和而不流，中立而不倚。这才是孔子要提倡的那种弘毅的新儒行。”而“柔逊谦卑不过是其一端而已。”孔子的业绩，主要也就体现在这种对儒的扩充上。“所以他把那柔懦的儒和杀身成仁的武士合并在一块，造成了一种新的儒行。”“这就是见危致命的武士道的君子。”把武士道、成仁与儒说在一起，是否反映了时代对强毅的要求呢？所谓从历史思想中发掘种种切合于现时的资源，同时这种对传统的姿态还能赢得同情？“可见孔子的新教义已能改变那传统的儒，形成一种弘毅的新儒了。”“这是一个新的理想境界，绝不是那治丧相礼以为衣食之端的柔懦的儒的境界了。”这样的描写，很使人想起新旧约全书的启示；好像历史中的新旧教之间往往有一个鲜明的分际似的。胡适在研究过程中是否受到了约书思维的启发呢？他用文学的笔调这样写孔子：他把儒抬高了、放大了，“他做了那中兴的儒的不祧的宗主；他也成了外邦人的光……凡有血气者莫不尊亲。”最后这句话，很有约书的味道，胡适大概是有意这样用的。结合前面胡适谈孔子的教主思想，我们可以明白，近世以来宗教在文化生活中的侵入，使得学人不自觉地会在平时的思考中留下种种的影响痕迹，或者关注。比如儒家是否宗教的问题，便是一个十分“近代”的问题。从大方面说，所有这些细节都在表明一个宗教博弈时代的来临。世界进入宗教博弈时代是必然的，胡适的文化研究及思路也不能脱离此氛围的影响。概言之，人文就是冲突。

## 儒教与宗教性问题

实际上，在《说儒》一文中，胡适专门有谈儒道之宗教性问题的一番话。他说：“我们看殷墟出土的遗物与文字，可以明白殷人的文化是一种宗教的文化。这个宗教根本上是一种祖先教。”事实上，早在利玛窦来华时就已经指出，中国民族是非宗教的，儒教并不是宗教。利玛窦是教会人士，是宗教中人，他的意见本来是没有多少讨论余地的。即以中国最宗教的道教也仍然是一个准宗教来说，华民族的非宗教性乃是不争的事实。但是为什么到了20世纪宗教问题却这样突出呢？这里面另有原因。那就是：儒教的宗教性问题已经不再是单纯文化学术的问题，而是演化为一种宗教博弈论、文化博弈论了。清末一大批学者想把儒家建设成一个宗教（如沈曾植谈佛道儒耶回等问题），作为民族的抗力，正说明了这一点。胡适的意见是，儒与道的性格都是知识的、智识主义的，至少是人文主义态度的，而不是含有宗教的臭味。他说："他们替这些礼文的辩护只是社会的与实用的，而不是宗教的。""这种意境都只是体恤生人的情绪，而不是平常人心目中的宗教态度。""这种智识与职业的冲突，这种理智生活与传统习俗的矛盾，就使这一班圣贤显露出一种很像不忠实的排优意味。""所以老子、孔子都是一个知识进步的时代的宗教家。"儒道所以都不能深入民间成为影响多数民众的宗教，都只能成为长袍阶级的哲学，其原因正在此。所以胡适说："民众还得等候几十年，方才有个伟大的宗教领袖出现。那就是墨子。"但是话说到这里，我们却不能不有一点讨论，即：墨家是真宗教，还是另有层次。因为我们在读墨子书时会发现（比如天志、明鬼等等），里面有这样一个意思：宗教是有利的吗？如果它是有利的，那么好，我们赞成宗教，提倡、宣扬它；如果它是不利的，那么我们反对、不要它。虽然墨家正好认为宗教有利，但这与严格宗教精神之间是否还是有距离，这个我们不能不问。

## 老子是更老的老儒

《说儒》另有一个同样重要的观点，即认为老子是更老的老儒，这个意见是无论如何不能忽略的。胡适关于儒与道的问题的论述，明显有反对钱穆、冯友兰一类学者认为老子年代靠后的意见的背景。所以胡适对老子的分析，里面有很可玩味的成分。从安排上看，似乎对儒与道的讨论是附属于儒这一正题的。"我们现在可以谈谈儒与道的历史关系了。同时也可以谈谈孔子与老子的历史关系了。"胡适开宗明义说："老子也是儒。儒的本义为柔，"《老子》的教义正是一种柔道，"老子的教义正代表儒的古义。""儒是柔懦之人，不但指那逢衣博带的文绉绉的样子，还指那亡国遗民忍辱负重的柔道人生观。"又说："柔逊为殷人在亡国状态下养成的一种遗风，与基督教不抵抗的训条出于亡国的犹太民族的哲人耶稣，似有同样的历史原因。"胡适这样批评钱穆、冯友兰一类学者的意见说："如果连这种重要证据都要抹杀，硬说今本《老子》里的柔道哲学乃是战国末年世故已深时宋钘、尹文的思想的余波，那种人的固执是可以惊异的，他们的理解是不足取法的。"甚至有这样的怪论："现在竟有人说道家出于颜回了。"胡适曾经指出过冯友兰定孔子年代在前含有立教主的意思，这是一种历史中儒宗道统心结的遗留。在《说儒》中胡适表达这一意思说："还有那个孔子问礼于老聃的传说，向来怀疑的人都学韩愈的看法，说这是老子一派的人要自尊其学，所以捏造'孔子吾师之弟也'的传说。""现在依我们的新看法，这个古传说正可以证明老子是个老儒，是一个殷商老派的儒。"韩愈是倡道统的，胡适说一些人学韩愈，其意所指甚明，并且引用史料加以说明（如《曾子问》）。胡适认为《曾子问》一篇颇能反映一个较早时期的情况：知道老子是一位丧礼大师，还能老老实实传述孔子称引老聃的丧礼意见，“这是老、孔没有分家的时代的老子。”谈到老子与周史的关系，胡适说：“这样看来，我们更可以明白老子是那正宗老儒的一个重要代表了。”简言之，胡适的基本意见是认为：“我们不能不承认这种柔逊谦卑的人生观正是古来的正宗儒行。”但是这种违反人情的极端教义（柔逊）是不足为训的，所以孔子也从老儒的教义里出来，而渐渐回到中庸的路上去，“要从刚毅进取的方面造成一种能负荷全人类担子的人格。”有了这一根本的不同，其他的教义自然都跟着歧异了。胡适这样说历史中的儒道分家，“在这个新儒的运动卓然成立之后，那个旧派的儒就如同满天的星斗在太阳的光焰里，存在是存在的，只是不大瞧得见了。”道的“原始儒”的一面就是这样隐没了。

## 沈曾植的看法

顺带说一下，胡适关于儒道的意见（诸如老儒之类）在历史中并不是独一无二的“孤见”。比如清末大学者沈曾植就谈到过这个问题，虽然十分简短。《海日楼札丛·柔道》云：“柔道阴行。柔道，儒道也。周家尊儒，盖文王以儒道取天下。”又《道德仁义》一节说：“老氏道德仁义之说，盖古易家微言，或《归藏》元旨。政如礼家说忠质文大同小康耳。”这里已明白说到儒道为柔道，周人大概正是看到了儒道阴柔的一面，所以正好利用它来安天下，尤其是镇抚殷人。归藏易为殷易，而大同小康也是甚古的说法，这里指出老子与殷的种种联系，与胡适老儒之说完全是相协调的。透过这件事我们能够看到什么呢？可以说，前代学者往往有很关键的见地不容易被我们觉察，这一方面是受写作形式的限制；比如，如果我们不读《说儒》那些详尽的论述，哪里容易透过沈曾植的寥寥数语窥见那么详细的条络原委、来龙去脉呢！所以这些都是问题，但同时也说明了学问中的真见识之“不孤”。不仅这一点，像沈氏《札丛》中《儒门刻急》一节还说：“儒门澹薄，容不得豪杰。此宋时某师之言也。今日儒门一味刻急，吾恐天下豪杰，将有望望然去之患也。”胡适也说过：“儒门淡薄，收拾不住一般老百姓、愚夫愚妇，他们都被低下的佛道两教引诱去了。”所有这些，都能反映学人之间真见识的种种暗合。

## 《说儒》对原始儒的还原意义

可以说，自20世纪以降的所有关于儒的问题的讨论与展开，看来都不得不以《说儒》为帽子。因为胡适这篇论文本身有一种标示意义，就是要把儒的原始情况之所是还原。而这篇论文又至少有三个人的工作为基础，就是章太炎、傅斯年、胡适对儒的问题的考论。说到这里，便不能不指出，民国以后新儒学的问题是不能脱离《说儒》

去考虑的。尽管儒学是一个历史活体，而不是死体；并且考史决定论也是难以成立的。但是基本的事实基础却很难完全离析掉，而剩下的乃是：对事实本身的考定能够精确到哪一步。《说儒》用自圆的论证，使我们可以初步相信原始儒的情况不会相去太远。因此很重要的一点就是，胡适对文化的批评不能单纯看作西学的作用，而更直接地有“对本身的观察和理智作用”为元素。简单地说，就是历史中的儒本身有很多胡适不能接受的东西；所以唐君毅要求胡适不要攻击传统文化显然不合适（参见王寿南先生主编《中国历代思想家·唐君毅》部分）。实际上，胡适对传统文化有很多回护，这些在《胡适全集》中反映得很清楚，不必枚举。总之，最重要的一点就是，《说儒》为20世纪以降的人文（尤其是儒的开展）提供了某种严整性，这才是最要紧的。

须要说明的是，思想的情况有时候就像一场演说。主讲人演讲结束以后要回答听者的提问，当他讲演的时候，他是自话自说的；只有在回答问题之际，他才知道听者想针对性地了解什么。这时他会基于自己的本位做出回答，而不是考虑有没有已经在演说中讲过了。人文方面也是如此。在与西学交接以前，与面对西学发问之际，情况是显然不同的。这并不是缺少什么或者不缺什么的问题，而首先是必须要回答提问的问题。如果这时候却不知所措，那么只能说明一点，即一开始自己就对自身缺乏了解，这是肯定的。所以讨论到最后还是一个知彼与知己的问题。假如我们像做尿检那样来做一个读检，就会发现：一切问题的根结可能还是在读书上。

## 二、儒学与当代教育

# “意义—感通”之学以情意为本

## ——以《礼记·大学》为中心的义理阐释

北京师范大学 于述胜

不知从何时开始，在现代中国的德育理论、特别是相关教科书中，德育过程曾被广泛化约为“知—情—意—行”的一般程序，中国教育史家亦常依此逻辑条理古人之“德育思想”。可能意识到此一般程序难以普遍规范具体的德育活动，人们又不得不以“多端”（具体的德育过程应针对不同情况选择不同起点）说补充之。可是，既承认其“多端”，又构造其“一般”，毋乃自相悖谬乎？其实，这是颇具现代性的“理论—实践”的思想范式在德育理论中的具体推演。“一般”之所以被视为“一般”，不过是知识本位和“工程—技术”思维反客为主、主宰人文学术思维的产物。至于一些学者欲从“自由”、“正义”之类的基本范畴出发，去建构所谓的价值教育内容体系，仍然是那一思维逻辑的自然引申。

这种学术思维，不能说完全没有传统思想的影子。譬如，宋代大儒朱熹就主张“知先行后”，并依此知、行观展开其“博学之、审问之、慎思之、明辨之、笃行之”的为学之序。其经典表述见于《中庸章句》、《中庸或问》和《白鹿洞书院揭示》等。在很大程度上，其所谓“致知”、“穷理”，系指明了“所以然之故”与“所当然之则”。但是，朱子之说后来遭到了王阳明的严厉批评，后者明确主张“知行合一”、“致良知”；而阳明所谓“知”，虽沿袭了朱子的概念，却弱化甚至消解了其“知识”义，而以“情意”为本，其“良知只是个是非之心，是非只是个好恶。只好恶便尽了是非，只是非便尽了万事万变”（《传习录下》）一语，足以尽之。阳明所谓“好恶”固然属于情，其所谓“是非之心”同孟子所谓“四端”一样，并非对于是、非准则的对象化认识，而是浸润着情意、感通于物我之间的直觉判断，亦属情意范畴。不仅如此，即便在朱子那里，“穷理”也并非近代认识论建立在“主—客”对立基础之上、以主体把握客体的认识活动，而是以“物我一体（一理）”为前提的内外感通过程：“万物各具一理，而万理同出一原，此所以可推而无不通也。”所以，当有人问：“观物察己者，岂因见物而反求诸己乎？”朱子答曰：“不必然也，物我一理，才明彼即晓此，此合内外之道也。”（《大学或问》）在物（人）、我感通中，情、意、知、行为一整体，密不可分。以《四书》为重要代表的原始儒学，其实更接近以情意为本的阳明心学。

中国现代教育学以“富国强兵”的国家功利主义为宏观历史背景，以“理论—实践”为根本思想范式，以知识本位和“工程—技术”化了的科技思维为基本特征。与之不同，以儒学为主干的中国传统思想，是名副其实的意义之学：“天人一体”，是其生存论前提；“生生”—（让）生命是其所是、成其为生命，既是天地之德，也是人生之的，是人类生存的根本价值和意义所在；物、我“感应（通）”，则是其意义生成和传达的根本机制或机理。其中的“感通”，又是以情意为本的。作为《四书》之首的《礼记·大学》篇，就集中体现了这一以情意为本的“意义—感通”之学。在笔者看来，《大学》的思想主旨可以概括为两句话：“亲亲”为意义生成之根，“修身”为意义传达之根。其旨与《论语》、《中庸》和《孟子》等书中之理念直接相通、密不可分，且可与近年出土之先秦简文互证。

## 一、“止于至善”，说到底，就是依止于亲亲之家

关于“大学”之意旨，古来诠之者众，但大要不出“大学问”、“大学校”及“大人之学”的范围。“大学之道”之所以“大”，在于它以修己安人为指归。在儒者心目中，人生在世、悠悠万事，莫重于安顿自己、安定他人。从事于此之学问，始为大学问；从事于此之场域，即为大学校（儒者致力于把整个社会营造成一兴行礼乐教化之大学校）；从事于此之人们，即是“大人物”（此以德言之，非以位言之）。所言不同，其致一也。欲通达《大学》之思想，必先明“三纲领”之间的关系。

“明明德，亲民，止于至善”，是所谓《大学》三纲领。“明德”，浅白言之即“光明之德”，质实言之即仁义之心、之性、之情、之德。所以视之为“明德”，乃因其本于天而俱于我，具有不言而喻、自我透明之性质，此性质在作为其发端的亲亲、敬长之情处尤为显明，故朱子以“因其所发而遂明之”释“明明德”（《大学章句》）。对于“亲民”，或许是为了凸显其“教养”义，朱子认为“当作‘新民’”，并以“革其旧之谓也”释之（《大学章句》）。王阳明不之许，于《传习录》中辨之甚详：

爱（阳明之徒徐爱）曰：“‘在亲民’，朱子谓当作‘新民’，后章‘作新民’之文似亦有据，先生以为应从旧本作‘亲民’，亦有所据否？”

先生曰：“‘作新民’之‘新’是自新之民，与‘在新民’之‘新’不同，此岂足为据？‘作’字却与‘亲’字相对，然非‘亲’字义。下面‘治国平天下’处，皆于

‘新’字无所发明，如云‘君子贤其贤而亲其亲，小人乐其乐而利其利，如保赤子；民之所好好之，民之所恶恶之，此之谓民之父母’之类，皆是‘亲’字义。‘亲民’犹孟子‘亲亲仁民’之谓，亲之即仁之也。百姓不亲，舜使契为司徒，敬敷五教，所以亲之也。《尧典》‘克明峻德’，便是‘明明德’；‘以亲九族’至‘平章协和’，便是‘亲民’，便是‘明明德于天下’。又如孔子言‘修己以安百姓’，‘修己’即是‘明明德’，‘安百姓’便是‘亲民’。说‘亲民’便是兼教养义，说‘新民’便觉偏了。”

阳明所辨切中肯綮。首先，《大学》之“亲民”，即孟子所谓“亲亲而仁民，仁民而爱物”（《孟子·尽心章句上》）。作为动词的“亲”、“仁”、“爱”三者，义实相贯，亲之即仁之、即爱之，反之亦然。所以更相分别，乃因亲、民、物于己有亲疏远近之不同，其“亲之”（“仁之”、“爱之”）之方式、程度、程序等自然随而有异，以示其情其理同中有异，普遍性即寓于特殊性之中也。不明以儒家为代表的中国式“人道主义”（或“人文主义”）所特有的这一“理一分殊”精神，分而不能合、合而不能分，于理会圣贤言语之时，必将滞固不通、不着边际。其次，“亲民”较之于“新民”于义为优，不仅因为《大学》古本本来如此，而且是因为君子的亲亲仁民之情、之行，本身即具有感通他人、使民相亲相爱之教化功能，为意义传达之根（后文更详之）；“新民”则在新与旧、成己与成人的割裂中落于第二着，故“便觉偏了”。

那么，“明明德”、“亲民”二者有何关联？还是王阳明说得好：“明明德者，立其天地万物一体之体也；亲民者，达其天地万物一体之用也。故明明德必在于亲民，而亲民乃所以明其明德也。是故亲吾之父以及人之父，以及天下人之父，而后吾之仁实与吾之父、人之父与天下人之父为一体矣；实与之为一体，而孝之明德始明矣！……君臣也，夫妇也，朋友也，以至于山川鬼神草木也，莫不实有以亲之，以达吾一体之仁，然后吾之明德始无不明，而真能以天地万物为一体矣。夫是之谓明明德于天下，是之谓齐家治国而天下平，是之谓尽性。”（《大学问》）若除却若其中干富有理学情调的字眼儿（如“体”、“用”之类），阳明之说，还是准确地表达了“明明德”与“亲民”并非两件事而是一件事，一件一体两面之事。如果说“明明德”是尽己之心、之性、之情、之德，属于“忠”、“成己”之范畴，那么，齐家、治国、平天下就是尽人（物）之心、之性、之情、之德，属于“恕”、“成人”之范畴。其实，《大学》文本中“古之欲明明德于天下者”一语，已经十分清楚地表明：“明明德于天下”即是“平天下”、即在“平天下”之中。

所谓“止于至善”，平白解之，就是“明明德”与“亲民”必达于至善之境。即此而言，“止于至善”与“明明德”、“亲民”亦非两事，它不过是后者的充分实现而已。可问题的关键在于，“至善”何所指？难道仅仅是“当然之则”吗？朱子似乎倾向于如此理解：“止者，必至于是而不迁之意。至善者，则事理当然之极也。”（《大学章句》）

阳明亦不许之，他说："至善者，明德、亲民之极则也。"（《大学或问》）其说看似与朱子不异，其实不然。他接着说："天命之性，粹然至善，其灵昭不昧者，此其至善之发见，是乃明德之本体，而即所谓良知也。至善之发见，是而是焉，非而非焉，轻重厚薄，随感而应，变动不居，而亦莫不自有天然之中，是乃民彝物则之极，而不容少有议拟增损于其间也。"除却其中的若干理学预设，则阳明之说意味着："止于至善"即本于天德良知应事接物，而切中事情者。此说凸显了至善之境中心达事理、情顺理通、物我一体之精神，于义为近。当然，"止于至善"之意趣并非局限于此。

《说文解字》释"止"曰："下基也，象草木出有址。"即"止"字取象于生出草木之根基，意指构成事物生成发展之出发点、根据地者。对于人来说，它的出发点和根据地即是家。与草木固着于一处不同，人有行动能力，不能总是龟缩在家中，总归要从家中踱出，步入一个更加广大也日渐陌生的世界。但是，只要人们能"亲亲而仁民，仁民而爱物"，做到了"为人君止于仁，为人臣止于敬，为人子止于孝，为人父止于慈，与国人交止于信"，则君子、小人各得其所——"君子贤其贤而亲其亲，小人乐其乐而利其利"，而"邦畿千里，惟民所止"——邦国、天下都将成为人们安居乐业之家。此即孔子所谓"耐以天下为一家，中国为一人"（《礼记·礼运》）、"依于仁，游于艺"（《论语·泰伯》）之境，亦便是王阳明所谓"君臣也，夫妇也，朋友也，以至于山川鬼神草木也，莫不实有以亲之，以达吾一体之仁"之意。故说到底，"止于至善"即是依止于亲亲之家。"亲亲"、"仁民"、"爱物"义虽相贯，《大学》却不言"仁民"，亦不言"爱民"，而独以"亲民"概之。盖以"亲亲"乃意义生成之根，而"明明德"与"亲民"，皆以将世界营造为亲亲之家为其极致也。生活于其中的人们，亦将有"在世即在家"的生命意义之感。

## 二、"格物·致知·诚意·正心"："亲亲"乃意义生成之根

对于《大学》之"三纲领"与"八条目"，中国现代教育史家常以目的与手段之关系视之。其实，朱子《大学章句》所说"此三者，大学之纲领也"、"此八者，《大学》之条目也"已清楚表明，二者乃大纲与细目也。也就是说，八条目乃三纲领，尤其是"亲民"即"亲亲、仁民、爱物"的具体推展形式。

关于"格物·致知·诚意·正心"，古今释之者众矣且意见纷纷，惟严立三先生所释至为简明而恰切：

> 身者，己也……心者，身之主，而情之所聚也。意者，情之注也。知者，情之感也。正者，是也；是者，直也。诚者，实也。致者，极也。格者，通也。通物而感，极感而实有诸己，则情动而直，德至而凝矣。

在孔、曾、思、孟一系的原始儒学中，广义之“情”与“性”相对，指人本其性与外部世界感应而生的各种情意状态。性静情动，故有“人生而静，天之性也；感于物而动，性之欲也”（《礼记·乐记》）之说，而《集韵》、《韵会》、《正韵》等皆以“性之动也”释情；性为未发之情，情为已发之性，故有“喜怒哀乐之未发，谓之中；发而皆中节，谓之和”（《礼记·中庸》）之说。“心者，情之所聚也”，是将情逆推于心的说法；反过来也可以说，“心者，性之所聚也”。“所聚”者，即性与情的居处之地。宋、明儒的“心统性情”及“性发为情”说，乃此种性、情观的直接表达。不用说，这是古人基于感应（通）原理（即“阴—阳”、“动—静”对生迭运）把握性、情关系的产物。

若况之于现代心理学，则情感、意志、认知者，皆隶属于古之“情”的范畴。不过，此仅为比况而已。儒者所言、所重之“情”，首先指向那种原发而尚未对象化（或前对象化）的情意状态。有如孟子的“恻隐、羞恶、辞让、是非”之心，它“不学而能”、“不虑而知”、人所共有。原发之情是物我感应的自然呈现，它本身是既“真”且“实”的，此即汉语“情实”、“真情”语义之所本。相反，昧此“情”而行事，则必然不真、不实，故孔子论“听讼”，力主“无情者不得尽其辞”。

此“情”既可上达，也可下达。孔子说：“君子上达，小人下达。”（《论语·宪问》）“上达”即达之于义、通之于理，是此“情”充分而恰到好处的开展与实现：“性自命出，命自天降。道始于情，情生于性。始者近情，终者近义。知情（者能）出之，知义者能入之。”（楚简《有性》，亦名《性自命出》）道是因性生情、因情而节的产物，其起始阶段即发乎其性的自然之情，故曰“其始近情”；即此而言，道是自然的，并不与人之性与情相对立。在其完成阶段，情恰到好处地得到了实现而成就为当然，所谓“其终近义”。“义者，宜也”，是情动而合乎生生之内在节奏的表现。正如《中庸》“喜怒哀乐之未发谓之中，发而皆中节谓之和”所表达的那样，“中节”之“节”当然包括静态的秩序和规则，但它首先体现为动态的“节奏”、“节律”和条理，是身心和谐、物我顺通的表现，这就是“致中和，天地位焉，万物育焉”之生命状态。道之兼有“情”、“义”两端，意味着它是自然且当然的：当然本于自然，自然成就于当然。真正懂得“情”的人能让情外发而合乎“义”，真正懂得“义”的人能让“义”内入而通乎“情”。“下达”即此“情”沉沦于欲、逐求于物，把自己所感之物对象化为占有的冲动。“物至知知，然后好恶形焉。好恶无节于内，知诱于外，不能反躬，天理灭矣。……是故强者胁弱，众者暴寡，知者诈愚，勇者苦怯，疾病不养，老幼孤独不得其所。”（《礼记·乐记》）物至心交，自生好恶之情；好恶之情漫无节制而一味追逐外物，人之心志便失去了回归而主宰己身之能力，不仅一己之天性、生命不能畅遂，他人、外物也无以各得其所。孔子说：“君子喻于义，小人喻于利。”（《论语·里仁》）君子为真纯的情义所吸引，小人为利欲所引诱。联系儒者之“中”道观，似乎可以说：“无情”是情之不及，追逐物欲则为情之过，而“义”或“理”则是情之恰好处，即章学诚所谓“适当其可之准”（《文史通议·原学》）。故孔子又说：“君子中庸，小人反中庸。”（《礼记·中庸》）以“无情”与“情之过”相较，后者因有情而胜于前者：“苟以其情，虽过不恶。不以其情，虽难不贵。苟有其情，虽未之为，斯人信之矣。未言而信，有美情者也。”（楚简《有性》）这表明，按照中华圣哲阴阳对生迭运的思想逻辑，并不存在事实与价值、自然与当然、情感与理智的二元对立或分裂，分裂只存在于人“阴阳失调”的生活或思想中。即此而言，《大学》所谓“至善”，其实质原理即是“生生”——物我两尽，共遂其生；其形式原理便是“中庸”——情顺理通，无过无不及。由此出发，方可有效通达《大学》自“格物”以至于“修身”等数重关节。

“格物”之“物”，是构成人的意向对象、被纳入人的意义世界而与人相感通之人伦物事。“格物”之“格”，有你与之相遇而来而至、而互动感通之义。[①] 故所谓“格物”实即“通物”，是与你不期而遇之物（主要指人）互动相通。此即严立三所谓“通物而感”。对于中华圣哲来说，最原本之物乃亲子以至于兄弟之伦，最原本之“知”（亦即“明德”）乃亲子、兄弟之情、之爱。它们作为人之生命的最切近源头，使人因近而亲、而爱，奠定了人认同世界的基础，是人进入意义世界的直接通道、基本出发点。故儒者有“孝悌也者，其为仁之本欤”（《论语·学而》）之说。亲子、兄亲之伦具有不期而遇而又必相关涉之性质，故曰“天伦”；亲亲之情具有不言而喻而又自我透明之性质，故曰“明德”。因此，张祥龙先生释“格物致知”为“格其亲亲之物而致其自明之知”。[②]“致知”不过是因感而应，让原发之情充分朗现，此即严立三所谓“极其感”也。《中庸》的“修身以道，修道以仁”的“仁”字，首先是指亲亲之情。它是“在世即在家”的意义生成之根。

亲亲之情发乎人之天性，是前对象化人际关联的反映，能让人超越功利性关系的羁绊，如“好好色”、“恶恶臭”般自然而真实。在事至物交、念虑发动之际，能不愧于自明之情如实承续之，让自明之情成为自己的真切意向，好者好之、恶者恶之，即是“诚其意”。故《大学》曰：“所谓诚其意者，勿自欺也。如恶恶臭，如好好色，此之谓自谦（“自谦”即“自慊”，自安、自快、自足之义）。”此即严立三所谓“极感而实有诸己”。“意”与“志”相类，只是“志”拥有更加明确的目标和更加强烈的行动意向。

---

① 《尚书·尧典》：“格于上下”，此“格”训“至”；《尚书·舜典》：“格汝舜”，此“格”训“来”；《尚书·说命》：“格于皇天”，此“格”训“感通”。诸训释并见《康熙字典》辰集中。

② 张祥龙：《先秦儒家哲学九讲》，桂林：广西大学出版社，2010年，第129页。

自然之情一旦成为人的活动意向，便有可能出现物、我分裂的对象化状态，或为物象所诱，或为己情所滞，因有“身有所恐惧（忿懥、好恶、忧患）则不得其正”的状况出现，不能时行则行、时止则止，恰如其分地实现物我感通，“心不在焉，视而不见，听而不闻，食而不知其味”，故须“正心”。所谓“修身在其正心”，即在以己通物之时，摆脱对象化情绪、情感的束缚，如其所是地作用于物，此即严立三所谓“正者，是也；是者，直也”，或如王阳明所谓莫“一向着意去好善恶恶”（《传习录上》）。

由此观之，从“格物”以至于“正心”，都是物、我感通的不同环节，而情意则贯穿始终，“亲亲”之情更是意义生成之根。

## 三、“修身·齐家·治国·平天下”：“修身”乃意义传达之根

如果说自“格物”以至于“正心”所重在尽其在己之性、之情，属于“忠”的范畴，那么，自“修身”以至于“平天下”则重在推己及人，属于“恕”的范畴。

关于“齐其家在修其身”，《大学》以“人之其所亲爱（贱恶、畏敬、哀矜，敖惰）而辟焉”明之。郑玄注云：

> 之，适也；辟，犹喻也。言适彼而以心度之曰：吾何以亲爱此人，非以其有德美与？吾何以敖惰此人，非以其志行薄与？反以喻己，则身修与否，可自知矣。

孔子说：“其恕乎！己欲立而立人，己与达而达人，己所不欲，勿施于人。能近取譬，可谓仁之方也已。”（《论语·雍也》）孟子说：“万物皆备于我，反身而诚，乐莫大焉。强恕而行，求仁莫近焉。”（《孟子·尽心上》）《中庸》曰：“君子以人治人，改而止。忠恕违道不远。”也就是说，“人之其所亲爱而辟焉”之“辟”，即“能近取譬”之“譬”，亦即“强恕而行”、“忠恕”之“恕”。说到底，它们体现的都是一“恕”道。郑氏此注打通了《论语》、《孟子》、《中庸》与《大学》思想，彰显了《大学》以身为譬、为喻之旨，可谓得其神韵！

“喻”者，晓也（《玉篇》）。从教、学关系上讲，“喻”乃教者用口与言来告、诫、导学之者，使之明通事理。“譬”者，谕（喻）也，匹而喻之也。（《康熙字典》）“譬”是教者在相同、相类事物的匹对、比方中晓喻学之者。由此而进之于“恕”，则教、学互动已超越了表面化、外在化的言与口，而深入到身与身、心与心、情与情的共振联动之中。“恕者，如心也”（《说文长笺》）；“恕，忖也，忖度其义于人也”（《礼记正义·中庸》疏）。“恕”即是在己之心、身与人之心、身的平等比观、互动中，既以自喻自修，亦以喻人导人。故所谓“人之其所亲爱（贱恶、畏敬、哀矜、敖惰）而辟焉”不过是以最切近的己身为譬，它意味着：自己对他人的情感反应与他人对自己的情感反应是相通的；自己对于他人的情感反映是否为积极的，与他人人格之是否美善相一

致，他人对自己的情感反应也是如此；一个人若能与他人共其情、同其欲，就能明白做人做事的道理，获得直接而切近的修身尺度。而所谓“齐其家在修其身者”，不过是“以人治人”，即以我这个人来对待他那个人；质言之，就是以一己之身去带动、感通他人之身。

关于治国、平天下之道，《大学》曰：

> 所谓治国必先齐其家者，其家不可教而能教人者无之。故君子不出家而成教于国。孝者所以事君也，弟者所以事长也，慈者所以使众也。……一家仁，一国兴仁。一家让，一国兴让。一人贪戾，一国作乱。其机如此。……是故君子有诸己而后求诸人，无诸己而后非诸人。所藏乎身之不恕，而能喻诸人者，未之有也。
>
> 所谓平天下在治其国者，上老老而民兴孝，上长长而民兴弟，上恤孤而民不倍。是以君子有挈矩之道。所恶于上毋以使下，所恶于下毋以事上。所恶于前毋以先后，所恶于后毋以从前。所恶于右毋以交于左，所恶于左毋以交于右。此之谓挈矩之道。

不难看出，同齐家之道一样，治国、平天下之道亦可归结为恕道。“絜矩之道”即是恕道的另一表述。“絜”者结也、挈也（《礼记正义·大学》注），度也（朱子《大学章句》）；“矩”者，规矩、法度也。是则“絜矩之道”即执持规矩以裁量事物之道也。此处所言之规矩不是别的，就是以情挈情、与民共其情而同其欲之己身。与外在、单一而僵硬的规律、原则、规范不同，此以情挈情之矩、之身即是鲜活而动态的生命尺度，它在物我互度中量物裁己、相互生发。此中哲理，亦与《老子》第54章之说相通：“修之身，其德乃真。修之家，其德有余。修之乡，其德乃长。修之邦，其德乃丰。修之天下，[其德乃普]。[以家观]家，以乡观乡，以邦观邦，以天下观天下。”（简本《老子》）《老子》此“观”也是在平等对待中的喻己通彼之道。

尤当注意者，《大学》论及治、平之道，多次提及“兴”字，如“一家兴仁，一国兴仁；一家兴让，一国兴让”、“上老老而民兴孝，上长长而民兴悌”等。此“兴”固然可译为今语如“讲求”“时兴”等，但远不足以尽其意蕴。如同《论语·泰伯》“兴于《诗》”一样，“兴”者起也（《尔雅·释言》），既是起始也是起情，是在起情中起始。且看《大学》所论修、齐、治、平，何一非在起情中起始？“亲爱、贱恶、畏敬、哀矜、敖惰”是情；“孝”、“悌”、“慈”固不失其人伦法则义，但它们首先表现为父子、兄弟之情；至于“所恶于”上下、左右、前后之“恶”，也还是情。这些情或许未必都像亲亲之情一样，具有原发而非对象化之特质，有的甚至还相当对象化。但是，在《大学》作者看来，即使那些对象化之情，只要能以情絜情，与人共其情、同其欲，所谓“民之所好好之，民之所恶恶之”，即可因情见理，在近身、近情的同时近仁、近义，成为最切近而有效的生活准则。

《大学》曰："自天子以至于庶人，壹是皆以修身为本。"这其实就是孟子所谓"天下之本在国，国之本在家，家之本在身"（《孟子·离娄上》）。"（修）身"是相对于"（齐）家"、"（治）国"、"（平）天下"而成为"本"（即根）的。"以修身为本"，并不意味着齐、治、平只要有了修身即已完足，不必讲求制度、生产货利。"以修身为本"仅仅意味着：第一，制度、货利必须深植于意义（仁义）之根，根深而叶茂；否则，"货悖而入者，亦悖而出"。第二，"修身"为意义传达之根，君子的美善之身本身即具有巨大的兴发力量，而言教、政令、刑罚，只有以此为根方能发挥其劝善禁恶之效力，"所藏乎身之不恕，而能喻诸人者，未之有也"。[①]

## 四、余论

综上所述，作为"意义—感通"之学的《大学》，旨在阐明依止于亲亲之家的意义生成与传达之道。其中，"亲亲"从而"格物致知"乃意义生成之根，"修身"乃意义传达之根。"修身"也好，"亲亲"也罢，说到底，又都是以情意为本的。此与《中庸》之说正相贯通："为政在人，取人以身，修身以道，修道以仁。仁者，人也，亲亲为大。"

在人的意义和价值世界的形成、发展过程中，情感、意向之作用，远比知识本位的中国现代教育学所予之者要大得多。人生从哪里开始，意义世界之建构便从哪里开始。亲子关系和亲子之情，因此成为建立世界认同的起点。认同首先是一个情意问题，而非知识问题。自然而正常的亲子之情一旦缺失，人便落入自我与世界相疏离的"被抛"状态，以及情意与理智相分裂的自我疏离状态。情意的缺失只能通过情意的重相感通来弥补，舍此不务而骋能于知识，则理智必陷于多歧而无尽的"理由"纷争之中，让人与世界更加疏远。不仅如此，意义、价值之理乃"情理"而非"物理"。"情理"需要因情见理，通情以达理；其理则充满了诗性，有情斯有理，无情必无理。

此情意为本之道，亦可推之于学术研究者的文化认同。文化认同首先也是一个情意问题，是人们对于自己所从属的那种文化传统的尊重、同情与承担。百余年来，文化自卑和文化功利主义使众多中国知识人走向了文化反叛之路，因有"中国文化救不了我，我为什么还要救中国文化?"之类的极端言说。其等而上之者，也只是把文化认同问题变成了一个知识问题，遂有"批判地继承"、"吸取其精华，剔除其糟粕"之类似是而非的理论话语。本该以"接着说"为根基，并在其与"借来说"的张力关系中

---

① 郭店简文《成之闻之》曰："君子之于教也，其导民也不浸，则其淳也弗深矣。是故亡乎其身而存乎其辞，虽厚其命，民弗从之矣。是故威服刑罚之屡行也，由上之弗身也。"《大学》之意正与此相通。

展开的中国现代教育学术，变成了比较单一的“借来说”。而我们所“借来说”的，恰恰又是隔离于西方人文主义思想传统的科技知识，以及科技化了的社会科学理论。在双重文化隔绝情势中，师范教育日益蜕变为专业化的知识、技能训练，道德和道德教育日益变相为知识问题，也就顺理成章了。

笔者为此一文，既欲以重现古人本有的意义与思维脉络，亦欲以救治疏远情意和文化认同的现代中国教育学术之弊。它本身就是笔者立于当今的思想学术情境扣动历史文本所感受到的历史回声。是耶？非耶？深耶？浅也？谨就正于方家。

**参考文献：**

[1]（清）阮元校刻．十三经注疏·礼记正义［M］．北京：中华书局，1980.

[2]（宋）朱熹．四书章句集注［M］& 四书或问［M］．朱杰人、严佐之、刘永翔主编．朱子全书（陆）［M］．上海：上海古籍出版社 & 合肥：安徽教育出版社，2002.

[3] 李零．郭店竹简校读记（增订本）［M］．北京：中国人民大学出版社，2007.

[4] 高亨．周易大传今注［M］．济南：齐鲁书社，1998.

[5] 程树德撰，程俊英、将见元点校．论语集释［M］．北京：中华书局，1990.

[6]（清）焦循撰，沈文倬点校．孟子正义［M］．北京，中华书局，1987.

[7] 王叔岷．庄子校诠［M］．北京：中华书局，2007.

[8] 刘笑敢．老子古今［M］．北京：中国社会科学出版社，2006.

[9]（明）王守仁撰，吴光、钱明、董平、姚延福编校．王阳明全集［M］．上海：上海古籍出版社，1992.

[10] 梁漱溟．梁漱溟全集（第四卷）［M］．济南：山东人民出版社，1989.

[11] 刘咸炘．推十书（甲辑）［M］．上海：上海科学技术出版社，2009.

[12] 张祥龙．先秦儒家哲学九讲［M］．桂林：广西大学出版社，2010.

# 荀子德性养成论及启示

北方民族大学 潘忠宇

在近几年开展的公民道德教育和近期开展核心价值观培育和践行活动中，公民德性养成始终既是一个重点，又是一个难点。德性何以养成？近日，重读《荀子》一书，联想到近几年开展的公民道德教育和核心价值观培育践行活动，惊叹两千多年前哲人德性养成论思想的天才直觉和高超智慧。

德性养成主要是指根据一定历史时期社会的道德要求和个体的品德心理发展规律，培养良好道德素质和道德品质的过程，它是以培养良好的品德为目标，通过积极努力，养成良好道德品质的实践活动。荀子以“性恶论”为基础，重视对人性的改造，提出“化性起伪”、“隆礼贵义”、“见得思义”、“注错习俗”、“身教示范”、“践行修身”、“学”“思”结合、“积善成德”、“致诚养心”等一系列德性养成主张，建立了具有鲜明东方特色的德性养成论学说，对后世影响深远，对我们当代公民道德教育和核心价值观培育提供了一系列启示，具有重要借鉴价值，值得我们认真探讨和总结。

## “化性起伪”

这是德性养成的基础。荀子十分重视后天教化。而他的后天教化思想是以其“性恶论”作为理论基础的。荀子明确认为，人性本恶。其具体表现是：“人生性生而有好利焉”，“生而有疾恶焉”，“生而有耳目之欲（有）好声色焉”。他认为，如果对上述恶的本性不加约制；任其发展，必将导致“争夺生而辞让亡焉”，“残贼生而忠信亡焉”，“淫乱生而礼义文理亡焉”。（《荀子·性恶》）荀子认为，道德教化对于人的成长至关重要。他说：“不富，无以养民情；不教，无以理民性。故家五亩宅、百亩田，务其业而勿夺其时，所以富之也；立大学，设庠序，修六礼，明七教，所以道之也。”（《荀子·性恶》）他举例说，上好的“莫邪”之剑，如果“不剥夺、不砥砺，则不可以断绳；剥夺之、砥砺之，则到盘盂、刎牛马忽然耳”。（《 荀子·强国》）对于社会中的人，若能用礼义“教诲之，调一之”，则“赏不用而民劝，罚不用而威行”，“夫是之谓道德之威”。（《荀子·强国》）为此，他主张对民众要“一以道”或“道之以道”（《荀子·正名》），他认为，人之所以为人，就在于有道德生活；离开了道德生活，人同禽兽就没有什么区别，指出：“水火有气而无生，草木有生而无知，禽兽有知而无义，人有气、有生、有知，亦且有义，故最为天下贵。”（《荀子·王制》）又说：“凡得人者，必与道也。道也者，何也？曰：礼义辞让忠信是也。”（《荀子·强国》）“故为人上者，必将慎礼义、务忠信而后可。”（《荀子·强国》）在这方面，古代圣王尧舜可以作为典范，故曰：“尧舜者，天下之善教化者也”。（《荀子·正论》）

## “隆礼贵义”

荀子认为：“国无礼则不正，人无礼不生，事无礼不成，国家无礼不宁”，“隆礼贵义者其国治，简礼贱义者其国乱。”“君法明，论有常，表仪既设，民知方，进退有律，孰私王！”要实现国家的安全稳定的统治局面，必须借助道德教化的作用，用“礼”来规范人们行为的。荀子在《荀子·大略》中说：“君人者，隆礼尊贤而王”。荀子认为礼制具有调节人们之间的社会关系和规范人们的社会道德行为的功能，把“礼义”作为衡量人道德的标准，希望通过礼制来规范人们的道德生活，认为人们能做到“隆礼贵义”，就是达到了思想道德的最高标准，因此荀子要求人们特别是君子，要严格按照礼义的标准来修养自身，荀子认为要通过以礼来规范人们的思想道德修养，通过礼来教化人们，他要求人们要知礼、学礼，通过知礼而践行，在道德修养上要反省自身，要持之以恒达到提高自身修养的目的。荀子认为修身的目的并不仅仅是为了自身的道德修养的提高，而是要使天下人都成为道德修养高的仁者，要修己以安人，修己以安百姓，要求人们不但要做到修养好自身，而且还要以自身的道德去教化他人，使所有的百姓都能够成为道德思想高尚的人，能找到自己安身立命之所。如果每个人能够自觉遵守礼制规范，社会就会变得和谐安定。

## “见得思义”

荀子在《荀子·修身》中明确指出：“以公义胜私欲”。荀子还提倡的“见得思义”、“见利思义”、“以义取利”等的道德思想，他认为利是义的物质基础，利离不开义，同样义也离不开利两者是对立统一的。在荀子的思想中遵循“以义制利”、“义以为上”的原则，这也是儒家一直把义作为目标追求。儒家的思想家认为义是把人和动物区分开的根本标志，义是人之所以为人的标准，是人的尊严体现，对于人具有积极的意义价值。儒家十分重视国家、民族以及社会的利益。因此，在对待个人利益上也表现出一定的宽容态度。荀子对道义的高度赞扬和追求，在面临义和利的选择时所表现出的那种“富贵不能淫，贫富不能移，威武不能屈”和“舍生取义”的精神，以及荀子的积极入世的情怀和社会担当意识，具有永恒的意义和价值。

## “注错习俗”

所谓“注错习俗”，指的是人们置身于一定的风习民俗，亦即人们所受的环境熏染。他说：“注错习俗，所以化性也；并一而不二，所以成积也。习俗移志，安久移质。”又说：“譬之越人安越，楚人安楚，君子安雅。是非智能材性然也，是注错习俗之节异也。”由于生活环境的不同，人们所走的道路及所形成的品性亦不同，“可以为尧禹，可以为桀跖，可以为工匠，可以为农贾，在势注错习俗之所积耳。”（《荀子·儒效》）据此，他把“注错习俗”称之为“仁义德行常安之术”。荀子特别重视环境的塑造作用。曾说：“蓬生麻中，不扶而直；白沙在涅，与之俱黑。”（《荀子·劝学》）这里说的是自然环境对周围事物的相互影响，这种相互影响的情况，在人类品格形成中亦同样存在着，故又说：“居楚而楚，居越而越，居夏而夏。是非天性也，积靡使然也。”（《荀子·儒效》）这一切，都不是先天就存在的，而是在生活实践中，潜移默化积累的结果。人的品性是在特定环境的作用下，后天养成的。由此可见，好的环境，对人产生好的影响，久而久之，就可以塑造出优良品格。

## “身教示范”

所谓“身教示范”，指的是教育者在对被教育者施行道德教育过程中，坚持以自身做楷模，给被教育者以示范启迪作用的教育方法。荀子对身教示范方法极为重视。他曾提出“师以身为正仪”（《荀子·修身》）的命题，强调做教师的，应当用自身为标准，去引导、启迪学生。他说：“以善先人者谓之教。”（《荀子·修身》）这是说，教育者必须带头立德，以善先人。他还说：“君子洁其身而同焉者合矣。”（《荀子·不苟》）荀子还将这一思维模式，运用于政权建设之中，要求当政者在实行社会规范方面，应当以身作则，要求民众做到的，当政者应当先做到。他说：“君者仪也，民者景也，仪正而景正；君者槃也，民者水也，槃圆而水圆。”（《荀子·君道》）这些比喻，生动地告诉人们，当政者的一言一行，对于被领导者来说，确实具有示范启迪作用。荀子还进一步指出：“君者，民之源也，源清则流清，源浊则流浊。”（《荀子·君道》）这是说，当政者（君）的言行举止，是社会风气的源头，对于民风的醇化，至关重要。其源头清正，则民风亦清正；其源头浑浊，则民风亦浑浊。荀子的以身示范的德性养成方法要求以行示人、以行教人、以行感人，具有极大的感召力和影响力。

## “践行修身”

荀子曾说：“不闻不若闻之，闻之不若见之，见之不若知之，知之不若行之，学至于行而止矣。”“故闻之而不见，虽博必谬；见之而不知，虽识必妄；知之而不行，虽敦必困。不闻不见，则虽当，非仁也，其道百举而百陷也。”（《荀子·儒效》）又说：“道虽迩，不行不至；事虽小，不为不成。”（《荀子·修身》）荀子认为听到的不如亲眼所见，见到的不如真正的知道，知道的不如行动实践。学习的东西应用到实践中才算真正学到。只有通过实践履行，才能使所学的东西更加明确。要使自己的言行和行动一致，把所学的付之于行动。这些思想表达了荀子重视践行的修身原则。荀子的践行修身，主要是强调把内心的思想道德观念应用于现实，成为个人行动，主要强调对思想道德观念和道德规范的履行和实施，重视道德品质的实践性。提倡践行修身，是古代先贤务实品格的集中体现，这一种品格在今天仍然是由它的积极意义，荀子强调的践行修养对我们民族的道德生活实践和文明进步都产生了十分深远的影响。

## “学”“思”结合

荀子认为人们能否成为思想道德高尚的人，主要在于思想修养和道德教育，“学”与“思”，都是修身不可缺少的重要环节，道德修养的方法是学思并重。关于“学”，他专门写了《劝学篇》，论述了许多关于“学”的理论观点，该篇首句就说：“学不可已矣”，强调任何时候都不能放弃学习。荀子在《劝学》中说：“故学数有终，若其义则不可须臾舍也，为之，人也；舍之，禽兽也”（《荀子·劝学》）。认为人要认真去学习，如果放弃学习，则和禽兽没有区别了。他还深有体会地说：“吾尝终日思矣，不如须臾之所学也。”（《荀子·劝学》）认为学比思更能使人得到提高，所以他明确提出“积学而不息”（《荀子·性恶》）的口号，要求人们专心于学，永不停息。荀子虽然高度重视“学”，但他并不贬低“思”。他曾说：“辟耳目之欲，可谓能自强矣，未及思也。”（《荀子·解蔽》）强调在学习上要“思索以通之”，“闲居静思则通”（《荀子·劝学》）。荀子曾提出“以心知道”的命题，说：“故心不可不知道；心不知道，则不可道，而可非道。”（《荀子·解蔽》）这“以心知道”的过程，实质就是“思”的过程。荀子认为在思想道德修养方面上，要时刻思考自己的言行是否符合道德的标准要求，用这种方法使自己的道德修养达到一个更高的思想境界。此外，荀子还主张见贤思齐的思想，荀子说：“见善修然必以自存也，见不善，湫然，必以自省。”这样可以激励人们来学习高尚的品德，抵制不良的道德习惯。可见，荀子在修身方面坚持“学”、“思”并重。

## “积善成德”

与孟子强调“反省内求”的思想不同，荀子的德性养成思想中偏重于“积善成德”。所谓“积善成德”，就是指在修身中，长期坚持行善积德，成就德性。荀子认为，圣人的高尚品格并非一夜之间成长起来的，而是长期积累的结果。他说：“积土成山，风雨兴焉；积水成渊，蛟龙生焉；积善成德，圣心备焉。”（《荀子·劝学》）荀子认为，按照“积善”的原则去做，即使是“涂之人”，也会在修身方面做出成就，曾说：“涂之人伏（服）术为学，专心一志，思索熟察，加日县（縣）久，积学而不息，则通于神明，参于天地。故圣人者，人之所积而致矣。”（《荀子·性恶》）又说：“百姓积善而全尽，谓之圣人”，“故圣人也者，人之所积也”，“积礼义而为君子”（《荀子·儒效》）。认为只需要长期的、自觉的学习优良的品德，用“礼”对人们进行教化和规劝，并且能不断的积善就能转化为善，圣人的品德高尚是因为长期行善积德的结果。

## “致诚养心”

所谓“致诚养心”，就是要求人们在德性养成中坚守“诚”德。荀子说：“君子养心莫善于诚，致诚则无它事矣。唯仁之为守，唯义之为行。诚心守仁则形，形则神，神则能化矣。诚心行义则理，理则明，明则能变矣。变化代兴，谓之天德。……夫此有常，以至其诚者也。”“天地为大矣，不诚则不能化万物；圣人为智矣，不诚则不能化万民；父子为亲矣，不诚则疏；君上为尊矣，不诚则卑。夫诚者，君子之所守也，而政事之本也。”（《荀子·不苟》）荀子把“致诚养心”作为德性养成的原则，这对于启迪人们在修身中严于律己，坚持“慎独”，有其特殊意义。

荀子德性养成论，包含丰富的精华内容，我们把它作为积极培育公民道德和践行核心价值观的基本价值资源，并不是不加分析地全盘吸收。荀子的德性养成论思想受当时社会的经济和政治背景及先秦诸子百家的影响，具有一定的历史局限性。我们应该站在社会发展的时代要求和人类文明发展进步的时代潮流的高度，取其精华，去其糟粕，发扬荀子德性养成论的合理内容，尤其要结合时代要求对其进行创造性转化，赋予其新的时代内涵，在传承中创新，在创新中弘扬，在弘扬中发展，从而使其更好地为我们社会的精神文明建设服务。

# 宋儒以仁修身之伦理意涵与工夫实践对当代教育之意义

暨南国际大学　齐婉先

## 一、前言

孔门学说首重“仁”之思想，孔子（公元前551－公元前479）讲“仁”，明白揭示“克己复礼为仁”，“为仁由己”，[①]“我欲仁，斯仁至矣”。[②]孔子距今虽已超越两千五百年之久，但由孔子所倡言之“仁”，不仅是儒家学说之核心观念，同时亦对后世人文生命产生深刻影响。牟宗三先生认为儒家思想对人类最大贡献就在于孔子经由反省夏商周三代文化而提出“仁”之观念，这个“仁”，“是可以在我们眼前真实的生命里头具体呈现的”。[③]正因孔子提出“仁”这个观念，人类之生命方向乃得以确立，这也正是儒家之本质意义所在，故牟先生直言：“开辟价值之源，挺立道德主体，莫过于儒。”[④]儒家之“反省”，牟先生认为主要是针对“周文疲弊”这个问题来进行，其中，最重要问题是“使人的生命站起来”。[⑤]因此，儒家思想所讲之“仁”，也就是儒者所赖以重建周文之核心伦理价值。孟子（公元前372－公元前289）根据孔子之“仁”讲“性善”，指出仁义礼智为人所固有，非由外铄而得；[⑥]孟子以“亲亲”作为“仁”之具

---

① 二语见《论语·颜渊》，（魏）何晏等注，（宋）邢昺疏：《论语注疏》，台北：艺文印书馆，1985年。影印清嘉庆二十年重刊宋本《论语注疏》附校勘记），卷12，第106页。本文以下所引《论语》篇章，俱出自《论语注疏》本，为行文简洁，此后不另标版本。

② 语见《论语·述而》，卷7，第64页。

③ 见牟宗三：《中国哲学十九讲》，台北：台湾学生书局，1983年，第35页。

④ 同前注，第62页。

⑤ 同前注，第60－62页。

⑥ 见《孟子·告子上》，汉·赵岐注，宋·孙奭疏：《孟子注疏》（台北：艺文印书馆，1985年，影印清嘉庆二十年重刊宋本《孟子注疏》附校勘记），卷11上，第195页。本文以下所引《孟子》篇章，俱出自《孟子注疏》本，为行文简洁，此后不另标版本。

体内容,[①] 以“恻隐之心”说“仁之端”,说“人皆有不忍人之心”,[②] 强调“居仁由义”之道德实践,才真正是“大人之事”。[③] 孟子也特别指出有能扩充四端者,不仅可以事父母,更进而可以保四海,并且行不忍人之政,运天下于掌上。[④] 牟先生对于孟子由孔子之“仁”转出说“性善”之解释是,孟子建立“道德的善本身”之善就在性中,以及“道德性本身”之性就是道德的善本身之“性善”意义,即是“直接从人的内在道德性说性”,换言之,直接从人的道德意识建立道德性的性。这个人的道德意识,就是孟子所强调可自四端去了解之“人的道德心”,代表“道德的主体性”。[⑤] 孔、孟学说以“仁”作为人之价值根源,挺立人之道德主体,为正处于礼崩乐坏之周代社会中的个人生命提供安身立命的支撑,同时,也给出儒家理想世界中人类的生命方向,影响着后世儒者对于理想世界与生命图像的建构与追求。

宋代儒者程颢(1032—1085)、程颐(1033—1107)及朱熹(1130—1200)三人对于“仁”之理解与诠释甚为重视,皆有用力处,也各具特色。程颢有“识仁”说,以“浑然与物同体”说“仁”,人能本其良知良能存习此心,以诚敬存守仁之理,便可得“反身而诚”之大乐;[⑥] 程颐以“公”说“仁”,“仁自是性”,“公而以人体之”为“仁”,“公”只是“仁之理”,一“公”就“物我兼照”,恕、爱则为仁之施用;[⑦] 朱熹则着〈仁说〉,以“仁”为人之得“天地生物之心”以为心之德,以“仁”为德之人之心,是“温然爱人利物之心,包四德而贯四端”,人能体“仁之道”而存之,则“众善之源,百行之本”,俱在人之心。[⑧] 二程与朱熹三人论“仁”,明显依据孔、孟文本,以孔、孟给出的理想世界与生命图像为基底,但又同时吸纳《中庸》、《易传》、《大学》中性命天道观,而提出具有伦理意涵之诠释,并且建构诚敬存守、以仁修身之工夫理论,反映出宋儒对于所处时代进行个人及人类生命方向之反省,以及宋儒出于道德的自觉建立由个人延展推扩至家国天下之伦理意识与道德价值。据此,因应全球化时代的来临,当代教育甚为关切之自我修身工夫及道德意识建立等议题,应当可以从宋儒对于孔孟“仁”学之教曾经做出的省思与诠释获得启发性意义。

---

① 语见《孟子·尽心上》,同前注,卷13上,第232页。

② 二语见《孟子·公孙丑上》,同前注,卷3下,第65—66页。

③ 二语见《孟子·尽心上》,同前注,卷13下,第240页。

④ 见《孟子·公孙丑上》,同前注,卷3下,第65页。

⑤ 关于牟先生对孟子论性之阐释,详细内容参见氏著:《中国哲学十九讲》,第67—74页。

⑥ 参见程颢语录“学者须先识仁”,(宋)程颢、程颐撰:《河南程氏遗书》卷2上,收入《二程集》(台北:汉京文化事业,1983),第1册,第16—17页。

⑦ 参见程颐语录“仁之道”及“问仁”,同前注,卷15及18,第153、182页。

⑧ 参见朱熹:《仁说》,《晦庵先生朱文公文集(四)》,卷67,收入朱傑人、严佐之、刘永翔主编:《朱子全书》,上海市:上海古籍:安徽教育出版社,2002年,第23册,第3279—3281页。

## 二、诚敬存守之修身工夫

当代教育重视公民道德的养成，原因之一是公民道德教育的落实有助于世界各国在全球化趋势下进行密切且频繁之跨国家、跨地区、跨文化之正向交流。全球化趋势对当前世界带来的影响，不仅是世界各国在政治、经济、社会、金融、文化、宗教等面向的发展越来越趋向相互依赖，彼此关联，同时也使得世界各地的发展出现同步、类似或同质的倾向。德国学者 Ulrich Beck 解释全球化是：

可经历的日常生活行为的疆界瓦解，这些行为发生在经济、信息、生态、技术、跨文化冲突和公民社会等面向……民族国家和民族社会的统一性崩解了；形成的是新形态的权力和竞争关系，以及民族国家的机构和行动者，与跨国行动者、跨国认同、跨国社会空间、跨国形态与过程间的冲突和交错。[①]

Beck 所谓“新形态的权利和竞争关系”及跨国、跨文化的冲突与交错，正剧烈改变着人类的生活形态与内容，产生关于生存技能的新形态需求，同时也造成个人因应新形态关系而产生对于生命意义、道德价值与是非判断的迷惘与省思。晚近因为跨国大型企业频繁出现管理上的伦理问题，美国企业管理学者戈夏勒（Sumantra Ghoshal，1948—2004）就直接批判美国著名商学院学者所发展出的管理学理论，空有符合科学性的精致数学模型及经验分析作为支持，但事实上却是全然无一物的虚假知识，这也使得商学院学生在学习过程中完全不能产生“任何道德上的责任感”。当法规条文与道德原则相抗时，不具道德意识的经理人自然将违法与否优位于道德原则，轻易做出未违法但却背离道德原则的错误决定。几个跨国大型企业严重的管理过失以及戈夏勒的诤言，导致美国著名大学如哈佛、史丹佛、达特茅斯学院（Dartmouth College）的商学院开始在企业管理课程中开设道德课程，教导道德困境的个案研究，部分学者甚至要求将企业道德课程列为必修课程。[②] 将道德教育引进商学院课程的改变，凸显出自觉的道德意识在全球化时代中高度的需求性，对于建立人类的生命方向及伦理意识具有重要意义。然则如何在当代教育中兴发道德情感，建立道德意识？二程与朱熹以仁修身的道德实践与伦理意识，强调诚敬存守的修身工夫应能为当代道德教育提供理论依据。

---

① 见（德）Ulrich Beck 著、孙治本译：《全球化危机——全球化的形成、风险与机会》，台北：台湾商务印书馆，1999 年，第 30—31 页。

② 见赖美译：《企业丑闻频传商学院开始教道德课》，《经济学人》，2005 年 2 月 19 日，收入，《商业周刊》第 901 期（2005 年 2 月 28 日）。取自：《商业周刊》知识库（2005—02—28）。陈一姗：《安隆前财务长的独家告白》，《天下杂志》第 551 期（2014 年 7 月），第 116—120 页。

程颢与朱熹二人论“仁”皆涵有宇宙论意义，陈来先生认为程颢以生生不息之“生意”论“仁”，将“仁”理解为宇宙的原理；朱熹则带入“天地以生物为心”之命题，提供“仁”在宇宙论上之意义支持。[①] 程颢以“识仁”为先，揭示识得“仁者浑然与物同体”之理，则知诚敬存守实为修身之工夫。观“识仁”说，通篇可以分为三大段落，首段为总纲，起首即言：

> 学者须先识仁。仁者，浑然与物同体。义、礼、智、信皆仁也。识得此理，以诚敬存之而已，不须防检，不须穷索。若心懈则有防，心苟不懈，何防之有？理有未得，故须穷索。存久自明，安待穷索？[②]

上述部分引文，可自三方面理解，此三方面亦正是“识仁”说通篇在理论建构上之三大支柱：第一，识仁乃为学之第一要务，所谓仁，即是“浑然与物同体”。第二，既已识得“浑然与物同体”之仁理，则仅须加“以诚敬存之”的功夫。第三，仁理在己，理会可得，既然实有诸己，因此，只须“诚敬”存久的功夫，全然用不上防检、穷索的努力。三者中以首出的第一个最为重要，即是“仁”之概念的义界，程颢以“浑然与物同体”解释“仁”之义涵，将“仁”推扩充之而为天地间之“大公心”，[③]“识仁”之说的义理间架，由是确立。然后再联系至“以诚敬存之”的道德实践功夫与“存久自明”的道德主体之贞定，“识仁”说之义理架构于是完成。值得注意的是，上述三个支柱彼此间建立一紧密关联之义理架构，即被给予之“仁”之概念的义界导引出“以诚敬存之”的修养功夫，而在“以诚敬存之”的修养功夫之实际践履中，“仁”之“存久自明”的本质亦一并具体表显，而“存久自明”之具体表显亦同时一并肯认被给予之“仁”之“浑然与物同体”的义界。三者间如此关联循环之义理架构，形成一持续活动之有机体，一如宇宙天地间创生生命且生生不息之恒久活动的有机结构。程颢即是通过如此之义理架构，揭示人之以天地万物为一体的自觉，即是人在超越意义上之主体性的显现，从而建立出“仁”之概念的形上道德意义。正是在此意义下，次段接续之内容，遂通至孟子“万物皆备于我”之说。“识仁”说之次段言：

> 此道与物无对，大不足以明之。天地之用皆我之用。孟子言“万物皆备于我”，须“反身而诚”，乃为大乐。若反身未诚，则犹是二物有对，以己合彼，终未有之，又安得乐！[④]

---

① 依陈先生之见，程颢虽以生生之“仁”作为宇宙的原理，但仍未将“与万物一体”概念关联至宇宙本体的意义上。相关分析，参见氏著：《仁学本体论》，北京：生活，读书·新知三联书店，2014年，第264—265、310—311页。

② 见《河南程氏遗书》，卷2上，第16—17页。

③ 参见劳思光：《新编中国哲学史（三上）》，台北：三民书局，2004年，第201页。

④ 见《河南程氏遗书》，卷2上，第17页。

上述段落文字承续首段总纲而下，用意不在补充说明首段，而是在描述已于首段中指示出之“仁”，在得以完全发用时所获得之“大乐”，亦即人之自觉与万物浑然同体得以完全而具体实践时达致“天地之用皆我之用”，一如孟子所言“万物皆备于我”，而又能自觉反省己身而能诚，即入于天人相合的“大乐”之境。然而常人多不能理会“仁体”乃实有诸己，故在践仁功夫上，总是向外远求。因此，程颢在“识仁”说之末段文字中，强调践仁功夫只是“以诚敬存之”，并以孟子存养“浩然之气”说之“必有事焉而勿正，心勿忘，勿助长”为教，指点“诚敬”功夫之践履。“识仁”说末段言：

《订顽》意思，乃备言此体，以此意存之，更有何事。“必有事焉而勿正，心勿忘，勿助长”，未尝致纤毫之力，此其存之之道。若存得，便合有得。盖良知良能，元不丧失。以昔日习心未除，却须存习此心，久则可夺旧习。此理至约，惟患不能守。既能体之而乐，亦不患不能守也。①

程颢论“敬”与程颐最大不同处，即在于程颢对“敬”之诠释，乃是置“敬”于直接发自道德本心之“纯亦不已”的自律道德中进行理解。② 上述段落中，程颢强调“敬”之功夫目的在“存之”，而此“之”字，即指“良知良能”。“良知良能”原为己所有，而是自知自能，自然从未丧失，故只须存而得之便有。然而人不能无“昔日习心”，对此，程颢认为去除习心之对治方法，即是通过“敬”之功夫“存习此心”。至于一再添加丝毫力气向外远求的努力，对程颢而言，既不需要，亦无所作用。正因如此，程颢只说“患不能守”，而一旦能体会仁体实有诸己，不待外求，则自能乐，至此境地，亦已无不能守之忧虑。故程颢又言：“敬胜百邪”。③ 又言：“执事须是敬，又不可矜持太过。”④

虽然程颢主张以“诚敬”存养，不须防检、穷索，但是程颢所欲实现之道德理性乃在“体之而乐”中，绝非过于矜持之样态。又言：

“鸢飞戾天，鱼跃于渊，言其上下察也。”此一段子思吃紧为人处，与“必有事焉而勿正心”之意同，活泼泼地。会得时，活泼泼地；不会得时，只是弄精神。⑤

观程颢之意，持守“敬”之道德实践功夫，正是落在“上下察也”上说，而在实践过程中，自是“活泼泼地”，入于“大乐”之境。若是过份把持，形成矜持模样，只

---

① 见《河南程氏遗书》，卷 2 上，第 17 页。

② 关于二程思想差异之梗概，参见蔡仁厚：《中国哲学史大纲》，台北：台湾学生书局，1999 年，第 215－218 页。

③ 见《河南程氏遗书》，卷 11，第 119 页。

④ 同前注，卷 3，第 61 页。

⑤ 同前注，第 59 页。

是劳累精神，则已失“诚敬”存养功夫之“正”，程颢所言“上下察也”即在此。

程颢、程颐兄弟二人在道德修养的工夫论上，虽然偏重处容或不同，但二人俱强调“敬”之内容与实践的重要性，认为此乃圣贤之学，学者之事，而以此勉励众弟子。[①] 钱穆（1895—1990）先生即曾指出程门提出最主要的一个字，是“敬”字。[②] 二程关于“敬”之认识，除来自阅读古代典籍，如《易传》、《论语》、《孟子》、《中庸》等之外，更为关键的是，出于自己立身行事与待人接物之日常生活中的实际体验而心有所得，二程语录中有段文字，可以说明二程以“敬”为达道之功夫的主张，曰：

> 学者须敬守此心，不可急迫，当栽培深厚，涵泳于其间，然后可以自得。但急迫求之，只是私己，终不足以达道。[③]

在二程思想中，达道之功夫不可急迫以求，而必须通过持续“敬守此心”之培养功夫，累积深厚至此心自得，方可谓完成。其中奥义，即是“敬”之功夫的实践必须至于“可以自得”。虽说“敬守此心”，然而程颢对于“敬”之功夫的主张，明显落在实事上讲求，程颢曾言：“敬者人事之本。”[④] 并尝自述其亲身践履之经验，他说：“某写字时甚敬，非是要字好，只此是学。”[⑤] 即使在写字时，程颢仍然保持“敬”之心态，原因不在求字好的结果，而是亲身经历“敬”之实践的一段过程并在此实践过程中自得学之真正义涵。又如以“敬”解释《论语》文献中关于孔子弟子颜回（BC521—BC481）不惰之学习态度，也是着重执事而能敬之功夫。程颢说：“子曰：‘语之而不惰者，其回也与！’”颜子之不惰者，敬也。”[⑥] 所谓不惰，即是持守而无间断，深厚培养，涵泳于其间，亦即是以“敬”自我修身之功夫实践。在程颢的思想体系中，“敬”之功夫的实践，虽行于人事上，然而始终符应于天命、天理。关于此，程颢之解释则是自“敬”之无间断的本质立说。程颢言：

> “天地设位而易行乎其中”，只是敬也。敬则无间断，体物而不可遗者，诚敬而已矣，不诚则无物也。《诗》曰：“维天之命，于穆不已，于乎不显，文王之德之纯”，“纯亦不已”，纯则无间断。[⑦]

上述文字显示，《诗经·周颂·维天之命》中所描述“文王之德之纯”遥契于“于

---

① 参见程颢语录之“学者不必远求”与程颐语录之“有人旁边作事，己不见”二则，同前注，卷2上，第20，154页。

② 有关钱穆先生之见解，参见氏著：《宋明理学概述》，台北：台湾学生书局，1987年，第73页。

③ 见《河南程氏遗书》，卷2上，第15页。

④ 程颢曰：“诚者天之道，敬者人事之本。敬则诚。”同前注，卷11，第127页。

⑤ 同前注，卷3，第60页。

⑥ 同前注。

⑦ 同前注，卷11，第118页。

穆不已”之天命的观念，经过《中庸》作者揭示“纯亦不已”之意，直接将文王之德上提至天命位阶，确立天人之间上下通贯之联系。程颢结合《周易参同契》之“天地设位而易行乎其中”，在理解该文本中带入周初人之“敬”的观念，建构出“敬”为一具无间断的本质，且是“体物而不可遗”之实践活动，而人通过“敬”之实践得以体现天命之“敬”的形上道德义涵。换言之，存在于天之德与文王之德间的关系，即是牟宗三先生所指出，“天命、天道贯注到个体的身上时，只要这个体以敬的作用来保住天命，那末天命下贯所成的个体的性可以永远呈现光明”，而文王即是彰显此一关系的典型例子。①

既然天命、天理之体现是在人之实践“敬”的功夫中进行，则人自然不须向外远求，仅须“近取诸身”，实用“敬”之功夫。因为，即令是如文王一般之圣人，亦别无他途可行。程颢即言：

> 学者不必远求，近取诸身，只明人理，敬而已矣，便是约处。《易》之干卦言圣人之学，坤卦言贤人之学，惟言“敬以直内，义以方外，敬义立而德不孤”。至于圣人，亦止如是，更无别途。……故有道有理，天人一也，更不分别。浩然之气，乃吾气也，养而不害，则塞乎天地；一为私心所蔽，则欿然而馁，却甚小也。“思无邪”，“无不敬”，只此二句，循而行之，安得有差？有差者，皆由不敬不正也。②

以“敬以直内，义以方外，敬义立而德不孤”作为圣贤之学的内容，并指出“浩然之气”即是人之气，倘人果能循圣贤之学，“养而不害”自身的“浩然之气”，则人所固有之“浩然之气”自然可充塞于天地之间。“敬”之观念在此显然已与孟子“浩然之气”的修养功夫建立道德实践意义之内在关联性。然而，由“近取诸身”，实用“敬”之功夫，持守不间断以养吾“浩然之气”，进而推扩、达致充塞天地之圣人之境，此一为学进程，程颢强调仍须先“识仁”，因为“仁者，以天地万物为一体，莫非己也，认得为已，何所不至”?③ 至于修养功夫之践履，则在“以诚敬存之”。因此，程颢说：

> 学要在敬也，诚也，中间便有个仁。“博学而笃志，切问而近思，仁在其中矣”之意。④

“博学而笃志，切问而近思，仁在其中矣”乃是子夏（BC507－BC420）之观点，⑤

---

① 参见牟宗三：《中国哲学的特质》，台北市：台湾学生书局，1990 年，第 28 页。

② 见《河南程氏遗书》，卷 2 上，第 20 页。

③ 同前注，第 15 页。

④ 同前注，卷 14，第 141 页。

⑤ 关于子夏之言，参见《子张》，《论语注疏》，卷 19，第 171 页。

对照二人文字，可见程颢所解释之“敬”、“诚”以学，即是子夏所论“博学而笃志，切问而近思”之为仁功夫。程颢之解释，不可谓无据，观孔子回答弟子樊迟问仁时，曰：“居处恭，执事敬，与人忠，虽之夷狄，不可弃也。”① 足见“仁”之内容，本即涵括“执事敬”之践履，尤其最后“虽之夷狄，不可弃也”二句话，明确说出孔子言“仁”，不仅强调在平日居家生活中谦逊和顺，在执事应对上专心致志、谨慎沉着，在待人接物上忠诚信实；尤其重要的是，个人之恭、敬、忠等行动必须随时随处进行并永久维持，不因所处时地之互异而有所不同。② 如此内容之“仁”，突显出“仁”之实践性。③ 而由程颢解释在“诚”、“敬”之修养功夫中已涵括仁之诠释进路观之，程颢主张“敬”之功夫，固然承继孔子“仁”学中“执事敬”之本质，但亦出现创造性的诠释义涵，即通过“识仁”说，人之“以诚敬存之”的修养功夫，乃具有在道德理性之实践上的意义。

## 三、主敬之道德实践意义

由二程提出具有理学意义之主敬修身工夫之所以能成为程门一套论述周延且体系完整的工夫理论，主要得力于朱熹之诠释。观二程阐述“敬”之义理内容、工夫用力处及修养成效，不仅以《易传》、《论语》、《孟子》、《中庸》等儒家典籍之文本作为主敬修身工夫之义理内容的根源，而且强调在平日待人接物、立身行事中，实践切身求仁，持敬主一，专求放心之道德修养工夫。程颢之专论“敬”，有三段颇为重要的言论。其一言：

> “居处恭，执事敬，与人忠”，此是彻上彻下语，圣人元无二语。④

其二言：

> 诚者天之道，敬者人事之本。敬则诚。⑤

其三言：

> 孟子曰：“仁也者，人也，合而言之道也。”《中庸》所谓“率性之谓道”是

---

① 关于子夏之言，参见《子张》，《论语注疏》，卷13，第118页。

② 英国汉学家A. C. Graham（葛瑞汉）将孔子在《论语》中曾经使用过之“敬”的意义，归纳为两类：一为个人对父母、君主、神灵等应有的态度，另一为自持、恭谨、专注的状态。参见氏著Two Chinese Philosophers（LA Salle，Illinois：Open Court，1992），第68页。

③ 牟宗三先生对于孔子之“仁”之解释为，“孔子提出仁，仁这个观念完全是个道德理性(moral reason)的观念，是属于实践的问题”。牟宗三先生此言主要在以孔子提出“仁”之观念及“仁”所涵摄之意涵为例，说明中国文化起始处即是著眼于“生命”，而且是“从德性上关心生命”，因此“重德”。相关详细论述，参见《中国哲学十九讲》，第3讲，第46页。

④ 见《河南程氏遗书》，卷2上，同前注，第13页。

⑤ 同前注，卷11，第127页。

也。仁者，人此者也。“敬以直内，义以方外”，仁也。若以敬直内，则便不直矣。行仁义岂有直乎？“必有事焉而勿正”则直也。夫能“敬以直内，义以方外”，则与物同矣。故曰：“敬义立而德不孤。”是以仁者无对，放之东海而准，放之西海而准，放之南海而准，放之北海而准。医家言四体不仁，最能体仁之名也。①

上引第一段文字说明程颢对于孔子通贯上下之圣人之学的理解，就是人在实事上切身践履“敬”之工夫。第二段则可见程颢论敬之工夫的实践是由敬而诚，由下学于人事入手而上达至天道，进入上下一贯、天人合一之境界。第三段重点有三，第一，程颢通过对《孟子》、《中庸》、《易》文本之理解，诠释“仁”为天命于人，且以“敬以直内，义以方外”为“仁”之具体表现。第二，程颢指出人若能具体表现“仁”，就能与万物同体，因此程颢强调成德工夫只须“敬以直内”地存养、持守而具体表现“仁”，就如孟子所言“必有事焉而勿正”，而非以“仁”为外在于人而刻意穷索以行仁义，刻意向外穷索就是“以敬直内”。第三，程颢通过《易·坤卦》“敬义立而德不孤”诠释仁者与物同体而无所对立之气象。

程颐论主敬工夫，也有三段颇为重要的言论。其一言：

闲邪则诚自存，不是外面捉一个诚将来存着。今人外面役役于不善，于不善中寻个善来存着，如此则岂有入善之理？只是闲邪，则诚自存。故孟子言性善，皆由内出。只为诚便存，闲邪更着甚工夫？但惟是动容貌、整思虑，则自然生敬，敬只是主一也。主一，则既不之东，又不之西，如是则只是中；既不之此，又不之彼，如是则只是内。存此，则自然天理明。学者须是将“敬以直内”涵养此意，直内是本。②

其二言：

闲邪则固一矣，然主一则不消言闲邪。有以一为难见，不可下工夫。如何一者，无他，只是整齐严肃，则心便一，一则自是无非僻之奸。此意但涵养久之，则天理自然明。③

其三言：

问：“‘出门如见大宾，使民如承大祭。’方其未出门、未使民时，如何？”曰：“此‘俨若思’之时也。当出门时，其敬如此，未出门时可知也。且见乎外者，出乎中者也。使民出门者，事也。非因是事上方有此敬，盖素敬也。如人接物以诚，人皆曰诚人，盖是素来诚，非因接物而始有此诚也。俨然正其衣冠，尊其胆视，

① 见《河南程氏遗书》，卷11，第120页。
② 同前注，卷15，第149页。
③ 同前注，第150页。

其中自有个敬处。虽曰无状，敬自可见。”[①]

在上述三段文字中，程颐认为闲邪工夫颇生弊端，因此强调敬之工夫就是主一，而一就是只心之专一。对照上述二程论敬之工夫，虽然二人皆强调主敬工夫，但在论敬之归趋上，仍旧存在差异性。陈来先生对此所作分析十分的当，陈先生指出：

程颢以诚与敬并提，他说的敬近于诚的意思，同时他十分强调敬的修养必须把握一个限度，不应伤害心境的自在和乐；程颐则不遗余力地强调敬，他所谓主敬的主要内容是整齐严肃与主一无适，要求人在外在的容貌举止与内在的思想情感两方面同时约束自己。[②]

二程论敬工夫之偏向虽不尽同，但主敬工夫经过二程之讨论，大致规范出建构一套工夫理论所需之蓝图。此份蓝图在朱熹手上，终于完成一套论述周延、体系完备、次第分明之工夫理论。

关于朱熹对二程主敬工夫之理解与诠释，有三段文字颇有意味，值得加以说明。第一段：

问："敬通贯动静而言。然静时少，动时多，恐易得挠乱。"曰："如何都静得。有事须着应。人在世间，未有无事时节；要无事，除是死也。自早至暮，有许多事。不成说事多挠乱，我且去静坐。敬不是如此。若事至前，而自家却要主静，顽然不应，便是心都死了。无事时敬在里面，有事时敬在事上。有事无事，吾之敬未尝间断也。且如应接宾客，敬便是应接上；宾客去后，敬又在这里。若厌苦宾客，而为之心烦，此却是自挠乱，非所谓敬也。故程子说：'学到专一时方好。'盖专一，则有事无事皆是如此。程子此段，这一句是紧要处。"[③]

第二段：

学者当知孔门所指求仁之方，日用之间，以敬为主。不论感与未感，平日常是如此涵养，则善端之发，自然明着。少有间断，而察识存养，扩而充之，皆不难乎为力矣。造次颠沛，无时不习。此心之全体皆贯乎动静语默之间，而无一息之间断，其所谓仁乎。[④]

第三段：

圣贤言语，大约似乎不同，然未始不贯。只如夫子言非礼勿视听言动，"出门如见大宾，使民如承大祭"，"言忠信，行笃敬"，这是一副当说话。到孟子又却说

---

① 见《河南程氏遗书》，卷18，第184－185页。

② 参见陈来：《宋明理学》，上海：华东师范大学，2003年，第81页。

③ 见朱熹：《朱子语类（一）》，卷12，收入朱傑人、严佐之、刘永翔主编：《朱子全书》，第14册，上海市：上海古籍：安徽教育出版社，2002年，第374页。

④ 同前注，第374－375页。

"求放心"，"存心养性"。《大学》则又有所谓格物，致知，正心，诚意。至程先生又专一发明一个"敬"字。若只恁看，似乎参错不齐，千头万绪，其实只一理。道夫曰："泛泛于文字间，祇觉得异。实下工，则贯通之理始见。"曰："然。只是就一处下工夫，则余者皆兼摄在里。圣贤之道，如一室然，虽门户不同，自一处行来便入得，但恐不下工夫尔。"①

此三段文字俱见于《朱子语类》卷十二，第一段详细阐释二程主敬工夫是随时随地，无论是否有事都持续践履，无一息间断，并且以应接宾客之实事为例说明程子主一持敬工夫。由此段内容可见朱熹兼容二程论敬工夫之要义，涵化合同二说差异性的诠释。第二段主要说明孔门求仁之方就是主敬工夫之持续践履，朱熹解释人能持续在日用之间践履主敬工夫，涵养到熟习处，察识存养扩充这一套工夫次第的实践自然不费力，亦能不受环境恶劣困顿之影响，继续用功不懈，层层递进转深，心之全体终能通贯透显生命整体之存在。在这段文字中，朱熹承继程颢对圣人上下、动静通贯之仁学的理解进行诠释，建构出具有存有论意义之主敬工夫论。第三段则将二程主敬工夫置于儒家思想发展之历史脉络中，建构出儒家修身工夫论传统。值得一提的是，朱熹在这段文字中对二程主敬工夫论所进行之诠释，颇具有当代诠释学经验的意义。德国哲学诠释学家高达美（Hans-Georg Gadamer，1900－2002，或译作伽达玛、加达默尔）在论及时间距离的诠释学意义时，说：

每一个时代都必须按照它自己的方式来理解历史流传下来的文本，因为这文本是属于整个传统的一部份，而每一时代则是对这整个传统有一种实际的兴趣，并试图在这传统中理解自身。②

据此以观，朱熹对二程主敬工夫之诠释，不仅建构出一套系统化之儒家修身工夫理论；同时，在朱熹依照其所处时代之方式理解《论语》、《孟子》、《中庸》、《易传》、《大学》以及二程论著（如高达美所言），对作为儒学传统一部份之"仁"做出诠释，也使得"仁"之意义开展由孔孟确立之道德实践，程颢理解之宇宙原理，程颐带入之性命天道，至朱熹则更将"仁"体系化关联到宇宙论之根源问题上。朱熹《仁说》对于"仁"之意义开展，陈来先生指出其贡献有两个面向，一是延续讨论先秦与汉代儒者论"仁"之内容，二是结合宇宙论说"仁"，扩大"仁"之意涵。陈先生说：

但《仁说》之作，从一开始就坚持在开首阐明"天地以生物为心"，作为天道

① 见朱熹：《朱子语类（一）》，卷 12，收入朱傑人、严佐之、刘永翔主编：《朱子全书》，第 14 册，上海市：上海古籍：安徽教育出版社，2002 年，第 367－368 页。

② 参见 Hans-Georg Gadamer 著，洪汉鼎译：《真理与方法——哲学诠释学的基本特征》，台北：时报文化，1993 年，第 388－389 页。

论的核心刻画，力图给予仁说最坚定的宇宙论的支持。在伦理学上，朱子仁说的主要倾向显然是，主张从爱来推溯、理解仁。……朱子重建了仁与爱、仁与天地之心的关联。天地之心元包四德，人之为心仁包四德，天地之元与人心之仁相对应，后者来自于前者。朱子的作法使得先秦儒与汉儒的仁说得以延续在新的仁说讨论中，其意义相当重要。①

又：

这里已经明确把“生意”和“仁”、“元”连结一体，不是只关注仁的实践意义，仁的伦理意义了，而向宇宙论去展开，把仁和宇宙论的生命问题、根源问题结合起来，赋予仁以更广大的意义。②

## 四、结语

公民教育是当代教育重要的一环，所谓公民教育，就是“国家或社会为培育健全的公民，所实施的一种教育”。其内容，就个人言，经由公民教育，个人“了解各种政治、社会之规范，训练政治、社会活动之技巧，以适应各种政治、社会之生活”。就国家、社会言，公民教育“传递政治、社会之文化遗产，规范个人政治、社会之行为，并建立共识，以促成政治、社会之理想”。③

在全球化趋势下，公民教育深受影响。由于全球化形成全球意识的升高、国家主权的削弱、公民参与的增强、大众文化的产生、社会正义的突显，地球村概念的形成、公民的权利义务关系模糊、文化与国家意识上认同的混淆、社会福利与劳工三权不明和非政府组织参与不足等问题。④ 面对这些问题，当前的公民教育是否足以承担并提供解答，这已经造成教育界各方面的诸多讨论。哈佛大学教育改变领导小组计划主持人华格纳（Tony Wagner）提出“全球成就鸿沟”（The Global Achievement Gap）之观点，指出“学校所教的、考的，跟 21 世纪工作场域最需要的能力，产生巨大的断裂”。⑤ 然而，美国教育学家 Ernest L. Boyer 则认为能力的教授从来就不是高等教育的问题，美国大学教育的真正问题在于并未超越能力的传授而回归至最初对于教育目的

---

① 参见陈来：《仁学本体论》，第 310－311 页。

② 同前注，第 314－315 页。

③ 参见杨日旭，《公民教育的政治学基础》，收入于史振鼎主编《公民教育之问题与对策（上）》，台北：台湾省教育会，1985 年，第 142－156 页。

④ 参见梁福镇：《全球化脉络下台湾公民教育的挑战与回应》，《教育科学期刊》第 8 卷第 1 期（2009 年 6 月），第 71 页。

⑤ 见无作者：《教你未来职场需要的七大能力》，《商业周刊》第 1113 期（2009－03－23）。取自：《商业周刊》知识库（2009－03－23）。

的承诺。① 这个承诺即是教育的目的在“培养能捍卫个人自由、从事负责任的政治决策的公民”。②

诚然，当高等教育已能成功传授并训练学生的能力时，对于高等教育，或者说，对于一切教育，在同时必须面对因应全球化所产生的各个面向问题，我们的期待应该是甚么？唐君毅先生曾说道德理性是为求实现文化理想所进行之文化活动之必然基础，其表现为实践理想之自觉，也是人文世界得以永久存在之重要支持，而人文世界所赖以成立之精神意识之基础，端在于人之文化意识中向上创造精神。③ 牟宗三先生也说人只有挺立道德的主体性，才可以堂堂正正地站起来，然后科学、道德、宗教、艺术等一切文化才有价值。④ 唐、牟二位先生之言论虽非就全球化现象而发，但二人所论道德主体性与向上创造精神，在今日尤其具有启发性。同时，反思二程与朱熹对孔孟仁学提出三人在所处时代之反省与诠释，以仁修身之伦理意涵与诚敬存守之道德实践，也有助于当代公民教育、道德教育之建立与施行。

## 参考文献

一、传统文献

[1]（魏）何晏等注，（宋）邢昺疏．论语注疏，《十三经注疏》本．台北：艺文印书馆．影印清嘉庆二十年重刊宋本《论语注疏》附校勘记，第 8 册，1985.

[2]（汉）赵岐注，（宋）孙奭疏．孟子注疏，《十三经注疏》本．台北：艺文印书馆．影印清嘉庆二十年重刊宋本《孟子注疏》附校勘记)，第 8 册，1985.

[3]（宋）程颢、程颐撰．二程集．台北：汉京文化事业，四部刊要本，第 1 册、第 2 册，1983.

[4] 朱熹．朱子语类（一)．收入朱杰人、严佐之、刘永翔主编．朱子全书．上海市：上海古籍：安徽教育出版社，第 14 册，2002.

[5]（宋）朱熹撰．晦庵先生朱文公文集（四)．收入朱杰人、严佐之、刘永翔主

① Ernest L. Boyer 在 1987 年曾针对 29 个美国大学及学院进行高等教育的目标之调查，调查指出“今日学院教得最成功的就是能力”，见 Ernest L. Boyer, College: The Undergraduate Experience in America.（New York: Harper Collins, 1987), p. 283. 相关 Boyer 之研究报告，亦可参见 Anne Colby, Thomas Ehrlich, Elizabeth Beaumont, and Jason Stephens, Educating Citizens (San Francisco: Jossey-Bass, 2003), p. 6. 又部分研究结果转引于林火旺：《审议民主与公民养成》，《台大哲学论评》第 29 期（2005 年 3 月），页 121－122。

② 参见林火旺：《审议民主与公民养成》，第 120 页。林先生自言在 Boyer 研究调查期间，林先生正在美国攻读博士学位，并且曾担任教学工作，因此他部分见证 Boyer 的研究结果，第 121 页。

③ 参见唐君毅：《文化意识与道德理性》，台北：台湾学生书局，1986 年，第 21 页。

④ 参见牟宗三：《中国哲学十九讲》，第 73－74 页。

编. 朱子全书. 上海市：上海古籍：安徽教育出版社，第23册，2002.

二、近人论著

［1］牟宗三. 中国哲学十九讲》. 台北：台湾学生书局，1986.

［2］牟宗三. 中国哲学的特质. 台北：台湾学生书局，1990.

［3］林火旺. 审议民主与公民养成. 台大哲学论评第29期. 2005（3），99—143.

［4］唐君毅. 文化意识与道德理性. 台北：台湾学生书局，1986.

［5］陈一姗. 安隆前财务长的独家告白. 天下杂志第551期. 2014（7），116—120.

［6］陈来. 宋明理学. 上海：华东师范大学，2003.

［7］陈来. 仁学本体论. 北京：生活，读书·新知三联书店，2014.

［8］梁福镇. 全球化脉络下台湾公民教育的挑战与回应. 教育科学期刊第8卷第1期. 2009（6），63—86.

［9］劳思光. 新编中国哲学史（三上）. 台北：三民书局，2004.

［10］无作者. 教你未来职场需要的七大能力. 商业周刊第1113期. 商业周刊知识库. 2009.3.23.

［11］杨日旭. 公民教育的政治学基础. 收入于史振鼎主编《公民教育之问题与对策（上）》. 台北：台湾省教育会，1985，142—156.

［12］蔡仁厚. 中国哲学史大纲. 台北：台湾学生书局，1999.

［13］钱穆. 宋明理学概述. 台北：台湾学生书局，1987.

［14］赖美译. 企业丑闻频传商学院开始教道德课. 经济学人. 2005.2.19. 收入，《商业周刊》第901期，2005年2月28日。取自：《商业周刊》知识库。

［15］（德）Hans-Georg Gadamer着，洪汉鼎译. 真理与方法——哲学诠释学的基本特征. 台北：时报文化，1993.

［16］（德）Ulrich Beck着、孙治本译. 全球化危机—全球化的形成、风险与机会. 台北：台湾商务印书馆，1999.

三、外文著作

［1］Boyer，Ernest L. College：The Undergraduate Experience in America. New York：Harper Collins，1987.

［2］Colby，Anne，Thomas Ehrlich，Elizabeth Beaumont，and Jason Stephens. Educating Citizens. San Francisco：Jossey-Bass，2003.

［3］Graham，A. C. Two Chinese Philosophers. LA Salle，Illinois：Open Court，1992.

# 儒学的进路：学以成人

上海华东师范大学　杨国荣

## 一

“为学”之“学”在宽泛意义上既涉及外部对象，又与人相关，“成人”则指成就人自身。从“学”与人的相互关联看，其进路又有所不同。首先可以关注的是以认知或认识为侧重之点的“学”，在这一向度，“学”主要表现为知人或认识人，其传统可追溯到古希腊。众所周知，在古希腊的德尔菲神庙之上，镌刻着如下箴言，即：“认识你自己”(Know yourself)。这里的“你”，可以理解为广义上的人，认识人自身，则旨在把握人之为人的特点。在当时的历史背景之下，对人自身特点的把握，一方面意味着把人和动物区别开来，确认人非动物；另一方面也关乎人和神之别：人既不是动物，也不是神。在此意义上，认识人自己，意味着恰当地定位人自身。

差不多同时，古希腊的哲学家苏格拉底提出了其著名的观点，即“美德就是知识”。这里的美德主要是指人之为人的基本规定，正是这种规定，使人人区别于其他对象。把人之为人的这种规定（美德）和知识联系起来，体现的是认识论的视域。作为与知识相关的存在，人主要被理解为认识的对象。以“美德即知识”为视域，与人相关的“学”，也主要展现了狭义的认识论传统和进路。

在近代，对“学”的以上看法，依然得到了某种延续。这里可以简单一提康德的相关问题。康德在哲学上曾提出了四个问题，即：我可以知道什么？我应该做什么？我能够期望什么？人是什么？最后一个问题（“人是什么”）具有综合性，涉及对人的总体理解和把握。当然，作为近代哲学家，康德对“人”的理解涵盖多重方面，包括从人类学的角度考察人的规定，以及从价值论的层面把握人的价值内涵，在康德关于人是目的的看法中，即体现了后一视域。然而，从实质的层面看，何为人（人是什么）这种提问的方式，仍然主要以认识人为指向：这里的问题并没有超对人的理解和认识。就此而言，康德对人的理解基本上承继了古希腊以来“认识你自己”、“美德即知识”

的传统。

当然，在康德那里，情况又有其复杂性。如前所述，他同时也提出了“我应该做什么”这一问题。“应该做什么”的提问，意味着把“做”、行动引入进来。但是，从逻辑上看，“我应该做什么”，是以人（“我”）已经成为人作为其前提，在这里，“如何成为人”这样的问题似乎并没有进入其视域。从这方面看，康德所关注的似乎主要还是人的既成形态，而不是“人如何成就”的问题。

除以上传统外，对与人相关之“学”的理解，还存在另一进路。这里，可以基于中国哲学（特别是儒学）的背景，对其作一简略考察。如果回溯儒家的发展脉络，便可注意到其中一种引人瞩目的现象，即对“为学”的自觉关注。先秦儒家的奠基人是孔子，体现其思想的经典是《论语》，《论语中》第一篇则是《学而》，其中所讨论的，首先便是“学”。先秦时代儒家最后一位总结性的人物是荀子，荀子的著作（《荀子》）同样首先涉及“学”：其全书第一篇即为《劝学》。从这种著作的系列中，便不难注意到儒家对“学”的注重。就“学”的内涵而言，儒家的理解较之单纯的认知进路，展现了更广的视野，后者具体表现为对“知人”（对人的认识）与“成人”（成就人）的沟通：在儒家的论域中，“学”既涉及“知人”，也关乎“成人”，从而表现为知人和成人的统一。这种理解，同时也体现了中国哲学关于“学”的主流看法。

理解人的以上视域，在中国哲学中首先与人禽之辨相联系。人禽之辨发端于先秦，其内在旨趣在于把握人区别于动物的根本所在，事实上，“人禽之辨”所指向的，即是“人禽之别”。就其以人之为人的根本规定为关切之点而言，“人禽之辨”所要解决的，也就是“人是什么”的问题。历史地看，中国古代的哲学家，也主要是从这一角度展开人禽之辨。孔子曾指出：“鸟兽不可以同群，吾非斯人之徒与而谁与?”① 在这里，他首先把人和鸟兽区别开来：鸟兽作为动物，是人之外的另一类存在，人无法与不同类的鸟兽共同生活，而只能与人类同伴（斯人之徒）交往。“人禽之辨”在此便侧重于人和动物（鸟兽）之间的分别。

对人的以上把握，在中国哲学中往往更概要地被理解为“知人”。孔子的学生曾一再地追问何为“仁”、何为“知”。关于何为“知”，孔子的回答便十分直截了当，即：“知人”。在孔子看来，“知”的内涵首先就体现在“知人”上。这里的“知人”既涉及人禽之辨，同时又在引申的意义上关乎人伦关系的把握。人伦（人与人之间的关系）展开于不同的层面，从家庭之中的亲子（父母和子女）、兄弟，到社会领域的君臣、朋友，等等，都体现为广义的人伦，“知人”一方面需要理解人不同于禽兽的根本之所在，另一方面则应把握基本的人伦关系。

---

① 《论语·微子》。

作为人禽之辨引申的“知人”，在中国哲学中常常又与“为己之学”联系在一起。这里又涉及“学”的问题。孔子曾区分了“为己之学”与“为人之学”：“古之学者为己，今之学者为人。”[①] 这里的“古”“今”不仅仅是时间概念，在更内在的层面，二者展现的是理想形态和现实形态之别：“古”在此便指理想或完美的社会形态，其特点在于注重并践行“为己之学”。此所谓“为己”，并不是在利益的关系上追逐个人私利，而是以人格上的自我完成、自我充实、自我提升为指向。质言之，这一意义上的“学”，旨在提升自我、完成自我，可以视为成己之学或成就人自身之学。与此相对的“为人”，则是为获得他人的赞誉而“学”，也就是说，其言与行都形之于外，主要做给别人看。不难看到，在区分“为人之学”与“为己之学”的背后，是对成就人自身的关注。

以“为己”、“成己”为目标的“学”，在中国哲学中同时被赋予过程的性质。在《劝学》中，荀子开宗明义便指出：“学不可以已”。“不可以已”，意味着“学”是不断延续、没有止境的过程。作为过程，“学”又展开为不同阶段，与之相应的是人成就自身的不同目标。荀子对此也作了具体的考察。他曾自设问答：“学恶乎始？恶乎终？”“其义则始乎为士，终乎为圣人。”[②] 这里，荀子区分了通过“为学”而“成人”的两种形态，其一是士，其二为圣人，学的过程则具体表现为从成就“士”出发，走向成就圣人。作为“学”之初始目标的“士”，关乎一定的社会身份、文化修养：所谓“士”，也就是具有相当文化修养和知识积累的社会阶层。从人的发展看，具有知识积累、文化修养，意味着已经超越了蒙昧或自然的状态，达到了自觉或文明化的存在形态。众所周知，中国传统文化中有所谓“文野之别”。这里的“野”即前文明的状态，“文”则指文明化的形态。中国哲学，特别是儒家，所追求的就是由“野”而“文”。荀子所谓“始乎为士”中的“士”，首先便可以理解为由“野”而“文”的存在形态：对荀子而言，通过“为学”而“成人”的第一步，便是从前文明（“野”）走向文明化（“文”）。“士”在此具有某种象征的意义：作为受过教育、具有文化修养和知识积累的社会成员，他同时体现了人由“野”而“文”的转换。

与“始乎为士”相联系的是“终乎为圣”，后者构成了学以成人更根本的目标。相对于“士”，“圣”的特点在于不仅仅具有一定的文化修养和知识结构，而且已达到道德上的完美性。正是道德上的完美性，使圣人成为“学”最后所指向的目标。在这一意义上，在中国哲学中的“人禽之辨”同时涉及“圣凡之别”：“人禽之辨”主要在于人和其他动物的区分，“圣凡之别”则关乎常人（包括“士”）与道德上的完美人格

---

① 《论语·宪问》。

② 《荀子·劝学》。

（圣人）之间的分别。从内在的理论旨趣看，以“圣人”为“学”的终极目标，意味着通过“为学”以“成人”不仅仅在于获得知识经验或达到文化方面的修养，而且同时应达到道德上的完美性。当然，与肯定“学不可以已”相联系，所谓“终乎为圣人”，并不是说人可以一蹴而就地成为圣人。事实上，从孔子开始，儒家便强调成圣过程的无止境性，在这一过程中，圣人始终作为范导性的目标，不断地引导人们趋向于圣人之境。

从另一方面看，无论“士”，抑或“圣”，其共同特点都在于已超越了自然或前文明（“野”）的状态，取得了文明化的存在形态。无独有偶，在西方思想史上，黑格尔也曾提出过类似的观点。黑格尔在谈到教育时曾指出：“教育的绝对规定就是解放”，这种解放“反对情欲的直接性”。[①]“绝对规定”是其特有的思辨用语，“情欲”则表现为一种自然的趋向，与之相对的“解放”，意味着使人从自然的形态或趋向中解脱出来。在这里，黑格尔似乎也把教育看作是人发展过程中超越自然的环节。“教”与“学”不可分，谈教育，同时也从一个侧面涉及“学”。不难看到，黑格尔的以上观念在逻辑上包含着肯定广义之“学”与超越自然的关联。

在中国思想传统中，由“野”而“文”、超越自然状态的成人的过程，同时离不开“礼”的制约。自殷周开始，中国文化便非常注重礼。“礼”涉及多重维度，从基本的方面看，它主要表现为一套文明的规范系统，其作用体现于实质和形式两个层面。在实质的层面，“礼”的作用又具体展开于两个方面：就肯定或积极的方面而言，礼告诉人们应该做什么、应该如何做：作为规范，“礼”总是具有引导的作用，后者体现于对应该做什么与应该如何做的规定。从否定的方面来说，“礼”的作用则表现为限制，即规定人不能做什么或不能以某种方式去做。在形式的层面，礼的作用之一在于对行为的文饰。中国早期的经典《礼记》在谈到礼的作用时曾指出：“礼者，因人之情而为之节文，以为民坊者也。”[②] 这里的“节”主要表现为节制，亦即实质层面的调节和规范，“文”则是形式层面的文饰。通过依礼而行，人的言行举止、交往的方式便逐渐地取得文明化的形态，这种文明的行为方式、交往形式，体现了礼的文饰作用。从“学”与“礼”的联系看，通过“为学”以“成人”即意味着基于礼之“节文”，使人逐渐地超越前文明的状态、走向文明的形态。

荀子对“学”与“礼”的以上关联给予了特别的关注。在前面提到的《劝学》中，荀子强调：学只有臻于“礼”，才可以说是达到了最高的境界，所谓“学至乎礼而止矣”。这样，一方面，如前所述，荀子认为学“终乎为圣人”，另一方面，他又在此处

---

① 黑格尔：《法哲学原理》，商务印书馆，1982年，第202页。

② 《礼记·坊记》。

肯定“学至乎礼而止”。在荀子那里，上述两个方面事实上难以分离：从为学目标上说，圣人构成了“学”的终极指向；从为学过程或为学方式看，这一过程又离不开礼的引导。学“终乎为圣人”和“学至乎礼而止”相互关联，从不同方面制约着为学过程。

与礼相联系的“学”，在中国哲学的传统中又与“做”、行动紧密联系在一起。在礼的引导之下展开的成人过程，同时也表现为按照礼的要求去具体的践行。《论语》开宗明义便指出：“学而时习之，不亦说乎？”① 这里，“学”和“习”即联系在一起，而“习”的涵义之一，则是习行，亦即人的践履。从“习行”的角度看，所谓“学而时习之”，也就是在通过“学”而掌握了一定的道理、知识之后，进一步付诸实行，使之在行动中得到确认和深化，由此提升“学”的境界。

“学”的以上含义，在中国哲学中一再得到肯定。孔子的学生子夏在谈到何为“学”时，曾指出：“贤贤易色；事父母，能竭其力。事君，能致其身。与朋友交，言而有信。虽曰未学，吾必谓之学矣。”② 这里所涉及的，是如何理解“学”的问题。“事父母”即孝敬父母，属道德领域的践行，“事君”，属当时历史条件下政治领域的践行，“与朋友交”，则涉及社会领域的日常交往行动。在此，“学”包括道德实践、政治实践，以及日常的社会交往。按照子夏的看法，如果个体实际地进行了以上活动，那么，即便他自己没有说在从事于“学”，也应当认为他事实上已经在“学”了。根据这一理解，则“学”即体现于“做”或践行的过程之中。孔子也曾经表达了类似的看法：“君子食无求饱，居无求安，敏于事而慎于言，就有道而正焉，可谓好学矣。”③ 这里涉及如何确认“好学”的问题。何为“好学”？孔子提出的判断标准便是：从消极的方面看，避免在日常生活中过度追求安逸，从积极的方面着眼，则是勤于做事、慎于言说（“敏于事而慎于言”），在积极践行的基础上，进一步向有道之士请教。在这里，“好学”主要不是抽象地了解知识、道理，而是首先体现于日用常行、勤于做事的过程。

荀子对学的以上意义作了更简要的概述。在《劝学》中，荀子指出：“为之，人也；舍之，禽兽也。”“为之”，即实际的践行，“舍之”，则是放弃践行。这里的“为”，也就是以“终乎为圣人”为指向、以礼为引导的践行。在荀子看来，如果依礼而行（“为之”），便可以成为真正意义上的人；反之，不按照礼的要求去做（“舍之”），那就落入禽兽之域、走向人的反面。这里再一次提到了人禽之辨，而此所谓“人禽之辨”，已经不仅仅限于从观念的形态去区分人不同于禽兽的特征，而是以是否依礼而行为判

① 《论语·学而》。
② 《论语·学而》。
③ 《论域·学而》。

断的准则：唯有切实地按照礼的要求去做，才可视为真正的人，背离于此，则只能归入禽兽之列。在此，实际的践行（“为之”）构成了区分人与禽兽的重要之点。

广而言之，在中国文化中，为学和为人、做人和做事往往难以相分。为学一方面以成人为指向，另一方面又具体地体现于为人过程。前面提到的道德实践、政治实践、社会交往，都同时表现为具体的为人过程，人的文明修养，也总是体现于为人处事的多样活动。同样，做人也非仅仅停留于观念、言说的层面，而是与实际地做事联系在一起。在以上方面，“学”与“做”都无法分离。

## 二

前文一再提及，在中国哲学尤其是儒学中，对“学”的理解首先与人禽之辨联系在一起。从狭义上说，“人禽之辨”主要涉及人与动物之别，在引申的意义上，“人禽之辨”则同时关乎对人自身的理解，后者具体表现为区分本然意义上的人和真正意义上的人。本然意义上的人，也就是人刚刚来到这一世界时的存在形态，在这一存在形态中，人更多地呈现为生物学意义上的对象，而尚未展现出与其他动物的根本不同。这种生物学意义上的存在，还不能被视为真正意义上的人。要而言之，这里可以看到两重意义的区分：其一，人与动物之别，亦即狭义上的人禽之辨；其二，人自身的分别，即本然形态的人与真正意义上的人之分。

从历史上看，中国哲学上不同的人物、学派不仅关注人禽之别，而且对后一意义的区分也有比较自觉的意识。以先秦而言，孟子和荀子是孔子之后儒家的两个重要代表人物，两者在思想观点上固然存在重要差异，有些方面甚至彼此相左，然而，在区分本然意义上的人和真正意义上的人这一点上，却有相通之处。孟子的核心理论之一是性善说，后者肯定人一开始即具有善端，这种“善端”为人成就圣人提供了前提或可能。但同时，孟子又提出“扩而充之”之说，认为“善端”作为萌芽，不同于已经完成了的形态，只有经过扩而充之的过程，人才能够真正成为他所理解的完美存在。所谓“扩而充之”，也就是扩展、充实，它具体展开为一个人自身努力的过程。从逻辑上看，这里包含对人自身存在形态的如下区分：扩而充之以前的存在形态与扩而充之以后的存在形态。扩而充之以前的人，还只是本然意义上的人，只有经过扩而充之的过程，人才能成为真正意义上的人。在荀子那里，也有类似的区分，当然，两者的出发点又有所不同。在荀子看来，人的本然之性具有恶的趋向，只有经过“化性”而“起伪”的过程，才能够成为合乎礼义的存在。所谓“化性”，也就是改变恶的人性趋向，“伪”则是人的作用或人的努力过程。总起来，“化性起伪”也就是经过人自身的努力以改变人的本然趋向，使之走向真正意义上的人——合乎礼义之人。在此，化性起伪之前的人和化性起伪之后的人，同样表现为人自身的不同存在形态。上述观念在先秦之后依然得到延续。明代的王阳明提出了良知和致良知之说，一方面，他肯定凡人都先天地具有良知，另一方面，又强调这种良知最初还处于本然状态，在这种本然状态之下，人还没有达到对其内在良知的自觉把握，从而“虽有而若无”。只有经过致良知的过程，才可能对这种本然具有的良知获得自觉意识，由此进而成为合乎儒家道德规范的、真正意义上的人。这里，致良知之前的人与致良知之后的人，也相应于本然的存在形态与真正的存在形态之分。

类似的观念，也存在于西方的一些重要哲学家之中，黑格尔便曾指出：“人间（Menson）最高贵的事就是成为人（person）。”[①] 所谓“成为人”，意味着个体一开始还未真正达到“人”的形态，只有经过“成”的过程，个体才成其为人。从逻辑上看，这里也隐含着“成为人”之前的个体与“成为人”之后的个体之分别。从以上方面看，中国哲学与西方哲学在对人的理解上，有理论上的相通之处。

本然意义上的人一方面尚不能归入真正意义上的人，但另一方面又包含着成为真正意义上的人的可能。儒家肯定“人皆可以为尧舜”，所谓“人皆可以为尧舜”，便是指每一个人都具有成为圣人（尧舜）的可能性，这种可能性即隐含在人的本然形态中，正是这样可能，构成了人成为真正意义上的人的内在的根据。进而言之，可能既为成人提供了内在根据，也使之区别于现实的形态，并使后天的作用成为必要：唯有通过这种后天作用，本然所蕴含的可能才会向现实转化。

真正意义上的人，也就是应当成为的人。作为“应当”达到的目标，真正意义上的人同时具有理想的形态。理想的特点在于“当然”而未然，从而不同于实际的存在形态。这样，一方面，本然不同于当然，本然形态的人也不同于理想形态的人，但这种本然形态之中又隐含着当然：本然之人具有走向当然（理想）的可能性。另一方面，当然又不同于实然（实际的存在）：作为理想形态，当然只有经过人的努力过程，才能化为实际的存在。这里可以看到本然、当然、实然之间的关联，通过“为学”以“成人”的过程，具体便展开于本然、当然、实然之间的互动：本然隐含当然，当然通过人自身的努力过程进而化为实然。本然隐含当然，具有本体论或形而上的意义：每一个人都包含着可以成为圣人的根据，这是从存在形态（本体论意义）上说的。化当然为实然，则侧重于理想形态向实际存在形态的转换，这一转换包含价值的内容。与以上内涵相应，本然、当然、实然之间的互动，同时体现了本体论与价值论的统一。通过“为学”以“成人”（成为真正意义上的人），具体表现为以上不同方面的相互作用，在这一互动过程中，价值论的内涵和本体论的内涵彼此关联，赋予成人过程以多方面

① 黑格尔：《法哲学原理》，商务印书馆，1982 年，第 46 页。

的意义。

从中国哲学的角度看，成人的以上的过程同时又与本体与工夫的互动联系在一起。作为中国哲学的重要范畴，“工夫”和“本体”的具体内涵可以从不同角度去理解。前面提到，本然蕴含当然，这里的本然，也就是最原初的存在，其中包含达到当然（理想形态）的可能性。在中国哲学中，“本体”往往与以上视域中的本然存在相联系，其直接的涵义即本然之体（original substance）。这一意义上的“本体”没有任何神秘之处，它的具体所指，就是内在于本然之中的最初可能。对中国哲学而言，正是这种可能，为人的进一步成长提供了内在的根据。以本体（内在于本然之中的可能）为根据，意味着成就人过程既不表现为外在强加，也非依赖于外在灌输，而是基于个体自身可能而展开的过程。

在中国哲学中，“本体”同时被用以指称人的内在的精神结构、观念世界或意识系统。人的知、行活动的展开过程，往往与人的内在精神结构以及意识、观念系统相联系。这种精神结构大致包含两方面的内容，其一，价值层面的观念取向，其二，认知意义上的知识系统。成人的过程既关乎“成就什么”，也涉及“如何成就”，前者与发展方向、目标选择相联系，后者则关乎达到目标的方式、目标。比较而言，精神世界中的价值之维，更多地从发展方向、目标选择（成就什么）等方面制约着成人的过程；精神世界中的认知之维，则主要从方式、目标（如何成就）等方面，为成人过程提供了内在的引导。

与“成人”相关之“学”既涉及认识活动，也关乎德性涵养，作为精神结构的本体相应地从不同方面制约着以上活动。从“知”（认识）这一角度看，认识过程并不是从无开始，将心灵视为白板，是经验主义者（如洛克）的抽象预设。就现实的形态而言，在认识活动展开之时，认识主体固然对将要认识的对象缺乏充分的认识，但总是已经积累、拥有了某些其他方面的知识，后者构成了认识活动展开的观念背景。这种以知识系统为内容的观念背景，构成了精神本体的认知之维，而现实的认识活动，即以此为具体的出发点。同样，德性的涵养也离不开内在的根据。在走向完美人格的过程中，已有的道德意识构成了德性进一步发展的出发点和根据。作为道德意识发展的根据，这种业已形成的道德意识，具体呈现为精神本体的价值之维。

以知识、德性等观念系统为具体内容，以上本体既非先天形成，也非凝固不变，而是在人的成长过程中，逐渐地生成、发展和丰富。关于这一点，明清之际的重要思想家黄宗羲曾作了言简意赅地概述：“心无本体，工夫所至，即其本体。”[①] 精神形态意义上的本体并非人心固有，而是形成于知、行工夫的展开过程。在知行工夫的展开过

① 《明儒学案·序》，中华书局，1985年，第7页。

程中所形成、发展和丰富的本体，反过来又影响、制约着知行活动的进一步展开。在这一意义上，精神本体具有动态的性质。

与本体相联系的是工夫。从学以成人的视域看，工夫展开于人从可能走向现实、化当然（理想）为实然（实际的存在形态）的过程之中，其具体形式态也包含多重方面。大致而言，上述视域中的工夫可以概括为两个方面。其一为观念形态的工夫，亦即中国哲学所理解的广义之“知”，其二，实践形态的工夫，亦即中国哲学所理解的“行”，“知”和“行”构成了工夫的两个相关方面。事实上，如前所述，广义之“学”便不仅体现于“知”，而且也包含“行”（“做”），对于后一意义上的工夫（“行”），中国传统哲学同样给予了相当的关注。以明代哲学家王阳明而言，作为心学的重要代表，他首先以心立说，然而，在关注心性的同时，王阳明对实际践行意义上的行，也给予了高度重视。他特别强调要“事上磨练”，“事上磨练”即践行的过程，后者同时被理解为工夫的重要内容。

与“事上磨练”相联系的工夫，具体展开为两个方面。首先是天人关系上人与自然的互动。在这一层面，人从一定的价值目的和理想出发，不断地运用自身的知识、能力作用于自然，使本然意义上的自然对象，逐渐地合乎人的需要和理想。在这一过程中，一方面，自然对象发生了改变：本来与人没有关联的自然之物逐渐被打上人的印记，成为合乎人的理想、需要的存在；另一方面，在人与自然的互动中，人自身的德性和能力也得到了提升。从以上方面看，以天人互动为内容的“行”或工夫，同样也与成人的过程密切相关：通过作用于自然，人不仅改变对象，而且也改变自身、成就自己。

工夫（行）的另一重形式，体现于人与人之间的互动过程，后者具体展开为政治、经济、伦理、法律等社会领域中多样的践行活动。在社会领域中，个体总是要与他人打交道，并参与多样的社会活动。这种活动，也可以视为“做”的过程，它对人的成长并非无关紧要，而是具有密切的关联。事实上，“是什么”（成为什么样的人）与“做什么”（从事何种实践活动），往往无法相分。具体而言，人正是在参与政治实践的具体过程中，逐渐地成为亚里士多德所说的“政治的动物”（政治领域中的主体）；在从事法律的实践活动中，成为法律意义上的主体（包括成为守法的公民）；在伦理、道德的实践（包括儒学所说的“事亲”、“敬长”等等）过程中，成为伦理领域中的道德主体，如此等等。在这里，“是什么”和“做什么”紧密相关。广而言之，正是在社会领域展开的多样活动中，人逐渐成为多样化的社会存在。

要而言之，“学”既涉及本体，又和工夫相联系。一方面，如中国传统哲学所强调的，“学”应有所“本”，这里的“本”既指本然存在中所蕴含的成人可能，也指内在的精神世界、观念系统。“学”有所“本”则相应地既意味着以人具有的内在可能为学以成人的根据，也指“本于”内在的精神世界展开“为学”过程。在通过“为学”以“成人”的过程中，一方面，“学”有所“本”，人的自我成就离不开内在的根据和背景，另一方面，“本”又不断在工夫展开过程中，得到丰富，并且以新的形态进一步引导工夫的展开。本体和工夫的以上互动，构成了通过“为学”以“成人”的具体内容。

当然，从哲学史上看，对本体和工夫的关系，往往存在理解上的偏差。以禅宗而言，其理论上趋向之一是“以作用为性”，理学家曾一再对此提出批评。“性”这一概念在中国哲学中蕴含本质之意，引申为本体（性体），所谓“作用”，则指人的偶然意念和举动，如行住坐卧、担水砍柴，等等。在禅宗看来，人的偶然意念、日常之举，都构成了“性”，由此，本质层面的“性”亦被等同于偶然意念和活动。这种观点的要害在于消解了作为精神世界、观念系统的本体（性体）。理学家批评禅宗以作用为性，显然已注意到这种观点将导致性体的虚无化。从当代哲学看，实用主义也表现出类似的倾向。实用主义的重要特点在于重视具体问题和情境，它在某种意义上将“学”的过程理解为在特定情境中解题的过程，对于概念、理论这种涉及普遍本体或内在精神结构的方面，实用主义往往也持消解的态度。就此而言，实用主义也表现出将本体虚无化的倾向。

另一方面，在工夫的理解方面，也存在不同偏向。王门后学中，有所谓“现成良知”说。前面曾提到，在王阳明那里，良知和致良知相互关联：本然的良知还不是真正意义上的良知，唯有经过“致”的工夫，良知才能达到自觉的形态。然而，他的一些后学，如王畿、泰州学派，往往仅仅强调良知的先天性，略去“致”良知的过程，将先天良知等同于现成良知。所谓“现成良知”，意味着先天具有的良知，同时已达到自觉地形态，从而，不需要通过工夫过程以走向自觉，这一看法最终将引向否定工夫的意义。从学以成人的现实过程看，工夫和本体这两者都不可以偏废，人的自我成就，乃是在工夫和本体的动态互动中逐渐实现的。

## 三

作为本体和工夫的统一，“为学”所要成就的，是什么样的人？从现实的方面看，人当然具有多样的形态、不同的个性。然而，在多样的存在形态中，又有人之为人的共通方面。概括而言，这些共通方面可以从两个方面去理解，其一是德性，其二为能力。中国古代哲学曾一再提到贤能，所谓“选贤与能”，亦即将贤和能放在非常重要的地位。这里的“贤”主要与德性相联系，“能”则和能力相关。不难看到，在中国古代哲学中，内在德性和能力已被理解为人的两个重要规定。从“为学”与“成人”的关系看，德性和能力更多地从目标上，制约着人的自我成就。

上述意义上的德性，首先表现为人在价值取向层面上所具有的内在品格，它关乎成人过程的价值导向和价值目标，并从总的价值方向上，展现了人之为人的内在规定。与德性相关的能力，则主要是表现为人在价值创造意义上的内在的力量。人不同于动物的重要之点，在于能够改变世界、改变人自身，后者同时表现为价值创造的过程，作为人的内在规定之能力，也就是人在价值创造层面所具有的现实力量。在中国哲学所理解的圣人这一理想人格中，也可以看到德性和能力的统一。孔子对圣人有一简要的界说，认为其根本特点在于："博施于民而能济众。"① 一方面，这里蕴含着对民众的价值关切，后者所体现的是圣人的内在德性；另一方面，博施于民、济众，又意味着实际地施惠于民众，这种实际的作用即基于价值创造的内在能力。根据以上看法，则在圣人那里，价值关切意义上的德性和价值创造意义上的能力，也具有相互关联性。圣人一般被视为理想的人格形态，对圣人的这种理解，从理想的人格目标上，肯定了德性和能力的统一。

德性与能力的相互关联所指向的，是健全的人格。人的能力如果离开了内在的德性，便往往缺乏价值层面的引导，从而容易趋向于工具化和与手段化，与之相关的人格，则将由此失去价值方向。另一方面，人的德性一旦离开了人的能力及其实际的作用过程，则常常导向抽象化与玄虚化，由此形成的人格，也将缺乏现实的创造力量。唯有达到德性与能力的统一，"学"所成之人，才能避免片面化。

从"为学"与"成人"的关系看，这里同时涉及德性是否可教的问题。早在古希腊，哲学家们已经开始自觉地关注并讨论这一问题。在柏拉图的《普罗泰戈拉》和《美诺》篇中，德性是否可教便已成为一个论题。在这方面，柏拉图的观点似乎有含混之处，就某种意义而言，甚至存在不一致。一方面，他不赞同当时智者的看法，智者认为德性是可教的，柏拉图则借苏格拉底之口对此提出质疑："我不相信美德可以教"。② 另一方面，按照前面提到的所谓"美德即知识"这一观点，则美德又是可教的：知识具有可教性，美德既然是一种知识，也应归入可教之列。事实上，柏拉图也认为，假定美德作为一个整体是知识，那么，"如果它不可教，那就是最令人惊异的"。③ 以上两种看法，显然存在内在的不一致。从总的趋向看，柏拉图主要试图由此引出德性的神授说：美德既不是天生的，也不是靠教育获得，只能通过神的施赐而来。④ 从逻辑上

---

① 《论语·雍也》。

② Plato, Protagora 320b, The Collected Dialogues of Plato, Princeton University Press, 1961, p320.

③ Plato, Protagora 361b, The Collected Dialogues of Plato, Princeton University Press, 1961, p351.

④ Plato, Meno100b, The Collected Dialogues of Plato, Princeton University Press, 1961, p384.

看，“教”与“学”相关，不可“教”，至少意味着与“教”相对应意义上的“学”无法实现。这里的“教”包括传授、给予，与之相对应的“学”则关乎获得、接受。德性既不可通过“教”而传授、给予，也就难以借助“学”而获得和接受。

以上观点与柏拉图的认识论立场具有一致性。众所周知，在认识论上，柏拉图的基本观点是将认识的过程理解为回忆的过程。对柏拉图而言，认识既不是完全发端于无知，也不能完全从有知开始：如果人一开始就已有知识，那么任何新的认识就成为多余的。反之，如果人一开始就完全处于无知状态，那么，他甚至无法确认认识的对象。由此，他提出了回忆说，即人的灵魂在来到这一世界之前已经有知识了，认识无非是在后天的各种触发之下，回忆灵魂中已有的知识。柏拉图关于德性不可教而来自神赐的观点，与认识论上的回忆说无疑具有相应性。

较之柏拉图，中国哲学对上述问题具有不同看法。按中国哲学的理解，不管德性，抑或能力，都既存在不可教或不可学的一面，也具有可教、可学性。中国哲学对这一问题的理解，以“性”和“习”之说为其前提。从孔子开始，中国哲学便开始讨论“性”和“习”的关系，孔子对此的基本看法是：“性相近也，习相远也。”[①] 这里所说的“性”，主要是指人的本性（nature）以及这种本性所隐含的各种可能。所谓“性相近”，也就是肯定凡人都具有相近的普遍本性，这种本性同时包含着人成为人的可能性。作为人在本体论意义上的存在形态，“性”是不可教的：它非形成于“教”或“学”的过程，而是表现为人这种存在所具有的内在规定；人来到这一世界，就已有这种存在规定。所谓人禽之辩，从最初的形态看，就在于二者具有相异的存在规定（本然之性）以及与之相应的不同发展可能和根据。与“性”相对的是“习”，从个体的层面看，“习”的具体内涵在广义上包括知和行，这一意义上的“习”与前面提到的工夫相联系，既可“教”，也可“学”：无论是“知”，抑或“行”，都具有可以教、可以学的一面。

可以看到，中国哲学对“性”和“习”的以上理解，展现了更广的理论视野。一方面，中国哲学注意到人在本体论意义上的规定，包括其中蕴含的发展可能、根据，具有不可教、不可学的性质，另一方面，中国哲学又肯定与人的后天努力相关的“习”既可以教，也可以学。这种看法在确认学以成人需要基于内在存在规定的同时，又有见于这一过程离不开人的知与行。以先天根据和后天努力的统一为视域，中国哲学对“为学”与“成人”关系的理解，无疑展现了更合乎现实过程的进路。

通过“为学”以“成人”不仅关乎价值取向意义上的德性，而且涉及价值创造层面的内在能力。从能力这一角度看，同样涉及可教、可学与不可教、不可学的问题。

① 《论语·阳货》。

与德性一样，人的能力既有其形成的内在根据，又离不开后天的工夫过程，两者对能力的发展都不可或缺。王夫之曾以感知和思维能力的形成为例，对此作了简要的阐述："夫天与之目力，必竭而后明焉；天与之耳力，必竭而后聪焉；天与之心思，必竭而后睿焉；天与之正气，必竭而后强以贞焉。可竭者天也，竭之者人焉。"[①] 目可视（不可听）、耳可听（不可视），心能思（不可感知），这一类机能属"性"，它们构成了感知、思维能力形成的根据，作为存在的规定，这种根据不可教、不可学，所谓"天与之"，突出的便是这一方面。"竭"则表现为人的努力过程（习行过程），这一过程具有可教、可学的性质。从视觉、听觉、思维的层面看，"目力"、"耳力"、"心思"，还只是人所具有的听、看、思等机能，作为"天与之"的先天禀赋，它们无法教、无法学，"明"、"聪"、"睿"则是真正意义上的感知和思维能力，这种能力唯有通过"竭"的努力过程才能形成。这里区分了两个方面，首先是"目力"、"耳力"、"心思"等先天的禀赋，这种禀赋属于"性相近"意义上"性"，它构成了能力形成和发展的根据，这种根据非通过教与学而存在。其次是"竭"的工夫，这种工夫构成了"习"的具体内容，其展开过程伴随着教和学的过程。中国哲学对能力形成过程以上理解，同样注意到了内在根据与后天工夫的统一。

以德性和能力的形成为视域，通过"为学"以"成人"具体便表现为"性"和"习"的互动，这种互动过程，与前面提到的本体和工夫的互动，具有一致性，二者从不同方面构成了学以成人的相关内容。当然，如前所述，人的现实形态具有多样性，人的个性、社会身份、角色等等也存在差异。然而，从核心的层面看，真实的人格总是包含德性和能力的统一，后者构成了人之为人的内在规定，并在一定意义上成为自由人格的表现形式。要而言之，一方面，通过"为学"以"成人"以德性和能力的形成和发展为指向，另一方面，作为德性与能力统一的真实人格又体现于人的多样存在形态之中。

---

① 《续春秋左氏传博议》卷下，《船山全书》第5册，岳麓书社，1996年，第617页。

# 儒家家庭伦理的核心精神与现代重构

北京师范大学 李祥俊

家庭是人的存在的基本境域，也是社会组成的基本单位，但家庭的形态却随历史发展而变化；家庭伦理是儒学的核心，而家庭伦理同样也在随历史发展而变化。儒家家庭伦理以家庭整体论为基础，强调亲情本位、差异关系，是传统中国社会指导家庭关系的主导思想。近现代中国社会形态转型，家庭形态也发生了巨大变化，传统儒家家庭伦理陷入困境，由此带来了严重的社会问题。如何顺应现代中国社会现实，回应西学，自我变革走出新路，这是儒家家庭伦理以至儒学现代转化所要解决的重要问题。

## 一、传统家庭形态与儒家家庭伦理主导地位的确立

在近现代的社会形态转型之前，中国传统社会在春秋、战国时期已经有过一次大转型。关于春秋、战国时期中国社会形态转型，学术界有种种说法，有的从生产力发展立论，有的从生产关系转变立论，也有的从学术文化融合创新立论，其中经典而宏观的表述是从奴隶社会到封建社会的转型。本文从家庭问题入手，认为春秋、战国的社会形态转型中，包含着一个极其基础性的变化，这就是家庭形态的变化，从上古、三代的宗法制社会向秦汉以降的以三代以内家庭为主的编户齐民的社会转型。

上古三代的中国社会从原始的氏族制度演进而来，它的王权政治是以宗法制的家族、宗族为社会基础的。受制于历史材料，这一时期家庭生活的具体存在形态还难以理清，但就已有的材料看，当时人们还是以宗族为社会生活的基本单位，贵族、占统治地位的原始氏族成员基本上是聚族而居，这个聚族而居是以宗族为本位的，它和秦汉以降以三代以内的家庭为本位的聚族而居不同。宗法制本就是从原始的聚族而居演变出来的，吕思勉先生分析说："盖一族之人，聚居一处，久则不足以容，势不得不分殖于外，此封建之所由兴。而分殖于外者，仍不可不思所以联结之，此宗法之所由

立。”[①] 吕先生讲到聚族而居久则分殖，但这是不可持续的，分殖到一定阶段则无地可分殖。商王朝末期对南方的战争就有开疆拓土以分殖的目的，但却最终导致小邦周借此灭了大邦商。西周末年不但无地分殖，反而遭到周边夷狄压迫，本有的土地还要被压缩。一旦无地可分，那么宗族按照几何级数繁殖出来的子弟就将“皮之不存毛将焉附”，像吴起、商鞅这些当时社会的改革者原都是宗法制中的成员，统治阶级自己无法按照原样生活下去了，这个时候宗法制的末日就要来临了，而家庭形态也将面临大转型。

从春秋、战国的历史实际来看，就是一个从宗族聚族而居到三代以内家庭本位的转型，这个转型大概经历了五百年的阵痛。在这个转型的过程中，诸子百家兴起并展开争鸣，百家争鸣涉及多方面，其中一个核心的方面就是关于家庭形态与家庭伦理的。诸子百家是虚称，除去兵家、医家、农家等研究实际事务的学派，产生重大影响的只有司马谈《论六家要旨》中的儒、道、墨、法、名、阴阳六家，而名、阴阳两家的侧重点在理论思维方面，真正在价值层面展开争鸣的主要是儒、道、墨、法四家，而它们对于春秋、战国社会转型所带来的家庭形态转变的态度是不相同的。

在宗法制解体，新的家庭形态产生的这个过程中，法家顺应潮流并积极推动政治上的变法以实现这个转型，从而打破社会中的宗族力量以加强君主专制，从这个目的出发他们甚至走到政府倡导两代以内的小家庭的地步，商鞅变法时颁布法令：“民有二男以上不分异者，倍其赋。……而令民父子兄弟同室内息者为禁。”[②] 墨家是工商阶层的代表，他们本身即是以行业公会为安身立命之地，所以对于宗法制度的解体是顺应的，他们提倡打破宗法制度、血缘亲情的无差别的“兼相爱，交相利”。道家站在个体性的立场上，对来自宗法制以及血缘家庭的对个体人的束缚有深切的体会，庄子感慨说：“天下有大戒二：其一，命也；其一，义也。子之爱亲，命也，不可解于心；臣之事君，义也，无适而非君也，无所逃于天地之间。”[③] 而儒家在这个问题上的态度与墨家、道家、法家都不同，它一方面维护旧的宗法制度，如孔子念念不忘“复周礼”，另一方面又顺应时代潮流维护新兴的家庭形态的稳定性，并通过对孝悌的大力提倡，从伦理秩序到道德情感，为这种新兴家庭的稳定提供理论上的服务。从孔子开始，儒家即把家庭伦理的孝悌上升到“为仁之本”，孟子提出：“仁之实，事亲是也；义之实，从兄是也；智之实，知斯二者弗去是也；礼之实，节文斯二者是也；乐之实，乐斯二

---

① 吕思勉：《中国制度史》，上海教育出版社，1985 年，第 373—374 页。

② 《史记》卷六十八《商君列传》，中华书局，1959 年，第 2230 页。

③ 《庄子·内篇·人间世》，陈鼓应：《庄子今注今译》，中华书局，1983 年，第 122 页。

者，乐则生矣；生则恶可以已也，恶可已，则不知足之蹈之手之舞之。”① 明清之际的大儒黄宗羲说：“仁、义、礼、智、乐，俱是虚名。人生堕地，只有父母兄弟，此一段不可解之情，与生俱来，此之谓实，于是而始有仁义之名。”②

秦汉以降，中国传统社会达到了相对稳定的形态并一直延续到清末，从家庭的维度来考察这种社会形态，它由三层结构组成：底层是所谓编户齐民的三代以内的小家庭，但穿插着强宗豪族；中间是春秋战国以来逐渐兴起并成熟起来的官僚阶层；上层是皇家。从这个三层结构来看，底层和上层都是家庭本位，中间的官僚阶层是面向社会各地域、各阶层的普遍性存在，但却深受上、下层的影响。就这个三层结构中的底层和上层的家庭而言，主要是三代以内的小家庭，虽然宗族的影响还很大，但家庭在经济、政治各个领域里都是独立的，从而使其不同于春秋之前的夏、商、周三代的宗法制社会。③ 所以，从秦汉到明清，中国传统社会可以定义为家庭本位的等级社会，三代以内的家庭和围绕着它的家族成为社会的基础，这是两千年中国传统社会的基本国情。

在中国传统社会由上古三代的宗法制向秦汉以降的家庭本位的等级社会转型中，先秦儒、道、墨、法各家都提出了自己的家庭伦理，但只有儒家的态度最适应秦汉以降中国传统社会的现实要求。法家在家庭形态上走得过快，把两代以内的小家庭作为社会基础，不符合中国传统社会的国情，但它反对宗法制度和强化中央集权的专制政治却适应了秦汉以后统一大帝国的要求，所以秦汉以降的中国传统政治基本上是儒、法合流，而在社会层面法家则被儒家取代。道家、墨家在这个问题上走得更远，它们对个体性的强调与秦汉以降的中国传统社会格格不入，也自然不为社会所接受。而先秦儒家在新兴的家庭制度与旧的宗法制度之间加以折中，秦汉以后的儒家则在三代以内的家庭与大家族之间搞折中，从而在这个关乎人的安身立命的核心问题上适应了中国传统社会的国情，并为后来的儒家学者发扬光大，使“独尊儒术”为历代统治阶层所接受。可以说，不理解家庭本位的伦理秩序、道德情感，就无法真正理解儒学，也无法真正理解中国传统社会。

## 二、传统儒家家庭伦理的核心精神

经过春秋、战国时期剧烈的社会转型，秦汉以至明清的中国传统社会呈现出相对稳定的政治体制和社会基础，而包括家庭伦理在内的儒学成为全社会的指导思想。儒

---

① 《孟子·离娄上》，杨伯峻：《孟子译注》，中华书局，1960年，第183页。
② 《孟子师说》卷四，《黄宗羲全集》第1册，浙江古籍出版社，2005年，第101页。
③ 参见陶毅、明欣：《中国婚姻家庭制度史》，东方出版社，1994年，第128—129页。

家的家庭伦理适应了秦汉以降中国传统社会的国情，同时也有效地服务于这个社会基础，那么，儒家家庭伦理的核心精神是什么，这是我们今天反思儒学的一个重要方面。我认为，儒家家庭伦理的核心精神可以概括为三个方面：家庭整体论、人际关系规范的差异秩序论、人际关系情感的亲情本位论。

家庭是在婚姻、血缘关系基础上亲属之间所构成的社会生活单位，在秦汉以降的中国传统社会中，最主要的就是三代以内、大约5—8人组成的家庭形态。在中国传统社会里，家庭是一个整体，这是一个事实性的存在，即家庭是当时社会运行中经济、政治的独立单位，经济生活中的生产资料、生活用度、财产分配等都是以家庭为单位展开的，政府的各种赋税征收、兵役劳役等也都是以家庭为单位实行的，这是儒家倡导的家庭整体论的社会存在基础。但儒家的家庭整体论将这种现实存在从形而上的层面论证其合理性、从伦理道德的层面落实其现实性。儒家学派认为，家庭是一个整体，所以家庭内部的父子、夫妇之间的关系都是内在的，家人之间的感情则是出于天性，这种整体主义的前提基础为儒家家庭伦理中的另外两个核心精神，即家庭人际关系差异秩序论和性善论基础上的亲情本位论奠定了基础。家庭整体论的实质则是父权至上，父亲是家庭整体的代表，所以孝德是万善之首，是一切伦理道德的源头。在儒家看来，家庭是一个整体，它不仅相对于个人来说是优位的存在，即使是相对于国家来说也是优位的存在，孔子的“子为父隐，父为子隐”，孟子的“瞽叟杀人”而舜窃负而逃的论述，就典型地表达了这个观念，只是秦汉以降在皇权政治的打压下，才把父权和君权尽量结合起来，但两者的内在矛盾始终存在，根本的原因即在于家庭整体论的前提。

其实就家庭作为社会的基础构成组织这一点而言，中、西方也是一致的，但西方传统中并没有因此而产生出像中国的儒家家庭伦理那样细密的学说，而这一点正是中、西方思想的根本性差异之一。在这个问题上，不仅中、西有差别，同在东方的中、日两国传统伦理中也有差别，相对于中国传统的父权至上以“孝”为本，日本文化中更重视对君主的“忠”德，这也和近现代之前日本社会的基础是家族而非三代以内的编户齐民直接相关。

以家庭整体论为基础，儒家在家庭人际关系规范上主张差异秩序论，这一点我们可以从分析儒学传统的人伦规范五伦、三纲来阐述。孟子论五伦说，“人之有道也，饱食、暖衣、逸居而无教，则近于禽兽。圣人有忧之，使契为司徒，教以人伦，——父子有亲，君臣有义，夫妇有别，长幼有序，朋友有信。”① 五伦包括父子、君臣、夫妇、长幼、朋友五种人际关系，其中父子、夫妇、长幼都属于家庭伦理关系，而其相应的道德规范是父子有亲、夫妇有别、长幼有序。三纲的提法在先秦两汉之际的诸家著作

① 《孟子·滕文公上》，杨伯峻：《孟子译注》，中华书局，1960年，第125页。

中多有出现，西汉大儒董仲舒提出："君臣父子夫妇之义，皆取诸阴阳之道。君为阳，臣为阴；父为阳，子为阴；夫为阳，妻为阴。阴道无所独行，其始也不得专起，其终也不得分功，有所兼之义。……王道之三纲，可求于天。"① 三纲包括君臣、父子、夫妻三种人际关系，其中父子、夫妻属于家庭伦理关系，而以阴阳比附父子、夫妇，强调父对子、夫对妻的主宰地位。从五伦、三纲中包含的父子、夫妇、长幼这些家庭人伦双方的关系上讲，五伦中的父子、夫妇、长幼基本上是一种在不对等基础上的互动互惠的差异关系，而三纲中的父子、夫妻则是一种单向的尊卑关系。如果从人际关系平等与否的视阈审视五伦与三纲，我们可以从中总结出支配儒家家庭人际关系规范的指导原则是差异性，它以等级、对等为两个极端，而随着时代与具体情境的变化而变化。儒家家庭伦理以差异性为本，但它的目的并不是要制造家人之间的对立，恰恰相反，它是要依据家人之间的现实差异制订出合理的人伦秩序，在秩序中求和谐，差异、秩序、和谐是儒家家庭伦理的基本内涵。

与人际关系规范的差异秩序论相对应，在人际关系情感上儒家主张亲情本位。儒家认为，家庭伦理以血缘关系为依据，而血缘关系又体现为人的情感亲疏的自然差异。孔子与学生讨论父母与子女关系时明确主张体现差异关系的孝道，其根据即在于内在的人情，"宰我问：'三年之丧，期已久矣。君子三年不为礼，礼必坏；三年不为乐，乐必崩。旧谷既没，新谷既升，钻燧改火，期可已矣。'子曰：'食夫稻，衣夫锦，于女安乎？'曰：'安。''女安，则为之！夫君子之居丧，食旨不甘，闻乐不乐，居处不安，故不为也。今女安，则为之！'宰我出。子曰：'予之不仁也！子生三年，然后免于父母之怀。夫三年之丧，天下之通丧也，予也有三年之爱于其父母乎！'"② 孟子曾与告子争论"仁内义外"说，力主"义内"，其核心也在于把人伦关系奠基于内在的道德情感之上。新出土的与先秦儒学关系密切的《郭店楚墓竹简》中有同意告子"仁内义外"说的，但它同时又说："门内之治恩掩义，门外之治义斩恩。"③ 仍然把家庭伦理奠基在亲属之间的恩情之上。正因为儒家的家庭伦理以亲情为本位，它们不是外在的宗教戒律、政治法律制度，而是一个出自自身本原的内在关系而非外在关系，只要家庭存在，父子、夫妇、长幼的差异伦理关系就会自然生成。

儒家在家庭伦理上倡导以亲情为本的内在关系说，但家人之间的情感为什么一定会导致良好的伦理秩序，而不是像荀子、韩非子那样理解为亲人之间的互相争斗，这

---

① 《春秋繁露·基义》，钟肇鹏：《春秋繁露校释》（校补本），河北人民出版社，2005年，第788、791页。

② 《论语·阳货》，杨伯峻：《论语译注》，中华书局，1980年，第188页。

③ 李零：《郭店楚简校读记》，北京大学出版社，2002年，第131页。

就不能不最终归结到在儒家学说中占据主导地位的性善论。孔子讲仁，本就有为人的情感合理性奠基的意义，不过他更多地是从人的德行修养上讲仁，仁是有待完成的本源之德。而孟子提出性善论，则为包括家庭伦理在内的儒家伦理奠定了源自人的天然性情的合理性，至于情感的不善则归因于外在的物欲与内在的私心，而去除私心、物欲既有待于内在的道德修养工夫，又有待于外在的礼乐教化，从而形成了一个完整的道德哲学的体系。

## 三、现代社会转型与儒家家庭伦理的困境

中国传统社会在春秋、战国之际有一个大转型，从宗族的家天下走向家庭的家天下，由秦汉时期确立的家庭的稳定形态一直延续到近现代。今天的中国正在走向现代化，在家庭结构与家庭伦理上又出现了一次大转型，晚清政界的头面人物李鸿章就慨叹："欧洲诸国百十年来，由印度而南洋，由南洋而东北，闯入中国边界腹地，……胥聚于中国，此三千余年一大变局也。"[①] 这个"三千余年一大变局"在家庭形态上有两个巨大变化，一个是家庭形式的小型化与多样化，另一个是家庭本位在政治、经济尤其是法制领域的丧失。

现代中国的家庭正在经历一个从传统的三代以内的家庭形态向两代以内的核心家庭形态转型的过程，这一过程随着改革开放以来的计划生育政策而进一步强化。放眼现代的中国社会，三代以内的大家庭在农村地区还有一定程度的留存，但两代以内的核心家庭成为主要形态。并且还出现了家庭形态多样化的状况：随着离婚率的提升，出现了很多单亲家庭；有一些夫妇，尤其是在高级知识分子阶层里，出于种种原因没有生育子女，这就是所谓的"丁克"家庭；还有一些保持独身主义的人群出现，这就是一种"单身"家庭；而且随着国内外在性、家庭问题上的宽容，同性家庭等也开始出现。家庭形态的巨大变化，相应地推动着家庭伦理的变化，它对传统社会占据主导地位的儒家家庭伦理构成了冲击。

家庭形态的小型化和多样化对于传统儒家家庭伦理构成了严重冲击，但这仍然是一种量变，而家庭本位的动摇与个人主体地位的确立则对儒家家庭伦理构成了致命的打击，这是一种性质上的转变。传统的中国是家天下，家庭真正是社会的细胞，它是经济、政治以至文化教育的不可分割的基本依托，传统中国人从根本上说是家里人，从皇帝到庶民无不如此；今天的中国则是国天下，个人是经济、政治以至文化教育的主体，今天的主席、总统不是宗族的代表，也不是家庭的代表，它是代表着亿万个人

---

① 李鸿章：《筹议制造轮船未可裁撤折》，《李文忠公全书》卷三十九《奏稿》，第11—12页。

来治理的，这亿万个人固然也还会“物以类聚，人以群分”，但家庭已失去其作为经济、政治主体的地位，也将逐渐失去其作为根本“群、类”的地位，这是现代的天下大势。近现代的中国社会正在经历着从家庭本位到个人本位的转型，从个人本位出发，传统儒家建立在家庭本位基础上的家庭伦理自然要受到批评，而与之相适应的是，近现代以来，以个人本位为基础的西方伦理文化大举进入中国，从而在家庭伦理层面掀起了一场场变革的风暴。儒家家庭伦理以家庭整体论为基础，在人际关系规范上主张差异秩序论，在人际关系情感上主张亲情本位论，这两点在近现代都受到了激烈批评。

首先受到激烈冲击的是儒家家庭伦理的差异原则，其所依据的是西方近现代以来以自由、平等、博爱为基础的伦理文化。近代中国介绍西学极有成就的严复就认为，西方的人际关系以个人自由、平等为基础，“自由既异，于是群异丛然而生。粗举一二言之：则如中国最重三纲，而西人首明平等。”[①] 五四运动的领袖陈独秀也认为：“盖共和立宪制，以独立、平等、自由为原则，与纲常阶级制为绝对不可相容之物，存其一必废其一。倘于政治否认专制，于家族社会仍保守旧有之特权，则法律上权利平等，经济上独立生产之原则，破坏无余，焉有并行之余地？”[②] 毛泽东提出君权、族权、夫权、神权为压迫中国人民的四大绳索，这就从根本上否定了以三纲、五伦为代表的包括家庭伦理在内的传统儒家伦理。

在对儒家家庭伦理的批评中，很多学者也逐渐从对外在的伦理关系的批评过渡到对其中内在的亲情依据的批评。在对儒家亲情伦理的批评中，有些学者认为儒家伦理局限于家庭成员、血缘亲属之间，但另外一些学者认为儒家伦理始于亲情但却由此推扩至“仁者浑然与物同体”，由此展开了多次学术争论。其实对儒家家庭伦理的批评还可以再进一步，这就是对家庭内部亲情的天然合理性、秩序性的怀疑，进而对儒家所秉持的性善论提出怀疑。在西方传统文化的“原罪”论视阈中，人是有限的存在，人的天然情感是靠不住的，道德是他律的，必须要有现实的法律和上帝的最后审判才能保证包括家庭伦理等的存在。而在中国传统文化中，法家等学派也主张人性自私，韩非就把家庭中人伦关系的阴暗面揭露出来，“且父母之于子也，产男则相贺，产女则杀之。此俱出父母之怀衽，然男子受贺，女子杀之者，虑其后便，计之长利也。故父母之于子也，犹用计算之心以相待也，而况无父子之泽乎！”[③] 在当代社会，儒家家庭伦理的人性论基础面临着中、西两方面学说的冲击，而中国社会现代化过程中产生的以工业文明、信息文明为主导的现代生活方式更为这种冲击提供了客观环境的支持。

---

① 《论世变之亟》，《严复集》，中华书局，1986 年，第 3 页。

② 《吾人最后之觉悟》，《青年杂志》第 1 卷第 6 号。

③ 《韩非子·六反》，李祥俊：《韩非子注释》，新华出版社，2003 年，第 357 页。

随着近现代的社会转型，儒家家庭伦理在面对日益现代化的中国社会时逐渐失去效应，一方面受到社会经济、政治生活变革的冲击，旧式的家庭组织逐渐解体或重构，另一方面受到西方伦理文化的冲击，儒家家庭伦理的基本原则饱受批评。儒家家庭伦理对于现实家人、亲属、友邻的人伦关系逐渐失去制约作用，它体现在当代中国社会尤其是乡村社会家庭伦理的失序，这一过程可以说贯穿整个20世纪，而在新世纪里愈演愈烈。如果说近现代是儒家家庭伦理不断失效的过程，那么它同时也是西方近现代伦理文化输入的过程。西方近现代伦理文化中对于家庭、亲情的理解与中国传统文化尤其是儒家文化差别很大，它以独立的个人为基础，倡导自由、平等、法制，在家庭的稳定性和亲情的重要性上相比中国传统的儒家文化要弱得多。并且，由于社会生活方式和伦理文化上的差异，西方近现代的一套伦理文化并没有在中国社会扎下根来。儒家的家庭伦理受到极大冲击，而西方伦理文化又不能扎根，结果是现代中国社会中普遍存在的家庭伦理失序现象。家庭伦理失序的意思主要可分为两类：一类指无序，回到原生态，按照家庭成员的自然情感相处，往往是没有规矩的凑合；一类是乱序，或者是中、西混用，但往往是将中、西家庭伦理中最不合理的部分相组合，或者是中、西抵触，依据其中一方家庭伦理生活的人往往受到来自依据其中另一方的人的伤害，当然也可能会伤害另一方。

家庭伦理的失序所带来的社会后果是极为严重的，因为以家庭关系为中心的亲情伦理绝不仅仅是一个感情、心理问题，它所确定的人伦关系秩序是和利益分配、社会地位、人际交往等直接相对应的。试看当下中国社会的家庭伦理，其中所存在的问题很多，大致可以从精神层面和物质层面两方面来讲。精神层面上，家庭内部以及相关的亲人之间几乎以自然情感、个人喜好定亲疏，缺少礼教大防，家人之间、亲属之间、友朋之间、邻里之间如何相处成为难题，由此导致情感上的冲突以至仇恨，当前的一些恶性案件往往与此相关。物质层面上，家庭内部的财产积累、分配等缺乏基本稳定的模式，再加上急剧变动的社会环境，各种关于遗产、房产、赡养费用等的争端蜂起。至于一般性的伦理失序在家庭内部和家庭之间的日常交往上的体现更是不胜枚举，以至于人们在庆生、送死、婚嫁等与家庭伦理相关的礼俗上无所适从，徒添无谓烦恼，徒增莫名冲突。

家庭是社会的细胞，在中国社会尤其如此。对于大多数中国人来说，一生当中的大多数时光是在家庭中度过的，家庭不仅关乎衣食住行的物质生活，更是人的精神的安顿之地。因此，家庭伦理失序所带来的危害是巨大的，家庭内部的利益分配不公正往往是最大的不公正，家庭内部的情感伤害往往是最大的伤害，处理不好的话，本来的安身立命之地就有可能变成人间地狱，但愿这不是危言耸听。

## 四、立足现实的儒家家庭伦理的现代重构

家庭是人的存在的本原性境遇，家庭形态的变化推动着家庭伦理的变化，面对当代中国社会的家庭问题和儒家家庭伦理的困境，完全复兴传统儒家的家庭伦理是不行的，那么能否完全去除儒家家庭伦理而代之以西方伦理文化或重新构成一套新家庭伦理呢？我认为这也是不行的，原因有两条：一个原因是事上的，在现代中国的社会生活中，儒家家庭伦理仍然有其存在的基础；另一个原因是理上的，儒家家庭伦理虽然以农耕经济、血缘家庭为基础，但它同样具有超越性、普遍性、永恒性的价值。况且，儒家家庭伦理主导中国传统社会家庭生活两千余年，它已经成为中国传统伦理文化的底色，根本无法去除，而西方伦理文化本身的局限性与民族性也使得它难以成为当代中国家庭伦理的根本指导原则。因此，合理的而且也是可行的方案就是重构儒家的家庭伦理。

实现儒家家庭伦理的现代重构，这并非是出于我们的善良愿望，而是具有深厚的社会基础。现代中国社会的家庭形态是以两代以内的小家庭为主，但小家庭内部仍然需要家庭伦理，此外，在广大的农村地区，家族内部的亲缘关系仍然很强大，所以，传统儒家家庭伦理对于现代中国人处理家庭内部的人际关系仍然具有重要的指导意义。有些学者认为中国社会已经走到了个人法权阶段，所以处理人际关系的伦理学已经失去了存在的意义，将来只需要依据法律等即可，这显然是把问题简单化了。我认为，在这个问题上，儒学恰恰有成功的经验，在春秋、战国的家庭形态转型中，墨家、道家、法家等均从宗法制的解体中走得太远，把两代以内的小家庭以至个体人当作社会基础来谈，不适应秦汉以降中国传统社会的国情，而儒家恰恰是在这一点上走了中庸之道。今天的中国同样面临着这个问题，“五四”以来的很多持激进主义思想的人认为现代中国会迅速走向以独立、自由的个人为本位的社会，而“文革”一段时间的单位制度有取代家庭的社会基础地位的倾向，但这两种思潮和先秦的墨家、道家、法家一样都走过了，他们不了解家庭在现代中国社会仍然具有基础性的地位，而儒学在这个问题正可以重走中庸之道，即一方面维护传统儒家家庭伦理的基本原则，另一方面与时俱进实现家庭伦理重构。

我们认为儒家家庭伦理在现代中国社会仍然有存在的现实基础，但不能否认的是，它面临着亟待解决的根本性问题，这就是如何处理家庭本位与个人本位之间的关系，从某种程度上说也就是如何处理传统儒家的家庭伦理与西方近现代伦理文化之间的冲突。我认为，人在世界之中，既是独立的主体性存在，又是与他人融通为一的存在，这是人生在世的两个基本面向。中国传统占据主导地位的儒家家庭伦理主要侧重个人

与他人尤其是亲人融通为一的存在方式，而相对忽略了个人的独立的主体性存在，而近现代传入的西方伦理文化则主要侧重人的独立的主体性存在，而相对忽略了个人与他人尤其是亲人融通为一的存在方式。今天，中与西、古与今的伦理文化传统在当下的中国社会交汇，形成了一种互相冲突的态势，但冲突中也存在着转生的契机。我认为，人是自由、独立的个体，要维护自己的权利，同时人又是家庭中人，要承担起自己的责任、义务，所以儒家伦理的家庭整体论和西方近代伦理文化的个人自由论可以在更大、更高的层面融通起来，而不必非此即彼。在这个问题上，我的态度是，独立、自由的个人是现代社会的基础，必须以独立、自由的个人为本，而以相对的家庭整体为辅，实现以自由、独立的个人权利为基础的家庭共荣，在这个基础上重构健康、和谐的新型的儒家家庭伦理。

人是生而自由的，但到目前为止却无往不在家庭之中，家庭无疑是人的生存的根源性境遇，但这不能成为桎梏人的自由的依据。传统社会由于经济、政治、文化等多种原因，导致人对物的依附、人对人的依附，而今天中国社会正在走向现代化，如何在肯定个体自由的基础上保持儒家家庭伦理的精华是一个问题。现代新儒家的一些前辈学者曾反复思考过这个问题，比如熊十力先生，他虽然推崇儒学，但却对传统儒家家庭伦理、家庭制度极为反感，甚至提出家庭社会化等一系列构想，他曾就解释《周官》经阐发其未来家庭制度设想："盖其社会组织，要在化家庭生活为大群共同生活，革其自私自利之习，发其与众同休戚之念，易散漫而为整齐，戒孤立而尚联合。"① 推究熊十力先生关于家庭问题的多处论述，其本意就是要维护个人的自由、独立，这不仅是熊先生一个人的观点，也是近现代一大批儒家学者的共识。熊十力先生关于家庭的设想和新中国成立后的一些制度是相合的，但历史的发展总是曲折的，"大群共同生活"的理想受挫于现实，以至今天在某种程度旧式家庭的伦理、制度有回潮的倾向和现实，但现代社会在个人与家庭、群体关系上走向个人自由、独立基础上的大分大合，这是社会发展的趋势，儒学也应当与时俱进。

以独立、自由的个人为基础，可以在肯定传统儒家性善论和家庭伦理内在关系说基础上，进一步凸显其同时作为外在关系的一面。传统儒家的家庭伦理把家庭看作是一个有机整体，而个体的人是家庭关系以及整个社会关系网络上的结，这是一种关系本位论，它把个人牢牢地吸附在家庭的母体中，这一点与现代社会追求人的自由全面发展是冲突的。我们认为，应该在独立、自由的个人的基础上，来建构一个家庭集合体而非有机整体，家庭成员既可以享受家庭生活的温暖，同时在不违反法律的前提下，也有维护个人自由、独立脱离家庭的权力，从而使家庭成为马克思所说的那种"自由

---

① 《论六经》，《熊十力全集》第五卷，湖北教育出版社，2001年，第701页。

人的联合体”。

在肯定人的自由、独立人格基础上，儒家家庭伦理的差异原则可以重新获得意义。儒家的家庭伦理肯定家人之间的人格地位的差异性，而人格平等是现代社会的基本共识，因此有必要在传统儒家的差异原则与现代社会的平等诉求之间进行理论沟通。传统儒学肯定人与人之间在先天、后天上的差异，肯定人与人之间在感情、才智、能力、德行上的差异，它来自于对社会生活中人际关系实际的概括，是一个现实性原则。而西方近现代的平等观念则是一个理想性原则，它奠基于自然人性论之上，把个体的人假设为抽象的平等、独立的原子，通过订立契约组成社会。从理论上讲，差异性与平等性都是人伦规范的永恒原则，都是建立包括家庭伦理在内的人伦秩序的基本支撑点，公正不应当是简单的平等，而应当是包容差异的平等，这种包容差异的平等是一种复杂的平等，也是更高层次的平等，只有这样，才能实现家庭成员关系的平等互助与差异互补，在社会最基本的组织单位家庭中实现公正。

儒家家庭伦理的差异原则有其合理之处，但在今天的社会转型中，其差异原则本身也需要调整。首先，从理论形态上讲，传统儒学往往将差异原则本体化上升为永恒的天理，没有意识到差异性本身的复杂性、变动性，我们则主张所谓的天理不过是对千差万别的现实差异关系的概括，它来自于人类社会生活实际，也要在人类社会生活的发展变化中不断更新其理论形态。其次，从概念内涵上讲，传统儒学以差异性为根本原则，差异性的特异发展应该是导向对等、等级两端，但在传统社会中，大多是向等级性一端靠拢，而远离平等性一端，这种偏颇理应得到纠正，今天应当以平等观念补充、修正儒家伦理，抛弃等级性，改差异、等级互动为差异、平等互动。再次，从差异性自身的依据上讲，传统儒学主要依据亲亲、尊尊、年龄、性别等因素，而我们应该根据今天的社会现实，对其进行扬弃，补充知识、能力等因素，提倡一种多元互动的差异性。第四，从应用范围上讲，传统儒学的差异原则往往是“天人合一”式的，而我们今天则应该实行领域分离原则，把它还原到以亲情为本的家庭伦理之中，而在公共生活、基本人权方面追求普遍平等。

传统儒家的家庭伦理主张性善论基础上的亲情本位，强调用感情来调节家庭人际关系，这种思路在现代社会仍然具有重要意义。人与物不同，人是具有深厚感情的存在，并且这种深厚感情并不仅仅是在后天交往中产生的，与生俱来的精神世界里“冲漠无朕，万象森然已具”。① 但同时我们也应该认识到，人的独立、自由是首出的价值，人与人之间包括家人之间的情感关系必须建立在对个体的尊重和人际双方的互动关系基础上，那种片面的情感诉求，尤其是用亲情的面纱掩盖下的人与人之间的依附关系

---

① 《程氏遗书》卷十五，《二程集》，中华书局，1981年，第153页。

必须打破。传统儒家家庭伦理中对于人的情感诉求大多是从自觉角度提出的，而我们今天更应该提倡自愿原则。同时，在倡导家人之间亲情的同时，也应该正视家人之间的权力、功利关系，形成情感与理智相互促进的家庭生活氛围。

重构儒家家庭伦理，应对转型社会的冲击，弘扬中华民族的传统文化、习俗，为当代中国人提供幸福的家园，这是一件影响巨大而又迫切需要的工作。不仅有学者呼吁这个工作，有些社会热心人士以及政府部门已经在这方面做出了努力，只是考虑尚不周全，也有与自由、平等、领域分离等现代社会基本理念相违背之处。如何在中与西、古与今思想文化冲突融合的现代境遇下实现儒家家庭伦理的重构，这是一件具有重要理论意义和现实意义的课题，也是一件艰巨的工作。

# 礼仪家教：构建礼仪之邦的基点

上海华东师范大学　陈卫平

当今社会流行的“家教”，是以给孩子请家庭教师补习文化知识为内涵的。其实，在中国本来的传统中，评价某个人是否有家教，主要不是指文化知识，而是指道德修养，其外在的表现就是行为举止是否合乎礼仪，通俗地讲就是懂礼貌或懂礼数。传统家教的名著《颜氏家训》就贯穿着礼仪教育，作者颜之推指出：“吾家风教，素为严密”，其礼仪家教十分系统，“晓夕温清，规行矩步，安辞定色，锵锵翼翼，若朝严君焉。”即早晚实行奉养父母的温清之礼，行走言谈都要合乎礼仪的要求，神色安详，谦恭谨慎。颜之推编撰这本家训，是为了使这样的家教门风得以传承，“整齐门内，提撕子孙”。中华民族以礼仪之邦而著称。孟子说：“天下之本在国，国之本在家，家之本在身。”（《孟子·离娄上》）礼仪家教正是儒家修身的第一课，是构建中华民族礼仪之邦的基点。现在重振礼仪之邦已成为培育践行社会主义核心价值观的重要课题，只有让礼仪回归家教，中华民族礼仪之邦的传统才能得到继承和发扬。

## 一、礼仪之邦：儒学价值观制度化的产物

中华民族成为礼仪之邦，是儒学价值观制度化的产物。这是礼仪家教作为构建礼仪之邦基点的前提。

孔子主张“道之以德，齐之以礼”（《论语·为政》）即以礼治国，这一主张在汉代以后一直主导着中国社会。儒家之礼仪集中表现于“三礼”即《周礼》、《仪礼》、《礼记》三部经典，内容包罗了政治制度、宗教仪式、法典刑律、道德规范、日常生活准则等。广义的制度是指组织人类共同生活、规范和约束个体行为的一系列规则，儒家之礼仪正可以这样的制度概念予以概括。对于价值观念之“仁”和制度规范之“礼”的关系，孔子认为前者必须通过后者才能得以普遍实现：“克己复礼为仁。一日克己复礼，天下归仁焉。”（《论语·颜渊》）。因此，礼仪的实施就是儒家价值观制度化的落实，礼仪之邦就是在这落实的历史进程中形成的。

显然，礼仪之邦形成的历史起点是儒学价值观成为主流价值观；而这又是通过确立礼仪即儒学价值观制度化而实现的。儒学价值观成为主流价值观无疑是在汉代。但这并非如一般人们印象中那样简单：汉武帝采纳了董仲舒“独尊儒术”的建议，于是儒学三纲五常的价值观就得到了确立。历史的事实是：汉武帝宣示“独尊儒术”的53年以后，在公元前81年召开的盐铁会议上，官位仅次于丞相的御史大夫桑弘羊和贤良、文学等儒生展开激辩，前者批驳后者的儒家重“仁义”的价值观，并明显地占据了上风。这表明儒学价值观即使在最高领导层内也没有得到普遍认同。盐铁会议是在汉昭帝时召开的，继汉昭帝之后的汉宣帝还是强调：“汉家自有制度，本以霸王道杂之，奈何纯任德教，用周政乎”（《汉书·元帝纪》）。

历史从西汉演进到东汉，公元78年召开了白虎观会议。这距盐铁会议已经有近百年之遥。陈寅恪认为根据这次会议编撰的《白虎通义》标志着儒家三纲五常价值观通过制度化而得以确立。他说：“吾中国文化之定义，具于《白虎通》三纲六纪之说”；“夫纲纪本理想抽象之物，然不能不有所依托，以为具体表现之用；其所依托以表现者，实为有形之社会制度”。[①] 在他看来儒学价值观在汉代以后的有效确立，不在其思想学说之精深（就此而言不如佛道），而在其社会历史过程中的制度化：“儒者在古代本为典章学术所寄托之专家。李斯受荀卿之学，佐成秦治。秦之法制实为儒家一派学说之所附系。《中庸》之‘车同轨、书同文，行同伦’（即太史公所谓‘至始皇乃能并冠带之伦’之‘伦’）为儒家理想之制度，而于始皇之身，而得以实现之也。汉承秦业，其官制法律亦袭用前朝。遗传至晋以后，法律与礼经并称，儒家《周官》之学说悉采入法典。夫政治社会一切公私行为，莫不与法典相关，而法典实为儒家学说之具体实现。故两千年来华夏民族所受儒家学说之影响，最深最巨者，实在制度法律公私生活之方面，而关于学说思想方面，或转有不如佛道二教者。”[②]所谓“制度法律公私生活之方面”，就是指儒家礼仪对于政治制度、法律制度和生活制度的影响，这说明了儒家价值观依托礼仪而成了制度化的存在，由此深入地左右了中国社会。这同时也使中国社会成了礼仪之邦。

汉代儒生认为儒学要成为主流价值观，必须通过礼仪而使其制度化，由此奠定了儒学价值观制度化的基础和礼仪之邦的基础。汉初的陆贾、贾谊、公孙弘等提出，汉朝要长治久安，必须吸取秦朝“不施仁义”导致二世而亡的教训；确立儒家仁义价值

---

① 陈寅恪：《王观堂先生挽词·序》，《寒柳堂集》附录《寅恪先生诗存》，上海古籍出版社，1982年，第6页。

② 陈寅恪：《冯友兰〈中国哲学史〉审查报告三》，《陈寅恪史学论文选集》，上海古籍出版社，1992年，第511页。

观则必须依靠礼仪："道德仁义，非礼不成；教训正俗，非礼不备；分争辨讼，非礼不决；君臣、上下、父子、兄弟，非礼不定；宦学事师，非礼不亲；班朝治军、莅官行法，非礼威严不行；祷祠祭祀、供给鬼神，非礼不诚不庄。"（贾谊：《新书·礼》）① 因此，公孙弘制订了朝廷和宗庙的礼仪，他的弟子撰成后来被收入《礼记》的《王制》。贾谊草拟了易服色、改正朔等礼仪制度，但未被采纳。在这前后不断有人提出同样的建议，但在浓厚的黄老之学氛围中均遭到失败。不过，由此可见汉代儒生意识到，只有通过礼仪来把儒学价值观制度化，儒学才能成为主流。董仲舒秉承这样的理念，在提出"独尊儒术"的同时，再次要求制订易服色、改正朔的礼仪制度，得到了汉武帝的赞同。但是"是时上方征讨四夷，锐志武功，不暇留意礼文之事。"（《汉书·礼乐志》）因而制礼的实际工作进展不大。董仲舒之后，一方面王莽建明堂等，"制度甚盛"（《汉书·王莽传》），把汉儒的制礼推向高潮；另一方面戴德、戴圣等对《仪礼》、《礼记》的整理，以及后来刘向、刘歆父子推崇《周礼》为周公致太平之书等，使得礼仪的制订更具操作性、可行性和权威性。由此我们可以明白何以直至白虎观会议，才标志着儒学价值观作为主流价值观得到了广泛，是因为经过汉儒上述的持续不断的礼仪建设，它显示了"由单纯的理论体系到制度体系的跨越具有决定性意义"。② 在汉代文献中，可以看到不少地方官员以礼仪建设使得儒家价值观因制度化而得到落实的记载。如《后汉书·循吏秦彭传》说：秦彭"以礼训人……每春秋飨射，辄修升降揖让之仪。乃为人设四诫，以定六亲长幼之礼。有尊章教化者擢为乡三老。"这也表明了儒学价值观因礼仪得以制度化而影响社会，同时促成了礼仪之邦的形成。

家庭礼仪是礼仪的重要部分。如果说礼仪建设是儒家价值观的制度化，那么礼仪家教则是这样制度化的落小落细落实。所谓落小，是因为礼仪家教以社会的微小细胞家庭为载体；所谓落细，是因为礼仪家教渗透于日常生活细节中；所谓落实，是因为礼仪家教落实于家庭成员从出生、成长到死亡的生命每一环节。礼仪之邦是儒学价值观制度化的产物，而礼仪家教是这一制度化的落小落细落实，由此礼仪家教就成了构建礼仪之邦的基点。

## 二、礼仪家教：文明的养成与化习惯为德性

礼仪家教作为构建礼仪之邦的基点，就其作为个体德性培养的作用而言，主要是文明养成的最初实践；就其作为个体德性培养的过程而言，主要化习惯为德性的自然

① 值得注意的是，这段话以后也出现在《礼记·曲礼》中，可见汉儒对于以礼仪而使得儒家价值观制度化的一贯努力。

② 姜广辉主编：《中国经学思想史》第2卷，中国社会科学出版社，2003年，第378页。

而然。

重视礼仪家教对于文明养成的作用，是与中国传统社会以家族为本位的特点分不开的。在以家族为本位的基础上形成的以儒家为主导的传统文化，如著名历史学家钱穆指出的：它有两个西方文化没有的概念，一个是“礼”，一个是“族”；“在西方语言中没有‘礼’的同义词。它是整个中国人世界里一切习俗行为的准则，标志着中国的特殊性。正因为西语中没有‘礼’这个概念，西方只是用风俗之差异来区分文化，似乎文化只是其影响所及地区各种风俗习惯的总和。如果你要了解中国各地的风俗，你就会发现各地的风俗差异很大。……然而，无论在哪儿，‘礼’是一样的。‘礼’是一个家庭的准则，管理着生死婚嫁等一切家务和外事”；“中国文化还有一个西方文化没有的概念，那就是‘族’”，家族的形成是与“礼”所规定的准则从家庭成员延伸到所有亲戚相联系的，“只有‘礼’被遵守时，包括双方家庭所有亲戚的‘家族’才能存在。换言之，当‘礼’被延伸的时候，家族就形成了，‘礼’的适用范围再扩大就成了‘民族’。中国人之所以称为民族，因为‘礼’为全中国人民树立了社会关系的准则”。[①]这就是说，由于作为全民族社会关系准则的“礼”，首先是以家庭为原点，然后扩展到家族和民族，所以，中国传统的家教就把礼仪放到极其重要和突出的位置了。俗话说“国有国法，家有家规。”家规的形成和延续无疑是依赖于家教的，各家的家规会有不同，但它们都是以普遍性的“礼”为依据的。因此，旧时所谓书香门第，在住宅的大门上，往往写着“诗礼传家”四个字，以标榜门风家教。这样的家教传统在孔子那里就已经存在了。《论语·季氏》记载，陈亢问孔子的儿子孔鲤：“你是老师的儿子，一定得到老师特别的传授吧？”孔鲤回答道：“父亲对我的教育，其实和大家是一样的。如果说有单独的传授，那只有两次。有一次，他老人家独自站在庭中，我从他面前走过。他问我：‘学诗了吗？’我说：‘没有。’他说：‘不学习诗，就不会说出有文采的话。’于是我开始学习诗。不久，他又站在庭中，我又从他面前走过，他问我：‘学礼了吗？’我说：‘没有。’他说：‘不学礼，就不能在社会上立足。’于是我又开始学礼。我独自受到父亲教导，就是这两次。”陈亢听后高兴地说：“我问了一件事，却得到了三件事，我知道了诗、礼的用处，知道了君子要求孩子继承的家风是诗和礼。”以后儒家思想被称作“礼教”，其中的重要涵义就是以礼为教，即通过礼制而实现教化的价值。因此，传统社会把礼仪作为家教的基本内容，并以是否知书达礼来评价某个孩子是否有家教。

在《论语》中孔子几次强调“不知礼，无以立”，把对于礼仪的家庭教育看作是孩子将来立足于社会的根基，是有见于人和动物的区分。人们呱呱坠地时是自然人，也

---

① 邓尔麟：《钱穆与七房桥世界》，社会科学文献出版社，1995年，第7页。

就是说只具有类似动物的本能，要从这样的自然人成长为被社会所认同的人，就必须按照社会通行的行为准则即礼仪来规范自己。这就是说，家庭礼仪教育是孩子走向文明的第一步。所以，《礼记·冠义》说："凡人之所以为人者，礼义也。"《礼记·曲礼》说："鹦鹉能言，不离飞鸟。猩猩能言，不离禽兽。今人而无礼，虽能言，不亦禽兽之心乎？……是故圣人作，为礼以教人，知自别于禽兽。"认为人与动物的区分不是语言的有无，而是是否有礼。就是说，如果没有礼仪的规范，人只是衣冠禽兽。正是有见于此，传统礼仪的有些规定是为了抑制人依然遗留着的动物习性。如《礼记·曲礼》中的如下规定："毋抟饭，毋放饭，毋流歠，毋咤食，毋啮骨，毋反鱼肉，毋投与狗骨，毋固获，毋扬饭，饭黍毋以箸，毋嚃羹，毋絮羹，毋刺齿，毋歠醢。"取饭时不要把饭抟成团，不要把手中的余饭放回食器，喝汤时不要倾流不止。上菜时舌头不要在口中作声，不要把骨头啃得有响声，不要把咬过的鱼肉放回食器，不要把肉骨扔给狗，不要专吃最好的食物，不要用手扬去饭的热气，吃黍时不要用错餐具，吃羹时不要连羹中的菜都不嚼就吞下去，不要重调主人已经调好的羹，不要当别人面剔牙，不要重调主人已经调好的肉酱。如此详尽的规定，是为了使人们自觉意识到，即便吃饭，也应该在端饭举筷之际体现有别于动物的进食习惯。就是说，家庭作为孩子文明养成的最初的摇篮，首先是从养成其合乎礼仪的行动规范开始的。《论语·宪问》记载：有位"阙党童子"常为党正（基层行政单位负责人）传信，孔子见其行为不合乎礼仪，大模大样地与长辈并排同坐和并肩而行，于是断定他只是急于出人头地，成人后无论在学问上还是在品德上都将不足为道："吾见其居于位也，见其与先生并行也，非求益者也，欲速成者也"。这个童子有如此举止，显然是缺少礼仪家教所致。可见，没有礼仪家教的最初文明养成，孩子很难真正地健康成长。

如上所述，儒家的礼仪建设是为了将其价值观念制度化，因而礼仪教育的目的在于涵养个体的德性。礼仪家教的重要在于使礼仪涵养德性的过程成为化习惯为自然的过程，而不是空洞生硬的说教。

《礼记·乐记》说："德辉动于内，而民莫不承听；礼发诸外，而民莫不承顺。"道德的光辉从内心萌动，礼的准则表现在仪表上，民众就不会不听从的。这是告诉我们，外在的礼仪教育是为了培养内在的德性。礼仪家教也是如此。人们常常把中国称作"礼仪之邦"，这固然是不错的。但是，我们还要进一步说，中国更是"礼义之邦"。这是因为中国传统文明不只是讲究形式上的礼仪，更注重的是"礼"以及与之相联系的"义"，就是说，更强调礼所依据和蕴含的道德之义理，因为这是礼之所以成立的伦理基础。所以，《礼记·仲尼燕居》说："礼也者，理也。"《礼记·乐记》说："礼也者，理之不可易者也"。前述汉儒编撰的《礼记》就是专门论述礼仪之义理。其首篇取名《曲礼》，意谓礼仪蕴含着迂回曲折的义理，需要认真思考领会。后来《礼记》在"三礼”中的地位越来越高，意味着儒家越来越看重礼仪之义理。其实，孔子早就强调重视礼仪不能停留于玉帛这些举行礼仪时使用的器具：“礼云礼云，玉帛云乎哉?”（《论语·先进》）但是，“礼义”又是和“礼仪”相联系的：只有从礼仪着手，才能让礼之义理在行动的体验中入耳入脑。儒家的《仪礼》和《礼记》正体现了礼仪和礼义的结合，前者是讲如何做，后者是讲为何要这样做。

礼仪家教正体现了这两者的统一基础上，因为它从培养礼仪的行为习惯入手，达到把礼义内化为德性的目的。道德规范是当然之则，道德教育是要人们懂得这些当然之则的义理，即为何应当如此。但是这对于儿童显然是不太容易明白的。而从行为准则尤其是家庭生活的行为准则入手，对于儿童来说，比较容易达到遵守道德规范的目的。因为在起居、就餐等家庭生活琐事中，每天按照礼仪来规范自己，久而久之就成了习惯，由习惯而成自然，遵守这些习惯仿佛成了他的第二天性，如孔子所说：“少成若天性，习惯若自然”（《颜氏家训》）。于是，就能“从心所欲不逾矩”，举手投足似乎并不刻意而为，但却合乎礼仪，由此这些礼仪蕴含的道德规范就内化为了人们的德性。如《礼记·曲礼》说：“邻有伤，舂不相；里有殡，不巷歌。”古人舂米，喜欢唱送杵的号子，当邻里有殡伤之事时，应该默舂，不在巷中歌唱。这样的家礼包含着同情他人的同哀之心。宋代朱熹的《家礼》、《童蒙须知》、明代屠羲英的等《童子礼》，对衣着、盥洗、洒扫、行走、语言、视听、饮食等等的行礼之法都有详细的规定，以此作为家庭礼仪教育的内容。如：“凡著衣服，必先提整衣领，结两衽纽带，不可令有缺落”。（朱熹：《童蒙须知·衣服冠履第一》）“走，两手笼于褎内，缓步徐行，举足不可太阔，毋得左右摇摆，致动衣服”。（屠羲英：《童子礼·行》）这里表现的是约束自我的道德自律精神。再如，“凡弟子须要早起晏眠”，“凡对父母长上朋友，必自称名；凡称呼长上，不可以字”，“凡侍长上出行，必居路之右，住必居左”。这都表达了尊敬长辈的道德品质。因此，无论是富贵还是贫贱的家庭，如果有效地进行了礼仪教育，就能培养他们良好的品德，“富贵而知好礼，则不骄不淫；贫贱而知好礼，则志不慑”（《礼记·曲礼》）。

由于儒家的礼仪教育是由养成习惯来培育德性，因而就十分注意生活习俗与礼仪的关系。人们常常把“礼俗”连在一起，这是有一定道理的。因为礼既源于俗，又是对俗的变易。《说文解字》云：“俗，习也。”俗，就是生活习惯。人们在特定的自然环境、社会环境中生活，久而久之，形成了各自的风俗。《礼记·王制》就对东、西、南、北四方的生活风俗作了描述。周公制作礼乐，就是要通过移风易俗来提升社会的文明程度。不过，儒家的移风易俗不是简单地把原来的风俗彻底破除，而是主张“因俗制礼”，即尽量利用原有的风俗形式和其中的合理部分，灌注新的精神，加以整理、提升，从而在人们本来熟悉的习俗中受到教化。很多家庭礼仪中也是这样的。比如冠礼，在远古氏族社会时代，曾流行过“成丁礼”。氏族中的未成年人享受氏族对他们的抚育，不用参加生产劳动和战争，但在他们达到成人年龄后，氏族要用一些方法来测定他们是否具备了生产、战争的技能，以确定他们是否能够成为氏族的正式成员。在社会发展的过程中，这样的“成丁礼”在很多地区消失了，而儒家看到了它的合理性，将它加工改造成冠礼。举行冠礼，不仅意味着生理上进入成年人的年龄，而且意味着应当具备与承担成年人社会责任相一致的道德品行。《礼记·冠义》说：“成人之者，将责成人礼焉也。责成人礼焉者，将责为人子。为人弟，为人臣，为人少者之礼行焉。将责四者之行于人，其礼可不重欤?”可见，将原来的成丁礼变易为冠礼，是赋予其提示行冠礼者，从此要践履为人子、为人弟，为人臣，为人少者的德行，担当起自己的社会角色。

## 三、让礼仪回归家教

自“五四”以来，传统礼仪在家教中基本上已经退出了。这有着很多原因，如传统礼仪的形式化和繁琐化，与现代社会生活节奏不相适应；还有对于传统礼教的封建性的批判，导致人们完全把传统礼仪当作糟粕予以抛弃。同时，由于西方礼仪随着西方文明涌入中国而广泛流行，改行西方礼仪成为“时髦”，还由于西方文明近代以来在全球占据主导地位，学习西方礼仪也成了中国与世界“接轨”的重要方面。于是，人们对于传统礼仪已经很生疏，甚至完全遗忘了。下面的故事可以印证这一点：1925年正在北京女子师范大学授课的鲁迅收到该校学生许广平的信，鲁迅在回信中称“广平兄”，许广平疑惑不解，在接着的回信中问道：“先生之意何居？弟子真是无从知道。不曰‘同学’，不曰‘弟’而曰‘兄’，莫非也就是游戏么”?[①] 其实鲁迅并没有与其开称兄道弟的玩笑，“兄”在传统书信礼仪中，和“同学”、“弟”一样，也是老师对学生辈的普通称呼。当时离开清朝的推翻只有14年，离开“五四”新文化运动至多也只有10年光景，许广平已经完全不知道这一传统师生礼仪的称呼了。现在人们对仍在使用的传统礼仪的称呼的无知，更是比比皆是。如常常有人在正式场合向他人介绍自己妻子时说：“这是我的夫人”。依据《礼记·曲礼》，天子的妃子称为“后”，诸侯、大夫、士、庶人的配偶分别称为“夫人”、“孺人”、“妇人”、“妻”。后来人们把他人的配偶称为“夫人”，是沿袭先秦礼仪而来的尊称，因而称自己的妻子为“夫人”，是自大的表现，完全违背了传统礼仪尊重他人的精神。可见，由于传统礼仪不再成为家庭日常教育和学校教育的组成部分，中国作为“礼仪之邦”已经出现了名存实亡的危机。

---

① 《鲁迅全集》第11卷，人民文学出版社，1981年，第17页。

克服这一危机的起点是继承以礼仪家教的传统，让礼仪回归家教。当年朱熹面对中国传统礼仪遭受佛教巨大冲击时感叹道："呜呼！礼废久矣。士大夫幼而未尝习于身，是以长而无以行于家。长而无以行于家，是以进而无以议于朝廷，施于郡县，退而无以教于闾里、传之子孙"（《朱子文集》八十三《跋三家礼范》）。因此，他专著《家礼》，要求礼仪成为人们年幼时家教的必修课。今天让礼仪回归家教，并非要回归"三礼"乃至汉、唐、宋、明乃至清代的家庭礼仪。从"二十四史"的《礼乐志》的记载来看，传统礼仪有两大发展趋势：一是形式日益烦琐复杂；二是服从皇权和特权的等级性日益明显；而且在两大趋势交织在一起，即形式的繁复是为了彰显皇权和特权的等级性。这也反映在家庭礼仪中，从《红楼梦》、《儒林外史》等有关描写中对此是不难感受到的。那么，今天应当如何让礼仪回归家教呢？

首先要将传统礼仪中蕴含的合理思想提炼出来。传统礼仪中有不少值得挖掘的至今仍有价值的思想：如反对把践行礼仪当作外在的形式，而要以内在的德性修养为灵魂，上述的"德辉动于内"而"礼发诸外"的观点就表现了这一点，还有"礼，与其奢也，宁俭"（《论语·八佾》）即将节俭作为礼仪的根本要求的观点。据《仪礼·士昏礼》记载，即使是作为"礼之本"（《礼记·昏义》）的婚礼虽然隆重，但也是相当简朴，不仅夫妇成婚的菜肴仅有数品，而且没有庆贺和举乐的仪式。再如强调礼仪"节"和"文"的观点，即礼是和人的情感是相称的，对情感、欲望起着有所节制和文饰美化的双重作用，如《礼记·坊记》所说："礼者，因人之情而为之节文。"《中庸》也说，礼的作用在于，使喜怒哀乐之情"发而皆中节谓之和。"《荀子·礼论》对于礼的解释是："称情而立文，因以群饰"。儒家讲"礼让"，就是注意到了礼的节制作用。孔子说："不能以礼让为国，如礼何？"（《论语·里仁》）北宋学者邢昺对此解释道："礼节民心，让则不争"。人们之间的欲望、利益是有矛盾的，这就需要由礼仪予以节制，从而使得人们的行为起到促进人际关系和谐的作用。孔融让梨就是一个典范，这也是传统家教在进行礼仪教育时，经常讲述的故事。儒家礼乐并举，是为了使礼成为美化的艺术形式，从《论语》等古代文献中可以看到，儒家的一些礼仪就是以歌舞、诵诗为载体的，于是人们在艺术的陶冶下认同了礼仪所表现的伦理关系。这些珍贵的思想遗产应当在今天礼仪家教中发扬光大。

其次，可以借鉴司马光、朱熹等对传统礼仪简化、改革的经验，把礼仪纳入学校教育中去。隋唐以来，佛、道两教盛行，乡风民俗多为其所化。司马光、朱熹等意识到，如果听之任之，儒家传统的礼义之邦很有可能不复存在。司马光首先编撰了家庭礼仪的《书仪》和《家范》，对繁琐的传统礼仪进行了大刀阔斧的删减，以《仪礼》为本，选择冠、婚、丧、祭四礼作为家庭基本礼仪，同时参酌宋代习俗予以变化。朱熹的《家礼》则在此基础上，进一步使其适用于普通百姓家庭，"虽贫且贱，亦得以大节，略其繁文，而不失其本意也。”（《朱子文集》八十三《跋三家礼范》）由此受到广泛的欢迎，成为进行礼仪家教的教材。我们应当吸取他们的做法，选择与日常生活紧密相关的家庭礼仪，融入一些具有传统色彩的礼仪，使礼仪家教在与时俱进中得到延续。还可以借鉴宋、明、清的韵语化蒙学读物，编写能够朗朗上口的进行礼仪家教的读本，在中小学推广。

再次，把礼仪家教与培育好家训、好家风结合起来，使礼仪家教更加凝练，也更加个性化。中国传统中，礼仪家教和家训、家风往往是合二为一的，著名的《颜氏家训》、《袁氏世范》、《朱子家训》、《弟子规》，还有上述司马光、朱熹的《书仪》、《家礼》等，既是礼仪家教的教材，也是家训、家风的体现。如司马光的《家范》不仅讲述了很多家庭礼仪，而且也宣示了家训：“以义方训其子，以礼法齐其家”。这是因为家训、家风的实质就是对礼仪家教提出的行为规范以及所体现的价值观念予以提炼，使其更加凝练生动。同时礼仪家教与家训、家风结合，使得礼仪家教彰显出各家各户的个性，这有助于激发家庭的礼仪自觉，也使得礼仪家教不是千篇一律而具有丰富性。事实上，现在很多地方正在开展的好家训、好家风活动，就是和礼仪家教紧密联系在一起的。

第四，家庭和社区联手，在举办青少年的活动中，融入传统的礼仪。家庭是坐落在一定的社区，礼仪家教的有效性往往和社区的道德熏陶有关，“孟母三迁”讲的就是这个道理。这方面韩国的经验是有启发的。至今韩国大约有 234 所乡校，与中国传统的民间乡校、社学相类似。这些乡校每逢假期为 7 岁到 14 岁的少年开设忠孝礼仪体验课程，学生必须穿着传统韩服上课，学习传统的生活礼节；也为成年人举行传统成年礼仪和传统婚礼，还举办耆老宴并表彰孝行者和善行者。总之，“乡校通过各种中小规模的课程和传统仪式，为当地居民提供实践传统儒家礼节的标准，使得一般韩国人能够体会到儒教的生活方式与儒教的价值观念”。[①] 显然，这样的体验课程会加深人们对传统礼仪的理解。射箭在韩国青少年中非常普及，这就和这些乡校把射箭和传统射礼的教育相结合有关。《礼记・射义》说：“发而不中，则不怨胜己者，反求诸己而已矣。”这就在射箭的活动中，使青少年体悟射礼中蕴涵的什么是君子式的竞争以及如何对待竞争遭遇失败的哲理。

中国正在大力推进城市化的进程，这就更加需要让礼仪回归家教。因为城市化进程不是简单的造城、扩城，也不仅仅是经济的升级更新。它在本质上是社会文明程度提升的过程。城市化的进程，从人口流动来说，是越来越多的家庭进入了城市。因此，随着城市化进程的加速，城市的家庭教育如何与城市文明建设相适应，就成为一个非

① （韩）金惠林：《韩国儒家文化的保护及弘扬》，《社会科学报》2007 年 4 月 26 日。

常需要正视的问题。城市化的进程，就人际关系来说，是越来越多的互不认识的陌生人汇聚在一起，陌生人之间应当以怎样的文明方式进行交往，也成为城市文明建设的重要问题。中国传统社会崇尚礼义，提出了以文明交往的礼仪来养成和体现良好的道德品性，而礼仪教育首先是从家庭教育开始的。这里蕴含着道德建设的传统智慧：在家庭的日常生活场景中，以温情和亲情来塑造道德人格；在以礼仪培养习惯的过程中。使道德行为成为自然而然的行为。就此而言，让礼仪回归家教，就是让道德回归生活、回归自然。这样的智慧应当成为“礼仪之邦”的传统在当代中国复兴的源头活水。

# 儒家礼乐教化思想与当代国民教育

贵州大学 龚妮丽

古老的中国曾被誉为礼仪之邦，这是文明走在前列的象征。文明必有理想，（即我们今天所说的中国梦）儒学最具生命力的根源就是其思想中的两个理想：一是社会理想，即《礼记·礼运》所言的“大同”、“小康”理想；一是文化理想，即《史记·周本纪》中“兴正礼乐”，“民和睦，颂声兴”的理想。前一种理想具有世界普遍性，后一种理想则最具中华民族特色。实现后一种理想的途径是教化，通过礼乐教化使人与人在情理上相互默契，达到社会和谐，个人行而乐之，乐而行之。新儒家代表人物徐复观先生说：“儒家的政治，首重教化，礼乐正是教化的具体内容。由礼乐所发生的教化作用，是要人民以自己的力量完成自己的人格，达到社会的和谐。由此可以了解礼乐之治，何以成为儒家在政治上永恒的乡愁。”①

以此看来，儒家礼乐教化的文化理想在当代社会仍然有着积极的意义，对于建构文明社会，个人修身提升道德，建构和谐社会，乃至获得“行而乐之，乐而行之”的生活模式，都可以是我们现代人的文化资源。

## 一、儒家礼乐教化的思想

儒家的礼乐思想发轫于周代，周公于成王年间制礼作乐，将上古祭祀祖先、沟通神明以指导人事的巫术礼仪，作了文化的转型，由重神道向重人道的方向过渡，使之理性化和体制化，成为治国兴邦，稳定社会的重要手段。到了春秋末期，周天子已经失去控制诸侯、卿大夫的实际能力，社会出现动乱，那些有权有势的卿大夫僭越周礼，自行其是，导致礼崩乐坏。先秦儒家的礼乐教化思想正是对周代礼崩乐坏反思的产物，经以孔子为代表的儒家群体对周公礼乐治国思想的继承和发展，对礼乐传统进行了系统的“述与作”，使礼乐文化基本定型，形成了一整套理想化的礼乐教化思想。

---

① 徐复观：《中国艺术精神》，沈阳：春风文艺出版社，1987年，第20－21页。

1. 何为礼？

礼是一套治理国家社会的重要手段，是治平天下的精神纽带，具体到社会中的个体来说，它是贯穿人一生无所不包的行为规范，礼的具体表现类型与表达方式涉及生命活动的方方面面，礼也必须随社会的发展而变化。

《礼记·曲礼上》说：

道德仁义，非礼不成；教训正俗，非礼不备；分争辩讼、非礼不决；君臣上下，父子兄弟，非礼不定；宦学事师，非礼不亲；班朝治军，莅官行法，非礼威严不行；祷祠祭祀，供给鬼神，非礼不诚不庄。

《礼记·仲尼燕居》又说：

"以之居处有礼故长幼辨也，以之闺门之内有礼故三族和也，以之朝廷有礼故官爵序也，以之田猎有礼故戎事闲也，以之军旅有礼故武功成也。是故宫室得其度……鬼神得其飨，丧纪得其哀，辨说得其党，官得其体，政事得其施。"

可见"礼"是对国家社会一切事务的治理，涵盖了政治制度、思想教育、道德诚信、立身处世、风俗礼仪、敬畏天地。小到个人修身齐家，大至治平天下。就如有学者指出："历史上所谓'周公制礼作乐'的礼乐，分明是指一套制度与文化的建构。若从后世《礼记》所说，'礼'根本是一个无所不包的文化体系"。[①]

2. 何为乐？

在先秦"乐"是包括音乐在内的诗、歌、舞融为一体的文化活动。《礼记·乐记》中说："乐者，乐也，人情之所不能免也。乐必发于声音，形于动静，人之道也……故人不耐无乐"[②]"乐"是与人的情感快乐相联系的生命活动，中国音乐的"乐"与快乐之"乐"同形异音，在很多时候其意义是相通的。儒家的理性精神中包含着浓厚的伦理道德意识，在认同音乐给予人耳目快乐的同时，将之与"善"紧密地联系在一起，强调音乐的美与伦理道德的善相统一。《礼记·乐记》强调"德音之谓乐"，"乐者德之华也"乐是德的外在光华。为什么儒家对音乐如此重视，因为音乐可以与礼相配合，不仅能很好地配合礼仪活动，更重要的是与"礼"互补，起到教化民众的作用。

3. 何谓礼乐教化？

中国的礼乐教化早在尧舜时代就出现了，如《尚书》中就有对舜命夔以礼乐教化百姓的记载："夔！命汝典乐，教胄子，直而温，宽而栗，刚而无虐，简而无傲。"周代礼崩乐坏之后，孔子呼吁继承周代礼乐教化，将西周以来"官学"的礼、乐、射、

---

① 陈来：《古代宗教与伦理：儒家思想的根源》，北京：生活·读书·新知三联书店，1996年，第225页。

② 《礼记·乐记》，《十三经注疏》，北京：中华书局，1980年，1544页。

御、书、数等“六艺”之教推广到民间，成为中国第一个兴办私学的教育家。孔子将教化视为社会的头等大事，由教观政，政由教出，《礼记·经解》载：孔子曰：“入其国，其教可知也。其为人也：温柔敦厚，《诗教》也；疏通知远，《书》教也；广博易良，《乐教》也；洁静精微，《易》教也；恭俭庄敬，《礼教》也；属词比事，《春秋》也。”[①]《论语·尧曰》记载孔子指出从政“四恶之首”为“不教而杀谓之虐”，他倡导通过礼乐教化使民知“仁”、而循“礼”；孟子也将教化提高到做人的前提，曰“人之有道也，饱食、暖衣、逸居而无教，则近于禽兽。”儒家非常重视通过礼乐教化，使人“明人伦”，懂得做人的道理，懂得按自己的名分尽职尽责，如何与人相处，如何与物相处，达到道德上的自我约束和提升。礼乐教化主要集中在社会性的道德伦理教化及个体人格修养两个方面，通过“礼教”、“乐教”、“诗教”为特征的“六艺”之教体现出来。用我们今天的话来说，形式是审美教育，核心是道德教育。

4. 礼乐何以能相互配合，实现教化作用？

“礼”是社会中人的行为规范，侧重理性的行为，“乐”合乎人性中的情，即所谓的“乐者，乐也，人情之所不能免也”，人不能无乐，乐即是人道、人性。所以“礼”需要与“乐”相配合，因为因此，一方面要规范人情、人性，另一方面又要顺乎人情、人性，于是就有了礼乐的内外结合。

“礼”通过事神致福，教民明人伦秩序；“乐（yuè）”能宣情，弦歌吟唱可转化为乐（lè），礼乐相济，为秩序化的社会生活增添情感的润滑剂。礼乐教化思想中包含着情理交融的教育理念，即在快乐中接受严肃的理性教育，使人们对“礼”的履践，乐而行之。

《礼记·乐记》对“礼”与“乐”各自的作用作了精辟的总结：

> 乐由中出，礼自外作……乐至则无怨，礼至则不争。揖让而治天下者，礼乐之谓也。
>
> 礼节民心，乐和民声。（乐本篇）
>
> 乐者为同，礼者为异。同则相亲，异则相敬。（乐论篇）
>
> 礼义立，则贵贱等矣；乐文同，则上下和矣。（乐论篇）
>
> 乐极和，礼极顺，内和而外顺。（乐化篇）
>
> 乐也者，情之不可变者也；礼也者，理之不可易者也。乐统同，礼辨异，礼乐之说，管乎人情矣。（乐情篇）

“礼”强调社会中人的行为规范，注重伦理秩序；“乐”能表现人的内心情感，礼乐教化使人与人在情理上相互默契，既有分疏又有融和，使社会达到有秩序的和谐。

---

① 《礼记正义》郑玄注：孔颖达疏，北京：北京大学出版社，1999年，第1368页。

从理与情的互补来看，礼乐活动中的行乐必然有对于人们心理情感的作用，乐舞以颇具感性特征的美感陶冶人情人性，在弦歌曼舞中，其乐融融，又恭敬肃穆，自然接受敬畏天道、尊祖崇德的教化。从序与和的互补来看，礼乐活动必然选择富有中庸精神的音乐以修正人心，在声律和谐的钟磬笙管合乐中，其乐奕奕，久而久之，温良文雅，自觉遵从君臣尊卑、明人伦秩序。《礼记·乐记》说："先王之制礼乐也，非以极口腹耳目之欲也，将以教民平好恶而反人道之正也。"因此，行乐活动中所体现出的审美心态一定是与道德教化相一致的，"乐者乐也"的美感意识也就更多地显示出崇德、致和、尚雅的特点。

孔子继承并深化了礼乐思想，认为礼乐教化必须以"仁"为前提，"人而不仁，如礼何？人而不仁，如乐何？"[①] 礼乐教化思想遂成为建构理想社会秩序的文化理念，成为中国儒家的文化向往。

## 二、儒家礼乐教化的内容与功能

礼乐教化的内容十分丰富，教化不仅是强调个人修身，还延伸到"齐家、治国、平天下"，修身是前提，而齐家、治国、平天下是目标。《礼记·王制》记载掌管教化司徒，对民众要施以"六礼"——冠、昏、丧、祭、乡、相见；"七教"——父子、兄弟、夫妇、君臣、长幼、朋友、宾客；"八政"——饮食、衣服、事为、异别、度、量、数、制，使人们通过礼乐的浸染，修养身心，变换气质，形成崇德、礼敬、诚信、和美的人文环境，以安顿人的身心。

《周礼·春官宗伯》记载：

> （大司乐）掌成均之法，以治建国之学政，而合国之子弟焉。凡有道者、有德者，使教焉……以乐德教国子：中、和、祗、庸、孝、友；以乐语教国子：兴、道、讽、诵、言、语；以乐舞教国子：舞《云门》、《大卷》、《大咸》、《大磬》、《大夏》、《大濩》、《大武》。[②]

乐德之教的内容："中、和、祗、庸、孝、友。"此为"六德"，郑玄注："中，犹忠也；和，刚柔适也；祗，敬；庸，有常也；善父母曰孝；善兄弟曰友。"实际上这六个方面包括了伦理道德的基本内容，乐德之教又是通过音乐教育方式，灌输受教育者德的内容，通过音乐活动，将"德"的内容化为情感体验，再上升为理性认同。一方面强调等级秩序，"教民明伦理"，一方面又注重沟通调和，使民乐于接受秩序而各安其位，礼乐同功，即是通过礼宜乐和来实现的。《礼记·乐记》中说：

---

① 《论语·八佾》，《十三经注疏》，北京：中华书局，1980年。

② 《周礼·春官宗伯第三》。

是故乐在宗庙之中，君臣上下同听之，则莫不和敬；在族长乡里之中，长幼同听之，则莫不和顺；在闺门之内，父子兄弟同听之，则莫不和亲。故乐者，审一以定和，比物以饰节；节奏和以成文。所以合和父子君臣，附亲万民也，是先王立乐之方也。①

在人伦有别的社会秩序中，同听同乐沟通了人与人的情感，达到情感的融洽，使社会分而有和。礼之理性秩序，配以乐之情感和悦，礼乐教化贯穿着“中和”精神，通过礼乐教化，使人行为端正，性情和美。

“礼乐”教化的意义还在于移风易俗，维护社会秩序的稳定、人群之和谐。荀子在《乐论》中说：

> 君子以钟鼓道志，以琴瑟乐心。动以干戚，饰以羽旄，从以磬管。故其清明象天，其广大象地，其俯仰周旋有似于四时。故乐行而志清，礼修而行成，耳目聪明，血气和平，移风易俗，天下皆宁，美善相乐。②

乐与百姓的日常生活有紧密的联系，所谓十五国风，都是各地民间的歌诗，它们产生于民间，也影响着各地的民风，《毛诗序》中有“风以动之”的说法，音乐就像春风吹化万物那样影响着人心，因而儒家认为教化百姓用音乐，“其感人深”可以“其移风易俗”。汉儒董仲舒十分重视通过礼乐改变民风，教化百姓。他认为“其变民也易，其化人也著”，的原因，那就是“故声发于和而本于情，接于肌肤，臧于骨髓”，乐不仅通过听觉器官，并进入到内心深处，他深深体会到“故圣王已没，而子孙长久安宁数百岁，此皆礼乐教化之功也”。③

儒家的“礼乐”教化又是与政治紧密联系的，《礼记·乐记》中言：

> 故礼以导其志，乐以和其声，政以一其行，刑以防其奸，礼乐刑政，其极一也，所以同民心而出治道也。

“礼”、“乐”、“政”、“刑”具有不同的性质、特征和功能，正好从不同的方面，相辅相成，相反相成，达到治理国家的目的。“礼乐”的作用是以不同的方式“治心”，“礼”侧重于“节民心”——通过以伦理秩序为基础的行为规范达到“治心”；“乐”侧重于“和民声”通过对情感的影响调和、调适人们的心性，修养完善人格。“礼节民心，乐和民性”，将人民自觉调适自己的心性、行为，完善人格作为治国的前提，之后才是“政以行之，刑以防之”，这实际上是一种以人为本的政治理路，有其深刻的一面。音乐是人们有感于现实而发出的情感性心声表达，社会的政治状况必然会在音乐中有所反映。音乐与政治之间的这种关系受到儒家特别的重视，认为既可以通过音乐

① 《礼记·乐记》。
② 《荀子·乐论篇第二十》。
③ 班固：《汉书·董仲舒传》点校本，北京：中华书局，1962年，第2499页。

观察政治得失，又可以通过音乐教化百姓，即所谓“本仁以聚之，播乐以安心”。[①]

礼乐教化还通过各种各样的礼仪，实现对人的教化。人的一生，要经历各种生命成长的阶段，以及各种重要的角色转变，乃至生命的终结，与之相配和的礼仪活动都内含着重要的文化价值观。礼仪是具有丰富内涵的象征体系，具体的礼仪各不相同，但都指向一致的“意义”，即通过礼乐教化，使体系中的人和事，皆“动得其宜”，从而达到个体、家庭、社会，乃至天人的秩序与和谐。如通过“冠礼”给予一个正在跨入成年的青年人以做人的尊严；通过“婚礼”，使你知道将要承担起家庭的责任，上对得起祖先，下对得起子孙；通过葬礼、丧礼慎重地对待一个死去的人，慎重地对待生命的终结。即谓“慎终”；通过祭礼，不忘以往的祖先，即所谓“追远”，祭礼还扩大到“祭天地”，感恩让我们能够生存的天地万物。《论语》中写道：“慎终追远，民德归厚矣”，如果大家都能做到慎终追远，心怀感恩，民风就纯化了。

## 三、礼乐教化的当代意义

当今的社会，在功利欲求与技术竞争的推动下，物质极大丰富，但同时，在欲望与功利的障蔽下，对于终极性的价值目标——信念、信仰、理想等精神上的追求正在淡化。极端的利己主义，使个人利益与社会价值产生冲突，出现人文精神的危机；残酷的市场竞争，使人与人之间产生激烈的利益冲突，导致道德的危机。人只要生活在社会中，就要与人和物打交道，人的生命热情不可能只来源于物，在冷漠的人群中，精神生命将失去光泽与温暖，在物的压抑下，人也只能是微不足道的存在。中国儒学充满生命的智慧，是我们解决人类生存危机的文化资源。礼乐教化理想根源于儒家的伦理哲学理念，虽然是宗法制等级社会的产物，但是它所包含的教育方式与价值理想是超越时空的。礼乐教化体现了儒家“生民之道，以教为本”的思想，是实现人与人在情理上相互默契，达到社会和谐，个人行而乐之，乐而行之的途径，对当代的文化建设仍然有着积极的意义。

1. 礼乐教化是构建文明社会的重要途径

今天的文明社会讲究行政法制，但仅仅依靠刑罚来治理社会是不够的，也是被动的。儒家的礼乐教化是对社会人群的人文教化，是对人的心灵与行为的价值建构，这是文明社会建设的重要途径。“礼乐不兴，则刑罚不中，刑罚不中，则民无所措手足。”[②] 礼乐教化是将礼的内在精神——仁爱、正义、和谐、节制、忠孝、诚信等，诉

---

① 《礼记·礼运》。

② 《论语·子路》。

诸人的理性精神，并通过人的行为表现出来。儒家讲“不知礼，无以立也”，[①]“知礼”是指思想行为的文化养成，“立”，是指以文化养成的行为融入社会、立身社会。礼乐教化通过“乐由中出，礼自外作”，“致乐以治心”，“治礼以治躬”，使人们从内部得到精神文化的提升，从外部习得与内部精神相应的、合乎礼仪的行为，美好的外在行为与内在的道德精神相统一，人人都成为有道德，有爱心、知廉耻、讲诚信的公民，社会风气就会好起来，国家的文明程度就会提高。可以说，礼乐教化与行政法制相配合，文明社会的建构才是完整的。

2. 礼乐教化是个人修身提升道德境界的重要途径

人与动物的区别，是具有理性的自觉与超越的生命境界。礼乐教化是情理的教化，通过礼的教育，“使人以有礼，知自别于禽兽。”[②] 儒家希望礼的教化，使每个人都能“明伦”，明白自己的身份，儒家把人与人之间的关系分成五大类——君臣、父子、夫妇、长幼、朋友。“明伦”就是要明白社会中人与人之间的这五种关系，明白自己社会角色的责任与义务，自觉地承担自己的责任和义务。通过礼的教育，每个人都能明白做人的道理，自觉地尽职尽责，在家庭中懂得孝敬父母，爱护子女；在社会中，懂得尊重他人，诚信待人，远离非理性的粗野、庸俗、愚昧、贪婪、迷乱，成为有道德修养的人，我们的社会就和谐有序，安定团结了。礼乐教化带给人的不应该是“禁令”，而是自觉地、愉快地接受从情感到理性的品格修养，自觉地、愉快地获得主体道德境界的提升。

3. 礼乐教化是建构和谐社会的重要途径

当今社会讲民主法治，人与人之间在政治上和人格上是平等的，应该取消等级的尊卑区别。但是人与人之间却存在着长幼、性别、亲疏、才能、特长、职业的区别，每个人在社会中扮演着不同的社会角色，各自发挥着相应的作用。礼教可以使有区别的人以自己的角色身份各安其位，各尽其责，使社会正常地、协调地运转，这样的社会才是健康的、有序的、长久的、稳定的。荀子说：“人何以能群？曰分。分何以能行？曰义。故义以分则和，和则一，一则多力，多力则强……”[③] 荀子还说：“人，力不若牛，走不若马，而牛马为用，何也？人能群，而牛马不能群。”荀子提到的这个“群”的概念，就是人与人联系在一起的社会性。礼乐教化就是要“致天下之和”，建构人人“安其位而不相夺”的和谐人际关系。乐教与礼教配合，让人们分中有和，通过音乐活动使人们在审美快乐情景中沟通情感，达到和谐。和谐社会的建构需要有分

---

① 《论语·尧曰》。

② 《礼记·曲礼》。

③ 《荀子·王制》。

有和，儒家礼乐教化的智慧中包含着人与人和谐相处的辩证道理。西方汉学家早在19世纪末20世纪初就注意到了中国礼乐文化的这一意义。英国汉学家亚瑟·韦利在他的《道德及其力量》这本书中说："全部中国哲学本质上就是研究如何才能最有效地促进人们在和睦与良好的秩序中生活在一起。"①

4. 礼乐教化是获得"行而乐之，乐而行之"生活模式的重要途径

礼乐教化思想中包含着情理交融的教育理念，所谓"言而履之，礼也。行而乐之，乐也。"中国音乐的"乐"与快乐之"乐"同形异音，其意义的关联有着中国文化的特色，唐君毅先生说："音乐者，人之所同乐者也。……音乐之乐者，下顺凡情之求乐，上希圣境之曰乐，故同其字而异其音，以见其义之相通，此亦唯中国有之，非他土之文字之异音者必异形之所能有者也。"②礼宜乐和的文化传统内含着充盈的"行而乐之，乐而行之"生活模式。礼乐教化使人与人之间的情感交流与思想交流充满积极的生命热情；礼乐双修，使受教者在快乐中获得恭敬而温文的气质，在快乐中修成正道。乐教帮助人们把道德教育规范变成自己内心情感的要求，自觉地与周围的世界建立和谐、美好的关系。例如，多声部的合唱，特别能激发人的向心力，各个声部协调一致，在这种完美和谐的音响氛围中感受到整体的理性美。这就是中国古代社会推崇的"乐从和"，"乐者敦和"的乐教思想。音乐中这些和谐、整体的观念如果变成人的纯理性的能力，人就会自觉地克服和战胜那些基于生理本能的自然感性和非理性的情绪，养成在生活中以人为善，真诚待人，宽容仁爱的道德修养。在一个充满和谐、友善、仁爱的人群社会中生活，这难道不是一种"行而乐之，乐而行之"的生活模式吗？

总之，礼乐教化——"兴于诗，立于礼，成于乐"③ 是中国人快乐人生的基础；礼乐教化，使仁人君子在"志于道，据于德，依于仁，游于艺"④ 的人生中获得生命的意义。

---

① 转引自金尚理：《礼宜乐和的文化理想》，成都：巴蜀书社，2002年，第37页。

② 唐君毅：《中华人文与当今世界》，南宁：广西师范大学出版社，2005年，第321页。

③ 《论语·泰伯》。

④ 《论语·述而》。

# 新时期高校儒家经典教育梳理

山东科技大学　杨立姣

新时期儒学研究与传承的快速发展主要指本世纪以来国家对儒学给予更多的重视，儒学研究、传播与普及得到了较快的发展。高校儒家经典教育主要包括三个层面：一是高校儒学研究的开展；二是高校儒学教育的探索；三是大学生儒家文化社团的活动。

## 一、儒学研究机构的设立与运作

2002年中国人民大学成立孔子研究院，其建院宗旨是："继承优秀传统文化，弘扬孔子思想精华，提高国民人文素质，建设人类美好未来"。孔子研究院学术研究机构分为国际儒藏与国际儒学研究中心、经学研究中心、和合文化研究中心、政治哲学研究中心、比较哲学研究中心、儒教研究中心暨儒教年鉴编辑部、儒商文化研究中心、中华气学研究中心。孔子研究院有自己专门的院刊，组织申报、评审、资助儒学研究课题。孔子研究院设立了各种奖励，奖励从事儒学与传统文化研究的学生与社会研究者。孔子研究院设立了孔子研究的常设性论坛《青年儒学论坛》，每月轮流举行一次儒学研讨会，每半年邀请学术权威举行报告会。中国人民大学孔子研究院在儒学研究启动方面走在前列。

2010年山东大学与山东省人民政府成立儒学高等研究院，后又与儒学研究中心、文史哲研究院、《文史哲》编辑部合并，成立新的儒学高等研究院。儒学高等研究院成为研究儒学的科研平台，在学术研究、人才培养、文献整理、信息交流、服务社会等诸多方面进行工作。儒学高等研究院下设儒学原理与方法研究所、儒学历史与文献研究所、儒学应用与传播研究所和《儒林》丛刊编辑部，将以研究课题为中心，整合校内外人文学科资源，形成创新团队，对儒学展开深层次、前瞻性及应用性研究。[1]儒学高等研究院聘请国内外学者兼职研究或联合培养研究生并积极拓展与其他团体的合作与联系，共同为研究和普及儒学做出自己的贡献。儒学高等研究院定期举行"尼山讲堂"，邀请本领域的专家授课讲解。同时定期举行"儒林学术研讨会"，一般有本学科的博士进行主题发言，众多老师进行点评，硕士生们可进行提问发言。山东大学作为山东的综合性部属院校，终于将儒学研究纳入自己的研究视野。也将自己的文史哲见长的优点得以发扬。

北京大学2010年在北大〈儒藏〉编纂与研究中心、北大中国哲学暨文化研究所和中国哲学教研室成立儒学研究院。儒学研究院的研究规划包括重大研究项目、经典典籍整理、专题研究项目、特色学术讲座四类。儒学研究院将开展一系列对人类社会有重大意义的项目，包括《儒藏》精华编的编纂、多卷本《中国儒学史》以及《儒学与马克思主义》等著作的编写。同时对于儒学人物的研究、儒学历史的梳理与当代儒学的实践等做出贡献。北京大学儒学研究院以儒学研究为中心，开展多项目的合作，注意儒学的时代性和世界性，推广儒学的跨文明交流，注重培养儒学研究人才［2］。北京大学以自己丰富的学术资源传承几千年来的儒家学术，推动中国学术的继续向前发展。

为了弘扬四川“重文尊儒”的蜀学传统，推进儒学研究和儒学人才培养，四川大学与国际儒学联合会、中国孔子基金会合作成立国际儒学研究院。儒学研究院致力于儒学研究、儒学教育与儒学普及工作。国际儒学院的建院方针是“弘扬儒学、服务社会、面向世界、刚健笃实”。儒学研究院继承了四川大学儒学研究“通经致用”、“关注现实”、“学术至上”、“推陈出新”的传统，国际儒学院整合了四川大学相关学科研究力量，下面设有中国儒学研究所、古籍整理研究所、蜀学研究所。另外设有儒商文化研究室、宋代文化研究室、海外儒教研究室、非物质文化遗产研究室等机构。四川大学国际儒学院研究成果丰硕，完成多项基金课题。完成了对《中国儒学通案》、《儒学大师文库》、网络《儒藏》、《巴蜀全书》、《宋会要辑稿》等典籍的整理和研究。在儒学方面、巴蜀文化方面、宋代文化方面都进行了深入的研究。国际儒学院以全国重点学科“历史文献学”、教育部“中国儒学”博士点、“纳通儒学”奖学奖教金为依托，构建了儒学人才培养基地与科研平台。国际儒学院出版了《儒藏》论丛、《儒藏论坛》学术辑刊，举办了《儒藏》学术系列讲座，开办了“儒藏网”与“国际儒学网”（与国际儒学联合会合办），发布儒学信息，展开儒学交流。应该说，作为西南重镇四川大学建立国家儒学研究院是相当有魄力的。

2014年，曲阜师范大学国学院成立，被称为山东首家国学院。国学院充分发挥在孔子故里的优势，在儒学研究和传统文化教育方面开展研究国学协同创新基地、国学人才培养基地、国学高端培训基地，国学信息资料中心和国学文化产业中心。曲阜师范大学与1956年成立了孔子研究会，以后又设立了孔子研究室、孔子文化研究所，是国内最早成立研究孔子儒学的高等学校，被称为研究经学的八大重镇之一。客观地讲，曲阜师范大学从建国至今持续不断、坚持不懈研究儒学的精神与做法值得尊敬。其学术带头人骆承烈教授几十年如一日进行孔子文化研究，退休后仍然活跃在研究与传播的前沿。2000年，曲阜师范大学与中国孔子基金会合建孔子文化大学，成为山东省儒学研究基地。此外，2009年清华大学重新设立国学院，秉承“中国主体，放眼世界”的原则开展工作。在具体工作上出版了《清华国学文存》，将老清华导师与学生的文献搜集出版。国学院开展了多层次的学术交流，设立“清华国学讲堂”，邀请国内外专家进行演讲。清华大学也逐渐认识到其传统研究的巨大优势，认识到国学与儒学研究的重要性。

## 二、儒学教育的探索与发展

现代高等教育与国学教学进行结合的尝试与探索。1994年北京大学举办“文史哲综合实验班”，目的是更多研习中国传统文化。但实验班的结果并不理想，同学们国学读的不多相反西学读的不少。所以，该班于2001年停止招生。应该说，社会的整体环境影响了广大学子的选择，同学们没有认识到国学的未来发展态势。2002年，武汉大学高级研究中心与人文学院合办国学班。国学班招生简章规定：“国学院旨在培养系统掌握我国传统文学、史学、经学、的基本知识，谙于基本典籍及治学之道，熟练阅读应用中国古典文献，懂得两门外语，熟悉当今世界人文科学基本走向的复合型人才。”该班最后选定20名同学进入实验班学习。该班的课程设置有两个突出方面：一是突出经典原著为特色。教材直接使用《四书》、《老子》、《诗经》、《楚辞》、《庄子》、《文选》、前四史等。这样在教学方式改变了重概论轻原著的现象，直通大家思想精髓。国学班的同学背诵了大量经典，如背诵了《四书》、《离骚》，并把背诵情况作为期末考试成绩的组成部分。二是突出外语特色。把日语和英语作为该班必修课，相当一部分课程使用英文原版教材。也有部分课程为英译的《论语》、《孟子》、《诗经》、《史记》等。总体看，在实际运行中，学生在外语方面占用的时间，花费的精力比较多，真正用于阅读国学经典的时间并不充分。还有如何处理古代经典与现代学术发展的关系问题考虑不足，系统的学术训练比较缺乏。另外，毕业生的出路过于狭窄，被保送到人大、复旦、武大等学校研究生占了一多半，其余考公务员、当记者、进公司等于普通文史哲类的毕业生没有区别。即使研究生、博士生最理想的还是在象牙塔中成为文化的传承人，如何为社会多方面工作多做贡献是国学人才培养需要考虑的问题。所以该国学班既积累了一定的经验，也有很多需要问题需要改进。2005年，中国人民大学承建国学院，冯其庸为首届院长。国学院学制六年，采用本硕连读的方式。但报名情况很不理想，主要原因是学生担心毕业出路问题。从国学实验的结果来看，与成立初衷有很大的差距，最终结果不甚理想。一是当今西学的广泛影响与学生未来职业定位。二是也存在着社会诱惑，学生也难以有刻苦学习经典的精神。最后，国学班的成立存在着一定的争议，就是国学班如何处理与一般文史哲学科的关系，有没有必要专门设立国学院，增强经典的研读能不能通过文史哲专业的改革实现。如何将美好的初衷变成持续的现实有很长的道路要走。2008 年，复旦大学设立国学班，隶属于哲学学院。教师主要是中国哲学教研室的老师与文史方面的教师。国学班是跨学科的专业，专业必修课为中国哲学史、国学通论、经学基础、古代汉语、校雠目录学和《论语》、《老子》等课程，专业选修课涵盖了经学、诸子学、史学（主要是前四史）以及集部中的篇目。课程中安排有大量的专题研究，包括汉代经学、魏晋玄学、宋明理学、经学、佛学、道教、简帛学、现代思想史等研究。复旦大学国学班主要为培养高层次人才打基础。复旦大学在国学人才培养方面不断进行新的探索，为中华文化的传承作了自己的思考。

儒家文化选修课程的广泛开设。中山大学推行通识教育，设计儒家经典类的课程有：儒林正史，以儒学传记为阅读底本，结合儒学两千多年的发展史，使同学们了解儒学的基本命题、从经学到理学的转变、历代儒生的精神风貌、儒学与传统文化的关联及其对现代化的意义进行反思。开设论语研读课程，系统介绍孔子及其儒家思想，加深对中国传统文化的认识。另外还有《周易》导读等课程，专门深入地介绍儒家经典课程。2006 年，东北师范大学文学院实施阅读经典计划，向同学们推荐了一百本经典书目进行阅读，其中儒家经典书目多篇。多读经典是培养学生的有效途径，只是需要同学们静心读书。

广西大学对高年级外国留学生开设了《论语》课程。课程共 72 学时，课程性质为必修课，分两个学期讲授。通过测评调查，留学生对此门课程兴趣较大，受到学生的好评。通过调查反映，97％的学生都希望进一步学习儒学经典，高达 41％的同学非常有兴趣参加以孔子的《论语》为专题的中华儒学经典课程。［3］需要解决的古字词的理解问题以及中国的古文化背景，另外《论语》的精神已经影响了中国的人生活的方方面面，成了中国人日常心理文化的一部分，在留学生中要加强文化传播方面的影响。在教学工作中尽量通俗易懂，化繁为简，使学生们易于理解、接受和践行。传播儒家文化，是汉语国际教育的重要内容。

曲阜师范大学从 20 世纪 90 年代以来，面向全校开设传统文化课程，把《论语》作为专业选修课，使孔子教育步入正轨。现在《孔子与儒家文化》成为全校学生的特色必修课。在学历教育方面，有儒学专门史的硕士点与博士点。学校举办“孔子文化月”品牌校园文化活动，受到各界的关注和高度评价。2011 年，山东大学将《论语》设为必修课，所有的学生都要学习。时任山东大学校长徐显明教授要把山东大学打造为道德高地，起到引领社会的作用。

清华大学、复旦大学、北京大学等面向社会面向企业家举办国学班。通过教师讲解经典、讲解原著，广大企业家更加熟悉中国文化，提高中国式管理能力。当然也有整合资源、构建企业家交往平台的目的。复旦大学举行国学精修班，邀请著名学者通过精讲原典，带领学习者领略国学的精华、传统文化的要略。中山大学举办商界领袖国学班，引领商界领袖品读国学经典，探讨治企之道，打造商业帝国。在课程设计上有儒家主题模块，掌握为政以德的精神与修身齐家治国平天下的管理思路，打造富有竞争力、青春常在的企业。通过解读《易经》，掌握整体变化与阴阳和谐的发展规律，提升宏观思维能力，增强决策正确性。

把儒家经典核心价值融入思想政治理论课程中。在大学生爱国主义教育中，吸取易经中自强不息的精神，克服改革中遇到的困难，实现中华民族的复兴，实现中国梦。在大学生品格塑造方面，推崇仁爱精神。发扬儒家的“己欲立而力人，己欲达而达人”，对人要温、良、恭、俭、让。发扬孟子的与人为善思想，“恻隐之心，人皆有之；羞恶之心，人皆有之恭敬之心，人皆有之；是非之心，人皆有之”，人要有责任感。从大学生修身的角度，继承儒家“内圣外王”的思想，不断完善自我，达到“修己安人”的境界。广大教师在教学工作中开辟第二课堂，教育部、国家语言委员会、国家文明办举行“中华颂·经典诵读行动”，很多学校都举行了经典诵读的活动。

## 三、大学生儒家文化社团活动的开展

继承和发扬儒家礼教的传统，各个学校成立大学生文明礼仪宣讲团。她们通过正确的站姿、坐姿、走路的方式等塑造大学生的自身形象。通过讲解餐桌礼仪、交往礼仪、乘车礼仪等加强大学生的自身修养。大学生文明礼仪宣讲团还走进社区、走向企业，不断把儒家“不学礼，无以立”《论语·季氏》秩序理念发扬开来。不少高校开始举行“成人礼”。“成人礼”能够唤醒大学生的责任意识，为进入社会进行角色定位。有的学校还成立文明礼仪督导队，在日常生活中监督、引导大学生的不文明行为。大学生穿上统一标志的红马甲，在校园中维护良好校园风貌，不断内化同学们的文明意识。

大学生国学社积极弘扬国学、普及儒家文化。笔者所在山东科技大学国学社本着“学习国学、传播国学”的精神开展活动。举行了传统文化节活动，大学生开展经典诵读比赛，开展传统节日文化知识宣传活动。国学社向“小草学堂”捐赠书包、图书等，以实践行动弘扬儒家注重教育的精神。同时，国学社成员参加“小草学堂”支教团，实现儒家快乐学习的理念，把近百本《三字经》和《弟子规》转赠给了“小草学堂”。不仅如此，他们还广泛联系其他社团、老师、校友募集更多的资源，为支教活动献出自己的力量。[4] 北京大学国学社明经读史，不受外界干扰困惑，同学们精读经典。

国学社利用北京大学的声望，邀请了众多名家进行专题解析，把学术演讲开展得有声有色。国学社还走进古老书院、文化圣地去实地感受传统文化的历史积淀。中国人民大学国学社和北京大学国学社都建立了自己的网站发布信息，进行网络交流，使广大的学生通过网络学习国学文化、儒家文化。

# 儒學與當代學校教育和社會教育

美国普林斯顿大学 郑锦玉 李淑芬

## 前 言

盱衡世局，放眼國際，廿世紀的確是輝煌世紀，卻也是大動亂的時代。人們已嚐過第一次、第二次世界大戰的苦頭，按理說，對於世局的發展，都該有所警惕，但不幸得很，如今第三次世界大戰似乎又迫在眉睫。人與人的關係或逐漸惡化，國與國的道義或蕩然無存，人類面臨種種難題，如：種族、宗教、限武、人權、經濟、能源……每一問題，都可能帶來毀滅性的危機。由於承襲甚多位聖人之遺產，致使中華文化精美博深，儒、釋、道三家思想深入人心，形成國人之處世南針，亦為能“重倫常”、“守道德”之主因。然卻因工商繁榮，歐風美雨侵襲，國人漸揚棄聖賢揭示的“道德人生觀”，而接受西方“特重物質的人生觀”，人性墮落，拜金主義、笑貧不笑娼之風氣，漸腐蝕人心。

眾所皆知，物質有限而心靈無限。因此，物質和心靈至少應該並駕齊驅。然而，今日的美國，甚至全世界，都是物質掛帥。許多高貴的精神為何流失了？只因為物質淹沒了心靈。

過去兩百年，科學快速發展，物質文明突飛猛進，影響社會價值。學術界，七〇年代達顛峰的“行為主義”便是典型。它重視外在行為和物質，蔑視內在心靈和道德。一九九一年底，蘇聯崩解，共產主義實驗七十多年後失敗了。曾在六九年預言此結局的美國布里辛斯基（Zbigniew Brzezinski）教授主張：“心靈主義將復興（the renaissance of spiritualism）。”他說：“因為共產主義的基礎是物質主義（唯物辯證法），它否定心靈的存在，說宗教是群眾的鴉片。它已經失敗了。而我們美國的資本主義何嘗不立足於物質主義？賺錢賺錢！其弊病已浮現。將來人類要尋找補救之路。”確實應透過長期家庭、學校、社會、及心靈與生命教育的努力耕耘，以恢復人類心靈和物質的平衡，將是未來的希望，這也是最重要的生命工程。

近來嚴謹的科學證實心靈的存在，是極有力的助因。二〇一一年九月，首款腦波電視問世，二〇一三年六月念力遙控飛機成功，都是不爭的事實，顯示出心靈哲學與生命教育的迫切需要，與不容被忽視。我個人淺見認為：英國經濟學家修馬克曾說："科技必須融入心靈與智慧，然後朝著有機、溫和、非暴力和優美的方向再出發。"真是鏗鏘有力的言論。而義大利詩人但丁曾說："道德可以彌補知識的不足，但知識卻不能填補道德的空白。"真是一針見血的主張。

所幸，中華文化可以一"道"字涵蓋，能從人心根本處滋潤全身，讓靈明的本性再顯和光。孔孟大道即本儒家精神的"神道設教"，以其"入世精神"配合"內聖外王"之學，正可解決東西方社會"道德"、"精神"上的危機，給人正確之規範、求得永恆生命之希望，達成至善和圓滿的境界。一個人若能鑽研儒學，潛修人道，以上達天道，必然是三達德兼具的人，以其"大智"而對生命意義有正確的認識，對是非善惡能有敏銳的判斷力；以其"大仁"而對苦難之人類有深切之同情，對垂危的文化，有拯救之悲願；以其"大勇"傾全力以實踐倫常，體現全德，成就完美的人格，並深信上帝與我同在，以挽救人類之浩劫。

環顧眼前這個世界，真可引用英國文豪狄更斯那部文學名著《雙城記》（英國文豪狄更斯，著有《雙城記》與《塊肉餘生錄》，去世於公元 1870 年，得年 59 歲。）的開場白："這是最美好的時代，也是最惡劣的時代；是智慧的時代，也是愚昧的時代；是信仰的時代，也是懷疑的時代；是光明的季節，也是黑暗的季節；是充滿希望的春天，也是使人絕望的冬天；我們的前途充滿了一切，但什麼也沒有；我們一直走向天堂，也一直走向地獄。"的確，二十世紀是人類有史以來，科學最發達，物質最得勢的時代，也是人類生活最奢華的時代，而今日台灣亦正處於商業掛帥、功利氣息彌漫之際，雖因歷經數十年之生聚教訓，物質建設一日千里，人民生活較以往富有，然而相形之下，一般並未享受到"高所得"帶來之成果，大眾所面對的，是一個治安日益惡化的環境，普遍心情上的不安，倍甚於往昔。故如何力挽頹風，因應急遽變遷之社會環境，締建富而好禮、守法守紀、和諧團結之美好社會，須賴有志之士提出，籲請各界針對此一目標，共同參與，戮力以赴。如眾所知，欲改造世界，先改造人心，當以科學精神求"真"，以倫理道德求"善"，藉文學藝術求"美"，透過宗教露修求"聖"，方可躋世界（社會）於"真善美聖"之境。儒學思想之本質為"中華文化"，擷取孔孟思想之精髓，以積極的"入世精神"來教化人心，改造世界。目前，儒學思想已經深受海峽兩岸黨政及社會各界肯定，並寄予厚望，其精神主張亦均與吾人日常生活息息相關，故獲得廣大知識份子之認同。

哲學專家說得好："中國自古雖無宗教之名，可是實際上仍有宗教。"的確，我們中國人喜歡講"天道好還"、"大道無私"、"公道自在人心"等的話語，足見是以"道"

(即西方人所言之“真理”)為國人普遍之信仰。當代哲學大師 牟宗三先生也說:“儒家(或云儒教)雖無宗教儀式,卻具有宗教之特質。”是故儒教始終對“人間世”有極度的關懷,孔孟思想特具廣大的包容精神,為其他種族之文化所望塵莫及。從前中國境內之各種著名宗教,幾乎全是外來的,如:佛教、基督教、天主教、回教等,我們都可接受,一視同仁,絕不排斥,更無所謂“宗教戰爭”,足證我們深受孔、孟、老、莊思想薰陶,心量廣闊。“孔孟大道”為“天啟”的信仰,亦秉承此一特色(《論語·八佾》篇說:“天下之無道也久矣,天將以夫子為木鐸。”而木鐸是啥?即古時宣布教令時所用的一種金口木舌的大鈴,就像是現今學校當中,鐘聲都是用電子式的鐘聲,但是當停電時所用的手搖鈴,就是古代的鐸。

而金口金舌者稱為金鐸,金口木舌者稱為木鐸。由於鐸有“振聾起聵”之意,所以被拿來當作夫子,即“教師”的代稱或代表物。孔孟儒家思想,欲透過切實可行之途徑,以造就“人間天國”!即“大同世界”,不太強調“死後上天堂”,是“把天堂搬到人間來”,這正是儒學的平易處,也正是“孔孟大道”信仰之可貴處,最能消弭戾氣、化解紛爭,解決現實社會的諸多問題。因此,歷來宗教泰半是由國外“輸入”的,而今“孔孟大道”卻是“輸出”的,由中國發展到外國,也最足以代表中華文化之精神與特色,這確是令人自豪的。“孔孟大道信仰”最合乎中國的國情,一本中國五千年歷史文化中心思想的“孔孟之道”,與國父孫中山先生演講“三民主義”所要建設的“理想社會”(即“大同世界”),完全不謀而合。其思想淵源正來自二千五百年前,記載於《禮記·禮運·大同》篇中短短的一百零六個字。以前台灣的謝東閔資政曾指出,我們祖先有這麼優秀的文化,可惜我們還沒有辦法做到那個地步,像目前鐵窗越來越多,心靈、環境……等各種污染愈來愈嚴重,離“路不拾遺、夜不閉戶”的境界還差得遠,實在對不起我們的祖先。

欲建設理想社會,是世界各國思想家一直在尋思的問題,他們也提出了許多辦法,也就是各種“主義”。例如:資本主義、社會主義,無政府主義等等,但實驗的結果,都有許多缺陷。比不上孔聖人以短短百餘字,將國家各種措施都包括在內,且會政治、經濟、社會、文化各方面,無所遺漏。《禮記·禮運·大同》篇首揭“大道之行也,天下為公”,凡事皆以天下眾人之利益為前提。“選賢與能”是內政運作,選擇賢且能的人參與國家政事;“講信修睦”是外交政策;“不獨親其親,子其子”則要發揮博愛精神,敬老慈幼,便如同對待自己的雙親子女一樣;“矜寡孤獨廢疾者皆有所養”是指“社會福利”措施;治安上則要做到沒有盜竊亂賊,也就是“路不拾遺,夜不閉戶”。集孔子大道精華於一書的《論語》,教導我們如何做人處事,雖是兩千五百前的思想了,但是到現在可用處還很多。在日本尤其受到重視,目前已成為他們“企業管理”的必備書籍了。因此,我們家家戶戶應該有一本《論語》,並加以研究,就像歐、美基督教家庭，戶戶有《聖經》一樣，《論語》的確堪稱是中國人的《聖經》啊。承襲中國文化的日本，從都市到鄉村，無論大街小巷都整理得整齊清潔；人的來往有禮貌，真正做到“富而好禮，貧而樂道”，他們更由“經濟大國”通向“教育大國”，以發展和重視教育為傲，值得我們效法。

我們前人曾慈悲開示“創造大同世界，應具備的學問”（底下十項標題，是參考“王鳳儀善人”的分類），大致如下：（一）心理學：須排除敵對心理，不要跟人起對待心，我們靜來常思己過，閒來莫談人非；我們心胸要寬宏大量，要原諒人、同情人，對人要有愛心，更要誠心誠意。（二）飲食學：我們吃東西要有節制，不可暴飲亂食，減少殺生害命，就是培 養道德心、佛心。（三）運動學：不管“外丹功”、“八段錦”或“太極拳”都好，要勤而不斷，有恆心，動中可以取靜，譬如：打太極拳一小時，心平氣和，雜念全無，想發脾氣也無從發了。（四）衛生學：講衛生得要細心，清潔外面，調和內心，少思寡慾。黎明即起，打掃屋子庭院，抹桌子，整理環境。在心理上也要衛生，不要胡思亂想、或生出“貪嗔癡愛、怨恨惱怒煩”的念頭，我們的身心靈，裏外都要衛生，而體內環保，似乎更為重要。（五）精神學：要精神振作有朝氣，還要有思考力。比如說：要策劃事情應該怎麼做，善用思考力，並保持樂觀、活潑、瀟灑。（六）家庭學：古人言：“一室之不治，何以天下國家為？”家不能治理，焉能治國？又如何創造大同世界？家要有規矩，五倫要守，勤儉持家，忍耐負責。五倫就是君臣、父子、夫婦、兄弟、朋友，各止於至善，為人父止於慈，為人子止於孝，兄則友、弟則恭。做兒子的要孝順父母，做父親的教養兒女，手足之間，要互相友愛。夫妻間，則應相敬如賓，家人均宜各守倫常之道。（七）社會學：要互助互諒，濟困扶危，熱心公益慈善事業，非禮則勿“視、聽、言、動”。在人際關係方面，與人交往須為別人著想，不可一味地要求人家幫助，而要互相幫助，並應救濟困難，扶助危急者，若能做到以上所說的，方算是正人君子。（八）倫理學：除了前面“家庭倫理”外，我們還要進一步講求“宗族、社會”倫理，要謹言慎行，敬老尊賢，長幼有序，恪遵綱常倫理，才能使六親和睦，社會安定。（九）社交學：我們要行“忠信”之道，“言忠信，行篤敬，雖蠻貊之邦行矣。言不忠信，行不篤敬，雖州里行乎哉？”一個人說話忠信，做事篤敬，到了 蠻貊等不開化之地，也可行得通。否則，連自己鄰里也行不開的。所以我們要有忠心，守信用，不貪不合理之財，不交無益之友，“無友不如己者，過則勿 憚改。”要交那些對我們有幫助的，德行比我們高的；有錢的不一定就是真朋友。此外，能“勸善規過”，才會使品德精進。（十）公德學：因為民主時代，更應養成“守法守紀”的好習慣。中國人一向注重“私德”，卻忽略了“公德”；注重“個體”而疏忽了“群體”。這是我們極待培養的。以前上海公園（法租界）門口招牌寫著：“中國人和狗，不准進入。”便是我們永遠不能忘懷的一項恥辱，絕對要知恥、雪恥。以上淺顯的道理，多半是源自儒家的“倫理道德觀”，只要能實踐在日常生活中，就能受益無窮。至於如何“弘揚儒學真諦，實踐倫理道德”？約有如下數端：

## 一、應本著孔孟大道精神啟發良知良能

由政府大力支持，各單位全力配合，鼓勵提倡“生命與心靈教育”，譬如：於台灣增設相關“學院、研究所”，以因應多元化之社會，而中國大陸設有幾處“社會科學院”與“民俗宗教研究所”來鑽研“生命、心靈、與宗教教育”等，或可於學校、社會教育課程中、社團中、週會時，請專人演講，並視實際需要，適當地介紹生命與心靈教育，適時地加入部份的生命與心靈課程。平心而論，台灣的“教會學校”的“生活教育”，總是比較成功的、徹底的；學生們的“倫理道德心”，也比較容易發揮出來。社會或青少年犯罪率不斷提高，而作奸犯科、殺人勒索者，十之八九，大概都是“無神論”者，甚至不知“良知”為何物的，大有人在。我們“孔孟聖道”，即本儒家精神的“神道設教”，能從人心根本處滋潤全身，讓靈明的本性再顯和光。（另外，日本“正則學園”高校，也是因重視儒家人格道德教育而頗為成功之一例）。

## 二、須從“教育”入手

使“心靈與生命、家庭、學校、社會”幾種教育，緊密結合，相輪相成，勿令各自為政，致效果不彰。目前最嚴重的，是幾種教育之間，都呈現脫節現象，欲振乏力。今日“孔孟聖道”或中國大陸“傳統文化”網站單位的所做所為，即是藉著積極的“自覺覺他”的教育效果，挽化世風人心，亦即彌補“學校、家庭”教育之不足，強化家庭教育，進而由孔孟聖道與中國大陸“傳統文化”，皆足以展現社教（社會教育）之功能，為一己和眾人創造幸福。以下是兩則真實故事。中國大陸“傳統文化”網站單位的實地採訪播出，有一位大嬸指出，透過中國“傳統文化”長期聽演講，受益非淺。早年，她與丈夫白手起家，於窮困中奮鬥，如今創業有成，經濟富裕，孩子們就讀著名的學校，養尊處優，喜好互相比較、炫耀炫富，深覺不妥，於是，她與丈夫、孩子們先後接觸大陸“傳統文化”節目，薰陶漸染的結果，找回正確的人生觀、道德倫理與價值觀。大嬸現身說法，語調幽默感人，令人動容（可參看大陸“傳統文化”網站）。另外，我有一位世代居住北京胡同的四合院的好朋友劉東興先生，他大門口貼著一副他尊翁傳承的對聯：“忠厚傳家久，詩書濟世長。”而在台灣，常見人生百年後的奠紀用的花圈，我最為欣賞的內容，就是：“餘蔭子孫”。因為祖先、長輩、父母積德行善，才能庇蔭後代子孫，所謂：“積陰德，蔭子孫”，這才是祖先留給子孫的最好財富。道家聖人老子不是說過：“金玉滿堂，莫之能守。富貴而驕，自遺其咎。”（見《道

德經·第九章》)。

中國歷史上，春秋時，楚國孫叔敖，幼年於路途中，遇見“兩頭蛇”，據當時傳說，遇見“兩頭蛇”，頗不吉利，但他將心比心，怕別人遇見不妥，設法將“兩頭蛇”掩埋了。隨即，哭著回家向母親報告經過，並且說：“孩兒看到雙頭蛇，恐怕活不成了。”只見母親安慰他說：“吾聞善積陰德者，天報之以厚福。”果然，孫叔敖後來做到楚國的宰相。

孫叔敖：生卒年不詳，春秋楚人。蔿賈之子。兒時於路上見兩頭蛇，聞人言，見此蛇者必死，自以為將死，而恐後人見之又死，乃殺而埋之。及長，性恭儉，代虞丘為楚相，施教導民，三月而楚大治。彼曾三得相而不喜，三去相而不悔，不以得失為意，史稱循吏。還記得我們求學時代，朗朗上口的青年守則十二條：一、忠勇為愛國之本；二、孝順為齊家之本；三、仁愛為接物之本；四、信義為立業之本；五、和平為處世之本；六、禮節為治事之本；七、服從為負責之本；八、勤儉為服務之本；九、整潔為強身之本；十、助人為快樂之本；十一、學問為濟世之本；十二、有恆為成功之本。幾乎都源自於儒家思想，都是立身處世，絕佳的座右銘呢！

《四庫全書 總目提要》有云：“聖人覺世牖民，大抵因事以寓教……。”)，藉著木筆沙盤，講孝順之道，說每人的做為，上天都有記載。若不聽父母的話而使父母傷心者，實在是有罪，言詞很令人感動。這位小弟當下良心發現，深感愧對父母，有負養育之恩。這天回家後，就變得很聽話了。其父母十分訝異，怎會前後判若兩人？忍了幾天，追問原因，才恍然大悟。父母心想：真不可思議！我們管不住的孩子，“孔孟大道”替我們管好了。於是他們立刻一起加入修身養性的行列。(當然，此類實例甚多，僅學此為代表)。這說明了兩種教育（宗教、家庭），互相配合則收效必宏。

## 三、寓教於樂，成果不凡

社會各界一再擔心青少年問題，政府當局亦呼籲為人父母者應重視青少年課餘生活，但是每逢暑假除了考生忙於應考，家長忙於陪考之外，其餘青少年則處於無人關心的時段，“孔孟聖道”領導前輩首先重視到青少年問題，乃是父母疏於關心，學校老師力所不及，社會的引誘，乃於公元 1983 年 籌辦青少年暑期國學育樂營，獲得廣泛迴響，台北市政府發現到由宗教團體來辦效果頗佳。引述畢班結業時，某位同學一段話來闡述心連心的迴響，一位就讀國中二年級的陳姓同學說：“十多年來只知道父母經常到講堂聽課，假日總是到較大的廟堂研究或當義工、志工，去服務別人，今天 我才知道父母親偉大的一面，捨己為人的情懷，真令我深深感動，以後我也要效法他們。”另一位同學說：“每個禮拜天，都有許多客人到我們家來，大家都非常客氣，有些熟面孔，有些生面孔，但是他們都對我很好，今天我才真正認識到為什麼他們那麼好。”許許多多的例子，每年都迴盪在全省數十間大的廟堂和講堂之中。

## 四、進修、陶冶、變化氣質

“孔孟聖道”的特色不在於誦經，不在於排場，而是在於從週一到週日，每天的研究或進修班，一個對信仰陌生的人，當他追求“孔、孟聖道”之後，接觸率性進修的儒學研究班，能使他當下迴光返照、有所頓悟，感嘆時光易逝、歲月不饒人，能使他覺悟名利的牽絆，使他發心、使他淡泊、使他明志、使他感受到數十寒暑不可輕易流失，因而他樂於再進修，新民班、至善班、培德班、行德班、崇德班，每班一年的進修期限，從感恩到發心，從飲水思源到敬老尊賢，從佈施到無為，從實踐到體悟，都是“孔、孟聖道”渡人，引人入勝的殊緣。

“孔孟聖道”領導前輩開示，道不是高深的學問，道就在日常生活當中，這就在自己身上，從濟世化人、說好話，做好事足以培功立德，誠如《左傳》記載，春秋時魯國賢大夫叔孫豹所說：“太上立德，其次立功，其次立言，雖久不廢，此之謂三不朽。”簡短淺顯的話語當中，寓含著字字珠璣，蘊藏著無限玄機。所以孔孟大道愛慕者都是從實踐中求證驗，從力行中得甘露，自然法喜充沛於其中。亞聖孟子曾說：“一人溺，援之以手；天下溺，援之以道。”（參見《孟子・離婁》篇）社會病了，且病得似乎不輕，風氣壞了，且壞得相當嚴重。但是大家不用灰心，不用頹志，最怕的是我們不知病在那裏，壞在那裏，今天我們已然知道，病在自私自利，壞在功利主義，只要有識者能共體上天好生之德，不忍民族幼苗受摧殘，為人父母有義務去栽培，為社會的一份子更有責任激濁揚清，所以我們必須結合各宗、各派，各宗教的人士，一齊為淨化世道人心而努力不懈。

〈台灣美麗的風景破碎了嗎?〉

每聞“台灣最美麗的風景是人”，都不免打心底感到驕傲；方今滔滔濁世，世風日下，僻處海隅的這一群人，卻以慈悲、善良、熱情、有禮而鶴立雞群，是多麼難得的事。

其實我們也曾粗鄙，引人側目。慶幸的是終於走過那個階段，自我提昇而備受肯定，仰仗許多來自四面八方的助力。慈悲與博愛，絕對深受千萬佛、道、西方宗教信徒的影響；熱情乃是這方土地數百年培養出的性格；善良、有禮則來自數千年傳統文化的薰陶，復受到東、西方先進國家公民風範的浸染。我們得天獨厚，將其共冶於一爐，數十年日積月累，終於修成正果。

然而從公元2014年“三一八學運”始，時見年輕人為逞一時之快或享瞬間之名而不擇手段、口出鄙穢之辭，忽然讓人驚睹我們這一群人未來的面目。一連串年輕人泯滅人性的殺人事件，其手段之凶殘，超出國人想像；隨之俱來的，是網路上年輕網友按讚稱羡的狂妄舉動，震驚整個社會。這就是最美麗的風景？

不讓其專“美”於前的，是仕途一帆風順的達官貴人，腰纏萬貫、事業如日中天的財團巨賈，行賄、受賄而鋃鐺入獄；學界聲譽正隆、呼風喚雨的設計、綠建築領域名教授為其奔走牽線；還可能牽連一批名校教授為虎作倀。在此之前，已有多少教授為戔戔之數甘供驅馳而身繫囹圄。其品格之低下，已到不堪聞問的地步。究竟誰為為之？孰令致之？

近年來不論文字還是電子媒體，經營者為追求獲利不擇手段，遊走於法律邊緣，誨淫誨盜、譁眾取寵、煽動撩撥，成為敗壞風氣、汙染性靈的頭號殺手。但不容諱言，其中自不乏深識大體、有所不為者。此亦顯示，關鍵不在市場競爭激烈、有司管理無方，端在主導者自身的品格、教養以及方寸之間對風氣良窳責任之自我承擔。一言以蔽之，這又是品格教育偏差的後果。

坊間侈言倫理道德者比比皆是，書籍文章汗牛充棟，而各級學校品格課程幾無日無之；何以上述種種怪現狀愈演愈烈，而在學受教、為人師表乃至書讀得愈多、愈好者尤烈？

多年來我們常以“禮義之邦”自詡，卻落到今日這般境地，仔細揣摩，應來自以下數端：

其一，威權專制王朝已敗亡，現代化蔚為新潮，台灣固未至將線裝書丟入茅廁的地步，典籍的地位日漸淪落，“去中國化”則更貶抑摧殘，年輕一代去傳統乃日遠，而得以取代的新倫理規範，則付諸闕如。

其二，西化繼之以日化、韓流，外來風氣席捲每個層面；但大眾趨之若鶩的，非其文化根柢、主流規範，而是聲色犬馬、紙醉金迷，未得其精髓卻飽饜其糟粕。

其三，傳統道德博大精深，卻愈來愈難被社會大眾透澈理解，往往淪為口頭禪。以“四維”禮、義、廉、恥為例，每一字均寓義深遠、包羅廣袤，卻非飽學鴻儒不能講解清楚；則自幼兒至大學生琅琅誦讀千遍、萬遍，與其品格教育有何交涉？

由此觀之，我們的品格教育已成花拳繡腿，華而無實；必須徹底改弦更張，腳踏實地從庶民百姓、莘莘學子的日常生活下手，揭舉親切易懂、易循可行的基本準繩，鼓勵人人身體力行，則國人品格自高。為拋磚引玉，我們集眾人之力融會傳統道德理想、西方品格規範及其他智慧；揚棄陳義過深、不知如何遵循者，選取見文知義、明確可行的條目，匯整為一兼容並蓄的規範，共五十項，名之為“品格 50”；每周全力奉行一項，一年周遍一次，次年再周而復始。持之以恆，雖不能人人為聖賢，但即無百分，或許可及其半。若能集思廣益，以此為起始點不斷向上，台灣最美的風景總有一日會吸引全球的目光。

〈台灣孩童讀經之推廣與普及〉

早已於各個社區與小學蓬勃展開，因為大家都能普遍接受台中市教育大學王財貴教授所提倡的兒童讀經理論，為民族幼苗，紮穩文化根基，必須從幼兒開始，可奠定良好基礎。

古學今用、“品格教育”的大智慧：《論語・為政》子曰：“道之以德，齊之以禮，有恥且格。”可說明“品格教育”重要性，往往就取決於日用尋常的“潛移默化”當中。現今中西方有關“品格教育”的書籍，琳瑯滿目，倒不如兩千多年，孔老夫子的這句話，就道盡了“品格教育”的精髓。雖然是教導上位者如何管理國家，但應用於教育上，更是受用不盡，值得所有為人父母者，一再深思！

在當今混亂的社會價值當中，培養足夠的羞恥心，是安定人心的首要關鍵。由於“倫理心”與“道德感”受到重視，法治紀律油然而生，社會自然安定。實際上，品格教育，就在日常生活當中。

例如：一位媽媽，處罰鞭打調皮的十歲小兒子，旁邊十三歲的大兒子，曾經參加過兒童讀經班，說道：“一個四十歲的大人，卻容不下一個天真的小孩。”媽媽嘴裡又唸道：“玉不琢，不成器；人不學，不知義。”十三歲的大兒子，卻說：“明明是一塊好玉，卻被不好的雕刻師給雕壞了。”暗指媽媽是不好的雕刻師。媽媽深切反省，認為十三歲的大兒子的話，很有道理。從此後以後，就再也不隨便責罰小孩了。參加讀書會時，還和大家分享這件事。

因此，聖人和我們前輩最重視“自覺”的功夫，一旦“自覺”之後，自然化掉脾氣、毛病、壞習慣，猶如老子所說“道法自然”，一點都不須勉強。譬如：當我們進入一間屋子，看到裡面髒亂，感覺很不舒服，立刻會捲起袖子來打掃乾淨，同樣的，當我們內心雜念叢生時，也感覺不舒服，立刻應反觀、覺照，讓身、心、靈都恢復清靜，如此一來，豈不“輕安又自在”呢？

以下是一項兒童讀經推廣的代表實例：台灣 溫世仁基金會舉辦孩童讀經：

〈新服務人才 靠《論語》培育〉公元2013年11月13日（“中央社”記者陳至中台北13日電）

溫世仁文教基金會紀念溫世仁逝世10週年，開創“新服務人才培育計畫”，在中小學推廣讀經教育，從小涵養服務熱忱。溫世仁文教基金會代執行長何能裕表示，新服務人才可分為特質、知識、技術3個層次，技專重視培育知識、技術，但“特質”的塑造，則必須深耕到中小學。何能裕苦思方法許久，在參觀台灣南部嘉義縣和興國小時，找到答案。何能裕說，原本該校風氣較差，訓導主任巡視校園時，手還要拿著球棒，隨時戒備。後來校長林金進推動讀經教育，學生有了很大改變，可以隨時出口成章，舉止氣質也變的不一樣了。

溫世仁基金會決定大力推展讀經教育，以《論語》為主軸，編寫活潑的故事內容，今年將到高雄、桃園、嘉義等 36 所中小學試教。何能裕說，經典學習不只是國文老師的事，必須融入各科學習，才能發揮效果。例如：音樂課時，可以吟唱詩詞，體育課作操答數時，也可改用經典字句取代數字，自然而然養成習慣。除了中、小學，溫世仁基金會也在台灣中部彰化的大葉大學、高雄的正修科技大學等校，開設一學年的實驗課程，讓學生選擇一個在地產業做實作題目，從做中學，體驗服務的意義與價值。

〈孩子教育的啟示〉

子曰：“愛之，能勿勞乎？忠焉，能勿誨乎？”（《論語・憲問》）是說：孔子說：“愛他，能不教他勤勞嗎？忠於他，能不規勸教導他嗎？”父母愛護子女，最怕溺愛；忠於長輩、長官，最忌怕一味逢迎。大陸有所謂“割草機父母”，意味什麼？即有些父母，為了讓獨生子女“健康成長”，隨時趕在孩子前面，像“割草機”般，幫他們清掃路上一切障礙。但在父母溺愛下，孩子性格容易扭曲、懶惰，失去生存力，反而不利“健康成長”。台灣也有所謂“直升機父母”，什麼意思？有一本親子教養書（《100 個教養傑出孩子優秀祕訣》，新手父母出版），提到：“我們不希望孩子忽視家事、忘記功課或不負責任，所以父母就像直升機般，時刻在他們身邊打轉，準備在第一個麻煩出現時，出面解救，接手孩子本身可以做的事。”書中建議：“在急於幫助孩子前，先停下來，花點時間，問你自己：‘我真需要做任何事嗎？如果我沒提醒他把課本帶回家，會怎麼樣呢？’有時候，孩子真正需要的是‘仁慈的’忽略。”我們一再強調“開放、尊重的父母不等於寵愛、溺愛的父母”，是因為“以孩子為主”的教養模式，基本是以孩子的全人發展為目標，方法是了解孩子、順應孩子的發展，並選擇適合孩子發展的教養模式，結果是讓孩子獨立自主、自信快樂且能尊重和關愛他人。舉例來說，當孩子在便利商店裡耍賴，想買某樣東西時：溺愛孩子的父母，為了怕孩子哭，就會買給他，讓孩子破涕為笑。而過於嚴厲的父母卻回答：我跟你說不行，就是不行！（嚴重一點的就會說：你這死孩子啥都想買，緊接著，一長串責罵並動手打人）。

◎※最好的情況是做有威信的父母：我知道你很喜歡這東西，不過我們今天不是來買這個，不妨把它畫下來，等聖誕節時，我們再從你的清單 選擇一項當作禮物（這也是從書本，偷學來的）。這方法所以有效或符合“以孩子為主”，是因我們接納孩子當時的需要，而不是否定它。我們受東西誘惑，也會興起慾望，孩子也一樣，但另方面，我們應教導孩子“想要的東西很多，不是每樣東西都可買回家啊（人生煩惱主要根源，就是需要的不多，想要的太多。）”，藉此立定規則，讓孩子學習遵守。

◎※或許有人覺得父母權威凌駕於一切，何必說這麼多，自己說不行就是不行，不容許改變。但我們提醒父母，孩子是人，有真實情感，需要在與人互動過程中，學習協商、妥協，放棄想要的東西，以遵守規範。這些歷程非常珍貴，讓孩子可一步步邁向與人理性互動，既能表達立場又能尊重別人，這才是我們教養孩子過程中，示範給孩子的最珍貴的事。如果我們只是任何事都自己做決定和判斷，一切否定孩子意見，孩子就無法學習協商和妥協，恐將變成無法尊重他人的小霸王，或任何事都沒主見。

◎※書中提到，教導孩子獨立，父母應遵守的原則：//1. 在你給孩子自己找出解決方法的機會前，不要太快介入。//2. 不要掉到想像的“如果……怎麼樣……”的泥沼中。//3. 不要太快下結論。//4. 不要告訴孩子，當他碰到問題時，覺得難過是傻事。//5. 不要迫使孩子處理超過能力所及的問題。//

◎※爸媽可做的是：//1. 讓結果來教導孩子。//2. 當孩子抱怨一個問題時，提供引導，而不是幫他解決。//3. 要有同理心，將心比心（就是應力行儒家孔子所提倡的“恕道”精神，將我心，比他心，讓孩子深深感覺，父母完全是站在孩子立場，替他們講話，替他們設想）。總之，孩子們總是朝著“被讚美的方向”發展，因此，父母們實不必吝於讚美孩子啊。//

〈不給做家事，怎怪孩子不懂事?〉蕭福松 台灣台東市教師// 2013.11.2. 聯合報

台灣有明星國中、小學，不讓學生掃廁所，而改向學生收取“廁所清潔費”，引發爭議。一所明星國小的校長，徵詢我的看法。他說：“家長會打算出錢，外包給清潔公司。”我問校長：“您覺得這樣好嗎?”校長搖頭說：“我認為不妥，畢竟學校是受教育的地方，掃廁所也是學習。”我建議他再跟家長會溝通。//現今少子化，孩子都是父母、家長們心目中的寶貝，家事都不讓他們做了，何況是學校骯髒的掃廁所工作？可是，另一方面，又有家長抱怨，孩子在家不幫忙做家事，不會體諒父母辛勞；問題是，家長有沒有給予孩子，做家事的機會？假使，家中的家事，都不給他們做，到學校也不用掃廁所，怎麼能怪孩子不懂事，不會體諒人？家長以為，只要孩子功課好，將來就有競爭力。忽略還有一種競爭力，更為重要，就是“生活教育”，簡單講，就是“晨昏定省（向父母問聲 早安、晚安），灑掃應對”。//最近，台灣有企業單位，聘請國外洗廁所專家，指導公司主管們洗廁所，以體會勞動者的辛勞，學習謙卑和感恩。學校卻花錢，請“清潔公司”幫助學生掃廁所。箇中道理，或許值得疼愛小孩的父母、家長們省思。//◎諾貝爾文學獎得主，英國哲學家羅素的名言：“人生而無知，但絕非生而愚笨。他們變得愚笨，都是教育使然。”不妥當或錯誤的教育，真的會讓孩子變得愚笨，賢明的師長與父母，您以為然否?

## 結 論

儒學真諦—孔孟大道六十年來在台灣默默推動倫理道德，實踐修身齊家，推動復興與力行中華傳統文化，已頗具磐基。相信海峽兩岸，今後傳統文化，與孔孟大道的愛慕者，責任將更形重大，為喚起人類良知，義務更深，同胞血肉濃於水，所以為天地立心，為生民立命，為往聖繼絕學，為萬世開太平，是您、我共同的使命。

# 儒学与通识教育

杭州师范大学 邓新文

## 一、当前通识教育存在的问题

“通识教育”是英文 general education 的译名，也有学者把它译为“普通教育”、“一般教育”、“通才教育”等等。自 19 世纪初美国博德学院（Bowdoin College）的帕卡德（A. S. Parkard）教授第一次将它与大学教育联系起来之后，有越来越多的人热衷于对它进行研究和讨论。可是至今对通识教育还没有一个公认的、规范性的表述。

众所周知，“通识教育”主要是针对现代分科教育“局而不通”之类的弊病而提出来的。19 世纪不少欧美学者有感于现代大学的学术分科太过专门、知识被严重割裂，从而导致种种弊病，诸如局而不通、杂而不精、烦而不密、专而过固之类。马一浮先生说：“执一而废他者，局也；多歧而无统者，杂也；语小而近琐者，烦也；滞迹而遗本者，固也。”① 局、杂、烦、固四弊，显然有违教育宗旨，于是有识之士创造出通识教育，目的是培养学生能独立思考，且对不同的学科有所认识，以至能将不同的知识融会贯通，最终目的是培养出完全、完整的人。由于这种通识教育符合人性的内在要求，顺应了历史的潮流，到了 20 世纪便已广泛成为欧美大学的必修科目了。

不可否认，通识教育从其开始的那一天起，就是作为“分科教育”的反题而存在的。其功过都与其“对症下药”的特性连在一起。其功，在于发现了现代分科教育的“局而不通”之弊，并行之有效地消减了这一弊病；其过，在于但治其标而不治其本。我认为，分科教育之病，并非出在分科上，而是出在人心上。中国有句古话，叫“事在人为”。心通则科通，心睽则科睽。圣人类族辨物，明察秋毫，“能善分别诸法相，于第一义谛而不动”。可见，合道则通，背道则隔。通识教育的根本弊病，在向外求通，而不知向内求通；在从事上求通，而不知从理上求通；在向知识才能上求通，而

① 《马一浮集》，浙江古籍出版社、浙江教育出版社，1996 年，第一册，第 130 页。

不知向道德修养上求通；在向思想上求通，而不知向心性上求通。若能从后一进路求通，则局、杂、烦、固四弊可去，通、精、密、专四利可得。“通则曲畅旁通而无门户之见；精则幽微洞彻而无肤廓之言；密则条理谨严而无疏略之病；专则宗趣明确而无泛滥之失。不局不杂，知类也；不烦不固，知要也。类者，辨其流别，博之事也；要者，综其指归，约之事也。”①

受上述通识教育的总体理念之制约，我国当前的通识教育，就笔者所了解的情况而言，普遍存在四大问题：

一是仍然沿袭西方知识论传统，把知识混同于学问，信奉“知识就是力量”，重视客观知识的介绍，而忽视性情的熏陶和德行的培养。此一问题，与我上文所谓“习上求通”而非“性上求通”之弊一脉相承。马一浮先生尝作《释学问》一文，其中对知识、才能同学问的区别解释得十分清楚。他说：“人人皆习言学问，却少有于此二字之义加以明晰之解说者。如见人读书多、见闻广，或有才辩、能文辞，便谓之有学问。古人所谓学问，似乎不是如此。此可说是有知识，有才能，若言学问，却别有事在。知识是从闻见得来的，不能无所遗；才能是从气质生就的，不能无所偏。（今所谓专家属前一类，所谓天才属后一类。）学问却要自心体验而后得，不专恃闻见；要变化气质而后成，不偏重才能。知识、才能是学问之资藉，不即是学问之成就。唯尽知可至于盛德，乃是得之于己；尽能可以为大业，亦必有赖于修。如此，故学问之事起焉。是知学问乃所以尽知尽能之事，而非多知多能之谓也。”由此可见，欲真求“通而不局”，非“尊德性而道问学”不可。

二是仍然沿袭分科教学模式，用“知识拼盘”对治“分科太过”，以为知识面越广、互补性越强，就越能克服“局而不通”的弊病。此一问题，与我上文所谓“向多处求通”而非“向深处求通”之弊一脉相承。教育家们发现了人性对于“通”的要求及其与“局而不通”的对立，却没能发现“人性本通”的真相与造成“局而不通”的真正原因。他们把“局而不通”的原因归咎于“分科太过专门”，以为打破这个格局，让学生按兴趣跨专业、跨学科广泛地学习“非专业、非职业性”的知识，就能有效地解决“局而不通”的问题。北京大学的“通识教育文库”与芝加哥大学的“名著课程计划”，在通识教学中都试图把“全人类的文明经典”介绍给学生。台湾大学、台湾辅仁大学、香港中文大学等，在通识教育中，也试图增加学生知识的广度，拓展学生视野，使学生兼备人文素养与科学素养，把学生培养成“全面发展的人”。我所在的杭州师范大学，全校的通识课程竟然多达 124 门，几乎每个学院每个专业都在面向全校学生开设通识课。这些课程的积极意义在于照顾到了学生的兴趣，扩大了学生的知识面，

① 参见《马一浮集》，第一册，第 130 页。

“对症下药”地解决了兴趣变化与专业固定的矛盾问题以及知识面的大小宽窄问题，而未能从根本上解决“局而不通”的问题。其功在“对症下药”，其过亦在“对症下药”。

三是任情而不依性，抱“兴趣是最好的老师”之俗见，过分看重学生兴趣，将通识课作为任意选修课完全交由学生兴趣来决定，不知“少习若天性，习惯成自然”的道理。迄今为止，我国高校几乎无一例外地是将通识课制作为菜单挂在网上，供学生任意选修。罕见有将通识课作为全校必修课者。这些通识课程主要面向大一的学生。这些学生新来乍到，选修通识课往往仅凭一时兴趣，甚或仅为几个学分。结果，很多选上了某门课程的学生会“后悔一学期”，漏选了某门课程的学生又“一学期后悔”。“兴趣是最好的老师”（Interest is the best teacher），这句口号，成了高悬于教育主管部门乃至所有教师头上的尚方宝剑！不仅因为它出自伟大的物理学家爱因斯坦，而且因为它看上去非常合乎大众的经验。然而，问题恰恰就出在这里！对于经验科学而言，或许兴趣是最好的老师；而对于心性之学而言，兴趣不一定是最好的老师。当今青年学子自我中心主义严重，动辄抱“兴趣是最好的老师”这句口号，任性取舍，随意臧否，不知天底下还有比自我的兴趣更重要的准则。

须知：通识教育，贵在“性其情”，不可任其情；通识之学，贵在得其正，不可依赖兴趣。一言以蔽之，本性之学，人人皆当习之，未可一味任情，徒恃兴趣。兴趣者，一时一地之情也；本性者，恒常不变之理也。一时兴趣，未必可靠；败兴而归，屡见不鲜。故老子云：“不知常，妄作，凶。”兴趣可助成才，难与成德。才者生于气质之偏，执着兴趣，往往偏上加偏，局而愈局。囿于兴趣，实属拘泥于习；听之任之，是为纵容习气，与祛习复性背道而驰。以此求通，无有是处。以此施教，即是失教。

孟子曰：“大匠不为拙工改废绳墨，羿不为拙射变其彀率。君子引而不发，跃如也。中道而立，能者从之。”我们不能因为学生不感兴趣就气馁，就放弃。我坚信“人同此心，心同此理”，心性之学最好的老师不应该是兴趣，而应该是天性，是良知。孔子曰：“生而知之者上也，学而知之者次也，困而学之又次也。困而不学，民斯为下矣。”知虽分生知、学知、困知三等，有快慢深浅之殊，有主动被动之异，然其能有成，一也。

四是在科学民主等西方价值主宰人心的时代背景下，讲解《四书》义理障碍重重。学生普遍痴迷于囫囵吞枣的西方观念，抱“天赋人权”、“生而自由平等”诸口号，不知此上还有更高的价值存在，与论礼义上下、尊卑贵贱，不出离愤怒，即嗤之以鼻。宋太祖尝问宰相赵普：“天底下何物最大？”普答曰：“道理最大。”赵普所谓“道理最大”，其实就是《论语》上孔子所说的“义以为上”。“义者，宜也”，就是说话做事、待人接物样样要合乎分寸，恰到好处。在孔子看来，天底下没有任何价值可以高过“义”。即便是通常人们所奉为的儒家最高价值的仁、智、信、直、勇、刚等，在孔子心目中都必须合乎礼义才是可取的，否则都不免其弊病。《论语·阳货第十七》记录了孔子与子路的一段对话，最能看出孔子的根本精神。

子曰："由也，女闻六言六蔽矣乎?"对曰："未也。""居！吾语女。好仁不好学，其蔽也愚；好知不好学，其蔽也荡；好信不好学，其蔽也贼；好直不好学，其蔽也绞；好勇不好学，其蔽也乱；好刚不好学，其蔽也狂。"

这里所谓"不好学"，即不好学礼义。可见，礼义的价值比仁、智、信、直、勇、刚这些价值还要高。无怪乎孔子要说："君子之于天下也，无适也，无莫也，义之与比。"还说："君子义以为上"。辜鸿铭先生认为，中华文化的精华是义与礼，"特别是礼，更为中国文明的精髓"。他说："欧洲宗教要人们做一个好人，中国的宗教则要人们做一个识礼的好人；基督教叫人爱人，孔子则叫人爱之以礼。"[①] 中国文化的礼义与西方文化的自由平等，高下本来一目了然，然而受西方文化的影响，今人普遍食西不化，偏信盲从，与讲四书义理，殊为困难。

## 二、两种理与东西教育之不同

我们今天研讨儒家与教育的课题，不能不深入区分两种"理"与两种"错误"，以及由此而来的中西教育的根本差异。近现代以来，文化人多因"中国文化落后"而盲目自卑，越来越喜言"真理"而耻言"天理"。实则中国人所说的"天理"与西方人所说的"真理"还是有微妙差别的。天理，侧重于"情理"；真理，侧重于"物理"。正如梁漱溟先生所说：

从前中国人常爱说"读书明理"一句话。在乡村中，更常听见指说某人为"读书明理之人"。这个理何所指？不烦解释，中国人都明白的。它绝不包含物理的理、化学的理、一切自然科学的理，就连社会科学上许多理，亦都不包括在内。却是同此一句话，在西洋人听去，亦许生出不同的了解罢！中国有许多书，西洋亦有许多书；书中莫不讲到许多理。但翻开书一看，却似不同。中国书所讲总偏乎人世间许多情理，如父慈、子孝、知耻、爱人、公平、信实之类。若西洋书，则其所谈的不是自然科学之理，便是社会科学之理，或纯抽象的数理与论理。因此，当你说"读书明理"一句话，他便以为是明白那些科学之理了。

科学之理，是一些静的知识，知其"如此如此"而止，没有立即发动什么行为的力量。而中国人所说的理，却就在指示人们行为动向。它常常是很有力量的一句话，例如"人而无信，不知其可也！""临财毋苟得，临难毋苟免！"它尽可是抽象的，没有

① 辜鸿铭：《中国人的精神》，海南出版社，1996年。

特指当前某人某事，然而是动的，不是静的。科学之理，亦可以与行为有关系，但却没有一定方向指给人。如说“触电可以致死”，触不触，却听你。人怕死，固要避开它，想自杀的人，亦许去触电，没有一定。科学上大抵都是“如果如此，则将如彼”，这类公式。

所谓理者，既有此不同，似当分别予以不同名称。前者为人情上的理，不妨简称“情理”，后者为物观上的理，不妨简称“物理”。此二者，在认识上本是有分别的。现时流行有“正义感”一句话。正义感是一种感情，对于正义便欣然接受拥护，对于不合正义的便厌恶拒绝。正义感，即是正义之认识力；离开此感情，正义就不可得。一切是非善恶之理，皆同此例。点头即是，摇头即不是。善，即存乎悦服崇敬赞叹的心情上；恶，即存乎嫌恶愤嫉不平的心情上。但在情理之理虽则如此；物理之理，恰好不然。情理，离却主观好恶即无从认识；物理，则不离主观好恶即无从认识。物理得自物观观测；观测靠人的感觉和推理；人的感觉和推理，原是人类超脱于本能而冷静下来的产物，亦必要屏除一切感情而后乃能尽其用。因此科学家都以冷静著称。但相反之中，仍有相同之点。即情理虽著见在感情上，却必是无私的感情。无私的感情，同样是人类超脱于本能而冷静下来的产物。[①]

理既分情理与物理两个方面，则随之而来的人类错误也应该有两种分别。梁漱溟先生说：“动物倚本能为活，几无错误可言，更无错误之自觉；错误只是人的事。人类是极其容易错误的，其错误亦有两种不同。譬如学校考试，学生将考题答错，是一种错误——知识上的错误。若在考试上舞弊行欺，则又是另一种错误——行为上的错误。前一错误，于学习上见出低能，应属智能问题；后一错误，便属品性问题。智能问题于理智有关；品性问题于理性有关。事后他如果觉察自己错误，前一觉察属于理智，后一觉察发乎理性。”[②]

西方文化偏重物理，中国文化偏重情理。中西方文化各有侧重，中西方的教育也各有侧重。辜鸿铭先生在他所作批评东西文化的一本书所谓《春秋大义》里边说到两方人教育的不同。他说：“西洋人入学读书所学的一则曰知识，再则曰知识，三则曰知识；中国人入学读书所学的是君子之道。”梁漱溟先生也说：“大约可以说中国人的教育偏着在情志的一边，例如孝弟……之教；西洋人的教育偏着知的一边，例如诸自然科学……之教。”[③] 关于东西方人的教育之不同，梁先生有两段话值得引用于此。他说：

---

① 梁漱溟：《中国文化要义》，上海世纪出版集团，2005年，第113页。

② 梁漱溟：《中国文化要义》，上海世纪出版集团，2005年，第114页。

③ 转引自梁漱溟：《东西人的教育之不同》，《梁漱溟全集》第四卷，山东人民出版社，1991年，第660—661页。

盖情志是本能，所谓不学而能，不虑而知的，为一个人生来所具有无缺尔者，不同乎知识为生来所不具有；为后天所不能加进去者，不同乎知识悉从后天得来（无论出于自家的创造，或承受前人均为从外面得来的，后加进去的）。既然这样，似乎情志既不待教育，亦非可教育者。此殊不然。生活的本身全在情志方面，而知的一边——包固有的智慧与后天的知识——只是生活之工具。工具弄不好，固然生活弄不好，生活本身（即情志方面）如果没有弄得妥帖恰好，则工具虽利将无所用之，或转自贻戚；所以情志教育更是根本的。这就是说怎样要生活本身弄得恰好是第一个问题；生活工具的讲求固是必要，无论如何，不能不居于第二个问题。所谓教育不但在智慧的启牖和知识的创造授受，尤在调顺本能使生活本身得其恰好。

本能虽不待教给，非可教给者，但仍旧可以教育的，并且很需要教育。因为本能极容易搅乱失宜，即生活很难妥帖恰好，所以要调理他得以发育活动到好处，这便是情志的教育所要用的功夫——其功夫与智慧的启牖或近，与知识的教给便大不同。从来中国人的教育很着意于要人得有合理的生活，而极顾虑情志的失宜。从这一点论，自然要算中国的教育为得，而西洋人忽视此点为失。盖西洋教育着意生活的工具，中国教育着意生活本身，各有所得，各有所失也。然中国教育虽以常能着意生活本身故谓为得，却是其方法未尽得宜。盖未能审察情的教育与知的教育之根本不同，常常把教给知识的方法用于情志教育。①

## 三、儒学的价值与通识教育目的之达成

从中国教育史来看，可以说中国从来就是通识有余而分科不足。说中国的通识教育博大精深、源远流长，是一点也不为过的。20 世纪 80 年代初，晚年梁漱溟在接受美国汉学家艾恺的采访时就曾经明确说过：“今日世界问题之形成，由于西方文化。要避免人类之毁灭，只有转向中国文化。中国问题之陷于今日局面，正为盲目学西洋之结果。”② 无独有偶，在 1988 年法国巴黎召开的题为“面向 21 世纪”的首届诺贝尔奖获得者国际大会上，物理学家汉内斯·阿尔文博士更是语惊四座地指出：“人类要生存下去，就必须回到 25 个世纪以前，去吸取孔子的智慧！”我们今天研讨教育问题，不能不深切检讨自弃国宝、盲目西化的教训。在我看来，中国分科教育之弊病，实在可以说是自弃国宝、盲目西化的结果。说句不中听的话，我们今天在通识教育源远流长、博大精深的中国，使用“通识教育”这个外来词，来谈论通识教育的问题，多少有点

---

① 转引自梁漱溟：《东西人的教育之不同》，《梁漱溟全集》第四卷，山东人民出版社，1991 年，第 663—664 页。

② 梁漱溟：《这个世界会好吗？——梁漱溟晚年口述》，东方出版中心，封底。

数典忘祖、拾人之土苴以为宝的意味。至少我个人是“别有一番滋味在心头”。

说实话，我们在中国讲通识教育，完全不必亦步亦趋步西方后尘。然而令人遗憾的是，在民族自卑感和文化落后论甚嚣尘上的大背景下，我国的通识教育却偏偏步人后尘，至今一切唯西方马首是瞻。从教学内容、课程设置到管理手段和方法，几乎样样效法西方。在我看来，在如何“通而不局”的问题上，西方人至今未能走上正确的道路。步西方后尘的中国通识教育亦不例外。

《周易·系辞上》曰：“一阖一辟谓之变，往来不穷谓之通。”又曰：“形而上者谓之道，形而下者谓之器；化而裁之谓之变，推而行之谓之通；举而错之天下之民，谓之事业。”孔子说：“性相近也，习相远也。”通者，性也；性则本通。局而不通者，习也。欲求通识，当向性上求，当走祛习复性之路！否则，习上求通，愈求愈远。

儒家所谓“性”，是宇宙的“纯然之理”，是事物的“当然之则”。其所谓“习”，乃指气边事，属于经验层面。道通万事，理一分殊。能通者，道也，理也，性也；非器也，事也，情也。道器一如，理事不二；真求通识，非“穷理尽性以至于命”不可。《周易·系辞上》曰：“通变之谓事，阴阳不测之谓神。”又曰：“易无思也，无为也，寂然不动，感而遂通天下之故。非天下之至神，其孰能与于此！夫易，圣人之所以极深而研几也。惟深也，故能通天下之志；惟几也，故能成天下之务；惟神也，故不疾而速，不行而至。”《同人》彖辞曰：“文明以健，中正而应，君子正也。唯君子为能通天下之志。”通识之学，君子之学也。孔子告诫后人唯向“深”处求，并未教人漫向“多”处求。此深处乃吾人心性之深处，非外物之深处也。心包宇宙，舍祛习复性，无以深入之。佛家所谓“性”，更是“不生不灭，不垢不净，不增不减”，不从缘生，不因习成，法尔如是，常住不灭。习不离识，性须智证。泯识显智，乃可见性。见性之后，方可入世无碍，一通百通。

马一浮先生尝言，说到“性”字，西方人实无一字道着。也就是说，全部西学，在马一浮先生看来不出“习”边事。我在这里斗胆说一句，通识之学，唯我东方儒学或佛学可以当之。《大学》开宗明义：“大学之道，在明明德，在新民，在止于至善。”《中庸》开宗明义：“天命之谓性，率性之谓道，修道之谓教。”此皆大通之道也。欲求通识，不向此中求，我未知其可也！

儒学的根本宗旨在求仁，在祛习复性。儒家实现这一宗旨的根本途径是礼乐教化。儒家礼乐教化的功效体现在两个方面：一是启发人性本具的向上之心，一是启发人性本具的相与之情。梁漱溟先生说：“就在儒家领导之下，二千多年间，中国人养成一种社会风尚，或民族精神，除最近数十年浸浸澌灭，今已不易得见外，过去中国人的生存，及其民族生命之开拓，胥赖于此。这种精神，分析言之，约有两点：一为向上之心强，一为相与之情厚。”关于中国民族的“向上之心”，《中国文化要义》中的一段话值得引用于此：

向上心，即不甘于错误的心，即是非之心，好善服善的心，要求公平合理的心，拥护正义的心，知耻要强的心，嫌恶懒散而喜振作的心……总之，于人生利害得失之外，更有向上一念者是，我们总称之曰："人生向上。"从之则坦然泰然，怡然自得而殊不见其所得；违之则歉恨不安，仿佛若有所失而不见其所失。在中国古人，则谓之"义"，谓之"理"。这原是人所本有的；然当人类文化未进，全为禁忌（taboo）、崇拜、迷信、习俗所蔽，各个人意识未曾觉醒活动，虽有却不被发见。甚至就在文化已高的社会，如果宗教或其他权威强盛，宰制了人心，亦还不得发达。所以像欧洲中古之世，尚不足以语此。到近代欧洲人，诚然其个人意识觉醒活动了，却惜其意识只在求生存求幸福，一般都是功利思想，驰骛于外，又体认不到此。现代人生，在文化各方面靡不迈越前人，夫何待言；但在这一点上，却丝毫未见有进。唯中国古人得脱于宗教之迷蔽而认取人类精神独早，其人生态度，其所有之价值判断，乃悉以此为中心。虽因提出太早牵掣而不得行，然其风尚所在，固彰彰也。

广义上说，人类的一切创造都是向上之心的表现。但梁漱溟先生所说的作为中国民族精神的"向上之心"，则是特指"于人生利害得失之外"的"向上之心"。孔子说："放于利而行，多怨。"故《孟子》开篇答梁惠王求利之问曰："王何必曰利？亦有仁义而已矣。王曰'何以利吾国'？大夫曰'何以利吾家'？士庶人曰'何以利吾身'？上下交征利而国危矣。万乘之国弑其君者，必千乘之家；千乘之国弑其君者，必百乘之家。万取千焉，千取百焉，不为不多矣。苟为后义而先利，不夺不餍。未有仁而遗其亲者也，未有义而后其君者也。王亦曰仁义而已矣，何必曰利？"怨由不通而来，怨又强化不通，因此欲求通识，必须开发人类本有的"向上之心"。

王阳明先生说："是故见孺子之入井，而必有怵惕隐恻之心焉；是其仁之与孺子而为一体也。孺子犹同类者也。见鸟兽之哀鸣觳觫，而必有不忍之心焉；是其仁之与鸟兽而为一体也。鸟兽犹有知觉者也。见草木之摧折，而必有悯恤之心焉；是其仁之与草木而为一体也。草木犹有生意者也。见瓦石之毁坏，而必有顾惜之心焉；是其仁之与瓦石而为一体也。"无怪乎梁漱溟先生会说："人类生命廓然与物同体，其情无所不到。"他还说："人在欲望中恒只知为我而顾不到对方；反之，人在感情中，往往只见对方而忘了自己。实则，此时对方就是自己。凡痛痒亲切处，就是自己，何必区区数尺之躯。普泛地关情，即不啻普泛地负担了任务在身上，如同母亲要为他儿子服务一样。所以昔人说'宇宙内事，即己分内事'（陆象山先生语）。人类理性，原如是也。"[①]《中国文化要义》第七章第三节有三段深刻的论述值得引用于此：

---

① 梁漱溟：《中国文化要义》，上海世纪出版集团，2005年，第120—121页。

然此无所不到之情，却自有其发端之处，即家庭骨肉之间是。爱伦凯（Ellen Key）《母性论》中说，小儿爱母为情绪发达之本，由是扩充以及远；此一顺序，犹树根不可朝天。中国古语“孝弟为仁之本”，又曰“亲亲而仁民，仁民而爱物”，其间先后、远近、厚薄自是天然的。“伦理关系始于家庭，而不止于家庭”，这是由近以及远。“举整个社会各种关系而一概家庭化之”（见第五章），这是更引远而入近，唯恐其情之不厚。中国伦理本位的社会之形成，无疑地，是旨向于“天下为一家，中国为一人”。虽因提出太早，牵掣而不得行，然其精神所在，固不得而否认也。

中国伦理本位的社会，形成于礼俗之上，多由儒家之倡导而来，这是事实。现在我们说明儒家之所以出此，正因其有见于理性，有见于人类生命，一个人天然与他前后左右的人，与他的世界不可分离。所以前章“安排伦理组织社会”一段，我说孔子最初所着眼的，倒不在社会组织，而宁在一个人如何完成他自己。

一个人的生命，不自一个人而止，是有伦理关系。伦理关系，即是情谊关系，亦即是其相互间的一种义务关系。所贵乎人者，在不失此情与义。“人要不断自觉地向上实践他所看到的理”，大致不外是看到此情义，实践此情义。其间“向上之心”，“相与之情”，有不可分析言之者已。不断有所看到，不断地实践，则卒成所谓圣贤。中国之所尚，在圣贤；西洋之所尚，在伟人；印度之所尚，在仙佛。社会风尚、民族精神各方不同，未尝不可于此识别。[①]

## 四、结论

综上所述，我以为当今世界要根本解决现代分科教育“局而不通”之弊，必须拨乱反正，反本开新，从儒家的传统教育中吸取智慧。其中最根本的，就是要从片面追求客观的知识型教育转向以情志教育为主、以知识教育为辅的综合型教育。借本次会议的机会，我想就“通识教育”的根本理念谨提出如下四项主张：

通识教育之要，在祛习复性，不在多知多能。

通识教育之途，在向内求深，不在向外务广。

通识教育之典，在吾华六经，不必舍近求远。

通识教育之效，在礼义复兴，不在知识创新。

---

① 梁漱溟：《中国文化要义》，上海世纪出版集团，2005年，第121页。

# 儒家道德本体论及其当代启示

重庆师范大学　李禹阶

由于中国古代社会与世界其他各大文明之间历史发展道路的不同，使中国古代国家在社会生产力还没有充分发展的情况下，就直接由氏族、部落进化到“三代”（夏、商、周）国家形态，形成“早熟”的文明社会。与此相适应，在这种“早熟”的文明社会中，具有多神崇拜意义的原始宗教和氏族、部落习俗遗留下来，并直接演化为中国古代国家的社会规范、思想意识、道德伦理。它使古代中国没有能够世界其他各大文明一样，建立起统一的宗教及其一神崇拜，而是将进化而来的原始宗教、社会规范、思想意识、道德伦理抽象、融合形成古代中国重要的文化特征——礼。在几千年中国文明史上，礼是华夏民族及国家的重要文化内涵。它不仅是指导人们社会生活的经典法则，而且还是具有形而上本体意义的“天理”“良知”。《大戴礼记·三本》：“礼有三本：天地者，性之本也；先祖者，类之本也；君师者，治之本也。……故礼上事天，下事地，宗事先祖而君师，是礼之三本也。”说明礼与形而上的“天道”崇拜具有内在的有机联系。而儒家思想的核心即是“礼”及其内在化了的道德规范总纲“仁”。可以说，在几千年的中国文明史上，由于缺乏世界各大文明都出现过的统一的宗教神及其崇拜，以及这种统一宗教下的道德指引，具有形而上与形而下两个层次的“礼”“仁”就成为中国古代社会在日常规范、道德伦理方面的指引和模式，构建了一种享誉世界的中华文明，在中国和世界文明史上具有极其重要的地位。

## 一、“礼”的三重特性及其形而上特征

“礼”字虽然晚出，但是在中国五、六千年前的新石器时代，包括宗教形式的原始礼仪就出现了。从考古材料看，早在6000年前的中原地区，便有了礼的萌芽。濮阳西水坡大墓中，出土一些非实用性器物。从形制、质地看，类似于其后各地出土的礼器，主要用于标明墓主人身份等级。以后，在中原龙山文化遗址中，则出土了成套礼器。如陶寺遗址中型墓中，随葬有成组陶器和玉（石）钺、琮、瑗佩饰等；大型墓中则随

葬有成套龙石斧、石镞、玉（石）钺、瑗、特磬、龙盘。其发现的石钺大都刃部钝，没有使用痕迹；与石钺相仿的有一种石刀，长方穿孔，青灰色，造型偏薄，无使用价值，应为“礼器”一类。特磬通高80厘米，上端两面对钻一孔，一般为庙堂重器，说明这时礼器发展已有一定规模。

距今5300—4000年的良渚文化，是一支分布在我国太湖流域的古文化。在浙江的反山、瑶山、汇观山等良渚文化时期的贵族墓地中，大都建有人工堆筑的大型墓台，有宽大的墓穴、精致的葬具，以及一大批制作精美的玉礼器。这些玉器种类多达20余种，有琮、璧、钺、锥形器、三叉形器、冠形器、璜、纺轮、圆牌饰等。玉琮是古代典型的礼器，后世有“苍璧礼天，黄琮礼地”之说，认为璧和琮象征着天圆地方，为重要的祭祀礼仪用器。而良渚文化遗址中，就发现作为礼器的玉琮，两端对钻孔，呈明显的喇叭口状，在大端射口中间部分雕琢一符号。同时在良渚文化遗址中，还发现制作精致的刻有繁缛的蟠螭纹或鸟禽纹图案的陶制双鼻壶、鼎、豆等器形，这正是礼器制度在陶器上的反映！它表明了良渚文化礼制已经产生并且有了一定规模。

新石器时期的部落“礼制”，是在社会等级分层的情况下，原始宗教与部落社会规范结合的产物。原始宗教在当时表现为三重特征。即：对超自然的自然山川神的泛灵崇拜；对超血缘的部落联盟内祖先神的权威崇拜；对日益发展的世俗公共职能的神化与敬畏。这三重崇拜，构成中国远古，尤其是中原地区史前宗教的基本特征。但是它又使中国古代的社会和文明抛弃了统一宗教神的模式，向着世俗化的道德崇尚的方向发展。例如在原始宗教的三重神统中，祖先崇拜及公共权力神化是世俗血缘与政治的一种抽象化。以祖先神为例，从世俗地位上看，他们都具有超越各血缘氏族部落的盟主首领地位，既是族神，又是“帝”（王）神；从神格上看，他们又都是超越各下属血缘部族神（分支图腾）的统一神。当这种超越性不断升华时，就超凌多神主义倾向，形成与上天同格的天神、“上帝”。这种抽象与现实、宗教思辨与日用常行的矛盾，一方面使祖先神在血缘感性认知的范围内，服务于形而下的现实需求，另一方面，它又配享或直接是最高的昊天神灵，对自然山川诸神有极大的神权规范。其结果导致神帝的崇高是一种基于感性认知范围的、服务于社会整合的崇高，人们对它的敬畏瞻望，只是求得它在天神灵的冥冥福佑。当进入阶级社会后，这种神灵则直接发展为阶级压迫与人性抑制的宗教工具。由于这种宗教抽象及宗教感情的浓缩是为现实的社会整合服务的，势必遏制原始宗教自身向超功利形而上的实体性概念发展的途径，而转入现实人世的功利祸福中来。其结果使最高的帝也就具有有血有肉的与现实人世的密切联系的功能性特征。神性的光辉是在有限的人类感性生活中为统治者求福受佑的短暂的“光辉”。所以，这种祖先崇拜与多神泛灵崇拜的原始宗教结构，从内部破坏着宗教的统一性，阻碍着纯粹、抽象的“上帝神”摒弃世俗功利的出世道路的延伸，最终导致宗教形式向人伦形式的转化，即宗法血缘与世俗权力相结合的“礼”的转化。①

远古中国大地上的三重神统并存，本质上是落后的生产力（木石器时代）与快速发展的生产关系的矛盾的产物。它打断了原始宗教自身的逻辑进程，使具有现实宗法内容的祖先崇拜和权力神化的“礼”脱颖而出，代替原始宗教与习惯法成为中原地区先民行事作人的规范、准则。同时由于“礼”的早熟性，它又带着原始宗教泛灵崇拜的各种特征。这些原始宗教的特征渗入到礼的构架中，成为礼的一部分。自虞礼以后，继之的有夏礼、殷礼、周礼。三代礼制虽有区别，但本质上是一致的，即都继承了中原地区一脉相承的文化特色，都离不开以祖先崇拜、权力神化、泛灵禁忌为构架的祭祀、丧葬、朝觐、聘问、婚姻、盟会、燕享、军礼等一套礼制内容。这套礼制包括了以血缘部落（族）为基本单位的地域性国家对内对外所涉及的各项政治、经济、法律、道德、艺术及人伦准则，并且具有一以贯之的性质。孔子说：“吾说夏礼，不足征也；吾学殷礼，有宋存焉；吾学周礼，今用之，吾从周。”“夏礼吾能言之，杞不足征也；殷礼吾能言之，宋不足征也；文献不足故也。足，则吾能征之矣！”正是说明了中国古代“礼”的这种一以贯之的延续性。

随着生产力发展，在中国春秋时期出现了“礼崩乐坏”的现象。“礼”的权威性受到挑战。如何在这个各种矛盾和斗争都十分激化的转折时期，重新建立起一种社会规范和道德信仰，来稳定变幻的社会局势与激发人们的道德自觉，是一个重要的思想和文化任务。孔子正是这么一位承上启下的哲人。他自觉承担起了这么一个历史的重任。在延续古代文化传统的基础上，他将“礼”及其文献载体《六经》加以整理、抽象，加上自己的道德理解，抽象，上升了“仁”及其相关道德范畴，形成以“礼”“仁”为内涵外延的儒家精神，构成了试图补益于世的儒家思想与道德文化体系。这个体系经过孟、荀以及董仲舒、朱熹等儒学家的发展，形成了中国古代的社会规范和道德传统，构成中国几千年来的政治、法律、艺术、道德及文化主流。可以说，儒家思想是在根植于中国这个特殊的宗法社会国情，继承与改造中国传统文化中形成、发展的。在古代中国缺乏统一形而上宗教及其道德指引的情况下，儒家学说则根据中国古代国家“早熟性”及其没有统一宗教的特点，自觉构建了具有形而上意义的世俗化社会规范及其道德指引，构建了一种享誉世界的中华文明。

## 二、儒家道德本体论的形而上特征

由于“礼”既有着形而上的哲学本体的意义，又有着世俗化的人伦规范特点，因

① 李禹阶《史前中原地区的宗教崇拜及“礼”的起源》，《中国史研究》1995年1期。

此它同时具有“天道”的信仰意义和“人道”道德伦理的双重属性。

这种属性决定了儒学中心命题的双重性，即“性与天道”的天人合一本体论。“性与天道”的命题本质上是从“礼”的内涵——“仁”发端的。“仁”在卜辞、金文中具未见。较早的《尚书》、《诗经》中仅几见，意义不很清楚。只有在春秋时代“仁”才大量出现，并被作为原始儒家学说的核心内容。这不是偶然的，而与中国古代“亲亲”“尊尊”的宗法礼制社会实际紧密相关。“仁”，古文作仁、巳，从人从二，会意为二人相处省形。《说文》“仁，亲也，从人二。”郑康成注：“读如‘相人偶’之人。”段玉裁《说文》释曰：“仁，……以人意相存问之意。”“《正义》曰：‘人偶者，谓以人意尊偶之也。’《论语》注：‘人偶同位，人偶同辞。’”证之“仁”原意，既有血缘亲族间的亲仁、存问、互敬、礼让，还有政治上“人偶同位”、“辅道治民”，经济上同生共食、相依相存的特征。在《论语》中，“仁”这种意义被概括、总结为宗法族类中人际间相互界定与关系，这便是“已欲立而立人，已欲达而达人”、“己所不欲，勿施于人”的“忠恕之道”。从先秦思孟学派开始，经董仲舒今文经学，直到宋明时期的程朱理学与陆王心学，儒学共同特点是将儒学所倡导的“礼”与“仁”上升为“天道”的内涵，使其社会规范和道德纲常成为绝对宇宙精神，从而导致长盛不衰的儒家伦理本位与道德本体论。这种道德本体论强调天道与人道的合一，而“天人合一”的中介则是人良知、良能的“性”与“心”。故《中庸》开篇曰：“天命之谓性，率性之谓道，修道之谓教”。而朱熹《四书章句集注·中庸章句》注曰：“命，犹令也；性，即理也；天以阴阳五行化生万物，气以成形，而理亦赋焉，犹命令也。于是人物之生，因各得其所赋之理，以为健顺五常之德，所谓性也。”以“天道自然论”著名的儒家学者荀子，亦不能逃离这一儒家本体论定律。荀子一方面推崇天的自然性；另一方面又将“礼”作为“天之大经”，宇宙万物普遍的规律。他说：“天地以合，日月以明，四时以序，星辰以行，江河以流，万物以昌，好恶以节，喜怒以当，以为下则顺，以为上则明，万变不乱，贰之则丧也，礼岂不至矣哉！……礼者，人道之极也。”[①] 而传承荀学的汉初儒者陆贾，则将先秦儒学的“礼”之属性加以发展，他说：“传曰：‘天生万物，以地养之，圣人成之。’功德参合，而道术生焉。故曰：张日月，列星辰，序四时，调阴阳，……苞之以六合，罗之以纪纲，改之以灾变，告之以祯祥，动之以生杀，悟之以文章。”[②] 从荀学的天道自然论直接推演出以道德为本体的“天人感应”的灾异谴告论，成为汉代董氏之学的滥觞。

宋明理学的一个主要特征，就是将“仁”上升为至高的“理”、最高的“善”、天地

---

① 《荀子·礼论》，北京：中华书局，1975年。

② 陆贾：《新语·道基第一》，北京：中华书局，1986年。

人物的共同品性，具有超越自然物我一体的性格。朱熹说:“仁者性也。仁自是性，性即是这道理。”[①]“仁者天地生物之心，而人、物所得以为心。则是天地人物莫不同有此心，而心德未尝不贯通也。”[②] 在朱熹等人看来，属于伦理范围的道德理性而非任何个体及其意志就是宇宙最高理性、天地人物共同本质宇宙万化的本源。“立天之道，曰阴与阳，是与气言；立地之道，曰柔与刚，是以质言；立人之道，曰仁与义，是以理言。”[③]时空、存在、理性相统一的天地人系统中，只有“人道”的“仁义”才是至高至大的“理”，而天、地不过是这个“理”派生的“气”与“质”，“有是理，便有是气，但理是本。”[④]同时它又是人类认识的对象及目标。“盖仁之为道，乃天地生物之心即物而在。……诚能体而存之，则众善之源，百行之本，莫不在是。”[⑤]大千世界，茫茫乾坤，没有什么天王上帝、鬼魅神道，只有人类自身理性，才是宇宙的中心与信仰的对象，识“仁”就是识得天地之机，万物之化。这样，基于传统人文的理学新“天人合一”论建立起来了。这种“天人合一”论用“理”去融会贯通自然诸物，将人类主观理性推向哲学的中心。这也正是朱熹对理学颇为自得的贡献:“仁者天地生物之心，而人、物所得以为心，……窃谓正发明得天人无间断处。”[⑥]

将道德本体化，从而使儒学伦理范畴取得最高“天道”的本体保障，是二千年来儒学“一以贯之”的原则。随着儒学成为中国封建社会主体意识形态，这种本体学说则导致中国封建社会政治伦理化，伦理政治化；法律伦理化，伦理法律化；同时也使儒家道德伦理信仰化。作为中国封建社会具有重要影响的意识形态，儒家道德本体化、信仰化有其负面影响不言而喻，并已为许多学者所指出。但是，其道德本体化的正面精神价值，当代却揭示甚少。按照历史唯物主义理论，人类认识是螺旋形发展的，唯心主义是人类认识之树上一朵不结果的花。它虽然片面夸大了事物发展的某一部分，但从人类认识史上看，它又具有对认识中矛盾的探索以及包含着辩证思想的合理性。正如黑格尔哲学中的唯心主义体系亦正包含着一系列关于矛盾辩证发展的真理颗粒，直接孕育了马克思辩证法的产生。对历史上的儒学亦应如此看待。儒学道德本体论虽然具有唯心主义先验论成分，其本质亦是为了维护地上人间的封建专制政治制度。可是，它作为古代中国一种世俗化的社会规范和道德形而上学，它所发挥的建立道德信仰的功能和作用，仍值得我们认真反思、研究、总结:

---

① 《朱子语类》卷五。
② 《朱子语类》卷七七。
③ 《朱子语类》卷九五。
④ 《朱子语类》卷一。
⑤ 朱熹:《仁说》,《朱文公文集》卷六七。
⑥ 朱熹:《答何叔京》,《朱文公文集》卷四十。

第一，儒家“性与天道”的天人合一本体学说，将道德伦理范畴上升为最高的“道”与“理”。从世界哲学史与思想史的意义上说，这是一种独特的理性形式。它的思辨意义在于当古代中国历史道路杜绝了世界各古老文明所共通的统一宗教形式在中国大地的发展后，而构建了一种新的道德信仰弥补形式，这种形式使中国文化传统与人们的精神信仰始终处于世俗与入世的范围之中。在世界各古老文明中，人们的精神世界往往通过宗教来寄托，而传统宗教的最高本体无一例外，均以人格化的一神教形式出现。如基督教的上帝耶稣，佛教的释迦牟尼，伊斯兰教的穆罕默德，中国道教教主老子等。但在中国，自儒学成为主流意识形态后，中国占主体地位的思想就基本采用半人格化或非人格化形式来建立其哲学本体论。汉代董仲舒主张的“天”“帝”，是有善恶、有情感但无人格形式的半人格化的伦理主体。在董仲舒看来，“天”“帝”能用灾异祥瑞遣告、告诫、激励人间帝王，使之向善惩恶；但董氏之“天”毕竟只是一种精神的“道”与“理”，故而“道之大原出于天，天不变道亦不变”。“天”“帝”的这种半人格化特征，在董仲舒看来是“天高其位而下其施，藏其形而见其光。”,[①] 即见其施予而不见其模样，所以至今中外尚无人能解得中国的“天”“帝”的人格范式与模样。经魏晋玄学体玄味道，至宋代周敦颐、邵雍、张载、二程、朱熹等理学家，“天”“帝”则完全采用非人格化的“道”“理”即伦理律令化、规范化、固定化的精神范式。周敦颐在《太极图说》中将“太极”（即“道”）作为最高本体，并衍生出一套以阴阳五行之气同仁义五常之性相结合的儒学宇宙生化论，至此开了理学本体说之先，同时亦全面完成对儒学道德本体论的建构以及对本体学说的非人格化改造。朱熹著《太极图说解》，则将周敦颐建构的道德本体论与宇宙生化论范式加以全面肯定，由此确立了理学形而上的道德本体论及宇宙发生说。在理学家看来，“天”即“理”、即“道”、即“性”，而所谓“理”与“性”、亦不过是地上的“仁、义、礼、智、信”五常之德。这样，儒学最高本体完全内化为伦理性的绝对宇宙精神与道德律令。理学家还将这种本体植入人性中，看成人认识（心）世界的最高境界，这就是返璞归真，直指心性，将天赋人性中之“理”完整地通过主体行为外化出来，从而达到封建社会的长治久安即“修、齐、治、平”。这样，“天”“帝”蜕化为直接的伦理原则，成为伦理本体的代名词。在这种伦理原则规定下，“礼”即“法”，即“教”，即“理”，即“天”，就成为天经地义的不变法则了。

将伦理本体化，将“礼”张扬为人生命价值的最高规定性，其结果是造就出无数以生命和青春去铸就其人生价值与道德信念，去殉节、殉道的贞女节妇烈士侠客，这些人为了实现“礼”、“义”的人格目标而献身；同样也造就出岳飞、文天祥一类为国

① 董仲舒：《春秋繁露·离合根》。

家、民族献身的、受儒学天地“正气”所熏陶的英雄豪杰，成为中华文明史上名垂青史的不朽人物。这些还不是最重要的。从哲学和思辨的意义看，重要的是，这种哲学本体论的非人格化道德信仰的建立，使中国人几千年来始终保持一种完整的对道德的理性认识，亦即一些学者所称之的“民族集体理性”。同时，人们对民族、国家、社会的认同，基本上是持一种以华夏文化价值与道德伦理认同的积极入世的“中和”态度，而非其他一些古代国家、地区的宗教人格模式的狂热崇拜。因为儒家道德本体论范畴中所蕴含的“中和”“中庸”，以及“温良恭俭让”的认知方式及行为态度，让人们始终保持了一种温和的行事方式及价值认同，从而避免了中世纪以人格化偶像崇拜为中介带来的一些情绪化的东西。

第二，儒学道德本体论，使中国封建社会“礼义之邦”之文明特征凸现，尽管这种“礼义之邦”的特征对于个体精神自由带有一定的制约性。在道德本体化的价值规范中，“礼”是最重要的范畴，而“非礼勿视”等行为尺度同人心的良知、良能、良心、“天理”结合，或为横亘在人心中的重要的道义约束。这种道义约束，以及我们民族对道德的理念，应是人类社会发展阶段文明整合的重要形式。从公元前 5 世纪始，在世界范围内开始了所谓文明整合的“轴心时期”，即各大地区的文明，普遍采用一种形而上的信仰形式（其中大多表现为宗教的方式）对人类精神加以整合，以超现实的宗教及其伦理精神来规范人们的行为，强调一种形而上的道德（即宗教）律令。这种人类精神文明的整合，世界各地区是以不同方式展开的，但由于它强调精神的形而上性质，因此普遍是通过宗教形式，这也是世界几大宗教产生的基础。中国却走了一条特殊的道路。上承“三代”的儒学在建立后，通过许多代人的努力，将世俗化的道德直接本体论，将“礼”“仁”作为生命过程的道德律令，来建构了一个架设在个人与整体（国家、民族、家族）间的礼法价值体系。由于它是以直接的“礼”即社会规范的形式架构，亦由于它没有一种教义与教派的封闭性，因此它不仅是世俗的、开放的，而且亦是中国国家、民族，乃至每一个家庭、个人直接的道德伦理法则。它的结果是使中国人在积极入世的态度下，在“礼”的道义约束下，迅速进行了对民族精神规范性的整合，而且这种整合采用了“中庸”“中和”的处事方式，避免了许多过激或偏执的行为，如西欧中世纪基督教对异教徒的态度以及十字军东征之战等。这种在“礼”的道德律令支配下的精神同化过程，尽管有许多负面影响，也是以牺牲个人精神自由为代价，但是它是一种世界各国文明发展都必须得付出的代价。尤其在古代中国水旱频仍、战争不断的情况下，通过人们对这种高置于自己心上的形而上本体价值观的认同，通过由这种价值观转化的“天理”“良心”的认同，来达到对国家、民族、文化价值观的认同，而使中世纪散沙般的小农生产者凝聚成一个具有东方式道德的“礼义之邦”，文明国度，在国家统一、经济繁荣基础上走在世界其他国家之先。从这一点意义上说，儒学道德本体论与价值观是起着重要作用的。

第三，它使儒学具有一种自我超越的精神功能。儒学道德本体论强调对“善”的主动欲求。这种自我内蕴的对主观能动性的强调，对“善”的积极追求，使儒学具有一种自我超越的精神价值。自孔孟开始，儒学就主张对社会、人生的理想主义即理想社会和理想人格的追求、探索，并把超越人生自我情欲，实现以“德”为内涵的人生价值作为人生命自我实现的最高目标。这使儒学具有一种自我更新的调节与开放机制，也使儒学熏陶下的士人具有一种对国家、民族人文关怀的情怀。张载重塑儒学伦常，主张“为天地立心，为生民立命，为后世开太平，为往圣继绝学”，范仲淹“先天下之忧而忧，后天下之乐而乐”，以及儒学士子“生于忧患，死于安乐”的情怀，应当说都是在道德律令、范式之下的一种对理想社会和圣贤人格的追索。这种自我超越精神，使儒学历经中国封建社会的大动荡、大变动、大分裂的年代而继往如新；也使儒学在佛、老二教的挑战中能始终保持其主流地位。通过升华道德规范来促使人们去遵循道德，完善主观世界，超越自我，在儒学家看来是一个连续不断的过程。从孔子到程朱、陆王，随着其本体价值观的不断完备，其完善，自新与超越过程也在不断发展，这即是道德本体论所包容的“新民”思想。所谓“苟日新，日日新，又日新”，“《诗曰》：‘周虽旧邦，其命惟新。’是故君子无所不用其极。”① 朱熹释此曰：“言诚能一日有以涤其旧染之污而自新，则当因其已自新者，而日日新之，又日新之，不可略有间断也。”②在儒家士人那里，“止于至善”已成为无限超越的一种理念目标，尽管这种“修、齐、治、平”的“至善”目标从未一日实现过。但儒家这种强调自我更新、自我超越的精神是有一定意义的。

直到明代王阳明心学，王氏所主张的心即理、知行合一与致良知，也是要通过重新发现人的精神价值，充分发挥人心的主观能动性而达到“至善”目标的一种执着的追求，即所谓“君子无所不用其极”也。正是由于这种对主观精神世界的不断探索与超越，致使儒学开始走向它主观意志的反面。王阳明主张无限自我超越的结果，是使道德本体论中天道与人道合一的中介——心与性中的道德内蕴发生了变化，即由天赋性善转向超越善、恶之上的无善无恶的至真状态，即王阳明主张的“无善无恶心之体，有善有恶意之动，知善知恶是良知，为善去恶是格物。”这样，“天道”“天理”“心性”均成为超越人间善恶评价的至真本体，人的主观意志成为达到这至真本体的唯一舟车。尽管王学从本质上是强调“性”“理”至善的，但因过分强调主观意志在自“心”中的作用，以至于将自我意识扩充成为人的自性。而道德本体论从这时起就不断出现其理

① 《礼记·大学》。

② 《四书章句集注·大学章句》。

论上的巨大矛盾。因此，自王阳明后，王门后学开始在道德主体和伦理本位上出现分化，出现了王艮的“百姓日用即是道”；李贽“不以孔子是非为是非”；刘宗周的仁义礼智喜怒哀乐合一的性情论；黄宗羲“四德”性情合一思想。历史和儒学道德本体论开了一个玩笑，从强化封建纲常，并将之推崇为与“天道”并立为三的“人道”起始，以“百姓日用即是道”为终点，儒学道德本体论在不断超越自身和走向极致中出现矛盾，但是也是在这种矛盾中深入普通百姓之中，成为人人所遵循的“天理”“良心”。这是王阳明心学学理的二律背反，也是由儒学道德本体论自我内在的精神价值规律即不断地自我否定、超越所决定的。

第四，儒学道德本体论主张“中和”的天人合一论，将“天之大德曰生”“生生不已”作为自然的伦理法则，使中国人在与自然的关系上保持着一种和谐、协调的关系。儒学道德本体论，不仅将社会，亦将自然之道即自然规律看成是一种“圣人化之”，“功德参合”的伦理法则，将天地自身的“体仁行义”看作“生生不已”的春生夏长，秋收冬藏，以借此获得天道、地道与人道在内涵上的一致性。这种本体论思想，使人们对自然采取了一种中庸、随和乃至妥协的态度。自然界在人们认识中不是作为社会的对立物与征服的对象，而是作为人们对社会改造和自身修养及超越的一种伦理律令的参照物。所谓“格物致知”，“致知在格物”，则是“穷极事物之理，欲其极处无不到也”，[①] 是与正心诚意，修身齐家，治国平天下相关联的三纲领、八条目，是人间治道的参照系。因此，人类社会“善”的属性至自然界就成为“生”的寄托。人与自然的这种情怀，使自然多了拟人化的面貌。中国的士子常常在天人合一的意蕴中去体味自然、宇宙所内含的“道”，从自然山水中去观赏宇宙的道德律令与伦理法则，由此人和自然在一个同化的进程中发展其谐和的关系。儒学这一法则，表现在文学、艺术上则是“文以载道”，艺以载道，书（法）以载道，乐（音律）以载道。所谓“志于道，据于德，依于仁，游于艺”，“兴于诗，立于礼，成于乐”。《林泉高致·山水训》载北宋绘画理论家郭熙论山水画，有云：“春山烟云连绵，人欣欣。夏山嘉禾繁阴，人坦坦。秋山明净摇落，人肃肃。冬山昏霾翳塞，人寂寂。看此画令人生此意，如真在此山中，此画之境外意也。见青烟白道而思行，见平川落照而思望，见幽人山客而思居，见岩扃泉石而思游。看此画令人生此心，如将即其处，此画之意外妙也。”人在画中，自然在人境中，人的山水情怀及自然的人文情致一览无余。它形成了中国人独特的含蓄、内蕴、回味的艺术理论与审美理念，也构成人和自然的妙合关系。这种理论在与当前地球环境急剧恶化的情况下尤其有着现实意义。

因此，儒家道德本体论，就其对中国人及传统社会的精神价值言，有着重要的意

---

① 《四书章句集注·大学章句》。

义。这种价值及意义造就了独特的东方文明，并对外影响到东亚大陆。可是，无可讳言，儒学道德本体论，虽然就其基本立场来说，是片面夸大了社会伦理法则，将之抬高到“天”“道”的高度，是一朵绚丽的唯心主义不结果之花朵。但是在人类文明发展史上的关键时期，在人类面临精神与物质、物欲泛滥的拜物主义与道德至上的“天理”“良心”对立的巨大矛盾中，它的作用是不能够简单否定的。它在人类认识史上虽然只存在一个阶段或过程，但它对于中华文明的整合，并且持续影响我们国人精神世界二千余年，其思想学说的贡献是巨大的。所以，儒家道德本体论思想，也是东亚文明整合与发展中的一朵奇葩。

## 三、儒学道德本体论的当代参照意义

自“五四”新文化运动以后，中国近现代文化历程开始了新的起点。同时中国人的精神世界与价值观也有着新的参照系统与构建原点。但是，在新旧文化的冲突和“破”与“立”中，旧的文化价值系统在逐渐远去，而新的文化价值系统，尤其是新的社会规范与道德信念始终未能够全面、深入地建立起来。各种思想与价值观的冲突，影响着中国社会普遍价值系统的建设。新中国建立后，将国家的统一、民族的团结，以及建立一种新的中华文化价值系统作为努力的方向，并且在实践新的道德信念及其社会主义价值系统方面做出了很大成绩。但是，当“文化大革命”开始后，在破除“四旧”，“破旧立新”的口号中，中国固有的许多道德观念及社会规范被扫除了，而有助于巩固中国人道德价值信念的新体系却没有及时建立、完备。必须看到，“文化大革命”的后果，不仅是使当时中国经济面临崩溃的边缘，而且中国人固有的道德信念、伦理价值观也在破“四旧”、尊法批儒的狂热斗争中被粉碎。相对于经济而言，道德信念的摧折具有更大的后延性及隐形破坏力。改革开放以来，中国政府致力于经济的恢复及发展，取得了举世公认的伟大成绩，使我国成为世界第二大经济体，正在实现强国之梦。但是在市场经济的发展过程中，金钱崇拜，道德沦丧，腐败丛生的情况也成为当前中国社会的一些严重问题。食品安全、环保问题、假冒伪劣商品、官员腐败等，正在销蚀我国改革开放的成绩。固然在市场经济的发展过程中，这些问题的出现是不奇怪的。但是对于这些问题的遏制不力，却可能牺牲我国改革开放的成果。解决这些问题的根本要素，一是法制，二是信念，即人的主体道德信仰。总的来看，目前我国社会主义法制正在不断完善并发生效能。但是在建立社会主义道德信念方面，却还有很长的路要走。目前中央倡导的建立社会主义核心价值观，而社会主义道德信念、伦理价值的树立应该是其中一个重要内容。因此，建立社会主义道德信念，提升中华民族的道德价值观念，是使中华民族崛起和强大的精神基础，也是当前我们面临的一个十分重要的任务。

在实现这个任务中，我们必须注重对于沉淀于民族血液的传统文化和思想的吸取。任何一个民族、国家的传统文化，既有精华，又有糟粕；既有其需要扬弃的东西，也有合理的可以发古为今用的精神价值。在今天，在社会主义市场经济呼唤道德信念，呼唤公平、道义的时候，儒家道德本体论应该说仍然有着积极的参考意义。

1. 社会存在决定社会意识，物质决定精神。但是在一个社会中，物质与精神是相互作用的。作为一个社会的人，在其人生观和价值体系中，道德信念与伦理价值观念须占着主导性位置。康德说过："世界上有两件东西能够深深地震撼人们的心灵，一件是我们心中崇高的道德准则，另一件是我们头顶上灿烂的星空。"道德信念与伦理价值观是社会赖以建立的重要价值观念，它虽然依赖于社会存在，但是当它一旦形成，就有着超越个体人的物质观念而引领人们社会行为的作用。因此，道德准则犹如灿烂的星空一般的崇高，具有个体信念的意义。马克思·韦伯认为，资本主义是伴随着基督教新教伦理而一同发展起来的。新教伦理为崇尚资本、倾慕金钱的资本主义发展提供了道德指引的功能。甚至在当今资本主义社会，形而上的基督教伦理仍然在发挥作用。事实上，在人类社会发展中，人对于美好生活的需求与人的道德观念、价值信念始终是相辅相承的。没有社会需求就没有社会经济、文化的发展。同样，缺乏价值与信念，一个社会也将停滞、腐朽、衰弱。因此，科学与人伦，始终既有差异，又相互融合的。儒家道德本体论，将道德提到一个崇高地位，尽管有着许多负面影响，但是在一个世俗化的社会中，如何提供一个人安身立命的思想基础，如何给人们一种超脱人欲的道德信念，防止物欲横流，达到社会的稳定，却是有着重要作用的。

2. 儒家思想十分重视道德的功能，重视做事必先为人，强调治国平天下必须先"正心诚意""修身齐家"，将个体人的道德修养提高到人生命价值的高度。修身、齐家、治国、平天下是否是儒家思想的核心与精髓，这个还可以讨论。但是儒学体系的基本内涵是道德伦理及修养学说却是无疑的。儒家讲修身，指的是道德和自律。道德和自律并非与生俱来，而有赖于后天的学习与修养，有赖于人心中超然于非分物欲的道德标尺。例如儒家的利义观念，主张以义为原则，不要谋求非分之利，在利、义冲突中强调以义制利，在物质利益面前，首先考虑是否合乎道义。这个"道义"就是一种价值理念，是超然于物欲的精神。虽然这种精神是社会存在的反映，但是它一经产生，就超然于个体人的物质欲望，形成一种独立的道德标尺树立在人心中。这种思想在当时是有着合理因素的。即使仅从内容上看，儒家义利观中的"义"，既是对于地主阶级整体利益的关注，也是对于国家稳定、社会整合的关注。任何一个理性国家，除了有着阶级压迫的工具职能外，还有着社会控制与整合的职能，有着表面上维护公共利益的职能。在儒家看来，维护社会稳定与公众利益，也是一种"义"，是人所必需的道德信念。所以，儒学是非常注重道德信念与人伦原则的，主张在物质面前要保持一定操守。儒家道德本体论，将社会道德形而上学，将其伦理原则推到极限，这是不对的。但是将人伦、道德作为每个个体的人行为做事的内在尺度，作为一个社会普遍的做人原则。通过道德自律，在物欲横流的商品经济中，注重心中的道德准则，使人摆脱功利化倾向，强调做事必先做人。在古代中国这么一个没有统一宗教的世俗化国家，这种价值观有着其重要意义。它在今天我国社会主义市场经济的发展中，对于人们如何正确选择“义”与“利”，仍然有其借鉴价值。

3. 儒家在道德修养方面，主张从小事做起，从身边事做起，将道德信念与日常生活、洒扫应对结合起来。1957年冯友兰提出了“抽象继承法”，从具体意义和抽象意义这两个尺度来评价儒学传统。他认为就前者而言，儒学传统没有什么当代价值。但就后者而言，几乎都可以分析出在当代还有价值的东西。冯友兰的这种认识应该说有着一定道理。在人类发展史上，有些方法和规律是共通的。尤其在民族文化发展中，往往是以继承、创新为前提，而非全盘否定。例如孔子强调的教育方法，“多闻择其善者而从之，多见而识之”，“学而不思则罔，思而不学则殆”，对于促使学生主动自觉地学习与品德培养，确有着很好的效果，这些东西至今是我们民族文化的精神财富。

孔子的一系列道德范畴几乎都围绕中国古代宗法社会这一实际展开，如“孝悌”、“忠信”、“惠敏”、“智勇”，无一不是这种以宗法血缘关系为基点进行社会伦理教育。在当时的社会情况下，是有着合理性的，它主张从小事做起，从身边事做起，将道德信念与日常生活、洒扫应对结合起来。这对于古代社会的稳定与控制、整合，有着重要作用。正是在这个支点上，孔子提出了个人与整体、宗法与社会、“小类”与“大类”的联系与区别，并以个体、宗法血缘为基点向社会人际全面展开。“弟子入则弟，出则悌，谨而信，泛爱众，……”换言之，孔子的伦理思想，根本上是将人的自然种属性与人性化的亲子之情作为社会、民族伦理的基本法则，将“类”的共耦心态的建立与固化作为伦理的最终归宿。正是因为它符合了中国古代社会的特点，才能够延续几千年而不衰。今天我们进行的社会主义精神文明建设中，同样也需要借鉴传统文化的一些优秀的、符合中国实际的文化精髓，这对于我们建立社会主义精神文明，建立社会主义核心价值观有着积极的意义。

# 儒家道德

清华大学　钱　逊

儒学的精神用一个词来表示，就是道德。与现代道德连言不同，古代道和德分言。道，为人之道，做人的根本原则；德，得也；道之得于己者为德。道德是这两个方面的总称。本文所说，即在这个意义上之道德。

## 一、道是儒家道德的最高层次

儒家道德是一个包含多个层次的体系。道和德，是传统道德的两个基本的层次。

道，“日用事物当行之路”，是一切人伦日用所当遵行，指示着为人的方向。懂得为人之道，就不至于走入邪路。

子曰:“朝闻道，夕死可矣。”(《里仁》)

子曰:“笃信好学，守死善道，危邦不入，乱邦不居。天下有道则见，无道则隐。邦有道，贫且贱焉，耻也；邦无道，富且贵焉，耻也。”(《泰伯》)

能知为人之道，生命就获得了意义，可以死而无憾。出入进退，富贵贫贱，生死抉择，一切都是为了善道。道之于人，不啻生命。

道的内容，所指为何?

仁以为己任，不亦重乎?死而后已，不亦远乎?(《论语·泰伯》)

提出一个仁字。孟子则兼说仁义:

仁义而已矣。居仁由义，大人之事备矣。(《孟子·尽心上》)

具体说:

子路问君子。子曰:“修己以敬。”曰:“如斯而已乎?”曰:“修己以安人。”曰:“如斯而已乎?”曰:“修己以安百姓。修己以安百姓，尧舜其犹病诸。”(《宪问》)

人生在世，面对两大基本问题：物质生命与精神生命的关系、个体与群体的关系。修己和安人、安百姓，是对这两大问题的回答，亦即为人之道的两大要义。

修己，即以精神生命为重，努力修身，提高自己的精神境界。

子曰："士志于道，而耻恶衣恶食者，未足与议也。"（《里仁》）

子曰："君子忧道不忧贫。"（《卫灵公》）

子曰："富与贵是人之所欲也，不以其道得之，不处也；贫与贱是人之所恶也，不以其道得之，不去也。"（《论语·里仁》）

谋道与谋食对举，说的就是就是精神生命和物质生命的关系，志于道，应致力于修己，而非孜孜于衣食等物质生活的追求；追求富贵，厌弃贫贱是人之常情，但对摆脱贫贱，得到富贵的追求，应服从道的要求，而不能以物质生命凌驾于精神生命之上。孔子又说：

"君子义以为上。"

以精神生命放在第一位，这是为人之道的第一要义。

安人、安百姓，即人不能只为个人，还需为他人，为百姓谋福祉。是对个体与群体关系问题的回答。

子贡曰："如有博施于民而能济众，何如？可谓仁乎？"子曰："何事于仁？必也圣乎！尧舜其犹病诸！夫仁者，己欲立而立人，己欲达而达人。能近取譬，可谓仁之方也已。"（《雍也》）

博施于民而能济众，是圣人之事，尧舜其犹病诸。而"己欲立而立人，己欲达而达人"，则是对仁者的要求，为仁之方。

前引子路问君子章，说到修己以安百姓，孔子也说"尧舜其犹病诸"，博施于民而能济众，即安百姓之意；己欲立而立人，己欲达而达人，即修己以安人。前者是圣人之事，后者是君子的要求。

孔子居乱世。当时的隐者，认为乱象恶事如滔滔洪水，无人能够改变，劝孔子的弟子，不如跟随他们避世隐居。孔子听后慨叹：

"鸟兽不可与同群，吾非斯人之徒与而谁与？天下有道，丘不与易也。"（《微子》）

人生不可离群，人生责任也无可逃于天地之间；正因天下无道而尤其加重其责任。离群避世，是放弃了自己的责任。

置身群体中，心系他人，与群体共命运，群己统一，是为人之道又一要义。

综上所述，义与群，是人禽相区别，人之所以为人之所在；义以为上，群己统一，是为人之道的根本要义，是为儒家道德之第一层次。

## 二、德的两个层次

德，得也；道之得于己者为德。道为德之本，德为道之用。道抽象而简单，德具体而丰富。只知道的抽象原则，不能成为行为的依据。只有了解其具体内容，得于己，落实于日常言行中，才能成为行为的依据，所以说据于德。《论语》多处谈德，提出众多德目。如：

夫子温良恭俭让得之。

能行五者于天下，为仁矣。曰：恭、宽、信、敏、惠。

刚、毅、木、讷近仁。

行己有耻。

智者不惑，仁者不忧，勇者不惧。

人之生也直，罔之生也幸而免。

主忠信。

弟子入则孝，出则弟，谨而信，泛爱众，而亲仁。

众多德目，可分为两个层次。一为共同的、一般人际交往之德，是一般人际交往中普遍适用的；一是个别的人伦之德，这种德的要求，只是在某一种特定的人伦关系中，对特定的对象适用。即孝悌忠信四端，也分属这两个不同层次；孝悌属于后者，忠信属于前者。

孝，善事父母；弟，善待兄弟。是专用于父子兄弟之间。孟子：

圣人有忧之，使契为司徒，教以人伦，父子有亲，君臣有义，夫妇有别，长幼有叙，朋友有信。(《孟子》)对父、子、君、臣、夫、妇、长、幼各有其不同之德的要求。如父慈子孝、兄友弟恭，以及妇女之三从四德等等，均属此类。此类专属某种人伦关系之德，也有人称之为角色伦理。

儒家提倡的德，更多的不属此类。如忠信，并不专限于某种人伦关系，而是适用于一般人际关系。忠，尽己之谓忠。曾子自省，为人谋而不忠乎？信，人而无信，不知其可也。均为待人立世的普遍共同要求。勇、智、直、刚、温、良、恭、俭、让等亦然。

德之两层次，性质有不同。个别的人伦之德，直接反映社会制度的要求，有较强的时代性，随时代变迁而变。人际交往的共同的一般之德，则为人与人交往的普遍共同之追求，超越时代及地域之限制，古今中外，概莫能外。这两类不同的德，构成整个德目体系。

从《论语》看，在这两类德中间，孔子重视忠信重于孝弟，重视共同一般的德重于各别人伦的德。《论语》中弟子问仁、问君子、问成人、问何如可以为士，孔子回答中极少谈到孝弟，只在《子路》篇答子贡问“何如斯可谓之士矣?”时提到孝悌。原文是说：

子贡问曰：“何如斯可谓之士矣?”子曰：“子宫 辱君命，可谓士矣。”曰：“敢问其次。”曰：“宗族称孝焉，乡党称弟焉。”曰：“敢问其次。”曰：“言必信，行必果，硁硁然小人哉！抑亦可以为次矣。”曰：“今之从政者何如？”子曰：“噫！斗筲之人，何足算也。”

是在回答“敢问其次”的时候才提到“宗族称孝焉，乡党称弟焉。”只是作为士的次等的要求。对于忠信，则多次提到“主忠信”，要以忠信为主，以此作为君子的一项重要要求和标准。7·24章“子以四教：文、行、忠、信。”以忠信为所教之本。5·27章还说“十室之邑，必有忠信如丘者焉，不如丘之好学也。”都是突出了忠信。还有，子贡问曰：“有一言而可以终身行之者乎？”子曰：“其恕乎！己所不欲，勿施于人。”（《卫灵公》）子贡问什么是可以终身践行的，孔子回答说是恕，也没有提孝。而曾子还说“夫子之道，忠恕而已矣。”可见，孔子更重视的是忠信、忠恕，以及这一类共同的一般的德。

五四时期，陈独秀说过：

记者之非孔，非谓其温良恭俭让信义廉耻诸德及忠恕之道不足取，不过谓此等道德名词，乃世界普遍实践道德，不认为孔教自矜独有者耳。士若私淑孔子，立身行己，忠恕有耻，固不失为一乡之善士，记者敢不敬其为人？（答《新青年》爱读者）

吾人不满于儒家者，以其分别男女尊卑过甚，不合于现代社会之生活也。（阴阳家）

可见当时新文化运动的领导人，就已经指出了儒家道德中两个层次的不同。并且明确说明他们反对旧道德，主要是反对反映等级制度要求，别尊卑明贵贱的那部分特殊的个别的德，而并非反对儒家道德之全部。

综上所述，儒家道德，包含道与德两个层次，德又有共同一般之德与各别人伦之德两层次。合而言之，可说是三层次。道与德，道为本，德为用。道是贯穿于整个道德体系中的根本精神，德是道的具体体现。

## 三、德和礼

据于德，就要说到礼。礼是德的载体；德通过礼而落实、体现。据于德，也就是要依礼而行。

颜渊问仁。子曰：“克己复礼为仁。一日克己复礼，天下归仁焉。为仁由己，而由人乎哉？”颜渊曰：“请问其目？”子曰：“非礼勿视，非礼勿听，非礼勿言，非礼勿动。”颜渊曰：“回虽不敏，请事斯语矣。”（《颜渊》）

颜渊问什么是仁，怎么做到仁？孔子说“克己复礼为仁”。克制、去掉自己一些和礼不符的东西，按照礼去做就是仁了。凡是不符合礼的，不要看，不要听，不要说，不要做，视听言动都按照礼的要求，这就做到仁了，即“仁”要落实到“礼”上。

> 孟懿子问孝，子曰：“无违”。樊迟御，子告之曰：“孟孙问孝于我，我对曰无违。”樊迟曰：“何谓也。”子曰：“生，事之以礼；死，葬之以礼，祭之以礼。”(《为政》)

父母生前依礼的要求侍奉父母，身后依礼的要求安葬和祭祀。这就是孝了。

仁和孝，体现在实际生活中，就是依礼而行。礼的规定体现了德的要求，德通过礼而得到落实和检验。德是内在的灵魂，礼是外在的规范、行为。德和礼不可分。离开德，礼就徒具形式，失去灵魂和意义；离开礼，德就流于虚空，难以落实和检验。所以说，不学礼，无以立。(《论语·季氏》)

所以，孔子说为政，说“道之以德，齐之以礼”；孔子说教育，“博学于文，约之以礼”；颜渊说孔子的教育，“博我以文，约我以礼。”“子以四教：文、行、忠、信。”文，“博学于文”，是学道；行，“约之以礼”，是据于德而行。礼的功能、作用是“齐”是“约”，约束和统一人们的行为。德的教育落实在礼的教育上，同时也是礼的教育。

## 四、德教的层次性

谈儒家道德，不能不谈到德教。

从前文所述，可知儒家道德是包含道、德、礼等不同层次的一个大体系。儒家道德的层次性，决定了德教的层次性。这种层次性表现于两个方面，一是从小学而大学的为学次第，一是士君子之教和庶人之教的层次差别。

道与德，道抽象而德具体。德之二层次，一般之德为共同之要求，人伦之德为个别之要求；后者又较前者具体而直接。三者依次由抽象而具体。从适用范围看，则前者宽而后者窄。人之道德修养，一般即由人伦之德始，由具体而抽象，由近而及远。道德的层次性，决定了修身进德由低到高的进程，是安排道德教育次第的依据。

《论语》：

> 子曰：“弟子入则孝，出则弟，谨而信，泛爱众，而亲仁。行有余力，则以学文。”

反映了由人伦之德孝弟而谨信、爱众、亲仁之一般之德，再至学文致道的次第。

古代教育有小学、大学之分。八岁入小学，十五入大学。所学各有不同。

> 小学涵养此性，大学则所以实其理也。忠信孝悌之类，须于小学中出。然正心、诚意之类，小学如何知得。须其有识后，以此实之。(《朱子语类》卷 19)

孝弟、谨信、爱众、亲仁属小学之事，为据德之学，以力行为主。“行有余力，则以学文”，说明修身应自力行据德之学始，而又不可止于此。

力行而不学文，则无以考圣贤之成法，识事理之当然，而所行或出于私意，非但失之于野而已。（《论语集注》）

《论语》又有：

子游曰："子夏之门人小子，当洒扫应对进退则可矣，抑末也。本之则无，如之何?"子夏闻之曰："噫，言游过矣！君子之道，孰先传焉，孰后倦焉，譬诸草木，区以别矣。君子之道，焉可诬也？有始有卒者，其惟圣人乎?"（《子张》）

就本末言，洒扫应对之行是末；圣贤之成法，事理之当然是本。就先后言，洒扫应对之行在先，行有余力学文。本末先后，不可不辨。而所以辨明此一切之基础，就在于分析把握儒家道德的层次性。

儒家德教的层次性也表现于士君子之教和庶人之教的差别上。

儒家道德包含由浅之深的不同层次，它植根于人们的日常生活，源于普通人日用常行的经验，为百姓所践行；特别如孝悌这等个别人伦之德，其最初的表现往往表现为不虑而知，不学而能的良知良能。而它所内涵的思想精神则深邃博大，不是一般人所能理解，甚至饱学之士，也难以穷尽。如《中庸》所说：

君子之道费而隐。夫妇之愚，可以与知焉，及其至也，虽圣人亦有所不知焉；夫妇之不肖，可以能行焉，及其至也，虽圣人亦有所不能焉。（《中庸》）

另一方面，人们接受能力的差异，是一切教育必须考虑的基本前提。儒家德教对此极为重视。孔子的教育因材施教，前提是"中人以上，可以语上也；中人以下，不可以语上也。"（《论语·雍也》）孟子说："行之而不著焉，习矣而不察焉，终身由之而不知其道者，众也。"（《孟子·尽心上》）基于此，儒家德教对士君子和庶人提出了不同的要求。这两个不同层次的要求，形成了德教的两个系列和传统。

孔、孟的教育，是以士为对象，以培养君子为目标，其内容"志于道，据于德，依于仁，游于艺"是对成人的全面要求，而中心是"致其道"。孔子谈对君子、士的要求，主要在道的层次。子路问君子，孔子答以"修己安人、安百姓"；子贡问士，孔子答以"行己有耻，不辱君命"；子路问成人，孔子答以"知，不欲，勇，艺，文之以礼乐"，退而求其次是"见利思义，见危授命，久要不忘平生之言"。孟子谈士则说"居仁由义，大人之事备矣。"都体现道的要求。更提出"朝闻道，夕死可矣"，"守死善道"，"有杀身以成仁，无求生以害仁"和"富贵不能淫，贫贱不能移，威武不能屈"，义与生不可得兼时"舍生取义"等要求。这些要求为历代士人所接受，是无数仁人志士毕生追求的最高人格理想。范仲淹"先天下之忧而忧，后天下之乐而乐"。文天祥临终遗言说毕生读圣贤书，所学为孔孟成仁取义之义；抗元失败，被俘不屈，捐躯就义，庶几无愧。顾炎武说圣人之道是博学于文，行己有耻。认为"士大夫之无耻，是谓国耻"，提出天下兴亡，匹夫有责的思想。他们深得儒家真谛，学习、追求、践行；儒家为人之道造就了他们伟大人格。他们是中国士君子的代表。他们和无数仁人志士的这种精神，集中体现了中国人的价值观和中华民族的民族精神，形成了我国士人的传统，影响着整个社会，也是维系中华文化五千年绵延不绝的重要支柱。

与士君子之教并行的还有庶人之教。孔子说“道之以德，齐之以礼，有耻且格”，提出“庶、富、教”的为政要求；孟子以“谨庠序之教”为仁政的重要内容，以对百姓的教化为施政的基础，是儒家的重要传统。而教化的内容，《论语》说“弟子入则孝，出则弟，谨而信，泛爱众，而亲仁。行有余力，则以学文”。孟子说是“教以人伦，父子有亲，君臣有义，夫妇有别，长幼有叙，朋友有信”；“申之以孝悌之义”。重点在据德之教。对于基本德目，历代有不同的概括，有的概括为“孝悌忠信”，“忠孝节义”等；影响较大的则有“孝悌忠信礼义廉耻”和“忠孝仁爱信义和平”。这种教育，渗透在中国人生活的一切方面。节庆礼俗，乡规民约，家训、治家格言，以及戏剧、小说、诗词歌赋等一切艺术形式中，无所不在，陶冶了中国人独特的生活方式，由此而使中国得到礼仪之邦的美誉。尽管多数百姓是处于“日用而不知”的状态，但却是实实在在的传统，中华文化的最主要的存在和表现。

针对不同人群的不同层次的德教，覆盖了全社会，渗透到社会的一切方面，构成极有效的教育体系，也成为中华文化传统的一个重要方面。这份宝贵遗产今天有着特别的意义，需要认真研究和继承。

## 五、两点思考

### （一）关于对中国道德（或儒家道德）的认识

有一种观点认为，儒家道德或中国传统道德的特点是人伦道德或角色道德。对此，有几点可以讨论。

第一，从前面所说，可知个别的人伦道德，或称角色道德，只是儒家道德的一部分，一个层次。儒家道德中，德的主要部分，是共同的人际交往中的一般的德，是一个人应该怎么做的普遍道理。

不仅如此。儒家道德，还是一个包含道、德、礼的体系。在现在一般所说的道德之上还有一个道的层次，而德又和礼不可分。这样的一个体系，反映出中西文化的差异，是儒家道德的更大特色。所以以角色伦理为儒家道德之特色，并不准确。以此作为儒家道德的一个特点则可，以此作为整个儒家道德的特点则不可。

第二，儒家道德的出发点和基础，是对人、人性的探究。我们的先贤从夏商周朝代的更替，认识到“天命靡常”，由此而思考天命与人事的关系。从周初“敬德保民”，“祈天永命”，到孔子“与命与仁”，建立人文思想体系，到《中庸》“天命之谓性，率性之谓道，修道之谓教”，再到孟子“尽心知性知天”，建立性道合一、天道与人道合一的思想体系，思考的对象始终是人、人性、人道；是与天、与自然、与禽兽相对的人，而不是单个的个人。思考的问题是“人是什么?”而不是“我是谁?”这里反映出中西文化在根本思维方式上的差别。以儒家道德为角色伦理，立论的基础是说儒家“基于将人视为处于互系的观念，将人家庭角色及关系作为修养道德能力的起步”（安乐哲《儒家角色伦理学：挑战个人主义意识形态》，《孔子研究》2014年第一期）虽然他也强调在儒家思想里“人不是个体的”，然而他所说的“互系”“角色”，出发点还是“个体的”人；互系是个体的人之间的互系，角色是个体的人的角色。他并没有真正跳出西方文化立足于个体的人来思考人的思维方式。

第三，把儒家道德理解为角色伦理，不能正确反映儒家道德的特点，不能充分反映儒家文化的根本价值观和中华民族民族精神的核心内容。无论内外，都不利于中华文化的发扬光大。五四时期陈独秀等人只把这一部分当作中国传统道德，而认为其他中华美德都是“世界普遍实践道德”而排除在传统道德之外，一定程度上导致对传统道德全盘否定的误解，也自外于世界多元文化，否定了中华文化、儒家道德所有的普世价值。全面认识传统道德，注重对传统道德的普世价值的发掘和发扬，才能更好地走出去，与其他文化交流；也只有这样，才能使传统道德更好地与现代社会和中国特色社会主义建设的要求相适应，成为建设当代中华民族共有精神家园的基础。

（二）关于中华传统文化教育

国内的社会状况，信仰缺失、价值迷乱、道德崩坏已经成为破坏社会和谐，阻碍经济社会发展的大患，也是广大民众关注的焦点之一。重建我们的信仰、价值、道德风气和秩序，复兴中华文化，是当前的重大问题。儒家道德，无论其内容还是德教的经验，对于解决这个问题都有重要的意义。

儒家道德的基本内容和精神，和社会主义核心价值，方向是一致的，内容是相辅相成的。对于社会主义核心价值体系建设，中华文化教育是带基础性意义的一环；而对于中华文化教育，社会主义核心价值体系建设则具有方向性的意义。

儒家道德的核心价值，可以提出五点来说：义、群、礼、和、耻、义，物质生命和精神生命的关系。人的生活，有两个方面：物质生活和精神生活，由此生命也有物质生命和精神生命两方面。物质生命的基础是人的生物本能，和禽兽没有根本区别；精神生命的基础是人的社会生活，是人所独有而禽兽没有的，是人不同于禽兽，人之所以为人的根本之处。所以，人要摆脱禽兽的境界，成为堂堂正正的人，就要“义以为上”，把精神生命的追求放在第一位。

群。个人和群体的关系。人是社会性的，生活在群体中，一刻不能脱离群体。所以应该把个人放在群体中，求个人和群体相统一。个人作为群体的一分子，个人发展和社会、民族、国家发展统一。群己统一。

和。义、群是从人禽之别，人之所以为人角度讲，和是从对宇宙、社会整体的认识讲。以和为贵不是单纯的美好愿望，是以对宇宙的根本认识为基础而提出的根本价值观．“和实生物”。宇宙万物都是不同成分和因素和谐共存的统一体。从自然到人类社会，从家庭、单位、社区、社会、国家、国际，以至生态，都是如此。所以以和为贵，在承认差别的基础上求各得其所。

礼。是从落实的角度讲。遵守道德、礼制的规范。以上义、群、和三点都通过礼而落实。总之，一切行为举止，不离礼的规范；“立于礼”，“不学礼，无以立”。

耻。是从道德的基础讲。行己有耻，有所不为。羞耻心是做人的底线，是道德自律的基础，有耻才能有所不为。无羞耻之心，就会无所不为。无所不为是危险的，不可救药的。所以人不可以无耻。

以上五项，从不同角度反映做人的根本要求，构成中国人为人之道的核心价值体系。这五项，反映了中西文化在根本宇宙观、天人关系等问题上，以及社会、国家治理问题上思维方式的根本差别；同时又都具有普遍的意义，可以成为普世价值。

“修道之谓教”，道德流行有赖于教育、教化。近年来，传统美德教育已经受到愈来愈多的重视，在政府和民间的共同努力推动下，有了极大的发展。但也还存在许多困难和问题，远不能适应社会的实际需要。总的来说，是以民间活动为主，表现出明显的分散、无序的特点，带有相当程度的自发性；教育的内容，主要在据德之教的层次，而又以孝道教育为主，较少注意到的层次，即理想信念、价值观的教育；读经活动广泛开展，但对读什么？怎么读？谁来教？等，都没有明确的回答；儒学学术的研究则走向专业化的道路，日益与教化脱节；民间教化活动难以得到学界及时有效的指导和帮助。

面对如此的现状，借鉴传统德教的经验，重要的问题是要做好顶层设计，建立和完善传承、普及儒学和中华文化，进行中华传统文化教育的体系。这个体系，应不局限于文化教育、思想宣传领域，而要统筹国家、社会治理的各个方面、各个部门，渗透到社会生活一切领域，涵盖各个阶层和群体，运用一切有效的方式，对不同对象有不同的要求和做法。

# 儒家良知教的现代性新开展

贵州大学 张新民

## 一、良知为人生社会的天则明师

至少一个多世纪以来，良知教不仅在学校教育中缺位，而且也在社会生活中隐遁，已是大家长期习焉不察的普遍现象了。我们知道有这样那样的分科分目的老师，我们都希望拜在名师门下求学，甚至政府也在树立道德模范，希望通过道德模范的宣传来影响和转移社会风气，但我们却遗忘了人人都天然拥有的且内在于心性之中的一位最好的老师——“天则明师”——良知，遗忘了依据我们的“天则明师”的绝对律命做出的行为才是真正的道德行为，遗忘了“天则明师”的存在才是人之所以为人的先验存在根据，遗忘了按照“天则明师”的旨意做出的选择才是最真实最本然的选择，遗忘了让“天则明师”恢复其应有的正位才能获得真正的主体自由。现代中国教育的失败乃是多方面的原因造成的，但良知教的缺位或隐遁无疑也是值得我们反思的一大历史原因。

提到“天师明师”和良知教，我们就会想到王阳明，就会想到龙场悟道，就会想到一群肖小对一个哲人的迫害，就想到哲人面对生死困境的生命沉思，就会想到哲人在黑暗现实中的挺拔和超越，就会想到哲人在受辱蒙垢的情况下仍对人性的光明面充满了信心，就会想到哲人在沉沦的世界中的惊天动地的良知呼唤，就会想到哲人即使身后也会遭到凡俗庸众的误读误解，就会想到哲人在现代社会消失退隐后的悲凉和无奈。

哲人消失退隐后的悲凉和无奈，当然在古代社会也时有发生，如明代高僧蕅益智旭大师便明确宣称：“近代传孔颜心法者，惟阳明先生一人；传佛祖心法者，惟紫柏大师一人。旭生也晚，习儒时，不得亲炙阳明，后学佛，不得躬承紫柏。所以虽于儒释源流，略窥一线，知与世谛流布之理学禅机，迥然不同，而障厚慧弱，福薄习强，遂尔半生误于虚名，罔臻实诣。[1]”与蕅益大师相较，我们今天当然更生活在一个无哲人的时代，或者说是生活在一个后哲人的时代，众声喧哗者全是凡庸的声音，而所谓“障厚慧弱”、“罔臻实诣”者，更百倍于倍于蕅益大师，时代的悲凉与无奈岂能不油然而生？

蕅益大师于佛教则推崇紫柏，紫柏与蕅益一样，均为明代著名高僧，影响后世甚深，其事迹可暂且不论；而儒家人物中，他最为看重者，即比他稍早的王阳明，原因是在他看来，王阳明颇得孔颜心法，故生无限向往之情，颇以不能亲炙为憾。蕅益大师非儒门内人物，评价反而相对客观。可见良知学说，不仅是对治时代弊病的良方，而且也是孔颜心法的发扬，值得我们重返自己的心性，再思再认人类自我拯救的路径。

更明白地说，尽管我们生活在一个后哲人的时代，后哲人的时代必然让人悲凉与无奈，但只要孔子所说的“仁”，颜回所体会的“乐”孟子所强调的“义”，朱熹所提倡的“理”，王阳阳所揭示的“良知”，其真实精神或实质涵义仍长存于天壤之间，人类社会就有希望，哲人就可能重新出现，悲凉就是暂时的心境，无奈也是偶然的现象。这就是为什么我们提倡良知教重返社会与校园的原因，无论“仁”、“乐”、“义”、“理’”、“良知”，都不应该是外在于我们生命存在的“他物”，

## 二、沟通先验与经验两重世界

以良知为“天则明师”，即是说价值的本源实则植根于我们的心性，既有着先验的形上的超越的来源，也可以转化为经验的形下的行动的事实。良知根源于最深层、最微妙的人性，又可通过心的能动运作而外显，不能不是天理的心灵化表达，当然也是天德的肉身化展开，同时更是天命的行动化落实。而人的生命亦在此过程——由“天”而“人”或由“人”而“天”的不断循环往复互动过程——与天理、天德、天命合一，获得终极性的意义与价值，步入天人合一的真实性的圣域。

以良知为“天则明师”，实即以人性之神明为师。“盖神灵之生有自来，故性识早定于童幼，如旭日初出，已自皎然大明；其后之进，不过升至中天，濛气渐解，而光耀更照耳。虽有增益，非如常人之性识，如聚薪而然之也。[2]”可见以良知为“天则明师”，当然就能凭借人性神明的烛照，根据生命固有的直观智慧，了解什么是真实和不真实，知道什么是应该和不应该，在自得进学的次第提升过程中，不断地实现生命的意义和价值。而“明师”则既在人的理性活动中呈现自己的存在，化为生命行动或生

① 蕅益大师：《灵峰宗论·赠石淙掩关礼忏占轮相序》，北京图书馆出版社，2005年，第377页。

② 康有为：《论语述》卷二，《康有为全集》，中国人民大学出版社2007年，第6集，第388页。

活实践的灵活指南；也能以情感的形式升华我们的实存感受，透过善的向度消弭一切人间隔阂，获得价值源源滚滚沛然涌出的体验愉悦，在生命的乐境中展示自己的存在，成为人生态度及人间事务的基本律则。良知的根源在天地宇宙，良知之知即是天地宇宙之知，但良知之知的活动本质上仍是人的切身性活动，必须经过人的活动而与现象界发生关联。因此，良知教作为“天则明师”示现和引导人生实现自身价值的活动过程，显然也是天理、天德、天命与人的实存生命浃然合为一体的成己之学的过程。

但良知与良知教，如果不徒作玩弄光影，不执着于文字表相，如果重新回到王阳明生死困厄的苦难处境，与古人同发于一境界，就不难发现它是何等的动心忍性的修持工夫才得出的人性结论，是何等的实存体悟的工夫才从心性中流淌出来的生命言说。良知及良知教学说，真可说是千古永存，不因时间有过去、现在、未来而改变，不因地域有东、西、南、北而消失。人不能没有良知，人必须有良知，因为良知是先天的、先验的，是天植灵根且内具于人性之中的。也就是说，生命存在，良知就存在。没有先天本然的良知存在，人便不能成为真正意义上的人，就完全丧失了完成自己德性生命和文化生命的可能。良知不思而能，不虑而知，乃是人与动物的一大根本性区别。良知一旦泯灭或丧丢，人就变成非人，人就退堕为动物，可见良知乃是人的真实存在依据，而良知教就是要使人成为真正意义的人——不仅凭借内观了解广袤精神世界的先验超越来源，更要依据行动将其转化为人间充满温情的可靠经验事实。

但是，良知尽管为先天的存有，可称为先验的形上本体，乃是含藏着理性、充满着情感的心灵的永恒法则，却可以治化为后天的行为，能够通过“事上磨练”的工夫变化人的气质，升华人的存在状态，见证生命意义和值的现实到场。凭借良知虽沉默却大声的呼唤，依据良知教所要求的生命实践的精义，能够唤醒我们最深层的善良意识，并透过善良意识过滤了的智慧直觉来认识人人皆有的真实人性。这就是儒家一贯重视的尽心知性的工夫，也是良知教之所以必要和必须的一大前提。由于良知教可以外显为客观的经验事实，良知教的要义即在于生命的磨试与道德的实践，因而它本身也是我们展开社会批判的价值活泉，积极从事人间秩序建构活动的力量来源。所以依据良知所开启的精神天地，一方面我们可以步入形上的境域，领悟不证自明的生命的神圣本源，获得单凭理性思辨根本就无从获得的人性形上学答案，体悟只有在智慧直觉的光明内照下才能如实证取的真知；一方面我们也能够据此踏进经验的世界，看到人间现实社会中各种善意的关怀，危难的帮助，绝境的安慰，厄困的解救，而一切人间的温情善意，都足以提示我们良知的存在，告诉我们“人之超然万物之上，而最为天下贵”的结论的可靠正确。[①]

---

① 董仲舒：《春秋繁露》卷十七《天地阴阳》，上海古籍出版社，1989年，第99页。

由此可见，良知既能沟通先验与经验两重世界，也具有先验与经验两重性格。一方面良知乃是形上的精神的心灵的，源于最深层的人性的内部，属于不可说的范畴；一方面良知又不能不是实践的行动的存在的，可以外化为社会的现象，属于可以言说的范畴。因此，良知的存在是先天自明的，它的存在及其起用流行既无须依赖也不必脱离外部经验的存在，根本就超越于权力世界之上，挺拔于功利市场之外，不仅不为权利世界和功利世界所左右，反而是权力世界与功利世界最强大的批判资源，是一切社会政治文化行为正当性的审理依据。而推行良知教的目的，即是打通先验与经验两重世界，避免经验与超验两重世界的割裂，既维护人的存在本有的庄严与神圣，也将生命的潜能转化为现实的意义与价值。

## 三、对治社会与时代的病症

先天自明的良知，乃是一切道德活动的本体论来源，也是一切社会建构活动的正当性来源。良知虽隐蔽而能外显，虽外显而又隐蔽。虽是个人的心灵的语言和召唤，但也可以转化为社会的公共的语言和召唤，是人之所以为人的灵性根据，是人人都有的天植灵根，是发潜道之幽光的最伟大的生命美感示范，是天壤间永不可朽坏的生命种子，是人类社会最需要珍惜护守的创造性力量，是人与人之间交往与沟通最活泼的情义触媒。离开了代表心性的虚明灵觉的良知的即体即用的活动，人类的一切才情艺术和哲学文化创造活动便都无从谈起。

然而，现实世界人性的扭曲、沉沦和堕落，却导致我们丢失了本有的良知，造成了生命的异化，产生了人与人之间的疏离。人不再向往价值理想，却长于工具理性计算，面对强大的体制与市场，感受到的只是自己的空虚和无力。而一旦人人都将工具理性奉为至上，人人都以工具理性为处世原则，人就难免不会多疑、猜忌、放纵、享乐，虽精于得失多寡的计算，却失去了根本就无法计算的生活意义。享乐的机会膨胀放大，固有的天性则枯萎蔫缩。人只能逃避自己，却不敢面对自己，既丧失了本属自己的主体性，也泯灭了与主体同在的生命自由。而主体性的自由一旦丧失，创造性的活力也就随之枯萎，不但个人生命会感到窒息，即社会国家也必然一派死寂。

更为严重的是，现代社会恰恰凭借消费市场的扩大，娱乐方式的增加，为人们提供了更多的逃避责任的空间，依靠物质繁荣的假象掩盖了精神贫困的真相。而现代教育之所以失败，也恰恰是只有知识灌输、技能训练，却缺乏人格教育、生命提升。既无个人心性体贴和良知肯认的工夫，当然就谈不上人与人之间的感通互助。人一方面不能不防范他人，变得贪婪、狂傲、乖暴、轻浮，一方面也封闭了自己，变得冷酩、自私、麻木、阴鸷。古人肝胆相照、气贯日月的侠义精神，现代社会是很难看不到了。

诚如萨特所说，他人不仅是激烈竞争的对手，他人也是必须防范的地狱。地狱埋葬的非仅是实存的自我，更是生命在世不可或缺的意义和价值。颓废与虚无弥天盖地，欺骗与假言无处不在，这显然是现代教育的最大失败，不仅暴露了社会的病相，也造成了时代的不幸。

因此，为了匡正文化的价值发展方向，为了改变现代人生的不幸，为了对治时代社会的病症，我们显然大有必要重新开出现代性的良知教，让良知教重返人生，重返家庭，重返校园，重返社会，并内化为活的人格形态，具化为活的生活内容。试想人一旦泯灭了良知，心灵只是一片黑暗，社会则必然充满戾气，国家亦将遍布乱象，不仅人与人之间会横生隔阂，即人与世界之间也会出现断裂。人有如一堆碎片，完全成为无灵性的行尸走肉；世界也将一片荒芜，完全退堕为率兽食人的丛林。所以恢复源自本心的良知教，就是恢复人与人之间的真诚、信任、坦荡与关怀，维护人的尊严、庄重、高贵和荣耀，让人重新回归生命的意义世界和价值世界，让良知的阳光雨露重新撒满人间大地，滋润一切蓬勃发展的创造性生命和存在。

## 四、良知必须参与历史文化的创造活动

面对今天的时代困境，寻找人类的未来希望，重提良知学说，恢复良知教育，让良知教重新进入家庭、校园和社会，从积极方面说，就是要恢复人的主体性自由，维护人的尊严，重现人的自性光明，回归人的真实生命，实现人的真实价值；从消极方面看，则是要改变人的不自由状态，打破人的封闭，化除人的桎梏，消解人的私欲偏见，对治人的存在迷惑。良知教即是人性之教，人格之教，生命之教，行动之教，必须做到知行合行，在行动中见证真理，在行动中体悟真实，在行动中领悟意义，在行动中实现价值，与一切虚假天然对立，与一切异化决然冲突，与一切丑恶势同冰炭，与一切污浊天壤判别。

良知作为本心本性的灵明觉知，当然也是求真、求善、求美的自觉心或认知心，是成全自己也成全别人的动力源泉，是人与人之间往来沟通的情义温暖，是人能够反省自己并通过反省不断提升精神境界的本体论依据，是人能对是非善恶进行判断辨识并展开批判的生命原则，是人可与日月争辉的既内在又超越的存在论源泉，是去弊兴利挽狂澜于既倒的救世悲愿，是文化生命机体虽百死千难仍能绵延传承的一线活脉。因此，良知只能呈现，只能到场，不能坎陷，不能遮蔽。良知所提供的价值应成为社会生活主导的价值，良知教也应成为第一义的安身立命的根本之教。

大家知道，存在不只是虚无的空壳，不只是肉体的外在的存在，不是萨特所谓的无用的激情。在有自己深刻的人性内蕴，有自己意义涌现的内在本体来源，有自己内

外打通无限开阔包容的天地。根据人的不同的存在选择，人既可以堕入污潭，走上自我欺瞒的虚假化道路，也能够不断超拔，踏上返归本心本性的真实化道路。

一如缺少了文化，社会就会退堕为沙漠一样，丧失了良知，人也会还原为野兽。因此，我从来都不赞成牟宗三先生“良知坎陷”的说法，因为“良知坎陷”就意味着人的异化，社会的败坏，生活世界的冷酷，意义世界的坍塌。良知坎陷即为生命灵性的泪没，只会造成生命的封闭，难以滋生任何真实的知识与价值，实为人生的大不幸、存在的大痛苦，不但动摇了第一义的良知教的立根基础，而且也破坏了社会秩序赖以存在的伦理原则。

从更深的层次看，良知运作的状态不仅与我们的心灵秩序本来一致，同时也与我们存在的秩序密契应合。良知、心灵与存在的状态或方式具有同构的关系，良知语言、心灵语言、存在语言也不可能成为相互脱节的系统。良知活动是先验与经验的统一，形上与形下的统一，本体与实践的统一，人格与存在的统一，代表了生命的创造性本质，展示了生生之道的活泼风姿，体现了存在的和谐性真实，见证了主体自由的人格化实现。[①] 失去了良知的存在只能是内外一片黑暗，不仅心灵锁闭在身体的黑漆桶子中，而且世界亦亦为黑暗所吞噬，人生在举目茫茫中，只能像孤魂一样随风飘荡，既无法贞定自己的生命，也失去了创造的可能。更直接地说，欲望、私利、冲动和贪婪的意象，既有可能遮蔽心性中的良知准则，也有可能搅乱头脑中的理性清澈，不仅会导致生命意义的迷失，而且也将造成认知方向的错乱。心性离不开价值，大脑不能乖悖理性，社会不能抽空秩序。而良知即意味着价值，理性即表征着秩序，秩序则蕴含着福祉。为了避免理性可能造成的死板或干枯，秩序必须以价值的方式来加以滋润。所以良知不仅不能坎陷，反而必须呈现升华。

特别重要的是，我们必须依据良知重建社会生活不可或缺的批判精神传统，即以良知为主脑来引导导现代科学的发展方向，以良知为主脑来匡正现代民主的弊病。无论科学或民主，都不能缺乏良知的到场。如果良知不参与历史文化的创造活动，历史文化能不崩溃吗？社会能不解体吗？国家能不窳败吗？良知缺位的世界只能是一个毫无生气的退堕的小人世界，而不可能是一个充满行健自强生气的君子世界。因此，我们要重建可以屹立于世界之林的华夏文化，就必须重建具有创性活力的君子形态的华夏文化，重建良知活泼发用的礼义之邦形态的华夏文化。没有良知参与其中的无道德的世界，只能是丛林莽野般野蛮蒙昧的世界。谈何礼仪，谈何文化，谈何传统，谈何社会！所以，我一有机会就要大声疾呼，我们必须让良知教重新发挥涵化人生、滋润社会

① 参阅张新民：《探寻精神生命的终极安顿：王阳明“良知”与“致良知”学说》，《王阳明国际学术讨论会论文集》，贵州教育出版社，1997 年。

的功能，让多元化的精神教育成为第一义的教育。[①] 我们必须重建君子形态的中国文明，重逮良知形态的华夏文化。人类应成为相互关爱的人类，以良知来交往的人类。而作为个体生命的良知，也应该成为社会性的集体良知，没有良知就没有生命存在的意义！

## 五、良知教是大圆融教

面对工具理性一脉偏大的现代功利社会，致良知和良知教的展开实现并非容易之事。然而无论良知说或良知教，都不仅是一种解释的理论，更是一种实践的哲学。也就是说，即使是解释的理论的向度，也必须踏上实践的行动的路途，将人导入终极性的善的价值境域，获得具体性的主体自由和存在真实。因此，同当年的王阳明一样，我们今天也有必要大力提倡知行合一。而将良知本体之善活化为生活实践之善，则是我们提倡知行合一说的一大基本出发点。

从根本上说，恢复良知教的意义即在于致良知，致良知的目的则在于人类整体的“至善”。因为良知的创造性活动不能不有实践的环节，人类只有在道德的实践过程中才能完成自己与天理、天德、天命合一的“至善”。致良知即是创造意义和价值的生命实践的行为，是作为本体的本心本性的展开、实现和完成的生命的实践过程。[②] 如同天地流行发用的创生性力量能够使万物活泼畅遂地生长一样，良知流行发用的创造性力量也可以让每一个人活泼畅逐地成长。可见知行合一说的根本要义，着眼处仍在与天地相通的价值经验感的获得，故心灵遂在饱满和谐的状状态中焕发出最大的创造力量，人类亦因此而有健康、全面、长足的发展。

知行的统一本身即是身心的统一和创造的表现，[③] 必须通过“事上磨练”的工夫，将知与行以统一的方式，完整全面地整合到我们的生命结构和生活结构之中，使“行”成为有价值理想导向和至善目的诉求的正义之“行”，而“知”亦成为可见诸行事并获得实践性经验意义的“知”。知与行不断展开对话式的良性循环互动，从而真正挖掘或开拓人生价值意义体验的深度或广度，既是创造性的活力永不枯竭的前提保障，也是人生实现和完善自己必须经历的命运考量。而良知教的推行与落实，显然也是为了确保知与行的统一，不仅要避免知与行分裂所造成的人生痛苦，同时也要尽量减少知与行脱节所滋生的社会弊端。

从知行合一的角度看良知说与良知教，则可说良知说是大圆融说，良知教也是大圆融教。因为知行合一的目的性诉求，决不允许“知”与“行”分裂成两个世界，也

① 参阅张新民《多元化的精神教育应该成为第一义的教育》，《阅江学刊》2010年第2卷第2期。
② 张新民：《生命行动的哲学：论王阳明的知行合一说》，《中国哲学》1997年第7期。
③ 成中英：《论王阳明心学之“知行合一”》，张明译，《阳明学刊》2011年第5辑。

拒绝一切欺瞒的言说和盲目的行为。无论“知”或“行”，都必须以良知为本体，都必须照耀在良知的阳光下，都应该透“至善”的境域，获得完整的统一性整合，不仅良知得以流行发用而无碍，即人生亦因此而满合创造性的生机，诚可谓先天而天弗违，后天而奉天时。如阳明子所说：“只是顺顺良知之发用，天地万物，俱在我良知的发用流行中，何尝有一物起于良知之外能作障碍。[①]”如此则大圆融教既成，人生亦臻于至善之境。

## 六、守住寂寞与孤独的边缘

然而稍加审视，即不难发现，市场主义取向的现实社会所呈现给我们的，乃是大量知行不一的恶劣习气和社会现象。尤其自20世纪初叶以来，由于激进主义的思潮一浪高过一浪，传统精英文化遭到了彻底的扫荡，中心与边缘发生了巨大的错置性颠覆，我们已失去了固有的“道不远人”的人文主义的传统，失去了具有凝摄和向心力的文化认同力量。尽管向上提升的大门依然向每一个人敞开，但堕落下坠的陷机也遍藏大地。因此，如果要真正恢复良知教，并透过良知教对宇宙人生的奥秘有一彻底的了解，就必须一方面在人性的本体论问题上怀抱乐观的自信态度，透彻地看到每一个体的心性本体都内蕴着良知的无尽活泼机藏，都有实现和完善自己的先天人性条和后天现实可能；一方面又在人性的实践论问题上采取忧患的致思取向，清醒地看到现实人生和现实社会的不完善或不完美，了解“事上磨练”的艰难困苦和复杂诡谲。也正是在这一意义上，我多年来始终强调，越是怀抱价值理理，就越应该以守道、行道为己任，就越应该正视社会的邪恶、病态和弊端，明悉历史文化发展的反复、多变、吊诡和曲折。概括地说，即乐观而不失于肤浅，始终看到人人都不能不面对堕陷的向下门的吞噬异化力量的考验；忧患而不动摇希望，始终坚信人人都可透过超越的向上门助成人生或社会的美好和完善。现实社会总是道魔消长，善恶夹杂。而孔子修《春秋》，凭借褒贬笔法，以微言示大义，为千秋留炯戒，无论知我罪我，是毁是誉，均一概超越，其所展示出来的，恰好正是乐观与忧患合为一体的历史智慧，以及敢于正视一切负面历史经验并善于将其转化为人间正面秩序建构力量的批判精神。所谓“将顺其美，匡救其恶，故上下能相亲也”，[②] 则不但要顺百姓民风之美，更要匡权力世界之恶。故“顺美”者不能不“匡恶”，而只有“匡恶”才能“顺美”，历史批判的目的乃是要开辟现实发展的方向，谁也不能躲脱历史的批判，除非他根本就没有进入历史。所以君子

① 王阳明：《传习录》下，《王阳明全集》（新编本），浙江古籍出版社2011年版，第1册，第117页；参阅张新民《中华典籍与学术文化》，广西师范大学出版社，1998年，第378－379页。

② 《史记》卷六十二《管晏列传赞》，中华书局，1959年，第7册，第2136页。

风骨人格的一大衡量标准，中国文化从来认为救过即是“正”，匡恶方为“忠”；反之，从人之过便是“邪”，顺之恶则为“佞”。正与邪不能两立，忠和佞也不许淆混。历史批判植根于华夏民族久远深厚的传统，它应该转化为制度性的建构，从而真正发挥权力督督的作用，让权力世界永远受到历史批判的震慑。

由此可见，儒家对人性本体及其现实表现的洞察，乃是极为深刻和十分实际的。一方面，儒家始终强调必须以尽心知性的生命实践工夫，切己切身地体贴人性本然的懿美醇善，长期提倡并积极坚持返求诸己的“复性”工夫；另一方面，儒家也以我不济世谁济世的精神勇猛直面现实社会与现实人生的各种问题，严格剖析和批判各种社会弊端和人生病相，敢于以道抗势或以道驭势，积极参与一切符合价值理想的秩序建构工作。良知说与良知教乃是既救心心又救世的学问体系。从救心的角度看，它对人性体贴的深刻超过了任何西方学说，可说是有大根大本的心性系统学说；从救世的立场说，它对世俗的悲苦从来都有极为深刻的同情性了解，总是表现出一种济世安民的宗教情怀，对现实政治批判的也积累了大量的经验资源。

以过往的历史为今天现实的参照，置身于效率为中心的工具理性的主流文化大潮，如果真要坚持价值理想，就必须甘于边缘；面对放纵主义的市场原则，倘若真要固守人格情操，亦必须安于孤寂。“应然”与“必然”能够统一固然很好，因为天下有道本来就是良知教的愿望，促使“应然”变成“必然”亦为君子的责任；惟“应然”与“必然”一旦分裂，良知教所要选择者则为“应然”而非“必然”，因为君子所从者只是“道”而“势”。纵使天下滔滔，所守者亦为“道”。

因此，一旦听从内在良知的严肃召唤，肩负天命下贯的时代责任，则良知边缘，自己亦甘愿边缘；良知孤寂，自己亦宁可孤寂。即便困难重重，乃至未来一无收获，根本就看不到人类的希望，也必须守护好自己的良知和人格情操，维护好亘古亘今永在的“道”。

今天，良知在无道德的冰冷的世界中早已边缘，良知在昏沉麻木的恶浊世界中格外孤寂，但良知仍然能在冰天雪地的世界中为我们带来一丝春天的信息，在冷酷算计的社会中为我们递送一丝人间的温暖。因此，我们心甘情愿地守住自己的边缘，坦然自在地接受生命的孤寂。我们深切地知道，尽管人类危机积久深重，社会病相触目惊心，思想无出路，前程无希望，生命无意义，存在无价值，但只要天植灵根尚在，天地生机获存，人心仍有所不满，人心尚在思变，则现实必变，社会必变。天地变化，草木必蕃。天地大道既然如此，社人生会又何能例外。

心灵是一切创造性活动扎根的原型家园，也是良知教得以成立的本体基础。只要美好的心灵尚在，良知的呼唤犹存，生命就有意义，主体就有自由，人间就有温暖，社会就有生气，人类就有希望，世界就有前途。

# 从儒家的“修身”到共产党的“修养”

中共中央党校 许全兴

毛泽东思想的显著特点之一是重视人的主观世界的改造，重视人的改造，而这一特点成了马克思主义在经济、政治、文化相对落后的中国取得伟大胜利的一个重要因素。毛泽东思想的这一特点是中国传统文化重视个人“修身”的继承和发展。重视共产党员的“修养”是保证中国共产党的无产阶级先锋队性质的一个法宝，也是中国共产党的一个优势和优良传统。“修养”是中国马克思主义的一个重要概念，也是中国对人类哲学思想和伦理思想的一个贡献。修养在当代中国仍有重要的现实意义。

## 一、从人类发展史上的一个奇迹说起

马克思主义是产生于西方资本主义社会的无产阶级的科学思想体系，然而，马克思主义并没有能在西方发达资本主义国家取得实践上的胜利，倒是在一个经济、政治、文化落后的半殖民地半封建的东方大国——中国取得了伟大胜利，不仅取得了新民主主义革命的伟大胜利，而且进而取得了社会主义革命和社会主义建设的伟大胜利，取得了建设中国特色社会主义的伟大胜利。今日社会主义中国已成为世界第二大经济体和世界贸易第一大国。新中国成立以来近65年来所发生的翻天覆地的巨大变革和所取得的超过了以往几百年、上千年的辉煌成就，堪称人类历史上发生的奇迹，令世界瞩目和惊叹。

马克思主义没有在西方发达资本主义国家而是在东方的中国取得胜利的原因是多方面的、复杂的，是多种因素综合作用的结果。从客观上讲，是世界历史发的产物，同20世纪发生的两次世界大战密切相关。没有第一次世界大战，就没有1917年俄国十月社会主义革命的胜利。没有第一次世界大战和俄国十月社会主义革命的胜利，就没有马克思主义在中国的迅速传播和中国共产党的成立。没有第二次世界大战和抗日战争的胜利，就没有中国共产党及其领导下的人民军队的迅速发展壮大，也就没有中国革命的胜利以及胜利后迅速走上社会主义道路。这说明中国革命和建设的成就是同整个资本主义世界的矛盾和危机密切相关的。

这一奇迹发生的最根本原因是半殖民地半封建中国社会矛盾的尖锐性、复杂性和不平衡性为世所罕见，中国成为十月革命后世界矛盾的焦点和革命的中心。中国社会尖锐、复杂的矛盾运动为马克思主义在中国的胜利提供了现实基础。中国又是一个具有五千年悠久历史的文明古国，有着丰富的优秀文化遗产，这为马克思主义在中国生根、开花和结果提供了丰厚的文化土壤。可以设想，最好的种子和种苗在贫瘠的荒漠中也不可能长成参天大树。中国悠久的、博大精深的历史文化遗产是马克思主义在中国取得胜利的重要条件。

从主观上讲，以毛泽东为代表的中国共产党人不仅善于把马克思列宁主义普遍真理同中国现实的革命运动相结合，而且也善于把它同中国历史文化实际相结合，继承和弘扬了中华民族的优良传统。中国化的马克思主义——毛泽东思想不仅是中国革命和建设经验的科学总结，而且也是中华民族智慧的结晶。实事求是、群众路线和独立自主是构成毛泽东思想活的灵魂的基本方面。有关这三方面同中国历史文化的内在联系已为许多论文和著作反复阐述，在此不再赘言。本文则从在中国特殊的社会条件下如何建设无产阶级政党视角看中国共产党人对中国传统“修身”的吸取和弘扬。

共产党是无产阶级的政党，在资本主义国家其主要成员来是无产阶级，其主要活动是在城市。由于中国特殊的社会条件和中国革命的特点，中国共产党同资本主义国家的共产党有很大的不同。它的党员主要来之于贫苦农民及小资产阶级，它主要的活动不是在城市，而是在经济、政治、文化十分落后的农村。在这样的环境下，要把共产党建设成为先进的无产阶级政党，这是一个国际共产主义运动史上前所未遇的历史难题。毛泽东在创建井冈山革命根据地时发出了这样的感慨：“在这种情形下，‘斗争的布尔什维克党’的建设，真是难得很。”为了破解这道难题，他强调“无产阶级思想领导”的重要。[①]

在一些外国人看来，要把中国党建设成为无产阶级政党，这简直是不可能的。他们认为，中国共产党只能是农民的党，中国的马克思主义不是真正的马克思主义，而是农民的马克思主义。周恩来在1944年做的有关中共党史的报告中说：“一九四〇年我到共产国际去，共产国际的领导同志还担心我们离开工人阶级太远了。我说我们在农村里经过长期斗争的锻炼，有毛泽东同志的领导，完全可以无产阶级化。共产国际

---

① 毛泽东：《井冈山的斗争》（1928年11月25日），《毛泽东选集》第1卷，人民出版社，1991年，第74、77页。

的一些同志听了之后大哗，不以为然。”[①] 也许正是出于这种认识和担心，共产国际在较长时间里并不认同毛泽东开创的以农村包围城市的中国革命道路。周恩来讲的“共产国际的一些同志”并非是普通同志，也不只是共产国际的一般领导同志，而是主要领导同志，包括斯大林。也许是一个偶然的巧合，就在周恩来在延安中央党校做报告后不久，1944 年 6 月 10 日，斯大林同莫洛托夫一起在会见美国驻苏大使哈里曼时不仅完全认同美国总统罗斯福说过的“蒋介石是唯一能把中国合在一起的人”的话，并说：“在目前情况下，蒋介石是最恰当的人，因而必须给予支持。”两人在谈到中共时，斯大林笑着说：“中国共产党人不是真正的共产党人，他们不过是些‘人造奶油’共产党人。”斯大林也承认，“他们是真正的爱国者，他们要跟日本作战”。[②] “人造奶油”是冒牌的奶油也。这是斯大林对中国共产党的看法。在此后不久，莫洛托夫也曾对美国总统罗斯福派往中国的私人代表赫尔利说过类似的话：“中国共产党事实上并非共产党，……苏联不支持中国共产党。”[③] 赫尔利从谈话中得出的印象是：俄国人认为中共只是一些虚假的共产主义者，因此，俄国不愿介入中国的国内政治。受此影响，赫尔利在当时相信，中共不是真正的革命者，而是看作美国当时的在野党——共和党。[④]

总之，要把中国共产党建设成为一个无产阶级的马克思主义政党，在那时的共产国际和苏共领导人看来，这简直是一件不可能的事，而在毛泽东的领导下，如周恩来所说，中国共产党“完全可以无产阶级化”。历史证明，中国共产党是经历了国际国内各种考验的成熟的马克思主义政党。有意思的是当苏共解散、苏东剧变时，中国共产党不仅岿然不动，而且风景这边独好，使中国特色社会主义走上新的历史阶段。

## 二、重视党员修养是中国共产党的一大特点和优势

毛泽东如何能使中国党无产阶级化，做到了外国人认为不可能做到的事情呢？这里的答案要从中国历史文化中寻找。

决定一个政党性质的不是党员成分的来源、出身，而是党的指导思想，党的理论、纲领和路线。毛泽东是一个坚定的马克思列宁主义者，深信中国革命必须坚持马克思列宁主义指导，但他不是教条主义者，坚持独立自主原则，反对盲目照搬照抄本本和

① 周恩来：《关于党的“六大”的研究》（1944 年 3 月 3 日、4 日），《周恩来选集》上卷，人民出版社，1980 年，第 178－179 页。

② 《战后世界历史长编》编委会：《战后世界历史长编》第 1 编第 1 分册，上海人民出版社，1975 年，第 353－354 页。

③ 世界知识出版社编：《中美关系资料汇编》第 1 辑，《美国与中国的关系（白皮书）》，世界知识出版社，1957 年，第 140、160 页。

④ 见费正清主编《剑桥中华民国史》第 2 部，上海人民出版社，1992 年，第 777 页。

共产国际指示，坚持马克思列宁主义普遍真理与中国革命实际、中国历史文化实际相结合，从而形成中国化的理论、路线和方针。这是把中国党建设为一个马克思列宁主义政党的首要条件。“中国革命斗争的胜利要靠中国同志了解中国情况”。[①] 独立自主是中国共产党立党、立国的基本原则之一，但它并非来自马克思列宁主义，而是来自中华民族自强不息的优良传统。[②] 也许正是由于毛泽东坚持实事求是、独立自主的原则，抵制了共产国际和斯大林有关中国革命的某些错误指示，从而引起他们对毛泽东和中国共产党人是否是真正马克思列宁主义者的怀疑。

虽说一个政党的性质主要不是取决于党员来源的成分，而取决于党的理论、纲领和路线，但主要是非无产阶级出身成分的党员，会给党带来大量的非无产阶级思想，这对执行正确路线、保持党的无产阶级性质确实是一个极严重的问题。如毛泽东所说的那样，在这样的环境中，“‘斗争的布尔什维克党’的建设，真是难得很”。“难得很”，并不是像有些人所认为的不可能。

如何解决这一难题？以毛泽东为代表的中国共产党人不仅坚持马克思列宁主义的科学指导，注重从理论上建党，而且坚持无产阶级的思想领导领导，注重在思想上建党，开展无产阶级思想与非无产阶级思想的斗争，注重党员的思想改造和党性修养，解决党员从世界观上入党。

笔者虽不是专门研究党建理论的，但为了写作毛泽东有关党建理论的论文，查阅了中央党校图书馆有关苏联从30年代到80年代的党建理论著作，其中有斯列波夫主编的《党的建设研究提纲》(30年代)、《苏联共产党的建设论文集》(第一、二集，50年代初)、苏共中央马克思列宁主义研究院集体编写的《社会主义国家党的建设》(1980年)等。笔者发现他们的党建理论主要是讲党的组织建设，较少讲理论建设、思想建设，更无党员为保持无产阶级先进性所进行的党性修养和世界观改造的内容。从这一个方面看，注重党性修养和思想改造确实是中国共产党特有的一大特点和优势。

毛泽东在1929年12月起草的《中国共产党红军第四军第九次代表大会决议案》(简称《古田会议决议》)首次初步显示了这一特点和优势。该决议有“纠正党内非无产阶级意识的不正确倾向问题”、“党的组织问题”、“党内教育问题”、“红军宣传工作问题”、“士兵政治训练问题”、“废止肉刑问题”等八个部分。第一部分最为重要，经作者校阅后以《关于纠正党内的错误思想》为题收入《毛泽东选集》第1卷。毛泽东

---

① 毛泽东:《反对本本主义》(1930年5月)，《毛泽东选集》第1卷，人民出版社，1991年，第115页。

② 详见许全兴:《中华民族优秀传统——毛泽东思想来源之一》，《毛泽东思想论坛》1994年第2期，收入《为毛泽东辩护》一书，当代中国出版1996年出版。

开宗明义地指出：红四军的共产党内存在着各种非无产阶级的思想，这对执行党的正确路线，妨碍极大。若不彻底纠正，则中国革命伟大斗争给予红四军的任务，是必然担负不起来的。为此，决议分类列举了红四军党内各种非无产阶级思想的表现及其危害，分析其来源，提出纠正的方法。决议的着眼点是开展无产阶级思想与非无产阶级思想的斗争，纠正各种非无产阶级思想，以保证党的正确路线的执行，保证党的无产阶级性质；其落脚点则是通过理论学习、思想教育、制度建设、批评与自我批评、解决实际问题等方式，纠正党员身上存在的各种非无产阶级思想，提高党员的觉悟和素质。决议指出，对于政治形势的主观主义分析和对于工作的主观主义指导，其必然结果，不是机会主义，就是盲动主义。决议主要纠正单纯军事观点、极端民主化、绝对平均主义、主观主义、个人主义、流寇思想、盲动主义等错误思想。决议首次把共产党的思想理论建设落实到纠正党员个人的非无产阶级思想和提高党员自身的修养上。决议的基本精神是，不纠正党内的各种非无产阶级思想就不能有效地执行党的正确路线，担负起领导革命的任务。决议虽然讲的是军队党的建设问题，但对整个党的“无产阶级化”有着普遍的意义。这个决议不但在红军第四军实行了，而且后来在红军的其他部分也先后不等地照此做了。1942 年整风运动中该决议的第一个部分列为十八个必读文件之一。

该决议的哲学意义在于，不纠正错误思想，不注重主观世界的改造，就难于贯彻党的正确路线，难于改造好客观世界。

“古田会议决议”是党和军队建设经验的总结，是现实革命斗争的需要，这是首先必须肯定的，但从深层次上看，把纠正党内错误思想落实到党员个人身上，落实到提高党员的思想理论修养上，这与我国古代文化注重个人修身的传统密切相关。

## 三、把儒家的“修身”转化为共产党的“修养”

中国古代的政治家、思想家认为，“德，国家之基也”，[①] 主张以德治国。孔子提倡：为政以德，以德服人；政者正也，己正才能正人；正己要在修身，修己以安人。[②] 中国古代社会，家是最简单的社会细胞，家与国同构，所谓“天下之本在国，国之本在家，家之本在身”，[③] “修其身而天下平”。[④] 荀子则著有《修身》篇，其中说“以修身自强，则名配尧舜”。《礼记·大学》则进而把修身看成治国之本，提出“修身、齐家、

① 《左传·襄公二十四年》。

② 见《论语》的《为政》、《颜渊》、《子路》、《宪问》诸篇。

③ 《孟子·离娄上》。

④ 《孟子·尽心下》。

治国、平天下”，“自天子以至于庶人，壹是皆以修身为本”。《大学》的“修齐治平”思想为历代的政治家、思想家、教育家所推崇，从而形成了一套完整的、丰富的修身理论，深深影响着中国的政治、思想、文化和社会生活。世界上任何一个民族、国家都有自己的伦理道德，都有自己的一套道德修养，这是毫无疑义的。但像中国这样把修身看成治国之本，形成如此完备的修身理论则确实是独一无二的。不信可以翻检一下世界伦理思想史。[①]

中国传统修身理论内容丰富深刻，包括修身的可能、必要和意义、修身的标准和内容、修身的途径和方法等方面。中国古代哲人主张，修身以立志为先，只有立志，才能有高尚而远大的人生理想、奋斗目标和内在动力。“志，气之帅”[②]、“立志则有本”[③]、“有志者事竟成”[④] 等，此之谓也。欲立真志，非盲从之志，则必先为学，求得真理。“吾十五而志于学”[⑤]、“学以致其道”[⑥]、“正心、诚意、格物、致知”[⑦] 等，此之谓也。中国修身论主张言行一致、知行合一、行己有耻，反对言行不一，伪言伪行。“为己之学”[⑧]、“君子耻其言而过其行”[⑨]、“君子强学而力行”[⑩] 等，此之谓也。人非圣贤，孰能无过。因此，古人修身养性，重视改过，不贰过，不断从改过中完善自己。“过而能改，善莫大焉”[⑪]、“过而不改，是谓过矣”[⑫]、“闻过则喜，知过不讳，改过不惮”[⑬] 等，此之谓也。古代先哲重视自省克己，检讨自己，自觉主动地开展内心的思想斗争，及时知过、改过、迁善。“吾日三省吾身”[⑭]、“见贤思齐也，见不贤而内自省

---

① 附带说明：东邻日本，一衣带水，深受中国哲学文化影响，自然也讲修身。近代明治时期，出现过国民“修养”热，修养类书籍大量出版，其中新渡户稻造的《修养》，作为青年通俗读物，影响甚大。1911年出版以后至1934年，重印了149次，成为日本人励志的经典书籍。详见《修养》一书中译本的译者前言《一本值得重读的名著》。该书由王成、陈瑜译，27万字，由中央编译出版社2009年出版。该书纯属通俗应用之书，故伦理学史少见涉及。

② 《孟子·公孙丑上》。

③ 《二程集·河南程氏粹言》卷一《论学篇》。

④ 《后汉书·耿弇传》。

⑤ 《论语·为政》。

⑥ 《论语·子张》。

⑦ 《礼记·大学》。

⑧ 《论语·宪问》。

⑨ 《论语·宪问》。

⑩ 扬雄：《法言·修身》。

⑪ 《左传·宣公二年》。

⑫ 《论语·卫灵公》。

⑬ 《陆九渊集》卷六《与傅全美》二。

⑭ 《论语·学而》。

也”[①]、“省察克治之功，则无时而可间”[②] 等，此之谓也。中国先贤圣哲强调，修身贵在自觉、诚实、严于律己，提倡慎独。“不诚则不独”[③]、“君子必慎其独也”[④]、“慎独即不自欺”[⑤] 等，此之谓也。

古人修身论虽有尽心知性、居敬涵养、脱离社会实践的缺点，但也有提倡“艰难困苦，玉汝于成”的诸多嘉言和世范。孟子的下列话成为众所周知的修身名言：“天将降大任于斯人也，必先苦其心志，劳其筋骨，饿其体肤，空乏其身，行拂乱其所为，所以动心忍性，曾益其所不能。”[⑥]“文王拘而演周易，孔子厄而作春秋。屈原放逐，乃赋离骚。……韩非囚秦，说难孤愤。诗三百首，大抵贤圣发愤之所为作也。”[⑦] 司马迁的这段血泪文字以历史人物的故事激励着后人在逆境中自强不息，奋发进取，勇于作为，做出传世的贡献。

中国传统修身理论自然有其历史的局限，把修身用作维护“三纲”专制制度的工具；片面强调以国家、社会为本位，忽视个人权利和个性自由；片面强调正谊明道，把人的欲望看作恶，忽视了物质利益，甚至发展到“存天理，灭人欲”，以理杀人等等。但传统道德中提倡和弘扬的“夙夜在公”[⑧]、“天下为公”[⑨]、“公耳忘私，国耳忘家”[⑩] 等的大公无私精神；“杀身成仁”[⑪]、“舍生取义”[⑫]、“以公义胜私欲”[⑬] 等的高尚情操；“生于忧患而死于安乐”[⑭] 和“先天下之忧而忧，后天下之乐而乐”[⑮] 等的忧患意识；“位卑未敢忘忧国”[⑯]、“天下兴亡，匹夫有责”[⑰] 和“苟利国家生死以，岂因祸福避趋之”[⑱] 等的爱国精神……皆是中国五千年文明生生不息、未曾中断的内在动力，也是

---

① 《论语·里仁》。
② 《王阳明全集》卷一《传习录》上。
③ 《荀子·不苟》。
④ 《礼记·大学》。
⑤ 《陆九渊集》卷三十四《语录上》。
⑥ 《孟子·告子下》。
⑦ 司马迁：《报任安书》。
⑧ 《诗经·召南·采蘩》。
⑨ 《礼记·礼运》。
⑩ 《汉书·贾谊传》。
⑪ 《论语·卫灵公》。
⑫ 《孟子·告子上》。
⑬ 《荀子·修身》。
⑭ 《孟子·告子下》。
⑮ 范仲淹：《岳阳楼记》。
⑯ 陆游：《病起书怀》。
⑰ 顾炎武：《正始》；梁启超：《痛定罪言》。
⑱ 林则徐：《赴戍登程口占示家人》。

中国悠久历史文化的精义所在。

注重人生修养是中国历史文化的一个极为重要的优良传统，即使在近现代，新思想、新文化、新道德的提倡者也仍继承着这一传统。严复的“开民智、鼓民力、新民德”；梁启超的“新民说”；陈独秀创办的《青年》杂志旨在商讨“修身治国之道”和“改造青年之思想，辅导青年之修养”；鲁迅的“立人”和“国民性改造”等都显示出在近现代思想变革大潮中，人生修养的传统并未中断，尽管其内容已是资产阶级民主主义的新思想、新文化、新道德。

作为革命民主主义者的李大钊，与新青年同人一样，竭力用新思想来改造、武装青年。他创办《晨钟报》，高擅自由之晨钟，“厚青年之修养，畅青年之精神，壮青年之意志，砺青年之气节，鼓舞青春中华之运动，培植青春中华之根基”，以创造新的青春中华。[①] 在转变为马克思主义者之后，李大钊虽然尖锐地指出“孔子所谓修身不是使人完成他的个性，仍是使人牺牲他的个性”，[②] 但他并没有抛弃修身的传统，而是赋予它适应新时代的新内容。他多次指出：学问最要紧的用处是“用他来助我们的人生修养”。“人要过优美高上的生活，必须要有内心的修养”。他专门论述了史学、文学、哲学与人生修养的关系。[③] 他本人的道德文章，如日月之经天，江河之行地，光明磊落，胆肝照人，成为世人楷模。

从保存下的毛泽东的《讲堂录》（尤其是听杨昌济先生“修身”课的笔记）和他早期通信、文章及新民学会的有关资料看，青年毛泽东深受时代思潮和老师的影响，亦十分注重人生修养。他在给同学的信中说：“吾人立言，当以身心之修养、学问之研求为主，辅之政事时务”。[④] 他本人身体力行，堪称品学兼优的学生。[⑤] 他和蔡和森等同学发起成立的团体取名“新民学会”，其“新民”一词就源于《尚书·康诰》和《大学》

---

① 李大钊：《〈晨钟〉之使命》（1916年8月15日），《李大钊文集》（上），人民出版社，1984年，第181页。

② 李大钊：《由经济上解释中国近代思想变动的原因》（1920年1月1日），《李大钊文集》（下），人民出版社，1984年，第178页。

③ 李大钊：《史学与哲学》（1923年4月17—19日），《李大钊文集》（下），人民出版社，1984年，第635、644—645页。

④ 毛泽东：《致萧子升信》（1915年9月27日），《毛泽东早期文稿》，湖南出版社，1990年，第28页。

⑤ 1917年6月，湖南省立第一师范学校开展考查学生德、智、体优秀的“人物互选”活动。全校十一个班四百多人参加选举，毛泽东得票最多。敦品（如敦廉耻，尚气节，慎交游，屏外诱）、自治（如守秩序，重礼节，慎言笑）、胆识（如冒险进取，警备非常）、文学（如长于国文辞章）、才具（如应变有方，办事精细）、言语（如长于演讲，论辩应对）等六项考察皆为优秀。其中，言语、敦品两项得票数第一，胆识项得票为他所独有。见中共中央文献研究室编《毛泽东年谱》（1893—1949），中央文献出版社2013年修订本，上卷，第26页。

及梁启超的"新民说"，旨在标明重视国民自身的改造、自新和修养。由他起草的新民学会章程则明确规定："以革新学术，砥砺品行，改良人心风俗为宗旨"和会员须遵守"不虚伪、不懒惰、不浪费、不赌博、不狎妓"规则。[①] 1921年，当他和蔡和森等人初步接受马克思主义之后，新民学会的宗旨发展为"改造中国与世界"，但注意学术研究与人生修养则没有变。他在新民学会的新年大会上提出，学会的活动，在重视"主义"研究的同时"须增'修养'"。[②] 可以认为，正是由于他继承了中国文化重视修养的传统，使得他在领导中国革命过程中十分重视纠正错误思想和改造主观世界，十分重视提高党员自身的修养。

基于党和军队建设的经验，毛泽东在《实践论》行将结束时提出改造主观世界的任务，并论述了改造客观世界与改造主观世界的关系。他指出，无产阶级和革命人民改造世界的任务包括改造客观世界和改造自己的主观世界——改造自己的认识能力，改造主观世界同客观世界的关系。[③] 这是对新民学会"改造中国与世界"的宗旨与重视主体自我修养这两者的统一和发展。《实践论》关于改造主观世界任务的论述在当时传入的马克思主义中是没有的。在改造客观世界过程中改造主观世界，又在改造主观世界过程中改造客观世界，不认真地改造主观世界，就不能有效地改造客观世界，这是人类认识世界和改造世界的一条根本规律。

中国共产党是无产阶级的先锋队，也是中华民族的先锋队，中国共产党党员是国际主义者，又是爱国主义者。在全面抗战爆发后，毛泽东指出：中国共产党及其所领导的民众和武装力量，"站在抗日的最前线，为保卫祖国流最后一点血"。[④] 又说："共产党员在各级政府中应该成为坚决勇敢、刻苦耐劳、急公好义、礼义廉耻的模范"。[⑤] 在中共六届六中全会上，毛泽东深刻论述了爱国主义和国际主义的统一，号召共产党员要在抗日民族战争中起先锋模范作用。他具体提出：共产党员在军队中，应该成为英勇作战的模范，执行命令的模范，遵守纪律的模范，政治工作和内部团结统一的模范；在和友党友军发生关系时，应该成为实行抗战任务的模范，言必信，行必果，不傲慢，诚心诚意地和友党友军商量问题，协同工作，成为统一战线中各党相互关系的

---

① 《新民学会会务报告》（第一号），《新民学会资料》，人民出版社，1980年，第3页。

② 毛泽东在1921年1月3日新民学会新年大会上的发言。《新民学会会务报告》（第二号，1921年1月），《新民学会资料》，人民出版社，1980年，第28页。

③ 毛泽东：《实践论》（1937年7月），《毛泽东选集》第1卷，人民出版社，1991年，第296页。

④ 毛泽东：《为动员一切力量争取抗战胜利而斗争》（1937年8月25日），《毛泽东选集》第2卷，人民出版社，1991年，第357页。

⑤ 毛泽东：《目前抗战形势与党的任务的报告大纲》（1937年10月），《毛泽东文集》第2卷，人民出版社，1993年，第54页。

模范；在政府工作中，应该是十分廉洁、不用私人、多做工作、少取报酬的模范；在民众运动中，应该是民众的朋友，而不是民众的上司，是诲人不倦的教师，而不是官僚主义的政客；在工作中，应该是实事求是的模范，又是具有远见卓识的模范。他强调："共产党员无论何时何地都不应以个人利益放在第一位，而应以个人利益服从民族的和人民群众的利益。因此，自私自利，消极怠工，贪污腐化，风头主义等等，是最可鄙的；而大公无私，积极努力，克己奉公，埋头苦干的精神，才是可尊敬的。"① 笔者在此做大段的引证，意在表明中国共产党人是中华民族优秀传统道德的继承者和弘扬者。还是在这次讲话中，毛泽东专门讲了学习问题。他指出，我们党的马克思主义的修养，很不普遍，很不深入，号召全党要研究理论，系统而不是零碎地、实际地而不是空洞地学会马克思主义；要研究历史，继承从孔夫子到孙中山数千年历史的珍贵遗产，使马克思主义中国化，具有中国作风和中国气派；要研究现状，认识当前革命运动的特点和规律。② "马克思主义的修养"命题的提出，进一步表明中国马克思主义者将中国传统的个人道德品质的修养扩展到党的"理论修养"。

长征到达陕北后，延安成了全国人民，尤其是革命青年向往的革命圣地。他们冲破重重阻力和障碍，纷纷从国民党统治区来到延安，参加抗日。为把这些青年转变成为抗日的先锋战士，时任中共中央书处书记、负总责的张闻天在陕北公学发表了题为《论青年的修养》的长篇讲演。他结合当时的抗日形势、党的历史和青年的优点、特点及弱点、存在的问题，系统地讲了"要有坚定的高尚理想"、"要为实现自己的理想奋斗到底"、"要学习实现理想的办法"、"要同群众在一起去实现自己的理想"等四个问题。③ 张闻天的《论青年的修养》刊中共中央机关刊《解放》，这是笔者见到的延安地区首篇有关马克思主义人身修养的专题论文④。

待人接物是中国传统修养的内容之一。为了动员全国绝大多数的人民参加抗日民

---

① 毛泽东：《中国共产党在民族战争中的地位》（1938年10月14日），《毛泽东选集》第2卷，人民出版社，1991年，第522页。

② 毛泽东：《中国共产党在民族战争中的地位》（1938年10月14日），《毛泽东选集》第2卷，人民出版社，1991年，第533－534页。

③ 张闻天：《论青年修养》（1938年4月12日），刊《解放》周刊第39期（1938年5月22日），《张闻天选集》，人民出版社，1985年，第161－185页。

④ 顺便指出：我国著名马克思主义哲学家、伦理学家冯定曾在青年时代写作过《青年怎样修养》（6万字），1937年3月由上海生活书店作为"青年自学丛书"出版，以后多次再版，收入《冯定文集》。该小册子在简要讲述了世界观、人生观的基础上结合青年的学习、工作和生活，用通俗语言讲解了青年在知识、思想、意志、技能、健康、学业、恋爱、家庭等方面的修养。这可能是我国最早用马克思主义观点专论修养的著作。冯定在名著《平凡的真理》中不仅以"修养"章结束全书，而且将哲学原理转化为人生修养的思想贯穿全书。冯定是我国最重视"修养"的马克思主义哲学家，他把"修养"作为重要的概念写进自己的哲学专著和诸多伦理学的论著。

族统一战线，做好与各方面人士的交往、接待工作，团结一切可以团结的人，张闻天向抗大第3期毕业同学发表了题为《论待人接物问题》讲演。他在讲演一开始就明确指出：站在马克思列宁主义立场上，估计到中国人在待人接物方面的传统和特点，再加以改造与发展，使之适合于中国革命的要求，这也是中国共产党人的重要任务之一。根据当时的形势，他讲了“要有伟大的胸怀与气魄”、“要有‘循循善诱’与‘诲人不倦’的精神”、“对人要有很好的态度”和“要适当应付坏人”等四个方面的内容。① 讲演引用《论语》、《孟子》、《左传》、《中庸》等中国古人有关人身修养、待人接物、处理人际关系方面的语录、格言近30处。《论待人接物问题》堪称是中国马克思主义的待人接物篇。

吸取和改造中国传统修养思想、对党的思想建设发生重大影响的名著则是刘少奇的《论共产党员修养》一书。刘少奇在长期的革命实践中重视党的建设。在中共中央六届六中全会前夕召开的中央政治局会议上，他提出在党内要制定一种党规、进行党的建设的建议。会议采纳了这一提议。在中共中央六届六中全会最后一天，刘少奇做了《党规党法的报告》。报告本身没有涉修养问题，但他对毛泽东在会上提出的“马克思主义的修养”的命题在思想上引起了强烈的共鸣，在会后产生了写作论共产党员修养的想法。经过一段时间的酝酿和准备，1939年7月8日，他在马列学院发表了《论共产党员修养》的讲演。他结合中国的实际和党的建设的经验，批判地吸取了中国传统文化有关修养的内容（引用《论语》、《孟子》等经书、格言十余处），系统论述了共产党员为什么要进行修养；怎样进行修养和在哪些方面进行修养；修养必须遵循的党员个人利益无条件地服从党的利益的原则；党内各种错误思想意识的表现、来源；对待各种错误思想意识的态度及党内斗争等问题。讲演主题是共产党员要努力学习马克思主义，提高马克思主义理论修养，正确认识社会发展规律，树立共产主义理想信念，坚持个人利益无条件地服从党的利益的原则，同各种错误思想意识进行斗争，把自己锻炼成为一个忠诚纯洁的进步的模范党员和干部。这天主要讲的是绪论和思想意识方面的修养，7月12日接着讲党员组织纪律的修养。7月8日的讲演整理稿经张闻天审阅后送毛泽东。毛泽东在审阅后给张的信中说：“这篇文章写得很好，提倡正气，反对邪气”，应尽快发表。②《解放》周刊第81、82、83与84合刊分三次连载。同年11月延安新华书店首次出版单行本。1942年延安整风时该书（第二章的第2—5节）列为中

① 张闻天：《论待人接物问题》（1938年7月26），刊《解放》第65期（1939年2月28日），《张闻天选集》，人民出版社，1985年，第202—222页。

② 转引自中共中央文献研究室编，金冲及主编的《刘少奇传》（上），中央文献出版社，1998年，第352页。

共中央规定的十八个必读书目之一，新华社做了广播，并编入解放社出版的《整风文献》。该书从初版到1962修订再版的数十年间，总计印数千万册，还译成英文、日文等多种译本。该书对中国共产党的思想建设，增强党员的思想意识修养，保持共产党的纯洁性发生了重大作用。①

1941年7月1日，在纪念党成立20周年之时，中共中央做出了《关于增强党性的决定》。《决定》指出了在政治、组织、思想意识等方面存在违反党性的倾向，提出了纠正的办法。决定要求，“要用自我批评的武器和加强学习的方法，来改造自己，使适合于党与革命的需要。要求每个党员，特别是每个负责的领导的干部，都深刻反省自己的弱点。把党的利益看得高于一切……”为了配合党的决定的贯彻，任弼时写了《关于增强党性问题的报告大纲》，对为什么要增强党性，怎样增强党性，“需要在那些方面修养和锻炼自己”做了说明。②

延安整风是一次普遍的马克思主义教育运动。参加整风的每一个干部和党员，对规定的文件，“必须逐件精读，逐件写笔记”。在学习与讨论过程中，“每人都要深思熟虑，反省自己的工作及思想，反省自己的全部历史”。③ 毛泽东在整风报告中亦强调反省总结的重要。他指出，整风“重心在自己”，领导同志“要以身作则”，“要反复研究自己的思想、自己的历史、自己现在的工作，好好地反省一下，要做模范。”④ 经过回顾、反省、总结自己的历史，自觉检讨缺点错误，每个党员提高了理论修养、思想意识修养和工作能力，增强了党性。共产党员的党性修养、改造主观世界，无论就内容、方法和形式而言，自然与中国传统的修身、修养有本质的不同。但也应承认，我们党创造的整风这一党的建设形式，与中国传统的修养有着内在的联系。延安整风实质上是中国传统修养在现代的一种有领导、有组织、有计划的实践形式，取得了极大的成功。在30多年后，邓小平依然评说：“没有那次整风，打败日本侵略者，打败蒋介石，

---

① 有学者夸大了影响，认为刘少奇在书中大量援用了儒家文化的资源，这使得他的书的得到青年及大众的高度认同，甚至“使其影响在60年代前期一度超过毛泽东”（陈来《现代中国文化与儒学的困境》，北京大学中国文化发展中心、北京大学马克思主义学院编《马克思主义与中国文化发展》，北京大学出版社，2011年，第9—10页）。确实，在那时期，凡有阅读能力的党员和入党积极分子无不把该书作为党性修养的教材学习，并努力践行之。但若说其影响“一度超过毛泽东”，这并不符合实际。

② 任弼时：《关于增强党性问题的报告大纲》（1941年），《任弼时选集》，人民出版社，1987年，第231—237页。

③ 《中共中央宣传部关于在延安讨论中央决定及毛泽东同志整顿三风报告的决定》（1942年4月3日），解放社编：《整风文献》（订正本），中原新华书店印行，1949年2月。

④ 毛泽东：《关于整顿三风》（1942年4月20日），《毛泽东文集》第2卷，人民出版社，1993年，第419页。

是不可能的。”①

生于1878年的革命老人吴玉章，从小受孔孟经典教育，深信“正心诚意、修齐治平、中庸忠恕之道”，经历辛亥革命、五四新文化运动，1925年参加共产党。他认为，共产党改造了我的思想，发扬了我旧的好思想，洗掉了我旧的坏思想。“我常常把我们共产党员的修养和处事的方法，与中国古圣贤所谓‘修己治人’之道相比较，只有过之而无不及，而且只有共产党员才能真正实行人类最高的道德”。“整风运动是一个有历史意义的伟大运动，也就是使我党更加民族化、使马列主义更能切实应用于中国具体环境中”。②

周恩来在学生时代就结合中外历史写过《论名誉》、《尚志论》、《诚能动物论》等诸多篇励志、修身的文章。他创建觉悟社，主编《觉悟》杂志，其目标是：“本着反省、实行、持久、奋斗、活泼、愉快、牺牲、创造、批评、互助的精神”，“做学生方面的‘思想改造’事业”。③ 可见，周恩来从学生时代起就继承了中国注重修养的传统，注意个人的思想改造。在长期的革命实践中，他严格修炼自己。他高尚的品德、情操和修养，在党内外有口皆碑，赢得赞誉和敬仰。1943年，他在整风学习中制订了《我的修养要则》，从学习、工作、与群众的关系到保持合理的生活规律等共七条。④ 这又从一个侧面表明，整风运动反过来又促进传统修养在现代的继承和发展。

总之，把中国传统的“修身”转化为现代的共产党的“修养”，在改造客观世界过程中自觉改造主观世界，纠正各种非无产阶级思想，是中国共产党能够使自己“无产阶级化”，经受各种考验，立于不败之地的一个法宝。

## 四、“修身”在当代的理论价值和现实意义

笔者在一些文章及许多场合的发言中指出，马克思主义与中国历史文化相结合是马克思主义中国化内涵不可或缺的一个重要方面，而这种结合决不能简单地理解在讲解马克思主义基本原理时引证中国历史文化资料来证明基本原理的普遍真理性。马克思主义与中国历史文化相结合的实质是，立足中国和世界的现实，运用马克思主义的

---

① 邓小平：《力强党的领导，整顿党的作风》（1975年7月4日），《邓小平文选》第2卷，人民出版社，1994年，第14页。

② 吴玉章：《共产党改造了我的思想》，延安《解放日报》1943年7月2日，引自中国社会科学院新闻研究所编的《延安文萃》下，北京出版社，1984年，第619、622、624页。

③ 周恩来：《“觉悟”的宣言》（1919年12月29日），刘焱编《周恩来早期集》上卷，南开大学出版社，1993年，第332页。

④ 周恩来：《我的修养要则》（1943年3月18日），《周恩来选集》上卷，人民出版社，1980年，第125页。

科学方法，总结和概括中国历史文化的优秀成果，用以解决现实问题，并在理论上丰富和发展马克思主义。两者结合的方面和形式是多样的，其中尤其要重视用中国历史文化中特有的、马克思主义鲜有论及的珍贵品来补充、丰富和发展马克思主义。[①] “修养”就是这样的“珍贵品”。

马克思在《关于费尔巴哈的提纲》的第3条论及人与社会环境关系时写道：“环境的改变和人的活动或自我改变的一致，只能被看作是并合理地理解为革命的实践。”[②] 在这之后不久，马克思恩格斯在强调革命的意义时说：无产阶级“只有在革命中才能抛掉自己身上的一切陈旧的肮脏东西，才能成为社会的新基础。”[③] 又说：“在革命活动中，在改造环境的同时也改变着自己。”[④] 他们在有的著作中也偶尔使用“修养”一词。但因历史的缘由，他们更多是讲改造客观世界，较少讲到改造主观世界和改造人自身。他们之后的马克思主义者同样很少讲改造主观世界和改造人，很少讲人生修养。我们在翻检马克思主义发展史、马克思主义哲学史和马克思主义伦理思想史时难觅马克思、恩格斯、列宁及国外马克思主义者有关改造主观世界和人生修养的论述。因此，从马克思主义发展史看，“改造主观世界”、“修养”这两个概念是由中国马克思主义者提出的，是对中国特有的优秀传统的继承和发展，是马克思主义中国哲学化的成果，也是对人类哲学思想和道德伦理的一个贡献。这两个概念应进教科书，进课堂。

前面讲到，重视改造主观世界，重视党性修养是民主革命时期中国共产党保持自己的无产阶级纯洁性、先进性的一个法宝。改革开放以来的历史表明，它依然是党在新的历史时期不可须臾的一个法宝。当我们轻视这一法宝，不讲改造主观世界、不讲修养时，党内的非无产阶级思想就滋长泛滥，贪腐奢靡之风就厉禁不止，有些党员、干部丧失了共产党人应有的理想信念，是非不分，美丑不辨，迷失方向，为资产阶级糖衣炮弹击垮，甚至触犯国法，锒铛入狱，成为罪人。针对党内存在的严重问题，江泽民同志指出：“我们党的一大长处和优势，就是把树立马克思主义世界观、人生观同坚持和发扬中华民族的优秀传统结合起来，讲求共产党员个人的思想品德修养。刘少奇同志写了一本《论共产党员的修养》，就曾专门讲过这个问题。革命战争年代，党

---

① 详见拙文：《马克思主义哲学与中国哲学相结合的思考》，《南京大学学报》2006年第3期，《新华文摘》2006年17期转载；《论马克思主义与中国传统文化相结合》，《党的文献》2009年第3期以，人大复印资料《马克思主义、列宁主义研究》2009年第8期。

② 马克思：《关于费尔巴哈的提纲》（1945年春），《马克思恩格斯选集》第1卷，人民出版社，1995年，第55页。

③ 马克思恩格斯：《德意志意识形态》（1945年秋－1846年5月），《马克思恩格斯选集》第1卷，人民出版社，1995年，第91页。

④ 马克思恩格斯：《德意志意识形态》（1945年秋－1846年5月），《马克思恩格斯全集》第3卷，人民出版社，1960年，第234页。

员、干部要讲个人修养；党执政了，搞改革开放和现代化建设，党员、干部同样要讲个人修养。”① 面对党内存在的严峻问题，习近平同志也指出，领导干部要严以修身、严以用权、严于律己。党风堪忧，党管不住自己是当代中国最大的问题和最严重的危机。要治好党在这方面的顽症，除了依靠群众管党和用法制管党这两条外，再一条就是要讲改造世界观，讲党性修养，讲修身律己，恢复和发扬我党在这方面的优良传统。

党员坚定的共产主义理想信念和高尚的道德情操不是靠外部强制的硬约束形成的，而是靠自觉的党性修养和内心意志力。“改造主观世界”、“修养”这两个概念应进每个党员和干部的头脑，使每个党员从入党那天起就要有自觉改造自己、修养自己的意识，使每个干部要认识到，只有严格修炼自己，才能“拒腐蚀，永不沾”。这也是笔者写作此文的旨意所在。

最后还要说明的是，修养不仅属于道德范畴，而且也是中国哲学认识论的重要概念。国内外的有关认识论的论著都不讲认识主体的修养。中国古代哲人则明确提出，不修养认识主体，怎么能认识客体②？中国哲学把求善看成是求真的前提，将求真与求善融为一体。中国哲学认识主体修养论有着丰富而深刻的内容，可以补充和发展当代认识论。为此，笔者发表过《中国哲学认识主体修养论》一文。③ 感兴趣的读者不妨一阅。

---

① 江泽民：《大力发扬艰苦奋斗精神》（1997 年 1 月 29 日），《江泽民文选》第 1 卷，人民出版社，2006 年，第 623 页。

② 《管子・心术上》：“人皆欲知，而莫索其所以知。[其所知]，彼也；其所以知，此也。不修之此，焉能知彼。”

③ 刊《哲学研究》2006 年第 8 期；人大报刊复印资料《中国哲学》2006 年第 11 期；“Theory on the cultivation of cognitive Subjective in Chinese philosophy”“ Frontiers of philosophy in China” 2008 Number 1 Volume 3。

# 读书是一种人生境界

中国人民大学 葛荣晋

21世纪，人类已经进入了“知识经济”的新时代。新时代的知识，呈现出三个明显的发展趋势，即书本知识爆炸现象的加剧、知识老化速度的加快和知识综合化、一体化的加强。面对知识老化和知识更新速度的加快，现代人若不能与时俱进，站在人类知识的最前沿，不断地增加自己的新知识，淘汰自己的旧知识，更新自己不合理的知识结构，就有可能随时被社会无情地抛弃，更谈不上跻身于世界知识前沿、使自己成为国际市场竞争的强者，构建自己的理想人生境界。

## 一、读书是一种富贵人生境界

在知识激增和信息万变的“知识经济”时代，知识是一种谋生的手段，是企业创新和人生成功的基石，是一种富贵人生境界。

英国哲学家弗朗西斯·培根（公元1561—1626年）认为知识本身就是一种巨大的力量，他指出：“人的知识和人的力量相结合为一”，“达到人的力量的道路和达到人的知识的道路是紧挨着的，而且几乎是一样的。”（《新工具》）培根的这一观点，被后人概括为一句著名的话：“知识就是力量”。培根肯定知识和科学技术的发明是“任何政权、任何教派、任何杰出人物对人类事业的影响都不能比拟的”，因为科学“发明的利益可以扩及于全人类，而政治的利益只限于特殊的地带. 后者经不了几代，前者则永垂无穷。”知识是财富增殖的基础，知识也是获取权力的源泉。阅读史书可以使人明智，阅读诗歌可以使人聪慧，演算数学可以使人精密，研究哲理可以使人思想深刻，修身养性可以使人道德高尚，逻辑修辞可以使人能言善辩。一句话，知识决定人生命运，人的知识是构建富贵人生境界的根本保证。

中国汉代哲学家王充（公元27—约97年）在其《论衡》一书中，早已认识到知识是人生成功的一种力量。他说：“人有知识（学），则有力矣。”（《论衡·效力篇》）

宋代皇帝赵恒（公元968—1022年）在其《劝学诗》中云：“富家不用买良田，书中自有千钟粟。安居不用架高楼，书中自有黄金屋。娶妻莫恨无良媒，书中自有颜如玉。出门莫恨无人随，书中车马多如簇。男儿欲遂平生志，六经勤向窗前读”。读书越多，人的“智商”越高，知识面越广，在社会中的发展空间也就越大，社会竞争力也就越强，发言权也就越多，社会地位也就越高。现代社会流行的“知识决定高度”这一警句，道理就在这里。

读书是苦也是乐。读书有两种：一种是把读书只视为谋取功名利禄的重要手段，带有浓厚的功利色彩。在今天的应试教育环境下，如果是在家长的设计与逼迫下，学生读书只是为了考取名牌学校，读外语只是为了出国留学谋利。这完全是一种功利化的读书。另一种读书是随个人兴趣爱好、抚慰心灵，选择阅读有益于世道人心的书。这种不带功利目的的读书，则是一种快乐的读书。孔子曰：“学而时习（复习、实习）之，不亦说（悦）乎？”这种读书犹如儿童读小人书，成人读小说一样，随人兴致所至，广泛涉猎，完全出于人的趣味爱好。正如鲁迅在《读书杂谈》一文中所说：“嗜好的读书，该如爱打牌的一样，天天打，夜夜打，连续的去打，有时被公安局捉去了，放出来之后还是打。诸君要知道真打牌的人的目的并不在赢钱，而在有趣。”

## 二、读书是一种健康长寿人生境界

读书是一种构建富贵人生的手段，同时也是一种追求健康长寿的人生境界。俗话说：“读书破万卷，不用去医院。”正如南宋诗人陆游所云：“读书有味身忘老，病需书卷作良医。”

清代学者李渔曾说：“予生无他癖，惟好读书，忧藉以消，怒藉以释，牢骚不平之气藉以除。”读书可以解除人的忧愁、寂寞、愤怒、孤独和牢骚不平之气，可以使人心神集中、杂念尽消、心平气和、神志安稳，从而有利于人的身体健康；读书可以清心明志，教人明理，遇到不平之事可以避免“怒伤肝、恐伤肺”等；读书还可以引导病患者专心于书中，暂时忘却病痛带来的苦恼，使患者意境开阔、心情舒畅，有利于人的身体康复。

读书还可以延缓衰老，预防老年痴呆症。医学研究表明，老年痴呆归根结底是因为大脑功能衰退，记忆能力丧失。人在晚年，如能勤于读书则能促“脑运动”，而不断的脑运动可以促进脑健康，从而通过脑协调与控制全身的功能，防止老年痴呆症的发生。勤于读书的人，大脑血管经常处于舒张状态，以输送充足的氧气和营养物质，从而延缓中枢神经老化，带动血液循环，使全身各系统功能保持协调统一，促进人体健康。美国哈佛大学心理学家德格斯・坡厄尔对1600多名25岁到92岁爱读书的人进行推理能力、记忆力、视力以及对空间的判断力的测试，发现80多岁的人，表现得几乎和年轻人同样良好；一部分80多岁与90多岁的人的智力，接近任何年龄段的最高水平。戏剧电影大师夏衍说得更具体："不爱动脑，不爱读书，不爱思考的人，容易得'老年痴呆症'。"由此可见，古人所云"至乐莫过于读书"，是一句千真万确的真理。

## 三、读书是一种道德人生境界

读书是一种健康长寿的人生境界，也是一种人所追求的道德境界。明代民族英雄和著名诗人于谦（公元1398—1457年）在《观书》一诗中，盛赞读书之乐，极写读书之趣，诗云："书卷多情似故人，晨昏忧乐每相亲。两眼直下三千字，胸次全无一点尘。活水源流随处满，东风花柳逐时新。金鞍玉勒寻芳客，未信我庐别有香"。在现代社会中，北京也有一位文化名人，在他的书房内，挂有一副对联云："抛他难抛身外物，读我平生未读书。"当你在静静的书房里，两耳不闻窗外事，一心只读圣贤书，以你的丰富人生阅历去解读书中所阐述的哲学智慧和人生理念有所悟的时候，可以明理，可以赏景，可以观史，可以鉴人。顿时，你会将自己一生所追求的钱、权、名、色"身外之物"全都抛到九霄云外，完全摆脱了令人痛苦的世俗的"功利境界"而升华为君子的"道德境界"。这里所说的"胸次全无一点尘"的"道德境界"，是一种快乐和谐的人生境界。这正是"世事浮躁唯拥书城而心静，人间烦嚣但闻墨香而气平。"这才是现代人所追求的道德人生境界。在这一境界中，读书使我超脱，读书让我宁静，读书令我满足。这是一种精神享受，更是一种心灵净化。所以，法国著名哲学家梅里特在《人是机器》一书中，正确地指出："征服全世界，也抵不上一个哲学家在他的书房里所尝到的那种快乐。"

## 四、读书是一种文化软势力

生活于市场经济中的现代人，既需要财富和健康的硬势力，更需要知识和道德的软势力。读书不仅可以提高现代人的文化知识水平，达到身体健康目的，而且也可以提高现代人的道德水平，构建他们的道德境界，培养他们的爱国热情，还可以坚定现代人的信仰，启发现代人的哲学智慧。这种文化软势力，才是每个人综合势力和国际竞争力的所在。所以，温家宝总理指出："读书关系到一个人的思想境界和修养，关系到一个民族的素质，关系到一个国家的兴旺发达。一个不读书的人是没有前途的，一个不读书的民族是没有前途的。"

因此，公元1995年，联合国教科文组织宣布每年4月23日（西班牙作家塞万提斯和英国剧作家莎士比亚的逝世纪念日）为"世界读书日"。近年，我国有识之士多次建议将孔子诞辰日9月28日以法律形式定为"中国读书节"。向全国人民发出"享受阅读乐趣，共创学习型社会”倡议，主张在全国范围内有计划地有组织地开展全民读书活动。

在读书远离我们的今天，现代人应牢固地树立“终身学习”的新理念，努力做到活到老学到老。早在中国春秋末年，著名教育家孔子就是“终身学习”、自学成才的典范。他敏而好学、不耻下问，一生都在努力读书，追求知识。他曾说过：“学而不已，阖棺乃止。”① 又说：“加我数年，五十以学《易》，可以无大过矣。”（《论语·述而》）他将读书学习视为人生的第一要义和终身目标。中国自古以来就有发愤图强、刻苦读书的优良传统，如战国苏秦锥刺股、汉代孙敬头悬梁、晋代车胤囊光读书、孙康映雪读书，等等。在现代中国社会中，毛泽东同志是“终身学习”的典范。他说：“我一生最大的爱好是读书。”“饭可以一日不吃，觉可以一日不睡，书不可以一日不读。”他从四五岁读蒙书开始，无论是在革命战争年代还是在日理万机中，真正做到了“枕上、厕上、马上”手不释卷，嗜书如命。在他弥留之际，还叫别人为他念书，直到去世，整整读了将近80年的书。我们应当继承和发扬孔子和毛泽东的这一优良传统，活到老学到老，在读书中不断地充实自己的知识，使自己具有终身学习和驾驭知识的能力，从而为自己走向成功人生之路奠定牢固的基础。

最后，我想赠送大家宋代诗人翁森的两句诗：“蹉跎莫遣韶光老，人生唯有读书好。”（《四时读书乐》）希望大家千万不要为世俗应酬所役，白白地浪费时光，让宝贵时间空自逝去。在这里，我愿与大家共勉：少一点应酬，多一点读书。不管你有多忙，每天至少保证一小时的读书时间。在努力构建自己的物质家园的同时，更要在读书中不断地提高自己的道德水平，努力构建心灵快乐、健康长寿的人生境界。

---

① 在《韩诗外传》中有这样一则记载：“孔子燕居。子贡摄齐而前曰：‘弟子事夫子有年矣，才竭而智罢，振于学问，不能复进，请一休焉’。……孔子曰：‘……学而不已，阖棺乃止，”这段话的意思是：孔子在家里休息，他的学生子贡就提着长袍下襟去见他，说：“我跟你学习好几年了，可是现在感到才能枯竭，智力疲惫，看来学问是停止不前，不会再有什么进步了。还是让我把学习停止一下吧。”孔子答曰：“学习是不能停止的，一个人应该是到了棺材的时候才能停止自己的学习。”孔子深刻地阐明了“活到老学到老”的“终身学习”理念。

# 国学与当代文化自觉

秦皇岛市国学研究会　郑安纲

## 一、文化自觉是一个民族成熟的标志

（一）何为文化自觉

自觉就是自知之明，就是觉悟、觉醒，就是自我理性认识、自我审视。文化自觉就是对文化的觉悟和觉醒，对文化深层次的理性认识，对本民族整体的审视和理性认识。

“文化自觉”是费孝通先生于1997年在北大社会学人类学研究所开办的第二届社会文化人类学高级研讨班上首次提出，目的是为了应对全球一体化的势必发展，而提出了解决人与人关系的方法。他提出“文化自觉只是指生活在一定文化中的人对其文化有‘自知之明’，明白它的来历，形成过程，所具有的特色和它发展的趋向，不带任何‘文化回归’的意思。不是要‘复旧’，同时也不主张‘全盘西化’或‘全盘他化’。自知之明是为了加强对文化转型的自主能力，取得决定适应新环境、新时代时文化选择的自主地位。”

中西不同文化语境下，对“文化自觉”的态度有不同的看法。

1. 费孝通则提出了著名的“各美其美，美人之美，美美与共，天下大同”的观点，非常形象地阐明了东方式的文化观。费孝通讲和合，大家求同存异，互相学习，共同建立美好世界，乐观中透着中国文化的自信。

2. 美国学者亨廷顿提出的“文明冲突论”，代表着西方的文化自觉观。亨廷顿认为世界上7个或8个文明，很容易冲突起来，伊斯兰文明因为缺乏中心会率先与基督教文明发生冲突，但对西方最大的威胁还是东方的儒教文明，甚至还假想了在2010年中越因南海问题引发的多国之间的冲突。（《文明的冲突与世界秩序的重建》）亨廷顿讲冲突，代表的是西方以力服人的文化观，不是东风压倒西风，就是西风压倒东方，照这个逻辑推下去，在当今原子弹时代人类没有活路了，可以说代表的是文化悲观主义。

（二）文化自觉的形成和过程

文化自觉往往是受到外部刺激引起。有其内在和外在的原因。内因包括自身条件、内部因素，如发展历史长自我成熟、制度变革等。外因往往表现的比较明显，一是受到外部刺激，如外族侵略、社会动荡、文化冲击等；二是思想自由的环境，多数出现在不受统治阶级严格控制的动乱时代，如春秋战国、魏晋南北朝时期。

文化自觉是一个过程，变现的程序为：落后──→失序──→骚动──→反思──→觉醒──→理性思考。

（三）文化自觉的特点和形式

文化自觉是全民族的自省，是全民族的，是整体的、全面的，不是局部的、单个人的；是深刻的、深层次的，不是浅显的、表象的。如：春秋战国时期百家争鸣（西方学者提出的文明轴心时期，人的觉醒）、魏晋南北朝时期文的自觉（人性的觉醒、文学自觉）、文艺复兴（神本位到人本位，西方文明现代化）、明治维新（日本大和民族自觉）、新文化运动（中华民族的觉醒）、新中国—文化大革命—改革开放—文化热（当代中国的文化自觉）等等。

（四）文化自觉的意义

文化自觉，是人类自身觉悟，是对人类自身深刻的认识；文化自觉是一个民族成熟的标志；文化自觉是民族自信、文化自信的表现；文化自觉是民族进步、社会发展、国家强盛的表征。

文化自觉是个过程，人的自觉、文的自觉、社会自觉（制度变革）都是文化自觉的一部分，是文化自觉的准备阶段。文化自觉是最深层次的觉悟，是对人类最高层次的认识和最准确的把握。人类发展的过程就是一个不断自我觉醒的过程。当一个民族在文化层面进行理性自觉时，说明这个民族已是一个成熟的民族。从文化的层面去认识一个民族，才是对这个民族的全面把握和真正的认识。

## 二、中华民族的文化自觉历程

在中华民族发展史上有三个文化自觉时期。前两个重要的文化自觉时期：

一是春秋战国时期。即文明轴心时期（中国先秦时期），这个时期世界三大宗教形成了。在中国，是中国文化的形成时期，出现诸子百家思想争鸣局面，是中国传统思想文化奠基期。这个时期的本质是人类的自觉。就是人类走过了童年，开始思考本源问题：人从何处来？到何处去？怎样认识社会、自然和人的自身。其特点是整个人类的思考，重对群体的认识。

二是魏晋南北朝时期。由于社会动荡、佛教思想影响，整个社会在思考。主要表现在：(1) 在对人生命的感慨。如魏晋时期诗歌文学，文人《古诗十九首》中许多诗句："生年不满百，常怀千岁忧。""人生寄一世，奄或若飘尘。""人生天地间，忽如远行客。"政治家曹操："对酒当歌'人生几何?"等等，感叹人生短促，这样的感叹几乎在所有的魏晋文人的作品中可以看到。(2) 思想上，反对名教，鼓吹自由，玄学兴起。佛教兴起，产生中国佛教。道教体系的完备，形成宗教形式。(3) 文学的自觉。文学觉醒，对文学本身的思考，《文心雕龙》、《文赋》、《诗赋》等大量文学理论。对文学载体和记载工具——文字的思考，如沈约的四声八病，音韵学的发展等等。这次文化自觉的本质是人性的觉醒，其特点重在对人生、生命、人性的觉悟，不在依附于群体（国家、族类）思考人的问题，是对自身生命的感悟，对自己怎样生活的思考。

现在处于第三个文化自觉时期（从明朝开始），表现为对中国传统文化的再思考和对外来文化的接受、认识和再思考。

中华民族的文化自觉历程（如下图）：

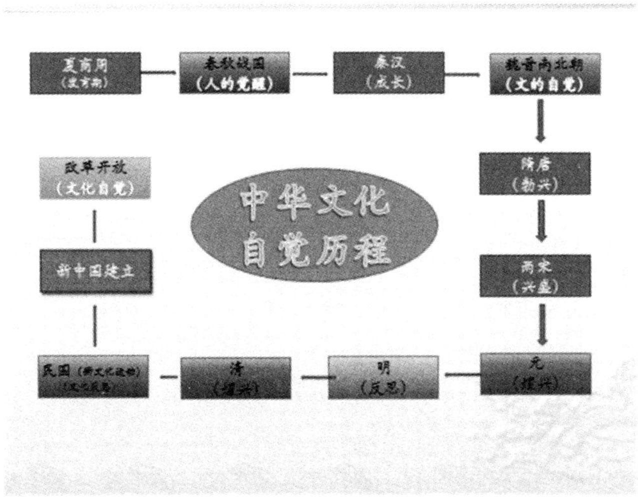


## 三、当代中国的文化自觉表现为对传统文化的再认识

文化自觉是立足于现实的历史性和世界性的思考。

当今中国文化建设取得了巨大成就：可以说从中央到地方，从学界的民间，从来没有像今天这样重视文化建设，文化的重要性从来像今天这样突出，文化软实力和精神家园的概念从来没有像今天这样广泛使用和空前普及，文化产业、文化体制改革从来没有像今天这样引人关注，文化建设呈现出良好的发展态势。

发展社会主义先进文化，建设和谐文化，推动社会主义文化大发展大繁荣，是20世纪第一个十年中国文化建设的战略构想，体现了当代中国的文化自觉。

（一）当下中国文化自觉主要表现

一是对文化的深刻认识。表现为“文化热”现象，思考：何为文化？文化之于民族、国家的意义？

二是对中国传统文化的重新审视。表现为“国学热”现象，思考：何为国学？国学之于当代中国的意义？

三是全社会全民族对民族文化的思考，特别执政党对文化建设的重视。

从知识分子热情坚守到党的自觉认识。由“精神文明建设”到“文化建设”。改革开放以来，解放思想，实事求是，改革开放，实践是检验真理的惟一标准大讨论。怎样看待西方，怎样看待现代化，怎样看待市场经济等到表现为对中国现实、中国特色和中国文化、西方文化的再认识。

执政党的文化自觉表现在：党的报告中的文化认识。党的历次代表大会的报告和文件中的提法：“中国共产党是一个具有文化自觉的政党”，“加强精神文明建设”，“文化建设”，“代表先进文化前进的方向”，“文化大发展大繁荣”“文化复兴”“建设文化强国”等等，这是一个历程，一个认识过程：

“民族的科学的大众的文化，就是人民大众反帝反封建的文化，就是新民主主义的文化，就是中华民族的新文化”（毛泽东）；邓小平第一次创造性地提出了“社会主义精神文明”的科学概念，并高度概括其基本内容，指出“所谓精神文明，不但是指教育、科学、文化（这是完全必要的），而且是指共产主义的思想、理想、信念、道德，革命的立场和原则，人与人的同志式关系，等等”；20 世纪 80 年代《中共中央关于加强精神文明建设的决定》；2006 年 9 月 13 日《国家“十一五”时期文化发展规划纲要》；十七届六中全会《关于促进文化大发展大繁荣的决定》。梳理一下不同时期中国共产党的文化建设的提法和观点：1. 引入马克思主义思想文化（建党之初，新文化运动时期）；2. 提出新民主主义文化（ 新民主主义革命时期），即无产阶级领导的人民大众的反帝反封的文化，民族的科学的大众的文化；3. 推进马克思主义理论建设（在建国之后），使得马克思主义文化在中国大地上蔚然成风；4. 建设有中国特色社会主义文化（改革开放之后），真理标准问题大讨论，社会主义精神文明建设；5. 建设社会主义先进文化（20 世纪 90 年代）；6. 建设社会主义和谐文化（弘扬民族优秀文化传统）；7. 推动社会主义文化大发展大繁荣（文化复兴）；8. 建设社会主义文化强国（建设优秀传统文化传承体系）。

2011 年 10 月 18 日中国共产党第十七届中央委员会第六次全体会议通过的《中共中央关于深化文化体制改革推动社会主义文化大发展大繁荣若干重大问题的决定》明确指出：“文化是民族的血脉，是人民的精神家园。在我国五千多年文明发展历程中，各族人民紧密团结、自强不息，共同创造出源远流长、博大精深的中华文化，为中华民族发展壮大提供了强大精神力量，为人类文明进步做出了不可磨灭的重大贡献。”“中国共产党从成立之日起，就既是中华优秀传统文化的忠实传承者和弘扬者，又是中国先进文化的积极倡导者和发展者。我们党历来高度重视运用文化引领前进方向、凝聚奋斗力量，团结带领全国各族人民不断以思想文化新觉醒、理论创造新成果、文化建设新成就推动党和人民事业向前发展，文化工作在革命、建设、改革各个历史时期都发挥了不可替代的重大作用。”这充分表明了中国共产党对文化建设的重视，同时也表明新时期党对传统文化的态度。

（二）当下传统文化即国学思潮的几种倾向

我们对国学的认识有一个过程，曾走过两个极端时期：一是清算传统文化，革传统文化的命。认为传统文化是落后挨打的源泉（新文化运动，砸烂孔家店），传统文化等于封建糟粕（文化大革命）。（二）传统文化救中国，救世界。文化热、国学热现象。

1990年代以后，“国学热”在各地持续升温，被称为是20世纪以来国学在中国出现的第三次高潮。

从目前发表的各种倡导国学的言论看，人们对此的认识并不一致，其中至少包含着以下几种倾向。

一是着眼于传统文化尤其是其知识性遗产的继承和发扬，认为传统文化是一个民族的根，关系到每个民族自身的归属感和内聚力，也是其得以自立于世界民族之林的基础，故“国学的当代意义是围绕着弘扬中华民族优秀文化传统这个目标来实现的”。《儒藏》、《子藏》等大型国学文献整理项目的推出，高校国学研究院等专业人才培养机构的建立等，便突出地反映了这方面的意向。

二是希望以儒家文化来补救当代社会人文素养和人伦道德方面的某些缺失。针对当前社会出现的一些“拜金主义”、唯利是图和诚信缺乏等道德滑坡现象，有人主张通过重建中华文化的主体性，尤其是将儒家注重自我人格修养和道德教化的一些重要意涵“渗透到人们的日常生活中”，以帮助化解商品经济条件下人们面临的道德和精神危机。目前各种民间的国学私塾、讲堂，以及一些儒家启蒙读物被引入中小学教学，大多与这一诉求有关。

三是主张全面恢复儒学旧有的社会政治和伦理功能，主张把孔孟之道作为国家的立国之本，恢复科举制度和经典教育制度，规定凡有志从政者须通过《四书》、《五经》的考试获得资格。

## 四、正视国学（中国传统文化）

正视国学（国学自觉）是当今中国文化自觉的重要表现和主要任务。

（一）认识国学的正确视角和态度

1. 国学是当下中国语境中的“国学”意义，非站在历史上、本世纪初那时对国学的思考定义。

2. 正确认识国学，必须放在当下经纬度中去把握国学，即放在历史经度（历时）和世界的维度（共时）坐标系里去认识国学（中国传统文化）。一是古今关系：在历史中的作用和当下的意义；二是中西关系：就对当下中国的意义角度，如何看待、对待西方文化。进而探讨华人梳理优秀和糟粕，有用和无用，以及科学性问题。

3. 对待国学的科学态度：

今天重振国学，不是对传统国学的简单回归与重复，而是以现代的理念指导国学的研究与发展。我们力求充满明确的创新意识和与时俱进的当代精神；坚持以历史唯物主义的立场、观点和方法对待中国传统思想与学术，取其精华，弃其糟粕，避免陷入单纯复古的泥淖。对于什么是糟粕，什么是精华，我们也要持慎重分析的态度。我们往往把精华当糟粕，把糟粕当精华，这都是历史的经验和教训，所以要慎言精华和糟粕。沟通历史与现实的畛域，摆脱为整理国故而研究国学的思路，立足于从丰厚的历史文化资源中寻求启迪，为建设共有精神家园提供服务；以博大的襟怀、坦荡的气魄，使今天的国学成为一个开放的文化体系，充分汲取和借鉴世界尤其是欧美近现代文化中的精华成分，给国学注入新的生机，升华新的境界；不断开拓视野，注重东西文化比较，在世界文明发展的大格局中进行定位，不张扬狭隘的民族主义，而是追求在世界文化多样化背景下，既各美其美，也美人之美，致力于将博大精深的中国文化作为“世界文化”的一部分，作为全人类共同的精神财富加以集成、阐释和光大。概而言之，我们所说的国学，乃是今人眼中的国学，乃是国际视野中的国学，乃是现代形态意义上的国学。

（二）科学界定国学概念和正确认识国学研究和传承的意义

1. 国学概念

国学是中国传统文化之学，是中华民族智慧的结晶，是人类文明的重要组成部分，是中华民族对全人类的伟大贡献，也是中华民族五千年生生不息的精神源泉，是当代中国人的精神寄托。

2. 国学的品质和特点

中华文化具有包容自新的品质；中华文化源远流长、博大精深；以孔孟为代表的儒家思想是中国传统文化的主流；中华文化整体性和混沌性，反映了中华民族的心理结构，即中国特色。思维方式（审美心理）的特征（悟性、感觉）：注重整体的把握，不重细密的逻辑分析（国画、古诗）；这种思维的准确性和正确性（人的情感因素和事物的普遍联系）。

3. 研究、认知国学的意义

中国文化的特色就是中国特色，研究中国事情必须懂得中国文化，中国的一切事情必须和中国实际相结合。比如认识西方和中国，认识四小龙和中国，认识国学就认识中国。

对国学概念、作用、意义的争议、思考、定位，就是当下中国的文化自觉。

国学热——国学冷思考——国学的国家认同，就是当今民众、知识分子和国家的文化自觉的过程。

# 儒学与科学

中国科学技术馆 王渝生

提起近现代科学技术三五百年来的发展，欧美处于世界领先地位似乎已成为不争的事实。但是在一两千年前，美洲还是未经开发的地区，欧洲则处于黑暗的中世纪时期。而此时东方的中国、印度和阿拉伯地区，则经历了科学文化大发展的全盛阶段。

中国是世界四大文明古国（古巴比伦、古埃及、古印度和古代中国）之一。古老的中华农业科技文明可以追溯到至少六七千年以前。四五千年以前的科学知识萌芽和农、牧、手工业以及青铜冶铸等技术都有了长足的进步。可以说，在四五千年以前，世界科技文明四分天下的话，中国有其一。

两三千年以前，中国逐渐形成了农学、医药学、天文学和数学等独特的科学体系，在地学、生物学以及制陶、矿冶、纺织、建筑等技术领域也取得了辉煌的成就。此时在欧洲地中海沿岸，崛起了一个新兴的奴隶联邦制的古希腊后来是古罗马的文明，而此前的古老文明，除中华文明外，其他的都衰亡了下去，出现了中断现象。可以说，在两三千年前，古代中国和古代希腊罗马的文明就像两颗璀璨的明珠，一颗在东方，一颗在西方，两者交相辉映，那时的世界科技文明两分天下，中国有其一。

一千多年以前，中国则先后完成了指南针、造纸术、印刷术和火药这闻名于世的四大发明，“并在 3 到 13 世纪之间保持一个西方所望尘莫及的科学知识水平。”（李约瑟：《中国科学技术史》）事实上，直到 14—16 世纪，数学家朱世杰的“四元术”及“招差术”、天文学家郭守敬的简仪和《授时历》、航海家郑和“七下西洋”、乐律学家朱载堉的“十二平均律”理论、医药学家李时珍的《本草纲目》以及 17 世纪初地理学家徐霞客的《游记》、科学家徐光启的《农政全书》和技术专家宋应星的《天工开物》，都在世界科技史上占有重要地位。也就是说，一千年前，中华科技文明在世界上一枝独秀！

从四分天下到半壁江山，到独领风骚，中华科技文明一直在大踏步前进，并在数千年中居于世界前列。

而在西方，到了一千多年前，确切地说，是公元 476 年，日耳曼雇佣军攻占了罗马城，西罗马帝国灭亡，标志着欧洲封建时代的开始。从西罗马帝国灭亡到14－16世纪欧洲文艺复兴之前，差不多一千年左右，欧洲开始了政教合一的封建时代，宗教裁判所可以因为布鲁诺信奉哥白尼的日心地动学说而判他死刑，把他烧死在罗马繁花广场上。欧洲的中世纪被称为是黑暗的中世纪，科技经济的发展和社会的进步在这个时期受到了极大的阻碍。而这一千年间中华封建文明在大踏步前进。

到了14－16世纪，西方出现了宗教改革、文艺复兴、科学革命三大近代化运动，出现了思想启蒙运动、资产阶级革命和资本主义生产方式，一下就把在封建老路上蹒跚爬行的中华封建大帝国远远抛在了后面。但是，西方的近代科学和资产阶级革命的进步和发展，中国古代科学成就在其中是产生了巨大推动作用的。

譬如说，关于中国的四大发明，英国哲学家弗兰西斯·培根在1620年就曾指出，印刷术、火药、指南针“这三种发明已经在世界范围内把事物的全部面貌和情况都改变了：第一种是在学术方面，第二种是在战事方面，第三种是在航行方面；并由此又引起难以数计的变化来，竟至任何教派、任何帝国、任何星辰对人类事务的影响都无过于这些机械性的发明了。”

马克思则在1863年这样评论道：“火药、指南针、印刷术——这是预告资产阶级社会到来的三大发明。火药把骑士阶层炸得粉碎，指南针打开了世界市场并建立了殖民地，而印刷术则变成了新教的工具，总的来说变成了科学复兴的手段，变成对精神发展创造必要前提的最强大的杠杆。”虽然没有提到造纸术，但是正是它为印刷术的产生和推广提供了必要条件。

1970年，英国科学史家贝尔纳在为其《历史上的科学》中译本所写的序中说：“中国许多世纪以来，一直是人类文明和科学的巨大中心之一。已经可以看出，在西方文艺复兴时期从希腊的抽象数理科学转变为近代机械的、物理的科学的过程中，中国在技术上的贡献——指南针、火药、纸和印刷术——曾起了作用，而且也许是有决定意义的作用。”

只是在四五百年前我们没有顺应历史潮流发展，没有像西方那样在近代科学指引下，以资本主义机器大生产方式飞速前进，总之是没有从农业文明跃升工业文明，从封建时代进入资本主义时代，后来我们又遭受帝国主义侵略，沦为半封建、半殖民地国家，所以我们落后了几百年。

有人把中国近代科学的落后，归罪于中国传统文化，特别是作为中国传统文化主流的儒家文化，这是既不合乎逻辑又不符合历史事实的。

如果说儒学阻碍了中国科技的发展，那么中国古代科学技术的辉煌成就从何得来？上述弗兰西斯·培根、马克思、李约瑟、贝尔纳等人对中国科技的评价岂不成了虚妄之辞吗？

下面我们简略回顾一下中国古代科技发展的辉煌历程，考察一下它们同儒学的关系。

## 原始社会迎来科技文明的曙光

人类社会的发展，迄今已有三四百万年的历史。中国境内发现的古人类遗迹，云南元谋人化石和山西芮城西侯度石器，距今也有170万年以上。从那时开始到公元前2070年前夏王朝建立的漫长岁月中，华夏人的祖先生活在原始社会时期。起初他们住的是天然山洞，穿的是树叶兽皮，吃的是野菜野果，过着茹毛饮血的生活。随着生活领域的扩大和生产水平的提高，他们逐步创造了初始的技术，萌生和积累了一些科学知识。传说中的燧人氏钻木取火，伏羲画八卦制九针，神农尝百草作耒耜，嫘祖养蚕抽丝织绸；羲和观日，隶首作数；刳木为舟，剡木为楫；从穴居野处到构木为巢，从室内分隔到方圆城池，从石器到陶器漆器黄铜器，迎来了中华文明的曙光。

## 夏商周三代灿烂的青铜科技文化

公元前2070年，以晋南、豫西为活动中心的夏族建立了中国第一个王朝——夏朝。夏自禹至桀470年。起自冀西南、豫北的商族于公元前1600年推翻了夏朝，建立了商朝。商自汤至纣约550多年；其间第十世盘庚迁殷，于河南安阳建都，史称殷商。其后便是原在陕西、陇东的周族，于公元前1046年灭商，建立了周朝，以丰京、镐京为都（在今陕西长安）。到公元前770年平王东迁洛阳为止270多年，史称西周。夏、商、西周三代，凡1300年。这期间，冶铜技术趋于成熟，创造了灿烂的青铜文化。夏爵商鼎西周簋，戈矛戟钺驷马车；规矩准绳测高下，九九筹算十进制；五色丝织以为锦、十二纹章入服饰。圭表测冬至，记录日月食，如顾炎武《日知录》称：“三代之上，人人皆知天文。”这是因为我们的先民“日出而作，日落而息”，观天象以便于生产和生活。

## 春秋战国百家争鸣铁器时代的风范

春秋战国时期是中国历史上的社会大变革时代，自公元前770年周平王东迁，至公元前211年秦始皇统一中国，在这五个半世纪中，春秋五霸，战国七雄，诸侯分封割据，战争连年不断。激烈的社会竞争促进了生产的发展和思想的解放。学术上诸子百家争鸣又为科学技术的进步创造了有利的条件。儒学的开门祖师孔子，是开创“私学”的大教育家，他以“有教无类”和培养“博学通才之士”为方针和目标，对学生进行礼、乐、书、数、御、射“六艺”教育。其中数即数学，乐和声学、金属冶铸有关，御和力学有关，射和机械有关。儒家的“六艺”教育具体付诸教材，即古代经典中，如《易》，“易道广大，无所不包，旁及天文、地理、乐律、兵法、韵学、算术，以逮方外之炉火”（《四库全书总目·易类小序》）；《诗经》包含有大量虫鱼、鸟兽、草木，以及天文、地理、农业生产等知识；《礼记》中有农业与季节相关的知识，《考工记》则是有关手工业技术的专门著作。孔子之孙孔伋（子思）的《中庸》：“博学之，审问之，慎思之，明辨之，笃行之。”学、问、思、辨、行，这完全符合认识过程和研究科学的方法，即获取信息，提出问题，逻辑推理，检验结果，躬身实践。作为“孔子之言而曾子述之”的《大学》，有八目，即：格物，致知，诚意，正心，修身，齐家，治国，平天下。所谓“物格而后知至，知至而后意诚，意诚而后心正，心正而后身修，身修而后家齐，家齐而后国治，国治而后天下平”。这本来是古代知识分子中家喻户晓的话，可惜后人多引后半段“修身齐家，治国平天下”而忽略了前半段“格物致知，诚意正心”。前半段指知识来源于实践，而又指导实践，“格物致知”为知之始，“诚意正心”为行之始，是为本。后半段是知行观的外推于家国和社会，是为末。在《大学》“经”之“传”中，引汤之《盘铭》曰：“苟日新，日日新，又日新。”引《康诰》曰：“做新民。”引《诗》曰：“周虽旧邦，其命惟新。”真是充满了创新精神！

中国古代没有“科学”这个词，直到清末，西方科学传入，我们还称之为“格致”。今天看来，中国传统科学技术中的农、医、天、算四大科学体系，机械、冶金、建筑、纺织四大技术门类，大都在这一时期形成了传统的框架，奠定了体系的基础。

吴王金戈越王剑，步入铁器新时代；齐纨鲁缟衣天下，耕耨并用事农桑；《易经》《墨经》《山海经》，《甘石星经》四分历；扁鹊华佗麻沸散，望闻问切治未病；开渠筑堰、泽被百代；国中营城，高台筑室；龙窑青瓷，荆楚彩漆。百花竞放的格致之学，五彩纷呈。

## 秦汉一统天下科技集大成的辉煌

公元221年，秦灭六国，建立了中国历史上第一个统一的、多民族的、中央集权的帝国。秦始皇废分封，立郡县，建驰道，修长城，书同文，车同轨，统一货币和度量衡。汉承秦制，400余年间，经济得到发展。古代科学技术各大门类的知识在先秦时期的长期积累，特别是春秋战国时期“百家争鸣”的基础上，集其大成，逐步形成了具有自己特色的体系。在儒家崇尚务实和“经世致用”思想影响下，中国古代科技具有强烈的实用性。具有适应大一统帝国政治经济各方面需要、密切联系社会生产实践、偏重解决经济发展和生活实际问题的鲜明特色。

中国古代以农为本，民以食为天，要使“黎民百姓不饥不寒”，国家兴旺，实施儒家的“王道”政治，在中国古代知识分子的心目中，农业这一行的社会地位仅次于官宦，“士农工商”，“农”排在第二位。医术以治病救人为宗旨，与儒学的仁义道德一致，称为“仁术”；儒家还以为医家治病的道理与治国的道理相一致。至于天文算学，则被视为历代王朝改正朔，易服色，“受命于天”的标志；而且“观象授时”，可以指导农业生产，所以受到统治者的重视。自汉以来，历代王朝政府机构中都设有大规模的皇家天文机构进行天文观测和历法制定，即使在大战乱的时代也没有中断过。所以，中国古代天象记录之丰富为世界之冠，历法也备臻精确。数学“夫推历、生律、制器、规圆、矩方、权重、衡平、准绳、嘉量，探赜索隐，钩深致远，莫不用焉”（《汉书·律历志》)。传统数学经典著作《九章算术》以方田、粟米、衰分、少广、商功、均输、盈不足、方程、勾股分类，列举246个数学应用问题求解，很有实用价值。在地学方面，《汉书·地理志》开创了按行政区划记述各地山川地形的地方志的先声，以后历朝历代，都重视编修地方志，内容扩大到各地的物产、户口、贡赋、沿革、古迹等，将自然地理和人文地理有机结合，其内容之广博，数量之庞大，历史之悠久，也居世界之首位；而其动因，当然是为了社会管理、发展生产和文化交流的需要。

汉代取得了诸多领先世界的辉煌成就。如张衡地动仪，蔡伦造纸术；《月令》记农耕，《尔雅》辨生物；引水溉田，治黄防洪；球墨铸铁，百炼成钢；南纱北锦并秀，机械巧夺天工；观象授时造历法，盖天浑天宣夜说。

## 三国两晋南北朝时期分立中的融合

秦汉天下一统凡440余年，到公元3世纪初，又进入了割据与纷争的时代，直至6世纪末。

古代科学的兴衰与王朝的统一或分立并无必然的对应关系。有时候，战乱恰恰使一些被阻断了正常入仕途径的学者放弃经学转向科学。而对立政权的竞争和战争，都对技术的发展有所刺激。南北的分裂与统一促进了中华各民族的摩擦、交往和融合，也推动了古代科学技术长足的进步。

这360多年间，科技成就要者有：贾思勰《齐民要术》，郦道元《水经注》，葛洪《抱朴子》，稽含《南方草木状》；刘徽“割圆术”，祖冲之圆周率；木牛流马千里船，失蜡佛像宿铁刀；石窟佛塔，鬼斧神工；贝锦斐成，濯色江波；施胶染色、洛阳纸贵；青瓷设釉，漆器脱胎；医典整理，医方汇聚。

## 隋唐大帝国盛世的繁荣

隋（581—618年）唐（618—907年）时期，中国再度统一。唐代实行对外开放政策，加强了同东亚、南亚和中亚的交流，经济文化空前繁荣，“盛唐”之誉驰名于世。唐代科举曾设有“明算科”，医学教育也建立有严格的制度。但总的说来，唐代的科技成就与强盛帝国的浩大声威相比，尚不能说是相称。不过，隋唐五代时期的科学技术仍得到持续发展。

请看：水田整地，《茶经》传世；生物图谱，环境保护；运河贯通南北，石鱼标记水位；船中轮磨，水密隔舱；长安都城，赵州拱桥；常平架，地监听，鉴重影；海内华夷图，大唐西域记；《缉古算经》，《算经十书》；戊寅历始用定朔，子午线一行首测；织为云外秋雁行，染作江南春水色；析诸病源侯，集千金医方；炼丹术盛极而衰，造纸术突飞猛进；金银平脱，瓷器胎雕；青白瓷南北辉映，唐三彩独树一帜；雕版印刷术和黑色火药堪称人类中世纪的伟大发明。

## 两宋王朝兴衰中的科技奇葩

两宋时代，与北宋（960—1127年）并存的是辽（947—1125年）和西夏（1032—1227年），与南宋（1127—1279年）对峙的是金（1115—1234年）。这300多年间，中原王朝的声威远逊于唐代，但就科学技术而言却达到了中国古代历史上的高峰。英国著名科学史学家李约瑟说：“对于科学史学家来说，唐代却不如后来的宋代那么有意义。这两个朝代的气氛完全不同。唐代是人文主义的，而宋代则较着重于科学技术方面。……每当人们在中国的文献中查找任何一种具体科学技术史料时，往往发现它的焦点就在宋代。不管在应用科学方面或在纯粹科学方面都是如此。”

据沈括《梦溪笔谈》记载，平民毕昇发明活字印刷术；指南针用于航海，也是在北宋时期；植物专谱，本草图经，地志地图，未艾方兴；苏湖熟、天下足；药政“和剂局”，法医《洗冤录》；治水利航运，修堤防海潮；水运仪象台，超新星观测；数理精微，大衍求一；胆水炼铜，巨型铸铁；南北瓷器，八大窑系；缂丝精巧疑鬼斧神工，《营造法式》立建筑规范。

## 元代科技恢宏的气象

元朝（公元1271—1368年）在将近一个世纪的时间内，于“北逾阴山，西极流沙，东尽辽左，南越海表”的辽阔疆域上，下马治天下，“恃北方之马力，资中原之技巧”，加强和发展了中华各民族间的融合，恢复农业、手工业和商业贸易，特别实施鼓励海外贸易的政策，促进了同欧亚各国之间的科技文化交流。中国的四大传统科学体系：天文学、数学、医药学和农学，都在这一时期达到顶峰；纺织、瓷器、机械、建筑等技术也有长足发展。

“天元术”“四元术”世界领先，观象台《授时历》海内独步；京杭运河，开通南北；黄河探源，《岛夷志略》；广植棉麻，精养蚕桑；金锦金碧辉煌，毛纺棉纺普及；彩色套版套印，转轮排字印刷；火铳火炮，威力无穷；指南《针路》，万里导航；光学实验，小孔成像；卵白青花釉里红，戗金剔红并剔犀；规模宏大元大都，中医中药四大家。

元代连同它以前的两宋、辽、西夏、金各代，统称宋元时期（960—1368 年），这 400 年来是中国科学技术发展的高峰，可谓人才济济、硕果累累。众多的科学家和能工巧匠，众多的科学发现和技术发明，为中华民族谱写了世界科技史上灿烂的篇章。

## 明代不绝的余响

1368 年，朱元璋建立明王朝。明代把中国的专制制度推向极致。特别是采取思想禁锢政策，规定科举考试必须用八股文体，“代圣人立言”，造成思想僵化。故顾炎武《日知录》说：“八股之害，甚于焚书。”宋元时期高度发展的天文学、数学等传统学科都出现了中衰现象。

明中叶以后，欧洲已伴随着资本主义的兴起而发生科学革命，中国却依然在昔日的封建驿道上蹒跚爬行。然而一些才识卓越的知识分子，如李时珍、宋应星、徐霞客等，仍在科学技术上做出了巨大的贡献；进入仕途的知识分子徐光启则在继承传统和吸收外来科学知识的基础上，力求中西汇通。总的说来，明代科技是传统科技体系的尾声，缺少蒸蒸日上的活力，比起西方先进的近代科技，已经是大大的落伍了。

明初有郑和扬帆下西洋，紫禁城和明长城的修建；巧妙的无梁拱殿，精美的江南园林；竹纸皮纸工艺，饾版套色叠印；景德釉瓷，宜兴紫砂；运河改建，攻沙治黄；人痘接种，天花免疫；徐光启《农政全书》，李时珍《本草纲目》，宋应星《天工开物》，徐霞客《游记》四大著作，堪称明末对中国传统科技方面的总结。

1582 年，意大利传教士利玛窦来华，带来了西方的科学著作和科技器物，中国朝野为之震惊，此乃西方近代科学传入中国之开端，具有中国科技史上从古代向近现代转变的里程碑式的意义。

## 清代的暮鼓与晨钟

1644 年清军入关，满人贵族成了中国的统治者。

明末清初，随着欧洲耶稣会士来华传教，西方科学开始传入中国。因夷夏之防、本末之辨的诸多文化屏障，中国只是被动地零星接受西方的科学知识。清中叶乾嘉学派大兴考据之风，对于搜集、整理和保存传统文化功不可没，然而忽视了另一个重要的方面：中国文化应该向世界文明汲取新的营养。

1840年鸦片战争以后，中国受到世界列强的侵略。随着1860年代洋务运动的开展，西方科学技术潮水般地涌进国门，逐渐改变了中国人对整个世界的看法。通过书局、译局和新式学校的开办，以及向欧美和日本派遣留学生，中国开始主动学习西方国家的科学和技术。

1682年，清廷在北京设立同文馆，1683年在上海和1684年在广州相继设立方言馆，1868年在上海江南制造局设立译书馆，魏源、严复、李善兰、徐寿、华蘅芳华世芳兄弟等同欧洲传教士合作翻译数学、天文学、地质学、物理学、化学、生物学等西方科学著作，哥白尼日心说、达尔文进化论都传了进来，是为中国近代科学的先驱。

1895年中日甲午战争，宣告了洋务运动的失败。是年盛宣怀在天津创设中西学堂，后改名为北洋大学堂、北洋大学校、国立北洋大学，是为我国近代科技教育的先声；1896年则在上海开办了南洋公学，即是现在的上海交通大学。1898年6月11日，清光绪帝颁布《明定国是诏》宣布变法 。1898年7月3日，光绪帝正式批准设立京师大学堂，由孙家鼐主持在北京创立。这是中国的第一所大学，北京大学的前身，也是戊戌变法至今唯一幸存的成果。

经过1898年戊戌变法，直至1911年辛亥革命推翻了清朝的统治，中国的现代科学技术才进入了步履维艰的起步和其后奋起的新时期。

中国没有爆发近代科学革命，没有产生建立在观察和实验的基础上并同数学的逻辑推理相结合的近代科学。中国近代科学的发展经历了一条充满艰辛和屈辱，而又有奋斗与辉煌的曲折历程。既然中国传统文化包括儒学孕育了中国古代灿烂的科技文明，今天，在以开放的心态学习西方近代科技、学习世界一切优秀文化的同时，对中国古代科技和传统文化中的优秀基因，借鉴、移植到当代科技前沿探索中，是有古为今用，继往开来的价值的。

例如，近代科学建立起了庞大的分析型学科体系，在很多方面精确地研究了自然界，取得了丰硕的成果。但是，近代科学有长处也有不足：重分析，轻综合；重结构，轻功能；长于线性研究，短于非线性研究；习惯于封闭系统研究，不善于开放系统研究。当然，这种说法只是相对而言的。事实上，客观自然界是局部与整体，结构与功能，线性与非线性，封闭与开放的统一。而中国传统的系统思维方式在当代和今后科技整体化中会起到越来越重要的作用。耗散结构论的创始人普利高津说："中国传统的学术思想是着重于研究整体性和自发性，研究协调和协和，现代新科学的发展，近些年物理和数学的研究，如托姆的突变理论、重正化群、分支点理论等，都更符合中国的科学思想。"创建协同学的哈肯也指出："事实上，对自然的整体理解是中国哲学的一个核心部分。在我看来，这一点西方文化中未获得足够的考虑。"

又如，在近现代科技发展中，特别是工业文明后期，人与自然是对立的，人对大自然着重征服、索取，而不注意保护，结果受到严厉报复：资源匮乏、能源枯竭、环境污染、生态破坏，全球气候变暖，珍稀物种灭绝，自然灾害频仍等。而中国传统文化、传统哲学、传统科技的核心是“天人合一”，中国的“天”，不是西方的“神”、“上帝”，而是自然界、客观规律。荀子曰：“天行有常，不以尧存，不以桀亡。”中国古代的区域开发和经济发展，强调天时、地利、人和的三才学说，所谓“人与天地相参”，“仰观天文，俯察地理，内省自身”，强调生物界的和谐和“各得其养以成”，这对当代生态经济学、生态伦理学的发展有指导意义，有利于促进身心健康和生活质量的提高，有利于建设生态文明和可持续发展。

再如，中国传统科技方法创造了古代光辉的科技成就。吸收和应用传统科技基因，开发现代科技，往往可以有大的创新。中国传统数学，不发展演绎几何学，但充分发展程序性算法，寓证于算，不证自明，在电子计算机出现后，二者巧妙结合，若合符节，中国学者创造了几何定理的机器证明法，并崛起了崭新的机械化数学。中国古代铸造中的失腊法，在现代已形成精密铸造产业。当代电子计算机打孔程序控制技术受到源自中国古代纺织中提花技术的启发而发明的。用现代科技原理和方法去研究龙洗、编钟、透光镜、“越王剑”等，已引发出若干有价值的科学前沿问题。

还有，天体演化、大地构造、地震预报、气候变迁、海平面升降、环境演替、生物进化等当代重大科学热点乃至社会热点，是与自然史和历史自然科学相关的问题。浩如烟海的中国儒学和经史子集等古文献中有大量类型多、系列长、连续性好、地域覆盖广阔、综合性强的有关自然现象特别是异常现象的观察记录，这是中国古人几千年来留给今人、贡献给世界的一个自然史信息宝库，它已经在射电天文学、地震震中分布图和烈度区划图、5000年气候史重建、500年旱涝史重建及其隐含周期的发现中发挥了重要作用。黄河小浪底工程大坝高程设计是以黄河1843年洪水的复原研究为依据，长江三峡工程防洪设计是以1870年洪水时下游荆州大堤不决口为前提。大型工程设计论证早期有物理模型法、数学模型法，现在中国学者又创立了历史模型法，服务于科技和经济建设重大工程中长期规划的自然背景评估。

当然，我们在充分估计儒学对中国科技发展的积极影响，挖掘中国古代科学思想方法和传统文化的现代价值的同时，也要防止对其作牵强附会解释而导致一些不科学的认识。《易经》的“天行健，君子以自强不息”鼓舞了多少人求新创新，《易经》中包含了一些科学思想和数学结构等成分，能为当代科学研究提供创造性的思想模式，但在历史上衍生出来与易经有关的方术活动，如算命、占卜之类，则要科学地、实事求是地认真分析其中的精华和糟粕，有所扬弃，这才是继承发扬儒学和传统科学文化所应取的正确态度。

## 三、儒学传播与普及

# 儒家思想早期在欧洲的传播

北京外国语大学 张西平

## 一、全球化初期的东方与西方

今天的世界成为一个世界，各个民族和国家真正开始作为全球的一个成员，参与世界的活动，世界在经济和文化上构成一个整体。这一切都源于16世纪的地理大发现。①

地理大发现的最早推动者是地处利比里亚半岛上的葡萄牙和西班牙。葡萄牙在恩里格王子（Infante D. Henrique，1394—1460年）的带领下，“将地理探险和发现成为一门艺术和科学，使远航成为全国感兴趣、与之有密切利益联系的事业。②”葡萄牙人首先攻下北非的休达，然后乘着三桅帆小心的沿着西非海岸前进。1488年迪亚士（Bartholmeu Dias，约1450—1500）发现了好望角；1498年，达伽马（Vasco da Gama，约1460－1524.12.24）绕过好望角，进入印度洋，沿东非海岸，过红海口，直达印度大陆。葡萄牙开辟了西方到达东方的新航线。1511年占领了马六甲，进而有占据

① 马克思在《共产党宣言》中说：“美洲的发现，绕过非洲的航行，给新兴资产阶级开辟了新的活动场所。”《马克思恩格斯全集》，第1卷，第252页；恩格斯在《反杜林》中说：“伟大的地理发现以及随之而来的殖民的开拓使销售市场扩大了许多倍，并加速了手工业向工厂手工业的转化。”《马克思恩格斯全集》第3卷，第313页。当代全球化史的研究者也认为，“我们已经养成了一种习惯，即根据实际上是西方史的世界史来论述现代时期起因。我们所养成的这种习惯只不过是收到了都市商业文明——其覆盖面在蒙古人入侵前从地中海沿岸地区一直到中国海——发达的影响。西方承继了这一文明的部分遗产，在其影响下才得以成就自己的发展。这一文明的传播受惠与12、13世纪十字军的几次东征和13、14世纪蒙古帝国的扩张。……西方的这种落后状况一点也不奇怪，意大利的城市……地处亚洲大型商业之路的终端。……西方只是由于海上的扩张才得以摆脱隔离状态；它的兴起正好发生在亚洲两大文明（中国和伊斯兰世界）面临威胁之时。”安德烈·冈德·弗兰克 巴里·K·吉尔斯主编《世界体系：500年还是5000年?》，社科文献出版社，2003年，第36页。

② 张箭《地理大发现研究：15－17世纪》，商务印书馆，2002年，第81页。

了暹罗和巴达维作为商业活动的据点。1517 年（正德十二年）葡萄牙人在船长费尔南·佩雷斯·安德拉德（Fenão Peres d' Andrade）和使臣托梅·皮尔资（Tomé Pires）的率领下从马六甲来到中国。这是中国与西方人的首次见面。① 广东巡抚林富奏疏言："正德十二年，有佛郎机夷人，突入东莞县界，时布政使吴廷举须其朝贡，为之奏闻。此不考成宪之过也。"②

1492 年 8 月 3 日哥伦布（Cristoforo Colombo，1451—1505）带领探险船队出发，1493 年返回出发的港口帕洛斯，开启了人类对北美新大陆的发现。1522 年麦哲伦（Ferdinand Magellan，1480—1521）的西班牙船队首次环球航海成功，从而开辟了从欧洲到达亚洲的另一条不同于葡萄牙人开辟的新航线。同时，西班牙人从美洲到达菲律宾，开始与居住在那里的中国人做生意，形成了"中国—阿卡普尔（墨西哥西海岸）黄金水道"，"马尼拉大帆船贸易"由此拉开序幕。

"寻找契丹是百年航海史的灵魂"。从马可波罗（Marco Polo，1254—1324 年）到柏郎嘉宾（Giovanni da Pian del Carpine，1180—1252 年），中世纪时这些旅游者的游记点燃着西方寻找富饶契丹的梦想。刺桐港堆积如山的香料，契丹大汗无与伦比的财富都成为枯燥无味的中世纪欧洲人的热门话题。哥伦布出发时，带着的是一份西班牙国王致大汗的国书，葡萄牙人则将寻找"秦人"作为他们来到东方的重要使命。③ 奥斯曼帝国的兴起后，中国与欧洲商路的阻断，寻找香料，与东方展开贸易是其海上扩张的根本目的。而基督教的扩张则和其商业利益、文化梦想融为一体。蒙元帝国将世界连为一体，欧洲人通过蒙古时代的游记知道了东方文明与东方的富饶，整个地理大发现的动机就是寻找"契丹"，寻找东方。

---

① "1500 至 1700 年间，葡萄牙人试图在从好望角的开普敦到日本之间建立一个贸易和权力网络的世界并不是静止不变的。它随时都在两个层次：制度和功能上发生变化。有些变化微妙得几乎不易觉察，有些变化则清晰可见。因此，要理解葡萄牙人在亚洲的所作所为，以及他们所要适应的环境和所使用的途径，我们不仅仅需要描述他们在上面表演的'亚洲舞台'，还需要考虑这 200 年中亚洲历史的活力。"参阅桑贾伊。苏布拉马尼亚姆著，何吉贤译：《葡萄牙帝国在亚洲 1500—1700：政治和经济史》，朗文书屋出版（Longman Group UK Limited），1993 年。

② （明）顾炎武：《天下郡国利病书》卷一三，昆山市顾炎武研究会点校，上海科技大学文献出版社，2003 年。

③ 葡萄牙国王曾颁布寻找"秦人"的敕令"你必须探明有关秦人的额情况，探明来自何方？路途有多远？探明何时到达满刺加或探明进行贸易的其他地方？探明带来什么商品？探明每年驶进多少艘船？探明船只的形式和大小如何？探明是否在来的当年就回国？探明在满刺加或其地方任何国家是否设有商栈？探明是富商吗？探明生性懦弱还是尚勇好战？探明有无武器或火炮？探明穿什么杨的服装？探明的身材是否高大？他们是基督徒还是异教徒？他们的国家大吗？他们是否不止一个国王？他们国中是否有与他们法律信仰不同的摩尔人（穆斯林）或其他民族？如果他们不是基督徒，那么他们信仰和崇拜什么？他们遵从什么杨的社会习俗？他们的国土扩展到何处？与那些国家为邻？"张天泽著，姚楠、钱江译：《中葡早期通商史》，香港中华书局，1988 年，第 36 页。

地理大发现所开启的全球化并非仅仅是在地理上人类第一次较为全面的认识了自己生存的家园——地球，同时，初期的全球化开始了人口的流动，贸易的沟通，科学的发展。在西方殖民主义的血与火中，世界从孤立分散走向联合与统一。农作物的传播极大促进了农业的发展，而疾病也在世界联系的各种通道中传播。①

更为重要的是：1500年后的初期全球化的另一个最重要的收获就是多元文化的相遇与碰撞，直到今日，这种文化的接触和碰撞、理解与纷争仍未完成。在全球化初期，西方文化在全球的扩张充满了血腥，但唯一有一个例外，这就是西方文化与中国文化的接触。正是在这200年间中国文化和欧洲文化相识、交融，开出了绚烂的文明花朵，成为全球化初期人类在文化上最大的收获、最宝贵的成果、最珍贵的文化历史遗产。这一宝贵成果的获得主要原因在于，中国在经济实力与文化实力都处在与欧洲不相上下，甚至高于欧洲的水平之上。远来的葡萄牙人和西班牙人无法采取他们在非洲和南北美洲所采取的殖民政策，只能以另一种形式开始与中国接触，② 而来自于欧洲的来华耶稣会士们为了自己的宗教利益采取了，开始探索在不同文化的天主教传播，从而为文化之间的接触和理解做出了的不懈努力和历史性的贡献。“12世纪耶稣会在华传教的历史与欧洲对中国的早期研究，或者成为早期汉学，是不可分割的。虽然传教这一首要任务将耶稣会士和早期汉学家区别开来，但耶稣会士作为有关中国地理、语言、政治、哲学、历史和社会生活情况的主要传播者和解释者，为那些后来成为早期汉学家的欧洲学者提供了学术基础。来华耶稣会传教士经常利用返回欧洲逗留的机会或通过从中国寄回欧洲的书信与这些学者保持直接的、密切的联系。”③

来华耶稣会士沟通中国和欧洲的一个重要成果就是他们开始第一次用欧洲的语言将中国的古代文化经典翻译出来，由此，传教士汉学和游记汉学的那种道听途说才有

---

① 张箭在其地理大发现研究中，谈到地理大发现的重大作用和影响时，主要从地理、科学角度谈的。当然，尽管也谈到了对社会科学发展的贡献，但主要是站在西方社会的角度来讲的。其实，地理大发现在文化上的主要价值是：文化的相遇与碰撞，它所带来的文化冲突，西方殖民主义在全球化中对待异族文化的野蛮态度的影响，至今仍未解决。经济的全球化并不意味着文化的全球化，文化的相遇和理解，求同与存异，至今仍是地理大发现以来一直未很好解决的问题。

② 西班牙传教士桑切斯在菲律宾制定了了一个攻打中国的计划，葡萄牙初到中国南海与明军的交战都以失败而告终。参阅张维华：《明史弗朗机吕宋和兰意大利四国传注释》，台湾学生书局，1972年；张凯：《中国和西班牙文化交流史》，大象出版社，2003年；万明：《中葡早期关系史》，中国社科文献出版社，2001年；金国平：《西力东渐：中葡早期接触追昔》，澳门基金会：金国平、吴志良：《过十字门》，澳门成人教育学会出版，2004年。参阅罗荣渠：《美洲史论》，中国社会科学出版社，1997；（美）普雷斯科特著，周叶谦、刘慈忠、吴兰芳、刘方译：《秘鲁征服史》，商务印书馆，1986年；郑家声主编《殖民主义史：非洲卷》，北京大学出版社，2000年。

③ （美）孟德卫著 陈怡译《奇异的国度：耶稣会适应政策及汉学的起源》第2—3页，大象出版社2010年。

了根本性的区别。“游记汉学”的一个根本性特点就是这些作者叙述的是个人的经历，他们很少亲自研读中国的典籍文献，自然也谈不上从事中国典籍的翻译。这些来到东方的“游客们”，游走四方，浪迹天涯。尽管他们也提供了大量关于中国的文化和历史信息，也给西方讲述了不少动人心弦的故事，但总体上他们提供给西方读者的中国就是一副多样的、感性的中国，是一个个性化的讲述。在这个时期由于西方人读不到中国典籍的原文，他们只能获得一个关于中国的感性印象，一个充满神奇，支离破碎，可以任意想象的中国，从而无论是西方的大众还是知识界都始终无法从精神层面上来把握和认识中国。① 自罗马帝国与汉帝国分别统治的欧亚大陆的两端起，欧洲与中国就开始沿着丝绸之路来往贸易，但直到大航海时代后，以耶稣会士入华为其标志，中国和欧洲才开始了真正思想文化意义上的交流，中国古代文化典籍中所包含的人类共同的价值和意义，才第一次在欧亚大陆两端同时彰显出来。

## 二、高母羡：儒家思想的最早翻译者

第一个向西方介绍儒家思想并翻译儒家经典的是来自西班牙传教士高母羡（Juan Cobo，1546—1592），②《明心宝鉴》是元末明初的中国文人范立本所编著的一本关于中国文化先贤的格言的一本蒙学教材，收入了孔子、孟子、庄子、老子、朱熹等先哲

---

① 参阅坞承钧译：《马可波罗行纪》，上海世纪出版集团，2001年；《海屯行记·鄂多立克东游录·沙哈鲁遣市使中国记》，何高济译，中华书局，1981年；（英）道森编：《出使蒙古记》，中国社会科学出版社；（美）柔克义（W. W. Rockhill）译注；耿升、何高泽译《柏朗嘉宾蒙古行记·鲁布鲁克东行记》，中华书局，2002年；（英）约翰·曼德维尔著，郭泽民、葛桂录译：《曼德尔游记》上海书店，2006年。

② “高母羡系西班牙多来都省 Toledo Spain 舒厄各拉人（Consuegra），死于一五九二年十一月。高母羡于一五六三年加入道明会（Order of Preachers），……并在赫纳斯的阿卡拉大学接受神哲学训练，然后从事神哲学的教学工作。高母羡于一五八六年加入由三十九位道明会士组成，志愿远赴远东的菲律宾传播基督宗教的传教团体行列，这一团体怀著打开亚洲大陆传教之门的梦想和远见来到了菲律宾，在途经墨西哥时，高母羡在该地一年以达成一项重要使命，然而他的同伴们已先赶往菲律宾，他们一行数十人在一五八七年七月抵达菲律宾。”摘自潘贝新《高母羡和玫瑰省道明会传教方法研讨》http：//www. catholic. org. tw/dominicanfamily/china cobo. htm＃ ftn3)

Sententiae plures et graves philosophorum etiam gentilium ut Senecae et similium ex eorum libris excertae et Sinicae reditae. Lingua sinica ad certam revocata methodum quatuor distinctis caracterum ordinibus generalibus，specificis et individualis；seu vocabularium sinensis.

“‘Juan Cobo’，是他在1590年寄给危地马拉会友信末的落款签名，也是同时代的欧洲作家对他的称呼；‘高母羡’，是1593年马尼拉出版的中文著作《辩正教真传实录》一书扉页上的作者；‘羡高茂’，是1592年他在翻译菲律宾总督致丰臣秀吉的回信中使用的署名。”摘自蒋薇硕士论文《高母羡(Fr. Juan Cobo) 出使日本再议》抽样本；参阅方豪：《中国天主教史人物传》上册，中华书局，1988年，第83—89页。

的格言，于洪武二十六年（1393年）出版。1592年高母羡翻译这本书时在菲律宾传教，为了归化当地的华人，他必须学习汉语，于是将《明心宝鉴》翻译成Beng Sim Po Cam，Espejo clar del Recto Corazón 也是为了让传教士们更好地学习汉语。[①] 学者们认为，这个以闽南话为基础的西班牙译本“书中的书名，人名及部分难以意译的地方，採取音译方式，其所注字音，当然也是闽南语音，因此《明心宝鉴》音译材料不但是现今通行的闽南语教会罗马字的老祖宗，在闽南语文献及记音方式上极其珍贵。”[②]

高母羡所翻译的《明心宝鉴》“后来由米格尔·德贝纳维德斯（Miguel de Benavides）神甫带回西班牙并于1595年12月23日呈现给菲利普二世。”[③] 因此，法国汉学家伯希和认为《明心宝鉴》是最早被翻译成欧洲语言的中国古代典籍。[④]

《明心宝鉴》至今仍受到西班牙人的欢迎，它的各种译本如下[⑤]

20世纪至今，西班牙共出版了四种高母羡《明心宝鉴》译本：

| | | | |
|---|---|---|---|
| 1924 | Ed. P. Getino, | Fr. Juan Cobo, El Libro Chino Beng Sim Po Cam o Espejo rico del Claro Corazón, traducido de Legua castellana por Juan Cobo, Madrid: Claudio Coello, 114, 1924 | |
| 1959 | Ed. Carlos Sanz | Beng Sim Po Cam o Espejo Rico del Claro Corazón, Madrid: Libreria General, 1959 | 自西班牙国家图书馆原件的影印本。中西文对照 |

① 尽管这本手稿知道1942年才第一次公开出版，但从历史学上到目前为止是一个被翻译成欧洲语言的中国古代书籍。当然，西班牙传教士拉达从福建回到菲律宾时，也带回了很多中国书籍，据说也在当地找人翻译了一些中文的书籍，但很可惜，至今学界尚无发现这些书籍。

② 摘自潘贝新《高母羡和玫瑰省道明会传教方法研讨》(http://www.catholic.org.tw/dominicanfamily/china cobo.htm# ftn3)；参见刘莉美，“当西方遇见东方——从《明心宝鉴》两本西班牙黄金时期译本看宗教理解下的偏见与对话”，台北：《中外文学》第33卷，第10期，2005年，第123页。

③ 参阅张凯《中国与西班牙关系史》，大象出版社，2003年，第206页。

④ Pelliot, Paul. “Notes sur quelques lives ou documents conserves en Espagne.” T’oung Pao 26 (1929), p. 46; Biemann, Benno, Die Anfänge der neueren Dominikanennission in China, Vechta: Albertus Verlag, 1927. Biermann, Bemo, “Chinesische Sprachstudien in Manila: Das erste chinesische Buch in europäischer Überse-tzung”, NZM 7 (1951), pp. 18—23.

⑤ 蒋薇《活跃于东亚各国之间的道明会传教士：高母羡》，载张西平 罗莹主编《东亚与欧洲文化早期相遇：东西文化交流史论》第5—56页，华东师范大学出版社2012年。

| | | | |
|---|---|---|---|
| 1998 | Ed. Manel Ollé | Rico Espejo del Buen Corazón (Beng Sim Po Cam) Barcelona: Península, 1998 | 是西班牙文原文的现代整理版 |
| 2005 | Annotated. Liu Limei | Espejo Rico del Claro Corazón, Madrid: Letrúmero 2005. | 中西双语版，并夹有西班牙文注释 |

留学西班牙的刘莉美博士在其论文《高母羡对〈明心宝鉴〉的翻译》中对高母羡的翻译做了深入的研究。她以西班牙中世纪文学的特点来分析高母羡用于翻译中国伦常词汇的西班牙文对应词以此探究高母羡对于中国典籍的理解理路。"高母羡阅读《明心宝鉴》时，在初学汉文且缺乏参考工具书的条件下他使用《圣经》的思想去理解中文原文的，再加上中古天主教适应希腊哲学的传统影响，高母羡先入为主地套用他预先建立的思想模式去诠释、附会眼前的新世界。这种'适应策略'早期广泛地被耶稣会利马窦等人应用于其宣教策略上。"[①]

## 三、罗明坚：儒家经典西译的开创者

《明心宝鉴》只是民间通俗读物，而将中国儒家经典著作首先翻译成西方语言的是来华的耶稣会士罗明坚（Michele Ruggieri，1543－1607 年）。[②] 在讲到耶稣会的汉学成就时，学术界给予利玛窦（Matteo Ricci，1552—1610 年）和他的一些后来者的赞誉太多了，[③] 无论在西方还是在东方学术界都忽视或者冷漠了来华耶稣会士的真正开创者，西方汉学的真正奠基人之一——罗明坚，他才是儒家经典西传的真正开创者。

---

① 转引自蒋薇《活跃于东亚各国之间的道明会传教士：高母羡》，见张西平、罗莹主编《东亚与欧洲文化早期相遇：东西文化交流史论》，华东教育出版社，第 17 页。参阅张凯《中国与西班牙关系史》，大象出版社，2003 年，第 204－205 页；陈台民《中菲关系与菲律宾华侨》，香港朝阳出版社，1985 年。

② 近两年来学术界开始注意到罗明坚的在中西文化交流史的贡献，参阅宋黎明：《神父的新装：利玛窦在中国（158－1610）》，南京大学出版社，2011 年；夏伯嘉：《利玛窦：紫禁城里的耶稣会士》，上海古籍出版社，2012 年。

③ De Christiana expeditione apud Sinas (see Trigault) Tetrabiblion Sinense de moribus, 1593, a Latin translation of the Four Books mentioned by other sinologists but never found or never published. ;

Alden, Dauril, The Making of an Enterprise: The Sociew of Jesus in Portugal, Its Empire, and Beyond 1540—1750, Stanford: Stanford Univ. Press, 1996. ; Betray, Johmnes, Die Akkommodationsmethode des P. Matteo Ricci S. J. in China, Roma: Univ. Pont. Gregoriana, 1955. ; Ricci Roundtable on the History of Christianity in China, several collections accessible online through the Ricci Institute for Chinese－Western Cultural History, University of San Francisco.

当1592年高母羡在菲律宾翻译《明心宝鉴》时，从中国回到罗马的来华耶稣会士罗明坚，也做着同样的工作，如果从翻译中国典籍的时间上看，高母羡先于罗明坚，但如果从在欧洲出版中国典籍的时间来看，罗明坚早于高母羡，因为，高母羡的书是在菲律宾出版的。

首次将罗明坚的这个《大学》的拉丁文译文在欧洲正式发表的是波赛维诺（Antonii Possevino，1533－1611）。他1533年出生，1559年加入耶稣会，以后成了耶稣会会长麦古里安（Mrecurian，1573－1581在任）的秘书，就是麦古里安把范礼安（（Alessandro Valignano，1538－1606年），派到了东方传教。波赛维诺以后作为罗马教皇的外交官被派到德国、匈牙利和葡萄牙、俄国等地工作。晚年从事文学和神学研究，其中最重要的著作便是百科全书式的《历史、科学、救世研讨丛书选编》一书（Antonii Possevino，Bibliotheca Selecta qua agitur de ratione stucliorum in historia，in disciplinis，in Salute omniun procuranda. Roma 1593）这部书1593年在罗马出版。（书中所标明的当时耶稣会会长阿瓜维瓦（Aquaviva）的出版许可日期为1592年4月16日。）

罗明坚返回罗马以后常常去波赛维诺那里，向他讲述自己在中国传教时所看到和听到的事，这样波赛维诺就在该书的第九章上介绍了罗明坚在中国的一些情况，并将罗明坚的译文一同发表。这本书以后又分别于1603年和1608年在威尼斯和科隆两次再版。[①]

以下是罗明坚在《历史、科学、救世研讨丛书选编》一书（Bibliotheca Selecta de Ratione Studiorum in Historia，In Disciplinis，in Salute Omnium Procuranda））发表的原文图片[②]

---

① Lundbaek，Knud，"The First European Translations of Chinese Historical and Philosophical Works"，in China and Europe (1991)，pp. 29－43.；麦克雷（Michele Ferrero）China in the Bibliotheca Selecta of Antonio Possevino (1593)，抽样稿.

② Lazarist Mission，Pekin CATALOGUE OF THE PEI－I″ANG LIBRARY 1949 第2504号 "Bbliotheca selecta de rat，ione stvdiorvm，Ad Disciplinas，& ad Salutem omnium gentium procurandam. Reoogn，ita novmme ab eodem，et avcta，et in duos Tomas distri－ buta. Triplex additus index，alter librarum，a，Iter Capitwn... tutius Verbonmz a Rerum a，Iter Capitum... tertj，us Verborum & Rerum I 603."

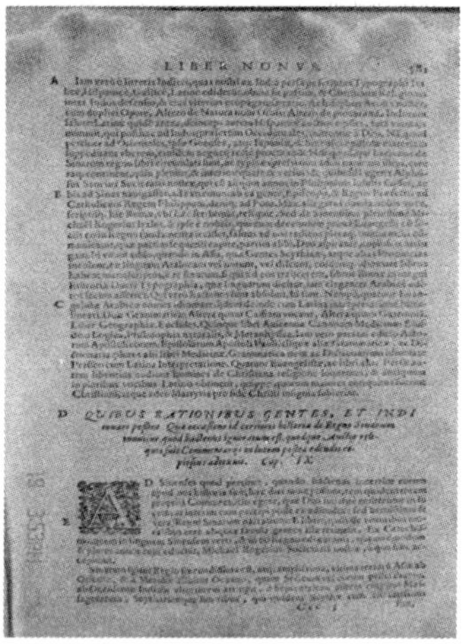
LIBER NONVS. 581

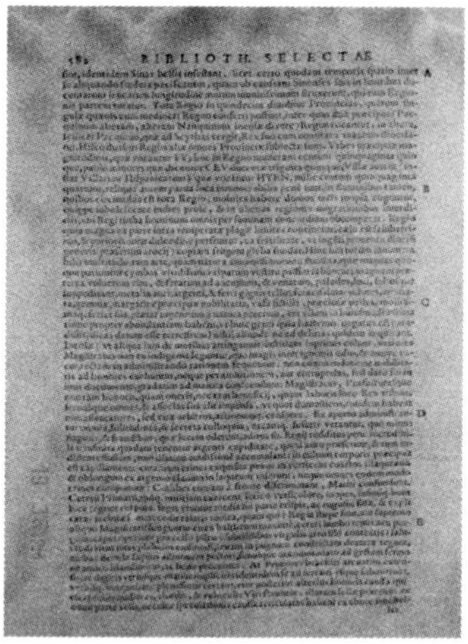
582 BIBLIOTH. SELECTAE

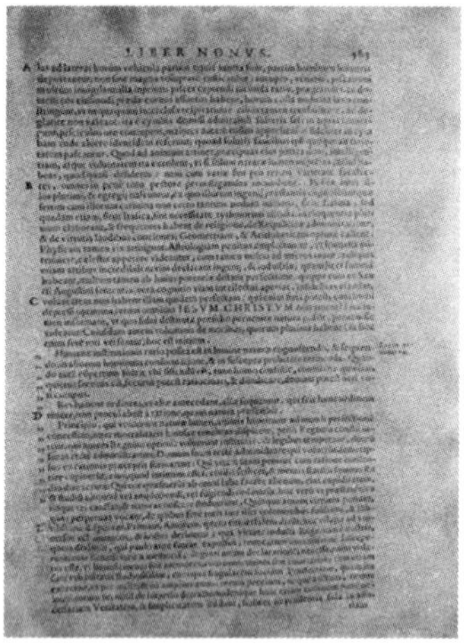
LIBER NONVS. 583

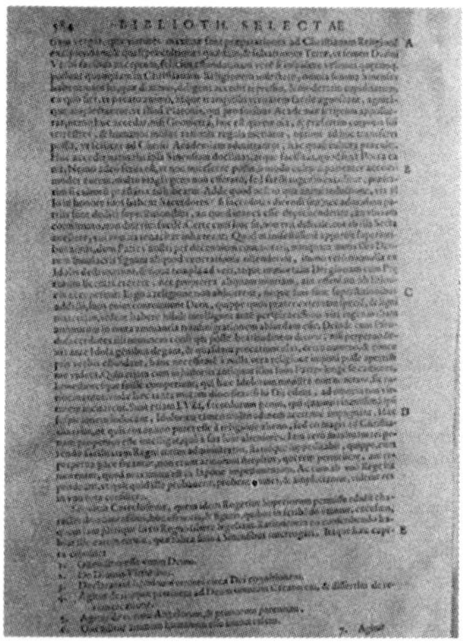
584 BIBLIOTH. SELECTAE

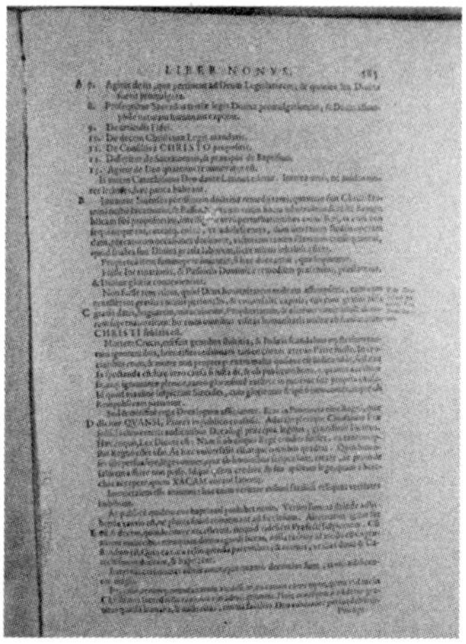
LIBER NONVS. 585

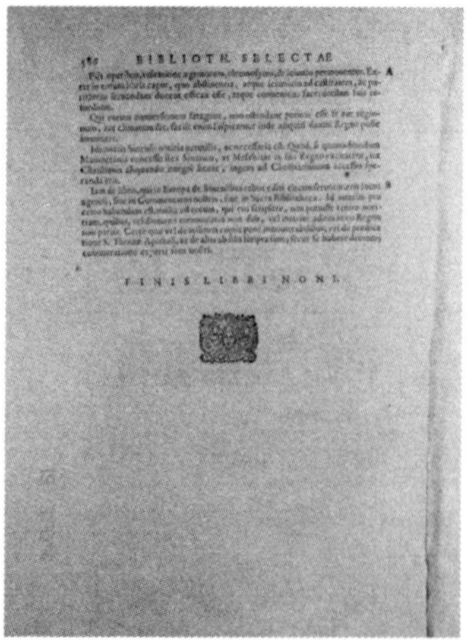
586 BIBLIOTH. SELECTAE

FINIS LIBRI NONI.

罗明坚所翻译的《大学》内容如下：

《大学》之道，在明明德，在亲民，在止于至善。知止而后有定，定而后能静，静而后能安，安而后能虑，虑而后能得。坊有本末，事有终始，知所先后，则近道矣。古之欲明明德于天下者，先治其国，欲治其国者，先齐其家；欲齐其家者，俞其身；欲修其身者，先正其心；欲正其心者，先诚其意；欲诚其意者，先致其知致知在格物。

波赛维诺在《选编》里发表罗明坚拉丁文译文如下[①]

Humanae institutionis ratio posita est in lumine naturae cognoscendo, & sequendo, in aliorum horr. inum conformatione ( & in suscepta probitate retinenda. Quando autem compertum fuerit ubi sistendum est, tunc homo consistit, consis-tens quiescit, quietus securus est, securus potest ratiocinari, & dijudicare, deraum potest fieri voti compos?

Res habent ordinem, ut aliae antecedant, aliae sequantur * Qui scit hunc ordinem tenere, non procul abest a ratione, quam natura praescribit.

Principio, quo voluerunt naturae lumen, animi6 hominum ad mundi perfec-tionem concessum, inter mortalitatis huiusce tenebras dispicere, prius Rognura consistuerunt; qui autem Regnum optirais voluerunt institutis, & legibus temperare, domum suam recte adminictrarunt; Domum suam recte admin-istrare qui voluerunt, semitipsos ex rationis praeceptis formarunt: Qui vitam suam penitus cum ratione consentire cupiverunt, eius, quod intimum esset, cordis scilicet, 8c mentis statura summo studio direxerunt: Qui cor quaesiverunt ab orani lahe facere alienum, eius cupidatatem, & studium aliquod vel amplectendi, vel fugiendi ordinarunt; hoc vero ut praestarent, cuiusque rei caussas, & naturas noscere studuerunt.

这是在西方16世纪的文献中首次对中国古代文化经典的翻译，在学术上意义很大。

首先，我们从文献学的角度来看这篇文献。罗明坚这篇文章是发表在波赛维诺的丛书中的，[②] 这套丛书选编共18有章，或者说18部分，分为上下两卷。“在第一卷中，波塞维诺介绍了文化与研究的崇高地位和重要性；圣经，包括其历史和解读方面的东西；神学；教理问答（传道的方法和传统）；关于神职人员和教会；如何应对东正教徒（希腊人，等等）；如何帮助异教徒（宗教改革）；神学和异教徒的无神论；如何帮助犹

---

① （丹）龙柏格（Knud Lundbaek）《儒家经典在欧洲最初的翻译》（The First Translation from A Confucian classic in Europe），CHINA MISSION STUDIES（1550—1800）BULLETIN，1，(1979).

② 笔者在《西方汉学的奠基人：罗明坚》（见《历史研究》2011年第3期）一文。

太人、穆斯林和其他人；谁可以帮助日本人及其他东方民族；如何帮助日本人及其他东方民族。第二卷包括：关于哲学；关于法律；关于医学；关于数学；关于历史；关于诗歌和艺术；关于以西塞罗为典型的正统写作艺术。”① 按照麦克雷教授的研究“耶稣会士企图通过这套书为欧洲天主教知识分子从事学术研究、教育以及制度设立提供保险的教义参考。因其内容所具的深度和广度，这套书也被称为“反宗教改革的百科全书。”②

波赛维诺在1593年出版第一版时的第十部分是“日本及其他东方民族”，但是这里没有提到中国人。而在1603年第二版时有了关于中国的部分““Quibus rationibus gentes et Indi iuvari possint. Qua occasione id certioris historiae de Regno Sinarum innuitur quod hactenus [so far] ignoratum est, quodque auctor reliquis suis commentariis in lucem postea edendis copiusius adiexuit.”他也明确说这些材料是来自罗明坚的“我们的教友罗明坚在那里编撰并宣讲这些问答多年，我们亦从他那获取这些材料。”而且说，这些材料都是“之前一直是未公开的”(hactenus ignoratum)。在拉丁文中他还提到了西班牙传教士桑切斯，他说：“这些材料大多来源于罗明坚，还有少数信息来源于另一位耶稣会士桑彻斯。桑彻斯在墨西哥、菲律宾工作过，后在澳门和广东做了短暂停留。……桑彻斯用口头或文字的形式在罗马留下了材料，我们在此创作。但是关于中国的最丰富的材料还是由罗明坚提供的。”③ 桑切斯主要在菲律宾活动，但他也来过中国，并与罗明坚有过交往。虽然同为耶稣会士，但由于传教的地点不同，两人对待中国的态度也完全不同，罗明坚采取的适应中国文化的政策，而桑切斯却说：“我和罗明坚的意见完全相反，我以为劝化中国，只有一个好办法，就是借重武力了。”④ 应该说，这份文献主要是罗明坚所写。

其次，我们来具体研究罗明坚对《大学》的翻译。《大学》原是《礼记》中的一篇，后被宋儒所重视，朱熹在《四书集注》中说：“子程曰：“《大学》，孔氏之遗书，而初学入德之门也。’”所以他认为“学者必由是而学焉”。

为更好理解罗明坚的这段拉丁文翻译，我们从拉丁文译文展开研究，拉丁文中文

---

① 参阅麦克雷(Michele Ferrero)《波塞维诺〈丛书选编〉(1593)中的中国》，感谢麦教授提供给我这篇论文。

② 尽管这是一本在欧洲也很难找到的一本书，但笔者在中国国家图书馆的北堂藏书中发现这本书，实在令人惊讶，但也说明了这本书在当时的价值和受到来华耶稣会士的重视。《北堂书目》藏号：1593和1603年两个版本。这再次证明了《北堂书目》的学术价值。

③ Donnelly n. 29, p 189，引用《丛书选编》，卷I，第581页。参阅麦克雷(Michele Ferrero)《波塞维诺〈丛书选编〉(1593)中的中国》。

④ (法)裴化行《明代闭关政策与西班牙天主教传教士》，载《中外关系史译丛》第4辑，上海译文出版社，1988年，第264页。

翻译如下：

“教育人的正确道路，在于认识与遵从自然之光，在塑造其他人，而且还在于能正确地的行和止。当人明白在哪里要停止时，他就停止，而停止时他便平静，且平静后他就感到安全，而安全后地方能推理与判断，就能实现他的愿望。事物本有秩序，有的事物是前提，有的事物是后果。能够掌握住事物秩序的人离自然所规定的原理不远了，因此，愿意探究自然的因有、先天光明，为了治理世界的人们，首先要管理好自己的国家，而要恰当地管理好自己的国家，则应先以正当的规则来建立自己的家庭。那些要以正当的规则建立自己的家庭的人，则应先建造自己的生活。要建造自己生活的人，则应先建造自己的精神；要建造自己精神的人们，则应先从众人的沉沦中拯救自己的灵魂。凡是试图从众人的沉沦之中拯救自己灵魂的，他便需要端正欲望，要先为自己准备知识。而知识的圆满在于认识事物的原因与本质。”①

我们来分析罗明坚的这段译文。首先，如何译《大学》这个标题？罗明坚译为“Humanal institutions ratio”，即“教育人的正确道路”。罗明坚之后来华的意大利传教士殷铎泽（Prosper Intorcetta，1625－1696）在他1662年的《大学》译本②中将其译为“Magnorum Virorum sciendi institutum”，即“大人的正确教育”，而1687年由著名的来华耶稣会士柏应理（Philippe Couplet，1624－1695）等人在《中国哲学家孔子》（Confucius Sinarum Philosophus，Paris 1687，S. I. ）③中将“大学”译为“magnum adeoque orum Principum，sciendi inseitatam”，即“大人，或者确切地说为君子的正确教育”。安文思（Gabriel de Magallaens，1609－1677）在他的《中华帝国史》（Nouvelle relation de Chine，Paris 1689）中将“大学”翻译为“La methode des grands hommes pour apprendre”即“伟大人的理解方法。”

如果对比一下这几种译法，我们会觉得相比之下，罗明坚的译文不如殷铎泽翻译的好，“大学”在这里不是指对一般人的教育，主要是对大人的教育，或者说是培养君

---

① 感谢雷立柏帮助我翻译了这段拉丁文，也感谢我的拉丁文启蒙老师贾西诚神父。

② 关于这个译本说法不一，费赖之认为这个《大学》译本是郭纳爵（Ignace da Costa，1599－1666）1662年在江西建昌所译，又说索默尔沃热尔书目上讲是1662年为殷铎泽所译。见费赖之书中文版上册，第226页，331页．考狄的“L'IMPRIMERIE SINO－EUROP'EENNE ENCHINE BIBLIOGRAP－HIE DES OUVRAGES PUBLIES EN CHINE PAR LES EUROPEENS”一书中附了《大学》在建昌刻本的封面，上有郭纳爵和殷铎泽共译。

封面的题字为：

Kién chān in nrbe Sinarū ‖ Proninciate Si. 1662 ‖ Superiorum permissu. 耶稣会档案馆藏有此书，书号为JAD SIN Ⅲ3－1．1998年夏我在该馆访问时曾翻阅此书。

③ 关于此书，下文还将展开重点论述，这里不做展开。

子的教育，如张居正说解释的“大学是大人治学，这本书中说的都是大人修己治人的道理。故书名为《大学》”。[1]

其次，如何译“在明明德”。罗明坚将其译为“Lumen naturae”，即“自然之光”，他用这种译法以表示区别于“超自然之光”，即“Lumen Sapranatarale”，这句话的英文翻译是“遵从自然的启迪”。这是一个很重要的理解。正是从罗明坚开始，来华传教士大都采用这种观点，以“自然神学”来解释中国的思想。这里的罗明坚没有用“超自然之光”，显然是在回避启示神学。1662 年殷铎泽的译本中则回到了“启示神学”，而改为“Spiritualis potentia a caelo indita”，即“由天所赋予的精神力量”，到柏应理时，则把这个概念引入了基督教的含义，译为“rationalis natura a coelo inditam”，即“天赋的理性本质。”这显然是面对欧洲的礼仪之争，柏应理在翻译策略上的转变。在当时的欧洲，以斯宾诺萨所代表的“自然神学”思想是受到主流神学思想的批判的。[2]

“明明德”，这里的第一个“明”字是动词，是彰明的意思，而“明德”意思是人原具有的善良德性，因后来受物质利益的遮蒙，个人偏狭气质的拘束，这种善性受到压制。教育的目的在于使人这种“明德”得以恢复。朱子说：“明，明之也。明德者，人之所得乎天，而虚灵不昧，以其众理而应万事者也。但为气禀所拘，人欲所蔽，则有时而昏。然其本体之明，则有未尝息者。故学者当因其所发而遂明之，以复其初也。”（朱熹《四书章句》）朱熹对“明德”之源做了提升，人这种原初的善“得乎于天”。这个天既不是物质的天，也不是神的天，而是理之天，“合天地万物而言，只是一个理”“未有天地之先，毕竟也只是理。有此理，便有此天地。若无此理，便亦无天地。”（《语类》卷一）

罗明坚从自然神学加以解释，殷铎泽和柏应理则表面上是套用朱熹的思想，实际上是向“启示神学”倾斜，他所讲的“天”显然是人格神的天，而柏应理的解释则已完全是从基督教来理解的。相比较而言，罗明坚的解释相对接近“明明德”的本意。从罗明坚到柏应理，在翻译上的变化则反映了当时欧洲对中国思想认识的起伏。

罗明坚把“亲民”与“明明德”合在一起译为：“in lunine naturae cognoscendo et sequendo，in aliorum hominum confirmatione”即“在于认识和遵循自然之光，在于成全他人”这里他实际上翻译了朱熹注的后半句，朱熹注：“新者，革其旧之谓也。言既自明其明德，又当推以及人，使之亦有以去其旧染之污也。”（朱熹《四书章句集注》），殷铎译在 1662 年译文中的“新民”译为“renovare sea reparare populum”“祈祷或更

---

[1] 参阅朱雁冰：《从西方儒家思的最早传说到利玛窦的儒学评价》载于香港道风山《神学论集》1996 年号。

[2] 参阅洪汉鼎：《斯宾诺莎评传》，山东人民出版社，1984 年。

新人民”但他在括号中加上了“in amore erga alios”即“向他人的爱”的解释，柏应理则是用“in renovando sea reparando”，（即“在于恢复或修整”）从这个比较中可以看出，罗明坚的译文不如殷铎泽的译文，主要是没有把“新民”译好。这点丹麦汉学家龙柏格（Knud Lundbaek）对罗明坚和殷铎泽两人的翻译评价比较合理，他说：“在1662年殷铎泽的译文中我们看到汉字‘亲民’（爱人民），但是翻译为‘使人民焕新’。在这个问题上，它后面加了一句插入语：‘在对他人的爱’（in amore erga alios）。《中国哲学家孔子》里则是‘重新塑造人’（in renovando seu reparando populum）。有个脚注指出第十个字不发‘新’的音，意思也不是‘新’或‘革新’。这个字发音为“亲’（cin），意思是‘如同父母或亲戚’（aware parentes propinquos）如果中文文章也放在一起，这个难以理解的阐述可能还能至少部分地获得理解。译者并没有说明他们面对的是朱熹的校正。事实上，亲/新的问题几个世纪以来都是中国政治伦理界的一个颇有争议的议题。朱熹学派的反对者王阳明就一直坚持那个字应该是‘亲’。[①] 罗明坚似乎没怎么意识到这个问题，看起来他试图用“在于认识和遵循自然之光，在于成全他人’‘……in lumine naturae cognoscendo et sequendo，in aliorum hominum conformatione’来处理回避了这个问题，这个表达就包括了两个意思：‘在于认识和遵循自然之光，在于成全他人’”。[②] 罗明坚没有很透彻理解“新民”的含义，没有明确翻译出“新”字所包含的“自明其明德。又当推以，鼓舞作兴，使之革去旧染之污，亦有其明德”的含义。[③]

“格物致知”是朱熹注《大学》时的另一个重要思想，罗明坚原译文为“Absolution scientiae posita est in caccsis et rationibus rerum cognoscendis”即“知识的圆满在于认识事物的根源和本质”后在波塞维诺的《历史、科学、技世研讨丛书选编》时罗明坚将其译文做了修改，将“欲诚其意，先致其知”联在一起翻译为“Qui cor quaesiverunt ab omni labe facere alievum eius cupidatatum，& studium aliquod vel amplactendi，vel fugiendi ordinarunt；hoc vero ut praestarent，cuiusque rei causas，et naturas noscere studerunt”即“凡是试图从众人的沉伦之中救出心灵者，他便需端正欲望，要先为自己准备知识，而知识的圆满在于学会认识事物的原因和本质”。英文译文翻译成：“为此他们努力学习万物的缘由和本质。”这两个译法都反映了罗明坚对“格物致知”理解与原意相差甚远，他基本上是从西方知识论和认识论来理解“格物致知”的，

---

① 冯友兰：《中国哲学史》，普林斯顿，1952年，第二卷600页。Fung Yu-lan，A History of Chinese Philosophy. Princeton 1952. II，600.

② （丹）龙柏格（Knud Lundbaek）：《儒家经典在欧洲最初的翻译》（The First Translation from A Confucian classic in Europe），CHINA MISSION STUDIES（1550－1800）BULLETIN，1，（1979）.

③ 张居正：《大学·中庸》评讲。

而实际上朱熹的“格物致知”是置于伦理学的框架之中的，因为宋儒中的“格物致知”“不在乎科学之真，而在乎明道之善，这才是朱熹格物致知论的本质。”① 由此看出罗明坚对中国文化的本质特征的理解还有距离，这反映了中西思想初次交流所遇到的困难。

已故的丹麦汉学家龙伯格（Knud Lundbaek）认为罗明坚的这段译文的有三个特点：

1. 它说明在中国的教育内容中包含着政治——伦一理的内容，或者说这二者是不能分开的；2. “这个劝诫人们追求事物的本性和缘由的讲道词所具备的伦理政治性已达到很高的水准，使读者震惊”；3. 这段译文给人印象最深的在于这样一种政治——伦理的思想劝告人们要研究“事物的性质和原因”。“一个人如何能实现这样一个过程？只有通过分析事物的性质和原因。”②

应该说龙伯格评价的前二条是对的。第一条说明了罗明坚的译文

还是抓住了《大学》的思想本质，即教育的政治化与伦理化。第二条评价也是客观的，因为罗明坚第一次将东方伦理思想介绍到了西方，应该说，这种伦理与政治治理的结合特点与西方是有重大区别的。龙伯格的第三条是揭示了罗明坚译文的一个重要特征，但正像我们上面已指出的，这正是罗明坚译文的一个重要误解，而不是应加以肯定的地方。龙伯格的这个评价也反映了他对宋儒明理学的认识论的伦理特征理解不够，按照他的思路，中国哲学思想在修身、齐家、治国、平天下这个思想中，最终要落实到“修身”，而修身在于“格物致知”，最终落到了认识自然，探求事物的原因和本质上。显然，这是从西方认识论的角度来理解的。在理学中“格物致知”是在伦理和道德的框架中发生的，朱熹的“格物致知”主要在“穷天理，明人论，讲圣言，求世故”，而不是求自然之因，科学之真。

罗明坚的译文发表后，当时并未引起多少人注意，龙伯格说17世纪西方最著名的伦理学和政治学著作都未提到他的这个译文。直到1615年随着利玛窦等人的著做出版，中国逐步被欧洲人所重视时，以往关于中国的报道才重新被人所注意。无论如何，罗明坚首次将中国儒家经典传向西方，开启了欧洲人翻译中国经典之先河，功不可没。

---

① 侯外庐、邱汉生、张岂之主编:《宋明理学史》，人民出版社，1984年，第399页。

② Knud Lundbaek，The first traslation from a confucian classic in Eurape，China Mission Studies (1500—1800) BuLLetin，1. 1979.

# 儒學在韓國的傳承過程及其推移

## ——以麗末鮮初新儒學導入爲中心

韩国木浦大学 金承炫

## 壹、緒論

弘益人間①

此乃韓國之精神命脈，與開國之大本，歷代來莫不以這理念爲教育之主旨。在這裏，我們可以發現韓國思想之終極在於人道。雖然，莊子等諸子百家也提到了人道，但“人道”則實爲儒家思想的主題。因爲儒家所推崇之道。實爲人道，亦卽仁道。乃人生行爲所必循之途徑與道路。因此，儒教在韓國的歷史展開上。非但負擔著決定性的角色，而且其倫理道德與規範可說是生活的軌道。

據於韓國儒學史的觀點，新儒學在韓國正式生根發展的時代，乃在高麗末期接納新儒學以後，至朝鮮開國採取抑佛崇儒政策開始的。這論點是韓國儒學界的衆論②

其實，儒教的轉入是在漢字傳到韓國之後，在高句麗的太學與扃堂裏傳授儒學思想，百濟輩出五經博士，主導其文化活動，並把漢字與儒學轉入日本，對日本古代社會的文化活動有所助益。在新羅時代骨品制度的統制體系中吸收儒教後，首創的制度組織是“讀書三品科”高麗時代實施“科舉制度”到了朝鮮時代成爲統治階級最根本的制度。另一方面以儒學爲中心新儒學在朝鮮廣爲初期流傳高麗末開始了新儒學的研究，發展到退溪與栗谷時形成朝鮮理學之哲學體系

新儒學非但是屬於宋明時期的學術思想，而從高麗末期到朝鮮後期爲韓國儒學道統和準據。

又到了朝鮮中期由導入清代考證學而爲了朝鮮實學之基礎。

綜合而言，在韓國儒學史上我們可以區分儒學的傳承時期和學術內容。

---

① 一然：《三國遺事 · 古朝鮮條》。

② 柳承國：《韓國的儒教》，頁 61－62。

一、三國時代－統一新羅："先秦儒學" 導入期

二、高麗前期－高麗中期："漢唐經學" 傳承期

三、高麗末期－朝鮮前期：新儒學（宋明理學）傳承期

四、朝鮮中期－朝鮮後期：清代考證學傳承期

但這四段時期儒學的傳承過程當中，我們注意的是在第三時期新儒學（宋明理學）傳承期的

因爲由新儒學的傳承朝鮮士大夫可以具備了朝鮮王朝開創的當爲性和朝鮮性理學之學的準據。

所以在本稿裏，我要特地敍述以"麗末鮮初[①]（高麗末期－朝鮮初期）"新儒學的傳承過程和學術內容爲中心。

## 貳、儒學在韓國的受容過程與發展

從韓國儒學思想史的觀點來看，儒學在韓國的導入過程可以區分下例的四個時期。

一、第一時期（三國時代～統一新羅）：先秦儒學導入期

高句麗：太學和扃堂設置/ 史書：李文眞《新集》5 卷[②]

百濟：五經博士設置/ 史書：高興《書記》[③]

新羅：國學設置/ 史書：居柒夫《國史》[④]

其中，新羅統一三國以後，對更加擴大的社會與政治來說，儒教理念更形成必要，故神文王設立國學[⑤]，置博士與助教，教授儒學與漢文學。教學課目分爲三科，《論語》與《孝經》爲三科共同必須科目，三科爲：(1) 主修《禮記》，《周易》(2) 主修《左傳》，《毛詩》；(3) 主修《尚書》，《文選》。國學的入學資格爲大舍以下無官位的貴族，修業年限爲九年。之後，元聖王時代便是以此教育機關爲基礎，設立"讀書三品科"[⑥]："國家考試制度"，樹立使用官吏的新原則；根據學問成績而不根據骨品制度。亦卽債用官吏時，依學問成績分三等級；能解讀《左傳》，《禮記》，《文選》兼諳《論語》，《孝經》者爲上品/ 能讀《曲禮》，《論語》，《孝經》者爲中品/ 能讀《曲禮》，《孝經》者爲下品。並擢用伯通五經三史者。

---

① "麗末鮮初"：指稱高麗末期（AD13 世紀）－朝鮮初期（AD15 世紀）約 200 年間的王朝交替時期。

② 《三國史記 卷 18 · 小獸林王條》。

③ 《周書 · 異域傳》，《舊唐書 · 東夷傳》。

④ 《三國史記 卷 44 · 居柒夫傳》。

⑤ 《三國史記 卷 8 · 神文王條》。

⑥ 《三國史記 卷 10 · 元聖王條》。

二、第二時期（高麗前期～高麗中期）：漢唐經學傳承期

高麗太祖創立新國家以後，已經登用新羅系統的文人學者，在開京與西京設置學校，但是教育機關完備乃在確立中央集權體系的成宗時代。成宗初年選拔地方子弟上開京研修學問，但由於一般人認識不足而失敗，因此派經學博士，醫學博士各一名分赴十二牧普及教育。在此之前，光宗時代開始實施科舉制度時[①]，曾在全國各地廣泛選拔人才參與政治；成宗亦致力於振興地方教育，爲了鞏固中央集權體制，需要接受漢學教育的官吏，而設立了“國子監”[②]。在開京的“國子監”，依據學生的身分可分爲“國子監”（三品以上的子弟），“太學”（五品以上），“四門學”（七品以上），已研修儒學與漢學。成宗爲了提高官吏的讀書風氣，實施了文臣月課法，要求中央文臣每月作詩三篇，賦一篇，地方官吏一年作一篇文章。

高麗之科舉分進士科，明經科，雜科。進士科的考試科目有詩，賦，策，頌等詞章；明經科有書，《易》、《詩》、《春秋》等儒教經典；雜科有法律，醫學，天文，地理等技術科目。

光宗代設置科舉制度，成宗代廣收書籍，培養可以實踐儒教政治思想的政治階層，奠定了高麗儒教政治理想基礎。又其成宗代有名的崔承老便以儒教政治理想基礎，舉出改革政治，社會的“時務二十八條”方案，其中大部分被採用施行，其改革方案是以儒教思想促進高麗社會的發展並保持高麗的傳統生活與習慣。

除了這官學之外，還有“私學”[③]。設置私學的代表家是崔沖。他退休後設置“九齋學堂”教授弟子，許多學者亦模仿其興辨私學。又睿宗時設置了“養賢庫”，爲一種獎學財團，以可强官學的經濟基礎。

三、第三時期（高麗末期～朝鮮前期）：新儒學（宋明理學）傳承期

高麗由於受到蒙古的侵略與統治，地方制度崩潰，社會矛盾更加激烈，高麗文化亦從基層開始解體；到了高麗末期新進知識階層與中小地主階層形成了社會意識與民族意識，以對抗附元的權門勢族並主張社會與文化改革。

其實從高麗中期已經有了顯了儒教無力感。於是儒教漸與佛教互相影響並聯合佛教，卽承認佛教的弊端。但是高麗末期新進士大夫興期，主張新儒學不僅攻擊佛教，並批評前期儒學本身的矛盾。新儒學士從儒教的立場接受佛教的禪宗思想而成立的新儒學。因此新儒學的特徵是以形而上學的解釋人生與宇宙根源的哲學；另一方面又以政治，社會倫理道德强調君臣，父子的義理，由安珦開始提倡，接著白頤正與朴忠佐直接

---

① 《高麗史 卷 93 · 列傳 雙冀》。

② 《高麗史 卷 74 · 選擧志 2 國子監試》。

③ 《高麗史 卷 93 · 列傳 崔承老》。

從元朝傳入，之後經歷李齊賢，李穡，鄭夢周，吉再等過渡期，到了麗末鮮初的鄭道傳權近等以理學爲中心，不僅對佛教弊端而高麗文化做全般性批評，並主張革新，在思想界引起相當大的震盪。他們不僅對深入家庭日常生活儀式而且對邱族婚姻古代習俗，巫俗等都欲加改革，以《朱子家禮》入家廟，全力普及儒教儀式，使理學不僅成爲政治理念，並擴大位社會與文化規範。另一方面，由於標榜理學的新進士大夫抬頭，過去一向以詞章，訓詁爲主的學風變成經學和理學方面，結果理學也展開新方向。

朝鮮初期致力於振興教育，尤其以地方教育爲中點，在全國所有郡縣設立“鄉校”爲小學機關；振興教育是守令職責中的重要一項。這鄉校的學生學習《小學》，《四書》等儒學。教授儒學的最高機關爲“成均館”。由生員。進士入學朝鮮前期之儒學是可以分爲兩個學派；一個是“事功學派”。另一個是“節義學派”。前者是開國朝鮮的同參者，後者是恰恰相反者。但是注意的是，以後者節義學派爲朝鮮儒學之道統（正統）。因此朝鮮儒學之道統是鄭夢周－吉再－金叔玆－金宏弼－趙光祖－李滉與李珥。朝鮮前期的儒學，沒有參加開國的儒臣們崇尚鄭夢周，重視義理與修己，以鄉村爲中心，致力於程朱學此學風在與吉再等節義之臣有淵源的嶺南地方較爲顯著；金叔玆等培養了許多門人，在 15 五世紀末形成一個學派，即所謂嶺南士林，於成宗時代大量參與國政，成爲牽制勳臣的一股勢力。

十六世紀對於程朱學有更深的了解，從嶺南地方擴散至京畿，湖南地方；但是隨著地區的不同學者也不同，以產生了各種學派。嶺南地方李彥迪，李滉的主理派；畿湖地方李珥的主氣派。大致而言，首爾附近畿湖學派主張王道主義，把程朱學應用於政治上，重視“經世”亦即“治人之學”；相反之嶺南學派重視修己與鄉村問題，並具有思辨傾向。

四、第四時期（朝鮮中期～後期）：清代考證學傳承期

朝鮮中期以後性理學本身內部展開主理說與主氣說的熱烈爭論，而陽明學，漢學，道教，讖言等逐漸興起。李滉確立的主理說由南人學者繼承發揚廣大，經歷了兩個患亂即一壬辰倭亂及丙子胡亂，此兩患亂以後 朝鮮士大夫要脫離於朱子學和理論的學術體制而爲接納現實的・實用的・科學的學術路線。我們指這學術路線稱”實學”。如此朝鮮實學的興起原因和學術背景與清代考證學的發生原因是同調的。

又受到天主教與西洋勢力的挑戰，發展成爲“理一元論”，排斥夷狄與異端，乃固守三綱五倫的保守派。但是即使相同的南人學派中，展開實學運動。這被受到清代考證學的影響。

朝鮮實學可以分爲如下之三個學派

1. 利用厚生學派：以重農主義爲中心/星湖李翼 等

2. 實事求是學派：以重金石學爲中心/秋史金正喜 等

3. 經世致用學派：以重商主義爲中心/茶山丁若鏞 等

## 參、麗末鮮初新儒學的形成過程和學的背景

高麗由於受到蒙古的侵略與干涉，國家統治體制崩潰，佛教的經濟活動更加激烈，文化思想亦基層開始解體。到了高麗中期門閥貴族登場具有事大保守性格，沒有解決這社會矛盾的力量。後來，武人執權之時，很多知識層在文化面或社會面上，感覺到了儒教的無力感。而且接著蒙古的侵略，他門加强了其事大性和派閥性，使社會更趨矛盾。於是儒教漸與佛教互相影響並聯合佛教，卽承認佛教的病弊却不否佛教。但到了高麗末期，地方中小地主階層出身的新興士大夫屈起，主張新儒學，不僅攻擊佛教，並批評前期儒學本身的矛盾。

又問臣曰：我國古稱文物侔於中華。今其學者，皆從學釋子，以習章句，是宜雕蟲篆刻之徒寔繁而經明行修之士絶少也。此其故，何耶？

臣對曰……不幸毅王季年不幸毅王季年武人變起所忽薰。同臭玉石俱焚其說身虎口者遯世窮山。冠帶面蒙伽梨以終餘年若神駿悟生之流是也。……故臣謂學者，從釋子習章句，其源蓋始于此。今殿下誠能廣學校，謹庠序，尊六禮，明五教，以闡先王之道，孰有背眞儒而從釋子，捨實學而習章句者哉！

將見彫蟲篆刻之徒 盡爲經明行修之士矣。[①]

顯然，李齊賢攻擊了“彫蟲篆刻之徒”和“釋子”的學術。事實上，他所謂“彫蟲篆刻之徒”，就是“句讀訓解”之類的儒者。根據金富軾所撰的《三國史記》，這類的儒學在高句麗小獸林王二年（AD372 年）時傳到韓國來。新羅則統一三國以後，神文王二年（AD682 年）在輸入。

因此，自統一新羅至高麗，佛教雖是國家所公認的國教，但儒學也竝行發展，其對文化，思想上的影響增多。尤其，高麗光宗九年（AD985 年）後周人雙冀建議，依唐制開設科擧之法；其制有“製述”，“明經”二科。從此高麗之教六及取士，皆用儒學爲基礎。文宗十五年（AD1061 年）和睿宗九年（AD1114 年）時，二王皆幸國子監，再拜儒教先師。又靖宗十一年（AD1045 年）時，命刻《禮記正義》，《毛詩正義》等經書，睿宗十四年（AD1119 年）設立養賢庫，培養儒學人材。除了這些之外，很多學者傳授儒教經典。尤其，崔沖（AD984—1068）退職後開私塾，教儒教經典。後來很多學者也效他，先後出現十一個私塾，因而世人稱爲“十二公徒”。在此儒學一時大盛，人人稱崔沖曰“海東孔子”，而指其徒弟謂“文憲公徒”。

但注意的是，崔沖類的儒學是屬於漢唐經學的範疇。所以在學術內容上，他門無法

---

① 李齊賢,《櫟翁稗說 · 前集二》。

克服佛教思想體系。這就是李齊賢所謂“今其學者，皆從釋子以習章句”的主要原因。然而，當武臣之亂，佛教之墮落，蒙古的干涉等內外憂患之時，高麗儒者不得不檢討自己本身的問題。因此，來往燕京的高麗使臣中，安珦尋找這出路。大體上說，他所接觸的新儒學是元代北方理學，而它以趙復，許衡之類的程朱學爲中心。所以安珦（AD1243—1306）較容易得到朱子學。安珦是一位高麗理學的始創者。故他一直强調新儒學的重要性。後來，高麗政府接納他的建議，而設置了“贍學錢”制度。白頤正，朴忠佐，李齊賢，李穀，李仁復，白文寶等繼之而研究新儒學。

《淡庵逸集》中說：

> 始性理之學未及東方。夷俗未祛。士趨不正。白彝齋入中朝。得程朱全書以歸。於是朴恥庵忠佐，李益齋齊賢，李稼亭穀，李樵隱仁復，白淡庵文寶首先師受。爲群儒倡。以明道學。使學者知吾道之可尊。異端之可斥。繼開之功。實有大焉。(本出於《白彝齋實記》)[①]

但是他們的理學，還沒有脫離了初步的階段。因爲在他們的著述中，詞章之學和經學的成分較濃厚。

後來，三隱 即一牧隱李穡，圃隱鄭夢周，陶隱李崇仁與三峯鄭道傳，陽村權近等接着他們的性理學後，高麗理學却找到了自己的眞面目。

綜上而言，從文化思想的角度來看，高麗理學掘起的原因，大致劃分爲下列兩個部分：

第一，爲了克服佛教的理論體系

第二，爲了找出儒學本身的理論結構

因此，當時元代的官學一卽程朱學在忠烈王時由安珦開始提唱，接著白頤正與朴忠佐直接從元朝傳入，之後歷經李齊賢，李穀等過渡期，到了麗末鮮初鄭道傳，權近等才建立高麗理學的體系。但李齊賢一李穡一鄭道傳和權近的學脈，也兼取了元代“和會朱陸”說。

無論如何，他們都以新儒學爲理學根據，不僅對佛教的弊端而且對高麗文化做全般性的批評，並主張革新，在高麗思想界引起了相當大的震盪。結果 他們不僅對深入家庭日常生活的佛教儀式，而且對親族婚姻，古代習俗等都欲加以改革，以《朱子家禮》入家廟，全力普及儒教儀式，使新儒學成爲社會文化之規範。

高麗末期新儒學的導入途徑和發展科程是如下的：

一、導入途徑

1. 使行儒臣

高麗與元講和後，高麗君王已非獨立王國的統治者，而以元帝室的駙馬，在元帝國

---

① 《淡庵逸集 · 史傳攝輯》。

內保障其鞏固的地位，並利用其地位在國內擴展王權。但此種有限的收獲是犧牲降低高麗王室的地位所換來的。因此，元政府不斷地要求高麗的特産物和金，銀等，甚至亦要求處女和宦官。爲了處理這件事情，高麗政府派遣了使臣。這就是“使行儒臣”的産生原因。如前所述，安珦是此類中最著者。他去燕京時（AD1290），碰到元代北方的理學。

庚寅忠烈王十六年留燕京，手抄朱子書，摹寫孔子，朱子眞像。朱子書未及盛行於世，先生始得見之，心自篤好，知爲孔門正脈，遂手錄其書，又寫孔朱眞像而歸。自是講究朱書，探致博約之工。三月從王還自元。[①]

事實上，朱學是元代北方理學的理論根據，而許衡理學較近於朱學。

由此可知，安珦等高麗使行儒臣所接觸的新儒學以程朱學爲中心。但在其學術內容上，我們很難尋他們的學術體系。因爲這“使行儒臣”之類的主要任務是在於進納貢物，而不在於講究學術。

結果，他們對高麗理學的貢獻，較局限於傳播或介紹性的工作方面。

2. 燕京留學者與萬卷堂

安珦傳播新儒學之後，白頤正和李齊賢承繼這路線，而講究新儒學。他們各各十餘年間留於燕京但二人所接觸的理學內容和範圍有所不同。

首先，根據《櫟翁稗說·前集二》，可知白頤正的學術以朱學爲主。

其後，白彜齋頤正從德陵（忠宣王）留都下十年，多求程朱性理之書以歸。我外舅政丞菊齋權公得《四書集註》，鏤板以廣其傳，學者又知有道學矣。

由此可見，白頤正實爲高麗最初的性理學者，而他的理學的內容和範圍，都有限於程朱學。

然而，李齊賢的不同。他雖是白頤正的學生，但他所接觸的學術對象與交遊人物，是較廣泛的。因爲他去燕京時，元代南方理學已經上京了。所以他可能接觸到元代的北方和南方理學。

按照《高麗史》的記事 可以推測這事實

甲寅，以長子江陵大君燾，見于帝，請傳位，帝乃策燾爲王。是時，朝廷欲王歸國，王無以爲辭，乃遜其位。又以姪延安君暠爲世子。王嘗封瀋王故，時稱瀋王。忠肅王元年，帝命王，留京師，王搆萬卷堂于燕邸，招致大儒閻復、姚燧、趙孟頫、虞集等，與之從遊，以考究自娛。[②]

當是之時，忠宣王亦特地招致了高麗學者李齊賢。這事實見於高麗史 李齊賢傳。

---

① 安裕：《晦軒先生年譜》。

② 《高麗史 卷34· 世家 忠肅王》。

值得注意的是，這些元儒中虞集是一位“和會朱陸”論者，並且是吳徵的直傳弟子；姚燧則是許衡的門人。由此可知，“萬卷堂”是高麗理學之主要輸入經路，而李齊賢所接觸的新儒學不只是程朱學。

3. 征東行省的“儒學提舉司”

元朝分全國爲十一行省。每一行省，所轄有路，府，州，縣，都沒有正式的學校。依照學校等級，設教授，學正，教諭登官，教材不外四書五經。學生均可參加鄉試。各行省的“儒學提舉司”擔當這方面的工作。如前所述，征東行省是關於征伐日本的軍政機構，後來便成干涉高麗內政的統治機構。因此，征東行省“儒學提舉司”管掌了高麗科舉制度和文教政策。結果，麗末儒者多應於儒學提舉司主辨的鄉試。例如，李穀、李穡等

忠肅王元年 中征東行省鄉試第一名 遂擢制科穀所對策，大爲讀卷官所賞，置第二甲。宰相奏，授翰林國史院檢閲官。穀與中朝文士，交遊講劘，所造益深。爲文章，操筆立成，辭嚴義奥，典雅高古，不敢以外國人視也。奉興學詔還國，尋復如元，本國授典儀副令。元授徽政院管勾，轉征東省行中書省左右司員外郎[①]

除了李穀之外，李穡也經過這途徑之後，都還國而掌文教學術方面的事。

由此可知，這些高麗儒者的理學以征東行省儒學提舉司的教科課程爲基礎。而且《四書》《五經》中，《四書》以《朱子集註》爲主；亦則以程伊川的易傳爲中心。所以“儒學提舉司”也是高麗理學之重要輸入徑路之一，而它較近於許衡理學之路線。

二、發展過程

如前所述的高麗理學家，大部分沒有超過幼稚的程度。換言之，他們是屬於高麗理學的第一段階的理學家。

經過這一段以後，麗，鮮交替之際，鄭夢周，李崇仁，鄭道傳，權近等優秀的高麗理學家出現了。也就是說，他們是屬於第二段階的理學家。但注意的是，在經世論上，他們之間有所不同之處。鄭夢周和李崇仁以“義理觀”爲主；鄭道傳和權近以“實用觀”爲主。因此，前二人堅決地反對新王朝“朝鮮”的開國，而後二人參加了開國事業。根據當時和後代的評價，鄭夢周是最出名的理學家。

例如 李穡評鄭夢周說：

十六年，以禮曹正郎兼成均博士。時經書至東方者，唯《朱子集註》而已。夢周講說發越，超出人意，聞者頗疑。及得胡炳文《四書通》，無不脗合，諸儒尤加嘆服。李穡亟稱之曰：夢周論理，横說竪說，無非當理。推爲東方理學之祖。[②]

---

① 《高麗史 卷 109 · 列傳 李穀》。

② 《高麗史 卷 117 · 列傳 鄭夢周》。

可惜的是，目前我們無法看得到鄭夢周的理學資料。我認爲爲朝鮮初期的政治家疾視他的徇節，可能毀滅了他的一些資料。李崇仁的理學資料也是亦然。結果，他們的現存資料，只不過是詩文幾十篇而已。

在現存資料的問題上，鄭道傳和權近則顯然不同。簡單地介紹他們的思想與著述的話，鄭道傳的學術思想以“斥佛”爲主，並且他所撰的資料以《佛氏雜辨》，《心問天答》，《心氣理篇》爲中心。權近的學術思想以“天人心性合一論”和“五經體用合一論”爲主，並且他的著述以《入學圖說》，《五經淺見錄》等爲中心。

無論學術資料的有無，很多學者一直忽視了鄭道傳和權近。因爲他們缺乏了“節義”精神。所以在韓國理學的道統上，道學者們很尊重了鄭夢周的徇節和義理，而批評了權近的出仕。我認爲這觀點是不能完全正確的。因爲在歷史上，我們無法否認“奉天承運”的肯定的因素。尤其，學術一定要客觀根據，而此根據以現存資料爲中心。所以自義理精神史的側面而看，可以肯認這些道學家的論法。但是從學術思想史的角度來講，這觀點很難成立。

因此，鄭道傳和權近在朝鮮理學上占有了非常重要的學術上地位。

重視了權近的理學。加以說明，三峯鄭道傳之理學思想以“斥佛排老”的政治社會哲學爲根幹；陽村權近之理學思想以教育倫理哲學爲基礎。因此，在學術的性格上，朝鮮初期的理學家多半受到陽村理學的影響。朝鮮中期巨儒許穆曰：“本朝權文忠公又考定經禮。作讀書分程，入學圖說，五經淺說。闡明六經之奧。…… 東方尊信浮屠。自新羅終麗之世千餘年。能斥異端崇禮教。明先王之道。定一世之治。其功大矣。……金文簡公論國初文學師道。推權文忠一人云。於是有吉注書，金祭酒亦各《五經》傳授 皆出於陽村。”

由此可知，陽村在麗末鮮初學術上所佔的地位和貢獻。

綜上而言，高麗理學經過初步階段之後，到了鄭夢周，李崇仁和鄭道傳，權近才形成了其體系。但在現存資料的限制上，我們不得不討論鄭三峯和權陽村的學術思想。此二人都是出於李穡之門，但在學術的目標與內容上有所不同。結果，朝鮮開國後，三峯積極地參與於政治方面；陽村參加於教育方面。

無論如何，我認爲他們加以代表麗末鮮初的理學界。所以在鄭，權的理學思想中，我要找出 元代“北許南吳”理學的成分和影響之問題。

## 肆、宋元理學在麗末鮮初新儒學中的影響

控制着高麗一代思想界的，便是佛教。自大覺國師義天開立天台宗以來，九山禪門以“曹溪宗”一名總稱之。其原因，在於義天原係華嚴宗出身，自始卽企圖以華嚴教理

爲基礎而包容禪宗。但至武臣執權時，由闍崛山（曹溪九山之一）掘起的普照國師知訥，與義天之“教觀兼修”對立，以“定慧倂修”爲標語，企圖以曹溪宗而融合華嚴教理，竟使日形衰微的曹溪九山爲之氣象一新。簡言之，知訥所主張的宗旨大意如此：古來禪，教兩家，各偏向一方；禪家“不立文字”，徒主“頓悟自性”，不事修行；教家却徒爲文字經所拘，而疏忽“見性悟道”工夫。所以爲匡正計，須兼倂二者，除努力“頓悟自性”以外，倂須漸修華嚴教理工夫，以逍除“無量劫來”所集積之“無明習氣”。結果，知訥的思想都歸結陽村的理學以他的經學的理解爲基礎，又他的經學以學，庸和五經爲根幹。所以我先討論他的經學思想。

陽村在《入學圖說》中說：

愚按易 五經之全體也，春秋五經之大用也，書以道政事，詩以言性情，禮以謹節文。雖各專其一事，而［易，春秋］之體用亦各無所不備焉。嗚呼 大哉！聖人五經之全體而五經聖人之大用也。［易］者 道在天地而聖人體之；［春秋］者道在聖人而天地不能違者也。故河出圖而易畫，春秋作而麟至也。①

顯然，他認爲《易》是五經之全體，而聖人體之。由此可見，陽村非常重視這一本書。値得注意的是，他研究《周易》時，以吳徵的《易纂言》爲主資料。

陽村在《周易淺見錄》中說：

觀草廬吳氏澄所著《纂言》。其於卦爻互體取象。多所發明。亦有功於此經者也。②

尤其，關於履卦九至爻辭和頤卦六四爻辭等的吳徵的見解，此朱子又清楚又合理。然而，陽村以爲吳徵所謂“心”近於佛教的“心”論。故在這問題上，陽村他在《周易淺見錄》。“易經上說”中說：

其說務立奇異。容有牽强。又倍先儒之說。而淫於異端者。亦或有焉。③

又曰：

吳氏務欲絶去外物。…… 此即釋氏所謂心無所住而能應變，見闢於先儒者也。若夫主敬。則天理常存。人欲自絶。④

事實上，吳澄也很重視了程朱的主敬工夫。如此看來，這是一種陽村的誤解。我認爲這問題與當時高麗的學術風度有關。因爲麗末新儒學者堅決地排斥了佛教的“心”說。所以這樣的情況之下，陽村容易誤解了吳徵所講“心”的眞意。

---

① 權近：《入學圖說· 五經體用合一之圖》。

② 權近：《周易淺見錄 · 易說上經》。

③ 權近：《周易淺見錄 · 易經上經》。

④ 前揭書。

除了《五經淺見錄》之外，還有《入學圖說》。這一書承襲了周濂溪的《太極圖說》。其中，最主要部分是“天人心性合一之圖”及“天人心性分釋之圖”

陽村在《入學圖說》中說：

右圖謹依周子大極圖及朱子中庸章句之說，就人心性上，以明理氣善惡之殊，以示學者。故不及萬物化生之象。然人物之生，其理則同而氣有通塞偏正之異。得其正且通者爲人；得其偏且塞者爲物。①

他先以爲人與物的氣稟不同，而後又說各人的氣稟也有所不同。事實上這觀點是宋代理學家的公論。陽村接納這觀點，而又採取了漢唐儒學的“性三品說”。因此，他把人的氣質分爲下例的三圈。

①“誠”圈 — 聖人的氣質（上智：生而知之者）

②“敬”圈 — 衆人的氣質（凡人：學而知之者）

③“欲”圈 — 與禽獸幾希者（自暴自棄者）

顯然，這觀點沿襲了吳徵的“性三品說”。他以爲氣質之性就是惡之來源。但我們把它可以改善。

他在“天人心性分釋之圖”。“圖說”中說：

性者，天所命而人所受其生之理，具於吾心者也。故其爲字，從心從生，人與萬物其理則同，而氣質之稟有不同者焉。告子曰生之謂性；韓子曰 與生俱生；釋氏曰作用是性，皆以氣言而遺其理者也。

《中庸》曰 天命之謂性，《孟子》曰盡其心者，知其性也；知其性則知天矣。②

由此看來，爲了回復“天命之性”，必須經過“明心”的途徑。陽村以爲人的“本心”有時被氣稟所拘，物欲所蔽。所以學者要當“敬以直內”去其昏，而後復其明德也。並且，他把此“心”區分了“道心”和“人心”。簡言之，發原於性命者謂之“道心”；其生於形氣者謂之“人心”。但是其體則是同一的。這就是許吳所謂“體用一源”的觀點。由這觀點，而他主張“知行竝進”說。

陽村在《入學圖說》中說：

知行二者，如車兩輪。學者，所當交致其力而並進者也。③

陽村說的“知行竝進”觀與吳澄的“知行兼該”觀是一脈相承的。因此，在實踐工夫上，他的思路更近於吳澄。

又說：

---

① 權近：《入學圖說 · 天人心性合一之圖》。

② 權近：《入學圖說 · 天人心性分釋之圖》。

③ 權近：《入學圖說 · 大學指掌之圖》。

既曰：物有本末，事有終始，知所先後，則近道矣。又曰：致知在格物，則物非外物，格非扞格，而與致知非爲兩事者，意甚明白。其傳雖闕，而於經文自有上文語 緒之可尋者矣。[①]

由此可知，他所謂“物非外物，格非扞格”的說法是和吳澄的“切己”觀類似的。

綜上而言，在萬卷堂裡麗元學者交遊之時，李齊賢可能接觸到“北許南吳”的“和會朱陸”說。這是一件重要的事實。因爲從高麗末期學脈的關係來講，牧隱李穡是齊賢的門人，而鄭道傳和權近都是李穡的門徒。故陽村可以看得到吳徵的《易纂言》。我以爲這事實絶不是偶然的。由此看來，鄭道傳和權近的理學是與“北許南吳”的“和會朱陸”說不能無關。但可惜的是，麗末學術界的風氣問題。換言之，麗末新興士族所採納新儒學的目的，是爲了克服佛教的“心”論。他們把這類的“心”說看待“狂禪”或“假幻”工夫。因此，他們無法接納象山的心學。這就是使三峯和權近不能公開地介紹“北許南吳”之“和會朱陸”說的主要原因。然而，我們不能否認鄭，權的理學含有一些元代“北許南吳”理學的因素。例如：盡心知性，本心以窮理，天人心性合一，主敬，知行竝進說等。

## 伍、結論

我們要談到關於韓國的儒家之傳統倫常與教育理念的話，麗末鮮初新儒學的導入問題是第一義之學術命題的。

韓國的儒教思想家認爲“天命”並不僅是外在迪一種天之命令，而是宇宙的生機。這種生機是與人生相連相通的，以人的眼光來看，就是天道。此天道是有它的理則，有它的法象，人可以憑藉這些理則，法象，以窺測天行，與天爲一。

天道之運行，所藉者一“誠”而已。故人應該思誠。“誠”與“誠之”之別；一爲先天，一爲後天。一爲自然，一爲教化。

《中庸》〈首章〉曰 ：“天命之謂性 率性之謂道 修道之謂教”，它們之別在乎此矣。誠的函義有二：一爲宇宙的本姓，一爲宇宙賦予萬物之性。此處之“天命”，卽 指賦予之性，“率性”卽謂“誠者”，誠者知天命，知先天之性，用先天之性，無拂逆，無叛離，故云率也。

人或不知率性，則教之以率性之方，是謂修道也，是謂“誠之”也。

例如說：

唯天下至誠 爲能盡其性。[②]

---

① 前揭書。

② 《中庸 · 二十二章》。

盡性與率性大同而小異，率性一辭，頗不見痕迹，盡性則 顯露矣。盡性於無所爲之中，即是率性，此非至誠，不能至也。故不誠者，必使之誠而後能也。因爲人能盡其性則能盡人之性，能盡人之性則，能盡物之性，此推而及之之理。盡其性爲“成己”，盡人之性爲“成人”，盡物之性爲“成物”。成己則與天地同化，成人則教人與天地同化，成物則使物與天地同化，知物之與天地同化。

綜上而言，在韓國的儒家之傳統倫常和教育理念中，天道可以展現於人的道德。而且，它的表現就是“命”。此命是眞實無妄而純粹至善的。因此，人先知“天命”以後，應該建立它的“當行之理則”即“義”而防止“自造的孽”。換言之，盡其性的話，人可以得到“樂天知命”的理想。

如此“天有命，人有義”的天人合一之道。較此朝鮮中期以後的理學家更詳細明白，且更合理。

還有麗末鮮初新儒學的特點在於《小學》般的實踐躬行之學。這一點可以認證了韓國的儒家之傳統倫常與教育理念都聚在於人道。

# 朱、陆的鹅湖论辩与韩国朱子学的展开

韩国启明大学 洪元植

## 一、绪论

2001年是开启“韩国朱子学”时代的朝鲜最具代表性的儒学者退溪李滉（1501—1570）诞辰五百周年。为此，当时韩国举行了各种纪念活动，并召开了国内外学术会议。笔者也在本人主管发行和担任主编的《今天的东洋思想》（半年刊，艺文东洋思想研究院）筹划了“退溪诞辰500年，退溪学研究50年”的特辑。在这里，由于笔者认为有必要从“东亚儒学的展开”视角看李滉的“退溪学”，而且非常有必要确定退溪学的本质和哲学史的地位，因此说了如下的一段话。

退溪学是心学。退溪学的本领在于心学。退溪理学处于退溪心学的从属位置，是支撑退溪心学的理论构造物。退溪理学不能脱离退溪心学而被独立讨论，在与退溪心学的关系性里有具体的意义。退溪哲学的中心不在于“世界”，而在于“心学”。朱子学是理学，退溪学是心学。在朱子学中也有心学的部分，在退溪学中也有理学的部分。但是哲学的重心不同。从世界到人间，哲学的重心发生了转移。由此，退溪学才成为一门独立之“学”而占据一席之地。①

那么，也许马上就会产生“退溪心学”与“阳明心学”有何不同的疑问，所以接着上文继续陈述如下。

退溪学与阳明学在处于朱子学解释史的延长线方面具有很多共同点。其中最重要的共同点在于，通过重读孟子使哲学重心从世界转移到人间。尽管如此，两者间还是有很大的差异。如果说阳明学使朱子学的道德形而上学体系完全解体的话，那么退溪学则实现了位置转换和缩小。退溪学不是单纯地回归到孟子，而是把孟子的道德之人提升到宋代以来朱子学构筑的道德形而上学最顶部。相反，阳明学可以说由于把朱子

① 洪元植:《退溪学，试问其存在》，《今天的东洋思想》第4号，艺文东洋思想研究院，2001年，第50页。

学的道德形而上学引入人的心性中而导致其解体。[①]

由于这是从广义的概括性观点上阐明了退溪心学与阳明心学之间的差别性，因此需要更详细的其他讨论。为此，论者在提出退溪心学论后回答了异见，为增强自身的论旨进行了大量研究。首先，以吴澄为中心探讨过“朱陆和会论”，翻出权近的性理说和李滉的《宋季元明理学通录》等，对“朱陆和会论”进行批判性探讨的同时，阐明了退溪心学处于朱子学里尊德性派的顶点。因为退溪心学论中有程敏政的《心经附注》，所以写了相关的几篇论文，同时对有关朝鲜时代《心经附注》的著述写了解题书和研究书等。在展开退溪心学论的过程中，因对李滉的“理气互发说”及其独创性等的论议而卷入论难，于是又写了几篇文章。

如前所述，到了16世纪中叶李滉，韩国朱子学时代正式开启。随着既是其弟子的李珥（号栗谷，1536－1584）批判老师的学说，之后朝鲜时代（1392－1897/1910）300多年间，韩国朱子学即李滉的退溪学派和李珥的栗谷学派不但在学问上，而且在政治、社会、文化等各领域以不同面貌被展开。在这种学派分化过程中，出现过类似“四端七情”和“人心道心”的论辩。退溪学派和栗谷学派各自主张“理气互发说”和“气发一途说”，因此也被称为“主理派”和“主气派”。

同时，退溪学派和栗谷学派在工夫论上也体现了很大差别性。由于朱子学是自己自觉地追求成为圣人的“希圣之学”，程颐和朱熹等曾经为此主张居敬涵养的尊德性工夫和格物致知的道问学工夫都是必要的，还以鸟之两翼与车之两轮为譬喻进行过说明。退溪学派和栗谷学派同为朱子学者，尽管在两种工夫都是必要的方面看法是相同的，但退溪学派偏重尊德性工夫的立场，而栗谷学派主张两种工夫的彻底并重。如此，在工夫论的差异成为韩国朱子学分歧的原因之一方面，南宋时代的朱熹（1130－1200）和陆九渊（1139－1192）之间曾经以工夫问题为中心展开的鹅湖论辩与韩国朱子学之展开有很深的关联性。

## 二、鹅湖论辩与朱陆同异

鹅湖论辩是从1175年（淳熙二年）朱熹与陆九渊、陆九龄兄弟在江西省铅山县的鹅湖寺相会，就工夫的内容和顺序等问题展开论辩开始，其后1188年（淳熙十五年）朱熹和陆九渊、陆九韶兄弟又通过书信就周敦颐《太极图说》中“无极而太极”的解释等问题展开了论辩。通过朱陆之争体现的“朱陆同异”问题在以后中国和韩国的理学展开中起到了里程标的作用。本文将以前者的工夫论辩为中心来考察朱陆学的差

---

① 洪元植：《退溪学，试问其存在》，《今天的东洋思想》第4号，艺文东洋思想研究院，2001，第52－53页。

异点。

当时朱熹和陆九渊兄弟在鹅湖寺的相会，在陆九渊的年报里记载如下：

鹅湖之会，论及教人。元晦之意，欲令人泛观博览，而后归之约。二陆之意，欲先发明人之本心，而后使之博览。朱以陆之教人为太简，陆以朱之教人为支离，此颇不合。[①]

在这里，朱熹和陆九渊在鹅湖寺相会并对各自工夫论进行讨论。朱熹主张“博览”，即“博文”之后“约”，即“约礼”；相反，陆九渊主张首先显露本心后再博学。朱熹认为陆九渊的这种工夫方法“太简”，而陆九渊则认为朱熹的工夫方法“支离”。由此可见，两者有很大的不同。基于此，后来黄宗羲在《宋元学案》里提出，陆九渊以尊德性工夫为主，而朱熹以道问学工夫为主：

先生之学，以尊德性为宗，谓“先立乎其大者，而后天之所以与我者，不为小者所夺。夫苟本体不明，而徒致功于外索，是无源之水也。”同时紫阳之学，则以道问学为主，谓“格物穷理，乃吾人入圣之阶梯。夫苟信心自是，而惟从事于覃思，是师心自用也。”[②]

陆九渊批判支离是因为朱熹过分重视经传工夫，即重视其道问学工夫；朱熹批判太简是因为陆九渊的工夫里遗漏了道问学的经传工夫。如此看来，两者间的论辩核心在于道问学的经传工夫。因此，陆九渊轻视道问学工夫，而朱熹重视道问学工夫；更进一步，陆九渊轻视道问学工夫，重视尊德性的心工夫，因此被认为是尊德性派，与此相比，朱熹被规定为道问学派的见解就产生了。最终，这种认识导致了很多误解和混乱。

陆九渊在多处提到当时学习者的工夫方法太繁多、太难，引用《周易·系辞传》章节说明自身的工夫方法“易简”：

天下之理，将从其简且易者而学之乎？将从其繁且难者而学之乎？若繁而难者果足以为道，劳苦而为之可也，其实本不足以为道，学者何苦于繁难之说。简且易者，又易知易从，又信足以为道，学者何惮而不为简易之从乎？[③]

后世言易者以为易道至幽至深，学者皆不敢轻言。然圣人赞易则曰，“乾以易知，坤以简能。易则易知，简则易从。易知则有亲，易从则有功。有亲则可久，有功则可大。可久则贤人入德，可大则贤人之业。易简而天下之理得矣。”[④]

---

① 陆九渊：《陆九渊集》卷36，《年谱》。

② 黄宗羲：《宋元学案》，《象山学案·案语》。

③ 陆九渊：《陆九渊集》卷34，《语录上》。

④ 陆九渊：《陆九渊集》卷1，《与曾宅之》。

陆九渊认为，当时学习的人进行如此繁多而艰难的工夫，是因为不知天下各种理是“天所以与我”，徒然地被束缚于“浮论虚说”，只局限于经典工夫：

此理本天所以与我，非由外铄。明得此理，即是主宰。真能这主，则外物不能移，邪说不能惑。所病于吾友者，正谓此理不明，内无所主。一向萦绊于浮论虚说，终日只依藉外说以为主，天之所与我者反为客。主客倒置，迷而不反，惑而不解。①

因此，陆九渊为了在工夫上有进展而抛弃艰难支离的方法，提出就像古代圣贤所说的做到“存心”、“养心”、“求放心”即可：

事业固无穷尽，然古先圣贤未尝艰难其途径，支离其门户。夫子曰，“吾道一以贯之。”孟子曰，“夫道一而已矣。”曰，“涂之人可以为禹。”曰，“人皆可以为尧舜。”曰，“人有四端而自谓不能者，自贼者也。”人孰无心，道不外索，患在戕贼之耳，放失之耳。古人教人，不过存心养心求放心。②

正因为陆九渊抛弃经典读书工夫，只强调心工夫，所以朱熹认为“太简”。③ 朱熹警戒说如果不进行读书工夫，很容易陷入“私意”，④ 认为尊德性的心工夫和道问学的

---

① 陆九渊：《陆九渊集》卷1，《与曾宅之》。

② 陆九渊：《陆九渊集》卷5，《与舒西美》。

③ 《朱子语类》卷124，“陆子静答贤书，说个易简字，却说错了。乾以易知，坤以简能，是甚意思？如何只容易说过了！乾之体健而不息。”

陆九渊。

陆九渊：《陆九渊集》卷1，《与曾宅之》。

陆九渊：《陆九渊集》卷5，《与舒西美》。

《朱子语类》卷124，“陆子静答贤书，说个易简字，却说错了。乾以易知，坤以简能，是甚意思？如何只容易说过了！乾之体健而不息，行而不难，故易。坤则顺其理而不为，故简。不是容易苟简也。”

朱熹《朱子语类》卷11，“又有一般人都不曾读书，便言我已悟得道理，如此便是恻隐之心，如此便是羞恶之心，如此便是是非之心，浑是一个私意。”

朱熹在解释《中庸》的“尊德性而道问学”时，在《中庸章句》里提出“尊德性，所以存心而极乎道体之大也。道问学，所以致知而尽乎道体之细也。二者修德凝道之大端也。”

朱熹《朱子语类》卷9，“涵养中自有穷理工夫，穷其所养之理。穷理中自有涵养工夫，养其所穷之理。两项都不相离，才见成两处，便不得。”

朱熹《朱子语类》卷9，“择之问，‘且涵养去，久之自明?’曰，‘亦须穷理。涵养穷索，二者不可废一，如车两轮，如鸟两翼’。”

朱熹《朱子语类》卷9，“务反求者，以博观为外驰。务博观者，以内省为狭隘。堕于一偏，此皆学者之大病也!”

行而不难，故易。坤则顺其理而不为，故简。不是容易苟简也。”

④ 朱熹《朱子语类》卷11，“又有一般人都不曾读书，便言我已悟得道理，如此便是恻隐之心，如此便是羞恶之心，如此便是是非之心，浑是一个私意。”

读书工夫是“修德”、“凝道”的大端绪。[①] 他还提出心的涵养功夫与读书的穷理工夫处于不可分离的关系。[②] 最后他认为，涵养和穷理工夫就像车之两轮和鸟之两翼一样，缺一不可。[③] 同时，他认为只局限于某一种工夫是弊端，[④] 陆九渊的工夫方法正是如此，因此说“太简”。

但是，后世学者中出现了类似朱熹所说的尊德性工夫和道问学工夫并重的主张，就好像鹅湖论辩之后受到陆九渊的影响一样。王守仁的阳明学出现之前，明朝程敏政在《心经附注》里把朱熹的道问学工夫和尊德性工夫分为早年说和晚年说。《道一编》里提出“早异晚同说”，认为朱熹早年主要以道问学为主，到了晚年因受象山学的影响而强调尊德性工夫，所以两者的学问变得相同。最后，王守仁写了《朱子晚年定论》，提出朱子学归一到象山学。这导致了明代和朝鲜朱子学者的激论。后来，明末清初时的黄宗羲也有过类似的想法，提出朱熹和陆九渊“始虽有意见之参差，终归于一致而无间”，[⑤] 使人感受到作为阳明学后裔的余韵。在现代学者中也间或有持这种观点的人。[⑥] 如此，提出朱熹重视尊德性工夫是受陆九渊影响的人经常谈及下面的书信：

> 熹衰病日侵，去年宰患亦不少，此数日来，病躯方似略可支吾，然精神耗灭，日甚一日，恐终非能久于世者。所幸迩来日用功夫颇觉有力，无复向来支离之病，甚恨未得从容面论，未知异时相见，尚复有异同否耳！[⑦]

朱熹在给陆九渊的来信进行回复时，提出近来用心于日用工夫，支离的弊病很多已经没有了，差异也就没有了。如果原封不动地理解朱熹在信中所说内容的话，可以说是受到了陆九渊的影响。然而作为回信，可以说这可能包含着礼节意义。实际上重要的在于，他是偏重尊德性工夫，还是只倾向于尊德性工夫一方面的问题。这里将直接考察陆九渊的想法。

---

① 朱熹在解释《中庸》的“尊德性而道问学”时，在《中庸章句》里提出“尊德性，所以存心而极乎道体之大也。道问学，所以致知而尽乎道体之细也。二者修德凝道之大端也。”

② 朱熹《朱子语类》卷9：“涵养中自有穷理工夫，穷其所养之理。穷理中自有涵养工夫，养其所穷之理。两项都不相离，才见成两处，便不得。”

③ 朱熹《朱子语类》卷9，“择之问，‘且涵养去，久之自明?’曰，‘亦须穷理。涵养穷索，二者不可废一，如车两轮，如鸟两翼’。”

④ 朱熹《朱子语类》卷9，“务反求者，以博观为外驰。务博观者，以内省为狭隘。堕于一偏，此皆学者之大病也!”

⑤ 黄宗羲《宋元学案・象山学案・案语》，“观此可见二先生之虚怀从善，始虽有意见之参差，终归于一致而无间。”

⑥ 作为一例，彭永捷认为朱熹重视尊德性工夫有陆九渊的影响。尽管如此，但就像王守仁所说的“朱子晚年定论”一样，朱子学并不是归一到象山学，朱子学与象山学之间存在无法一致的差异。彭永捷，《朱陆之辩－朱熹陆九渊哲学比较研究》（北京：人民出版社，2002年），第213－236页。

⑦ 朱熹：《朱文公文集》卷36，《答陆子静》。

朱元晦曾作书与学者云，“陆子静专以尊德性悔人，故游其门者多践履之士，然于道问学处欠了。某教人岂不是道问学处多了些子？故游某之门者践履多不及之。”观此，则是元晦欲却两短，合两长。然吾以为不可，既不知尊德性，焉有所谓道问学？[1]

陆九渊认为朱熹想“去两短，合两长”，这是不可能的，所以反问若不知尊德性，何以谈道问学。这是陆九渊批判朱熹树立尊德性工夫一边的立场而提出两种工夫并重。即他也不认为朱熹转向了尊德性工夫一边。不过可以解读为他只是因为自身的原因，认为朱熹从偏重道问学工夫转向两种工夫的并重。但这与事实不相符：

> 致知力行，用功不可偏。偏过一边，则一边受病。如程子云，“涵养须用敬，进学则在致知。”分明自作两脚说，但只要分先后轻重。论先后，当以致知为先。论轻重，当以力行为重。[2]

这里，朱熹从开始就提出道问学工夫和尊德性工夫的并重，如果实在要追究重要性的话，那么尊德性工夫比道问学工夫更重要。知和行也是在同样的脉络说明。[3] 这是起初朱熹所持的基本立场。朱熹早年重视道问学工夫，到了晚年重视尊德性工夫，这与事实不相符。只是看到弟子们流于偏重道问学工夫而强调过尊德性工夫的重要性，朱熹不可能因为看到这种现象就改变自身的观点。这只是站在象山学和阳明学立场上的学者的看法而已。

## 三、朱陆的尊德性、道问学工夫论辨析

我们在前面看到，黄宗羲认为朱熹是以道问学为主，而陆九渊以尊德性为宗，起初两者间虽有这种差异，但到了后来“始虽有意见之参差，终归于一致而无间”。即归一于尊德性工夫一边。根据这种观点，他在《宋元学案》里以吴澄和郑玉等为例，把元代理学放在“朱陆和会论”的框架内进行了解读。这种观点与事实不符。朱熹既没有以道问学工夫为主，也没有从以道问学工夫为主转为以尊德性工夫为主。只是主张两种工夫要并重，经常警戒不要过于偏重某一边。如果一定要追究两种工夫的轻重的话，那么尊德性工夫更重要。到了晚年看到弟子们陷入道问学工夫，为加以警戒他强调了尊德性工夫的重要性。尽管他提出两种工夫的并重，但在他死后，后裔们倾向于某一边，分为“道问学派”和“尊德性派”而展开。其实黄宗羲提出“朱陆和会论”正是朱子学尊德性派的展开。

---

① 陆九渊：《陆九渊集》卷34，《语录上》。

② 朱熹：《朱子语类》卷9。

③ 朱熹《朱子语类》卷9，“知行常相须，如目无足不行，足无目不见。论先后，知为先，行为重。”

结果，黄宗羲的观点不符合事实，导致了很多误解和混乱。反倒像陆九渊所说的，如果说朱熹并重两种工夫的话，那么陆九渊以尊德性工夫为主，也许更符合事实。但即便这样整理，还会有几种疑问。首先，对两者的尊德性工夫论是否真的相同存在疑问。如果说陆九渊的工夫论以尊德性工夫为主的话，那么就会对他的道问学工夫是什么内容，以及与尊德性工夫有何关系产生疑问。

首先如果说朱熹提出尊德性工夫和道问学工夫的并重，陆九渊以尊德性工夫为主的话，那么两者的尊德性工夫内容是否相同？事实上，到目前为止，对此的疑问还没有被认真地提出过，不知不觉中被认为好像是一样的。然而并非如此。两者间的尊德性工夫论有很大不同。最重要的是，朱熹的尊德性工夫论的核心是从程颐那里继承的“居敬涵养”。但陆九渊则不同：

> 且如“存诚”“持敬”二语自不同，岂可合说？“存诚”字于古有考，“持敬”字乃后来杜撰。[①]

这里陆九渊认为“存诚”和“持敬”是不同的，提出虽然“存诚”被包含在很多经典里，但“持敬”不过是到了后代被杜撰的而已。结果，陆九渊认为朱熹的“持敬”、“居敬”中心的尊德性工夫论是没有经典根据的。实际上，两者间尊德性工夫论的差异渊源很深。尊德性工夫的对象首先是心。但两者对心的理解从根本上讲是不同的：

> 道塞宇宙，非有所隐遁，在天曰阴阳，在地曰刚柔，在人曰仁义。故仁义者，人之本心。孟子曰，“存乎人者，岂无仁义之心哉?”，又曰，“我固有之，非由外铄我也。”愚不肖者不及焉，则蔽于物欲而失其本心。贤者智者过之，则蔽于意见而失其本心。[②]

陆九渊认为道即理充满于宇宙，对人而言，那是仁义或本心。他认为“人心至灵，此理至明。人皆有是心，心皆具是理”，[③] 所以提出不能把心与理分开来看。[④] 对此，他提出“宇宙内事，是己分内事。己分内事，是宇宙内事”，[⑤] 最后“宇宙便是吾心，吾心即是宇宙”：

> 四方上下曰宇，往古来今曰宙。宇宙便是吾心，吾心即是宇宙。千万世之前，有圣人出焉，同此心同此理也。千万世之后，有圣人出焉，同此心同此理也。东

---

① 陆九渊：《陆九渊集》卷 1，《与曾宅之》。

② 陆九渊：《陆九渊集》卷 1，《与赵监》。

③ 陆九渊：《陆九渊集》卷 22，《杂说》。

④ 陆九渊《陆九渊集》卷 1，《与曾宅之》，“盖心，一心也。理，一理也。至当归一，精义无二，此心此理，实不容有二。”

⑤ 陆九渊：《陆九渊集》卷 22，《杂说》。

南西北海有圣人出焉，同此心同此理也。[①]

同时，陆九渊提出吾心就是圣人之心。因此，就像六经不过是圣人之心的注脚一样，也不过是吾心的注脚而已。[②] 他认为工夫必须像孟子所说的“先立乎其大者”，应该把天本来赋予我的本心加以存养和扩充。这就是他的尊德性工夫，对六经等的道问学读书工夫自然就落到次要的或从属的位置。

就像陆九渊在前面所说的，如果说六经等经典不过是吾心注脚的话，那么他认为道问学的工夫学习没有必要吗？不是。

如中庸大学孟子诸书，不可不时读之，以听其发扬告教。戕贼陷溺之余，此心之存者，时时发见，若火之始燃，天之始达。苟充养之功不继，而乍明乍灭，乍流乍窒，则渊渊其渊，浩浩其天者，何时而可复耶？[③]

这里陆九渊提到有必要经常读《中庸》和《大学》等很多经典，接受教诲，发扬自身。尽管如此，他认为如果存养和扩充的工夫不在先，并且没有被传承的话，读书工夫就会很快明灭和窒塞。他特别警戒的是，过分死抠经典内容或推出自己的想法，提出新学说：

此心之良，人所均有，自耳目之官不思而蔽于物，流浪展转，戕贼陷溺之端不可胜穷。最大害事，名为讲学，其实乃物欲之大者，所谓邪说诬民，充塞仁义。质之懿者，乃使之困心疲力，而小人乃以济恶行私。[④]

今讲学之路未通，而以己意附会往训，立为成说，则恐反成心之蟊贼，道之榛棘，日复一日而不见其进。志与事乖，说与行违，首尾衡决，本末舛逆，未可归之禀赋，罪其懈怠也。[⑤]

如此，陆九渊认为勉强穿凿经典内容而提出自己学说，只会因“物欲之大”、“成心之蟊贼”而“困心疲力”，这就是“所谓邪说诬民，充塞仁义”，其结果“志与事乖，说与行违，首尾衡决，本末舛逆”，反倒会导致伤害本心。显然他的这种批判是针对朱熹工夫论的。对此，他提出如下正确的读书工夫的方法：

至于圣贤格言，切近的当，昭晰明白，初不难晓。而吾之权度，其则不远，非假于外物。开卷读书时，整冠肃容，平心定气。训诂章句，苟能从容勿迫而讽咏之，其理当自有彰彰者。纵有滞碍，此心未充未明，犹有所滞而然耳，姑舍之

---

① 陆九渊:《陆九渊集》卷22,《杂说》。

② 陆九渊《陆九渊集》卷34,《语录上》,“或问先生何不著书？对曰，‘六经注我，我注六经。’”

③ 陆九渊,《陆九渊集》卷5,《与戴少望》。

④ 陆九渊:《陆九渊集》卷5,《与徐子宜》。

⑤ 陆九渊:《陆九渊集》卷7,《与彭子寿》。

以俟他日可也，不必苦思之。苦思则方寸自乱，自蹶其本，失己滞物，终不明白。但能于其所已通晓者，有鞭策之力，涵养之功，使德日以进，业日以修，而此心日充日明，则今日滞碍者，他日必有冰释理顺时矣。如此则读书之次，亦何适而非思也。如是而思，安得不切近？安得不优游？若固滞于言语之间，欲以失己滞物之智，强探而力索之，非吾之所敢知也。[①]

这里陆九渊提出在读书时，首先"整冠肃容，平心定气"，不要着急，要悠闲地"讽咏"，如果不能很好地把握意义的时候，不要"苦思"，而是以已经掌握的内容为基础，用心涵养，进修德业，不知何时必然就像冰融化一样，能理解文理。朱熹对读书法也像陆九渊一样详细说明时，提出过读书时心不要"迫切"，而是"放宽"，[②] 但他在特别强调"精读"和"熟读"时叙说如下：

看文字，须大段着精彩看。耸起精神，树起筋骨，不要困，如有刀剑在后一般。就一段中，须要透。[③]

看文字，须是如猛将用兵，直是鏖战一阵，如酷吏治狱，直是推勘到底，决是不恕他，方得。[④]

朱熹提出，读书时就像后背被刀顶着，猛将把敌军全部杀死，狱吏以逼人的气势对待犯人一样，用心才行。朱熹的读书法还萦绕着悲壮感。因此，对就像玩味一样的读书进行了辛辣的批判：

人言读书当从容玩味，此乃自怠之一说。若是读此书未晓道理，虽不可急迫，亦不放下，犹可也。若徜徉终日，谓之从容，却无做工夫处。[⑤]

尽管朱熹也提出读书时心不能"迫切"，但认为因此而"从容玩味"的态度也不正确。这与陆九渊有很大的不同。这可以说是源于两者对道问学工夫的根本立场之差异。

从上述可见，陆九渊没有说过道问学的读书工夫是不必要的。但并不意味着他认为那是必要的。即他认为虽然对经典的读书工夫间或是必要的，但因为六经不过是吾心的注脚而已，所以不必拘泥于此，对后代的训诂或传注更是如此。他认为读书工夫必须"先立乎其大者"之后，要先有尊德性的涵养功夫，无论何时，损害"其大者"的自己本心都是不行的。因此，既不能认为陆九渊把道问学的读书工夫与尊德性工夫并重，也不能看作是并举，可以看作只是把道问学工夫放在尊德性工夫的次要的、从

---

① 陆九渊：《陆九渊集》卷3，《与刘深父》。

② 朱熹《朱子语类》卷10，《读书法上》，"读书，放宽着心，道理自会出来。若忧愁迫切，道理终无缘得出来。"

③ 朱熹：《朱子语类》卷10，《读书法上》。

④ 朱熹：《朱子语类》卷10，《读书法上》。

⑤ 朱熹：《朱子语类》卷10，《读书法上》。

属的位置。尽管朱熹与陆九渊都重视尊德性工夫，但是其内容完全不同。因此，仅依据两者都重视尊德性工夫的事实就说产生了影响或转换、归一的提法是勉强的。

## 四、退溪李滉的尊德性工夫偏重论

退溪李滉在晚年与其弟子高峰奇大升展开了韩国哲学史上最有名的所谓“四端七情论辩”。该论辩的核心是有关对四端和七情的“理气分属”和“理的动静”的问题。李滉的最后定论是“四端理发而气随之，七情气发而理乘之”，他同时认定气和理的“发”和“动静”。在这点上，他的学说经常被称为“理气互发说”。另一方面，奇大升的观点被栗谷李珥所继承和发展，主张四端与七情因为是包含关系，所以无法分离，理与气也是“一而二，二而一”的“妙合”关系，理作为形而上者不能发，只有气才能发。李珥的这种观点与李滉的“理气互发说”相对比，被称为“气发一途说”。因为李滉以理气不相离为基础谈理的绝对优位性，而李珥以理气不相离为基础谈气的相对重要性，所以在韩国哲学史上各自被称为“主理派”和“主气派”。如此，李滉和李珥的观点被清楚地加以区分。在他们死后，朝鲜的朱子学分为李滉的退溪学派和李珥的栗谷学派而展开，同时正式开启了“韩国朱子学的时代”。

但是本人认为李滉的退溪学和李珥的栗谷学，以及退溪学派和栗谷学派的最本质的重要差异在于工夫论。因为作为朱子学者，他们的穷极目标都是自己成为圣贤，只是在如何实现的具体方法上分为两个学派，前面谈论的两学派的哲学差异不是别的，而是根据其方法的差异而立说产生的。李滉及其后裔们为了成为圣贤，认为就像“鸟之两翼，车之两轮”一样，尽管道问学的读书工夫和尊德性的涵养功夫都必要，但两者之中，尊德性的涵养工夫是最根本的和最重要的。相反，李珥的后裔们主张两种工夫要彻底并重。对此，如果说李滉的退溪学派在偏重尊德性工夫方面是朝鲜朱子学的尊德性派的话，那么李珥的栗谷学派由于主张两种工夫的彻底并重，比退溪学派相对地更重视道问学工夫，可以被看作是朝鲜朱子学的道问学派。不但在理论上，而且在实际上两个学派也体现了这种差别性。如果说退溪学派认为由于到了朱熹从理论上完成了孔孟儒学，把李滉漏掉的完全进行补充，现在只剩下实践了的话，那么栗谷学派则认为由于朱熹学说中有很多异论的余地，以致经常提起很多论辩，所以三百多年间致力于补充《朱子大全》等。

这种对工夫论的两个学派间的观点差异很好地体现在栗谷学派对李滉特别尊崇程敏政的《心经附注》的批判中。李滉的叙述如下：

滉初感发兴起于此事者，此书之力也。故平生尊信此书，亦不在四子近思录之下矣。许鲁斋尝曰，“吾于小学，敬之如神明，尊之如父母。”愚于心经亦云。[1]

这里所说的《心经》是指程敏政的《心经附注》。我们可以由此充分得知李滉是非常尊崇《心经附注》的。但是该《心经附注》在朝鲜成为问题的原因在于，程敏政在给真德秀的《心经》最后章节《尊德性斋铭章》添加附注时，把朱熹的工夫说分为早年说和晚年说之后，认为晚年倾向于重视尊德性工夫，提出所谓“早异晚同说”。他在另外的著作《道一编》里主张朱子在初年攻击陆象山，晚年意识到错误，与象山达成一致，这就更成为问题。对此的批判是由其弟子赵穆提出的。李滉在苦思冥想之后回答如下。

是则不然也。吾观是书，其经则自诗书易以及于程朱说，皆圣贤大训也，其注则由濂洛关闽，兼取于后来诸贤之说，无非至言也。何可以篁墩之失而并大训之论，不为尊信乎？……徒务博文，而少缓于约礼，则其弊必至于口耳之习。故朱子于当时，其忧之戒之之切，诚有如此注所引十二条之说。其门人之述行状又云，“晚年诸生，缴绕于文义，始颇指示本体云云”，则尊德性以救文义之弊，非篁墩之说也，乃朱子之意固然也。篁墩于此，但不当区区于初晚之分耳。若其遵朱子之意，赞西山之经，注此于篇终，欲以救末学之误，实亦至当而不可易也。况只引朱说，而补以诸儒发明朱说之条，未尝一言及于陆氏之学，以为朱子晚悔而与此合，如道一编之所谓乎！[2]

上述内容可以整理如下。

第一，李滉指出朱子学和象山学绝不是相同的，这点连朱熹和陆九渊也都否定。他批判了程敏政把朱熹的学说分为初年和晚年，把重视尊德性工夫作为晚年说，更进一步地批判王守仁关于朱熹在晚年接受陆九渊的影响而倾向于重视尊德性工夫的“朱子晚年定论”是荒谬的。

第二，李滉提出朱熹把尊德性的心工夫和道问学的读书工夫比作“鸟之两翼，车之两轮”。这样，他虽然提出尊德性工夫和道问学工夫的并重，继承了朱熹的观点，但另一方面他认为朱熹在晚年看到弟子们偏重道问学工夫，为加以纠正强调了尊德性工夫是事实。

第三，李滉提出不但真德秀的《心经》经文，而且程敏政添加的附注内容也都是诸位先贤的话，所以不成问题。最成为论难的是《心经附注》最后章节《尊德性斋铭章》的附注。其中朱熹的话自不必说，就连吴澄的话也因为“遵从朱子的意思，赞同西山的经传，在篇末添加注解”，所以都不成问题。另外，李滉提出在程敏政的附注里对象山学连一句也没提及，也没有说过朱熹晚年醒悟与象山学一致，所以没有任何问

---

① 李滉：《退溪先生文集》卷41，《杂著·心经后论》。

② 李滉：《退溪先生文集》卷41，《杂著·心经后论》。

题。这里可以看出他对《心经附注》很强的尊信态度。

如前所述，李滉借用朱熹的比喻来说明尊德性工夫和道问学工夫的并重。尽管如此，这既是对倾向于象山学嫌疑的答辩，也是对朱子学正统见解的一次确认。可以看出他的工夫论已经倾向于重视尊德性工夫。其后裔中还有人干脆提出尊德性工夫和道问学工夫的比重是 7 比 3。因此，栗谷学派不断地对李滉和退溪学派投来怀疑的眼光，主张两种工夫的彻底并重。

## 五、结论—“退溪心学”的展开

朱熹与陆九渊曾经在鹅湖寺相会，就工夫的问题展开过一次论辩。这里论辩的核心在于道问学的读书工夫。陆九渊批判朱熹的读书工夫“支离”，对此，朱熹批判陆九渊过于轻视读书工夫“太简”。结果，朱熹主张尊德性的涵养功夫和道问学的读书工夫的并重，陆九渊只强调尊德性工夫。尽管如此，朱熹并不是完全否定陆九渊的读书工夫。他把道问学的读书工夫放在尊德性工夫的次要的、从属的位置。因此，朱熹和陆九渊读书工夫的内容和方法只能是不同。不论陆九渊还是朱熹，并不是因为都重视尊德性的涵养功夫而连内容和方法也相同。朱熹的尊德性工夫核心是“敬”。对此，陆九渊批判说，只不过是没有经典根据的杜撰而已。两者对尊德性工夫的差异源于包括对心的理解的哲学根本差异。

朱、陆死后，在南宋和元代，虽然陆九渊的象山学传承是微不足道的，但朱子学经历了多样的分化与变貌而被继承。大体而言，分为尊德性派和道问学派而被展开。朱子学的尊德性派自然强调心的涵养工夫，体现了“心学”的倾向。后代心学系列的学者认为这正是朱子学受到象山学影响的结果。明末清初的黄宗羲称之为“朱陆和会论”。然而，这与事实不相符。

从整体来看，朱子理学到了后代，经历了向心学的转换。从东亚视角来看，体现为“阳明心学”和“退溪心学”。退溪心学站在了朱子学尊德性派的顶点。退溪心学与偏重尊德性工夫有很深的关联性。退溪李滉偏重尊德性工夫可以从极为尊崇程敏政的《心经附注》得到很好的体现。即使程敏政在被批判为是倾向于象山学人物的情况下，他最终也没有否定《心经附注》的价值。这是因为对偏重道问学工夫的现实批判意识与自身的心学倾向相符合的缘故。

那么，通过对退溪心学的内容进行整理将结束本文。

第一，退溪学的本领和穷极目的是自觉完成的人格，即成为圣贤，这是“圣学”。即便是君主也不例外，制作《圣学十图》呈献给年幼的宣祖。这到后来成为“圣君”的教科书。

第二，他认为，为成为圣贤，尊德性的涵养功夫最重要。他提出作为朱子学者，为成为圣贤，与尊德性的涵养功夫一起，道问学的读书工夫也不能漏掉。这种想法与朱熹一样，曾以鸟之两翼和车之两轮的譬喻为例说明了两种工夫的互发、并进和并重。尽管如此，但不能由此就认为他同样重视两者，这体现为他的后裔偏重尊德性工夫。同时，从主张两种工夫并重的栗谷学派那里受到对他及其后裔偏重尊德性的涵养功夫的嫌疑和持续的批判也可以得知。

第三，他的尊德性的涵养功夫重视未发心体的存养工夫，把敬作为要体。这就产生了对心的存在论的、哲学分量的要求，提出了心不是单纯的气，而是“理气之合”的主张。这就打开了强调本心和心之主宰性的路。

第四，因为他更重视尊德性的涵养功夫，所以尽管道问学的读书工夫不具有独自的领域，但在与此有很深联系的同时，间或也处于次要的位置。他认为读书工夫必须以涵养功夫为基础，不能只局限于文字而勉强地掌握意义，或者急于树立自身的创见都是不行的。在他看来，与其追求新知识，还不如到先贤的门庭寻求指正，进行对话，从而得到超过文字的意义和全人格的感化。因此，比起朱熹的其他著作，他更重视朱熹通过与弟子们的对话进行讲授的书札，编纂了《朱子书节要》和《宋季元明理学通录》。有必要重新记忆其中大部分内容是为成为圣贤的涵养工夫内容。

# 韩国儒学的传统及其特性

韩国传统文化大学　崔英成

## 一、韩国儒学思想的时代变迁与社会功能

韩国的儒学思想史是个“理论完善”的历史。韩国的儒学思想既敏感于时代要求，又重视符合时代的理论启迪，在良好继承以人为本的儒家思想本质的同时，又注重现实性与时宜性，并能根据所处环境的变化做出主观能动性应变，在韩国民族史的发展中起到了至关重要的作用。

从宏观的角度审视韩国的儒学思想史，可以看出其在不同时期彰显出不同的特征。韩国三国时代由于三国鼎立、争霸存亡，“忠”成为最高的道德条目，提倡“团结”和“牺牲”精神。新罗时代青少年组织花郎所谓的世俗五戒一事君以忠、事亲以孝、交友以信、临战无退、杀生有择，从中也可看出与“孝”相比，尤为强调“忠”。记载两位花郎少年盟誓的壬申誓记石上也刻有“忠道执持”，强调“忠”的思想。此外，随着新罗社会情况的变化，佛家“不杀生”的戒规也变更为“杀生有择”，这亦从侧面反映了当时的社会气氛。三国时代形成了整体重于个体的社会风气，佛教的“护国・佛国土”思想对这种社会风气的形成也产生了积极作用。在抵御外侵的过程中，三国时代的儒家思想对自主精神与反抗意识的形成和部族社会共同体精神的倡导都起到了关键作用。因此，集智慧与勇气于一身的领导者被认为是理想的人物形象。

统一新罗时代为与平和安定的社会氛围相吻合，以“仁”、“孝”为政治礼教的根本。在这种环境下，儒教文化制度逐渐扎根，儒教秩序及伦理意识也达到了相当高的水准。到了高丽时代，儒教的政治思想进一步被强调，并加以机构化、组织化、功能化。而且儒教的政治原理也被广泛地应用于中央集权统治体系和王权强化上。科举制的实施成为通过官僚体制整顿而形成的王权强化政策与仁政主义的象征。至1170年武臣政变为止，以儒教仁政主义为基础的文教发展已经达到了相当高的水准。

高丽末期传入的朱子性理学给韩国带来了深远的影响，甚至在记述韩国儒学史时，

以性理学的受容情况为界，将其划分为性理学受容之前与性理学受容之后。性理学是从形而上学的层面上探究宇宙自然原理与人间社会秩序的儒教哲学，通常又被称为“新儒学”。性理学从传统信条式的伦理道德范畴中挣脱出来，将儒学哲学体系化。性理学将陈旧的儒学进行再创造，在儒教的伦理规范上赋予形而上学的依据，在这样的基础上，既欲克服佛教的理论，又想确保儒教的正统性，因此深受高丽末期改革势力—新进儒学者的欢迎。高丽末期，性理学被接受之后展开了抑佛扬儒运动，以此为基础，高丽最终完成了儒教和佛教思想的交替。恭愍王之后经过四十余年的革命，朝鲜王朝成立。随着王朝的更替，其统治理念也由佛教转变为儒教。

朝鲜初期，在整顿文化制度的过程中发挥指导理念作用的性理学自 16 世纪中叶后逐渐向文学和哲学方面深化，展现出具备深奥理论和综合体系的学问风貌。朝鲜的性理学重视现实问题，在现实问题中又特别重视人的问题、人性的问题。也就是说，自主又切切实实省察自我的人学倾向非常明显。从周濂溪的理，张横渠的气，邵康节的数，二程的理气论可以看出中国的性理学概以天人关系为主，存在着探讨客观性与宇宙论的倾向，相比之下，朝鲜时代的性理学以宇宙论为基础，并从人性论的角度进行深入地探究，通过人内在的诚实性自主地掌握真理，四端七情论与人物性同异论便是实证。

以人性论为中心的朝鲜性理学，与以本体论为中心的中国性理学之间存在着一定差异。中国的性理学大致是朝着客观性、宇宙论、远心的方向发展，而朝鲜的性理学可以说是朝着求心的、向内的方向汇集。在此，大陆风气与半岛特性可以说是其中的原因之一。朝鲜的性理学从各个方面逐渐向外延伸拓宽，向内又围绕着某一重要问题集中论点、增加深度、维持高水平与凝练性，同时追求普遍性和独立性。朝鲜性理学的代表者退溪李滉和栗谷李珥便很好地证明了这一点。

回顾以往，李滉和李珥之前的性理学研究倾向相对来说较为单调。但自 16 世纪中叶，四端七情论之争发生后，最终形成了不同的学派。17 世纪后，探讨人与万物关系的人物性同异论成为主要研究课题，至朝鲜末期为止，关于人物性同异论的论争持续了 2—3 个世纪。由此也证明了朝鲜的性理学把人的问题，即人的尊严性和人的修养（实践）问题作为重点研究课题。从这点可以评价朝鲜的性理学胜过中国性理学，迈入了进一步发展的领域，扭转了研究方向。

壬辰倭乱后，韩国进入到朝鲜后期，在政治、社会、经济等各方面都发生了不同程度的变化。随着变化的发生，一场为克服各种体制性矛盾，迈入新时代的运动在部分先觉者中展开了。这便是实学运动的兴起，而这种实学思想则是当时社会全盘性变动的历史产物。

在历史上，实学这一用语，无论在哪个时代，都是指当时时代具有现实性或现实意义的学问。到了宋代，与老子、佛的“虚无寂灭”形成对照，更加彰显儒学的现世主义性格，将儒学称为实学，后来实学几乎成为儒学的代名词。此外，标榜修己治人的儒学的“修己”与“治人”，或是“道”与“器”在不同时代所占的比重也不同。随着时代的要求，更为需要的那个层面便被称为实学。

实学的概念不仅在中国，在韩国也随着时代而变迁。丽末鲜初时期批判佛教和老庄思想、辞章学的性理学被称为实学。在经历过倭乱和胡乱后，为了反对朝着烦琐支离方向发展的性理学与礼学的弊端，部分学者高喊经世致用、利用厚生、实事求是的口号，并将以此为目标的学问称为实学。

从主导朝鲜时代思想史主流的朱子学的角度来看，朱子学虽然对“道”和“器”的侧重有所差异，但并非是只注重道的学问。因此在朱子学的发展期乃至兴盛期，不仅精通性理学，而且明于时务、对经世见识高深的学者辈出。但是从整体来看，性理学者对人伦道德和内在修养急功近利，对很多社会问题和产业、经济等闲视之，这也是事实。尤其在学派分化，学说多样化、精密化的过程中，逐渐疏忽迫在眉睫的现实问题，学风朝着思辨性与观念性发展，这也是不争的事实。

从宏观上看，朝鲜后期的实学可以说是以《周易》的变通论为根据，在恢复“道器、本末、内外体用皆应兼备”的儒学本质精神的过程中产生。总而言之，与正德问题相比，更注重于安民问题。这可以说是在儒学思想的发展过程中必然要提及的问题。

另外，19世纪中叶，以鸦片战争为契机，西方势力加速对中国的侵略，这也加重了对华夷论深信不疑的朝鲜有识之士的恐惧心。丙寅洋扰、辛未洋扰和开港等一连串冲击性事件的发生，部分政界和学界对西洋和日本的恐惧心和危机意识膨胀。最终固守儒教秩序的正统性和纯正性，并以资本主义为基础的，反对外国侵略势力的尊王攘夷的斥邪卫正运动开始了。

斥邪卫正是排斥“邪学”，维护“正学”的意思。斥邪和卫正彼此是表里一体的关系。正如佛教所说的“破邪显正”，排斥“邪”就可以确保“正”，维护“正”就可以排斥“邪”。到了19世纪，斥邪的“邪”的对象发生了变化，由原来的佛教和老庄思想变为西洋的学术、思想及从中衍生出的科学、文物。开港（1876年）后排斥的对象具体化为“斥洋斥倭”。

这场运动以全国在野的儒林为中心展开，广泛波及信奉性理学、持有保守倾向的“两班”阶层。斥邪论者在警惕西洋与日本的政治、经济、文化侵略的同时，坚守保守排他的立场。对于外国势力的侵略，他们坚守反侵略的立场，宣传民族自尊性和自立性的意志十分强烈。斥邪论者在历史危机之际，将性理学的义理思想升华为救国理念，掀起了自觉维护民族传统、抵抗外国势力侵略的“内修外攘”精神热潮。斥邪运动紧接着通过义兵运动得以实践化、行动化，又在国权丧失期通过抗日义兵运动和独立运动得以继承，成了这些运动的精神思想源流。

## 二、韩国思想的传统与儒学思想的结合

### 1. 韩国思想与尊重人的精神

在讲韩国儒学的特性之前，不得不先谈一下韩国固有思想的传统。“固有思想”不是指自古以来传承下来的某种不变的思想体系，而是指韩国人在自己的风土里，在思维过程中形成的共同特性。韩国固有思想与儒学思想之间存在着紧密的关系。

韩国固有思想概起源于檀君神话。由于篇幅有限，无法详细讲述檀君神话所蕴含的思想，但天人合一、神人相和、弘益人间的精神可谓是其精华。天人合一、神人相和思想将“天”和“神”作为思想形成的基准，同时认定人、天、神在某种层面上可以共存。这与把天和人看作是造物主和被造物，认为两者是对立关系的认识完全不同。天人合一思想从宽泛的角度来看，虽可在整个东洋思想中可以觅得共性，但在普遍性中又可以寻得特殊性，所以“固有思想”值得探讨。

从檀君神话来看，虽然提到了天与神，但在整体脉络中以人为中心的人本主义思想是很明显的。檀君神话中将神设定为为人的世界而存在。理想中的人物形象也被设定为“达到天人合一境界的人”。这与以原罪说为基础，欲摆脱现世的西欧宗教不同。鉴于此，可以说“以人为中心”、“以人为尊”的思想是韩国思想的奠基石。[①] 所谓的弘益人间思想正是在这样的基础上应运而生。

以人为中心，以人为尊的思想向重视人的生命，爱护和平，强调“以人为主体”的方向展开。[②] 韩民族的相生哲学、爱护和平的哲学是以“弘益人间”的理念作为根据。近世哲学家一夫金恒（1826－1898）说到“天地匪日月空壳，日月匪至人虚影”[③] 一语道破了主体的问题。主体虽然在政治、经济、社会、文化等人类社会的诸领域中被论及，但这其中处于中心位置的主体仍然是人。从宏观上看，现代社会两分为“以天为中心的宗教”和“以物质为中心的科学”。在这两者中，人被排除在外，但是没有人参与的宗教或科学是没有意义的。以人为重，强调以人为主体的韩国思想的传统可以说是恢复被宗教遮蔽、被科学埋没而存在价值受到威胁的人的尊严的最佳方案。我认为“宗教和科学的人类化”是解决这个问题的方法，这种方法可以在韩国思想的传统中找到。

接下来，我们来看看檀君朝鲜之后韩国故国——君子国与青丘国的思想传统。中

---

① 这应该与“人是万物中心”的人本主义思想区别看待。

② 19世纪宗教东学中的“人乃天”思想可谓是重视人的思想的结晶，是最高峰。

③ 《正易》，18b“天地匪日月空壳，日月匪至人虚影。”

国古代历史典籍《山海经》对韩民族有如此描述：“君子国，其人好让不争”、“青丘国，有柔朴民”。君子国位于韩半岛，青丘国位于满洲辽东地区，这已是学术界的定论。介绍君子国和青丘国的《山海经·海外东经》和《山海经·大荒东经》也与甲骨文的内容相一致。与此记录相关的甲骨卜辞是殷代武丁时期的，从这也可以看出君子国和青丘国至少在公元前1400年前便已存在。[①]

“君子”是儒教中所说的理想型人物形象。“柔朴”是老庄哲学的根基，重视柔和与无为自然。孔子集大成形成儒教之前，韩半岛就存在被称为“君子不死之国”的君子国。此外，老庄哲学出现之前，重视“柔朴”的韩民族的一个分支便已生活在辽东地区。如果上述内容是历史事实的话，那么新罗末期的思想家孤云崔致远（857－?）在《鸾郎碑序》中证言韩国民族固有思想“风流”的存在时，所说的风流思想“包含着儒教、佛教、老庄思想三个核心要素”（包含三教），[②] 并非夸张或舞文弄墨。

从君子国可以看出重视正义和仁道的“仁”的风气，从青丘国可以看出重视柔和与自然，进而重视“无为”“无欲”朴实自然的风气。从“仁”和“朴”、“刚”和“柔”的侧面看，可以说相互间存在对照，但也具有互相补充完善的性质。君子国的“仁”思想和青丘国的“朴”思想并非不同，归根到底是一脉相通。儒教的中心思想“仁”乃“人”之意。《论语》或是《中庸》、《孟子》等儒教经典中也说“仁”乃“人”也。[③] 从甲骨文也可得知“人”源于“仁”。[④]“人”和“仁”之间存在不可分割的关系，意味着“仁”思想源于以人为主体意识。道家的核心理念“朴”以“自然”来看待人性，刻画了完完整整保存人性的人物形象。这也意味着朴实自然的“以人为主体”。自韩国上古时代的君子国和青丘国起，重视以人为主体的思想代代相传，形成了悠久的传统，这点值得我们重视。同一民族共有着性质不同的价值观，还为“中庸价值观”的创造打下了基础，在这点上，韩民族的思想源泉值得我们回味。

2. 阴阳相合精神与中和思想

韩国思想的特性之一便是“阴阳相合”精神。众所周知，太极阴阳思想虽是在周易中得以系统化，但其思想源泉却追溯到周易之前。阴阳的原理从周易以前的殷代甲骨文中可以寻得。在甲骨文中，较之龟甲卜辞，牛骨卜辞出现的时间更早。用牛骨来

---

① 参照柳承国：《韩国思想的渊源与历史展望》，成均馆大学出版部，2009年，第71－72页。

② 《三国史记》卷4，新罗本纪，真兴王37年（576）条“国有玄妙之道，曰风流. 设教之源，备详仙史。实乃包含三教，接化群生。且如入则孝于家，出则忠于国，鲁司寇之旨也。处无为之事，行不言之教，周柱史之宗也，诸恶莫作，诸善奉行，竺乾太子之化也。”

③ 《论语·微子》：殷有三仁焉。《中庸》第20章：仁者人也；《孟子·尽心下》：仁也者人也。

④ 中国殷代称东夷族为“人方”。这里的“人”并不是指人的普通名词而是固有名词。从众多文字中选用“人方”来指称东夷族，这与以人为重的东夷族的风气有关。

占卜是东夷族之间流行的风俗文化。至今在中国东部地区，即渤海至辽东地区，牛骨卜辞遗物仍在流传。

阴阳是相互对立的关系。但阴和阳首尾相连，同时也存在着相互依存的关系。这种关系称为“待对关系”。用一圆相表示的太极是宇宙万物的本源。太极是阴与阳的调和。韩国太极旗中的太极图样早在7世纪末，新罗感恩寺的塔中便已出现。这比11世纪中国性理学始祖周敦颐（1017－1073）在《太极图说》中描绘的太极图样要早数百年，比中国道教的象征太极徽章渊源还要甚早。这是证明太极阴阳思想的形成与我们东方有关的重要例证。

韩国的太极旗是在世界其他任何国家中都无法找到的、具有浓厚哲学色彩的国旗。太极旗肯定了任何存在都具有“不同的价值”，还蕴含着从更高的境界来克服两极对立与矛盾的寓意。调和两极，以求和解实现和平，并不是自然而然的事。要依靠调节阴阳对立关系的主体——德性与知性，加以人的创造性与能动性来实现。由此我们可以说，如果在宇宙论角度存在太极的话，那么从人学角度就存在“人极”。①

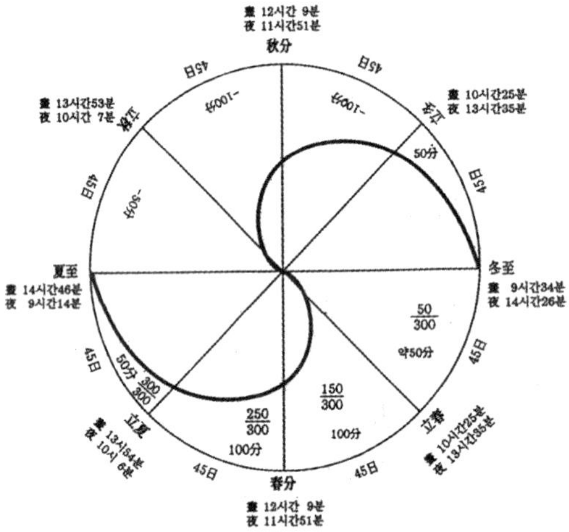


太极图原理解

## 三、韩国儒学的特性

1. 道学的义理思想

儒学的人道主义思想尊重人、爱护人，并且要求排除了非人道因素的正义感和义理感。从“为己”、“克己”上升到在政治、社会层面上亦要求义理思想。

中国的儒教以“仁”为中心，具有很强的包容性，相反，韩国的儒教更强调

① 参照柳承国：《韩国思想的渊源与历史展望》，成均馆大学出版部，2009年，第187页。

“义”，这一重要特征持续了数百年。中国曾有过统治其他民族的历史，而韩国在政治上受他国侵略或被统治的情况更多，因此义理思想成了核心，仁人和志士对韩国人来说是所期望的人物形象。高丽末期，随着性理学正式被接受，义理思想成为代表韩国儒学的最重要的特征之一。韩国儒学用一句话来说就是“道之学”，这种“道之学”是以义理思想为基础的。道学性质的义理思想在道德、政治、历史等各领域中都得以发挥。

被称为“海东孔子”的栗谷李珥对关于道学者的重要标准提出了以下几点：①得道学之正脉②习圣贤相传之心法③进退出处有度④经世济民与学识兼备。[①] 他认为违背这些标准就不能认定为是道学者。如此看来，不能单纯地将学习性理学的人称为道学者。

在韩国儒学史上静庵赵光祖（1482－1519）是如实展现“道学”是怎样一种学问的学者，又是在道学的基础上，追求哲人政治的政治家。他所追求的政治是至治主义的王道政治。虽然年仅38岁便被人杀害，但是他撒下的种子结下了丰硕的果实。事实上，之后朝鲜王朝是按照赵光祖定立的道学和王道政治理念，进行了学问和政治。

到了朝鲜后期，标榜“山林”的道学家辈出。他们受益于重用在野道学者的朝廷政策，得到了极高的礼遇。但是他们中的部分人过于追求空虚的名誉，没有深入了解现实问题，对国利民福没有起到太大的作用。在这一时代，道学的性质已经发生了变质。但道学绝不是不理会或忽视现实问题的一门学问，反而是要求对现实有着莫大的关心，具有强烈的实践感的学问。朱子当时所说的“道学之人”并不是指我们现在所熟知的“古板的形式主义者”或对现实了解不够深入的“迂阔人士”，而是指对现实具有着莫大的关心和正确的判断力，甚至在某一方面能够激烈批判现实的人士，这点值得我们注意。[②]

道学的义理思想在性理学中得以系统化。性理学把关于人的本性与天理的问题作为主要课题，同时又与善恶正邪的问题，即价值的义理，有着直接的关系。[③] 朝鲜的性理学不仅在追求内在诚实的人性论层面上发挥着重要作用，同时在历史社会现实中，在人的行为准则与规范的实践层面上也发挥着积极作用。这与重视理性的思考方式成为主流，被认定为正统性相通的情况一脉相承，是韩国性理学派（义理学派）的特性。国难危急之时，以坚强的主体性和不屈的斗志来维护民族的自尊和正统性，冲在前线的烈士与志士们当中有许多性理学者，是一力证。特别是韩国近代思想史中，抵抗外

---

① 参照李珥：《圣学辑要》之《第五圣贤道统》。

② 户川芳郎（外）：《儒教史》，赵诚乙、李东哲（译），理论与实践出版社，1990年，第272页。

③ 《近思录》卷1，第15则：“在物为理，处物为义。”

敌侵略，倡导自主精神的春秋义理学兴起和义兵举义也很好地证明了这一点。

提到义理精神，不得不提“士人精神”。“士人”是指体现儒教理念的人格体或集团。士人摆脱追求欲望的世俗价值观，奉行以人性为基础的仁义思想。士人将儒家价值的仁义，进一步说是人的价值，看的比生命更重要。“杀身成仁”或“舍生而取义”是士人精神世界的真实写照。士人是义理精神的化身。不拘于成败，良心的指令在前，甘受任何坎坷与苦难，这就是士人的精神。朝鲜时代的士人被认为是该社会的良心，是知性人，是人格的标准，也被比喻为生命的动力——“元气”。这样的士人精神在延续国脉的过程中起到了推动作用。由此可见，朝鲜后期学者牛山安邦俊（1573－1654）在下文所说的内容非常切实。

> “节义之于国家，犹元气之于人也。人有元气，则虽甚病，不至于死。国有节义，则虽大乱，不至于亡。故国之存亡，惟在于节义之扶植如何耳。”①
>
> “夫节义国家元气，人无元气则死，国无节义则亡。是以古之创业中兴之君，莫不以褒崇节义为急先之务者，良以此也。”②
>
> “无论环境何等艰难，只要国家子民的精神尚在，国家就不会灭亡。”

这句话是所有国民应铭记于心的金言。

韩国儒学史上树立“士人意识”传统的应是圃隐郑梦周（1337－1392）。郑梦周人品高尚，学识渊博，经纶卓越，是道德、学问、功业兼备的人才。他用自己的身躯支撑着濒临灭亡的高丽王朝，恭让王四年（1392）与五百年江山社稷一起走到了生命尽头。他的牺牲是为了成全儒教中所追求的杀身成仁的大意，因此应该说他的牺牲不是殉节，而是殉道。他的精忠大节真实体现了儒教所追求的价值比生命更高贵。

曾子曾云“可以托六尺之孤，可以寄百里之命，临大节而不可夺也，君子人与，君子人也。③”此话中所说的具有卓越经纶、坚定节操的人，指的就是像郑梦周这样的人。后来郑梦周与李穑、李崇仁一起称为“丽末三隐”，备受世人推崇，成为后代学者的师表。并且在整个朝鲜时代，被视为众儒者义理精神、士人精神的表率，同时被尊为东方性理学鼻祖，他给后世带来的精神影响是巨大的。后人宋时烈在追慕郑梦周时说“先生之生，非丽氏之幸，而我朝之幸也。④”这句话值得我们回味。

2. 心性学的风气与主理论

儒学思想基本上说是重视现实的，重视人的价值与生命。为了维护人的高贵性、

---

① 《隐峰全书》卷 3，5b，《与延平李相公别纸》。

② 《隐峰全书》卷 2，28a，《言事疏》。

③ 《论语・泰伯》。

④ 《宋子大全》卷 137，6b，《圃隐先生诗集序》。

营造适合人类的社会，不断探求人的本质，并通过教育与教化使人领悟到人性本善。同时将“所有的人都可以信赖、可以教化”作为国家政策的根本，以教化为中心，并积极地反映在政治和制度上。① 儒学中的本性探究以德治主义为焦点，这与现代伦理学中探讨善恶问题存在一定的差异。朝鲜时代的性理学者对人的心性问题，尤其是善恶问题的探讨特别集中，其目的就是从个人修养进一步上升到建设德治主义和道德社会的层面。退溪李滉和栗谷李珥各自向君王呈献了《圣学十图》与《圣学辑要》，强调儒教中所说的帝王学的根本——“格君心”。朝鲜中期的“圣学”旨在培养“具备圣人之德的王者”，与心法之学相一致。帝王学从“人性教育”出发，这对只重视能力与技能的现代社会风气有着很大的启示意义。

到了朝鲜时代，韩国儒学的发展与中国有所区别，确定了韩国儒学的特殊性。16世纪以后，性理学鼎盛，从哲学、精神层面为后代留下了丰厚的财富。韩国的儒学以性理学为中心，四端七情论、人物性同异论等关于人性的论议构成主流。若用一句话来概括朝鲜儒学的特性，可以说是心学（心性之学）。

韩国性理学自16世纪以来至朝鲜末期为止，其论争贯穿了数个世纪，在学术史、理性史上留下了灿烂的一页。这在世界哲学史上也是罕见的例子。将人的问题、人的尊严性与心性修养问题作为重点研究课题，数百年间滔滔不绝地展开论辩，充分展示了韩国人的哲学头脑与力量。韩国性理学的代表学者有五位：静庵赵光祖、退溪李滉、栗谷李珥、沙溪金长生（1548－1631）、尤庵宋时烈（1607－1689），他们亦被称为五贤。近代韩国新儒家学者柳承国（1923－2011）教授将五贤尊为韩国学术史的正脉，评价说“静庵高，退溪深，栗谷正，沙溪确，尤庵大”。用一个字概括了主导朝鲜儒学史潮流、深思儒学在当时时代如何发挥技能的先儒们的学术倾向。

朝鲜时代的性理学与事实论相比，更重视价值论，主理论被视为正统。在朝鲜王朝的开创中起了主导作用，被指责为“变节汉”的郑道传（1337－1398），还有之后开创“勋旧派”先河的权近（1352－1409）都倡导主理论，可见朝鲜性理学自开创起便具有着主理性倾向。② 如果在价值论方面，将气置于理之上，那么全世界的人将无穷尽地追求本能的欲望，最终导致天理人欲颠倒，变成灭伦乱常的世界，这就是通常所说

---

① 按照从善还是从恶来看待人的本性，政治的基调也有所不同。从以对人性的信赖为基础的性善说立场上看，更注重“教化”与“事前预防”。与此相比，从怀疑性善的角度上看，必然更注重“法律”与“事后处罚”。举个例子说，“矫导所”和“刑务所”这两个名称上就反映着两者不同的见解。

② 但是即使是在主理论被认为是正统的大趋势下，各时代也都出现具有“气重视的”倾向的学者，他们为纠正以主理论为中心的学问风气所衍生或伴随出现的局限性与弊端，提供一定的哲学基础，起到了很大作用。16世纪以后具有“气重视的”倾向的栗谷学派将气与现实的变化相联系，提出了变法更张论。

的忧患意识，而朝鲜性理学的主理倾向便源于此。强烈的价值论思考也是值得与中国儒学史相比较的与众不同的一面。这与整个朝鲜时期，名分论优于实利论有着直接的关系。

本来儒学是一门哲学、伦理、道德，进一步说是与政治相结合的综合学问。特别是在性理学心性论方面的研究达到了很高的水平。在与全人教育、乃至人性教育相关的学问中，达到如此高水准并具备了一定体系的学问传统是很难找到的。儒学—性理学并不止于以个人心性修养为目标，而是通过自我省察与觉醒，与天下人沟通，实现“精神世界化”，这就是其最终的理想。在《大学》中提到“明明德于天下”时，叙述如下：

“古之欲明明德于天下者，先治其国，欲治其国者，先齐其家。”①

“明明德于天下”是指让天下所有人恢复其自然本性，按照本性而活。上述引用文以倒叙的方式对《大学》八条目进行了说明。若按照正常伦理逻辑或说明方式来推想的话，引用文中位于开头的应该是“欲平天下者”。但引用文却执意写作“欲明明德于天下者”，这是不容忽视的。这里的“明明德于天下者”不仅是点化世人内心的方法，还是通过人的本性，即内在的自我统一性，进而实现精神世界化的方法。通过恢复“人类本质的普遍性”可以营造出文明世界、大同世界，这样的境界即高深又宽广。儒学—性理学所具备的价值在当今社会值得弘扬。

## 四、结语：关于人性教育

在人类智慧并不发达的古代，圣人以堪称社会准则的教诲来规劝戒训人。之后至文明程度较低的前近代时期为止，以圣人的教诲为中心，少数的精英团体从“启蒙的”、“教化的”层面上来治理社会。如果说蕴含着宇宙原理的是“太极”，那么包含着人类世界标准的是“人极”，帝王的大中至正的标准则是“黄极”。前近代时期的政治始于制定“极”（标准，standard）。在文明程度较高的当今民主时代，过去的权威主义标准是行不通的。这是一个“价值观多样化的时代”，但是由于价值观的多样化引发出一系列众多的冲突也是事实。由此我们深深感觉到对韩国传统思想，尤其是对韩国儒学思想价值进行再发掘的必要性。

东洋思想和学问其自身也可以称得上是人性教育，故与人性教育有机地结合，以学习做人为根本，以哲学和伦理为中心。这与以心理学为中心的西欧人性教育存在一定的差异。在东洋的传统里，自创造了人类赖以生存的社会，便开始重视人性教育，

---

① 《大学》，第一章。

这个传统已经绵绵不断延续了数千年。特别是代表儒教哲学的性理学，作为一门关注心性问题的学问，旨在恢复人的自我本性（复其初），率真而活。

韩国儒学的特性从重视人的思想与义理思想、士人精神、重视共同体的精神中均可找到。这种不偏重于某一方面的教育，培养德智体兼备的人才教育，就是全人教育，可谓是韩国的悠久传统，在当今社会也值得提倡。我们的思想传统、教育传统有着悠久的历史和完整的体系。随着西欧实用主义、新自由主义教育的失败，我们的思想传统及教育传统的价值受到关注。正所谓“水不洗水”，用西欧思想去消除西欧教育思想所导致的弊端，这是很难的。

切切实实地实行人性教育，即便从现在开始也为时不晚。东洋思想，尤其是韩国儒学思想传统的特性相信在人性教育中能够得以充分发挥，在确立主体意识方面也会发挥显而易见的作用。韩国儒学的传统本身就是人性教育，如今对其进行重新认识比以往任何时代都显得更为迫切。

# 儒学在印尼的发展

印度尼西亚华裔总会 马咏南

## 一、儒学的兴起

18世纪初，在印尼传播的“儒学”不是直接由中国传来的，而是由在印尼土生的华人把英文版和荷兰文版的“四书五经”翻译成马来由文，即印尼土生华人日常用的交际语言，以后马来由文也成为印尼的官方语。

根据荷兰统治者之一官员 Dr. F. De. Haan 之调查，1729 年在巴达维亚（印尼首都雅加达之古称）已有私孰，教土生华人子弟背诵四书五经，是用福建方言来念，开办私孰者是祖籍福建的土生华人。当时统治印尼的荷兰东印度公司委派有势力的华人当买办，来管理华人事务和税收，处理事务的地点叫作“公馆”，由“公馆”按照旧礼节来负责红白喜事及人们的日常生活，儒学守旧派的繁文缛节，让人不胜其烦。

1753 年，“公馆”开办私塾“养济院”，当时也有荷兰儿童学习，后因管理不善而停办。

1787 年，雅加达公馆有几个“雷特南”头衔的华人领袖在雅加达寺庙“金德院”开办义学，叫作“明德书院”，其经费由公馆负担。教材是四书五经，师资不良，学生念了五六年，还不能书写简单的书信，书院渐渐没落。

## 二、儒学的改革

1897 年，印尼儒学主要人物李金福写有关孔子的书《华人的宗教》，他虽然不会中文，但是他精通荷兰文、马来由文，因为他只受荷兰教会学校之教育。他对于儒家思想的了解是通过西方书籍认识的。另外还有土生华人陈银忠和游再祥用马来由文出版《大学》和《中庸》，游再祥还办了《理报》，专门宣扬孔子学说，上述《华人的宗教》就是于 1903 年发表于《理报》，内容如下：

“宗教是一种活着的人与死人的灵魂相互沟通的风俗习惯。所以，宗教是文化的一部分。真正的华人文化存在于四书与孝经，即孔子的学说。因此，华人的宗教包含在孔子的学说，这是华人文化的主要源泉。

文化是发展的，宗教也不例外。孔子学说后来与其他宗教学说渗合在一起，例如道教与佛教。许多在中国的中国人相信这三种宗教，但是在荷属印尼的华族，除了相信上述三教外，也相信回教。然而，孔教仍然是华人文化中最主要的成分。所以，在荷属印尼的华人有义务遵循孔子的教义。

孔子并没有为人类创自己的条规，但是他引用了古代圣贤的学说，才创出了许多教条。凡是孔教的信徒，都要遵守这些教条。

孔子相信“天”，“天”是万物的主宰，他拜“天”，而“天”就好像是生者的先父。信封孔教就要祭拜天或天公。向天求保佑或求天赐福，是被允许的，但是必须从简。“天”有无限权力，而且知道人类的一切。“天”存在每一个地方。但“天”是公正的，完美的，也是慈悲的。孔子自己也拜“天”。当他生病时，他的弟子要为他祷告。他对她们说，他已经向“天”祈祷了一个很长的时间。

拜“天”，人们就得检点行为，做应该做的事。他必须热爱自己的父母，因为父母被当成“天”的代表，也是人类自己的代表。

孔子要我们“孝顺”。“孝道”是孟子所发扬光大的，孟子受业于孔伋（子思）的门人，子思是孔子的孙子。(出于《史记·孟子荀卿列传》)

孔子并没有谈及人死后的世界，但很明显地，他相信灵魂的存在。他甚至要人们尊敬灵魂。有些灵魂，同某个家庭有关系，那么，那家庭中还活着的成员，就必须祭祀它。

作为祭祀的一部分，必须准备好祭品，因为祖先的灵魂要享受这些祭品。人们必须祭祀他们祖先的灵魂，因为这是孝子所应该做的。然而，祭祀祖先的灵魂应该只限于家庭的成员。一个人不应该祭祀那些与自己的家庭没有关系的灵魂。

1900年，印尼土生华人成立了“巴达维亚中华会馆”，取代了儒学守旧派的“公馆”。中华会馆的章程明文说明：“它旨在改变华人的风俗习惯，使人能与圣人孔子的原则相配合，以便有文明的举动，同时，也促进对中国语言文化的知识。”把守旧的儒学和礼教进行大改革，把那些烦琐的婚礼、落伍的丧礼等改革。

1901年，为了宣扬新文明的儒学，改良派于1901年成立了“中华学堂”，第一任校长是闽籍卢桂芳，他仿效日本华侨办的新学校，以浅显易懂的汉语作为小学课本，使学生感兴趣和读书有进步。

1903年中国改良派康有为逃难到印尼爪哇岛，他鼓吹维新思想，大大的鼓励印尼土生华人对儒学的改革。

1907年，儒学改良派在爪哇岛许多县城都纷纷成立了“中华学堂”，5月5日，成立了爪哇华侨学务总会。

另外，受中国流亡到海外展开革命活动的革命派影响，唤醒了新客华人之民族觉醒，新客华人是指那些从中国来的新移民，未被侨居地同化的华侨，他们是清末时候或民国初期，因为列强入侵中国，军阀割据混战，中国连年战祸，民不聊生，只好当契约华工移民到海外。这些革命人士，成为新客华人的领袖。他们都是属于印尼儒学改良派的先锋。

1911 年 6 月在中爪哇三宝垄创办第一所华侨中学。

## 三、儒学的两派分化

1911 年孙中山先生领导辛亥革命，并成立了中国民国，鼓励了新客华人，成为改良派的中坚分子，他们控制了中华学堂。这些新客华人在二十年代末期把孔子思想和学说从章程中取消。而那些土生华人因为不懂得中文，无法操纵中华学堂，他们就把儒学转变为儒教，后来又把儒教改名为孔教。

1923 年，在万隆成立了孔教总会，土生华人社群的宗教信仰也开始多元化了。

1934 年，郭德怀先生成立了“三教会”，即儒、道、佛三合一的宗教。

1949 年，中华人民共和国成立，影响了印尼的中华学校分成左右两派。左派是倾向于中华人民共和国，右派是倾向于中华民国。右派学校仍教儒学，宣扬四维八德这些儒家思想，直到 1958 年，因台湾支持印尼反革命，使得右派学校、报纸和社团被禁。而左派学校，就宣扬民主和科学，“打倒孔家店”。

1955 年，土生华人为了“纯化”孔教，重新组织印尼孔教联合会，易名为“印尼孔教中央理事会”。华侨大学王爱平教授曾经深入研究印尼的孔教，在其著作《印度尼西亚孔教研究》中写道：印尼孔教源于中国的儒学，是印尼土生华人特有的宗教形式与文化认同标志。中国儒学在印尼的传播最初主要是通过华人家庭教育、庙堂、宗教祭祀及私塾、书院的文化教育。

## 四、儒学发展陷入低谷

1965 年，印尼发生“九卅事变”，苏加诺被迫下台，新政权由军人垄断。军人政府反共和仇视华人，所以 1966 年封闭了全印尼的华校、华报、华社，连土生华人所成立的社会组织“印尼国籍协商会”及其教育机构“共和大学”、“国籍协商会”全遭封闭，因“国籍协商会”被诬蔑成印共属下组织。

1967 年，苏哈托第 14 号总统令，禁止华文汉字在公共场合使用，也禁止支那宗教风俗习惯。印尼孔教为了求生存，和配合印尼政府对宗教信仰的规定。所谓宗教，必须有圣者，圣经，圣地。所以“印尼孔教中央理事会”决定印尼孔教制度化，和定下祈祷时的各种仪式。孔教的圣者是孔子，圣经是《四书》，圣地是有安放孔子像的礼堂。

1969年，印尼军人政府为了防止印共复活，不容许无神论者存立于印尼，提倡宗教的重要性和必要性，故政府颁布在印尼有六大宗教：回教、天主教、基督教、巴厘印度教、佛教、孔教。由于中华学校遭关闭，华人子弟多数就读于天主教、基督教学校，少部分进入孔教和佛教学校，因为基督教会校风严格，程度高，同时，有强制性规定，学生必须上基督教课，如不及格则留级。作为佛教和孔教的家长，也必须签字同意孩子接受基督教教义，渐渐地，华人子弟改变了宗教信仰，而佛教、孔教开办的学校因师资力量薄弱，素质较差，设施简陋，学生多数为中下层华人子弟，所以学生人数逐年下降，甚至有贫穷华人子弟生转校公立回教学校。而那些受过华校教育的新客华人，认为孔教是不伦不类的宗教，形成对儒学的偏见和对其影响力的冲击，自此，印尼儒学只好在逆境中求存，自生自灭。

## 五、儒学的复兴和历史的期望

自中国与印尼于1950年4月13日建交。后1965年印尼发生“9・30事件”后，两国于1967年10月30日中断外交关系，从此进入长达三十多年的冷冻期。直到1990年8月8日，李鹏总理访问印尼期间，两国外长分别代表本国政府签署《关于恢复外交关系的谅解备忘录》，宣布自当日起正式恢复两国外交关系，印尼的儒学复兴初现一丝曙光。

旧华校的师生纷纷成立校友会和基金会，他们当中很多是经商成功的儒商，同时，90年代亚洲经济“四小龙”，即日本、韩国、台湾地区、新加坡，经济能够腾飞，是因为“四小龙”的企业家接受“中华文化圈”的教育和影响，其中儒学思想和伦理影响最深，亦受此影响，印尼的儒商去新加坡国立大学商学院进修中文现代管理课程，自1982年到1997年，就有400多名前往进修，他们于1987年成立国大商学院中文校友会，限于当时印尼政府禁止华文在公共场合使用，只好以基金会的形式在1992年成立印尼国民福利基金会，并推动和组团华校师生去新加坡参加汉语水平考试，考虑到基金会的安全，遂又于1993年成立东方语言文化中心，借此来推动印尼华文教育的复兴。

1997年4月11日到15日，印尼儒商前往新加坡参加第二届世界儒商文学研讨会，校友会与基金会紧密结合在一起，合作推广印尼的华文教育的复兴。

1998年，统治印尼的军人政权下台，2000年瓦希德总统取消对华文之禁令，使儒商们可以名正言顺和印尼文教部一起推广华文教育，支持华文教育协调机构，同时，儒商们也开办三语学校。当年，在国大商学院中文校友会的力荐下，由吴永嘉，吴宗盛，马咏南邀请台湾的王财贵教授来雅加达讲解儒学教育的重要性。王财贵教授认为“‘流传千古’的经典，‘流传千年’的教育，古今中外的贤明，皆由经典教育而来。”希望儒学的复兴从学习《大学》《中庸》《论语》《孟子》四书开始，但因为印尼华文长达 32 年的教育断层，和自 1949 年左派教育的影响，华文水平也大幅度降低，白话文尚未精通，更不要说晦涩深奥的文言文，因此旧华校的师生对儒学深感陌生，要求王财贵教授由浅入深辅导儒学的学习，而不是要求的从少儿时期就开始读《论语》《大学》，王财贵教授勉为其难，只好同意由浅入深，从《弟子规》《千字文》《三字经》开始，逐渐过渡到四书的学习，从此，印尼的三语学校普推《弟子规》的学习，并以其作为招生宣传。

除了学校教育推广《弟子规》，印尼佛教净宗协会也大力培养《弟子规》师资，和翻译印刷其印尼文版，免费赠送给各界人士，包括回教习经院，也认可印尼文版《弟子规》是一部很好的道德教育书籍。另外，印尼华裔总会属下的印华妇女会也积极参加经典华文教育，以下为参加经典华文教育的历程：

2004 年 7 月 4 日至 6 日，参加在香港举办的第一届全球中华文化诵读大会，届时，印华妇女会唯一参加者居士马咏南见证北京 4 岁小男孩背诵《大学》，高雄 4 岁小孩背诵《中庸》，自此才信服王财贵教授提倡的少儿经典教育；

2005 年 7 月 27 日至 31 日，参加在北京举办的第二届中华文化经典诵读大会，雅加达必利达二校师生也赴北京参加诵读大会，参加人数为 11 人，从此以后，印尼的三语学校开始以必利达Ⅱ校为榜样，推广《弟子规》教育和交流。

2006 年 8 月 7 日至 11 日，参加在台北举办的第三届中华文化经典诵读大会，印华妇女会和必利达Ⅱ校参加人数共为 19 人，为历届人数之最。当年，由必利达Ⅱ校表演的《经典文化传遍全世界》节目在大会获得一致好评。

2007 年 7 月 14 日至 17 日，参加第四届中华文化经典诵读大会，会场分为香港会场，印华妇女会有 6 人参加；深圳会场，必利达Ⅱ校有 9 人参加。

2011 年 1 月，印华总会和印尼净宗协会联举办“中华传统文化企业家论坛”，希望加深对中华文化的了解，建立信心，传承中华传统文化，完善自我，振兴事业，并且确实落实个人的社会责任，成就美满人生。印华总会特派印华妇女会负责参与整个论坛活动。

第五届全球中华文化经典诵读大会自 2008 年不见举行，印华妇女一年又一年等待着，从焦急盼望到渐渐淡忘，突然 2011 年 6 月 28 日接到香港国际经典文化协会主席温金海先生传来的电邮和第五届全球中华文化经典诵读大会的通知。鉴于雅加达“必利达学校”师生于 7 月 10 日至 20 日去柳州参加夏令营，无法参加上述大会，另请已 86

次推广《弟子规》讲座的杨瑞旭老师出席上述盛会，无奈杨老师抽不出时间来，而《印尼中华国学研究社》社长吴宗胜先生也刚从香港回来，不便出国，只好由马咏南单独赴会。

2011年7月15日至18日，参加在湖南长沙举办的第五届中华文化经典诵读大会，印华妇女会由马咏南前往，而且还参加北京市延庆县，于从7月18日至8月18日举办的第二届“相约论语一百”的开幕礼。共约有800人参加为期一个月的活动，借用王财贵博士的话：“是闭关自修30天”，马咏南看到许多大学生热衷于学习《论语》，受到极大的鼓舞。

2013年7月12日至16日，参加在山东曲阜，孔子故乡举办的第六届中华文化经典诵读大会，此时印华妇女会参加人数才又恢复到常态，印华妇女会4人参加，必利达Ⅱ校12人参加。当年，必利达Ⅱ校表演了《经典牵动印尼情》的节目，受到广泛好评。

2014年4月18日至22日，参加在台湾高雄佛光山举办的第七届中华文化经典诵读大会，印华妇女会10人参加。来自海内外的近七千人齐聚佛光山于开幕典礼当日共同诵读了《弟子规》、《论语》、《老子》等中华经典，并举行多场经典与教育研讨会。

印尼三语学校师生对中国文化经典诵读大会的积极参与，反映了儒学文化的复苏，也扩大了儒学文化在印尼的影响，这个历程波澜曲折，尽管有外力及国际环境的冲击和影响，印尼的儒学文化的复苏仍然如星星之火可以燎原，是历史的潮流和时代需要。

## 六、总结

发扬推广儒学，可以通过很多途径：

（一）通过学校和学术机构，虽然印尼华文教育断层32年，儒学学者、专家人数并不多，且这条路并不那么容易走，但是只要愿意播下儒学的种子，势必会破土而出，生根发芽，茁壮成长。

（二）使用宗教的形式，即儒、道、佛三合一体，这条路更容易普及和推广华文教育，进一步提高华语水平，让更多人一起学习，会说、看得懂、能写华文，以便弘扬经典教育。

（三）由华校校友会的儒商来推广儒学，回馈社会，请儒商们开办平民化的三语学校，加强《弟子规》的教育和实践，扩大受教育者的人群。

学习儒学，《论语》强调“理之用，和为贵”。《中庸》指出“以中为用，凡事发乎‘中和’，取乎折衷，将心比心”，和谐社会不远矣。《大学》讲“诚心正意”，心诚求之，虽终不成亦为美矣。

中国历史上的各派思想家都重视孝道，儒家尤其强调“百善孝为先”。《论语》言曰：“孝悌乃仁之根本”，一个人倘若连父母亲人都不能善待，又怎能指望他把爱心“推己及人”？推崇孝悌之义，弘扬儒学思想，经典是亘古不变的道理，是古今中外的人们永久遵循的常理、原则。儒学经典乃中华文化瑰宝，诵读经典，学习儒学，这对疗治现代世风日下，人心不古，道德沦丧的社会普遍现象具有积极的作用。

印尼的儒学文化发展虽历经沧桑，但其强大的生命力和普世价值，正如“传承中华美德，培育民族精神，功在当代，利在千秋”，是中华文明薪火相传的钥匙，使中华文明昂首屹立于世界民族之林！

附：《经典寄语》

经典

经典是各民族文化的根本，是全人类文明智慧的结晶，经典所蕴含者乃常理常道，“经也者恒久之至道，不刊之鸿教也”（《文心雕龙》），“天经地义”之“常理常道”便是“经”字本义，因此，经典乃文化之宝藏，其价值历久而弥新，人类任何一个文化系统均有其永恒不朽的经典作为源头活水，它博造文化，推动历史、取之不尽，用之不竭。

文化

人类因文化而文明，文名因文化而传承，文化，乃人类生活之特征。“经典文化”凝聚着全人类最优秀的精神财富，是人类的智慧之果，是人类的精神之花，它承载历史，传承文明，养育人类，与个人乃成人之本，与民族乃民族之魂，与国家乃立国之基，“国者，人之聚；人者，心之器，”吾之人“心”，浸润于文化，藉文化而养育，故国家、民族、社会、个人，皆以文化为根本。

教育

目前举世的教育模式皆偏重于知识和技能的传授，却缺乏文化的熏陶与人格的养育，及早让儿童诵读中西文化经典，接受传统优秀文化的熏习，即是让他在心灵最纯净、记忆力最佳的黄金时期（13岁以前），接触最具智慧和价值的文化宝藏，在他幼小的心灵中潜移默化，“以文而化”，逐渐培植起福德、开启其智慧，从而奠定他一生的高远见识和优美人格，经典遂成为他一生开智、受益、励志、成长的源泉。

# 印尼孔教：中国儒学的宗教化、印尼化

华侨大学 王爱平 鲁锦寰

印尼孔教源于中国儒学，以孔子学说（儒学）为宗教信仰，是印尼一部分土生华人特有的宗教形式与文化认同标志。[①] 作为印尼的一个“Agama”（宗教，印尼语），印尼孔教目前是与伊斯兰教、基督教、天主教、佛教和印度教并列的印尼六大宗教之一。

近年我们采取历史学、人类学和宗教学相结合的研究方法对印尼孔教进行研究，多次深入印尼进行田野调查，广泛搜集各种形式的研究资料，将搜集、分析文献资料与参与观察、深入访谈相结合，在尽可能了解印尼华人社会、历史与文化的基础上考察印尼孔教，力图对印尼孔教进行较为全面、深入的考察研究。[②] 在此研究基础上试将其归纳为：印尼孔教是源于中国儒学而在印尼发展起来的制度化宗教；或可以表述为，印尼孔教是中国儒学的宗教化、印尼化或本土化。[③]

20世纪以来，尤其是近二十多年来，中国学术界对儒教是教非教问题的激烈争论中一个十分关键的问题，即宗教的定义和标准问题。儒教的最大特点，就是它并非像西方基督教教会组织那样的“制度宗教”，这是讨论中各种不同观点者一致的认识。但是，源于中国儒学/儒教的印尼孔教显现出不同于中国儒教的制度型宗教的特征。本文所称之儒教是中国文化传统中与佛、道并存的“儒教”；题目中“宗教化”之宗教则是以基督教为代表的“religion”为定义标准。

所谓制度型宗教（InstitutionaI reIigeon）与弥散型宗教（Diffused reIigion）是根据宗教的组织程度与特性来区分的。美籍华裔社会学家杨庆堃受宗教社会学家瓦赫

① 参见（新加坡）廖建裕：《现阶段的印尼孔教》，见《现阶段的印尼华人族群》，新加坡国立大学中文系、八方文化企业公司联合出版，2002年；王爱平：《印度尼西亚孔教研究》结论部分，中国文史出版社，2010年。

② 笔者的调查研究，得到印尼孔教最高理事会及其地方组织和许多印尼华人及团体各方面的支持与帮助，谨在此表示衷心的感谢。

③ 参见王爱平：《印度尼西亚孔教研究》结论部分，中国文史出版社，2010年；王爱平：《组织与制度：印印度尼西亚孔教制度化的表征》，《文史哲》2008（3）。

(Wach）的影响，对此作了深入的阐述，并将其运用于对中国宗教的研究而闻名于西方。他指出，在中国，制度型宗教的主要代表包括佛教和道教；弥散型宗教则主要指祖先崇拜、社区神崇拜以及伦理—政治神崇拜。[①]

台湾著名人类学家李亦园在大量田野调查、实证研究的基础上也采用了这一分析框架，而称之为“制度化宗教”和“普化宗教”。“制度化宗教”是指“有严格的教堂组织，严谨的宗教执事，有明显的经典，同样有明显的教义，而宗教事务跟一般的日常生活分开”，如天主教、基督教、伊斯兰教、佛教、道教和其他有组织的宗教。“普化宗教”则是指“宗教信仰扩散到我们生活的各方面，跟我们日常生活密切地联系在一起，但是没有形成一个有组织的制度，同时跟日常生活密不可分，没有明显教会组织、经典教义等的一种信仰仪式”，如祖先崇拜、风水测算等中国民间的信仰和仪式。[②]传统中国宗教的一项重要特色就是表现在“普化的宗教”的形态，而与一般西方宗教的“制度化的宗教”有异。

中国宗教学家吕大吉提出“宗教要素说”，认为宗教须具备宗教的观念或思想；宗教的感情或体验；宗教的行为或活动；宗教的组织和制度四种基本因素，[③] 被认为是尤其适宜用来分析各种发展完善的宗教，即所谓“制度化宗教”。

按照上述宗教学、人类学的有关理论，制度化宗教必须具有：宗教组织和制度；宗教经典和较完整的神学或哲学、伦理体系；明确、固定的祭祀礼拜场所；系统、规范的宗教仪式；约束信徒的教规或戒律等。我们将以此作为把握一个宗教的具体维度，来考察印尼孔教发展的历史；并注意把印尼孔教置于印尼社会特定的环境中，置于印尼华人一个世纪以来的发展脉络中进行考察。

## 一、印尼孔教的缘起与发展历史

据目前所掌握的资料，印尼孔教源于中国儒学/儒教，形成于19世纪中晚期。孔教在印尼，自有较具规模的正式组织算起，至少已有100余年的历史。印尼孔教的形成与发展，大致可以分为以下五个阶段：

（一）印尼孔教的缘起与形成（华人移居印尼——19世纪末）

印尼孔教源于中国儒学儒教缘起于由印尼华人所承载的中国儒学/儒教在印尼的传

---

① C. K. Yang：Religion in Chinese Society：A Study of Contemporary Social Functions of Religion and some of Their Historical Factors，pp20—21，294—295.

② 李亦园：《宗教、仪式与象征》，载马戎、周星编：《田野工作与文化自觉》（上），群言出版社，1998年，第282页。

③ 吕大吉：《宗教学通论新编》，中国社会科学出版社，1998年，第76页。

播；形成于19世纪中晚期，印尼华人民族意识觉醒，开始有目的的维护华人文化传统之时。

中国儒学/儒教在印尼的传播由来已久，是伴随着华人移居印尼开始的。最初主要是通过华人的家庭教育和庙堂宗祠的祭祀以及私塾、书院的文化教育。

19世纪中晚期，随着印尼华人民族意识的觉醒，印尼华人开始有目的的维护华人文化传统。当时华人团体为了阻止华人被同化，开始建立公共宗祠和丧葬组织，在祭祖、婚丧仪式、妇女着装等方面着力恢复华人传统习俗。同时把儒学经书由中文翻译成马来文，或从荷兰文、英文翻译成马来文而且把经书原文改写成“口语”（白话文）。这一时期，《论语》、《大学》、《中庸》都被翻译。

特别是早在19世纪80年代在印尼第二大城市东爪哇首府泗水（soerabaja）出现了孔诞纪年的使用。这一切都早在康有为到印尼之前以及戊戌变法之前。

（二）从中华会馆到孔教会、孔教总会（1900－1945荷兰殖民统治时期）

1900年巴达维亚中华会馆成立，这是第一个正式的公开的孔教组织。公开宣称“要以圣人孔子学说为指导改进华人的风俗习惯要进行孔教的教育，要推广华人学习中国语言文化”。

此前在泗水已经建立了亚洲最大规模的文庙，并成立了孔教组织“斯文会”。

1923年印尼各地的孔教会联合成立了印尼孔教总会。

（三）从闽南语的“孔教会”到印尼语的“宗教”（Agama）（1945—1978）

1945年印尼独立以后，1955年在梭罗重新成立了印尼孔教联合会，这就是现在印尼孔教最高理事会的前身。

1965年苏加诺总统发布第一号总统法令，宣布孔教与伊斯兰教、基督教、天主教、佛教和印度教并列为印尼六大合法宗教之一，政府给予资助。苏加诺总统当时是把孔教当作印尼土生华人的宗教，他认为印尼土生华人已经成为印尼国家民族的一部分。

1965年9.30事件后苏哈托执政，最初对宗教采取利用的政策，宣布承认苏加诺总统的1965年一号法令。

（四）为争取合法宗教地位而斗争的印尼孔教（1978－1998）

苏哈托政府对华人实行强制同化政策，并很明确地把清除华人的文化特性作为其同化政策的重点，源于中国儒学/儒教的孔教被认为是阻碍华人同化的力量。自1978年开始，苏哈托政府不承认孔教为合法宗教，对孔教从各方面进行打压。宗教部、内政部、教育部发布一系列法令，身份证上不得登记宗教信仰为孔教，学校里的孔教宗教课被取消，政府不再承认孔教主持的结婚仪式和注册等等。孔教面临着生死存亡的严重考验。

此后直到1998年的20年间，印尼孔教顶住了各方面的压力，他们以有关法律为依据，一直坚持宗教活动，使得许多年轻人仍然有机缘接触孔教，加入孔教。

目前孔教年轻一代的领导人和骨干，如现任总主席黄耀德，前任总主席、现孔教总会主席团秘书长黄金泉（Candra setiawan），前任总主席陈清明（Budi. S. Tanuwibowo），雅加达西区孔教会主席罗伟源（Januardi. S. E）都是那一时期加入孔教的。

（五）孔教争取恢复合法地位获得成功并有较大发展时期（1998年——至今）

1998年苏哈托下台不久，印尼孔教即不失时机地召开了第13届全国代表大会。自2000年开始，先后有印尼三任总统瓦希德总统、梅加瓦蒂总统和苏西洛总统每年都参加孔教的新年（华人新年——春节）庆祝活动，他们以此表示对华人的态度和政策。梅加瓦蒂总统更把春节定为全国公共假日。到2006年上半年，在苏西洛总统命令下，印尼宗教部、内政部和教育部都发布有关文件，最终解决了印尼孔教的法律地位问题。

目前印尼政府的高层领导对印尼孔教都很重视，2007年11月第四届国际儒学研讨会暨首届世界孔教国际研讨会在雅加达召开，印尼宗教部长和宪法院院长亲自出席致辞祝贺。

印尼孔教和伊斯兰教等也都保有友好和谐的关系。

印尼孔教分布已由爪哇扩展到廖内、西加等外岛。印尼孔教的中央组织、地方组织及其机构、制度等也在进一步完善。

## 二、印尼孔教是制度型宗教，是中国儒学/儒教的宗教化

近20多年来，中国国内关于儒学是教非教的讨论与争论十分激烈，不过大家公认的是：我们是以西方宗教学关于制度型宗教的定义作为判断宗教的标准。

那么即使按照西方宗教学关于制度型宗教的定义、标准来看，印尼孔教是制度型的宗教也应是无疑义的。在这一点上，印尼孔教明显与中国儒教（儒学、儒家）不同，印尼孔教是中国儒学的宗教化。

首先，印尼孔教有系统的宗教教义体系：印尼孔教的教义就是孔子思想。

其次，印尼孔教有自己的宗教经典——也就是儒学经典《四书五经》。孔教徒每周做礼拜时都要携带孔教的圣经《四书》。

第三，印尼孔教有规定教规：八诚箴规等等。

第四，印尼孔教有自己专门的宗教活动场所：泗水文庙、分布在印尼各地的孔教“礼堂”、三教会庙宇里面的孔圣神坛，等等。孔教将宗教活动场所称为“礼堂”凸显了儒教重“礼”的特点，明显有别于基督教的“教堂”。

第五，印尼孔教有教徒——印尼孔教总会估计，全印尼大约在400万以上，印尼孔教总会认为，凡是敬天、拜祖先、尊孔者都被承认为孔教徒。

第六，印尼孔教有比较完整的宗教组织及制度。

印尼孔教有它的中央组织（印尼孔教最高理事会、主席团、宣道师委员会）和地方组织（孔教会、孔教宣道会、孔教青年会、三教会的孔教组织、大学生孔教组织、华人庙宇等）。印尼孔教每四年召开一次全国代表大会，选举最高理事会、主席团、宣道师委员会。现任最高理事会、主席团、宣道师委员会是在2010年11月举行的全国代表大会上选举产生的。

印尼孔教有专门的教职人员（神职人员），并实行教阶制度，分为三级：学师、文师和教生，学师为最高级。其名称充分表明了重教、重“师”的儒家传统。

第七，印尼孔教有一整套系统的宗教仪式体系，包括有：

（1）礼敬仪式。

（2）礼拜宣道仪式。印尼孔教每周都有礼拜宣道仪式：孔教礼堂摆着一排排椅凳，上面放置着《四书》《圣歌集》等，每逢星期天要举行礼拜仪式，读经、讲道和唱歌。

（3）祭祀仪式：包括祭天仪式、祭孔仪式、祭神仪式、祭祖仪式。

（4）人生仪式：包括出生仪式、命名仪式、成人仪式等；婚姻仪式；丧葬仪式；宣誓就职仪式，等等。

印尼孔教的崇拜对象及信仰体系分为四大类：天；圣人孔子；神明和祖先。最核心的部分可以认为是闽粤民间信仰体系的架构。

印尼孔教把中国传统的岁时节庆的主要节日几乎全部纳入仪式体系（元宵、端午、中秋、冬至等），这些节日也就是孔教的宗教节日。

印尼孔教把孔子自述人生修学成长的各个阶段都纳入了仪式体系，如三十而立仪式等，笔者将其命名为“修学成长仪式”。

总之，印尼孔教制度化的特征是十分明显的。具体来说，制度化宗教一定具有宗教组织和制度、宗教经典和较完整的神学或哲学、伦理体系、有专职的教职人员和教阶制度，有明确的、固定的祭祀礼拜的场所，有系统的规范的宗教仪式，有约束信徒的教规或戒律等。

印尼孔教拥有自己的基本观念和自己的结构体系，即拥有自身的神学、仪式和组织系统，它独立于其他建制的宗教，作为一种独立的社会系统发挥功能。印尼孔教的组织制度经过多年以来的建设是比较完备的，它有着全国性的中央组织和各种类型的地方组织，并形成自己的体制与运作模式。孔教有自己的宗教经典——“四书五经”；制定有比较详尽的各方面的教规；设有专职的教职人员及其组织和教阶制度；有固定的祭祀礼拜的场所——礼堂、文庙以及祭孔的华人庙宇；有系统的规范的宗教仪式，等等。

从孔教的组织形式来看，俨然是十分现代化的社会组织，但是又突出了它的宗教性，其中有专门的教职人员组织，自成系统而且教职人员组织的最高首领不需选举，自然成为印尼孔教最高理事会主席团成员和副总主席。另外，承认不同形式的孔教徒，包括没有加入孔教会的孔教徒，这是从印尼的实际情况出发而定的。

## 三、印尼孔教是中国儒学/儒教的印尼化（本土化）

（一）印尼孔教源于中国儒学/儒教，是以制度化宗教的形式传承中国儒学

从基本教义来看，印尼孔教的教义承继了源于中国的儒学及孔子学说。基本教义是一种宗教的基本成分，这些基本成分可以跨越时间和空间，超越派别，始终被认为是宗教的精髓。虽然可能对教义有不同的理解与解释，但总有能达成共识的基本教义。

印尼孔教的教义基本上是遵照孔子学说、儒学的四书五经而来的。印尼孔教明确规定，以“四书”为主，以“五经”为基。教义基本上是用四书五经来阐述的。如孔教对天、天道、天命；天与圣人、与孔教、与人的关系；以及“五常”（仁、义、礼、智、信）、五伦关系基本上是按照四书五经来阐述的，也体现出中国儒教尤重伦理道德，或说是伦理化的特点。当然，作为一种制度化的宗教，印尼孔教的阐述比较强调“天道”和“神性”，更注重儒教宗教性的表述。另外，虽然大多数情况下是用印尼语来表述的，运用四书五经的原文很少，但翻译中出现的差异尚未影响到对孔子学说、儒学基本理论的理解与奉行。

值得一提的是，从印尼孔教的教义、宗教观念、崇拜对象、信仰体系及仪式的程式等来看，不仅源自正统的中国儒教，而且大量的属于中国闽粤地区民间宗教信仰的内容。如果说中国儒家文化可分为国家层面、士大夫层面的“大传统”和民间“小传统”的话，印尼孔教是将中国儒家文化的“大传统”和“小传统”都结合在一起的。

印尼孔教的崇拜对象及信仰体系明显地、较多地吸纳了民间“小传统”的内容。其崇拜对象及信仰体系可分为四大类：天；圣人孔子；神明和祖先。信仰体系中最核心的部分，实际上就是闽粤（其中可能主要是闽南地区）民间信仰体系的构架，这个体系以“天公”为最高神祇，下面各种神明各司其职，有土地神、灶神，还有许多人神，伏羲、周文王、周公、关公、屈原，孔圣人也是一位人神。另还有祖先和鬼魂。当然也赋予孔教新的诠释。同时，孔教的祭祀礼仪，从祭祀时间的确定，祭品、祭礼及程序，礼敬的姿势和祭礼上以及日常进行的“点香”礼仪等，基本与中国闽粤民间社会文化传统类同。尤其是将中国民间传统岁时节庆的主要节日几乎全部纳入仪式体系，作为孔教祭祀的宗教节日，这对于华族文化的传承与认同、对于华族身份的保留影响甚大。

孔教信仰体系中有很多象征和有意义的组合。在孔教的“八诚箴规”中有“诚敬

鬼神”的教规，但是在孔教的制度与规范中没有明确的把所有信仰的神祇全部公布出来，明文规定的重大节日的祭祀对象，除了“天”，只有土地神、灶神以及人神屈原。这可能是由于处在印尼，必须按照印尼国家所规定的宗教“一神论”的标准，即信仰唯一的独一无二的上帝，所以不宜公开明确地将太多的中国传统神祇纳入孔教祭祀体系，但实际上对中国传统神祇，尤其是人神尊崇有加，人神的标准仍然是按照儒学之道、孔子学说、《礼记》。同时重要的是谨遵孔子的教导“敬鬼神而远之”。

从组织上看，印尼孔教的许多地方组织及礼堂都设立在三教会之中，设立在华人庙宇之中如说泗水北极庙、玛琅永安宫、杜板关圣庙等等，印尼华人的庙大多数是三教合一的庙，三教的标志是木铎（儒教）、太极图（道教）、卍字符（佛教），所祭拜的是孔子、老子、观音菩萨或释迦牟尼。他们可以在这些庙宇中举行孔教的仪式，而与其他的宗教仪式相安无事。

但实际上所祭拜的还有许多人神。如列入中国古代国家祭祀大典，又从闽粤民间社会传如东南亚，在印尼华人中一向有崇高威望的人神关羽，印尼华人称他为关公、关圣。《规范》在孔教徒任公务员宣誓就职仪式中提到，可以拜关公。在西爪哇丹格朗的孔教礼堂中，中间立有孔子的塑像，左右两边一边是土地神，一边是关公。这样供奉关公的礼堂还有很多。关公被视为孔教的神，这在孔教看来，似乎是不言而喻的，当我问及为什么，他们回答说关公是忠义的代表人物，这正是孔子所提倡的；也有的说因为关公也读春秋，也有的说中国古代的皇帝，官府都祭拜关公。在印尼严厉禁止孔教活动、禁止公开拜孔子的地方，他们就以拜关公所代替。当泗水孔教会的主席傅孙铭、布迪和戴德龙到法庭诉讼时，法庭不许拜孔子他们就以拜关公代替。这一是因为印尼的法律规定若担任公务员以及政府的工作，或在法庭上诉讼作证的时候都必须以宗教名义起誓；二是他们也需要从自己的宗教信仰中获得勇气和信心。看来，一些宗教行为实际上也是孔教在恶劣环境下的一种生存策略。

再如祭孔。孔教的《圣歌》集收入了列入国家祭祀大典的中国孔庙的祭孔礼乐——《大成乐章》，但是长期未使用过（可以确知的是近五十年来没使用过），虽然每年的孔子诞辰和忌辰印尼孔教都有祭祀仪式。孔教的一些核心人物，曾去过中国曲阜朝拜、亲眼或通过媒体看到大陆、港台地区以及其他国家祭孔典礼，也发现了与印尼孔教祭孔典礼的一个不同之处——祭祀乐舞等另有专人在月台之上表演。[①] 这似可说明印尼孔教祭孔仪式承继的更多的不是源于中国传统中国家体制层面的儒教；也从另一角度说明了中国儒教祭孔仪式在各国各地区的变异。

---

① 据2006年8月23日访问印尼最高理事会陈克兴先生口述记录资料。

（二）印尼孔教是中国儒学/儒教的印尼化，是印尼的宗教

印尼孔教的发展历史实际也是源于中国的儒教不断本土化、印尼化的过程。这一过程从印尼的角度去看，可以表述为一种源自外国的宗教“中国儒教”在印尼的本土化。

印尼孔教是印尼化（本土化）的宗教，是中国儒教的印尼化，可以从以下几个方面去看。

1. 印尼孔教使用的语言文字是印尼语。印尼孔教的经典、教义的解说及举行仪式的过程，大多数是使用印尼文、印尼语表述。《四书》已全部翻译成印尼文，《五经》现已翻译了三经。这是因为孔教的信徒大多是既不懂华文，也不懂华语的土生华人和年轻一代华人。

2. 作为宗教最核心的部分——印尼孔教的教义也已经带有十分明显的印尼色彩，而没有完全照搬中国儒学。最突出的是对“天”的解释，把天解释和表述为“独一无二”的唯一的上帝，这些与中国儒学的解释明显不同。这是因为，在印尼，对宗教教义、对上帝、天的解释都必须遵循印尼国家的规定，这往往是以伊斯兰教为标准的。

印尼宗教部以及1965年总统宣布国家承认伊斯兰教、基督教、天主教、印度教、佛教和孔教为合法宗教的命令中，都谈到宗教的标准最基本的应具备四条：一是信仰唯一的、独一无二的真主或上帝；二是有先知、圣人；三是有宗教经典；四是有系统的仪式和信徒。[①]

3. 印尼孔教的组织、机构、宗教活动场所等也都体现了印尼化的特点。

印尼孔教的中央、地方各级组织、各类机构都是在印尼国家的有关法律、政策框架下形成与发展起来的。“礼堂”及学师、文师、教生等三级教职人员的名称不仅体现了儒家文化的特点，而且也体现了在印尼特殊环境和历史背景下，印尼孔教有意区别于基督教等其他宗教的特点。

由于历史的原因，孔教可以在这些庙宇中举行孔教的仪式，而与其他的宗教仪式相安无事。

4. 孔教的宗教仪式体系也有鲜明的印尼化、本土化的特点。

其一，纳入了印尼国家颁布的纪念节日。如8月17日国庆节、10月28日青年宣言日、11月10日英雄节等，这些都是印尼独立以后制定颁布的，大都与印尼独立及现代国家意识有关。每年之中，凡遇上述国家颁布纪念日，印尼孔教或单独举办纪念礼

---

① MATAKIN：《Ada Pendidikan Tiada Perbedaan：Golden anniversary MATAKIN 16april 1955—2005》MATAKIN，Jakarta，2005. 印尼孔教最高理事会编：《有教无类：印尼孔教最高理事会成立50周年纪念刊》，雅加达，2005年，第37页。

拜仪式，或参加地方政府、社会团体举行的纪念活动。

其二，纳入了地方认同、面向社会的慈善活动的内容。如每年农历七月的中元节，又称为“敬好朋”，孔教要这时组织孔教徒和其他华人捐赠，以救济本地贫困居民（不分民族和宗教信仰）。如泗水文庙每年的“敬好朋”慈善活动规模很大，在当地造成很大影响。这实际上是中国闽南地区的农历七月“普度”习俗的变异。类似的还有农历腊月廿四日的送神节（祭灶节），也要举办面向社会的慈善活动，并被称为“社会节”或“友谊节”。目前印尼孔教的一年两次宗教节日的慈善活动已成为尽人皆知的惯例。这对于形成与保持华人与当地居民的友好和谐关系有很大的作用。在孔教受到打压时期，泗水文庙曾多次在前来领取救济粮、油物品的伊斯兰教徒支持下，说服或赶走了前来禁止华人文化活动的官员和警察。

其三，纳入了作为印尼国家公民义务的内容。在国家规定纪念日、节日，孔教都要举行仪式；并且按照印尼国家法律规定，制订和举行就职宣誓仪式，制订印尼孔教婚姻法、制订和举行孔教订婚和结婚的立愿仪式，等等。

其四，对原有的华人传统节日加上了宗教意义的内容，比如将冬至节加入了纪念孔子的周游列国的开始和孟子的忌辰的内容，使其成为印尼孔教的“木铎节”。等等。

有一些孔教仪式看起来明显与印尼基督教、伊斯兰教有相像之处。比如星期天的礼拜仪式，礼堂里摆着一排排的椅凳，椅子上摆着孔教的经书、圣歌集，礼拜、读经、讲道、唱歌，看起来似乎与基督教很相像。

目前尚无法得知，孔教这种每周一次的礼拜仪式究竟怎样创立？究竟从何时开始？仅就所能观察了解到的材料来看，这实际上也是与现代城市生活节奏相适应的一种安排。而且孔教与基督教并不完全相同。孔教只是规定每周一次，并未如同基督教一律定为星期天上午，而是可以由各个孔教会根据所在社区的、教徒的工作和休息具体时间，为方便大家而决定。所以，除了大、中城市定为星期天上午外，各地区各个孔教会有所不同。丹格朗地区地处乡村的孔教会礼拜大都在晚上，笔者曾去过的设在祖师公庙的孔教会，成年组的礼拜时间定在星期天晚上，青年组的时间定于星期天下午。一些小城镇许多定在下午四、五点钟，而且并不限于星期天。另外，孔教作为重要宗教节日的“冬至节”，既使用孔圣诞历法（即中国农历）计算日期，又为了教徒方便起见，直接定为公历12月22日，这也是从印尼的实际情况出发而定的。

以上这些突出的印尼化特点，使得印尼孔教成为与中国儒学/儒教风貌迥异的、印尼的一个宗教。

## 四、印尼孔教对于印尼华人的意义以及在印尼的地位和影响

1. 印尼孔教是一部分不愿意被同化的印尼华人保持华人身份认同和文化认同的合

法的形式，而且在一个相当长的历史时期其他承传华人文化的手段几乎丧失殆尽，孔教是唯一合法的形式。

印尼政府规定印尼公民必须有宗教信仰，宗教在印尼国家有合法的地位。

印尼孔教成为在印尼特殊的、恶劣的政治环境下印尼华人的精神支柱。在1998年以前的30多年中，只有印尼孔教以宗教节日的名义坚持公开过孔圣诞新年——华人的传统节日春节。

2. 印尼孔教的本土化（印尼化）有利于实现华人与当地各民族和谐相处，有利于华人在地生根。

现在印尼的孔教徒也有爪哇族等其他民族，也有伊斯兰教和基督教信徒转教过来的。

印尼孔教和占印尼人口总数88%以上的伊斯兰教也都保有友好和谐的关系。

3. 印尼孔教现在印尼是六大合法宗教之一，并获得政府资助。宗教部每年可以提供一些经费；大中小学开设的宗教课也必须有孔教的内容。目前印尼政府的高层领导对印尼孔教都很重视，2007年11月第四届国际儒学研讨会暨首届世界孔教国际研讨会在雅加达召开，印尼宗教部长和宪法院院长亲自出席致辞祝贺。

在印尼，孔教的确是充满活力的宗教，至今仍在不断发展、建设之中。印尼孔教的领袖们坦言，由于过去孔教面临的主要问题是如何争取合法生存，对自身的建设无法给予更多的关注，各种制度还有待完善，有些仪式规范尚未有实践，教职人员的素质、水平尚有待提高，等等。2006年重新获得合法地位之后，他们适时地提出“谦受益，满招损”的口号，正在努力进行自身的建设，以迎接新形势的挑战。

## 五、印尼孔教研究给我们的启发

印尼孔教以活生生的事例表明了：

第一，中国儒学/儒教能够在海外以多种形式存在，可以以宗教的形式存在；而且可以以制度化宗教的形式存在。这说明中国儒学/儒教可以适应各种复杂不同的环境，显示出儒学及中华传统文化多元、开放、包容的特质和很强的生命力。

第二，东南亚华人移民在海外对儒学的传承播布，不是简单地、原封不动地照搬和复制；而更重要的——是一种生机勃勃的文化创造（用中国大陆当代流行语言来说就是文化创新）。这种文化创造表现为华人以及儒学对移居国当地文化的适应、吸纳、融合，表现为儒学及中华文化与华人移居各地文化的交流、会通与发展。

海外华侨华人是文化的载体，又是文化的创造者，在文化创造中传承着儒学文化及中华文化，从而创造出丰富多彩的各国华族文化。

第三，这一文化传承和创新的过程，体现了作为儒学及中华文化载体的华人族群富有文化创造力的民族特性，显示出他们在儒学与世界文明多元共处中的重要作用。

笔者个人认为，作为中国学者，在研究儒学/儒教时，应努力做到以下三点：

第一，应该放眼世界，具有世界眼光。应该看到孔子、儒学/儒教不仅仅是中国的，而是属于世界，属于全人类。人类、世界需要孔子、孔教、儒学和中华文化，尤其是现在的状况是“礼失求诸于野”，中国大陆多年来对传统文化、儒学传统的破坏十分严重，在某些方面反而是海外华人中有较多较好的保留。台湾对于传统文化的珍视与传承更无须多言。我们的研究应该放眼世界，不应局限于中国大陆本土。

第二，需要眼光向下，看到民间。

印尼孔教是以民间宗教的形式存在，长期是被边缘化的。在台湾、香港，在新加坡、马来西亚、越南、日本、韩国、美国等，孔教往往是以民间的形式存在。

杜维明先生2005年5月到印尼接触了孔教，并亲到泗水文庙等处考察，对其儒学研究产生了很大的影响。

台湾及东南亚学者对民间儒教、儒学传播的研究可以给我们很好的启迪，很值得学习借鉴。

第三，研究儒学的世界传播，一定要做具体的研究，一定要做实地考察。要将其放在所处的具体环境和历史背景下，或者包括华侨华人发展历史脉络之中去研究。

第四，研究海外儒学，一定要有文化意识。在研究过程中，既要注意从各种迥异不同、繁杂缭乱的现象中发掘出不变的文化内涵，追寻出其源流及传承的路径；更要重视研究文化的发展与变化、文化的革新与创造、文化传承播布的深层原因等。

不当之处，尚祈方家指正。

# 东南亚儒学传播特点初探

华侨大学 鲁锦寰 王爱平

东南亚地区作为中国的近邻，儒学的传播、影响由来已久。儒学传入时间早，传播和发展时间长，从儒学传入越南算起，至今已达两千多年。有不少学者认为，世界儒学可分为东方儒学与欧美儒学，东方儒学包括日本、韩国东亚儒学和东南亚儒学。东南亚一些儒学研究者认为，从世界儒学发展来看，已经逐步形成了与东亚、北美鼎足而三的新兴区域儒学——东南亚儒学。①

儒学在东南亚地区传播具有鲜明、突出的特点：

首先，从传播学的视角来看，东南亚地区的儒学传播是一种文化传播；并且主要是以人为载体和媒介的传播，以华人移民为载体的传播。

除越南与中国历史上的关系比较特殊，儒学的发展与其他东南亚国家明显不同，应归于东亚儒学文化圈之外；其他国家儒学的传入基本上始于中国的移民——华侨华人的到来，儒学的传播是以华侨华人为载体的一种文化传播。本文的论述也基本上不包括越南在内。

毋庸置疑，儒学乃中华文化之主脉，儒家文化乃中华传统文化之核心。从文化研究和传播学角度看，人是文化的载体，也是文化传播的主要媒介。中国的海外移民——华侨、华人、华族，是儒学及中华文化的重要载体，也是儒学及中华文化在海外传承播布的重要载体与媒介。随着一代又一代中国移民走向世界各地，在不同的国度落地生根，形成各不同国家的华人族群，也把儒学带到世界各地。

东南亚地区是中国海外移民最集中、人数最多、历史最久的地区。中国向海外的移民，最早就是东南亚地区，比较成规模的移民已有千余年的历史。华人移居东南亚时，儒学文化随之而至。东南亚华人的历史有多长，该地的儒学文化的发展就有多久。

其次，东南亚儒学源自中国儒学，但又与中国儒学有很大不同。

---

① （马来西亚）郑文泉：《东南亚儒学：与东亚、北美鼎足而三的新兴区域儒学论》，马来西亚孔学研究会，2010 年。

文化的多样性是人类世界的基本特征，文化的继承与创新是文化存在和发展的基本规律。随着一代又一代中国移民走向世界各地，在不同的国度落地生根，形成各不同国家的华人族群——“华族”，他们虽然传承中华文化的基本特质，但已有所变异——他们吸纳了移居国当地不同的文化，在各不同的居住国创造出各具特色的华族文化。

在有上千年华人移民历史背景下的东南亚儒学，即是源自中国的儒学在与东南亚各国不同文化的长期互动中发展形成的，在其传播过程中，曾先后与印度的佛教文化，阿拉伯的伊斯兰教文化及近代西方文化相文汇，形成东南亚地区的多元文化结构。东南亚儒学已经成为华人所在国多元文化的一个组成部分。

由于东南亚儒学的传播是以华侨华人为载体的一种文化传播，因此也使东南亚儒学呈现出一些突出的特点，形成一处处缤纷多彩的文化景观。可以从以下五个方面来看。

## 一、东南亚儒学表现在华人族群的伦常日用践行的传统

千百年来由华人移民为载体传播的东南亚儒学，在很长时间里和很大程度上主要不是表现为一种知识体系的“儒学”的传播，而体现在大多数普通华人的生活之中，体现在华人对儒学之践行、伦常日用之中。

中国与东南亚地区的经济文化交往以及华人移居的历史，可溯源于两千多年前的汉代。据文献记载，自唐代开始已有成批的华人移民定居于东南亚，在17世纪荷兰、西班牙、英国等西方殖民者大规模入侵东南亚之前，华人已大量移居东南亚，形成了在地的华人社会。东南亚的华人大多是通商贸易的闽粤两省商人和手工业者，他们在南洋群岛沿海和内地经济中已经有了很重要的地位和作用。鸦片战争以后，南下移民东南亚的华人越来越多，华人社会进一步扩大。

随着华人的大批移民东南亚，也把中国传统文化带到东南亚，中国文化及孔子思想学说借此逐步在东南亚传播，中国儒学也开始了在东南亚群岛“落地生根”的过程。

儒学文化，或称儒家文化，是以孔子学说为依归，以儒家伦理为核心价值的文化体系。它包括学术思想、伦理规范、思维方式、生活方式和民俗信仰等诸多文化层面。移居东南亚的华人，多为谋生而去，属于穷苦下层的较多。这些穷苦下层的华人虽然没有很深的儒学理论教养，但是孔孟之道、儒家伦理在他们的为人处世、家庭观念和生活习俗中得到充分的反映和体现。大多数华人都是儒家思想的践行者。他们身体力行儒家所尊奉提倡的孝悌忠信、礼义廉耻、敬天法祖、慎终追远的道德伦理，保持和发扬刻苦耐劳、勤俭朴实、尊老敬贤、仁爱宽恕等优秀品质，并且世代相传。儒学思想已经渗透在他们的心灵深处，儒学于他们实在是日用而不自知也——这也是东南亚

作为知识体系的“儒学”传播的基础所在。

在评价儒家文化在新加坡现代化成功中的作用时，人们都关注到新加坡人口结构中华人所占比例和新加坡华人的儒学传统。1991年8月10日，新加坡前总理李光耀在新加坡召开的世界首届华商大会开幕式的讲话中指出：“世界各地华人成功的主要因素是节俭、刻苦耐劳、重视教育、社群的信任和互相扶助。简单来说，就是中华文化的核心价值观。”新加坡副总理吴庆瑞也说：“华人很早以来就开始向海外移居，他们把孔子学说及儒家思想所发展出来的精神，带到所移居的社会。华人的勤奋、节俭、讲求信用，对法律的尊重，对社会的关怀，对家庭的爱护，以及对子女教育的重视，使他们不但在海外打开新的世界，同时也保持了祖先所遗留下来的美德和传统。总之，移居海外的华人能够有今天，能够为他们的后代创立下繁荣、文明的社会，同孔子及儒家的潜移默化的影响有密切的关系。”

华人对儒家思想的日用践行即为儒学的传承，主要通过几个途径：一曰为人处世，行为规范；一曰生活习俗及节庆习俗，包括衣食起居、婚丧嫁娶人生礼仪；一曰祭祀、崇拜与信仰；从中体现出儒家的家庭伦理、社会伦理，体现出儒家的伦理道德观念乃至价值观、宇宙观。本篇恕不展开论述。儒学从而成为海外华人安身立命的思想基础。

当代新儒家学者也都注意到儒学、儒家传统内部的分层。杜维明曾把儒学划分为三种类型：即作为意识形态被政治化的儒学，成为权力者的统治工具；作为一门学问的儒学，涉及复杂的阐释技巧和对儒学经典的注释、训诂；作为为人处世和基本意义上的伦理与生活方式的儒学……①余英时曾经借用美国人类学家罗伯特·雷德菲尔德对于文化传统区分为“大传统”和“小传统”的二元分析框架，提出儒家传统也分为“制度化的儒家传统”（大传统）和“民间的儒家传统”（小传统），前者是指知识精英和政治统治者所共同传承维护的儒家传统，而后者则是指儒学通俗化之后，在民间草根阶层中传递的儒家传统。② 刘述先则把知识阶层独立出来，把儒家传统分为三种类型：精神的儒家、政治化的儒家和民间的儒家。③

东南亚华人所体现的这种儒学传统即为“伦理与生活方式的儒学”，或亦可称之为“生活儒学”、“民间的儒学”，可视为中国民间儒学传统跨洋越海在东南亚的传播。这一传播过程伴随着移民而来。作为“伦理与生活方式的儒学”和“民间的儒学”，家庭的教育（多是不见于文字的言传、身教，潜移默化），代际影响，华人社团的存在与熏

---

① 参见曹长青：《儒学：文化中国的源头活水—杜维明教授和他的“三个意义世界”》，载（美）《世界日报》1991年12月8日。

② 余英时：《现代儒学论》，上海：上海人民出版社，1998年，第241—249页。

③ 刘述先：《儒家思想开拓的尝试》，北京：中国社会科学出版社，2010年，第16页。

陶在其中起着巨大的作用，在很长时期内完全是一种自然的、无意识的自发传承。这种文化传统一直延续至今，并不以有了作为知识体系和体制内的儒学而有所偏废，而是并行不悖，且如水润万物，悄无声息地滋养着东南亚华人。

## 二、东南亚儒学传播与当地华文教育紧密结合

东南亚儒学的传播与华文教育有着密切的关系。在东南亚地区，作为知识体系的“儒学”的传播与当地的华文教育紧密结合在一起。在兴办华文教育的过程中，儒学的传承逐步由自然的、无意识的状态演变出有意识的、主动的传承。

（一）东南亚早期华文教育与儒学教育的一体性

在东南亚华人社会中，最初的文化教育是一些华人业余在家庭或家族内部进行的。随着华人的增多，开始设立私塾。一些富有的华人请家庭教师任教，也出现教读先生“设帐授徒”的私塾，以后出现了专供华人子女读书受教育的义学和书院。

1690年（康熙二十九年）巴达维亚（今印尼雅加达）华人创办的“明诚书院”是印尼以及东南亚最早创设的义学，也是世界最早的海外华人教育机构。1775年（乾隆四十年）又设立巴达维亚“南江书院”。1787年在巴达维亚金德院庙内加办义学，名“明德书院”。新加坡第一所华人学校是1849年在天福宫建立的崇文阁，接着1854年萃英书院成立；1888年创立于槟城的南华义学，等等。这些是整个19世纪东南亚最重要的华人学校。

这些私塾、义学、书院均使用汉语方言进行教学，其教学内容、方法、仪规等都与中国国内相同，教师来自于中国，教学的内容即是三字经、千字文以及儒家经典四书五经，还有华人重视的写字与珠算等。学生入学要向孔子像或牌位行礼。南江书院等书院还“崇祀紫阳（朱夫子）圣像”。① 崇文阁和萃英书院两所学校石碑上的碑文表明：它们都是为传授儒学而建立的。创建崇文阁的目的，就在于希望建成之后，“从兹成人小子，读孔孟之书，究洛闽之奥，优柔德性培养天真，化固陋为文章，变鄙俗为风雅”。②

当今的印尼孔教最高理事会认为，“明诚书院”、“明德书院”就是如同伊斯兰教习经院的儒学院，因为这是教导“明明德”（《四书》之《大学》的开篇语句）的书院，

---

① （荷）包乐史、吴凤斌：《18世纪末吧达维亚唐人社会》，厦门：厦门大学出版社，2002年。

② （新加坡）陈荆和，陈育崧《新加坡华文碑铭集录》，香港：中文大学出版社出版，出版时间不详.

人们在里面学习和研究儒教。[1]

总之，当时华人的文化教育与儒学教育实属一体，儒家思想文化藉华人文化教育在东南亚得以承传。

（二）19 世纪末东南亚儒教复兴运动与新式华文教育

19 世纪末至 20 世纪初与中国相互影响的儒教复兴运动，是作为知识体系的“儒学”传播的集中表现，当时波及整个东南亚，包括新加坡、马来西亚、缅甸及荷属东印度（印尼）等地区，声势浩大，对东南亚华人社会产生了重大和深远的影响。

兴办新式华文教育即是这场儒教复兴运动的主要内容之一，同时提出的还有建孔庙、宣讲学习孔子学说。当时人们认为要真正了解孔子学说就必须懂得中文，为了提倡孔子学说，也就必须改变华人受教育不足的状况。所以，各地华人都积极筹办新式华文学校。

新马孔教复兴运动一般被划分为两个阶段，第一阶段的主要活动集中于倡建孔庙和现代学堂，第二阶段则从纪念孔子诞辰开始，将孔子诞辰日作为一个民族的节日予以庆祝，后来又逐渐地恢复为建立孔庙和现代学堂。

林文庆、邱菽园以及吴寿珍等是这一文化复兴运动的重要领导人物，尤其是林文庆，不仅被公认为是第一阶段孔教复兴运动的核心人物，他还对荷属东印度地区的孔教复兴运动发挥了虽说是间接的，但却无疑是重要的影响作用。

清政府驻新加坡首任领事左秉隆及其继任者黄遵宪二人在任时对儒家文化不遗余力的传播与推广，对儒教复兴运动的兴起起到了奠定基础的作用。左秉隆曾设立一个成人教育机构“会贤社”，每月出题征文，主要是以儒家思想为题目，如：臣事君以忠；言忠信、行笃敬；满招损谦受益论；致知在格物论；人之行莫大于孝论；学而不思则罔；夫子之道忠恕而已矣等。

荷属东印度（印尼）的情况有些不同，从时间上要更早一些。早在中国戊戌维新之前的 19 世纪中叶，印尼华人已经开始努力复兴以儒家思想为代表的文化传统，在此不赘。

在东南亚儒教复兴运动中，印尼 1900 年成立了第一个正式的孔教组织巴达维亚中华会馆。中华会馆董事会成立不久即发布《巴城创设中华会馆兴办学堂公启》，很快成立了“巴达维亚中华会馆中华学堂”。

中华学堂的指导思想即是“尊孔”，明确规定：凡中华学堂必高悬孔子像；在孔子生辰和忌辰，分别放假一日，尤其是在孔子生日，须举行演讲会等，以示纪念。同时

---

① MATAKIN，Ada Pendidikan Tiada Perbedaan：Golden anniversary MATAKIN 16april 1955－2005，MATAKIN，Jakarta，2005。

还规定，至少每周一次在会馆举办孔教讲座，由中华学堂的校长、教员向大众宣讲孔子学说。当时大都用闽南话讲授《四书》、《五经》，但同时把讲义翻译成马来文，印发给听众。讲座内容还刊登在马来文报纸上。这种讲座活动很快推广到各地，后来即发展成为各地孔教会组织。中华会馆还创办了图书馆，并专门成立编译组，出版马来文小册子，主要是宣传孔教教义，如《孝》等，解答如何才符合中国儒教礼俗等问题。另外，还翻译出版了《四书》《孝经》等。巴达维亚中华会馆的成立很快在全国引起热烈的反响，各地纷纷效法成立中华会馆，创办新式的中华学校。

在苏拉威西岛的望加锡，福建公祠创始人的长孙李连喜于1899年创办男、女两所华文学校，并在学校中供奉孔子。供奉孔子的殿堂大门之上挂着“宣圣庙”的匾额。开学后不久，举行了盛大的孔子诞辰纪念活动，有四十多位知名人士参加。1900年时还专门托人到厦门聘请儒士苏易夫妇担任男女教习之职。①

戊戌变法失败之后维新运动领袖康有为到访东南亚，更推动了这一发展。东南亚各地中华会馆、中华学堂如雨后春笋般地相继成立。

（三）依托现代华文教育的儒学传播

在新加坡和马来西亚，20世纪40年代开始，中学的华文课本成为传统上传播儒家思想的重要媒介，而本地大学的中文系以及延续的研究院则从六七十年代开始成为儒家思想传播和研究的最理想场所。依托于华文教育体制，新加坡和马来西亚得以开始进行儒学的研究。现代意义的东南亚儒学可以以20世纪50年代上半期马来亚大学成立中文系为起点。

尤其是马来西亚华人始终坚决、强烈地维护华人族群自身民族语言文化教育的权利，为此虽九死而无悔，在付出沉重代价下终于保持了还比较完整的华文教育体系，所以在马来西亚教育体制内使得儒学有可能作为知识体系得以继续传播，包括教学、践行与研究。

20世纪初新式教育的学校成立后，在学校仍然保持尊孔的传统和儒学的教育。1904年（光绪三十年）在槟城设立中华学校，这是马来西亚华人新式教育的第一所学校，但这所学校保留了“修身”、“读经”、“讲学”等课程，并保留了尊孔、祭孔等传统。后来儒学传播在马来西亚虽然曾一度式微。20世纪90年代，儒学研究在马来西亚开始有明显发展，华文学校的儒学教育和马来亚大学中文系的儒学研究还能存续，或多或少占有一席之地。

如创立于1906年的著名的吉隆坡尊孔独立中学仍然名实一致，通过校训等各种方

① （新加坡）《天南新报》，第277号，1899－5－6，梁元生：《宣尼浮海到南洲—儒家思想与早期新加坡华人社会史料汇编》，香港：香港中文大学出版社，1995年。

式与途径进行儒家思想的教育。甫进校门即可看到其左侧楼壁上写着一副大字对联："尊重精神扬宇宙，孔师风范立春秋。"位于怡保市的怡保国民中学，其校门两侧写着作为校训的"孝悌忠信，礼义廉耻"八个大字。尊孔中学、怡保国民中学等诸多华文学校，一直坚持每天早晨均诵读儒家经典30分钟的传统。并开设有道德课，其中的儒家伦理内容更为丰富。

马来亚大学中文系于1962年成立，早期有关儒学研究的成绩可观，后来开始偏向文学，儒学研究减弱。但是在老师的指导下，仍然有一些研究生论文研究儒学，主要有：《儒家思想和中国古典小说：〈三国演义〉研究》（1997年）、《鲁迅与儒学：中国反传统主义的悖论》（1999年）、《马来西亚一个华人甲必丹家族之儒家文化现象》（1999年）、《先秦政治思想研究：孔子、孟子与荀子》（2000年）等。

1990年还成立马来亚中文系毕业生协会（简称"中协"），开展儒学研究，并取得丰硕成果。曾先后与马来西亚中华大会堂、马来西亚华社研究中心、马来亚大学中文系合作，举办国际学术研讨会。大量出版杜维明、余英时及本土学者儒学研究专著和论文集。

## 三、东南亚儒学是信仰化的儒学，宗教化特点突出

东南亚华人继承的儒学文化也同时表现在宗教的层面。东南亚地区的儒学往往体现出华人族群的信仰所在，可以说是信仰化的儒学，表现出明显、突出的宗教化的倾向。儒学的宗教性在东南亚的影响较大，源远流长。

纵观整个东南亚儒学传播的历史，这一特点十分明显。

（一）华人家庭的祭祀、华人宗祠、传统庙宇是儒学传承的重要依托。

从最初儒学的传播到迈入现代社会的华人世界，具有宗教意义的华人家庭和庙堂、宗祠的祭祀一直是儒学教化与传承的重要途径。

儒学的基本信仰就是"敬天法祖"，包括敬天祭天、祭祖敬宗和圣贤崇拜等。圣贤崇拜包括祭拜关公、妈祖、先医、贤良、昭忠等。按照东南亚华人的说法，是华人就要拜天公、拜祖先。对天地和祖先的崇拜、孝道的尊奉、家庭伦理的维护、往往是与生活和民间信仰相融合的。

宗祠，亦称祖祠、祖堂、祖庙，如同在中国国内，宗祠的设立是为用来祭祀去世的祖先，以使后代报本追远。正如东爪哇泗水著名的郑氏家族宗祠营建碑和管理立碑（1884年；1914年）中所记：

家之有祠庙，所以为禴祀蒸尝之区，为子孙勿忘祖宗之念，爰是我兄弟四人，同心协力，捐赀营建我先考原任泗水大妈腰绍阳郑公之祠堂。庶孙支百世相承奉祀于勿

替。爰勒贞珉，俾后人知此祠堂之所由建也。[①]

盖闻自古三代圣王治天下者，皆以孝道为先，故人生于世，莫不以祀事为重，考自经传，乃有春禘秋尝之礼，此教民，则终身不可忘其先人之禋祀也。……营建先祖之祠堂，……欲尽人子报本追远之大端，留仟佰年之基础，而兼欲免后世子孙之忧，其思虑深远，非常人所能及也。[②]

在东南亚，凡是华人聚居之地都有华人所建的宗祠。这些祖祠，一直保留着春秋两季大祭的传统习俗。在爪哇，目前所知创建确切时间最早的是1754年建于巴达维亚的陈氏祖庙，其前厅供奉唐朝开发福建漳州被称为“开漳圣王”的陈元光。

孔子注重祭祀，认为祭祀是维持伦理的一种教化方法。“孝”为伦理之中心价值，对于孝道的培植，重点在“生则养，死别敬享”。故有“生事之以礼，死葬之以礼，祭之以礼”的教导。祭祀祖先有“报本、追远、崇德”的意义，期望民德因而归厚。是故，儒教文化特别重视祭祀祖先的宗教礼俗。儒教重视祖先祭祀，并不只局限于有血缘关系的祖先，也祭祀为民族做出贡献的英雄或领袖。

华人所建庙宇更是遍及东南亚各地，也更早于宗祠的建立。可说是自有华人定居之时就“有华人必有庙”。崇拜神明为海外华人的精神寄托与精神支柱，华人的庙宇大多是祭拜中国传统儒教中所祭祀的天神、地祇、人杰，特别是祭祀《礼记》所说的那些“以死勤事”、“以劳定国”、能御大灾、能捍大患，“有功烈于民”的人神。

仅雅加达一地就有17、18世纪所建古庙多处，较有名气的有：金德院；安卒大伯公庙，主要崇奉土地神大伯公，又称福德正神；丹绒玄天上帝庙；妈祖庙，即天后宫；关帝庙，又称关公庙；等等。现今的东南亚华人依然崇祀传统儒教诸神明。

华人庙宇大都是儒释道三教合一。马来西亚最古老的华人庙宇——创建于1673年的马六甲青云亭，也是一间儒释道三教信仰合一的古庙宇。青云亭的儒教色彩不仅仅在于崇祀孔子，其中尚保留的碑文、纪念甲必丹及亭主的“立功立德”功德祠、供奉神祖牌或亡灵的大众爷祭祀堂及祭拜文昌帝君与仓颉的神龛，这些都是民间的儒教信仰。

在华人庙宇，儒学与儒教是一体的，“儒教”即为“儒学之教育”，儒学的教育不止于学术与知识层面，更包含生活礼俗，包含祭祀天地先人的宗教成分。在荷兰统治（1641—1824年）时期，成为华社的政务及宗教信仰中心。甲必丹及亭主都曾为华侨社区为华人社会谋求福利，做出贡献，其行为体现出“仁、义、勇、孝”等儒家价值观。青云亭内还设有功德祠，供奉了对青云亭有贡献的甲必丹及亭主之牌位，亦体现出儒

---

① 傅吾康主编，苏尔梦、萧国健：《印度尼西亚华文铭刻汇编第二卷（下册）》，新加坡：新加坡南洋学会，巴黎法国远东学院，巴黎群岛学会，1997年。

② 同上。

教之精神——因“立德”、“立功”及“立言”为儒者追求之人生理想，亦为儒者人生追求的三不朽价值观。

（二）东南亚儒教复兴运动的宗教性

席卷整个东南亚的19世纪末儒教复兴运动的主要内容，即为大力倡导复兴孔教。除了建学堂，重视进行的还有纪念孔子圣诞、建孔庙、采用孔历——孔圣诞纪年法等。1899年农历八月二十七日纪念孔子诞辰2450年之际，印尼与新加坡、缅甸仰光等地的华人行动一致，都举行了热烈的庆祝活动，并借此庆祝活动“议建孔庙，建学堂”。①

巴达维亚中华会馆创办人之一并任宗教部负责人的李金福，早在1897年就撰写了孔子的传记《至圣孔夫子》。1903年他写下《华人的宗教》的长文，表达了中华会馆宣扬孔教的基本立场与看法。② 其基本观点可以归纳为以下几点：

其一，孔教为一种宗教。孔教是华人文化中最主要的成分，在荷属印尼的华人，都有义务遵循孔子的教义。

其二，天是万物的主宰，孔子是从天得到灵感，而在华人之间宣扬孔教教义。信奉孔教就要祭拜天，孔教的上帝就是“天”。

其三，孔子是圣人先知，他就是孔教的教主。

其四，父母、祖先就是天的代表，信奉孔教就要发扬孝道，祭祀祖先。

印尼巴达维亚中华会馆关于孔教的看法，实际上很有代表性，也表达出了整个东南亚华人复兴儒教的心声。如运动发起者缅甸仰光李凤鸣等也发表演说，指出“种种求治之道，教化实为其基”。③ 他们认为传播孔教“宜仿耶回传教”，并“特遣教牧，周流四方”；在教牧临讲之时，“伐鼓三”，并“高声朗吟大学圣经一章”，④ 等等。这些都表明，东南亚华侨企图使儒教宗教化，把孔子当圣人，儒学当教义，把孔教建设成为一个全体华人信仰的宗教，从而在华人社会中复兴儒家的伦理价值，以对抗西方文化和在这一地区的其他宗教文化的影响。

（三）以孔子学说、儒家思想为教义的制度化宗教——印尼孔教

在以上所述东南亚儒教复兴运动的大背景下，终于发展出据目前所知为中国以外、世界唯一的以孔子为教主、以孔子学说、儒家思想为教义的制度化宗教——印尼孔教，

---

① 《南洋各埠建孔庙学堂》，光绪二十五年九月二十一日，（澳门）知新报社：《知新报（影印本）》，上海：澳门基金会，上海社会科学院出版社联合出版，1996年。

② Nio Joe Lan：Riwayat 40 Tahun dari Tiong Hoa Hwee Koan—Batavia（1900—1939），Batavia，1940。

③ 《说教—圣诞日仰光辅仁李鸣凤演说》，《知新报》，光绪二十五年十月十一日，第一百〇五册。

④ 《鹭门明新旧主拟各处华人联立孔教会章程并序》，《知新报》，光绪二十五年十一月二十一日，第一百〇九册。

历经一百余年的磨难与曲折，现已成为与伊斯兰教、基督教、天主教、佛教和印度教并列的印尼六大合法宗教之一。

近三十余年来，中国学术界对儒教是教非教问题的激烈争论中一个十分关键的问题，即宗教的定义和标准问题。儒教的最大特点，就是它并非像西方基督教教会组织那样的“制度宗教”，这是讨论中各种不同观点者一致的认识。但是，源于中国儒教的印尼孔教却显现出不同于中国儒教的宗教特征。

美籍华裔社会学家杨庆堃提出中国宗教包括两种不同的类型：即制度型宗教与弥散型宗教，制度型宗教的主要代表包括佛教和道教；弥散型宗教则主要指祖先崇拜、社区神崇拜以及伦理—政治神崇拜。[①] 台湾著名人类学家李亦园在大量田野调查、实证研究的基础上也采用了这一分析框架，而称之为“制度化宗教”和“普化宗教”。“制度化宗教”是指“有严格的教堂组织，严谨的宗教执事，有明显的经典，同样有明显的教义，而宗教事务跟一般的日常生活分开”，如天主教、基督教、伊斯兰教、佛教、道教和其他有组织的宗教。“普化宗教”则是指“宗教信仰扩散到我们生活的各方面，跟我们日常生活密切地联系在一起，但是没有形成一个有组织的制度，同时跟日常生活密不可分，没有明显教会组织、经典教义等的一种信仰仪式”，如祖先崇拜、风水测算等中国民间的信仰和仪式。[②]

具体来说，制度化宗教一定具有宗教组织和制度、宗教经典和较完整的神学或哲学、伦理体系、有专职的教职人员和教阶制度，有明确的、固定的祭祀礼拜的场所，有系统的规范的宗教仪式，有约束信徒的教规或戒律等。

印尼孔教明显与中国儒教（儒学、儒家）不同，比较全面地具备了制度化宗教的特征。

首先，印尼孔教有系统的宗教教义体系，印尼孔教的教义就是孔子思想。

其次，印尼孔教有自己的宗教经典——也就是儒学经典《四书五经》。孔教徒每周做礼拜时都要携带孔教的圣经《四书》。

第三，印尼孔教有规定教规：八诫箴规等。

第四，印尼孔教有自己专门的宗教活动场所：泗水文庙、分布在印尼各地的孔教“礼堂”、三教会庙宇里面的孔圣神坛，等等。孔教将宗教活动场所称为“礼堂”，凸显了儒教重“礼”的特点，明显有别于基督教的“教堂”。

---

① C. K. Yang：Religion in Chinese Society：A Study of Contemporary Social Functions of Religion and some of Their Historical Factors，pp20－21，294－295.

② 李亦园：《宗教、仪式与象征》，载马戎、周星编：《田野工作与文化自觉》（上），北京，群言出版社，1998年，第282页。

第五，印尼孔教有教徒——印尼孔教总会估计，全印尼大约在400万以上，印尼孔教总会认为，凡是敬天、拜祖先、尊孔者都被承认为孔教徒。

第六，印尼孔教有比较完整的宗教组织及制度。

印尼孔教有它的中央组织（印尼孔教最高理事会、主席团、宣道师委员会）和地方组织（孔教会、孔教宣道会、孔教青年会、三教会的孔教组织、大学生孔教组织、华人庙宇等）。印尼孔教每四年召开一次全国代表大会，选举最高理事会、主席团、宣道师委员会。印尼孔教有专门的教职人员（神职人员），分为三级：学师、文师和教生，学师为最高级。这也充分表明了孔教重教、重“师”的儒家传统。

第七，印尼孔教有一整套系统的宗教仪式体系，包括礼敬仪式；礼拜宣道仪式；祭祀仪式；人生仪式等等。其崇拜对象及信仰体系分为四大类：天；圣人孔子；神明和祖先。并且把中国传统的岁时节庆（元宵、端午、中秋、冬至等）纳入仪式体系，成为孔教的宗教节日。

综上，印尼孔教作为制度化宗教的特征是十分明显的。

（四）民间儒教的广泛存在

还有盛行于东南亚的一贯道、德教等以华人为主体的宗教，虽然都声称是“五教合一”（儒释道耶伊），实际上均可视为民间儒教。

一贯道约三十多年前自台湾传到马来西亚，现已遍布东南亚各国。其道场称为佛堂，分为公共佛堂和家庭佛堂，估计马来西亚佛堂有一千间以上。一贯道的讲经说法大部分是四书五经等儒家经典，几乎所有的佛堂都办有儿童读经班，是最早开始组织儿童诵读儒家经典的。一贯道在马来西亚办的读经“小状元”活动，每年参加者有数千人，入榜“小状元”居然可以读诵《弟子规》《三字经》《大学》《中庸》《孟子》《论语》《易经》选读，《礼记·大同》……七八部之多，可见日常功课之努力。后来每年同时举办读经“大状元”活动，推动了成年人学习儒家经典。一贯道教徒注重修身，待人接物彬彬有礼，往往是“佛化家庭”，齐家和谐。

20世纪30年代起源于广东潮州的“德教”，在新、马、泰十分兴盛，近年也传入印尼。德教以“孝、悌、忠、信、礼、义、廉、耻、仁、智”十章为教旨，行教则以“八则”（不欺、不伪、不贪、不妄、不骄、不急、不怨、不恶）为基础。十章亦为“十德”，很明显，十德的基本方面是属于儒家的。

## 四、儒学的传承是东南亚华人族群文化认同、族群认同的标志与途径

东南亚儒学的传播是和东南亚华人族群的文化认同、文化选择、族群认同紧密联系在一起的。

跨洋越海来到并长期生活在迥然不同的异文化环境之中，东南亚华人面临着异文

化的压力和多种文化选择。在西方殖民者来到东南亚之前，华人移民自然地被同化也是一种时常发生的现象。但长期以来，在各种内外因素的影响下，大部分华人不愿意被同化，也就没有被同化。不愿意被同化的华人族群具有强烈的华人身份认同意识，他们意识到以儒家文化为主干的中华文化是海外华人的文化之“根”、民族之“根”，具有强烈的“保根”意识和儒家文化认同意识。虽然历经居住国殖民统治者、民族主义者的排斥歧视政策、同化政策的打击，同时还时常要面对来自中国反孔反儒反传统运动的冲击，他们仍矢志不渝，运用各种方式传承儒学命脉，以此来表示文化认同、华人身份认同和华人族群认同。

东南亚华人社会早期兴办华文教育时已经具有明确的文化认同意识，这种文化认同意识表现为儒学认同、儒教认同。如19世纪40年代，巴达维亚荷印殖民当局颁布禁止华文教师等“文人学士”入境的条规，巴达维亚华人公馆据理力争，向荷印总督申诉：

然可来者匠人百工，所禁者文人学士，实有负于圣教所云，恐仁、义、礼、智之风，尽泯于今矣！余诚私心痛之！夫童子自幼须教以礼仪，致其长大方能知诗识理，通权达变而利生焉。既无贤人教督，势必至于庸愚，商贾贸易，谁能掌数（数，闽南话，指账目、账本）？又且愈久愈忘，其危害伊于胡底耶？[①]

由此可看出：华人社会的领导阶层、中坚力量崇尚儒学，遵奉“圣教”——儒教，认为华人儿童必须自小教以“礼仪”，使其长大成人能“知事达理、通权达变”，他们以维护儒教传统为己任，希望能够藉教读文化传承仁、义、礼、智儒教之风。

前述19世纪晚期波及整个东南亚轰轰烈烈的儒教复兴运动，即是在东南亚华人民族意识开始觉醒、族群意识和文化认同意识形成的大背景下发生的，不论是建孔庙、庆孔诞、兴办学堂、宣讲孔子学说，确定服饰、婚丧嫁娶规制礼仪……无不是将儒学儒教、孔子学说视作华人文化，视作华人族群的精神支柱，通过对儒学文化的认同表达对华人身份、华人族群的认同，儒教的复兴与传承成为在异文化环境中东南亚华人文化认同、身份认同的标志，这明显地是一种文化民族主义的表现。[②]

在二战之后，东南亚华人开始由华侨身份转变为加入当地国籍的华人，中国由祖国变成了祖籍国，国家认同或政治认同由认同中国转变为认同居住国，坚持儒家伦理道德和生活习俗成为保持华人身份认同、文化认同的重要途径，也往往是一个标志。

以曾经长期对华人实行强制同化政策的印尼为例：印尼政府对华人同化政策的核

---

① （荷）包乐史、吴凤斌：《18世纪末吧达维亚唐人社会》，厦门：厦门大学出版社，2002年。

② 颜清湟：《新加坡和马来亚华侨的民族主义（1877—1912）》，载其著《海外华人史研究》，新加坡亚洲学会，1992年。

心内容并公开宣称，是以消灭华人文化为宗旨，而印尼华人坚持华人民族认同的发展趋势，就是愈来愈注重保存华人的文化，也就是通过文化认同来确定自己的华人身份，保存华人民族特性。

从文化的角度来看，在印尼延续了三百多年的华文教育，在华人社会中传承了中国的儒学，为华人提供了精神的支柱。印尼孔教产生与发展一百多年的历史，正是表现和反映了一部分不愿意被同化的印尼华人确立文化认同和华人身份认同的历程——那就是：认同印尼国家，同时又对自身的华人身份持有强烈的认同，只不过这种认同表现为儒学文化认同，并且采用了一种宗教的形式。他们打出了儒学的旗帜，孔子的旗帜，这是源自祖籍国——中国，同时也被西方世界和印尼的伊斯兰文化所承认的。①

如此，印尼孔教就成为在印尼特殊的、恶劣的政治环境下印尼华人的精神支柱，成为不愿意被同化的印尼华人保持华人身份认同和文化认同的合法的形式，在其他承传华人文化的手段几乎丧失殆尽的特定历史时期，甚至是唯一合法的形式。在 1998 年以前的三十多年中，只有印尼孔教以宗教节日的名义坚持公开过孔圣诞新年——华人的传统节日春节。

## 五、东南亚儒学发展呈现出多元化的方向及特征

由于东南亚各个国家、地区在历史文化传统、华人华侨比例、华人政策、文化政策和社会现代化进程等方面存在明显差异，因此，东南亚各国及地区儒学文化的发展也呈现出不同的面貌与特征。

在 19 世纪末至 20 世纪初期的儒教复兴运动结束之后，新马地区和印尼的儒学各自走上不同的发展道路。多元化的发展之中体现出一个共同的特征，即中国儒教/儒学的本土化——或印尼化，或马来化，或新加坡化等，从而出现了不同风貌的东南亚各国儒学。

### （一）印尼孔教的不断本土化、印尼化的发展

在对华人严厉实行同化政策的印尼，最终形成一个源于中国儒学、以孔子为教主的印尼化、制度化宗教。这一过程也可以表述为一种源自外国的宗教“中国儒教”在印尼的本土化。印尼孔教是印尼化（本土化）的宗教，是中国儒教的印尼化，可以从以下几个方面去看。

---

① 印尼著名伊斯兰教领袖哈姆加把孔子列为真主的使者之一，他认为孔子的教导同穆罕默德的教导是一致的。在每次参加华裔青年入教仪式上，他总是把孔子的教导同伊斯兰教教义相提并论。参见郑仁良：《对印尼华人同化和回教化问题的讨论》，（新加坡）《亚洲文化》第八期，1987 年 10 月，第 77 页。

1. 印尼孔教使用的语言文字是印尼语。经典、教义的解说及举行仪式的过程，大多数是使用印尼文、印尼语表述。《四书》已全部翻译成印尼文，《五经》现已翻译了三经。这是因为孔教徒大多是既不懂华文，也不懂华语的土生华人和年轻一代华人。

2. 作为宗教最核心的部分——印尼孔教的教义也已经带有十分明显的印尼色彩，而没有完全照搬中国儒学。最突出的是对“天”的解释，把天解释和表述为“独一无二”的唯一的上帝，这些与中国儒学的解释明显不同。这是因为，在印尼，对宗教教义、对上帝、天的解释都必须遵循印尼国家的规定，这往往是以伊斯兰教为标准的。印尼宗教部以及1965年总统有关的命令中，都谈到宗教的标准最基本的应具备四条：第一条即为“信仰唯一的、独一无二的真主或上帝”。[①]

3. 印尼孔教的组织、机构、宗教活动场所等也都体现了印尼化的特点。

印尼孔教的中央、地方各级组织、各类机构都是在印尼国家的有关法律、政策框架下形成与发展起来的。“礼堂”及学师、文师、教生等三级教职人员的名称不仅体现了儒家文化的特点，而且也体现了在印尼特殊环境和历史背景下，印尼孔教有意区别于基督教等其他宗教的特点。由于历史的原因，不少地方组织及孔教礼堂都设立在三教合一的华人庙宇之中。

4. 孔教的宗教仪式体系也有鲜明的印尼化、本土化的特点。

其一，纳入了印尼国家颁布的纪念节日。

其二，纳入了地方认同、面向社会的慈善活动的内容。如每年农历七月的中元节，农历腊月廿四日的送神节（祭灶节），孔教举办面向社会的慈善活动。

其三，纳入了作为印尼国家公民义务的内容。按照印尼国家法律规定，制订印尼孔教婚姻法，制订和举行孔教订婚和结婚的立愿仪式、就职宣誓仪式，等等。

其四，适应印尼社会实际情况规定礼拜宣道仪式节期。如每周一次的礼拜仪式，改变了华人初一、十五祭拜的传统，但也不同于基督教一律定为星期天上午，只是规定每周一次，具体时间由各个孔教会根据所在社区具体情况，方便教徒而决定。作为重要宗教节日的“冬至节”，既使用孔圣诞历法（即中国夏历），又为方便起见，直接定为公历12月22日。

以上这些突出的印尼化特点，使得印尼孔教成为与中国儒教（儒学）风貌迥异的、印尼的一个宗教。

---

① MATAKIN：《Ada Pendidikan Tiada Perbedaan：Golden anniversary MATAKIN 16april 1955—2005》MATAKIN，Jakarta，2005（印尼孔教最高理事会编：《有教无类：印尼孔教最高理事会成立50周年纪念刊》），雅加达，2005年，第37页。

（二）马来西亚：在与伊斯兰教文化的交流中探讨儒学的发展

在马来西亚华人依托完整的华文教育体系，儒学/儒教得以比较好的传承。但是长期马来民族主义高涨以及“国家文化政策”的推行，华人文化、儒学的发展备受抑制。20 世纪 90 年代以来，政府领导人突破种族思想的樊篱，倡导各族文化交流与融合，马来西亚的儒学迎来发展的契机。

副首相安华·易卜拉欣赞扬中国古典文化，率先学习华语，并喜欢引述孔子的话语，曾经出访中国参观孔庙。他认为，“马来人学习孔孟思想是迎合时代及回教的需要”。1995 年 3 月，马来亚大学举办“伊斯兰教和儒学：文明对话”国际学术会议，他到会发表祝词演讲。来自马、中、美、日的多名专家学者发表专题演讲，探求回儒两大世界文明在过去和现在的共同点．以及两者面对的问题和解决问题的方法途径。

在政府的支持下，马来亚大学宣布将“文明对话”活动作为马来亚大学常设性活动之一，成立“文明对话”中心，并筹建“东亚研究所”。

儒学研究团体纷纷成立，开展儒学研究，取得丰硕成果，并多次举办研讨会。除了前已述及马来亚中文系毕业生协会，还有：朱熹学术研究会，成立于 2001 年 12 月。孔学研究会 2003 年正式成立。各种文教团体的儒学研究纷纷兴起，并创办多种刊物。如由董总出版的《资料与研究》1992 年 5 月创刊；马来西亚中华大会堂总会 1999 年 7 月创刊《愿景》，华社研究中心 2000 年 1 月创办出版《人文杂志》等。

由民间儒教一贯道支持的吉隆坡崇德文教研习会 1997 年邀请台湾儿童读经教育的倡导者王财贵博士抵马国作全国巡回演讲，很快成立了马来西亚儿童读经推广中心，使诵读经典（儒家为主）活动在马、新、印尼各地迅速推广开来。

（三）潜龙在田、细水长流：新加坡第二次儒学复兴高潮之后

在新加坡，在实行英语至上和迅速西化政策多年之后，由于担心过于西化，可能会导致道德的堕落和社会经济发展的停滞，20 世纪 80 年代又发起推行儒家伦理的“儒学复兴运动”，盛极一时。但到了八十年代末，这场文化运动却由热转冷，盛况不再。

在儒学传播失去了官方强力支持的背景下，1990 年代以后，儒学在新加坡的流传又恢复了之前“潜龙在田、细水长流”的状态。① 在新加坡儒学的“潜龙”、“长流水”中，除了国立大学、南洋理工继续保持儒学的课程与研究以及新加坡儒学研究会、新加坡儒学会等儒学团体，还有一支很重要的力量，即是民间儒学社团——具有百年历史的新加坡南洋孔教会。

南洋孔教会的前身是为实得力孔教会，成立于 1914 年，这也是一个世纪前儒学复

---

① 苏新鋈：《儒家思想近十五年来在新加坡的流传（1982－1997）》，林纬毅主编：《别起为宗：东南亚的儒学与孔教》，新加坡亚洲研究学会，2010 年。

兴运动终结后遗留下来的唯一硕果。康有为的弟子、哥伦比亚大学博士陈焕章继承老师的未竟事业，于1912年在上海建立中国孔教会，成功地在中国各地建立起了一百多个分支机构，并且出版《孔教会杂志》。为推动孔教复兴运动在海外的发展，陈焕章还在香港策划并创立了孔教学院，亲自兼任院长，使得“该院遂成为国内外各分会相互策应之枢纽。”但是在遭遇“五四运动”的重创后，迅速地走向失败。然而在海外华人社会中，尤其是在东南亚，却获得了相当的成功。实得力孔教会（另名为中国孔教会新加坡分会）的成立，就是这一运动在新加坡活动的直接结果。[①] 实得力孔教会集中了林文庆等一批热衷于孔教的中坚分子，一直为建立孔教体制而努力。

1949年改名为南洋孔教会，活动日渐频繁。历年之活动，“最持久而富有意义者，莫若征文比赛”。自1967年之后，每年举办圣诞纪念征文比赛，参加比赛人士，不但数量极多，并且包括许多不同的职业；其中有校长、教师、记者、店员、医师、大专中学生等，影响相当广泛。南洋孔教会还发起并树立了当时东南亚第一座、也是“世界上第四座大成至圣孔子先师青铜像”。

南洋孔教会作为一个“弘扬孔教的团体，数十年来毁誉参半”，但他们“苦心孤诣，屹不为动”。后来由于多方面原因，很长时间委顿不举，奄奄一息。2007年，以郭文龙会长为首的新一任董事会成立，分析国情，适应社会，为孔教会重新定位，提出作为“文化团体”开展新的活动和树立践行儒家伦理规范的目标，吸引了大批年轻人参加，成立了青年团，会员增多，规模扩大，并经过多年的努力，终于购得会所，实现了几代人的夙愿。还与新加坡儒学会、新加坡国立大学、新加坡国家图书馆、喜耀文化学会、东亚人文研究所、宗乡会馆联合总会等团体合作，邀请新加坡及中国学者，举办了一系列儒学课程及传统文化讲座，据统计，自2008年至2013年讲座达50余场，影响越来越大，百年老树終得再发新枝散新叶，为新加坡儒学的传承发展带来新的希望。

总之，东南亚华人移民在海外对儒学的传承播布，不是简单的、原封不动地照搬和复制；而更重要的——是一种生机勃勃的文化创造（用中国大陆当代流行语言来说就是文化创新）。这种文化创造表现为华人以及儒学对移居国当地文化的适应、吸纳、融合，表现为儒学及中华文化与华人移居各地文化的交流、会通与发展。

这一文化传承和创新的过程，显示了儒学多元、开放、包容的特质及其强大的生命力；同时体现了作为儒学及中华文化载体的华人族群富有文化创造力的民族特性，显示出他们在儒学与世界文明多元共处中的重要作用。

许多问题尚在思考之中，内容及附注尚有待完善，请勿转载引用。不当之处，尚祈方家指正。

---

① 盛碧珠：《本会简史》，盛碧珠主编：《孔圣降生二五四五周年纪念（暨）南洋孔教会成立八十周年纪念双庆特刊》，新加坡：南洋孔教会，1995年。

# 马来西亚国学：儒学可以学些什么?

马来西亚拉曼大学　郑文泉

## 百年来儒学的国学化、古学化及其不满

儒学对百年来作为概括中国“本国固有的学术文化”的“国学”一词，并不陌生。从文献学的角度来看，这个名词在20世纪20年代以来即指向余英时所析说的“经过（清朝）考证方法洗礼之后的‘四部’（经史子集）之学”之意,① 而“四部之学”恰恰是儒家学术的目录分类之说,②二者实是一名异而实同的概念关系。

但是，这种同实异名的关系，却是儒家学术的重大时代转折与标志。这种转折，就是将“四部之学”视为中国过去的（且已死了的）学问传统，是国故学的意思：

可以说，早在1919年，在胡适等人影响之下的毛子水、傅斯年这帮年轻学生的心目中，从章太炎那里转手过来的“国故”，便已经不是章太炎、邓实、刘师培们的“国粹”，而是一堆杂乱零碎的材料，等待着西方传来的“科学精神”对之进行整理。而且在这里，“国故学”也已经不是一个独立的学科门类，而是表示整理中国传统典籍的意思，整理的结果，是将之放在各门学科之中。毛子水以一个26岁的青年，非常精准地把握了当时新派学人的“中国文化观”，即中国成为历史，中国典籍成为史料。而将这种国学观进行全面阐述，并产生重大影响的，是胡适之。③

这个“故”，在胡适心目中恰是“死亡”或“过去”的意思，表示“四部之学”已经是和现时代无涉的陈堆故纸：

概而言之，国故已经死亡，“因为国故是过去的已经僵化的中国旧文化，所以

---

① 见余英时:《“国学”与中国人文研究》,《人文·民主·思想》，北京：海豚出版社，2011年，第6页。

② 对“四部之学”乃至《四库全书》是否是“儒藏”文献的析释，见王锦民，《古典目录与国学源流》，北京：中华书局，2012年，第346—351页。

③ 见陈壁生:《经学的瓦解》，上海：华东师范大学出版社，2014年，第80—81页。

它与现在中国人的生活实在没有什么关系”。[①]

换句话说，20世纪将传统儒学的“四部之学”称之为“国学”，并没有礼敬的雅意，而是表征其已与本时代无涉的一套“古学”之贬义。

这种“与现在中国人的生活实在没有什么关系”的“古学”模式的儒学或“国学”影响有多深远？可以说，从1949年以后在港台乃至东南亚大学建立的中文系，一直到近年中国大陆又复苏的国学院，其课程建制无一不是上述“中国传统典籍”意义的“四部之学”，其作为中国过去的学问表征之意并未有根本变异。不能理解儒学在现时代的上述“国学”处境与背景，就很难理解如下学人之不时对儒学业已成为一套“口耳记诵之学”所发出的不平与不满之情。

在谈儒家思想时，许多人都会强调儒家学问并不只是一套玄思或言说，它具有极强的实践性。所谓：“读圣贤书，所学何事？”读书不光要明理，更须把所明之理具体表现在为人处事上，故读圣贤书，目的是学圣人那般让自己也努力成为圣贤，否则就只是口耳记诵之学，与自己的身心性命无关。

这个儒学的基本原则，相信没有人不明白，但落在具体实践层面却又怎么样呢？

大部分人其实仍只是在理论上明白了、在言说上强调了而已，在具体为人处事上如何表现圣贤气象，恐怕甚少人在此自我要求。因此，儒家所讲的修齐治平之道，根本在“修身以为本”这一关上就极少人真去实践，实况如此，儒学焉能复苏乎？[②]

有些不仅要求儒学要“与自己的身心性命”有关，甚至还要能够解决当今社会的重大问题，如“大陆新儒家”群体之谓：

从情感倾向和学术立场上来看，此群体的特征是非常鲜明的。他们强调儒学在今天社会问题中的优先地位，也就是认为，儒学作为一种思想资源，能够为今天的诸多社会问题，提供更佳的解决方案。这也是称其为“儒家”的根本原因。[③]

由此可见，对当今儒学的思考，甚至一个人是不是、能不能算是“儒家”，几乎就形同是对上述儒学的“国学”化、“古学”化的建制接纳与否的态度问题，足示儒学作为“国故是过去的已经僵化的中国旧文化”的时代已经相当久远了。

话说回来，要求儒学不应该只是一套国故学，或只是一套随之而来的“口耳记诵之学”，这些与儒学既有的“四部之学”的文献与学问分野有何联系与障碍，还未被认真提上议事日程来讨论。众所周知，从传统的“四部之学”要走向过去百年来的“整

---

① 按：这是钱玄同的话，见同上注，第92—93页。

② 见龚鹏程：《序言》，朱翔非：《新孝道：〈孝经〉新解》，北京：京华出版社，2011年，第14页。

③ 见进罡：《总论：如何切中活的思想史》，崔罡等：《新世纪大陆新儒家研究》，合肥：安徽人民出版社，2012年，第29页。此一新儒家群体的思想近况，可见曾亦、郭晓东编著：《何谓普世？谁之价值？当代儒家论普世价值》，上海：华东师范大学出版社，2013年。

理中国传统典籍”的国故学途径，乃至一套“口耳记诵之学”，是很相顺且自然的理路联系。一旦儒学要变成现时代的“身心性命之学”乃至“儒学在今天社会问题中的优先地位”的学问性质与方向，这个“四部之学”的文献与学问体系是否需要加以调整、拆解甚至重组，以满足这个“优位”的需要，似乎不是一个无关紧要的学术课题。换句话说，我们除了眼前的“四部之学”体例之外，是否还有别的“国学”体例以改变其现时代的过去的（且已死了的）国故学境况，恰是本文拟为探讨的课题所在。

本文对此一课题的探讨办法，正如题目所署，是“马来西亚国学：儒学可以学些什么?”。与上述儒学远在《隋书．经籍志》即已形成“四部之学”的（唯一）定制而易趋于僵化的历史形势不同，马来西亚国学是近三百年在西学的刺激、启发之下而形成的现代建制，体例多元且各有其因应时代问题的内涵与目标在。从这个角度来说，马来西亚现有四大国学体例，是否有颇堪儒学借鉴以满足其不徒是一套国故学或“口耳记诵之学”的时代变革与要求，就是本文此下分析的焦点所在。

## 马来西亚国学的四大体例

承上所述，儒学对“本国（中国）固有的学术文化”的目录学研究，从汉代刘向、刘歆父子算起也已有逾两千年的历史，而马来西亚的国学研究则是相对晚近的事。“国学”既是指“本国固有的学术文化”，则马来西亚国学就是指马来西亚自古以来的学术文化之总体。这里的区分与重点是“学术文化”而不是一般所指的“传统文化”：传统文化是指流传下来的自然类与人文类的文化总和，学术文化则是对传统文化的学术整理与研究的结果，二者的区分是一个是第一序（未经整理）和另一个是第二序（经学术整理）的文化整体与构成，彼此既有区隔但又相互联系的文化体系。作为“本国固有的学术文化”之马来西亚“国学”，其历史肯定远比马来西亚传统文化还要短暂，且可能可以套用梁启超、钱穆的同名著作《中国近三百年学术史》那样只有三百年的历史光景。

如果说马来西亚传统文化（指“信史”以来的文化传统）始于公元78年，也就是萨迦（Saka）1年，那么马来西亚国学也就是学术文化可能要迟至18世纪才开始（详下表一）。熟悉东南亚古代碑铭和文本的人都知道，萨迦历是马来西亚在采用伊斯兰历之前所通行了一千两三百年之久的古代（印度）纪元方式，除了少数被刻写（碑铭）、书写（抄本）的文献之外，这一期间的文化（和印度一样）多是口传的。在后来伊斯兰文明的要求与影响之下，这些口传的（如 Hikayat Seri Rama）和伊斯兰本身的（如 Hikayat Muhammad Hanafiah）文本才被书写成今天所见的爪威文（马来语的阿拉伯文字）抄本流传下来。但是，只有在据信是最早的 Francois Valentjin 和 G. H. Werndly

分别于1726年、1736年对这些文本进行目录汇编和文本研究之后，[1]才逐渐开启和形成后世（也就是现在所说的）“本国固有的学术文化”与传统。

**表一　马来西亚文化—学术史分期**

| 公　元 | 朝　代 | 文明属性 | 学术属性 |
|---|---|---|---|
| 79—669 | 古列国时期 | 印度文明 | 口传文化 |
| 670—1274 | 室利佛逝王朝时期 | | |
| 1275—1401 | 爪哇—暹罗统治时期 | | |
| 1402—1873 | 马六甲—文莱列国时期 | 伊斯兰文明 | 撰著文化 |
| 1874—1956 | 英国统治时期 | 英国文明 | 学术文化 |
| 1957 | 马来西亚联邦时期 | | |

换句话说，马来西亚“国学”大致是一个受惠于西学的近现代产物，迄今约有三百多年的历史。撇开“马来西亚”作为一个“本国固有的学术文化”的国家单位也是于1963年去英国殖民化（意即无英国即无今日马来西亚）的结果不说，本文现在所可考察出的四大“国学”体例实际上有些是远在此之前即已滥觞，只是到了1963年以后才扩大其范围至今日的东马地区。举例来说，诸如“伊斯兰文明与亚洲文明”（Tamadun Islam dan Tamadun Asia，简称TITAS）的“文明研究”之国学体例，远在马来亚于1957年独立后即因学校历史教学的需要，已以“马来亚居民的文化背景”（Latar Belakang Kebudayaan Penduduk—Penduduk di Tanah Melayu）的名目出版了以下四大册材料（1962年初版，1978年重印）：

伊斯兰文化（Muhammad Zaki Badawi著）

中国文化（王赓武著）

印度教文化（此一册1963年出版，N. M. Idaikadar著）

欧洲文化（Anthony Short著）

据上述第三册的〈前言〉所示，这一系列其实还包括有第五册《马来文化》，但未被落实。[2]换句话说，在当时的马来西亚人即已觉得“马来亚居民的文化背景”应包含了伊斯兰文化、马来文化、中国文化、印度教文化及欧洲文化，始为周全，和今日

① 此可详Siti Hawa Salleh, Kesusasteraan Melayu Abad Kesembilan Belas (Kuala Lumpur: Dewan Bahasa dan Pustaka, 1997), hlm. 73—139。

② 见Syed Nasir Ismail, ‘Kata Pengantar’, N. M. Idaikaar, Latar Belakang Kebudayaan Penduduk—Penduduk di Tanah Melayu: Bahagian Kebudayaan Hindu (Kuala Lumpur: Dewan Bahsa dan Pustaka, Kementerian Pelajaran Malaysia, 1963), hlm. vi。

“伊斯兰文明与亚洲文明”的“文明研究”以为“被对话的文明以与本国各个族群及宗教的生活方式、价值观有密切关系者为对象”而具体包括了“伊斯兰文明、马来文明、中国文明及印度文明；尽管不是以一个独立的单元来讲授，西方文明也是被讨论的范围”的五大范围来说，①是何等的不约而同而又殊途同归法!?

承上所述，马来西亚从15世纪以前的口传文化（中经伊斯兰化时期的撰著文化）进入到目前的学术文化，西学的传入和输导既是一个关键因素，且迄今已至少有四大符合且满足“本国固有的学术文化”的“国学”之内涵体例者：

“马来西亚百科全书”体例，即吉隆坡法属Editions Didier Millet出版公司的十六卷本《马来西亚百科全书》(The Encyclopedia of Malaysia)，不是采取一般常见的词条体而是篇章体，分别纳入了马来西亚制度的十六个门类即自然类四种/卷（环境、植物、动物、海洋)、历史类四卷（古代史、现代初期、当代政府与政治、当代经济)、社会阶层类二卷（统治者、人民与其传统）及（人民）文化类六卷（建筑、表演艺术、语言与文学、宗教与信仰、手艺与视觉艺术、体育与娱乐)，此相当传统儒学或今国学中的史学纪传体的“书志体”而可视之为马来西亚国学的“书志体”体例。

**表二 《马来西亚百科全书》卷目**

| 卷 次 | 出版年 | 门 类 |
|---|---|---|
| 第1—5卷 | 1998 | 第一卷《环境》、第二卷《植物》、第三卷《动物》、第四卷《古代史》第五《建筑》卷。 |
| 第6—7卷 | 2001 | 第六卷《海洋》、第七卷《现代史初期》 |
| 第8—9卷 | 2004 | 第八卷《表演艺术》、第九卷《语言与文学》。 |
| 第10卷 | 2005 | 第十卷《宗教与信仰》。第11卷2006第十一卷《当代政府与政治》。 |
| 第12—14卷 | 2007 | 第十二卷《人民与传统》、第十三卷《当代经济》、第十四卷《手工与视觉艺术》。 |
| 第15卷 | 2009 | 第十五卷《体育与娱乐》。 |
| 第16卷 | 2011 | 第十六卷《马来西亚统治者》。 |

资料来源：郑文泉：《马来西亚“国学”的研究与体例》，钟瑜编：《马来西亚文化与艺术》，吉隆坡：华社研究中心，出版中。

① 见由教育部授权马来亚大学文明对话中心起草的“伊斯兰文明与亚洲文明”课纲：Osman Bakar, Azizan Baharuddin, Zaid Ahmad eds., Modul Pengajian Tamadun Islam dan Tamadun Asia (Kuala Lumpur: Penerbit Universiti Malaya, 2009), hlm xiii。

“马来西亚五百人物志”或“马来西亚二十名人丛书”体例，相当传统儒学史学纪传体中的“列传体”：前者是Arus Intelek出版公司于2013年6月出版的二十卷本《马来西亚五百人物志》(Malaysia 500 Khazanah Insan Aset Negara)，从二十个不同领域（卷目见下）来涵盖马来西亚所有的学术文化与其人之现象；后者是Medium Publications出版的三十二册本（也就是三十二个不同门类或领域）的《马来西亚二十名人丛书》(Siri 20 Tokoh Malaysia，尚未出齐，理论上涵盖640位名人）来涵盖“本国固有的学术文化”之人物；

**表三　《马来西亚五百人物志》卷目**

| 卷　次 | 人　物　门　类 |
| --- | --- |
| 1 | 国家元首 |
| 2 | 各政党首领 |
| 3 | 历届部长与政治元老 |
| 4 | 国家首席秘书与杰出行政人物 |
| 5 | 民族英雄 |
| 6 | 警察人物 |
| 7 | 军队人物 |
| 8 | 公私立机关主管 |
| 9 | 教育局长与杰出教育人物 |
| 10 | 语言、文学与传媒界学问家 |
| 11 | 艺术与文化名人（一） |
| 12 | 艺术与文化名人（二） |
| 13 | 体坛健将 |
| 14 | 科学家 |
| 15 | 工商推手 |
| 16 | 专业人士 |
| 17 | 非政府组织领袖 |
| 18 | 伊斯兰精英 |
| 19 | 专业组织推手 |
| 20 | 思想家 |

资料来源：郑文泉：《马来西亚“国学”的研究与体例》，钟瑜编：《马来西亚文化与艺术》，吉隆坡：华社研究中心，出版中。

“伊斯兰文明与亚洲文明”体例，即时下公、私立大学必修的“伊斯兰文明与亚洲文明”（Tamadun Islam dan Tamadun Asia，简称 TITAS）一课，是将马来西亚“本国固有的学术文化”理解为一个文明整体，内含有伊斯兰文明、马来文明、印度文明、中国/华人文明与西方文明的子体系，每一体系含有该文明之地理、社会与文化、哲学与宗教、政治与政府体制、家庭与社会体制、各文明领域之成就等，在传统中国史学似未有严格对应的体例，故名之谓“文明研究”体例。

**表四 《伊斯兰文明与亚洲文明》课程内容**

| 单　元 | 内　容 |
|---|---|
| 第一单元 | 文明研究导论 |
| 第二单元 | 伊斯兰文明 |
| 第三单元 | 亚洲文明：马来文明 |
| 第四单元 | 亚洲文明：印度文明 |
| 第五单元 | 亚洲文明：中华文明 |
| 第六单元 | 时事课题与未来 |

资料来源：郑文泉：《马来西亚“国学”的研究与体例》，钟瑜编：《马来西亚文化与艺术》，吉隆坡：华社研究中心，出版中。

马来传统文献体例，由国家图书馆、语文出版局及各大学马来研究机构所执行，相当儒学传统的文献学研究，彼此均有两方面的共同特点可言：一是“本国固有的学术文化”是指主体学术文化，所以中国的“国学”实际上是“汉学”而马来西亚的“国学”也因此是“马来学”而不是全部的学术文化、二是这个“学术文化”是指历史文献或文本，所以中国今日的“国学”是指“‘四部’（经史子集）之学”而马来文献也有它自己的文献分类与说法（详下例）。

**表五 语文出版局《马来传统文献》目次**

| 章　次 | 内　容 |
|---|---|
| 第一章 | 概念与进路 |
| 第二章 | 历史背景 |
| 第三章 | 人民文学 |
| 第四章 | Hikayat 类文献 |
| 第五章 | Panji 类文献 |

| 章　次 | 内　容 |
| --- | --- |
| 第六章 | 史诗类文献 |
| 第七章 | 历史类文献 |
| 第八章 | 伊斯兰先知与伟人故事 |
| 第九章 | 伊斯兰经籍类文献 |
| 第十章 | 法律与国体类文献 |
| 第十一章 | 传统知识类文献 |

资料来源：郑文泉：《马来西亚“国学”的研究与体例》，钟瑜编：《马来西亚文化与艺术》，吉隆坡：华社研究中心，出版中。

以上四大体例，即为本文所可考察的学界之试图概括、爬梳“本国固有的学术文化”之马来西亚“国学”的模式与结晶，其中既有儒学并不感陌生的“马来西亚百科全书”体例、“马来西亚五百人物志”或“马来西亚二十名人丛书”体例及马来传统文献体例（详下），但也有一时不容易找到其对应体例的“伊斯兰文明与亚洲文明”模式，既可看出马来西亚国学研究与其体例趋于多元且尚未定于一尊，也足可让我们借此回头探索是否有足堪儒学借鉴的“四部之学”以外的其他体例之变革需要。

马来西亚国学可供儒学借鉴的几个要点：

如上所述，马来西亚之有国学是相当晚近的事，它迄今为止的四大国学体例对已有逾两千年国学历史的儒学来说，也并不见得都有新意与创意。仔细地说，我们即可轻易地找出“马来西亚百科全书”的对应体例为郑樵的《通志（二十略）》，[①]“马来西亚五百人物志”或“马来西亚二十名人丛书”体例相当儒学三大纪年、纪传、纪事的史学体例中之“列传”体裁，马来传统文献体例甚至与刘向、刘歆以来的目录学成果相较还逊色许多。换句话说，马来西亚现有国学体例对儒学有新意且可能提供其变革国故学或“口耳记诵之学”之现时代需要者，或可集中于“伊斯兰文明与亚洲文明”一例来探索之。

严格说来，“伊斯兰文明与亚洲文明”的“文明研究”体例与“马来西亚百科全书”的“书志体”还多少有重叠关系，并不截然构成二种不同体例。这是因为，一旦我们进入到每一文明单元的内部情形来看，它们与“书志体”的门类都呈现出异曲同

① 这点我在以下论文已有详尽证明：Tee Boon Chuan（郑文泉），‘Sains Ketamadunan Ensiklopedia Malaysia dan Historiografi Konfusianisme’，kertas kerja Seminar Sains Ketamadunan：Ke Arah Pembentukan Paradigma，Kajang：Akademi Kajian Ketamadunan，Kolej Dar al－Hi*km*ah，11－12 Mac 2014。

构的对应关系（详下对照表），如下“中华文明”单元所示：

**表六 《伊斯兰文明与亚洲文明》的“中华文明”目次**

| 节次 | 内容 | 《马来西亚百科全书》 | 对应程度 |
|---|---|---|---|
| 5.1 | 引论 | — | — |
| 5.2 | 概念与定义 | — | — |
| 5.3 | 疆域<br>5.3.1 地理位置 | 第一卷《环境》、第六卷《海洋》。 | 前者为略 |
| 5.4 | 社会与文化<br>5.4.1 中国语言与文字系统<br>5.4.2 中国文明中的世界观<br>5.4.2.1 天<br>5.4.2.2 道<br>5.4.2.3 太极、阴阳和五行<br>5.4.2.4 天人合一<br>5.4.2.5 中庸之道 | 第九卷《语言与文学》、第十卷《宗教与信仰》。 | 基本对应而后者较详 |
| 5.5 | 多元的中国宗教与哲学<br>5.5.1 儒家<br>5.5.2 佛家<br>5.5.3 道家<br>5.5.4 墨家<br>5.5.5 法家<br>5.5.6 伊斯兰 | 第十卷《宗教与信仰》。 | 基本对应 |
| 5.6 | 政府制度与政治组织 | 第十一卷《当代政府与政治》、第十六卷《马来西亚统治者》。 | 基本对应而后者较详 |
| 5.7 | 家庭制度 | 第十二卷《人民与传统》 | 后者较详 |
| 5.8 | （按：此节与下节重复而较简略，故整并入下节） | — | — |

| 节次 | 内容 | 《马来西亚百科全书》 | 对应程度 |
|---|---|---|---|
| 5.9 | 各文明领域的成就<br>5.9.1 文学<br>5.9.2 艺术<br>5.9.3 科学与技术 | 第九卷《语言与文学》、第八卷《表演艺术》、第十四卷《手工与视觉艺术》。 | 后者较详而缺“科学与技术”类 |

资料来源：Osman Bakar，Azizan Baharuddin，Zaid Ahmad eds.，Modul Pengajian Tamadun Islam dan Tamadun Asia，hlm viii.

综上所析，马来西亚国学的“伊斯兰文明与亚洲文明”的“文明研究”体例，可见是建立在类似“马来西亚百科全书”的“书志体”上，是以“书志体”来归纳一个文明的内涵的结果。从这个角度来说，“伊斯兰文明与亚洲文明”就是“（甲）书志体与（乙）书志体”的复合体例，是“书志体”的进阶体例而非另一体例。

尽管如此，这种“（甲）书志体与（乙）书志体”的复合原因和意义，却和单一“书志体”体例本身大不同，需要在此一提。本文此前已提及马来西亚“国学”诞生的原因与背景在于近现代西学的刺激与启发结果，不同体例各有其回应的具体对象与目标，如“伊斯兰文明与亚洲文明”的情形是：

**表七　“伊斯兰文明与亚洲文明”体例编年**

| 日　期 | 大事记 |
|---|---|
| 1993 | Samuel P. Huntington 在《外交政策》(Foreign Affairs) 发表题为《文明的冲突》一文，原是对 Francis Fukuyama 的 The End of History and the Last Man 一书回应之作，却引起广泛的世界媒体与学术效应。 |
| 1995 | 时在美国的 Seyyed Hossein Nasr 托其两位马来西亚学生 Anwar Ibrahim（时为马来西亚副首相）、Osman Bakar（时为马来亚大学副署理校长）开办“伊斯兰与儒家的文明对话”的学术会议，以示对 Samuel P. Huntington 理论的不认同以及文明间对话的促进需要。 |
| 1996 | 马来亚大学成立文明对话中心，并受教育部之托筹划文明对话相关之课程与教材，最后拟成两学分之“伊斯兰文明与亚洲文明”（Tamadun Islam dan Tamadun Asia，简称 TITAS）一课，分别讲解伊斯兰文明、中国文明、印度文明、马来文明等四大文明并穿插西方文明的相关影响与挑战。 |

| 日　期 | 大事记 |
|---|---|
| 1996 | Samuel P. Huntington 将〈文明的冲突?〉一文扩写为《文明的冲突与世界秩序的重建》（The Clash of Civilizations and the Remaking of World Order）一书于是年出版，并应马来亚大学之邀前来观摩文明对话中心与其活动。 |
| 1998 | 教育部规定于是年起公立大专必修“伊斯兰文明与亚洲文明”一课。 |
| 2001 | 联合国宣布今年为“文明间对话年”（Year of Dialogue among Civilizations），马来西亚借此推介“伊斯兰文明与亚洲文明”一课并获得众多国家推举。 |
| | 第一部“伊斯兰文明与亚洲文明”课本由马来亚大学出版社出版，内有教育部长序言，文明方面增加“马来西亚原住民文明”和“日本文明”二种。 |
| 2006 | 联合国再次于 Qatar 首都举办“文明间联盟”（Alliance of Civilizations）国际会议，“伊斯兰文明与亚洲文明”一课的正面作用再次获得首肯。 |
| 2013 | 高等教育部规定于是年九月起私立大专亦必修“伊斯兰文明与亚洲文明”一课。 |

资料来源：Osman Bakar，‘Kata Pengantar’，dlm Osman Bakar，Azizan Baharuddin，Zaid Ahmad eds.，Modul Pengajian Tamadun Islam dan Tamadun Asia，hlm xi-xvii.

由此可见，这个体例诞生的原因是为反对文明冲突论的国际现实，而透过“（甲）书志体与（乙）书志体”的复合体例来促进文明间对话，以遏止文明冲突论成为现实，从而达到文明间和平相处的目标。这么一来，在“书志体”之上形成的“（甲）书志体与（乙）书志体”的复合体例的马来西亚“伊斯兰文明与亚洲文明”的“国学”体例，就有了鲜明的现实意义，而不尽然是“国故学”之作，这是儒学可以借鉴的第一个论点。

其次，这个“（甲）书志体与（乙）书志体”的复合体例变成现实的“伊斯兰文明与亚洲文明”而不是别的文明间对话，其原因即在立足于“本国利益”（kepentingan negara）的取择结果。诚如“伊斯兰文明与亚洲文明”体例的重要推手 Osman Bakar 所释，“要包容所有还活着的世界各大文明的知识和讨论，既不可能也不现实”，所以文明间对话必须要有具体的范围和目标。

众所周知，马来西亚是一个多元民族、宗教和文化的国家。这个社会事实使到民族间团结构成本国最重大的国家问题。由此之故，文明间对话必须是与本国人民最为相关的文明间对话，也就是只有那些与本国族群、宗教的人生观、生活方式密切相关的文明才会被选取为对话的范围。

在这个课程里，与本国多元社会现实相符应的四大文明将会专章讲解，它们是伊斯兰文明、马来文明、印度文明和中华文明。除此之外，西方文明虽然未被设为一章，但是在讲解四大文明的现时代发展是如何脱离不了它的影响和作用的角度来看，西方文明还是多少都被讨论到。[1]

换句话说，这个"本国利益"就是指本国的"民族间团结"，是被认为可以透过文明间对话来达成。而这个文明间对话的办法，就是透过与本国民族相攸关的文明传统间之对话，以及对本国各民族文明均有重大影响的现代西方文明间之对话来促成，是可供儒学借鉴的第二个论点。

再次，这个本国"民族间团结"导向的文明间对话要取得实效，无疑需要在各阶层间展开，而学生这一阶层又最不能省免。受惠于"伊斯兰文明与亚洲文明"这一体例的两大推手的体制内条件，即时任马来西亚副首相的 Anwar Ibrahim（后于 1998 年亚金融风暴中被革职）和马来亚大学副署理校长的 Osman Bakar，这一体例最终于 1998 年化为公立高等学校的部定必修课，并于 2013 年进一步扩大至私立学校而为全国高等学校的共同部定必修规定，从而使文明对话成为举国"事业"。换句话说，"伊斯兰文明与亚洲文明"此一"文明研究"体例可供儒学借鉴的第三个论点是，就是举凡具有时代意义（第一论点）而又兼能解决本国重大问题（第二论点）的国学建制必须能与体制结合，才能产生实效，而不是止于学界的言论意见。

复次，对文明间对话的内容与意义本身，也要有所规导，才不至于产生或减免与此一体例目标相背反的负面效应。从"伊斯兰文明与亚洲文明"作为一个课程的内容设计来看，不管是教育部还是课纲的负责人都一再强调文明间的"求同存异"之必要。当时的教育部长在第一部《伊斯兰文明与亚洲文明》教材的序言就明白指出：

出于对大学生必须对重大文明的历史、文化与思想背景均有所认识，我们就在大学阶段推行了文明研究这一门课。这个认识对多元宗教、族群和文化的群众阶层培育相互尊重的态度以及真诚的一体化精神是至关重要的。除此之外，我们也希望大学生在对普世价值观的体认之余也能因此拥有更全球化的视野和开阔的心胸。经过这样的文明认识，我们由衷期许能产生新一代具有高文明且能捍卫普世价值观的马来西亚民族。我们更期待新一代在面对当前乃至未来的种种挑战之时，始终不失且能坚守人性

---

① 本文意译，见 Osman Bakar，'Kata Pengantar'，dlm Osman Bakar， Azizan Baharuddin，Zaid Ahmad eds.，Modul Pengajian Tamadun Islam dan Tamadun Asia，hlm xiii。

的尊严。①

如果说上述序言对文明研究的“求同”的正面内涵与意义着墨较多，那么课纲的负责人在“各文明之间具有共同的人性和社会价值观”可联结起各大文明的一体感之余，也坦诚“文明间的差异也必须加以睿智的处理”。

对不论是信仰间或价值观、观念、习俗之间的差异，必须有一积极的面对态度。这个态度就是要对与我们日常生活相异的其他生活方式表达出宽容之意……我们不希望大学生由于有太多不同的差异把我们的社会切割成不同族群、宗教的现实，而对国家未来感到悲观。相反，我们希望他们相信对这个国家和谐构成挑战的多元性、差异性问题是可以被解决的，从而充满乐观和自信的态度。②

言下之意，这个文明间对话也不能沦于为对话而对话的纯学术课程，而必须有一个明确的“求同存异”的教学任务与目标：“求同”是对文明间的“普世价值观的体认之余也能因此拥有更全球化的视野和开阔的心胸”，“求异”则是“对与我们日常生活相异的其他生活方式表达出宽容之意”。这个始终谨记并自觉此一文明间对话乃为“民族间团结”目标服务，从而遏制文明间冲突成为国际现实的最终目标，是马来西亚国学可供儒学借鉴的第四个论点。

## 小结：儒学走出百年的国学化、古学化窘境是否可能？

承上所析，儒学在现代中国的国学化也是一古学化的趋势，历来已引起不少学人的不安和省思。本文上节所提几点可供儒学借鉴的马来西亚国学的要点，前二项意在提醒儒学的整体学问应有一鲜明的既对现时代国际问题有所因应且同时又立足于“本国（中国）利益”的现实问题为依据，后二点则是其问题解决方式的实施办法与提醒。

从马来西亚的“伊斯兰文明与亚洲文明”体例来类推，身处在多元族群、文明、宗教的世界社会中的儒学，是否觉得应该为文明间的和谐共处尽绵力（此第一要点）？此一尽力又是以本国的文明间和谐共处之达成为现实目标（第二要点）？是否有积极的体制内办法（第三要点）？此一办法之实施是否又始终不背其原来的立项目标？从这些角度来看，一个既是“国学”但同时又是“今学”的马来西亚“伊斯兰文明与亚洲文明”的“文明研究”体例，是可供儒学走出其现时代的国学化、古学化窘境的模式思考之一。

---

① 本文中译，见 Musa Mohamad，‘Pengantar’，dalam Tamadun Islam dan Tamadun Asia（Kuala Lumpur：Penerbit Universiti Malaya，2001），hlm xix。

② 本文中译，见 Osman Bakar，‘Kata Pengantar’，dlm Osman Bakar，Azizan Baharuddin，Zaid Ahmad eds.，Modul Pengajian Tamadun Islam dan Tamadun Asia，hlm xv。Osman Bakar 在文中一再指出“多元性是社会强盛的来源”、“差异和多样性是社会强大和丰饶的泉源”，可惜未展开论述。

# 越南儒学的发展与现代意义

新加坡国立大学　李焯然

儒家思想对越南的历史和发展有深远的影响。越南从陈朝（1225－1400）开始便已经开科取士。官制礼教，均以中国为依据，深受儒家文化的影响。在陈朝以后，越南被中国明朝政府统治达二十年之久，儒家文化更加根深蒂固。但越南的儒学主要继承中国的官方儒学，深受程朱学说的影响，对儒学的探究，创获较少。加以越南学者的著作流传不多，要了解越南学者对儒家文献的释解，甚为困难。本文尝试探讨越南儒学的发展及以河内文庙为例，分析儒学在现代越南的地位。

## 越南儒学的发展

越南在文化上深受儒家思想的影响，自10世纪（939）争取独立，建立大越国后，便开始接受以儒家学说建设国家，其后一直没有中断。① 儒学在传统越南的发展，汉喃研究院前院长潘文阁曾分为四期：②

李朝（1010－1225）：儒佛并重期

陈朝（1225－1400）：佛儒势力的消长期

黎朝（1428－1788）：儒学统治地位的确立及鼎盛时期

阮朝（1802－1945）：儒学复兴期

---

① 详参 Nguyen Ngoc Huy，“The Confucian Incursion into Vietnam”，in Walter H. Slote & George A. De Vos eds.，Confucianism and Family，(Albany：State University of New York Press，1998)，pp. 91－104；John K. Whitmore，“Vietnamese Adaptations of Chinese Government Structure in the Fifteenth Century”，in Edgar Wickberg ed.，Historical Interaction of China and Vietnam：Institutional and Cultural Themes (Kansas：Center for East Asian Studies，University of Kansas，1969)，pp. 1－10. 朱云影：《中国政治制度对于日韩越的影响》，见《中国文化对日韩越的影响》，台北：黎明文化事业股份有限公司，1981年，第407－438页。

② 潘文阁：《深受中国文化影响的越南传统文化》，（新加坡国立大学汉学研究中心专题演讲，1999年1月9日）。

陈朝和黎朝在越南儒学发展的过程中扮演非常重要的角色，但这段期间的儒家著作最为缺乏。目前遗留下来的著作，阮朝时期的比较多，了解当时的儒学情况，相对来说会较为容易。史载阮朝儒学家辈出，如郑怀德、吴仁静、黎光定等文章经学，为世推重。阮朝诸帝对儒学诗文，均有研究，诗文遗作甚多。[①] 中叶以后，儒家文士有潘清简、范富庶、高伯适、阮文迢、阮庭昭、高春育、潘巢南、黄叔杭、邓文瑞等人，所著书立说，皆以发挥儒家孔孟思想为依归。[②] 但在19世纪初期，随着时代的转变和外来文化的影响，对传统文化以至儒家思想提出质疑的人，亦大有人在。Alexander Woodside对高伯适的研究，就反映了当时知识分子的疏离心态。[③]

儒学在越南奠定基础，大概是在三国时代士燮治理交趾四十年期间。越南史家对其在越南兴办文教，甚为推崇。[④] 士燮因为本身有儒家经学修养，且精于《春秋左氏传》，与他推动文教不无关系。但较有系统的进行儒学教育，则始于丁朝和李朝。越南自丁朝（968—980）建国初年，便崇尚儒学，官制礼教，均以中国为依据。至李朝（1010—1225）太宗时，更建立文庙，奉祀孔子及先贤，儒学地位日隆。李仁宗（干德，1066—1138）时始开三庠科试，选拔文学之士入朝为官。又设国子监，延请文学之士任教，儒学自始更盛。当时的儒学主要受中国官方儒学的影响，其中尤以明永乐年间遣监生颁赐《五经四书性理大全》、《为善阴骘》、《孝顺事实》等书于各府州县学校，对当地的儒学教育影响至深。[⑤] 从史料去看，儒学在越南发展的记载并不多。中国方面的文献，甚至如《明实录》，当中有关安南的记载约共一千二百多条，但只纪录当时明朝和安南的政治和军事冲突，甚少提及文化和教育方面的活动，这使中国儒学如何输入和影响越南的儒学发展的问题，有点扑朔迷离。[⑥] 例如《大越史记全书》外纪、本纪、续编共二十四卷，有关儒学的记载只有数十条。比较早的记录是在陈朝时，政府开始选用儒生作为国家的栋梁。《陈纪》太宗绍隆十年（1267）记：

---

① 有关阮朝的文化与政制的研究，目前最详细的，仍为 Alexander Barton Woodside, Vietnam and the Chinese Model: A Comparative Study of Nguyen and Ch' ing Civil Government in the First Half of the Nineteenth Century, (Cambridge: Harvard University Press, 1971).

② 详参罗怀：《中越文化论集·儒学在越南》，第143—158页。

③ Alexander Woodside, "The nature of Vietnamese Confucianism and the Alienation of Cao Ba Quat", Vietnam and the Chinese Model, pp. 223—233.

④ 吴士连编、陈荆和校：《大越史记全书·外纪》，东京：东京大学东洋文化研所，1984年，卷3，上册，第132页。

⑤ 有关明代的官方儒学，可参阅李焯然：《儒学传统与思想变迁》，《亚洲学术文库》第16种，香港：香港教育图书公司，2003年，第123—143页。

⑥ 有关《明实录》中记载安南的史事，可参考赵令扬、陈璋、陈学霖、罗文等编：《明实录中之东南亚史料》，香港：学津出版社，1968年；孙湘云、王玉德等编：《明实录类纂：涉外史料卷》，武汉：武汉出版社，1991年。

夏、四月，选用儒生能文者充馆阁省院。时邓继为翰林院学士、杜国佐为中书省中书令，皆文学之士也。旧制非内人不得为行遣，未尝用文学之士，文学得柄用，自此始。[①]

儒学很早已经为古代越南政府的人才培养，扮演非常重要的角色。建于1070年的河内文庙有一片题1442年的进士题名碑，内容便说："贤才国家之元气，元气盛则国势强以隆，元气馁则国势弱以污。是以圣帝明王，莫不以育材取士、培植元气为先务。"根据当时的记载，陈朝也开始在经筵讲述儒家经典。[②] 越南的开科取士也是自陈朝开始。[③] 科举制度在后来的朝代继续有推行，并与越南的地方学校教育配合。《黎纪》太宗绍平元年（明宣德九年，1434）条重申科试四场要目：

定取士科，诏曰："得人之效，取士为先；取士之方，科目为首。我国家自经兵燹、英才秋叶、俊士晨星，太祖立国之初，首兴学校，祠孔子以太牢，其崇重至矣。而草昧云始，科目未置，朕纂承先志，思得贤才之士，以副侧席之求。令定为试场科目，期以绍平。五年各道乡试、六年会试都省堂，自此以后，三年一大比，率以为常，中选者并赐进士出身。所有试场科目，具列于后：第一场，经义一道、四书各一道，并限于三百字以上。第二场，制、诏、表。第三场，诗赋。第四场，策一道、一千字以上。"[④]

黎圣宗（1460—1497在位）洪德三年（明成化八年，1472）曾会试天下举人，取黎俊彦等二十六人，当时的会试内容是"第一场，四书八题。举子自择四题以作文，《论》四题、《孟》四题。五经每经三题，举子自择一题作文，惟《春秋》二题并为一题，作一文。第二场，则制、诏、表各三题。第三场，诗赋各二题，赋用李白体。第四场，策问一道，其策题以经书旨意之异同、历代政事之得失为问。"[⑤] 越南虽然甚早便举行开科取士，但并不是定期。以黎朝为例，其初或六年一举，或五年一举，未有定例。光顺四年（1463）以后，始三年一科，并以子、午、卯、酉为乡试，辰、戌、丑、未为会试。[⑥]虽然应考人数无法与中国相比，但人数仍续有增加，到19世纪初阮朝时，平均每次会试应考人数平均约170人。[⑦]

史料中并未提及当时科试所用经典和注释，但明朝所颁赐的经书，对越南的科试

---

① 《大越史记全书·本纪》，卷5，上册，页345—346。

② 《大越史记全书》，卷6，上册，页388。

③ 《大越史记全书》，卷8，上册，页471。

④ 《大越史记全书·本纪》，卷11，中册，页577。

⑤ 《大越史记全书》，卷12，中册，页691。

⑥ 《大越史记全书》，卷15，中册，页818。

⑦ 科举考试在后来的发展，详参 Alexander B. Woodside，"An Overview of the Vietnamese Examination System in the 1800's"，Vietnam and the Chinese Model，pp. 170—181.

应该有一定的影响。《大越史记全书》记明永乐十七年（1419）成祖遣使颁赐明政府所编四书五经范本予安南，时为黎太祖己亥年："春、二月，明遣监生唐义颁赐《五经四书性理大全》、《为善阴骘》、《孝顺事实》等书于府、州、县儒学。立僧学，传佛经于僧道司。"① 明初对越南的统治，使儒学的传播更为广泛。② 其后儒家思想便很明显的成为越南知识分子的主导思想，儒家经学中的道理，常常被大臣引用作为治理国家的根据。③ 儒家思想也普遍反映在史臣的评论中，如吴士连在《大越史记全书》中"史臣曰"的意见，便可以看出儒家的价值观在当时大臣心目中的地位。④当时儒生死后能从祀文庙，被认为是最高的荣誉。其中如陈宪宗绍庆元年（明洪武三年，1370）十一月二十六日，国子监司业朱安卒，赠文贞公，以其学业精醇，性刚介，清直严毅，赐从祀文庙。⑤儒学在越南的影响，并不局限在儒臣的范围，当时从个人的修养到国家天下的治平，都以儒家之学作为根据和标准。

## 中国官方儒学在越南的影响

越南的儒学比较单纯，发展亦缺乏多样化，学派的对立，如程朱、陆王的学风分歧，并不多见。其中原因，越南本身的条件限制颇为重要，加以所受的影响都是来自中国的官方儒学，朱学的影响应该是最主要的，与邻近国家如日本、朝鲜的儒学发展相去甚远。程朱之学大抵是在陈朝开始在越南传播，当时在中国已经是南宋末年。陈太宗（1225—1257 在位）时开始下诏学者讲四书五经。《大越史记全书》记载："元丰三年（1253）六月，立国学院，塑孔子、周公、亚圣，画七十二贤像奉事。"同年九月，又"诏天下儒士诣国子院，讲四书五经。"⑥ 陈圣宗（1258—1278 在位）时亦诏贤良明经者讲四书五经。〈陈纪〉记绍隆十五年（1273）"冬十月，诏求贤良明经者为国子监司业，能讲谕四书五经之义，入侍经幄。"⑦ 陈顺宗（1388—1397 在位）时又诏诸

---

① 《大越史记全书》，卷 10，中册，页 517。

② 有关明朝在政治和文化上对越南的影响，参考 Alexander B. Woodside，"Early Ming Expansionism：China's Abortive Conquest of Vietnam"，in Papers on China，Vol. 17，(1963)，pp. 1—37；Lo Jung-pang，"Intervention in Annam：A case study of the foreign policy of the early Ming government"，Tsinghua Journal of Chinese Studies，8：1—2（1970），pp. 154—182；John K. Whitmore，"Chiao-chih and Neo-Confucianism：The Ming attempt to transform Vietnam"，Ming Studies，No. 4（1977），pp. 51—91；赵令扬：《大越史记全书有关明初五朝资料》，见《明史论集》，香港：香港大学中文系，2000 年，第 369—392 页。

③ 《大越史记全书》，卷首，上册，页 83。

④ 《大越史记全书》，卷 6，上册，页 401。

⑤ 《大越史记全书》，卷 7，上册，页 455。

⑥ 《大越史记全书·本纪》，卷 5，上册，页 336。

⑦ 《大越史记全书·本纪》，卷 5，上册，页 348。

路各置学官，教授四书五经，并每年终选优秀者晋京，由皇帝亲自考试，授予官职。四书为程朱学的重要文献，陈朝对四书的重视，反映朱学在越南的流行。从文献的纪录，在陈朝曾经发生越南儒学史上对程朱学说提出挑战的事件，其主角是后来篡位自立的黎季犛（1400—1407在位）。[①] 陈顺宗光泰五年（明洪武二十五年）十二月：

季犛作《明道》十四篇上进。大略以周公为先圣，孔子为先师。文庙以周公正坐南面，孔子偏坐西面。《论语》有四疑，如子见南山、在陈绝粮、公山佛肸、召子欲往之类。以韩愈为盗儒，谓周茂叔、程颢、程颐、杨时、罗仲素、李延平、朱子之徒学博而才疏，不切事情而务为剽窃。[②]

黎季犛的观点不是每个人都可以接受，如国子助教段春雷便上书反驳，但因季犛大权在握，段春雷被斥，并牵连其他官员。对于黎氏所上意见，顺宗亦只能赐诏奖谕。后来的史家对其观点，无不提出谴责，如吴士连便说："前朝之道，非孔子无以明，后圣之生，非孔子无以法，自生民以来，未有盛于孔子者，而敢轻议之，亦不知量也。"[③] 黎季犛的《明道》十四篇今天已经看不到，我们无法知道这次学术论争的程度有多广泛和内容是怎样，但朱学在当时占有一定的地位，从这次事件中可以肯定。黎季犛本身对程朱之学可能亦深有研究，其贬斥程朱之学是纯粹学术立场抑或有政治意图，则不得而知。[④]四年以后，光泰九年（1396）十一月，又作《国语诗义》并序，"令女师教后妃及宫人学习，序黎季牦中多出己意，不从朱子《集传》。"[⑤] 当时黎氏对《诗经》的释义，所谓"国语"大抵是指越语，其内容已不可知，但引来批评和非议却是肯定的。后黎时代儒学家吴士连便痛斥其非，并为朱子辩护，推崇朱子衍述儒学之功。他说：

自孟子没，师各专其门，士各私其学。源分而流支，差之毫厘。谬以千里。或流而为他歧，或倒戈而相攻，莫能归一。其可称者，虽大醇，未免小疵，未有克醇乎其醇者也。朱子生于宋末，承汉唐诸儒笺疏六经之后，溯流求源，得圣人之心于遗经，明圣人之道于训解，研精殚思，理与心融。其说也详，其指也远，所谓集诸儒之大成，而为后学之矜式者也。况有程子倡之于前，而朱子补其未圆于后，则其义精矣。后之

---

① 有关黎季犛的背景和篡位过程，可参考 John K. Whitmore, Vietnam, Ho Quy Ly and the Ming (1371—1421), (New Haven: Yale Southeast Asia Studies, 1985).

② 《大越史记全书·本纪》，卷8，上册，页467—468。本文标点断句按是书陈荆和编校原文。

③ 《大越史记全书·本纪》，卷8，上册，页468。

④ 何成轩认为黎季犛排斥宋儒，是因为宋儒特别强调君臣之义，把三纲五常提到"天理"的高度来认识。黎氏要篡位，自然讨厌宋儒。但如果据此而断言黎季犛"反儒"，那是不符合历史实际的。他的崇儒思想十分明显，只是他对儒学有自己的一套见解。参考氏著：《儒学南传史》，北京：北京大学出版社，2000年，第345—346页。

⑤ 《儒学南传史》，第471页。

有作，恢廓而充大之，膏沃而光泽之，如斯而已，乌得而非议之哉。[①]

吴士连为朱学的辩护及其对朱子的推崇，可见朱子学说在越南士人心目中的地位，后来有学者认为，黎季犛虽然篡陈自立，但因为轻议儒家学说，不能获得士大夫的支持，又于1406年以伏兵攻杀陈天平及护送之明军，导致明成祖大举征伐安南，并于1407年攻入安南，大败黎军，俘其父子，改安南为中国郡县，政权只延续了七年便灭亡。[②]

虽然说儒学在士大夫中有重要的地位，但儒学并不是唯一的思想源流。佛、道二教在黎朝以前，与儒学成鼎足之势，而佛教甚至一度比儒家强盛。这与政治影响有一定的关系，而儒家知识分子亦只能够尽其力量，大声疾呼。[③] 直至后黎皇朝（1428—1788）建立以后，一反李、陈两朝以来的三教并重政策，独尊儒学。除在开科取士方面以儒家经典为根据外，明显可以看到朱学影响的，便是刊行明朝颁赐以朱子学说为依据的《四书大全》、《五经大全》。《越史通鉴纲目》记黎纯宗龙德三年（1734）：

春，正月，颁《五经大全》于各处学官。先是遣官校阅《五经》北板，刊刻书成颁布。令学者传授，禁买北书。又令阮效、范谦益等分刻《四书》、诸史、《诗林字汇》诸本刊行。[④]

黎朝三百余年间，大儒辈出，如阮秉谦、潘孚先、吴士连、黎贵惇（1726—1783）等，均享盛名。阮秉谦精通《易》理，号白云先生。吴士连兼长经、史学，曾参与《大越史记》的编修工作，往往通过其史笔以发扬儒学精神。黎贵惇则为经学大师，著有《群经考辨》、《易经层说》、《春秋略论》、《四书约解》、《圣贤模范录》等。其《四书约解》的内容，主要依据朱熹《四书章句集注》，如释《大学》首句“大学之道，在明明德，在亲民，在止于至善”，朱熹《大学章句》曰：“大学者，大人之学也。明，明之也。明德者，人之所得乎天，而虚灵不昧，以具众理而应万事者也。但为气禀所拘，人欲所蔽，则有时而昏；然其本体之明，则有未尝息者。故学者当因其所发而遂明之，以复其初也。新者，革其旧之谓也，言既自明其明德，又当推以及人，使之亦有以去其旧染之污也。止者，必至于是而不迁之意。至善，则事理当然之极也。言明明德、新民，皆当至于至善之地而不迁。盖必其有以尽乎天理之极，而无一毫人欲之

---

① 《儒学南传史》，第472页。

② 朱云影：《中国文化对日韩越的影响》，第57页。

③ 详参 Alexander Woodside，“Vietnamese Buddhism，the Vietnamese Court，and China in the 1800’s”，Historical Interaction of China and Vietnam：Institutional and Cultural Themes，pp. 11—24；朱云影：《中国文化对日韩越的影响》，第647—698页。

④ 潘清简等：《越史通鉴纲目》（阮朝嗣德二十四年刻本），卷37，第6页。

私也。此三者，大学之纲领也。”① 黎贵惇《四书约解大学解》注释同句谓：

大学者，大人之学也。在明明德者，己之德本明也，而不能不昏于气禀物欲，故学者当因其所发而遂明之以复其初也。民之德本新也，而不能不污于习俗，又当推吾之所明，立法垂教，使革其旧而自新焉。止者，必至于是而不迁之意。至善则事当然之极也，言明明德、新民，皆止于至善之地而不迁。此三者，大学之纲领也。②

《四书约解》在解经方面可谓没有什么创获，只是对朱子之说亦步亦趋。但其特色是每句均加上越音喃文，使越南士子易懂易明，故是书全名为《四书约解国音义增补大全备旨》。卷前有《重刻四书约解序》谓：“圣贤言行载之四书备矣，读者体认而力行之，修身齐家，治国平天下，举此而措之，非难也。是故河南、紫阳两夫子迭出而发明之，理学诸儒又从而剖析之，一字一句，靡不坦然明白。”③ 其对朱学的推崇，是颇为明显的。

阮朝为越南最后的王朝，对儒学的推动，比起前朝，有过之而无不及。④ 1802 年建立的阮朝面对西方殖民主义侵略的威胁和天主教传播的挑战，为巩固封建秩序和国家统一的局面，仿效清朝，大力推崇国学，在各大城镇遍设文庙，举行春秋祭祀；学校教学、政府文书、科举考试，一概采用汉子，不准使用或混用喃字。⑤阮朝国史馆又汇集史家编纂《钦定越史通鉴纲目》、《大南实录》、《大南列传》及《嘉定通志》等，均“本儒家精神为主论之旨”，以加强历史文化的认同。《大南实录》正编〈圣祖人皇帝实录〉卷 21 记明命四年（1824）五月朝臣吴廷价等奏请讲学规程，引清高宗〈御制乐善堂全集序〉，指出《四书五经大全》、《性理大全》、《通鉴纲目》、《大学衍义》、《古文渊鉴》为最重要的讲学经籍。⑥ 至于明命三年（1823）刊行的范阮攸《论语愚按》，主要发挥朱子之说，卷前有郑怀德《论语愚按序》：

世之读书者，莫不曰吾孔子之徒，考其所学，则大异乎孔子之所谓学焉。嗟夫，孔子往矣，今固不可得而亲炙矣。而其言行气象，载在《论语》，皆为万世师法者。……学者之学孔子，舍是书奚求哉？寥寥千载，微言弗章，幸得晦庵朱子为之集注，发挥宗旨。后学于是乎折中，岂非大幸欤。⑦

---

① 朱熹：《四书章句集注》，北京：中华书局，1983 年，第 3 页。

② 黎贵惇：《四书约解大学解国音义增补大全备旨》（明命二十年〔1840〕郁文堂重刊本），卷 1，第 1 页。

③ 黎贵惇：《四书约解大学解国音义增补大全备旨・重刻四书约解序》，第 1 页。

④ 参考 Alexander Woodside，Vietnam and the Chinese Model，第 169－233 页。

⑤ 参考梁志明：《论越南儒教的源流、特征和影响》，《北京大学学报》第 1 期（1995 年），第 28 页。

⑥ 详参朱云影：《中国文化对日韩越的影响》，第 59－60 页。

⑦ 范阮攸：《论语愚按》（明命三年〔1823〕琼洞胡士刊本），卷首，第 4 页。

以上所举，虽然只是零碎的史料，但足以反映朱熹思想在越南儒学发展中的痕迹。越南儒学发展最为蓬勃的几个朝代，大臣的思想主要还是受朱学的影响。配合政府所推动的，又是中国的官方儒学，我们可以说越南的儒学所表现的，就是中国官方儒学的特色。①

## 从河内文庙看越南儒学的特色

文庙是越南儒学发展的重要标志，其中尤以河内文庙历史最为悠久。河内文庙是一座典型的中国式建筑群，位于河内还剑湖西侧，是越南古代王朝的祭孔庙宇和国子监。越南李朝的开国君主以孔孟之道治国，1010 年下诏书把安南国都从花芦迁到升龙(河内)，于城内建庙祀孔子，教化臣民。1070 年文庙建成。《大越史记全书》记载："庚戌年，李朝圣宗皇帝神武二年（1070 年）八月秋建文庙，立孔子，周公及四配塑像，画七十二贤肖像，四季供祭，并让皇太子前来学习。"文庙正殿供奉至圣先师孔子塑像，两侧供奉复圣颜回、宗圣曾子、述圣子思、亚圣孟子等四配的塑像。左右厢房则供奉孔门七十二贤以及越南各朝名儒的牌位。②文庙建成后，又于 1076 年在文庙旁建国子监，成为越南第一所最高学府。因此，河内文庙内的奎文阁（Khuê Văn Các）亦称为"文庙一国子监"（Văn Miếu-Quốc Tử Giám）。文庙主要用于祭祀孔子及其四大弟子。1802 年，阮朝迁都顺化，河内国子监毁而庙存，成为只奉祀孔子的庙宇。文庙建筑群位于河内还剑湖西面，坐北朝南，围墙长约一公里，红墙绿瓦。占地 26000 多平方米，当时仿照山东曲阜孔庙修建，因此布局上与中国的文庙大致相同：具备棂星门、奎文阁、泮池、杏坛、大成殿等主要建筑。河内文庙前后共五进庭院，代表中国文化中"水木火金土"五行，以及"仁义礼智信"五德。大成门前的天光池位于院落中央，左右遍立进士碑林，共 82 块。大成殿内有清康熙皇帝手书"万世师表"横匾。正殿内设有孔子供桌，供奉孔子及其七十二弟子塑像，两侧奉祀中越两国先儒。

① 详参李焯然：《朱子思想与越南儒学》，香港中文大学《中国文化研究所学报》新第 12 期(2003 年)，第 453—471 页。

② 有关河内文庙的规格，参考颜文：《河内文庙—越中文化交流的见证》，《中外文化交流》第 1 期（1995），第 38—39 页。

越南河内文庙的“文庙门”

河内文庙的“奎文阁”

越南河内文庙天光井

越南国子监又称太学，仿照中国宋、明制度，国子监既是教育的管理机构，也是培育官员的最高学府，始建于李朝圣宗神武二年（1070），历经陈朝、黎朝的修缮扩大，成为今天河内文庙的规模。主要的扩建在黎圣宗洪德年间（1470—1497），建东西讲堂以讲肄诸生，增秘书库，以藏书板；东西三舍生房屋各三连，每连二十五闲，共七十五间，以宿诸生。[①]

奎文阁与大成门之间，有一方明净的池水倒映着蓝天白云，就是有名的天光井。天光井东西两侧为“进士坊”，整齐地排列着 82 块进士碑，每侧为 41 块。因越南没有状元，所以没有状元碑而只有进士碑。1484 年，以重视文学著称的黎圣宗下令在文庙国子监树碑，记载从黎圣宗大宝三年（1142）起考中的进士名单。所以越南民间常用这样的话鼓励子弟用功读书：“金榜石碑，千秋永存。”

越南河内文庙进士碑林

康熙皇帝御书牌匾

进士坊的 82 块石碑均由石龟驮着，形态各异，每块高约 1.5 至 2 米不等，记录从 1442 年到 1779 年 337 年间 82 届科举的 1306 名进士的姓名与籍贯。其中包括 12 岁考中的阮贤和 68 岁才考中的郭童寅两位进士。从大宝三年到 1779 年的最后一场科举考试，按黎朝的制度应进行 110 多次考试，但由于战乱，现在河内文庙只存有这 82 块进士碑。每块碑上部标有科举考试的时间，碑文的撰写者、书写者、雕刻者以及考取的进士名单，是越南科举考试的重要历史文献。

---

① 详参陈文：《越南黎朝时期的国子监教育》，《南洋问题研究》第 1 期（2006），第 84—92 页。

## 结语：儒学在越南的现代意义

儒学虽然曾经对越南思想和文化有深远的影响，但目前越南学者对儒学的现代意义和作用，却是意见颇为分歧的。有些学者认为儒学仍有积极作用，但大部分的人只从功利的角度或儒学的消极面去理解儒学，质疑儒学对越南的现代化能够做出什么贡献。部分越南史家甚至认为西方文明和资产阶级革命思想的传入，是通过儒家学者；天主教早期在越南传教时，外国传教士也是利用儒家经典的道理，去阐释天主教的教义。[①]这类的看法，更令儒学的现代意义蒙上阴影。

汉字的不再使用，对儒学的传承亦不无影响。汉字大约从东汉开始大规模的传入越南。到了宋朝，汉字已经成为越南政府以及民间的主要文字，随着汉字在越南的传播，一些人开始尝试以汉字作为基础创造新的文字来纪录越语词汇。大约在8世纪的时候喃字开始出现，13世纪的时候，越南文人开始用喃字进行文学创作。越南上层社会由于有很浓厚的“尊汉”思想，一直很排斥这种文字，国家教育机关也没有将它作为正式文字看待，也没有对它进行整理规范的工作。1945年8月革命胜利后，汉字才最后退出历史舞台，代之以完全的拼音文字。越南文中称这种新的拼音文字为“国语字”。现今通用的越南文“国语字”，是17世纪葡萄牙、西班牙、法国等国到越南的传教士开始创造的。罗超的研究指出：

19世纪后半期，越南不断遭受外国侵略者的滋扰和侵犯，封建统治趋于没落。1884年《顺化条约》签订后越南沦为法国的殖民地，阮氏王朝成为法国殖民者的傀儡，被法殖民者统治达七十多年。殖民者为了控制越南人民的思想，极力打压越南社会受儒家文化浸润的传统文化，力图以此来打消越南人民的民族意识。1918年甚至要求废除汉字和以汉字为基础创作而来的喃字，改以拉丁语文字取而代之，这就为年轻一代学习儒学造成了障碍。1919年，越南中部和北部先后废除了科举制度。没有了功名的刺激，儒学自然也就丧失了吸引力，儒学教育因此一落千丈。[②]

随着汉字被喃文所取代，最后发展为拼音文字，儒家思想也随着汉字的消失而没落。年青一代不但无法阅读过去以汉文书写的古籍，儒家伦理再也不是道德教育的根据。少数研究汉文古籍和儒家思想的学者，他们所关注的是究竟儒家思想是否可以促进越南的现代化？

过去代表儒学重镇的文庙，现今只被视为是历史遗迹，失去其道德价值的内涵。河内文庙经历过战乱和殖民统治，受到严重的破坏。1962年越南文化部将文庙列为

---

① 参考陈文饶：《从19世纪至八月革命前越南思想的发展》，第二集，河内：越南社会科学出版社，1973年，第39页。

② 罗超《越南国子监文庙研究》，广西民族大学硕士学位论文，2009年，第17页。

“国家级历史文化遗址”，1988年河内市常务委员会成立“国子监文庙科学文化活动中心”，专门负责文庙遗址的管理、修缮、维护和使用管理工作，大规模的修复工作则在1991—1996年进行。作为文化活动中心，文庙举办过不少传统文化教育和文化交流活动。如黎圣宗550年诞辰祭典和胡志明100年诞辰纪念活动等。每逢春节，国子监文庙科学文化活动中心也会在文庙举行进香、舞龙蛇、武术表演、书画展等节目。对官方而言，文庙是有代表性的文化遗产，教育部每年的“教授和副教授职称颁授典礼”和表扬全国高校成绩优异毕业生的“首科礼”都在文庙举行。文庙的历史和文化地位，并未因为时代的改变而褪色。对民间而言，文庙是越南学子祈求金榜题名的地方，每逢考试季节，文庙的香火都特别旺盛。[①]但文庙所代表的儒家思想，却不知不觉的消失在人民的记忆和心灵中。

河内文庙举办的文艺活动

① 罗超《越南国子监文庙研究》，广西民族大学硕士学位论文，2009年，第34页。

# 越南文化中的《忠》与《义》

## ——以关公崇拜为例

越南胡志明市国家大学 阮玉诗

## 一、越南传统信仰文化

(一)“信”是对某个固定对象的相信与依靠。“仰”是仰慕、仰望的意思。从通俗观念角度而看,“信仰”这个术语是属于人心灵方面,由人创造为表示人对超然势力或者神圣的相信与仰望的信心价值系统,通过信仰人类寄托自己各种美好的价值以及得到超然势力的保安、避免灾祸及客观世界的恐怕。信仰显示人类对客观世界与其规律前无能为力的原来。自然现象,例如黑暗、死亡、地震、火山、洪水等的那种现像都带给古代人一种害怕、无能为力的感觉。因此人类把这种自然现象看成一个需要崇拜的超然势力。

在人类文明的黎明,人类因被限制于知识与抑制天然的能力而且害怕,以及为了得到自然保安而开始出现了崇拜自然的思想(Edward L. Shaughnessy 2005:102)。这种传统在东方显得更浓重,因大部分的东方人意识到大自然很超等,是“母亲”,他们都希望同“母亲”平安地一起生活。

信仰在东亚地区文化中均处于优势,很深刻地投入本地人的心灵生活,支配了很多社会与精神生活各个方面,如风俗,礼节、占卜、艺术等。通过文化传统的研究,科学界容易地认得此地人民有多神信仰生活的特色,偏重母亲崇拜(阮玉诗 2009)。

当时,有多大宗教都在亚太地区发展,有一些的在此地起源(道教、儒教),也有一些的从外边输入,然后在这里找到了顺利的发展环境(北传佛教)。最后,还有一些从远方起源的宗教,如基督教、伊斯兰教、犹太教以及印度教。

讲于一个文化现象的一些信仰基础功能,美国社会学家认为各种事物、现象有两个功能层次:体现功能与潜在功能。各种各样的社会体制的潜在功能是不得认识到的社会因素的角色。社会功能有时被提高成心灵功能。按照马林诺斯基来讲(马林诺斯基，1994），一个文化现象通过革新与传播的两个方法而转播到社会时，会从另一个社会扩散。一个文化现象的存在属于它向文化适应的影响，或者叫作“存在价值”。他特别注重传播的重要性。实际上，一个文化现象并不如遗传基因。他可以从这一个人被传到别的一个人，从这个社会到别的社会。战争的要素对于文化进化过程不是必须的。

这样来说，一个文化现象总带有两层基础功能，就是应急实际的必须（biological needs），同时也是文化现象存在的基础。第二层次是从第一功能脱胎的意义。这里，第二的功能层次继续分成心里一社会功能（psychological and social needs），以教育社会为主，另一个的是心灵功能（religious needs）。在一些情况中，心灵功能显得不清楚，所以显得深刻的知识心理社会的功能。

我们把忌辰大比，除了应急休息、饮食的需要，还当作亲族关系（纵向）与邻居关系（横向）被巩固和发展的地方。同时，它还是活人与归人的无形连接的空间和时间。

（二）至今，越南文化曾经过多么风雨，变迁由社会历史的影响，不过带着水稻文化农业的特征的越南都没有损失或被杂乱。那就是重阴，重静的水稻农业文化类型而被形成通过东南亚的文化背景。这种类型被发展在文化区域之内而最初为中华文化。那个过程一直不停着演变多千年不管在几个世纪中为了跟西方文化的交流而有猛烈的转变。

越南学者陈玉添 Tran Ngoc Them 教授（2001）曾确定越南文化对水稻农业文化的资格之基础特征包括下面的五个大特征，包括（一）、集体精神/共同体精神 Collectivism；（二）、综合性思维 Syntheticity；（三）、和谐性 Harmony-oriented；（四）、灵活性 Flexibility；（五）、向阴性的趋向 Feminization。其中，综合性思维与灵活性极为明显，两者浓厚地支配外来信仰宗教的接收及运用。

谈到思维，从古到今的越南居民大部分都有总和思维，“神秘 mysterious”，甚至还比华南人有深刻。正是那个相同特点在文化性格已经造成条件，为了在越南民间与华南信仰之间造成相同。

在越南文化中，民间信仰跟着民族对自然与社会环境挑战而斗争的漫长历史而存在了，生动地显出三种基础特色：1. 多神，2. 女性偏重，3. 简易性。越南信仰中的神圣包括然神（想象中的自然神）和人神（历史人物）。从北到南，成千上万的神灵已被承认，其中的大多数是自然神（河神、山神、火神、水神），其余的是历史圣人。在历史圣人之内，从起源于越南的二征夫人、陈兴道到起源于中国的关公、天后、胎生圣母等当作很普遍的信仰。

被崇拜的越南神圣大部分跟抗外侵或者抗敌对势力的正义有关，所以他们最突出的表达是爱国、仗义、忠孝及勇敢。起初时，供奉风俗形成在感谢卫国的历史英雄的基础上，崇拜他们的品德，给后世当作榜样。这些功能逐渐发生了副功能，如连接西天与尘世、除去魔鬼、给予福音。其中的，关公是以为特别神圣，通过文化交流连接到越南文化，但是贯串越族的两个伟大抗战：抗法、抗美在越南人的脑际存在。

（三）中国官方社会政治思想的儒教从进入越南以来，一直为越南本土阴性文化补充了极为重要的文化因素。但由于两种传统根源、形式、内容不同，所以两者之间存在着一定的距离。随着历史的演变，其距离缩小，因为两者各自调整，各自为对方补充，最后成为一体，建造了越南传统文化。儒教直接支配越南封建社会思想体系的形成，直接参与国家组织、国家管理、国法、教育事业，在一定的程度上影响到越南人的生活方式、风俗习惯。儒教深深地影响到越南传统文化性格。

反过来，进入越南之后，原有的儒教原则被打破，儒教因受本土阴性文化传统而严重扭曲。它走向阴性化方向，缩小其哲学理论以便于运用到综合性思维越南人的生活实践中去。越南人以水稻农作文化性格为主前后用了祖国棱镜，村落式文化棱镜，东南亚农业阴性文化棱镜及身份论棱镜四大棱镜来看待儒教。公元前后儒教的到来及其影响已经把越南文化推到东亚汉字文化圈去。经过两千年的冲突、纠正及融合，儒教和越南传统文化互相参透，互相补缺，成为推动国家发展动力的基础.

## 二、关公信仰传入越南的过程

关公信仰的传播与承认过程在越南通过两种主流表达：有机流的官方式与以机学流的民间式。

（一）第一主流为带有传统有机性的官方交流式。越南文化受中华文化的深刻影响，特别是传统社会思想体系、国家组织与运行管理模型、哲学宗教、心灵观念等，其中之一就是关公信仰，所以越南人在崇拜本地信仰的同时，也崇拜关公或其他华传信仰宗教。

在实际上，汉属时代从公元前延长了10世纪，不中国汉、吴、魏、晋、宋、齐、梁、随、唐等朝代断互相侵略及统治，把越南北部一带改成郡、县，进行统治与同化(周氏海：2)。通过这段漫长历史，很多中华文化要素作用于越南，其中含有信仰心识，后来就是接受关公信仰的基础。那是拜孔夫子的儒教、孟子亚圣、程颢与程颐兄弟、朱熹等以及越南人的根深蒂固的儒教价值。那是道教的太上老君、原始天尊、太乙真人、太白金星等。神仙教的姜子牙与诸位仙圣。那是北宗佛教的带有中国色的佛教神谱系统，从释迦佛、阿弥陀佛、观音、弥勒佛、地藏菩萨、普贤菩萨等。还有中华古代信仰的伏羲、女娲、盘古，鲁班等。汉属时代后，越南封建政府与东亚地区的关系深刻得不赖，已经为更火爆的越、中两国的文化交流过程创设很多条件。让越南人知道中华名人的方法之一是文学交流。中华作品，特别的著名作品是《西游记》、《水浒》、《红楼梦》、《西厢记》、《聊斋志异》等曾引起越南人的热情兴趣，因按照马林诺斯基的理论，它们满足越南人的心理需求。

河内关公祠门楼额题“千古伟人”之参照：清化东山广照总锐村关圣寺之“千古伟人”拓片，汉喃研究院拓片编号：16637［阅览陈益源 2013］

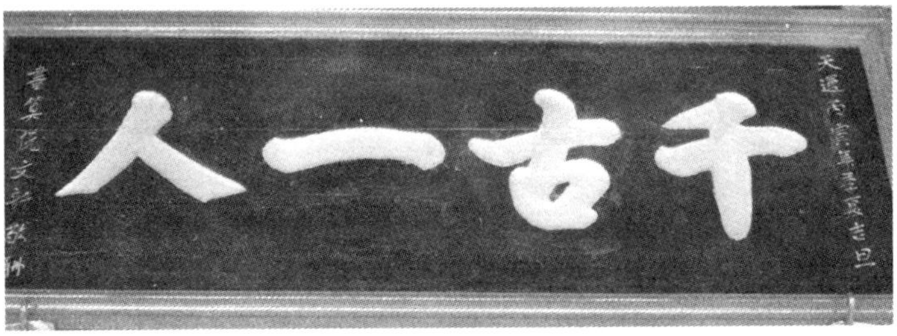


坚江省何仙市关帝庙门楼额题（阮玉诗摄）

在起源于中国文化中的各圣仙之中，关公早就被越南官方与民间接受为忠诚、尚义、勇敢与爱国的表象。深受忠、孝、礼、义、勇等儒家道德体系的越南封建统治阶层希望通过关公的精神向老百姓弘扬忠君、爱国的教育。从 16 世纪末期至 20 世纪中叶，经过了几百年充满战争的历史阶段，越南人真实地体验到尚义、忠诚的盖世英雄角色，进而推广关公崇拜之俗。

据官方的记载，官方信仰最迟第 17 世纪上叶已经成立了。《升龙古籍考并绘图》一书中提到升龙京城正东门的关公祠，世传唐交州度护府所建，黎中兴郑帅府重修，门楼挂着《千古伟人》一牌。《高平实录》记录越南后黎朝黎永治三年（1678 年）已经建立观庙。据《兴安一统志》记载，兴安仅东北地区原轻伤居住地区有个关庙，阮朝皇帝嗣德三十二年（1879）下令省官员重修此庙。《南定省地舆记》说明该省城南门外观庙是阮朝绍治三年（1842）所建，成泰三年（1891）重修。《清化省志》记录本省静嘉府玉山县有个关帝君祠，以烧至二年（1842）造的。《大南一统志》卷之一也描写城外春禄邑天姥寺左边的关公祠由绍治皇帝五年（1845）移去的，而《大南一统志》卷之二记载在县地灵社的关公祠不知何时所建，阮朝明命皇帝十二年（1831）重修，于嗣德三年（1850）被赐木匠金湘。中部《广南省志略》中特别详细地描写本省会安市明乡人所建立的关公祠，没记录具体何时，但说明明命六年（1825）驾幸广南过其祠，赐银三百两。南部《嘉定通志。城池。边和镇》一文记录 17 世纪末期明乡人迁移，在边和镇大铺州地区建立七府古庙的关帝庙，于 1799 年淋大水灾，后人想重修但未能。按照庙中的牌子记载，此庙最迟于 1684 年建立的，均在南部有名华人文人郑怀德（1765—1825）记录中有具体描写。按现存的关帝庙记录文献或碑铭拓片的结果得知，河内行帆庯关圣庙于 1814 年重修，清化省东山广照总锐村关圣寺建庙年代不详细但在东山碑记 1785 年有记录，于 1833 年立外碑，1839 年立内碑；顺华关公祠于 1861 年立祠碑等等。上述证明越南官方北、中部各地于最迟 17 世纪建立关祠或关庙，说明中国明朝的关公崇拜早已扎根在越南文化中。

按照陈益源教授的考察（2013），存的经文可也不少，譬如河内玉山祠中现存着关于关公的九种文献，包括《桃园明圣经》、《明圣经》、《明圣经注解》、《明圣经大板》、《觉世真言》、《劝孝十八条》、《关帝救劫宝训》、《宝训像注》、《关圣灵经》。其外还有关帝《经文演音》四种，包括《二帝救劫真经》、《关帝警世文》、《关帝劝孝十八条》、《桃园降笔经》。目前越南社科院至汉喃研究院收藏有关于关公的文献挺多，譬如《关夫子经训合刻》、《关帝宝训像注》、《关帝桃园明圣经注》、《关帝明圣经》、《明圣经旁训》、《关帝永命真经》、《关圣帝君觉世真言》、《关圣帝君感应明圣经注解》、《关圣帝劝学文》、《关圣帝君救劫永命经》、《关圣帝君妙药灵文》、《关公帝君训世文》、《关圣垂训宝文》、《关圣帝君警世文》、《关圣帝君救劫劝世宝训演音》、《关圣帝君刻仪》、《关圣科》、《关圣灵签》、《文武二帝救劫真经》。除了含钠研究院之外，其他地方还收藏着众多文献，比如越南国家图书馆的《关帝垂训宝文》，河内玉山祠的〈关圣帝君感应明圣经注解〉，南定、清化、顺化、会安、潘切、边和、胡志明市等地关公秒均有保存关圣帝君经文。

（二）第二种方式是由 17 世纪末期以来华人移民带到越南南部地区来。本方式的关公崇拜文化具有机学性。跟其他大多数民族不一样，华族是“非原住民”而从中国东南地区、台湾金门乘船渡海过去。华南地区的人早就把海上丝绸之路搞熟，移民到越南、鲁松、南阳等地越来越多。华人大多数居住城镇以便于买卖，其中越南潮州人、闽南人多喜欢移住湄公河三角洲各地，好好做大米买卖工作。在越南，他们自称明乡人，后改为明香人（香＝香火）。

从北南下，越南中代五大港口都有华人的参与，它们是北部兴安省宪铺、广宁省云墩市、中部广南省会安市、南部边和市及西贡市。按照上边官方的记载，南部边和市大铺州关帝庙与 1684 年由明乡人建立的。其他港口原有明乡人或清商检的关庙均没有具体记录的现存，只知道重修年代。

在华人广东、潮州、海南、福建、客家华人五帮会之中，潮州人与福建人多崇拜关公，其余偏重祭祀天后。而越南华人崇拜关公、天后的主要风格是华南风格。跟着历史流长，通过跨组文化交流的动态，越南人、高棉人也随着接受，进而把关公、天后当做自己的神。对于关公来说，当越南人从中部地区依据南部时早就认识到一种官方的关帝崇拜热潮了。同奈省边和市宝龙区天后宫原来是客家人木作、铁作与石作的三祖师庙，后来因为促进华人五帮会之间的合作，同时促进华、越两民族的文化交流而改为主要祭祀天后与关帝的天后宫。此事说明关公与天后对于跨民族交际起这么重要的角色。

总体而言，关公信仰以官方与民间两种方式传入了越南，关公本身代表着 1. 忠诚、尚义、英勇、爱国的象征人物；2. 福神、财神、保护神、赶鬼神等两大风格的文化涵义。这两种含义正好配上越南人传统文化性格（集体精神、综合性思维、灵活性、开放性等等），所以很容易被接受下去。

## 三、关公信仰在越南的表现

（一）越南文化中，关公崇拜既有官方文化涵义（正气的象征）又有民间风味（福神）。因此，越南官方与民间人对关公形象的理解与运用非常丰富。

中国学者颜宝[①]说，“越南和中国国一样，人们非常崇拜小说中的主角之一关羽，很多家庭供奉关羽的画像”。跟华南人一样，越南人拜关公如一个表象总体而包裹忠、

① 阅览陈益源《越南的关公信仰》，关公信仰与现代社会研究论文集，国力成功大学出版社，2013 年：490－528 页。

勇、君子（华北质）也像一位神的形象（华南质）。如果据社会阶层之分类，过去的越南封建政府主张立关圣帝庙因为想要鼓励君子精神（忠诚、英勇、爱国）与之对应的是垒文圣帝君孔子，其中民间拜关公在家偏于拜男神对垒拜观音之中。在越南西南部的很多家庭，男人拜关公而女人拜观音菩萨与各佛在寺庙里面。

茶荣市福明宫的关帝像

关于这种祭拜的特征，不管什么人都认出来其综合性之特征。谈到关公跟佛门之良缘，山南曰：

“在关公寺庙里是一位老爷爷，脸色红红，胡子剪短，手提大刀；十方之客可以到此跟这位老头子求卜。西贡的很多寺庙，提岸与在各地，市场，当再看就是拜关公而之后添加详细的就没有人疑问。”（山南 1993：100，101）

西南部的佛教的一个系派是四恩孝义也拜关圣（山南 1971：72）。如上有谈，综合性最明显的表现通过总和趋向意义是拜忠、义、勇、志与信这些德性属于拜神之官方文化。

在一定的程度，越南人已经“越南化”关公形象，让他成为“爱国”之形象，或者直接或间接对反抗外来敌人的越南志士的爱国精神之影响。在越南，有把关公当成爱国形象之趋向，这就深刻的接近官方性质。原因就是自古的升龙京城本来是越南各朝代的首都，接任从中国进入的官方儒教。

自从 20 世纪起，当越南南部长期深入属于法国之黑暗，中华长篇小说受到南部读者的关心，其中要讲到是：《三国演义》、《东周列国》、《红楼梦》、《水浒传》、《游龙戏凤》、《正德游江南》、《孟丽君》、《岳飞》、《十二寡妇》、《争西》等等。就《三国演义》著作在越南文学系统存在这好几种翻译的版本。南部人特别喜爱中心人物的“重义轻财”这些性格。“艚传”反映一个分化社会政治堕落，与当战争混乱之中，有一些从群众出现的英雄完全没有认领朝廷的命令而冲锋救国，重义轻财，成为升高争议的争议英雄。

越南的关公信仰的共同性表现在于越南人已经“越化”关圣形象，把它当成一位英雄与一位救助的神，扶助越南人的共同。有一些相关活动跟关圣有关的是关圣礼节，关平，周仓与桃园礼节都受到越南人共同的响应与跟华人一起广泛参加。在越南人的祭坛也拜关公影与关公像就如保护平安，镇压魔鬼，邪气的意义。大部分越南人都这样做。

越南人生活的关圣祭拜带着非常有和谐的特征。越南人无独立拜关圣而配自共于女神如观音佛为了和谐，阴阳平衡（而在越南人的说法是男神女神双重祭祀）。这特征很相同华南人的祭拜风格。平阳省土龙木市顺天庙主要供奉顺天圣母，正殿当然有供奉关公之处。由越南文化偏于情感所以越南人很容易接近关公形象进入自己的文化生活。虽然，关公不是越南人，可是，因为爱慕他的品性、道德与其佳的人格而祭拜他，学习与教育自己的儿孙。平阳省土龙木市关帝庙中除了关公之外，越南始祖国王雄王、13 世纪三次打败蒙古军的陈兴道大王、18 世纪末的英雄光忠皇帝、20 世纪的英雄胡志明主席以及其他当代英雄的照片也得到供奉。

平阳省土龙木市关帝庙中的陈兴道大王牌位

平阳省土龙木市关帝庙中的胡志明主席尊像

高台教神殿上有关公、孔子、老子的参与

东、西、南、北之会聚的高台教（从左向右：中国革命大师孙中山、法国文学家 Victor Hugo，越南儒家 阮丙谦）

在中部顺化地区，当前关公崇拜主要是由阮朝官方成立的。1945年阮朝崩溃，官方阶层逐渐消灭。依靠于官方的关公崇拜逐渐走向民间，融合语本地被传佛教中去。许多官方关公祠改称佛教寺庙，庙里主要崇拜释迦牟尼、阿弥陀佛、观音，侯殿常常配祀关公（譬如顺化市妙谛寺、国恩寺等等）。南部地区没有越南人官方关公祠，主要为华人建立的或者越南人民间自己建立的庙宇。大部分越南人民间关庙成为佛教寺庙。唯一华人关庙因特殊情况还保持民间信仰的状态。

在拜关圣的，越南人表现出深刻的灵活性。虽然越南人没有华北人拜关圣那么独立和僵直，也没有华南人为了阴阳和谐而一起拜关圣和女神。有时候，越南人在寺庙里面一起拜关圣和其他佛像，菩萨。也有时候，我们可以看到在寺庙里面越南人独立的拜关圣（华北）还是跟观世音菩萨（华南）或者在寺庙里面一起拜城隍或者在土地庙，神财庙里面拜关圣。特别的是，南部人还在高台教一起拜关圣和释迦牟尼佛，老子，孔子，姜子牙，李太白。总之，在两种影响之间：有机交流与无机交流（上面已谈），我们可以看到：在越南有机交流有最猛烈的影响对拜关公信仰。经过时间越南人在接触中国文化和华南文化区域而渐渐的吸收关公形象。

左边为四杰庙又变为协天宫

在做经济业的华人商贩眼里，关公是位“财神”，此想法其实起源于华南地区。因此，许多华人把关公与财神等同起来。搞买卖的越南人家把关公神像或牌位放在土地上祭祀，此俗起源于越南人原有的土地爷崇拜，土地爷当然离不开土地，而在蕴藏着浓厚水稻农作文化的越南人信念里头，关公跟财神一样，都是财神，而财富都从土地开始（意味着种植农业），所以关公或财神、土地爷的祭坛都放在土地上。

关公是标志着善良、诚实、忠诚、义气等精神的象征。此品德对蕴藏着高大志气、除奸祛害、保家卫国的人带来极大的影响力。这里的关公远离了三国时代的关羽本人，他是民间中的神。人们崇拜关公是因为他含着多么美好品德。在南部地区，许多村庄没建立村共所（越南称作《村亭》），人们把关公庙来代替。在抗法的时期，为了避免法军发现与杀害，许多战士或游击避身在关公庙里，等着顺利的时期进攻法军。举一个例子，越南作家山南先生写着：

“南部前江省 Cai Lay 市当时有四位英雄称作慎翁、龙翁、德翁、宽翁为民除害，后牺牲。人们建立四杰庙祭祀‘四位神魂’，并恭请关公牌为一起祭祀。法国人当然不知道此事。”

那么说，从前许多越南爱国者经常利用关公形象来跟同胞交道，把爱国同爱联结起来，此事一直都很顺利，因为人们在忠、勇、坚强的关公的普度下，在革命领导的统领下人们会得到保佑，一定平平安安地走过这一场战争。

越南爱国英雄阮安宁（1900—1943），爱国学者阮安羌之子，甲象与湄公河地区，小时离开老家到西贡学习，21 岁就获得法律毕业证说，进而赴法工读博士。回国后就加入越南南圻劝学会，挥动爱国青年力量，除了当作 La Cloche felee 报的主笔之外还很用心地编写弘扬爱国精神的书籍，因此被法军抓去东海的昆岛小道上坐牢。在牢中，他“天天祭祀关公，巩固义兵的精神”。许多人根本不了解它的来龙去脉，但通过他的行为很佩服他，听着他，有人还把他当作“活圣”。

打另一个例子，起源于中国的明师教跟着华人移植到越南南部地区。明师教崇拜三圣，但多倾于道教。在胡志明市第一郡到目前还存在着明师教总会玉皇殿（也称佛堂），南部其他地方偶尔也能看到明师教的佛堂。按照山南先生的记载，19世纪末期，芹苴市郊区 Tra Ngoa 乡明师教很盛。

名义上崇拜关公但实际上是真正的明师教根基地。在抗法时期，许多佛堂当作革命根据地。因此，关公形象在佛堂中偶尔可以看到。那么说，关公信仰传入越南之后遇上两场艰苦的战争，默默地扎根在越南人的心中。因此，关公信仰在越南南部地区影响力很广，人们借用关公的文化涵义代表着爱国心，弘扬着忠诚、勇敢、坚强不屈的精神，利用他来把爱国战士、义兵汇合在一起。

（二）在越南民间中，关公是位代表着阳性各种特征的神，早得到封建个朝代与民间共同崇拜。在华南地区，关公独祀、配祀两种方式都存在，越南南部地区也不例外。南部人并不把关公看作孔子的对象，而是观音、妈祖天后、胎生圣母、处住女神等女性神的对偶。他被祭祀在关帝庙，在天后宫，在佛教寺庙，在明师教佛堂，在高台教圣室，或者在老百姓家里。在许多平民家里，女人祭祀观音菩萨、胎生圣母、九天玄女等，男人就是崇拜被称作“度命神/护身神”的关帝。

黄水黎家客厅中的关公祭坛

南部地区同塔省沙沥市（Sa Dec，Dong Thap）20世纪初望家黄水黎住宅客厅祖先祭坛之左边就是供奉关公的祭坛。在贵族与平民的眼里，关公是传统上是家族教训子女道德的形象之一。

（三）在华人社区，山南先生曾记载：

“湄公河地区的 Rạch Giá，Sóc Trăng，Bạc Liêu 等地，华人从中国迁移过来，他方陌生，分散居住农村各地而不是集中在大都市里。因此，他们能够保持旧俗。金钱、家产不多但他们很用心捐钱建立关帝庙余天后宫”（山南 1993：175）

当华人落地南部地区的时候，他们成立主张“反清复明”的《天地会》。“天地会很深刻地接受关云长三兄弟的精神”（山南 1993：175）。入会仪式要经过两个星期的鞠躬典礼，先做四鞠躬，后八鞠躬。四鞠躬代表着《桃园结为兄弟》之礼，其中第三鞠躬是承诺学习关公之德。天地会存在的时间不长，但它的影响力远远超越华人社区。

当前的越南南部很多地方，特别是中部与南部地区，关帝诞日是当地的大节日。此庙会逐渐成为文化多样的中、南部地区之遗产，其价值充分（个人道德教育、家族文化教育、社会和谐精神教育、华人民族认同教育等功能），为越南文化加增丰富度。以下是三个表型的庙会活动：

中部广南省的会安市，关帝庙[1]于农历 4 月 24 日举办关帝诞节。会安华人与越南人早在 1653 年就开始建庙崇拜关公以及白马、赤兔两匹神马。会安人以及远方而来的善男信女赶来供奉香火。那日子庙内外都满满是人，脸庞都充满一种神秘的信心。上午 10 点典礼开始，经过 90 分钟才结束。典礼包括奉献就差，香火，花果与其他祭物，办礼时均有祭乐伴奏。正是典礼后在庙前原子往往举办越剧演出或各种民间文艺、民间玩艺活动。庙主任提前立着一根挂满祭物的柱子，描绘要结束时会有人把柱子拉倒，人们争着夺走祭物，心想得到福气。

在九龙江平原的芹萱市，每当农历 4 月 24 日时，关帝庙相济会成员，华人与越南人一起办理祭祀活动。典礼上午 9 点开始，祭物常见的是烤猪、糯米饭、水果、饼干等。当地的关帝庙庙会就是当地华人汇合诉旧、团结互助的美好场合，也就是华、越、棉三族会见、交流的重要时刻。

前江省丐皮市闽安会馆关帝庙的关帝像与观音菩萨

位于湄公河北岸上的前江省 Go Cong 市，关帝庙的最大庙会活动举办在正月 10 日至 13 日，也就是当地华人各帮会以及越南人一起来供奉关帝，重温人生美好道德、共创社会和谐。此庙会每年迎接尽两万人参加，是前江省的重要节日。

在胡志明市，同奈省，平阳省等地关帝盛会也非常热闹，一直保持华人典型的祭神仪式、传统服装、传统艺术、传统饮食文化等方面，大幅度地丰富化越南文化

从上述活动指出，关公不知而绝地成为华人本身的民族认同教育，是华人对于传统文化特色的守护者，是华、越、棉三族文化交流的凝聚力量。

---

① 位于会安市陈富路 24 号，曾被越南文化、体育与旅游部封为国家级文化遗产。

## 四、结论

传统越南是儒学为主的东方国家。在国民的思想体系中“忠”，“孝”，“义”，“仁”，“德”等儒学观念当作社会道德的基础。在不同的时间与不同地区，儒学价值体系会有变更或增减，不过基本的儒学美德永不褪色。

从一个相当安静的《三国志》与《三国演义》文学作品中走出来，文化中的关公并是报恩、忠诚、勇气、尚义等儒家崇高美德的化身。华北人通过上述美德敬拜关公（武业之师），把他当作孔子（文业之师）的对象，两者互相参透，共同酿造中华文化。在华南地区，由于特殊的心理状态与客观的来源，关公除了忠、勇、义等官方意义的象征之外还是一位赐福、赶鬼、致恩的福神。在华南地区，关公是天后圣母的对象。

关公信仰以越南的封建朝代官方资源接受与17世纪以后华人民间从华南地区介绍过来的两种方式传入越南文化，因此官方与民间的两种文化意义系统都共同存在。在越南南部地区各个关公庙举办的信仰文化活动系列逐渐成为华、越、棉三民族的共同文化遗产，是三民族之间的文化大融合的桥梁。

**参考文献：**

[1] Bùi Đức Anh 裴德英，2001. Thử so sánh một số nhân vật trong Tam Quốc diễn nghĩa với những nhân vật có thặt cùng tên có thật trong lịch sử Trung Quốc《三国演义》诸主角与中国历史上相关历史人物比较研究”，khóa luận tốt nghiệp ngânh Trung Quốc học，khoa Đông phương học，ĐH Khoa học Xãhội và Nhân văn TPHCM 胡志明市社会科学与人文大学东方学系中国学专业毕业论文.

[2] Châu Thị Hải 周氏海 . Người Hoa trong lịch sử Việt Nam. 越南历史上的华人 Viện Khoa học và Xã hội Việt Nam 越南社科院 .

[3] La Quán Trung 罗贯中 . 1994. Tam quốc diễn nghĩa《三国演义》. Phan KếBính dịch 潘继丙译，NXB Văn học 文学出版社.

[4] Lê Anh Dũng 黎英勇 . 1995. Quan Thánh xưa và nay 古今关公 . NXB Văn hoá Thông tin 文化通讯出版社.

[5] Phạm Đức Dương-Châu Thị Hải 范德陽—周氏海 . 1998. Bước đầu tìm hiểu sự tiếp xúc và giao lưu văn hóa Việt-Hoa trong lịch sử《歷史上華越文化交流》。Nxb Thế Giới，Hà Nội 河内世界出版社.

[6] Sơn Nam 山南 . 1993. Đờng bằng sông Cửu Long：nét sinh hoạt xưa《古今九龍江平原》，NXB Thành phố Hồ Chí Minh 胡志明市出版社.

[7] Thái Thiếu Hương 蔡少香，2004. Đặc điểm và chức năng xã hội của các tín ngưỡng dân gian《民間信仰的社會功能及特點》，Tập san Đại học Giang Tô，TQ，NXB Khoa học Xã hội TQ 中國社會科學出版社.

[8] Trần Ngọc Thêm 陳玉添 . 2001. Tìm về bản sắc văn hóa Việt Nam 尋找越南文化特色，NXB TP. HCM 胡志明市出版社.

[9] Trịnh Huy Hoá biên dịch 鄭輝化 . 2006. Đối thoại với các nền văn hoá - Trung Quốc《各文化之間的對話》。NXB Trẻ青年出版社.

[10] Theodore M. Ludwig，2000. Những con đường tâm linh phương Đông《東方心靈之道》，(Dương Ngọc Hà，Hà Hữu Nga，Nguyễn Chí Hoàn dịch) . NXB Văn hoá Thông Tin.

[11] Vũ Ngọc Khánh 武玉慶 . 2006. Đạo Thánh ở Việt Nam《越南的聖道》. NXB Văn hoá-thông tin Hà Nội 河内文化通訊出版社.

[12] Will Durant. 2002. Lịch sử văn minh Trung Hoa《中華文明史》. Nguyễn Hiến Lê dịch 阮憲黎譯，NXB Văn hoá Thông tin 文化通訊出版社.

[13] Chan Siu-po. 2007.《香港關帝信仰研究：以關帝廟為中心》. Degree of Master of Arts at The University of Hong Kong August.

[14] 袁鐘仁. 嶺南文化. 遼寧教育出版社，1998.

[15] 陳澤泓. 廣府文化. 廣東人民出版社，1991.

[16] 陳澤泓. 潮汕文化. 廣東人民出版社，2006.

[17] Henri Maspero. 1981. Taoism and Chinese Religion. The University of Massachusettes.

[18] Fred Inglis. 2004. Culture. Polity Press.

[19] Van Peursen. 1974. The Strategy of Culture. North Holland Publishing Company. California.

# 日本普及《论语》教育的历史与现状

神户市外国语大学 秦兆雄

## 一、序言

日本现存最古的孔子庙为枥木县足利市足利学校的大成殿。东京的汤岛圣堂、茨城县水户市弘道馆的孔子庙、冈山县备前市闲谷学校的圣庙、佐贺县多久市的多久圣庙亦享有盛名。

笔者近几年在考察研究这些孔子庙①的历史变迁与当代功能期间，耳闻目睹了日本各地政府以及很多精英人士全力保护各地孔子庙，认真学习《论语》等儒家经典，定期举行释奠礼推动社会和谐发展的情形。

本文主要以汤岛圣堂、足利学校、弘道馆以及闲谷学校为例来介绍日本各地《论语》普及教育的历史现状及其成因。②

需要说明的是，有关这方面的简单介绍虽然在一些学术著作以及各种媒体上可以看到，但各有偏重，不够全面深入。在笔者的研究范围内，目前还没有看到有关对日本孔子庙诵读《论语》等儒家经典进行人类学与儒学、教育学以及历史学等相结合的综合性考察报告。

首先让我们回顾一下《论语》在日本社会不断被传承发展与教育普及应用的历史概貌。

---

① 在调查研究期间曾得到公益财团法人斯文会事务所、史迹足利学校事务所，弘道馆事务所以及特别史迹旧闲谷学校显彰保存会等机构相关人员的理解与支持，在此谨表谢意。另外，此稿是在纪念孔子诞辰2565周年国际学术研讨会暨国际儒学联合会第五届会员大会上发表稿修改版。

② 2014年3月18日至20日专程考察了多久圣庙以及多久市横尾俊彦市长在圣庙、市立中小学以及政府各部门、各行业大力推动《论语》普及教育的盛况，于是推荐横尾俊彦市长参加了纪念孔子诞辰2565周年国际学术研讨会暨国际儒学联合会第五届会员大会并发表了相关论文（参见Yokoo 2014）。因此本文对相关实况不加论述。

## 二、《论语》在日本的传播推广历史概述

学术界关于《论语》传入日本的年代是公元285年还是405年存在争议。公元285年的根据是，成书于712年的《古事记》与成书于720年的《日本书纪》都分别记载：应神天皇16年（285年）2月，朝鲜百济王朝五经博士王仁应邀访问日本并带去《论语》十卷与《千字文》一卷，献给应神天皇。

但诚如孔祥林与孔喆所言，《古事记》没有纪年，《日本书纪》虽有纪年但因为所记有些天皇在位七八十年甚至百年以上而令人难以置信，而且所记史实与中国、朝鲜史籍不符。有的学者据《日本书纪》应神天皇16年“是年、百济阿花王薨”记载，由朝鲜《三国史记》推定为公元405年（孔·孔2011：731）。笔者也赞同这一推断。

当时日本只有口头语言，没有书面文字，书记官都由来自中国大陆或朝鲜半岛的移民来担任。应神天皇求贤若渴，敬请王仁做太子菟道稚郎子的老师，教授太子学习《论语》并在朝廷皇室推广汉字与儒家思想，为古代日本文化的发展繁荣奠定了坚实基础。

飞鸟时代的推古朝改革推行者圣德太子不仅笃信佛教，而且尊崇儒学。他把《论语》的道德思想总结为“礼”和“仁”两方面，并以此为基础于推古天皇11年（603年）12月制定《冠位十二阶[①]》，用大德、小德、大仁、小仁、大礼、小礼、大信、小信、大义、小义、大智、小智来表示官吏等级的高低；次年4月，圣德太子还参考儒家和佛教经典制定了作为各级官吏道德训诫的《十七条宪法[②]》，其中直接引用《论语》的就有五条。[③] 另外，圣德太子还首创派遣使者与留学生到中国交流学习制度，人们熟知的小野妹子与鞍作福利作为遣隋使于607年被派遣到中国交流，608年高向玄理与南渊请安等日本留学生开始跟随小野妹子到中国留学深造。

645年6月19日，孝德天皇宣布模仿中国建立年号，定年号为“大化”，以645年为大化元年。大化二年（646年）正月初一，孝德天皇颁布《改新之诏》，以唐朝律令制度为蓝本，正式实施“大化改新”，从经济到政治方面进行改革，完善了日本的政治经济制度。

为了将“大化改新”的成果以法律的形式固定下来，天智天皇元年（668年），日本历史上第一部成文法《近江令》颁布，其中涉及教育机构“大学寮”的规定。另外，

---

① 官位十二等表示干支十二属性，乃天地之循序。

② 按照阴阳五行学说，阴的极数为八，阳的极数为九，十七乃阴阳之和、天地之道。

③ 如第一条“以和为贵，无忤为宗”出自《论语·学而》的“礼之用，和为贵”。但值得留意的是，《十七条宪法》并没有提及《论语》中特别强调的孝。

701年[①]8月制定的基本法典《大宝律令》以及孝谦天皇治世的757年5月施行的《养老律令》都对教育设专章“学令”。大久保利谦介绍，当时“学令”仿照唐制，规定中央设大学寮，各国（地方）设国学，各置博士、助教，招收五位以上的贵族子弟，授以儒家经典，教科书为《周易》、《尚书》、《礼记》、《仪礼》、《毛诗》、《左传》、《孝经》、《论语》等，而《孝经》与《论语》是大学或国学的必修课程（大久保1997：26—27）。因此，儒家思想及其道德伦理在上层社会得到推广和普及。

据藤原佐世于宽平3年（891）所著《日本国见在书目录》记载，《论语》版本除了中国汉魏以来盛行的郑玄与何晏《论语集解》外，还有梁皇侃《论语义疏》十卷与褚仲都《论语义疏》等数种手抄本。因此，町田三郎由此认为，镰仓时代（1185—1333年）以前的儒学研究者主要使用何晏的《论语集解》作为阅读教材，同时参考梁皇侃与褚仲都的《论语义疏》进行学术研究（町田1991：88）。正平19年（1364年），《论语集解》由手抄本翻刻出版，成为日本最早翻刻的儒家经典。

至镰仓时代末期，前往中国大陆的禅僧也往来频繁，他们从中国带回了新注《论语》，即朱熹《论语集注》。当初，京都五山的僧侣只是将《论语集注》作为介绍中国的新学问，同时宣传宗门的部分资料而已，但后来逐渐让当时日本正宗国学清原家的学者们用来解释古注《论语》时的参考书。这样，人们的读书兴趣自然慢慢偏离古注而转向新注，且成为一种学术发展趋势。

至江户时代（1603—1867年），酷爱《论语》并践行孔子德治思想的德川家康[②]重用由“近世儒学之祖”藤原惺窝推荐的得意门生林罗山，尊孔崇儒、兴办学校、普及教育、推行文治，并将朱子说规定为官学，成为幕府的正统思想。《论语集注》也因此成为教科书被大量印发、大力推广、成为从上到下、家家户户都在热心诵读的通用版本。

当时从武士到庶民，男女老少，“没有不知道《论语》，没有不读《论语》的”。另外，还有一句“读《论语》而不知《论语》”的谚语特别有名，广泛流传至今。它的原意是普通老百姓讽刺挖苦那些只会读《论语》，而不在日常生活中应用或践行其思想的人，但从另外一个侧面也反映了当时《论语》在社会上被广泛普及并深入人心的程度。实际上，《论语》自江户时代已经逐渐成为日本人生活中孝忠主君的武士道精神及其行为规范的思想源泉。

---

① 据《续日本纪》记载，文武天皇治世的大宝元年2月14日（701年3月27日）日本正式举行释奠。

② 德川家康有很多格言都来自《论语》。如著名的“人生有如负重致远，不可急躁”出自《论语·泰伯》：“曾子曰：士不可以不弘毅，任重而道远。仁以为己任，不亦重乎？死而后已，不亦远乎”？

江户时代的等级制度是“士农工商”，武士居统治地位。德川幕府为了有效地控制各地大名与各级武士，制定并颁布了“武家诸法度”，要求他们不仅要苦练武艺，还要勤学《论语》，成为忠孝信义、遵纪守法、文武双全、廉洁奉公的主流楷模阶层，从而维护幕府统治以及整个社会秩序。

幕府最高学府“昌平阪学问所”与各藩所办的藩校与乡校以及寺庙所办私塾“寺子屋”① 等各类公私学校基本上仿制了中国的“庙学合一”，因此孔子庙也伴随这些学校的诞生在各地陆续登场。

藩校与乡校以及寺子屋通常模仿汤岛圣堂，建正厅（学馆）与大成殿，师生上课时不仅要诵读《论语》等儒家经典，而且还要向孔子像或木主牌位敬礼并定期举行释奠。

明治五年 8 月 2 日（1872 年 9 月 4 日），太政官颁布了历史上第一个近代教育法令《学制》，对江户时代的各级各类儒式学校进行了大规模的统一整编，或更改为西式学制或关闭废除。因此很多孔子庙也随之受到了不同程度的冲击，或被没收征用为其他设施或被毁坏荒废。

但《论语》的教育普及并未受到否定批判。明治维新开始后，以明治天皇为首的日本政府决心学习西方的科学技术，但同时抵制自由民权思想，为此，明治天皇于明治十二年（1879 年）颁发了《教学圣旨》，规定“道德之学以孔子为主”，使《论语》在日本道德教育上的地位再次得到明确肯定。

至明治后期，日本各界有识之士还努力复原并保护了部分孔子庙。另外，虽然许多孔子庙曾毁于天灾（雷击）、火灾或者战火，但都在有识之士的呼吁以及政府的支持下按原貌得以修复或重建。

## 三、汤岛圣堂与诵读《论语》的历史与现状

汤岛圣堂坐落在东京都文京区汤岛一丁目“御茶之水”车站近旁。宽永七年（1630 年），林罗山得到尾张藩主德川义直的资助，在上野忍冈（现上野公园）的林家私邸里创办私塾，两年后在私塾旁创建了孔子庙“先圣殿”。元禄三年（1690 年）7 月 9 日，幕府第五代将军德川纲吉下令，将孔子庙及私塾搬迁至汤岛现址并加以扩建，增添了学寮与附属校舍等建筑群，取孔子故乡昌平之名，称新庙为昌平阪圣堂。但因新

---

① 寺子屋是寺院开办的主要以庶民子弟为对象的初等教育机构，学童年龄大都是六至十多岁，以训练读、写及算盘为主，发源于室町时代（15 世纪）后期，江户时期共有 1 万 5 千所左右。当时，武士子弟纷纷前往学者的私塾和幕府或藩设立的学校就学，只有庶民子弟仍在寺院学习。随着庶民教育要求的不断提高，就学儿童大量增加，小寺院已经难以全部容纳。为此，一些破落武士、町人、浪人、神官、医生和有能力的庶民也开设了实施初等教育的民间教育机构，这些民间教育机构也被称为即寺子屋。明治五年（1872），日本颁布《学制》，各地纷纷设立小学，寺子屋遂逐渐消失。

庙所处汤岛，因此也称作汤岛圣堂。

第五代将军德川纲吉以谦虚好学、尊孔崇儒、酷爱《论语》并热心讲经“讲释”而闻名，他曾担任课时达 240 次，儒官谋臣们都去恭听。受他影响，新庙仰高门东舍内开设以讲授《论语》等儒学经典而著名的“东舍讲释”。平时因身份等级差别不相往来的武士与庶民听讲时因没有足够的座位而不得不混杂并坐。

宽政二年（1790 年）5 月 24 日，幕府颁布了《宽政异学禁令》，重申朱子学为幕府“正学”，阳明学等儒学流派乃至新兴的“兰学”均为“异学”并一律禁止。[①] 在强化实施这一禁令的基础上，表彰成绩优异者并提高幕臣的儒学求知欲，从宽政四年（1792 年）开始实施“学问吟味”，次年开始实施“素读吟味”的考试制度。

“素读吟味”的考试内容为《小学》、《四书五经》、历史书、诗文等经典。及第者的成绩优劣用甲、乙、丙表示，分别相当于优、良、可的评估。甲级与乙级的及第者获得银子、衣服以及布料等物质奖励，丙级合格者只有“褒词”（口头表扬）。落第者无奖励。“学问吟味”虽然在形式上模仿了中国的科举制度，但并不是为任用官吏实施的考试，与科举制度有着根本上的区别。[②]

宽政九年（1797 年）12 月，十一代将军德川家齐正式将林家经营管理的汤岛圣堂收归幕府作为“官学”，主要用于教育德川幕府的直属家臣“旗本”与武士家族“御家人”的子弟，并将其更名为“昌平阪学问所”，直属幕府管辖，并将其整修扩建，成为幕府的最高学府，俗称“昌平黉”。不过在日常生活中，与昌平坂学问所这一正式名称相比，人们更习惯称之为汤岛圣堂，并一直延续至今。

笔者从 2012 年 3 月 31 日开始对汤岛圣堂进行了数次实地考察，专程拜访了公益财团法人斯文会，并参加了他们在汤岛圣堂举办的 2012 年度释奠礼。

明治十三年（1880 年）6 月 6 日，斯文学会在东京成立。“斯文”二字取自《论语·子罕》。学会以此命名即有传承孔子思想之意。东京高等师范学校教职员中有志之士，为了表达对孔子教化日本国民的谢意，于明治三十九年（1906 年）10 月 10 日结成孔子祭典会，决定次年 4 月 4 日恢复释奠，并将 4 月第 4 个星期日定为祭祀孔子的释奠日。自此每年成为惯例，但释奠礼基本上沿袭德川时代后期采用的神道仪礼。

---

① 值得一提的是，尽管幕府禁止阳明学等，但实际上阳明学后来仍然成为时代主流。阳明学派始祖中江藤树（1608－48 年）十六岁从京都禅僧学《论语》，后又精研《四书大全》，开始信奉朱子学。二十七岁为回乡奉养寡母而私自离开伊豫，抛弃武士身份。回故乡后办私塾，著《翁问答》，认为儒道即士道，将武士精神和朱子学结合在一起。他根据王阳明的知行合一说，注重学问的实践，提倡经世，有“近江圣人”之称。2014 年 3 月 29 日笔者参观了藤树书院遗址与近江圣人中江藤树纪念馆等。

② 当然“学问吟味”考试合格者谋职时与其他人相比通常会受到重视或优待。因此考试合格被看作一种能力测验而颇具魅力。

大正七年（1918年）9月27日，斯文学会与孔子祭典会合并，成立财团法人斯文会。从大正九年（1920年）开始至今，斯文会一直负责管理汤岛圣堂并组织主办释奠礼等一系列传承传统儒学的文化活动。

据斯文会理事长石川忠久先生以及斯文会宣传资料介绍，斯文会于平成二十二年（2010年）6月1日由财团法人改为公益财团法人，目前拥有1200名会员，每年出版一期学术刊物《斯文》，并定期举办各种传统纪念活动。如1月1日至4日为“正月大成殿特别开放日”，元旦当天举行《论语》讲座，对外免费展示明朝遗臣朱舜水带至日本的孔子像；4月第4个周日举行祭孔仪式与纪念讲演会；5月第3个周日举行祭针灸仪式与纪念演讲会；10月第4个周日举行祭先儒仪式与纪念演讲会；11月23日举行祭神农仪式与纪念演讲会；每年1月和7月举办两次文化演讲会。此外，这里还继承了宽政九年德川幕府设立“昌平坂学问所”举办汉文讲座的传统，每周举办《论语》朗读、《论语》阅读、汉文入门、《孟子》讲读、汉字起源、《易经》讲义、阴阳五行说、素问讲读、《老子》讲读、《史记》讲读、十八史略讲读、汉诗作法入门、圣社诗会、江户汉学讲义、唐诗鉴赏、江户汉诗、古文书解读、书法、中国古典音乐、中国画、健康太极拳等各种文化讲座。

2012年4月22日上午，在汤岛圣堂大成殿举行的释奠礼第18项仪式上，由东京外国语大学名誉教授高桥均先生讲经《论语》先进篇第十一章“子路、曾皙、冉有、公西华侍坐”，大约35分钟。事实上，自林罗山于宽永十二年（1635年）2月举行的释奠礼上首次讲经《论语》第一章以来，每次释奠礼中都有讲经一项，成为传统，流传至今（秦2013：39—49）。

笔者于2013年6月1日上午考察汤岛圣堂时，看到在斯文会馆门口的右侧挂着白布旗幡，上面印有“汉文检定”的黑字标语。据斯文会常务理事谣口明先生介绍，汉字文化振兴协会是在得到日本政府“总务省”认可后成立的一般社团法人，所从事文化事业有三项：

一是举办藩校峰会，促进与旧藩校的学术·文化交流；

二是召集汉文教育工作者举办研讨会，促进汉字的传承；

三是实施“汉文检定”，普及汉文。

“汉文检定”即汉文经典考核。他们认为汉文是日本文化的根基，学习汉文的重要性不言而喻。因此从2013年开始，每年6月和10—11月两次在汤岛圣堂实施初级，中级以及高级等各等级的“汉文检定”考试。考规是：考题内容主要来自《论语》与汉诗；考试形式有口试与笔试；无年龄限制，任何人都可以报名参加。协会向考试合格者颁发相应的合格证书，表彰他们的儒学素养与汉文水平。以此来鼓励他们更加努力学习，提高汉文能力。对考生来说，该合格证不仅是自己汉文水平的见证，而且是汉语言学习获得汉文专家认可，且得到社会表彰的荣誉证。从这个意义上说，“汉文检定”类似上述“素读吟味”。其合格证书为年轻人升学或进入社会带来积极的促进作用；对老年人而言，亦可丰富其晚年生活。

2012年7月7日，笔者到汤岛圣堂讲堂参观了正在举行的市民《论语》素读讲座。讲堂基本满座，学员以中高龄男女居多，这与日本近年高龄少子化有关。年长的讲师在台上领着很多基本上不会汉语的学员进行日式“素读”。

## 四、足利学校普及《论语》教育的历史与现状

足利学校位于东京北部的枥木县足利市，创建年代不详，有奈良时代国学遗制说、平安时代初期天长九年（832）小野篁创立说、镰仓时代初期足利义兼以及室町时代中期永享十一年（1439）年关东管领上杉宪实创立等，说法不一。虽然各执一词，但大家普遍认为它是日本最古老的学校。

足利学校一直受到官方的支助与保护，自室町时代开始走向兴隆。当时由于上杉宪实的鼎力支持，成为日本僧侣学习研究易学中心，全校学生多达三千余人。除易学之外，其他教授科目为孝经、四书、五经、老庄，兵法、医学、卜筮等，同时还制造名品刀剑。西班牙出生的天主教传教士弗朗西斯科·扎比尔（Francisco de Xavier）于天文十八年（1549年）称其为“日本全国最大最著名的坂东大学”。

江户时代，幕府扩建校舍，安置圣像，刊行书籍，宽文八年（1668年）建筑圣庙，成为全日本最古老的圣庙。殿堂正面龛座内供奉着木雕孔子坐像，据木胎内铭文记载，此像造于日本天文四年（1535年），是日本现存最古的木雕孔子坐像。

明治四年（1871年），足利学校被迫关闭（两年后改为新式小学），而圣庙及附属的古籍、器物等由枥木县政府管理，明治九年（1876年）归还并设立足利文库，明治三十六年（1903年）改为足利学校遗址图书馆。大正十年（1921年）3月，孔子庙与校门等建筑被指定为“国家史迹”。

2012年3月29日，笔者曾赴东京郊外的枥木县足利市，参观了被誉为日本最古老的学校——史迹足利学校，并拜访了该校事务所所长前桥勋先生及孔子第76代孙女孔佩群女士。

现在的足利学校于1990年重建复原，采用左庙右学的建制。其大门称为“入德门”，左侧有中国山东省济宁市赠送的巨大孔子全身雕像。中门为“学校门”，门楹上“学校”二字由明人蒋龙溪挥毫。最后一门为“杏坛门”。穿过杏坛门，即为大成殿，建筑风格模仿明代庙宇。从大成殿正门可以分别看到孔子与小野篁的坐像。

传统释奠曾在明治初期伴随学校关闭而中断，但明治四十年（1907）[①] 冬至日得到恢复，从大正四年（1915）至今，每年 11 月 23 日（文化节）在大成殿举行。仪式完毕后，进行“论语素读”以及记念讲演会、雅乐演奏会。

面向大成殿，左侧为遗址图书馆，藏书 3 万 2 千册，其中古书 1 万 7 千册。古书宋刊本 4 种 77 册，即宋刊《文选》21 册于昭和 27 年（1952）、宋版《礼记正义》35 册、宋版《尚书正义》8 册、宋版《周易注疏》13 册于昭和 30 年（1955 年）被指定为“国宝”；另外，《周易传》、《周易》、《古文孝经》、《附释音毛诗注疏》、《附释音春秋左传注疏》、《论语义疏》、《周礼》和《唐书》等 8 种 98 册成为“重要文化财”。

大成殿右侧分别是大讲堂、食堂以及师生宿舍“寮”等设施。大讲堂入口处与学校大门入口购票处一样，摆设不少本校编辑发行的各种《论语》版本以供出售。各种资料显示，足利市教育委员会从 1992 年起就编辑出版了《论语抄》，1999 年又编写成面向小学生的《假名论语》，印制《论语》纸牌，供学生阅读。

值得注意的是，与上述斯文会馆入口类似，大讲堂入口处也高挂着“足利学校汉字检定”考试的宣传标语。考试内容主要是以《论语》著名章节为主，类似上述“汉文检定”与“素读吟味”因此也称为“论语吟味”。“足利学校汉字检定”从 2010 年 4 月开始施行，实施时间比斯文会的“汉文检定”更早。

足利学校工作人员早上“朝礼”时必须朗读《论语》一篇，营造了普及《论语》教育的环境和气氛。2004 年，茨城县立高中退休教师、史迹足利学校研究员须永美和夫先生提出了举办“周日论语素读体验”的建议，旨在吸引游客到史迹足利学校参观访问。此建议得到采纳。所以从 2005 年开始，主要以普通游客为对象，免费举办“周日论语素读体验”文化活动。2009 年，“史迹足利学校论语素读运营委员会”成立。从此，担任“论语素读”的讲师由其委员会指派。2010 年开始，以市内中小学生以及来自全国各地的普通团体为对象，开设了“论语体验项目”，每次收费 2000 日元。

从 2007 年 4 月起，足利市政府提倡足利市所有的市立小学、中学均开设《论语》课程，规定中小学有义务进行《论语》诵读。市教育委员会提出了参访足利学校就是实现培养学生“热爱乡土”的教育目标，规定各小学四年级学生和各中学一年级学生必须以学校为单位确定日期，积极主动到史迹足利学校去参加“享受论语素读”。对此，史迹足利学校不仅不收费，而且还向每个学生免费赠送一本《论语抄》。

另外，史迹足利学校还邀请日本各界儒学研究者来此举办学术讲座，讲授《论语》等儒学经典。尤其是在足利市大豆生田市长的倡导与主导下，为了继承足利学校的儒学教育传统，面向日本全国普及论语并弘扬“论语城市足利”精神，于 2012 年 3 月 17 日在

① 这可能与上述同年 4 月汤岛圣堂释奠恢复及其影响有关。

足利学校正式成立民间团体“全国论语研究会”① 后，《论语》教育普及达到高潮。在大讲堂几乎每月都要举办“全国论语素读集会”以及各种关于论语的学术研究会、诵读讲座和践行活动。全国各地爱好《论语》的男女老少前来足利孔子庙参拜孔子，然后聆听论语讲师的儒学演讲以及齐声朗读论语。目前，足利学校与下述弘道馆以及闲谷学校等传统校舍，以日本的教育遗产为主体，正在为联合申请登录世界文化遗产而努力。

## 五、弘道馆与诵读《论语》的历史与现状

笔者于2012年3月31日拜访斯文会石川忠久理事长先生时，得知他作为“汉字文化振兴协会”会长在茨城县水户市与其他同仁一起负责主办了全国藩校峰会的会议，时间正是当年2月18—19日，地点在水户市。从2002年在汤岛圣堂举行第一届以来，全国藩校峰会每年在全国各地原江户藩校②轮流举办，至今已历经十届，共有35所藩校代表参加。

2013年5月31日，笔者考察了弘道馆并受到弘道馆事务所专业研究员“学艺员”小圷纪子女士的热情接待与鼎力协助（秦2014）。

水户藩位于江户（东京）东面，第一代藩主为德川家康的第十一子赖房（1603—1661年），尚武好学，崇神尊儒。其子光圀为第二代藩主，不仅重视编修史书，而且对儒家思想及其应用亦非常重视，于宽文五年（1665年）6月将朱舜水从长崎聘请到水户担任顾问，协助编撰《大日本史》，管理藩政，振兴儒学并学以致用。后来又创立了以经世济民为己任的“水户学”，政绩显著、社会经济繁荣安定而在各藩中享有盛名。

水户虽然是水户学的发祥地，但是兴建藩校和孔子庙却比其他藩晚很多。文政十二年（1829年），从小喜好水户学的第九代藩主德川齐昭，为维护封建体制稳定并解决日益严重的财政危机，于天宝八年（1837年）开始推行“天宝改革”，重视文化教育，建设藩士子弟学文习武的藩校，同时为农村有志之士设立乡校。

天宝九年3月，齐昭公布了亲自撰写的《弘道馆记》，其中“奉神州之道，资西土之教，忠孝无二，文武不歧，学问事业不殊其效，敬神崇儒无有偏党，集众思，宣群力，以报国家无穷之恩”，反映了齐昭确定的五项建校与教育理念。

馆名“弘道”二字取自《论语·卫灵公》第十五。子曰：“人能弘道，非道弘人”。

---

① 会员不分职业年龄，只要赞同研究会宗旨并缴纳个人会费1千日元或团体会费3千元，任何人即可入会。

② 在江户时代，拥有一万石以上的领主“大名”均称作藩主，藩主家臣为藩士，明治维新之前共有276个藩，各藩都有藩校，维新后1871年废藩置县，大部分藩校废除，其他少数藩校则变为旧制初级中学。

其实，此前已经有佐贺藩与彦根藩等五所藩校命名为弘道馆，但因为〈弘道馆记〉的内容与学校教育特色以及占地面积等因素使创立最晚的水户弘道馆后来在各藩校中最为著名。

弘道馆于安政四年（1857 年）5 月 9 日正式开馆（须藤 2001：254－5）。当时占地 54000 坪（17.8 公顷），规模相当于屈指可数的加贺藩明伦堂（约 17800 坪）与长州藩明伦馆（14000 坪）的 3－4 倍，成为各藩中最大藩校，比上述汤岛圣堂大近 5 倍。全馆由校区、神社孔子庙区以及练武场三大区构成，相当于带有浓厚宗教色彩的近代综合性大学。

学生入学资格为藩士子弟，但入学之前必须在家塾里学习基础知识。之后由家塾教师向学馆提交希望升学的学生名单，然后在指定的日期领着 15 岁左右的学生登馆，并按规定首先参拜鹿岛神社与孔子庙，方能报名登记。进武馆不用考试，但入文馆必须通过入学考试，考题内容出自《论语》与《孝经》等，合格者才能入学，而不合格者则继续留在家塾"素读"经典。

与汤岛圣堂类似，学生入馆后称为"讲习生"，分班编组，先修"会读"，然后升进"轮讲"课程。"轮讲生"必须轮番依次讲解《论语》、《孟子》、《春秋左氏传》等汉书。"轮讲生"考试合格升为"居学生"。他们会被分配到 3 叠榻榻米的个人房室，有资格听"教授头取"（主任教授）的讲义并参加每年秋季在藩主临场主导下举行的"大试"。此外他们要在教授指导下轮讲，每月参加两次笔试"试问"与一次诗歌创作。

上课日数因年级差异而不同。通常高年级学生上课天数多。上午在文馆学文：儒家经典、历史、诗歌、天文以及数学等课程；下午则在武馆习武：剑术、枪术、兵术以及马术等多种武道科目。学习成绩根据每年一次"文武大试"与每月两次"小试"判定。值得一提的是，这里没有毕业年限，可终生学习，中老年人也可以随时申请入馆就读。

弘道馆虽然培养了大批优秀藩士，成为水户学的发展中心，但在幕府末期因为政治立场不同而分裂为"天狗"勤王派与"诸生"佐幕派，彼此互相抗争，并陷入战乱达数年之久。明治元年 10 月 1 日，两派发生最后交战，文馆、武馆以及医学馆等主要建筑毁于战火，只剩下正厅、正门、八卦堂、鹿岛神社以及孔子庙等建筑。

明治八年（1875 年），根据太政官颁布的公告，荒废的空地被指定为国家公园。1945 年 8 月 2 日遭受美军空袭，八卦堂、孔子庙以及鹿岛神社等建筑被烧毁。战后逐渐得到重建修复。

据和田祐之介介绍，为传承并弘扬弘道馆宗旨，纪念 1841 年 8 月 1 日弘道馆临时开馆日，从 2009 年 8 月 1 日开始，在弘道馆内由民间团体每月举办一次"弘道馆亲子论语塾"，邀请安冈定子女士作为讲师指导亲子一起学《论语》（和田 2012：104）。安冈定子女士是著名阳明学者安冈正笃的孙女，在东京银座开办论语私塾，弘扬儒学，享有盛名。

## 六、闲谷学校的《论语》教育传承

闲谷学校位于冈山县备前市和气町闲谷地区的深山峡谷，热心文教事业的冈山藩主池田光政于宽文八年（1668年）在领内12郡设立的123所乡村学校的“手习所”之一，两年后扩建时由延原更名为闲谷。延宝元年（1673年）讲堂竣工，次年圣庙建成。延宝3年藩政府由于财政压力，所以将所有的“手习所”废除，统一编入至闲谷学校。元禄十四年（1701年）新讲堂竣工，历时23年之久建造的校舍顺利完工，形成现今的规模。

当时学规是：凡来此学习者，交上不多的学费，准备好必要的文具，便可入学。在所学课程中，必修的有《孝经》、小学、四书、五经。继续深造者有《左传》、《国语》、《史记》、《汉书》等。学生在“孝、悌、忠、信”的前提下，有的学习农业知识，有的学习经商之道。每月初一讲《白鹿洞揭示》，每年的释菜礼，师生都要按时参加。首次释菜礼在贞享二年（1685）年举行。当时，释菜礼与“新春初读仪式”（后述）为此校每年定期举办的两大传统仪式。

池田光政还于宽文九年（1669年）创办了冈山藩校。此校比汤岛圣堂早21年，但与弘道馆等藩校一样都是只供武士阶层的子弟就读的藩立学校，而闲谷学校则是为普及平民教育而开设的。池田光政临终前，特意留下了要将闲谷学校永远办下去的遗言，并被历代后任者坚守其遗志并忠实地执行。封建社会平民百姓被武士阶层统治，社会经济地位低下，所以建成这所平民学校具有划时代的意义，被誉为日本最古老的庶民学校。

明治维新后，闲谷学校曾一度关闭，但没有遭到破坏而完整无损地保存至今。至昭和时代，闲谷学校的历史传统由和气闲谷高级中学继承下来。旧址校舍已停止教学活动，主要作为重要史迹保存，通称为“旧闲谷学校”。①

大正十一年（1922年），根据《史迹名胜天然保护法》，旧闲谷学校被指定为国家史迹；昭和十三年（1938），讲堂、圣庙、神社等25个建筑被指定为国宝。而这些国宝在昭和二十五年（1950年），根据《文化财保护法》更名为“重要文化财”。其中讲堂于昭和二十八年（1953）被指定为国宝，旧闲谷学校于昭和二十九年被指定为“特别史迹”，昭和四十年（1965年）成为冈山县青少年教育中心闲谷学校。至今来此参观者连续不断，来此受教育的全国各地青少年也络绎不绝。

2013年11月23日至24日首次参访了旧闲谷学校，受到公益财团法人特别史迹旧

---

① 但其“旧”字在日常生活中往往被省略。

闲谷学校显彰保存会事务局局长、冈山县青少年教育中心闲谷学校所长国友道一先生等工作人员的热情接待。

目前旧闲谷学校的门票为大人 400 日元、65 岁以上 200 日元、中小学生 100 日元。据国友道一先生介绍，近年来访人数逐渐减少，2008 年为 16 万 3274 人次，2013 年为 9 万 8694 人次。

学校正门名鹤鸣门，里面是坐北朝南的宽大院落，正对大门的高台上是上述圣庙，圣庙门外东西有两株粗大的楷树，大成殿内供奉着孔子铜像。圣庙东侧是为祭祀池田光政修建的芳烈祠，明治八年（1875 年）更名为闲谷神社。但为了表示对孔子的尊敬并突出圣庙的崇高地位，闲谷神社的地基要比圣庙深 1 米左右。

圣庙西南面，即大院西边是上述讲堂，为学校最大、最重要的建筑物。堂之正中高悬“克明德”三个遒劲的大字，其旁悬挂朱熹制定的《白鹿洞书院学规》匾额。

笔者参访旧闲谷学校的契机之一是在其网页中看到他们每月第三周日上午在讲堂举办一次诵读《论语》的介绍宣传。但因为各种原因没有找到机会参加体验。据国友道一先生介绍，“旧闲谷学校周日论语讲座”自 2007 年开始，每年原则上从 6 月至次年 3 月，每月第三周上午 10 点半至 12 点，聘请高级中学的汉文教师在讲堂讲授《论语》，并带领听讲者一起诵读《论语》。每次参加讲座的费用为 500 日元，缴费即可参加，报名听讲人数在 20—50 名之间，每次都不一样。

公益财团法人特别史迹旧闲谷学校显彰保存会自平成九年（1997）学术刊物《闲谷学校》创刊以来，每年发行一期。笔者自费购买了一整套（17 册）。据 2005 年 5 月发行的第 5 号刊介绍，闲谷学校显彰保存会在备前市教育委员会与和气町教育委员会的指导下，自 2005 年新年开始，恢复了中断近一个世纪的“新年初读仪式”,① 诵读《论语》章节，以象征一年学习生活的开始。

新年初读仪式每年 1 月 4 日上午 9 点半开始在闲谷学校讲堂举行，已作为定制确定下来。参加者主要是上述和气闲谷高级中学②的师生，学生家长以及其他男女老少都可

① 释菜礼在明治初期因废藩置县与学制改革而中断，大正四年（1915）年纪念创学 250 周年由私立中学闲谷黉师生自发恢复。

② 2014 年 9 月 4 日，笔者通过国友道一先生介绍访问了和气闲谷高级中学。据该校校长香山真一先生介绍，从昭和时代至今旧闲谷学校每年 10 月第四周日举办释菜仪式时，该校教职工担任主祭官成为惯例。2001 年为纪念建校 330 周年，编辑出版了论语教材《论语百章》，供全校学生诵读论语使用。该校每年有 5 次集会，全体师生都要在集会开始时一起诵读论语，铭记孔子教导，省思自己的言行举止。从 2014 年开始，全校师生携带使用名为《论语手帐》的袖珍日历手册，每页右侧供记录一周的安排，左侧印有论语章节。另外，该校于 1999 年 9 月 25 日于中国曲阜市第一中学签订了友好交流合作协议，2014 年 8 月 5 日师生第四次访问曲阜，4 名学生费用来自冈山县教育委员会拨发的“和气 AIAI 项目”专款，其目的是为了普及论语教育。

自由报名免费参加，但须购买进入校内的上述门票。

2014年1月4日清晨，笔者从神户专程参加了这项新年初读仪式。仪式内容顺序如下：

| | |
|---|---|
| 9：30—9：50 | 圣庙大成殿集合 |
| 10：00—10：15 | 向孔子像献香、敬礼 |
| 10：30—11：00 | 朗读《论语》 |
| 11：00—11：20 | 畅谈新年抱负 |
| 11：20—11：30 | 学生亲手用白毛巾擦地板 |

据第二天《朝日新闻》报道，此次参加仪式的人数为220名。其主体为和气闲谷高级中学的学生，其次是该校教师与学生家长，还有不少65岁以上的一般高龄男女，坐在前排。

值得一提的是，为了完美地继承江户时代师生的苦学精神，讲堂内至今特意没有安装空调，也没有使用其他任何取暖设备。当天上午气温在8—9度，比较寒冷，但参加者都脱下外套，身着单薄的学生制服或西装，聚精会神，正坐如钟。当笔者把这一现象与自己的敬意告诉国友道一先生等学校工作人员时，他们会心地说："前年这天的气温更低，降至零度左右，但大家一直热情很高，并不感到寒冷。"由此可见，从江户时代开始诵读《论语》章节的优良传统作为学校的开学仪式得到了传承及发展。

笔者得知国友道一先生作为公益财团法人特别史迹旧闲谷学校显彰保存会事务局局长、冈山县青少年教育中心闲谷学校所长，经常积极主动参加各种学术活动并到各地介绍弘扬闲谷学校传统精神及其当代意义，诚挚邀请他作为"Guest Speaker"，于2014年6月23日到我校，给学生们做了题为"旧闲谷学校的历史变迁与论语教育"的学术报告，受到热烈欢迎与高度赞扬。①

近年旧闲谷学校大力推行论语普及教育，与县政府的经济援助与思想指导有密切关系。比如，冈山县教育委员会为了促进心灵精神教育与日常生活教育，让学生更健康成长，决定在中小学导入传统的论语教育，于2013年3月编辑出版了题为《学校教育活用论语章句集》的教学参考资料并免费颁发给各校师生以及相关机构人士。另外，冈山县教育委员会为了更好地推进论语教育普及工作，于2014年10月25日在旧闲谷学校召开题为"学《论语》学术研讨会"。

为何冈山县教育委员会热衷于《论语》普及教育呢？"学《论语》学术研讨会"通知书开头公开说明：人与人为了健全地交流、舒适地生活，离不开规范意识、做人常

① 此次演讲允许社会人士旁听，相关信息在大学网页上公布。结果有10多名社会人士参加旁听，其中一名来自横滨。

理以及人际关系等因素。而《论语》以讲解如何“做人”为中心话题，所以此次研讨会决定以此为基础，主要讨论“为何现在出现论语热”以及“学校教育导入《论语》学习的可能性”。

但笔者认为除了这些客观原因外，至少还有以下两方面的因素值得留意。

一是与日本社会精英人士自发推广《论语》普及教育的传统有关。比如，冈山县井原市的兴让馆高级中学自嘉永六年（1853）创办以来，一直保持每天早上全体师生齐声诵读《白鹿洞书院 揭示》并坚持普及《论语》的传统教育方针。2014 年 9 月 5 日笔者访问了该校，受到小谷彰吾校长的热情接待，并旁听了他以及冲久教人老师的论语课。

据小谷彰吾校长介绍，该校战后论语教育停止，但在他的倡导下于平成十六年（2004）年 4 月的新学期开始正式将《论语》作为教材并定为必修课程，规定一年级各班学生一起上《论语》课，为一个学分。小谷校长还于 2011 年 4 月主持编辑了《“论语”与“人学”学习资料集》，供该校师生学习参考并免费赠送给其他相关机构与《论语》学习爱好者。

第二个因素是，这些中央政府的法令无疑促进了冈山县教育委员会以及上述足利市政府推动《论语》的普及教育。根据日本文化科学省于平成元年（1989）3 月颁布的旧《学习指导纲要》，高级中学于次年将《论语》作为国语古典与汉文的主要内容。另外，根据日本文化科学省于平成二十年（2008）3 月颁布的新《学习指导纲要》，以《论语》为主要内容的古典与汉文于 2011 年与 2012 年 4 月分别正式纳入小学与中学的国语课程。但值得一提的是，东京都世田谷区教育委员会因为取得了不受《学习指导纲要》的“日语特区”优待证，已经早于平成十九年（2007）4 月将以《论语》主要内容的古典与汉文正式纳入全区所有中小学的国语课程。由此可见，《学习指导纲要》普及《论语》教育不仅继承发展了传统的教育方针，而且集中反映了当代社会各阶层的需求。

## 七、结语

本文主要是以汤岛圣堂、足利学校、弘道馆以及闲谷学校为例来介绍日本各地《论语》普及教育的历史现状以及社会功能。虽然日本各地普及《论语》教育的历史现状多样，每个时代尊孔崇儒的情形有所差异，但总的来说，《论语》传入日本一千数百年以来，基本上一直受到皇室、僧侣与武士以及商人等精英阶层的青睐敬仰。经过他们长期由上至下推崇普及教育，《论语》已经在日本社会各个领域深深地扎下了根，至今对日本社会的发展变化产生着巨大的影响力。

尤其是自江户时代以来，日本各界许多著名人士对《论语》给予极高的评价，对其普及教育产生了深远的社会影响。比如，古学派代表人物伊藤仁斋在《童子问》中曾对《论语》推崇备至，高度评价“论语实为最上至极宇宙第一书”（伊藤 1970：22）。

明治时代，很多出生在江户时代的武士读过《论语》，儒学者及其企业家曾努力介绍推广《论语》超时代的普遍性价值。武士（幕臣）、官僚与实业家涩泽荣一（1840—1931 年）可谓其典型代表。

涩泽荣一出身琦玉县豪农家庭，自幼读《论语》，习剑术。他弃官从商，将《论语》作为第一经营哲学，创办了 500 多家企业，被誉为“日本资本主义之父”。他在大正五年（1916 年）出版的名著《论语与算盘》中指出：后儒对孔子学说误解最突出的是富贵观念和理财思想，他们错误地把“仁义正道”同“货殖富贵”完全对立起来。涩泽以自己的经验来说明《论语》与“算盘”可以一致，互相融合，并明确表示一定要把《论语》作为商业上的“经典”，认为自己的工作就是要通过《论语》来提高商人的道德，使商人明晓“取之有道”的道理；同时还要让其他人知道“求利”其实并不违背“至圣先师”的古训，尽可以放手追求“阳光下的利益”。因此，《论语》与算盘的关系是远在天边，近在咫尺，缩小《论语》与算盘间的距离，是当时最紧要的任务。

昭和时代阳明学者安冈正笃在名著《学论语》中曾高度评价《论语》是最古同时也是最新的经典，并指出“说如果想要把握当代并得出正确的结论，那么说一本《论语》就足够了并不过分”（安冈 2007：42）。

当代著名儒学者加地伸行（加地 2004：11）以及真田但马与吹野安（1999：1）等认为，《论语》与基督教的《圣经》一样，是在世界上被广泛阅读的“世界古典”。

著名社会活动家一条真也认为：“《论语》可与《圣经》并列，是世界上最著名的古典。……在遇到难题时，西洋人常常会打开《圣经》，听从耶稣教导来采取对应方针；同样，日本的许多政治家和企业家等往往会想起《论语》中的名句并以此作为依据决定自己的行动与态度。《论语》一千数百年以来一直被我们的祖先爱读传承至今。无论我们是否自觉意识到都应承认，像《论语》这样给予日本人的心灵以巨大影响的书籍可谓绝无仅有。”（一条 2007：191—197）

2007 年 12 月 27—30 日福田康夫首相一行访华期间，于 30 日访问了曲阜孔庙大成殿，在孔庙题词“温故创新”，在孔子的“温故知新”上做了一字之改。在接受记者简短采访时表示，中国两千多年的历史和文化使他印象深刻，《论语》等儒家作品在日本非常流行，因此选择来孔庙参观。这可视为当今日本精英人士尊孔崇儒、“知行合一”并将孔庙作为一种文化资源或外交手段充分开发利用的实例。

笔者也认为孔庙相当于基督教的教堂，《论语》可与《圣经》媲美。在孔子庙诵读《论语》，类似在教会诵读《圣经》。因此，在孔子庙及其相关校馆诵读以《论语》为代表的儒家经典来传承推广儒家思想，用儒家伦理道德来缓解各种社会矛盾，促进社会和谐发展，具有特别深远的历史与现实意义。

如果说孔庙与《论语》普及教育的兴盛是国家统治者及其社会精英尊孔崇儒的象征，也是社会繁荣、和谐发展的标志之一的话，那么经过强大的欧美近代文明冲击洗礼，逐渐由日本社会精英阶层自发组织而得以持续复兴的各地孔子庙以及《论语》普及教育史实，也和中国大陆正在持续复兴的各地孔庙以及各种形式的读经讲经行经浪潮一样，充分反映了源自中国的儒家文化（文明）不仅与欧美的基督教文化（文明）之间有着继续共存、互补乃至共同发展的必然性和可能性，而且还有着自身不可忽视的普世价值及其坚忍顽强的生命力。

但不能忽视的是，日本对《论语》的理解应用及其普及教育程度与中国是有很大差异的。上述圣德太子在制定《十七条宪法》时，首先强调的是《论语》中的“和”，而不是中国人公认的“孝”。林罗山等提出了神儒合一论（堀 1990：410－420；铃木 2012：145－149），但林罗山认为“君国大事”比“家父私事”更重要，即相对于中国人对“孝”的强调，更重视“忠”（加地 1995：112－113；歴史の謎を探る会 2005：48）。因此，儒教的忠孝仁义之道、重视社会秩序等被日本本土化，导致对上效忠比孝敬父母更具有社会价值，成为普遍接受的道德标准。“忠”在日本儒教中是无条件的，而在中国儒学中是有条件的。

值得一提的是，中国儒家特别重视的四书中，《孟子》一直没有像《论语》那样受到欢迎并推广普及。这是因为日本精英认为孟子的易姓革命思想不符合日本天皇“万世一系”、世代相传的尊皇忠君国体观念。事实上，历史上日本一直没有接受孟子所提出的易姓革命思想（松本 2014），很少发生中国式“革命”，即便是现在，日本社会也依然维持着等级森严的序列体系，人类学者中根千枝（1967）称之为“纵式社会”。无论是在战争年代，还是和平时期都能上下一致，秩序稳定，高度统一。

另外，江户时代的“学问吟味”虽然在形式上模仿了中国的科举制度，但并不是为采用官吏实施的考试，与科举制度有着根本上的区别。而日本当代各地孔子庙实施的“汉文检定”以及“论语吟味”与“学问吟味”基本上一脉相承。

至江户时代后期，日本阳明学成为主流，与尚文的中国文人士大夫重视“知”与抽象思维的传统相比，尚武的日本武士则更注重“行”与具体实践。

历史上日本没有全盘接受中国传统科举制度，也是日本精英人士一直热心普及《论语》教育的重要原因。诚如林泰辅在《论语年谱》序言中所言：“中国、朝鲜以及越南，因为热衷于将《论语》用于科举考试，所以虽然盛行诵读《论语》，但都是为了谋取名利，结果嚼取了糟粕，而不是精华。[1] 但吾邦人诵读《论语》则剥去外皮，取其精髓，故取得了培养国本的显著效果。”（林 1916：37）

如果以上所述日中两国对《论语》的理解应用及其普及教育程度存在的差异性属实的话，那么以《论语》为象征的中国传统儒学在日本的本土化过程既反映了日本精英阶层吸纳传承儒家文化的积极性与选择性以及创造性，但同时也充分体现了中日两国文化既有着深厚的历史渊源，又存在着不可混淆的异质性。

关于这方面的调查研究，今后还需要进一步吸收儒学、历史学以及教育学等领域前人研究成果并深入展开，同时对江户时代遍及日本各地的“寺子屋”[2] 和私塾《论语》普及教育的历史变迁与社会现状也要进行比较研究。这是本研究课题的遗留问题，也是今后要进一步深入调查研究的课题与方向。

**参考文献：**


[1] Hoobler，Thomas & Hoobler，Dorothy 2009 ConfucianismNew York：Chelsea House.

[2] Yokoo，Toshihiko 2014 “Confucius and Education of Taku City”，《纪念孔子诞辰2565周年国际学术研讨会暨国际儒学联合会第五届会员大会论文集》2121－2131页。

日文

[1] 足利市立美術館編 2013『論語と足利学校』、足利市教育委員会。

[2] 井沢元彦 2012『仏教・神道・儒教集中講座』東京：徳間書店。

[3] 石川松太郎 1985『藩校と寺子屋』東村山：教育社。

[4] 一条真也 2007『知ってビックリ！日本三大のご利益：神道 & 仏教 & 儒教』東京：大和書房。

[5] 伊藤仁斎（清水茂校注）1970『童子問』岩波書店。

[6] 石毛直道 2003『サムライニッポン：文と武の東洋史』東京：中央公論新社。

[7] 大久保利謙 2008『日本の大學』東京：玉川大學出版部。

[8] 岡山県教育委員会 2013『学校教育で活用できる論語章句集』


① 当然，何谓《论语》精华要看我们站在哪个角度、用什么标准来衡量。笔者在此不予深究。

② 目前总部位于大阪，支部几乎遍及日本各城镇的“论语普及会”可谓当代“寺子屋”版。2014年7月18日笔者专程到论语普及会事务室拜访了村下好伴先生。据先生自我介绍，他今年83岁，原来是买菜专业户，30年前开始与买菜专业户伊舆那先生一起崇拜安冈正笃而创办了论语普及会，目前拥有会员700名。创办初期曾得到过政界与财界的鼎力支持，但后来逐渐独立经营，主要靠会员会费维持运营。

［9］加地伸行 2004『論語』東京：角川書店。

［10］小谷彰吾 2014『興譲館の教え・徳の学び：興譲館高等学校「論語」「人間学」学習資料集』学校法人興譲館高等学校。

［11］財団法人「孔子の里」編 1991『時空を超えて——孔子と現代——』、多久：財団法人「孔子の里」。

［12］閑谷学校研究委員会編 2005『閑谷学校研究』9 号、財団法人特別史跡旧閑谷学校顕彰保存会。

［13］渋沢栄一 1977『論語講義』（全 7 巻）講談社。

［14］2010『渋沢百訓　論語・人生・経営』角川ソフィア文庫。

［15］2012（守屋淳編訳）『現代語訳　渋沢栄一自伝：「論語と算盤」を道標として』東京：平凡社。

［16］清水熙康 1994『論語と警察』東京：展転社。

［17］秦兆雄 2010「東アジアからみた儒教復興の展開」『宗教と現代がわかる本 2010』146－149 頁、東京：平凡社。

［18］鈴木三八男編 1989『日本の孔子廟と孔子像』東京：斯文会。

［19］第十回全国藩校サミットin 水戸実行委员会编 2012『第十回全国藩校サミットin 水戸記念誌』水户：第十回全国藩校サミットin 水戸実行委员会。

［20］鶴蒔靖夫 1996『心の革命——東日本国際大学の挑戦』東京：IN 通信社。

［21］特別史跡旧閑谷学校顕彰保存会編 2007『閑谷学校あいうえお論語』、特別史跡旧閑谷学校顕彰保存会。

［22］中根千枝 1967『タテ社会の人間関係』東京：講談社。

［23］橋本昭彦 1993『江戸幕府試験制度史の研究』東京：風間書房。

［24］林泰輔編　龍門社編纂 1916『論語年譜』東京：大倉書店。

［25］真田但馬・吹野安 編 1990『論語集註』東京：笠間書院。

［26］町田三郎　1991『日本の「論語」』財団法人「孔子の里」編『時空を超えて——孔子と現代——』、多久：財団法人「孔子の里」。

［27］松川健二編 1994『論語の思想史』東京：汲古書院。

［28］松本健一 2014『「孟子」の革命思想と日本―天皇家にはなぜ姓がないのか』いわき：昌平黌出版会。

［29］宮崎市定（砺波護編）1996『論語の新しい読み方』東京：岩波書店。

［30］安岡正篤 2002『論語に学ぶ』PHP 研究所〈PHP 文庫〉。

［31］矢羽野隆男 2013「新『学習指導要領』「伝統的な言語文化」に即した入門期漢文教育法：『論語』副教材・カルタを用いて」『天王寺大学紀要』56：45－

373頁。

中文

［1］北京特殊钢厂工人理论组编.《论语》是反动阶级的復辟经. 北京：人民教育出版社，1975.

［2］馆冈邦雄.《论语》在日本的传播与影响. 河南师范大学研究生院硕士论文，2013.

［3］郭飞鸿. 日本高等教育对儒学思想的提倡与实践——以东日本国际大学为例. 孔德成先生逝世五周年纪念会暨儒学的理论与应用国际学术研讨会论文. 2013，9.

［4］黄进兴. 优入圣域. 北京：中华书局，2010.

［5］黄俊杰. 德川日本《论语》诠释史论.（中日文化研究文库）、上海古籍出版社，2008.

［6］孔祥林，孔喆. 世界孔子庙研究（上下）. 北京：中国编译出版社，2011.

［7］駱承烈. 漫步孔子文化圈. 北京：中国言实出版社，2009.

［8］平坂谦二.《白鹿洞学规》在日本还活着. 国际儒学研究第三辑，2013.

［9］秦兆雄，王建新、刘昭瑞编. 汉族的家庭结构与宗教传承. 地域社会与信仰习俗：立足田野的人类学研究. 中山大学出版社，2007，128－139.

［10］2013a“东京的汤岛圣堂与释奠礼”《神户外大论丛》第63卷第4号35－54页.

［11］2013b“日本读经讲经行经的回顾与展望”国立台中教育大学语文教育学系编《第三届读经教育国际论坛会议论文》36－59页.

［12］2013c“试论日本孔子庙的历史演变与当代功能”台湾中央研究院编《孔德成先生逝世五周年纪念会暨儒学的理论与应用国际学术研讨会论文》共34页（即将出版）.

［13］2014“弘道館與偕樂園考察記”《神户外大论丛》第64卷第4号109－126页.

［14］张崑将. 德川日本“忠”“孝”概念的形成与发展：以兵学与阳明学为中心. 台北：国立台湾大学出版中心，2004.

［15］日本德川时代古学派之王道政治论：以伊藤会斋、获生徂徕为中心. 台北：国立台湾大学出版中心，2004.

［16］德川日本儒学思想的特质：神道、徂徕学与阳明学. 台北：国立台湾大学出版中心，2007.

［17］张崑将编. 东亚论语学：韩日篇. 上海：华东师范大学出版社，2012.

# 人间佛教实践对推进大陆儒学世俗面向的启示

山西社会主义学院　李祥熙

自 20 世纪 70 年代以来，在海峡两岸先后涌现出两大人文思潮，即以人间佛教为标志的台湾佛教兴盛运动，和以“国学热”为标志的大陆儒学复兴活动。这两个看似不相干的社会文化事象，实际上有着一定的内在呼应和联系。自佛法西来，儒释之间就一刻也没有停止过相互吸收与借鉴。海峡两岸同根同祖、血脉相连、互为镜像，台湾人间佛教作为由传统佛教向现代佛教转化的成功案例，对大陆当代儒学的转化与创新具有宝贵的启示和借鉴意义。本文拟在综述台湾人间佛教基本经验及大陆儒学复苏进程的基础上，就如何推进大陆儒学世俗面向的若干问题做一探讨。

## （一）

台湾人间佛教发端于 20 世纪 70 年代。以星云大师 1967 年开创佛光山为标志，历经 40 多年的辛勤耕耘，台湾佛教一改当初“社会地位低落”，“出家人不受重视，在社会上难以立足，到处被人瞧不起”的“苟延残喘”处境，成为以佛光山、慈济功德会、法鼓山和中台禅寺等四大道场为代表，其规模之大、信众之多、活动影响之巨、组织之严密，在中国佛教史上前所未闻，即便放在当代世界宗教的整体视野中亦堪称翘楚的奇迹。仅佛光山就在世界拥有两百多处佛光别院、分院，一百七十余个佛光协会、分会，真正实现了“佛光普照三千界，法水长流五大洲”的宏伟愿景。慈济功德会在世界五大洲都设有分会和联络处，从事慈善、教育、医疗、文化、国际赈灾、骨髓捐赠到环境保护和小区志工，其影响遍布全球。由法鼓山创办人圣严法师积极倡导“以健康、快乐、平安的身心，照顾自己、照顾社会、照顾大自然，使得你、我、他人，都能健康、快乐、平安地生活在同一个环境之中”的心灵环保思想，更是为越来越迷失于物欲与感官享受和追求的现代人，提供了安顿安心、继续前行的指南。

台湾人间佛教的做法和经验主要有：一是在理念层面着力通俗化。星云大师将人间佛教的理念定义为，人间佛教“主要是倡导生活的佛教，以促进人际间的和谐，带来社会的公平，达到世界的相互尊重包容，让所有人都能幸福安乐地生活为目标”。简而言之，人间佛教就是“佛说的、人要的、净化的、善美的，凡是有助于幸福人生增进的教法，都是人间佛教”。二是在实践层面着力世俗化。星云大师提出，“人间佛教要有人间的性格、人间的伦理、人间的秩序”。他打破僧俗有别的传统观念，积极提倡并开启寺院生活的世俗面向。星云大师强调，人间佛教要与生活结合，要利益大众，要能给人受用，为“维护社会秩序、净化社会人心、改善社会风气、端正人生行为”尽到社会责任。过去的佛教是不出寺院，星云大师率先把佛法从寺院带入社会生活的每一处角落。三是在内涵层面着力包容化。人间佛教包容不同教派，“与其他宗教建立同体共生的关系；包容儒家文化，邀请牟宗三、唐君毅等儒学大家到各地讲学，甚至邀请日本东京大学教授水野弘元到台湾讲演；包容民间信仰，认为“为了度化众生，观世音菩萨应化各种身相，妈祖也是观世音菩萨的化身”。四是在诠释层面着力当代化。星云大师认为，传统佛教只能“以佛法解释佛法”，而不能弘法应世。他打破常规，以世间法来融合佛法，以主动变革来适应社会现代化，不断赋予人间佛教时代内涵。他在古今映照、传统与现代融合方面进行积极探索，不断思考“平等与和平、尊重与包容、自然与生命、同体与共生、发心与发展、人间与生活”等当代人类共同话题，甚至对“战争与和平、宗教之间、族群问题、生态环保、安乐死、优生保健法、生命教育、生死学”等当代问题，都用人间佛教理念给予重新诠释。他在观念改革方面，以“行佛”代替“拜佛”，提倡“身做好事、口说好话、意存好念”的三好运动，提出“你大我小、你对我错、你有我无、你乐我苦”的处世准则，并以“学佛不是个人清修，而是要为大众服务”等理念作为僧众的修行准则。五是在传播层面着力多元化。包括弘法形式多元化，早在佛光山开山之前，大师就从寺院走向社会，通过文艺作品、佛教歌曲、歌咏演唱、舞台剧等多种形式，在台湾各地进行弘法表演；寺院功能多样化，星云大师认为，寺院是人生道路的加油站，是去除烦恼的清凉地，是善友往来的聚会所，是修养性灵的安乐场，是采购法宝的百货店，是悲智愿行的学习处，更是一所疗治心灵的医院、维护社会正义的因果法庭、启发道德良知的教育学校、提升文化修养的艺术中心。六是在视野层面着力国际化。星云大师立足台湾，放眼全国，前瞻世界。他冲破狭隘的地域观念，打破人我、国家、民族的界限，提出人间佛教的国际观，把佛法传播到全世界。七是在主体层面着力表率化。星云大师一开始就对“怎样做个佛光人”提出明确要求，强调佛光人要“有宗教情操、有因果观念、有惭耻美德、有容人雅量”。他还总结出作为一名合格弘法利生僧伽必须具备的三要素，即学问、德行和人缘。他常说：“求观音，拜观音，更要自己做观音”；坚信“出家人身教重于言教”，佛门，僧相威仪，甚至连袈裟的一角都能度众。

台湾著名出版人，同时也是著名经济学家、教育家和新闻传播学家的高希均先生曾经说："四十年来，台湾经济是一种奇迹，而星云大师将佛光山组织得有条不紊，让佛教无远弗届送至全球各地，也是一种奇迹。""星云大师的一生，改革了佛教、改善了人心、改变了世界。"

## （二）

大陆儒学复苏于20世纪90年代。30年来，在民间、学界乃至官方的合力推动下，儒学振兴探索前行，渐成气候。这当中值得记录的标志性事件有：1984年，由国家拨款作为启动资金的全国性学术基金组织，中国孔子基金会在山东曲阜市成立。1985年，由教育部主管，以研究孔子、儒家学说和中国传统文化为主旨的全国性民间学术团体，中华孔子学会（原名中华孔子研究所）在北京孔庙成立。1986年，由中国孔子基金会主办的国际性中文学术期刊《孔子研究》创刊。1987年，儒学国际学术讨论会、朱子学国际学术会议、王阳明心学讨论会，分别在曲阜、厦门、贵阳召开。1988年，孟子学术讨论会在山东邹县召开。1989年，由中国孔子基金会和联合国教科文组织联合主办的孔子2540诞辰纪念与学术研讨会在北京举行，与会学者来自二十多个国家共三百多人，这在首都北京历史上是第一次。1990年，冯友兰哲学思想国际研讨会在北京举行。1991年，海峡两岸首次儒学学术讨论会在曲阜举行。1993年，中韩孔子思想与21世纪学术讨论会在曲阜召开；孔孟荀学术思想国际研讨会、浙东学术国际研讨会，汤用彤、梁漱溟、张申府三先生百周年纪念与学术研讨会，分别在威海、杭州、北京召开。1994年，由中国、韩国、日本、美国、德国、新加坡、越南等国家和中国香港、中国台湾地区与儒学研究有关的学术团体共同发起的国际儒学联合会在北京宣告成立；纪念孔子诞辰2545周年国际学术研讨会在北京隆重举行，世界五大洲近30个国家和地区的学者和社会贤达，近千人出席了大会；台湾台中师范大学王财贵教授发起青少年读经运动，后经南怀瑾、杨振宁等人的倡导和推动，大陆学界和民间迅速跟进。1996年，国务院批准设立的国家儒学研究机构，中国孔子研究院在山东曲阜市成立。2001年，武汉大学首创国学试验班；民间公益国学教育机构一耽学堂在北京创立。2002年，来自包括台湾、香港在内的中国19个地区的2000多名华人，在中国孔子研究院隆重举行"首届华人中华文化经典诵读友谊赛"。2003年，大型文化丛书《儒藏》被列入教育部哲学社会科学研究重大攻关项目，汤一介担任主编；由团中央中国青少年发展服务中心、中华文化经典诵读全国组委会选定的10所中华文化经典诵读示范学校在北京授牌。2004年，中国政府在海外设立的第一家孔子学院落户韩国；许嘉璐、季羡林、任继愈、杨振宁、王蒙等70多人联名发表《甲申宣言》；曲阜市举办新中国成立以来第一次孔子诞辰公祭活动。2005年，中国人民大学率先设立国学院；中国社会科学院成立“儒教研究中心”；首届“全球中华文化经典诵读大会”在香港举行，儿童读经活动成为时尚。2006年，《光明日报》正式推出《国学》专版；于丹在央视百家讲坛开讲“论语心得”。2007年，教育部所属中国国学文化艺术中心成立；由国际儒联主办的首届儒学普及工作座谈会在北京召开；于丹《论语心得》卖超千万册，“国学热”引发了改革开放后第二次价值观大争论。2008年，第一届世界儒学大会在中国孔子研究院隆重开幕；中国社会科学院举行首届“国学研究论坛”；张艺谋导演的29届奥运会开幕式展示龙、汉字、孔子思想等传统文化。2009年，钱文忠在央视百家讲坛开讲《三字经》、《弟子规》；清华大学国学研究院成立。2010年，中国山东首届尼山世界文明论坛，在孔子诞生地尼山开幕；胡玫导演的电影《孔子》上映。2011年，全国“小学国学经典课程规划暨教学观摩”培训大会，在北京大学百周年纪念讲堂举行。2012年，孔子第79代嫡长孙、衍圣公孔垂长首次来访大陆，并在尼山举行春祭、在孔林举行家祭；四川省把中华经典诵读活动纳入文明城市、文明村镇、文明单位和未成年人思想道德建设考核测评；文化部与山东省政府在济南签署《关于合作推进文化强省建设框架协议》，建设曲阜中国“文化特区”纳入议事日程；作为教育部“十一五”规划课题国学教育专项研究课题组八年研究成果的人教版《中国传统文化教育全国中小学实验教材》正式发行；山东大学设置儒学学科并单独招生。2013年，“儒学与马克思主义”研究项目在北京大学启动；儒家思想与当代中国文化建设国际学术研讨会在深圳举行；全国首届省级以上儒学团体会长联席会议在杭州召开；两岸高中中华传统文化教育交流研讨会暨中华传统文化（高中）教学研究基地共建启动仪式在北京中华书局举行。2014年，人民日报发表署名文章《尼山的月光——再读孔子》；教育部印发《完善中华优秀传统文化教育指导纲要》的通知，《纲要》从“加强中华优秀传统文化教育的重要性和紧迫性”，“加强中华优秀传统文化教育的指导思想、基本原则和主要内容”，“分学段有序推进中华优秀传统文化教育”，“把中华优秀传统文化教育系统融入课程和教材体系”，“全面提升中华优秀传统文化教育的师资队伍水平”，“着力增强中华优秀传统文化教育的多元支撑”，“加强中华优秀传统文化教育的组织实施和条件保障”等七个方面进行了安排部署；由凤凰网、岳麓书院主办的“致敬国学——首届全球华人国学大典”启动仪式在北京举行。

在民间、学界和有关方面合力推动儒学再度勃兴的同时，党和国家对弘扬以儒学为主体的中华优秀传统文化给予了高度重视和大力支持。党的十七届六中全会通过的《中共中央关于深化文化体制改革，推动社会主义文化大繁荣大发展若干重大问题的决定》强调：“中国共产党从成立之日起，就是中华优秀传统文化的忠实传承者和弘扬者，又是中国先进文化的积极倡导者和发展者。”尤其是党的十八大以来，习近平总书记每次在国内外的重要讲话中，几乎都要引用孔子及诸子百家思想。2013年8月19

日，在全国宣传思想工作会议上，习总书记提出“四个讲清楚”，即“要讲清楚每个国家和民族的历史传统、文化积淀、基本国情不同，其发展道路必然有着自己的特色；讲清楚中华文化积淀着中华民族最深沉的精神追求，是中华民族生生不息、发展壮大的丰厚滋养；讲清楚中华优秀传统文化是中华民族的突出优势，是我们最深厚的文化软实力；讲清楚中国特色社会主义植根于中华文化沃土、反映中国人民意愿、适应中国和时代发展进步要求，有着深厚历史渊源和广泛现实基础。”这次讲话打通了中华文化与中国特色社会主义的关系。2013 年 11 月 26 日，习总书记视察孔子研究院并发表重要讲话，总书记以全球视野和战略眼光，从历史与现实、国际与国内、治国与做人等多个维度，深刻阐述了孔子及儒家思想、中华优秀传统文化的重要价值、重大影响和时代意义。重申毛泽东同志的经典论述，指出我们是马克思主义的历史唯物主义者，要总结和承继从孔夫子到孙中山这份珍贵的遗产。这次讲话打通了中华文化与马克思主义的关系。用许嘉璐先生的话说，习近平的“曲阜之行”解决了人文社科领域的“姓孔”和“姓马”的对立问题，实际上提出了马克思主义与儒学的关系问题。马克思主义和儒学不是对立的，不是非此即彼的，而是互补的，能够兼容的。今年 2 月 24 日，习总书记在主持中共中央政治局第十三次集体学习时强调，“培育和弘扬社会主义核心价值观必须立足中华优秀传统文化”，要“使中华优秀传统文化成为涵养社会主义核心价值观的重要源泉”。这次讲话打通了中华文化与社会主义核心价值观的关系。今年 5 月 4 日，习总书记亲临北大人文学苑，特地看望了哲学系老教授、中华孔子学会会长汤一介。总书记同汤教授亲切握手、促膝交谈，了解大型文化丛书《儒藏》编纂情况，赞扬他为中华优秀传统文化继承、发展、创新做出了很大贡献。在北京大学师生座谈会上，总书记对儒家经典语句信手拈来、如数家珍。习总书记有关中华文化的一系列新思想、新论断，是自“五四”以来，党和国家最高领导人对中华文化定位和作用的最新表述、最高概括。我们有理由相信，以习近平为总书记的党中央对弘扬以儒学为主体的中华优秀传统文化是真提倡、真重视、真支持。我们同样有理由认为，经过社会各界和海内外同仁的不懈努力，儒学的历史价值和当代意义再次受到党和国家的肯定和重视，虽然杂音甚至反对之声仍然存在，但儒学走向复兴的大趋势已不可阻挡。

## （三）

比较海峡两岸的两大人文思潮，我们不难看到，以人间佛教为标志的台湾佛教兴盛运动，更多呈现出“世俗化、生活化、通俗化、大众化”等特点。而以“国学热”为标志的大陆儒学复兴活动，则更多表现出“论坛化、书卷化、蒙学化、乡贤化”等趋势。前者由山林走向社会有余，后者从书斋走向世俗不足。儒学本来是“切于人生日用之实”（薛瑄语）的实学，儒学的生命在于对当下中国世俗社会不可或缺。在经历半个多世纪的衰微之后，孔子和儒家传统要想从重新回到当下中国人的生活世界，就必须在大众化、通俗化、生活化等世俗面向上有大作为。在这方面，台湾人间佛教的成功做法和经验，至少对我们有如下几点启示：

启示 1. 人间佛教的成功在于，将原本面向善男信女的小众佛教，变成了面向社会众生的大众佛教。为此，儒学面向要大众化：把儒学从小圈子中解放出来。大陆儒学复苏虽然走过了 30 年的奋斗里程，但远未产生像人间佛教那样广泛的影响。其中一个重要原因，就是长期局限在小圈子里面做道场。这些年民间、学界举办的活动、论坛，发表的文章、专著，不可谓不多，但热衷与参与者总是一些熟悉的面孔。活动进行时大家热热闹闹欢聚一堂，活动一结束便各奔东西忙自家的事。即使主办单位编简报、发综述，阅读简报和综述的还是小圈子里面的人。一方面是圈子内部少数人的坐而论道，另一方面是圈子外面多数人的无动于衷。儒学复苏形成了一个从小圈子到小圈子的路径依赖，始终没能找到将小圈子变成大圈子的有效途径。虽然不时有人苦心倡导并力行“进校园、进企业、进机关、进社区、进军营”的点对面传播模式，但儒学与大众的联系界面仍处于华而不实的状态。小圈子的儒家文化自信，如何转化成为社会大众的儒家文化自觉？小众化的儒学体验经历，如何转变成为大众化的儒学生存方式？专家学者们极力推崇的小众儒学，如何拓展成为老百姓普遍认可的大众儒学？是大陆儒学世俗面向需要破解的课题。

启示 2. 人间佛教的成功在于，将原本难学难解的经典佛教，变成了一听就懂的通俗佛教。为此，儒学阐释要通俗化：让街道老大妈都能听得懂。一种价值观念要想被受众所接受，首先要通俗易懂。儒家经典本来是与中国人密切相关的修齐治平之道，但由于以文言文为载体，对当下许多国人来说如同天书，如果原文照搬照转，必然令人望而生畏。现阶段的儒学传播离不开对经典有研究有感悟的专家学者。问题是眼下有一种怪象，在面向大众的儒家文化传播过程中，受众对一些“肚子里有货”的专家学者反应平平，却对“半斤鸭子四两嘴”的“大师”们叫好叫座。这就需要我们的专家学者“反求诸己”，名师讲座可能抓住在校的大学生，但难以吸引尚不知儒学与己何干的普通百姓。应切实改变“曲高和寡”的经院式授课方式，要有受众可能是“儒盲”的底线思维，善于用浅显易懂的语言、寓教于乐的方式，讲好甚至连街道老大妈们都能听懂的儒学课程。也许我们有的专家学者没有时间和精力，或者不愿意放下身段去作儒学扫盲工作，但拓展儒学市场的现实，既需要能在各种高端论坛上侃侃而谈的学界精英，更需要能在大众场合娓娓道来讲好“老大妈儒学”的通俗高手，因为就对当下社会人生的影响和作用而言，后者的意义和价值决不在前者之下。

启示 3. 人间佛教的成功在于，将原本长篇大论的烦琐佛教，变成了三言两语的简约佛教。为此，儒学叙事要简约化：在五分钟拿下传播话语权。现代社会的生活工作节奏日益加快，人们获取资讯的方式空前便捷，对古今中外各种观点、学说的取舍权，完全掌握在时间就是金钱、就是生命的受众手中。据有经验的电视制作人介绍，抓住和保持观众是视频产品成败的关键。电视广告如不能在前七秒抓住观众，文献和政论片如超过两分钟不出现新故事，就有被转台的可能。同样的道理，儒学传播要想在多元化的“观念市场”中赢得应有份额，就必须遵守现代传播规律，把抓住和保持受众作为发展和壮大儒学受众的关键环节。这就要求我们的儒学工作者，不仅要具备在时间充分的场合下系统阐释儒家文化的能力，还要具备利用时间的“边角料”说短话、说关键话、说有吸引话的能力，善于抓住一切可以利用的机会，简约叙事，数语中的，在五分钟内拿下儒学传播的话语权。只有讲好了“五分钟儒学”，你才有可能争取到下一个讲一小时儒学、二小时儒学和 N 小时儒学的机会，才有可能让对方坐下来听你的折子戏，并期待“且听下回分解”。

启示 4. 人间佛教的成功在于，将原本晨钟暮鼓的出世佛教，变成了服务世俗的生活佛教。为此，儒学内容要生活化：让儒学回归伦常日用本色。儒学本来是入世的学问，正如明代大儒薛瑄所言：“濂、洛、关、闽诸儒之书，皆根据至理，而切于人生日用之实。”然而，在一百多年的白话、普及化过程中，包括儒家经典在内的“中国原典多是书斋的、学派的、蒙学的，是经典自证的，它在个体的学子时代和学者生涯中有限地自我循环，是学问式的正解或未解之谜，尚未能成为歌哭、联谊、雅聚、行旅、养生送死途中的常识和资粮，未能成为农民、诗人、工匠、歌者、樵夫、哲人、渔夫、史官、武士、高僧、禅师、隐士、大师天才、匹夫匹妇、政要商贾、贩夫走卒……的习语和救赎。先秦精神一如飘零的花果，惨淡，在父子、师徒间艰难地传承。”（余世存语）因此，让儒学走出过去父子、师徒间的封闭式传承，走出目前从经典到经典、从论坛到论坛、从论文到论文的路径依赖，老实回到当下中国人的生存现场，进而成为每个阶层、每个家庭及至每个人各取所需的“常识资粮”和“习语救赎”，是大陆儒学世俗面向的最终落点。什么时候，当你我他在举手投足、进退取舍、嘘寒问暖、衣食住行、婚丧嫁娶之时，自觉不自觉地共识于中国人曾经拥有的古朴儒雅和温润，儒学就真得回到我们生活中来了。

启示 5. 人间佛教的成功在于，将原本出家人的戒律佛教，变成了众生皆宜的普适佛教。为此，儒学教育要普适化：营造从蒙童到成人的儒化环境。儒学的本质是人学，其核心问题是如何使人成其为人，与禽兽相区别；如何使社会成其为人的社会，与动物世界相区别。在儒家看来，“人之所以异于禽兽者几稀”（孟子语），人不是生而为人，而是教化成人。人之初，性本善，没有经过“复性”、“明明德”、“致良知”教化的人与禽兽没有区别，即便穿上衣服、戴上帽子，也不过是衣冠禽兽。天下生民，每个人都需要经过儒家的道德教化，都必须在做人上“苟日新，日日新，又日新。”总之要“作新民。”从某种意义上讲，儒家的全部事业就是“新民事业”、“儒化工程”，其梦想是要把天下的男人都教化成谦谦君子，把天下的女人都教化成大家闺秀。当男人都成为谦谦君子，女人都成为大家闺秀的时候，家国天下政通人和就在其中了。当下中国社会最突出的问题是精神的混乱和迷茫。混乱是因为没有社会秩序层面的共识，迷茫是因为没有人生价值观层面的共识。儒家文化是当下中国在社会秩序、人生价值观层面形成共识的最大公约数，对全体国人进行普遍适用的儒化教育是当务之急。

儒化是一个系统工程。首先，在国家层面，需要出台关于继承和发扬以儒家文化为代表的中华优秀传统美德的决定，明确阐述党和政府对弘扬中华优秀传统文化的政策主张；借鉴新加坡和韩国的经验，组织编写适合我国社会的儒家伦理道德教育教材，并纳入党校、行政学院和干部培训学校主体课程，纳入公务员公开招聘考试科目，纳入从幼儿园到大学的教育体制；将孔子诞辰作为国家公祭日。其次，在地方层面，需要成立省、市、县中华文化传播机构，主要负责中华文化和地方特色文化资源的开发和应用；允许开办民间传统文化培训机构，支持举办以弘扬中华文化和地方特色文化为主题的各种社会公益活动；充分利用现存文庙，举办春秋祭、成人礼、开笔礼等传统礼仪活动；举办以淳厚世风民俗为目的的清明公祭和慎终追远活动；切实推进“让居民望得见山、看得见水、记得住乡愁”的新型城镇化建设。其三，在社会层面，需要正确引导、充分发挥相关社团组织、民间文化机构在传承和弘扬中华优秀传统文化和传统美德中的作用；开展全民经典诵读活动，启动银发、黑发、童发、乳发全民补课工程，从零开始重新培养国人对自己民族历史文化的温情和敬意；重点倡导重建仁义礼智信、温良恭俭让的社会氛围，最大限度地消除社会戾气。其四，在家庭层面，需要恢复以达成完美人格为目标的家教传统。当代美国著名社会学家爱德华·希尔斯在《论传统》一书中指出，家庭、教会和教派、教育机构、国家、党派和法律秩序，在传统延续中具有不可或缺的作用。其中，“家庭是联系过去、现在和未来，使其成为一个社会结构的第一环节。”在家庭里，“孩子从父母那里获得他第一批词汇和最一般的道德标准”，“孩子通过吸收传统而具备了人的特征。”在人国，当下许多孩子处于有人养无人教的状态，他们是吃喝嫖赌抽、坑蒙拐骗大军的预备队，是许多体面家庭和父母永远的痛和掘墓人。央视今年春节播放的“家风是什么”系列报道，光明日报发起的“家风家教大家谈”，抓到了当下中国社会之痒和家庭之痒。家风乃吾国之民风，中国向何处去、中国社会向何处去，在一定程度上要看中国家庭向何处去。以孝悌忠信、仁义礼智为代表的儒家道德伦理和传统美德如果不能落实到家庭，一切都将是空谈。

本文的结论是：种种迹象表明，大陆儒学走向复兴已是大势所趋。经历半个多世纪衰微的孔子和儒家传统，能否真正从“博物馆中的陈列品”（列文森语）重新回到当下中国人的精神生活，赓续“为天地立心，为生民立命，为往圣继绝学，为万世开太平”之使命，不仅取决于当下有于儒学再度勃兴的天时、地利、人和环境，而且在更大程度上取决于儒学自身在大众化、通俗化、简约化、生活化、普适化等世俗面向上能有多大改变和创新。从某种意义上说，世俗化而不是政治化和官僚化，才是当代大陆儒学发展的正确方向。

**参考文献：**

[1]（明）薛瑄. 薛瑄全集. 山西人民出版社.
[2]（美）约瑟夫·列文森. 儒教中国及其现代命运. 广西师范大学出版社.
[3]（美）爱德华·希尔斯. 论传统. 上海世纪出版集团.
[4] 牟钟鉴. 大陆当代儒学巡礼. 中国儒学网.
[5] 余世存. 六经责我开生面. 余世存的共识网·思想者博客.
[6] 李祥熙. 儒学普及应借鉴台湾人间佛教的做法和经验. 共识网.

# 吉林省的儒学研究与传播

吉林省社会科学研究所 刘 辉

吉林省地处东北腹地，多民族聚居，多种文化交融，经历了由少数民族为主到汉族为主的发展历程。历史上有夫余、高句丽、渤海、辽金、明、清时期古文化遗存，有汉、朝、满、蒙、回、锡伯等民族长期创造的农耕文化、游牧文化、渔猎文化，有关东移民文化、东北抗联红色文化等。一方水土养育一方人，吉林山水成就了吉林的地域特色文化，也影响了吉林儒学的发展轨迹。历史上吉林儒学基础薄弱，发展滞后，直至20世纪70年代后期改革开放以后，吉林省的儒学研究与传播取得了长足进步。

## 一、吉林儒学研究与传播的历史基础

自古以来，吉林地区一直是多民族聚居地区。在中国古代史上，吉林地区长期为少数民族政权统治，包括汉魏时期的夫余、汉魏至唐的高句丽、唐朝时期的渤海、两宋时期的辽金，以及元朝、清朝。古代吉林无论是作为属国还是由中央王朝直接管辖，都在积极地借鉴和吸纳中原文化，学习和实践儒家文化。

高句丽王朝的治国方略、社会秩序、社会伦理、行为规范深受儒家文化影响，素有“书有五经”之说，他们将儒家经典奉为至宝，“尤爱重之”①

渤海号称“海东盛国”，“是继夫余和高句丽之后，第三个以今吉林省境内为统治中心的少数民族政权。渤海国时期也是古代吉林历史发展的辉煌时期之一”。② 渤海文化与唐朝文化车同轨、书同文，“车书本一家”，③ 儒家文化是渤海治国安民的指导思想。中央机构以忠仁义礼智信为六部名号，两个公主墓的碑文所体现出的内容

契丹建立的辽朝，在辽太祖时期就建立了孔子庙，还诏告太子春秋释奠。④ 儒学在

---

① 李殿福 孙玉良：《高句丽简史》，韩国三省出版社，1990年，第448页。

② 《吉林通史》第一卷，吉林人民出版社，2008年，第150页。

③ 《全唐诗》卷五八三《送渤海王子归本国》，国际文化出版公司，1993年，第1945页。

④ 《辽史》卷七二《耶律倍传》，中华书局，1982年，第1210页。

辽居正统地位。辽重用汉族儒士，开设科举，“程文分两科辞赋和经义，魁各分焉”。[①]所设官学和私学，以儒家经典为教材。契丹人还著书立说，耶律俨著有《六义集》。

公元1234年女真建立的金朝灭亡，享国120年。对于金亡的原因，素有“辽以释废，金以儒亡”之说，这种说法是否合理有待商榷，但这种说法之盛行本身足证儒学在金朝的影响之深远。金建国伊始，即确定儒学为国家意识形态，儒学是统治者“致治”的指导思想，金代的女真教育与科举皆以儒学为主要内容，女真人伦理观念也表现出明显的儒学化倾向。

清朝在康熙三十二年创设宁古塔儒学，此后又有永吉州学（后改为吉林厅儒学）、三姓、阿勒楚喀儒学、伯都讷儒学等。雍正以后清朝倡导书院教育发展，嘉庆十九年吉林地区建长白书院。后又有吉林府崇文书院、伯都讷厅种榆学院、长春府养正书院等。乾隆元年建吉林文庙，光绪三十三年择定新址新建，即现址。清同治十一年建长春文庙，1894年和1924年历经两次大规模维修。

中华民国成立后，吉林省发展近代文化教育，改良取缔私塾，发展新式教育，儒家文化教育受到弱化。1931年“九一八”事变后，日本迅速占领东北全境，对包括吉林在内的东北地区实行法西斯文化专制。为了削弱吉林人民的民族意识，日本统治者在吉林建立文化专制体系，实行奴化教育。为了欺骗中国人民，日本侵略者打着儒家传统文化招牌，提出所谓“王道主义”教育方针。伪吉林教育厅当局指令各学校以《四书》、《五经》为讲授教材，同时各类教科书将《即位诏书》、《建国宣言》、《回銮训民诏书》等内容编选其中，规定日语为学校重要课程，由日本人讲授。此时，儒家文化成为日本侵略者在精神上麻痹和奴化中国人民的工具，儒家文化被断章取义，遭受曲解和摧残。

新中国成立后，受国内发展大环境的影响，包括儒家文化在内的中国传统文化一直被弱化，甚至作为落后文化被批判。这种状况一直延续至20世纪70年代末期改革开放之前。

综上所述，吉林省的儒学研究与传播与中原、江南地区相较明显历史积淀不足，基础薄弱，呈滞后发展状态，分析其原因在于：

首先，偏远的地理位置、相对滞后的生产方式使然。秦、汉、魏晋、隋唐和两宋时期姑且不论，元明时期，吉林地区已经由统一的中央王朝直接管辖，尤其是明朝是汉族建立的统一中央政权，但是儒家文化在元明两代并未有所发展。元代吉林省大部

---

① 《契丹国志》卷二三《试士科制》，上海古籍出版社，1985年，第226、227页。

属辽阳省辖区，辽阳省元代修建孔庙9所，多处山海关以内，[①] 吉林境内却一所没有。吉林地区在明朝属奴儿干都司辖区，明朝对之实行羁縻怀远政策，这一时期是吉林建置发展史上的停止且有些后退时期。究其原因，导致吉林儒学发展的停滞不前的主要原因，应该是地理位置的偏远、固有的生产方式落后使然。

其次，古代民族政权更迭造成文化发展的间断性、不平衡性。古代吉林民族政权更迭频繁，被不同的民族交替统治。民族不同则风俗文化不同，则政权结构和统治方式相应有所差异，直接导致儒家文化的间断性和不平衡性发展。

其三，少数民族矛盾心理使然。各少数民族对先进的汉族文化态度不是一成不变的。他们在积极接受汉文化同时，也在担心本民族文化元素的弱化和丧失，维护本民族文化的心理使其对儒家文化的接纳常常持保留态度。道光二年，著名学者、原工部郎中朱瑞辰有罪发遣黑龙江，因长白书院“教读乏人”，吉林将军富俊奏请将马瑞辰“改发吉林，专司教读。”道光皇帝则强调八旗应“以清语骑射为重”，不得“议课生徒，学习文艺。”[②] 直至光绪年间，才增加了教习三员，汉教习一员，教八旗子弟汉文。

其四，清代封禁政策对吉林儒学发展的影响至为深远。吉林是满清王朝的龙兴之地。清朝为维护龙兴之地的神圣，对吉林实行封禁政策，这虽然在一定程度上起到保护吉林自然资源的作用，但总体上是严重滞碍了吉林的发展，也包括吉林儒学的发展。应该说清代封禁政策对吉林儒学发展的影响深远，直接影响到近现代吉林儒学的发展步伐。

其五，抗日战争时期奴化教育的恶劣影响。日本帝国主义为奴化包括吉林在内的东北人民，推行“王道主义”教育，训练所谓“忠良国民”。中华民族优秀的传统文化——儒家文化，成为他们利用的工具。他们对儒家文化的推行，不仅不能推动儒家文化的传播，反而在国民中激起反感和抵触情绪，极大地损害了儒学在平民百姓心目中的地位和形象。

## 二、吉林儒学研究现状

改革开放以来，伴随着“文化热”、“国学热”的兴起，吉林省的儒学研究取得了长足进步，在吉林大地先后有60余位专家学者活跃在儒家文化研究领域。目前在职的专职从事儒家文化研究者24人，其中教授和研究员8人，副教授和副研究员10人，博士18人，享受国务院特贴者2人。就年龄结构而言，55岁以上5人，50—55岁4人，

① 胡务：《元代庙学——无法割舍的儒学教育链》四川出版集团巴蜀书社，2005年，第79、80页。

② 《清宣宗实录》卷三七，道光二年六月辛未，《清实录》，中华书局，1986年。

40—50 岁 9 人，30—40 岁 6 人。多年来吉林省的儒学研究主要集中于周易研究、儒家主要思想研究、儒学史研究、现代新儒家研究、儒学现代化研究、东亚儒学研究、礼学研究、比较问题研究、儒学与马克思主义中国化研究以及大众儒学研究等研究领域。目前吉林省儒学研究机构主要分布于长春和延吉两市，包括吉林大学中国哲学史教研室、东北师范大学哲学学院中国哲学史教研室、延边大学东方文化研究中心、吉林省社会科学院哲学与文化所中国哲学与传统文化教研室。此外吉林大学历史系、吉林大学古籍研究所、吉林师范大学政法学院、长春大学国学研究中心、通化师范学院、长春师范学院、北华大学也有一些教师和研究人员在从事儒家文化研究。篇幅所限，本文仅就具有代表性的吉林大学中国哲学史教研室、延边大学东方文化研究中心、吉林省社会科学院哲学与文化所中国哲学与传统文化教研室的基本情况做一简要介绍，以期对吉林儒学的研究情况有一个基本把握。

吉林大学哲学社会学院中国哲学史教研室成立于 1961 年前后，历任研究室主任有吴锦东、吕希晨、乌恩溥、陈庆坤、李景林，现任研究室主任为张连良。教研室先后拥有吴锦东、吕希晨、乌恩溥、陈庆坤、朱日耀、刘建国、刘国梁、顾宝田、蒲荣高、李景林、张连良、刘连朋、邱高兴、连瑶、华军、赵海英、李聪、翟奎凤等老中青多名学者，分别从事中国哲学与宗教学两个专业方向的学术研究工作。现有教学和研究人员 8 人，其中教授 3 人，副教授 3 人，致力于中国哲学史研究、史料典籍研究、儒学专题研究领域研究。先后出版了《中国哲学史通》、《中国近代启蒙哲学》、《中国近代哲学史》、《中国哲学史史料学概要》，此外还有《先秦伪书辨正》、《先秦哲学要辑选释》、《左氏春秋译注》、《新译谷梁传》、《新译仪礼读本》、《尔雅义疏》、《周易—古代中国世界图式》、《教养的本原》等著作。

延边大学东方哲学研究所成立于 2000 年，其发展历史可追溯至 1979 年的延边大学朝鲜问题研究所朝鲜哲学研究室和日本哲学研究室。目前，拥有 2 名教授（博导）、5 名副教授、1 名讲师，全部为博士。现任所长为金哲洙博士。

东方哲学研究所由李洪淳教授、朱七星教授许能洙教授、李宗耀教授等为核心构成第一代学者群，20 世纪 80、90 年代中国第一部《朝鲜哲学思想史》就出自他们的研究中。他们还完成《哲学大辞典》、《外国哲学大辞典》、《中国伦理学百科全书》等大型辞书的朝鲜哲学条目的全部撰写工作；完成国家教委“八五”人文、社会科学基金项目《中国朝鲜日本传统哲学比较研究》，从 1979 年至 1993 年还和中国社会科学院哲学所共同主办出版 15 期国内唯一的《东方哲学研究》学术内刊。进入本世纪初，延边大学东方哲学研究所进入了第二次发展高峰。先后承担国家社科规划基金项目 4 项，包括《现代韩国哲学研究》、《儒家思想对构建东北亚区域“和谐”文化环境的角色定位》、《中国儒学的韩国本土化研究》和《影响韩国历史文化发展进程的儒家思想研究》

等。教育部人文社会科学研究基地重大项目 1 项；承担日本国际交流基金项目 1 项，国际学术会、韩国中央研究院项目 2 项。出版《日本近代哲学史纲要》、《儒学思想与东北亚“文化共同体”》、《东亚儒家文化圈价值冲突》《中韩日儒学比较论》、《儒学与丁若镛哲学思想》、《“太极图”和“天命图”——朱熹和李滉理气论比较》等十余部有关韩国、日本哲学思想研究专著，出版研究所系列丛书《东亚哲学研究丛书》5 部；在《哲学研究》、《孔子研究》、《新华文摘》、《日本学刊》、韩国的《哲学研究》等刊物上发表论文、译文百余篇。

吉林省社会科学院哲学与文化研究所中国哲学研究室成立于 1979 年。历任负责人为吕颜博、曹福敬、刘辉。先后有吕颜博、徐志锐、张秉楠、曹福敬、邵汉明、郭志成、宋立民、王霆钧、王永平、刘辉、杨永亮等研究人员任职于此，主要研究方向为周易研究、儒道哲学研究、近代哲学研究以及中国传统文化研究。先后出版的儒学研究著作有《周易大传新注》、《周易阴阳八卦说解》、《〈易传〉今译》、《宋明易学概论》、《孔子传》、《稷下钩沉》、《走进伏羲——破解易学千古之谜》、《精校新释大六壬大全》、《大六壬精解》、《大易阐真》《儒道人生哲学》、《中国文化精神》商务印书馆 2000 年 12 月版、《中国文化研究 20 年》《中国哲学与养生》等。近年来，吉林省社会科学院整合院会中国哲学研究力量，形成了以邵汉明研究员为学术带头人的吉林省社会科学院中国哲学与中国传统文化研究团队。团队成员 5 人，其中研究员 3 人，博士和在读博士 3 人，主要致力于儒家哲学的现代阐释、大众儒学、金代儒学、周易、马克思主义中国化等领域研究。先后主持完成了国家社科基金青年项目《三纲五常与现代生活》，国家社科基金项目《大众儒学》、《金代儒家思想研究》。出版《儒家哲学智慧》、《中国文化研究 30 年》、《国学新论》、《周易本义校注》、《马克思主义中国化新探》、《大众儒学》等著作。在《哲学研究》、《中国哲学史》等刊物发表学术论文 100 余篇。

总之，吉林省的儒学研究呈良性发展态势。就研究队伍而言，年龄和职称结构合理，学历结构合理，形成了老中青结合的梯队组合。就研究内容和成果而言，吉林省的儒学研究特色突出，延边大学的东亚儒学研究、吉林省社会科学院的大众儒学研究都具有一定优势。吉林省的儒学研究不足之处在于，历史上优势学科呈断档趋势。譬如周易研究，吉林省的周易研究成果突出。以金景芳先生为代表，以吉林大学和吉林省社会科学院周易研究中心为核心，一大批专家学者从事周易研究，包括吕绍纲、陈恩林、徐志锐、曹福敬等，取得了突出的成绩。尤其是金景芳先生先后出版《学易四种》、《周易讲座》、《周易全解》、《〈周易系辞传〉新编详解》等著作，力主《周易》为哲学著作，运用马克思主义观点，结合经学、史学方法研究《周易》，多窥前人未止之境，创获颇丰，培养了一批省内、国内、国际著名的易学研究专家。随着老一辈专家学者的故去和离退，吉林省的优势学科周易研究后继乏人。此外人员流失严重也是现在和未来影响吉林省儒学发展的重要问题。

## 三、吉林省的儒学普及概况

国内学术界于20世纪90年代提出了儒学大众化、普及化的问题。吉林省的专家学者除了在刊物和会议上鼓与呼，还身体力行，以学会团体为依托，以各种公益活动为平台，积极投身到儒学大众化和普及化的实践中去，在各种国学讲习班、儒学讲习班和孔庙的祭孔活动发挥主力军作用。吉林省各学会团体发挥积极作用。包括吉林省中国哲学史学会、吉林省周易学会、吉林省孔子研究会、吉林省孔子学会、长春市孔子学会、吉林省国学研究会、吉林省易经学会、吉林省素质教育研究中心、吉林市孔子学会、吉林市国学研究会、延边孔子学会、松原市国学研究会、北华大学孔子学会、梅河口市国学研究会、长岭县国学研究会、北华大学孔子学会、北华大学机械学院计算机学院孔子学会等。他们广泛联系吉林省儒学研究、传承方面的专家学者、爱好者，积极致力于儒学推广普及，努力提升吉林大众的儒学修养，积极促进儒学在各个领域的应用推广。吉林省"国学大讲堂"和吉林省文庙的儒学普及活动开展得有声有色。

1. 全国第一个公益性国学系列讲座——吉林省"国学大讲堂"

"国学大讲堂 "是由吉林省社科联主办、长春电视台、长春市图书馆、长春文庙等单位协办的我国第一个国学方面的公益性系列讲座。2005年是孔子诞辰2556年，以此为契机，2005年12月25日，吉林省"国学大讲堂"在长春举行了开课仪式。截止至2013年12月28日，吉林省"国学大讲堂"举办了500多期。吉林省国学大讲堂表现出以下几个特点：其一是应民众需求而生，受到百姓欢迎。每期讲座听众最少时200人，最多时有五六百人，各个阶层、各种职业、各种知识水平的人都有。为了满足不同听众需求，"国学大讲堂"讲座不局限于长春文庙及图书馆等地，还办到了长春市一些中小学、部队、社区甚至监狱，在中央党校国学班和邯郸国学讲堂都曾举办过"国学大讲堂"，无论在省内还是省外，每次讲座都反响热烈。每次讲座都有不少听众踊跃发言、提出问题或者向老师以纸条的形式写明自己在听讲中遇到的疑惑，或者希望下一讲能听到什么内容，在固定的听众中，甚至已经形成了松散的班委会，他们在听讲前做查相关资料等准备工作，课后还收集大家的意见反馈，为下一讲确定题目提供参考。"国学大讲堂"的举办在长春市乃至吉林省掀起了一场"国学热"，为传承国学经典精神、弘扬优秀中华传统文化发挥了良好的作用。其二是着眼现代生活，解读传统文化。"国学大讲堂"以诸子百家理论为主，讲座内容遵循循序渐进的原则，从讲人、讲事再到讲理。邀请的主讲嘉宾来自社会各个层面，既有专家、学者也有政府官员。他们以渊博的国学知识、通俗易懂的讲解，运用大量的史实材料、耐人寻味的故事、精辟的分析，着眼现实、用现代眼光解读传统文化是“国学大讲堂”的鲜明特色，这一特色使“国学大讲堂”成为兼具知识性与趣味性的叫好又叫座的国学讲座。讲座的内容包括国学及其经典的解读、历史人物与历史事件讲解以及其他专题讲解，选题紧贴百姓需要。2011 年 5 月 21 日，在一年一度的高考来临的前夕，12 年寒窗苦读的学子们进入冲刺阶段，考前的紧张气氛对每位考生和家长都是一种无形的压力。每年中、高考临近时，考生不免出现考试紧张，甚至出现因焦虑而引起的注意力不集中、失眠、茶饭不思等考前综合症状，如果学生对上述情绪无法得到及时的疏导和缓解，很可能会影响冲刺备考及中、高考当日的发挥，那么，在我国的古代，参加科举考试的举子们又是如何应对心理压力，缓解紧张情绪的呢？为了帮助今年高考生轻松赶走焦虑，增强自信迎接高考，“国学大讲堂”开展高考心理解压辅导讲座《折桂蟾宫，冠冕龙门》，帮助考生和家长守好“心理阵地”，自信从容迎高考。国学大讲堂受社会各界高度评价，听众曾寄语“国学大讲堂”云：

长河千古祈太平，春草万象吹更生。
文华瑰宝拜圣迹，庙筑经藏仰先生。
国泰安民思论语，学以致用集大成。
讲古说今启心慧，堂堂育人铸真诚。

这是对“国学大讲堂”的恳切期望，也是听众对“国学大讲堂”的认可。

2. 作为东北文庙代表连续十一年举办“全球祭孔”的长春文庙

长春文庙始建于公元 1872 年（清同治十一年），历史上经历过 1894 年和 1924 年两次大规模的维修。1986 年，长春文庙被确定为吉林省重点文物保护单位。2002 年长春市政府出资复建文庙，2008 年又复建文昌阁，恢复面积为 12000 平方米。目前长春孔子文化园建设工程正在施工，竣工后长春文庙占地面积将达到 5 万平方米左右。

2003 年 9 月 28 日至今，长春文庙作为东北文庙的代表连续十一年举办了祭孔大典，引起世人关注。中央电视台多次报道长春文庙举办“全球祭孔”、“海峡两岸同祭孔”和“全球华人同祭孔”等活动实况，而每一次都是场面壮观、万人空巷。2005 年 12 月 28 日起，长春文庙在吉林省国学大讲堂中担当了重要角色，截止至 2013 年 12 月 28 日，共举办国学大讲堂 455 期。几年来，长春文庙发展创新，与时俱进，先后开创举办了启蒙礼、成人礼、书画笔会、文昌会、走状元桥、传统婚礼、春节祈福礼、新年送祝福红蛋、重阳送祝寿糕等丰富多彩的文化活动，深受民众欢迎。每逢节假日，大量的游客涌向长春文庙拜谒至圣先师和文昌帝君，聆听国学讲座，领略中华民族优秀传统文化的无穷魅力。现在的长春文庙已经成为吉林省弘扬中华传统文化、对外展示文化形象的重要窗口。

总而言之，吉林省的儒学研究与传播在近30余年取得了长足的进步，并从以往的学术研究与儒学普及分途向相互借鉴学习、互相交叉渗透大幅度转变，学术研究与儒学普及互为依托，互相促进，相得益彰。但是也存在着明显的不足，主要表现为无论是儒学研究还是儒学普及都存在地域发展的严重不平衡性，且在相当一个历史时期内无法得到根本性改善。

历史上优长研究后继乏人，佛教、道教也传入高句丽金代萨满教、佛教、道教，挖掘中的积极元素，挖掘和现代工业文明蕴含的文化精髓，深入研究吉林文化内涵，提炼吉林文化精神。

意识形态上受“华夷有别”与“中华一体”东亚儒学研究主要集中于东北师范大学和延边大学。东北师范大学韩东育教授领导的东亚思想史研究团队、延边大学东方哲学研究所在东亚儒学研究领域取得可喜的业绩。

大众儒学研究主要集中于吉林省社会科学院，邵汉明研究员领导的中国传统文化研究团队主持完成了国家社科金项目大众儒学研究，借项成果鉴定等级优秀，大众儒学2014年由人民出版社出版。

# 传承儒学文化　实现教育创新

## ——河南省儒学文化与教育创新示范学校综述

河南省儒学文化促进会　王廷信

以孔子为代表创立的中华儒学文化源远流长、博大精深，在中华文明发展史上发挥了重要作用，是中华民族团结奋进、自强不息的不竭动力，成为中华民族非常宝贵的精神财富。在教育上，儒学文化仍然发挥了重大的历史作用，因为孔子不仅是思想家、政治家，而且首先是教育家，他开办了私人办学的先河，是中国乃至世界上第一个职业教育家。儒学文化在中国长期教育发展史上居于主导地位，一部中国教育思想史基本上是儒学教育思想发生、发展的历史。儒学提出的教育思想和教育理论，在中国教育发展史上做出过不可磨灭的贡献，在当今的学校教育中仍然具有重要的启迪作用。结合河南省儒学文化促进会在全省命名的传承儒学文化示范学校的情况，说明在当代我国学校教育中，学习和传承儒学文化而实现教育创新仍然是历史的必然。

## 一、儒学教育思想和教育理论的再认识

儒学教育思想和教育理论是中国传统教育的主体，有极其丰富的教育思想、教育原则、教育内容和教育方法等，在中国长期教育发展中做出过重要的历史贡献。进一步学习和认识儒学教育思想和教育理论，对于现代教育中继续传承儒学文化有着非常重要的指导意义。

（一）教育思想是“有教无类”

孔子在教育上最早提出“有教无类”，就是教育不分类，人人都享有教育权，从而把教育从官府中解放出来。在孔子提出“有教无类”之前，是“学在官府”，只有少数统治阶级的子女才能在官府上学，其他占绝大多数人民群众的子女没有受教育的权利，被排斥在官府学堂之外。人类生活在世界上，第一个权利是生存权，剥夺了生存权，人就没有一切权利；但是人还有一个更重要的权利是受教育权，如果人没有受教育权，人和其他动物就没有什么区别了。所以，在教育上提出“有教无类”，使人人都享受受教育的权利，在中国和世界的教育发展史上具有划时代的意义。在当今我国的社会主

义教育事业中，人人都有受教育的权利，在九年义务教育中，任何青少年到学校学习，既是一种义务又是一种权利，就是儒学倡导的“有教无类”的最好体现。

（二）教育原则是“因材施教”

“因材施教”就是根据学生的不同特点和实际情况进行教学，是儒学的重要教学原则之一。孔子指出：“知之者不如好知者，好知者不如乐知者。”“中人以上，可以语上也；中人以下，不可以语上。”（《论语·雍也》）在这一论述中已经有了“因材施教”的思想。孟子是“因材施教”的实践者，他认为，虽然每个人都具有先天的“善质”、善性，但由于后天客观影响的不同，人们的兴趣、志向、德才学识、主观努力的程度的不同，从而很自然地形成了个体之间的差异。他列举了一些生动事例，说明教育者因善于根据学生的不同情况，采取不同的教育方式、方法，分别给以不同的教育。之后的儒家学者对“因材施教”的教学原则多有发展。张载在教学中认为，世界上人和人是不相同的，也各有自己的特点，教育者必须根据教育对象的不同特点和实际情况，因势利导，因材适教，才能把学生教好，而不至误人子弟。朱熹也深有感触地指出：“教人之至难，必尽人之材，乃不误人。观可及处，然后告之。”（《近思录·教学之道》），并就贯彻“因材施教”的原则，提出了一些行之有效的具体措施和方法，取得了显著的教学成效。

（三）教育内容是“文、行、忠、信”

文是指知识教育，重点是传统文化的内容。行是实践，儒学强调用知识指导实践的行动。忠信指品德教育，儒学强调德育领先地位。

儒学所讲的文化知识，主要指中华传统文化。学生在小学阶段，主要是学习儒学蒙学读物——《弟子规》、《三字经》、《百家姓》、《千字文》等教材。在小学高年级和初中、高中阶段，从低年级到高年级逐步学习儒学的四书、五经到十三经。儒学文化内容丰富、博大精神，涵盖了中华民族的伦理道德思想。如果说儒学的启蒙读物涉及中华五伦（父子有亲、君臣有义、夫妇有别、长幼有序、朋友有信）和八德（孝、悌、忠、信、礼、义、廉、耻）等内容，概括起来就是一个“孝”字。“百善孝为先”，在孝的基础上建立起中华伦理道德，使中小学生学习以后，从小树立优秀的道德品质，学会做人做事，为以后成长打下基础。那么儒学的高级读物就是——四书、五经等，则涉及儒学五常（仁、义、礼、智、信）与八德等丰富内容，用一个字概括就是“仁”。仁者爱人，通过仁可以表现和外化为礼、义、忠、信、孝、悌、廉、耻等内容。从根本上讲儒学就是讲仁、义、忠、信等道德品质教育，学生能学以致用，将终身受益。所以“文、行、忠、信”可以体现儒学的全部教育内容。

（四）教育方法主要是知与行的结合

在儒学文化中，知主要是道德知识，而行是道德实践。儒学强调道德知识和道德实践的结合，提倡言行一致和身体力行，认为只有躬行践履，修身才能成为自觉行动，最终成为圣贤的理想境界。孔子历来提倡言行一致，反对言行不一，他认为“君子欲讷于言，而敏于行”。（《论语·里仁》）“先行其言而后从之。”（《论语·为政》）“君子耻其言而过其行。”（《论语·宪问》）“巧言令色，鲜矣仁。”（《论语·学而》）孟子在仁政学说里，提出理想人格的造就全在于道德实践，在于将自己的天赋善性推及他人。儒学的后继者荀子、朱熹、王阳明、王夫之等都进一步提出了知行统一的观点。荀子提出“见之不若知之，知之不若行之”的著名论题，认为“学至于行而止”。王夫之甚至提出行高于知的观点，提出：“知非先，行非后，行有余力而求知。”（《尚书引义卷三》）强调学以致用，用以致学，提倡重在于行。

另外，启发式教学和教学相长等也是儒学的主要教育方法，在中国教育发展上是行之有效的成功经验。还有学思并重、温故知新、循序渐进、言传身教、尊师爱生等等也都是儒学教育思想与教育方法，从不同的方面反映了教育教学规律，成为中国教育思想中的宝贵遗产。

在这里，之所以提出儒学教育思想和教育理论的再认识，是为了避免在传承儒学文化时，只重视诵读经典，而轻视儒学教育思想和教育理论的重要社会价值。只有全面的、历史的、辩证的认识儒学文化，才能对儒学文化有准确的理解与现代阐释，有利于学校传承儒学文化和实现教育创新工作的健康发展。

## 二、传承儒学文化与实现教育创新的新气象

近几年来，特别是党的十七届六中全会以来，在全国上下教育系统出现了积极弘扬中华优秀传统文化，涌现出一批传承儒学文化的先进典型。经各级教育部门推荐，由河南省儒学文化促进会认真考察研究，先后在全省命名了50所中小学（幼儿园）为“儒学文化与教育创新示范单位”。这些学校（幼儿园）在传承儒学文化教育中出现了崭新的气象，学校及幼儿教育出现了教育创新的局面。

（一）建设显性文化校园，为学习儒学文化创造了良好环境

优美的环境可以净化人的心灵，良好的文化氛围可以陶冶人的情操，转变人的行为习惯，激励人们向上的精神和意志。建设显性校园文化，打造书画诗韵校园，经过精心设计，高品位制作，成为学校文化一道靓丽的风景。

学校在对校园进行硬化、净化、绿化、美化、靓化的基础上，进一步建设文化校园，提高校园文化的档次和品位。进入校园，崇尚科学知识和儒学文化的温馨书院型的春风迎面扑来，学校的每一个角落都飘浮着经典格言、名人语录和历史故事，图文并茂，形象逼真。《弟子规》解读、《三字经》新解、品经典悟人生、讲故事学做人、

圣人教诲改变人生等文化系列，展现在人们面前。每一栋楼房都有传奇故事，每一个墙壁都会说话，每一个版面都像过电影，每一个教室门面都有校领导和教师承诺与感悟，让师生入眼入耳入脑入心，促使学生学习精神倍增，为师生学习经典、增长知识、修德育才创造了优美和谐的校园景观。洛阳市洛龙区龙城双语小学、南阳市唐河县第一小学、漯河市双慧幼儿园等校园文化建设内容好、形式新、档次高，值得学习借鉴。

（二）坚持形式多样的经典诵读，把学习儒学不断引向深入

以儒学为主体的中华优秀传统文化，博大精深的内容凝结成流传千古的经典美文、诗词、歌赋，是中华民族传统文化的精华，让儿童从小浸润在中华优秀文化瑰宝之中，以奠定儿童理想的人生品格、良好的人生道德及谦恭的人生礼仪。中华经典穿越时空，历经数千年，仍如天籁之音，惊醒浑浊的人生，荡涤世尘的污垢，洗礼师生的灵魂。

为了调动学生经典诵读的积极性，有效地开发学生的智力，使学生对经典诵读产生浓厚的兴趣，学生长期坚持仍能声音洪亮，激动人心，情绪盎然。坚持形式多样的经典诵读活动，使学生在潜移默化中学到知识，提高素养。在经典诵读与学校各项实体活动相结合的过程中，通过各种形式展示学生对经典的学习和理解：一是诵经典，二是唱经典，三是写经典，四是画经典，五是演经典，六是对经典，七是赛经典，八是研究经典，九是亲子共读经典，十是校园文化融合经典等形式。晨诵经典 10 分钟，是各示范学校的必修课。每天早上 8 点整，当悠扬的古乐响起，学校的广播里就会传出那稚嫩纯真的童声："现在是经典诵读时间，请大家跟我读……"顿时，朗朗的经典诵读声在校园回荡，穿过院墙、围栏，飘向校外，飘向路人，飘向社区，飘向村镇，使晨练的人群也跟着吟诵起经典来。每天上午 30 分钟快乐阳光大课间，同学位多种行为艺术与经典诵读同行更是一道靓丽的风景线。每天中午放学，不少示范学校按既定路线排队放学，依次走出校门，齐声背诵规定的经典篇目，诵经之声此起彼伏，被群众称为"诗文路队"、"经典童声"，产生了极好的社会反响。在下午的课外活动中，学生开展丰富多彩的文化体育等活动，其中有学生用经典诵读的内容排练文娱节目或进行"经典美文"、"古诗歌赋"、"经典书法"等评比、竞赛活动，全方位推动经典诵读活动的深入开展。

许多学校学生在多种多样娱乐形式经典诵读活动中，从低年级到高年级，结合学校实际，编写了校本教材，学习了《弟子规》、《三字经》、《百家姓》、《千字文》等蒙学读物；又学习了《论语》、《孟子》、《大学》、《中庸》、《道德经》、《易经》、"唐诗"、"宋词"等成人读物。师生们对学习经典由熟记背诵，到理解践行，到提高思想素质，增长知识才干，服务奉献社会，使学校的面貌发生了全新的变化。郑州市二七区外国语小学、洛阳市洛龙区龙城双语小学、南阳市唐河县第一小学、漯河市漯河小学等形式多样的经典诵读活动开展得生动活泼，激情满怀，成为经典诵读的一流示范学校。

（三）快乐大课间行为艺术，把经典诵读推向新的境界

学校的经典诵读与快乐大课间活动结合，学生在集体体操和舞蹈中背诵经典，队形千变万化、诵读之声此起彼伏，非常壮观，可以充分体现中华文化博大精深和鼓舞人心、聚集人气的力量。有的学校还将经典诵读与研发的大课间多种行为艺术有机结合。如钻山洞、竹竿舞、跳皮筋、跳绳、拍手操、武术操等，无不体现学校的经典诵读活动的特色，让学生在玩中学，在学中玩，寓教于乐，乐中寓教，从中理解、感悟中华传统文化特别是儒学文化的魅力。不少示范学校每天上午30分钟的快乐阳光大课间，学生们听着雄壮的进行曲，踏着节奏，步调一致，一边行进，一边变化队形，一边背诵《三字经》、《弟子规》、成语接龙、诗词对仗、英语短句等，成了以经典诵读为主要内容多学科融合的行为艺术。洛阳市洛龙区龙和小学的大课间采取多种形式行为艺术与经典诵读相结合，出现生动活泼、激动人心的场景。仅竹竿舞背诵经典，就研发了50多种，学生在体育娱乐中学习了文化知识。南阳市唐河县第一小学的快乐大课间展现的多种行为艺术，队形变化大，体操舞蹈形式多，经典背诵声音洪亮，把师生共读经典活动推向一个崭新的境界。凡是第一次参观这种场景的人都为之震撼！

（四）传承儒学文化，实现教育创新

学校通过学习、传承中华儒学文化，把儒学文化融入教育之中，学校的教学和管理均发生了崭新变化。这种异常的变化可以用十个字概括：靓丽、文明、自觉、提升、创新。所谓“靓丽”是出现了一个诗情画意的校园文化，任何人一进校园就如同进入了一个丰富的科学文化殿堂，一个美好的催人上进的学习场所。“文明”是师生在道德上的巨大变化，到处是尊师爱生、父（母）慈子孝、仁爱礼教、遵纪守法，学校的校风和学风焕然一新。“自觉”主要指在学习上学生更加自觉、更加勤奋、更加深入。许多学生变被动学为主动学，变苦闷学为快乐学，变让我学为我要学，学习的收效明显提高。“提升”主要指学校教育质量的提升、学生素质的提升、学生能力的提升、学校办学的群众满意度提升。“创新”是用中华优秀的传统文化特别是儒学文化融入学校教育之中，解决了学校教育中难以解决的问题，促进了教育改革，使学校教育发生了根本性的变化，实现了教育创新发展。河南少年先锋学校早在15年前就在学生中全面学习儒学文化，学校的教育质量和学生的综合素质全面提升，成为省内外传承中华优秀传统文化的一面旗帜。郑州一中创启学校学习儒学经典文化，用科学的方法促进学生超常记忆，在教育改革与教育创新中发挥重要作用。一句话，许多学校开展经典诵读活动以来，出现了生动、活泼、激情、创新、和谐的新局面。

## 三、坚持六个结合，把传承儒学文化落到实处

在河南省儒学文化与教育创新示范学校的经验中得到一个重要启示：儒学文化在

国民教育中、特别是基础教育中有不可替代的作用，目前儒学经典诵读是学习儒学文化的最好形式。怎样能把儒学经典诵读落到实处？我们总结出“六个结合”。

（一）领导和教师带头相结合

要使学校深入持久地学习儒学文化，开展好师生经典诵读活动。一是学校领导和教师统一认识，组织大家带头学习儒学文化，领导、教师带头学，认识到位，就会积极、主动组织学生开展有计划、有步骤的经典诵读活动。二是成立有领导和教师参加的组织机构，以校长为组长，以副校长、骨干教师为副组长，以语文、历史、政治课教师为主要成员的学习指导机构，制定切实可行的计划，一级抓一级，谁主管谁负责，把经典诵读活动抓出成效。三是制定领导、教师共同遵守的规章制度，以保证学习儒学文化，开展经典诵读活动深入、持久、健康的发展。

（二）经典诵读同班级各项活动相结合

一个班级是学校的基层单位，班级活动蕴含着巨大的潜力，把儒学经典诵读同班级的各项活动结合在一起，如经典诵读同主题班会结合，同班级文化活动结合，同班级文体活动结合，同班级课外实践活动结合等，使经典诵读和班级各项活动实现双丰收，形成师生互动、班级互动、年级互动、全校互动，使师生学习儒学文化形成一种氛围，经典诵读蔚然成风。

（三）经典诵读同各学科教学活动相结合

把学习儒学文化融入各个学科的教学内容和教学实践活动之中。每天都从学科教学时间中抽出 10—15 分钟，作为学生晨读、师生共读、集体诵读时间。有的学校根据学科特色开设特色课堂，编写“儒学经典”校本教材，结合学生的接受能力，从低年级到高年级先后讲授《三字经》、《弟子规》、《百家姓》、《千字文》《论语》、《大学》、《中庸》、《孟子》等校本教材，使学习内容由浅入深，逐步提高学生对儒家经典的理解，进而使学生增长知识和才干。河南少年先锋学校建校十几年来，一直按照中华优秀传统文化特别是儒学文化制定教学大纲、编写教材，已经成为河南省乃至全国的办学先进典型，培养人才的质量和水平相当高，已经得到社会广泛的认可。其他儒学文化示范单位把经典诵读融入各学科教学之中，按国家规定的教学大纲和自编的儒学校本教材，进行各学科教学，同样使学校教育改革出现新的局面。

（四）经典诵读与德育教育活动相结合

儒学文化主要是讲道德的学问，而儒学最高的道德是仁义，就是以仁爱之心处理人与人的关系。而当前各类学校的德育教育相对比较空泛，若把儒学经典诵读融入德育教育活动之中，可以收到显著效果。围绕“德育课堂教育”、“中华传统文化节日教育”、“敬亲敬老教育”、“爱国爱民教育”、“热爱自然、珍爱生命教育”等活动，组织学生学习和理解儒学经典，培养学生以实际行动孝敬父母，感恩祖国，回报社会，报答人民，敬畏自然，珍爱万物和生命，使许多学生思想道德素质有很大提高，精神面貌和行为焕然一新。不少学校把学习儒学经典与德育教育活动有机结合，涌现了许多孝敬父母、感恩老师、文明礼貌的先进典型。

（五）经典诵读同学校团队活动特别是与学雷锋活动相结合

小学有少先队组织、中学有共青团组织，所有学校都有学生会组织，有的学校还有学雷锋团队等。把博大精深的儒学经典列入各团队学习的必读书目，在团队活动中建立学习儒学经典的机制，搭建学习经典的交流平台，这样既丰富、浸润了学校的团队活动，又把学习儒学文化引向深入。如儒学文化所倡导的“自强不息”、“厚德载物”、“仁者爱人”、“兄友弟恭”等，既符合我们当前社会主义核心价值体系倡导的主流思想道德、“全心全意为人民服务”、“助人为乐”的雷锋精神是一致的。学习传承优秀传统文化与新时期学习弘扬雷锋精神是完全可以融合的。我们应该坚持这种结合，通过儒学经典学习与学校团队活动的有机结合，许多学校各项活动生机勃勃，又处处飘逸着儒学书香，所有团队活动中的好学博雅源于儒风的吹拂。

（六）经典诵读同家庭教育活动相结合

儒学优秀文化的传承教育不仅需要学校的努力，而且家庭和社会也有不可替代的重要作用。因此，学校积极开展亲子共读活动，促使家长和学生一起学习儒学经典，也是一种好办法。为了充分利用家、校共建资源，许多学校建立了家长委员会，通过家长委员会，学校主动和家长交流教育孩子的经验、方法和学习体会，取得了家长认可。洛阳市洛龙区龙城双语小学、龙和小学、唐河县第一小学、登封市崇高路小学、通许县第一实验小学等开展家长与学生共读一本书的“亲子共读”活动，既有力推动了学校的经典诵读活动，又引领和鼓励更多的家庭成为“书香家庭”。郑州市二七区外国语小学、汉川街小学还把儒学文化的学习引入社区，实现了学校、家庭、社区共建的良好育人环境。

## 四、努力做好对各示范学校的指导和服务工作

自2010年1月1日河南省儒学文化促进会成立之日起，我们怀着高尚的社会责任感和神圣的历史使命感，积极在河南各地认真弘扬与普及儒学文化，特别是把教育系统及中小学作为工作的重点，遵循儒学教育最好从青少年抓起的原则，调动各方面力量，采取有效措施，认真抓好落实，取得了显著的成效。首先，我们把传承儒学文化已有十多年历史、并且取得了显著效果的河南少年先锋学校和郑州十四中学作为促进会的儒学文化示范基地，及时总结、宣传、推广他们传承儒学文化的先进经验和做法。同时，我们又由促进会主要负责同志牵头成立了调研考察小组，及时到河南有关市、

县教育局及中、小学校进行考察论证工作，在条件成熟的情况下，于2012年1月在部分市、县中小学中及时命名10所儒学文化与教育创新示范学校和10所儒学文化与教育创新试点学校，对他们创造的好经验及时进行了总结、宣传和推广工作。截至2014年2月，我们命名的儒学文化与教育创新示范学校已经达到50所（包括10所儒学文化与教育创新试点学校转为示范学校），并对他们的工作及时进行了有效的指导和服务工作，促进了全省中、小学传承儒学文化和实现教育创新工作的顺利开展。

第一，积极做好各示范学校的宣传推广工作。

我们采取多种措施和办法，做好各示范学校的宣传、推广工作：一是充分发挥各新闻媒体的作用。我们在各新闻单位发展一批热爱儒学文化的同仁为理事和会员，并把他们组织起来，统一规划，分工负责，重点做好各示范学校的宣传、报道工作，不断为宣传儒学文化做出新贡献。二是充分发挥促进会的会刊、网站的作用。会刊《中州儒学文化》每期都开辟有“儒学文化与教育创新”栏目，有计划、有步骤、分期分批地刊载各示范学校传承儒学文化的好经验、好做法，促进会网站也及时转载。这种做法，为宣传、推广各示范学校的经验发挥了积极的作用。

第二，认真选派专家到各示范学校巡回演讲儒学文化。

为了更加广泛地宣传推广儒学文化，我们于2011年3月成立了儒学文化宣讲团，先后吸收40多名专家、教授为宣讲团讲师。宣讲团应各示范学校和会员单位的邀请，到各地各单位巡回演讲儒学文化，成为促进会工作的一个亮点。据不完全统计，四年多来，宣讲团到各地示范学校和会员单位演讲达600多场次，受众达二十多万人。副团长闫合作一人巡回演讲超过300场次，听众达十多万人。副团长聂振弢不仅在示范单位讲，而且还到非示范单位讲；不仅在河南讲，而且到香港地区、台湾地区、韩国讲，而且乐教也很叫好。宣讲团讲师们的巡回演讲，受到广大听众、特别是教师和青年学生的欢迎和喜爱。正是宣讲团的讲师不辞劳苦，无私奉献，把中华优秀传统文化用通俗易懂的形式传播给师生，使师生学习儒学文化产生了浓厚的兴趣，有效地促进了儒学文化与教育创新示范学校的工作开展。

第三，努力做好各示范学校教师的教育培训工作。

为了促进儒学文化与教育创新示范学校工作的开展，我们在选派讲师走出去的同时，还采取了请进来的办法，在促进会的教育培训基地进行教育培训工作。从2010年5月以来，先后组织13次儒学文化教育培训班，请各示范学校和会员单位的领导、教师和职工计300多人参加学习培训，抽调促进会的数十名主讲教师，讲授儒学经典和儒学文化专题讲座，参加培训的人员普遍反映，思想收获大，认识提高快，不断加深了对儒学文化学理性的认识及其社会价值的理解，增强了对学习传承儒学文化的信心，大部分学员已经成为本单位弘扬、传承儒学文化的带头人。

第四，及时组织各示范学校校长参加现场经验交流会。

为了更好地推广和普及各示范学校的先进经验，我们于2012年5月中旬在洛阳市成功召开了“河南省儒学文化与教育创新示范学校现场经验交流会”，有关市、县教育局长、中小学校长120多人参加了会议。与会代表参观了洛阳市洛龙区儒学文化与教育创新示范学校龙城双语小学和龙和小学，他们的校园文化、经典诵读和阳光大课间行为艺术独具特色，学校面貌焕然一新，师生的综合素质明显提升。与会代表普遍反映：“参加这次经验交流会，特别是参观了两个示范学校，使人感到非常震撼！学到了从书本上从未学过的好经验。”时任中共河南省委常委、洛阳市委书记毛万春同志亲自到会、并发表讲话，他指出：“弘扬中华优秀传统文化、特别是儒学文化，是一件功德无量的大善事、大好事，学校把树人放到首要地位，创造了先进经验，值得大力提倡!”2013年5月下旬，我们又在洛阳市嵩县隆重召开了“中华优秀传统文化进机关、进学校、进乡村现场经验交流会”；2013年12月18日，我们又在南阳市唐河县顺利召开了“河南省儒学文化与教育创新示范学校现场参观学习会”，实地参观学习唐河县第一小学的先进经验和做法。几次现场会的召开，反映出传承儒学文化不仅在学校有声有色地进行，而且在更大范围内得到了各方广泛的认可，必将推动河南省更多的学校把儒学文化与教育创新活动迈上个新台阶。

此外，我们还组织多种形式的儒学文化宣传教育平台——学术报告会、演讲报告会、国学高层论坛、公益大讲堂、道德大讲堂等，由省内外数十名专家、教授作主讲嘉宾，有效地弘扬和传播了儒学文化。其中中华国学高层论坛和洛阳儒学公益大讲堂已成为促进会的品牌，产生了良好的社会效应，包括各示范学校的领导、教师在内的广大听众，从中感受到中华儒学文化的博大精深、魅力无穷，受到了很大的启发和鼓舞，在传承儒学文化、实现教育创新活动中同样发挥着促进作用。

# 乡村儒学的缘起与意义

中国社会科学院 赵法生

从 2013 年 1 开始，我们在尼山周围的乡村开始了乡村儒学建设实验，到目前为止已经有一年零七个月的时间，受到了农民的热烈欢迎，成效较为明显。我们搞乡村儒学并非心血来潮，而是长期以来就徘徊于脑海中的想法。乡村儒学的出现得到了很多鼓励，也伴随着一些质疑，不管是鼓励还是质疑，都是对我们的支持，促使我们进一步总结经验和不足，以便使乡村儒学更健康地向前发展。

## 一、乡村儒学兴起的历史文化背景

目前乡村社会面临三大挑战是信仰缺失，治理紊乱和生态失衡，我们关注的首先是乡信仰缺失问题，这一问题在目前乡治中占有特殊地位，许多其他问题都与其密切相关。传统中国乡村是一个独特的社会文化生态系统，梁漱溟先生将它定性为“伦理本位，职业分立”。[①] 所谓伦理本位就是以伦理关系和伦理情谊为本位，而与西洋社会的个人本位相对照；而职业分立则是有职业分工而无固定阶级，社会阶层轮流变迁而不世袭继承。伦理本位和职业分立相互作用，彼此强化，形成了传统中国乡土社会的特征。支撑此一社会系统的，从外部组织形式讲是自耕自足的农业社会，从内在价值观念讲则是以儒家为主又儒释道合一的价值观，此一价值系统的基础又是以慎终追远为核心的孝道观念，它赋予了农民以生活的意义，构造了传统乡村的家族体系、伦理情谊和自治制度，也构建了现实生活中的五伦关系。实际上，不管是基督教文明还是中华文明，不管是乡村采取哪种治理形式，家庭伦理都是社会有效治理的前提，破坏家庭伦理势必动摇文明的根基，带来严重的社会后果。

“文革”中的文化革命和以人民公社为代表的经济革命，摧毁了数千年的价值观念和宗法体系，却并未立即引发乡村的信仰危机，因为当时的意识形态实际上发挥了信

---

① 梁漱溟:《乡村建设理论》，上海世纪出版集团，2006 年，第 29 页。

仰替代作用。20世纪50、60年代出生的人想必清楚地记得人人高唱革命歌曲以及早请示、晚汇报时的虔诚与庄严感，那是一种近乎宗教崇拜的感情。一些人假设，如果这种替代性信仰在“文革”结束后得以延续，或许不至于出现后来严重的道德滑坡，但历史不能假设。由于“文革”的极端非理性，以及由于一大二公的人民公社在生产上的低效率所导致的乡村的普遍贫穷饥饿，决定了这一运动注定是短暂的。20世纪70年代末开启的改革运动以彻底否定文革为起点，这种彻底否定主要表现在经济领域和政治领域，在文化领域则十分有限，自然，被关闭的寺庙和道观先后恢复活动，但作为传统中国人信仰支柱的儒教系统——书院、宗祠、孔庙等却都没有恢复，普遍性的民间信仰（如曾经遍布中国北方乡村的土地庙）也未恢复，为儒家思想的正名也迟迟不能进行。

改革以来否定了极“左”思想，却没有尽快为传统文化正名。如果说文革给了已经饱受重创的乡村传统文化最后的一击，然而文革为它提供的替代物却在改革进程启动以后迅速失去了感召力。如果说，从近代到文革完成了对于传统乡村精神信仰的解构，改革则在实际上完成了对于传统信仰替代物的解构。经由此两次解构，客观上造成了乡村信仰的空心化，我们现在面对一个既没有了传统宗教信仰和人文精神，又没有现代法治理念的乡村。历史的断裂就这样发生了，价值的真空就这样造成了。以市场化为导向的改革在此一精神背景下高歌猛进，却使得拜金主义大行其道，因为金钱至上已经失去了任何精神抗体，而拜金主义的肆虐客观上又给了乡土中传统文化残余以更为沉重的打击，此次打击的力度某种意义上并不亚于文革。如果“文革”是对于传统文化的政治冲击，拜金主义则是对于传统伦理的经济解构，此一解构深入到社会生活的每一个方面，使得乡村社会所剩无几的人与人的温情迅速消弭，人与人之间的关系更加功利和冰冷，从而引发了乡村深层的价值认同危机，其中最突出的孝道的式微和老人处境问题。

我们从2012年下半年开始对于济宁市泗水县圣水峪镇北东野村的老人状况进行调查，村子离尼山只有一千米，发现即使在孔子的诞生地，老人的生活状态普遍不佳。村里老人住的房子是最差的，被称为老人房。村支书庞德海说，如果老人还能下地干活，境况还过得去，一旦失去劳动能力，或者老来得病，就会被看成是家庭包袱，其境况便更加悲惨。甚至村里一些先富起来人的老父老母也处境惨淡，有人家境富裕却不愿意给自己的老父亲缴纳每年几十块钱的医疗合作基金。孔子当年曾感叹有人把养老人与养牲口看成一回事，但是，一旦拜金主义在大脑里占了上风，人们就会宁愿养牲口而不养老人，因为牲口毕竟可以卖钱。据统计，北东野村七十岁以上的老人62位，其中八十岁以上的22位，年底书院想从中挑出部分困难老人给予补助，村干部们竟然颇费踌躇，因为不困难的老人太少。有一儿媳妇公然在大街上打婆婆的耳光，因为媳妇命令婆婆去骂村干部而婆婆没有从命。有一个老人没有儿女，过继了一个侄子做儿子，这个过继的儿子不但对老人一毛不拔，还从老人每月的400元五保和老年补贴中克扣300元。有良知的村干部痛恨不孝，同情老人，可是他们往往爱莫能助，他们感到那毕竟是村民的家务事。

近年来，农村自杀问题引起了社会的广泛关注。根据人民网2013年年11月22日资料：我国人口占全世界五分之一，自杀率却占四分之一，每年约有28.7万人自杀，200万人自杀未遂，农村人口自杀率是城市的三倍，其中农村妇女的自杀率又高于男性，前者是后者的1.24倍，农村妇女自杀多为失范性自杀，人际关系恶化和家庭不和谐是重要原因，妇女的抗压力较弱使得他们更容易成为牺牲品。[①] 农村老人也属于高自杀人群，中国农村老人的自杀率是世界平均水平的四到五倍。（成都商报，2009年8月30日）据中国青年报2014年7月30日报道，武汉大学社会学系讲师、国家社会科学基金项目《农村老年人自杀的社会学研究》项目主持人的刘燕舞走进湖北、山东、江苏、山西、河南、贵州等11个省份的40多个村庄，用驻村调查400多天的数据表明，从1990年开始，中国农村老年人自杀率大幅上升，这一比率在2000年以后又进一步提升，高湖北京山地区的老人自杀率竟然达到了百分之三十[②]乡村妇女和老人的高自杀率都与家庭伦理问题息息相关，不管人生的困难多么严重，一个温暖的家庭足以支撑起人们活下去的勇气。老人们的处境尤其如此，他们为了抚育后代付出了一生的心血精力，到了无力生活的晚年而被儿女遗弃，极容易在心灰意冷中选择绝路，长期致力于乡村问题研究的三农专家贺雪峰教授将湖北京山老人自杀的原因归结为“老无所依”，[③] 可谓抓住了问题的关键。因为各种条件的限制，中国百分之九十九的乡村老人选择居家养老，只有百分之一选择社会养老，儿女的孝心和家庭的关爱就是他们生活的全部希望之所在，当孝道观念在青年一代心目中最终消失的时候，也就是老人们走上绝路之时。

价值真空也导致基督宗教和一些邪教在乡村快速传播。在尼山一带的乡村，基督教家庭教会迅速发展，据我们调查，北东野村有七、八十个基督徒，一般每周聚会两次，周日到附的教堂做礼拜，该教堂可以容纳500余人。该镇的另一教堂能容纳2000余人。由于乡村多为老弱病残，且不识字的人居多，封闭式的家庭教会有时演变为邪教，全能神教和东方闪电等大概都是这样产生的。最近的一份基督教调查表明，基督教在江南农村的发展远逊于北方，因为江南农村的宗祠等儒家组织和民间宗教在“文革”中所受到的破坏较北方为轻，近二十来年来自发恢复较快，自然形成了与基督教

---

① 刘燕舞:《中国农村自杀率的现状分析和原因探究》，2014年7月14日。

② 《中国青年报》，2014年7月30日。

③ 三农中国网站，2014年，4月12日。

等的对冲力量。[①] 有宗教学者预言，15年后，中国将会取代美国成为全世界基督徒最多的国家，[②] 人们或许对于具体数字统计尚有分歧，但基督教在中国社会德尔快速发展是个不争的事实。

八十多年前，梁漱溟已经感叹中国近代史就是一部乡村的破坏史，指出近代以来中国乡村的主要问题在于文化失调，必须通过重建乡村礼俗来统领经济与社会生活，这的确抓住了乡村治理的核心问题：儒家文化才是乡村的根，也是乡村走向和谐有序的关键。目前乡村伦理问题比梁漱溟时代更为严峻，那时，传统乡村的教化体系如祠堂、乡绅、家训、家谱等基本还在，可是，由此后来过激的反传统运动，乡村的一切教化体系已经荡然无存。因此，重建乡村伦理依然是乡土重建的当务之急。

## 二、重建现代乡村儒学传播体系

乡村儒学的基本理念是：以乡村儒家文化的重建来带动乡土文明的重建，通过儒家的孝道和五伦教育，培育民众的人生信仰和价值观念，重建乡村的人伦秩序和文化生态。我们将这一理念变成定期化的课程，以课程为核心建立其一套儒家教化体系，再通过教化活动将理念变成农民的生活方式。

（一）建立定期化的乡村儒学讲堂

最早开展乡村儒学教育的是泗水县圣水峪镇北东野村，该村有1200多人，百分之七十是庞姓，其余为冯、孔、赵等姓，因为庞姓人家占了绝对多数，多年来的村支书并村主任一直是由庞氏担任。该村离书院只有一公里左右，书院所占土地就书院该村农民。由于担心农民不来听，第一次讲座为前来听课的农民每人准备了一块毛巾和一条香皂，预计最多来90人，结果来了110多人，支书庞德海便号召村干部发扬风格，让群众先领。第一次讲的是孝道和家庭教育，庞书记说当场有不少老人落泪，有的老人回家之后还哭，看来是“男儿有泪不轻弹，只是未到伤心处”。有些中年妇女抱着孩子来听孝道，村民反映，她们有的在家里可是经常甩脸色给老人看的。可是，这些不孝敬公婆的媳妇竟然也抱着孩子来听孝道了，因为她们心里希望自己的孩子将来会孝顺自己，这就是儒家文化的生命力所在，孔子的教诲是发自人心又合乎人性的。第二次恰好是2013年农历的正月二十一，继续讲孝道，人数比上次还多，备用的凳子用完了，还有村民陆续赶来，晚来的只能站在走廊里，共有130多人。本来这次准备每个村民发一只面盆，结束时，庞书记感到刚过了大年就发面盆，有些不太吉利而作罢。第三次也是130人左右。经颜炳罡教授介绍前来参观乡村儒学的台湾佛光大学的谢大

① 杨华：《农村地下基督教的南北差异》，观察者网，2014年7月5日。

② 环球网，2014年4月24日。

宁教授，被眼前的景象感动得热泪盈眶，说他仿佛拿到了阳明后学儒学会讲的盛况。又发了几次礼品后便不再发放，因为书院的财政十分拮据。但一个相对固定的听众群体已经形成，每次大概在八十人左右。为了统计出勤率，每次都点名，并对出勤率高的群众进行表彰。

当年梁漱溟先生搞乡村建设最大的问题之一是乡村建设运动而农民不动。[①] 可是，眼前农民对于乡村儒学却是如此热切期待，这不令我们深思。大概我们以孝道为切入点抓住了农民最关心的问题，另外，在梁先生从事乡村建设的20世纪30年代，乡村的儒家伦理体系还大体保存着，可是，今天，由于北方乡村儒学体系已经荡然无存，农民心中对于人性、人道和人伦的饥渴大概是乡村儒学能够一炮打响的重要原因。

开局的成功极大地鼓舞了我们的士气。讲了五次之后，我便到夫子洞和周庄两个村庄进行调研，向老百姓介绍乡村儒学讲堂，对于愿意参加的群众登记电话，并事先进行电话通知，将停课群众扩展到三个村庄。后来发现来听课的也有其他村庄的村民，他们是听了亲戚的介绍后主动前来的。

经过试验，确定了半月一次的常态化乡村儒学讲堂制度，一开始村干部和村民嫌太频繁，说能不能一月一次。在我们的坚持下，半月一讲的制度终于形成，具体时间为每月中间和最后一个礼拜天，即使农忙时间也尽量不中断。目前，社会上的国学传播多采取大讲堂的形式，由一些受佛教影响的人士组织，一般是集中讲课，每次两三天甚至一个礼拜，讲课者多数介绍自己的亲身经历，如《我被十九个学校开除》，《一九零后个坏女孩儿的忏悔》等，由于是现身说法，声情并茂，颇能动人，听众当时也能涕泗滂沱。但是，由于这种活动不定期，长期效果难以巩固，眼泪流过之后大多依然故我。我们建立定期化的儒学讲堂，正是要通过持之以恒来化民成俗。

乡村儒学讲堂的设置经历了从农民进书院到学者下农村的转变。最早的乡村儒学讲堂设在书院，周围的村民进书院听课，后来，陆续在全镇各村设立讲堂，2014年3月份后，在圣水峪镇先后开设了小城子、椿树沟、南仲都、镇驻地、官庄、庠场六个讲堂，加上书院里的一个，共有七个。镇驻地讲堂是改造的旧法院，小城子借用了小学教室，椿树沟借用了奶牛场的会议室，南仲都讲堂在一间大棚里，庠厂小学在教室里。最早的一批儒学讲堂可谓八仙过海，各显神通。由于一个讲堂能自然辐射到三四个村，七个讲堂能够辐射到全近三十个村庄，约占到圣水峪镇六十个村庄的一半。

（二）构建完整的乡村儒学传播体系

我们以定期化的乡村儒学讲堂为依托，试图构建一个现代儒学传统体系，主要包括以下内容：

---

① 梁漱溟：《乡村建设理论》，上海世纪出版集团，2006年，第369页。

行孝。孝悌为仁之本，乡村儒学讲堂开始的话题主要围绕着孝道进行，讲解父母的恩德，行孝的好处，使村民知孝、重孝、行孝。村庄的文化氛围的营造也紧扣孝道主题，对于孝道模范给予奖励，唤醒村民的孝亲敬老之情。来听课的孩子们有一道家庭作业，就是每天要帮助长辈做一件事，有的饭前给爷爷奶奶搬凳子，有的给爷爷奶奶叠被子，一年级小朋友庞传奇的奶奶有腿疾，他年龄小还不会叠被子，就每天给奶奶端便盆。孩子们们的心中已经播下了孝的种子。

读经。儒学课堂以讲经为主，通过经典讲习向村民传授儒家的价值观和人生观。最先讲解的是《弟子规》，群众很欢迎《弟子规》，不少村民还给自己的孙子或者外甥要一本。由于目前的《弟子规》课本大多不能令人满意，我便用一个月时间重新注释并自费印刷了2000多本，解决了急需的教材问题。通过讲课，乡亲们对《弟子规》的人生道理产生了浓厚的兴趣，出现了祖孙同学《弟子规》、母子同学《弟子规》的场景，这本传统蒙学教材，是教孩子如何孝敬尊重长辈的，现在，他却成了孙子和爷爷们共同使用的教材，这是在为一个时代补课。此外，还计划讲授《王凤仪言行录》，《朱子家礼》，《童子礼》、《了凡四训》，以及乡土版的《论语》、《孟子》、《大学》、《中庸》等。

习礼。中华文明号称礼乐文明，此外，还没有任何其他民族曾经获得的过此一殊荣。可是，由于连礼仪也成了革命对象，终于造成了今天礼崩乐坏的现实，曾经的礼仪之邦因此而陷入尴尬，如何摆脱尴尬，得有点孔子所说“知耻近乎勇”的勇气，更需要闻过则喜的力行精神。于是，乡村儒学建设在开展《弟子规》教育的同时引入礼仪教育，请礼仪专家来给老百姓讲授和演示一些儒家礼仪，比如成童礼、开笔礼、冠礼、婚礼、射礼、释奠礼等等，并在课堂上教导乡亲们行礼如仪。乡村儒学讲堂的课堂制定了课堂仪规，要求所有听众向至圣先师孔子行四鞠躬礼，再向讲课老师二鞠躬礼，青少年还要给在座的长辈们行敬长礼。孔子故里的礼让之风就在这些生活化的礼仪熏陶之中逐渐归来。

乐教。移风易俗莫善于乐，讲堂请来了志愿者给村民教唱“跪羊图”等孝道歌曲，并录制了一些优美的家庭伦理歌曲定期在村里播放，从此，尼山脚下便再度响起了感人的乐声。为了使得乐教经常化，从常来听国学的孩子中挑选了二十几小学生组成了一个小小国乐团，孩子们每周末都到书院里学唱歌曲，并经常在国学课堂上为村民演唱。君子之风的种子已然在孩子们的心中播下，也必将伴随着他们优美和稚气的歌声传遍四方。

乡约。乡约为北宋儒家的关学所首倡，对于传统社会的乡村治理影响甚大。梁漱溟先生曾将其乡村建设的思想归结为“本古人乡约之意以组织乡村。”[①] 乡约是乡民的自我约定，是基于道德自我约束的农村宪章，它不同于强制性的法律，又具有某种强制力量，是从个人修养过渡到公共理性的重要媒介。传统乡村所以以无讼著称，乡约发挥着重要作用。目前各地农村也有一些村干部制订的乡规民约，主要内容有严禁偷他人的东西，严禁哄抢国家物质，严禁购买枪支，严禁损坏公共财物以及计划生育政策等，其实是村干部单方面提出的对于村民的强制性要求，失去了儒家乡约“齐之以礼”的精神而变成了单纯的“齐之以刑”，这样的乡规民约受到农民的冷漠是不足为奇的。我们在试点村的道德重建取得一定成效之后开始了乡约试点，其内容主要包括孝道、齐家、睦邻、公益、环卫、持戒、权利等内容，充分体现古代乡约中“道之以德”的精神，将乡约变成村民砥砺道德和人生向上的手段。我们专门在乡约中加入了权利部分以保障村民利益，并选出德高望重的乡绅作为乡约的约长，来监督乡约的执行。

救助。为了和农民交朋友，我们时常到农民家里串门聊天，并帮助那些生活困难的农民。八十多岁的孤寡老人庞德顺身体有病，还要坚持下地干活，生活困难，我们便接济他两千元。另一位 79 岁的老大娘，儿子在淄博打工失踪，儿媳妇扔下两个孩子一去不回，她不得不担负起了抚养两个孩子的重任，靠放羊、捡垃圾为生，她大概是支撑不下去了，表示要将两个孩子送给书院。孙女已经十一岁了，爸爸失踪后就从一年级退学在家，书院的学者资助老人并让她孙女复学。2013 年底，我们还给村里十几个困难老人发放了生活补助。2014 年，书院副秘书长张晓雨先生又资助了两家孤寡老人，每人每月补贴他 200 元。另外，还请城里的大夫下乡义诊。这些帮助老弱的行动拉近了我们和农民的距离，也提高了他们参加乡村儒学讲堂的积极性。

熏陶。为了配合儒学教育，在村里设立了传统文化宣传栏，墙壁上写上了修身齐家的格言。村里的大喇叭每天都定时播放《弟子规》与音乐光盘，使整个村子浸透在浓郁的文化氛围之中。学习《弟子规》半年后，为了检验学习成绩，组织了一次村民有奖背诵比赛，村民们参与的热情超出预料，许多人主动上台背诵，使得整个比赛结束时间一再推迟。年底由全村村民投票，评出了奖孝亲媳妇、模范公婆和谐家庭，给优胜者带上大红花现场发奖，然后介绍他们的家道家风和先进事迹，使大家学有榜样。

乡村儒学能否取得成功，关键在于能否将儒学重新变成乡村的内生性教化活动，为此，必须实现由学者主导向村民主体的转变，这一转变的成功与否直接决定着乡村儒学建设的成败，可谓生死攸关的一环。为此，我们从开始就注意充分调动群众的学习积极性，将村民变成学习主体，而不仅仅是被教化的对象。为此，我们将村民划分为不同学习小组，选出组长组织学习活动，并开展不同小组之间的学习竞赛。

---

① 梁漱溟：《乡村建设理论》，上海世纪出版集团，第 156 页。

## 三、乡村儒学实验的初步效果

一年半多来，乡村儒学建设实验取得了良好效果。头半年效果尚未显现，半年后村民开始品尝出儒学的味道，一年之后家风和村风都发生了显著变化，村民的学习积极性也更加高涨。乡村儒学给村庄带来一系列可喜变化：

首先是打娘骂老的风气被刹住，孝亲敬老风气渐浓。二年前调查时，让村干部最头疼的问题是许多村民不孝敬老人。在头半年，孝道教育好像没有产生立竿见影的效果，但是，寒冰在悄无声息地被仁爱的春意消融着，终于，到了春节前后，量变引起了质变，一股孝亲敬老的暖流从村民心中涌流出来。村里有一个叫刘德娥的老太太，三个儿子，事先约定每人每年应该给老人200块钱，二儿媳妇不但不交纳，反而说婆婆偏向老大和老三。经过一年的学习，去年大年三十，二媳妇不但送来了二百元，而且请婆婆去她家过年。婆婆正月初一跑到村主任家里，说："他三叔，书院的班可管用了，可千万不能停!"那个公开在大街上打婆婆的耳光的恶媳妇，也来听孝道课，尽管她不好意思坐到前面而总是坐到最后一排，经过一段时间的听课，对于公婆的态度大大改善，过春节时竟然破天荒地给婆婆买了一身新衣裳，最近时常用三轮车拉着婆婆赶集。那个气死公爹而且不出来送葬的媳妇，听课后也有改变，尽管公婆都已经去世了，可这个一向与邻居关系不好的村民，变得比以前和气多了，时常给邻居帮忙。记者来采访她是，他以为公家派人追究她不孝敬老人的过错，吓得躲到亲戚家里一天没敢回家。一对婆媳因为计划生育问题形成积怨多年，现在和好了；一位乡亲在雨季到来之前忙着给他的老娘修房子，以前他才不管这些闲事呢。现在，打娘骂老的现象不见了，用一位村民的话讲，村民们不好意思这样做了。原先不孝老人是正常的，现在感到脸红了，内心中的变化必然反映到行动上来。

家风的改善带动了村风的好转，村里的风气也发生了明显改善，一是邻里关系变好了，原来是互相不服气和彼此看热闹，现在邻里关系融洽多了。两个中年妇女因为矛盾多年不说话，学习了儒学后，现在经常一起去赶集。二是酒后骂街的现象不翼而飞了，这本来是这一代乡村的一大人文景观，也是村干部无可奈何的事情。有人心中不高兴，喝醉了酒就骂街，有人丢了一只鸡能在大街上骂六七个小时，什么难听骂什么，直骂得两嘴翻白沫。一年之后，这种景观消失了。三是小偷小摸明显减少了，村里的"秋里忙"（秋天到田野里偷人家的花生和果品的人）不见了，在最早开始儒学讲堂的北东野村，按照村民的话说，去年下半年以来连一双袜子都没有少过。四是村里的卫生大大改善，乱倒垃圾的少了因为人们宁愿多走几步将垃圾倒在坑里。五是干群关系有所改善。原来，村干部和群众打架是家常便饭，有一年因为土地调整，干部和群众打架4次，现在不用了。上一次农网改造，需要砍伐村子里的一些树，但有个别村民就是不许动自家的树，还骂村干部，结果导致村干部和群众打群架，当年参加战斗的几个小组长现在还记忆犹新。可是，今年的农网改造却进行得波澜不惊，没有一家出来打横炮，村支书说到这里露出了一脸的笑容。

北东野村主任庞德海说，我原来以为农民天生就是油盐不进、四六不分，是教育不好的，现在来看不是这样。官庄的村主任也说，看来没有天生的坏人。言行变了，风气变了，是因为心里变了，心里变得柔软了，这正是儒学教化的力量。实践证明，儒家的孝道和五伦是可以内化于心、外化于行的。现在，每到学堂开讲时间，村民们就从四面八方赶来，有拄着双拐的，有眼睛失明让人领着路的，那有的胃癌手术后出院才10天就赶来来听课，那种扶老携幼的情景令人感动，显然，农民心中沉寂已久的某种东西已经被唤醒了，那被唤醒的究竟是什么？是人伦、人道和人性。2500多年前的孔夫子曾说：诚信、恭笃和礼让，即使到了蛮夷之地也是不能丢弃的；亚圣孟子也说：人心喜欢圣贤的义理，就如同人的嘴巴喜欢珍馐美味儿一样。尼山脚下的乡村儒学实践证明，由孔子开出的儒家道德原则不仅是古典的，也是现代的；不仅是传统的，也是永恒的，它注定将在中华文明现代转型中的历史进程中发挥重要的作用。

## 四、反思与前瞻

现在的乡村被称为荒芜的乡村，逃离的乡村，记忆中的故园。多少有些能力的人都在争先恐后地逃离乡土，奔向城市，即使他们根本没有在城市里谋生的能力，也要拼命逃离故土。乡村成了老弱病残留守的荒原，成了盗贼横行罪犯出没之地，这就是我们的故乡吗？我去过英国和德国的乡村，那里风景如画，恬静祥和，如同伊甸园；我去过新西兰的乡村，雪白的羊群飘动在碧绿的草原上，与高空的云朵交相辉映，那里的农民比城里人人还要富庶。日本的农民的收入与城市居民持平。临渊羡鱼，不如退而结网，如何重建我们的故乡呢？我们选择了乡村儒学。从人伦道德的重建作为乡村重建的出发点，一年半的实验效果有些人意料之外，但这仅仅是起点而已。从总体上说来，乡村儒学依然处于起步阶段，总结回顾一年半来乡村儒学的实践，我们对于儒学和乡村的发展都有一些新的体悟。

我们在实践中发现，尽管遭遇了百余年的打压摧残，儒学在乡土文明中的根并未断绝。尽管乡村的伦常出现了许多问题，但是，那里仍然有许多感人的人伦美德，它们是儒家文化长期熏陶的结果。比如82岁的朱大爷号称是北东野村第一好人，此人年轻时是个木匠，最喜欢帮人做活，全村人找他帮忙随叫随到，农忙时他宁愿扔下自己的活也要尽快修好别人的犁头。老伴晚年长期卧病在床，他细心照料，给她洗脚、搓澡、梳头，好天气便推出老伴来天井里晒太阳。他平常包水饺都是两种陷儿，肉的给老伴吃，白菜的自己吃。去年腊月里，有一天比较暖和，他还推着老伴来到书院听儒学，今年春节期间老伴不幸去世了。这位乡村木匠以他的行动诠释了传统儒家伦理中的夫妇合敬同爱的美德。朱伯忠老人家里依然保持着四世同堂的格局，那不是外来的命令，而是家庭的自由选择，因为大家舍不得分开。女儿常年在外地打工，将小儿子寄养在他家，儿媳妇视若己出，这样的人伦情谊，岂非福报？儒学的根本虽经百年摧残依然不绝，甚至在维系儒学教化的体系彻底崩塌之后，依然顽强地存在于民间，是因为它是从人心深处生发出来的，它植根于人性的深处，才有“野火烧不尽，春风吹又生”的顽强。

乡村儒学的成效也是我们对于儒学的本质有了新的认识。儒学究竟是什么？它是非常特殊的一门学问，一门完全不同于目前学校里绝大多数课程的学问，一门极其重要却又从民国初年就已经从我们的教科书中删除了的学问。它是道，而不是一般的知识，而是修己安人之道。它以忠恕与内省将人领回到自己的内心，寻找到真正的自我。孔孟教诲无不落实到人的心性，以开启心性作为修养历程的发端。先秦儒学是道，是百姓日用而不知的人伦之道，是“不可须臾离也”之道。汉儒将其政治化，宋儒将它理学化，固然有当时的历史文化背景，却未免对于原始儒家的本来面目有所遮蔽。道是一团元气，它情理兼顾，圆融而丰沛，外圆而内方，退藏于密而又弥漫六合，与它比起来，理学家的理未免显得枯瘦和僵硬。由道而理，固然强调了原始儒家的某些方面，但它使得儒学的整体层次有所降低。先秦儒家之道从哪里发端？人情，《诗大序》所谓“发乎情止乎礼义”，既从人情出发，又能将人情提升到公共理性的高度，合情入理，正是儒道教化的奥秘所在。

儒学在乡村教化成效与乡土文明自身的特点密切有关。村庄是个熟人社会，这里的人是要面子的，甚至一个杯子、一支暖瓶这样的奖品他们都是在意的。一位妇女说，我不是在意那个东西，我打一天工就挣七八十块，可是为什么人家能有，咱家就没有？她感到脸上挂不住。孝心媳妇评奖、慈爱公婆评奖所以有效，正是建立在这一心理机制上的。爱面子是一种上进心，反映了梁漱溟所说的人生向上的意愿和动力，这种上进心和荣辱感乃是乡村的熟人社会特有的精神，它将私人道德最终提升到了村庄的公共道德，是儒家教化得以发生作用的前提。如果说良知是儒家教化发生作用的心性基础，爱面子则是儒家教化显效的社会动力，这两种力量结合起来，才最终造就了“君子之德风，小人之德草”的教化景观。反之，如果人连面子都不要了，那就变成了“我是流氓我怕谁?”，接下来便是“人要不要脸，神仙也难管”的哀叹了。

乡村儒学也让我们重新反思乡土文明中法治与德治的关系问题。孔子提出了“道之以德，齐之以礼”的治道理念，反对单纯“道之以政，齐之以刑”，这依然适合于当代的乡村。人必自治而能治之，古今中外皆然，乡村也不例外，中华文明固然正迈向民主法治时代，但是，这并不意味着要抛弃乡村历史悠久的德治传统。相反，德治是法治有效发生作用的必要前提。一位法院院长到农村蹲点，给农民讲法治，但农民死活不听，一见他就躲得远远的。他后来明白了："你所谓法治，就是要用法来治我的意思"，这一方面说明了我们当前的法治尚未落实到民权的保障上，而近乎孔子所说的"齐之以刑"，而农民对于什么是良治具有天然准确的判断力。另一方面，农民对于村主任召集的会议也兴趣索然，能躲就躲，这大概是出于同样的理由，如果说，法院是想"齐之以刑"，村主任是想"道之以政"，均遗失了孔子"道之以德，齐之以礼"的意蕴。民主法治之本意，在于划定群己权利边界，限定公权力的范围，提升社会的公共理性，这种现代法治与法家的法治南辕北辙，却与儒家的德治具有天生的亲和关系，因为它们皆以"己欲立而立人，己欲达而达人"和"己所不欲勿施于人"为宗旨，所不同者，现代法治为儒家的此一人道理想寻求到了更加理性化和制度化的实现形式，它并不否定社会的自律基础，反而是以此种自律为条件的。一个没有了起码道德自律的社会，不可能建成现代法治社会，就如同不可能在空中建起高楼大厦一样。当然，法治与德治，在农村治理中所起的作用并不完全等同，德以修身，法以治世；道德教化重在提升个体品德，法治重在解决公共事务。

因此，乡村儒学并不是单纯的复古，它尤其需要更化，传统儒家教化体系尽管有效，但它毕竟是小农时代的产物，具有鲜明的宗法社会的印记。但是，国家市场乃至于世界市场的形成，要求儒家在乡村的复兴也必须站在普遍人性和普适价值的出发点上。它应当拥有更为超验的神灵世界，它的神应该从祖神提升为人的神，以便为不同姓氏、肤色、种族和语言的人所信奉，并从家族道德理性提升为公共道德理性。这并不意味着要否定传统的宗祠文化，而是要促使它发生现代转变。比如广东已经出现了跨姓氏的祠堂，这是一个传统儒家组织与现代社会融合的典型例证。另外，儒学的组织和传播系统也要有新的变化，完成此种历史演变，既需要借鉴基督教、佛教的制度化经验，又要充分体现儒家特色。

那么，儒家教化体系的再生能够成功吗？乡村儒学能够承担起此一重大的历史使命吗？我们对此持有谨慎乐观的态度。无疑，重构儒家教化体系是一场历史性变革，是儒学三期的核心内涵。它意味着儒家的信仰系统、组织系统，传播系统和政教关系的全面革新，而此种改革的走向与成败，注定将成为中华民族未来命运的重要决定力量之一。乡村儒学只能从社会的最低端为此进行探索。目前的乡村儒学仍然是一项外来的事业，如何将儒学的软件重新植入乡村依然是一个挑战，这就要求实现由学者主导到村民主导的本质性转变，要求培育出新时代的儒家传道者，能够独立担负起向村民传播儒家教化的使命，只有这些条件具备了，重新形成乡村自发性和内生性的儒学传承体系的使命才算是完成了，也才能够为儒家教化体系的再生提供出一套乡土版经验。

# 国学教育的开展：国学系列公开课

《光明日报》国学版主编　梁　枢

由光明日报国学版策划发起的“国学系列公开课”项目，自2013年春开始实施，先后于孟子故里——邹城推出《孟子公开课》，在介子推故里——介休开讲《慈孝文化公开课》，在老子故里——涡阳举办《老子公开课》。在国学界众多学者的支持和参与下，国学系列公开课在公开课举办地引起关注，激活了名人故里的文化资源，有力地促进了当地的文化建设。同时，由于光明日报作为国内主流媒体的深度介入，以及其他媒体的宣传报道，公开课在中国社会各界产生了比较大的影响，成为当代具有重大文化意义和推广价值的新的国学教育方式。

## 一、什么是国学系列公开课？

国学系列公开课计划整合全国高校、地方政府、大型企业等各种社会资源，由国内二十余家高校国学机构等共同参与，通过在各高校及社会公共场合公开讲授国学课的形式，推进国学教育、普及国学知识、传承中华文化。国学系列公开课由光明日报国学版发起，并承担宣传推广之责。

附：

国学系列公开课第一课

孟子公开课课程安排

主办单位：山东师范大学齐鲁文化研究中心、邹城市人民政府、光明日报国学版

授课地点：邹城市择邻山庄会议中心

第一讲 从孔子到孟子（2013年4月27日上午）

主讲人：牟钟鉴（中央民族大学哲学与宗教学学院教授）

内容简介：孟子创造性地发展了孔子的思想。他把仁学与民生密切结合，高扬民本主义，确立了士人的独立性格，首倡心性之学。孟子是孔子之后儒家思想史上影响最大的思想家。

第二讲　孟子与齐鲁文化（2013 年 4 月 27 日下午）

主讲人：王志民（山东师范大学齐鲁文化研究中心教授）

内容简介：邹鲁之风与稷下气象影响了孟子思想的形成；孟子对齐鲁文化的提升与拓展发挥了重要作用。

第三讲 孟子其人其书（2013 年 5 月 11 日上午）

主讲人：颜世安（南京大学历史学系教授）

内容简介：典籍中所见孟子生平活动；战国初、中期的社会变动与孟子政治理想；孟子著述及编纂成书；《孟子》在中国古代思想史上的地位。

第四讲 居仁由义：从孟子的性善论说开去（2013 年 5 月 11 日下午）

主讲人：郭齐勇（武汉大学哲学学院暨国学院教授）

内容简介：孟子仁义并举，以“四端”之心阐发性善论；性善论的内涵、理论价值与现实价值；性善论在中国文化中的贡献。

第五讲 孟子的仁政思想（2013 年 5 月 25 日上午）

主讲人：李景林（北京师范大学哲学与社会学学院教授）

内容简介：从孔子论管仲谈起；道义至上与事功成就；论天人关系的超越性意义；道义功利一体论。

第六讲 孟子的民本思想（2013 年 5 月 25 日下午）

主讲人：王钧林（山东师范大学齐鲁文化研究中心教授）

内容简介：民本理念的起源与内涵；孟子对民本思想的新发展、新贡献；孟子民本思想的当代价值。

第七讲 孟子的为官之道（2013 年 6 月 8 日上午）

主讲人：梁涛（中国人民大学国学院教授）

内容简介：孟子倡导立志为先；孟子论述为臣如何对上进谏，对下关注民生。

第八讲 孟子的正气论（2013 年 6 月 8 日下午）

主讲人：颜炳罡（山东大学儒学高等研究院教授）

内容简介：孟子的“浩然之气”；“修天爵”、“尊良贵”、“养大体”的修养之术；居仁由义的“大丈夫”精神与创格完人；孟子修养论的历史影响与当代价值。

第九讲 题目：“国际正义观：孟子的‘王道’信念”

主讲人：王中江（北京大学哲学系教授）

内容简介：“战国”时期的国际局势：利益与冲突；天下秩序与“民意”；从强权、霸道到王道；“义战”与“国际干预”；孟子的王道思想。

第十讲 孟子是如何成为亚圣的（2013 年 6 月 22 日下午）

主讲人：徐洪兴（复旦大学哲学学院教授）

内容简介：孔子以后儒家学派的流变；外来思想文化的冲击与挑战；孟子升格运

动的兴起及演变过程；孟子升格运动的原因与目标；孟子升格运动的意义。

第十一讲 孟子思想的当代价值（2013年7月6日上午）

主讲人：王杰（中共中央党校哲学部教授）

内容简介：孟子注重大丈夫精神的培养，主张百善孝为先，强调民贵君轻。这些思想均具有重要的当代价值。

第十二讲 孟子思想在海外（2013年7月6日下午）

主讲人：林安梧（台湾慈济大学宗教与文化研究所教授）

内容简介：孟子思想海外传播概况；孟子思想在东亚；孟子思想在欧洲；孟子思想之于世界文化的贡献。

国学系列公开课兼有当前高校公开课的共同性，同时又有其独特性，主要体现在以下几个方面——

1. 授课形式。纳入高校教学计划或讲座计划。有条件的高校可以给予选课学生学分，条件暂不成熟的学校可以以讲座形式代替开课。国学公开课的可以走出校门，在开讲高校所在城市的文化馆、图书馆等场所进行公开讲授；亦可以邀请社会上的公众走入校园，坐进教室；还可以与诸如名人故里或历史文化名城的地方政府合作开办专题公开课。目前，高校校园的公开课正在筹划之中，已有华东师范大学、山东师范大学、曲阜师范大学提出合作意向；已经组织实施的公开课都是在名人故里举办的。

授课教师。以往的公开课一般由一门教师主讲，国学公开课则突破学院、学校壁垒，以相关课程最有权威性的海内外学者为主。

主办单位。于名人故里举办的国学系列公开课均由各司其职、相互协作的三个单位合作主办：光明日报国学版为策划发起单位，某大学院系所为教学单位，某名人故里当地政府为接地单位。

教学要求。国学系列公开课有一个总的指导原则及开设方案，每门课均有统一的教学大纲与教学日历。每门公开课都要事先召开备课会，由主办单位召集授课学者以讨论的方式确定讲什么，谁讲，每讲之间如何衔接。这样，每门课虽然有多位老师授课，且各讲各的内容，但散而不乱，按部就班地围绕一个主题，逻辑分工，循序推进，有始有终，形成一个相互衔接的有机整体。

授课对象。在大学校园，授课对象为本科生、研究生；在名人故里，是以五大班子为首的党政干部。人数达百名以上。

课程类型。一类为思想家：孔子、老子、庄子、墨子、孟子等；第二类为经典：《论语》、《周易》、《诗经》等；第三类为地域文化，如关学、湖湘文化等；第四类为专史专论，如孝文化、思想史等；

课时。每门公开课开设时间为一学期，每门公开课分12讲。每讲时间100分钟。国学公开课属于通识教育类选修课，有条件的学校可以纳入必修课，2学分。

讲授风格。科学严谨，求实创新，脱稿演讲，通俗易懂，欢快互动，幽默风趣。

## 二、为什么要搞国学系列公开课？

1. 提高全社会国学普及水平的需要。当前的国学教育多以民间书院与讲座为主，主要存在以下问题：单兵作战，讲国学或是学者个人行为，或是政府、企事业单位等机构组织的各种演讲。由于没有统一的教学目的、纲领与计划，造成内容上随机，没有连贯性，缺少整体性；有功利色彩，有的还收费不菲；总体层次低，虽有高校参与，但民间自称国学大师者居多，难以保证国学教育推广的科学性与严谨性；缺乏高水平的统一教材。国学公开课的推广有利于纠正以上弊端，改善当前国学教育的散乱局面，整合优势资源，提高国学教育质量。

2. 名人故里与历史文化名城推进文化建设的需要。文化名人是文化名人故里的最宝贵资源，是无可替代的光荣。文化名人的思想、精神历久弥新，直到 21 世纪的今天，仍然是中国之所以为中国的文化象征，仍然在中国乃至全世界产生深远的影响。利用这种宝贵资源，延续这种独特光荣，与时俱进，推进特色文化建设，为建设社会主义文化强国做出自己应有的贡献，是历史赋予文化名人故里的神圣使命。公开课项目通过高校与相关地方政府合作，把公开课开到名人故里去，让名人故里的干部群众更多地了解故里名人，全面深入地学习他的思想，让名人的精神在其故里发扬光大。这就是最好的城市特色文化建设，也是对故里名人最好的纪念。

3. 高校服务社会的要求。高校的国学课向社会公开，是让国学进出校门，把国学教学从校内扩展到社会。这种新型公开课将把只为校内学生的开设的优质国学教学资源，转化成可为社会大众所共享的公共资源。这是高等教育服务社会的直接体现，也是高校传承创新中华文化的具体实践。同时，高校开设国学公开课，必然带动该高校的人才培养、科学研究、服务社会、文化传承创新等水平的提升，从而提高高校社会影响力。

附：

### 光明日报：孟子公开课在孟子故里邹城开讲

邹城 4 月 27 日电（记者罗容海）由光明日报国学版发起，并与山东省邹城市人民政府、山东师范大学齐鲁文化研究中心联合主办的“国学系列公开课”第一课——孟子公开课今天在孟子故里山东邹城开讲。

开讲之前举行了简短的公开课启动仪式。邹城市委副书记、市长谢成海在致辞中指出，邹城古称“邹鲁圣地”，是国家历史文化名城、中国优秀旅游城市、全国综合实力百强县（市）。源远流长、博大精深的孟子学说，为中华民族精神的形成和发展做出了极其重要的贡献。特别是孟子的性善论、仁政学说以及君子人格思想，在当前仍然具有重要价值，是实现中华民族伟大复兴“中国梦”的重要思想资源。知名高校、媒体与地方政府合作，以公开课的方式让孟子思想回归故里，让孟子故里的干部群众更多地了解这位故里名人，全面深入地研究孟子的思想，并发扬光大，不仅是对孟子的最好纪念，也是传承儒家文化、推进国学教育、培养优秀人才的重要措施，必将对邹城加快名人故里特色文化建设，打响“孟子故里”文化品牌起到有力的推进作用。

中央民族大学教授牟钟鉴先生担任第一讲主讲人。他以“从孔子到孟子”为题，从传承与创新的思想史角度，梳理了儒学两大代表的思想演进过程。牟先生着重指出，孟子创造性地发展了孔子的思想。他把仁学与民生密切结合，高扬民本主义，确立了士人的独立性格，首倡心性之学。

山东师范大学齐鲁文化研究中心主任王志民指出，孟子是孔子之后最伟大的思想家之一，孔孟思想作为儒家核心思想成为中华传统文化的主干，长期以来对孔孟思想的研究已经成了国内外学术界的热点。此次公开课聘请了全国知名专家学者在孟子故里开讲孟子思想，是贯彻落实十八大精神的具体体现，抓住了名人故里文化建设的关键。

光明日报报副总编辑李春林参加了启动仪式。他指出，光明日报国学版倡议发起的国学公开课是一种新的国学教育的方式，旨在整合全国高校、地方政府等各种优势社会资源，改善当前国学教育的散乱局面，提高国学教育质量，有利于全社会国学普及。李春林表示，孟子是中华文化的核心人物，在孟子身上集中体现了大丈夫的浩然之气，集中体现了真理力量和人格力量的完美结合，孟子的道德文章正是中国精神、中国力量的重要源泉。孟子公开课在邹城的开讲，有助于站在延续中国文化的道统、承接中华民族文脉的高度，站在弘扬中国精神、凝聚中国力量的高度，持续推动孟子思想文化的继承和弘扬，让孟子思想文化在当代中国发挥重要而深远的社会效益，提升邹城人民的文化自觉、文化自信和文化自强。

据悉，孟子公开课的主讲教师分别来自北京大学等十几所重点高校，首批学员为邹城市的机关、学校、企业等单位的领导与职员。孟子公开课由相互连贯的12讲构成一个整体，其内容涵盖孟子的思想渊源、齐鲁文化与孟子、孟子其人其书、孟子思想的当代价值与海外影响等方面。

## 中青报：在邹城，听“孟子公开课”

近日，在山东邹城游走，恰逢此地举办“孟子公开课”，第一讲由中央民族大学教授牟钟鉴先生开篇。于是，走进会场做了一回旁听生。

老实说，虽身在孟子故里，但潜意识里，常常会对孔孟之道“不感冒”。要知道如今乃全球化的信息时代，地球村里的新知识层出不穷，谁有时间咀嚼两千多年前的那套伦理道统……

身着一袭中式灰褂的牟钟鉴先生，话语不疾不徐，却是开门见山：大半个世纪以来，从新文化运动，到新中国成立，到“文革”时期，孟子几乎一直被批判，然而“孔孟之道”打而不倒，绵延几千年，今天孔子学院已经走出国门，在106个国家的350多个教育机构落户，这是为什么呢？

先生的公开课也就个把小时，让人有所触动的却是他的开场白——

“‘文革’时给孟子扣了两顶帽子：其一，‘万物皆备于我’——典型的宣扬主观唯心主义；其二，‘劳心者治人，劳力者治于人’——鼓吹剥削阶级统治有理。”牟先生讲，其实“万物皆备于我”下面还有一句：“反身而诚，乐莫大焉。”孟子的原意是说，天地万物我都能够思考、认识，所以天地万物我都具备了；反躬自问，我所认识的一切都是诚实无欺的，所以非常快乐。接下来，先生要解释“劳心者治人，劳力者治于人”时，笔者忽然想起，一位著名的美籍华裔诺贝尔物理学奖获得者对此亦有自己的见解，大意是：我是在旧中国长大的，因此，想借这个机会向发展中国家的青年强调实验工作的重要性。中国有句古话“劳心者治人，劳力者治于人”，这种落后的思想，对青年有很大的害处。由于这种思想，很多发展中国家的学生都倾向于理论的研究，而避免实验工作……希望由于我这次得奖，能够唤起发展中国家的学生注意实验工作的重要性。

那么，物理学家对孟子名言的引用与理解是否就是孟子的原意呢？牟先生说，其实，孟子讲“劳心者治人，劳力者治于人”的前面还有一句：“且一人之身，而百工之所为备，如必自为而后用之，是率天下而路也。”然后才是“故曰，或劳心，或劳力；劳心者治人，劳力者治于人”。这其实是讲社会分工啊！用白话说就是，每一个人所需要的生活资料都要靠各种工匠的产品才能齐备，如果都一定要自己亲手做成才能使用，那就是率领天下的人疲于奔命。所以说：有的人脑力劳动，有的人体力劳动；脑力劳动者管理人，体力劳动者被人管理。

呵呵，什么叫似懂非懂、似是而非、自说自话啊？这回笔者真服了：不读原著，人云亦云，大科学家也会误读先贤的本意！晚上回到住处上网一查，这孟子名句的后面还有话呢——治于人者食人，治人者食于人，天下之通义也。即：被管理的养活人，管理人的被养活。平心而论，这真是典型的“民贵君轻”啊！

然而，孔孟之道绵延几千年，不只是当下，它却被人们一再误读！

“丢了仁，人还像人吗？这个社会还像人的社会吗？同时，义也不能丢，现在的人见利忘义，为了钱不择手段，丢了就乱了套，所以丢了是根本不行的。现在社会诚信缺失，我们都感到很痛苦，人与人之间冷漠，这都是因为没有仁、义造成的痛苦。而仁学是孔子、孟子及儒学的精华所在，是儒学实现理论现代转型最有价值的思想资源。”牟先生的分析直面现实。

由此又想到，在今天不少年轻人心目中，“孟子”已经成为一个被淡忘的历史符号。在孟子身上，我辈“知道分子”感觉的多是“陈腐”、“迂腐”、“过气”、“糟粕”，而牟先生却能拂去尘埃，看到“底蕴”、“根脉”、“浩然之气”。这种视角的差距，认知的差距，不仅仅缘于我辈对传统文化的误读与无知，同时还折射了人们对民族文化遗产的不同心态、不同情怀。从牟先生的公开课里，我们更听到了一个兼济天下的学者那种难得的民族自信、文化自觉的使命感。

# 卷　二

# 儒学与社会发展

# 目 录

## 卷二 儒学与社会发展

### 一、儒学与经济发展



### 二、儒学与生态

## 三、德治与法治



## 四、儒学的现代价值

# 一、儒学与经济发展

## 儒家思想的道義觀對企業經營之影響

高雄孔孟学会 李樑坚

### 一、緒論

道是一切自然的源頭，如何順道而行，一直是古人積極追求的路徑。義者，正理也，做人做事要循公理正義才是基本規範，也才能受到人們的認同及尊敬。而孔子在論語中所闡述的道義精神相當多，如“君子喻於義，小人喻於利”，一個不循正道的小人，只是汲汲營利，為了賺錢卻是不擇手段一點都不講道義，等到有一天事情爆發，不僅讓世人唾棄，更是有所批評，非人生之正確運作方向。

講求道義也是做人做事的根本，如果只為私利不顧道義，久而久之就會被人察覺，受到眾人指責或是背後暗罵，就算家財萬貫，也是不義之財。如同放高利貸業者，只想謀取暴利，而不顧別人死活，這種行徑並沒有得到善終，甚至在自作惡孽，禍害自己及子孫。因此論語顏淵篇提及仲弓問仁：“己所不欲，勿施於人”，自己面對同樣的困境，可是都遭受相當不合理的待遇，等到有一天自己也碰到了，那真是情何以堪。因此孔子強調要能為他人設身處地著想，如果自己有相同的狀況，那又會如何。然而在現今社會中，企業經營者有時為了賺錢，卻忘記作人的本分、做事的原則，以蒙騙的手段來欺瞞消費者，如胖達人麵包，廣告號稱純天然，可是都用了化學香精，等到消息被媒體報導出來，所有消費者都嚇到了，用高價買進的麵包，竟然被業者騙了，如此憤怒的心情將是不言可喻，當然消費者也就群起拒買，而胖達人的諸多主管及負責人，以及在公司股票中炒作獲利的人都被起訴吃上官司，就連知名藝人小 S 也被捲入代言不實的官司中，如此也映證“法網恢恢，疏而不漏”，千萬不要逞一時之快及貪念，想著一夕致富的慾望而種下錯誤的動機。當然企業經營者有時也想依循正道公義而行，可是看到別人競爭對手賺錢就起了貪慾之心，用了錯誤方法，來賣起黑心產品來了，如同大統沙拉油事件，負責人高振利董事長號稱地方慈善家，可是都是披了羊皮的狼，不僅用假油、混油來充當高級油品，從軍中、批發中心及一般消費者皆在不知情下買了一大堆黑心油品，不僅可能造成身體的病變，也賠了諸多的損失，如此損人利己的不公道、違背正義的作法，終究被舉報出來，也查封了負責人高振利的財產，更要面臨高額索賠及身陷囹圄之狀況。所以一個具有誠信的企業經營者，講究道義是經營企業的基本要件，也是永續經營的穩定內涵。

本研究將從孔子所著論語的道義佳句來闡述道義的基本精神和核心理念，並分析其運作的思維及探討對從事企業經營者的影響層面為何？另外也將列舉台灣發生的食安案例加以分析探討道義的重要性，最後提出在企業經營管理中，如何善用論語提出的話語當作運作圭臬的具體作法，以建立更為富含道義社會的企業環境。

## 二、論語中對於道義思維運用在企業經營之分析

孔子不僅是一位偉大的政治家、教育家，更是追求誠信和建立道義的實踐家，其平時言語的智慧，不僅可以發人深省，而幾千年的智慧傳承，歷經諸多朝代的演進變革，仍然可以屹立不搖，也代表其精神核心的一貫性，並具有長治久安的特性，可讓後人多加思考運用。

（一）生活居住觀：要跟有仁義道德者為鄰，才能提升自我的道德涵養，在論語里仁篇中提及子曰："里仁為美，則不處仁，焉得知"。

孔子說：人如果能跟有仁義道德的人做鄰居是很好的，如果選擇居處，而不會找有仁德的人作鄰居，怎能算是個有智慧的人呢？而如果住在不執行仁義道義的地方，這樣是很不智的。

管理意涵：良禽擇木而居，一個人選擇在那一個企業工作，乃是希望跟有誠信行事、有原則的同事及主管一起共事，如果周遭都是貪婪之徒，滿心詐騙而沒有誠信經營為目的，採用不擇手段的員工及老闆，這種公司如何待的下去呢？這種公司企業如何招到好的員工呢？而且有良好品性及仁義之人也不會想要來這種公司上班。

（二）個人價值觀：自己要體認合理的價值觀，自己不想要應該也不要施加於人，在論語顏淵篇中，子曰："己所不欲，勿施於人，在邦無怨，在家無怨"。

孔子說：自己不想要做的，也不要加諸在別人身上，這樣在社會上較無怨言，在家裡也較不會有抱怨。

管理意涵：一個人在工作職場上的行事作為及對待顧客都要以真誠的服務心態，而對待或管理員工，也能以合宜的態度相互要求，如此較能獲得別人的肯定與尊重。因為自己不想要面對的服務行為及態度，員工不喜歡的領導模式，就不要任意施加在別人身上，這樣在社會及家裡的互動也會較為合宜，也可以減少許多無謂的衝突。

（三）做人道德觀：所謂做人是要循公理正義而行，而不是一昧在追求自己的私利，在論語里仁篇中提及，子曰："君子喻於義，小人喻於利"。

孔子說：君子了解的是義理的重要，小人只知道如何爭取私利。

管理意涵：經營企業要建立的是長久的互動關係，因此講究誠信道義相當重要，如果只追求短暫的小利，而成為一種小人行徑，就相當得不償失，也無法讓企業建立可長可久的發展基礎。

（四）誠信道德一貫性：做人做事要本諸誠信，具有道德感，才能安身立命，在論語子張篇中提及"君子之道，焉可誣也？有始有卒者，其惟聖人乎！"。

孔子說：君子之道不能隨便加以誣衊扭曲！有始有終的人就是聖人啊！

管理意涵：對於個人修身立業所堅持的準則沒有大小之別，都是要加以遵守的，所謂誠信和道德誰先誰後呢？其實都是差不多的，沒有先後次序，都是在管理企業重要立事、立業根本。只有小人才會加以區別，要先遵行那一個準則，給自己下台階找藉口，這是不對的，也是自我怠惰的開始，所以皆要認真地自我約束，努力以赴，才是自我管理首要之務。

（五）結交朋友之道：要多結交具有仁義道的的人，這樣自己的品行、品格就不會受到汙染，在論語衛靈公篇提及："群居終日，言不及義，好行小慧，難矣哉！"

孔子說：整天在一起生活，可是談話的內容都缺乏仁義，而且喜歡賣弄小聰明，這就很困難可以自我提昇了。

管理意涵：所謂近朱者赤、近墨者黑，如果一天到晚混在一起，相處在一起的工作夥伴，談話都沒有什麼內容及深度，則自己的能力及學識要成長的機會就很難了，久而久之，自己也會很墮落，愈來愈不進入狀況，在工作職場上就很快會被淘汰掉了。

（六）追求有正道的人一起合作相處："所謂近朱者赤，近墨者黑"，人要跟有正義道德多相處及合作，則做人做事也會較符合社會常規，在論語衛靈公篇提及："道不同，不相為謀"。

孔子說：對於道的想法不同，就不要在一起共事。

管理意涵：對於企業經營過程中，一般人都希望找到志同道合的人，能一起合作共事，在理念及想法上也比較容易溝通，而且在推動一些事務上也比較不會產生溝通上的落差，也較能在相同價值觀下去完成企業的目標。

（七）講話誠信的重要性：一個人所言要能被肯定及接受，如此才能被信賴，公司經營企業也才有合作的基礎，在論語學而篇提及，子曰："信近於義，言可復也：恭近於禮，遠恥辱也；因不失其親，其可宗也"。

孔子說：與人講話有信用，符合道義之精神，講話才能執行；對別人恭敬有禮，符合道德規範，才可以避免遭受恥辱。所以跟可靠有信用的人來往，互動過程才可以靠得住。

管理意涵：與別人互動往來要講究信用，這樣以後跟別人談生意或要履約，別人才會信服。跟人交往要有一定的互動禮節，不能過度隨便，而不尊重別人，這樣人家也才會以禮相待，而不會被別人看不起，故意給你難堪。因為跟正直可靠、講話有信用的人經常來往，所以別人也會有相同信賴感，所謂近朱者赤，近墨者黑，就是這個道理。

（八）行為要以道義為依歸，不要過度講究私利：一個人所作所為，如果只看到利害關係是很現實的，如此獲致的感受及評價應該不會太好，在論語里仁篇提及，子曰："放於利而行，多怨"。

孔子說：每個人完全依照利害關係來做事，是很容易招來別人的抱怨

管理意涵：經營企業完全依照利益關係來作為決策因應準則，缺乏一些互動及關懷的心境，縱然事業有賺錢，也不容易交到真心的好朋友，別人也會覺得這個企業毫無同情心或有朋友道義。一旦有碰到一些不好狀況，也會遭受到別人無情的對待，因此要能創造雙贏，對往來的廠商有時也可以稍微犧牲一點，存有一點同情心或江湖道義，可以適度協助度過難關才有好的企業商譽。

（九）立基根本在於道德仁義，企業立基要有核心理念及精神，而道德仁義是企業經營的核心根本，在論語述而提及，子曰："志於道，據於德，依於仁，游於藝"。

孔子說：要立志求道，立基根德，行事靠仁義，而悠遊於在禮、樂、射、御、書、數等六藝之中。

管理意涵：企業經營要有經營願景及基本立業根本，講究仁義誠信是基本精神，而且自我不斷創新求變，以因應市場環境的變革，而且在管理技能方法也要不斷自我學習，才能提昇整體團隊效能，尤其員工如能堅守基本原則，誠信對待顧客，並且學習多元化的應用知識及技能，如此才能因應競爭對手的加入及挑戰而不會快速崩解，進而屹立不搖。

（十）明辨是非，不要過度鄉愿：企業做事及經營不能太過鄉愿，否則便宜行事，終究影響信譽的還是自己，在論語陽貨篇中提及，子曰："鄉愿，德之賊也！"

孔子說：鄉里間那些不能明辨是非的人，是敗壞倫理道德的小人啊！

管理意涵：在公司做事，有時候總是礙於同事情誼，很多事情就便宜行事，破壞規則，久而久之，也就形成一種文化而無法改變，結果許多應該要發揮效能展現績效的時候就無法達成，如此公司團隊競爭力也就愈形下降，因此身為主管或上司應該要堅持原則，否則倫理道德一旦流失就很難挽回了。

（十一）講話要有誠信，所謂人而無信，不知其可也，一個人如果沒有信用，那如何獲致別人的信賴，從企業經營角度來說，更是自斷生路，企業沒有信用做基礎，那

誰敢跟你做生意，而且一旦信用關係崩解，要再重建談何容易，因此想追求永續發展的企業主話講出去，就很難收回，就算賠錢做生意，也要咬牙苦撐，如此才能贏得別人對你的信賴，否則講話反反覆覆，不知真正的想法如何，那彼此雙方如何建立信賴關係呢？孔子在論語子路篇中就提及，“言必信，行必果，硜硜然小人哉”。孟子也說“大人者，言必信，行不必果，唯義所在”，而仁義是彼此環環相扣的，孔子曰：“仁者，義之本也；義者，仁之節也，仁者人也；道者，義也”，可見到忠義以誠信為本質的重要性。

## 三、台灣發生食安之道德危機案例與企業經營之關係分析

**食安案例一：鼎王公司**

鼎王公司陳世明原先從夜市賣火鍋起家，而後陳世明老闆自行研發創新以多種中藥結合火鍋湯底形成特色，並在客人吃完後，主動加湯讓客人帶回，因此生意相當不錯，並且已規畫準備上市，然而就在上市前遭人爆料，火鍋湯底及豆腐專業工廠並沒有按照宣傳所做，並以雞湯塊做湯底，而非完全天然及中藥材，一開始陳世明左閃右躲，而後被一再檢視查核，跟宣傳有很大落差，因此在整個火鍋市場頓失信譽，生意大幅下降，上市也不能完成。原先鼎王的獲利相當可觀，可是負責人一念之差，把自己累積顧客對其信賴蕩然無存，“一步錯，滿盤錯”的決策行為，實在非常可惜，而企業要重新再出發就相當困難。

案例分析：企業經營之持續成長對負責人是一種挑戰，有些企業主為了賺錢就不擇手段，把原先標榜的信用誠實就拋在腦後，一旦被察覺顧客感覺受騙，就以拒置或拒吃作為抗議，結果企業就面臨倒閉及減低業績之困境，真是得不償失，可見企業誠信不是空口說說，是要一路走來始終如一，才能獲致顧客的具體認同及支持。

**食安案例二：胖達人事件**

胖達人是由基因食品公司投資，董事長徐洵平以標榜純手工無香料製作的高價值麵包，並邀請知名藝人小S進行代言，一時之間在全台灣及中國大陸造成轟動，因為標榜天然、健康，因此麵包單價不低，結果香港顧客消費感受怪怪的，因此提出質疑，而一經查證，所謂天然的香料就是化學香料，顧客一聽全民譁然，更為可惡的是，基因公司因為投股胖達人麵包，因此股價大幅攀高，有些人從中謀取暴利，等到事情被爆發出來，許多顧客相當不高興，雖然胖達人同意顧客憑發票可以退貨，可是對其商譽及商品信心已經打擊很大，生意大不如前，最後胖達人已經倒了幾家，企業運作榮景已經無法恢復。

案例分析：公司企業要善用顧客對其購買高價商品的支持態度，既然強調天然、

健康，就要持續貫徹，不能為了省錢，就自毀前程，好不容易累積的形象破壞殆盡。更為可惡的是，有人卻由不當行銷而從中獲取暴利自肥，這些皆不是民眾可以接受的，所以身為企業負責人，要珍惜得之不易的品質及信用，一旦被顧客唾棄，就回不去了。

**食安案例三：大統沙拉油事件**

位於彰化彰濱工業區境內的大統沙拉油觀光工廠，不僅全台銷量相當大，標榜的高價油品包括橄欖油等，竟然用其他棉籽油替代，不僅罔顧民眾消費安全，並從中謀取暴利，而且大量銷售至軍中、批發中心十幾年，這種作法被員工舉報出來，全國譁然，也引起諸多討論及撻伐，對於負責人高振利賺取不當獲利，並經由民代做依靠關心之作法相當不齒，因此經由法院的提告，除了將其財產沒入外，也經由相關受損民眾提起告訴求償，原先一年獲利幾億的公司，在一夕之間就宣告破產，真是情何以堪。

案例分析：原先知名企業的運作及管理，絕大多數民眾都選擇相信，可是企業主濫用民眾對其的信賴，而將食品內容混搭及混用，其目的只是想降低成本，而賺取暴利，這種為了錢不管民眾健康的負責人，不僅讓人憤慨，對其人格更是不能忍受，而在捐贈做慈善的作為更是認為是披著羊皮的狼，而這種負責人完全以”利益”為依歸，就是一個真小人、偽君子，一旦被爆發出來，了解其真面目，企業想要東山再起，就難上加難。

根據三個食安案例之分享，我們可以瞭解到，”道義”對企業經營的重要性，一旦違背公理正義，民眾在了解真相後，是會以實際行動來展現對不良企業之反撲，這跟論語提及之諸多思維不謀而合。

自我修養面：“己所不欲，勿施於人”就是最好的寫照

道德提升面：孟子主張要培養法然正義，士大夫要“貧賤不能移”，有仁義的人要“殺身成仁，捨生取義”，孔子也說：“仁者，義之本也!”

人格操守：子曰“仁者不憂”，有仁義的人，不會受到物質引誘，也能安於貧賤，而不會貪求富貴，而犧牲自己的仁義道德之心

知人之道：子曰“眾好之，必察焉”，大家都認為好的，就要好好仔細觀察，有些企業善於包裝行銷，結果是包藏禍心

重視誠信：子曰“言必信，行必果，硜硜然小人哉!”，講話誠信是做人做事的基本要求，而且言行合一，才能符合社會的要求

## 四、道義觀念如何融入在企業經營理念中

道義是經商之基礎要件，如何有效將其融入在企業經營之體質中，以下提出幾個作法加以說明如下：

1. 表揚“企業社會責人（CSR)”：以提昇社會大眾對其認同，並對企業善盡CSR者，給予適當的表揚，並透過報章雜誌媒體作具體宣傳。

2. 發揚儒商的影響力：儒商的特性就是以孔孟思維作為核心經營理念，發揚善的精神及道義的本質，以作為全世界的典範。

3. 對不法所得的企業主予以重懲及處罰：有些企業主不惜鋌而走險，而賺取不法之錢，一旦被察覺查獲，就要予以重罰，以正視聽。

4. 鼓勵員工舉報企業不法情形：許多食安事件之爆發，諸多皆是由有良心的員工加以舉報真相才能被揭露，因此政府也要鼓勵員工之行為。

5. 政府要加強查核及管理：政府之職責是為安全性把關，善盡人民保障之職責，因此要對企業加強查核及管理，以減少不當行為及事件之發生。

## 五、結語

道義是一切正理的源頭，不能遵守義理，如何有效經營企業，就算一時獲利也是心驚膽顫，所以孔子在論語主張的以及提出之至理名言“己所不欲，勿施於人”、“君子喻於義，小人喻於利”，這些皆是歷經千古運作及社會過程的考驗，表示其精神是可以發揚光大，也是企業經營者要引以為榮的不變法則，而諸多失敗的案例及經營思維探討，皆已驗證孔子在論語主張且可以經得起考驗，並能放諸四海而皆準。企業經營主把道義放在心中，也要落實在企業經營的圭臬中，並視為核心價值，才能引以為戒，視為自我警惕的核心思維，因為沒有道義做根本，諸多企業經營只能淪落成為私利的掠奪，缺乏善意的體現，就算賺了錢，也不是很正當，如何搬上檯面。所以能本諸道義的原則做出發，如此行事作為才能安心無懼，也才能達到永續經營之目標。

**參考文獻：**

[1] 宋一霖. 儒家道義新解. 中山大學出版社.

[2] 李林. 食品老闆都要學習儒家道義. 慧聰網企業管理頻道，2012.12.15.

[3] 儒家的道義承擔：困境是“道”與“勢”衝突. 中華讀書報，2010.1.21.

[4] 儒家文化促進經濟發展的若干進路. 哲學動態，2012.11.2.

[5] 劉凌：儒家的道義承擔. 中國網，2010.1.26.

# 儒学对当代经济和社会发展的影响

苏州工业园区鸿坤环境工程公司　谢　兵

当代经济和社会发展，离不开儒家思想的指导，每个人都必须具有社会责任心和道德修养，责任重于泰山，厚德才能载物。我们已经进入21世纪，21世纪是一个充满挑战的世纪，经济全球化趋势必将给我们带来巨大的冲击，科学进步与社会文明的发展日益成为人们关注的话题。面对我们具有五千年文明史的中华民族和泱泱古国传统文化的深厚积淀，感受着现当代社会文化融合带给我们的芬芳。源远的儒家思想无时无刻不在影响着我们，使我们树立远大理想，激扬爱国之志，陶冶情操。从先秦诸子的天人之辩，到汉代董仲舒“天人合而为一”命题的提出，再到宋明理学家“万物一体”论的形成，犹如一条红线贯穿了中华民族传统文化的主流观念，这种主流观念对于中华民族的形成、发展和凝聚，起到了积极的作用。在社会主义文化百花齐放的今天，走建设有中国特色的社会主义，继承和发扬中华民族传统文化，剔除其封建宗法和唯心主义，弘扬其整体、和谐、统一的合理内容，树立严谨的人文科学发展观，进而使先进的文化传统得到繁荣和升华，实现习总书记提出的中华民族伟大复兴的远景梦想，显得尤为重要和紧迫。

## 一、儒家思想对当代社会发展影响的两面性

儒家思想对促进社会更加文明进步，尤其是对现代经济发展有着重要的积极因素。中国社会数千年的发展史，特别是在长期的君主专制社会中这样告诉我们，无论是思想观念、伦理道德、学术、教育、宗教、文学艺术、科学技术、典章制度、文物宝藏，还是衣食住行、风俗习惯等等，都与儒家思想的继承和发展息息相关。儒家文化是中国历史文明的主流，儒家思想在中华民族传统文化中是最富有生命力的思想体系，对中国的经济、政治、文化领域产生着广泛而深远的影响，也曾是中国封建社会的统治思想及精神支柱，对中华民族的民族精神、民族性格和民族心理的形成起过重要作用。这已经成为民族生命传承的纽带，积淀在民族的心灵里，流淌在民众的血液中。儒家

文化中深藏着值得认真研究和弘扬的适合于现代化经济发展的积极因素，而且市场经济越向前发展，越能够为儒家文化作用的发挥提供更广阔的空间。因此丰富儒家文化中可以适应和促进市场经济发展的思想内涵，对之进行与时俱进的整合，使儒家文化作为一种软资源去为中国特色市场经济的健康发展服务，不失为当前的明智之举。但是，当着人们在儒家思想传承的过程中，也难免精华与糟粕杂陈。时至今日，仍然有许多糟粕束缚着人们的思想，影响着社会发展。其负面影响主要有以下两个方面。

1. 受君主专制制度和专制主义思想的影响。在中国历史上，春秋战国时代思想最为活跃。诸侯国日益强大，逐鹿中原，争霸称雄，征战不已。知识分子受到很大重视，“重士”、“征士”、“养士”成为一种风气，思想相当活跃。他们对社会的各种问题以及自然界进行了新的观察探讨，出现“处士横议”、“百家争鸣”的盛况，形成儒、墨、道、法、阴阳、名辩、纵横、兵、农、杂家及史家等各种学派，互相争论诘难，又互相吸收补充，有力地促进了思想文化的发展，为以后中国思想和文化的发展演变奠定了坚实的基础。后来的思想如两汉经学、魏晋玄学、隋唐佛学、宋明理学、清代汉学或实学等，对思想观念、伦理道德、哲学宗教、学术理论等都有所发挥或发展。但是，这种发展越到后来也越为缓慢，乃至成为八股教条而僵化，科举考试只能在经书中寻章摘句作文章，特别是尊卑贵贱，君道臣节，专制主义尤为严重，这也是影响当代社会人文思想的根源所在。中国君上专制的历史很长，从商代开始，君主就自称“余一人”，以示其独尊无二。周代君主称为“天子”，开始“奉天承运”，管治兆民。春秋战国时，法家主张君主专制独裁和中央集权。在传统的治国之道中，儒家主张仁政德治礼教，被称为“王道”。法家强调“不贵义而贵法”，“以法为本”“以法为教”被称为“霸道”。其实两者并不是截然对立，而是相通互补的。孔子在《论语》中说：“道之以政，齐之以刑，民免而无耻。道之以德，齐之以礼，有耻且格。”这当然是肯定德政礼制，否定政刑。但是，他又称赞法家的代表人物郑国大臣子产的“宽猛相济”。孔子说：“善哉！政宽则民慢，慢则纠之以猛；猛则民残，残则施之以宽。宽以济猛，猛以济宽，政是以和。”所谓“猛”，即最严刑酷法，不惜民残的。“宽猛相济”，亦可谓德法互补、礼刑结合，这种传统的影响也很大，以后儒法结合即源于此。这种中央集权的专制政治对后世有深远的影响。到了秦始皇，依据法家学说，厉行法制，富国强兵，削除六国，建立起中央专制集权的统一大帝国，废除分封，实行郡县制，采取车同轨、书同文，统一度量衡，颁布严厉的刑法，建立起绝对皇权。西汉初年，鉴于秦法繁苛，以致很快灭亡的教训，曾实行“黄老之术”，“与民休养生息”，但仍坚持了秦朝的法制原则。以后历代的儒法互补、儒法结合、外儒内法等，实际上都是“宽猛相济”，“霸王道杂之”，这是中国文化传统中的基本传统。正是由于这种专制的长久性和固有性，使得我们很容易在当代社会生活中看到它的影响，如特权思想、家长制作风、官僚主义、以权代法、权大于法、贪污腐败等种种现象也就顺理成章。

2. 受儒家思想长久的文化专制氛围的束缚。在中国古代，文化专制的传统也是相当长久的。春秋战国虽然是百家竞说，互相争论诘难，又互相影响吸收，但是仍然出现了异样的声音。如孔子说的“攻乎异端，斯害也已”和孟子的“辟杨墨”即是。秦王朝建立后，秦始皇废封建改郡县制，是个进步。但是他接受李斯的建议，实行“焚书坑儒”，成为文化专制主义的开端。董仲舒向汉武帝建议“罢黜百家”，“独尊儒术”。虽然“坑”与“尊”正相反，但君主统治的文化专制则是一样的。从汉代起，历代王朝实行的多是儒法结合，或曰“外儒内法”、“霸王杂之”，而在思想文化方面又有儒释道结合，但孔子儒家思想的地位仍然高高在上。儒家被视为官学，科举考试只能在经书中寻章摘句作文章，八股教条严重束缚了人们思想的发展。最为严重的还有文字狱，统治者可以从奏议文书乃至诗词、书信中寻找某些词句任意歪曲，制造冤狱，杀头或流放。从秦始皇“焚书坑儒”开始，到以后的历朝历代文字狱愈演愈烈，严重阻碍了社会思想文化的进步。近代中国的落后和所经历的屈辱无不是这种专制思想束缚的结果。20 世纪以来，中国人为摆脱外国列强压迫和国内专制统治，进行了长期英勇顽强的斗争，同时努力向西方国家学习，引进民主民权、自由平等、进化论、人权说，进行过变法，发动过革命，推翻帝制，建立了民国，宣布国家主权属于“全体国民”，具有伟大历史意义。但是并未能改变专制统治，专制主义和专制思想可谓根深蒂固。五四新文化运动热情宣扬民主和科学，宣传人格独立、人权平等、个性解放、思想自由，向封建专制主义及其意识形态发动了猛烈进攻，反对旧思想、旧道德、旧文学，发出“打倒孔家店”的呼声，有力地促进了人们特别是广大青年的思想解放，发现自我，追求真知，探索改造中国社会的出路。但是由于民族危机的加深，这个启蒙运动未能彻底进行下去。毛泽东就曾说过，五四运动时期反对旧思想、旧道德、旧文学，提倡民主和科学，立下了伟大的功绩，但是，那时还只是开始。要使全国人民完全摆脱封建专制主义的统治，还须费很大的力气，还是今后革命改造路上的“一个大工程”。邓小平在总结新中国成立以来经验教训时曾说过：旧中国留给我们的，封建专制传统多，民主法制传统很少。新中国成立以后，我们也没有自觉地、系统地建立保障人民民主权力的各种制度，法制很不完备，也很不受重视。他还谈道，在我们党政机关存在的特权、家长制、官僚主义、以权代法、贪污腐败等都带有封建主义色彩。所以，他提出肃清封建主义传统影响，“解放思想”，“重点是切实改革并完善党和国家的制度。从制度上保证党和国家政治生活的民主化、经济管理的民主化、整个社会生活的民主化，促进现代化建设事业的发展。”这是非常重要的，应该逐步贯彻实行。

## 二、儒家思想对当代社会生活的积极影响

儒家思想的传承，除去糟粕外，仍有许多精华对当代社会生活的发展具有积极影响，应该给予肯定。我认为儒家思想在关于人的问题上表现的积极作用更为突出。在儒家思想的形成和完善的过程中，对于人生价值的内涵、类型、层次、标准等问题，都有充分而精辟的论述，这些是构成中国传统文化的核心内容。儒家思想的人生价值观包含着对人的内在价值和外在价值的观点，包含着怎样做人，怎样实现个人价值的看法。人不是孤立的存在，每个人都处在一定的社会关系中，也与一定的自然环境发生联系。怎样做人，实质上就是怎样对待自己，以及怎样对待与自己构成相互作用的其他三组基本关系。这三组关系是：与他人的关系、与民族和国家的关系、与自然环境的关系。一个人的人生价值正是通过对待自我、他人、民族和国家以及自然的关系而实现的。

1. 关于人与自我的关系。人与自我的关系是一个人格塑造的问题，人格也就是古人所说的人品。什么是具有崇高人格的人，怎样才能达到和保持崇高的人格？这是古代思想家所热心讨论的一个中心问题，孔子说："三军可夺帅也，匹夫不可夺志也。"强调人人应具有独立的意志，也就是肯定人人都具有独立人格。孟子说："富贵不能淫，贫贱不能移，威武不能屈，此之谓大丈夫。"所谓大丈夫的崇高人格，就是始终如一地坚持自己的原则，在任何情况下都决不动摇。庄子也提倡崇高人格，他说："至人神矣！大泽焚而不能热，河汉冱而不能寒，疾雷破山、飘风振海而不能惊。"认为至人具有不受任何环境影响的独立精神和自主精神。庄子还提倡追求"天地与我并生，而万物与我为一"的精神境界，主张从万物平等无差别，即没有价值区别的理念出发，超越自我，以与天地同在。儒家认为一个人的生命价值与道德价值、人格价值相比较，道德价值和人格价值更为重要，孔子的"杀身成仁"和孟子的"舍生取义"，就是儒家为了保全仁义道德价值而不惜牺牲个人生命的典型表述，这些论述对后世深远影响。不难看出要正确对待自己，塑造崇高人格，最关键的就是要正确对待生命与道德、人格的关系。一个人的人格尊严是生命中最为宝贵的、人格尊严超过了生命价值。

2. 关于人与他人的关系。人与他人的关系是关于人伦与群己的关系问题。古代思想家，尤其是儒家学者提倡人与人应当互相亲爱，以保持人际关系的和谐，并对人伦的准则与规范有着详细的论述。荀子论述人类合群的必要性时提出"群道"的概念，他认为，人所以能群，在于有职分与道义；合群是人类能够战胜万物的保证。荀子重视合群之道，强调对待他人的方法要得当，这就为妥善对待自己与他人、个体与群休的关系提供了社会学的依据。儒家思想的仁、礼、和、义、信，就是关于人与他人关

系的准则与规范。“仁”，是孔子伦理道德的最高准则，其含义是“爱人”“泛爱众”。孔子解释说：“夫仁者，已欲立而立人，已欲达而达人”，人我具立，人我具达，也即是人人和谐。孔子提倡爱人，但又承认等级差别。墨子主张兼爱，谓“爱人若爱其身”，“视人之室若其室”，认为应当不分远近亲疏地爱一切人。孔子的爱人和墨子的兼爱都表现了崇高的人道主义精神。“礼”是古代的社会规范和道德规范。孔子重视礼，说：“不知礼，无以立。”认为必须知礼才能自立，自立然后才能立人。他又说：“克己复礼为仁”主张克制自己的言行，使之符合礼，以达到仁的境界。也即以礼待人，尊敬他人。应有的礼节、礼貌还是维系人与人之间关系的重要行为规则。儒家以“和”为价值的中心原则，“以他平他谓之和”，“和”是不同事物相互联系、会聚而得其平衡，也就是多样性的统一。此外“义”的基本意义是公正，公正是对待他人应有的规范。“信”则是诚实、信用、守信。认为朋友之间应当遵守信用。信用是基本的道德规范，是任何时代最起码的公共生活规则。

3. 关于个人与民族和国家的关系。中华民族正处在伟大民族复兴的进程之中。民族的复兴必然与民族文化的复兴相关联，而 儒学在我国历史上曾居于主流地位，影响着我国社会生活的方方面面。因此，儒学的复兴和中 华民族的复兴是分不开的，这是由历史原因形成的。儒学自孔子起就自觉地继承着夏、商、周 三代的文化，从历史上看它曾是中华民族发育、成长的根，我们没有可能把这个根子斩断。如 果我们人为地把中华民族曾经赖以生存和发展的根子斩断，那么中华民族的复兴就没有希望了。我们不能在没有文化传统的空地上建设“ 和谐社会”。我们只能适时地在传承这个文化命脉的基础上，使之复兴，为建设“和谐社会”提供精神力量。民族是历史形成的一定人们组成的共同体，中华民族是由多民族汇合而成的统一体。国家既指政权，也指该政权治理范围内的国土和人民。中国自古以来就有一个以关心社稷民生，维护民族独立和捍卫中华文化为基本内容的爱国主义传统，以爱国主义为人生的崇高价值。中国古代还提倡“忠”，忠的原则是对别人尽心尽责。到了汉代以后转义为对国君尽忠，强调对君主的绝对服从，以维护君主专制。辛亥革命推翻了君主专制，废除了君主，尽管对儒家思想的“忠”我们曾一度存在偏见，但是在当代社会我们应大力提倡的“忠”，是忠于民族、忠于祖国，忠于人民的忠，是责任心、事业心的体现。忠于民族、忠于祖国、忠于人民是每一个国民的崇高职责。

4. 关于人与自然的关系。人与自然的关系如何、人应当怎样对待自然是人类社会必须首先和着重解决的问题，也是历来中国哲学探讨的一个根本问题。古代所论“天人之际”的“天”含义多样，一般是指自然界，“人”指人类，“天人之际”主要就是讲人与自然的关系。孟子最早提出“知性则知天”的天人统一思想，认为人性是天赋的，天与性相通，知性也就能知天。董仲舒提出“人副天数”说，宣传人体结构与天体结构相副的“天人相类”的观点。张载明确提出“天人合一”的命题，强调天道与人性的统一。至于“天人之分”说，主要有荀子的“制天命而用之”的说法，含有征服自然的思想。再就是刘禹锡的“天人交相胜”说，认为天与人各有特殊的功能，自然界的自然规律与人类社会的道德准则是不同的。应当指出，“天人合一”说，是侧重于宣扬天人的统一，但并不排斥天人的区别，而承认区别正是强调统一的前提。此外，在人对待自然的态度上，儒家思想还有“因任自然说”，即自然界是和谐美好的，应当排斥一切人为，以免破坏自然状态。“控制自然说”，即主张治理自然，利用万物以提高人类的物质生活。“相互协调说”，即要重视自然变化及其规律的客观性，掌握自然规律，又要发挥人类的主观能动作用，调节自然的变化，协助万物获得完满的成就。这是把人与自然的关系视为相辅相成的关系，以人与自然的协调和谐为最高理想。综观上述四个方面，是中国传统文化，特别是儒家思想关于人生价值以及实现人生价值的基本观点，它构成了互相联系的统一的人生价值观。正确对待自己是正确对待他人、民族和国家以及自然的基础，而一个人人生价值的完满实现，又是通过正确处理与他人、民族和国家以及自然的关系体现出来的，这也就是说，借鉴“天人合一”的整体性思想实现自身价值与服务祖国人民是统一的。

5. 关于“天人合一”的辩证统一思想。儒家“天人合一”的观念将会为解决“人与自然”之间的矛盾提供某些有意义的思想资源。人与自然的和谐发展一直是中国古人心目中的社会理想。儒家用“天人合一”这一命题来概括人与自然的关系。天人合一即肯定人与自然界的统一，亦即人与自然界不是敌对的关系，而是具有不可割裂的关系，就是要充分尊重自然，平等地对待人与自然，使人与自然达到高度和谐，协调发展。

《易传》提出天人合德的理想：“夫大人者，与天地合其德，与日月合其明，与四时合其序，与鬼神合其吉凶。”与天地合德即谓人具有天地品德，与自然界相互适应、互利共生。孟子将天道与人性联系起来，认为人性是天赋的，他说：“尽其心者，知其性也，知其性则知天矣。”宋代大儒程颢强调：“仁者，以天地万物为一体莫非己也。”还说：“仁者，浑然与物同体。”

可见，儒家文化视域内的天人合一就是人与自然界的对立统一，是把人和自然界看作是休戚与共的共同体，既不是原始蒙昧状态下的天人混一，只是自然界作用于人，也非西方所谓“战胜自然”、“克服自然”。一方面，人在自然界面前具有能动性，人是天地之灵明，天地无思无虑化成万物而无心，但人要有思有虑，有悲悯有忧患，要投身到天地生化万物的过程当中去，无私的化育万物。正所谓“先天而天弗违”，就是敢于和善于先天时而动，大胆创新，预见自然规律以指导人们的行动。另一方面，人又不能凌驾于自然之上，面对外界麻木不仁，随意戕害、践踏自然生灵，而要做到“后天而奉天时”，即遵循自然变化按规律办事，能够认识和正确运用自然规律。

现代化是一个充满悖论特征的过程。在人类消受工业文明所带来的物质财富的时候，也逐渐面临前所未有的困境和难题。西方资本主义国家在实现工业化的过程中走的是一条先污染后治理的道路，尤其是二战后，虽然世界各国都把发展作为主题，但是却一度把经济的增长等同于发展，单纯追求 GDP 的扩张，在开发和利用自然资源的能力空前提高的同时，也造成了一些对于科学技术使用不当所导致的严重后果，环境污染与生态破坏使人类陷入生存困境。20 世纪 80 年代，联合国首次使用“可持续发展”的概念，以后这一概念得到逐渐明确和完善其核心思想是经济的增长不能超过资源、环境的承载能力，社会经济的增长既要考虑当前发展的需要，又要考虑未来发展的需要，不要以牺牲后代人的利益为代价来满足当代人的利益。直到今天，环境污染、生态破坏、资源枯竭、能源危机和气候异常等问题依然是人类所共同面对的全球性问题。

在中国，这些问题随着市场作用的逐渐发挥也日益凸显出来。新时期，中国最显著的成就就是快速发展，但基本上走的是一条高投入、高污染、高排放和高消耗的发展道路，在经济总量跃居世界前列的同时，也出现了人与自然关系的紧张。在人与自然的矛盾中，人是矛盾的主要方面，因为造成污染的是人，治理环境、保护生态还要靠人，有效引导市场的力量，化解人与自然的冲突终究要靠人的努力。这当然需要制度、科技、模式和流程的创新，但首先要端正观念，解放思想，思想的解放最终会落脚在实践的解放上。把中国老百姓喜闻乐见的儒家“天人合一”的整体性思想与可持续发展的现代文明理念相融合并引入市场机制，以“天下万物无一物非我”的宽广胸怀体察个人与宇宙的关系，把握人与自然的整体统一，促进人与自然的和谐，才能引领中国市场经济的正确发展，才能走上完善市场机制的康庄大道，才能实现经济社会的永续发展。

## 三、儒家思想“以义为上，厚德载物”的核心价值

井然有序是市场经济的内在要求，建立和维持秩序既需要法治，也需要德治。市场经济不仅是一种法制经济，需要法律的制约，而且也是一种道德经济，需要道德的规范。使市场经济从无序走向有序，除了采取法律手段外，从价值取向上，继承和弘扬儒家的“义以为上，厚德载物”的义利观念，也是一剂对症良药。

在儒家文化中，义利之辩是一个永恒的主题。所谓“义”，是指社会的公共福利；所谓“利”，是指个人的功利。为了个人的利益牺牲他人或社会的利益是不义，为了他人和社会的利益而牺牲自己的功利则是仁义，所谓“德”，就是社会道德，只有具备了一定社会道德，承担着社会责任，才能成就自己的事业，有德才能驶得万年船。

1. 儒家把“义”看作是君子最高贵的品质。孔子说“君子义以为上”强调一个君子必须“先义后利”、“见利思义”，这是儒家思想指导现代经济的核心。在处世处人的交往中，孔子并非主张贵义贱利，一味排斥物质利益和社会权势，而是要表明应该有比个人获利更重要的东西，那就是获得什么样的利，如何获利。如果“义然后取”、以义取利，未尝不可，因为“富与贵，是人之所欲也”。但是，如果义利冲突，则舍利取义，所谓“不以其道得之，不处也”，甚至处在人所不堪的贫贱，亦无不可。总之，对于取得和享有富贵，不可不义，孔子所说的“不义而富且贵，于我如浮云”就表现了这样的境界。义利双行是儒家的一贯主张，重利轻义不符合儒家思想本意。在儒家来说，不是要不要利的问题，而是利当取不当取的问题。儒家把利置于义的统摄之下，用义来规范利、引导利，既讲“制民之产”，又讲“以义正我”，要求道德与经济、现实与超越的和谐发展。“天行健，君子以自强不息。地势坤，君子以厚德载物”，天（即自然）的运动刚强劲健，相应于此，君子处世，应像天一样，自我力求进步，刚毅坚卓，发愤图强，永不停息；大地的气势厚实和顺，君子应增厚美德，容载万物。君子应该像天宇一样运行不息，即使颠沛流离，也不屈不挠；如果你是君子，接物度量要像大地一样，没有任何东西不能承载。

2. 儒家把“诚”上升到“天道”的高度。如果说计划经济是用行政权力来配置资源的方式，那么市场经济则是用资本的力量来配置资源的方式。而资本是逐利的。为了追求自身物质利益，进而实现利润最大化，资本所有者可以无所不用其极。马克思的《资本论》中有一条注释：资本害怕没有利润或利润太少，就像自然界害怕真空一样。一旦有适当的利润，资本就大胆起来。如果有10％的利润，他就保证到处被使用；有20％的利润，它就活跃起来；有50％的利润，它就铤而走险；为了100％的利润，它就敢践踏一切人间法律；有300％的利润，它就敢犯任何罪行，甚至冒绞首的危险。这就敢犯任何罪行，甚至冒绞首的危险。这幅图画形象地描绘了资本只追求本身增值而不顾公共利益的本性。改革开放之初，我们的总设计师邓小平提出，摸着石头过河，勤劳致富，不管是白猫还是黑猫抓住老鼠就是好猫，而我们有些人，把白猫黑猫论错误地理解，造成了今天社会人文道德沦陷，没有诚信。利用一切机会主义去投机倒把，丧心病狂的谋取黑利，一些化工厂，不顾环境污染，到处排放污水，一些养殖户，利用一切机会，不顾道德和良心，使用瘦肉精，催熟剂，一些食品厂在食品中添加各种不符合标准的添加剂，残害人类的健康。儒家大师们从道德意义上讲，把诚信，作为社会最基本的道德价值观，诚信对修身、齐家、治国，平天下起着基石的作用，即一个人成长轨迹的起点，对个人和社会的发展起着尤为重要的作用。如《中庸》篇中，把“诚”上升到“天道”的高度，“诚者，天之道也，诚之者，人之道也，诚者不勉二中，不思而得，从容之道，圣人也，择善而固执之者也。”因此，我们要用儒家思想，引导人们，培养人们诚信的道德观，是我们为之追求的最终目标，这样才能使社会进步，经济发展，高度文明。才能国强民富，社会和谐，实现中华民族伟大复兴的中国梦。

3. 儒家思想提醒人们关注“义”“利”问题。在中国建立市场经济，意味着资本力量的逐渐发挥，资本支配的领域逐渐扩大，从农村到城市，从商品到土地等生产要素，从物质资源到人力资源。随着资本作用的发挥，一方面促进了整个社会效率的提高和生产力的发展，另一方面，也产生了资本自发力量和社会公共福利之间的矛盾，即儒家所说“义”、“利”之间的冲突。各种假冒伪劣产品严重威胁到消费者权益和相关产品知识产权，甚至损害了中国产品在世界上的形象和声誉；中外资本的扩张使中国环境受到污染、生态遭到破坏，有的企业所排放的废烟、废气、废水直接影响了当地甚至更为广大地域的空气、水源、植被等自然环境，这种本应由企业承担的内部成本却转嫁为外部化的社会成本；以“钱”为本，一“利”障目，人受役于物，见物不见人，金钱至上，利润至上，而人的价值、尊严失落。

总之，中国市场经济建立之初尚不成熟，出现过许多有待克服的问题。主要是如何把资本逐利的本性纳入“义”的轨道。当然，这里的“义”不再局限于封建道德的狭窄圈子，而是具有了社会主义条件下法制和价值体系的现代内容。但儒家对义利关系的辩证理解，对将“义”作为人的行为准则的强调，对人应具有理想的德性和责任的要求，则可以使当下中国人警醒，更可以为完善市场经济体系提供肥沃的文化土壤。

# 从市场经济看儒学的现代转化

中国人民大学 宋志明

市场经济是现代性最突出的体现。从经济学的角度看，传统社会转向现代社会，就是从自然经济转向市场经济。在自然经济时代，生产力水平比较低，从事生产的主要目的是满足最基本的生活需求，而不是去进行商品交换。大多数生产者比较看重使用价值，而不甚看重交换价值。由于生产力水平比较低，生产规模小，只能维持简单的再生产，无力于扩大再生产。与这种情况相适应，社会主流的价值导向不是求发展而是求稳定、求秩序。产生于自然经济时代的儒学，典型地体现出这种时代特征。如孔子所说："不患寡而患不均，"《大学》中讲的"修身、齐家、治国、平天下"，都反映出求稳定的价值导向，而不是求发展的社会导向。在市场经济时代，儒学的价值导向的局限性是显而易见的。在市场经济时代，从事生产的目的已不再是满足于基本的生活需求，而是为了进行商品交换，不再看重使用价值，而特别看重交换价值。社会的主流价值导向不仅仅是求稳定、求秩序，而特别重视发展。面对这种新情况，现代新儒学当然不能再照着传统儒学讲，只能接着传统儒学讲，并且找到新的讲法，对中国的现代性取向做出回应。

## 一

在西方现代化的起步阶段，曾经出现过启蒙主义运动。这一运动高扬理性主义，反对权威主义，主张解放思想，倡导自由、平等、博爱等现代价值观念，对于西方的现代化进程起到了推动作用。马克斯·韦伯称之为"理性化"，称之为"祛魅"，看成是现代性的集中体现，看成现代化进程的必要步骤。但是，这一运动也有缺点，主要表现为对立性思维：把传统与现代对立起来，把理性与信仰对立起来，把个人与群体对立起来，把工具理性与价值理性对立起来。由于片面地强调工具理性，导致后来实证主义思潮流行；由实证主义又引发盲目崇拜工具理性的科学主义思潮。由于片面地贬抑价值理性，损害了人文精神，造成了人格扭曲和异化，形成了"单向度的人"，导致意义世界与精神世界的迷失。由于片面强调个人的作用，片面强调人与人的竞争，导致个人主义流行，形成个体与群体的严重对立，从而损害了社会群体的互助与和谐。现代化之后暴露出的问题：由于过度追求市场价值，导致消费主义流行。文化越来越商业化、世俗化乃至低俗化，造成人的主体性的再度丧失，实际上沦为媒体的奴隶、物欲的奴隶。于是，使西方现代性不能不表现为二律背反：一方面推进了现代化的进程，一方面有导致“现代病”的流行。第一次世界大战以后，西方现代性的负面效应充分暴露出来，在思想界出现了反省现代性的人本主义思潮。

中国的现代化进程不是原发型的，而是后发型的，必须寻找到一条有别于西方的发展模式。如何在培育中国社会的现代化进程中，即培育有中国特色的现代性，又避免出现西方社会的现代病？这是摆在中国人面前的一个重要的课题。西化派显然没有察觉这一课题的重要性，出于追求现代化的迫切心情，出于对当时中国社会落后状态的深恶痛绝，他们选择了“全盘西化”的道路。在他们看来，既然现代性是从西方引进的，那么，就必须尽弃中国固有的思想传统，扫清一切阻碍现代化进程的思想障碍。他们模仿西方的启蒙主义模式，主张在中国发动启蒙主义运动，像西方对待中世纪的基督教那样，把传统儒学当作“祛魅”的对象，于是发出“打孔家店”的呼喊。

在现代性向度上，现代新儒家选择的路径与西化派不同。他们没有把西方的现代化当作唯一的理想模式，反对把传统与现代截然对立起来。在梁漱溟看来，西方的现代化模式固然有成功的方面，可是也存在着相当大的问题。西方的现代化发展主要体现在物质文明方面，而没有体现在精神文明方面。诚然，西方发达国家在物质文明方面取得了很达到成就，“然而他们精神上也因此受了伤，生活上吃了苦，这是19世纪以来暴露不可掩的事实！”[①] 中国搞现代化，可以借鉴西方成功的经验，但不能照搬照抄，尤其应当吸取他们的教训。中国作为后发的建设现代化的国家，一方面应当积极追求现代化，另一方面也应当避免西方发达国家已经出现的“现代病”。基此，现代新儒家做出“现代化不等于西化”的论断。冯友兰在《新事论》中明确提出：“现代化并不是欧化。现代化可；欧化不可。”[②] 他提出的这种看法在现代新儒家当中得到普遍的认同，至今海外的新儒家们仍把“现代化不等于西方”视为他们的基本主张之一。站在现代新儒家的立场上，冯友兰反对“全盘西化”，反对照搬照抄别国的发展模式，主张探索有中国特色、有中国“旧情”根据的发展道路。他的这一主张无疑是正确的。他认为具有深厚文化底蕴的中国人完全可以做到这一点。“真正底‘中国人’已造成过去底伟大底中国。这些‘中国人’将要造成一个新中国。在任何方面，比世界上任何

---

① 梁漱溟：《东西文化及其哲学》，上海：商务印书馆，1922年，第107页。

② 冯友兰：《三松堂全集》第4卷，郑州：河南人民出版社，1987年，第314页。

一国，都有过之无不及，这是我们所深信，而没有丝毫怀疑底。”[①] 这充分表现出他对中国文化传统的挚爱，对中国文化的现代转化充满信心，对中国的未来充满信心。

## 二

儒学能否与现代化相适应？这是现代新儒家必须面对的问题。马克斯·韦伯曾写了《儒教》一书，断言儒学不能适应现代经济，不具有促进市场经济的因素，因而对于现代化进程只有负面作用，而没有正面作用。他的结论遭到现代新儒家的反对。余英时在《士与中国文化》一书中，以大量事实反驳韦伯的结论。他指出，韦伯在新教伦理中遭到的那些促进市场经济的思想要素如敬业、勤俭等等，在儒学中都可以找到。亚洲四小龙的经济腾飞，似乎验证了现代新儒家的结论，他们提出了“儒家资本主义”的新概念，证明儒学是现代化的助力甚至是动力，并不是阻力。

现代化虽然以发展为主题，但发展也需要有稳定的秩序为条件。儒学在论证发展的必要性方面，思想资源比较匮乏，可是在维护稳定秩序方面的资源却十分丰富。冯友兰提出“由社会必有社会之理”的论断，证明儒家伦理与现代社会是相容的。他指出，儒家伦理虽然产生于农耕社会，但所阐述的并不限于农耕社会之理，而是“社会之所以为社会”之理。农耕社会改变了，“农耕社会之理”无疑过时了，可是“社会之所以为社会之理”却没有过时，仍然适用于现代社会。在市场经济时代，每个人依旧是某个家族的一员，依旧担当某种社会角色。“不论一个人所有底伦或职是什么，他都可以尽伦尽职。为父底为尽父之道是尽伦；为子底尽为子之道亦是尽伦。当大将底，尽其为将之道，是尽职；当小兵底，尽其为兵之道，亦是尽职。”[②] 他把儒家传统的家族伦理改造为职业伦理，使之与市场经济有了相容性。

现代新儒家没有像西化派那样把传统儒学当成“祛魅”的对象，而是看成可以实行现代转化的宝贵资源。他们认为，传统儒学虽然是农耕时代的产物，不可避免地带有历史的局限性，但不能因此而否认其具有普适性。中国人搞现代化，没有必要模仿西方启蒙主义的路线。一些西方国家在现代化起步阶段，曾发动了一场清算中世纪的基督教的思想运动，要求把“人”从“神”的控制中解放出来。中国的情况显然与这些国家不同。在中国，儒学并不是神学，儒学本身就不是“魅”，当然也就不必成“驱魅”的对象。中国在现代化进程中遇到的问题，并不是开启现代性，而是批判的接纳现代性，并且同时避免现代病，避免价值世界的迷失。在这种情况下，可以把儒学的普适性发掘出来，使之与市场经济相适应，从而成为促进中国现代化的精神动力。

---

① 冯友兰：《三松堂全集》第4卷，第365页。

② 冯友兰：《新原人》，重庆：商务印书馆，1943年，第165页。

## 三

认同儒学与市场经济的兼容性，可以说是现代新儒家的共识。在他们之中，对这一观点阐述最为充分的人，当属贺麟。他明确指出，在传统儒学中，儒者通常是指“耕读传家”之士。这样的儒者人格显然不能适应市场经济时代的要求了，必须更新内涵，做出新的诠释。他在《文化与人生》一书中写道：

“何谓‘儒者’？何谓‘儒者气象’？须识者自己去体会，殊难确切下一定义，其实也不必呆板说定。最概括简单地说，凡有学问技能而又具有道德修养的人，即是儒者。儒者就是品学兼优的人。我们说，在工业化的社会里，须有多数的儒商、儒工以作柱石，就是希望今后新社会中的工人、商人皆为品学兼优之士，参加工商业的建设，使商人和工人的道德水准知识水平皆大加提高，庶可进而造成现代化、工业化的新文明社会。”①

贺麟对“儒者”作了最广泛的解释。在他看来，儒者应该是一种高尚的道德形象，一种合乎理想的人格。儒者人格不是抽象的，而是具体的存在。所谓“儒者，圣之时者也”，就是说，儒者的内涵是变化的，将随着历史环境的变迁而改变。在农耕时代，儒者指的是耕读传家之士，而在市场经济时代，则是指品学兼优之士。贺麟指出，中国只有造就一大批新式儒者，现代化事业才有望成功。“若无多数重忠孝仁爱信义和平的道德修养的儒商、儒工出，以树立工商的新人格模范，商者凭其经济地位以剥削人，工者凭其优越技能以期令人、傲慢人，则社会秩序无法安定，而中国亦殊难走上健康的工业化的途径。”②

贺麟突破了传统儒学重农抑商的观念，提出“儒商、儒工”等新观念。他指出，以往把士列为四民之首，视商人为利禄之徒，是错误的。他说：“我觉得几千年深入人心重农轻工商的旧观念，使应加以改变。……其实平心而论，且就大多数看来，农人固属勤劳自食其力，商人也何尝不夙兴夜寐，操其业务。农人固朴实耐苦，商人亦多急功近利的人。农人固劳力，商人恐有时亦须劳力且兼须劳心。总之，农人与商人皆是良好的公民，皆是组成健全的社会国家所不可缺的中坚分子。似不宜有所轩轾其间。……且即从道德生活言，商贾大都比农人好动，远离乡井，旅行冒险，精神可佩。农人则比较安土重迁，好静而守旧，于维持传统的道德文化，颇有力量。商人游历的地方多，见闻亦多，每每非故乡的旧风俗习惯所能束缚。故商人于打破旧风俗习惯，改

---

① 贺麟：《文化与人生》，北京：商务印书馆，1989 年，11—12 页。

② 贺麟：《文化与人生》，第 11 页。

革旧礼教，促进新道德的产生，常有其特殊的贡献。”① 他认为在市场经济时代，商人不能再被排除在儒者的范围之外，而必须获得应有的尊重。

贺麟也突破了宋明儒学的理欲对立的旧观念，强调在市场经济时代二者之间的兼容关系。他说：“近代伦理思想上有一大转变，早已超出中古僧侣式的灭人欲、存天理、绝私济公的道德信条，而趋向于一方面求人欲与天理的调和，求公与私的共济，而一方面又更进一步去设法假人欲以行天理，假自私以济大公。”② 从现代伦理思想的发展趋势看，宋儒“存天理灭人欲”之说显然已经过时，因此现代新儒家不必再拘守这种旧观念，应当跟上时代的步伐，对理欲关系提出新的诠释。在贺麟看来，人欲与天理并不是敌对的或对立的关系，而是相容的、互济的关系。过分地凸显人欲，当然会助长为非道德的消极因素；但是，过分限制人欲，不利于调动人的进取精神，也会妨碍经济发展。如果恰当地看待人欲，人欲也可以构成使天理得以实现的积极因素，甚至是必不可少的前提与条件。如果道德生活完全脱离了人的欲望、需求，则必然陷入空虚与贫乏。这样的道德生活绝不是现代人所要求的充实丰富、洋溢着生命力的生活。贺麟认为，视人欲为洪水猛兽，乃是经济不发达的旧时代的人所难以避免的偏见，随着时代的发展，原本对人类有害的消极因素也可以转化为对人类有益的积极因素。洪水可能泛滥成灾，但把洪水控制起来，也可以用来发电，从而造福于人类；猛兽可能伤人，把猛兽关在动物园里，也可以供人们欣赏。

贺麟提出的儒学可以促进市场经济发展的观点是很有见地的，显示出儒学经过现代转化以后，仍然可以有用武之地，仍然可以发挥积极的促进作用。

## 四

儒学对于当前的社会主义市场经济是否也有促进作用呢？笔者借鉴现代新儒家的理论思维成果，也抱着一种肯定的看法。

毫无疑问，在新的世纪中，中国经济将缩短与西方发达国家之间的差距。不是有英国人预测，到2050年中国经济将赶上美国吗？不是有不少学者认为新的世纪将是中国人的世纪吗？当然，我们不会因为几个洋教授的几句赞誉之辞和美好预测而沾沾自喜，但不容置疑的是，一个改革、开放的中国，经济上必将越来越强大，东方睡狮正在觉醒！中国共产党正在全心领导十几亿中国人民想尽一切办法赶超发达国家，而社会主义市场经济体制的确立为中国经济的腾飞找到了正确的道路。经济发展的强大动力和惯性，将按照自己的规律而发展，绝不是个别人或任何主观意识所能改变得了的。

---

① 贺麟：《文化与人生》，第33—34页。

② 贺麟：《文化与人生》，第209页。

当然，这个过程决不会一蹴而就，城乡发展的巨大差别、东西部地区之间的巨大差距以及人口重负、落后意识等对中国现代化都具有巨大的制动作用。但是，希望的萌芽破土之后，不是就有大量的农民在农闲时外出打工、看看精彩的外面世界、接受城市新观念的洗礼了吗？不是也有华西村、刘庄等新农村出现了吗？事实证明，有儒学文化背景的中国人接受市场经济的新观念并非不可能。传统观念固然应当转变，但把传统观念同新观念对立起来，否认其现代转化的可能性，显然不符合事实。

新世纪的中国经济在“适度的中央集权”体制之下，在执政党正确的路线、方针和政策指引下，是可以飞速发展的。因为市场经济的繁荣和社会生产力的迅速提高，依赖于对人们经济利益的承认、依赖于对经济竞争中自由与公平的保障、依赖于对人们财富私人占有的认可，而这三点在目前的中国来说，正在逐渐变为现实，或者说是中国共产党和政府正在努力从事的工作。“水往低处流，人往高处走”，当人们有了追求更美好生活的愿望时，也就有了前进的动力。在当今的世界上，没有哪一个国家会因工业文明的副作用（如环境污染等）而降低自己的发展速度。公开承认人们占有物质财富的合理性，必将极大地激发人们的创造能力的发挥，极大地提高社会的生产力水平。回顾改革开放后我们所取得的成绩，不能不承认这一点。

中国封建社会后期长期停滞不前落后的一个重要原因，就是没有公开承认人们追求经济利益的正当要求，宋明理学“存天理灭人欲”的说法，有思想禁锢的作用。但是，也应当看到，“存天理灭人欲”不过是一种说法而已，并没有社会的实际状况。在理论上不承认人欲的正当性，不等于人欲因此而真的消失，只不过是转化了形式而已。在中国封建社会中，对政治权力的占有，强烈的官本位意识，实际上就是通过对政治权力的占有来掩盖对经济利益的占有。“三年清知府，十万雪花银”，非常形象地说明了这一点。在中国封建社会中，人情大于王法，“利”掩盖在“情”之中，只要有了权，就会获得各种各样的“情”和各种各样的“利”。在市场经济时代，公开承认求利的正当性，将会使“情”的色彩淡化，使“法”的色彩强化，并进一步会导致“权欲”的淡化和“官本位”的淡化。中国人历来对于形而上的纯本体论问题不太感兴趣，历来关注的焦点是活生生的人，儒家的“未能事人，焉能事鬼”的观念集中体现了这种倾向。在市场经济的条件下，儒家文化中的务实精神已经开始、并最终会得到极大程度的弘扬。宋明理学“存天理灭人欲”的说法，笼统地讲，确实不妥；如果加以限制，在市场经济时代并非没有积极意义。在市场经济条件下，固然应当承认个人利益的正当性，但绝不是主张放纵人欲。对于金钱拜物教，对于商品拜物教，对那些唯利是图、损人利己、利欲熏心的人，讲讲“存天理灭人欲”的古训，有何不可？

儒家重义轻利的观念在市场经济的发展过程中仍有其独特的现代价值，那就是可以对过度膨胀的功利追求发挥制衡作用。随着经济的快速发展，人们对个人利益的追逐将日益强烈。在这种情况下，就迫切需要“义”来予以调节。“义”与“利”的平衡，实际上是维护社会稳定、协调社会发展的有效方式。在现代社会，讲“义”实际上就是讲法治和信誉，也就是说，在追求利益的时候，要遵守公众制定的游戏规则。具有丰厚积蕴的中国儒家文化，在协调现代社会中义与利的关系方面，完全可以提供许多有益的启示。在市场经济的冲击下，现代人常常会感受到意义失落、价值失衡的困惑；极端的功利主义将造成人们文化素质和道德水准的滑坡。对于这些现象，儒学将发挥制衡作用，以崭新的面貌再现于现代人的精神世界。

由于儒学人文主义的导向，使得中国人非常务实，只要有利于自己的生存和发展，均可采取“拿来主义”的态度。“洋为中用，古为今用”，不管是玉皇大帝，还是太上老君，抑或释迦牟尼，只要能保佑我，都可以供奉他，甚至可以放在一起供奉。在人们的经济利益得到认可的情况下，这种务实精神必将产生极大的影响，人们会自觉自愿地参与到市场经济中去，改变自己的贫穷状况和国家的落后面貌而努力工作。在这个过程中，党和政府迫切需要制订出相应的经济法规和制约机制，以保证人们的经济活动按照一定的合理规则行事。使人们处于公平的自由竞争当中，从而避免产生民众的心理失衡。这种情况虽然还有一个完善的过程，但我们目前正在做。转变经营机制、明晰产权关系、转变政府职能等等，都是这种努力的组成部分。建立公平的竞争机制，可以避免务实精神滑向它的另一个极端——为了占有经济利益而不择手段。

当然，中国在前进的道路上，并不会是一帆风顺的，还会遇到许多的制动因素，其中有些确实与儒家文化有关系。例如，儒家文化中的官本位意识已如上述；再如传统儒家文化中的小农意识和轻商意识（如“士农工商”的排序和“奸商”的蔑称等），对于现代化进程也会形成负面影响。但是这种影响并不是不可以克服的。现代化的一个重要标志就在于工业化水平，因此，随着中国工业化水平的提高，机器大工业在农业中的大量运用，人多地少的矛盾将会越来越突出，这样，农村中大量的劳动力必将从祖祖辈辈固守的土地中解放出来，接触到更大范围的现代化进程，参与到市场经济的大潮中去，或者经商，或者把自身的劳动力充实到城市人不愿干的工作中去，这是社会的必然，也是农村走向现代化的一个重要方面。我们不能以狭隘的眼光（如社会治安、计划生育等）来看待“民工潮”，也不能以行政手段强制农民固守在无活可干的一点点儿土地上。农村人自觉自愿地要求改变小农意识，正是我们现代化过程中求之不得的事情，理应加以积极引导。

在当代中国，传统的小农意识和轻商意识已经在改变，与现代意识相融洽的务实精神正在蓬勃发展。轻商、贱商的意识虽然还在不少人的脑子里具有一定的地位，但在市场经济大潮的冲击下影响必定越来越小。目前对儒家轻商意识的批判，除了换得一点点微不足道的稿费之外，已经没有太多的实际意义。意识形态在现实的经济基础面前，永远占据不了主导地位。儒学作为一种传统的意识形态，一直都非常重视义利之辨，宋儒则把义与利对立起来，提出“存天理灭人欲”的口号，对中国封建社会后期经济的发展有不良的影响，这是事实，但这毕竟不造成中国经济落后的主要原因。造成中国经济落后的主要原因还是应当到社会制度方面去找，不能要儒家来负责。

# 儒家“义利之辨”的基本内涵及其当代意义

北京大学 李翔海

重“德”是中华文化深厚绵长的传统。经过殷周之际的变革，周人就有了“天命靡常”（《诗·文王》）、“皇天无亲，惟德是辅”（《尚书·蔡仲之命》）的认识。在春秋战国时代，儒家思想就形成了从人与动物的区别来看待人、要求人的思维方式，并把人区别于动物的根本点归结为具有仁、义、礼、智等德性。由此，中华民族很早就形成了高度注重克己修身的传统，高尚的道德是中华民族一以贯之的精神追求。这一点集中体现在儒家的“义利之辨”中。通俗地说，所谓“义”就是道德上的“应当”，“利”则指物质利益。“义利之辨”所集中讨论的是道德与利益的关系问题。在儒家思想中，“义利之辨”具有重要地位。它不仅直接与“君子小人之辨”相关联，而且与儒家的一些核心论题如人禽之辨、理欲之辨、王霸之辨等之间亦存在着相当密切的关系。由此，“义利之辨”构成了儒学的核心论题之一。对此，不少宋明理学家都曾不约而同地做出过明确的论述。二程指出：“孟子辨舜跖之分，只在义利之间。”（《二程遗书》卷十七）陆九渊教人，首在辨义理（参见《象山集》卷三十四）。张栻在《孟子讲义》“序”中指出，“学者潜心孔孟，必得其门而入，愚以为莫先于义利之辨。”朱熹更是鲜明地强调：“义利之说乃儒者第一义。”（《朱文公文集》卷二十四）由于“义利之辨”所关涉问题的重要性，也由于中国现代社会与中国传统社会之间的差异，儒家“义利之辨”大概是近代以来受到中国思想文化界误解最多亦最为集中的问题之一。正因为此，虽然改革开放以来已出现了大量力图合理阐释儒家“义利之辨”的研究成果，但对儒家“义利之辨”的一些误解却依然没有得到有效澄清。造成这一状况的原因当然是多方面的。在笔者看来，对儒家“义利之辨”的完整内涵阐释尚不充分应该也是其中的缘由之一。本文拟对儒家“义利之辨”的基本内涵及当代意义做出概括和讨论，并有针对性地对一些有代表性的误解儒家“义利之辨”的观点做出辨析。由于儒家“义利之辨”的思想源头显然是在先秦，因而本文对儒家“义利之辨”基本内涵的阐述主要是立足于先秦儒家的有关思想。为了论说的方便，本文从梳理误解儒家“义利之辨”的三种有代表性的观点入手开始探析问题。

## 一

笔者认为，围绕儒家“义利之辨”的误解主要包括了以下三种：一种是根本否定在今天讨论儒家“义利之辨”仍具有积极意义；一种是强调儒家“义利之辨”的基本精神在于义利对立基础上的取义舍利或重义轻利；还有一种则是从肯定儒家“义利之辨”的积极意义出发，认为其中包含了主张“以义取利”的内容。以下我们对这三种观点分别加以概要的梳理。

有论者根本否定在现时代讨论儒家“义利之辨”归根结底仍具有积极意义。有一篇刊登在《哲学研究》上的文章对此做了颇有代表性的论说。在作者看来，“今日的‘国学’复兴，搬出‘义利之辨’这个古老的问题套到市场经济条件下去建设社会主义精神文明，或者从儒学的近代形态的‘重利’去为儒家‘正名’，认为它符合现代精神有利于促进物质文明建设，都是牵强附会的。”为什么呢？作者的回答是：“因为‘义利之辨’毕竟是陈旧的古典课题和话语，以为它可以解决今日的问题不外乎是一种由观念史观而来的‘预成论’的设定，即认为现在的问题已在古圣先贤的‘名言’规定好了的，只要‘落实’或略作调整就行了。……在维特根斯坦强调了一种表述只有在生活之流中才有意义之后的40多年后，还有人‘庄严地’做‘义’、‘利’、‘轻’、‘重’的纯语言文字组合游戏，充其量不过是无意义的空谈”。作者认为的正确做法应当是：“事实上与此恰恰相反，不是按古代的‘金科玉律’去行动，而是一方面批判它的伪善性，一方面消除它的负面影响，我们才能有所前进。这是历史前进的题中之意，即我们不能停留于以使用价值为表征的古代社会，在以交换价值为特征的市场经济条件下，再去炒这些陈年老货，其实是刻舟求剑。”[①] 这也就是说，在市场经济条件下，谈论儒家“义利之辨”无异于炒“陈年老货”，“充其量不过是无意义的空谈”，因而不仅不具有积极意义，而且还事实上成了历史的负担。

认为儒家“义利之辨”的基本精神在于由义利对立出发而主张重义轻利甚至取义舍利，是一种有一定普遍性的误解。在与墨家的比较中将儒家的相关主张归结为义利对立、重义轻利甚至取义舍利，是一种长期以来一直存在着的对于儒家“义利之辨”的基本评断。这种看法随着改革开放以来相关研究的不断深入已在相当程度上得到了改变，但却依然有一定市场。在这一点上，老一辈著名学者、清华大学历史系教授何兆武先生的相关主张颇有代表性。直至1987年，在谈到儒家“义利之辨”时，何先生依然明确认为：“孔门义利之辨对后世的历史影响，大体上是坏的不是好的，消极作用

---

① 吕世荣：《义利之辨的哲学思考》，《哲学研究》1998年第5期。

大于积极作用。理论上它犯了把概念绝对化的形而上学错误，在实践上则往往流入假道学之一途。个人与集体，这个问题可以说是古今中外的思想家都在想解决的。正统儒家并没有解决好。……越是仁义叫得响的，大概就越是为了阶级、阶层、集团、小圈子乃至个人的利欲。……孔孟无论正面明确阐明了没有，但实际上都蕴涵有义利对立的观念。……一种理论的科学价值，需看是否合乎实际。少数例外不能成为普遍的规律。理论家不可以以理想、空想或幻想代替现实。少数特立独行者的典型并不真正能成为普遍性的规律。在这种意义上，强调义利之辨，强调两者的对立或对抗性的，都可以说是唯心论者而非唯物论者。他们都是以假大空代替了对现实的严谨的理论探讨。"① 时至今日，虽然随着时间的推移，已有越来越多的人不再简单地认定儒家"义利之辨"的基本精神在于义利对立并进而由此从整体上对儒家"义利之辨"予以否定性评价，但在对中国思想史上关于义利问题的不同主张予以分类时，不少人还是直接把儒家的相关思想归结为"重义轻利"派。

如果说前两类误解主要与部分或整体地否定儒家"义利之辨"的现代价值相关联，另一种误解则恰恰是从肯定儒家"义利之辨"的积极意义出发而事实上曲解了其基本精神。这方面的一个集中表现，就是从市场经济"重利"的现实要求出发，在为儒家"义利之辨"的"辩护"中，强调其中包含了主张"以义取利"的内容，即认为儒家"义利之辨"主张通过主动自觉地"行义"而获得利益。有论者指出，"以义取利"是儒家"义利之辨"的一个重要特征。他以孔子的相关主张为例，来对此加以论证："孔子并不否认利，问题是怎样取利。他主张'见利思义'，'见得思义'（《季氏》）。这就是说，取财要符合义的要求，称为'君子爱财，取之有道'。孔子说：'富与贵，是人之所欲也；不以其道得之，不处也。'（《里仁》）又说：'不义而富且贵，于我如浮云。'（《述而》）'邦无道，富且贵焉，耻也。'（《泰伯》）这都说明孔子重视以义取利，反对为富不仁。这一认识虽仍没有脱出重义轻利思想的窠臼，但具有义利兼行之意，这是孔子义利观的进步。"② 不难看出，作者正是立足于努力阐扬以孔子为代表的儒家"义利之辨"的积极意义，而将"重视以义取利"视为儒家思想中具有"进步"意义的观念。有的论者还在此基础上，按照"完整而准确地理解义利关系的内涵，挖掘传统义利关系理论中有价值的部分并进行现代转换，以适应和推进当前经济社会的发展"的要求，在对于"建构社会主义义利观"的探讨中，提出了"确立'尚利贵义'的指导思想，推行'正义谋利、义利统一'的实施原则，树立'以义取利，见利思义'的道德风尚"的主张，明确强调，"'尚利贵义'，是指对义与利的选择上，既尚利且贵义"；

① 兆武：《关于"义利之辨"》，《清华大学学报》（哲学社会科学版）1987年第1期。

② 吕明灼：《义利之辨：一个纵贯古今的永恒主题》，《齐鲁学刊》2000年第6期。

“正义谋利、义利统一”,就是“反对将义与利截然对立的观点,坚持‘正义谋其利,明道计其功’的辩证义利观”;“‘以义取利’,意即以义作为获利之手段”。①

在我们看来,上述误解儒家“义利之辨”的第一类观点出现的基本原因,是因为仅仅从“时代性”这一单一维度来看待文化与中国文化,在“传统”与“现代”之间僵硬地持守了二元对立、非此即彼的立场,从而遮蔽了“现代”对于“传统”既继承又超越的辩证关系。这种观念在直接的思想渊源上与中国自由主义西化派的影响有着紧密的关联,进而言之,又可以说是在相当程度上反映了西方“现代性”理论对中国学界的重要影响。强调时间对于空间的首要性,是在源起于西方的现代化过程中所成就的现代性的一个重要的特质。在这样的视野下,西方文化与非西方文化都被置放于时间等级序列的考量中,前者被等同于现代文化,后者则被等同于前现代文化。前者在时间序列上的优先性就被确立为在空间序列中相对于后者的优越性,并最终落脚于对西方文化之中心地位的维护。由于在人类社会的世界历史阶段,缘起于西方的现代性在相当的程度上被等同于人类文化的时代性,因而从时代性的角度来看待中国文化往往能更清楚地见出中国文化传统的自身局限之所在。但是,正像上举论文所显示的,如果从时代性来论衡中国文化传统成为基本的乃至唯一的尺度,它所可能带来的一个基本问题就是容易由此而走向在整体上否定包括中国文化传统在内的非西方文化传统的现代价值。这就显出了这种主张事实上所包含的内在局限:这一主张实际上隐含着以特定时期西方文化的民族性充任人类文化共同的时代性的理论义涵;轻忽乃至抹杀了非西方民族文化传统的超越性与继承性;它的一个基本的理论前提是将西方式的现代性看作是一个封闭的、完备的价值系统,而人类文化发展演进的历史已经说明,这一理论前提是难以成立的。② 时至今日,这种主张的片面性已为越来越多的研究者所认识,这里不再多加讨论。由于对上述误解儒家“义利之辨”的后两种观点的辨析直接涉及对儒家“义利之辨”具体内容的把握,接下来本文就先对此加以梳理。

## 二

我们认为,儒家“义利之辨”包含了四个方面的基本内容,即:第一,明确反对见利忘义;第二,肯定合理之利的正当性;第三,在动机上反对“以义求利”,但在结果上可以接受“因义得利”;第四,在特殊情况下则牺牲利益而成就道义,其极端的情

---

① 孔祥宁:《义利之辨:中国价值观的核心内容及现代意义》,《南昌大学学报》(人文社会科学版)2005年第5期。

② 详论请参见李翔海:《对中国现代哲学研究中“时代性”观念的反省》,《南京大学学报》2006年第6期。

况就是孔子所谓“杀身成仁”、孟子所谓“舍生取义”。需要指出的是，由于在其后两千多年的发展历程中，尽管不同时代的儒家对“义利之辨”提出了不尽相同的主张，但其根干则是生长于先秦时期的，而且其基本精神亦与以孔子、孟子和荀子等为代表的先秦儒家之间存在着不可割舍的内在的精神联系，因而本文对儒家“义利之辨”基本内涵的梳理主要是立足于先秦儒家的有关思想。

第一，明确反对见利忘义。正如人们已注意到的，“成人”或曰具备人之所以为人的基本属性、成就人之所以为人的理想人格，在一定意义上堪称儒学展开自己思想系统的逻辑起点。顺此而进，儒学把人区别于动物的根本点归结为具有仁、义、礼、智等德性，表现出对“德性”与“德行”的高度注重。为此，作为儒家开山鼻祖的孔子一改此前以社会地位来区分“君子”与“小人”的观念，而将是否具有“德性”与“德行”作为区分“君子”与“小人”的根本标准，进而做出了为此后儒家“义利之辨”奠定了基本精神方向、事实上也流传十分广泛的论断：“君子喻于义，小人喻于利。”(《论语·里仁》)这也就是说，在孔子看来，作为生命的个体究竟是做“君子”还是做“小人”，两者的分界线正在于是追求“义”还是追求“利”，或者说是按照仁道的要求规范自己的言行还是只顾为自己谋取一己之私利。做有德君子而不做只知道追求自己私利的小人，正是儒家对人的基本要求。如何才能做到这一点呢？儒家一方面明确提倡“见得思义”(《论语·述而》)、“见利思义”(《论语·宪问》)，另一方面也明确反对见利忘义、“放于利而行”(《论语·里仁》)。也就是说，一个人面对利益时，首先应当有道德的自觉，应当把做一个有德君子作为自己的自觉追求，一定要对所面对的利益究竟是否属于自己“应当”得到的有清楚的认识。与此相对应，见到利益就完全把道德置诸脑后甚至于把追求个人利益当作自己行事的基本准则，则是儒家所坚决反对的。

第二，肯定合理之利的正当性。由于儒家从重德、成人的基本要求出发，充分突显了“义”的首要性，而且从孔子那里，就开创了“罕言利”(《论语·子罕》)的记录，再加上孟子有“王何必曰利？亦有仁义而已矣”(《孟子·梁惠王上》)的说法，《汉书·董仲舒传》留下了“正其谊不谋其牙利，明其道不计其功”的记载，以及宋明理学家严辨“义利”的影响，这就易于给人们一种印象，似乎儒家在“义利”问题上是只重“义”而不及“利”的。应该说，这一认识是不完整、不全面的。实际上，在提倡“见得思义”而反对“放于利而行”的基础上，儒家肯定了合理之利的正当性。对此，作为先秦儒家主要代表人物的孔子、孟子与荀子均做出过明确的论述。

《论语·里仁》中记载了孔子的一段话：“富与贵，是人之所欲也，不以其道得之，不处也；贫与贱，是人之所恶也，不以其道得之，不去也。君子去仁，恶乎成名？君子无终食之间违仁，造次必于是，颠沛必于是。”透过这段话，我们不难得出三点结论。其一，孔子明确承认，富与贵，是一般人之所欲求的；贫与贱，是一般人之所厌恶的。这其中显然包含了认肯合理之利的正当性的意涵。其二，无论是得到富贵还是去除贫贱，都应当为之以道，而不能肆意妄为。其三，对于一个君子而言，首要地是成就仁德，因为这是君子之所以为君子的本质之所在。《论语·里仁》中的这段话，可以与《论语·述而》中的另一段话相互印证："富而可求也，虽执鞭之士，吾亦为之。如不可求，从吾所好。"正是立足于这样的认识，《论语》标举了"义然后取"（《论语·宪问》）的原则。这说明，在孔子那里，在提倡"见得思义"而反对"放于利而行"的基础上，只要是合乎道德要求的、理当得到的利益，完全可以心安理得地取得。

孟子同样也明确地肯定了一般人或曰普通民众之物质利益的合理性。面对战乱时代一如既往地追求王道，是孟子思想的一个重要特点。为达此目标，孟子提出了"仁政"的主张，并在政治、经济、教育等方面系统地提出了行"仁政"的具体举措。其经济上施行"井田制"、制民之产、使民以时、轻徭薄赋等具体举措的一个基本立足点，就是首先保障普通民众物质利益方面的需求。这其中显然同样包含了认肯普通民众合理之利的正当性的意涵。可以说，在孟子这里，不仅肯定普通民众合理之利的正当性，而且采取制度性的措施保障普通民众获得其正当利益，恰恰构成了"王道"的基础和前提。孟子的下面一段话清楚地体现了这一点："不违农时，谷不可胜食也；数罟不入洿池，鱼鳖不可胜食也；斧斤以时入山林，材木不可胜用也。谷与鱼鳖不可胜食，材木不可胜用，是使民养生丧死无憾也。养生丧死无憾，王道之始也。五亩之宅，树之以桑，五十者可以衣帛矣；鸡豚狗彘之畜，无失其时，七十者可以食肉矣；百亩之田，勿夺其时，数口之家，可以无饥矣；谨庠序之教，申之以孝悌之义，颁白者不负戴于道路矣。七十者衣帛食肉，黎民不饥不寒，然而不王者，未之有也。"（《孟子·梁惠王上》）在这里，孟子明确地把"养生丧死无憾"视为"王道之始"。在保障普通民众的物质利益以"富之"的基础上，再施以教化，就有可能推行王道于天下。孟子还进一步分析了何以会如此的原因。他指出："民之为道也，有恒产者有恒心，无恒产者无恒心。"（《孟子·滕文公上》）"若民，则无恒产，因无恒心。苟无恒心，放辟邪侈，无不为已。及陷于罪，然后从而刑之，是罔民也。焉有仁人在位，罔民而可为也。是故明君制民之产，必使仰足以事父母，俯足以畜妻子，乐岁终身饱，凶年免于死亡。然后驱而之善，故民之从之也轻。今也制民之产，仰不足以事父母，俯不足以畜妻子，乐岁终身苦，凶年不免于死亡。此惟救死而恐不赡，奚暇治礼义哉？王欲行之，则盍反其本矣。"（《孟子·梁惠王上》）在这里，我们甚至可以得出对于普通民众而言，"有恒产"是"有恒心"之"本"即合理的利益是讲究礼义之"本"的结论。当然，我们同时也不要忘记，对于士或曰君子，孟子同孔子一样，也提出了更高的要求。在他看来，"无恒产而有恒心者，惟士为能。"（《孟子·梁惠王上》）这句话的另外一面也就是说，如果一个人不能做到“无恒产而有恒心”，他就没有资格做一个不同于普通民众的士或曰君子。这其中显然包含了君子应当“以义为先”的要求。

作为先秦儒家的殿军，荀子同样也明确地肯定了一般人或曰普通民众之物质利益的合理性。在他看来：“义与利者，人之所两有也，虽尧舜不能去民之欲利，然而能使其欲利不克其好义也。”（《荀子·大略》）当然，在归根结底的意义上，荀子仍然像孔子和孟子一样，明确强调了义是第一位的、利是第二位的观念。他指出，“先义而后利者荣，先利而后义者辱”（《荀子·荣辱》）。因此，行义是做人处事的首要原则：“从道不从君，从义不从父，人之大行也”（《荀子·子道》）。而究竟是“以义为先”还是“以利为本”，其结果则鲜明地表现为“治世”与“乱世”的差别：“故义胜利者为治世，利克义者为乱世”（《荀子·大略》）。

第三，在动机上反对“以义求利”，但在结果上可以接受“因义得利”。也就是说，反对在主观动机方面假仁义之名而行谋利益之实，但却并不反对在客观效果上因为行义而得到正当的利益特别是公共的大利。这一点体现得最典型的就是《孟子·梁惠王上》。正如人们所注意到的，这一章的确可以视为孟子直接讨论“义利”关系问题的重要文献之一。面对梁惠王“叟不远千里而来，亦将有以利吾国乎”的提问，孟子回答说：“王，何必曰利，亦有仁义而已矣。”表面看来，孟子似乎是将道德与利益对立了起来，只讲义，不讲利。不少现代研究者正是由此而认定孟子乃至儒家是主张义利对立的。但是，仔细的分析表明，这种认识是不够准确、完整的。

面对梁惠王的问题，孟子给出“何必曰利，亦有仁义而已矣”这一回答的理由何在呢？因为“上下交征利而国危矣”：“王曰‘何以利吾国’？大夫曰‘何以利吾家’？士庶人曰‘何以利吾身’？上下交征利而国危矣。万乘之国弑其君者，必千乘之家；千乘之国弑其君者，必百乘之家。万取千焉，千取百焉，不为不多矣。苟为后义而先利，不夺不餍。未有仁而遗其亲者也，未有义而后其君者也。王亦曰仁义而已矣，何必曰利？”接下来，孟子进一步讲明了在上位者应当“与民偕乐”，应当保障庶民的物质生活需求并富之、教之，不能“率兽而食人”，“仁者无敌”，应当“不嗜杀人”，应当以不忍之心行不忍之政等方面的道理。最后强调指出，如果凭借武力“欲辟土地，朝秦楚，莅中国而抚四夷”，只能给国家和人民带来比“缘木求鱼”还要严重的灾难性；相反，如果“发政施仁”或曰“施仁政于民”，就可以“保民而王，莫之能御”。概括而言，孟子此章的基本主张在于：如果整个社会的各个阶层都只知道讲利并互相陷入利益的纷争，必将给国家与包括君主在内的社会各阶层均带来亡国灭身等巨大的危害；如果希图凭借武力而开疆拓土、一统天下，其结果也必将因为四面树敌而危及国家与社会的安定与存亡；只有行仁践义、以不忍之心行不忍之仁政，才能“沛然莫之能御”而“王天下”即结束战乱、走向统一。毫无疑义，这不仅符合君主自身的利益，而且也是当时黎民百姓最大的利益。而这种“利”又是在行义的过程中得以实现的。这怎么能说是要将“义”与“利”对立起来呢？就其客观效果而言，甚至可以说是“义利双成”。当然，正如孟子“何必曰利，亦有仁义而已矣”的回答中所显示的，孟子的相关主张不能归结为是主动自觉地“以义求利”。而是在动机上反对“以义求利”，但在结果上可以接受“因义得利”。亦即反对在主观动机方面假仁义之名而行谋利益之实，但却并不反对在客观效果上因为行义而得到正当的利益特别是公共的大利。对此，本文在后面还要做出更具体的辨析。

第四，在特殊情况下则牺牲利益而成就道义，其极端的情况就是孔子所谓“杀身成仁”、孟子所谓“舍生取义”。由于社会生活与具体的人生际遇都是纷繁复杂的，因而，在某些情况下，也会出现“义”与“利”尖锐对立、不可调和，只能做出非此即彼的选择的情况。在这种情况下，应当以怎样的原则来对待“义”与“利”呢？正是在这里，儒家“义利之辨”的确体现出了更为注重道义而非更为注重利益的倾向，成为儒家“义利之辨”相对于墨家与法家的一个重要特色。在这方面，孔子和孟子均有明确论述。孔子指出：“志士仁人，无求生以害仁，有杀身以成仁。”（《论语·卫灵公》）如果说这里孔子是直接在一般性的意义上对“仁人志士”提出了“无求生以害仁，有杀身以成仁”的要求的话，孟子则是清楚地展示了在特殊情况下“义”与“利”之间所具有的巨大张力，并明确地揭示了何以必须“舍生而取义”的理由。孟子曰：“鱼，我所欲也；熊掌，亦我所欲也，二者不可得兼，舍鱼而取熊掌者也。生，亦我所欲也；义，亦我所欲也，二者不可得兼，舍生而取义者也。生亦我所欲，所欲有甚于生者，故不为苟得也；死亦我所恶，所恶有甚于死者，故患有所不辟也。如使人之所欲莫甚于生，则凡可以得生者，何不用也？使人之所恶莫甚于死者，则凡可以辟患者，何不为也？由是则生而有不用也，由是则可以辟患而有不为也。是故所欲有甚于生者，所恶有甚于死者。非独贤者有是心也，人皆有之，贤者能勿丧耳。”（《孟子·告子上》）透过孟子的上述话语，我们可以得出如下四个方面的结论：第一，正像对于“鱼”与“熊掌”并不是任何时候都只能二者择一样，“义”与“生”也是可以共存并同为“我”所“欲”的；第二，只是在“二者不可得兼”的情况下，才不得不做出“舍鱼而取熊掌”、“舍生而取义”的选择。第三，之所以做出“舍生而取义”即为了道义而安然赴死的选择，是因为在“义”与“生”相互冲突的情况下，追求“义”的价值超过了生命本身的价值，对于违“义”的厌恶超过了对于死亡本身的厌恶。第四，仍然同孔子一样，在孟子这里，“舍生而取义”的要求也是首先针对“贤者”或曰“仁人志士”而提出的。

可见，在儒家看来，当遇到义与利发生尖锐冲突而不可调和的特殊情况时，志士仁人决不为了苟活而做出损害仁义的事情，而是宁可牺牲自己也要成仁践义。

## 三

在对儒家“义利之辨”的基本内涵做了梳理之后，为了更为具体亦更有针对性地讨论问题，本文接下来就前文所论及的误解儒家“义利之辨”的第二种、第三种观点做出概要的辨析。

第一，从上述对儒家“义利之辨”基本内涵的梳理中不难看出，将儒家“义利之辨”的基本精神视为由“义利对立”出发而主张取义舍利，是对于问题不符合实际的、简单化的理解。儒家的确是首重“义”，但这并不意味着儒家是以“义利对立”作为理解义利关系之基本前提的。以孔子、孟子及荀子为代表的先秦儒家，不仅均肯定了合理之利的正当性，而且在客观效果上接受“因义得利”，这表明：在儒家对于“义利”关系的整体理解中，是包含了“义利统一”之向度的。因此，即使儒家因为相比较而言更为重“义”因而对“利”的注重没有达到对“义”的程度，其所谓“重义轻利”也不是简单地建立在“义利对立”的基础之上。只是在特殊的境遇中，出现了“义”与“利”尖锐对立、不可调和的情况，儒家才明确主张在“义”与“利”之间做出非此即彼的选择，牺牲利益而成就道义。其极端情况就是“生”与“义”“二者不可得兼”，因为“所欲有甚于生者”、“所恶有甚于死者”而“杀身以成仁”、“舍生而取义”。我们显然不能否认在实际生活中义利之间出现尖锐对立、不可调和境况的可能性，也不能简单地将儒家“义利之辨”所针对的这一境况的相关主张扩大化甚至绝对化，而应当对儒家“义利之辨”完整内容做出具体的、实事求是的认识。

第二，在客观效果上接受“因义得利”不能归结为“以义取利”。我们认为，这也是讨论儒家“义利之辨”时必须加以认真辨析的一个原则性问题。所谓“以义取利”，就是主动自觉地打着道义的旗号而追求、谋取利益。这实际上是儒家所一直明确反对的一种行为方式。当齐宣王问到“齐桓、晋文之事可得闻乎”这一问题时，孟子对曰：“仲尼之徒无道桓文之事者，是以后世无传焉。臣未之闻也。”（《孟子·梁惠王上》）为什么“仲尼之徒无道桓文之事者”呢？我们从孟子的相关论说中可以看出一些端倪。在谈到齐桓、晋文等五霸与尧舜、汤武的不同时，孟子指出：“尧舜，性之也；汤武，身之也；五霸，假之也。久假而不归，恶知其非有也。”（《孟子·尽心上》）这是说，尧舜实行仁义是根于本性，商汤周武实行仁义是身体力行，五霸实行仁义则只是借来牟利，因而齐桓、晋文是不能与尧舜、汤武等儒家圣贤等量齐观的。在另一处，孟子说道：“天下有道，以道殉身；天下无道，以身殉道。未闻以道殉乎人者也。”（《孟子·尽心上》）而如果一味以仁义之名去谋利，在儒家看来，就可以说是“以道殉人”了。荀子则进而具体地论说了何以“仲尼之徒无道桓文之事者”的原因。当有人问到

“仲尼之门，五尺之竖子，言羞称乎五伯。是何也?”这一问题时，荀子的回答是：“然！彼诚可羞称也。齐桓五伯之盛者也，前事则杀兄而争国；内行则姑姊妹之不嫁者七人，闺门之内，般乐奢汏，以齐之分奉之而不足；外事则诈邾袭莒，并国三十五。其事行也若是其险污淫汏也。彼固曷足称乎大君子之门哉!”（《荀子·仲尼》）概要而言，在荀子看来，即使是作为五霸之首的齐桓公，虽建立过一些功业，但却因为行事不合于道义而不足以“称乎大君子之门”。宋儒朱熹则更是直接对这一问题做出了明确回答。当有人不赞成《汉书·董仲舒传》所载“正其义不谋其利，明其道不计其功”一语，认为“仲舒说得不是。只怕不是义，是义必有利；只怕不是道，是道必有功”时，朱熹鲜明地指出：“才如此，人必求功利而为之，非所以为训也。固是得道义则功利自至，然而有得道义而功利不至者，人将于功利之徇，而不顾道义矣。仲舒所立甚高，后世之所以不如古人者，以道义功利关不透耳。”（《朱子语类》卷一百三十七）朱熹一语中的地道出了其中的症结之所在：如果为“利”而“义”，其最终结果必然是人们“不顾道义”而“徇”利。这就涉及“儒家”之所以为“儒家”的根本。作为一种成德之学，儒学所关注的中心是德性人格的成就。在儒家看来，真正的德性是高度自主而不为外在利益所左右的。而所谓“以义取利”即自觉地以“义”为旗号而行牟利之实，显然不是一种真正的道德行为。因此，如果把儒家“义利之辨”在客观效果上可以接受“因义得利”归结为“以义取利”，无论出于怎样的主观愿望，都可以说是不仅完全消解了儒家讨论“义利”问题的价值意义，而且有违于儒家的基本理论立场。这也正是古代儒者明确加以反对的基本原因。

## 四

综上所述，儒家“义利之辨”归根结底体现为一种“义以为上”（《论语·阳货》）即以德性的要求作为人之所以为人的安身立命之本的精神追求。当道义与利益、德性精神与感性欲求发生冲突时，志士仁人理当超越利益的纠结与感性的欲求而致力于对道义与德性的追求，并在其中得到精神的满足与心灵的自由。由此，超越物欲与私利的诱惑，不断提升自己的精神境界，成就以德性精神为依归的理想人格，就成为儒家精神追求的一个重要特色。所谓“不以物喜、不以己悲”；所谓“安贫乐道”、“淡泊明志”；所谓“先天下之忧而忧，后天下之乐而乐”；所谓“富贵不能淫，贫贱不能移，威武不能屈”；所谓“人生自古谁无死，留取丹心照汗青”；所谓“天地与我并生，万物与我为一”；所谓“上下与天地同流”、“仁者与万物为一体”，都是这种精神境界的不同表述方式。

在儒家思想中，是做一个孜孜以求利、放于利而行，因而无德性、无操守、肆无忌惮的小人，还是做一个义以为上、行仁践义，因而重德操、求上达，行己有耻的君子，可以说是人在梦觉关头的一次重大的生命抉择，是关系到究竟做一个真正的人还是做一个衣冠禽兽的大问题。这对于现代人无疑仍能起到相当程度的警醒作用。面对物欲横流的生存环境，现代人并没有远离究竟是做一个真正的人还是做一个衣冠禽兽的生存考验。如果说儒家传统义利观特别是其流变在某种程度上存在着对“利”注重不够的偏颇，现代社会则似乎走到了另一个极端，即单方面地把利突出到了甚至完全不顾“义”的程度。在今天，面对市场经济的冲击，要想有效地抵御拜金主义、享乐主义以及极端个人主义的侵蚀，通过提升境界而筑起精神的堤防，同样具有不可替代的重要意义。在这方面，儒家思想中“义以为上”的精神追求无疑有着重要的借鉴意义。而如何既坚持“义以为上”的主导，而又面对现代社会而达成客观效果方面的“义利双成”，更是在现代市场经济条件下儒家传统义利观的现代转化所必须认真面对的急迫而富有挑战性的时代课题。

## 二、儒学与生态

# 《周易》哲学中人与自然的和谐

韩国成均馆大学　金圣基

## 一、前言

处于地球村时代的今天，在传统文化中占有重要地位的儒家思想再次面临“恢复自我本体性”的要求和对“现代意义”问题的回答。虽然很微薄，但是各自要准备诚实的答案。这就成为儒家哲学研究者们共同肩负的责任。

本文也想为了阐明儒家哲学的现代意义，重新回味《周易》的神人关系，思考其和谐观念现代意义。

本文虽然选择了“神人关系”这一主题，但是其目的不仅仅是倾向于神人关系研究其本身。反而通过这个主题对西欧的文化，特别是宗教、神学界今天所面临的核心问题做出儒家的回答。根据笔者的见解，西欧宗教界现在正不断地受到“神观”新解释的要求。

这些要求可以简单概括为：①人格的、超越的、传统的神观念的崩溃；②重新探讨超越的价值观念；③新人观等。

本文将其中“神”观念的转变，特别是：①人格意义的神观念向发现于内在深度之神的转变；②向人生的深度和广度之神的转变理解为现代宗教性的特征，以儒家哲学和《周易》的意义为中心为其准备了答案。本文中，采取与世界宗教发展史同步的方式，同时为了确保儒家的特质围绕着：①神观念的脱人格性；②深度之神观念；③广度之神观念等三个方面分别进行考察。本文通过这种分析要阐明儒家和谐思想的主要涵义。

## 二、儒家哲学神人关系的解释框架：“绝地天之通”

那么，为了分析周易的神人关系要使用哪种解释框架？这里首先提出解释的角度。

本文拟通过《尚书·吕刑篇》的“绝地天之通”概念来提出解释的基本角度。《吕刑篇》有如下的内容：

“……民兴胥渐，泯泯棼棼，罔中于信，以覆诅盟。虐威庶戮，方告无辜于上。上帝监民，罔有馨香德，刑发闻惟惺。皇帝哀矜庶戮之不辜，报虐以威，遏绝苗民，无世在下。乃命重黎，绝地天通，罔有降格。群后之逮在下，明明棐常，鳏寡无盖。皇帝清问下民，鳏寡有辞于苗。德威惟畏，德明惟明。”

对于“绝地天通”，孔安国说：“使人神不苗，各得其序，是谓绝地天通”，所以“言天神无有降地，地祇不至于天，明不相干。”

这里再引用《国语·楚语》的内容进行补充说明。

“……昭王问于观射父曰，《周书》所谓重黎实使天地不通者，何也？若无然民将能登天？对曰，非此之谓也。古者民神不染，民之精爽不携贰者，又能齐肃衷正，其智能上下比义，其圣能光远宜朗，其明能光照之，其聪能听彻之，如是则明神降之，在男曰觋，在女曰巫。是使制神之处位次主，而为之牲器时服，而后使先圣之后有先烈，而能知山川之号，高祖之主，宗庙之事，昭穆之世，齐敬之勤，礼节之宜，威信之则，容貌之崇，忠信之质，禋絜之服，而敬恭明神者，以为之祝，使名姓之后，能知四时之生，牺牲之物，玉帛之类，采服之仪，彝器之量，次主之度，屏摄之位，坛场之所，上下之神，氏姓之初，而心率旧典者，为之宗。于是乎有神明类物之官，是谓五官，各司其序，不相乱也。民是以能有忠信，神是以能有明德，民神异业，敬而不渎，故神降之嘉生，民以物享，祸灾不至，求用不匮。及少皞之衰也，九黎乱德，民神杂糅，不可方物，夫人作享，家为巫胎，无有要质，民匮于祀，而不知其福，烝享无度，民神同位，民渎齐盟，无有严威，神狎民则，不蠲其为，嘉生不降，无物以享，祸灾荐臻，莫尽其气。颛顼受之，乃命南正重司天以属神，命火正黎司地以属民，使复旧常，无相侵渎，是谓绝地天通。”

分析本文的内容，可以看出其中包括以下的几个特征。

第一，按照孔安国的说明，“绝地天通”是人和神互不纠缠、互不妨碍的状态，人和神各自维持着自身秩序的状态（使人神不扰，各得其序），在这种状态下天神不会降临到地界加以干涉，地神也不想登上天界，分明是互不干涉的状态。

孔颖达和《国语·楚语》也分别把“绝地天通”说明为“民神不杂”和“民神异业”的状态，将其设定为神人关系的理想状态。尤其是《国语》中，“民神异业”状态被描述为民有忠信之德、神有明德的状态，“绝地天通”状态是民与神各自实现自己理想的最和谐的状态。

第二，与此相反，民神关系不理想的状态则表现为“民神杂糅”和“民神同位”。这是神与人的世界混杂的状态，其结果灾难频繁降临，出现民神不互敬、互相鄙视的状态（敬而不渎）。

第三，因此，为了克服这种民神不和谐的状态，恢复理想状态而提出的就是“绝地天通”。这个“绝地天通”的目的在于恢复从前的“民神异业”和“民神不染”，使民神互不干涉（使复旧常，无相侵渎）。

第四，“绝地天通”要求给人设定一个最合理的地天关系，即神人关系，其要求可以概括为“对神人关系的适度限制”。其实这种思维形态可以在孔子那里找到，即是“敬而远之”的态度。可见儒家哲学是为了摸索并设定神人关系的合理关系而努力的。

但是，要想把“绝地天通”的观点作为本文论述的角度，就有必要对以下的几点进行说明。

第一，“绝地天通”概念与所谓儒家哲学特征的“天人合一”概念具有相反的意思。怎么能说明这个关系？对于这个问题，本文首先同意“天人合一”概念相当具有说服力，只不过这个概念的成立时期至少要和《中庸》、《易传》内容的成立时期是接近的。这里存在如何说明“天人合一”观点成立以前时期的问题，仔细寻味“绝地天通”的意思就能说明“天人合一”以前思维形态的发展过程。总之，经过“天人不杂”、“天人相通”、“天人合一”等结构上的变化，先秦儒家的思维框架得以完成，这时“天人合一”、“民神合一”概念才具有说服力。

即是说，为了说明儒家哲学的特征，与其从一开始就为导出“天人合一”概念而努力，不如经过“天人矛盾”、“天人感通”等阶段之后再导出“天人合一”的概念。这反而在世界“宗教史”的观点上也会具有说服力。只不过，强调“天人合一”概念在更早的先秦时期就已经基本完成了，能突出儒家的特质。

有必要把这种神人关系的结构变化作为理解《周易》或儒家哲学的关键，对其进行具体的分析和解释。

最后，“绝地天通”概念还可以看作是留给人类的一个新课题，即在“合理而妥当”的程度上将神人关系的结构变化设定下去。本文在周易神人关系的解释上适用这个观点，并且作为其具体方法，考察从设定为神人关系原始出发点的“民神异业”到“民神合一”的内容，从而阐明其现代意义。

## 三、周易神人关系的结构：“民神相分”

### （一）周易的原初神观念：“高度之神”

现在来考察本文的主题——周易神人关系的特质。

众所周知，周易是由卦和爻、卦辞和爻辞组成的“经”部分及其解说内容“传”部分，即“十翼”所构成。

首先从《易经》是占筮书的事实入手开始我们的讨论。占筮，即占卜行为才是《易经》的原始目的和功效。

在占筮已经具有掌握神的旨意的意义上，我们可以看出它具有很强的“高度之神”，即传统意义上的人格性、超越性的性格。

作为表示《周易》的原初神概念，可以例举帝、天、神。《易经》卦爻辞里出现几处在外观上具有人格意义的宗教性、咒术性的帝、天概念。有《大有卦·上九》爻辞“自天祐之，吉无不利”和《益卦·六二》爻辞“王用享于帝，吉”。此外，还有《豫卦·象传》的“殷荐之上帝，以配祖考”和《涣卦·象传》的“先王以享于帝，立庙”等等。通过以上的文章可以看出，《易经》的帝、天概念表现为赐予人类帮助的主宰者和祭祀的对象。这证明《易经》的卦爻辞与古代殷周代的上帝、帝出自同一脉络，很好地反映了当时具有人格神意义的宗教性、咒术性的世界观。

直接考察《易传》的神观念，可以发现其中还保留着传统的意义。下面看一下《易传》中具有传统观念的天神、鬼神、神灵意义的解释。

鬼神害盈而福谦。(《谦卦·彖传》)

天地盈虚，与时消息，而况于人乎，况于鬼神乎？(《丰卦·彖传》)

圣人以神道设教。(《观卦·彖传》)

以上，鬼神观念被描写为能给人的吉凶祸福带来一定影响的存在，可见它包含着传统意义。然而它的意义仅仅是依据天地自然的循环规律，已经很难找到从前具有主宰性、创造性意义的人格性了。

以上考察了《周易》神观念含有上古以来的传统意义。不能否认，这时的神观念多少含有一些宗教性、咒术性的意义。

（二）人与神的连接：“占筮之神明”

前面我们已经谈过《周易》本为占筮而作。占筮的意义原本在于设定神人关系，人问神的旨意，可见在某种程度上已经提示了神人关系的结构。

根据考古学的报告，人类从新石器后期开始用各种各样的占卜方法来预测吉凶。殷代使用龟壳的占卜活动形成主流，当时的占卜活动把人类的吉凶原因归结为神的旨意。这时，人类占卜行为的目的不是为了认识客观世界，而是为了把握神的意志。对于所有事情，他们都必须通过占卜来决定行动（每事必卜），最终的判断依据是甲骨裂开的形状，人只能服从和信仰占卜的结果（听命行事期）。

即，这时占卜是连接神与人之间关系的唯一交通手段。周初，作为神与人的连接手段，占筮形成主流，还并用了卜占。

如前所述，《周易》以占筮为目的出发，毕竟其首要目的在于阐明占的神妙功效，这时神人关系也表现为领悟占筮之神明，要与神的旨意合一的形态。因此《易经》到处都并存着对卜筮之神明的信赖。可以说，《周易》是从确保“占筮之神明”出发的，以此为基础摸索“人之神明”转变的过程就是周易的成立过程。

现在看一下关于具有原始意义的“占筮”功能的内容。

昔者圣人之作易也，幽于神明而生蓍。

这里，“作易”的目的是为了阐发“神明”，反映其意志，为此创造了使用蓍草的占筮法。这说明“作易”的原来目的转向认识超越“神明”的领域并把握其意志的一环。这与原来的卜筮精神是同出一辙的。因此，“占筮”功能被描述为《周易》的重要部分。

《易》有圣人之道四焉：以言者尚其辞，以动者尚其变，以制器者尚其象，以卜筮者尚其占。是以君子将有为也，将有行也，问焉而以言，其受命也如向，无有远近幽深，遂知来物。非天下之至精，其孰能与于于此？

将占筮包含在易之“四德”中，是了解占筮在《易》中所占地位的重要手段。对于这种占筮功能的信赖是人类的行动原理——通过占卜来获得行动指南的传统占筮态度有效发挥了作用。

对于占筮的这种态度，当然表现出对神与人的媒介——蓍草的信赖。《系辞传》中有“蓍之德，圆而神”的描述，朱子对此说明：“圆神，谓变化无方。”表现了对蓍草功能的变化无常和神秘感的信赖。

此外，对占筮功能的信赖还表现在下面这段高度评价蓍龟的文章中。

探赜索隐，钩深致远，以定天下之吉凶，成天下之亹亹者，莫大乎蓍龟。

从以上内容可以看出，周易的神人关系包含着一定程度的传统关系，这时占筮是神人关系的唯一交通手段。

## 四、周易神人关系的转变：“民神相通”

### （一）神观念的转变：“变化之神”

我们在上一章考察了《周易》原始观念中的神观念和具有主宰性、人格性特征的传统的帝、王、神等思维体系在一定程度上出自同一脉络。神依然具有人格的、超越的属性，维持着人处于“受命者”地位的基本结构。

人们为了摸索神人关系的合理关系而做出的努力首先依赖的还是“神的命令”，这时神人关系的连接点是“占筮之神明”。这种以“高度之神”为本，将“占筮之神明”作为交通手段的结构，由于春秋末期占筮思想上的变化已经暗示着新的思维体系即将到来。

随着人类智慧的发展《易经》通过新的思维体系来解释神人关系的努力再一次开

花结果，使其面貌焕然一新。如果和我们的主题联系起来看，可以说为“绝地天通”结构创造了重新解释的空间。这种变化同时出现在《易传》的两个方面：一个是神观念的变化，另一个是人的地位与作用的变动。而且，这两种变化在“绝地天通”的结构分析框架中，以连接神与人的交通手段的变化产生作用，完成了新的转变，这时神人关系的结构从“卜筮之神明”变为“人之神明”，将易经哲学的意义提高了一个层次。

那么，我们来看一下《易传》中神观念的内容是如何转变的。首先《易传》的神观念中“传统宗教咒术层次的实体性神观念”表现出强调宇宙秩序的“神妙”及其“不可测性”等作用的“脱实体化”的倾向。例如：

“阴阳不测之谓神。”

值得注意的是，这里是从“阴阳不测”的观点上看“神”的意义的。就是说，神概念从超越性、人格性的意义上摆脱出来，进行“阴阳变化之奥妙”的意义转变。对于这个“神”，孔颖达在《周易正义》中说：

“天下万物，皆由阴阳或生或成，本其所由之理，不可测量之谓神也。”

韩康伯也对“神”说：

“神也者，变化之极，妙万物而为言，不可以形诘者也，故曰阴阳不测。”

以上可以看出，“神”被解释为阴阳变化的极致及其神妙的“不可测性”。通过《系辞传》的其他文章来看一下这种例子：

神无方而易无体。

这里也提到了“神”的“无实体”和“不可测性”。即是说，因为神的奥妙没有一定的场所和方向，所以无法预测。而且变化无穷，没有一定的形体。孔颖达指出，“无方、无体”分别具有两个含义。“无方”的含义：一个是看不到“神”的处所，另一个是由于“神”的周游运动而不常在一处。“无体”的含义：一个是因为其变化是自然形成的，所以不知道变化的根源，另一个是由于它是随着变化而移动的，所以不固定在一个实体上。

以上也能看出“易”的不可测性和神妙的意义。在《说卦传》中也能找到这种例子：

“神也者，妙万物而为言者也。”

这里所谓“神”，是指大自然的运行规律的神妙。关于“易”本体之无整形性、作用之奥妙的议论，还可以举出下面的例子：

“易无思也，无为也，寂然不动，感而遂通天下之故，非天下之至神，其孰能与于此。”

当我们说“易”包含着宇宙万物的原理时，其作用和属性表现为无思、无为、寂然不动的状态，于是和万物感应，通达天下的道理。“至神”是说，只有天下的至极神妙，才能参与到这个原理之中。这里为“至神”解释为“易”的本质、主体——圣人的最高境界保留着余地。因此不是把“天下之至神”局限在蓍草或占筮的本质上，而是解释为“圣人之心”的见解反而更为妥当。

以上我们考察了《易经》的“神”观念向“神妙”、“不可测”等概念非实体化的过程。

在“神”观念的转变中，作为人格性、超越性实体概念的“神”转变为非实体化的“神”概念，其意义也转向“神妙”、“不可测性”等。这在易经哲学意义的发展阶段中，对下一个“神”观念转换到体现人的最高德性的阶段起到了承前启后的作用。

（二）人与神的连接：“人之神明”

《周易》的神观念实现了在“神妙”、“不可测性”等内容上的变化，从人的角度来看，人又被赋予了重新解释“绝地天通”的可能性。如果《周易》的原始神观念能理解为“高度之神”，这时人与神的合理通道是“卜筮之神明”，那么在神以“神妙”、“不可测性”等新的超越性观念登场的今天，人将如何重新解释这个“神”的世界？

本文将重点放在从“高度之神”到“深度之神”的意义转变中在人的观点上设定的新内容的讨论上。

《周易》的神观念从传统观念中摆脱出来转变为“神妙”、“不可测性”等，而需要注意的是价值根源者的移动这一事实。如果说过去是帝、天、神作为价值的根源者主管所有人间事，又作为吉凶祸福的主宰者统治人间，那么现在的神不再作为价值的根源者而存在。因此，人是站在掌握天地宇宙的神妙道理并立法的新价值的根源者的立场上。即，站在要重新解释“神”的主体、主人公——人的立场上。现在看一下其内容。首先《系辞传》说：

“精义入神，以致用也。”

如果“入神”是指人进入神妙的境界，那么作为其方法而提出的“精义”则是精密地穷究事物的道理。这里有必要更仔细地考察一下作为“入神”条件而提出的“精义”的意义。

如果说“精义”是使天地万物达到奥妙的神明境界的方法，那么作为其具体内容，首先《周易》提出了“观”、“见”、“察”、“知”等方法。这里的“观”是比较广义上的观察，“见”则是狭义上的观察。

古者包犧氏之王天下也，仰则观象于天，俯则观法于地，观鸟兽之文与地之宜，近取诸身，远取诸物，于是始作八卦，以通神明之德，以类万物之情。

这里，“观”是观察“天”、“地”、“鸟兽之文”、“地之宜”等自然的人的观察活动，这种活动为可以说是“易”成立的关键——八卦奠定了基础。然后通过它达到

“通天下之志”。这说明“观”的方法成为通达事物神明的出发点。《系辞上传》第四章里还有描述“观”与“察”的方法成为“知幽明之故”、“知死生之说”、“知鬼神之情状”的第一步的内容。

而且作为“见”的方法，圣人看到天下万物的深奥原理（见天下之赜），在此基础上制成卦象，看到天下万物的运动（见天下之动），从中找出普遍规范，运用到实际行动上。这时又出现了“见”的方法。“见”也成为接近万物“神妙”的方法。

与“观见”的方法同时作为人进入“精义”境界的方法提出了“察微”、“知几”等。“微”是“事之始”，“几”是“动之微”。所以，人通过“观见”的方法来培养宏观观察宇宙的眼光，同时通过“察知”的方法继续对宇宙万物进行微观观察，从而人成为具有“极高明”、“尽精微”能力的主体，进入“入神，致用”的境界。例如，“观乎天文以察时变”、“俯以察于地理”、“明于天之道而察于民之故”、“彰往而察来”中，“察”的对象是“时变”、“地理”、“民之故”等，与“观”相比较，可以看出其对象已经扩大到更加具体而细致的部分。

另外，“知几”也被作为从“精义”到“入神，致用”阶段的关键而提出。

再来看一下“入神，以致用”的关键——“知几”。

几者，动之微，吉之先见者也，君子见几而作，不俟终日。

作为人进入“神”领域的条件提出“知几”。如果说“几”是“动之微”，体会“几”就是“知神”的基本。“动之微”主要有三种解释：第一，“动之微”；第二，“心念初动时”；第三，“动之奥妙处”。其中第三种解释最接近于本意。以上可以看出“几”具有征兆的含义。

以上的方法在《易传》中又被提示为“极深研几”的方法。

夫《易》，圣人之所以极深而研几也。唯深也，故能通天下之志；唯几也，故能成天下之务；唯神也，故不疾而速，不行而至。

对此朱子认为，“研”是审察，“几”是微妙，“极深”是通过“至精”而实现，“研几”是通过“至变”而可行。对于“精义入神”的方法，他同时提出了“至精”和“至变”，可见是一个卓见。

通过以上的途径，人不断地摸索通往“神”领域的道路，达到“知微知彰”、“知柔知刚”的境界，就接近“精义入神，以致用也”的实现了。

然而，易经哲学中作为神人关系的连接构造所提出的“观见”、“察知”等活动，并不是西欧的那种纯粹的抽象的理性工作，而是将人的主体自觉精神全部投入到宇宙万物中，体验到宇宙万物规律的神妙境界，然后再把它归纳为一种普遍的原理。在这个过程中，不但能掌握、建立“易道”，还能进一步摸索出宇宙的神秘原理与人类智慧合一的境界。

在这种意义上想再次回味一下，“神”的意义向神妙的宇宙原理的转变，在从单纯受命者的立场上摆脱出来的人的主体自觉精神的基础上摸索与“易本体”合一的过程所具有的意义。

## 五、周易神人关系的转变:“民神合一”

（一）神观念的转变:“深度之神”

《周易》的神观念，从人格性、超越性、主宰性的“神”转变为“神妙”、“不可测”等脱实体化的“神”，人与神的关系也从“卜筮之神明”中摆脱出来，在人的主体能力下不断探索着宇宙的神妙。

现在再看一下《周易》神概念又一次实现转变，成为体现人主体德性最高状态的概念的内容。

《孟子》里，神概念从人格性、主宰性、宗教性的神观念发生转变，作为形容人内在德性的“神”概念来使用。即，大而化之之谓圣，圣而不可知之之神。君子所存者神，所过者化，上下与天地同流。

这里作为人德性的最高阶段举出“神”的境界。这种转变被《易传》和《中庸》所继承，通过深化发展得以确立。

现在看一下《易传》中“神”观念被用于形容人的神明德性的例子。正如前面从《说卦传》“幽赞于神明而生蓍”中所看到的，《易》“神明”的原来概念是具有超越世界或宗教领域意义的用语。因此，这个“神明”的境界就成为圣人，即人所要达到的目标，这也是“作易”的主要动机。然而这个具有超越性意义的“神明”境界被专用于表示人的德性或其德性的神明境界。例如:

子曰，乾坤其易之门邪，乾阳物也，坤阴物也，阴阳合德而刚柔有体，以体天地之撰，以通神明之德。

又如前面引用过的《系辞下传》的文章:

“于是始作八卦，以通神明之德，以类万万物之情。”

由此可以看出，“作易”的动机在于与天地万物的“神明”之德合一。

《易传》中“神”的意义又一次转变为新的意义，即是从宇宙的“神妙”、“不可测性”等意义转变为表现人的德性的意义。这时的“神”当然不是人格神，也不是单纯表示宇宙的神秘原理——不可测性，而是表示体会了宇宙奥妙的人的德性境界处于最高状态。例如，《系辞传》说:

“子曰，知几其神乎？君子上交不谄，下交不渎，其知几乎!”

即，君子是知道“几微”的人，这时作为表示君子德性境界的形容词来使用的是

"神"。传统神观念的意义转变为表现人的德性的最高境界。这样的例子还出现在："唯神也，故不疾而速，不行而至。"这段文章的意思是说："因为圣人善于体会易的神秘原理的本质，所以似不见其急速，而自然快速，似不见其行，而能到达"。即是说，因为《易》中"神"的作用被理解为神秘而不可测，所以这里的"神"也是表现圣人德性的程度。再看其他例子：

"易无思也，无为也，寂然不动，感而遂通天下之故，非天下之至神，其孰能与于此。"

这里的"至神"在表现易的深奥功能的同时，也表现了圣人在"极深研几"之后所具有的德性的高度境界。

最能表现神观念向人内在德性转变的例子正是下面这段文章：

"神而明之，存乎其人。"

这里明确指出，《易经》的重点归结为"其人"和"德行"，《易经》的所有卦爻变通的原理只有通过人才能得到发挥。如果说前面提到的"神明"的原意是表示外在的"神"的领域或超越的世界，那么现在"神明"的意义则在于它是赋予人的一个"人"的领域。由此《易》"神明"的主题和关心领域从卜筮功效或占卜功能终于发展到以"人之神明"为主要对象的完成阶段。这就意味着，成就神明的责任也转到了人的身上。下面关于"神明的主体是人"的解释恰到好处地表现了本文的意思：

"心者神明之舍。如果人能洗尽尘埃，则此心的寂静与神明合一。为了占卜而摊开蓍草茎求卦时，如果能斋戒，则此心动而与神明相通。有心则有神。"

这是说，"易道"最终是由人的德行来发见的。又说明这时人的心成为神明的居所，从而实现了"人之神明"与"神之神明"的合一。

（二）民与神的连接："神之神明"与"人之神明"的合一

以上我们看到了《周易》的神观念完成了表现体会宇宙奥妙的人的德性境界处于最高状态的意义转变，可见这时已经打开了"神之神明"与"人之神明"合一的可能性。那么，这里简单考察一下合一的具体内容。

如前所述，"精义入神，以致用也"中的"入神"是经过"精义"过程以后达到的境界。首先举出表现这一阶段的文章。《系辞传》说：

"显道神德行，是故可与酬酢，可与祐神矣。子曰，知变化之道者，其知神之所为乎？"

这里的"显道"有两种含义：第一，天道由此而彰显；第二，仁道由此而发扬，即"弘道"。"神德行"的"神"作为动词，是使"德行"达到形而上的境界。

此外，表现"人之神明"的文章是：

"过此以往，未之或知也，穷神知化，德之盛也。"

这里，从治用和崇德实现神化，能够“穷神”、“知化”的根据就在于“德之盛”。有趣的是，这里提示了一个“德”一旦成熟就会达到“穷神知化”境界的超越的归纳式模型。

另外，《易传》中“斋戒”或“洗心”等也都是完成“人之神明”的方法。

而这些各种各样的方法能联系到《易传》中的“感应”、“感通”的方法。《系辞传》中这样说道：

“易无思也，无为也，寂然不动，感而遂通天下之故。”

这里，“易”虽然也是指易的本质——占筮的功能，但是之所以人能够察觉到这种事物的动向和几微，终究是因为人具有“感通”的能力。

这里提示的“感通”、“感应”的方式，在《易经》中作为通达万物道理的方法受到高度重视。

人“穷神知化”、“斋戒”、“神明其德夫”、“感通”、“法天地”等取决于连接神与人关系的交通方法——人的德性，这种能力是通达宇宙万物的原理，实现神人合一的途径。

《易传》中，这种人与神的领域合一的形态主要表现在《乾卦·文言传》中：

“夫大人者，与天地合其德，与日月合其明，与四时合其序，与鬼神合其吉凶……”

这里的“大人”是与天地和日月、四时和鬼神等合其神明的存在。

## 六、周易神人关系的扩展：“广度之神”

《周易》的神概念，通过“精义”、“入神”的阶段不断地重新解释与人的关系，形成了易的本质。那么，现在来看一下《周易》神人关系的最终意义到底在哪里。

《周易》的“神”观念最终的关注点在哪里？

前面所举的“精义入神，以致用也”的例子，说明“神”的解释最终是与“致用”相连。《周易》中把这种关系描述为：屈行虫把身子屈缩起来，是为了伸展身体；龙蛇深藏在洞穴里，是为了保全自身。同样对于人来说，精义、入神是为了致用，即是为了将来利用它成就天下大事。铃木由次郎说，“以致用也”是“成就天下之大事业”。

“致用”一词还可见于《系辞上传》第十一章：

“备物致用，立成器以为天下利，莫大乎圣人。”

即，按照孔颖达的解释，“致用”就是“天下所用”。而且它和“天下利”的意义是相通的。

“致用”和“开物成务”也具有同样的意义。即“开物成务”，是指“开发创造万物以创造未来”、“成就和完成天下万物应尽的职责”。

以上考察了“致用”的意义，接下来将“致用”的意义与“利”的概念联系起来加以理解。

下面举出《周易》中说明卦爻变化的最终目的在于“利百姓”“事业”的例子：

“子曰，圣人立象以尽意，设卦以尽情伪，系辞焉以尽其言，变而通之以尽利，鼓之舞之以尽神。”

以上“变而通之以尽利”中，卦爻变化最终关心的焦点在于百姓之“利”，进而用《易经》的道理鼓舞天下之人尽到神化妙用。而且说明，“鼓舞尽神”是尽神明的方法论，同时也是说达到的境界是神妙不测的境界。

再看一下“利”表示什么。《易经》中是怎样给百姓带来“利”的？《乾卦·文言传》说：

“乾元者，始而亨者也，利贞者，性情也，乾始能以美利利天下，不言所利，大矣哉！”

这里，“以美利利天下”的意思是说，用最美的利益利天下。众所周知，其实儒家哲学对于“利”并非持有肯定态度。可是《论语》中却有体现儒家所追求的“利”的真正意义的文章。《尧曰篇》说：

“子曰，因民之所利而利之，斯不亦惠而不费乎？”

儒家所追求的“利”，是指“民之所利”。《大学》说：“此谓国不以利为利，以义为利也”，把儒家的“利”规定为“以义为利”。在此基础上，可以看出《乾卦·文言传》的“美利”与儒家的“利”出自同一脉络。《集解》中也把“美利”解释为“云行雨施，品物流形，故利天下也”，认为“美利”之所以能成为“美利”，其根本原因在于“云行雨施，品物流形”。这里的“云行雨施，品物流形”是谓“云行雨施，品物流形，言亨也。天道运行，生育万物也。”易经哲学中“利”的含义还表现在《乾卦·文言传》“利者，义之和也”、“利物足以和义”中。对“利者，义之和也”的意义，王船山做出明确的解释。

“义之和”者，生物各有其义而得其宜，物情各和顺于适然之数，故利也。

《坤卦》的注释中，也将“利”说明为“益物而合义”。综合起来看，万物是各自具有事物固有之理的独立存在，能够满足这些事物维持其固有性的最佳条件的状态是“利”。因此可以看出，所谓“益物”，是指让万物施展其固有的道理。王船山的“益物而合义”不仅顺应了儒家“以义为利”的态度，而且最适合表现《易传》中“利”的含义。

这种“利”的含义还表现在《系辞传》“制器尚象”的利民精神上。“制器尚象”的基本精神是观察天地间的一切道理，用这种道理为百姓谋“利”。这说明，儒家和《易传》的“利”可以延伸到开创文物典章，谋求文明进步。

以上，通过“利”的概念我们解释了“精义，入神，以致用也”的含义。概括来说，“精义，入神”的目的在于“致用”，这个“致用”的具体内容是为天下万物保障合理的“利”。在这种意义上可以看出，下面这段文章包含着《周易》“神”概念的解释中最重要的意义。

民咸用之谓之神。

对此吴怡说，“所谓‘民咸用之’，是指不脱离人们日常生活的东西。这才是真正的‘神之用’。这句话虽然是说‘神’确实是阴阳不测的，但也绝非空话。这正是‘显诸仁，藏诸用。’”

以上，“神”的意义与我们的日常生活密切地联系在一起，成为与我们合一的概念。

现在本文对“神人关系”的解释似乎可以得出结论了。

变而通之而尽利，鼓之舞之以尽神。

万物生命最和谐的保障和鼓舞激励我们所有人都达到神妙境界，就是《周易》神人关系的意义最终所要达到的智慧。

这时，民与神是合一的。

## 七、结论

现在我们将在《周易》神人关系解释的基础上考察其所具有的和谐意义，以此作为本论文的结论。

目前为止，对于易经哲学中出现的神人关系的特征，主要是通过原文分析来考察其演变过程。《周易》神观念原来是与形成于夏殷周时代的帝、天、神等概念出自同一脉络，而到了《易传》便形成了与前代有所不同的独特的神观。神概念的特征表现为：①脱实体化的本体概念的确立；②脱人格性、超越性概念的意义转变；③作为人德性的“深度”之神；④作为人生与生活中的“和谐”之神。在这里，被称之为儒家哲学特征的“天人合一”一词才可以成立。这时，本体与人合为一体，开启了由人的主体自觉直接通达本体意识的可能性，从而不同于西方。

本文为了理解神人关系而致力于直接分析周易的原文，但前提是对现时代所面临的文化危机要具有基本的角度。特别是为了恢复儒家的自我本体性，如果能认识到在世界思想史、宗教史的意义中儒家的定位是非常重要的，那么对现状的基本角度将是非常重要的。

笔者认为，贯通 20 世纪 20 年代以后西欧神学及宗教学的观点是“世俗化”。“世俗化”无疑是西欧宗教今天的现状。虽然不能提出所有“世俗化”的错综复杂的理论，但是作为共同关心理论的宗教的衰退、神观念的崩溃、超越世界与超自然世界的崩溃等，都要求我们具有相当深刻而冷静的辨别力。首先现代宗教学或神学给我们的教训是，有必要从我们的角度以更加积极的态度去了解对方，确立对话的观点。无论怎样，在这个时代儒家热切渴望着与基督教或西欧宗教思想的相遇，但绝对不是他们的上帝、超越和原罪观念等。

我们要注意，在先秦时代儒家就已经成功地去除了高水准的神话和巫术的领域，至少已经从现时代西欧文化的共同现象——“解体的中心”摆脱出来。平凡中的伟大、日常中的求道早已超越“圣俗二分法”，提出最有说服力的在现代宗教神学的情况下所渴望的“真正超越”的意义。在这种意义上，要注意第二章的基本角度：儒家的出发点本身经历了神人之间脱咒术、脱神话的思想过程，将“有节制的相遇”设定为理想的状态，进而把适度超越的态度——“敬而远之”作为儒家哲学的出发点。分别通过第三章“周易的出发点也是宗教史上共有的咒术、迷信的阶段，被逐步机智地克服”，第四章和第五章“神观念从脱人格性、主宰性、垂直性的神观念中摆脱出来，转变为‘人生深度之神’、‘人内在的深度之神’”，第六章“‘在人生当中’神观念具有的意义”等方面重新解释其意义。

《周易》的64卦384爻要求所有人每时每刻在主体判断下度过真正的人生，可以说是最明智地成就了“宗教的日常化”、“神的真正超越”。这才是儒家哲学送给现代世俗化时代的最卓越的“含蓄意义”。从这个观点来看，儒家思想不仅会有无穷无尽的重新解释的空间，其在现代思潮中具有的意义也将得到重新评价。

夫大人者，与天地合其德，与日月合其明，与四时合其序，与鬼神合其吉凶……

这里的“大人”是与天地和日月、四时和鬼神等合其神明的存在。

这就是周易人与自然的和谐思想之内含。

# 浅谈《诗经》中的儒家生态伦理思想

天津师范大学　杜　勇

《诗经》是我国西周初年至春秋中叶的诗歌总集，自汉代以来就一直被奉为儒学经典之一。孔子说："不学《诗》，无以言。"（《论语·季氏》）强调它对规范个人言行的重要作用，以及外交辞令中赋诗见意的特殊功能。孔子又说："《诗》三百，一言以蔽之，曰'思无邪'。"（《论语·为政》）"思"字在《诗·鲁颂·駉》中本为语词，无义，孔子沿袭当时赋诗断章的风习，把它作为一个实词来使用，认为《诗经》的思想是纯正无邪的。《礼记·经解》记孔子说："其为人也，温柔敦厚，诗教也。"儒家重视《诗》对人道德修养的教化作用，说明《诗经》在一定程度上代表了儒家学说的价值取向。因此，深入探讨《诗经》中的儒家生态伦理观念，对于继承中国优秀传统文化，大力推进当今生态文明建设，不失为一件有意义的工作。

《诗经》本是文学作品，当然不可能直接阐述某种理论学说，但它通过文学意象表达出某种思想观念，却给人以启迪和影响。在人与自然的关系问题上，《诗经》蕴含着丰富的生态伦理思想，可以大体归纳为以下三个方面。

## 一、关爱自然的环境友好观念

《诗经》时代，生态环境尚未恶化，对经济社会发展亦未造成严重威胁。但在长期的生活实践中，先民们逐渐认识到人类与自然环境有着密切的依存关系，初步形成了关爱自然、以物为友的生态伦理观念。这在《诗经》运用赋、比、兴的艺术手法时有较多的体现。

赋、比、兴的表现手法在《诗经》中被广为运用，它所凭借的审美对象主要是自然界中的动植物和山水景物。这种选择不是随意的，实际是先民们热爱自然、寄情自然的思想写照。

《诗经·周南·葛覃》是一首描写女子准备回家探望父母的诗。首章云：

"葛之覃兮，施于中谷，维叶萋萋。黄鸟于飞，集于灌木，其鸣喈喈。"

诗人采用赋的艺术手法，描写山谷中蔓延着清碧的葛藤、飞翔着鸣啭的黄雀、生长着繁茂的灌木丛，展示出一幅动植物和谐相依的美丽画面，寄托着女主人公将与父母团聚的喜悦之情。《郑风·溱洧》是一首游春诗，描写郑国三月上巳节青年男女在溱河、洧河岸边的踏青活动。关于诗的表现手法，朱熹《诗集传》以为是“赋而兴”，其实只是赋。篇首“溱与洧，方涣涣兮”两句，作用不在起兴，溱水、洧水实际是诗中人物活动的场景，是“且往观乎”的踏青对象，故为赋法。游春的男女手持兰草和勺药，来到溱河与洧河岸边，去迎接春天的光临，去寻求爱的心迹。河水涣涣，冰雪消融，清澈微激，一派春意盎然的景象。在这春天的日子里，溱水、洧水给人们带来喜悦和满足，成为人们深情眷恋的审美对象。《小雅·无羊》一诗，歌咏牛羊蕃盛，畜牧兴旺。首章描写牛羊众多，“三百维群”，呈现出羊角簇立、牛耳耸动的奇妙景象。次章写散布四近的牛羊，“或降于阿，或饮于池，或寝或讹”，即有的在山坡缓缓下行，有的去山涧俯首饮水，有的卧草而眠，有的半睡半醒，何其自得！《魏风·伐檀》写劳动人民对剥削阶级不劳而获发出正义的责问：“不稼不穑，胡取禾三百廛兮？不狩不猎，胡瞻尔庭有县貆兮？彼君子兮，不素餐兮？”但篇首三句直赋伐木之事：“坎坎伐檀兮，寘之河之干兮，河水清且涟猗”，表明这些伐木工在艰辛的劳动中，即使对剥削者心怀强烈不满，也仍然对微波起伏的清澈河水保持着一种亲近亲和的情致，倾注着人们对大自然的热爱与赞美。

《诗经·小雅·鹤鸣》全篇描写自然景物，以比人事。诗中写道：

“鹤鸣于九皋，声闻于天。鱼在于渚，或潜或渊。乐彼之园，爰有树檀，其下维榖。它山之石，可以攻玉。”

诗中用来比喻的事物，或为动植物，或为山石，其中以鹤、鱼、树、石比喻贤人，以榖（楮树）比喻小人，表达出一种广为罗致人才、为国所用的渴望。《大雅·卷阿》有云：“凤凰鸣矣，于彼高冈。”是说凤凰在高冈上鸣叫，叫声震动四野，比喻周朝人才济济，各得其所。《小雅·车辖》中“高山仰止，景行行止”的诗句，以高山大路比喻人的崇高德行。《周南·汉广》云：“南有乔木，不可休思。汉有游女，不可求思。汉之广矣，不可泳思。江之永矣，不可方思。”以汉水、长江的宽广难渡为喻，表达出诗人对“汉有游女”的企慕难求之情。

《诗经·周南·关雎》是描写一位青年热恋采集荇菜女子的诗。其一、二章云：

“关关雎鸠，在河之洲。窈窕淑女，君子好逑。/参差荇菜，左右采之。窈窕淑女，寤寐求之。”

诗中以河水、沙洲为山水背景，以雎鸠相随和鸣起兴，描写主人公愁肠百结、缠绵悱恻的爱情追求。《召南·草虫》云：“喓喓草虫，趯趯阜螽。未见君子，忧心忡忡。”诗以蝈蝈（草虫）、蚱猛（阜螽）起兴，倾吐妻子对远行丈夫的忧思。《秦风·蒹葭》首章云："蒹葭苍苍，白露为霜。所谓伊人，在水一方。溯洄从之，道阻且长。溯游从之，宛在水中央。"其中前两句用于起兴，描绘秋日清晨，水边芦苇上的露珠结成斑斑白霜，凄清苍凉，借以反映主人公苦苦追求在水一方的意中人，虽近在咫尺却遥不可及的迷茫。

《诗经》用赋、比、兴的表现手法，把自然万物纳入审美视野，虽然不是直接对大自然的讴歌，却寄寓着人们对大自然热爱与友好的情感。这种价值取向实际代表着一种最为基本的生态伦理观念，与先秦儒家思想多相契合。孔子说："诗，可以兴，可以观，可以群，可以怨。迩之事父，远之事君。多识于鸟兽草木之名。"（《论语·阳货》）这是说诗三百除了具有兴观群怨的诗教作用外，还可让人对动植物多一些认知。这种认知固然有利于增长人的博物学知识，但增长知识的目的在于运用，从而使"多识于鸟兽草木之名"蕴含着关爱自然、与物为友的思想意义。孔子又说："知者乐水，仁者乐山。"（《论语·雍也》）认为热爱山水自然、乐观山水风光是仁智之举。孟子主张："亲亲而仁民，仁民而爱物。"（《孟子·尽心上》）把对人民的仁爱推及自然万物，同样是难能可贵的生态伦理情怀。

## 二、取用有度的生态保护观念

《诗经》时代，先民们对大自然的热爱与友善，不只出于审美活动的需求，也因为大自然为人们生产生活提供了不可或缺的物质资源。珍惜自然资源，取用有度，保护生态环境，以时禁发，这种实践层面的行为规范进一步丰富了当时的生态伦理内容。

《诗经·小雅·黍苗》是徒役赞美召穆公营治谢邑之功的作品。诗中写道："原隰既平，泉流既清。召伯有成，王心则宁。"这是说召伯在营治谢邑的同时，还将高田低地修治平整，井泉河流疏理清澈，使谢邑具备良好的生态环境。《鄘风·定之方中》云："定之方中，作于楚宫。揆之以日，作于楚室。树之榛栗，椅桐梓漆，爰伐琴瑟。"春秋时期，卫文公在齐桓公帮助下，迁都楚丘，重建卫国。诗中说卫文公除了兴建"楚宫"、"楚室"外，还大量种植榛、栗、椅、桐、梓、漆等多种名贵树木。这既有取其果实用作祭品，取其材质制作琴瑟的目的，也是为了改善和优化自己的生存空间，营造一个美丽宜居的生态环境。

由于人们认识到对自然环境的过分索取和干预将会带来不利影响，所以对保护生态资源和维系生态平衡格外重视。《诗经·周南·麟之趾》云："麟之趾，振振公子，于嗟麟兮。"在古人眼中麟是仁义之兽，陆玑《毛诗草木鸟兽虫鱼疏》说它"不履生虫，不践生草"。诗人用不践踏幼虫小草的麟趾来比喻贵族公子的仁厚与贤能，也是对其精心保护自然生态行为的礼赞。《大雅·行苇》云："敦彼行苇，牛羊勿践履。方苞方体，维叶泥泥。”这是说路旁的芦苇，绿叶初生，含苞未放，不能让牛羊践踏，以利于生长。《大雅·旱麓》是一首祭祖受福的诗，首章云：“瞻彼旱麓，榛楛济济。岂弟君子，干禄岂弟。”毛传说：“言阴阳和，山薮殖，故君子得以干禄乐易。”郑玄笺：“林木茂盛者，得山云雨之润泽也。喻周邦之民独丰乐者，被其君德教。”这是以旱山脚下茂密的榛树楛树起兴，比喻周邦治下的民众被其德泽，和乐平易。这首诗曾被春秋时期单穆公引用，以谏阻周景王“铸大钱”。他说：“夫旱麓之榛楛殖，故君子得以易乐干禄焉。若夫山林匮竭，林麓散亡，薮泽肆既，民力雕尽，田畴荒芜，资用乏匮，君子将险哀之不暇，而何易乐之有焉?”（《国语·周语下》）单穆公反对景王铸造新的大钱流通于市，与民争利。他认为，茂密繁生的山林是国家财用的来源，也是君子求取禄俸的依托。而铸钱需要开山取矿，还要耗费大量木材冶铸铜矿，势必对山林资源和自然环境带来严重破坏。如果山林薮泽的自然资源过度消耗，必将造成民力凋敝，国家财用匮乏，使士人处于忧虑危难之中，哪里还有安详快乐可言呢？这是把保护生态环境上升到了关系国计民生的高度。

《小雅·鱼丽》是一首描写贵族宴飨宾客的诗，它所表达的生态保护观念尤其值得注意。诗云：

“鱼丽于罶，鲿鲨。君子有酒，旨且多。/鱼丽于罶，鲂鳢。君子有酒，多且旨。/鱼丽于罶，鰋鲤。君子有酒，旨且有。/物其多矣，维其嘉矣。/物其旨矣，维其偕矣。/物其有矣，维其时矣。”

这确是一场豪华盛宴，席上鱼丰酒美，宴飨八方宾客。《诗小序》说：“鱼丽，美万物盛多，能备礼也。”诗中言及鲿、鲨、鲂、鳢、鰋、鲤等众多鱼类，进而赞美万物盛多，佳肴精美，最后称“物其有矣，维其时矣”，深刻表达了周人的生态保护观念。毛传对此多有阐发：

太平而后微物众多，取之有时，用之有道，则物莫不多矣。古者不风不暴，不行火。草木不折，不操斧斤，不入山林。豺祭兽然后杀，獭祭鱼然后渔，鹰隼击然后罻罗设。是以天子不合围，诸侯不掩群，大夫不麛不卵，士不隐塞，庶人不数罟，罟必四寸，然后入泽梁。故山不童，泽不竭，鸟兽鱼鳖皆得其所然。

意思是说，物产所以丰足，鱼兽所以敷用，关键在于人的“取之有时，用之有道”的物产养护、生态维系意识。[①] 人类要生存发展，不可能不开发利用自然资源，但开发利用必须合理适度。这就是《鱼丽》一诗强调的“时”字，正如毛传所说，不到严冬风疾时不可烧山猎兽，不到秋木枯落时不可砍伐山林；豺食兽时才可以田猎，獭食鱼时才可以捕鱼。这个“时”代表了动植物的生长规律，遵循这一规律则山中草木、水

---

① 王政：《〈诗经·鱼丽〉与先秦生态观念略说》，《文献》2002年第2期。

中鱼鳖、林中野兽就会成为人们可以持续利用、永不枯竭的生活资源。如果说《鱼丽》因诗歌体裁的限制在表达上尚过简略，那么，《礼记·月令》则把这种“时禁”思想转化为制度层面的行为准则了。《月令》规定，春夏两季，严禁采伐林木，季秋之月“乃伐薪烧炭”，仲冬之月“则伐木取竹箭”，以保护山林资源。又规定在动物繁衍生长的春夏季节，严禁捕捞、斩杀，孟春之月“无覆巢，无杀孩虫，胎夭飞鸟，无麛无卵”，仲夏之月“无大田猎”，季夏之月“令渔师伐蛟取鼍，登龟取鼋”，以保护动物资源。还规定夏季“毋起土功”，冬季“土事毋作”，以保护土地资源。这些“时禁”思想与措施，“在古代生态保护和资源合理利用中起到重要的导向作用”。①

《诗经》这种取用有度的生态保护意识，在先秦儒家思想中有更为明确的理论表达。《礼记·祭义》记曾子说：“树木以时伐焉，禽兽以时杀焉。夫子曰：‘断一树，杀一兽，不以其时，非孝也。’”在孔子看来，不按生长季节伐木杀兽是不孝的行为。《大戴礼记·易本命》谓孔子说：“故帝王好坏巢破卵，则凤凰不翔焉；好竭水搏鱼，则蛟龙不出焉；好刳胎杀夭，则麒麟不来焉；好填溪塞谷，则神龟不出焉。”这些话未必真为孔子所说，但其思想与儒家学说是相通的。意思是说破坏自然生态将会招致严重后果，凤凰、蛟龙、麒麟、神龟这些代表和平安宁的吉祥动物不会出来，自然灾害就会发生，甚至可能诱发政治危机。《大戴礼记·卫将军文子》又谓孔子说：“开蛰不杀则天道也，方长不折则恕也，恕则仁也。”是把“时禁”纳入恕与仁的范畴。孔子躬自践行“钓而不纲，弋不射宿”（《论语·述而》）的生态原则，即不用大绳结网系钓取鱼，不射杀归巢的飞鸟，悉心保护小鱼幼鸟的繁殖。孔子说：“节用而爱人，使民以时。”（《论语·学而》）强调对资源的利用要合理适度，有所节制。孟子认为，临淄附近的牛山因为过度砍伐放牧，致使成为秃山。“故苟得其养，无物不长；苟失其养，无物不消。”（《孟子·告子上》）他说：“不违农时，谷不可胜食也；数罟不入洿池，鱼鳖不可胜食也；斧斤以时入山林，材木不可胜用也。谷与鱼鳖不可胜食，材木不可胜用，是使民养生丧死无憾也。养生丧死无憾，王道之始也。”（《孟子·梁惠王上》）这是说农事不误季节，捕鱼不用密网，伐木不违时禁，粮食、鱼鳖、材木供给丰足，不致匮乏，百姓生养死葬都可得到保障。这就是以仁义统治天下的王道。荀子也说：“圣王之制也：草木荣华滋硕之时，则斧斤不入山林，不夭其生，不绝其长也。鼋鼍、鱼鳖、鳅鳣孕别之时，罔罟、毒药不入泽，不夭其生，不绝其长也。”他主张设立虞师，“养山林薮泽草木鱼鳖，百索，以时禁发，使国家足用而财用不屈。”（《荀子·王制》）这是说对山林薮泽的各种索取不能无度，必须“以时禁发”，即按时节禁止和开放，以保障资源环境的持续利用和国家财用的丰足。

---

① 刘海鸥：《〈月令〉的生态保护思想与中国传统生态法律》，《光明日报》2010年6月29日。

## 三、和谐共生的天人合一观念

《诗经》时代，先民们热爱自然、与物为友，保护环境、取用有度的伦理观念，来自于更深层次的物我相谐的天人合一信仰。这种精神信仰，既是先民生态伦理的重要内容，也是构成人们如此行为的基本动机和内在基础。[①]

《诗·大雅·烝民》云："天生烝民，有物有则。民之秉彝，好是懿德。"《孟子·告子上》记有孔子对此诗的评论曰："为此诗者，其知道乎！民之秉彝也，故好是懿德。"认为诗的作者是知晓"道"的人，这个"道"不是别的，而是人们应予遵循的自然法则。正如赵岐注所言："天生蒸民，有物则有所法则，人法天也。"这个天是自然之天，即自然界自身的运行规律。《左传·昭公二十五年》子大叔说："天地之经，而民实则之。则天之明，因地之性"。所谓"经"亦即"道"，天地之常道也是指天地万物运行的自然法则。《诗经》说"天生烝民，有物有则"，蕴含着"人法天"亦即"则天"、"因地"的理念，要求人们遵循自然规律办事，建立人与自然和谐统一的社会秩序。

《诗经》时代，人们以真切的生活感受，把自然万物融入自己的内心世界，谱写出不少动人的诗篇。在先民的农事、徭役、战争、宴飨、婚恋等各种活动中，时时可见自然界的身影，处处洋溢着一种人与自和谐融洽的气氛。《王风·君子于役》写妻子思念远出服役的丈夫说："鸡栖于埘，日之夕矣，牛羊下来。君子于役，如之何勿思！"女主人公看到夕阳西下，鸡群回窠，牛羊进栏，便情不自禁地想起久别的丈夫何时才能返家。《小雅·采薇》写守边战士久役归来的悲伤，与当初出征时的乐观心情形成鲜明对照："昔我往矣，杨柳依依。今我来思，雨雪霏霏。行道迟迟，载渴载饥。我心伤悲，莫知我哀。"诗中霏霏"雨雪"、依依"杨柳"与人的哀乐切相呼应，情景交融。《豳风·七月》云："春日载阳，有鸣仓庚。女执懿筐，遵彼微行，爰求柔桑。"也是以文学意象展示出人与自然和谐融合的意趣。

《大雅·生民》、《公刘》、《緜》是一组叙述周人创业历程的史诗，反映了先民追求与自然和谐共生的理念。《生民》有一章描写后稷初生被弃，历险不死，诗中写道：

诞寘之隘巷，牛羊腓字之。诞寘之平林，会伐平林。诞寘之寒冰，鸟覆翼之。鸟乃去矣，后稷呱矣。实覃实訏，厥声载路。

周人始祖后稷生下来被弃之小巷，有路过的牛羊用奶喂养他；弃之山林，有砍柴的樵夫救起他；弃于寒冰，有大鸟用羽翼温暖他。透过这些神话故事，也可看到人的

---

① 何怀宏：《儒家生态伦理思想述略》，《中国人民大学学报》2000年第2期。

命运与自然万物生死相依的密切关系。《公刘》叙述周人祖先公刘带领族众由邰迁豳，那里有林木山冈，有百泉流淌，矿藏丰富可以“取厉取锻”，原野广阔可以“彻田为粮”。但在新建都邑过程中，既要“相其阴阳，观其流泉”，又要“度其原隰”，“止基乃理”，精心规划，合理开发，保持人与自然的和谐相处。《緜》叙述古公亶父自豳迁岐，诗谓“周原膴膴，堇荼如饴。爰始爰谋，爰契我龟。”周原土地肥美，宜于建都，但仍要通过龟卜获知天意，达到天、地、人的和谐统一。

《小雅·信南山》是周王室祭祖祈福的乐歌。诗中写道：“信彼南山，维禹甸之。畇畇原隰，曾孙田之。我疆我理，南东其亩。”这是说周人深受大禹恩泽，才有南山平整的原野可供耕种。“疆埸翼翼，黍稷彧彧”，“中田有庐，疆埸有瓜”，表明田地里的庄稼和蔬菜生长茂盛，丰年可望。这既是祖先赐福，也是“受天之祜（福）”。这里的“天”既是神明之天，也是自然之天，故诗中有云：“上天同云，雨雪雰雰，益之以霢霂，既优既渥，既霑既足，生我百谷。”说明天降雨雪可为五谷丰登创造条件。《小雅·大田》前三章云：

“大田多稼，既种既戒，既备乃事。以我覃耜，俶载南亩，播厥百谷。既庭且硕，曾孙是若。/既方既皁，既坚既好，不稂不莠。去其螟螣，及其蟊贼，无害我田稚。田祖有神，秉畀炎火。/有渰萋萋，兴雨祈祈。雨我公田，遂及我私。彼有不获稚，此有不敛穧。彼有遗秉，此有滞穗，伊寡妇之利。”

诗中用白描的手法，写春耕、夏耘、秋敛的农事过程，处处有“我”，物“我”相依，曰“我覃耜”，曰“我田稚”，曰“我公田”。周人把“我”深深融入大自然的怀抱之中，表现出一种人与自然的和谐关系。

在周人看来，人与自然和谐共生，拥有良好的资源环境，是国家富饶的标志。《大雅·韩奕》说司马蹶父愿意把女儿嫁给韩侯，所看重的是韩国自然生态环境比其他诸侯国优越。诗中写道：

“蹶父孔武，靡国不到。为韩姞相攸，莫如韩乐。孔乐韩土，川泽訏訏，魴鱮甫甫，麀鹿噳噳。有熊有罴，有猫有虎。庆既令居，韩姞燕誉。”

蹶父身任王室司马，威武不凡，常常出使各国，见识高远。他选择女婿相中韩侯，认为其他地方“莫如韩乐”，即没有哪个诸侯国能够像韩国那样给女儿带来欢乐。其原因正如郑笺所说：“甚乐矣，韩之国土也。川泽宽大，众鱼禽兽备有，言饶富也。”这里所谓富饶是指韩国大川大泽生长有鳊鱼、鲢鱼等众多肥美的鱼类，山林有鹿群聚集，熊罴、山猫、猛虎出没其间，拥有良好的生态资源与环境。

《诗经》这种物我相谐的天人合一观念，在先秦儒家那里亦有踪迹可寻。孔子说：“天何言哉？四时行焉，百物生焉，天何言哉？”（《论语·阳货》）这里的天也是自然之天。一年四季的运转，自然万物的生长，都受自然法则的支配，尽管它并不说话。荀子更明确指出："天行有常，不为尧存，不为桀亡。应之以治则吉，应之以乱则凶。"（《荀子·天论》）可见人道是不能随意背离天道的。相传子思所做的《礼记·中庸》云："唯天地至诚，为能尽其性；能尽其性，则能尽人之性；能尽人之性；则能尽物之性；能尽物之性，则可以赞天地之化育；可以赞天地之化育，则可以与天地参矣。"这是说，人只有如此至诚尽人、尽物之性，才能在地位上与天地相配并称，加入生生不息的"天地之化育"。《荀子·天论》说："天有其时，地有其财，人有其治，夫是之谓能参。"这是把人看作自然的一部分，主张天、地、人三者和谐统一的生存哲学。

综上可见，《诗经》所蕴含的热爱自然的环境友好观念，取用有度的生态保护观念，和谐共生的天人合一观念，不只与先秦儒家思想一脉相通，而且在某种程度上可以说是儒家生态伦理思想的重要来源和组成部分。尽管这些生态伦理思想是朴素的，甚或有些不科学的成分，但总体上是积极健康的，有利于推动人类社会的进步与发展。近代工业文明时代的到来，物质财富虽然极大地丰富起来，但人类中心主义的泛滥，使整个大自然失去了应有的和谐状态，生态危机日益凸显，人类社会的可持续发展受到严重影响。深入发掘《诗经》中的儒家生态伦理思想，批判继承中国传统文化的精华，为保护和改善生态环境提供深厚的价值支持资源，有助于把我国生态文明建设不断推向新的高度。

# 儒家的生态智慧及其当代价值

中共中央党校哲学部 王 杰

儒家思想中蕴含着丰富的生态智慧资源，研究、整理和挖掘这些资源，对解决当前我国面临的生态困境和危机，对人类继续走可持续发展之路，可以提供十分有价值的参考和借鉴，提供一个解决问题的思路和方法。下面我们从几个方面对儒家的生态智慧做一介绍，然后对它的当代价值做一简要评判。

## 一、天人一体、天人合一的和谐共存

一般说来，西方文化在天人关系问题上所持的是一种“天人二分”、“天人对立”的思维方式，那么，“天人合一”、“天人一体”可以说是中国传统文化的基本特点。天人合一与天人二分可以说是中国文化与西方文化的最主要区别之一，这种区别决定了中西文化不同的性格及发展走向。天人合一既不是人类中心主义，也不是自然中心主义，它是一种思考问题的方式，这种方式就是把人类与自然环境看作是一个大化流行、生生不息、一气贯通的生命整体，这是中国文化观察问题、思考问题的出发点和落脚点。

那么，儒家所说的“天”是指什么？在儒家哲学那里，所谓“天”，不同的场合，不同的语境下，有各种不同的含义，如有人格之天、命运之天、义理之天、自然之天等含义。我们在天人关系中所理解的“天”不是指人格之天、命运之天，而是指自然之天，指外在于我们人类的自然界。这种理解，就与我们现在对天的理解很接近了。在儒家看来，作为自然现象的“天”有其恒常不变的秩序和运动规律，孔子说：“唯天为大，唯尧则之”，“天何言哉？四时行焉，百物生焉。”天虽然不言不语，无声无息，但自然界的春夏秋冬四时依然在交替轮回，自然界的万事万物依然在生灭变化；孟子也说：“天之高也，星辰之远也，苟求其故，千岁之日至，可坐而致也。”荀子也说：“天行有常，不为尧存，不为桀亡”，即是说，天有其恒常的运行规律，不因为尧的存在而存在，不因为桀的灭亡而灭亡。天还是那个天。荀子还说：“天不为人之恶寒也辍冬，地不为人之恶辽远也辍广。”即是说，天不因为人讨厌冬天就没有冬天了，大地不因为人讨厌它太辽阔，就不再广袤无垠了。孔孟荀在这里所说的“天”，显然就是指外在于我们人类之外的自然界，他们所要表达的是这样一个道理，就是说，自然界的万事万物虽然变化莫测，但都有其固有的运行规律，这种规律是客观存在的，是不以人的主观意志为转移的，这种规律是可以被我们人类所认识的。只有严格按照自然规律办事，才能够做到趋利避害、逢凶化吉，违背了自然规律，就会遭到大自然的惩罚，人永远不可能凌驾于自然之上，也就是孟子说的“顺天者昌，逆天者亡”。一句话，自然界就是独立于人类而存在的客观实体。

那么，接下来的问题就是，自然界既然不以人的主观意志为转移而独立存在，那么，它与我们人类之间究竟是一种什么样的关系？是先有自然界，还是先有人类？早在老子那里，就已经提出了一个宇宙演进的模式，这个模式就是“道生一，一生二，二生三，三生万物”。在这个宇宙生成模式中，略显得笼统，它只是谈到了自然界的生成过程，至于人类世界是怎样产生的，它并没有谈及。在《周易・易传》那里，则提出了一套相当系统精致的宇宙——人类社会的演进图式，《周易・序卦》对这个问题做了很好的回答，“有天地，然后万物生焉，”“有天地然后有万物，有万物然后有男女，有男女然后有夫妇，有夫妇然后有父子，有父子然后有君臣，有君臣然后有上下，有上下然后礼仪有所错。”很显然，在《周易・序卦》看来，男女、夫妇、父子、君臣、上下等等都是从大自然中孕育产生的，人来源于大自然，人是大自然中的有机组成部分，是大自然造化的产物。人不能游离于自然之外，更不能凌驾于自然之上，在这一点上，儒家的这种思想观点与马克思主义的观点是不相违背的，马克思主义认为，“人直接地是自然存在物”，人与动物一样，要依赖“无机自然界来生活”。自然界是人的存在的基础，是人无法离开的对象世界，万事万物及人类都来源于自然界，可见，在人与大自然究竟孰先孰后问题上，儒家思想与马克思主义是相当一致的，并没有相矛盾相冲突的地方。同样，在这个问题上，儒家思想与西方思想之间也看不出有什么矛盾分歧。

那么，矛盾分歧究竟在哪里？通过对中西文化的比较，我们发现：分歧就出在人类对待自然界的态度上以及人类在自然界中居于一种怎样的位置？在回答这个问题上，儒家思想与西方文化便有了明显的分野：西方文化主张人类是自然界的主宰，自然界是没有生命的客观存在，人类的终极目的就是要征服自然、战胜自然，人类是宇宙的中心，这是典型的人类中心主义观点，是西方文化天人二分思维方式所必然导致的结果。马克思主义看到了西方这种人类中心主义所产生的结果，及时发出了忠告：“我们不要过分陶醉于我们人类对自然界的胜利。对于每一次这样的胜利，自然界都对我们进行了报复。”而儒家文化则认为，人和一切生命体，都是来自大自然，人不可能离开大自然而存在。人与自然万物都是秉承天地而生的，是生生不息的生命整体，人与天是相通的，不可分离的，人中有天，天中有人。人通过反观内求，就能够认识天，即孟子所说的："尽其心者，知其性也；知其性，则知天矣。"天人是贯通的，人只要充分发挥其先验的道德之心，就可以认识自己的本性；认识了自己的本性，就能够认识天。我们这样来表述中西文化的矛盾差异，并不是说西方文化只有天人相分，而中国文化只是天人合一，不是的，作为人类对大自然的探究，永远不会只有一种单一的模式，西方文化在天人相分的模式下仍然有天人和谐、天人合一的思想，中国文化在天人合一的模式下仍然有天人相分、天人对立的观念。对这一点，我们应该辩证地看。孟子尽心知性知天的天人合一思想对后世思想界影响很大。以后的董仲舒提出了"天人感应"说；司马迁提出了"天人之际"说，刘禹锡、柳宗元提出了"天人相交"说，程颢提出了"天人同体"说，认为"天人本无二，不必言合"，主张"仁者以天地万物为一体"，张载提出了"天人合一"说、王夫之提出了"天人一气"说；朱熹提出了"天人一理"说，认为"惟仁，然后能与天地万物一体"。陆象山、王阳明提出了"天人一心"说，认为"宇宙内事乃己分内事，己分内事乃宇宙内事"、"大人者，以天地万物为一体。"等等。这些历史上著名的思想家们都把天人关系看作是自己思想体系中的一个重要内容。北京故宫的核心建筑太和殿、中和殿、保和殿以及皇家园林"颐和园"，也反映了天人和谐一体的思想理念。这种天人合一的宇宙观，强调主体与客体的统一，主张有机地、整体地去看待天地间的万事万物。可见，在中国文化系统中，天人合一问题始终是被中国哲学家看作最重要的哲学问题，是中国哲学思考一切问题的出发点和归宿点。

## 二、仁民爱物、民胞物与的生态情怀

在儒家思想看来，人与宇宙万物是贯通一体的，都是禀受天地之理、阴阳之气而生的，正如荀子所描述的那样："水火有气而无生，草木有生而无知，禽兽有知而无义。人有气有生有知亦且有义，故最为天下贵也。"（王制）草木禽兽都是有气有生有知的生灵，人也只是万物中的一物而已，在本源构成上，人与他物之间并没有根本的差别。在自然属性上，人与万物没有区别；区别就在于社会属性上，人与草木禽兽相比，只是多了理性思维和道德观念而已。自然界中的一切生命体与人一样，都是地球生命社区中的一员，都有自身存在的权力和价值，它们的生命是不可以随意被剥夺的。这是一种把大自然当作伙伴、当作朋友的观念，在这种观念支配下，人与自然之间冷冰冰的关系就被纳入到了伦理思考的框架中来，被赋予了人性的、道德的、有生命活力的含义。

早在远古时期，我们这个民族就确立了保护生态资源的观念，如殷商时期商汤

“网开三面”讲得就是这个意思。再看看孔子，孔子思想的核心是讲仁讲道德修养，但他要求我们人类要把仁爱之心拓展到自然万物身上，要求我们人类以友善的态度对待自然万物，对待鸟、兽、草、木，充分表现了孔子对大自然的热爱。他提出了“钓而不纲，弋不射宿”，主张只用鱼竿钓鱼，反对用大网拦河捕鱼，并反对射杀夜宿回巢的鸟。反对人类对大自然生命的滥捕滥杀，反对破坏生态平衡；孔子还说：“刳胎杀夭则麒麟不至郊；竭泽涸渔则蛟龙不合阴阳；覆巢毁卵则凤凰不翔”，意思是说，剖腹取胎，杀死幼兽，麒麟就不会来到郊野；竭泽而渔，一网打尽，蛟龙就不会调和阴阳；捣毁巢窠，打碎鸟蛋，凤凰就不会飞翔再来。从这段话中，也可以看出孔子对破坏生态环境和资源持一种批判和否定的态度。孟子提倡人性善，他也是主张把仁爱之心从家庭伦理之亲投射到自然万物之中，提出了“亲亲而仁民，仁民而爱物”的生态伦理主张。《礼记》提出了“断一树，杀一兽，不以其时，非孝也”的主张，董仲舒提出了“泛爱群生”、“鸟兽昆虫莫不爱”的主张，二程提出了人不仅要爱人类，而且还要爱一切有生命之物，要把仁爱的对象扩大到天地万物和整个自然界中，以实现人道与天道的彻底贯通。张载更是把苍天看作是父亲，大地看作是母亲，天地是人类生存的根本。提出了民胞物与的思想，即天地间所有的人都是我的兄弟姊妹，所有有生命和无生命的事物都是我的朋友。人类之爱由近及远，由父母、兄弟、夫妻、家族之爱推及朋友、邻人、乡人、国人、天下人之爱，然后再推及动物、植物直到宇宙间的一切生灵。所以，儒家在生态观上始终认为，人的生命与大自然的生命是贯通的、协调的，而不是对立的。以这种观念审视自然界，自然界就不再是一个被动的、死寂的机械世界，而是一个生机弥漫、生命流行的有机世界。这种天人一体、天人和谐的理念成为中国文化中非常重要的有价值的思想资源。

儒家是这样，看看道家是怎样的。道家也是主张人与自然和谐相处，老子就主张人法地，地法天，天法道，道法自然，反对人类用强制的方式对大自然进行人为的破坏，道家所向往的是那种“禽兽成群，草木遂长……禽兽可系羁而游，鸟鹊可攀援而窥”、“同与禽兽居，族与万物并”的自由自在的生活。强调那些任意破坏生态环境，任意残害大自然生灵者，必将遭到报应。道家还从道法自然中悟出长生不死、羽化登仙的道理。希望达到一种“天地与我并生，万物与我为一”、“独与天地精神往来”的理想境界，把生态环境与生命的终极追求完美地结合在了一起。道家的理想境界就是：“与天和者谓之天乐，与人和者谓之人乐。”（《天道》）追求的是人与自然、人与人的完美和谐。

道教与道家一样，同样强调人与万物的平等性，北宋末年出现的道教书《太上感应篇》就明确指出，“昆虫草木犹不可伤”，元代道教劝善书《文昌帝君阴骘文》也告诫人们，要“救蚁”，“救密罗之雀”，要人们“或买物而放生，或持斋而戒杀，举步常看虫蚁，禁火莫烧山林，……勿登山而网禽鸟，勿临水而毒鱼虾。”道教也是把保护、救助飞禽走兽看作是“功”，而把上海一切众生看作是一种“过”。这一点与儒家非常相似。

儒家、道家是这样，佛教也是这样。佛教中的生态思想，同样是把生命个体和生态环境看作是一个统一体，承认万物皆有佛性，因而万物都具有内在价值，主张“不杀生”、“泽被草木”、“慈悲为怀”、“万物平等”等，反对人类对大自然生灵的伤害，“郁郁黄花无非般若，青青翠竹皆是法身”，认为“诸罪之中，杀罪最重；诸功德中，不杀尤要。”因此，佛教徒大多都是素食主义者、和平主义者、生态保护主义者。

可见，中国传统的儒释道三家在对待自然的态度上，都是主张人与自然的和谐相处，尊重自然，善待自然中的一切生命。这一思想给了我们重要启示：在进行社会主义市场经济过程中，我们要更加重视人与自然的和谐相处，协调统一。要树立正确的生态保护意识，要善待大自然，减少对资源的无限制的掠夺和对环境的破坏，因为自然界是人类生存的基础，如果盲目破坏自然，破坏了我们赖以生存的自然环境，最终只能导致人类自身的灭亡。为实现人类的可持续发展，我们不得不回过头来重新审视人类与大自然之间的关系。

## 三、古代生态遭破坏、环境遭污染现象一瞥

是不是说中国古代就没有生态环境遭到破坏和各种污染现象存在的记载呢，不是的，现在人们把环境污染基本上分为大气污染，水污染，噪声污染，固体废弃物污染几大类。古人虽然没有这种划分，但这些污染现象在中国古代是存在的。这里举两个例子：一个是生态环境遭到破坏的例子，一个是环境遭到污染的例子。关于生态环境遭到破坏的例子，《孟子》中记载了这样一件事，他说：“牛山之木尝美矣。以其郊于大国也，斧斤伐之，可以为美乎？是其日夜之所息，雨露之所润，非无萌蘖之生焉，牛羊又从而牧之，是以若彼濯濯也。”就是说，牛山这个地方的树木曾经很繁茂，因为它离大都市太近，人们常常上山去砍伐它，结果成了一片光秃秃的山；本来，山上的林木受到雨露的滋润，生出了嫩绿的枝芽，但人们又在这里放牧牛羊，原来郁郁葱葱的牛山就变成寸草不生的秃山了。孟子在这里本来是要说明一个道理：人的善心，如果像刀斧砍伐树木一样天天去砍伐，就很难保住。但在不经意间，孟子为我们后人保留了战国时期牛山曾经遭到人为破坏的珍贵信息。显然，这是一起战国时期生态环境遭到破坏的典型事件。关于环境污染，唐代诗人李群玉在《石潴》一诗中为我们记载了这样一件事：“古岸陶为器，高林尽一焚。焰红湘浦口，烟浊洞庭云。田野煤飞乱，遥空爆响闻。地形穿凿势，恐到祝融坟。”这首诗，反映了当时手工业如陶瓷、开矿等的作业情景，但也把人对环境的破坏，包括毁坏森林，空气污染，噪音污染等描写得

淋漓尽致，反映了作者很强的环保意识。唐另一位大诗人岑参在《走马川行奉送出师西征》一诗中也描绘了在当时的西北地区“平沙莽莽黄入天。轮台九月风夜吼，一川碎石大如斗，随风满地石乱走”的狂风弥天、飞沙走石的恶劣生态环境。在中国古代，还有一件对自然环境造成危害的就是炼丹术。炼丹家认为，人的肉体可以借助于某种神奇的药物而获得永生。中国的皇帝和贵族希望能够长生不死，永享人间快乐。秦始皇是想吃而没有吃到，派徐福到处寻找长生不死药，药没有找到，徐福却带着三千童男童女到了日本，开始了中国和日本的最早文化交流。像晋哀帝、唐宪宗、唐穆宗等就是因服食了丹药而中毒身亡。什么是“丹”？丹就是丹砂，就是硫化汞，炼丹的原料大多含有对人体有害的重金属，如砷，铅，汞。术士们炼完丹后，由于缺乏环保意识，往往是随意倾倒，结果造成了大气的二次污染，古书记载说：“丹砂置之于田，则苗尽死”，把丹砂倾倒在田地里，各种幼树幼苗都死了。与王安石同时的苏颂在《本草图经》也谈到了丹砂对水体的污染。他说：在春州、融州这些地方都有很多丹砂，所以，这些地方的水都是红颜色的。沈括在他的《梦溪笔谈》中也写道：在鹿延境内有石油，燃烧之后，烟雾弥漫，什么都是黑色的，石炭燃烧的烟也很大，人穿的衣服都变成黑色的了。这里所描述的是煤、石油燃烧给环境造成的污染。可见，我们现在存在的各种污染现象，在古代都有。

## 四、保护自然生态平衡的实践措施

是不是古人对自然、生态环境的保护不到位呢？不是的。就像我们现在有很多制度规定，有的人就是不执行，从而造成了各种各样的环境污染和人为的灾难。在儒家思想中，保护自然生态环境的思想贯穿始终，主要体现在两个层面上：一是理想层面的呼吁，二是制度层面的规定。也就是说，既有指导思想，又有现实可操作性。

（一）在理想层面上

儒家主张不但应该遵循自然规律，合理开发和利用大自然，而且还要自觉地去养护自然生态资源，以保证自然生态环境的可持续利用和发展。孟子说：“不违农时，谷不可胜食也；数罟不入洿池，鱼鳖不可胜食也；斧斤以时入山林，树木不可胜用也。”孟子告诫人们不要过度向大自然索取，“苟得其养，无物不长；苟失其养，无物不消。”（孟子·告子上）荀子不但把人和人赖以生存的自然界看作是一个统一有机的生态系统，而且把自然界的各种要素也看作是不可分割的生态链条。由生态环境的保护联想到现实政治的清明幽暗，他说：“川渊深而鱼鳖归之，山林茂而鸟兽归之，刑政平而百姓归之。”相反，“川渊枯则龙鱼去之，山林险则鸟兽去之，国家失政则士民去之。”（致士）还说：“欲致鱼者先通水，欲致鸟者先树之。水积则鱼聚，木茂则鸟集。”就是大自然的飞禽走兽都要选择良好的自然环境，何况我们人？荀子告诫我们说：人们在任何时候都不应该去破坏自然界的生态链，否则，就有可能危及人类的生存。基于这种理性思考，荀子主张我们应该合理开发和利用自然资源，“草木荣华滋硕之时，则斧斤不入山林，不夭其生，不绝其长也；……春耕，夏耘，秋收，冬藏，四者不失时，故五谷不绝，而百姓有余食也。污池渊沼川泽，谨其时禁，故鱼鳖犹多而百姓余用也。斩伐养长不失其时，故山林不童而百姓有余财也。”（王制）“谨其时禁，不失其时”，就是指对需要捕杀的鱼鳖之类或需要砍伐的林木之类从节令上、时间上做出禁止或开放的明确规定，是从合理开发和利用自然资源的角度来养护自然生态环境，以达到“万物各得其和以生，各得其养以成”、“万物皆得其宜，六畜皆得其长，群生皆得其命”的人与自然生态环境协调发展的理想境界。

（二）在制度化规定层面上

儒家不但主张人要保护自然生态环境，而且还把它上升到了制度化管理的高度，主要表现在以下三个方面：

1. 对土地资源的利用和养护

土地是我们人类的栖息地，是我们的家园。中国自古以来就是一个以农立国的社会，土地是人们生存的命根子，没有土地，人们就没有了生存的基础，因此，拥有一块属于自己的土地，就是人们梦寐以求的事情。孟子就把土地、社稷与人口看作是一个国家最重要的资源。一个国家要想长治久安，首先就要想办法解决老百姓的土地问题。土地就是恒产。在这方面，孟子有非常丰富的思想，他提出了制民恒产、取民有制、道德教化等思想，荀子也提出了老百姓“得地则生，失地则死。”（天论）“无土则人不安居”（致士）等思想，可见土地对老百姓的重要。“但存方寸田，留与子孙耕”，有了土地，并不是万事大吉了，还要对土地进行养护。一是合理利用开发土地，《礼记·月令》中就规定了要根据季节的变化，合理使用土地的时间，让土地尽力发挥其最大的生产功效；在冬季，则应该使土地得到修整，使土地能够得到可持续利用。二是反对乱垦乱占用土地。孟子就把那种“辟草莱”、“任土地”的乱垦乱用土地的行为看作是仅次于“善战”、“连诸侯”的罪行，应该处以重罚。

2. 对水资源的利用和保护

水是人类生活中的重要资源。一切都离不开水，没有水，就没有生命；没有水，也就没有农业的丰收，水利是农业的命脉。因此，在生产生活中，合理利用水资源就显得尤为重要。《礼记·月令》中就提出了根据气候季节的变化，要对水资源给予合理利用的思想。如认为春天是万物复苏、生长的季节，在这个季节，万物生长需要大量的水，但这个季节又往往干旱少雨，如何解决这个矛盾？《礼记·月令》就明确规定了，在仲春之月，不得竭取流水，不得放干蓄存的水，最大限度地保护了水资源。二是加强对水资源的维护和管理。君主要在仲春之月派官员到各地巡视，看看堤防是否牢固，沟渠是否畅通，道路是否平整；仲秋之月，为了防止秋涝，命令各地官员“完堤障，谨壅塞以备水潦”，检查堤岸是否完好，沟渠有没有堵塞，以防备水涝的发生。

3. 对生态资源通过立法进行保护

《国语·鲁语上》记载的一个“里革断罟匡君”的故事。鲁宣公在夏天鱼类繁殖的季节到泗水深处撒网捕鱼，太史里革看到后，就把鲁宣公捕鱼的网割断，并理直气壮地说：“按照古训，在鸟兽鱼类生育繁殖的时节，禁止张网捕猎，不能砍伐再生的嫩枝，连捕虫都要留下虫卵和幼虫。现在鱼类正产子，不让鱼生长，反而下网捕捞，这是贪得无厌!”。里革告诫宣公要根据“古训”，合理利用生物资源，不应该在鱼类生长繁殖季节用网捕鱼。宣公认为里革的话很有道理，就不再张网捕鱼，并把这张“有意义的网”保藏起来，以示警诫。在中国传统历史典籍中，有关这方面的记载俯拾皆是。传说早在夏禹时代（公元前21世纪），就已经有了“春三月山林不登斧，以成草木之长；夏三月川泽不网罟，以成鱼鳖之长”的规定（《逸周书·大聚篇》）；周文王在临终前告诫武王要加强对山林川泽的管理，他说：“山林非时，不升斤斧，以成草木之长；川泽非时，不升网罟，以成鱼鳖之长。”这可能是我国最早的关于环保的法规了。《韩非子》记载，商代已有不得随意倾倒垃圾的法律，“殷之法，弃灰于公道者断其手。”可见处罚之重。秦国商鞅变法，他制定的秦律中有“弃灰于道者被刑”的条文，这是商朝法律的延伸。《礼记·祭义》记载曾子说：“树木以时伐焉，禽兽以时杀焉；夫子曰：‘断一树，杀一兽，不以其时，非孝也。’”《礼记》还记载说：“孟春之月：禁止伐木……仲春之月：毋竭川泽……孟夏之月：…… 毋伐大树；季夏之月：树木方盛……毋有斩伐。”《吕氏春秋》也记载说，春季“祀山林川泽，牺牲无用牝。禁止伐木，无覆巢，无杀孩虫胎夭飞鸟，无麛无卵”，“无竭川泽，无漉陂池，无焚山林”。《大戴礼记》也对帝王提出了忠告：“故帝王好坏巢破卵，则凤凰不翔焉；好竭水搏鱼，则蛟龙不出焉；好刳（KU）胎杀夭，则麒麟不来焉；好填溪塞谷，则神龟不出焉。”什么时候砍伐呢?《礼记·月令》记载说：“草木黄落，乃伐薪为炭。”《礼记·王制》说：“草木零落，然后入山林。”到了秋季草木凋零枯黄了，才可以到山上伐木。这些都是说的是，我们人类对自然界的生灵不要斩尽杀绝，要给它们提供生存生长的空间，要维持生态链的可持续发展。那么，这些制度规定，由谁来管理呢?自然是由专人来管理，古代还设立了一些环境管理的官员，如“林”，“虞”，“牧”等官，他们分别管理山林，川泽和畜牧。《易经·屯》卦六三爻说：“即鹿无虞，惟入于林中；君子几不如舍，往吝。”意思是说，进山打鹿，没有熟悉地形和鹿性的虞官帮助，那是白费气力。可见，对山林湖泽的管理是由专人负责的。就像现在的林业部、农业部、水利部等，专管一个领域，荀子认为，虞师是管理“山林薮泽草木鱼鳖百索”之事的；乡师是管理“养六畜，间树艺”之事的；司空是管理“修堤梁，通沟浍，行水潦”之事的等等。其目的就在于通过制度化管理，使各部门官员能够在养护自然方面，各司其职，承担起自己的责任来。《周礼》对此也有详细的记载。如《周礼·秋官·司寇》就记载了管理山林川泽的山虞、林衡、川衡、泽虞、迹人等官职，；其中山虞是“掌山林之政令”，泽虞是“掌国泽之政令”，林衡是“掌巡林麓之禁令而平其守”，川衡则是“掌巡川泽之禁令而平其守”，迹人是“掌公私田猎之政令”，还规定：“不树者无椁”、“窃木者有刑罚”。为什么？因为“天生之物有限，人之用物无穷。若当然无制，暴殄天物，则童山竭泽，何所不至！刑罚之施，至是不得不行。”《吕氏春秋》中也提到“野虞”、“水虞”和“渔师”等类似的官名。可见，在中国古代，设立专职官职，通过立法管理自然资源已经是一种共识了。

## 五、儒家生态智慧的现代价值

1. 儒家的生态智慧为当前人类面临的种种生态危机提供一种解决的途径

在人类中心主义观念的支配下，人类成了自然的主宰，天人二分、戡天役物、人定胜天成为人与自然关系的主要模式，并由此导致了人与自然关系的紧张、扭曲与错位，人类在征服自然、改造自然的过程中，采取的是一种人类中心主义的行为方式，一种竭泽而渔的掠夺式的行为方式，经济高速发展、工业日益繁荣的背后，隐藏着人与自然关系的严重错位，经济发展与社会发展出现了极度的不协调。我们赖以生存的美好家园遭到了人为的破坏，人类真切地感受到了毁灭的脚步，感受到了死亡的声音。人类和自然正在走上一条相互抵触的道路。人类如果不尽快调整自己的行为，除了毁灭外将别无选择。这不是危言耸听，而是真真切切的现实。人类越来越深刻地认识到，物质生活的提高是必要的，但不能忽视生态环境的保护，人类不能一味地向大自然索取，而必须保护生态链的平衡。而儒家天人合一的生态观念，主张尊重自然，亲近自然，把自然看作是我们人类的朋友，亲亲仁民，仁民爱物，民胞物与，矫正了人与自然的不正常关系，为在当今社会解决人与自然关系提供了很有价值的视角和途径。因此，儒家思想是属于全人类共同的文化遗产。

2. 儒家的生态智慧与中央提出的建设生态文明的观念相契合

可以说，生态文明问题是在经济发展的基础上必然要提出来的一个问题，是人与自然关系和谐共处过程中必然要提出来的一个问题，人类目前正处在一个十字路口，未来人类发展的出路在哪里？那就是走生态文明发展的道路。要保持良好的自然生态环境，就必须抛弃西方文化中天人对立、人定胜天的思维模式；要想实现文化生态环境的多样性特征，就必须破除文化霸权主义的思维模式，确立多元文化共生共存的理念。这一思想给了我们重要启示：在进行社会主义市场经济过程中，我们要更加重视人与自然的和谐相处，协调统一。要树立正确的生态保护意识，要善待大自然，减少对资源的无限制的掠夺和对环境的破坏，因为自然界是人类生存的基础，如果盲目破坏自然，破坏了我们自己的生存环境，最终只能导致人类自身的灭亡。在这种背景下，如何保持人类经济与社会的可持续发展就成为人类不得不思考和面对的一个重要问题。由此相继提出了“可持续发展”问题，“生态文明”问题，资源节约型、环境友好型社会等，其主旨就是在于“促进人类之间以及人类与自然之间的和谐。”这种崭新理念的提出，是对人类对所面临种种生态危机的一种调整，是对人与自然的关系做出了新的理性的思考，是对西方工业革命以来人类中心主义价值观的彻底颠覆，是以追求一种更公平合理、更资源优化、更生态和谐的可持续发展模式。就像一百多年前，恩格斯所警告的那样：“我们不要过分陶醉于我们人类对自然的胜利。对于每一次这样的胜利，自然界都对我们进行了报复。”当我们回首中国传统文化的时候，我们惊奇地发现，现代可持续发展的理念与儒家所主张的生态伦理思想具有惊人的相似相通之处。为实现自身的可持续发展，人类不得不重新审视与自然的关系，把人与自然的和谐相处作为一项重要的内容。

3. 儒家的生态智慧告诉我们：对儒家文化，作为炎黄儿女和龙的传人，应该心存温情和敬意

并不是说儒家思想一切都是好的，有精华有糟粕，作为封建时代的意识形态，其中有许多对当今社会有负面影响的内容，这些需要我们在工作、学习及社会实践中认真辨别与筛选，但是，儒家思想作为支撑中华民族几千年的指导思想，也有许多思想精华，需要我们继承和弘扬，如以德治国、以人为本、和为贵、民贵君轻、尊师重教等思想就是精华，这些优积极的秀的思想文化遗产经过现代创新和转换，在现代社会仍具有重大的思想价值，都已经融化到了我们今天的思想观念和指导思想中，成了我们今天制定治国方略的重要历史资源和思想资源。也表明中国共产党人能够在儒家思想被否定了150多年后，能够主动的自觉的理性的从儒家思想中汲取治国安邦的智慧和养分。因此，对待儒家文化，不管你是一位学富五车的学者，还是一个大字不识的白丁，它毕竟是我们民族自己的传统、自己的文化，我们对待自己的民族文化，应该心存温情和敬意、尊重和认同，这应该成为每一个炎黄子孙对待民族文化的最起码心态，一个没有传统文明的民族，是一个不完美的民族；而有了传统文明却不知道珍惜的民族，则是一个可悲的民族。一个不尊重自身历史文化传统的民族，是不可能赢得其他民族的尊重的。一个智慧的民族，绝不可能与自己悠久灿烂的文化传统一刀两断。我们不能做那种“抛却自家无尽藏，沿门托钵效贫儿”的傻事，我们不能再犯过去那种无知无畏无耻的被人耻笑的“三无”的低级错误了。

# 论张载的生态伦理观及其现代意义

陕西师范大学 林乐昌

在北宋理学家张载（字子厚，学者称横渠先生，1020－1077）的思想中，含有丰富的生态伦理观，包括“太和”之道、“天人合一”、“乾父坤母”、“民胞物与”等著名命题。这是儒家生态伦理思想中极富远见卓识而又影响深远的精神财富，能为今天反省人与自然的关系问题，解决人类的生存危机，建构适合中国现代社会的新型生态伦理观、生态文明观和社会发展观提供富有启发性的思想资源。值得注意的是，张载的生态伦理学与社会伦理学之间具有很强的相关性乃至一致性，而这二者又都是以张载的天道论或宇宙论哲学为基础的。本文拟以张载的天道论或宇宙论哲学为基础，从“太和”之道、“天人合一”：人与自然和谐的原理，“乾父坤母”、“民胞物与”：人与自然和谐的根源和准则，张载人与自然和谐观的现代意义等三个方面，对这一论题展开探讨，以求教于学界同好。

## 一、“太和”之道、“天人合一”：人与自然和谐的原理

在张载的用语中，与今天所说的“自然”或“自然界”在语意上有对应性的是“天地”。张载所谓天地有其整体性意涵，具体指由太虚（天）和阴阳之气所创生的万物（“动植”、“金铁”、“山川”等等）生生不息的世界。在张载看来，宇宙自然的存在和运行是有机的、有序的，而支撑宇宙万物生存、推动其运行的则是“太和”之道。

张载在其代表著《正蒙·太和篇》之首章开宗明义便提出了宇宙的“太和”之道：

> 太和所谓道，中涵浮沉、升降、动静、相感之性，是生絪缊、相荡、胜负、屈伸之始。其来也几微易简，其究也广大坚固。起知于易者乾乎！效法于简者坤乎！散殊而可象为气，清通而不可象为神。不如野马、絪缊，不足谓之太和。语道者知此，谓之知道；学《易》者见此，谓之见《易》。[①]

① 张载：《正蒙·太和篇第一》，《张载集》，北京：中华书局，1978年，第7页。

虽然这里没有出现“天地”等字眼，但描述的是自然界生生不息的图景却不会有疑义，它体现了张载肯定世界真实性的态度，也表明了他与佛教不同的天道论立场。

古今不少学者将张载所谓“太和”之道归结为“气”。这就给我们提出了一个重要问题：应当如何理解张载“太和”之道的构成和实质？孔颖达在《周易正义》中把“保合太和”归结为“太和之道”，但对于“保合”则仅从字面上解作“保安合会”。[①]与汉唐义疏家不同，北宋理学家重在对经典做义理发挥，例如程颐解“保”作“常存”，解“合”作“常和”。[②] 张载则依据《周易》咸卦之“感”义解“合”。张载说：“咸，感也。”“说者多以咸、恒配天地，殊不知咸自可配天地。”[③] 张载显然欲以“感”之中介作用来构建自己的宇宙生成之道。且看张载对“感”是如何解释的，他说：“无所不感者虚也，感即合也，咸也。以万物本一，故一能合异；以其能合异，故谓之感；若非有异则无合。”[④] 在张载看来，虽然太虚本体“至静无感”，[⑤] 但太虚作为宇宙生成万物的主导力量则又是“无所不感者”。感，亦即感应或感通，指特定主体对异质的他者发挥关联整合作用的机制。在张载看来，经由这一感应或感通机制，能够使“有异”亦即异质的东西关联整合为一体，这里具体指太虚本体能够将自身与阴阳之气整合为统一的宇宙创生力量。这也就是《太和篇》首章所谓“相感之性”。张载把这种宇宙创生力量视作“万物之一源”的“性”，而此“性”又是“合虚与气”才得以构成的。[⑥]“合虚与气”，其实也就是异质的虚与气相感相合。张载在论“感”与“性”二者之间的关系时说：“感者性之神，性者感之体”，[⑦] 认为感应是生成的神妙机制，而性则是感应的直接根源。正是在此意义上，张载认为“太和”之道是“中涵”了“相感之性”的，就是说“太和”之道内在地包涵着“性”，二者的意蕴是一致的。也正是在此意义上，张载才一贯坚持“性与天道合一”，或“性即天道”。[⑧]

张载在其理学“四句纲领”中提出：“由气化，有道之名。”[⑨] 张载以“气化”言“道”，这可能是有人把“太和”之道归结为“气”的理据之一。但实际上张载所谓宇

---

① 王弼注、孔颖达疏：《周易正义》卷一，阮元校刻：《十三经注疏》(影印本)，北京：中华书局，1980年，第14页。

② 程颐：《周易程氏传》卷一，《二程集》，北京：中华书局1981年，第698页。

③ 张载：《横渠易说·下经·咸》，《张载集》，第124—125页。

④ 张载：《正蒙·乾称篇第十七》，《张载集》，第63页。

⑤ 张载：《正蒙·太和篇第一》，《张载集》，第7页。

⑥ 张载：《正蒙·太和篇第一》，《张载集》，第9页。

⑦ 张载：《正蒙·乾称篇第十七》，《张载集》，第63页。

⑧ 张载：《正蒙·诚明篇第六》，《张载集》，第20页；《正蒙·乾称篇第十七》，《张载集》，第63页。

⑨ 张载：《正蒙·太和篇第一》，《张载集》，第9页。

宙的“气化”过程恰恰是由“太虚”本体亦即“天”本体所主导和推动的，这里涉及张载“天惟运动一气，鼓万物而生”的“天能”观念。[①] 张载说：“天能谓性”。[②] 同样在理学“四句纲领”中，张载是以“合虚与气”而言“性”的。已如上述，张载认为“性与天道合一”，故其“道”亦并非单纯言“气”不言“虚”（“天”）。在张载看来，太虚作为先于并高于天道的宇宙终极根源和最高实在，有其独立性，[③] 故曰：“言虚者未论阴阳之道。”“天地之道无非以至虚为实”，“凡有形之物即易坏，惟太虚无动摇，故为至实。”[④] 可见，张载是把太虚视作宇宙间的最高本体和终极实在的。然而，太虚（天）不可能总是停留于“未论阴阳之道”的无生状态，它必然要下贯、参与宇宙的生化过程，并成为太和之道的主导力量，以显其“天德”、“天能”。[⑤] 而这就是《太和篇》首章所谓“是生絪缊、相荡、胜负、屈伸之始”，末句的“始”字，与始句“是生”之“生”字相呼应，说的是宇宙生成过程的开始。依据《太和篇》首章，聚散之气是“可象”的，亦即形而下的；而作为“天德”、“天能”的“太和”之道则是“不可象”的，亦即形而上的；这也表明形而上的“太和”之道不可归结为形而下的聚散之气。《太和篇》首章说：“不如野马、絪缊，不足谓之太和”。张载在解释何谓“絪缊”、“野马”时说：“气坱然太虚，升降飞扬，未尝止息，《易》所谓‘絪缊’、庄生所谓‘生物以息相吹’、‘野马’者欤。”[⑥] 这说的不正是太虚参与“太和”之道运行过程的情景吗？这就足以说明太虚是参与太和之道的生化过程的。在张载学说中，如果说“太和”之道强调的是宇宙间万物生成的动力性、万物关系的有序性及和谐性的话，那么，“太虚”（天）本体强调的则是其本身的纯粹性和最高实在性，以及它作为“太和”之道亦即宇宙生成力量的终极根源性和主导性。

张载还依据《易传·系辞》“太极”、“两仪”的观念提出了“天参”说，他指出：“天所以参，一太极两仪而象之，性也。”[⑦] 这里的“参”与“叁（三）”，古字通用，有同一结构中三方面力量参错会合之意。张载的“天参”宇宙结构模式，涉及作为统一体的宇宙及其三重结构这一古老问题。早在屈原的《天问》中便提出：“阴阳三合，何本何化？”著名学者游国恩在其主编的《天问纂义》一书中，采诸家之说，比较异同，认为诸说中“当以柳宗元《天对》自注所引《穀梁》之解为正。”[⑧]《穀梁传》曰：“独

---

① 张载：《横渠易说·系辞上》，《张载集》，第 185 页。
② 张载：《正蒙·诚明篇第六》，《张载集》，第 21 页。
③ 林乐昌：《张载两层结构的宇宙论哲学探微》，《中国哲学史》2008 年第 4 期，第 79 页。
④ 张载：《张子语录·语录中》，《张载集》，第 325 页。
⑤ 张载：《正蒙·诚明篇第六》，《张载集》，第 21 页。
⑥ 张载：《正蒙·太和篇第一》，《张载集》，第 8 页。
⑦ 张载：《正蒙·参两篇第二》，《张载集》，第 10 页。
⑧ 游国恩主编：《天问纂义》，北京：中华书局，1982 年，第 26—27 页。

阴不生，独阳不生，独天不生，三合然后生。”[1] 显然，“三合”指阴阳二气和天这三种力量的会合参错、互感互动，从而成为宇宙万物生成的结构性根源。依乎此，再来看屈原“何本何化”的发问，就不难解答了：“本”指作为天道之本体的天，在张载哲学中指太虚之天；“化”指阴阳互动的天道生化作用，在张载哲学中指由天所推动的阴阳之气的生化过程。其实，“天参”亦即张载所谓“太虚即气”的天道，是由“天”所主导的、天与阴阳之气共存互动的，具有结构性的宇宙根源。这一宇宙根源同时即是创生万物的力量。在这种力量的推动下，宇宙万物在其生生不息的过程中才有可能达致最高的和谐（太和）境地。总之，张载把源于《易传》及《春秋穀梁传》系统的“天参”生成论模式归结为“性”，这与“太和”之道的结构模式“中涵”“相感之性”是一致的。而且，“天参”模式和“太和”之道模式的结构都是三位一体的，在这一点上两种模式也是一致的。

人类自诞生于世，就必然要置身于宇宙万物生生不息的过程当中。因此，在张载宇宙论哲学中还有一个与“天参”模式并行的“三才”模式。张载所谓“三才”，是以《易传》的《系辞》和《说卦》诸篇为经典依据的，这一模式的特点是把宇宙视为由天、地、人这三个基本方面构成的整体。尽管“天参”模式和“三才”模式是并行于张载宇宙论哲学中的，但二者又有所区别：“天参”模式凸显的是宇宙本体论和宇宙生成论，而“三才”模式则强调宇宙中天、地、人的整体存在以及人在天地之间的位置。就是说，“三才”模式所揭示的是人生在世的基本关系，亦即人与自然（天地）之间共生共存的关系。在此意义上，张载所谓“天地”便又有“天地之间”的意思，既包括自然世界，也包括人间社会。在张载哲学思想中，如果说“天参”模式所体现的主要是宇宙创生力量的话，那么，“三才”模式所反映的则主要是宇宙整体意识。德国著名哲学家卡西尔（Ernst Cassier）在考察作为“人类认识世界方式”的神话思维时发现，在人类早期文化的不同时代里便已经认识到“三构成数字系列的终端，因而成了完善的、绝对整体本身的一种体现。”[2] 张载所谓“天参”和“三才”模式与这种整体思维有类似之处。张载依据《易传》、《穀梁》，并吸收道家观念，明确地提出太虚（天）或太极与阴、阳之气是由“一”和“两”构成的三位一体式的存在，丰富了儒家的宇宙论哲学。这是对儒家天道论或宇宙论哲学建构的重要贡献，[3] 也为人与自然的和谐观念提供了坚实的天道论或宇宙论哲学基础。

---

① 范宁集解、杨士勋疏：《春秋穀梁传注疏》卷五，阮元校刻：《十三经注疏》（影印本），北京：中华书局，1980年，第2381页。

② （德）恩斯特·卡西尔：《神话思维》，黄龙保等译，北京：中国社会科学出版社，1992年，第168页。

③ 庞朴：《一分为三论》，上海：上海古籍出版社，2003年，第132页。

总之，前引《太和篇》首章为人们揭示的是："太和"之道是宇宙间创生万物的力量，这种力量表明，在"太和"之道中包含着作为万物生成根源的"相感之性"；而且，"太和"之道创生万物的性能离不开宇宙的太虚（天）本体与阴阳之气这些不同力量之间的相感互动，而这正是万物的生成机制及生化过程的开始。张载强调，只有通晓这种"一以贯天下"的"乾坤"之道和"易简"之理，[①] 才有资格被称作"知道"和"见《易》"之人。简言之，张载所谓"太和"之道不仅是阴阳之气的整合，而且还是太虚与气的整合，是宇宙间由太虚与阴阳之气相感互动、整合而成的创生力量及其运行过程。

值得注意的是，包括张载"太和"之道在内的儒家所谓"道"有别于道家所谓"道"。道家探索的是自然之道，而非人类社会之道；[②] 儒家不仅关注自然之道，而且也关注人类社会之道。与其他派别的理学家不同，张载特别重视天道论或宇宙论哲学，认为宇宙秩序与伦理秩序之间具有统一性。张载不仅认为人类社会秩序根源于自然秩序，而且认为人类道德价值也有其宇宙论根源。这涉及张载宇宙论哲学的目的论思想。[③]

在张载看来，虽然宇宙有其多重复杂结构，但其运行却是有秩序的，即所谓"天序"、"天秩"。他指出："生有先后，所以为天序；大小、高下相并而相形焉，是谓天秩。天之生物也有序，物之既形也有秩。知序然后经正，知秩然后礼行。"[④] 张载认为，"天序天秩之类"，是永恒的，是自然之礼当中的"不须变者"。[⑤] 这是张载对《尚书·皋陶谟》"天序有典"、"天秩有礼"思想的发挥。张载强调，天序、天秩是根源于宇宙自然的本有之礼，是作为宇宙万物生成和存在的顺序或规则。认为宇宙自然存在着"天序"、"天秩"，这是目的论的说法。[⑥] 张载的目的论思想还表现在，他认为天或天地也像人一样有"心"、有"德"、有"能"，这就是所谓"天心"、"天地之心"和"天德"、"天能"。张载说："大抵言'天地之心'者，天地之大德曰生，则以生物为本者，

---

① 张载：《正蒙·作者篇第十》，《张载集》，第 36 页。

② （英）李约瑟：《中国科学技术史》第二卷《科学思想史》，何兆武等译，北京：科学出版社；上海：上海古籍出版社，1990 年，第 35 页。李约瑟还认为，道家对目的论是持否认态度的。（第 61—62 页）

③ 林乐昌：《"为天地立心"——张载"四为句"新释》，《哲学研究》2009 年第 5 期，第 59—60 页。

④ 张载：《正蒙·动物篇第五》，《张载集》，第 19 页。

⑤ 张载：《张子语录·语录下》，《张载集》，第 328 页。

⑥ 金春峰：《〈月令〉图式和董仲舒的目的论及其对宋明理学的影响》，《汉代思想史》附录二，北京：中国社会科学出版社，1987 年，第 649 页。

乃天地之心也。”“天地之心惟是生物。”[①] 他又说：“天本无心，及其生成万物，则须归功于天，曰：此天地之仁也”。[②] 张载还依据《中庸》把“知道者所谓诚”称作“天德”，[③] 这与张载把万物生成根源和创生力量的“性”称作“天能”是一致的。张载目的论思想的特点是把宇宙秩序同时视作价值秩序，并把宇宙自然过程拟人化，除“天心”之类的说法外，还有称“乾坤”为“父母”的著名说法（详下节）。

张载在先秦思孟学说的基础上，第一次把“天人合一”作为一个重大命题明确地提了出来。他说：“儒者则因明致诚，因诚致明，故天人合一，致学可以成圣，得天而未始遗人。”[④] 这里所谓“天人合一”，指儒者坚信经由为学的努力便能够实现“成圣”理想，而为学的方法则是“穷理”（“明”）与“尽性”（“诚”）这两个重要方面互为依据、交互为用。粗看之下，张载有关“天人合一”的论述似乎并未明确指涉人与自然的关系问题，这就难怪有学者认为，“虽然天人合一的理论也涉及人与自然生态的关系，但这种关系是以政治、伦理和精神境界为本位的。”[⑤] 言下之意是，“天人合一”是以伦理、境界意义为主，以自然生态意义为次的。这种观点不够确切，也缺乏根据。本文认为，从学理上看，张载“天人合一”思想的人伦道德意义与自然生态意义之间并不是主次关系，而是交织关系；正是在这种交织关系中，才使得“天人合一”命题既具有了伦理境界意义，同时也具有了自然生态意义。至于学理在实际运用当中自然生态意义往往不如人伦道德意义强，则主要限于时代的要求，中国古代面对的自然生态问题不像当时社会伦理问题来得更加迫切。

首先，张载“天”观两重涵义的交织。如前所述，对“自然”的整体理解应当包括“天”（太虚）在内。在张载的思考脉络中，“天”既是自然万物生成的终极根源，又内在于自然万物之中；在作为“天道”或“太和”之道的终极根源和生成万物的主导力量的意义上，“天”完全可以作为自然的表征。同时，“天”（“太虚”）还具有人的存在根源和道德价值根源等涵义。[⑥] 在张载的道德价值系统中，其核心部分便是“生生”之“仁”和“天秩”之“礼”。张载所谓“天”作为整体观念，其自然、物质涵义与伦理、价值涵义之间并没有被割裂，“天”并没有失去自然意蕴。对于张载“天人合一”思想中的“天”，似可作如是观。

---

① 张载：《横渠易说·上经·复》，《张载集》，第113页。

② 张载：《经学理窟·气质》，《张载集》，第266页。

③ 张载：《正蒙·乾称篇第十七》，《张载集》，第65页。

④ 张载：《正蒙·乾称篇第十七》，《张载集》，第65页。

⑤ 刘立夫：《“天人合一”不能归约为“人与自然和谐相处”》，《哲学研究》2007年第2期，第69页。

⑥ 林乐昌：《张载对儒家人性论的重构》，《哲学研究》2000年第5期，第50页。

其二，张载“天人合一”思想的人伦道德与自然生态两重意义的交织。从张载对“天人合一”的论述中可以看出，其主要经典依据是《中庸》有关天道与人道、诚与明的原理。虽然“天之道”作为宇宙万物的创生力量和自然秩序的基础，其本身是一个自然过程；但是，人却能够从中领悟出作为自己行为根据的道德价值观。例如，上述的“生生”之“仁”，以及“天秩”之“礼”，就是以天或天道作为人的伦理道德价值的宇宙论根源的。通过下节的论析我们将看到，在张载学说中，礼和仁、孝等价值既被运用于人与人的关系中，也被运用于人与天（包括自然、万物）的关系中。于是，张载所谓“天人合一”思想就既具有人伦道德意义，同时又具有自然生态意义，二者是交织在一起的；任何把这两重意义加以割裂只做单方面归约的企图，都有失偏颇。若把“天人合一”命题置于几千年来中国社会所具有的农业文明类型这一宏观历史背景当中，[①] 那么，它所包含的自然生态意义则更无法淡化或消解。可以认为，张载提出的“天人合一”思想的确同时构成了人类如何正确对待自然的基本态度和实践原则，并使我们有可能借助这一传统资源实现儒学在现代的“生态转向”。[②]

其三，张载“天人合一”思想对人类提出了很高的要求。这可以从“知”（知识）和“用”（实践）两个层面加以诠释。一是如何在“知”的层面实现“天人合一”？张载提出：“天人异知，不足以尽明。”[③] 在张载看来，人们必须“先识造化”，[④] 经由“尽明”亦即“穷理”等为学工夫，使人从宇宙秩序中汲取智慧。二是如何在“用”的层面实现“天人合一”？张载提出：“天人异用，不足以言诚。”[⑤] 在张载看来，人们还必须“本天道为用”，在“与天地参”亦即参与宇宙自然的创生过程中，经由诚、明互动的工夫，调整人自身的性情，提升人的道德水准，以“尽人道”，[⑥] 顺从而不违逆自然秩序之礼，[⑦] 从而实现人与自然的和谐相处。

---

① 金岳霖：《道、自然与人》，北京：生活·读书·三联书店，2005年，第149页。

② 杜维明首次提出了儒学的现代生态转向这一重大问题。参阅杜维明：《新儒家人文主义的生态转向：对中国和世界的启发》，《中国哲学史》2002年第2期，第5—7页。

③ 张载：《正蒙·诚明篇第六》，《张载集》，第20页。

④ 张载：《横渠易说·系辞上》，《张载集》，第206页。

⑤ 张载：《正蒙·诚明篇第六》，《张载集》，第20页。

⑥ “尽人道，并立乎天地以成三才，则是与天地参矣。”（张载：《横渠易说·系辞上》，《张载集》，第176页）

⑦ “知极其高，故效天；礼着实处，故法地。人必礼以立，失礼则孰为道？”（张载：《横渠易说·系辞上》，《张载集》，第192页）“天之生物便有尊卑大小之象，人顺之而已，此所以为礼也。”（张载：《经学理窟·礼乐》，《张载集》，第264页）

## 二、“乾父坤母”、“民胞物与”：人与自然和谐的根源和准则

在张载看来，不仅宇宙的自然秩序本身是和谐的，而且，人与自然、人与人之间的关系也应当是和谐的。张载在其著名的短论《西铭》中，提出了影响深远的社会伦理原则和自然伦理原则。《西铭》全文如下：

乾称父，坤称母；予兹藐焉，乃混然中处。故天地之塞，吾其体；天地之帅，吾其性。民吾同胞，物吾与也。大君者，吾父母宗子；其大臣，宗子之家相也。尊高年，所以长其长；慈孤弱，所以幼吾幼。圣其合德，贤其秀也。凡天下疲癃残疾、惸独鳏寡，皆吾兄弟之颠连而无告者也。于时保之，子之翼也；乐且不忧，纯乎孝者也。违曰悖德，害仁曰贼；济恶者不才，其践形，唯肖者也。知化则善述其事，穷神则善继其志。不愧屋漏为无忝，存心养性为匪懈。恶旨酒，崇伯子之顾养；育英才，颍封人之锡类。不弛劳而底豫，舜其功也；无所逃而待烹，申生其恭也。体其受而归全者，参乎！勇于从而顺令者，伯奇也。富贵福泽，将厚吾之生也；贫贱忧戚，庸玉女于成也。存，吾顺事，没，吾宁也。[①]

对于《西铭》本旨，古今学者历来解释不一，歧见纷呈。限于篇幅，本文不以辨析歧见为主，而是扣紧论题，以前三句为中心，基于自己的浅见，对《西铭》的论旨纲要、义理内涵、思路脉络略作阐论。

我认为，《西铭》本旨是：基于宇宙根源论的社会伦理原则和自然伦理原则。这些伦理原则涉及自然与社会的多重关系结构，既包括人与作为宇宙根源的“乾坤”大父母的关系，也包括人与人之间的伦理关系，还包括人与物之间的伦理关系。《西铭》的主要义理内涵包括：以“乾坤”大父母为表征的宇宙根源论，以仁、孝为核心的道德价值论，以人在宇宙间的自我定位、角色担当为基本内容的伦理义务论。按照《西铭》的义理内涵及思路脉络，可以把宇宙间一切关系及其结构归纳为两层、四重。所谓两层，一指宇宙间以纵向上下关系为特征的“父子”关系结构，二指宇宙间以横向平行关系为特征的“民胞”、“物与”关系结构。在第一层次中，又可以分为人与“乾坤”大父母的关系，及人与生身父母的关系；在第二层次中，又可以分为人与人之间的同胞关系，及人与物之间的伙伴关系。从“乾称父”至“物吾与也”，《西铭》的这前三句涵盖了所谓两层、四重关系结构，因而可以将其视作《西铭》的纲要。以下，对这些关系及其结构逐层、逐重论析如下。

关于第一层次以纵向上下关系为特征的“父子”关系结构。这是本文所要论析的

---

① 张载：《正蒙·乾称篇第十七》，《张载集》，第62—63页。

重点。

《西铭》三句纲要的前两句，论说的是作为宇宙间第一层次的上下“父子”关系结构。

首先看第一句“乾称父，坤称母；予兹藐焉，乃混然中处”。“乾称父，坤称母”，直接依据《易传》而来。《易传·说卦》在论述“乾坤生六子”的宇宙生成模式时说：“乾，天也，故称乎父；坤，地也，故称乎母。”① 《说卦》以八卦中的乾坤为父母，其余震、坎、艮、巽、离、兑则为六子女，把作为宇宙根源的乾坤与六种自然现象视为父母与子女之间的关系；《西铭》则据以说明作为宇宙根源的乾坤与人类及自然万物的关系。值得注意的是，《易传》并不区分“乾坤”和“天地”，而张载却特意对二者加以区分，他说：“不曰天地而曰乾坤，言天地则有体，言乾坤则无形，故性也者，虽乾坤亦在其中。”② “言天地则有体”，是说“天地”表征的是有形的实体世界；而“言乾坤则无形”，则是说“乾坤”表征的是无形的万物生成根源。在张载看来，“乾坤”比“天地”更具有抽象性质和形上意义，与他所提出的“性”的涵义大体一致。在此意义上，《西铭》首句把“乾坤”称作创生万物的“父母”，其实也就是说“乾坤”乃是宇宙创生万物的根源之“性”。这与张载所谓“性者万物之一源”③ 的界定是完全一致的，只不过《西铭》首句的表述借助了比喻而已。总之，张载对于万物的生成根源有几种不同的称谓：“天地”是在具象的意义上加以使用的，“乾坤”是在抽象的意义上加以使用的，而“父母”则是在喻象的意义上加以使用的。另外，《西铭》所谓“乾称父，坤称母”的真实意图，并不在于一定要划分“乾坤”（“天地”）或“父母”，而是格外强调乾坤、天地是作为统一的宇宙生成根源的“道”或“天道”，而且这与张载所谓“太和”之道的意涵也是一致的。因此，张载指出：“《订顽》（即《西铭》）之作，只为学者而言，是所以订顽。天地更分甚父母？只欲学者心于天道，若语道则不须如是言。”④ 提醒学者不必拘泥于天地、父母的区分，其实天地、父母的说法无非是“语道”而已，对作为宇宙根源的“道”真正有所识解和体认才是《西铭》乾父坤母观念的着眼点。

紧接在“乾称父，坤称母”之后的是“予兹藐焉，乃混然中处”。这里的“予”与下文的“吾”，都指人而言。此句中的“兹”字，向为学者所轻忽而无人予以解释。古汉语专家杨树达指出，“兹”字可作为承接连词，有“则”、“斯”等义。⑤ 清儒王引之

---

① 王弼注、孔颖达疏：《周易正义》卷九，阮元校刻：《十三经注疏》（影印本），第 94 页。

② 张载：《横渠易说·上经·乾》，《张载集》，第 69 页。

③ 张载：《正蒙·诚明篇第六》，《张载集》，第 21 页。

④ 张载：《张子语录·语录上》，《张载集》，第 313 页。

⑤ 杨树达：《词诠》卷六，上海：上海古籍出版社，1986 年，第 236 页。

认为，“兹者，承上起下之词。”[①] 这启发我们把乾父坤母亦即天道与人类双方视作宇宙论意义上的父子关系，这种关系从各自的地位看是有上下之分的。古今不少学者将“兹”后之“藐”字仅解释为人自身形体的藐小。笔者认为，全面地看，“藐”固然有人体态藐小之义，但在这里的语境中其重点却是人在面对乾父坤母时的自我定位，“藐”既指人的体态，更指人的心态。前引张载说：“生有先后，所以为天序；大小、高下相并而相形焉，是谓天秩。”关于“天秩”，张载还说：“天之生物便有尊卑大小之象，人顺之而已，此所以为礼也。”[②] “天序”，说的是在先的宇宙创生根源与在后的万物（包括人类）之间是生成与被生成的关系；“天秩”，说的是作为创生根源的天道与万物（包括人类）之间是大小、高下、尊卑的关系。在宇宙的这种基本关系中，“自感人类藐小的意识，同时伴有敬畏、尊崇和羞耻心；这种情感通常通过仪典得到表达和加强。”[③] 这里的“藐”字，是人作为乾坤之子的自况，是相对于乾坤父母的尊上而言的，故反衬出人的藐小和卑下之意。这也表现出张载继承西周“敬天”、孔子“畏天”、孟子“事天”的传统，以地位在下的人对地位在上的无限广大的天或天道的尊崇，以及报本返始的情感。“乃混然中处”的“中”，指上述宇宙秩序及其基本关系，表明人有自知之明，并通过自己“存心养性”、“知化”和“穷神”的工夫，从而与宇宙根源保持一种亲近的、没有隔阂的一体关系，最终达致“圣其合德”的境界。

其次看第二句“故天地之塞，吾其体；天地之帅，吾其性”。在前句阐明了乾坤天道是人类的生成根源这一理据之后，此句进而说明人类的形体和品性这两个方面都是由天地（乾坤）所赋予的。而在人类的形体和德性中，人的道德品性是人的身体和行为的统帅。南宋陈亮在引这句话时，将其改为：“塞天地者，吾之体也；帅天地者，吾之性也。”[④] 经陈亮改动后，人的身体和品性是由天地（乾坤）所赋予的这一本意竟变为：天地要由人的身体去充塞，要由人的品性去统帅。显然，这是一种以人为宇宙中心、以人为宇宙主宰的解读，将人在宇宙中的地位膨胀到了极点，完全颠倒了《西铭》本意。其实，用现代语言来表达，张载所要强调的是人在宇宙中、在乾坤面前的有限性和谦卑性，是一种非人类中心主义的思想。

根据《西铭》的义理实质看，相对于“乾父坤母”而言，“予”或“吾”应当被理解为乾父坤母之子，乾父坤母的天性或天道与人之间是一种宇宙论意义上的“父子”

---

① 王引之：《经传释词》卷八，南京：江苏古籍出版社（据王氏家刻本影印），1985年，第76页。

② 张载：《经学理窟·礼乐》，《张载集》，第264页。

③ （美）保罗·伍德拉夫：《尊崇：一种被遗忘的美德》，林斌等译，北京：商务印书馆，2007年，第73页。

④ 陈亮：《西铭说》，《陈亮集》（增订本）卷二十三，北京：中华书局，1987年，第260页。

关系，这种相互关系应当遵循《周易正义》所说的“父子之道”,[①] 亦即父子之间应当奉行的行为准则。张载赋予“父子之道”以具体内涵，这主要是礼和仁、孝等价值。《中庸》第十九章引“子曰：‘武王、周公，其达孝矣乎！’夫孝者：善继人之志，善述人之事者也。”张载把《中庸》的孝祖与《易传》的“穷神知化”观念联系起来，敦促人们首先要做天地父母的孝子。张载还依据《中庸》“诚者天之道，诚之者人之道”，“君子诚之为贵”等命题，提出，“天所以长久不已之道，乃所谓诚。仁人孝子所以事天诚身，不过不已于仁孝而已。故君子诚之为贵。”[②] 在张载看来，“仁人孝子”便是人在宇宙间所应当承担的角色，根源于“诚”之天道的“仁孝”便是人所应当履行的道德规范，而“事天诚身”便是人所应当履行的首要伦理义务。在张载及其弟子看来，由于人“能知其所自出，故事天如事亲”,[③] 以虔敬之心敬畏、事奉乾坤天道。与此同时，孝敬自己的生身父母也是“仁人孝子”所应尽的基本伦理义务。

关于第二层次以横向平行关系为特征的“民胞”、“物与”关系结构。

依据乾坤是人类和万物的父母这一认识，张载提出了著名的“民胞物与”口号。这是说，人对所有的民众都应当视作自己的同胞，对所有的物类都应当视作人类的伙伴。因此，一切人、物都是这个宇宙大家庭的平等成员。从限于人类谈仁爱，到不限于人类谈仁爱,[④] 这是张载对儒家仁爱观的重要发展。这种把宇宙间所有物类视作人类伙伴的观念，可以作为人类平等对待自然的重要行为准则，其实践意义是不言而喻的。

总之，张载把人和万物所生存于其中的宇宙自然视作一个由纵横关系交织而成的大家庭，一切人或物都是这个大家庭的成员。从这里，我们可以看出张载哲学宇宙观、自然观与伦理观交织融合的突出特征。上述张载所谓“太和”之道、“天人合一”、“乾父坤母”、“民胞物与”等观念，都既是人与自然和谐相处的基本准则，也是社会伦理原则。与其他学派的理学家把生态伦理建基于内在心性论[⑤]有所不同，张载的人与自然和谐观及生态伦理，则是以外在的宇宙论亦即天道论为基础和根据的，属于儒家人与自然和谐观及生态伦理的另一种类型。

---

① 王弼注、孔颖达疏:《周易正义》卷九，阮元校刻:《十三经注疏》(影印本)，第 94 页。

② 张载:《正蒙·诚明篇第六》,《张载集》，第 21 页。

③ 王霆震编:《古文集成》卷四十九注释引张载门人吕大临语，《文渊阁四库全书》本。“事天如事亲”的思想，源自《礼记·哀公问》。

④ 黄建中:《比较伦理学》，济南：山东人民出版社，1998 年，第 252 页。

⑤ 陈来:《宋明儒学仁说的生态面向》,《中国近世思想史研究》，北京：商务印书馆，2003 年，第 50 页。

## 三、张载人与自然和谐观的现代意义

综合以上论述可知，张载的伦理学建基于天道（乾坤）之上，既是社会道义伦理学，同时也是自然道义伦理学。具体言之，张载关于“太和”之道、“天人合一”等人与自然的和谐原理，关于“乾父坤母”的宇宙根源意识、“民胞物与”等保持人与自然和谐的基本准则，对于今天重建人与自然之间的新型关系应当有所启迪。

第一，“太和”之道对重建人与自然和谐观的现代启迪。张载“太和”之道强调宇宙自然本身是一个有秩序的、不断变化的持续过程。这一道理昭示人们，人类及其活动必须尊重自然秩序，使人类社会与自然之间的关系也变得越来越有序，越来越友好。因此，应当首先转变人类对待自然的态度，从与自然“斗争”、“征服”自然的心态，逐渐转变为以自然万物为伙伴、为朋友的心态。对自然及其万物的态度友善了，就有可能使人类在处理与自然之间的关系时从惯于算计利害得失，逐渐转变为站得更高，以“太和”之道的思考方式化解人类与自然之间的冲突，积极谋求人类与自然的相互补充、相互和谐，从而使人类居住的自然环境不断趋近于平衡的境地。

第二，“天人合一”对重建人与自然和谐观的现代启迪。“天人合一”，是张载在《正蒙·乾称篇》中第一次明确提出的纲领性口号。如前所述，张载“天人合一”思想的人伦道德意义与自然生态意义之间是一种交织关系。正是在这种交织关系中，才使得“天人合一”命题既具有了伦理境界意义，同时也具有了自然生态意义。张载所谓“天人合一”，可以看作对“乾父坤母”的宇宙根源意识及“民胞物与”的人与自然和谐准则的概括。因而，“天人合一”既是人们在实现人与自然和谐过程中善待自然的基本信念，也是实现人与自然和谐的最高境界。

第三，“乾父坤母”对重建人与自然和谐观的现代启迪。如上所述，天及天道是宇宙万物的生成根源，万物与其生成根源一起构成了完整的自然界。故对天及天道的敬畏，也就是对自然的敬畏。张载把乾坤天道视作“父母”，这与今天“大地母亲”① 的说法有某些类似之处。建立正确的自然观，必须依赖深层的精神基础或信念基础。对天、天道、自然怀有敬畏和感激之心，是儒家的重要传统之一，是埋藏在中华民族心理深处的信念基础。长久以来，这种敬畏天、天道、自然的心理越来越淡漠。因此，当务之急是恢复这种优秀的民族心理，克服人们在自然面前的傲慢自大和人类中心主义，使敬畏自然成为以科学态度善待自然环境的普遍前提。

第四，“民胞物与”对重建人与自然和谐观的现代启迪。在本文的语境中，“民胞

---

① （英）阿诺德·汤因比：《人类与大地母亲：一部叙事体世界历史》（上下卷），徐波等译，上海：上海世纪出版集团，2012年，第9、18、611、633、640、611页。

物与”观念的重点在于其“物与”方面。张载“物吾与也”这一观念的深刻意义在于，它要求在人与人之间和睦如兄弟的基础上，人与自然之间也应当和睦相处。如果人们能够把世界万物都当作自己的伙伴而平等地善待之，地球上物种灭绝的步伐将会减慢，人们与所居住的自然环境将更加友好，我们生存于其间的生态环境也将逐步得到改善，变得越来越适合人类居住。

总之，以上张载有关宇宙根源意识及人与自然和谐的原理和准则，有益于人类对自然态度的根本转变——从敌对转变为亲善、和谐。“为万世开太平”，是张载提出的著名的“四爲”句之末句。[①] 对于这句名言，以往人们多着眼于其社会政治理想意义。在人类居住的地球环境是否安全、是否太平已经愈益成为我们不得不面对的尖锐问题的今天，我们理应拓展这一口号的意义：在努力开拓人类社会万世太平的同时，也努力调整好人与自然之间的关系，从而使人类生存的自然环境也能够万世太平。

---

① 张载的“四为句”是：“为天地立心，为生民立命，为去圣继绝学，为万世开太平。”（张载：《张子语录·语录中》，《张载集》，第 320 页）

# 论儒家三才之道与当代生态伦理建设

山西省当代儒学会 柳河东

伦理是指人与人、人与社会之间的关系及处理这种关系的规范和道理，而生态伦理则是指人与自然的关系及强调人对赖以生存的环境和大自然应负有的保护责任、爱护义务和道德操守。三才之道影响下的儒家生态伦理思想具有超越时空的永恒价值和不朽意义，同时亦是一个不断演进、与时俱进、常研常新，具有很强现实价值的时代论题。本文拟从历史的智慧与启迪——三才之道与儒家生态伦理、当下的危机与共识——世界努力与中国超越、未来的建构与思考——当代儒家生态伦理建设与实践展开三方面进行论述与探研：

## 历史的智慧与启迪：三才之道与儒家生态伦理

（一）三才之道——“天人一体”的卓越智慧

“三才之道”源于万经之首、大道之源的《易经》。《易传》对天、地、人三才之道做了最早而比较系统的论说：《易·系辞》中讲“《易》之为书也，广大悉备。有天道焉，有人道焉，有地道焉。兼三才而两之，故六。六者非它也，三才之道也。”

《孝经》十八章中专有一章讲述了三才：“夫孝，天之经也，地之义也，民之行也。”并以《三才章》为篇名。流传最广、影响最大的童蒙读本《三字经》中亦讲，“三才者，天地人。”可以说三才之道在古代中国流传久远，影响巨大，深入人心。

《易·说卦》讲，“昔者圣人之作易也，将以顺性命之理。是以，立天之道，曰阴与阳；立地之遭，曰柔与刚；立人之道，曰仁与义。”儒家所主张的人道之仁与义，效法、顺应地道之柔与刚；而道之柔与刚，又顺应天道之阴与阳，即人之性命之理，顺应、符合天地运行规律。《易·序卦》讲：“有天地然后有万物，有万物然后有男女”。天之道是“始万物”；地之道是“生万物”；人之道是“成万物”。可以说，三才之道包含着天、地、人一体，即天人合一的思想。

“天人合一”是中国哲学史上一个重要命题，季羡林讲，“天人合一论，是中国文化对人类最大的贡献。”历代儒家圣贤对天人合一、天人一体多有不断完善的体悟与论述：

先秦儒家讲，“唯天下至诚，为能尽其性。能尽其性，则能尽人之性，能尽人之性，则能尽物之性。能尽物之性，则可以赞天地之化育。”最终人类“可以与天地参矣。”（《中庸》）

董仲舒第一次明确提出，“事物各顺于名，名各顺于天。天人之际，合而为一。”（《春秋繁露·深察名号》）

理学先驱程颢在宋代道学家中第一个最明确地提出了“仁者以天地万物为一体”的论断，“若夫至仁，则天地为一身，而天地之间品物成形为四肢百体，夫人岂有视四肢百体而不爱哉?”（《河南程氏遗书·卷二》）

最早正式提出“天人合一”命题的是北宋大儒张载，他说：“儒者因明至诚，因诚至明，故天人合一。”（《正蒙·乾称》）

理学宗师朱熹在为《礼记》作序中讲，“人者，位乎天地之间，立乎万物之上，天地与吾同体，万物与吾同气。”（《礼记·朱熹序》）

南宋大儒陆九渊幼年读书时就悟到，“吾心即是宇宙，宇宙即是吾心”，“宇宙内事乃己分内事，己分内事乃宇宙内事。”（《陆九渊集》）

明朝大儒王阳明则明确提出“天地万物一体之仁”，讲到，“盖天地万物，与人原是一体……风雨露雷、日月星辰、禽兽草木、山川土石，与人原只一体。”（《传习录卷下》）

清初大儒王夫之发展“天人合一”思想，认为天地人不可分割，“夫易，天地之合用也……天之所以天，地之所以地，人之所以人，不相离也。”（《周易外传》），提出以仁爱之心礼待自然、尊重自然。

天道、地道、人道为一体的“三才之道”集中体现着“天人一体”、“天人合一”的极高智慧。人道合于地道、天道，人类与天地之大型生命体相合为一，融为一体，人类社会的运行规则能够顺应和符合天地运行规律，则必然“人与天地参”，长生、长兴不衰。天地人三才一体的整体观、系统观是中华文化的基本精神，是中国文化异于西方文化的最显著特征，亦是中国哲学和中华文化精神的最大优势所在。

（二）儒家生态伦理思想——“仁民爱物”的道德自觉

儒家文化中包含着丰富的朴素的生态伦理意识、超越的生态伦理思想。儒家“为天地立心，为万世开太平”的治学方向和奋斗目标，体现了强烈的自然与人类终极关怀。对自然（天地万物）的关爱与保护，亦是儒家文化核心价值观“大仁”的体现。儒家博大的“仁”道主义精神，将人与人之间的相亲相爱推及天地万物，即泛爱，把人与自然的道德关系推向了一个至高境界：“大仁”境界、大人境界、圣人境界。

至圣孔子在二千多年前就主张“子钓而不纲，弋不射宿。”（《论语·述而》）

述圣子思讲，“万物并育而不相害，道并行而不相悖。”《中庸》

亚圣孟子讲“君子之于物也，爱之而弗仁。于民也，仁之而弗亲。”倡导君子要“仁民而爱物”。（《孟子·尽心上》）

荀子讲，“鼋鼍鱼鳖鳅鳣孕别之时，网罟毒药不入泽，不夭其生，不绝其长也。”（《荀子，卷五·王制》）

张载提出“民胞物与”的伟大思想与胸怀，“乾称父，坤称母；予兹藐焉，乃混然中处。故天地之塞，吾其体，天地之帅，吾其性。民吾同胞，物吾与也。”（《正蒙·乾称》）

并提出最能张显儒者襟怀、器识、宏愿与儒学立学宗旨的横渠四句，“为天地立心，为生民立命，为往圣继绝学，为万世开太平”。

王阳明提出山川、鬼神、鸟兽、草木亦当亲之，“君臣也，夫妇也，朋友也，以至于山川、鬼神、鸟兽、草木也，莫不实有以亲之，以达吾一体之仁……”（《阳明全集·〈大学〉问》）

以上，无不透显出儒家先驱的高明远见，亦足现儒学朴素而超前的生态意识，朴素而崇高的博爱境界。

（三）儒家生态保护实践——“礼法并举”的集体自律

伴随着儒家文化在古代中国民间社会、政治上层建筑的深入流传、广泛影响，儒家生态伦理思想学早已深入中华民族的灵魂深处，通过“礼”与“法”贯穿于中华民族的政治生活和人伦日常之中，培育了中华民族乐于与天和、乐于地谐的民族性格与精神，对天地自然持有虔诚、敬爱的“仁心”与“礼俗”、“礼法”，因而也铸就了一个能与天地共存数千年的伟大民族与国度。

夏禹曾下令以禁伐和限渔：“春三月，山林不登斧斤，以成草木之长；夏三月，川泽不入网罟，以成鱼鳖之长。”（《周书·大聚篇》）

西周时期曾颁布《崇伐令》以禁伐：“毋填井，毋伐树木，毋动六畜，有不如令者，死无赦。”（《说苑》）

《礼记·祭义》规定伐木杀兽要遵时节，“树木以时伐焉，禽兽以时杀焉。夫子曰‘断一树，杀一兽不以其时，非孝也’。”

《大戴礼记·卫将军文子》中讲，“开蛰不杀，当天道也，方长不折，则恕也，恕则仁也。”

《礼记·月令》则详细规定，按月份保护森林、动物，禁止伐木、杀戮捕捉、“竭泽而渔”等措施。

秦汉以后，以礼入法，自然保护的规范进一步演变为比较严格遵守的法律、法令：

《秦律·田律》明文规定了春天保护动植物的内容，“春二月，毋敢伐材木山林及雍堤水。不夏月，毋敢夜草为灰，取生荔麋卵谷，毋毒鱼鳖，置井罔，到七月而纵之……麋时毋敢将火以之田。”

迄今为止我国发现最早的一部较为完备的环境保护法规——汉代诏书《使者和中所督察诏书四时月令五十条》规定，“毋□水泽，□陂池、□□：四方乃得以取鱼，尽十一月常禁；毋焚山林：谓烧山林田猎，伤害禽兽□虫草木……”

《唐律疏议》规定，“诸失火及非时烧田野者，笞五十”；而“非时”，即二月至十月底。

唐玄宗开元21年下诏规定，“献岁之吉，迎气方始，敬顺天时，无违月令。……诸有藏伏孕育之物，蠢动生植之类，慎无杀伐，致令夭伤。”

《唐律·杂律》规定，“诸部内。有旱、涝、霜、雹、虫、蝗为害之处，主司应言不言，及妄言者，杖七十。”“诸失火，及非时烧田野者笞五十。”“诸弃毁官私器物及毁伐树木、庄稼者，准盗论。”

南宋《庆元条法事类》“河渠令”规定用水的“时禁”，“诸小渠灌溉，上有碾硙，即为弃水者，九月一日至十二月终方许用水。八月以前，其水有余，不妨灌溉者，不用此令。”

宋太宗太平兴国三年下诏，“方春阳和之时，鸟兽孳育，民或捕取以食，甚伤生理，而逆时令，自宜禁民，二月至九月无得捕猎。”

为了保证环保礼、法的实施，中国古代历朝历代还设置了环保机构和专职官员：

帝舜时期设立了管理山林川泽草木鸟兽的官员——虞，可以讲是世界上历史最早的环保管理机构，以后又设立虞部下大夫、大司徒等。

周代的环保机构虞，归地官司徒管辖。当时的司徒是朝廷六卿之一，主管农业林牧渔业的税收。虞人则专管“山泽所生之物及其禁令”，并做分工：野虞，掌管保护鸟兽禁令；山虞，执掌护山禁令；林衡，看管平原地区林木；川衡，掌握山川物产；泽虞，掌管湖泽及物产；水虞，掌管渔泽禁令……

秦汉时期，山林川泽的事务归九卿之一的少府，其下设置有专管苑囿围池的苑官、管理森林的林官、湖官、陂官等。

汉武帝时的主管官员改称为水衡都尉。

隋唐以后，除元朝设置有专门的虞衡司外，其他各朝由掌管全国工程事务的机关“工部”负责环保工作，主管山林川泽的开发和保护。

## 当下的危机与共识：世界共识与中国超越

（一）当下的危机与出路

在200多年的工业化进程中，人类所创造的物质财富超过了以往几千年农业社会所创造财富的总和。高科技飞速发展，生产力大幅提高，现代工商业高度繁荣，人类改造自然的能力突飞猛进，在人类物质生活水平空前提高的同时，人类的生存环境却日益恶化，人与大自然之间矛盾日益尖锐，人类长存和繁荣面临严峻挑战：

资源过度消耗和枯竭：据有关统计，整个20世纪人类消耗了1420亿吨石油、2650亿吨煤、380亿吨铁、7.6亿吨铝、4.8亿吨铜。按照传统的消耗量计算，世界石油仅够维持50年，煤、天然气仅够开采200—300年。《活着的地球》报告称，人类对自然资源利用超出其更新能力的20%，以目前消耗速度和人口增长速度计，到2050年，大约需两个地球才能满足人类的需求。

物种以惊人的速度减少和灭绝：世界自然保护基金会报告认为，在过去的30年里，地球上的生物物种减少了35%。地球上平均每天就有一个物种灭绝，预计未来30—40年中，将有6000种植物灭绝。

全球核武随时有毁灭人类的威胁：据《俄罗斯报》2006年称，全球核武总数已达3万枚。而据有关分析，美国拥有世界上最大核武库，在役战略核弹高达7200枚，战术核弹1700余枚，爆炸威力足以摧毁地球数十次。据美国“科学与国际安全研究所”估计，截至2003年底，超浓缩铀和钚的全球总库存量已超过3700吨，分散在世界约60个国家，可用来加工成数十万颗核弹。

森林锐减和土地沙漠化：20世纪50年以来，全球森林资源已失去了一大半。据联合国粮农组织统计，地球上每分钟有2500平方米森林被毁掉。世界沙漠化土地已经达4800万平方公里，几乎是中国、印度、美国和俄罗斯国土的总和。

与此同时，还有全球气候变暖、海平面提升、臭氧层破坏、酸雨增多、湖泊消失、河水断流、热带雨林减少、电子垃圾猛增、土壤侵蚀、海洋污染、太空污染……全球性生态危机已严重威胁着人类的生存安全。

恩格斯曾在《自然辩证法》一书中警告说：“我们不要过分陶醉于我们对自然的胜利。对于每一次这样的胜利，自然界都报复了我们。美索不达米亚、希腊、小亚细亚以及其他各地的居民，为了想得到耕地，把森林都砍完了，但是他们梦想不到，这些地方今天竟因此成为荒芜不毛之地。”曾经辉煌的南美洲玛雅文明、中东苏美尔文明、印度河哈拉帕文明等都最终走向衰落和消亡，探其原因，很可能均由于人对当地自然资源，如林、草等植被，进行了的严重的掠夺破坏。

美国科研机构提出，到公元2050年，地球生态环境将急转直下，最坏的结果是全部生物一起消亡，最好的结果是其他生物留下来，而全部人类从地球上消失……暂且不论结论正确与否，数千年人类文明发展史告诉我们，凡是对自然进行疯狂掠夺的文明最后都遭到了自然的报复。我们今天穷奢极欲、急功近利的生存与发展方式是难已持久的，毁灭性的灾难会像泥石流顷刻摧毁村庄一样随时向我们袭来。

人类要永续长存，出路只有一条：达成共识，形成合力，深刻反思，克制贪欲，不急功，不近利，改变当前难以持续的生存与发展方式，敬畏大自然，爱护生态，保护生态，实现人与天地万物的和谐共荣。

（二）现代世界的努力与局限

1972年6月，联合国在瑞典首都斯德哥尔摩召开第一次人类环境会议，通过了《人类环境宣言》，向全世界郑重告诫："如果人类继续增殖人口、掠夺式地开发自然资源、肆意污染和破坏环境，人类赖以生存的地球必将出现资源匮乏、污染泛滥、生态破坏的灾难。""人类有权在一种能够过尊严和福利的生活环境中，享有自由、平等和充足的生活条件的基本权利，并且负有保护和改善这一代和将来的世世代代的环境的庄严责任。"

《宣言》在警示危机和明示责任后指出，保护和改善人类环境不仅关系到全世界各国人民的幸福和经济发展，同时也是全世界各国人民的迫切希望和各国政府的责任，呼吁各国政府和人民，为保护和改善人类环境、造福全体人民、造福后代而共同努力。

时隔十年，1982年10月，联合国大会通过了《世界自然宪章》，提出呼吁："人类是自然的一部分，生命有赖于自然系统的功能维持不坠，以保证能源和养料的供应。""文明起源于自然，自然塑造了人类的文化，一切艺术和科学成就都受到自然的影响，人类与大自然和谐相处，才有最好的机会发挥创造力和得到休息与娱乐。"此呼吁合于"天地人一体"的中华古老智慧，是人类共同认识上的巨大进步。

《宪章》规定：应尊重自然，不损害自然的基本过程，不得损害地球上的遗传活力，各种生命形式都必须至少维持其足以生存繁衍的数量，保障必要的栖息地。这符合儒家"同则不济，和实生物"（《国语》）的主张与思想。

又过了十年，1992年6月，"联合国环境与发展大会"（又称"地球会议"）在巴西的里约热内卢举行，通过了规范国际环境行为准则的纲领性文件《里约热内卢宣言》（又称《地球宪章》），提出："各国应本着全球伙伴精神，为保存、保护和恢复地球生态系统的健康和完整进行合作"。"和平、发展和保护环境是互相依存和不可分割的。"

《地球宪章》号召各国人民建立一种新的公平的全球伙伴关系，为实现保护环境的共同目标而奋斗。

又过了十年，2002年9月，第二届可持续发展世界首脑会通过了《约翰内斯堡可持续发展承诺》和《可持续发展世界首脑会议执行计划》，标志着人类实现可持续发展的努力正在从口号变为实际行动。

十年之后的2012年9月，以“自然的恢复能力”为主题的世界自然保护大会在韩国济州岛召开，来自180多个国家的1100多个团体、1万多名人士参加该大会，对176个提案进行了讨论，发表了《济州宣言》。宣言称：与会各方将为保护生物多样性，寻求气候变化、能源、粮食安全等问题的解决方案；努力实现可持续发展，承诺在政府制定公共政策、企业进行生产活动时追求“绿色发展”。

由以上梳理中我们颇喜地看到，从1972年联合国第一次人类环境会议发表《人类环境宣言》，到2012年世界自然保护大会发表《济州宣言》，四十年时间里，全球在应对生态危机、保护人类共同生存环境大自然、实现可持续发展上做出了积极的努力，达成了可喜的共识和初步行动。

现代国际社会这些努力与共识所彰显的现代环保与生态保护理念，与儒家文化中三才之道之天人一体、天下一家为基础的超验而朴素的生态伦理思想与智慧表现出高度的一致性。

成果是可喜的，但现实的情况是：这些阶段性成果在大会上讲起来和听起来令人激动与振奋，但大会之后，很快被很多人遗忘，真正实施起来、落到实处，则举步维艰。参与这些大会、关心这些伟大事业的人只是全球70多亿人口中的极少数，而能真正付诸行动与持续做出有影响力工作的人又少之又少。

析其原因，主要有五大方面：人和自然二元分离之西方传统世界观的广泛影响、现代市场功利主义的强势、现代享乐主义价值观的盛行、利益集团超强利益的驱动、各国发展不平衡而导致的利益冲突。根本原因则是：以利己、尚智、对立为主导价值的西方文化强势所致。当代生态危机实质上讲，是西方文化主导下所造成的危机，需要弘扬以尚和、崇德、利他为核心价值的中华文化补偏救弊。

为换句话讲，全人类需要张扬优良价值观，提高觉悟与境界，遏制贪欲，改变近功近利的与思想与行为。

（三）现代中国的生态问题与治理成效

新中国建国60多年，特别是改革开放30多年来，我国经济建设取得了举世瞩目的成就，但环境和生态却受到了巨大破坏，据有关统计分析，自20世纪90年代中期以来，中国经济增长中有2/3是在环境污染和生态破坏的基础上实现的。据世界银行估计，每年中国环境污染和生态破坏造成的损失占GDP的比例高达10%。2006年全国流经城市的河流中，70%的江河水系受到污染，3亿农民无法喝到安全饮用水，75%的湖泊出现了富营养化问题。酸雨的影响面积占到国土面积三分之一。世界上污染最严重的20个城市我国占了16个……洪涝、沙尘暴、热浪、雾霾等自然灾害变得越来越频繁。

我国各种资源总量虽富，但若按人均拥有量计却属“贫”：水资源人均占有量为世界人均的27%，居世界第119位，是全球13个贫水国之一，660多个城市中三分之二城市供水不足，其中110个严重缺水；人均耕地面积仅相当于世界人均的40%；国际上公认的工业化过程中不可缺少的45种矿产资源，我国人均拥有量不足世界平均水平的一半，石油、天然气人均剩余探明储量占世界的7.7%和7.1%……国内资源难以支撑现有发展方式的持续增长。

面对危机和问题，近二十年来我国党和政府，将环境保护确立为一项基本国策，把可持续发展作为一项重大战略，在保护环境和生态方面做了一系列努力：

1994年3月，中国通过了《中国21世纪议程——中国21世纪人口、环境和发展白皮书》，制订和组织实施《中国21世纪行动议程》，提出走可持续发展的道路。

建立健全了环境与资源保护法律体系：制定《环境保护法》、《节约能源法》等30多部有关环境保护法律，制定、修订了《建设项目环境保护管理条例》、《水污染防治法实施细则》等50多项行政法规。

加强环境保护机构建设：1998年国家环境保护局升格为国家环境保护总局（正部级），2008年建立环境保护部，成为国务院的组成部门，加大了保护环境工作的力度。

发展民间组织和环保志愿者行动：据统计目前国内有非政府环保组织3000多个，有力推动中国环保事业的进步。

2007年10月，十七大首提生态文明，并写入党的报告，提出“建设生态文明，基本形成节约能源资源和保护生态环境的产业结构、增长方式、消费模式”。

2012年11月，十八大第一次把生态文明建设作为中国特色社会主义建设总体布局的重要方面，提出“要大力推进生态文明建设”，“加大自然生态系统和环境保护力度”，提出了“建设美丽中国的目标”，并写入党章，成为执政党的战略任务和长期国策。

积极参与环境保护国际合作，取得了可喜成就：参加了《联合国气候变化框架公约》、《京都议定书》、《联合国防治荒漠化公约》等50多项涉及环境保护的国际条约；完成了《蒙特利尔议定书》规定的阶段性削减指标，据世行估计，中国淘汰消耗臭氧层物质占所有发展中国家淘汰总量的50%。中国政府郑重承诺，到2020年我国单位国内生产总值二氧化碳排放比2005年下降40%—45%，作为约束性指标纳入国民经济和社会发展中长期规划，远高于美、欧减排目标。国家教育部原副部长章新胜2013年就职新一届世界自然保护联盟理事会主席。有关机构先后荣获联合国环境规划署、世界银行、全球环境基金授予的“笹川环境奖”、“绿色环境特别奖”、“全球环境领导奖”、“地球卫士奖”等，到国际社会的肯定。

尽管当前问题严重，尽管中国正处于工业化和城市化加速发展的阶段，环境保护面临很大的挑战和压力，但我们信心十足，我们有着数千年保护生态环境的文化智慧、实践经验和优良传统，在中华义理和圣贤智慧的滋养、指引下，我们有能力化解当前的危机，并实现超越。

## 未来的建构与思考：当代儒家生态伦理建设

（一）儒学的当代化与当代儒家生态伦理理论建设

辉煌属于过去，新的建树才更有意义和价值。儒学是在农业文明社会中富有影响和成就的思想理论，在工商业占主导地位的现代市场经济社会中，儒学需要理论上的与时俱进。儒学进行卓有成效的现代化、当代化的一个重要路向，在于当代儒家生态伦理理论建设。

在当代儒家生态伦理理论构建中，顺应当代人类社会生活方式、结构与特征，吸收当代科学理论成果，我们尝试将传统儒家天道、地道、人道三才之道创化阐释为：宇宙生态伦理、全球生态伦理、国家生态伦理；国家生态伦理须服从、符合全球生态伦理，全球生态伦理须服从、符合宇宙生态伦理，从而达致新时期的天、地、人一体，使传统天道、地道、人道合一的系统观、整体观、和谐观得到发展和弘扬。

首先，提出当代儒家人道论——国家生态伦理。现代人类文明体系中，国家愈来愈成为强有力的利益共同体和意志共同体，国家意志往往是一国全体国民认识、道德水平的反映。传统儒家政治治理的核心理念为“家国同构”、“王道仁政”。全体国民需要对国家赖以存在的国土、矿产、动植、水域等所有自然资源及人文资源，在享有利用、享受的权力同时，就像家庭成员一样，自觉负有保护责任、爱护义务和道德操守。

在现代社会中，由于国家政权的存在和现代法制的崇尚，生态保护理论和理念一旦上升为国家意志和国家法律规定，生态保护工作即有了强制保障和长效生命。与此同时，现代国家的国民教育体系愈来愈完善，生态保护理论和理念一旦得到国家重视，便会通过教育体系深入国民人心。因此，国家生态伦理在现代社会体系中最易得到实施。

其次，提出当代儒家地道论——全球生态伦理。地球是一个大生命体，现代人类有机地融入地球这个在生命体中，实现人与地球长生共荣，人类需要对赖以生存的地球及地球上的所有生物、物质负有保护责任、爱护义务和道德操守，地球公民就像地球大家庭成员一样，自觉爱护、保护和维护全球生态平衡。

随着现代市场经济的发展，国与国之间的贸易往来，经济依存度的加深，加之现代交通、通讯的便利，现代全球愈来愈成为一个“地球村”。另外，联合国、世界贸易组织、世界银行、国际货币基金组织、世界自然保护联盟等这些重要国际组织经过六、七十年的发展，成员国家愈来愈多，在国际事务中的影响力愈来愈大。特别是在面对共同的生存与发展危机时，世界各国很快达成了共识：近四十年间形成了联合国《人类环境宣言》、联合国大会《世界自然宪章》、联合国环境与发展大会《地球宪章》、世界首脑会《约翰内斯堡可持续发展承诺》、世界自然保护大会《济州宣言》五大全球共识。因此，全球生态伦理的建设与实现也不再是难题。

第三，提出当代儒家天道论——宇宙生态伦理。宇宙（天地万物）是一个更大的生命体，现代人类有机地融入宇宙这个在难探终始、无边无际的神圣生命体中，实现人与宇宙的长久和谐生存与共同发展，人类需要对赖以生存的宇宙及宇宙中的所有无机物、有机物和精神财富负有保护责任、爱护义务和道德操守，人类作为宇宙公民就像宇宙神圣大家庭成员一样，自觉爱护、保护和维护宇宙生态平衡，以求人类族群像宇宙一样长寿无限。

自 20 世纪 50 年代始，人类已向宇宙发射了 4 千多次航天运载火箭。据不完全统计，太空中现有直径大于 10 厘米的碎片 9 千多个，大于 1.2 厘米的有数十万个，而漆片和固体推进剂尘粒等微小颗粒可能数以百万计。“2003 年近地天文学”国际会议上称：目前在近地轨道上的太空垃圾已经有大约 30 万吨。对航天器和宇航员生命形成致命威胁，对地面的生命财产安全也构成一定威胁。随着科技的迅猛发展、人类“改造大自然”能力的提升和人类在宇宙探索的广度延伸，宇宙生态伦理亦会成为日渐升温而极具意义的论题。

（二）儒学的复兴与当代儒家生态伦理实践展开

1. 危机压力下的必然选择——世界形成合力，提升人类境界，保护人类共同家园安全

商业化过度而反道德，工业化过度而反自然；工业化助长了商业功利主义，商业功利主义的泛滥反过来又加剧了反自然的工业化进程；尽管大家都认识到了危机的严重性，亦形成了全球性的共识和行动纲领，但却难以真正实施。如何破解人类形成了生态保护共识而难以行动的局面，需要对治根因：弘扬优良价值观，提升人类的觉悟和境界，提高道德操守。否则，只会流于治标不治本，形成补了东墙西墙破、按下葫芦浮起瓢的局面。

而欲提高人类的觉悟、境界和道德操守，则须得从文化启蒙和人文精神张扬上着力。唯有尚和、崇德、利他的精神价值张扬，唯有高扬天、地、人三才之间协调、和谐、统一的人文精神与价值取向，唯有生态伦理深入人心，才能形成共同爱护、保护和维护生态的强大合力和有效行动。

在尊重世界各国、各民族优秀文化的大前提下，推动儒学在世界的创新和复兴，

有似于欧洲文艺复兴运动一样，高扬儒家人文情怀、仁道主义、天下主义，积极在全球倡导儒家“协和万邦”、“四海之内皆兄弟”、“和而不同”、“己所不欲，勿施于人”等和谐共处思想和理念，以有化解国与国、民族与民族之间的根本矛盾，减少或消除军事对抗、军备竞赛，制止战争，促进人类和平与发展。

推动儒学在世界的创新和复兴，积极在全球弘扬儒家文化关于环保和生态安全的观念与思想，开展儒家当代生态伦理建设、宣传和实践，倡导遵守“仁民爱物”、“天人一体”、“天人合一”为核心价值与理念的国家生态伦理、全球生态伦理、宇宙生态伦理，让数千年的儒家生态智慧活化于今、广为流传，以有效促进人类与自然的和谐相处，化解人与自然的矛盾，消解人与自然之间的张力，保护人类家园地球与宇宙，改善人类的生存发展环境。

面对人类社会前所未有的巨大危机，全世界儒学、儒商、儒官等当代儒者联合起来，勇于担当，躬身践行，积极倡导，推动当代儒家生态伦理建设和儒学复兴，光大儒家人文精神与光辉价值，开启人类恒久永续生存发展之大慧，提升全人类的道德觉悟和精神境界，引导人类走上天人合一、天人一体的可持续发展大道，则功莫大焉。

2. 道德升华后的自觉之路——中国实现超越，引领人类生态文明建设新纪元

中华文明是唯一以大一统的国家形态、民族形态同根、同文、同种保存数千年的文明体，正如本文第一部分分析，这是因为以儒家文化为主干与精髓的中华文明精神里蕴含着朴素而深刻的生态智慧，与现代生态文明的内涵和要求一致。

作为中华文明的核心与精髓、中华文化的主干与主流的儒家文化是建设现代生态伦理、解决生态危机、超越工业文明的重要文化资源和智慧支撑。而当代生态文明建设又将是创新发展儒家文化、丰富振兴中华文明的有力举措和重大历史契机。

作为儒学产生与发展的母体之国，党和政府坚持科学发展观，走可持续发展之路，在两次党的全国代表大会提出“生态文明”建设，并写入党的报告和党章，上升为党的意志，表明全党和全国人民加强生态文明建设的决心和智慧，既是时代的选择，也是深受儒家文化滋养的中华文明固有的生态保护思想、精神之再度彰显和时代升华。

十八大提出“把生态文明建设融入经济建设、政治建设、文化建设、社会建设各方面和全过程”，无疑为中国当代生态伦理实践展开、生态文明建设进行全方位着力提出了纲领性举措：

在经济建设中，我们当遵循儒家先贤关于“天地与吾同体，万物与吾同气”、“天人合一”、“民胞物与”、“中和并育”、“天地万物一体之仁”等的智慧教诲，在爱物、惜物、省物、节物上下功夫，学习借鉴西方发达国家市场经济先进经验的同时，坚定不移地走符合自己国情和文化传统的中国特色之路，建设道德张显、法制完备的当代市场经济文明，转变经济增长方式和消费模式，调整产业结构，坚持全国、协调、可

持续发展，实现良财与美德相生相长，形成节约能源资源、保护生态环境、惠人利物益己的产业结构和发展方式，为当代生态文明建设提供物质保障和示范发展模式。

在政治建设中，中国共产党不仅要学习借鉴西方发达国家的先进政治文明建设经验，还应勇于、善于从中国传统政治文明和文化中汲取经验和智慧，将古圣明王关于“内圣外王”、“修身、齐家、治国、平天下”、“为天地立心、为万世开太平”等的优秀思想、理念和价值观在新时期创新发扬光大，将自己建设成为民众欢迎、国际尊重、顺应时代潮流、富有朝气、大有前途的现代君子集团、准圣贤集团；积极实行现代民主法制机制下的王道政治、贤能政治，重德尚贤，进贤举能，健全法制，复兴礼乐，开创当代政治文明建设新篇章，为当代生态文明建设提供坚实的政治保障。

在文化建设中，继承古代儒家中国数千年来形成的尊师重教、崇文尚学的优良传统，复兴关注个体差异、因材施教、注重人文德化、讲习互动的古代书院教育，以弥补重知轻德、重教缺化的现代教育弊病；保护和开发文庙、贤祠，推动祭孔、祀贤活动，倡导敬拜“天地君亲师”，培养国民的敬畏之心和感恩之情；提倡学术自由，复兴儒家文化，培育核心价值观，重视传统节日文化宣传，弘扬中华美德，增强国家文化安全和软实力，重建中华礼仪之邦，再造现代君子国度，将中国人塑造成为有修养、有觉悟、高素质的现代公民，成当代生态文明建设的生力军和先进表率。

在社会建设中，根据市场经济下“小政府、大社会”的发展趋向，继承古代儒家中国数千年来形成的学习型社会、和谐自治型社会的优良传统，大力扶持当代儒家社会组织、环保社会组织等的建设与创新发展，支持生态和环保志愿者行动，支持宗教团体和社会教化事业，建设终身学习型社会与和谐社会，建设资源节约型社会和环境友好型社会，充分发挥现代社会的监督、自治、服务功能，推动当代生态伦理的社会化宣传、教育、推广，形成当代生态文明建设的社会化长效机制与行动合力。

党和国家最高领导人习近平同志去年年底考察曲阜孔府和孔子研究院，细看《论语》和《孔子家语》，今年五四青年节又专程看望中华孔子学会会长汤一介，促膝交谈《儒藏》，在多次讲话中大量引用儒家经典，明确提出要大力弘扬中华优秀传统文化，中华儒学复兴的春天可谓真正到来了。

面对伟大的历史机遇——三千年未有之巨大变局，中国当代儒者，当“以舍我其谁”、“我欲仁，斯仁至矣”的弘道勇气和担当精神，修己以立范，精进而立功，弘扬“天地万物一体”之大“仁”精神，铸就“返本开新”、“修齐治平”之功业，为提升全体国民素养、道德水平和精神境界，实现全民族的高尚道德自觉、崇高道德自律，以引领人类集体走上克制贪欲膨胀、“以义制利”、“仁民爱物”、关心万世后代与宇宙天地万物、真正的可持续发展之路，建设儒家新三才之道和当代生态伦理文明，保障人类族群的繁荣永续，谱写时代新华章！

**参考文献：**

［1］人类环境宣言. 联合国斯德哥尔摩第一次人类环境会议通过，1972（6）.

［2］世界自然宪章. 联合国大会通过，1982（10）.

［3］地球宪章. 里约热内卢“联合国环境与发展大会”通过，1992（6）.

［4］（明）王守仁撰，吴光等编译. 阳明全集. 上海古籍出版社，1992（12）.

［5］中国21世纪议程——中国21世纪人口、环境和发展白皮书，1994（3）.

［6］李史峰. 十三经. 上海辞书出版社，2006（3）.

［7］薛惠峰等. 中国经济发展进程中的资源环境问题根源与对策. 能源环境保护，2008年22卷5期.

［8］乔清举. 儒家生态文化的思想与实践. 孔子研究，2008年06期.

［9］陈克明. 群经要义. 中国人民大学出版社，2009（11）.

［10］刘海鸥.《月令》的生态保护思想与中国传统生态法律. 光明日报，2010.6.29.

［11］柳河东. 儒学的当代使命及其现代复兴之路. 第三届“世界儒学大会”学术论文集，2010（9）.

［12］苗俊玲.“天人合一”思想与生态文明的渊源. 人民论坛，2010年第14期.

［13］柳河东. 儒家三才之道与当代生态伦理建设之思考论文纲要. 中国人民大学“第九届国际儒学论坛”论文集，2012（12）.

［14］胡锦涛. 中共十八大报告“坚定不移沿着中国特色社会主义道路前进为全面建成小康社会而奋斗”. 2012（11）.

# 从“天人合一”回到《易经》“天、地、人”三才哲学

## ——兼论儒家环境哲学的基本构架

新加坡南洋理工大学　李晨阳

根据刘笑敢教授对“天人合一”这一文化现象的详细研究，“20世纪以来，‘天人合一’已经是代表中国文化传统特点的熟语或成语，有人称之为中国哲学的基本命题，或思维模式，或思维定式。”① 这方面的一位重要的代表人物是国学大师钱穆。在他96岁高龄时的绝笔之作《中国文化对人类未来可有之贡献》中，钱穆先生表明他晚年彻悟出“天人合一”乃是“中国传统文化思想之归宿处”。他说，“‘天人合一’论，是中国文化对人类文化的最大贡献。”② 钱穆先生这一论断对中国学界有很大影响。也许是因为《易经》为诸经之首，不少人往往把“天人合一”的思想归源于《易经》。讨论“天人合一”的人常常引《易经》来论证这一哲学思想。当代大力推崇“天人合一”并把这一命题直接与《易经》联系起来的著名学者包括季羡林。季先生明确说，

《周易·乾卦·文言》说：“‘大人’者与天地合其德，与日月合其明，与四时合其序，与鬼神合吉凶，先天而天弗违，后天而奉天时。”这里讲的就是“天人合一”的思想，这是人生的最高的理想境界。③

2012年2月28日凤凰网专稿用“百位专家探讨易经‘天人合一’把握整体”的题目，总结报道海南中华传统文化研究院和国际易学联合会共同主办的易学研讨会。该讨论会规模宏大，有来自全球的200余名易学专家参加。④ “天人合一”论究竟是不是中国文化思想之归宿处，其实是值得讨论的。刘笑敢等学者的研究说明，“天人合一”至少不是中国古代思想传统的中心理念。本文认为，把“天人合一”的思想归源于《易经》或者把《易经》的基本思想归结于“天人合一”是没有根据的。季羡林等学者

---

① 对“天人合一”学界讨论的详细研究，见刘笑敢“天人合一：学术、学说和信仰—再论中国哲学之身份及研究取向的不同”，《中国哲学与文化》第十辑，20112：73页。

② 见刘笑敢文，74页。

③ 季羡林，“天人合一新解，”见 http：//www.aisixiang.com/data/23861.html

④ http：//phtv.ifeng.com/program/whdgy/detail _ 2012 _ 02/28/12844222 _ 0.shtml

希望从儒家传统中发掘“天人合一”来对应我们当代所面临的环境问题。其实，“天、地、人”的“三才”思想才是既忠实于《易经》而又有理有效的环境哲学理念。季羡林先生上面所引用的那段话其实是《易经》的“三才”思想的展开，说的是“（大）人”与“天”和“地”合其德。即通过三者彼此之间的合作为宇宙和谐提供一个整体性的框架。《易经·系辞下》曰：“《易》之为书也，广大悉备。有天道焉，有人道焉，有地道焉。兼三才而两之，故六。六者非它也，三材之道也”[①]。“三才”之道通过阴阳二性表现为六爻。没有三才就没有六爻；没有六爻就没有六十四卦；没有六十四卦当然也就没有《易经》之理。所以，“三才（材）之道”乃《易经》之理的根本。这里的重要概念就是“兼三才”，亦即整合三种不同的能源，而不是使三者化约为任何的一种或者两种。

“三才”思想是《易经》中一以贯之的思想。《易经·说卦传》曰：“昔者圣人之作《易》也，将以顺性命之理。是以立天之道曰阴与阳，立地之道曰柔与刚，立人之道曰仁与义。兼三才而两之，故《易》六画而成卦，分阴分阳，迭用柔刚，故《易》六位而成章”。这里，天道乃三才之首。天道表现为阴阳。阴与阳使得“兼三才而两之”成为可能。柔与刚，仁与义虽然可以被看作是阴阳的体现。但它们不是阴阳一般的体现。而是自然大地和人类社会的重要的存在形式。《乾卦·彖》曰：“大哉乾元，万物资始，乃统天，云行雨施，品物流形。大明终始，六位时成，时乘六龙以御天。乾道变化，各正性命。保合太和，乃利贞”。乾代表天道。在乾的统摄下，天道变化，品物流形，各正性命。在天地之间，“人”是最重要的存在。《泰卦·象》讲“天地交而万物通”。人作为“天地交”的积极参与者，起着“财（裁）成天地之道，辅相天地之宜”的作用。周振甫先生解释“财成”为“裁成，制定”；余敦康先生解释“财（裁）成”为“通过裁断决定而使之成就”。[②] 在《易经》的作者看来，“人”之“参天地”构成“三才”。“人”“参天地”包含裁断并辅佐天地的大任。

“三才”对儒家传统至为重要。“三”在儒家哲学思维中有很重要的作用。庞朴先生认为，儒学的基本方法是“三分法”。他说，

道家向往一，法家保持二；而儒家则提倡三，有所谓圣人“与天地参”，“德配天地”（《礼记·经解》）。[③]

儒家讲究“参”的存在形式。只有在“三”的前提下才有“参（与）”。如果仅仅是

---

① 《十三经注疏》，北京：中华书局，1985年，第90页。

② 周振甫：《周易译注》，北京：中华书局，1991年，第47页。余敦康：《周易现代解读》，北京：华夏出版社，2006年，第74页。原文把“财（裁）成天地之道，辅相天地之宜”的能力赋予君王。在古代人看来，人类社会的作用是通过君王而实现的。

③ 庞朴：《儒家辩证法研究》，北京：中华书局，1984年，第101页。

一，就不必“参”，因为本来就在一起了。如果仅仅是二，当然也不必“参”，而只能是“对”，即“对应”或者“对立”。而《易经》的“三才”思想恰恰是儒家所倡导的人类“参天地之化育”哲学基础。

从环境哲学的角度看，《易经》的“三才”思想为当前西方环境伦理学面对的“物”“我”两分提供了第三条道路。西方的“资源保护主义”（conservationism）主张唯有人拥有内在价值（intrinsic value），[①] 而保护环境的终极目的就是要为人类造福。用著名资源保护主义者吉福德·平超特（Gifford Pinchot）的话说：“保护资源意味着在最长的时间里为最多的人造就最大的福利”。[②] 平超特将自然界只视为一种资源；不有效开发这个资源相当于浪费资源。他认为人类的义务除了在于负责任地使用现有的自然资源以外，还要积极的发展出新的资源。与此相反，“自然保护主义”（preservationism）主张自然界除了拥有工具价值以外，同时还拥有内在的价值。虽然保护环境可以为人类带来利益，但这绝不仅仅是保护环境的唯一原因：自然界的存在本身具有其自身的价值，不能将这种内在价值完全化约为对人类谋福利的工具价值。“资源保护主义”与“自然保护主义”的主要哲学方面的差异在于保护环境的终极目的。资源保护主义者主张，保护环境的主要目的是为了让人类能够从大自然中获取更多的长远利益；自然界所受到的保护只是服务于人类利益的副产品。从哲学上来说，这个观点是人类中心主义的。自然保护主义者则主张，保护环境除了对人类有益以外，同时也对拥有其自己的内在价值；环境保护所带给自然界的好处是其内在的重要组成部分，而并非资源保护主义者所说的只是一种微不足道的副产品。从哲学上来说，这后一个观点可以借由非人类中心主义的立场得到证成。在最近的几十年里，自然保护主义的观点已发展为全面整体性的环境哲学。一些持这种观点的人甚至认为人类只是整个生态系统中没有任何特殊身份的一分子，与其他动植物平等，而我们影响自然环境的一切行为之对与错，将取决于这些行为能否促进整个生态系统的整体健康及完整性。

相比较而言，儒家的“三才”说既不是“环境保护主义”也不是“自然保护主义”。儒家一方面不认为唯有人类才具有内在的价值，不主张“天”“地”只是为满足人类的需求而存在。儒家哲学承认万事万物在宇宙间的正当地位，主张“各正性命，保合太和”。另一方面儒家也不主张人类只是处于与其他非人类成员相等的地位。儒家哲学赋予人类在宇宙间的特殊地位。人类的使命即是与“天”和“地”一起共同实现宇宙的和谐。我们可以将这个儒家“三才”理念称作“三才和谐”的结构。在这种

---

① “内在价值”有时也被指为“固有价值”（inherent value），亦即独立于人类利益之外的价值。

② Pinchot，Gifford（2004）The Fight for Conservation，Whitefish，MT：Kessinger Publishing（2004）：17.

“三才”观中，人类虽然不是世界的中心，但也绝不仅仅是动植物界里的一员。人类一方面是生态环境中的一名成员，另一方面其地位与生态环境中的其他成员并不完全相等，主要原因是人拥有改变世界的创造性能力。就人类在宇宙间的状况来说，一种顺着三才和谐的理念而产生的儒家环境哲学应该处于西方“资源保护主义”与“自然保护主义”两者的中间。也可以这么说，按照儒家的观念，人类在这个三才的宇宙中承担着三分之一的角色和责任，是这个宇宙的三个“合伙人”之一。相对于大地伦理学（Land Ethics）与深层生态学（Deep Ecology）等西方的整体性环境哲学而言，儒家整体性的环境哲学赋予人类在宇宙间以一个更崇高的地位。

儒家非人类中心主义的环境哲学是一个整体性的系统，包含了儒家宇宙观中的三个主要组成部分，分别是天、地、与人。这三者一起组成了至大至尊的“和谐”共同体。按照儒家“和谐”观的设想，天、地、与人各自都有其适当的功能，而且都在自身的范围以内对宇宙的总体和谐运作做出积极的贡献。它们在相互之间的促进中推动整个宇宙的和谐化进程。在这种和谐“三才”结构中，“地”与“人”的意涵基本上并不难了解，但是这两个概念都有一些精微的特征是我们在理解儒家哲学时所必须掌握的。“地”指的是我们人类所居住的地球；它本身即是一个拥有自己生命的活生生的实体。在儒家的设想中，“地”是维持万物生命形态的有德之物。但它不能离开太阳，即《乾卦·象》所说的代表乾道的“大明”。“人”指的是具有清醒的道德意识的人类。人类不只是大地上众多物种当中的一种。作为一种独特的存在，人类不仅被赋予了超出一般生物之上的卓越能力，而且还被赋予了积极参与宇宙之和谐化进程的特殊使命。“天”的意涵比较复杂，它对于不同流派的儒者来说可以指向不同的内容。对杜维明等哲学家来说，“天”指的是一种掌握世界的终极意义的“无所不在、无所不知”的神圣力量。[①] 但是，这种意义的“天”不同于西方一元论的“上帝”；“天”虽是宇宙中主导的创造性力量，但并非唯一的创造性力量。[②] 按照儒家所构想的和谐“三才”的结构，“天”是同“地”与“人”一起并行的共同创造者。对世俗的儒者来说，“天”则是指地球以外的宇宙，尽管这个宇宙本身可能有灵性或者精神性。随着人类努力发展自己

---

① Tu Weiming 杜维明：“An ‘Anthropocosmic’ Perspective on Creativity,”见 Zhao Dunhua (ed.) Dialogue of Philosophies, Religions and Civilizations in the Era of Globalization: Chinese Philosophical Studies, XXV, Washington, D.C.: The Council for Research in Values and Philosophy. (2007): 147。

② 蒋庆似乎对“天”持有一种比较“原教旨主义”的观点。有关蒋庆天道观的批评，见拙作 Chenyang Li, “Transcendent Heaven? A Critique of Jiang Qing’s Grounding of the Right to Rule,”见 A Confucian Constitutional Order: How China's Ancient Past Can Shape Its Political Future, eds. Daniel A. Bell and Ruiping Fan, Princeton: Princeton University Press, 2012, 129—138。

的能力并且逐渐对外太空施加影响，三才结构中的“天”就更应该得到我们的重视。[1]有了这种三才的“和谐”结构的概念，有关“天”的诠释就不必限制于一家，既能包容世俗性的诠释，也能包容宗教性的诠释。

儒家的三才和谐观不应该同“天人合一”的思想混淆在一起。“天人合一”这个命题最早并不见于先秦的儒家文献中。有关思想首次在道家经典《庄子》中清楚的表述出来。《庄子·山木》将“人与天一也”的观点归之于孔子，并且借孔子之口赋予了这个命题以特殊的道家含义：“‘何谓人与天一邪?’仲尼曰：‘有人，天也；有天，亦天也’”。[2] 按照《庄子》作者的构想，“人”完全被“天”所消融了。一切作为（包括人类自身的作为）都是“天”的作为。这个观点并没有在《论语》或其他先秦儒家文献中出现，而孔子本人也不会赞同这样一种典型的道家主张。真正持有这种人类必须完全顺应自然之道及天之道的观点的是庄子。

儒家哲学家对待庄子“天人合一”观的态度基本上莫衷一是、臧否不一。譬如荀子主张“明于天人之分”(《荀子·天论》)，批评庄子的观点“蔽于天而不知人”。[3] 孟子虽曾论及人如何可以通过“尽心知性”而“知天”，[4] 但是他从来没有提出“天人合一”的观点。《易经·文言传》主张人的道德能与天、地的功能相合，主要意味的是当人的行动先于天的法则时，天的法则不会违逆他。[5]《中庸》则指出，天与地只有在“致中和”时才能取得和保持其正当的位置，[6] 而人类无疑是实现“中”与“和”的主要推动力。换句话说，《易传》与《中庸》都不主张将人消融于天道，而是充分肯定了人在此和谐的“三才”结构中的独特作用。

第一位将“天人合一”的观念纳入儒家传统中的是董仲舒。与荀子不同，董仲舒并不提倡天道与人道相分，而是明确主张“天人一也”。[7] 对他而言，天与人是直接关联在一起的，以致天能够对人事产生相对的反应。当人做坏事时，天会惩罚他；当人做好事时，天会奖励他，亦即所谓的“天人感应”。这个观点呼应了董仲舒有关天与人具有相同的结构，而且天道与人道之间有着重要的相似之处的思想。总之，相对于主流传统儒家在阐发和谐“三才”的理念时所持的观点，董仲舒更有意识地将天与人的关系拉近了一步。

---

① “天”还有第三层含义，亦即天下的“义理”。我们这里不做详细的讨论。
② 《二十二子》，上海：上海古籍出版社，1986 年，第 58 页。
③ 《荀子·解蔽》，《二十二子》，第 340 页。
④ 《孟子·尽心上》，《十三经》，第 2764 页。
⑤ 《十三经》，第 17 页。
⑥ 《十三经》，第 1625 页。
⑦ 《春秋繁露·阴阳义》，《二十二子》，第 791 页。

三才和谐的理念与“天人合一”观之间有相似之处。它们都既不主张人类是孤立于天地之外的单独实体，也认识到人类的行为能够影响整个世界的运作。但是，这两个概念之间又具有重大差异。首先，“天人合一”的命题提出了一个二元性的世界观，而三才的理念却提出了一个三元性的世界观。三才和谐的理念有意将“地”这第三种因素包含在内是非常值得重视的，尤其当我们从环境哲学（主要关注与地球的状况）的角度来思考这个命题。其次，在一种“天”与“人”所构成的二元结构中，人很可能将被强势的“天”所覆盖和遮蔽，正如在庄子的情况那样。这种二元结构也可能朝另外一种方向发展，亦即对自然界进行过分的人化或浪漫化，甚至像董仲舒一样按照人类的特征塑造出一个不切实际、虚幻的自然图景。相反，一个三元性的结构基本仿效着三角形的形状，因而拥有更大的平衡性与稳定性。儒家一方面赋予人类一定程度上的独立性，另一方面又不完全使其从“天”与“地”隔离出来。天、地、人就犹如一个富有凝聚力的团队中的成员：它们既是各自独立的，拥有属于自己的特殊身份，同时又是相互依存的，因为它们在共同促进宇宙的和谐化进程中是不分离的。

在儒家三才和谐的结构中，宇宙中的和谐是通过这三种因素来加以实现和维持的。如果没有“地”，“人”就不可能存在，因为人类若没有一个蓬勃发展、生生不息的地球环境，是根本无法生存的。如果没有“天”，世界或者将从宗教的意义上失去其精神上及道德上的根源，或者将从世俗的意义上中止其正常的运行，因为地球是太阳系的一部分。最后，如果没有“人”，整个世界将失去意义，而宇宙间也将没有积极参与和促进和谐化进程的自觉的主体。

有些人可能认为“天人合一”只不过是三才和谐的理念的一种简便的说法。我在前面已经说明情况并非如此。在《易经》里，天不是地，乾不是坤。我们不能以天代地，不能以乾代坤。否则，就会乾坤不分，阴阳无别。现在，我们有必要对这些概念做出澄清。通过“正名”，我们可以对三才和谐的理念的三元结构进行明确的梳理和表述。

儒家的三才和谐的理念在某种意义上代表着一种形上学或者宇宙论的观点，因为它展示了天、地、与人之间深层关系的基础框架。这种观点虽然还不是环境哲学的观点，但是它与环境哲学有着直接的关联。按照三才和谐的理念，宇宙不是由任何一方所垄断的。人类不是宇宙的中心，而天与地存在的目的也不单纯是为了给人类提供满足其需求的资源。天、地、与人三者各自都有自身的功能与价值。身为三才和谐结构中的积极参与者，人类拥有促进与维持宇宙和谐的重要责任。如果顺着这个思路，我们就不难推论出一套关于自然环境的儒家原则了。事实上，一些由杜维明等学者所阐述的环境哲学理论都可以很容易地在三才和谐理念的基础上加以重构。杜维明写道：“君子的行为传达了这样一个观念，即人参与创造了宇宙。作为共同创造者，理想的人就是宇宙的创始者、参与者、护卫者”。[①]我们可以对这样的论述做出与三才和谐理念相符合的诠释。所谓“共同创造者”的概念表明人与天并非同一个东西，而是两个各自独立而又密切相关的东西。而且，这个“宇宙”中不能不有“地”的位置。人类是天与地的守护者及合作伙伴。

儒家三才和谐的理念可以通过三个原则来阐明。其中一个原则是“人”的原则。根据这个原则，人类代表着天地之间的“万物之灵”。没有“人”，世界将被剥夺了其最宝贵的因素，因此人类的生存相对于保存地球上其他生物来得更重要。但是，正因为人是“万物之灵”，他在努力促进世界的和谐化进程上也就拥有不可推卸的责任。用儒家的话说，唯有人类才可以积极推广天下之“正道”，即天下的整体和谐。以此对照天地即是万物之“父母”的隐喻，人类在这里不宜理解为一般意义上的孩子，而是指“长大成熟的孩子”。因此，人类在宇宙的“大家庭”中必须承担起与其“父母”相同的，甚至更为重大的责任。

另一个原则是“地”的原则。地球不单是人类居住的家园，而且也是世间万物栖居繁衍的场所。它滋养世间所有的生命。“地”为人类提供重要的资源。但是，它又不仅仅是人类所需资源的来源。“地”在宇宙间具有属于自己的生命和地位。儒家将“地”称作母亲，[②] 而当我们联想起母亲在儒家哲学中所受到的敬重与推崇时，就不难体会“地也，故称乎母”背后的深刻含义了。在保护环境的过程中，“地”无疑是主要的关注点。儒家认为世间上的一切存在物都根据其所处的特殊环境而加以个体化。每一个存在物都是在某种特定的环境中作为独立的个体而存在。在自然进化的过程中，世间万物是在陪同其他存在物或与其他存在物相关联的情境下进化而来的。世间万物在进化过程中的相互关联可以理解为它们彼此之间的一种合作关系或协调关系。每一个存在物在整体的存在界中都拥有属于自己的地位。如果我们相信自然界的进化过程大致上是均衡与协调的，我们就可以说自然界中的所有因素在促进世界的整体和谐上都必须扮演好自己的角色。《易经》的“各正性命”指人和自然界的一切存在物都能在其性命之途上获得证成，亦即自然界的一切存在物都拥有属于自己能够获得证成的权利。如果我们将整个世界看作是“太和”，所有存在于这个世界中的万物都是这个至大的和谐场域的组成因素，而每一个因素都必须为此至大的整体做出贡献。按照这个理解，世间上的所有事物必须在“太和”中扮演其特定的角色。当每一个因素能够在其正当的角色中发挥其功能时，它们就能各得其所，而整个世界也将能够实现理想的和

---

① 杜维明 Way, Learning, and Politics: Essays on the Confucian Intellectual. Albany, NY: State University of New York Press. (1993): 53。

② 《十三经》，第 94 页。

谐状态。

还有一个原则是“天”的原则。儒家将“天”称作“父”,[1] 从而赋予了它在儒家三才和谐结构中的最高地位。“天”对于不同思想支流的儒家哲学家来说可以指涉不同的内容。拥有宗教倾向的儒者将“天”视为人类道德的终极根源;对他们而言,如果没有“天”,宇宙将完全丧失其灵性。从结构上来说,“天”为“人”与“地”之间的关系提供某种平衡。由于人们一般是以自己为中心的,“天”的原则要求我们超越自身的利益,积极促进整个宇宙的和谐化进程。即使对于世俗的儒者来说,“天”依然具有重要的意义。“天”代表地球以外的所有天体。因此,虽然人类与大地都非常伟大,但是它们并非宇宙间的唯一实体。从世俗的眼光看,“天”主要指的是地球以外的太空,而正是太空提供了地球及人类得以生存的环境。世俗意义上的“天”原则要求人类充分尊重太空的尊严和地位,而不是用它来实现某些狭隘的人类或地球的目的。随着当代的科技逐渐允许人类将自己生活圈子扩大至太空,“天”的原则就显得格外重要。一个合乎儒家“和谐”观的环境哲学只会支持那些能够让“天”、“地”与“人”同时受益的太空计划,而不是那些仅仅为了人类或地球利益的太空计划。

总而言之,“天”、“地”、“人”三个原则共同促成儒家宇宙观的高度和谐。[2] 从整体上来看,儒家三才的宇宙和谐观既不同于西方所发展出来的“人类中心主义模式”也不同于“泛价值模式”。与西方的人类中心主义模式不同,儒家不将世间万物仅仅视为满足人类需求的工具,而是赋予了非人类实体以伦理价值。与西方的泛价值模式(比如,大地伦理学与深层生态学)不同,儒家不主张世间所有事物都具有平等的伦理价值,而是在众多存在物中唯独赋予了人以主导的位置。当然,这套儒家环境哲学还有待进一步的发展及更具体的阐述。但是,我相信儒家传统的“三才和谐”观已经为未来更深入的研究与诠释奠定了坚实的基础。而这种和谐观的源头正是儒家诸经之首的《易经》。

---

① 《十三经》,第94页。

② 对儒家和谐观的详细论述,读者可参见拙作 Chenyang Li,The Confucian Philosophy of Harmony,London,UK/New York:Routledge (2014) .

# 儒、道哲学生态观之比较

陕西师范大学 刘学智

大约从十六世纪始，人类就进入了为工业化而努力的时代。随着一百多年来工业文明步伐的加快，科学技术的猛进，人类在取得一个又一个“辉煌成就”的同时，也造成了人与自然关系的高度紧张。当人类在欢呼自己对自然界的每一个胜利的时候，危机却无情地降临了。人类对水、空气、土地的需求和无限度开发利用，已经消耗了地球上近三分之一的可再生资源，但地球却不能及时得以补给，于是导致了森林资源逐渐在缩量、土地日渐沙化，空气和水源严重污染致使洪涝和干旱交替频繁发生，由此也带来了物种的大量减少。当生态的恶化已严重威胁到人类的生存的时候，我们不得不敬畏我们的古人，他们在地球并没有出现严峻生态紧张的情况下，早已在思考自然生态的问题，思考如何建构人与自然和谐关系的问题。早在春秋末期产生的儒、道诸家那里，都对此进行了有价值的思考。重要的是，儒家和道家关于自然生态观的思考，不是在现实生态危机威逼之下的权宜之虑，而是带有在天地万物一体化基础上的本原性思考。

儒、道两家对生态问题虽然有诸多相通之处，但是其相异之点还是比较明显的。本文试图探讨其同中之异，以期揭示儒道哲学生态观与其各自哲学观的内在关联和二者在相同的问题意识指向上所持的不同方法和视角，从而为我们今天关于生态问题的思考提供借鉴。哲学生态观问题涉及多个方面，本文着重就儒、道两家的生态本体观、生态价值观，做一点比较，以就教于同仁。

## 一、生态本体观之比较

存在问题是哲学的根本问题之一，它关注的是宇宙万物何以存在，即存在的方式和根据等问题。生态存在当是指人的生存环境对于人的生命存在来说何以才是合理的状态，此涉及人与万物的关系。如果宇宙间没有人类，宇宙无所谓生态问题，也无所谓生态文明的问题。在生态观问题上，中国传统哲学中的儒、道两家既有其相通之处，也存在着较大的差异。其相通之处在于，二者都能把人与宇宙联系起来思考生态问题，即都在天人合一的理路上思考生态问题，都注意到人的活动的目的性与规律性相统一的问题。但是二者的差异也是有的，表现在：

（一）儒家的生态本体观的根本点是“生”，而道家生态本体观的根本之点是“道”（自然）

“生”是涉及生命创造和生命过程的概念。从一般意义上说，儒、道两家都重视这一问题，但是，儒家是以“生”为其生态哲学的根基，诸多生态问题皆由此而引发；而道家认为宇宙相对于人的生态方式是合“道”，“生”仅被视为万物基于道的生成过程而已。在道家看来，道的本性是自然，故自然是万物根本的存在方式。

儒家将“生”定位为万物的根本存在方式。《易传》：“天地之大德曰生”，“生生之谓易”，认为天地万物最根本的特性（德）就是“生”，这个“生”表征着“生命存在及生命创造的内在联系”[①]（蒙培元）。“生”包括生出的原发性、生养中人的参与性以及生长过程的变化、更新等生命性意义的展现，体现了儒家对生命本源性的理解。儒家所理解的“生”，是在人与自然的内在关系上说的，如《五经正义》孔颖达释“天地之大德曰生”，说：“欲明圣人同天地之德，广生万物之意也。言天地之盛德，在乎常生，故言曰生。若不常生，则德之不大。以其常生万物，故云大德也。”这里所说的“大德”是指根本的特性、本性。一方面，人是天地所生，自然界对于人的生命存在有着决定的意义；另一方面，是说圣人与天地其性相通，天地根本之特征（盛德）在于“生”，圣人也有敬畏自然生命的本性。可见，“生”之德是在天人互动中实现的。又说，“日新之谓盛德”，韩康伯注：“体化合变，故曰‘日新’”《正义》释曰：“圣人以能变通体化，合变其德，日日增新，是德之盛极，故谓之盛德也。”就是说，宇宙之所以能发生日新之化，是因为圣人能够“变通体化”“合变其德”，参与了其中变化的缘故。“生生之谓易”，《正义》释：“生生，不绝之辞。阴阳变转，后生次于前生，是万物恒生，谓之易也。”“生生”，张载曰：“生生，犹言进进也。”（《横渠易说·系辞上》）是说宇宙不绝如恒的阴阳转化是持续不已的过程，所以“生”是宇宙间永恒的原理，这个永恒的原理谓之易。这一永恒易理的核心，正在于揭示宇宙在天人互动中的万物生生之理，体现了儒家对自然生命连续性和无限性的认识。“生”在儒家这里，不单纯是一个纯粹自然哲学的问题，而涉及“自然界对人的生命存在的意义究竟何在的问题。”[②]显然，“生”在儒家这里是作为人与自然联系的纽结而出现的概念。

儒家吸收了阴阳家的观念，从阴阳之气循环不已的流行来说明“生”是宇宙万物

---

① 蒙培元：《中国哲学生态观的两个问题》，《鄱阳湖学刊》，2009年第1期。
② 蒙培元：《中国哲学生态观的两个问题》，《鄱阳湖学刊》，2009年第1期。

的根本存在状态。《易》曰“一阴一阳之谓道”，按照朱熹的解释，其所说“一阴一阳”指“阴阳气也”，即是就气的两种对立的属性和力量上说的。而“道”是就阴阳之气“循环而不已”的过程上来说。（参见《朱子语类》卷九五）这是说，阴阳之气交替运行，循环不已，才有万物的生成。《易》在这句话之后接着说“继之者善也，成之者性也”。《易》说“大哉乾元！万物资始”，故“继之者善也”。“继善”是一阴一阳之气交替运行，循环不已所表现出来的生生不息之理。又说“乾道变化，各正性命”，故“成之者性也”。是说人与物都是在阴阳之气运行变化过程中获得了自己的规定性的，故说“成之者性”。以往我们多是从人性论方面理解这句话，其实这是不准确的。朱熹说：“这一段是说天地生成万物之意，不是说人性上事。”（《朱子语类》卷七四）可见，儒家认为，由于基于阴阳之气运行的“生生”，才使人与物得以形成，从而有了自己的规定性遂成为自身，故“生”是宇宙万物的根本存在状态。

儒家认为，“生”的前提条件是阴阳二气的相互感通。《易传·彖传》：“天地感，而万物化生。”《正义》释：“天地二气，若不感应相与，则万物无由得应化而生。”故《易传·系辞》：“天地絪缊，万物化醇，男女构精，万物化生。”也是说天地相互感通，是人与万物得以化生的根本条件。张载对“感”做过较为全面而细致地分析，特别指出“感”的普遍性、多样性、复杂性，说：“不可止以夫妇之道谓之咸（感），此一事耳，男女相配，故为咸也。感之道不一：或以同而感，圣人感人心以道，此是以同也；或以异而应，男女是也，二女同居则无感也；或以相悦而感，或以相畏而感，如虎先见犬，犬自不能去，犬若见虎则能避之；又如磁石引针，相应而感也。若以爱心而来者自相亲，以害心而来者相见容色自别。‘圣人感人心而天下和平’，是风动之也；圣人老吾老以及人之老而人欲老其老，此是以事相感也。感如影响，无复先后，有动必感，咸感而应，故曰咸速也。”故曰感是万物的生成条件。

如果说儒家把“生”视为宇宙生态的根本观念，那么道家则在“生”之上安置了一个终极的本原即道，强调宇宙生态观的根本是“道”。所谓“有物混成，先天地生。寂兮寥兮，独立而不改，周行而不殆，可以为天下母。吾不知其名，字之曰道。”（第25章）“道生一，一生二，二生三，三生万物。”（第42章）都表达了道是万物本原、道生万物的思想。庄子不仅明确指出道的本原性，同时也表达了道是万物的所以然之根据的思想：“夫道，有情有信，无为无形，可传而不可受，可得而不可见，自本自根。未有天地，自古以固存，神鬼神帝，生天生地。”在道家看来，“道”的根本特性是“德”即自然，“自然”是万物其生态存在的基本方式：“人法地，地法天，天法道，道法自然。”就是说，天、地、人作为宇宙中三个基本子系统，都应该以道为法则，而道的本性则是任自然。《老子》说：“道生之，德畜之，物形之，势成之。是以万物莫不尊道而贵德。道之尊，德之贵，夫莫之命而常自然。”（第51章）道以自然的方式生成了万物，又以自然的方式养育了万物。万物皆自生自成，自然天成，自己如此，非他力所为。突出道的实在性、本原性和万物生成过程的自然性，是道家区别于儒家哲学生态本体观的重要之点。

自然是万物根本的生态方式，由此道家强调人与万物的“自生”“自化”。自然的生态方式，指万物的组成要素是自然形成的，万物的内在结构是自然形成的，万物的运行秩序是自然的，或万物都有其自组织系统。也就是说，宇宙万物因其都有自身自然形成的组成要素，也有自己自然形成的内在结构、内在秩序和自组织系统，从而决定了万物特有的自然生态本性，于是其运化过程也是自然而然发生的。这样，自然演化过程本身就具有其内在的规律性、有序性。所谓“道”的规律性，不是说“道”本身是万物遵循的普遍规律，而是说“道”尊重万物自身的本性和规律，任万物以自身的本性和规律去自生、自长、自成。这是因为，如韩非子所说的，“万物各异理，万物各异理，而道尽稽万物之理”，道是“无常操”的，所以“天得之以高，地得之以藏，维斗得之以成其威，日月得之以恒其光。”（《韩非子·解老》）“无常操”而任万物之性，正体现了道家关于万物基于道的生态本体观。

（二）儒家是立足于“生生”基础上的“与天地万物一体”的生态观，而道家立足于自然基础上的“人与天一”生态观

儒家的“仁”不仅具有道德的意义，而且具有生态的意义。仁的生态义在孔子的思想中已经有了，此后经过历代儒家的发展，形成了较为系统的建立在“生生”基础上、以“仁民爱物”为轴心，以“与天地万物为一体”为特征的仁性生态观。

仁学与“生生”之德的结合，进一步深化了儒家仁的生态本体论意义。《易传》说“生生之谓易”，是说天地生养了万物，使万物生生不息，这正体现了天地的仁德。所以《彖传》说：“大哉乾元，万物资始，乃统天。云行雨施，品物流形。”“至哉坤元，万物资生，乃顺承天。坤厚载物，德合无疆。”由于天地的生生之德，才使“万物资始”、“万物资生”，于是才有“品物流形”，才有“品物咸亨”。这种“生生之德”正是仁爱的德性对万物的体现，由此，仁具有了天地生生不已的生态意义。

宋明理学家对仁与生的关系做了深入地考察。朱熹特别强调“须先识得元与仁是个甚物事”。他主张天地间只是一个生理，循环无穷，如元亨利贞，春夏秋冬，其中都蕴涵着、体现着这个生理。他说：“（四德）统是一个生意。如四时，只初生底便是春，夏天长，亦只是长这生底。”秋、冬“亦只是这个生”，即使“恻隐、羞恶、辞逊、是非，都是一个生意。”他所以认为仁有“生意”，原因是仁义礼智四德其核心是“仁”，而仁是四德之元。而“元”为初、始，有“生意”，所以“要理会得仁，当就初处看。故元亨利贞，而元为四德之首。就初生处看，便见得仁。”并举例说，“程子谓‘看鸡雏可以观仁’，为是那嫩小底便是仁底意思在。”（《朱子语类》卷九五）程子通过观鸡

雏之“生意”，乃体认出仁的道理。所以“仁者，天地生物之心。”（《朱子语类》卷五）朱子进一步举例以说明如何“乃见天地生物之心”，他说：“春气温厚，乃见天地生物之心。到夏是生气之长，秋是生气之敛，冬是生气之藏。若春无生物之意，后面三时都无了。”（《语类》卷二〇）在他看来，天地广大，万物流行，生生不息，“天地以生物为心，而所生之物，因各得夫天地之心以为心，所以‘人皆有不忍人之心’”（《朱子语类》卷三五）这与二程所说“仁本生意，乃恻隐之心便发”，意思完全相通。所以二程强调要“复其见天地之心”，意即“《复》之初爻，便是天地生物之心也。”并举例说，“心，譬如谷种，生之性便是仁。”（见《朱子语类》卷九五）是说心譬如谷种，其能生的本性就是仁。既然心是生生的道理，而恻隐之心亦是“得天地生物之心”的人心的道理，这样，生生就由外在的天地之德内化为人心的德性了。人心之仁就必然表现出对万物生命的珍爱，表现出促进和保护万物生长的德性。这种仁与生与性的内在统一，正是儒家本体生态观的核心和基础。

在此基础上，儒家进一步强调仁者“与天地万物为一体”，这是其仁学生态观对天、地、人统一观的集中表述。《易传·象传》：“夫大人者与天地合其德，与日月合其明，与四时合其序，与鬼神合其吉凶。先天而天弗违，后天而奉天时。”所谓圣人与天地合德，就包含了人与天地自然其性相通的思想，其“合明”“合序”也包含了天人合一的观念。因为如此，人才能而且必须“奉天时”而“弗违”。如果说《易传》所表述的尚是一种外在的“合”，到宋明理学那里，则强调的是天人在仁性相通相感基础上的内在的合，如二程所说，“天人本无二，不必言合”（《河南程氏遗书》卷六）。理学家认为，天与人都是一气之流行，其中又都是一理之贯通，当然二者本为一体，不必言合。张载说：“感者性之神，性者感之体。在天在人，其究一也。”（《乾称篇》）又说：“乾称父，坤称母；予兹藐焉，乃混然中处。故天地之塞，吾其体；天地之帅，吾其性。民吾同胞，物吾与也。”（《西铭》）这就赋予了天地所生万物自身内在的、固有的价值，明确说出了基于一气流行的“民胞物与”的天人合一思想。此后王阳明在心学的理论架构上讲“盖天地万物与人原只是一体，其发窍之最精处，是人心一点灵明。风雨露雷，日月星辰，禽兽草木，山川土石，与人原只一体。”这种天人合一思想成为儒家哲学生态观的核心理念。不过，张载又通过“因明致诚，因诚致明，故天人合一”走上与《中庸》相通的道德本体与价值境界统一意义上的“天人合一”，强调道德本体与心性工夫的统一。程颢所说“仁者浑然与物同体”（《识仁篇》），也与孟子所说“万物皆备于我，反身而诚，乐莫大焉”（《孟子·尽心上》）的道德境界论相通，这则是道德心性论和道德价值论意义上的天人合一了。

与儒家建立在生生基础上的仁性生态观不同，道家则强调建立在“道”基础上的“人与天一”说。如果说儒家把“生生”视为宇宙万物的本原性，而道家则把道之性即

"自然"视为宇宙万物的本原性，强调道性自然。其所说的"自然"即尊重万物天然本有的状态，亦即未有人的主观意志打上印迹的本然状态。老子把"自然"视为宇宙大道的根本属性，称为"玄德"。在老子看来，事物是"本然如此"，"自己如此"的，皆按照自身的本性存在的，按照自身的规律变化和发展着。道家所说的本真的状态，就是"朴"、"素"、"静"的状态。未雕者为"朴"，未染者为"素"，不躁者为"静"，故老子主张"复归于朴"（第28章），"素朴而民性得矣"（《庄子·马蹄》），"归根曰静"（第16章）。返璞归真，去染归素，返躁归静，就可以回归到事物的本然，即返归原始的天性、真性。就人来说，就是回归到"如婴儿之未孩"（第20章）的状态。庄子将此境界称为"与道合一"或"人与天一"，即人要无为而顺从天，从而达到与天之本然合一的状态。什么是"人与天一"？郭象注："皆自然。"（《庄子·山木注》）庄子借仲尼之口回答说："有人，天也；有天，亦天也。人之不能有天，性也，圣人晏然体逝而终矣。"（《山木》）就是说，人与天，皆天为之。天日逝而不停，人只能顺应天而不可与天抗，这就是"人与天一"。按庄子的说法，就是"无以人灭天，无以故灭命。"（《庄子·秋水》）郭象说："天地以自然为体，而万物必以自然为正。自然者，不为而自然者也。"（郭象《庄子·逍遥游注》）可见，自然是道家哲学生态本体观的核心和基础。

儒学以"生"为本的生态观和道家以"道"（自然）为本的生态观，二者虽不同但却有相通之处。儒家所说的万物"生生"的过程，也是自然的过程，只是道家的自然更多地排斥人的主观干预，而儒家的"生生"则总是与人、与人的活动相关联。

## 二、生态价值观之比较

生态价值观是指关于自然的价值的观点，这涉及在人与自然的关系问题上，人类是宇宙的中心，还是人内在于自然，融合于自然之中。如果人类是宇宙的中心，那么自然就可能是无价值的。如果人内在于自然，融合于自然，那么人与自然就有着共同的利益和命运，就要建立人与自然相互协调发展的价值观。在农业文明背景下，人类由于求生存和发展的需要，必须顺应自然，尊重自然。所以在春秋时期形成的儒家和道家，都认识到自然的价值，尊重自然的价值，所以二者在生态价值观上有诸多相通之处。但是在表现形式上又有着某些差别。

（一）儒家的生态价值观

首先，儒家主张"人为天下贵"与"参天地，赞化育"。关于人类在自然界的位置，儒家有着明确的态度。孔子在马厩焚毁后问"伤人乎？"而"不问马"（《论语·乡党》），说明他最看重人的价值。荀子说"水火有气而无生，草木有生而无知，禽兽有知而无义，人有气、有生、有知、亦且有义，故最为天下贵也。”（《荀子·王制》）刘向《说苑》卷一七：“天生万物唯人为贵”。儒家这些说法都明确表达了人与自然万物相比是最重要的观点。不过，儒家虽然讲“人为贵”，只是肯定人的相对价值，却没有走向人类中心主义，因为儒家总把人与自然联系在一起，且非常重视人生活在其间的与人的生命息息相关的宇宙自然万物的价值。在儒家看来，人是自然的产物，也是自然的一部分，与自然有着内在的生命联系。从价值的意义上说，自然内在于人而存在，没有人，自然是无所谓价值的。所以儒家总是把人与自然天地联系在一起来思考人与自然的价值的。《易》主张人要“顺性命之理”，即强调自然的价值，又说“立天之道，曰阴与阳；立地之道，曰柔与刚；立人之道，曰仁与义。”“兼三才而两之，故易六画而成卦”，是说天地人三才具有一体性的特征，而其内部又各有其对立的两方面，所以《周易》才以每卦六爻来彰显其运行变化的规律，这叫“易六位而成章”。（见《易传·说卦》）并且人与天地并立而相互作用，由此自然界就不是离开人、与人无关的自在。荀子亦说：“天有其时，地有其财，人有其治，夫是之谓能参。舍其所以参，而愿其所参，则惑矣。”（《天论》）天地人各遵循自身的规律，人虽然“不与天争职”，但可以与之相“参”，也说明天、地、人具有交互作用的一体性。《中庸》则明确提出人可“与天地参”的命题，说：“惟天地至诚，故能尽其性。能尽其性，尽人之性，能尽人之性，则能尽物之性，则可以赞天地之化育，赞天地之化育，则可以与天地参。”是说天地之道至诚而生物无穷、生生不息，但是，人却可以“尽其性”（尽天性、人性、物性），以“赞天地之化育”。能赞天地之化育，“则可以与天地参矣”，即人能够参与并完成自然界之化育，故能与天地“参”，即并立而为三，这样天地已经是既与人并立又内在于人的存在了。此后董仲舒说得更明确：“何为本？曰：天、地、人，万物之本也。天生之，地养之，人成之。……三者相为手足，合以成体，不可一无也。”（《春秋繁露·立元神》）这就在“天人一体”的意义上肯定了自然的价值。显然儒家的生态价值观从根本上不是人类中心主义的，而是天地人并立而相参的，自然对于人来说具有内在价值的。

其次，“和谐”观：“万物并育”而“皆得其宜”。由于儒家是在人与天地并立基础上肯定自然的价值，所以，从一开始就注意建立人与自然的和谐关系。《中庸》强调要“上律天时，下袭水土”，这样按规律去做，则“万物并育而不相害，道并行而不相悖。”这正是儒家追求的和谐的宇宙秩序。荀子主张人与万物都在“群”中生活，如果建立这种“群”的原则是合适的（“群道当”），“则万物皆得其宜，六畜皆得其长，群生皆得其命。”这个“群道当”的原则就是合乎规律。“故养长时，则六畜育；杀生时，则草木殖；政令时，则百姓一，贤良服。”“养长”合时，则六畜繁育；“杀生”合时，则草木繁殖；政策法令合时，则社会和谐。荀子进一步解释所谓“时”，就是“草木荣华滋硕之时，则斧斤不入山林”，“鼋鼍鱼鳖鳅鳣孕别之时，罔罟毒药不入泽”，这样就可以“不夭其生，不绝其长”；农业生产“春耕、夏耘、秋收、冬藏，四者不失时”，这样就会“五谷不绝，而百姓有余食”，有“余用”。在这里，儒家提供了一个极具人天和谐特征的生态图景。由于儒家没有走向人类中心主义，而是在人“与天地万物一体”意义上提出这一和谐的生态价值观，这无疑对中国传统农业文明的持续发展发生过积极影响。

再次，“仁民爱物”。孔子提出了“仁者爱人”的思想，其基本的含义是强调以人与人之间相亲的原则处理人际关系。孔子的仁最初更多指向伦理关系中的人，如孝悌等伦理原则。但后来他也讲到“泛爱众而亲人”（《论语·学而》），“爱众”当然其施爱者还主要限于众人。不过，《论语》中也提及孔子“子钓而不纲，弋不射宿”（《论语·述而》），主张不用大网捕鱼，不射归宿的鸟，说明他把爱的对象已从“众”人扩展到动物。到孟子则明确提出“亲亲而仁民，仁民而爱物”（《孟子·尽心上》），郑玄注：“仁，爱人以及物。”显然儒家已经有了近于博爱的情怀。孟子“不忍其觳觫”，主张祭祀不杀牛而“以羊易之”（《孟子·梁惠王上》），都是“仁民爱物”的体现。儒家这种“仁爱万物”的理念，以高尚的道德情怀、博大的生命意识，引发了人们对万物、对生命、对自然的心灵关怀。此后，韩愈提出“博爱之谓仁”（《原道》），其心灵关怀则进入到一个新的境界。到宋儒，这一心灵关怀更上升到一个新的高度。张载在《西铭》中所讲“故天地之塞，吾其体；天地之帅，吾其性。民吾同胞，物吾与也。”指出人类与万物都是禀气而生，所有的人都是我们同胞兄弟，万物都是我们的同伴朋友，人与万物构成自然界的生命共同体，所以我们都应该平等地尊重、同情和爱护万物。这一“民胞物与”的价值观，标志着“天人一体”意义上的儒家生态价值观的成熟。

（二）道家的生态价值观

如前所述，在农业文明的背景下，道家更强调尊重自然的价值。如果说儒家是在“天人一体”的意义上看待自然的生态价值，而道家则是在一个更多地强调自然的价值，即在自然为本的基础上看待自然的绝对价值，主张“与道合一”、“人与天一”。

首先，道家把人视为自然界中的一个部分，没有一点人类中心主义的意味。《老子》说：“道大，天大，地大，人亦大。域中有四大，而人居其一焉。”（第25章）即认为“道”是先于天地而又内在于天地之中的最高存在。如果把宇宙中的一切分为四大类的话，那么道是最高的存在，人只能算作“四大”之一，而且是宇宙间相对脆弱的存在物。不过，人不是大自然的异在，而是自然界的一部分。同时，自然界还为人类的生存与发展提供物质前提，生养和哺育了人，所以，人类应该尊重自然，爱护自然，善待自然，并努力保护自然，以与自然和谐相处。

其次，“道法自然”。《老子》说：“人法地，地法天，天法道，道法自然。”这是说，在宇宙“四大”中，天、地、人都以道为法则，而道则以“自然”为法则。所以，在道家这里，“自然”处于最高的价值地位。由于天、地本身就是自然的存在物，而人却具有意志性和目的性，所以，人必须自觉地合于天，与天为一。这样，相对于人来说，自然就居于天人关系的中心地位。于是，天地就不能被简单地视为人类征服的对象，而应该是顺应和保护的对象；自然也不是人类随意违背的原则，而是人应该顺应的原则。“知和曰常”，《老子》认为，当人自觉地遵循自然的规律，顺应自然的本性的时候，就会达至“和”的价值境界。天与人的和谐乃是道家追求的价值境界。所以，庄子说“与天和者，谓之天乐”（《庄子·天道》），把人与自然的和谐称为“天乐”。“天乐”的境界，就是如庄子所说“天地与我并生，而万物与我为一”（《庄子·齐物论》）的境界。主张顺应自然，尊重自然的运化方式，以使“人与天一”，这与参与自然、“赞天地之化育”的儒家生态价值观是有明显区别的。

**参考文献：**

[1] 蒙培元．人与自然．人民出版社．2004．

[2] 蒙培元．中国哲学生态观的两个问题．鄱阳湖学刊．2009.1．

[3] 乔清举．泽及草木，恩至水土．山东教育出版社．2011．

[4] 陈红兵．传统儒家、道家哲学生态观比较．管子研究．2005.4．

# 对18—19世纪韩国儒学中人物性同异论的生态学解释

成均馆大学，栗谷学会 崔英辰

## 一、绪论

我们在使用望远镜或是显微镜时，会观察到很多肉眼看不到的现象，而“科学”正是如此，将我们用肉眼看不到，想象不出来的世界呈现在我们面前，感叹造物的神奇。从这个角度来说，物理学者张会翼所看到的“生命”的现象，为我们呈现了一个非常重要的事实。[①] 这些重要的事实之中其中有所谓的“全生命（Global Life)”是生命的单位。[②] 他将生命的概念规定为“宇宙内部形成的持续自由的能量不断流动，以此为基础，既有的秩序成为新秩序的母体，是一个能够使持续成长成为可能的一种‘情报秩序的总体’”,[③] 认为生命可以分为“全生命”，“个体生命”和“补生命”。全生命作为一个自主的单位是“最基本的自由能量的根源，并灵活运用其物理条件对此进行确保，同时利用其流动的各个阶段的个体构成了一个有机的整体”,[④] 个体生命作为依存的单位是构成全生命个体的生命，而补生命则是“除了全生命自身以外所剩余的部分”。[⑤] 因此，各个个体生命不仅要作为个体生存下去，同时还要持续的与补生命和谐共存。它具有双重的性格，即在补生命共存时要不断吸收其有利于自己的方面，同时为了与其共存要有一定的生态上的照顾。也就是说个体的行为趋向之中，通过个体之

① 张会翼（1938—今），首尔大学物理系名誉教授。他以物理学为中心，结合现代科学的研究成果对生命的现象进行研究，创立了“全生命”的概念，并以此为基础批判现代文明中所出现的问题，提出新的解决方案。特别是他从物理学的角度对朝鲜性理学和《周易》进行了解释，最近以周濂溪的《太极图说》和现代物理学理论为基础发表了其论文《宇宙和人类》，而其著作更有《生活和全生命》，《如何理解生命》等。

② 张会翼：《“全生命”和现代文明》，《科学思想》，1995年春季刊，汎洋社，第139—160页。

③ 同上，第140页。

④ 同上，第143页。

⑤ 同上，第144页。

间的竞争去追求自身相对利益的“个体中心倾向”和通过与自身周围个体的协作来达道整体和谐的“生态中心倾向”是共存的。如果将这种个体生命的倾向适用于社会之中，那么以竞争为主的社会多一些生态性的思考，就会减少对利益最大化的关心，而以协作为主的社会多一些生态性的思考，就会最求更长远的利益，共同的善。①

根据以上观点来分析由现代文明所带来的生态界危机的话，可以从人类这一个体生命所具有的个体中心倾向中找出根本性的原因。人类不是追求与周边个体的共存与和谐，而是对他们进行榨取，有时甚至消灭周边的个体来满足自身的欲望，使人类这一种生物产生了异常繁殖，其结果直接导致了作为人类生存必要条件的补生命受到了破坏，最终是全生命也处于了危机之中。这种现象我们可以将之比喻为人的癌症，身体一处细胞的非正常繁殖，导致了其他细胞的损坏，最终是人体丧失了平衡，产生了癌症。② 这也是为什么我们将机械论的自然观和人类中心主义作为生态危机根源的原因。

根据人类中心主义是生态危机的根本原因之一这一诊断，有人提出生态主义或者说是自然主义就是其处方。这种说法不仅使人类，动物，植物，就连一土一石也都有其所应有的价值和权利，因此他们也应该得到相应的尊重，而人类也对他们负有一定的道德义务。但是这种主张的合理性很难得到证明，而且西方的传统伦理学反对将道德共同体扩大到动植物或是整个自然界。自然事物中类似美术作品或遗址虽然能得到一定的法律权利，但是却不能上升为道德权力的主体。③ 可是如果将自然单纯的规定为保护的对象，最终只会有回到了人类中心主义。这是因为人类中心主义者们只在人类中心主义所接受的范围内拥护对于生态危机或是环境保护重要性的主张。

如果将“人类如果还将自己作为世界的中心是不可以的”这一观点作为克服生态危机的关键，那么又会聚焦到最基本的问题上，即“如何规定除了人以外的自然生物”？是将它规定为没有灵魂的单纯物质还是能够组成机器的精巧装置？抑或是根据人类的需求和利害关系需要保存的资源？如果这些最基本的观点不加以改正，那么人类中心主义就无法克服。带着这样的问题意识，我们来研究 18 世纪朝鲜性理学最大的论争—人物性同异论。这是一场对“物”这一自然事物是否具有和人类一样的道德性问题的讨论，由于看待这一问题角度的不同，也有人会认为这是一场幼稚的论争，但是在这场论争中用“物”这一词语所表现的“对他者的认识”则会让我们发现儒家自然观和人类观的一个断面，并可以以此来展望对生态学的新探索。

---

① 张会翼：《“全生命”和现代文明》，《科学思想》，1995 年春季刊，汎洋社，第 145 页。

② 同上，第 156—158 页。

③ 黄敬植：《科学时代的伦理反省》，《科学思想》，12 辑，第 129—135 页。

## 二、巍岩与南塘对于“人物性同异”的见解

“人物性同异论”是湖洛论争中的理论之一，在18世纪初期产生于畿湖学派的老论之内。

图表：朝鲜后期 学派与政派

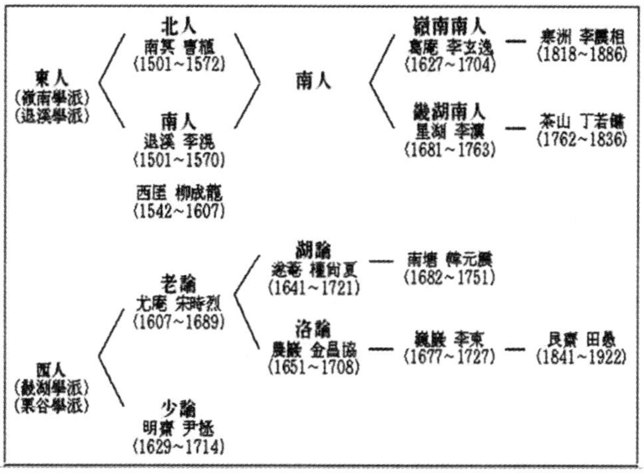


湖洛论争与四端七情论争都使中国的朱子学更加本土化，逐渐形成了朝鲜性理学，进一步的发展深化了儒学思想。这场论争的争论点南塘整理为：“先生之說，不同于公舉者有二，曰未发气质之性有无之辨也，曰人物五常之性同异之辨也”，[①] 也就是说他认为争论点有两个，一是未发论辩，一是人物性同异论争——五常论辩。巍岩否定未发时的气质之性，认为圣人和凡人都得到了明德本体，其本心都是一样的，即“圣凡心同论”，[②] 他以此为基础认为人性和物性也是一样的，所以他支持“人物性同论”。南塘则认同未发时的气质之性，当然他就以圣人和凡人的本心不同，即“圣凡心不同论”[③] 为基础认为人性和物性有着本质上的区别，所以他支持“人物性异论”。[④] 如果说巍岩的理论基调是“同”，那么南塘的理论基调就是“异”。

众所周知人物性同异论是以朱子对《中庸》第一章“天命之谓性”和《孟子·告子章》“生之谓性”的注释为文本根据的。

---

① 《南塘集·28·李公举上师门书辨》。

② 《巍岩集·卷2·未发辨》。

③ 《南塘集·卷11·拟答李公举》。

④ 未发论辩和人物性同异论争中哪个探讨的更接近本质？二者理论发展的前后有何种关系？对此的见解各有不一，但是可以肯定的是二者在逻辑上有着非常紧密的联系。（全仁植：《李谏与韩元震的未发·五常论辩研究》，精神文化研究院韩国学大学院博士论文，1998年，第6—9页。）

1. 天以陰陽五行，化生萬物，氣以成形，而理亦賦焉，猶命令也，於是人物之生，因各得其所賦之理，以爲健順五常之德，所謂性也。

2. 人物之生莫不有是性，亦莫不有是氣，然以氣言之則知覺運動，人與物，若不異也，以理言之，則仁義禮智之稟豈物之所得而全哉？此人之性所以無不善而爲萬物之靈也。

根据引文1的解释，人类与万物都秉受了“仁义礼智信”这五常之德，而这一点也充分体现在在巍岩的理论中。

蓋人物均受五行之氣，而偏全煞有分數，今論其分數多少，（“分數多少”，本朱子語.）發用與否（“發用與否”，本程子語）則可。於其五者之中，謂一有而一無則不可。凡一草一木，何莫非二五所造，而况較靈於草木者，寧有不盡稟五者之理哉？①

巍岩根据有理则必有气这一性理学前提，主张万物都是由阴阳五行之气所构成，而其理就是五常，五常平均的分配在所有事物当中。

根据引文2我们可知，虽然“物”不是完全没有“仁义礼智信”的脱道德性存在，但是人类拥有全部，而物则只具有其中的一部分，从这点来说他们要比人类低一等。反过来说，由于人类具有全部的四德，保留了其本性的绝对善，因此成了万物的灵长。南塘对此做了如下的说明：

夫以爲知覺運動人與物同者。豈謂人之無不知無不覺者。物亦同之耶。蓋以知覺之在人在物者。雖有精粗之不同。其有是知覺則同。至於仁義禮智。則初無精粗之混。而非物之所得以全者。故謂知覺運動則人與物同。而仁義禮智則人與物異也。若論其仁義禮智之或存或亡或全或偏者。則又不在他。在乎其知覺之氣有不同耳。何以言之。物之知覺。其氣得五行之粗濁者。故其理只得爲粗濁之理。雖未嘗無其理。亦不可謂仁義禮智也。②

南塘认为人与物虽然在知觉能力上有所差别，但是在具有知觉能力的事实上却是相同的。他还认为类似仁义礼智的这种较高层次的道德性，二者有着本质性的差异，即从严格意义上的仁义礼智上来看，只有人才有可能具有仁义礼智。

## 三、茶山的人物性异论及其与湖洛论争的关系

人物性同异论争并不仅仅停留在性理学派系之间，朝鲜后期道德代表性实学者湛

---

① 《巍岩遗稿·卷7·与崔性仲》。

② 《南塘集·卷29·论性同异辨》。

轩洪大容和茶山丁若镛的著述里也出现了人物性同异论。首先我们来看茶山的《中庸注》：

1.《天命之謂性》注释：況草木禽獸 天於化育之初 賦生生之理 以種傳種 各全性命而已. 人則不然 天下萬民 各於胚胎之初 賦此靈明 超越萬類享用萬物.

今乃云 健順五常之德 人物同得 孰主孰奴 都無等級 豈上天之生物之理 本自如此乎.

仁義禮智之名 本起於吾人行事 並非在心之玄理 人之受天 只此靈明 可仁可義可禮可智 則有之矣 若云上天 以仁義禮智四顆 賦之於人性之中 則非其實矣. 人猶然矣 況云五常之德 物亦同得乎.①

2.《中和》注释：愼獨之爲至誠。至誠之爲愼獨。旣然無疑。則未發之中已發之和。惟愼獨者當之。不能愼獨者。方其未發之時。心術先已邪辟。及其旣發之後。行事又復偏陂。安得以中和二字許之於此人乎。況致中和則天地位焉。萬物育焉。明中和二字爲聖人之極功。安得爲衆人之所與乎.②

引文1是茶山对“天命之谓性”的注释，他完全否定朱子人与物都得到了健顺五常之德的观点，认为物只具有“生的道理”，即只具有对物种复制的道理，而人从降生之初就得到了灵明，是比物更优等的存在，并享有使用物的权利。人与物的关系可以说就像主人与奴隶。

引文2是茶山对“中和章”的注释，他认为由于喜怒哀乐在未发之时，只有圣人和君子才在中的状态，一般人都已经有了邪辟，所以“中和章”只是针对了圣人和君子，并不是对人类普遍性的性情进行的论述。这种说法与湖论一脉相承，都认为未发之时即使心体湛然虚明，但由于气禀有清浊粹驳必然导致善恶的产生。

当然茶山并没有直接言及湖洛论争，只是我们从他对朱子“人物性同论”的批判上推断出了他的立场。他认为朱子兼具人和物，解释《中庸》第一章中的性和道，以及命、性、道、教是由根本性的错误的。“天命之谓性”就是人类的性，“率性之谓道”就是人类的道，“修道之谓教”就是人类的教，而朱子却误认为这是人与物的普遍之道。③ 茶山认为朱子中庸注释当中把“天命之谓性”的定义为了本然之性，因此认为人与物同得此性。他说“朱子中庸之注曰，天以阴阳五行化生万物，气以成形，理亦赋焉。此所谓本然之性，谓赋生之初，其理本然，此所谓人物同得也。然臣独以为本然

① 《中庸讲义补》。

② 《中庸自监》。

③ 《中庸讲义补》，“朱子看此二句太拘太泥，每以命性道教四字兼人物而言之，然所謂天命之謂性，人性也，率性之謂道，人道也，修道之謂教，人教也。”

之性，原各不同。”[1] 是对朱子人物性同论错误的批判。

茶山和南塘都认为人与物虽然都有知觉，但在道德的层面上却有着本质性的差异。南塘认为万物都具有善和灵明，是接受了部分的朱子学理论，与茶山有着根本性的差异。南塘肯定自然界也有道德性，并断言物虽不全具有仁义礼智和纯粹性，但却绝不可以说完全没有，人与物的差异只在于“偏全”。由于偏全所产生的差异巍岩称之为“气质之性”，而南塘则认其为“本然之性”。从这里我们可以看出南塘理论体系的基调就是自然与人类有着联系性的朱子学，更广一点可以说是儒学的基本前提，[2] 而茶山则否定这一基调，将自然和人类，事实与当为分离。

## 四、湛轩的人物性同论以及其生态学的意义

18世纪北学派的代表学者湛轩洪大容在洛论的基础上构成了新的理论。他在《医山问答》中对人与物的关系做了如下解释：

1. 我復問爾。生之類有三。人也。禽獸也。草木也。草木倒生故有知而無覺。禽獸横生。故有覺而無慧。三生之類。坱軋泯棼。互相衰旺。抑將有貴賤之等乎。

2. 天地之生 惟人爲貴 今夫禽獸也草木也 無慧無覺無禮無義 人貴於禽獸 草木賤於禽獸.

3. 五倫五事人之禮義也 群行呴哺禽獸之禮義也 叢苞條暢草木之禮義也 以人視物 人貴而物賤 以物視人 物貴而人賤 自天而視之 人與物均也…… 夫大道之害莫甚於矜心 人之所以貴人而賤物 矜心之本也.

湛轩指出了构成生态的人、禽兽、草木之间的差别，并强调这种差别性并不是构成差等性的原因，并批判主张人、禽兽、草木这一等级秩序的虚子，认为禽兽和草木也会有各自的礼和义。人与物的贵贱是相对的，如果从天这一绝对的立场上来看时人与物是均等的，只有执着于人类的立场才会认为物贱人贵，人类中心主义才是妨碍真理的根本原因。

湛轩进一步又说：“君臣之义，盖取诸蜂，兵阵之法盖取諸蚁，礼节之制盖取提拱鼠，网罟之設盖取诸蜘蛛，故曰圣人师万物”，[3] 将物规定为道德的规范和事物的原则。

---

① 《孟子要义·生之谓性犬牛人之性章》，“朱子中庸之注曰 ，天以阴阳五行化生万物，气以成形，理亦赋焉。此所謂本然之性，谓赋生之初，其理本然 ，此所谓人物同得也，然臣独以为本然之性原各不同。”

② 拙稿，《儒教的真理观》，《现代人读儒学》，亚细亚文化社，1999年，第211—213页。

③ 《医山问答》。

他还解释说“夫无慧故无思，无觉故无伪，然则物贵于人，亦远矣”，认为物比人有着更优秀的道德性，并赋予了雨和露珠这类生命道德性。

雨露旣零萌芽發生者 惻隱之心也 霜雪旣降枝葉旣落者 羞惡之心也 仁卽義義卽仁 理也者一而已矣. 毫釐之微只此仁義也 天地之大只此仁義也[①]

众所周知，笛卡尔的精神和物质是两种绝对不同的实体的二元论思想是对西方近代自然观的形成产生了决定性影响的思想之一。他认为物质是不包含任何形式的精神意识的，那么我们就可以将作为所有存在集合体的自然理解为是一个没有灵魂，只具有复杂结构的机器性存在，而这种认识自然的机械的因果作用原理则会使自然沦为人类可以随心所欲的拥有和榨取的对象。与这种西方近代的自然观不同，儒家自然观的代表之作《周易》则将自然看作是一个生命体，是具有目的指向性的存在，并肯定心这一要素的存在。这一点我们从复卦的《象传》“复见其天地之心”一句中可以看出。[②]

如上所诉，以农耕生产方式为基础而建立起的易学思维中，四季变换所代表的自然的运动，就是一系列关于生产出作为最高价值的生命的过程。因此天地就是以生育万物为目的的有机体，也称之为目的指向性存在。如果将天地看作是一个目的指向性的存在，[③] 我们就可以说“天地之心”是天地生育万物的“目的意识”，也就说自然界的变化并不是盲目的机械运动，而是有一定目的和意义的，我们将此表现为“天地之心”。

肯定自然之中具有心这一要素的另一有力资料就是战国时代的诸文献。《周易・系辞传・上篇》有“精气为物”一句，就是将气看作是物的构成要素。根据之前的研究我们可以知道，在《孟子》、《庄子》、《吕氏春秋》中出现的气不仅仅指身体・自然，甚至包含了精神的领域，而这样的气在物中的话就不得不肯定他所具有的精神要素。从这种角度来看，阿弗烈・诺夫・怀海德（Alfred North Whitehead）说“就连岩石这类的东西，也会具有最低形态的心理体验（mental experience），物质的宇宙包含了所有被要求的心理体验”，给我们带来了很大的启示。[④]

湛轩认为雨水、露珠、霜、雪降落的这一自然现象就是“恻隐之心”、“羞恶之心”，这是从传统的自然观出发，肯定了自然中所包含的精神。“恻隐之心”和“羞恶之心”是仁和义的端绪，同时又是仁和义的发现体。因此从细小的尘土到整个天地，所有的存在都充满着道德性，世界超越“生命共同体”成了一个“道德共同体”。

---

① 《医山问答》。

② 以下论述见拙稿《易学对于精神和物质的理解》，《哲学》，35辑，1991年，第4—12页。

③ 徐复观：《中国人性论史》，台湾：商务印书馆，1972年，第207页。

④ 山本诚作：《怀海德的宗教哲学》，京都行路社，1988年，第1页。

如上所述人物性同异论对“物”是只具有部分的四德或是五常，还是具有全部的问题展开的论辩，也就是说不管是“同论”还是“异论”其实都是肯定“物”的道德性的，而这种观点在“天地万物”这一词语上则得到非常好的体现。其代表性的著作为《周易·大象传》，构成两个三爻短卦所象征的就是从自然物的存在形式导出人类规则。[①] 以最典型的乾卦为例：

天行健，君子以自强不息。

“天行健”说的是天象，是一种事实判断，这种天象要君子去体得，在需要之时就会转换成“自强不息”的当为法则。这里天成为人的法则，也可以称之为“自然的法则化”，[②] 从这种层面上说自然的法则的根源就是绝对善。

## 五、结论：超越人类中心主义

一位神学者对于西方人类中心主义的源泉有如下的看法：

根据圣经所言，自然不是‘神’，而是被人类支配的被造物，将自然作为观察和分析的对象，可以随心所欲操作的科学技术是由基督教所孕育出来的。基督教以人为中心，以历史为中心，崇尚人类优越的自然观……莫尔特曼（Jurgen Moltmann）认为基督教像这样走向错误之路是始于中世纪末出现的新概念唯名论。根据唯名论神是全能的，而神具有绝对性的力量就是神性最大的特征。人类从神那里得到了“支配大地”的许可，于是也拥有绝对的力量，当然要优于自然。培根（知识就是力量）和笛卡尔（人类是自然界的主人和统治者）受到这种思潮的影响，他们对自然进行支配的程序就是自然科学和科学技术。[③]

对于人类的优越性认识不仅仅存在于基督教，也同样存在于儒教之中。荀子说：

水火有氣而無生，草木有生而無知，禽獸有知而無義，人有氣有生有知亦具有義 故最爲天下貴也。

荀子为我们展示了由无生物——植物、动物、人类构成的存在的阶级构造，将人类放在最上位以确保人类的优越性。有开启宋代性理学先河之称的周濂溪，再起代表性论文《太极图说》中也有类似的主张。

無極之眞。二五之精。妙合而凝。乾道成男。坤道成女。二氣交感。化生萬

---

① 以讼卦为例：“天与水违行，讼；君子以作事谋始。”文中从天和水这两种自然物导出了君子需要遵守的当为法则。

② 崔珍源：《江湖歌道研究》，成均馆大学博士论文，1975年，第150页。

③ 边宣焕：《科学技术和基督教的伦理》，《科学思想》，12辑，第94—95页。

物。萬物生生。而變化無窮焉。惟人也得其秀而最靈。

周濂溪主张只有人最灵，因此相对于其他自然物来说具有优越性，但是他在这里并不是要合理化人类对自然的支配，就像《论语》所述“人能弘道，非道能弘人”，只是在强调人类所具有的主体性。人心如果正，那么就会“天地立，万物化”，人是帮助天地完成化育的存在，是构成世界的“三才”中重要的一才。①

但是我们也要看到，儒教的这种观点稍有偏差就会成为湛轩所说的矜心，有变成人类中心主义的危险。历史的教训也告诉我们，人类中心主义也容易产生拥护“华夷论”这种以中华为中心的国际秩序。② 因此我们应该从“明明德于天下”，“平天下”中所谓的“天下”中发展到“天地位焉，万物育焉”的境界上来。

周濂溪在《太极图说》中“立人极”的主张也应该进一步发展为“立物极”，借东学的语言来说就是从“人乃天”向“物乃天”的转变。③ 当然，这里所说的“物”当然是不仅仅包含了禽兽草木，同时包含了无生物的广义概念。从这种层面上看时，我们需要特别注意《中庸章句大全》中如下的注释：

> 如鳶率鳶之性 必飛 魚率魚之性 必躍 於此 見物物有自然之天 物物有天命之性④

文中认为所有物都具有“自然之天”和“天命之性”，强调鸢和鱼也具有和人类一样的绝对价值。

从“人类中心主义”向“自然中心主义”转变的思想并不是什么新的提案，只是对个体生命本来所具有的“个体中心倾向”和“生态中心倾向”中生态的部分进行了强调。个体生命如果想要成功的生存就必须在这两个看似冲突的倾向中找到一个平衡点。⑤ 但是现代社会过于强调个人中心倾向，使二者产生了严重的不平衡，最终导致人类与其他补生命，甚至全生命都受到了生存的威胁。所以我们现在必须要强调生态中心主义倾向，这也是周易“一阴一阳之谓道”的原理。

为了克服阶级秩序下近现代社会对人权的蹂躏，产业化和大众化所带来的人与人之间的疏离，需要强调人的尊严性，建立起针对人类为中心的一系列法规是当时的当务之急。同理，由于人类的急速破坏导致包括人在内的整个生态系统都在受到威胁的

---

① 能尽物之性则可以赞天地之化育，可以赞天地之化育则可以与天地参矣。(《中庸》22章)

② 俞奉学：《18－19世纪燕岩与北学思想的研究》。

③ 东学主张“人乃天”的同时还主张“物物天，事事天”(《天道教经典·海月神师法说·以食天下》)“物物天，事事天”是东学第二代教主崔时亨的理论，“人乃天”是第三代教主孙秉熙的理论。

④ 胡云峰：《中庸章句大全》，12章小注。

⑤ 张会翼，同上，第145页。

现在，当务之急就是将“人乃天”的观念转变诚“物乃天”。

上文也有言及，人类中心主义向自然中心主义的转换是生命体所具有的个体中心倾向向生态中心倾向转变的过程，要对人类已经享有的一些权利做出一些放弃，所以对此进行批判和反对的声音应该不在少数，但是为了人类共同的利益我们是时候做出选择和放弃了。

在这种层面上与西方文化进行比较时，相对重视生态主义的东亚文化，特别是儒学思想应该会产生积极的作用。而赋予全部生命道德性的湛轩的人物性同论，在克服人类中心主义的今天，应该说也具有指导性的意义。

**参考文献：**

原典：

[1] 孟子要义

[2] 中庸讲义补

[3] 中庸自监

[4] 中庸章句大全

[5] 南塘集

[6] 巍岩遗稿

[7] 巍岩集

[8] 医山问答

[9] 天道教经典

单行本：

[1] 徐复观. 中国人性论史. 台湾：商务印书馆，1972.

[2] 山本诚作. 怀海德的宗教哲学. 京都行路社，1988.

论文：

[1] 张会翼. “全生命”和现代文明. 科学思想，12 期. 汎洋社. 1995 年春季刊.

[2] 黄敬植. 科学时代的伦理反省. 科学思想，12 辑.

[3] 全仁植. 李柬与韩元震的未发 · 五常论辩研究. 精神文化研究院韩国学大学院博士论文.

[4] 崔珍源. 江湖歌道研究. 成均馆大学博士论文，1975.

[5] 崔英辰. 儒教的真理观. 现代人读儒学. 亚细亚文化社，1999.

［6］———，易学对于精神和物质的理解．哲学，35辑，1991．
［7］边宣焕．科学技术和基督教的伦理．科学思想，12辑．
［8］俞奉学．18－19世纪燕岩与北学思想的研究．

# 儒学与生态环境保护

## ——从泛“天人合一”论说现象说起

马来西亚南方大学　林纬毅

早在春秋战国时期，由于人们原始的生产方式、统治者修建宫殿苑囿以及和战争所需物资、御敌以及所作造成的破坏等原因，频频发生生态环境恶化的事件。也正因此，中国自古就设有管理生态环境的官吏和法律，许多古代典籍中也有涉及生态环境的论说。以儒学经典来说，虽然蕴含有丰富的生态意识，但是儒家典籍中没有“生态”这一名词；“生态文明”更是在近现代生态平衡失调、造成生态危机之后才有的事。而且，不论中外，古代人对生态环境的破坏，绝对没有现代工业、科技与自利的国家与企业的排放、污染、辐射以及对地下资源的无所不用其极的开采，来得严重。

提起儒学与生态环境，许多学者会提出儒家的“天人合一”思想；把人与自然和谐共生的思想归于“天人合一”，而有“天人合一”的生态哲学。我们常常可以看到、听到：先秦儒家生态伦理思想的关注对象是人与自然的关系，主张人与自然应当和谐相处，追求“天人合一”的境界。我把这种论说成为“泛天人合一”论说现象。在这样的论说下，更有把先秦儒家思想中的“天”视为“自然之天”。在此，我必须先指出两点：一、生态这一词在中国文献中是后起的，先秦并没有儒家生态伦理思想。虽然我们从先秦儒家经典中可以找到有关涉及生态和保护环境意识的论说，并可以作为我们今日实践生态文明的启示与参考，但是我们不能将这些论说说成是先秦儒家的生态伦理思想；二、儒家“天人合一”的天是从天作为道德形上实体来说的，从“自然之天”说“天”，是不可能说到“天人合一”的。

“天人合一”是儒家中心义理骨干，有丰富、深入与全面的内容，也是以儒家思想为主流的中华文化与其他文化的重大差别所在。“天人合一”有纵向的本质意义，也有横向的成己成物的实践意义。如果将“天人合一”局限在人与自然和谐和善用资源上，是窄化了“天人合一”的精义。当然，从“天人合一”的内涵来说，是可以开出涉及生态文明、保护生态环境的理论来的。在中华文化上探索人与自然的关系上，儒学不但有其哲学基础，也有丰富的资源，并对现代生态文明的实践有着积极的启示。但是，不能由此而说先秦儒家有生态伦理思想。

以下先从纵向的理论上阐述“天人合一”的哲学理论基础，再从“天人合一的”的横向的成己成物的实践，论述“天人合一”在生态保护上，有它形而上的根据。

## “天人合一”的哲学理论基础

“天人合一”，也称“天人合德”，是这是从天命、天道下贯为人的性而说的。作为形上道德实体的天赋于人的生命以道德，人的道德因此有了超越的价值根据。因此，超越的天道和现实的人的性命是相贯通的，是可以通过道德而合一的。人的性既然是理性的天所赋予的，人的性也因此而有了天作为价值根源。人能够以天道为根本来建立人道，又通过人的道德实践来配合天德。天道、人道和人德、天德，是相互回应的。

“天人合一”必须从超越而内在，内在与超越以“德”相贯通来说的。《论语·述而》篇子曰：“天生德于予”。孔子认为其德为天所赋予，隐约实有将天作为形而上道德实体、把天作为超越处的价值根源的意思。同篇子曰：“仁远乎哉？我欲仁，斯仁至矣。”是直扣仁的主体性和内在性。由于仁是内在于自己的生命内，仁不远离生命，才可能欲仁而仁至。因此，为仁必然由己，只要克己复礼，即为仁。由于人的生命所固有的德是有其超越的价值的根源，因此这德性不是寡头。道德实体的天也不是孤悬，而是下贯人性。

孔子从十五志于学到五十知天命以至于六十、七十云云，并自称“知我者其天”，是孔子下学上达、践仁知天，由知性生命转向德性生命的历程，是孔子知天与天知孔子的历程。孔子与天的相知是双向的相通与相知。这是“天人合一”的表述。到了孟子由心善言性善，讲尽心、知性、知天，则是以孔子善性为基础，直接从道德的进路讲“天人合一”。

“天人合一”思想在《中庸》中有深入的展现。《中庸·首章》的第一句就是：“天命之谓性”，开章明义就指明了人的道德性是理性的天所赋予的 。这是直言纵向的贯通。在天道、性命相贯通的基础上，《中庸·二十章》又提出“诚”是天道，而人则是“诚之者”的道德实践者。天命的性、天道的诚，都是人性的超越根据，“天命”和“天道”赋予人可以表现最高理想与无限价值的性和诚。所以，这样来说性，即是说超越的。理性的天的最高理想与无限价值是内在具备于人自己的生命之中，这又是内在的。这不但在主观的道德基础上，更在既超越又内在的理路上，正面地建立了天人关系。唯有这样，“天人合一”的说法才有其哲学理论的基础。

## “天人合一”成己、成物的实践蕴涵生态环境保护

《中庸》的“致中和”即是“至诚”“天人合一”实践所达到的的境界。“致中和”

在超越和内在的基础上，由率性、修道的自我而外扩到与人和物的成己、成物，实已蕴涵了生态环境保护的内容。“致中和，天地位焉，万物育焉”，即是说能够达致“中和”的境界，天地便各在其位了，万物便生长繁育了。致中和，使到普天之下，凡为天所覆、为地所载的各个禀天命而来有普遍性与差别性的一切事物，都能各遂其生、各得其所、各定其性，使天地万物共成一和谐的生生不息的景象：天成其为天，地成其为地，人成其为人，一草一木一瓦一石都无不成其为一草一木一瓦一石。整个生态环境中的动、植、矿物，都能顺其本性，自然存在、成长，不受任何破坏。所以说：“致中和，天地位焉，万物育焉。”

《中庸·二十二章》：“唯天下至诚，为能尽其性；能尽其性，则能尽人之性；能尽人之性，则能尽物之性；能尽物之性，则可以赞大地之化育；可以赞天地之化育，则可以与天地参矣。”是对生态环境饱和的总纲领。圣人之至诚，能完全实现其性。人能够这将禀自于天的德性全面展现，就是在尽人之性，能够尽人之性，就能够尽物之性，使物各遂其性，各得其所，人与物共成一个各得其所的和谐的理想社会，而人就在这社会中，参与并且赞助了这社会的成长，并与天地并立为三。

因此，天道的诚，通过天道的诚的实践者，在做“诚之”的人道时，能无息，发挥悠久、博厚、高明的人道，以实践天道的为物不贰、生物不测。人道的悠久、博厚、高明，也是天道的悠久、博厚、高明，因而，成就了一幅这是天道、人德的合一所完成的一幅多么美好和谐的位天地、育万物之宇宙图，如《中庸二十六章》所述：

故至诚无息，不息则久，久则征，征则悠远，悠远则博厚，博厚则高明。博厚所以载物也，高明所以覆物也，悠久所以成物也。博厚配地，高明配天，悠久无疆。如此者，不见而章，不动而变，无为而成。天地之道，可一言而尽，其为物不贰，则其生物不测。天地之道：博也，厚也，高也，明也，悠也，久也。今夫天，斯昭昭之多，及其无穷也，日月星辰系焉，万物覆焉。今夫地，一撮土之多，及其广厚，载华岳而不重，振江海而不泄，万物载焉。今夫山，一卷石之多，及其广大，草木生之，禽兽居之，宝藏兴焉。今夫水，一勺之多，及其不测，鼋鼍蛟龙鱼鳖生焉，货物殖焉。

人能至诚无息，则其德悠久、博厚、高明，如地德天德之载物覆物；一切动作都本天理而中节，天地间人、我、万物都各得其所、各遂其性、各得其生，不受人们由于过分的非理性的生理欲望、心理情绪所形成的乖戾之气之摧残，由此以见天地之道的为物不贰、生物不测，并由此反见天地之道的高明博厚。《易经》也有这种天地之道“为物不贰、生物不测”的意思。《周易》乾卦《象》曰“大哉乾元，万物资始”；坤挂《象》曰“至哉坤元，万物资生”；《系辞上传》“乾知大始，坤作成物；乾以易知，坤以简能”，以乾、坤二元分别作为创生于终成原则，万物因而得以生成。

从以上的“致中和，天地位焉，万物育焉”，尽人性、物性以赞天地之化育，以及天道、人德的合一所完成的美好和谐的宇宙图像，其中实已经不需言喻的包含了生态环境保护的内容。

性德的仁、知确保生态环境保护自律实行。

在先秦儒家的“天人合一”思想中，生态环境保护没有被当作一个人、物对立的课题来讨论，它是成己、成物过程中一个必然的环节。最具体的论说框架可见《中庸·二十五章》：“诚者，自成也；而道，自道也。诚者，物之终始，不诚无物。是故君于诚之为贵。诚者，非自成己而已也，所以成物也。成己，仁也；成物，知也。性之德也，合外内之道也，故时措之宜也。”

这一章指出，诚不只是实现自己而已，也要成物，尽物之性；尽物之性就包含了让所有生物、非生物得到良好的存在和生长环境，不破坏自然生态环境。之所以能完成成己、成物，全在与天赋的性德中的仁与知。成己是仁的实现，仁的成己，属于内；成物是知的作用，知的成物，属于外。仁、德都是本性所有之德，使人能合内外，与万物为一体的。成物的完成，不能只靠“仁”，而必须有“知”来完成，而知是统摄在仁之下的；这样知性的作用才能在德性的主宰下完成作用。涵盖于成物的生态环境保护的实行，属于知的范围。对应着生态环境保护来说，这“知”可以是生态环境保护的知识、技术、科技以及法律。在成己成物的过程中，以人固有的道德主体为依据，在成物中完成了保护生态的道德行为，这是自律的道德行为，不必依靠法律条文。

以上论述，指出儒学的“天人合一”思想在现代环境保护所提供的哲学理论和实行上的形而上根据。与自然和谐共处、保护自然生态是儒学“天人合一”思想的一个横向的必然自律行动；如果将“天人合一”局限于和自然和谐共处、保护自然生态，那是将“天人合一”局部化与贫乏化。

# “天人合一”思想与现代生态观念

深圳大学 景海峰

张岱年先生在《中国哲学大纲》中指出，“天人合一”是中国哲学的根本观念，人生的最高理想就是自觉地达到天人合一的境界，从天人不二到泯绝物我、内外合一，这是中国哲人的宇宙观与西洋哲学的最大不同处。“天人相通的观念，是中国哲学尤其宋明道学中的一个极根本的观念。不了解此观念，则许多思想都不能了解，而只觉其可怪而已”。[①]“天人合一”思想，历经秦汉、隋唐、宋明，下至晚清，经历过极为复杂的演变和发展过程，就儒学主流而言，大致有汉儒的天人感应说、汉唐间的自然论、宋明时期的“天理”以及性即理、心即理等，一直到近代西学传入，又有了科学诸解释。在现代学术研究的方式和视野下，“天人合一”观念成为历史叙述的内容，同时也作为传统文化现代转化的重要资源之一，被重新加以理解和阐释。总的说来，在科学宇宙观和自然进化论已经成为常识，并为一般大众所了解和接受的情况下，再来谈所谓“天人合一”，其论说的前提必然包含了对科学知识的承认，也预设了现代性批判的眼光，即对所谓迷信观念的鄙夷和对宗教信仰的排斥，以及知识的分类意识和科学研究方法的运用等等。在全球生态问题日益严峻的今天，人们往往又把“天人合一”思想作为东方智慧的典范，用来分析人与自然的关系，试图借助于传统之观念以作化解现实之顽疾的良药。这类的想法，基本上是以科学解释为基础的，即随顺着科学理解的路数，按照科学的逻辑，将天人合一划归为人与大自然的关系，或简约化为人类生存的自然环境问题。相反，对于“天人合一”的本意及其哲学内蕴的阐发，却显得较为薄弱，甚至有所偏离。

## 一

随着近代科学的兴起，传统的宇宙观、神创论、人与自然的关系说，以及对于人

① 张岱年：《中国哲学大纲·序论》，中国社会科学出版社，1982年，第7页。

自身的理解等等，均发生了翻天覆地的变化。西学东渐，自然科学普及，天人关系解构，天与人同时经历了彻底的祛魅化过程，传统的“天人合一”论不再有任何说服力。首先是天与人的相分，天是自然之天，人是进化之人，天自天，人自人，各有各的演化路径和运行规律；如果相合，那也只是外在的、两个事物之间的关系，即人与自然环境之间的关系。在此科学认知的基础上，人天分离，人是认识活动的主体，自然环境为客体，讲人与天之间的关系，立论前提就是要区分出主（体）、客（体）来，所有叙事都必须纳入到这个二分的逻辑框架之中。在此情景下，传统儒家本之自然之天和德化之天的独特理解及其所建构起来的天人关系，就难再成立了，无论是汉儒的“天人感应”之说，还是宋儒的“天人合一”理境，均失去了立足的支撑点，传统的天人观逐渐被科学的人与自然的关系之新范式所取代。

19世纪末叶，进化论传入中国，自然演化的图景和人与天地的关系具有了全新的视野，人只不过是宇宙洪荒、天地演化、万物流变过程之中的瞬间存有和沧海一粟而已，如何得天人合一？不啻是痴心妄谈。按照自然科学对于宇宙和生命认识的事实剖析和直白陈述，人与天地的关系是从属性的，它只是宇宙整体之中的一小部分，不可能平列在一起谈所谓“合一”的问题。[①] 作为物质运动变化和自然生物演进的序列式构件，人之存在的片段化和渺小性，在宏大的宇宙面前简直不值一提，天人合一只能是意识活动的假设和浮游无据的精神想象而已。在自然科学的视域和理解当中，天人合一命题是不可理喻的，更是无法证明的，所以完全可以被证伪掉。如果按照科学的理路来继续讲论天人合一，那就走到了死胡同里，百口莫辩，难圆其说。换言之，天人合一不可能是科学的假设，或者说用科学的眼光来理解天人合一，那是牛头不对马嘴。所以科学主义者或崇尚科学真理的人，自此后就不再理会所谓天人合一的话题。

但科学的解释不能够解决所有的价值疑问，科学判断的真假值也无法消弭人们面对自然之时内心所产生出来的种种困惑。故近代以来，在两种文化——科学与人文的对峙格局之下，或者在做中西文化之比较研究的时候，对于天人合一的另一种理解还是不时地浮现出来。譬如，严复（1854－1921）在传播进化论的同时，就用了分疏科学与宗教、学术与政治的方式，指出了儒家天人观在义理上的独特性。他在解释斯宾塞之天演界说“翕以聚质，辟以散力，由纯之杂，由流之凝”的质力之天时说：“前篇皆以尚力为天行，尚德为人治。争且乱则天胜，安且治则人胜。此其说与唐刘、柳诸

---

① 张岱年先生在写于40年代的《天人简论》一文中，也基本上接受了进化论的思想，用物质演进来理解天人关系。他说：“宇宙演化之大历程是由物质（一般物质）而生命（有生命的物质）而有心物（有心知的有生物质）。物为基本，生命心知为物质演化而有之较高级的形态。”（见《真与善的探索》，齐鲁书社，1988年，第221页）。

家天论之言合，而与宋以来儒者，以理属天，以欲属人者，致相反矣。大抵中外古今，言理者不出二家，一出于教，一出于学。教则以公理属天，私欲属人；学则以尚力为天行，尚德为人治。言学者期于征实，故其言天不能舍形气；言教者期于维世，故其言理不能外化神。”① 这意思便是，西学所谓的天，是就天之自然性的质力而立论的，属于科学的说明和学术研究的范畴；而中学的天，则具有拟人化与想象的色彩，是宗教信念和政治期待的一种特殊寄寓方式。当时大力传播科学新知的杜亚泉（1873—1933）亦曾就西学之时空观和宋儒的无极太极说做了中和性的理解和解释，他说：“自吾顶而上之，空气已尽，其境无名，名之曰天。天者其虚境乎，抑实质乎？其为虚境，则长此虚境，无尽程乎？乘虚而上，靡有底止乎？假令不然，必遇实质。此实质也，有尽程乎？无尽程乎？吾能步虚，又能蚀实，凿之镕之，钻而过之，实质尽则虚境又来，是故纯虚纯实，何谓尽程；虚实相间，亦无止境。”② 这里是在随顺着科学的逻辑一直往上推，这显然是难有止境，作为物质性和时空存有意义的天，如何确证它的虚实特征及其无限性，在经验世界里依然是个难题。面对此一不可究诘的困境，杜亚泉认为用无极太极观来做说明，恰能补足其缺憾。他指出，无极就是一个无尽的设定与想象，可以以光喻之；太极就是最大之“止境”，即在无极之内截取一段，立为太极，建立起想象的确定性来。这样，用无极太极观来解释天，就可以补充感觉经验之天的不足，将思议的天和物性的天结合起来，以丰富天论之内涵。

这类以差异的眼光来衡量东西方文化的模式，在物质主义的迅速演进中，说服力越来越式微，而更具有普遍性的理解是：地球是一个，人类的生存环境是一样的，因而处理人与自然的关系之手段也应该是相同的，这便是依靠科学的思维方式和技术能力的不断进步。所以，在科学主义大行其道、人类所面临的环境问题日显窘迫的情形下，随顺着科学治理的思路，将天人合一解释为人类的适应能力或顺应自然的哲学，显然是有吸引力的，这也成为现代阐释的主流方式。过去大讲唯物主义，宇宙观重天人相分，进步论言人定胜天，强调人征服自然、改造自然，天人分离，严重对峙，并由此否定了天人合一。在科学观和唯物论的结盟下，儒家的天人合一学说被作为反面教材肆意曲解，或批判的体无完肤。拨乱反正之后，科学批判的眼光有所收敛，对传统的理解多了一丝温情和敬意，天人合一又渐渐地成为被肯定的、具有正面价值的思想。在这个转变过程当中，除了社会意识形态的因素之外，天人关系的重构式理解——由对抗变为合作、由二元对立趋向于同一体的建构，这一内在要求的转向促成了

---

① 严复：《天演论》按语，《严复集》，中华书局，1986年，第五册，第1395页。

② 杜亚泉：《无极太极论》（1901年），《杜亚泉文选》，华东师范大学出版社，1993年，第3页。

对天人合一学说的重新审视和评价。既然科学解释并不排斥天人合一，那么天人合一当然就可以按照科学的逻辑来进行阐发和说明，于是乎，当代儒学与生态哲学之间便形成了结盟的关系，对天人合一的解释也大多沿着生态的思路在前行。以往的新儒家诸哲所苦心孤诣坚守和揭橥的天人合一义理，也成了新时代儒学发展的不竭动力。杜维明就认为，钱穆、唐君毅、冯友兰的相关论述，已经构成了儒学“生态的转向”，用“他们所钟爱的传统为形成中的‘地球村’带来了信息”。①

但是不是简单的回到东方思想，就能够解决过分的物欲膨胀所带来的对自然的戕害，遏制对地球过度的开发利用，以及人类理性漫越的狂妄？实际上，问题并不像人们所想象的那么简单，当代中国的传统意识和具有活性的历史资源无比的稀薄，我们要真切地感受这样的“传统”，在现实社会中是何其的困难？唯科学主义和过时的旧工业时代的价值观念依然泛滥，在盲目的竞速发展和无节制的开发利用中，人们对自然的敬畏之情仍显得如此匮乏。近些年来，生态问题日显突出，但环境保护意识和“绿色”和平诸观念，特别是其可以操作的手段，并不是来自东方，而是仍在依靠发达的西方之不断的输送，就像东方实现工业化的过程一样，还是在亦步亦趋地跟着走。对于这个状况，狄百瑞（Theodore de Bary）在《东亚文明——五个阶段的对话》一书中，用反讽的口吻说道：“具有讽刺意味的是，既然东方哲学以‘自然神秘主义’的形式往往被看作是对这类运动的一种鼓舞力量，我们便有了一个明显的悖论：西方以其文化的与政治的多元主义接受了东亚传统的某些方面，而现代的东亚几乎是带着一种复仇心理经历了工业化和商业化之后，却在控制污染的斗争中落后了。于是在这方面，东方与西方的会合和交融就已经走到了这种地步，即现代的东亚可能需要赶上在西方所体现出来的某些东方最好的传统。”② 这的确是一个悖论，其中包含了几多的苍凉与无奈！试图用科学主义的生态观来呈现中国传统“天人合一”的价值，往往是难以自圆其说的，这其中的无力感也是显而易见的。

## 二

对儒家“天人合一”思想的科学化解释，虽然求得了当下的合法性和心理上的某种安稳感，向生态问题的滑转，也为儒学话语的现实介入拓展了空间；但主客体的分离、自然世界的对象化以及天地人文精神的祛魅后果，都将使儒学面临着新的困境。

---

① 杜维明：《当代新儒家人文主义的生态转向》，《儒学与生态》，Mary Evelyn Tucker、John Berthrong 编，彭国翔等译，江苏教育出版社，2008 年，第 284 页。

② 狄百瑞：《东亚文明——五个阶段的对话》，何兆武等译，江苏人民出版社，1996 年，第 136 页。

再者，完全按照西方的生态理念，亦步亦趋，紧随其后，固然有添砖加瓦之功效，但缺乏思想主体性的劳作，可能永远只是听人吆喝的小帮工。汤一介先生指出："如果我们从科学的意义上了解中国哲学中的'天'，无疑会提出种种问题。但是，在中国哲学中的'天'只是一哲学概念，因而体现天人关系的'天人合一'命题，也只能从哲学意义上了解它。"① 近代以还，学界讲论天人，以科学为殊胜，而谈学理，则多走史学一途。现代学人所做的大量的学术史、思想史的研究工作，保存了我们对"天人合一"传统的丰富记忆，也厘清了历史积累过程之中的重重迷雾，加深了人们的印象，也使得这些宝贵的资源有了更好的清晰度和可辨识度，这些都功不可没。但历史记忆的叙述和我们的现实需求毕竟不是一回事，特别是在历史的理解和解释之中，实际上已经包含了观念的演绎和思想的创造，所以哲学的阐释便呼之欲出、紧随其后。

和历史叙述的复杂性相比，哲学把握则相对要来得简洁些。对所谓"天人合一"的哲学式概括，一般是从主体和客体，或宇宙与人生的大关节处来入手的。现代新儒学开山熊十力就将儒家的天人合一视为是宇宙人生的根本问题，属于哲学本体论，力主"体用不二"。他指出：立基于自然科学的近代西方哲学总是将宇宙人生割裂，"其谈宇宙，实是要给物理世界以一个说明，而其为说却不从反己体认得来，终本其析物之知，以构画而成一套理论"。② 这就使得天与人是相分离的，宇宙和人生没有了关系，宇宙论的对象成为自然状态的块然之物，而人生论也失去了存在环境的根系性，变得没有意义。所以他凝思于体用，抉发真源，重新阐释宇宙人生合一的传统，用本体论来统贯天人。"《新论》直将本体论、宇宙论、人生论融成一片，此是老夫苦心处，亦是不失吾先圣哲精神处"。③ 走哲学化路向的新儒家，大体都坚守了精神本位的立场，反对物质主义的宇宙人生观，认为天地自然和人文精神是融贯在一起的，不能割裂开来理解。唐君毅便指出："吾人谓中国儒者之天或天地，至少在《孟子》、《中庸》、《易传》作者之心中，乃一具形上之精神生命性之绝对实在。由是可知中国人之祀天地，或祀天，与天地君亲师神位中之有天地，亦不能谓之只祀一块然之物质天地，或只有生命之自然；而实含视之为一精神实在之意。唯先哲因恒对物质、生命、精神三者，不加截然区别，故人恒易不知觉间以天或天地唯指感觉界之自然。实则中国后儒亦多以天或天地，直指形上之精神实在。"④ 这一主客浑沦、宇宙人生不分的天人观，可以

---

① 汤一介：《论"天人合一"》，《汤一介集》第五卷《在儒学中寻找智慧》，中国人民大学出版社，2014年，第58页。

② 熊十力：《新唯识论》（删定本），《熊十力全集》，湖北教育出版社，2001年，第六卷，第301页。

③ 熊十力：《摧惑显宗记》，《熊十力全集》第五卷，第539页。

④ 唐君毅：《中国文化之精神价值》，台北：正中书局，1953年，第454—455页。

说是我国与西方最大的不同。

对于中国哲学的生命化特质，不仅新儒家诸哲有很好的把握，就是治西方哲学的现代哲人也大多能体会得到，他们对“天人合一”的独特意义，多具同情的理解。譬如，张东荪在《知识与文化》(1940年)一书中，讲到中国思想之特征时，就特别分析了这个“天”的意义——它是自然，也是上帝；是宇宙观，也是社会、道德、政治诸论；是包括了人在内的“整体”。[①] 金岳霖也准确地意识到了：“这‘天人合一’说确是一种无所不包的学说，最高、最广意义的‘天人合一’，就是主体融入客体，或者客体融入主体，坚持根本同一，泯除一切显著差别，从而达到个人与宇宙不二的状态。”[②] 金氏的学生张世英沿着这个理路，在近些年来的中西哲学之比较研究中，大大地扩展了其丰富的内蕴。他认为，就最广泛的意义来说，“天人合一”代表了一种思想类型或思维模式，强调主客体的互融性，乃至主客无分。“西方哲学史上占统治地位的旧传统是‘主客二分’式，中国传统哲学的主导思想是‘天人合一’式”。[③] 西方早期的自然哲学在讲到人与世界、自然、万物的关系时，也有“天人合一”的色彩，即人与自然不分；在柏拉图之后，特别是笛卡尔以来的近代哲学，才走上了“主客二分”的道路；后现代主义兴起之后，又有了向“天人合一”模式回归的倾向。中国古典哲学则长期是以“天人合一”为主导的，儒释道概莫能外，只是到了近代，才有了所谓“主客二分”的挑战和应对问题。今后中国哲学的发展，就是怎样在这两种思想方式之中会通出一条新路来。

“天人合一”说到底，是对于一个思想观念的理解和解释问题，属于哲学诠释学的范畴。近代以来的科学宇宙观将人与自然完全隔开，主客二分的认知模式又强化了这种对立的趋势，使得天人关系的解释要么是机械论的，要么是形式论的，自然、宇宙与人之间的有机联系或者种种情境化的问题往往被忽略掉，更不要说人的精神主体性的存在了。要走出天人相隔的困局，就需要重新理解世界、自然、宇宙这些概念，从机械论和唯物论的狭隘解释中逃离出来。怀特海（A. N. Whitehead）指出：“作为完整宇宙论的目标之一，就是要建构起一种观念体系，把审美的、道德的、宗教的旨趣同来自自然科学的那些世界概念结合起来。”[④] 儒家的“天人合一”观念，恰恰是建立在审美、道德、政治和宗教的基础之上的，如果去除了这些情境化的因素，只是孤零零地谈宇宙论，则中国哲学就成为不可理解的臆说。实际上，近代以来的科学宇宙观只

---

① 张东荪：《知识与文化》，岳麓书社，2011年，第117—120页。

② 金岳霖：《中国哲学》(1943年)，《金岳霖学术论文选》，刘培育选编，中国社会科学出版社，1990年，第355页。

③ 张世英：《天人之际——中西哲学的困惑与选择》，人民出版社，1995年，第5页。

④ 怀特海：《过程与实在》，李步楼译，商务印书馆，2011年，第2页。

是人类对自然和世界认识的漫长历史过程之中有限而短暂的一种形式而已。“哲学史表明，在不同时期支配着欧洲思想的有两种宇宙论，即柏拉图的《蒂迈欧篇》所表达的那种宇宙论，以及17世纪以伽利略、笛卡尔、牛顿和洛克为主要代表的宇宙论。在进行同一种事业中，也许正确解决问题应当遵循的明智的途径就是把先前的这两种宇宙论体系结合起来，并且根据自洽性和知识发展的要求作必要的修改”。① 就中国哲学而言，宇宙不是一个外在的世界，它一样是可设计的、合目的性的、自洽的，并且有着精神的意义灌注其间；因而它也是可以感知和可以理解的对象，与人的情志、判断力、审美情趣以及道德追求是联系在一起的，所谓自然、宇宙可以说完全是“人化”的结果。在这样一个有机的世界里，充满了各种诗意的想象，孕育着无限的生机和创造力，为人的现实存在提供着多种多样的可能性，这可以说是一种有机哲学的宇宙论图景。

张岱年先生早在上个世纪30年代就已经阐述了中国哲学宇宙论的特点，特别是变化和历程的观念，认为除了研究本原问题的本根论之外，中国哲学的重心是在大化论，即“宇宙中一切都是在时时的变化中，宇宙便是一个大化”。他说：“中国哲学关于宇宙大化之根本见解，即在于认为宇宙是变动的，宇宙是一个生生不已的变易历程，所以名之曰大化。”② 张先生将这一古老的变易思想和近代历程哲学的观点联系起来思考，提出了“存在是变化历程，宇宙中之一切皆历程，世界是历程之总和”、“凡物皆一历程”、“宇宙大化是一切之大全”等命题。③ 这些思想在一定程度上呼应了怀特海所预想的新宇宙图景，并且把这种新宇宙观和中国传统哲学的特点结合了起来。正像怀特海所指出的：“在有机哲学中，这种终极的东西叫作‘创造性’……就一般的立场来看，有机哲学似乎更接近于印度或中国的某些思想特征，而不是像西亚或欧洲的思想特征。一方面使过程成为终极的东西；而另一方面则使事实成为终极的东西。”④ 从这个意义上来说，中国传统的“天人合一”思想，也可以说是一种想象，只是一个理想，因为它不存在任何终极性的追求，永远只是一个目标，也永远逸动起伏于人生努力的途程之中，代代相延，永无止歇。

## 三

这样一种天人观，表达的是人对自我存在意义的追问，是人的精神世界寻求价值

① 同上，第5页。

② 张岱年：《中国哲学大纲》，第162页。

③ 张岱年：《宇宙观与人生观》（研思札记之一），《真与善的探索》，齐鲁书社，1988年，第256—257页。

④ 怀特海：《过程与实在》，第15页。

安立的积极内省，也是道德主体性的觉醒和解放。与神话时代和巫史传统的天人隔绝相比较，这里的天已经没有了外缘化的效果，神秘性大大地减弱了，而向着人自身的存在意义无限敞开。正像雅斯贝尔斯（K. Jaspers）在“轴心时代”理论中所描述的，此时“人证明自己有能力从精神上将自己和整个宇宙相比照，从自己的生命中发现了可以将之提升为自我与世界的内在根源”。[①] 这一被后人称之为“哲学的突破”的伟大转折，将离人之天变成了即人之天，把外在于人的天地自然内化成为人的生命存在价值的有机组成部分，天的不可知性也通过礼乐教化的文明形式而被彻底地祛魅化了。余英时指出：“轴心突破标志了古代中国宗教史和哲学史新纪元的开端。一方面，它终结了神话中长期‘绝地天通’的状态；另一方面，它也向所有‘好学深思’的个人（士）表明，他们完全有可能纯然仰赖自身力量与‘彼世’交通。”[②] 这一内在式超越的路向，奠定了中国古典学术与思想的基础，也成为之后人们理解天人关系的主流形态。

就拿儒家来说，最能够体现此种精神的当推《易》、《庸》传统。清初易学家胡煦（1655—1736）说：“《周易》乃天人合一之书，言天道当知有人道，言人道当知有天道。”[③]《易》道本之于自然，但又充盈着理性的精神。《易传》对宇宙全体做了哲理化的抽象与演绎，明确提出了一套天之自然生成与万物变化的模式。这其中，天的存在是万事万物所展开的具体性之根源，也是人的活动能够被解释和说明、从而获得意义的最终依据，没有了形而上的天道，人的行为就变得荒谬和不可理解。反过来，天的价值也是在人的活动之中得以呈现的，“富有之谓大业，日新之谓盛德，生生之谓《易》”（《系辞上》）。没有了万物变化的具体性，天就成为死体，《易》道也就无从谈起了。《易传》的宇宙大化论，为天人关系的说明奠定了重要的理论基础，天人合一成为自然之事，天道与人道是一体之两面，谈天道不能离开人道，谈人道亦不能离开天道，天人本不二。《中庸》所讲的天人合一，则是以德性为纲宰的。它把空泛而寂寥、乃至于神秘莫测的天的世界给意象化和道德化了，使之成为境界性的形而上实体；同时，庸众的日常生活，甚或是无意味的普遍现象，也因为至诚无息的天作为其存在的形而上根据，而变得熠熠生辉、意义非凡。诚，本为人的道德品节，讲人心之信实状态，《中庸》将之投射到无声无臭的天上，就将天拟人化、德性化了；然后作为形而上普遍存有的天之意义又反诸人自身，加强了“诚”的厚度，使之具有了更大的权威性和说服力。这一“诚”的意义，自由穿梭在天与人之间，使得天人关系的各个层面和相关

① 雅斯贝尔斯：《历史的起源与目标》，魏楚雄等译，华夏出版社，1989年，第10页。

② 余英时：《天人之际——中国古代思想的起源试探》，《国学与中国人文》（余英时文集，第十二卷），沈志佳编，广西师范大学出版社，2014年，第248页。

③ 胡煦：《周易函书约存》卷七，《周易函书》，中华书局，2008年，第一册，第225页。

的问题都可以得到融会贯通的解释，从而圆融无碍。

宋代理学正是沿着《易》、《庸》的路向来往前拓展的。张载在《正蒙·乾称篇》中第一次明确提出了“天人合一”的命题：“释氏语实际，乃知道者所谓诚也，天德也。其语到实际，则以人生为幻妄，以有为为疣赘，以世界为阴浊，遂厌而不有，遗而弗存。就使得之，乃诚而恶明者也。儒者则因明致诚，因诚致明，故天人合一，致学而可以成圣，得天而未始遗人，《易》所谓不遗、不流、不过者也。彼语虽似是，观其发本要归，与吾儒二本殊归矣。道一而已，此是则彼非，此非则彼是，固不当同日而语。其言流遁失守，穷大则淫，推行则诐，致曲则邪，求之一卷之中，此弊数数有之。”[①] 他借着批判佛教人生观之虚幻，重返《易》《庸》传统，用天道自然、大化流行的宇宙观和致学成圣、诚明真际的人生态度来重新诠释天人关系，创造性地转换了传统的元气论和释道之虚无观。张载的学说，以太虚之气为天，同时容涵了天道、自然、神化、天命、心性诸义，将这些不同的属性和功能熔铸为一体，成一人天合一的大系统。在这个系统中，“天地之帅吾其性，天地之塞吾其体”（《正蒙·乾称》），人以天地之性为其性，以天地之气为其体，此因“天性在人，正犹水性之在冰，凝释虽异，为物一也”（《正蒙·诚明》）。这个水乳交融的状态，是因为人有特殊的天性，可以在实践中与万物相合，这就是“大其心”以“合天心”，超越自身的局限性而达于天德之无限，“穷神知化，与天为一”（《正蒙·神化》）。程颢也有类似的思想，明确提出了“仁者以天地万物为一体”的命题。他说：“医书言手足痿痺为不仁，此言最善名状。仁者，以天地万物为一体，莫非己也。认得为己，何所不至？”[②] 这里所举医家之语，形象地说明了心之仁与万物之间的关系，凡是保有“仁”之天性者，皆能与天地万物不相隔而为一体，故能爱人爱物，如同爱己。

阳明心学继承了“仁者以天地万物为一体”的思想，对“天人合一”说发挥得更为圆巧。在阳明看来，人与天地万物是一气之流通，“盖天地万物与人原是一体，其发窍之最精处，是人心一点灵明”。[③] 人心即天地万物之心，天地万物的意义是由人心之“发窍”所赋予的，离开了人心，天地万物的意义就无从谈起，所以人与天地万物的关系是融合无间的。阳明所说的“一体之仁”是根于人的良知的，没有良知，就无从体味得到人与天地万物之间的紧密关系，有了良知，才能“视天下犹一家，中国犹一人焉”。这也就是他在《大学问》中，所反复申述的“其心之仁本若是”、“虽小人之心亦

① 《张载集》，中华书局，1978 年，第 65 页。关于对张载这段话的理解，历代注释者众，详见林乐昌撰《正蒙合校集释》一书，中华书局，2012 年版，第 946—950 页。

② 《河南程氏遗书》卷第二上，《二程集》，中华书局，1981 年，第一册，第 15 页。

③ 《传习录》（下），《王阳明全集》，吴光等编校，上海古籍出版社，1992 年，第 107 页。

莫不然”，因为是人，就“必有怵惕恻隐之心”，亦“必有不忍之心”、“悯恤之心”、“顾惜之心”等，这个“仁”是与天地万物融合在一起的，大人与小人的差别只是“灵”、“明”和“昧”、“蔽”之不同，其关联性皆是植根于一体之仁的表现。[①]“一体之仁”的普遍性，不但使得“天下之人无外内远近”，而且万事万物都具有了相互联系、相互依存的紧密关系。这样，人类道德价值不止对社会生活有意义，而且辐射到整个存在的环境，对人类生存问题做了本体论意义的论证，也为人与自然的和谐相处提供了理论上的依据。

从“仁者以天地万物为一体”，到“一体之仁”，这些思想都包含了很深刻的道理，具有哲学本体论的意义。同时，中国古代哲学家在谈论这些话题时，又都特别强调“差等”的原则和运用“推及”之逻辑，所以并不抹杀事物的具体性，不持相对主义的观点，反而很看重情景化的认知方式与处理方式，这些对我们理解人与环境的关系无疑都是有帮助的。所以今天大家拿“天人合一”的思想来讨论环境问题，来处理人与自然的关系，来对治因各种污染所造成的生存之危机，这些从大的原则和哲学本体意义上来讲是没有问题的，因为这些思想会给我们以启迪。但是，“天人合一”学说并不是在一般地谈论人与自然的关系，更不是好像为了解脱我们今天的困境才特产的良药，它的论域和工业化时代才日渐突显的环境问题有着相当的距离，所以就和我们本之于当下的感知、理解以及期许所热议的许多话语，都有着明显的横隔，这不可不知、不得不言。那种认为强调了“天人合一”，就可以解决当前问题的看法，显然是过于简单化了，因为只是一般性地谈论人与自然的和谐相处，甚或是提供了某种哲学本体上的论证，都不足以面对今天日益复杂的环境问题，更不要说具体操作的层面了。中国哲学的慧识有助于我们提斯精神境界，却并不能为如何做到人与自然的和谐、特别是解决当前的环境困局提供具体的方法和途径，这显然还需要知识的层面，需要具体的认识和实践活动，在改善环境的方式上寻找到有效的手段，这离不开科学技术的进步。而在这些方面，我们仍需要向西方学习，需要开放的胸襟和现代的意识，走中西文化与哲学的会通之路，而不是简单地回到过去，一味地“去西就中”，甚或沉溺于只是想象中的“天人合一”里面。

---

① 《大学问》。同上，第968页。

# “天人合一”与生态环境失衡的人文拯救

北京东方道德研究所 傅永吉

## 一

钱穆先生生前最后的一篇文章中说：“中国文化中，‘天人合一’观，虽是我早年已屡次讲到，惟到最近始澈悟此一观念实是整个中国传统文化思想之归宿处。”① 此文写于1990年5月，先生谢世前不久。文中先生还说：“中国文化过去最伟大的贡献，在于对‘天’‘人’关系的研究。”“中国人喜欢把‘天’‘人’配合着讲。……西方人喜欢把‘天’‘人’离开分别来讲。换句话说，他们是离开了‘人’来讲‘天’。这一观念的发展，在今天，科学愈发达，愈易显出它对人类生存的不良影响。”

先生那里已年逾九十，自台湾赴香港参加中文大学新亚书院创校四十华诞庆典，虽在港数日，却因年事已高、行动不便而大部分时间待在宾馆中享受“闲暇”，遂专一玩味“天人合一”观念，先生对这次思考的断语是：“有澈悟，心中快慰，难以言述”。说明先生这次思考是大有心得的，但具体思考的结果是什么，却无具体记述。比及次年，逢中华书局建立八十周年庆，有编辑向先生索稿，钱穆先生遂将有关“天人合一”的感想简要写出，虽系应景之作，却颇似先生毕生学术生涯之高度概括与总结。钱穆先生续道：“近百年来，世界人类文化所宗，可说全在欧洲。最近五十年，欧洲文化近于衰落，此下不能再为世界人类文化向往之宗主。所以可说，最近乃是人类文化之衰落期。此下世界文化又以何所归往？这是今天我们人类最值得重视的现实问题。以过去世界文化之兴衰大略言之，西方文化一衰则不易再兴，而中国文化则屡仆屡起，故能绵延数千年不断，这可说，因于中国传统文化精神，自古以来即能注意到不违背天，不违背自然，且又能与天命自然融合一体。我以为此下世界文化之归趋，恐必将以中

---

① 钱穆《天人合一论——中国文化对人类未来可有的贡献》，刘梦溪主编《中国文化》1991年8月第四期 。

可参阅网页：http：//www.douban.com/group/topic/15796923/

国传统文化为宗主。”先生满怀信心地说：“我深信中国文化对世界人类未来求生存之贡献，主要亦即在此”① 这篇小文极短，精要已如上述抄录，而更多更深的内容，先生却未谈及，令先生产生“快慰”之感又“难以述及”的那番“澈悟”的具体内涵，随着先生撰此文后不久的仙逝，遂成为永世之谜，吾辈后生末学岂能无大憾与？

钱穆虽未读完大学，系自学成才，但传统经典功夫十分扎实，学贯文史哲，著述丰富，才华横溢，并以贯通中西文化——以天人合一会通人类文化为使命，晚年所提出的这一课题，关涉到中华传统文化的现代性转化，与现代城市新生活之契合也关涉到人类文化的未来发展的总体愿景。

## 二

何谓“天人合一”?《中华思想大辞典》说：“强调天与人的和谐一致。”作为中华传统文化的核心精神，“天人合一”在中国文化史上被反复讨论，如孔子、孟子、董仲舒、程颐、张载、老子、庄子、墨子等，都对这个思想有所论述。20世纪末叶以来，随着回归中华传统文化的趣向渐次升温，对此问题的学术讨论也逐渐多起来了。

本文试行到知网中搜罗“天人合一”，以篇名搜之，共得2170篇，再以全文关键词搜索，却得20951篇。2005年讨论“天人合一”的文章超过千篇，而以之为专门题目加以专论者，在2004年超过百篇，2010年更接近了两百篇。2012年，关涉同一主题的文章超过两千篇。由此可见，在当下中国，任何一个题目，一个学术议题，早已是众人争相咀嚼的肥肉——是被各路神仙啃过千遍万遍的“老”馍。各路学人想嫩嫩地吃口鲜馍，大致是痴心妄想了。于是，大家不得不将这老馍抱起来细细腻腻、反反复复地来啃去，满口里是别人唾液的滋味也就顾它不得了。

## 三

钱穆先生这篇文章写于1990年5月，可视为先生的绝笔之作。季羡林先生读到这篇小文，感触颇多，也接连写了《“天人合一”新解》、《关于“天人合一”的再思考》和《钱穆的“天人合一”观——中国文化对人类的伟大贡献》三篇短文，情不自禁地发表自己的思考结果。季先生说：“这个代表中国古代哲学主要基调的思想，是一个非常伟大的、含义异常深远的思想。”先生认为，对于“天人合一”这一中国哲学处于核心地位的根本问题，学术界没有足够重视和充分研究。

---

① 钱穆《天人合一论——中国文化对人类未来可有的贡献》，刘梦溪主编《中国文化》1991年8月第四期 。

可参阅网页：http：//www.douban.com/group/topic/15796923/

季羡林先生认为，作为东方综合的思维模式之具体表现的“天人合一”，是东方文明之主导思想。季先生曾郑重指出，以分析思维为基础的西方近现代文化已呈强弩之末之势、走向衰竭，并进一步提出挽救之法，即“以东方文化的综合思维模式济西方的分析思维模式之穷，在西方文化已经达到的基础上，更上一层楼，把人类文化提高到一个前所未有的高度”。这一立场与钱穆先生的倡议不谋而合，消化吸收西方现代性文化成为这一任务的关键要素之一。这令我想到了钱穆先生为新亚书院设计的办学方针：“上溯宋明书院讲学精神，旁采西欧大学导师制度，以人文主义之教育宗旨，沟通东西文化，为人类和平、社会幸福谋前途。”我们今天可以清晰体会到“沟通东西文化”这一良苦的用心，也是中国跨越并超越现代文明这一历史进程的必须。在中华文化之现代进化的大图景中，可以勾勒出一个黑格尔式的“正反合”图式：鸦片战争或新文化运动前中华数千年的固有传统是正题阶段，鸦片战争之后逐渐滋生出的走出中国传统并热情拥抱西方文明代表中华文化发展的反题阶段。在漫长的正题阶段，内在地又包含有许多大大小小的“正反合”，不断地自我否定并自我发展，生生不息而永葆青春，成就为独具魅力、古老而年轻、活力永具的极独特的文明形态。我们今天，则已经面临着跨越、超越现代性的“新合题”的自觉深化、深度开掘、全面拓展的铺陈，一个具有历史大跨度特质的神圣任务。当然，对于这一巨大无比的文化“合题”，我们以及所能经历的短暂的时空，都不过是宏大的历史演进的微不足道的垫脚石，如我辈后生末学，甚或不足自称一颗微芥细沙。但这并不能阻止我们向引“合题”奋然、勉力前行的勇气、毅力、意志。

季先生对“天人合一”这一东方哲学的核心理念可谓情有独钟，三篇短文似乎是对钱穆《中国文化对人类未来可有的贡献》一文的回应，细读之，可以发现实为季先生对“天人合一”这一东方哲学核心观念的框架性解读与建构。季先生明确表态：“我完全同意宾四先生对这个命题的评价：涵义深远，意义重大。”因为，在季羡林先生的文化视野中，天人合一“代表中国古代哲学主要基调的思想，是一个非常伟大的、含义异常深远的思想。”当然，他也不是简单认同钱穆把“天”理解为“天命”而把“人”理解为“人生”，而主张将“天”理解为大自然，将“人”理解为人类。季先生由此而判断，“天人合一”理念“是一个非常伟大的、含义异常深远的思想”。于是季羡林先生同意钱穆先生的意见，即要专门并深入地研究“天人合一”理念，特别是这一理念在现代社会的生成与转化。这成了当代国学研究的一个热点课题。本文前述提及学术界两千余篇专论及两万余篇文章涉此题目，足见学术界已经重视并着手多方探索。

## 四

中国传统社会中，强调人的身心（性命）修养的综合全面调节，追求个体人格的内和谐，并进而加强与他人、群体关系之协调，追求群际和谐，以期促进人类社会的完善、和谐、秩序。以个体人格内和谐、群际和谐、社会和谐为条件，中华民族特别崇尚、追求人与自然的和谐相处，从大自然所收获的反馈则是个体、群体、社会生活所必须的优良生态环境的生成与滋育。这一与大自然和谐相处的理念集中表现为“天人合一”思想。

中华原始宗教进入文明时代仍重视“神人交通”，具浓郁的宗教膜拜色彩。殷周之际，人文主义开始勃兴，“大写的人”开始觉醒，《周易》是“人的发现”与人性自我觉醒的代表、标志，夏商时代占据主导地位的极富宗教迷信色彩的“神人交通”观，由强烈的主体性自觉之人文主义理念所取代。

## 五

儒家思想是中华人文精神之核，对“天人合一”理念也有系统表述。孔子作《易传》，系统阐述了人文主义与自然主义综合、合一的观念，提出以天命观为基础的儒家学说，成为中华人文精神五千年贯通的枢纽。在《论语》中孔子说：“天何言哉！四时行焉，百物生焉，天何言哉!”,[①] 这里的“天”系指“自然之天”；孔子又说：“天生德于予，桓魋其如予何?”[②] 此处之“天”则指“天命之天”，在孔子心目中“天”是有道德倾向并与人的生活密不可分的存在。后来钱穆先生强调后者，而季羡林先生则主张多关注前者。孔子还说过：“君子有三畏，畏天命，畏大人，畏圣人之言”,[③] “五十而知天命”,[④] 毕生以探悉并承载天命的君子人格自况，以强烈的使命担当精神，始终不渝地追求“克己复礼”即恢复社会基本秩序并进而追求和谐、小康之升平之世、大同之太平盛世。

儒家“天人合一”思想所突出、强调的重点，是“人在宇宙中的地位以及人类的精神价值来源”这一关键问题。《中庸》开宗明义：“天命之谓性”，断言人性之根源在天道之中。《周易》则讲：“昔者圣人之作易也，将以顺性命之理。是以立天之道曰阴与阳，立地之道曰柔与刚，立人之道曰仁与义，兼三才而两之”,[⑤] 这是将天地人会通来讲论的，“道”则为一，而所表现却各有不是，分“阴阳”“柔刚”“仁义”三种不形态。《易传》又说：“大人者，与天地合其德”,[⑥] 此处“德”的含义较之现代汉语中所

---

① 《论语·阳货》。
② 《论语·述而》。
③ 《论语·季氏》。
④ 《论语·为政》。
⑤ 《易传·说卦》。
⑥ 《周易·乾卦·象言》。

理解的“道德”更为宽泛，意指人类的精神属性或精神价值，即人要在精神上与天地万物（自然）追求统一性，也即“为天地立心”。

## 六

荀子是儒学发展中承前启后的关键人物。与孟子“性善论”不同，荀子持“性恶论”，认为个体的自然本性系近乎纯粹的生理特征，可视为天然的恶，而经社会教化即可弃恶而从善，所以，荀子断言：“人之性恶，其善者，伪也。”特别强调教化在人类向善中的作用。他主张“明天人之分”，并主张“人定胜天”，将儒家所重视的主体独立性、能动性置放在更加突出的位置，强调“天人相分”，并由此而对天人关系做出更深入的开掘。在五四以来激烈反传统的氛围中，荀子是硕果仅存的传统文化巨匠之一，他在两千多年前所发出的“制天命而用之”的论断曾为当世所特别关注。笔者认为，荀子是孔子“外王”思想的继承和发扬者，是儒家道德理想主义向现实政治构架转化的枢纽，而他对儒家“天人合一”思想的特别阐扬，亦有特殊的文化意义与当代实践意义。荀子说：“天有其时，地有其财，人有其治，夫是之谓能参”，这是他对“人与天地参”的研究心得，所主张的仍是人类要不违天时、顺应自然，自觉地追求“天人合一”，只有掌握天时才有可能利用万物——制天命而用之，强调只有尽人、物的自然之性，方能参与（赞）天地之化育。当代对荀子思想多有夸大与曲解处，尤其将之比附于西方“主客二分”“二元对立”以至于人类征服、掠夺大自然的理论渊源，是误读或刻意的曲解。

## 七

汉初大儒董仲舒杂众家之长，以阴阳家“五行学说”说为基础提出了“天人感应说”，所表述的是极具代表性的宇宙系统论，也具有相当的哲学深度。

董仲舒说：“天有十端，……天为一端，地为一端，阴为一端，阳为一端，火为一端，金为一端，木为一端，水为一端，土为一端，人为一端，凡十端而毕，天之数也”。[①] 将宇宙万物是化为十个元素所组成的系统。到20世纪，西方人贝特朗菲发明了“系统论”，有一套现代的术语很严谨地表述，而中国人，至少自《周易》诞生起，早已将宇宙视为一个有内在联系的系统，也就是系统化思想在轴心时代已经明确并“系统地”确立了，也以东方式的简约与细腻完成了。董氏的“天人感应说”是《易》的系统论精神的发微、展开。董氏认为，在天地宇宙这个大系统中，计有天、地、阴、

① 《春秋繁露·官制象天》。

阳、金、木、水、火、土、人十大要素，以“天次之序”即五行法则为基而运行——五行间相生、相克、相胜，而阴阳五行也恰是这个系统的骨架。此之谓“天地万物的直接合一”。此论常常被斥为迷信。其实与愚昧无知者众密切相关。自己愚蠢，又常常感觉受骗，其实殊不知上当受骗其实常常是自愚之恶果。董氏这套理论或为封建大一统的政治框架提供“道之大原出于天，天不变，道亦不变”的理论基础（论据），也为儒家学说上升为封建社会的意识形态铺平了道路，这一儒学融入现实政治生活的理路的趣向，本文以为倒需要认真研究，因为与中华文明大尺度兴衰密切相关。

董氏之论实不止于此。尚有“天与人的合一”“天的运行与人类社会运行的合一”二度层面，方构成立体的“天人感应论”之整体意象。“天与人的合一”是谓天与人直接之合一，董仲舒从人的身体构造上讨论“人副天数”，说：“人之身，首②而员，象天容也；发，象星辰也；耳目戾戾，象日月也；鼻口呼吸，象风气也；胸中达和，象神明也；腹胞实虚，象百物也……颈以上者，精神尊严明，天类之状也；颈而下者，丰厚卑辱，土壤之比也；足布而方，地形之象也……天地之符，阴阳之副，常设于身，身犹天也。数与之相参，故命与之相连也。……心有计虑，副度数也；行有伦理，副天地也……于其可数也，副数；不可数者，副类。皆当同而副天，一也。”[①]不仅如此，董氏还认为人的血气性情也与天数演化直接契合：“为人者天也……天亦人之曾祖父也。……人之血气，化天志而仁；人之德行，化天理而义；人之好恶，化天之暖清；人之喜怒，化天之寒暑；……天之副在乎人，人之情性，有由天者矣。”[②] 如是，董氏所勾画出的人类，无论外在形体还不是内在性情气质上，莫不与天数（天道）相合、相类，董氏的结论是：“唯人独能偶天地”。[③]

董氏的“天的运行与人类社会运行的合一”论，所讲亦即是天道与人道之关系，董氏以为二道本为一体，当从的合一而论。他董仲舒说：“天亦有喜怒之气，哀乐之心，与人相副，以类合之，天人一也。”[④] “是故春气暖者，天之所以爱而生之；秋气清者，天之所以严而成之；夏气温者，天之所以乐而养之；冬气寒者，天之所以哀而藏之。”[⑤] 将“人道”简单地比附于“天道”，是传统哲学的特点，当然有缺陷，而放在远古的历史情境中，则容易理解。董仲舒说这些话的目的无非当是为“人道”寻找依据，令之具有某种必然性。他以阴阳之道比喻社会中诸种关系：一个必然的依据，即君臣、父子、夫妇之义，皆取诸阴阳之道。“君为阳、臣为阴；父为阳、子为阴；夫为阳、妻

① 《春秋繁露·人副天数》。
② 《春秋繁露·为人者天》。
③ 《春秋繁露·人副天数》。
④ 《春秋繁露·阴阳义》。
⑤ 《春秋繁露·阳尊阴卑》。

为阴”。“天之亲阳而疏阴，任德而不任刑也。是故仁义制度之数，尽取之天。天为君而复露之，地为臣而持载之；阳为夫而生之，阴为女而助之；春为父而生之，夏为子而养之……王道之三纲，可求于天。”[①]三纲五常所设定的基本秩序理念，就在天数、天道中找到了神圣的根据。

## 八

魏晋开始，由西域传入的佛教渐入佳境，与儒道二家成分庭抗礼、三足鼎立之势，“三教合一”的文化趣向渐具雏形，迄至宋明理学心学，儒家吸纳道家、释家思想精华而集其大成，对“天人合一”理念的阐释转换为系统的哲学本体论视角，张载“为天地立心，为生民立命”可谓这一阐述的点睛之笔。清代王夫之重提荀子“天人相分”立场，儒学之实学精神之一维得到发扬。

至此，儒家一脉之“天人合一”论，经由天人之间有“相分”始得人性全面自觉基础上的“合一”，与夏商时代人完全从属于天命、天道的关系，立意与文化趣味上升到全新阶段。故荀子等后儒所着重论述的“天人相分”思想应得到更高估价和更多重视，以期充分展示儒家的“天人合一”思想的丰富内涵（思想内容和思维方式）。

## 九

道家更注重、强调“天地人”三者的统一。中国文化史上，无论道家、道教（无论仙道抑或方道）都视“道”为宇宙万物之本源。老子有言：“道生一，一生二，二生三，三生万物万物负阴而抱阳，冲气以为和。”，[②] 普遍认为这里所表达是“宇宙生成论”。

道家认为，天地人（包括宇宙万物）都是由道化生的，并且都不能离开道而独立存在，因而，道家“天人观”的核心范畴或理念是“天人一体”。如老子在《道德经》中所论断：“人法地，地法天，天法道，道法自然。”对老子“自然”概念的解读，代表性解读是“自然而然”，即非由自外力的意思。“道”是天地万物的本原，是包括人在内的“天地人”存在、发展的总源泉，有“虚”、“无”之表象，而又充盈而无所不在、无所不为，是理解世间一切的根本途径。是物质性和规律性的统一体。由此，可以理解道家的“天人观”可以简单概括这“天人一体”。道家之“天”又可进一步解析为“外在之天”（指大自然及其客观必然性）与“内在之天”（指源于大自然的人之

① 《春秋繁露·基义》。
② 《道德经》第42章。

“天性”)。

道家把天地人万物看作是一个整体，包含人与万物的天地宇宙则一个大系统，人是其中一个相对独立的子系统，如《丹书》云：“人身一小天地，天地一大人身”，人即可视为一小宇宙，与大宇宙同构——同样由“道”、“气”、“阴阳”与“五行”构成，并与大宇宙（天地自然）同源、同构、互感。人有生死，其生不过是精、气、神这聚集，其死则是精、气、神的离散。

汉代道家的一支向宗教发展，更突出强调“全真葆性”“性命双修”的文化趣向，主张人们要注意保持精、气、神充盈（饱满）状态，并以婴儿之姿态为理想生命状态，而不要令其虚耗，更不可致其枯竭，返璞归真、返老还童是值得崇尚的生命理想。为此，道教逐渐提炼出一整套修炼技术，诸如“积神生气”、“积气生精”、“炼精化气”、“炼气化神”、“炼神还虚”，很大程度上走向了神秘主义，在民间则演变成装神弄鬼的邪术妖法的变种。当代人仍有提防神仙术等迷信的极大必要，但又可通过学习道家哲学而使精神境界得到提升（升华），节制物欲，主动地修炼身心，提高生命质量，为成功和幸福生活打基础——以“性命双修”的志趣，追求最大限度地开掘人体的生命潜能，亦无为不可。这其实也可视为个体生命之小宇宙凝练精、气、神以与大宇宙沟通、契合的精神努力，是追求人天合一境界之一法。

道家强调人是大自然的产物和组成部分，与大自然具同一性、一体性，简言之即是“天人一体”，也就是要求人类们对人性深处的“内在之天”要有清醒、明晰之认知，这即可形成人类恰当的自我认识自我，确立人在天地自然之间的恰当位置，在精神上有向自然回归的主体自觉，与自然“天道”合一即本于规律之行为视为生命追诉之主旨，主动克制、化解与“外在之天”的矛盾、冲突，同时化解人类的生存困境，自觉抵冲人与自然的张力，驾驭物质与物欲，成为生命的主人，并实现大化自然的主宰之使命。

## 十

佛家主张“四大皆空”且“万法皆空”，以“空”和“无”的视角审视人生世界，强调世间万物的变化和无常，引领人们向内寻求人生意义和价值：弃绝俗欲而追随“真我”（真如）即“不生不灭，不垢不净，不增不减”的生命真谛，并进而向大我之境反复不断递升——升华，所强调的其实是人类特有的精神生活的深度、高度、宽度、广度的开拓、挖掘。将“真我”之境的抵达和修持作为人生主旨，对色身则看作虚空、虚无，（“色即是空，空即是色”、“有即是无，无即是有”），乃有真切而厚重的精神生活之追求并充实而快乐，终得极乐——往生净土。

佛教认为人人皆有佛性，这恰如儒家所认定的“人性本善”“人人皆可为尧舜”，即强调人有善良根性的一面，用西人语言则为“人的一半是天使”。

人虽本禀赋有佛性，但又有与禽兽同类的欲望本能，大儒荀子所言“人性本恶”，而西人亦云“人的一半是魔鬼”。人性中的这一侧面则会诱导人类沉迷于原欲，如无当头棒喝则往往（常常）不能觉醒，身在迷途而不自知返，在欲海中会愈陷愈深直至不能自拔。在佛教的文化视野中，四大皆空（地水火风、生老病死），人的欲望所指向的对象都不是真实的。人如能悟得此真谛，则真如本性就显现，一心向佛（向善）地修持身心，就可以抵达成佛的境界。佛家认为：“烦恼即菩提，凡夫即佛”，追求天人合一是佛教主张的修行的一个侧面。“佛”也可视为抵达了“天人合一”之境那些人（个体）。

《金刚经》之“般若波罗蜜”说，义译则为“大智慧之彼岸”，般若就是智慧，彼岸就是梦想、目标。般若波罗蜜意指借助大智慧而实现直抵彼岸的梦想目标，这即是佛教智慧中的“天人合一”理念。天即西天极乐世界，是梦想与智慧的象征，而求取佛性智慧的人则是追求、发现之思考者与行动者的统一体。《金刚经》还说：“世间有为法，如梦幻泡影，如露亦如电，应作如是观”。所阐释的是“色即是空”的佛学理念，强调的是“不著于世，不离于心”的具超越精神的世俗生活主张。

禅宗是佛教中国化的代表。禅宗讲究“即心即佛”“明心见性，立地成佛”“即出世即入世”“以出世之心行入世之教化”，将出世色彩明显的佛教转化与日常生活一体化的人间宗教，并发明出在家修行这一广为普及的修持佛心的求道得道之路径，为与儒、道合一铲除了障碍、铺平了道路。

## 十一

中国特色的以儒释道三家为代表的“天人观”与长期持续、稳定的农耕文明直接密切相关，但并不拘泥于这一文明形态，对于现代工业化生产为基础的人类社会之处置与天地自然的关系都样的基础价值。

“天人合一”中华人文精神的核心理念，为儒释道以及诸子百家所共有，可以尝试从“系统整体性”、“平等公正性”、“价值内在性”三个视角进一步分析。传统文化讲究“天人和谐”，我们今天则强烈期求“人与自然和谐”，在中华人文精神的视域中，可称为传统文化精华在当代的发扬。

系统整体性。把天地人视作一个严整的系统，一个处于内在有机联系和相互作用中的整体，人在宇宙这个大系统中与天地万物的关系是“处于一焉”、“人与天一”、“天地一体”，也就是圆融为一的有机之系统。人与天地自然是一体而不可分割的，人类不只是自然界的有机组成部分，并且是能动自觉的部分（因素），所强调的是相互联结与有机统一的辩证特征。这与西方的机械主义、形而上学的“主客二分”“二元对立”的理念是本质上完全不同的“天人观”。

平等性。“天人合一”理念主张人与万物平等，与西方式的“人类中心主义”所主张的主客二分、人与自然二元对立的立志截然不同。儒家主张人“与天地参”，道家主张“万物一齐”，佛家主张“众生平等”，这种理念在西方世界只到19世纪末叶至20世纪中叶创生后现代性的“主体际性”理念后才初窥精微，第一次抵达了同样的思维境界。因之，中华传统人文精神的“天人合一”理念，较之现代性所突显、高扬的以主客二分、对立、冲突为基本特点的“主体性”、“理性主义”（工具理性）等更具超前性和后现代性，是中华文明在“轴心时代”所凝聚成的十分独特的文化建构。在中国人文精神视野中，主体并非彻底独立于天地自然，发现并承认“天人之分”，是为了复归于并自觉地完成“天人之合”，而人生的重要价值与使命、理想则是追求“天人合一”境界。此是正题，是起点，又经历异化、分化、离异与“有分”——现实中的分与理念中的分，儒家等反复强调、强化的是：人类的清明理性须指向自觉地抵达“合一”——“与天地参”，将人的智慧之力自觉地纳入天地运化的宏构之中，为造化之功增添如花妙笔而不与天地争功。这样的人文理念并非消解了人类的主体性，而是“主体际性”这一人之为人的理性特质的更为高妙的表达。因为，人是自然（天父地母）之子，是万物之灵，是唯一有心性（灵性）特质的存在，不是天地造化的收获（寄生）者，更非压迫、征服、劫掠者，而以天地自然中灵性的拥有与实现者为使命，承担起这一角色所必负有的神圣责任，消解对立、冲突，而追求秩序与和谐。因而，中国儒道释三家的天人观，其核心是相契、和谐，是以天（道）为根本，即以客观规律为根本，而以人为核心（能动因素）的高妙的系统论思想。我们可以通过借用西哲的“主体际性”理念进一步理解“天人合一”理念的后现代意义上的深刻内涵。主体际性，所强调的是人类特有的自觉性，即人是能动的主体。人与天地自然的关系与是一种交往关系中，人作为天地之心，是充分自觉的主体，既与天地平等，却又是天地灵性之系统表达者，并承认天地所具有的主体性（灵性），着力避免从主客二分之二元对立视角审视天人关系，是以人可以轻巧、顺利地完成“与天地参”的使命

价值内在性。也可概括为内生性价值。广袤宇宙所构成这一巨大的生态系统，任何事物都自具不假于外的内在价值。自然界并非人类纯粹的改造、征服、劫掠的对象，而是自在自生的天然存在物，具天然的存在权和内在价值，如果一定要谈论目的与手段等关系的话，天地自然本身即是终极目的，并非为他物（如人类）之食物、宠物、观赏、玩弄等等工具性目的，而是目的本身，正如人（人的群体和每一个体）是目的本身一样。外力对自然界之介入、干预，必引起自然界的相应反应，以改造、征服、

劫掠大自然为事，迟早必遭遇大自然的报应。

## 十二

当代生态环境持续恶化这一问题，如何应对？有一种唯科学主义的态度，认为全部的问题可以通过所谓“发展”而得到解决，而且是唯一有效的办法。窃以为，这种迷信于科学的态度是误入歧途了。

毫无疑问科学技术为人类带来了许多福音，近代以来的生产力的巨大发展和人类物质生活的持续性善可资一再证明。然而，人们长期地有意无意地忽视、漠视的是，科学技术是一柄双刃剑，其发展的积极效益被无限夸大，而其不可避免的诸多负面效应及其对人类的巨大伤害，则被屏蔽、忽略。中国三十多年的快速发展，以低端制造加工（代工）为主要形态，生态环境保护问题被置于事实上可有可无的地位，结果是大气、江河、土壤、地下水的系统性污染，直至大半个国家已雾霾重重包围的悲惨现状，种种怪病绝症纷至沓来，生态污染所导致的生存安全成为全民性的日常焦虑。这一恶果的共享极具讽刺性，其实是几十年来违背客观规律、漠视生态环境保护的畸形发展，所遭遇的报复；从另一角度看，则是科学技术被无节制滥用的恶果，是唯科学主义猖獗的果报——恶有恶报。科学技术与人文精神的关系被倒置、颠倒了。科学精神取代人文精神主掌人类精神生活乃至整体社会生活，恶仆乱政，胡作非为，最终贻害的是人类整体利益。因为，科学技术是典型的工具理性，直指具体的利益诉求；而人文精神则代表价值理性，直指人类的道义担当及崇高神圣等超越性价值目标的向往与追求。只有将科学技术置于人文理想的制约、管束之下，才能保证科学技术经常地发挥积极的、正向的作用；而缺乏人文精神（或人伦理性）引导和制约的科学技术，必然会以直接的短期的利益为主要或唯一目标，时日一长就会堕入市侩式的功利计较，堕入唯利是图的邪恶渊薮，最终危及人类的总体的（根本的）利益——道义。这是人类进入近现代社会以来最大的教训。

因而，尝试开掘中华传统的人文资源，特别是“天人合一”这一丰厚的中华人文精神资源，以对治环境污染、生态失衡等深层危机，对现代社会建设具有特殊意义。

## 十三

重归整体性、综合性的哲学思维。

近代以来，西方科学的一大突破是分析主义、归纳逻辑的发现，这奠定了近现代科学技术的基础。这一思维的路向对于缺乏分析、归纳习惯的东方式生活（生存理念与生活方式，逻辑的与现实的），显然有重大的补益价值，当然不可简单否定。然而，过分简单地模仿、“拿来”，并断然放弃传统的整体、综合、有机思维方式，陡然走向了另外一个极端，陷入“主客二分”与“二元对立”的思维陷阱——另一种片面性，导致上整体生存理念和生活方式的扭曲。

为矫治这种片面性，我们主张重归中华传统所注重的整体、综合、有机的东方式逻辑思维，并自觉地将分析和综合、统一、一体化起来。这一思维模式，强调总体性的视角，强调事物之间的彼此相因、交融互摄、旁通统贯，突出强调运动、变化、发展（生生不易），明确主张宏观、整体、综合的思维路向，具有模糊逻辑等后现代式思维特质，值得深入挖掘、开掘、培植。“天人合一”理念可资这一古老而年轻的东方式思维模式的代表或原型标志，本文认为，它抑或足以成为新时代（世纪）以中华人文精神为本位、根基，实现中西文化大整合的核心与枢轴。

世界是一个有机的整体，万事万物之间并不彼此隔绝，更非陌不相关，而是存在着密切而内在、普遍而客观的联系，人类是这种联系中的智能环节——“天地之心”，是拥有意识能力和意志品质的灵长动物，是事物间相互联系、贯通的能动（自觉）因素，是宇宙作为超级机体的生命、生机的文化发现者、表达者、实现者。如果说，近代以来西人的思维逻辑曾经呈现明显的形而上学的机械性偏颇的话，这种机械性偏颇在当下中国人的工作和生活中则已经相当严重而普遍地存在，是“西化”路径内在的天然缺陷的显露。在经历了分析主义、归纳主义等科技理性、工具理性的洗礼后，时代精神已表露出回归传统人文精神的客观需求。这一回归的现实路径，将是双重文化扬弃——本土儒道释为代表的人文精神的批判性传承与欧美文化为代表的域外人文精神批判性吸纳的统一，而基本目标则是达到综合、圆融的现代性人文精神这一理想境界。本文认为，以扬弃为实质的传统人文精神的回归，既是可欲的，又是现实的与必然的。强调事物间的客观、必需的联系性，天地宇宙自然所内在具有的有机性关联，自然并不与穷究个体事物的特殊矛盾、独特存在状态形成简单的冲突、对立，却存在明显的张力，实为事物客观存在的两个侧面，又是人类思维必须具备的两种主要路径和方式。当然（显然），重建总体性、综合性、系统性思维，必须将分析主义、归纳主义的科学精神和逻辑方法包容其中，消化为内在的有机组成，抵达辩证的系统的新整体逻辑之境界。

## 十四

全面建构现代性人文精神。

这是一项浩大的文化工程，其核心是现代性道德观（人生价值观）的构建，而其现实的路径可考虑中华传统人文精神之复归与再造。中华传统人文精神高度重视人际和谐和人与（天地）自然的和谐，儒道释诸家所系统思考与表述的“天人合一”理念，所体现的是“仁民”“爱物”这一极具包容性的“大爱”，其核心则是整体性（一体化）的“致中和”“允执厥中”的人文理念，而其关键则在人自身的精神世界（人格）的健全、健康的持续修炼和生活养成，所以，《大学》强调“自天子以至庶人，一是皆以修身为本”。修身是普遍要求，但儒家特别强调政治家为代表的精英群体加强修身的重要性。孔子说：“政者，正也”，将政令的畅通建立在管理者具备良好道德修养的基础上。突出强调政治精英修身的特殊重要意义——范导、引导意义，这自然与中国长期的官本位传统相关，更与政府对各类资源的掌控度密切相关。总体而言，政治精英在中国社会治理中长期处于并仍将继续处于绝对强势位置，对全社会的影响、辐射力远远超出其他精英群体。当然，知识精英、商业精英、文体精英及其他精英或准精英群体等，在修身问题上者亦共同负有无可推卸的率先垂范之职责。

这里讨论的是操作的或微观的人文精神建设层面，榜样的价值、实践的养成，显得格外突出。于是，我们主张重温、牢记、信守并践行孔子所强调的“为政以德”“政者，正也”“其身正，不令而行”等社会治理理念、原则，由政治精英为代表的精英群体带头，高扬“义以为上”“义以为质”的道义担当旗帜，在日常生活中自觉践行并长期坚守，在追求人际关系和谐、人与自然关系和谐的努力中成为大众的表率，在物欲的节制与精神生活雅致趣味的追求上亦成为大众的表率，并进而在人与自然的关系中成为大众之表率。质言之，精英群体要率先养成健康（健全）的现代人格，即自我培养成为具备内在（心灵）和谐的健康、健全的现代新人，并以此作为外在的人际和谐、群体社会、社会和谐、人与天地自然和谐的心性根基。本文坚信，内和谐是人生修养最关键处，有之，则足以造成人们对普遍和谐的真诚而自然的追求；无之，则一切皆归于空洞、虚无、虚伪。内和谐既有，则个体必能讲究心态平衡，必可化解人与人、人与社会、人与自身心灵之间的种种偏执，促进社会全面发展，践履“仁爱”，从而创造良好的社会氛围，并可为这一人文目标提供心性之根基；于是，“贵和”、“尚中”的生命志趣才能现实地转化为“致中和”的生活现实。

## 十五

建构现代生态伦理，悉心追求永续发展。

当代生态环境危机的解决，根本上并不在技术路径的挑三拣四、予取予夺，而是人文路径这一根本方向的抉择，是改造世道人心这一核心课题的重新彰显与自觉强化，初级目标是人类欲望的适当节制、遏制、控制，解决近代以来日益严重的欲望（本能）放纵、泛滥、沉沦、堕落这一根性的人文危机。具体而言，则要求建构起以“天人合一”理论为心性向导的现代生态伦理观。近现代以来的西方生态伦理观，“主客二分”“二元对立”的形而上学机械论事实上占据主导地位，在人与自然的关系中，采取的是改造、奴役、索取、劫掠的拙劣甚至邪恶之态度。人类是过分狂妄了，因为人类对于自然的规律的认识还十分有限，人类改造自然的能力以及应用科学技术应对环境污染、生态失衡的能力都很初级、幼稚。欧美国家 20 世纪下半叶以来，对付环境污染的策略，其实就是放弃传统大工业生产而转向高新技术新产业，同时将传统制造业、加工业等基础产业及其附带的种种环境污染源统统向新兴工业国家转移、转嫁，以牺牲后发现代化国家（第三世界）的生态环境的“巧妙”方式赢得蓝天白云青山绿水的重归。世界工厂转移到哪里，严重的环境污染和生态失衡也就追随到哪里。总体而言，环境污染威胁着整个地球这一人类的生存的唯一基础、凭依。全球变暖、环境污染、生态失衡、土壤沙化、森林锐减、湿地萎缩，大批生物快速灭绝，资源特别是能源的极速枯竭。这一切昭示着，罗马俱乐部的黑色预言（人类在自我毁灭并毁灭掉整个地球）似乎将提前兑现，不能不令人类的良知惊醒。

面对这一似乎难以解脱的超级困境，必须重构生态伦理观，必须回归“天人合一”理念所代表的人文精神路径，重构人与自然的关系。最为关键处，是人类从自私自利的原欲崇拜、本能放纵的物质主义、功利主义、实用主义等粗陋文化中跳脱出来，摒弃现代丛林主义为代表的邪恶价值观，既保持充沛的阳刚进取精神，又对个体和群体的欲望有足够的（法律制度和文化精神的）节制，从而既能分享现代化的物质文明的果实，又能将生命意义的精神文化内涵充分开掘，引导人们更注重精神文化生活的质量，注重精神文化品质的提升，注重精神世界的拓展，共同呵护精神家园，在有德、成功、幸福的人生正途上坦然前进，成就自我，利乐他人（群体），造福人类，在和谐与秩序中共享现代文明。

# 后现代视野中的儒家生态文明观（论纲）

深圳大学　王兴国

一、今天所谓的“儒家生态文明观”是根据中国古代儒家关于生态文明思想的现代诠释与建构之说。虽然中国古代儒家没有提出与使用过“生态”与“生态文明”的字样，但是这不表示或意味着中国古代儒家没有近代以来被称为“生态”与“生态文明”的思想意识。事实上，在中国古代儒家的思想中存在着大量丰富和宝贵的生态文明思想智慧。然而，中国古代儒家的生态文明思想在过去一直没有得到应有的重视，因而也没有能对现代社会产生应有的积极影响与作用。不乏悲剧意味的是，中国古代儒家的生态文明思想及其重要价值被极力追求现代化的现代社会践踏与抛弃了。只有当文化生态学作为显学登上现代世界文化的舞台以后，才能照亮中国古代儒家的生态文明思想以及其他诸家的生态文明思想。中国儒家的生态文明观，虽然曾经只是历史地存在，但是对于人类社会的今天和未来，仍然具有重要的价值。

智慧是永远也不会过时的。我们必须重新去学习和接受中国古代儒家和其他诸家的生态文明智慧，让它照亮我们眼前和通往未来的道路。

文化生态学是我们进入中国古代生态文明思想的一座不可或缺的桥梁，同时也是我们理解中国古代生态文明思想的一个重要参照系。唯有在文化生态学这一参照系的光照和启示下，并通过这座“桥梁”，才能进入后现代的视野中，去发现中国古代儒家生态文明观及其重要价值。这有助于我们从一种“后生态”的观点与立场去反思我们今天的主流文化及其价值观，同时也可以由一种具有“后现代精神”的“后现代文化”来引领我们顽疾缠身的社会自我拯救，并走向未来的康庄大道。

二、诞生于20世纪中叶的文化生态学（cultural ecology 或译为“生态文化学”），由美国人类学家朱利安·斯图尔德（Julian Haynes Steward，1902—1972）在《进化与过程》（1953年）一书中所提出，它旨在从人类生存的整体大环境，包括一般的自然环境和社会环境（乃至已知的宇宙全体）中的各种可能的因素之间的交互影响和作用，来研究人类不同文化的类型与模式。换言之，它是由宇宙之中的人、自然、社会、文化的各种参变量的交互影响和作用的关系来理解与把握人类的文化样态，包括文化的起源与发展轨迹的描述，以求能对不同地域民族的不同文化的存在模式进行归类（分为不同类型）研究。这就决定了它必须与人类生态学（或称社会生态学）区别开来。后者欲在探索和解释作为纯生物的人种在适应环境的变化中的机能和遗传功能，前者则以描述与解释存在于适应不同环境中的特殊的文化样态的类型和模式为鹄的。在文化生态学家看来，人作为从自然界的动物进化出来的产儿，其实只是文化的一种符号，人在体质上完全受其文化活动的影响、制约与决定；人与文化是在相互影响和作用中共同进化的。因此，人的进化“方程”与文化的运行轨迹之间是休戚与共的，导致人种形成的文化因素委实超过人的体质因素。这表示人必须进入文化及其符号的活动中，才能成其为人而存在。据此可知，人类的文化行为与人种的生物进化是截然（具有本质的）不同的，从遗传上推导与解释一种文化样态，并对其模式进行归类是绝对错误的，唯一正确的道路，是必须而且只能从文化的适应上去寻求结论。

然而，“文化生态学”是基于“生态学”（Ecology）和“文化”（Cultural）这两个概念的基础上而产生的。“文化”在“生态学”之前早已出现了，“生态学”则要到19世纪70年代才能由德国生物学家E. H. 海克尔（全名：恩斯特·海因里希·菲利普·奥古斯特·海克尔 Ernst Heinrich Philipp August Haeckel，1834—1919）提出。因此，文化生态学的问世必须以生态学的存在为前提和基础。这就决定了文化生态学离不开生态，并且必须研究生态。因此，文化生态学，必须以生态学的研究为前提。实际上，对于文化生态学来说，人类生存的整体大环境在本质上是一种生态概念，人类生存的整体大环境中的各种可能的因素（包括社会制度以及各种经济模式、政治模式、文化模式和生活方式）之间的关系，在实质上，是被理解为生态关系的。据此可知，文化生态学表现为两个基本的向度：它一方面是以生态学的范式来理解与解释人类文化样态的类型和模式，以彰显各个民族文化的独特性；另一方面则是以文化人类学的范式来理解与诠释，人类赖以生存的整体大环境系统（乃至已知的宇宙全体），在本质上，是多样性的生态关系。就像文化样态的多样性一样，作为人类生存的整体大环境（系统）的生态关系，在不同民族的历史与地域中，也是具体的不同的（表现为社会制度以及各种经济模式、政治模式、文化模式和生活方式以及生态本身的不同）。如果说它的前一个向度强调与突出文化样态的特殊性，那么它的后一个向度则追求与强调人类生存环境生态系统的统一秩序或一般秩序。统一的生态系统秩序对于人类生存的重要性与紧迫性正日益显现。

与其说人类文化的不同类型和模式，决定了人类不同生存环境的生态关系，不如说是不同人类环境的生态关系，决定了不同的人类的不同文化类型和模式。然而，只要持着一端，不一定陷入文化决定论，就必然陷入生态环境决定论；反之，亦然。事实上，文化人类学与环境生态学互为其根。因此，文化生态学是文化与生态环境交互决定论。在这个意义上说，人一方面是作为社会文化的动物而存在的，另一方面又是环境生态的符号之存在。归根结底，人在本上是社会文化与环境生态结合与统一的产儿。

文化生态学涉及人类学、生态学、生物学、社会学、环境学、地理学、历史学、政治学、哲学等多学科的交叉，无疑是一门综合的交叉学科，似乎有许多个端点。然而，上升到哲学人类学的观点来看，文化生态学只有文化人类学和环境生态学两个基本的端点。尽管文化生态学在20世纪问世，但是关于文化生态的思想却早已存在了。中国儒家早在2000多年以前，就已经在“以人文化成天下”的观念指引下，自觉地将自然的生态观纳入社会的文化或文明之中，形成了一种独具特色的生态文明观。

在文化生态学的照察中，儒家的生态文明观变得清楚起来。

儒家生态文明观，一方面以人文的观念来关照与审视自然以及人所赖以生存的整个环境的生态关系，另一方面也从神圣的自然生态关系来关照与检视人类的社会文明。其根基在于人文的宗教的“生命”与“感通”（或“感应”）观念。

三、虽然儒家生态文明观是农耕文明时代的产物，但是儒家的生态文明思想早已超越了农耕时代与农业经济社会；它没有在科技时代与现代社会充当过主要角色，甚至没有扮演过什么重要的角色，而是在儒学被妖魔化而遭受政治化的大革命性批判与追求社会的所谓“现代化”的浪潮声中完全沉寂与落寞，被现代社会无情的践踏埋没了。因此，只有到了人自身裂离（身心裂离、自我裂离），与他人裂离（完全以私欲之我为中心）、与社会裂离（以把持和操控国家政治权力的方式垄断社会的一切资源，实现自己个人利益以及少数利益集团利益的最大化，制造新的不公正，破坏道德与法律，蔑视正义，践踏人权，欺压弱势群体，制造巨大的贫富两极分化；同时以政治操控经济，而又一味地追求经济的高速畸形发展，工业与军事的飞速扩充，企业的最大利益化，不惜以严重毁坏自然和污染环境为代价，）、与自然裂离（掠夺与毁坏自然资源，诸如：森林泛伐、水土流失、土壤恶化、新的沙漠出现并且面积不断扩大、水资源日益短缺并不断被污染，海洋资源也遭到巨大掠夺、海水也不免被大面积污染，排碳量失控、空气污染、雾霾严重，地下资源枯竭……，不一而足，严重破坏了自然的生态秩序，社会与自然的和谐平衡被打破，导致生存环境的日益恶化，各种疾病怪病大肆流行，生命健康失去了保证，越来越多的人死于不治之症，而且新的疾病纷至沓来，层出不穷，防不胜防）、与“神”（宗教）裂离（终极关怀与人生信仰丧失），变成了披着“文明人外衣”的十足的“经济动物”的时候，时代与社会出现了前所未有的重大危机的时候，人作为“存在者”的“存在”面临重大危机的时候，儒家生态文明的思想智慧才会被发现与被发煌光大。换言之，现代社会不幸与儒家生态文明思想擦肩而过，只有在鱼肚白中出现了“后现代文化”观与“后现代社会”观的曙光，才能照亮中国儒家的生态文明智慧。从某种意义上说，儒家的生态文明观是一个提前了2000多年问世的“后现代生态文明”观。

四、儒家的生态文明观建立在人与自然之间的相互感通或感应的“天人合一”这一核心基石之上，讲求与强调人必须“知天命”（对于生态文明的自觉的前提），“爱万物”（一草一木），“致中和”，“未发”和中，“发而皆中节”，保护与维持宗教的“天命”之神圣（所谓“惟天之命，於穆不已”），自然的生态之美（孟子所谓“牛山之美”），“尽心”“知性”，“修身”“俟命”，“与天地参”，“赞（天地之）化育”，德与天地配，融文化与生态为一体，从而实现“上下与天地同流”的生命超越境界。

五、儒家生态文明观的天人感通（或感应）模式分别由：（一）生命的形上学；（二）贯通的实践观；（三）赞生的美学观；（四）王道政治观；（五）天地境界观五大支柱所撑起而凸显出来。

以下分别对它们加以简略的叙述。

（一）生命的形上学。视宇宙为一个生生不息的大生命（存在）。人作为在宇宙中的具体的“存在者”的“存在”是与宇宙的大生命（的“存在”）为同一的。因此，人只是宇宙生命的具象表征。人的生命终将回归宇宙的大生命之中去。圣人是人类的先知先觉者，意识到自己的生命与宇宙生命的同一，自觉地把自己的生命与宇宙的大生命相连同与连通，自觉地回归于宇宙的大生命之流行。所以，圣人境界就在天地气象中表现出来。

宇宙大生命生生不息的动力乃在于它自身之中，是内在的动力而不是外力。这种内在动力是由阴阳的交互感通作用而产生的。阴阳相反而相成，互为其根，一翕一辟，一动一静，负阴抱阳，阴平阳秘，交感为用，形成永不枯竭的鲜活动力。这种动力不仅使宇宙恒转不息，而且贯穿于宇宙中的一切事物，当然也就贯穿于人的个体生命。

阴阳的交感形成了宇宙之道或心。《易传》所谓“一阴一阳之谓道”，表示的就是宇宙之道。也不妨称为宇宙之心或宇宙心。说宇宙之道，是就道器关系而言；说宇宙之心，是就心物关系而论。道凸显宇宙之为存在的状态，心所凸显的则是宇宙之为生命。宇宙的存在无论为道或为心，都不是静止不动的实体，而是自本自根自生自化的流行过程。

宇宙道或宇宙心乃是宇宙间的生态存在的根基。当人在宇宙大生命的创造化育流行之间无动于衷，不知对宇宙道或宇宙心存有敬畏之感的时候，生态环境的灾难就不可避免地降临了。

宇宙之为大生命的“存在”，是一个鲜活的不断创生与化育的过程。宇宙间的万事万物作为具体的“存在者”既是这一过程中的产物，又是宇宙之为大生命的“存在”（道或心）的表征。在宇宙万物中，唯人为万物之灵。宇宙之为大生命的存在，只有透过人之具体存在的智慧生命，才能显露与被揭示。这是一个永不完结永无止境的以生命亲证生命（以人之具体存在的智慧生命亲证与体验宇宙大生命），生命与生命（人的具体生命与宇宙大生命）互相感通与合一的过程。这也就是天人交感与合一的过程。这一过程对人来说，就是工夫践履的过程。广义地说，就是实践与体证的过程。

人只有在这一实践与体证的过程中，才能具体和真切地洞察和悟解：宇宙之为大生命的"存在"（活的道或心），乃是人类生态文明的源泉与本根。

（二）贯通的实践观。实践的目的在于体证与觉悟宇宙大生命永恒健动的创生流化与载物之德的精神，并以个人的生命与其感通互动，自觉参与到宇宙大生命的创化活动与流行过程之中去；实践的过程是以个人的修身工夫开始，经过社会化规模化的群体实践或集团实践，最终达到超越的天地实践，使个人的具体生命与宇宙大生命之间感通合一，实现天人合德；实践的基本形式表现为：1. 个人的修行工夫实践，2. 社会群体或集团的规模化的事功实践；3. 超越的天地实践。在实践的整个过程中，以"仁"为本的道德精神贯彻始终，人类生存的环境生态与宇宙生命秩序的（固有）生态之间保持贯通和谐一致，一而不二。

（三）赞生的美学观。儒家的美学观虽然是从诗教出发的，孔子所谓"不学诗无以言"，但诗教本身并不是目的，而只是一种审美情趣与审美鉴赏力的熏陶和培养，是为了发现美、鉴赏美和体验美做准备的。实际上，儒家的美学观是围绕着"生"的精神的意味与情趣而展开的。"生"的意味和情趣是由宇宙大生命所决定的。因此，对宇宙大生命之"生"的精神领略与把握，鉴赏与体验，便成为儒家美学的最高追求。作为儒家美学的最高对象，宇宙大生命之"生"的精神是真善美的统一体。如果通过审美鉴赏与审美体验活动，使审美主体个人的有限生命与无限的宇宙大生命之"生"的精神合一无间，那么就在审美鉴赏与审美体验中实现了真善美的统一，达到了审美与美的最高境界。因此，唯"生"为美，就成为儒家美学的一个基本原则。这一原则贯穿于儒家的一切审美鉴赏活动与审美体验的过程之中。与此同时，"生"也就成为美之为美的一个最重要的标准了。对儒家来说，审美就是观"生"。因为有"生"之物才是美的。无疑，"生"本指宇宙生命的精神，在审美活动中引申为生动活泼可爱，使人愉悦的意味与情趣。"天地有大美而不言"。天地万物自身具有无穷无尽的生意盎然的精神、情趣与意味，本身就是一种趋向完美艺术地活动和存在。因此，天地万物永远都是最美的，而且是最真实的，具有无声无臭，於穆不已的德性，使人百看不厌，并开悟生命的智慧。一件艺术品之所以是美的，是因为他气韵生动并且具有艺术之真生命的活力贯注其中。美的食物也一定得是具有新鲜与生活的意味的。

总之，儒家的美学无外乎是求一个"生"字而已。儒家对宇宙之美的鉴赏与体验如此，对宇宙间的万物之美的鉴赏和体验如此，对人生之美与社会之美的鉴赏与体验依然如此。儒家以“生”的审美标准看一切，总是对“生”敬畏不已，赞美不已。孔子说：“未知生焉知死”，就是对“生”的最高赞美。“未知生”的“生”，在孔子的精神或意识中，已经直通到宇宙大生命之中了。那是何等的崇高、圣神、庄严与美丽啊！“焉知死”，并不表示孔子不明了死的意义与对死的漠视。孔子提倡养生送死，慎终追远，便是最好的证明。对孔子来说，“死”在“生”中。能知“生”便足矣。所以，孔子以“生”的眼观来看一切，以“生”的态度来对待一切（在这一意义上，死也是生）；孔子总是乐观的，对人生与世界充满了“生”的希望。

儒家的美学是美生论。从人的生存环境生态的审美要求出发，必然追求环境生态之美，这自然包括自然生态环境之美。孟子论“牛山之美”，就是一个范例。

（四）王道政治观。孟子提出“以民为本”的“仁政王道”，也是宇宙大生命的“生生之德”精神在人世间的政治上的一种表现而已，所谓“替天行道”。董仲舒的“天人感应”的政治观，也是儒家政治生态观的一种表现。这要求社会的政治生态与信仰的宗教和道德的生态统一起来、社会的人文生态与自然的原始生态统一起来。

（五）天地境界观。人的一切活动或所作所为，都是为了成人、成物、成己，不断地提高生命的觉悟，不离世间而出世间，内在于世间而超越世间，自觉地达到天德与实践天德，与天地同流。

天地境界就是圣人境界。在圣人境界中，宇宙万物皆非手段，而都是目的，与圣人平等，各得其所而各尽其性。宇宙成为圆满的大生命。

以上五个方面的内容表明，儒家把人的生存环境，乃至整个宇宙，都视为具有内在关系的互相感通或感应的生命机体的关系。因此，儒家在这一基础上建立了一种生态文明观的天人感通模式。

六、深入儒家思想可以发现，在古老的儒家生态文明思想与现今的“后现代精神”之间不仅具有惊人的相似，而且存在着一种平行与相通的关系。具体地说，这主要表现为：（一）机体主义思想；（二）万物一体思想；（三）天人感通思想；（四）人与人以及自身，人与社会，人与自然，人与神或“天”（宗教）之间具有内在和谐、同一、感通与平衡的思想；（五）敬畏生命与生命太和健全的思想；（六）社会生生不息发展（可持续生成与发展）思想；（七）宇宙生命内动力的思想。具体展开略。

七、基于一种后现代视野的文明对话观来看，“后现代文化”和“后现代精神”不应该只有唯一的西方文化来源，而是应该具有广泛的不同背景的异质文化的来源，其中就应该包括东方文化，尤其是中国文化与中国思想。事实上，“后现代文化”和“后现代精神”并不完全在西方产生，也不完全为西方所独有。在中国文化与中国思想中，具有丰富可观的与西方“后现代文化”和“后现代精神”相似的并保持着一种平行关系的思想或精神，儒家的生态文明观就是其中的一个典范和代表。

八、儒家的生态文明观固然不是今天的“后现代思想”，但是这并不妨碍儒家生态文明思想可以参与到“后现代社会”观的建设中去，丰富“后现代文化”和“后现代精神”，为人类社会自身生态的平衡发展提供有益的启示与灵感的源泉。因此，中国儒家的生态文明思想理当为西方“后现代文化”和“后现代精神”所许可与融摄。李约瑟、卡普拉、朱利安等是重要的先驱。相信一定会有更多的后继者出现，并取得更多更辉煌的成就。

基于一种后现代文明的视野来看，中国和世界都必须重新回到人与人以及自身，人与社会，人与自然，人与神或“天”（宗教）之间的内在和谐、同一、感通与平衡的基础上来，才能重建适合作为“存在者”的“存在”之人类宇宙的新秩序。这一宇宙新秩序的建立与维系，有赖于世界文化的生态多样性的存在与平衡发展。在这一意义上来看，东西方文化发展之间形成与保持一种综合交融，不失自性与平衡的关系不仅是必要的，而且是非常关键的。

# 三、德治与法治

## 孔子思想中缺乏法治精神吗?

中国农村杂志社总编辑　冀名峰

孔子的治国思想集中反映在《论语》之中,《论语》十分强调德治在社会治理中的重要作用,孔子推崇和追求以德治统帅和覆盖社会治理,认为如果社会能够在德治体系有效运行下达成安定和谐,那将几乎是成本较小、效果较优的社会秩序状态。比较而言,孔子专门论述法治的内容确实相对较少,但是,言不可因其少而谓其轻,我们不能因为孔子专门论述法治内容相对较少而得出孔子只重视德治、不大重视法治的结论。事实上,孔子高度重视法治在社会治理中的重要作用,并特别强调法治精神和德治精神内在统一的重要性,这对完善现代社会治理有着重要意义。本文将对此进行分析。

### 一、孔子的德治思想和法治思想

在《论语·为政》中,孔子从总体上描绘了德治功成之后所形成的和谐而美好的社会秩序状态,这成为中华传统文化高度重视德治、孜孜追求德治的重要动因之一:

子曰:“为政以德,譬如北辰,居其所而众星拱之。”(《论语·为政》)

在孔子看来,以德治国如果能够实现的话,那就会产生北极星一样的政治效应:居其所而众星拱之。朱熹对此进行了进一步诠释:“为政以德,则无为而天下归之”,“为政以德,则不动而化、不言而信、无为而成。所守者至简而能御烦,所处者至静而能制动,所务者至寡而能服众”。(《论语集注》)可见,在朱熹看来,德治成功意味着我们坐在那里不干什么就可以实现天下大治,何其美好诱人!

同样在《论语·为政》中,孔子还比较了德治和法治的优劣和效果:

子曰:“道之以政,齐之以刑,民免而无耻;道之以德,齐之以礼,有耻且格。”(《论语·为政》)

这是说,用法令来引导百姓,用刑罚来统一百姓言行,百姓或可为免于刑罚而服从管治，但并不会以违法为耻，也不会以守法为荣。用道德教化百姓，用礼的规范来统一百姓言行，百姓就会懂得守法之荣与违法之耻，因而会自觉改正。

以今天的视角来看，“政”可以理解为法律和行政法令，是条文或文字形态的制度，其颁布者为行政司法部门等社会管理机构。“政”，解决的问题是明确人们不得干什么或必须干什么，这是建立社会秩序的一种手段。“罚”，是由行政司法部门实施的，对违反“政”的行为的一种惩罚。例如杀人者偿命，其中所含有的不得杀人之意，即为“政”，而偿命即是“罚”。“德”，是社会共同价值观或一个社会所倡导的标准价值观体系。“德”，可以是行政司法部门等社会管理机构倡导的，也可以不是这些部门倡导的。“礼”，是儒家或传统社会所建立的保持社会秩序和调节社会行为的一种规范。从一般意义上说，“德”和“礼”是软约束，“政”和“罚”则是硬约束。但也不尽然，“德”和“礼”的观念可以转化为“政”和“罚”。例如，人都应尽孝，这属于“德”的范畴，尽孝以礼，按照“礼”的规范去尽孝，是“德”通过“礼”的规范实现了孝的目的。但政府部门也可以规定，不尽孝则不得做官或者鞭笞五十，这就属于“政”和“罚”的范畴了。“德”和“礼”重在治心，通过治“心”达到治“行”（行为），以达成保持社会秩序的目的。“德”和“礼”的落实，主要靠社会力量和人们自我约束。“政”和“罚”，则主要以强制力甚至暴力方式直接规范行为。“政”和“罚”的落实，主要依靠社会管理机构，如行政司法部门。

孔子这句话所揭示出的重要思想是，以德治国，“民”知耻；单纯以法治国，“民”不知耻。如果治国“以法”而不“以德”，“民”缺乏价值观这个内核，“民”将失去其民族性因而失去其凝聚力。这是单纯德治和单纯法治的不同效果。这一思想何其深刻！我们需要不需要高度重视以什么样的价值观和思想体系塑造人民，不言而喻。同时，因为“以德治国”使得“民”知耻而自觉，社会管理者可以依靠吸引力、号召力而不必使用强制力达成社会秩序，如此看来，“以德治国”也是一种痛苦指数比较小的社会治理方式。

果然可以“以德”而不是“以法”实现天下大治，那最好不过了。然而，当我们从理论回到现实的时候就会发现，单纯以德治国将是一种很难实现的治国方式。以德治国，主要依靠价值观体系规范人们行为，靠价值观力量凝聚人心、人气和人力。价值观对行为的约束主要是软约束。在这种情况下，如果社会成员中少部分人不按价值观原则行事，那么，这部分人很可能就会在损失不大的情况下，获得很大的个体利益。而坚守道德原则的人会成为利益损失者，时间长了，这种利益的逆向分配会造成越来越多的人突破道德约束，最后导致价值观体系约束力的崩塌，形成道德建设领域的“劣币驱逐良币”现象。所以，以德治国，所治之国是君子国才会产生良好效果。在君子国中，君子们具有共同价值观；同时，君子们都按价值观要求进行自治，这样治国成本就必然下降，无为而治就可以实现了。

那么，现实社会并非君子国，是不是就可以把“以德治国”放在一边了呢？也不是。儒家治国，主张先从修身开始，所谓“修身、齐家、治国、平天下”，这句话简约总括了儒家在各个社会层面的责任，实际是强调要从个体改造开始，通过提高每一个社会成员的道德水准，以充分发挥道德力量在社会治理中的作用，这是非常正确的。应该说，道德水准提高就会导致社会治理成本下降，这是一条规律。所以，即使单纯以德治国不能够实现良好的社会治理，也必须坚定不移地推进以德治国。

孔子在其自身的实践中并非只重视以德治国而不重视以法治国。历中上的孔子，不仅仅是理论大师和中华传统文化价值观体系的主要构建者，他同时也是一位行政管理大师，最高官职曾至鲁国大司寇并行摄相事，在孔子执鲁国国政期间，鲁国以很短的时间实现了大治，这还引起齐国的恐慌：

“（孔子）与闻国政三月，粥（鬻）羔豚者弗饰贾（价）；男女行者别于涂（途）；涂（途）不拾遗；四方之客至乎邑者不求有司，皆予之以归。齐人闻而惧……”（《史记·孔子世家》）

而孔子执政鲁国伊始所做的一件重要事情就是“诛鲁大夫乱政者少正卯”（《史记·孔子世家》）。据称，少正卯这个人乱德乱政，心机很深且心术不正，能言善辩，很有迷惑性，对群众有一定的号召力，已经达到了孔子在政治上的“三恶”的标准（恶紫之夺朱也，恶郑声之乱雅乐也，恶利口之覆邦家者《论语·阳货》），成为孔子推行政治主张的主要障碍。孔子的办法是杀掉少正卯，并没有以道德教育的方式来改造少正卯，这是以法治国方式的运用，同时也彰显了孔子在治国中所坚持的法治精神。

深入理解孔子的德治思想和法治思想除了需要研究《论语》中的相关论述之外，我们还需要高度重视记录于《孔子家语》中的一段话，这一段话在展示孔子德治思想和法治思想方面意义非凡。

闵子骞为费宰，问政于孔子。子曰：“以德以法。夫德法者，御民之具，犹御马之有衔勒也。君者，人也；吏者，辔也；刑者，策也。夫人君之政，执其辔策而已。”“善御马者，正衔勒，齐辔策，均马力，和马心。故口无声而马应辔，策不举而极千里。善御民者，壹其德法，正其百官，以均齐民力，和安民心。故令不再而民顺从，刑不用而天下治。”《孔子家语·执辔》

闵子骞要到“费”这个地方担任最高行政长官，临行前向孔子请教如何为政，孔子对此进行了长篇论述，集中而全面地表达了孔子的德治思想和法治思想及其对治国“以德”和“以法”二者之间关系的看法。对于如何管好“费”这个地方，孔子的回答很明确：“以德以法”，就是要靠两手，一手是德治，一手是法治，并且认为“德”和“法”都是“御民之具”，并无孰重孰轻的问题，同时也强调“刑”的重要性，“刑者，策也”。而“刑”，则更多的是体现了法治精神。接下来的话更为重要：“善御民者，壹其德法，正其百官，以均齐民力，和安民心。故令不再而民顺从，刑不用而天下治。”突出强调德治精神和法治精神必须高度统一，二者必须保持一致的思想和行为规范方向，不能依“德”应向北，依“法”则应向南。而且，不论是“以德”或“以法”，其最终目标是不用“刑”而天下治。可见，说孔子不重视法治只重视德治，显然不是事实。

那么，治国“以法”不“以德”或无法“以德”又会如何呢?

如果治国“以法”不“以德”或无法“以德”，将很难长久维持下去。历史上一个典型失败的例子就是秦国。商鞅使秦国由弱致强，韩非虽然不见用于秦王，但是秦国用他的思想统一了六国，可是只过了十几年，统一后的秦王朝就崩溃了。秦国崩溃的原因可有多种分析，但是六国民心没有收复是其中之关键。我认为秦国的统治者并不是没有意识到这方面问题的严重性。公元前 213 年秦相李斯就曾进言，说诸子百家“入则心非，出则巷议，夸主以为名，异取以为高，率群下以造谤。”用今天的话说，是社会上出现了价值观的混乱和文化的冲突，这不利于秦的统治。秦始皇为了解决这个问题实行了上历史上著名的“焚书”和“坑儒”，当年下令销毁除法家以外的所有诸子百家的著作，次年在咸阳将 460 余名儒士和方士坑杀。秦国这样做的目的显然是为了收复和统一六国民心，但是武力改造心灵并不能产生立即的效果，没有文化优势的秦国无法推行有效的德治，民心不服之下国家垮掉也是很容易的。结合这一史实，再回到孔子说过的话：“道之以政，齐之以刑，民免而无耻；道之以德，齐之以礼，有耻且格。”我们一定可以从中读出强烈的震撼。有耻或无耻实际上是文化或价值观上的认同或不认同。这个史实告诉我们，只有“硬实力”而没有“软实力”一定不是可以长久的治国之道。

实际上，德治和法治是相互依赖、相互补充的，很多情况下分别承担了不同的社会管理功能，它们具有不同的约束方式和约束体系，分别具有各自的社会管理优势。例如，如何实现德治?孔子讲了要“齐之以礼”，即通过“礼”的规范实现德治，“德”是指出的一个方向和标准，向这个方向前进，要靠“礼”。比如说“男女授受不亲”，这是一种礼的规范，通过实施这一规范以达到纯净男女关系的“德”的要求。那么谁来落实和监督“男女授受不亲”这一礼的规范呢?社会大众。每一个人都是落实者，每一个人都是监督者，包括授受者本人。如果把这条原则变成“政”和“罚”，男女亲密接触者双方都不是对方的监督者，只有政府才是监督者，那么落实起来就很困难。总体而言，“德”和“礼”是在每一个人心中设立一个管理者，而“政”和“罚”是在整个社会共同设立一个管理者，这是二者的不同。但是，是不是“德”和“礼”就是一个优于“政”和“罚”的社会管理手段呢?不见得。这要具体问题具体分析。比如杀人偿命，可能通过“政”和“罚”的手段去规范会更有效。所以，“以德治国”和“以法治国”必须相辅相成，相互补充，才能实现最佳的社会治理效果。

总结上述分析，孔子显然具有崇尚德治的强烈倾向，在孔子看来，实现社会和谐，最重要的是人民心灵的改造，而价值观教育和塑造所达到的效果是以单纯治国“以法”的方式所不能获取的，而且德治这种“软实力”建设具有更为长久的社会治理效果。事实上，千百年来虽然传统中国的国家形态反复遭到各种力量的摧毁，但中华民族始终保持强大的凝聚力，其中重要原因是中国有着一脉相承的德治传统，即不断强化以儒家为核心的传统文化体系来塑造民族心理和民族精神，尽管这个体系本身也是不断变迁的。孔子虽然崇尚德治，但他丝毫没有轻视法治的想法，相反孔子高度重视法治手段的运用，在他看来，德治和法治都是不可或缺的治国利器，德治和法治互为补充、相辅相成，在实现社会有效治理方面分别承担着不同的功能。孔子也指出，强化德治和法治的方法是不同的，二者的发展遵循着不同的规律。在推进法治和德治过程中，要高度重视“壹其德法”，保持德治和法治精神的高度统一，这是运用“德”、“法”治理社会所必须坚持的重要原则。

## 二、孔子德治思想与法治思想的时代意义

孔子的德治思想和法治思想法对于今天的社会治理有着重要意义。就笔者观察和思考所见，这里谈两个问题。

（一）以科学的方法推进德治建设

通常认为传统中国社会缺乏法治精神而不缺乏德治精神（不是孔子缺乏法治精神）。十九世纪以前或许中国社会就是这样。但是，经过二十世纪文化领域的不断变革和革命，既有的以中华传统文化为核心的德治体系至少相当一部分已经崩塌和湮灭。“礼失求诸野”。如果想要体会传统中国的社会气息和文化氛围，恐怕要到日本和韩国农村去感受；如果想要体会中华传统文化和现代城市建设融合之后可能产生的结果，这恐怕要到新加坡去感受。事实上我们丢掉了相当一部分中华优秀传统文化精神。如果坚持说这些精神还存在，那也只能说是存在于“典籍”里，而没有渗透到社会各个方面而成为塑造“中国人”的有效材料和范式，所以重振中国特色的德治体系和模式十分必要。

运用孔子德治思想观察当今社会，我认为当前德治建设在以下两个方面存在缺失。

第一，德育方式没有严格遵循价值观教育规律。

德育应当遵循怎样的规律？先秦儒家认为应当遵循“行为教育——概念理论教育”的先后顺序，关于这一点《论语·子张》有着明确的说法：

子游曰："子夏之门人小子，当洒扫、应对、进退，则可矣。抑末也，本之则无。如之何？"子夏闻之曰："噫！言游过矣！君子之道，孰先传焉？孰后倦焉？譬诸草木，区以别矣。君子之道，焉可诬也？有始有卒者，其惟圣人乎！"（《论语·子张》）

可见，在子夏看来，"洒扫、应对、进退"这些日常行为教育是德育之本，德的概念和理论教育则是"末"，当然"末"也不是不重要，但"末"一定应是立于"本"之上。反观我们现在实行的少年儿童价值观教育方式，总体上过度偏重于概念教育而不是行为教育。不论是学校里的德育或是社会上的德育甚至于家庭德育，基本上是偏重说教，阐释一些较为高深的价值观概念，讲一些大道理，这样做背诵或考试固然没有问题，但就是成不了个人素质的组成部分。比如说进行爱国主义教育，重要是让他们认识到什么样的行为是爱国、什么样的行为是不爱国和怎样正确地爱国，而不是简单地讲爱国道理，以至于一些少年儿童的爱国理念和个人实际行为无论如何也不能产生关联。

再比如说教育孝顺父母。我们天天告诉他"要孝顺父母"，讲一些孝顺的大道理，或许有一定作用，但并不会有太大作用。如果我们的德育课采取行为教育方法，在课堂上设置父母与孩子的角色，教孩子如何与父母说话，面对父母时应有什么样的态度，如何对待父母的教诲，与父母一起吃饭时应如何表现，等等。同时实行一致性的学校教育、家庭教育和社会教育，这样反复训练，慢慢就会在其心里建立一种孝顺的习惯，形成了孝顺的价值观。甚至他可能不知道"孝顺"这个词，但他的一切言行会体现出孝顺的精神。

现在社会广泛存在的陌生人之间相互不尊重，彼此言语行为中间缺乏"敬"的范式，已经成为一个严重的社会问题，比如问个路都难以以礼相待，发生争执时必定恶语相加才算够"横"。在我看来，这也是德育行为教育普遍缺失所产生一个严重后果，因为我们从小没有学会"好好说话"，我们没有学会如何以"尊重对方的方式去反对对方"，没有学会以"尊重对方权益的方式来维护自己的权益"，没有学会"人之间本来就应当客客气气"，而不是有利益需求时才"客客气气"。这些都属于行为教育的范畴。我们不应轻视传统社会教育孩子"站有站相、坐有坐相、吃有吃相"方式，而恰恰是这种简单的行为教育塑造了人。

总之，对于当前社会而言，如何进行有效的价值观教育显得极其重要和紧迫，它关系到民族素质的整体提高，关系到国家的强盛和民族的长远发展。

第二，德治约束体系弱化，德治价值观导向存在某种程度的混乱。

孔子认为，推进德治要靠"礼"的约束，所谓"道之以德，齐之以礼"。比如说"孝"这个儒家文化的重要基石。在过去，如果不孝，首先会受到宗法的严厉惩处。现在，如果一个人不孝怎么办呢？或许一般的不孝不会得到惩处，搞到十分严重地步则只能走法律途径，而法律只能解决赡养费用问题。子曰："今之孝者，是谓能养。至于犬马皆能有养；不敬，何以别乎？"（《论语·为政》）是的，"不敬，何以别乎"。可见，法治不能解决"敬"的问题，这个要靠德治来解决。这样说不是要恢复过去的宗法制度，过去的宗法制度对人的权利造成了很多伤害，但是宗法制度对于传统中国社会保持秩序具有重要作用，这是客观实际。问题是我们摧毁了不合时宜的德治约束体系（或者说传统社会"礼"的体系）之后，新的德治约束体系并没有完整确立和特别有效地确立，以至于目前社会大众保持道德水平主要靠各自"良心发现"，这是我国德治水平始终无法有效提升的重要症结之一。

在"举孝廉"的时代，在家里孝与不孝、在乡里是不是具有良好的道德形象，都是决定是否可"举"的重要维度，官员的提拔和任用高度重视个人的社会道德形象。但是现在行政人员提拔任用，很少考察个人私德。所谓"德才兼备"中的"德"更多的是指的是"政治道德"而不大包括个人私德。他是不是一个好儿子、好父亲、好丈夫、好公民似乎是私人的事，并没有制度化地进入组织人事部门考察范围。如此，政治上很强、工作能力很强而私德很差的人就有可能进入社会管理集团，一些行政人员追求特权固然是吏治不严之过，但是我们对这些人缺乏有效的德治约束机制也是其中重要原因。

媒体和社会舆论是德治约束体系的重要组成部分。现在要求媒体坚持正确的舆论导向，有的人就说这影响"新闻自由"。应当指出，作为德治约束体系重要组成部分的媒体必须以弘扬真善美、引导社会道德水准不断提高为己任，新闻自由必须位于宪法和法律框架之内，一切人和机构并无传播"恶"、冲击宪法精神的自由。如果试图引导怀疑和颠覆宪法精神所倡导的价值观，就应当进行坚决纠正和实施必要的管理，以确保社会主流价值观的正确方向。20世纪80年代媒体曾经报道过这样一件事，一个七十多岁的老农落水了，一个风华正茂的大学生入水去救，结果老农得救了，大学生却淹死了。事情发生后，一些评论认为用大学生的命去换老农的命不值得，是社会损失。实际上，见危致命是一个健康社会的价值观，不能用合算不合算这种计算"利"的方式来评判其正当性。否则，每一个救人的人在救人之前都与被救者进行价值对比，就不会有救人行为发生了。媒体进行如此评论，混淆了我们的价值观导向，就应当进行澄清和纠正。前一段时间网络上流行语所谓"我爱国家，国家爱我吗?"，以此作为个人向国家无度索取权利和自由的"说辞"，似是而非，故意混淆价值观导向，应当进行纠正和管理。孔子讲的"恶紫之夺朱也，恶郑声之乱雅乐也，恶利口之覆邦家者《论语·阳货》"，实际上指的就是要坚决反对一些以对抗主体价值观为目标的似是而非、惑乱视听的论述和"说辞"，因为这种似"是"实"非"的东西最有欺骗性，而"黑白分明"的东西反而容易识别，所以孔子对前者特别警惕。目前网络上的德治约束体系建设明显滞后，网络成了各种奇谈怪论大行其道的乐园，一些言论常常以挑战人类社会基本价值观取向为能事，其对社会和谐的破坏力不容小视。我们的原则应当是，所有的领域，只要是对社会道德水准产生影响的地方，都要有相应的有效德治约束体系跟进，而不能留下“死角”。一些主流媒体常常不屑于与网络上的“散兵游勇”进行价值观论战，这是不对的。

我们应当清醒地认识到，较高道德水平的社会是“管”出来的，而不是“喊”出来的，现在的德治总体上偏于“软”，因此必须要敢于“管”。不论如何加强道德教育，不论树立多少道德楷模，如果我们没有建立广泛有效德治约束体系，社会的总体道德水平就难以实现一致性提高。如果“闯红灯”、在社会上“耍横”、随地乱扔垃圾、在公共场合抽烟等等法治所不及的事项均成为与个人就业创业和在社会上生存发展相关的记录要素，归入德治范围，我们很可能就会通过这一德治约束机制的有效运作而实现社会整体道德水平的显著提高。

（二）坚持法治精神和德治精神的高度统一

孔子提出“壹其德法”，坚持法治精神和德治精神高度统一。不论是“道之以政，齐之以刑”或是“道之以德，齐之以礼”，都应坚持统一的价值观导向。反思今天社会现实，这一思想尤为宝贵。

我们面临的大量问题是法治精神和德治精神不一致甚至相悖，造成了巨大的社会困惑，导致“民无所措手足”。

例如，很多“见义勇为”、“见危致命”这类德治精神所褒扬的行为，法治精神却不支持。一位疾病突发的老人倒在地上，大家只能围观，谁也不敢上前施救。因为没有法律法规会保护他的清白、奖励他对社会成员的关怀，如果他上前施救，他或者被家属讹诈或者被警方问话，由此可能导致他时间、精力、名誉、资财等各方面的损失。电视上有的专家对处理此类事情提出了所谓合理建议：一是打 110，二是打 120。这类办法对提升德治水平没有任何正面意义，如此我们必将面对一个极端冷漠的社会。

再比如“过马路要坚持绿灯行、红灯停”，这既是德治的要求，也是法治的要求，但大量的现实是我们没有“守法”的条件，结果不得不突破心理上“德”的约束。有的人行横道没有装红绿灯，过往车辆认为自己有通行权，过路行人也认为自己有通行权，两个群体相互拥堵交织在一起，互相影响对方的通行权，相互骂“缺德”，其实不是“缺德”，而是“缺灯”。有的人行横道上设置了红绿灯，但绿灯开放时间短到永远无法保证行人正常通过，结果横穿马路的人群不论自身道德水准高下，都一致视“红灯”而不见，因而都成为不守交通秩序的“缺德”且“不守法”之人。这些情况都是法治实施条件缺失导致德治崩塌，从某种意义上说也是没有“壹其德法”所致。这些固然是小事，但我们不应小看这些“小事”对社会道德水平建设的影响，人们就是在这样的环境下形成了对“德”、“法”两种约束的看法和态度。

类似的事情太多了。比如我们反对随地小便，这是德治的要求，可是有的高速公路休息区间隔相当长，人们不得不随地小便。有的公园厕所不足，小孩子只能随地方便。公共场所女厕所永远不足，对女性身心健康造成严重危害。这些问题大量存在，如何让我们的国民保持“优雅”？所以德治精神和法治精神的高度统一，既应统一于同一的价值观导向上，也应统一于社会建设各个方面包括各种基础设施建设。

总而言之，我们从事社会各个方面的建设和管理必须将德治精神和法治精神高度统一贯彻其中，把这一原则作为检视各项工作的重要维度，这样才能更加有效地推进和谐社会的建设。

# 孔子对礼制与刑罚关系的认识及其法治思想

辽宁省孔子学会名誉　王恩来

在孔子的政治主张中，德治是最理想的境界。在孔子看来，“为政以德，譬如北辰，居其所而众星共之。”（《论语·为政》。下引《论语》只注篇名）孔子德治思想的核心是“仁”，而“礼”是“仁”的外化，即“人而不仁如礼何?”（《八佾》）所以，孔子便理所当然地将推行礼制视为治理国家的重要手段，即所谓“以礼让为国”（《里仁》）和“为国以礼”（《先进》）。为了推行德化和礼制，孔子曾将二者的作用与政令和刑罚做过比较：

子曰：“道之以政，齐之以刑，民免而无耻；道之以德，齐之以礼，有耻且格。”（《为政》）

用政令去引导，用刑罚去整治，民众虽可免于罪过，却没有廉耻之心；用道德去引导，用礼制去规范，则民众不仅有廉耻之心，而且会内心叹服。这一结论虽有夸大德治作用的偏向，但从治本的角度看，也不无道理。政令与刑罚虽有吓阻作用，但事实表明，仅此尚不能从根本上解决问题。起长久作用的，还是自律意识的增强和文明程度的提高。

有些学者根据孔子的这一比较说明，断言孔子轻视法治。政令、刑罚与道德、礼制相较孔子重视德化和礼制，是没有问题的；但由此认定孔子轻视乃至否定法治的作用，则是过度推论。

## 一、孔子所言之“刑”并不完全等同于今天所说的“法”，而且以严酷和针对平民为主要特征

刑罚在我国产生较早，如夏代的“禹刑”，商代的“汤刑”，西周的“九刑”，以及春秋时期一些诸侯国制定的“刑书”等。据考证，古代刑罚大多比较残酷，如破面涂黑的“墨刑”，削除鼻子的“劓刑”，断足的“刖刑”，男子去势、女子幽闭的“宫刑”、“蚕室刑”等。剥夺生命的刑罚也多种多样，如挖心、活埋、晒干以及烹、枭首、戮尸

等。对这些严刑峻法的负面作用，一些比较进步的政治家在当时即有比较清醒的认识，并提出了反对或修正的意见。如周初的统治者吸取殷商灭亡的教训，强调要“明德慎罚”。周穆王初年，大司寇吕侯有感于滥用刑罚、政乱民怨的现实，作《吕刑》，主张“明于刑之中”、“轻重诸罚有权”，即用刑适中，惩罚罪犯的轻重要灵活掌握，从轻、公正、慎用刑罚（详见《尚书·周书·吕刑》）。

明德慎罚的主张虽在周初即被提出，也取得一些实际效果，却并没有得到普遍、持久的施行。到春秋时期，因“礼崩乐坏”和诸侯争霸，一些诸侯国君和当政者维护统治的主要手段，就是军事与刑罚。譬如齐国，就因为断足的“刖刑”被滥用而致使鞋子滞销、假肢成为市场上的紧俏商品，即齐相晏婴谏景公时所言之“踊贵屦贱。”（《左传·昭公三年》）鲁哀公时执政上卿季康子，也曾想用杀戮的办法解决社会问题：

季康子问政于孔子曰：“如杀无道，以就有道，何如?”孔子对曰：“子为政，焉用杀？子欲善而民善矣。君子之德风，小人之德草，草上之风，必偃。”（《颜渊》）

孔子反对杀戮与刑罚，除来自其对德治作用的认识外，也是针对了当时滥施刑罚和以刑代德的实际。

还有一个值得注意的情况，即当时社会存在“礼不下庶人，刑不上大夫”（《礼记·曲礼上》）的规定或理念。所谓“刑不上大夫”，并非大夫犯法可不受任何追究，而是与平民的处理方式和结果不同。例如，“凡命夫命妇不躬坐狱讼，凡王之同族有罪不即市。”（《周礼·秋官·小司寇》）凡大夫以上的贵族及其妻子的违法犯罪，不用亲自参加诉讼活动，而由其属吏代理；王室中人被判处死刑，可以不像庶民那样被陈尸于市。更为重要的是，从夏代起，便有“赎刑”即缴纳罚金免除刑罚的规定，如《尚书·舜典》中的“金作赎刑”。春秋时期，齐国亦通过赎刑的办法扩充军备（《国语·齐语》）。赎刑虽不必特为贵族所设，但平民却很难有条件利用。这样一来，其严刑峻法的实施对象就主要是平民百姓。在这种情况下，孔子主张用“齐之以礼”的办法减少或减轻刑罚，也体现了对百姓的同情。

在崇尚武力征伐和视民众生命如草芥的时代，孔子从总体上反对杀戮，限用刑罚，这与他痛斥“俑殉”一样，更反映出对人的生命的珍视和人道主义情怀。我们已经看到，随着社会文明程度的提高，法治已不再依赖或体现于血腥的刑罚手段，死刑在许多国家亦被废除。以此来关照孔子重德礼而慎刑罚的主张，更能从中体会出其进步意义。

## 二、孔子虽将道德和礼制视为治本之策，但并没有否定政令与刑罚的作用

孔子认为：“善人为邦百年，亦可以胜残去杀矣。”（《子路》）就是说，要实现克服

残暴、免除虐杀的社会理想，需要有一个漫长的过程。在此过程中，对各种犯罪的刑罚就不可避免。据《左传·昭公十年》记载，郑国执政上卿子产在去世前嘱其儿子大叔说：“我死，子必为政。唯有德者能以宽服民，其次莫如猛。夫火烈，民望而畏之，故鲜死矣。水懦弱，民狎而玩之，则多死焉。故宽难。”大叔执政后，不忍心使用严厉的手段而施行宽松政策，结果盗贼蜂起。大叔后悔没有听从子产的教诲，兴兵剿盗，从而减少了贼患。对此，孔子大为赞赏：

仲尼曰：“善哉！政宽则民慢，慢则纠之以猛。猛则民残，残则施之以宽。宽以济猛，猛以济宽，政是以和。”

孔子称许宽猛相济的为政方略，认为这样可实现政事协和。这就明确地表明了其对德政与刑罚关系的认识。

孔子对子产为政方略的认同，也体现在其自己的诸多论述中。

孔子曰：“圣人之治化也，必刑政相参焉。太上以德教民，而以礼齐之。其次以政焉导民，以刑禁之，刑不刑也。化之弗变，导之弗从，伤义以败俗，于是乎用刑矣。”《孔子家语·刑政》

这是孔子在其学生仲弓请教政令与刑罚运用的问题时给出的答案。孔子认为，圣人治理教化民众，必须是刑罚和政令相互配合使用。最好的办法是用道德来教化民众，并用礼来统一思想。其次是用政令来教导民众，用刑罚来禁止他们。用刑罚的目的是为了不用刑罚。对经过教化还不改变，经过教导还不听从，损害义理又败坏风俗的人，于是就要使用刑罚。比较可见，孔子此论，与对子产父子的评价是一致的。在《孔子家语·执辔》中，还有孔子把治国比喻为驾车，把德、法比喻为驾车的缰绳和鞭子的记录：“夫德法者，御民之具，犹御马之有御勒也。君者，人也；吏者，辔也；刑者，策也。夫人君之政，执其辔策而已。”“执其辔策”，就是德法并用。类似的认识，还见之于《孔从子·刑论》，可用来参阅。孔子在评价周武王时也说过：“武王正其身以正其国，正其国以正天下，伐无道，刑有罪，一动而天下正，其事正矣！”（《说苑·君道》）可见，对公正得当的刑罚，孔子也是主张使用的，只是反对只用刑罚一种手段和滥施刑罚而已。

据上海博物馆藏战国楚竹书中记载，在鲁国遭遇旱灾、鲁哀公向孔子讨教应对之策时，孔子以加强刑、德之治答之，并告诫鲁哀公不要沿用民间的做法举行大旱之祭。原文如下：

鲁邦大旱，哀公谓孔子：“子不为我图之?”孔子答曰：“邦大旱，毋乃失诸刑与德乎?”“唯之何在?”孔子曰：“庶民知说之事，视也，不知刑与德。女毋薆珪璧　帛于山川，政刑与。”（见马承源主编《上海博物馆藏战国楚竹书（二）》，上海古籍出版社2002年，第204—206页）

据专家测定，上博楚简系战国晚期文物，其抄写的文章当来自孔门后学。这一新材料的发现，对《孔子家语》和《孔从子》孔子相关论述的真实性，提供了有力的佐证。起码可以说明，这些记录是有史料来源的。

对礼乐与刑罚的关系，孔子在与子路讨论“正名”的问题时，有直接的推演：

名不正，则言不顺；言不顺，则事不成；事不成，则礼乐不兴；礼乐不兴，则刑罚不中；刑罚不中，则民无所措手足。（《子路》）

在孔子看来，礼乐是刑罚的基础，如果礼乐得不到实施，社会风气不好，刑罚就不会得当；刑罚不得当，民众就无所适从。反过来说，礼乐得到实施，法官公正执法，刑罚就会得当；刑罚得当，民众就知道该如何行事了。孔子没有否定刑罚的作用，由此亦可看出。

不仅如此，孔子还把刑罚与道德同样视为君子应该怀有或关注的东西，即“君子怀德，小人怀土；君子怀刑，小人怀惠。”（《里仁》）君子既关心道德，也关心刑罚，就是“刑政相参”的“圣人治化”。其中的“怀刑”不仅是为政之需，也有以刑自律的意义，是道德自觉基础上的遵守法律的自觉。

## 三、“礼”在中国古代具有习惯法的性质，有一定的外在强制作用

《礼记·曲礼上》在阐述礼的作用时，有“分争辨讼，非礼不决”和“班朝治军，莅官行法，非礼威严不行”的结论，说明礼已被运用到司法领域，具有一定的强制性。《管子·枢言》指出：“法出于礼。”此认识也是有事实根据的。在《周礼·秋官·司寇》中，有对大司寇以下数十官职在刑罚和狱讼中的分工、标准、程序等明确规定，其精细程度超乎今天的想象。在《礼记·王制》中，也有关于司寇听讼应遵循的原则，案件从审理到定案应履行的程序等规定，相当于法律文献。这些情况表明，中国古代的礼制并不完全是现代意义上的德治，而是包括部分制度、刑罚和法律精神在内的德治与法治融合的形态，所以才具有一定的强制性。孔子讲“道之以德，齐之以礼”，即用道德去引导，用礼仪去规范和整顿，就言明了二者的联系和区别。“道之以德”是通过道德教化增强人的自律意识，“齐之以礼”是通过礼法规范人的行为，是自律与他律的结合。

荀子极重视礼，也是看到了这一点：“《礼》者，法之大分，群类之纲纪也，故学至乎《礼》而止矣。”（《荀子·劝学》）荀子认为，《礼》是法制的前提，是各种条例的纲要，所以学习到《礼》才终止。礼既然是法制的前提，那么，学礼就是为了用法。对此，荀子也有明确的解说：“好法而行，士也；笃志而体，君子也；齐明而不竭，圣人也。人无法则伥伥然，有法而去其义则渠渠然，依乎法而又深其类，然后温温然。”

(《修身》) 人无法度就会不知所措；有法度而不懂它的意义，就会窘迫不安，遵循法度并能依法类推，就会轻松自如。荀子此论，揭示了学礼用法的作用和不同境界。荀子还总结说："礼之所以正国也，譬之犹衡之于轻重也，犹绳墨之于曲直也，犹规矩之于方圆也，正错之而人莫之能诬也。"荀子重礼，礼与法又有如此紧密的联系，这也就不难理解，荀子的两个学生李斯和韩非，何以能够成为法家代表人物了。

传统礼制形态向后发展，便一分为三，一部分成为政治制度，如官职的设置和官员的考察任用等；一部分成为法律和法规，如刑罚和狱讼；一部分成为反映道德意识的礼仪、规范或公序良俗，这是分化之后礼的主体。

从传统礼制的结构看，尽管其具体内容和形式需要随着社会发展、时代变迁而不断进行调整和改革，但作为道德规范的具体化，作为反映社会成员之间、社会成员与社会组织之间关系的准则，礼一旦形成并取得习惯法的地位，就具有一定的外在强制作用，要求社会成员共同遵守，否则就无法发挥"经国家，定社稷，序民人"的作用。《左传·昭公二十年》载有一个事例和孔子的评论，可证明这一点：

十二月，齐侯田于沛，招虞人以弓，不进。公使执之，辞曰："昔我先君之田也，旃以招大夫，弓以招士，皮冠以招虞人。臣不见皮冠，故不敢进。"乃舍之。仲尼曰："守道不如守官，君子韪之。"

按照当时的礼法和官制，国君狩猎时，用旗帜召唤大夫，用弓召唤士，用皮冠召唤猎场的管理人员。而齐侯在沛泽打猎时，用弓召唤管理人员，管理人员不敢应召，齐侯便派人逮捕了他。当管理人员依礼说明原因后，齐侯释放了他。孔子对此评论说："遵守官道不如遵守官制，君子认为是对的。"臣下听从君主召唤，是为官之道；但不依成规礼法召唤则不至，是遵守礼制的表现。孔子赞成后者，说明在"非礼勿"的问题上，对君主也是一样的。如果君主凭借自己的地位和权势不依礼行事，恣意妄为，就会使人无所适从，就会乱制，使礼法成为一纸空文。有人将孔子的"非礼勿"视为僵化、教条、守旧的主张，是因为没有真正领会这一主张所具有的规则和制度意义。无论道德、礼制还是法律，如果其中某些内容和要求是错误的、不合时宜的，就应该及时修正、完善或废止，如我们曾经有过的"投机倒把罪"和"反革命罪"。但要求人们守德、守礼、守法，不能缺德、无礼、违法，则没有什么错误。任何国家和民族，若不守规矩、不讲规则，就不能济身世界先进民族之林。

## 四、孔子本人有过直接的司法实践，并提出了一些进步的司法理念

《史记·孔子世家》记载，孔子在鲁定公十年初"由中都宰为司空，由司空为大司寇"，并"由大司寇行摄相事"。"司寇"是掌管刑罚狱讼和纠察的官职，后世以大司寇

为刑部尚书的别称。如果孔子轻视乃至抵制法治，就不会担当此任；如果孔子在这一职务上没有取得较好业绩，也不会被再次提升。

孔子不仅担任过审理诉讼的官职，而且提出并运用了一些进步的司法理念。

（一）“使无讼”的司法愿景

孔子曾自述说：“听讼，吾犹人也。必也使无讼乎！”（《颜渊》）“听讼”即审理诉讼。孔子自认其“听讼”的水平与其他法官差不多，不同之处在于，孔子希望使诉讼案件完全消失。有人认为，孔子的“使无讼”是反对运用法律手段解决纠纷，是“君子不入公庭”的“非讼”观念的滥觞。实际上，孔子所说的“使无讼”，表达的是通过有效治理不再有诉讼事件发生的美好憧憬，是对执法目的的理解。没有案件发生，当然也就可以“无讼”了。这种愿望虽过于理想化，却并非轻视司法的作用。《汉书·刑法志》引孔子的话说：“古之知法者能省刑，本也。今之知法者不失有罪，末矣。”古时执法的人能让犯罪的减少，这是抓住了根本。如今执法的人不放过有罪的，这是抓住了末节。在仲弓向孔子请教古今刑罚教化的问题时，孔子以同样的认识回答说：“古之刑省，今之刑繁。其为教，古有礼然后有刑，是以刑省；今无礼以教而齐之以刑，刑是以繁。”（《孔从子·刑论》）这些认识，可视为“使无讼”的解说，与前引之《论语·为政》中孔子对政、刑与德、礼关系的认识，是完全一致的。

（二）“不可失平”的司法理念

鲁昭公十四年，晋国的邢侯和雍子两位大夫争夺鄐（chù）地，韩宣子令晋大夫叔向的儿子叔鱼判处这一积案。罪过本来在于雍子，但由于雍子进献他的女儿给叔鱼做妻子，叔鱼便判邢侯有罪。邢侯发怒，在朝廷上杀了叔鱼和雍子。韩宣子向叔向询问，叔向没有隐瞒其子叔鱼的罪过，指责其“鬻狱”即出卖法律，认为与雍子的“知其罪而赂”和邢侯的“专杀”同罪，于是杀掉邢侯，并将叔鱼的尸体与雍子、邢侯一同在市上示众。对此，孔子给予了很高评价：

仲尼曰：“叔向，古之遗直也。治国制刑，不隐于亲，三数叔鱼之恶，不为末减。曰义也夫，可谓直矣。”（《左传·昭公十四年》）

孔子称赞叔向有古代流传下来的正直作风，原因是他将制度刑法视为治国之要，对于亲人也不包庇隐蔽，不替叔鱼减轻罪名。孔子认为这样做合乎道义，可谓正直。孔子接下来对此案评论说：“邢侯之狱，言其贪也，以正刑书，晋为不颇。”邢侯这起案件，是由贪婪引起的。按《刑书》公正处理，体现了晋国的不偏颇。这就表明，孔子主张的秉公严格执法，也包括“刑上大夫”；“刑不上大夫”的规定，起码在春秋时期的晋国已被突破，并得到孔子的赞赏。与这种认识一致，孔子提出了司法公正的理念：“概者，平量者也；吏者，平法者也。治国者，不可失平也。”（《韩非子·外储说左下》）“概”是量粮时刮平“斗”一类容器的器具，孔子以“概”喻“吏”，认为

“概”是使计量公正的，“吏”是使法令公正的，治理国家的人不能失去这种公正。以称量粮食的统一尺度喻司法公正，把司法公正视为官员的责任和职业操守，比喻之恰切，认识之深刻，是前无古人的，具有超越时空的普适价值。

（三）“置法以民”的立法原则

《礼记·表记》记孔子言曰：“无欲而好仁者，无畏而恶不仁者，天下一人而已矣。是故议道自己，而置法以民。”在孔子看来，无私欲而爱好仁德者，和无所畏惧而憎恶不仁者，天下就那么个把人而已，因此，就不能将其作为道德规范和法律制定的普遍标准。正确的做法是，议论道德应从自己出发，即推己及人；而设置法律要着眼于民众，即根据多数人的实际情况。既不能用少数人才能达到的标准去要求和责罚多数人，也不能只维护少数人的权益而置多数人的利益于不顾，如“只许州官放火，不许百姓点灯”，这是维护法律的公平正义，特别是为多数人服务并被多数人接受的重要立法原则，可防止法律成为统治阶层和立法者的私器。

（四）“狱必三讯”的司法程序

在《孔子家语》中，记有孔子“大司寇正刑明辟以察狱，狱必三讯焉”的论说。对其中的“三讯”，王肃注为“一曰讯群臣，二曰讯群吏，三曰讯万民。”这大概是受了孟子“左右皆曰可杀，勿听；诸大夫皆曰可杀，勿听；国人皆曰可杀，然后察之，见可杀焉，然后杀之”（《孟子·梁惠王下》）的影响。其实，孟子所言之听取意见的主体是国君，而大司寇位列三卿之下，是没有“讯群臣”资格的。此外，司寇审理断案，若不是国家重犯，“讯万民”亦大可不必，也难以做到。孔子所说的“三讯”，当为多次问讯审理或听取意见之意，即《礼记·王制》中所说的“司寇正刑明辟，以听狱讼，必三刺。有旨而无简，不听。附从轻，赦从重。”“三刺”就是三番审理的意思，这从孔子接下来的阐释中亦可看出：

大司寇正刑明辟以察狱，狱必三讯焉。有指无简，则不听也；附从轻，赦从重；疑狱则泛与众共之，疑则赦之，皆以小大之比成也。（《孔子家语·刑政》）

孔子对“三讯”的解释，一是有指证而核实不了犯罪事实的，就不治罪；二是量刑可重可轻的，就从轻，赦免时则以重刑为先；三是对有疑点仍不能消除，就赦免他。从核实证据、量刑到合议，从重证据、把握量刑尺度到“疑罪从无”，这些程序设计和认识主张，是足以与当代法制理念接轨的。

孔子审理案件的具体怀形，也有史料记载：

孔子为鲁司寇，断狱讼，皆进众议者而问之曰：“子以为奚若？某以为何若？”皆曰云云。如是，然后夫子曰：“当从某子几是。”（《孔子家语·好生》）

孔子在审理案件时，均广泛听取陪审人员的意见，然后择善而从。这样做的目的，当然是为了使裁决公正、准确。用孔子自己的话说，即“毋杀无辜，毋释罪人，则民不惑。”（《说苑·政理》）这是历史上较早出现的防止冤假错案的主张，也可能是陪审制度的最早记录。《史记·孔子世家》亦说：“孔子在位听讼，文辞可与人共者，弗独有也。”孔子任鲁司寇审理诉讼案件时，文辞上有可与别人商量的时候，他从不独自决断。这是民主意识在司法领域的最早体现。

（五）“先教后诛”的司法主张

孔子认为：“不教而杀谓之虐。”（《尧曰》）不经过教育就横加杀戮，叫作暴虐。这是孔子指认的四种恶政之一。先教育，不遵从然后用刑，教育的内容当然就是刑法。这是我国历史上较早出现的普法主张。对此，孔子有更为具体的论述：

孔子为鲁司寇，有父子讼者，孔子拘之，三月不别，其父请止，孔子舍之。季孙闻之不说，曰：“是老也欺予。语予曰：为国家必以孝。今杀一人以戮不孝，又舍之。”冉子以告。孔子慨然叹曰：“呜呼！上失之，下杀之，其可乎？不教其民而听其狱，杀不辜也。三军大败，不可斩也；狱犴不治，不可刑也；罪不在民故也。嫚令谨诛，贼也。今生也有时，敛也无时，暴也。不教而责成功，虐也。已此三者，然后刑可即也。《书》曰：‘义刑义杀，勿庸以即，予维曰：未有顺事。’言先教也。故先王既陈之以道，上先服之，若不可，尚贤以綦之，若不可，废不能以单之，綦三年，而百姓往矣。邪民不从，然后俟之以刑，则民知罪矣。”（《荀子·宥坐》）

孔子担任鲁国司寇时，有父子二人打官司，被孔子拘留，三个月不判决。作父亲的请求停止打官司，孔子释放了他们。季孙听到后不高兴，认为应该杀其子以惩罚不孝。孔子听说后讲了不杀的理由，基中便有“不教育百姓而治罪，等于滥杀无辜”一条。他还引用《尚书·康诰》中的话，说明“先教”的重要。“先教”之后，需要自上而下服从。如果有奸邪的人不服从，再用刑罚来对待他们，百姓就懂得什么是犯罪了。通过“教而后刑”使民“知罪”，从而免于刑罚，是对“教而后诛”目的的诠释。

讨论至此，就不能不涉及孔子“反对晋铸刑鼎”的问题。

《左传·昭公二十九年》中，有孔子反对晋铸刑鼎的记载：

“冬，晋赵鞅、荀寅帅师城汝滨，遂赋晋国一鼓铁，以铸刑鼎，著范宣子所为刑书焉。仲尼曰：‘晋其亡乎，失其度矣。夫晋国将守唐叔之所受法度，以经纬其民，卿大夫以序守之，民是以能尊其贵，贵是以能守其业，贵贱不愆，所谓度也。文公是以作执秩之官，为被庐之法，以为盟主。今弃是度也而为刑鼎，民在鼎矣，何以尊贵？贵何业之守？贵贱无序，何以为国？且夫宣子之刑，夷之蒐（搜）也，晋国之乱制也，若之何以为法？’蔡史墨曰，‘范氏，中行氏，其亡乎，中行寅为下卿，而干上令，擅作刑器，以为国法，是法奸也。又加范氏焉，易之，亡也。其及赵氏，赵孟与焉。然不得已，若德可以免。’”

此记录虽被经常使用，并成为一些人评判孔子法治思想的重要论据，但在笔者看来，从史实到内容，均比较可疑。

其一，“范宣子所为刑书”一事，不仅《左传》中此前没有记载，《史记·晋世家》等史书中亦不得见。晋国的法令，是晋襄公时执政上卿赵宣子（赵盾）制定的：

六年春，晋蒐于夷，舍二军。使狐射姑将中军，赵盾佐之。阳处父至自温，改蒐于董，易中军。阳子，成季之属也，故党于赵氏，且谓赵盾能，曰：“使能，国之利也。”是以上之。宣子于是乎始为国政，制事典，正法罪，辟狱刑，董逋逃，由质要，治旧洿，本秩礼，续常职，出滞淹。即成，以授大傅阳子与大师贾佗，使行诸晋国，以为常法。（《左传·文公六年》）

赵宣子是晋卿赵衰之子，其执掌国政，是从鲁文公六年晋国在夷地阅兵、经赵衰原来的属下阳处父举荐开始的。赵宣子上任后所采取的重要举措，就是制定规章，修正刑法，清理诉讼，督察逃犯，使用契约，清除积弊，恢复礼制秩序和官职，举用屈居下位的人才等。政令法规制定完成后，交给太傅阳处父和太师贾佗，让他们在晋国推行，作为经常的法律。既然是在全国推行的“常法”，就意味着臣民均应遵守，也就有公开的文本——无论刻在竹简上还是铸在鼎上。若是，则晋国公布成文法，不仅远在昭公二十九年“铸刑鼎”前，比“郑人铸刑书”还要早六十多年。在“刑鼎说”中，有“夫宣子之刑，夷之蒐也”句，即宣子的刑书，是在夷地检阅时制定的。但查阅相关史料，并无范宣子此行此作的记录，所能看到的，便是赵宣子在夷地阅兵后执政并“制事典，正法罪”一事。由此可以推测，即使存在晋铸刑鼎一事，其所著刑书也当为赵宣子所制作而非范宣子。更值得注意的是，“刑鼎说”中所言之铸鼎者之一的赵鞅是赵宣子的侄孙，昭公二十九年时，与范宣子之子范献子（士鞅）同为晋国下卿，执政上卿是有恩于赵家的韩氏。且不说范献子的儿子范吉射在赵鞅执政后被赵鞅所灭的后话，即使在当时的背景下，赵鞅也不可能舍弃其先祖制定的刑法而将范宣子的刑书铸在鼎上，更何况是否有范氏刑书还是个疑问。

其二，对赵盾（赵宣子）的作为，孔子是极赞赏的。据《左传·宣公二年》记载，在赵盾推行“常法”十八年后，因“晋灵公不君”（不行君道）而“宣子骤谏”，晋灵公想借请赵盾进宫饮酒之时将其杀掉，在实施的过程中，赵盾在别人的帮助下幸免于难并准备逃往国外。在尚未走出晋国山界时，赵盾听说晋灵公被自己的同族赵穿杀掉，就回来了，于是发生了预想不到的事情：

“乙丑，赵穿攻灵公于桃园。宣子未出山而复。大史书曰：‘赵盾弑其君。’以示于朝。宣子曰：‘不然。’对曰：‘子为正卿，亡不越竟，反不讨贼，非子而谁？’宣子曰：‘乌呼，“我之怀矣，自诒伊戚”；其我之谓矣！’孔子曰：‘董狐，古之良史也，书法不隐。赵宣子，古之良大夫也，为法受恶。惜也，越竟乃免。’”

赵穿将晋灵公杀掉，史官董狐因赵盾当时尚未出国境，回来后又没有讨伐赵穿，便以“赵盾杀掉了他的国君”记录在案并公之于朝廷。这种认定虽不够公平，却符合当时史官的记事原则，因而孔子称赞董狐为“古之良史”即古代的一位好史官。但是，对晋灵公这样的无道之君被杀，就像武王伐纣一样，孔子显然并没有反对，故在称赞董狐的同时，称许赵盾为“古之良大夫”，对其因为史官的记事原则背负了弑君的恶名而感到惋惜。孔子对赵盾的赞赏，不可能仅仅因为他“为法受恶”这一件事，必定是根据了他此前推行常法十八年取得的政绩和作为。如前所述，文公六年赵宣子所制定的法典，也是公开的成文法。倘若孔子反对公布成文法，就不会对赵盾给予如此高的评价。

其三，在春秋时期，公布成文法并非晋国一家。在赵宣子之后，公元前536年（赵宣子制常法85年后，“晋铸刑鼎”二十三年前），子产将刑法条文铸在铁鼎上，即所谓“郑人铸刑书”（《左传·昭公六年》），被视为我国历史上首次把法律刻在器物上公布于众的著名事件。实践证明，子产治郑是很成功的，得到百姓的拥护。对子产铸刑书一事，孔子不仅没有任何非议，而且对子产的执政理念极为赞赏：

子谓子产，“有君子之道四焉：其行己也恭，其事上也敬，其养民也惠，其使民也义。”（《公冶长》）

孔子对子产的认识和肯定，是颇为全面的。在得知子产去世的消息后，孔子流着眼泪表达了惋惜和敬意（《左传·昭公二十年》）。孔子既然对郑人“铸刑书”毫无反感，怎么能反对晋“铸刑鼎”并预言其会因此而败亡呢？

其四，“刑鼎说”中所记“仲尼曰”的内容，与孔子的一贯主张亦不相投合。从文中所记看，“仲尼”之所以反对晋铸刑鼎，主要原因是有了刑鼎之后，民众都能看到鼎上的条文，就会按条文规定行事而不尊重贵族了，这样就打破了“贵贱不愆”即贵贱不变之序，也就无法治理国家了。这显然并非孔子的思想。我们知道，孔子是我国历史上最早提出人性相近、差距由后天决定这一带有人生而平等认知倾向的思想家，并以此为根据，提出了“有教无类”（不分出身贵贱一律给予教育）和“从先进”（优先选用先学习礼乐后做官的没有贵族身份的“野人”）的主张。他不仅把“天下为家”的世卿世禄看作“大道既隐”的结果（见《礼记·礼运》），而且盛赞泰伯的“三以天下让”（《泰伯》），主张“尊贤为大”（《中庸》），甚至认为其出身卑微的弟子冉雍可以当面南之君（《雍也》），直接表明了对“贵贱不愆”的反对。孔子主张“治国制刑，不隐于亲”，指向便是握有刑罚权力的统治阶层而非平民百姓。他赞赏叔向“三数叔鱼之恶”并将自己儿子与另外两位大夫的尸体一起示众，也表明其并无担心百姓因此而不“尊贵”的意念。孔子主张公正执法，认为“刑罚不中则民无所措手足”，亦是反对将“刑罚”的“国器”作为“私器”滥用而惑乱民众，所以才反对“不教而杀”，并将其视为四种恶政之一。这与铸刑书或刑鼎的目的是一致的。孔子认为,“上有制度,则民知所止。民知所止则不犯,故虽有奸邪贼盗靡法妄行之狱,而无陷刑之民。”(《孔子家语·五刑解》)孔子既然如此坚持这些主张,怎能反对使民知罪守法的“刑鼎”呢?

综上,我认为,《左传》中关于孔子反对晋铸刑鼎的记载,是值得怀疑的。或许有人在当时说了这样一段话,但在我看来,可以肯定并非孔子。在此聊备一说,待方家考察。

# 先秦儒家"德政"与"礼治"思想对当今建立法治国家的意义

德国杜伊斯堡·埃森大学　杜　仑

## 一、为什么最好说"德政"，而不是"德治"

首先，笔者想澄清一个概念的问题。学者在谈到孔子政治思想的时候，往往用"德治"的概念。这个概念也常常和可以翻译成 rule of law 的"法治"思想联系在一起讨论。比如梁晓杰写道："德治就是以道德作为立国之本的政治，法治就是以法律作为立国之本的政治"。[①] 笔者认为，如果认真分析孔子政治的思想，那么，用"德政"的概念更合适。首先，先秦儒家对"德"的理解与西周"敬德保民"和"以德配天"中的"德"相距不远。虽然其宗教意义弱化，但其基本意义仍是今天所说"美德"或者"德性"，而不是"道德"。翻译成英语，是 virtue，而不是 morality。明确而言，先秦儒家在政治上讲"德"，主要强调一种能力，即道德水平。所以，"德"不太可能是梁晓杰上面所说的作为"作为立国之本"的标准。进而言之，"德"不是外在于行为者（包括执政者）的规范，不像"法"或者"礼"那样，从外向内对人施以外律性的约束作用。其二，"政"的含义是政治权力的运用，包含政策和政令的实施。从这个角度说，"德政"的意思是，执政者必须通过修身提高自身的道德水平（也即美德），以身作则，并以此感化老百姓，使之服从自己，贯彻执行自己的政策。我们可以把"德政"用英文译成 to govern by the virtue 或者 to govern by power of the virtue。

孔子的"德政"思想，集中体现在"为政以德"和"道之以德"两句话上。先谈"为政以德"。孔子的全句是"为政以德，譬如北辰，居其所而众星共之。"（《论语·为政》）。这句话强调了执政者本人的"道德能力"在政治治理中重要性。首先，执政者本人必须具有道德水平，这是任何统治的前提。这不仅和儒家政治思想"人人向善"

---

① 梁晓杰：《德法之辩——现代德法次序的哲学研究》，上海：上海人民出版社，2007 年，第 31 页。

的统治目标一脉相承，也符合“内圣外王”的精神。只有执政者本人具有道德水平，才能感化老百姓。而感化的前提是执政者起到榜样作用。孔子说：“其身正，不令则行；其身不正，虽令不从。”（《论语・子路》）。当季康子向孔子询问“执政”的问题时，他回答道：“政者，正也。子帅以正，孰敢不正？”（《论语・颜渊》）。这不仅间接地批评了季康子，也强调了中国人当时对“执政”的一般理解，即“政者，正也”，执政就意味着“端正执政者自己和老百姓的行为”。孔子对季康子的话，今天说来，就是“你自己在端正行为方面起到了带头作用，还发愁老百姓不端正自己的行为吗？”

当鲁哀公向孔子请教政治问题，孔子也谈了类似的观点。在《孔子家语》有下面一段对话。“孔子侍坐于哀公。公问曰：‘敢问人道孰为大？’孔子愀然作色而对曰：‘君及此言也，百姓之惠也，固臣敢无辞而对。人道，政为大。夫政者，正也。君为正，则百姓从而正矣。君之所为，百姓之所从。君不为正，百姓何所从乎！’”（《孔子家语・大婚解第四》）

再讲“道之以德”。这句话出自“道之以政，齐之以刑，民免而无耻；道之以德，齐之以礼，有耻且格。”（《论语・为政》）我们虽然可以把“道之以德”和《礼记・缁衣》中的“教之以德”相联系，把“德”解释为社会所公认的“美德”或者“道德”，[①] 由此把这句话解释为执政者“以道德作为立国之本”，以道德作为“行为标准”引导老百姓，而不是把“德”解释为“为政以德”中的执政者的“道德力量”。尽管如此，“德政”的思想依然跃然纸上。朱熹解释说：“道，犹引导，为先之也。”[②]也就是说，这句话仍然包含了“德政”思想，强调执政者首先要具备道德水平，以身作则，给老百姓起榜样作用，在“己正”基础之上，达到对老百姓“正人”的效果。在同样的意义上，孟子说：“君仁莫不仁，君义莫不义，君正莫不正；一正君而国定矣。”（《孟子・离娄上》）我们看到，他不仅直言“君正莫不正”，更是说，执政者若是行为端正，会直接对国家的治理产生正能量。孟子的“仁政”和“王道”思想正是体现了这一“德政”精神。他说：“以力假仁者霸，霸必有大国；以德行仁者王，王不待大。汤以七十里，文王以百里。以力服人者，非心服也，力不赡也；以德服人者，中心悦而诚服也，如七十子之服孔子也。”（《孟子・公孙丑上》）。

这里，再简单分析一下“有耻且格”的含义。这是讲“德政”所要达到的目的和效果。即不是让老百姓仅仅表面上服从，而是让之产生羞耻感，并由此而“行为端

---

① 参阅刘宝楠《论语正义》，北京：中华书局，第 41 页。

② 朱熹《四书章句集注》，北京：中华书局，第 54 页。李泽厚把“道之以德”译成“用德行来管理、领导”。参阅李泽厚：《论语今读》，北京：三联书店，2004 年，第 50 页。

正”[①] 和“出自内心的归服”。把“格”解释为“出自内心归服”大概是参考了《礼记·缁衣》中孔子所说的类似的话：“夫民，教之以德，齐之以礼，则民有格心；教之以政，齐之以刑，则民有遁心。”孙希旦把“遁心”解释为做坏事不知羞耻，反而逃避刑罚；与之相反，他把“格”解释为“向善”。他说：“格，至也，为至于善也。”[②] 笔者认为，“羞耻感”是培养和树立道德观念的“心理”基础。要培养老百姓道德观念，关键在于让他们产生做了坏事和不道德的事而感到羞耻。这种“羞耻感”和“心不安”的心理类似。笔者可以举《论语》的一个例子来说明。宰我认为守孝三年时间太长，孔子生气地说：“女安，则为之！夫君子之居丧，食旨不甘，闻乐不乐，居处不安，故不为也。今女安，则为之！”宰我走后，孔子说他“不仁”。（“予之不仁也！”《论语·阳货》）总之，“德政”的教化是为了让道德观念深入人心。所以，孟子强调“善教”的作用：“仁言不如仁声之入人深也，善政不如善教之得民也。善政，民畏之；善教，民爱之。善政得民财，善教得民心。”（《孟子·尽心上》）

无论怎样，“德政”的关键是以身作则。执政者首先得自己内化美德，自觉地做符合道德之事，从而起到“上行下效”的榜样作用。上面引了《礼记·缁衣》中孔子“夫民，教之以德”这句话。孔子继续说：“故君民者，子以爱之，则民亲之；信以结之，则民不倍；恭以莅之，则民有孙心。”。同时，他更明确地说：“下之事上也，不从其所令，从其所行。上好是物，下必有甚者矣。故上之所好恶，不可不慎也，是民之表也。”

虽然我们强调执政者必需“以身作则”，首先得自己具备美德，才有道德感召力。但从逻辑上来看，只有社会承认某些行为的道德性，这些成为“美德”，才会有效力；执政者才会有基于这些美德的“其身正，不令则行”的道德感召力。换言之，虽然我们强调“德政”，却并不是说，执政者个人从上到下单方面地规定“美德”的内容。可以想象，在古代中国，不论是儒家思想道德的核心价值“仁”，还是包括具体目类的所有道德价值，都是在社会成员，特别是社会上层在相互交往中约定俗成，并慢慢渗透到的全社会的。我们从《左传》中可以看到一些“德”的具体内容。除了“仁”[③] 以外，还有“义”[④]、“孝”、“敬”、“忠”、“信”[⑤] 等等。

---

① 即把“格”解释为“正”。参阅刘宝楠《论语正义》，北京：中华书局，第41页。

② 孙希旦：《礼记集解》，北京：中华书局，第1323页。

③ 见《僖公十四年》：庆郑曰：“背施无亲，幸灾不仁，贪爱不祥，怒邻不义。四德皆失，何以守国?”、《襄公九年》：“固在下位而有不仁，不可谓元。不靖国家，不可谓亨。作而害身，不可谓利。弃位而姣，不可谓贞。有四德者，《随》而无咎。”和《哀公七年》：“小所以事大，信也。大所以保小，仁也。背大国，不信。伐小国，不仁。民保于城，城保于德，失二德者，危，将焉保?”

④ 见《僖公十四年》，同上。

⑤ 见《文公十八年》：“孝敬忠信为吉德。”和《哀公七年》，同上。

## 二、人人践“礼”是“礼治”的基本含义

先秦儒家“礼治”的思想，学界一般认为来源于西周“宗法制”的实践。西周的礼乐制度是否真的像《周礼》和《仪礼》里描述的那么完备，而且有成文的东西，还不能百分之百的证明。但是，我们仍然能够从这些历史文献中找到西周统治者和先秦儒家在“礼治“方面的思想。《左传》说：“天子建国，诸侯立家，卿置侧室，大夫有贰宗，士有隶子弟，庶人、工、商，各有分亲，皆有等衰。”（《左传·桓公二年》）这段话也间接地描述了被称为西周礼乐制度的两个原则：“亲亲”和“尊尊”。《礼记·世子第八》里记载了孔子的话：“君之于世子也，亲则父也，尊则君也。有父之亲，有君之尊，然后兼天下而有之。”而《中庸》则引用孔子的话说：“仁者人也，亲亲為大；义者宜也，尊贤為大。亲亲之杀，尊贤之等，礼所生也。”

对儒家来说，“礼”的作用是规范和理顺[①]社会关系，使之虽有上下远近之分，却带有亲情，并形成有效的社会及政治运作机制。荀子说：“故先王案为之制礼仪以分之，是有贵贱之等，长幼之差，知愚、能不能之分，皆使人载其事而各得其宜，然后使穀禄多少厚薄之称，是夫群居和一之道也。”（《荀子·荣辱》）

因为“礼”是社会规范和理顺社会成员行为的外律标准，所以，一方面，“礼”有使社会成员社会化的社会整合的功能。孔子说的“约之以礼”（《论语·雍也》、《论语·颜渊》）、“不学礼，无以立”（《论语·季氏》）以及“不知礼，无以立也”（《论语·雍也》）就是这个意思。另一方面，对执政者来说，“礼”是治理国家的治国大纲。孔子在指明“为国以礼”（《论语·先进》）的同时，也解释说：“治国而无礼，譬犹瞽之无相，伥伥乎何所之?”（《孔子家语·论礼第二十七》）荀子也说：“为政不以礼，政不行也。”（《荀子·大略》）

当然，“礼”不仅仅是规范性的礼仪和制度，也包含价值，也即今天所说的“道德”（morality）或道德标准，所以，“礼”是规范和道德的综合体系。社会成员在实践“礼”的过程中会自然而然地内化包含在“礼”中的道德价值。所以，“礼治”，既是治理方法，通过礼来治理国家和整合社会，即孔子所说的“齐之以礼”，也是这种治理的结果。（《礼记·礼运第九》）中描写了称为“十义”的五种关系：“父慈、子孝、兄良、弟弟、夫义、妇听、长惠、幼顺、君仁、臣忠。”这句话概括地描述了“礼治”作为结果的基本内容。

当然，我们也可以认为，无论是“父慈、子孝”还是“君仁、臣忠”，这些内化了

① 孔子说：“夫礼者，理也。”（《孔子家语·论礼第二十七》）

道德价值的“礼”的实践告诉我们，人人都实践“礼”是“礼治”的基本含义。先从老百姓实践“礼”的方面看。西周统治层约定俗成的“礼”已经完全渗透到全社会，虽然我们不能完全肯定，以至我们可以说，老百姓已经有实践“礼”的事实。但是从孔子“齐之以礼”的政治要求看，执政者至少应该以“礼”为标准和准则来教化老百姓。达到“有耻且格”的目的。《礼记》里说：“故礼之教化也微，其止邪也于未形，使人日徙善远罪而不自知也。是以先王隆之也。”（《礼记·经解第二十六》）

再从执政者实践“礼”的方面看。《左传·隐公十一年》记载了君子称赞郑庄公做了符合“礼”的事。原文是：“郑庄公于是乎有礼。礼，经国家，定社稷，序民人，利后嗣者也。”不过，春秋时代，已经慢慢出现了“礼崩乐坏”的状况。《左传》中可以看到很多诸侯、甚至周王做了不符合“礼”的事。用当时的话来说，就是“非礼也”。这里，可以举两个周王本人违反“礼”而遭到批评的例子。第一个例子：“十五年春，天王使家父来求车，非礼也。诸侯不贡车、服，天子不私求财。”（《左传·桓公十五年》）。第二个例子：“十八年春，虢公、晋侯朝王，王飨醴，命之宥，皆赐玉五瑴，马三匹。非礼也。”（《左传·庄公十八年》）这里虽然只是一些小事，但是却反映了这样一个信息，即每个人都得实践“礼”，每个人都得扮演与之社会地位和社会关系相应的角色，处于这个等级制最高位置的周王也不能例外。作为天子的周王虽然在等级制的最上面，却不在制度之外，也即不高于“礼”。虽然等级制不平等，但在实践“礼”和遵守“礼”上，虽不能说“人人平等”，却可以说“人人一样”。这就是“礼治”的基本原则。

那么为什么社会成员会实践“礼”呢。或者说，“礼”为什么会对社会成员有约束力呢？可以设想，是因为人人都尊“礼”，把“礼”看的至关重要。也许是当时春秋时代“周礼”越来越不受到应有的重视，孔子反复强调执政者尊“礼”的重要性。他对鲁哀公说：“丘闻之，民之所以生者，礼为大。非礼则无以节事天地之神焉；非礼则无以辩君臣、上下、长幼之位焉；非礼则无以别男女、父子、兄弟、婚姻、亲族、疏数之交焉。是故君子此之为尊敬，然后以其所能教顺百姓，不废其会节。”（《孔子家语·问礼第六》）

至于为什么要尊“礼”。我想，第一，践“礼”本身就是一种日常生活的礼仪行为，且一开始与宗教仪式有关。第二，人人都应该遵“礼”大概是一种共识，是一个天经地义的事。《左传·昭公二十五年》记载了郑国子大叔引用子产的话说：“夫礼，天之经也，地之义也，民之行也。天地之经，而民实则之。”换句话说，尊“礼”是出于对天道的宗教信仰，尊“礼”本身就是一种价值。鲁国的季文子说：“礼以顺天，天之道也。”（《左传·文公第十五年》）

上面说过，儒家认为，过去的圣王非常重视“礼仪教化”的作用（“是以先王隆之也。”）。这里，儒家把从圣王尊天道的角度来看这个问题。我们可以用《礼记・礼运》中两句话来说明。其一，“夫礼，先王以承天之道，以治人之情，故失之者死，得之者生。”；其二，“是故夫礼，必本于天，殽于地，列于鬼神［…］。故圣人以礼示之，故天下国家可得而正也。”。①

再回到刚才提的第二个问题：“礼”为什么会对社会成员有约束力呢？我们说，“礼”对社会某个成员有约束力，不是说作为外在于人的“礼”本身能对人产生效力，而是说，社会成员对“礼”的一般认可，会对不遵“礼”的人形成一种实施惩罚的压力。我们说“礼”有外律的功能，并不是说“礼”本身有威力，而是说，人们承认它的权威。

也就是说，“礼”对人的效力产生于人对其权威性的承认。孟子说的“徒法不能以自行”（《孟子・离娄上》）同样适于“礼”。这时因为，人是否践“礼”最终取决于人自己。这里，执政者能否起到榜样作用，又是“礼”是否具有有效力的关键。明确而言，不论是“以礼治国”还是“礼治”，都意味着执政者首先实践“礼”。孔子说：“上好礼，则民莫敢不敬。”（《论语・子路》）、“上好礼，则民易使也。”（《论语・宪问》）反之，如果执政者不首先得实践“礼”，就会祸国殃民。他说：“如有不由礼而在位者，则以为殃。”（《孔子家语・礼运第三十二》）

## 三、“德政”和“礼治”相辅相成的关系以及当代意义

综上所述，“德政”的核心是执政者的道德榜样，以便人人可以向之看齐。“礼治”的基本含义是人人实践“礼”。如果说“德政”更侧重于讲统治者的自身道德修养，那么，“礼治”则更侧重于讲任何统治都得有一种外在的行为标准，以便人们能够在日常生活中知道做什么好，做什么不好。所以，“德政”和“礼治”不仅不相抵触，而且是相辅相成。

当今，先秦时代的很多“礼仪制度”已经失去了意义，而且被新的“礼仪制度”所取代。同时，当今开放社会中，社会成员更是与陌生人打交道。不须在日常生活的时时刻刻都践行的“法律”在调解社会成员关系中起着越来越重要的作用。

人们通常说，传统的“礼”强调了社会成员之间的等级关系。但是要知道，等级是任何社会都存在的事实。对于某些领域（比如行政部门、军队甚至医院），等级对政策和指令得以贯彻是必不可缺的。关键是，社会成员之间必须存在着公众领域中的人

---

① 当然，鉴于践“礼”往往对很多人来说，只是“走走形式”，孔子致力于发现和发展“礼”中所含的“仁义”等价值。这里且不讨论。

格尊严上的平等。社会地位高的人并不能在人格尊严上高人一等。[①]

换句话说，人人都得尊“礼”，任何人不能高于“礼”的“礼治”原则可以作为当代建立法治国家的资源。这种在“礼”面前，任何人都一样的原则，也许会促进社会建立“法律面前人人平等”的观念和共识。

当然，一般来说，在任何社会中，地位高的社会成员对地位低的社会成员自然而然地会起到榜样的作用，无论是正面的，还是负面的。所以，地位高的社会成员，特别是执政者在遵守“法律”方面，必须起到模范作用。这又回到了“德政”的问题。

一言以蔽之，“法治”能否实行，还得靠“德政”。关键是能让自觉遵守社会规则成为一种美德。同时，在当今现代社会中，道德标准的建立和改变不能只靠执政者从上到下的教化，更得依靠全社会成员的共同努力，互相教育，通过讨论形成道德的共识。

---

① 在任何社会，“人人平等”都不是实然，而是应然。关键是，能让“人人平等”的观念去减弱事实上不平等产生的负面作用。

# 由法返德：商鞅思想特点新论[①]

山东大学　曾振宇

商鞅在历史上是一位备受争议的人物。太史公称其为“天资刻薄人也”。[②] 司马贞《索隐》：“刻谓用刑深刻，薄谓弃仁义，不悃诚也。”[③]纪昀的评价与太史公如出一辙：“观于商鞅、韩非诸家，可以知刻薄寡恩之非。”[④] 与此同时，数千年来对商鞅同情、理解甚至赞赏的衡评也不绝如缕。韩非将商鞅在历史上的贡献高度评价为“此亦功之至厚者也”。[⑤] 在韩非心目中，商鞅就是“圣人”。[⑥] 韩非是历史上第一位、同时也是最后一位称颂商鞅为“圣人”者，这与历代儒家对商鞅的评价可谓有云泥之别。章太炎先生撰有《商鞅》一文，为商鞅申二千多年来不白之冤：“商鞅之中于谗诽也二千年，而今世为尤甚。其说以为自汉以降，抑夺民权，使人君纵恣者，皆商鞅法家之说为之倡。呜呼！是惑于淫说也甚矣。”[⑦]《商鞅》一文是章太炎为商鞅翻案的巨篇宏文，笔底波涛起伏，对于还商鞅以历史本来面目大有裨助。其后牟宗三先生又立场鲜明地指出：商鞅“不坏”。[⑧]“这样的法家是不坏的。商鞅是法家的典型。”[⑨] 法家是从申不害、韩非开始变坏的，其中缘由在于申不害的“术”与道家相结合，“法家也变坏了”。[⑩] 孰是孰非？或谠论，或诽语，其间必有当而不可易者。商鞅思想与行事是一面多棱镜，立场与视角的不同，必然导致商鞅这一历史人物影像重叠杂乱。笔者不揣简陋，力图在前

---

① 基金项目：本文为国家社科基金重点项目“中华文化元典基本概念研究”（项目批准号：12AZD082）和山东大学儒学院项目“中国思想史基本概念研究”阶段性成果之一。

② 司马迁：《史记》卷六十八《商君列传》，北京：中华书局，1959 年，第 2237 页。

③ 司马迁：《史记》卷六十八《商君列传》，北京：中华书局，1959 年，第 2237 页。

④ 纪昀总纂：《四库全书总目提要》卷 101“法家类”，石家庄：河北人民出版社，2000 年，第 2565 页。

⑤ 陈奇猷：《韩非子新校注》，上海：上海古籍出版社，2000 年，第 287 页。

⑥ 陈奇猷：《韩非子新校注》，上海：上海古籍出版社，2000 年，第 287 页。

⑦ 汤志钧编：《章太炎政论选集》上册，北京：中华书局，1977 年，第 68 页。

⑧ 牟宗三：《中国哲学十九讲》，长春：吉林出版集团有限责任公司，2010 年，第 56－59 页。

⑨ 牟宗三：《中国哲学十九讲》，长春：吉林出版集团有限责任公司，2010 年，第 56－59 页。

⑩ 牟宗三：《中国哲学十九讲》，长春：吉林出版集团有限责任公司，2010 年，第 56－59 页。

贤今哲研究基础上，对商鞅思想特点与性质，尤其是法与德内在关系，进行一些新的探讨。不当之处，敬祈指正！

## 一、“至德复立”：商鞅思想并非完全否定道德文化

在学术史上，有人批评商鞅废灭文化、遗弃道德。换言之，商鞅思想反儒家道德文化。譬如，贾谊指责商鞅“遗礼仪、弃仁恩，并心于进取，行之二岁，秦俗日败”。[①]《淮南子·泰族训》作者也认为商鞅偏重刑法而弃绝道德，“今重法而弃义，是贵其冠履而忘其头足也”。[②] 平心而论，学术史上前贤今哲对商鞅的针砭并非纯粹空穴来风，因为在《商君书》中可以发现大量的批判、抹杀甚至灭绝道德与文化的言辞：

“六虱：曰礼、乐；曰《诗》、《书》；曰修善、曰孝弟；曰诚信、曰贞廉；曰仁、义；曰非兵、曰羞战。国有十二者，上无使农战，必贫至削。十二者成群，此谓君之治不胜其臣，官之治不胜其民，此谓六虱胜其政也。”[③]

“辩慧，乱之赞也；礼乐，淫佚之徵也；慈仁，过之母也；任举，奸之鼠也。乱有赞则行，淫佚有徵则用，过有母则生，奸有鼠则不止。八者有群，民胜其政；国无八者，政胜其民。民胜其政，国弱；政胜其民，兵强。”[④]

商鞅把仁义诚信孝悌等等称之为“六虱”，这与韩非“五蠹”提法有异曲同工之处。但是，两者之间也有区别。韩非明确点明“儒者”是“五蠹”之一，是必须“灭”的。但是，在整部《商君书》中，从未提及“孔子”、“孔丘”，也没有“儒”或“儒者”概念。这说明商鞅及其后学所批评的对象并非单纯针对孔子学说，而是针对当时社会上普遍流行的、占主导地位的价值观与主流文化。《靳令》篇所说的“非兵”、“羞战”，也很难说专门针对儒家学派，因为墨家和公孙龙也有类似的思想。至于《靳令》篇的“贞廉”、《说民》篇的“任举”，儒家和墨家都有类似共同的主张。商鞅之所以猛烈抨击礼、乐、仁、义、诚、信、孝、悌主流文化与价值观，有其深刻的社会历史背景。细而论之，盛行于世的礼乐文化和价值观与秦国力行的治国方略相抵牾，甚至水火不容。当年商鞅四见秦孝公，先以“帝王之道”游说，结果“未中旨”。[⑤] 然后以

---

① 班固：《汉书》卷四十八《贾谊传》，北京：中华书局，1962 年，第 2244 页。

② 刘安著、高诱注：《淮南子·泰族训》，《诸子集成》第 7 册，北京：中华书局，2006 年，第 364 页。

③ 高亨：《商君书注译》，北京：清华大学出版社，2011 年，第 500 页。

④ 高亨：《商君书注译》，北京：清华大学出版社，2011 年，第 425 页。另《韩非子·二柄》有“任贤，则臣将乘于贤以劫其君”，与《商君书·说民》“任举”近似。

⑤ 司马迁：《史记》卷六十八《商君列传》，北京：中华书局，1959 年，第 2228 页。

“强国之术说君”，孝公才“大说之”。[①] 孝公追求的是“各及其身显名天下”，既然如此，不用极端手段就无法达到这一社会目标。所谓“极端手段”，就是将秦国变成一座军营，用什伍军事组织方式把全国人民组织起来。只用一种文化（“壹教”）来教育平民百姓，“壹教”的具体内容就是“以法为教”、“以吏为师。”顾颉刚先生认为，秦始皇借助刑罚的裁制，不允许人民读书；汉武帝通过利禄的诱引，只允许人民只读一种书。结果“始皇失败了，武帝成功了”。[②] 其实秦国与秦王朝并非不允许人民读书，而是只允许人民读一种书，即“以法为教”的“壹教”。凡是符合“利出一孔”治国大略的价值观与文化都是合法的；反之，都是非法的，都是“淫道”。“淫道必塞”，[③] 否则“学者成俗，则民舍农”[④]

但是，必须点明的是，将道德文化斥之为“六虱”、“淫道”，只是秦国特殊时期的特殊文化政策。在“当今争于气力”的时代，要想彻底扭转“诸侯卑秦，丑莫大焉”[⑤] 落后局面，将礼乐文明打入冷宫，是一时权宜之策。“故以王天下者并刑，力征诸侯者退德。”[⑥] 瞿同祖先生指出，法家“行刑重其轻”，只是“止奸息暴的手段，不得已才用之”。[⑦] 因此，对礼乐仁义诚信道德文化的批判并不是商鞅思想的全部内涵，更不是其思想本质：

首先，商鞅在内心深处从来就没有否认或弃绝道德文化。从商鞅知识背景与师承关系考察，他在入秦之前实际上是一个杂家。他的老师尸子思想的特点就是兼儒墨、合名法，无所不窥。尸子思想这一特点影响了青年时代商鞅的知识结构。入秦之初，商鞅之所以能分别以“帝道”、“王道”和“霸道”游说秦孝公，得益于他广博的知识来源。因此，我们不能断言商鞅弃绝道德文化，只是在何谓“德”问题上，与其他学派存在着较大分歧。“天下行之，至德复立。此吾以杀刑之反于德，而义合于暴也。”[⑧] 在商鞅看来，依法治国、社会安定、无邪恶之行，“大邪不生，细过不失”，就是最高的“德”。高亨先生指出，“法家反对儒家所谓仁义，但并不弃绝仁义，认为实行法治，社会安定，就是做到仁义了。”[⑨]

其次，法家之仁义观与儒家思想存在着相通相容之处。“所谓义者，为人臣忠，为

---

① 司马迁：《史记》卷六十八《商君列传》，北京：中华书局，1959 年，第 2228 页。
② 顾颉刚：《秦汉的方士与儒生》，上海：上海世纪出版集团，2005 年，第 36 页。
③ 高亨：《商君书注译》，北京：清华大学出版社，2011 年，第 587 页。。
④ 高亨：《商君书注译》，北京：清华大学出版社，2011 年，第 408 页。
⑤ 司马迁：《史记》卷五《秦本纪》，北京：中华书局，1959 年，第 202 页。
⑥ 高亨：《商君书注译》，北京：清华大学出版社，2011 年，第 555 页。
⑦ 瞿同祖：《中国法律与中国社会》，北京：中华书局，2003 年，第 328 页。
⑧ 高亨：《商君书注译》，北京：清华大学出版社，2011 年，第 462 页。
⑨ 高亨：《商君书注译》，北京：清华大学出版社，2011 年，第 504 页。

人子孝，少长有礼，男女有别。非其义也，饿不苟食，死不苟生。”① “义”概念内涵比较广博，实际上是指道德自觉与道德践行。在这一层面上，商鞅对“义”范畴的界定，与儒家有相近之处。孟子云：“大人者，言不必信，行不必果，惟义所在。”② 义是最高价值原则，所以程颐认为“人皆知趋利而避害，圣人则更不论利害，惟看义当为不当为，便是命在其中也”。③ 所谓“命在其中”，实际上是指义不是一种外在的行为规范，更重要的还在于，“义”内在于人心，是德性之心的外在显现。④ 义出于心，具有绝对性，所以称之为“命”。正因为如此，义又是人生之乐。冯友兰评论说：“对儒家来说，人为什么要行仁义，是不需要提出的问题，因为这是人的本性。”⑤人既是人，就应该扩充其本性。扩充其本性就是实现人之所以为人，这与外在利益毫无关系。可以说，这一阐释与孟子思想合若符契。也恰恰在这一文化意义上，儒家与法家显现出根本的分歧。在商鞅思想中，义是外在的行为规范（墨家其实也是如此），义属于“有以为”，而非“无以为”；在儒家思想中，义却是内在于人心之“命”，仁与义皆属于“无以为”。换言之，用孟子与告子的争辩术语来概括，“仁义内在”，而非“仁内义外”。⑥

其三，法家与儒家对仁义忠孝等伦理价值观性质与适用范围评价不一。“仁者能仁于仁，而不能使人仁。义者能爱于人，而不能使人爱。是以知仁义之不足以治天下也。”⑦ 商鞅认为，仁义忠孝等等伦理道德价值观只对君子有效，对小人无法产生规范效应。仁义忠孝的适用范围是有限的，君子之德只能是单株的小草，无法形成草上之大风。换言之，仁义忠孝并非是超越时空的绝对真理，并不具备普适性。但是，儒家的伦理观显然与法家截然不同。朱熹认为，天理是一“谷种”，是百无欠缺的自在之物，人伦道德自然也是天理内在属性之一。“理者物之体，仁者事之体。事事物物，皆具天理，皆是仁做得出来。仁者，事之体。”⑧ 理是本体，仁是理在人心之落实；理是人伦道德存在正当性之根据，仁义礼智信“五常”是天理之分名。“天理既浑然，然既

---

① 高亨：《商君书注译》，北京：清华大学出版社，2011年，第555页。

② 焦循：《孟子正义》，北京：中华书局，2006年，第327页。

③ 朱熹：《近思录》卷七，上海：上海古籍出版社，2002年，第238页。

④ 郭店楚简《五行》有“义形于内谓之德之行，不形于内谓之行”记载，正与孟子“仁义内在”说相印证。

⑤ 冯友兰：《中国哲学简史》，北京：新世界出版社，2004年，第65页。

⑥ 韩非主张“仁内义外”，与告子思想接近，与商鞅思想分歧较大。《韩非子·解老》云：“义者，君臣上下之事，父子贵贱之差也，知交朋友之接也，亲疏内外之分也。臣事君宜，下怀上宜、子事父宜，贱敬贵宜，知交友朋之相助也宜，亲者内而疏者外宜。义者，谓其宜也。宜而为之，故曰：‘上义为之而有以为也’。”（陈奇猷：《韩非子新校注》，上海古籍出版社2000年版，第374页）义是“有以为”，与仁不同，仁是“无以为”。

⑦ 高亨：《商君书注译》，北京：清华大学出版社，2011年，第555页。

⑧ 黎靖德编：《朱子语类》卷98，北京：中华书局，1994年，第2510页。

谓之理，则便是个有条理底名字。……须知天理只是仁、义、礼、智之总名，仁、义、礼、智便是天理之件数。”[①] 天理浑然不可分，天理与仁义礼智信“五常”的关系不是本原与派生物之间的关系，而是本原与属性之间的关系。仁义礼智并非由理“旋次生出”，理是人伦道德的“总名”，仁义礼智信则是天理之“件数”。二程曾指明“人伦者，天理也”，已从哲学高度将仁义定性为天理固有之性，朱熹在二程思想基础上继续论证仁义礼智是天理落实在每一人伦关系上的“一个道理”，如果豁然贯通，“便都是一理”。[②] 朱熹把以仁义礼智信为内涵的理实有化，目的在于论证儒家伦理的普适性与永恒性。

其四，在法与德关系上，儒法两家的分歧十分明显。孔子主张先德后刑、先教后杀，父子相隐，“直”在其中。直是仁之表现，仁是价值体系之核心。在法与德关系上，仁是法之内在文化精神，这一观点在孔子思想中已有所显露，但还没有进行深入论证。在儒家思想史上，真正阐发孔子法律思想的人物是荀子。在荀子思想中，“礼”规范了社会各阶层的权利和义务。礼不仅“正身”，而且是国之“大分”，礼既有西方自然法的色彩，也被赋予了根本法的性质。“故人之命在天，国之命在礼。”[③] 礼的根本作用是“正国”，[④] 所以礼是“国之命”。基于此，荀子进而提出了“礼法”新概念：“礼法之大分也。”[⑤]“礼法之枢要也。”[⑥]“礼法”新概念的提出，具有划时代的文化意义，援礼入法、以礼论法，既是对法之性质重新界定，更是对法背后隐伏之伦理精神进行论证。有礼之法才是良法，无礼之法是恶法，“故非礼，是无法也”。[⑦] 出于礼、入于刑，隆礼重法，礼法合一，其实质意在表明：法已不再是刑罚的汇合，而是建基于礼文化基石之上的新法，法被赋予了焕然一新的文化内核。因此，“礼法”思想的提出，为儒家王道政治文化根基的培植起到了关键作用。与儒家思想相对，法家探讨法与德关系的角度和观点都大不相同。“刑生力，力生强，强生威，威生德。德生于刑。”[⑧] 类似文句反复出现于《靳令》、《去强》等篇章中，“威生德”在有些篇章中表述为“威生惠。”蒋礼鸿认为，“惠生于力，犹惠生于刑矣”。[⑨] 德来源于刑，有刑罚才有道德文明。“非其

---

① 朱熹：《朱熹集》卷40《答何叔京》，成都：四川教育出版社，1996年，第1885页。

② 黎靖德编：《朱子语类》卷98，北京：中华书局，1994年，第2519页。

③ 王先谦：《荀子集解》，北京：中华书局，2006年，第194页。

④ 王先谦：《荀子集解》，北京：中华书局，2006年，第136页。

⑤ 王先谦：《荀子集解》，北京：中华书局，2006年，第139页。

⑥ 王先谦：《荀子集解》，北京：中华书局，2006年，第144页。

⑦ 王先谦：《荀子集解》，北京：中华书局，2006年，第20页。

⑧ 高亨：《商君书注译》，北京：清华大学出版社，2011年，第432页。

⑨ 蒋礼鸿：《商君书锥指》卷1，北京：中华书局，1986年，第32页。

义也，饿不苟食，死不苟生。此乃有法之常也。”① “常”之含义为内在条理、特性、本质，《说苑·修文》有“常者，质也”记载，含义基本一致。仁义诚信是“有法之常”，无法则无德。社会通过轻罪重罚，达到“以刑去刑”社会理想境界之日，就是仁义诚信大行于世之时。“圣君独有之，故能述仁义于天下。”② 认清了法与德关系，才能真正把握仁义的内在真谛。儒家的理论缺陷在于空谈“老老、幼幼”社会大同理想，缺乏对实现社会大同理想途径的理论与制度设计。“背法而治，此任重道远而无马牛，济大川而无舡楫也。”③ 法是实现社会道德理想之必由途径，犹如船之桨、车之马。在商鞅看来，儒家因为没有厘清法与德内在关系，因果颠倒，所以其学说善而无徵、空而无果。

## 二、“比德于殷周”的社会理想愿景

在梳理德与法内在关系基础上，商鞅大张旗鼓地施行“行刑重轻”。“轻罪重罚”的目的并不仅仅在于惩罚犯罪者本人，而在于通过几十年甚至上百年的“刑不善”，最终达到“以刑去刑”的社会理想境界，这恰恰是商鞅矻矻以求的终生奋斗目标。明乎此，才真正读懂了商鞅的内心世界。概而论之，商鞅所追求的“至德复立”的理想社会，至少有两大愿景：

其一，“比德于殷周”，④ “移风易俗”，男女有别。商鞅相秦十年，已处于各种社会矛盾的交汇点上，“宗室贵戚多怨望者”。⑤ 隐士赵良力劝商鞅急流勇退、明哲保身。商鞅对自己十年改革进行辩护，“始秦戎翟之教，父子无别，同室而居。今我更制其教，而为其男女之别。大筑冀阙，营如鲁、卫矣”。⑥ 值得注意的是，商鞅的辩护词中首先提到的并非政治制度、徭役制度与军事制度上的改革，而是社会伦理道德建设方面的成就。鲁卫代表周文，以商周文明建设秦国道德文化，“比德于殷周”，是商鞅一生自我期许之奋斗目标。“营如鲁、卫矣”一句，掷地有声！其中蕴含着诸多感慨与慰藉。李斯对此评论说：“孝公用商鞅之法，移风易俗，民以殷盛，国以富强，百姓乐用，诸侯亲服，获楚、魏之师，举地千里，至今治强。”⑦ 我们必须将商鞅“移风易俗”改革置放于中国历史大背景中综合考察，才能认识清楚其间的文化巨变。在周代文明中，

---

① 高亨：《商君书注译》，北京：清华大学出版社，2011 年，第 555 页。
② 高亨：《商君书注译》，北京：清华大学出版社，2011 年，第 503 页。
③ 高亨：《商君书注译》，北京：清华大学出版社，2011 年，第 581 页。
④ 司马迁：《史记》卷六十八《商君列传》，北京：中华书局，1959 年，第 2228 页。
⑤ 司马迁：《史记》卷六十八《商君列传》，北京：中华书局，1959 年，第 2233 页。
⑥ 司马迁：《史记》卷六十八《商君列传》，北京：中华书局，1959 年，第 2234 页。
⑦ 司马迁：《史记》卷六十八《商君列传》，北京：中华书局，1959 年，第 2542 页。

“男女有别”是社会伦理道德程度高的一项标杆。《礼记·内则》云:“道路,男子由右,女子由左。”[①]“女子出门,必拥蔽其面,夜行以烛,无烛则止。”[②] 宋伯姬之所以死于一场大火,就是一直在等待傅姆的到来。“妇人之义,傅姆不在,宵不下堂。”[③]傅姆晚至,结果宋伯姬葬身于火海。在家庭伦理中,“男女授受不亲”也有详细规定,《礼记·曲礼》云:“男女不杂坐,不同椸、枷,不同巾、栉,不亲授。嫂叔不通问,诸母不漱裳。外言不入于梱,内言不出于梱。”[④] 叔、嫂相接,在中原文明国家是被禁止的。齐人淳于髡曾以“嫂溺,则援之以手乎”向孟子发难,孟子则以知“礼”通“权”应答。[⑤] 但是,中原国家的文明之风丝毫没有传播至边陲之外的秦国,这与秦国历史密切相关。秦人原为东夷,生活在山东沿海一带,夏末向西迁徙。周武王灭商后,秦人迁至陕、甘一带与戎狄杂处。西周孝王时期,秦人首领非子因养马有功,被封于秦(今甘肃陇西一带)。秦人立国时间,远远晚于中原各国,社会文明化程度也远逊于鲁、宋诸国。以至于到秦孝公时代,中原各国盟会,仍不邀请秦国。因为在中原各国眼中,秦国“与戎翟同俗,有虎狼之心,贪戾好利而无信,不识礼义德行”。[⑥] 秦人不知礼义德行,寡廉鲜耻,“若禽兽”。[⑦] 有鉴于此,商鞅治秦,依照鲁、卫风俗,雷厉风行在秦国推行道德文明建设。秦孝公三年(前359年),商鞅变法颁布《分户令》:“民有二男以上不分异者,倍其赋。”[⑧] 兄弟必须分家,各立门户,否则“一人出两课”。[⑨] 秦孝公十二年,又重申《分户令》精神,“令民父子兄弟同室内息者为禁”。[⑩] 在兄弟分居基础上,又规定父子也必须分户。“同室”即同户,睡虎地秦简《法律答问》有:“可(何)谓‘同居’?户为‘同居’,坐隶,隶不坐户谓殹(也)”。[⑪] 商鞅两次“分户令”,既有经济与政治管理上的考量,也有“移风易俗”、摒弃“戎翟之教”的社会教化目的。杨宽教授指出,商鞅变法禁止父子兄弟同室居住,目的在于“革除残留的戎狄风俗。”[⑫] 商鞅以中原礼教文化革除秦国恶风陋俗的措施,在出土文献中多有体现。“某里士五

---

① 孙希旦:《礼记集解》,北京:中华书局,1989年,第736页。

② 孙希旦:《礼记集解》,北京:中华书局,1989年,第736页。

③ 傅隶朴:《春秋三传比义》,北京:中国友谊出版公司,1984年,第200页。

④ 孙希旦:《礼记集解》,北京:中华书局,1989年,第43—44页。

⑤ 杨伯峻:《孟子译注》,北京:中华书局,1960年,第177页。

⑥ 张清常、王延栋:《战国策笺注》,天津:南开大学出版社,1993年,第625页。

⑦ 张清常、王延栋:《战国策笺注》,天津:南开大学出版社,1993年,第625页。

⑧ 司马迁:《史记》卷六十八《商君列传》,北京:中华书局,1959年,第2230页。

⑨ 司马迁:《史记》卷六十八《商君列传》,北京:中华书局,1959年,第2230页。

⑩ 司马迁:《史记》卷六十八《商君列传》,北京:中华书局,1959年,第2232页。

⑪ 睡虎地秦墓竹简整理小组:《睡虎地秦墓竹简·法律答问》,北京:文物出版社,1978年,第160页。

⑫ 杨宽:《战国史》,上海:上海人民出版社,1980年,第193页。

(伍) 甲诣男子乙、女子丙，告曰：‘乙、丙相与奸，自昼见某所，捕校上来诣之。’”[①] 秦律强调“男女洁诚”，对通奸之罪，绳之以法。如果发生家庭乱伦之行，更是严惩不贷。“同母异父相与奸，可（何）论?”[②] 兄妹通奸，论为“弃市”。汉承秦制，强调男女有别，对家庭乱伦之行惩罚更趋酷烈。汉衡山王之子刘孝先自告谋反，朝廷“除其罪”。但最终却以“坐与王御婢奸，弃市”。[③] 通奸罪竟然重于谋反罪，汉朝整齐风俗之礼法，与秦律相比有过之而无不及。

其二，从“壹刑”到“去刑”。商鞅思想中的“壹刑”蕴涵三层含义：

首先，法之公正性。“民本，法也。”[④] 法是体现国家意志的外在强制性约束力量，法应该具有普遍的约束力，上自君王，下自庶民，人人必须遵循。商鞅一再把法比作规矩、准绳与度量衡。“故法者，国之权衡也。”[⑤] 因为只有这样论证法之性质，才可以说“法令者，民之命”。法既然是衡评是非功过的客观准绳，当然蕴涵公正之特点。法之公正性源自何处？换言之，法律公正性的依据何在？商鞅和其他法家一样，皆从“天道”寻求法之公正性存在之合理性。天之运行有其内在的规律和法则，其中一条最根本的法则为“天道无私”。天对万物无远无近，无偏无私。得天之道为“德”，天之道显现于人之道、落实于法是为“公”。“公私之分明，则小人不疾贤，而不肖者不妒功。”[⑥] 天下人的普遍权益为“公”，个人利益为“私”。代表天下整体利益的法就是“公法”，体现君王个人利益之法就是“私法”。因此，统治者当“立法为公”，“故尧舜之位天下也，非私天下之利也，为天下位天下也。论贤举能而传焉，非疏父子亲越人也，明于治乱之道也。故三王以义亲，五霸以法正诸侯，皆非私天下之利也，为天下治天下”。[⑦] 商鞅于此提出了两个著名的论断：“为天下位天下”和“为天下治天下”。天下不是君王一姓之天下，而是天下人之天下，如果君王把天下当成自己私有之物，必将身亡国危。只有像尧舜那样，以天下为公，立法为公，“论贤举能”，实行禅让制，才真正通晓治国之道。“故公私之交，存亡之本也。”[⑧] 商鞅这些表述，与墨家禅让思想存在相通相近之处。“为天下位天下”社会政治思想既是对宗法社会“家天下”传统的

---

① 睡虎地秦墓竹简整理小组：《睡虎地秦墓竹简·封诊式》，北京：文物出版社，1978年，第278页。

② 睡虎地秦墓竹简整理小组：《睡虎地秦墓竹简·法律答问》，北京：文物出版社，1978年，第225页。

③ 司马迁：《史记》卷五十八《淮南衡山列传》，北京：中华书局，1959年，第3097页。

④ 高亨：《商君书注译》，北京：清华大学出版社，2011年，第544页。

⑤ 高亨：《商君书注译》，北京：清华大学出版社，2011年，第507页。

⑥ 高亨：《商君书注译》，北京：清华大学出版社，2011年，第509页。

⑦ 高亨：《商君书注译》，北京：清华大学出版社，2011年，第509页。

⑧ 高亨：《商君书注译》，北京：清华大学出版社，2011年，第509页。

否定，又是对西周早期以来民本主义思潮的继承与发展。

其次，法之公平性 。法既然代表国家和社会整体利益，就应该具有普遍适用的平等性特点。刑罚应该不分贵贱等级，不因人而异。司马迁虽然对法家多有微词，但对法家“不别亲疏，不殊贵贱，一断于法”[①] 普遍适用的平等性原则仍给予高度评价。“所谓壹刑者，刑无等级，自卿相将军以至大夫庶人，有不从王令、犯国禁、乱上制者，罪死不赦。有功于前，有败于后，不为损刑。有善于前，有过于后，不为亏法”。[②]“刑无等级”意味着不分贵贱亲疏，一断于法。在“刑无等级”理论中，商鞅还适度地提出了君王应守法的思想。尽管君王拥有立法、司法和行政诸大权，但法律一旦颁行，君王也有恪守法令的义务。《商君书·君臣》篇云：“故明主慎法制。言不中法者，不听也；行不中法者，不高也；事不中法者，不为也。言中法，则辩之；行中法，则高之；事中法，则为之。”[③] 商鞅从言、行、事三方面论述君王与法的关系，“不为”、“不听”和“不高”是君王自身对待法律应持之态度。不合法律原则的“不为”，合乎法律原则的积极“为之”，此乃“治之至”。[④] 商鞅关于法律面前贵贱平等、“一断于法”的立法思想，并未仅仅停留于思辨领域。在司法实践上，商鞅也力图维护法的平等性原则。在推行新法过程中，太子驷在公子虔、公孙贾等宗法贵族势力唆使下，公然诋毁与阻挠新法推行。对于太子驷的违法行为，商鞅主张依法惩处，后来可能孝公出面求情，又考虑到太子驷是君位继承人不便施加肉刑，只好让太子师傅代其受刑，黥其师、劓其傅。太子犯法，刑及师、傅，这一案例实际上等于处罚了太子，况且太子师傅又都是宗室贵族。由此可以看出，商鞅不仅在理论上倡导“刑无等级”，在司法实践中也力求贯彻法的平等性原则。

复次，法之公开性 。商周时代存在着“刑不可知，则威不可测”的神秘法传统，依恃不成文的习惯法和君主的命、诰来调整各种社会关系。迨至春秋晚期郑国子产铸刑书，开创公布成文法先例。此事甫出，立即遭到叔向等人极力反对，其理由为“昔先王议事以制，不为刑辟，惧民之有争心也”[⑤]。“议事以制”是指“临事制刑，不豫设法。”[⑥] 商周时代的法制特点是“以罪统例”，而非“以罪量刑”。对于子产在法制方面开时代风气之举，叔向不仅抨击，而且诅咒：“民知争端矣，将弃礼而征于书。锥刀之

---

① 司马迁：《史记》卷七十《太史公自序》，北京：中华书局，1959 年，第 3291 页。

② 高亨：《商君书注译》，北京：清华大学出版社，2011 年，第 533 页。

③ 高亨：《商君书注译》，北京：清华大学出版社，2011 年，第 597 页。

④ 囿于时代的局限，商鞅尚不可能提出“刑君王”思想，更不可能在司法上真正做到君王犯法，与庶民同罪。对此，我们必须站在历史主义高度，对商鞅思想进行客观的评价。

⑤ 杜预：《春秋经传集解》，上海：上海古籍出版社，1988 年，第 1275 页。

⑥ 杜预：《春秋经传集解》，上海：上海古籍出版社，1988 年，第 1276 页。

末，将尽争之。乱狱滋丰，贿赂并行，终子之世，郑其败乎！”① 商鞅继承了法家先驱子产等人公布成文法的传统，主张“宣明法制”：“故圣人为法，必使之明白易知，名正，愚知遍能知之。”② 商鞅认为，成文法颁布有两大优点：其一，“万民皆知所避就。”③ 成文法意味着法是刚性的行为规范，人们知道合法与非法的界限，了解自己的权利与义务；其二，“故吏不敢以非法遇民，民不敢犯法以干法官也”。④法令公开、透明，意味着法的可预见性。平民大众都通晓法律所赋予法吏的权利界限，法吏就不敢徇私枉法、任意断罪，罪犯也不敢法外求情或刁难法吏。韩非子评论说：“故法莫如显，而术不欲见。是以明主言法，则境内卑贱莫不闻之也。”⑤法必须“布之于百姓”，才能达到“刑罚必于民心”的社会效果。商鞅治秦二十余载，在思想与舆论上高倡法律公开性同时，在制度层面上也采取了诸多措施保障法律的公开、透明。譬如，“为法令置官吏”。⑥ 商鞅后学建议全国建立统一的司法官吏队伍，在中央设立三名司法官吏，其中天子殿中置一名法官，御史置一名法官，丞相置一名法官。诸侯郡县皆分别设置一名法官，配备法吏若干名。由法官与法吏组成的司法机构具有两大职能：其一，定期向天下吏民颁布法令条文。出土秦简《尉杂》律有“岁雠辟律于御史”⑦ 的记载，“掌刑辟”的廷尉每年要到御史处核对法律条款，以免传抄讹误，这与《定分》篇中关于司法官吏每年定期核对并颁布法令条文的内容正相吻合。从秦简分析，地方官吏有定期公布法律条文之义务，《语书》实际上就是南郡郡守“腾”颁发给本郡各县、道的法律文告，“发书，移书曹，曹莫受，以告府，府令曹画之。其画最多者，当居曹奏令、丞，令、丞以为不直，志千里使有籍书之，以为恶吏”。⑧ 法律文书传达到县、乡、里时，各级政府须及时公之于众，“明法律令，事无不能”者为“良吏”。“不智（知）事，不廉絜（洁）”，⑨ 阻滞延宕法令施行者，将被视为“恶吏”。此外，《内史杂》律的

---

① 杜预：《春秋经传集解》，上海：上海古籍出版社，1988年，第1276页。

② 高亨：《商君书注译》，北京：清华大学出版社，2011年，第625页。

③ 高亨：《商君书注译》，北京：清华大学出版社，2011年，第625页。

④ 高亨：《商君书注译》，北京：清华大学出版社，2011年，第619页。

⑤ 陈奇猷：《韩非子新校注》，上海：上海古籍出版社，2000年，第923页。

⑥ 高亨：《商君书注译》，北京：清华大学出版社，2011年，第615页。

⑦ 睡虎地秦墓竹简整理小组：《睡虎地秦墓竹简·秦律十八种》，北京：文物出版社，1978年，第109页。

⑧ 睡虎地秦墓竹简整理小组：《睡虎地秦墓竹简·语书》，北京：文物出版社，1978年，第20页。

⑨ 睡虎地秦墓竹简整理小组：《睡虎地秦墓竹简·语书》，北京：文物出版社，1978年，第19页。

“县各告都官在其县者，写其官之用律”[①] 的记载表明，各县都官必须抄写法律条文，这也是官府公布法律条文的一种形式。其二，司法官吏有向吏民解释法令条文的义务。“吏民知法令者，皆问法官。”[②]《定分》篇这些阐述司法理论与制度的记载，已转化为秦国与秦朝的司法制度。秦简《法律答问》实际上就是司法官吏与吏民之间关于法令条文的答问录，“甲盗牛，盗牛时高六尺，系一岁，复丈，高六尺七寸，问甲可（何）论？当完城旦”。[③] 秦朝成年男子平均身高是六尺五寸，尚未成年的孩子偷了别人一头牛，吏民问司法官吏应如何处罚？司法官吏回答说：先囚禁一年，一年后再量身高，如果身高已达 6.7 尺（约合今 1.54 米），就收录为城旦隶。这种答问录同样具有法律效力，在审理案件中经常援引，以资判决时参考。在商鞅之前，尚无思想家如此全面深入地论述司法原则、司法机构性质与职能。在这一意义上，商鞅学派学说代表先秦时期司法理论所达到的最高水平。

法之公正、公平与公开，构成商鞅学说“壹刑”的基本架构。从法之公正、公平与公开，才有可能臻于“以刑去刑”、“至德复立”的理想社会境界。换言之，“壹刑”合乎逻辑的发展趋向就是“去刑”。“重刑，连其罪，则民不敢试。民不敢试，故无刑也。夫先王之禁，刺杀，断人之足，黥人之面，非求伤民也，以禁奸止过也。故禁奸止过，莫若重刑。刑重而必得，则民不敢试，故国无刑民。国无刑民，故曰：明刑不戮。”[④] 商鞅所言“去刑”，并非“无刑”，或完全消弭犯罪现象，而是指通过公正、公平与公开的“壹刑”训导，全社会有望进入“明刑”的理想境界，“明刑之犹至于无刑也”。[⑤] 所以，商鞅“去刑”的涵义为“明刑”，韩非称之为“明法”。[⑥] 其思想实质一方面旨在表明法律的公正、公平与公开；另一方面意在说明，经过长期的“以壹辅仁”社会治理之后，法之性质已悄悄改变：“国治，断家王，断官强，断君弱。……故王者刑赏断于民心，器用断于家。治明则同，治闇则异。同则行，异则止。行则治，止则乱。治则家断，乱则君断。治国者贵下断，故以十里断者弱，以五里断者强。家断则有余，故曰：日治者王。官断则不足，故曰：夜治者强。君断则乱，故曰：宿治者削。故有道之国，治不听君，民不从官”。[⑦] 在“有道之国”理想社会中，是非对错，已能

---

① 睡虎地秦墓竹简整理小组：《睡虎地秦墓竹简·秦律十八种》，北京：文物出版社，1978 年，第 104 页。

② 高亨：《商君书注译》，北京：清华大学出版社，2011 年，第 619 页。

③ 睡虎地秦墓竹简整理小组：《睡虎地秦墓竹简·法律答问》，北京：文物出版社，1978 年，第 153 页。

④ 高亨：《商君书注译》，北京：清华大学出版社，2011 年，第 533 页。

⑤ 高亨：《商君书注译》，北京：清华大学出版社，2011 年，第 533 页。

⑥ 商鞅所言“明刑”，韩非称之为“明法”。

⑦ 高亨：《商君书注译》，北京：清华大学出版社，2011 年，第 435 页。

“断于民心”，平民大众既不“听君”，也不“从官”，他们唯一“从”的是“心”。此“心”既是德性之心，也是法性之心。法已不再是外在强制性的制约力量，法已内化为人内在的生命本然欲求，法与德交融为一“心”。① 通晓治国之要的统治者，商鞅称之为“王君”、“圣君”，“圣君”知道“以壹辅仁”的治国之道：社会高度法治化之日，就是社会道德文明大行于世之时。“耆老得遂，幼孤得长，边境不侵，君臣相亲，父子相保。”② “杀刑”与“圣德”相反相成、相生相依。“德礼为政教之本，刑罚为政教之用，犹昏晓阳秋相须而相成者也。”③ 至大至刚的法之精神与至善至美的伦理境界水乳交融，犹如气之阴阳相辅相成。圣君深谙德与法相须而相成之“道”，所以真正“能述仁义于天下”。④ 商鞅明乎此“道”，所以韩非称赞他是“功之至厚者。”“有道之国，治不听君，民不从官”的思想，与老子“自正”、“无为”思想，多有相通之处，其间的逻辑联系有待学者进一步探究。

## 三、结语

综上所述，研究商鞅思想及其行事，有三点有待于我们深入探讨：

其一，对商鞅知识背景、知识结构和价值取向应全面深入研究。从商鞅青年时代治学与游学经历分析，将青年时代商鞅定位为杂家比较符合历史事实。根据司马迁、班固和刘向等人记载，商鞅年轻时拜杂家尸子为师，杂家的特点在于“兼儒墨，合名法。”商鞅四见孝公，分别以“帝道”、“王道”和“霸道”试探孝公所好，足以证明商鞅的知识背景与知识结构。商鞅的核心思想与价值取向不可单纯以“刻薄寡恩”、“轻罪重罚”、“利出一孔”来综括，“比德于殷周”、“以刑去刑”也是商鞅梦寐以求的社会理想。在历史舞台上，存在着两个影像交叉重叠的商鞅：一个是师事尸子的杂家公孙鞅，另一个是被封于商、於之地的秦相商鞅。历史最终选择了商鞅以法家面目出现于世，而非商鞅自己愿意以法家面目显现于世。点明此区别，不无必要。

其二，商鞅并未全盘否定和废灭仁义道德文化，只是在仁义范畴的界定、仁义理想实现之途径、法与德的内在关系等方面，与儒家存在一些分歧。在商鞅看来，法之内在文化精神是“爱民”、“利民”，⑤ 这一观点与儒家可谓殊途而同归、一致而百虑。也正是在这一层面上，商鞅与韩非不可混为一谈。商鞅思想深处有人文关怀成分，“法

---

① 曾振宇、崔明德：《由法返德：商鞅社会理想之分析》，《中国史研究》，1997年第1期。

② 陈奇猷：《韩非子新校注》，上海：上海古籍出版社，2000年，第287页。

③ 刘俊文：《唐律疏议》卷一《名例》，北京：法律出版社，1999年，第3页。

④ 高亨：《商君书注译》，北京：清华大学出版社，2011年，第503页。

⑤ 高亨：《商君书注译》，北京：清华大学出版社，2011年，第370页。

者所以爱民”、“以刑去刑”、“至德复立”、“为天下位天下”、“为天下治天下”、“比德于殷周”等等论述，足以证明商鞅思想性质与儒家、老子道家相比有相通相容之处。《韩非子》一书多篇是帝王权谋之术，功利主义价值观贯穿全书始终。[①]

其三，中国古代法律的指导思想既有儒家成分，也有商鞅法家思想色彩。秦、汉律的蓝本可追溯到至战国李悝《法经》，秦、汉时代法律文化精神（或言灵魂）“纯本于法家精神”自是不易之论。陈寅恪先生也尝言：“汉家法律，实本嬴秦之旧。”[②] 但是，如果认为汉之后的中国古代法律文化之灵魂完全由儒家思想垄断，可能也是偏于一曲之论。首先，商鞅思想就不否定与排斥仁义道德文化，正文中已详论，此不赘述；其次，与其说儒家思想支配了一切古代法律，“一准乎礼”。不如说儒家与法家思想联袂支配了一切古代法典，这恰恰正是古代中国法系一大特色。长孙无忌在《唐律疏议》中开门见山的一段话值得我们细细品味：“夫三才肇位，万象斯分。禀气含灵，人为称首。莫不凭黎元而树司宰，因政教而施刑法。其有情恣庸愚，识沈愆戾，大则乱其区宇，小则睽其品式，不立制度，则未之前闻。故曰：‘以刑止刑，以杀止杀。’刑罚不可弛于国，笞捶不得废于家。时遇浇淳，用有众寡。”[③] 这是一段具有总纲性意义的言论，其思想贯穿于《唐律疏议》始终，事实上也渗透于宋元明清法律文本之中。“德礼”固然是法律文化之灵魂，“崇法”何尝又不是古代法律一以贯之的指导思想？长孙无忌所引“以刑止刑，以杀止杀”一语，出自商鞅等法家思想，这足以说明古代法律文化的内在精神是“王”“霸”兼用、“隆礼重法”、“礼法并举”。“汉家自有制度，本以霸王道杂之，奈何纯（住）【任】德教，用周政乎？”[④] 汉宣帝一语，道破数千年古代法律文化内在玄机。

---

① 根据容肇祖先生考证，《韩非子》中的《喻老》、《解老》两篇文章确定非韩非所著。如果将《喻老》、《解老》两篇文章排除在外，韩非思想中的人文关怀成分微乎其微。

② 陈寅恪：《陈寅恪集·金明馆丛稿初编》，上海：三联书店，2009年，第145页。

③ 长孙无忌等撰、刘俊文点校：《唐律疏议》卷一《名例》，北京：法律出版社，1999年，第1页。

④ 班固：《汉书·元帝纪》，北京：中华书局，1962年，第277页。

# 德治与法治的辩证关系

## ——以《孟子》“天子舜窃负杀人之父而逃”章为例

新西兰坎特雷大学 伍晓明

我这里想要重读的是《孟子·尽心上》中的一段著名文字。我要为这一文本加一个稍长一点的、因而更能表示其大致内容的标题：“天子舜窃负杀人之父而逃。”

桃应问曰：“舜为天子，皋陶为士，瞽瞍杀人，则如之何?”

孟子曰：“执之而已矣。”

“然则舜不禁与?”

曰：“夫舜恶得而禁之？夫有所受之也。”

“然则舜如之何?”

曰：“舜视弃天下犹弃敝蹝（屣）也；窃负而逃，遵海滨而处，终身訢（欣）然，乐而忘天下。”

我们知道，这一文本近年来激起过很多热烈的讨论，甚至激烈的争论。但我今天并不想加入这个争论的行列。也就是说，我将不试图对这一文本做出评价，因为“评价”意味着采取立场，而我很怀疑，如果我们发现我们自己处在这样的伦理困境之中，我们是否真能为自己找到任何简单、明确的立场，一个可以让我们从而或者拥护，或者批评，或者甚至同时拥护和批评天子舜或者圣人孟子在这一伦理困境中所做出的选择和决定的立场。我说舜“或者”孟子，是因为我想强调，如果我们认真对待这一文本，而这也就是说，如果我们把这一文本首先作为文本来对待，那么我们就应该更加注意我们在谈论这一文本时的措辞。在这一文本呈现给我们的伦理困境中，其实不是舜自己做了某个选择和决定，也不是孟子自己作了某个选择和决定，而是孟子“让”——我还不敢说“代”或者“为”——舜在这一困境中做了某个——或者某些——选择和决定，因为孟子“让”舜做的选择和决定似乎不止一个。而这就是说，我们在这一文本中看到的伦理选择和决定既不能说完全是舜的选择和决定，但也不能说完全是孟子的选择和决定。或者，我们也可以反过来说，这些选择和决定既可以说是舜所做出的，同时也可以说是孟子所做出的。是孟子藏在舜的身后说话——说他自己要说的话——吗?还是舜藏在孟子的身后或“通—过”孟子说话,说舜自己要说的话?我们应该如何分析这一文本的“作者”与这一文本中的“人物”之间的关系?我们其实很难立即就给出自己的明确回答,或做出我们自己的明确决定。

因此,我才不要急于对这一复杂文本做出任何简单明确的评价,因为一个需要采取立场的评价也意味着,我们把文本仅仅视为思想—认识的某种对象。而在这样做的时候,我们其实可能会削弱甚至压抑文本的“生产力”,亦即,一个思想—哲学文本的继续为我们生产或产生思想的力量。而我今天想要做的在某种程度上就是,尝试让孟子的这一文本继续为我们发挥它的生产力量。所以,我今天要做的会带有某种试验性,因为也会带有某种冒险性。

阅读这一文本,我们可能应该首先注意这一文本中孟子说话的语气。在这一文本中,孟子的话似乎说得很轻松。亦即,他的话至少从表面上看似乎并非全然认真之语。而此一可能是假装出来的“并非全然认真”则很可能是因为,面对此一困境,一个弟子放在老师面前的、设想出来的伦理困境,一个会让舜吃惊地发现自己竟然会置身于其中的伦理困境,孟子知道舜也许从根本上说就很难做出“合情合理”的选择和决定。因为,即使是天子之父,犯了杀人之罪也得依法论处,不然就没有公平与正义,因为公平与正义蕴含着:对所有人都“一视同仁”。所以孟子知道,在这种情况下,舜即使身为天子可能也会无可奈何。自己是天子,但父亲杀了人,自己的执法官就应该依法办理。这种情况下,舜又能怎么办呢?在孟子看来,舜大概也没有什么别的好办法。于是孟子才用了似乎很轻松的口气回答说,“抓起他来就是了。”(“执之而已矣。”但此一回答中其实已经蕴含着孟子对于法之必要及执法之必要的承认。)我们应该注意,这是孟子在此情况下为舜设想的决定,而不是舜自己所下的命令。舜自己不必说话,不必命令,因为在这种情况下该做什么是明确的。“那么舜就不管了吗?”(“然则舜不禁与?”)“舜又怎么管得了呢?”(“夫舜恶得而禁之?”)管不了是因为,皋陶把瞽瞍抓起来是有法律根据的,因此是有道理的(“夫有所受之也”)。那么舜又该怎么办呢?他就这样看着自己的父亲被抓起来吗?这似乎也不行。情急之下,于是孟子“让”舜做了这样一个选择和决定。这是孟子为舜设想的一条出路:把天下像用旧了的草鞋那样扔掉,偷偷地背着自己的父亲逃走,到远远的海边住下来,一辈子高高兴兴的,把天下全都忘掉。

孟子说这些时的某种轻松语气——至少是表面上的轻松语气,假装出来的轻松语气——其实非常值得注意。他似乎是在想让他的话不要被听得太认真,而这可能意味着,他也许想与自己的话保持某种距离,他也许并不想完全为这些话负责。这也就是说,他可能是想与他“让”舜在这种情况下做的选择和决定保持某种距离。为什么?是否因为孟子自己也隐隐感到,他“让”舜做这样的选择和决定有些不妥?是否因为他觉得自己也不能确定，如果舜发现自己处于这一伦理困境之中，舜真会做出他让舜所做的选择和决定？是否正因为如此，孟子才想让自己听起来似乎是在跟学生开某种玩笑：在自己的父亲因杀人而违反了法律这种情况下，你说舜又能怎么办呢？他既不能禁止皋陶抓人，但也不能眼看着父亲被抓吧？因为，如果舜禁止皋陶因瞽瞍杀人而执法，那么他就否定了法之为法，从而使公平正义没有保证，而如果舜听任其父被抓，那么他就树立了一个不孝的榜样，从而宣布人可以出卖自己对父亲的伦理责任。那他就带着父亲跑吧。跑得远远的，跑到法律可能管不到的地方住下来。这样，舜就可以继续尽他对父亲的孝了。当然，“代价”——如果我们这里可以谈论代价的话——似乎也不小，因为这得以抛弃整个天下来换取。但既然是为了自己的父亲，那也就顾不了这么多了。而且，还不仅如此。孟子“让”舜以为，拿天下来跟自己的父亲比，天下又算什么呢？天下就只是穿旧的鞋子而已。这似乎就是孟子所能为舜设想的“最佳”解决方案，所以孟子就“让”舜在这一伦理困境之中做了这样的选择和决定。但是，舜真能“心安理得”地接受或认同孟子“让”他做的——或者是“为”他做的——这个选择和决定吗？这样的选择和决定真能是“最佳”决定和最终决定吗？

现在我们首先应该问，在这一设想出来的伦理困境中，为什么舜会发现自己面对一个困难的选择和决定问题？如果只有一个他人，如果我只面对一个他人，我就不需要选择。面对他者，我会发现自己必然已经被置于需要为这个他者负责的地位之上了。而这个对于他者的责任必然是无条件的，因而也是无限的。（如果需要阐明这一无条件的无限责任，我们可以回到孟子的将入于井之孺子。）只有当还有另一个他人之时，或者有所谓“第三者”之时，才会有所谓“选择”问题（也就是说，做出某种选择的需要，或者说，需要去做出某种选择）。而这也就是说，才会有公平正义问题（如果有两个孺子将入于井，我应该先救谁？如果妈妈和媳妇同时落水了，丈夫应该先救谁？所以莱维纳斯才会言简意赅地说：有两个人的时候是伦理，有三个人的时候就是政治）。但是这个选择不是“价值选择”（杨泽波），也不是在父亲的生命和天子之位二者之间的选择（丁为祥）。舜并非在较不重要者与较为重要者之间做选择，也不是选择以放弃天子之位为“代价”而换取父亲的生命（也就是说，以极为重大的代价来换取父亲的生命）。需要选择是因为还有他人，还有其他的人。这些其他的人也必然与我有关。这也就是说，必然是我应该对之负责者和为之负责者。对于一个“普通人”来说，这个对于天下他人的普遍无限责任可能会隐而不显，但对于天子舜来说，这应该是非常显而易见的。舜必须为天下之人负无限之责。而每一他人都是独一无二的、不可替代的、不可比较的（舜只有一个父亲，但那个被假设为是舜的父亲所杀的人也必然是某子之父或某父之子，或某个家庭的成员）。所以，如果此处有所谓“选择”这一问题的话，如果舜真是需要在此困境之中做出选择的话，他的选择不是在可比者（因而“有价”

者，或有确定“价值”者）之间的选择，而是在不可比者（因而“无价”者，或超出一切价值者）之间的“选择”。（谁能在每一个人——每一个他人——身上放上一确定的价格或价值？谁能说舜之父就比他人之父“值”得更多？或更加宝贵？）但既然在不同他人之间不可能进行真正的比较（因为每一他人都是独一无二的，不可比较的），我们在此已经超出比较的可能性。比较的可能是因为有普遍标准。例如，在治国人才的选拔上我们可以任人唯贤，而这是因为这里我们有一个特定的普遍标准，贤。但是，在自己的父亲杀了人这一困境之中，我们却不可能将一个他人与另一个他人进行比较。而既然他人与他人不可比，那也就无从选择，无可选择，无法选择。如果我们此处还想坚持“选择”这个词的话，那么此一选择是在无法选择者之间做出的选择，因而是一个没有选择的选择。而所谓“没有选择的选择”是说，在不可能根据任何确定的原则或标准或规矩而进行选择之时却必须做出某种选择。而这也就是说，必须做决定，并且必须为自己的并无绝对保证的决定负责。

那么，舜真能让自己为孟子“让”他或者“为”他做出的这个选择和决定负责吗？他会发现自己真能承担这样一个决定吗？一个“后圣”为“先圣”所做的决定？我们可能会怀疑。所以我才不厌其烦地坚持，在《孟子》文本中，在这个假设出来的伦理困境中，在面对自己的父亲杀人这一极端情况之中，不是舜自己，而是孟子“让”舜做了这样一个最终选择窃负杀人之父而逃的决定。而孟子“让”舜所做的决定又是孟子自己在被弟子的提问逼入困境之时仓促做出的。让我们回到文本：

桃应问曰：“舜为天子，皋陶为士，瞽瞍杀人，则如之何？”

孟子曰：“执之而已矣。”

“然则舜不禁与？”

曰：“夫舜恶得而禁之？夫有所受之也。”

“然则舜如之何？”

曰：“舜视弃天下犹弃敝蹝（屣）也；窃负而逃，遵海滨而处，终身訢（欣）然，乐而忘天下。”

桃应设三问而孟子做三答。此三问步步进逼，盯住不放地追问舜在这一假设的父亲杀人的事件中最终将会如何。桃应在第一问中设想了一种情况，其中至少有四人被直接涉及，而此四人则纠缠于以下数种复杂的相互关系之中：

立法者与授权执法者（舜与皋陶）的关系；

子与父或父与子（舜与瞽叟）的关系；

加害于他人者与受害者（瞽瞍与其被杀者）的关系，或犯罪者与受害者的关系；

执法者与执法之对象（皋陶与瞽瞍）的关系；

以及法之代表者与法之应该保护者（舜与被他的父亲所杀者之间的关系，此受害者应该受到法的保护，或者说，法必须让此受害者与其他人一样受到公正的对待）。

在桃应的第一问中，“舜为天子，皋陶为士，瞽瞍杀人，则如之何?”，这个“如之何”问的是在此种复杂情况中，所涉及的每一个人将会如何或将应如何，他们各自将会做出什么反应，应该采取什么行动。因为，就其问题的表述本身来看，问者问的不仅是舜的可能的反应和决定，不仅是皋陶的可能的反应和决定，而且也是瞽瞍的可能的反应和决定（尽管据说瞽瞍以顽劣著称，但我们没有理由对瞽瞍的可能的反应和决定不加考虑），甚至还是与瞽瞍的受害者直接有关者的可能的反应和决定，因为我们必须记住，此受害者也必然是某人之子，或某人之父，或某一家庭的成员。

对于这样一个问题，一个至少是潜在地涉及所有“当事人”的问题，孟子的第一反应虽非面面俱到，却似乎是最直接的或最“自然”的反应。这里的基本问题看起来是有人非法杀人，而非法杀人即必须被法传唤和质问，亦即，必须在要求一视同仁的法的面前为自己之行为负责，并接受由法所规定的相应惩罚。孟子的第一与第二回答似乎直接而干脆（语气也轻松）：“执之而已矣。”即使天子之父瞽瞍杀人，皋陶也必须依法逮捕之。这意味着，当时的法在杀人问题上是“一视同仁”的。

如果桃应没有发其第三问，我们也许永远不知道，除了让舜眼睁睁地看着其父被皋陶抓起来，孟子还会为舜设计出什么“出路”。孟子让舜坐视皋陶依法逮捕其父，其实已经表明了孟子的立场：让其父被带至法律面前（这蕴含着，让公正得以特定的然而却是有限的方式实现）。但桃应却非要继续追问：此种情况之下，舜究竟会如何。我们可以想象，孟子在此被逼入了某种困境。他本来已经让舜坐视其父被抓，因为这是当时公认的正义之举（这是否也符合舜的形象：“恭己正南面”而天下治？既然有可以信任的皋陶在执法，舜确实已经不需要再做什么了）。但是，桃应的第三问“然则舜如之何?”蕴含着，难道舜真的会坐视其父被抓吗？瞽瞍不是舜的父亲吗？作为儿子的舜真可以对父亲这样吗？这样做“合情合理/礼”吗？孟子一想也对，的确，舜不能让他爸爸就这么被抓走，尽管他爸爸对他从来都不好，而且不是一般地不好，而且这次又犯了杀人罪，但这毕竟是他爸爸啊。而爸爸只有一个。所以，还是得给舜想点儿办法。什么办法呢？孟子不能让舜利用自己的权力禁止皋陶抓人，尽管舜似乎完全能做到这一点。因为，这样就破坏公平正义。孟子也不能让舜为他爸爸说情，因为这样做可能更坏。作为天子的舜如何能为自己的父亲请求让自己所代表的公平正义网开一面呢？仓促之间，孟子想出了办法：舜可以放弃天下（注意，是放弃天下，而不是如丁为祥所说，放弃天子之位，二者之间是有重要区别的），背上自己的父亲偷偷逃走，逃到法律/正义还管不到的海边去（或者说，逃到法律 / 正义之外）。孟子觉得舜会高高兴兴地跟他爸爸在那儿住下来。但是，孟子转念一想，可能就会后悔了，舜真能这样逃走吗？这样逃走他高兴得了吗？

孟子在让舜窃负其父而逃之时，是否是在让舜为他人的过错负责？舜是否必须为他人的过错负责？历来论者，包括近来卷入舜窃负而逃之争论者，似乎皆以舜挈父而逃为出于亲情之孝（刘清平）。但尚未被认真考虑的一个问题是，如果在有关舜之家庭的经典叙述中，舜之父与舜之弟对舜皆毫无那据说应该是天然的血亲之情可言（而这其实已经证明着，所谓天然的血亲之情并非天然，或并非完全天然），亦即，毫无父对子之慈与弟对兄之悌，那么我们又如何能够坚持说，舜窃负其父而逃乃是完全为其出于亲情之孝所推动？此处难道没有别的考虑，或许是更重要、更基本的考虑？难道舜之窃负其父而逃不正是因为瞽瞍恰为其父，而父之于子乃是一极为特殊的他人，即我作为我而与之发生关系的“第一他人”？当然，每一他人之于我皆为特殊之他人，皆为独一无二者，而就此而言，父其实并不比其他的他人更为特殊。但作为我之第一他人的父（或母）的特殊之处可能在于，我与此一他人的关系是生来就“注定”了的，或者，是由我之生所决定的。所以，如果我不可能推卸和逃避我对他人的责任，那么我最不可能推卸和逃避的就是我对父母的责任，不是因为所谓血缘关系，而是因为我生来即注定与此他人最近。此近并不使我对此他人的责任更“重”，但却使我对此他人的责任更直接，更不能不无动于衷。所以，舜之窃负其父而逃，并非出于通常总是被理解为基本上是由血缘关系决定的父子之情，或亲子之爱。我们可以说舜是出于孝，但此孝必须首先被理解为：为一特殊他人负无可推卸和无可逃避之责。而此一“负责”也必然包括：为此他人的过错负责。

的确，如果舜果真如孟子设想的，会放弃天下，带着父亲逃到海边住一辈子，那么舜的此种行为也许首先乃是一种为他人——为一个特殊的他人，父亲——受过的行为，而不是简单纯粹的徇情枉法。本来，经历了一切磨难之后，舜似乎已经可以安安稳稳地恭己正南面而治天下了。然而，他的顽劣的父亲，这个特殊的他人，在桃应的设问中，又一次将他置于磨难之中。当然，作为圣人，舜为了他人，为了一切他人，为了全天下的人，什么都可以做，包括放弃天下。然而，如果他人是一个整体，如果他人只有一个声音，一个要求，或者，如果只有一个他人，问题就简单得多：舜会为此“他人”献出一切，以至于生命。但问题是，这里涉及至少两个他人，两个互不相容的他人：他自己的父亲，和一个（假设的）被他父亲所杀者。怎么办？死者虽然不能复生，但以命抵命却似乎是人类社会的最古老的原则（但最古老的也并不一定就是最合理的和最公正的）。但是，能让自己的父亲如此去死吗？如果让父亲如此去死，舜作为子之孝何在？但这一问题其实却远不止于孝，其实已经远远超出了孝。因为，这一问题蕴含着，我能让他人——任何他人——去死吗？我能听任或允许他人由于任何原因或任何理由去死吗？我对他人有此权力吗？不要以为这是纯粹的现代问题，抽象的哲学问题。处于真正的悲剧性的伦理困境之中，面对是否要让自己之父去面对一个以杀人偿命为原则的法律，舜难道不会提出这样的问题吗？

当然，我们只能设想。替舜设想。就像孟子当年替舜设想一样。孟子仓促之间替舜做出的最好设想是，背着父亲逃到海边。让我们不要忽视这个细节：窃负而逃，背着父亲偷偷逃走。孟子知道舜必然知道，这样做是违法的，违他作为圣人为天下所立之法。所以才是“窃”，所以才要“窃”，偷偷地，不让天下看见。而且，舜虽贵为天子，此时却不仅要“窃”，偷偷地，而且还要“负”，亲自背着：偷偷地亲自背负着自己的父亲逃走。作为天子，舜应该不会没有任何车驾吧？那么，他为什么放弃不用？却要偷偷背着父亲逃走？难道不是因为他知道自己已经无法面对天下之人，已经“对不起”天下之人？在这样的情况之下，舜还会高兴得起来吗？他今后能够欣然而忘天下吗？很难。真正的“忘天下”是离开天下。但舜和他的父亲不可能离开天下。“天下”意味着普遍性，意味着与他人共在，意味着要对天下之人一视同仁。因此，孟子的最后一个回答是有矛盾的。我们是以说孟子的这一回答，他为舜做的这一设想，是仓促之间来不及深思熟虑的回答，但也是一个无法超出这一伦理困境的回答。如果舜选择背着自己的父亲偷偷逃到海边，那么他当然不是在“视弃天下犹弃敝蹝”。他的背负会很沉重，因为在如此背负着有过之父时，他也是在背负着父之过。而在如此背负着父之过时，他也是在背负着因其父之过而受害者。在将父亲偷偷背负到海边之时，他不仅会把父亲之过背到了海边，而且也会把父亲之过的受害者背到了海边。在这样的情况下，在这些重负之下，舜会“终身欣然，乐而忘天下”吗？很难。所以，如果我们分析孟子的最后一个回答，就会看到其中的冲突之处。如果舜真是“视弃天下犹弃敝蹝”，他就不会“窃负而逃”。因为，“视弃天下犹弃敝蹝”中有股孟子所说的浩然之气。而此气概只有相信自己拥有正义的人才能具备。我们都记得孟子是怎么形容浩然之气的：“其为气也，至大至刚。以直养而无害，则塞于天地之间。其为气也，配义与道。无是，馁矣。是集义所生者，非义袭而取之也。行有不慊于心，则馁矣。”“窃负而逃”，不正是因为自己并非理直气壮，因而“行有不慊于心”吗？在此种情况下，舜就算是偷偷背着父亲逃到了海边，他还能高兴得起来吗？他能忘得了他所欠于天下之人的吗？

因此，因为其父之过，舜，按照孟子的设想，尽管可能选择窃负而逃，但却不会——而且我想孟子可能也并不完全相信——真能“视弃天下犹弃敝蹝”，因而也不会真能“终身欣然，乐而忘天下”。如果舜选择跟他的杀了人的父亲一直住在海边的话，他就会背负着他人的过错（他自己的父亲）和他人的痛苦（受害者，被瞽叟所杀者之父或子的痛苦）郁郁而终。

作为圣人，尤其是，作为立法者，舜就没有更好的——准确地说，是更负责的——选择了吗？孟子似乎没能为舜找到。因为，让皋陶抓走瞽叟就意味着，根据杀人抵命的古老原则，瞽叟将需要为被杀者抵命。谁能忍心让自己的父亲如此？换了我们自己又能如何呢？因此，我们同情舜，也同情孟子。然而，舜的不忍心，孟子的不忍心，或者我们的不忍心，却不是因为父亲是父亲，而是因为父亲也是一个他者。我们的不忍心是不忍让他者痛苦，哪怕这个他者是犯有过错甚至罪恶的他者。因此，我们才不仅承担他者的痛苦，而且也承担他者的过错。我们为他者的过错而受苦。然而，在为一个他者——一个特定他者，一个特殊他者——如此绝对地承担痛苦和过错之时，我们——或者舜自己，或者在仓促之中“为”舜做出这一决定的孟子——却已经对他者不公正了。因为还有被瞽叟所杀者，以及此死者之父或子，以及期待着公平正义的天下之人，等等。

那么，我们能为舜设想一个更好的选择吗？一个更加负责的选择？一个更加公平正义的选择？舜当然不应该听任父亲被依照杀人抵命的法律处死。但是这并不是因为他出于亲情而要偏袒父亲，而是因为——让我们这样设想——面对自己的父亲杀人的问题，作为立法者的舜可能会被迫去考虑这样一个根本性的问题：我有权批准杀人吗？人有权批准杀人吗？一个人有权批准杀他人吗？依据对等原则的以命抵命的法律真是天经地义吗？等等。而这也就是说，为了公平正义能够具体地实现，必须有法律。但是法律是建构的，因而总是不完善的，并总是可以不断完善的。而使法律可以不断趋于完善的是公平正义的要求。公平正义与法律并不相等。因为，公平正义的要求从根本上说是他者的要求：公平正义只能来自他者，而且也只是为了他者。而既然他者总是独一无二的，不可比较的，不可替代的，所以其实没有——不可能有——普遍的公平正义。请不要误解这句话。所谓没有普遍的公平正义是说，我力求对每一他者都尽量公正，而每一他者都是独一无二，不可比较，不可替代的。因为，每一次我都需要在具体的、特定的语境中（重新）发明/创造他者所要求的公平正义。因此，在孟子的学生让舜所面对的这一设想出来的伦理困境中，因为不仅要为一个非常独特的他人——父亲——负责，而且也要为其他的人——受害者，乃至天下之人——负责，舜也面对着这样一个发现/发明/创造公平正义的任务。而正是这一任务，这一在某种意义上几乎是不可能的任务，可能会推动舜去改善那本质上必然是旨在保证公平正义的法律。

也许，舜因而会试图立法废除死刑？而且，他是否也可能会让法律更加人性化？因为，为了公平正义，舜可能不会不让自己的杀了人的父亲面对法律。孟子自己也首先承认了这一点。然而，舜也许应该能够做一个比孟子让他做出的选择和决定更好的——更加公平正义的决定？也许，舜不仅不会要窃负而逃，而且会去为父亲请求受害者的宽恕？并且可能会请求代父受刑，或陪同父亲一起服刑？是否他这样就会更加坦然，因为他这样做的时候，既对得起父亲，也对得起天下之人？他没有放弃父亲，没有“不近人情”地放弃父亲，但他也没有放弃天下，没有无动于衷和不负责任地放弃天下。而这也就是说，没有放弃天下之人，没有放弃他对天下每一个人的责任。他不会郁郁而终。相反，作为立法者，他为中国开创了一个未来，一个仍然有待于到来的未来：一个废除了死刑的文化。

一个废除死刑的文化：这难道不是为了防止我们对他者的无可挽回的不公正所必须的最低限度的制度要求？

# 试论德治与法治的辩证关系

中共太原市委党校 贾陆英

在中国，德治思想起源于西周。春秋末期，孔子继承、丰富和发展了周公的德治思想。法家思想起源于春秋时期，形成于战国时期。生活在战国晚期的荀子，溶礼法于一炉，提出“隆礼重法”的治国理念，成为历代统治者维护和巩固国家政权的基本国策。

无论是西方文化还是中国文化，都把人性作为研究道德与法的逻辑起点。中国文化对人性的认识，大致有四种观点：一是性善论，二是性恶论，三是人性无善无恶论，四是人性既善又恶论。孟子从“性善论”出发，强调主体修养在人性完善过程中的作用，丰富和发展了孔子的德治思想。荀子从“性恶论”出发，强调道德教育的重要性，融合法家观点，提出了“隆礼重法”的思想。由秦朝二世而亡引发的大讨论，是事关立国思想、治国方略的大讨论，也理所当然地追溯到人性问题。西汉哲学家杨雄提出了“人之性也善恶混”的观点，认为人性具有善恶两种因素，经过后天的熏染和学习，发展善的因素则成为善人，发展恶的因素则成为恶人。这些观点，为汉代日渐成熟起来的“阳儒阴法”治国方略提供了理论上的依据。

综观人类文明史，人性既有善、又有恶的判断才符合人的实际。道德与法就是根源于人性的这一基本特征而产生的。道德的基本功能在于劝善，法律的基本功能在于惩恶。二者各有优长，也各有不足，天然地具有互补性。抓住互补性这一关键，就抓住了认识和把握德治与法治辩证关系的切入点。德治是内在的自律，法治是外在的他律。从个人角度看，人的自我发展很重要的内容是人格的自我完善，而人格的完善主要依赖于道德水准的提高。从社会角度看，只要人类社会存在，就离不开道德的规范。德治既是治国的手段，也是社会发展进步的目标。而人性中恶的因素是不可能单靠教化解决的，离开了有效的他律作保障，个体的自律是难以实现的，也是靠不住的，法治就是为了抑制和惩处人性中恶的因素，维护和增强人性中善的因素所发明的一种社会机制。法律的产生是以道德为基础的，法治建设需要思想道德建设先行，法治的运行和法律的实施都要靠社会道德的支撑，法治的完善也离不开道德制约。法律重在惩罚已经违法犯罪的人，道德重在教育尚未违法犯罪的人；法律能惩“贪”，道德能养“廉”。法律的规则是有限的，社会生活中相当多的问题需要通过道德教育来解决。无限夸大法律惩处的作用而贬低道德教化的作用，或者无限夸大道德教化的作用而贬低法律惩处的作用，都是要不得的。德治与法治相辅相成，缺一不可，忽视其中任何一个方面，都不可能达到使国家长治久安的目的。

依法治国与以德治国相结合的治国方略，是对传统社会治理模式的扬弃，也是适应新时代要求的创造性转换。要从“法治”与“德治”相关联的角度推进法制建设和道德建设，把推进法治中国建设和培育社会主义核心价值观紧密结合起来。

今年，是孔子诞辰 2565 周年。孔子创立的儒家思想经过千百年的传承、积淀、丰富和发展，成为中国传统文化的主干，并且经过在亚洲、欧洲和世界其他地区的传播及其与当地文化的融合，成为世界文化的一个重要源流和组成部分。

21 世纪，儒学在世界和平与发展的历史进程中将扮演什么角色、发挥什么作用?世界著名历史学家汤因比先生曾经预言：儒家的人文主义价值观使得中国文明符合了新时代人类社会整合的需求。只有中华文明，才能真正给予世界永久的和平。一个历史上一直是和平主义和世界主义为取向的天下文明也将在 21 世纪成为全人类的共同精神财富。

无论在西方还是东方，道德与法都是治理国家、调节社会的重要手段。然而，就道德与法的关系而言，西方文化更注重法，法是科学理性从外部强行规范人们行为的产物；中国文化则更注重德，德在儒家的人文主义价值观中占有十分突出的位置，是人文精神从人的自身修养出发自觉规范人们行为的产物，从个人品德、家庭美德到社会公德，无所不在，如影随形地指导着中国人的言行。德治与法治作为两种基本的社会控制模式，不是对立的，而是互补的，二者有机结合，相得益彰，共同贡献于人类的文明，贡献于 21 世纪的世界和平与发展。

下面，我将以中国文化为例，阐释德治与法治的辩证关系。

## 一、德治与法治的形成和发展

在中国，德治思想起源于西周。范文澜先生说，商是“尊神文化”，周是“尊礼文化”。这个礼的实质，就是周朝的德治思想。西周初年，周公摄政，分封建国，制礼作乐，推行了一整套维护君臣宗法和上下等级的典章制度，对于巩固周天子的统治，保证社会秩序的稳定，促进经济文化的发展，发挥了重要作用。为了论证周朝取代商朝的合法性，周公提出“天命靡常”和“皇天无亲，惟德是辅”的观点，以改造夏、商时代的“天命观”，强调天意不能脱离人意，统治者的地位主要靠德行来维持，从而在一定程度上限制了“天”及鬼神的作用，看到了人的力量。与此同时，强调德治的治国理念，提出“敬德保民”、“明德慎罚”、“以德配天”，激发了人们道德意识的觉醒。

春秋末期，孔子继承、丰富和发展了周公的德治思想。孔子极为推崇周公和周礼，他说：“周监于二代，郁郁乎文哉！吾从周。”周礼是对夏、商两代典章制度进行因袭、损益而成的，达到了前所未有的高度，因此，他主张遵从周礼。周礼所蕴含的德治思想，在孔子创立的儒家学说中占有突出位置，其要义是用道德教化来规范人们的言行，借助道德的作用对社会进行调节和控制，以达到治理天下的目的。孟子进一步提出以民本为核心的仁政学说，把德治思想推向了新的高度。孔孟德治思想的要点是：第一、为政以德。要求国君率先垂范，统治者集团以身作则，修身立德，勤政尽责，充分发挥道德感化作用，并选拔任用贤才来管理国家。第二、爱民惠民。强调为政不可违背人心，要“泛爱众”，给民众以实惠和“恒产”（土地），让他们安居乐业。重视对民众的道德教化，以使他们的善心得到扩充和发扬。第三、德主刑辅。孔子并不否认“政”“刑”的作用，但他更强调“德”“礼”在教育人，感化人，引导人，提升人方面的重要作用，由此奠定了儒家德礼优于政刑，德礼为主、政刑为辅的治理模式。

法家思想起源于春秋时期，形成于战国时期。法家是中国历史上主张富国强兵，以法治国的重要学派，在法理学方面对于法律的起源、本质、作用以及法律同社会经济、国家政权的关系等基本问题，进行了卓有成效的探讨，强调“不别亲疏，不殊贵贱，一断于法”，这是难能可贵的。孔子对法家的先驱人物管仲、子产都有高度评价，孔子创立的儒家思想与法家思想并非截然对立。生活在战国晚期的荀子，溶礼法于一炉，提出“隆礼重法”的治国理念。他立足于儒家的“礼治”观，在“礼”与“法”的关系上，继承孔子的观点，认为礼是高于法的。而对于法的重要地位和作用的认识，却突破孔子，汲取法家的“法治”观，主张“礼法并重”，从而把“礼”与“法”当作治国安邦的两大根本手段。《唐律疏议》以“德礼为政教之本，刑罚为政教之用”两句脍炙人口的言辞，将这一治理模式做了简明的概括，使之成为历代统治者维护和巩固国家政权的基本国策。

## 二、德治与法治的人性根源

无论是西方文化还是中国文化，都把人性作为研究道德与法的逻辑起点。《论语》中孔子很少谈及人性，只是说：“性相近也，习相远也。”人性是从人的先天的本能发展而来的，人的本能是相近或相似的，是人性形成的内因，人与人在习性上的差别是后天造成的，是不同的环境影响和个人努力程度的结果，后天的环境因素和个人努力，是人性形成的外因。对于人性究竟是善还是恶，孔子没有说，这也为后世关于人性的探讨留下了空间。中国文化对人性的认识，大致有四种观点：一是性善论，以孟子为代表，认为“人性之善，犹水之就下也。人无有不善，水无有不下。”二是性恶论，以荀子为代表，认为“人之性恶，其善伪也。”三是人性无善无恶论，以告子为代表，认为“生之谓性”，人性无所谓善与恶。四是人性既善又恶论。以西汉的扬雄为代表，认为“人之性也，善恶混。修其善则为善人，修其恶则为恶人。”这四种观点中，对中国文化影响最大的是孟子的性善论，其次是荀子的性恶论。他们虽然各执一端，但都从一个侧面对人性问题进行了深入的探讨，形成了中华文化特别注重自我修养和道德教育的传统。

讲人性，离不开人与人的关系。因为人性是在人与人的关系中形成的，社会性是人的根本属性，是人与动物的本质区别。人类在长期的发展中，在处理人与人之间的关系上，形成了“义”和“利”这一对基本的伦理道德范畴。一事当前，是“义”字当先，还是唯利是图，这是人们衡量一个人是性善还是性恶的基本标准。也就是说，人类异于其他物种的一个显著特点，在于道德性。

孟子从“性善论”出发，强调主体修养在人性完善过程中的作用，丰富和发展了孔子的德治思想。孔子创立了以“仁”为核心的儒学思想体系，注重从人自身的情感和行为上，从人心之仁上去探究礼的根源。孟子循着这一思路作了进一步探索，他说：“仁义礼智根于心”，只要把人心中善的本性充分发扬起来，“人皆可为尧舜”。这一观点有力地启发了人们道德实践的自觉性，奠定了儒家在道德修养中更多地借助于自我反思、自我完善的基础。在社会治理上，孔子强调德治的重要性，突破“刑不上大夫，礼不下庶人”的旧观念，主张“为国以礼”，“为政以德”，不仅要求为政者要率先垂范，而且对百姓也要“道之以德，齐之以礼”，体现了对人的某种尊重。孟子进一步提出了“仁政”思想，强调“民为贵，社稷次之，君为轻”，君王只有实行仁政，才能得民心，从而巩固其统治基础。君王实行仁政必须以民为本，“民之为道也，有恒产者有恒心，无恒产者无恒心”，只有给民众以稳定的产业，使他们安居乐业，才能逐步引导他们提升道德水平。孟子的这些观点，把德治思想发展到新的高度。

荀子从“性恶论”出发，强调道德教育的重要性，并且融合法家观点，提出了“隆礼重法”的思想。和孔孟从人心之仁出发去探讨礼的根源不同，荀子从人心之欲出发去探讨礼的根源。他说：“礼起于何也？曰：人生而有欲。欲而不得，则不能无求。求而无度量分界，则不能不争。争则乱，乱则穷。先王恶其乱也，故制礼义以分之，以养人之欲，给人之求，使欲必不穷于物，物必不屈于欲。两者相持而长，是礼之所起也。”荀子还从人的社会性上探究礼的根源及其重要性、必要性，他说；人，“力不若牛，走不若马，而牛马为用，何也？曰：人能群，彼不能群也。人何以能群？曰：分。分何以能行？曰：义。……故人生不能无群，群而无分则争，争则乱，乱则离，离则弱，弱则不能胜物。故宫室不可得而居也，不可少顷舍礼义之谓也。”荀子的观点很明确，人性所固有的欲望和人类所特有的社会生活，是“礼”产生的根源。“礼”的制定和推行离不开“义”，“礼义”的本质内涵就是“分”，也就是贵贱、长幼之别。荀子说：“人无礼则不生，事无礼则不成，国家无礼则不宁。”“礼义”之于人类，不是先天就有的，而是人为的，是先王、圣人为了治理天下而制定的。生活在战国晚期的荀子，在稷下学宫“三为忌酒”，深受百家争鸣的影响，其学术内容和背景显得更加丰富和宽广。正如郭沫若先生所说：“荀子是先秦诸子的最后一位大师，他不仅集了儒家的大成，而且集了百家的大成。”荀子思想中对后世产生巨大影响的，是他融合法家观点提出的“隆礼重法”，礼法并用的思想，他把“礼”与“法”当作治国安邦的两大根本手段，事实上成为汉以后历代统治者的治国方略。

由秦朝二世而亡引发的大讨论，是事关立国思想、治国方略的大讨论，也理所当然地追溯到人性问题。战国时代后期的秦国，用法家思想富国强兵，于公元前 221 年消灭六国、完成统一大业，建立了中央集权的大帝国，这是中国历史上划时代的大事。然而，强大的秦帝国继续沿用法家思想，以武力治理国家，用严刑酷法实行残暴统治，对百姓横征暴敛，大兴土木，劳民伤财，结果仅存在 16 年就灭亡了。西汉初年著名的政论家贾谊在《过秦论》中深刻指出，秦朝迅速灭亡的原因在于“仁义不施而攻守之势异也。”由此引发了一场持续而影响久远的大讨论。这场大讨论总结出“可以马上打天下，不可以马上治天下”的历史教训。西汉大儒董仲舒在国策上提出“春秋大一统”和“罢黜百家，独尊儒术”的主张，在人性论上提出性三品说。他认为，人性区分为“圣人之性”、“中民之性”和“斗筲之性”。“圣人之性”是天生的，一般人先天不可能，后天不可及；“斗筲之性”无“善质”，生来就“恶”，只能采用刑罚的手段来处置他们；“中民之性”可上可下，可善可恶，是万民之性，是“有善质而未能善”，必须通过王者的教化才能成善。西汉后期著名的哲学家杨雄，提出了“人之性也善恶混”的观点，认为人性具有善恶两种因素，它们都是与生俱来的，经过后天的熏染和学习，发展善的因素则成为善人，发展恶的因素则成为恶人。他强调后天的学习和修养，是对孔子“性相近也，习相远也”思想的发挥。西汉学者在人性问题上的这些观点，为汉代日渐成熟起来的“阳儒阴法”治国方略提供了理论上的依据。“阳儒”，就是公开倡导儒家思想，实行德治，教化人心，以使人性中善的因素得到弘扬，这说明汉代统治者从秦朝灭亡的教训中认识到“得人心者得天下”的重要性；“阴法”，就是在实际政治活动中推行并依靠法家的法治，以维护其专制统治，这说明汉代统治者认识到人性中恶的因素是不可能单靠教化解决的，因而在治国方略的选择上具有了清醒的政治现实感。“阳儒阴法”的治国方略，既避免了纯任儒家的柔弱，也避免了纯任法家的严酷，是一种兼容并蓄的政治制度。

## 三、德治与法治的优劣比较

综观人类的文明史，人性既有善、又有恶的判断才符合人的实际。中国的阴阳思想认为，天地万物之中都包含着阴、阳两种既相反又相成的因素。人性也是如此。人性中阳的因素即是善，阴的因素即是恶。我们说某人是善人，其实是指在这个人身上善的因素占据着主导地位；说某人是恶人，其实是指在这个人身上恶的因素占据着主导地位。道德与法就是根源于人性的这一基本特征而产生的，是人类社会特有的现象。道德的基本功能在于劝善，法律的基本功能在于惩恶。二者各有优长，也各有不足，天然地具有互补性。抓住互补性这一关键，就抓住了认识和把握德治与法治辩证关系的切入点。

德治是内在的自律。德治着眼于弘扬人性中善的因素，强调教化在人格塑造中的重要性和必要性，认为教化是使人弃恶扬善，强基固本的基本途径。一个人的进步，是修身克已、弃恶扬善的结果。一个民族文明程度的提高，也是在经济社会不断发展的过程中弃恶扬善、革故鼎新的结果。孔子的仁爱思想最可贵的价值，并不是仅仅主张以孝为本，亲亲为大，而是抓住“孝”这个根本，对人进行教化，使人超越自我，实现从亲亲，到爱人，再到爱天下万物的人生境界升华。这种博大的人文情怀，正是孔子学说、中华文明的精华所在。马克思曾经说过：“道德的基础是人类精神的自律。”道德属于社会意识形态，是调整人与人、人与社会之间关系的行为规范的总和。它以真与假、善与恶、美与丑、是与非、好与坏、荣与辱、正义与非正义、公正与偏私、诚实与虚伪等基本范畴作为评价人们行为的标准，通过教育和社会舆论的力量使人们形成一定的信念、价值观、习惯和传统，从而引导人们对社会实际生活中的各种事物、思想和行为进行价值判断和选择。道德并不是超自然的、先验的或主观自生的东西，而是社会存在的反映，又对社会存在有着巨大的反作用。无论是对于一个民族或国家，还是对于一个人来说，道德都是至关重要的。作为一种理想信念和精神支柱，它是人类前进的“日的地”；作为一种思想境界和内在力量，它是人类前进的“发动机”；作为一种价值标准，它是人类前进的“方向盘”；作为一种行为规范，它是人类前进的“交通警”。从个人角度看，人的自我发展很重要的内容是人格的自我完善，而人格的完善主要依赖于道德水准的提高。从社会角度看，只要人类社会存在，就离不开道德的规范。德治既是治国的手段，也是社会发展进步的目标。

法治是外在的他律。人性中恶的因素是不可能单靠教化解决的，离开了有效的他律作保障，个体的自律是难以实现的，也是靠不住的。特别是对于掌握一定权力的人来说，如果没有健全有效的他律，疏于监督和管理，就必然会产生腐败，这是被无数事实反复证明了的一条铁律。法治就是为了抑制和惩处人性中恶的因素，维护和增强人性中善的因素所发明的一种社会机制。惩恶扬善，正是制定和实施法律的出发点和归宿点。法律的基本特征，一是它具有国家意志性，由国家制定或认可；二是它具有国家强制性，由国家强制力保证实施。对于公民而言，它是外部力量对个体进行的刚性约束，也就是他律，是一种不可违背的强制力，是一条不可逾越的底线。违背了，逾越了，就要受到惩罚，甚至要付出生命的代价。对于社会而言，它带有根本性、全局性、稳定性和长期性，可以有效地防止把国家的稳定和希望“寄托在一两个人威望上”的悲剧发生，是维护社会有序运转，维护国家长治久安的根本保障。

然而，法律的强制力也具有天然的缺陷。生活在 2500 多年前的孔子，就已经看到法律和刑罚并不能从根本上达到维护社会秩序的目的，已经看到人们的道德面貌、道德思想和道德素质在维护社会秩序中的重要作用。他说：“道之以政，齐之以刑，民免而无耻；道之以德，齐之以礼，有耻且格。”孔子认为，用行政命令去实施领导，用严刑苛罚去整治民众，民众虽然会因为畏惧而求免于处罚，但是却不知道违反法律是可耻的。因此，他们就不可能在内心中形成一道防御犯罪的堤防，而只是力求逃避法律的惩罚，甚至想方设法去钻法律的空子，一犯再犯，从而陷入邪恶的深渊。这种强制、压制的手段，其效果必不能深入人心，使民众感而自化。用仁德去引导民众，用礼乐去教化民众，民众就会有廉耻之心，而且会收到人心归服的效果。孟子也说：“徒法不足以自行。”法律的产生是以道德为基础的，法治建设需要思想道德建设先行，法治的运行和法律的实施都要靠社会道德的支撑，法治的完善也离不开道德制约。法律重在惩罚已经违法犯罪的人，道德重在教育尚未违法犯罪的人，提高他们的素质，使他们不去犯罪；法律能惩“贪”，道德能养“廉”。法律的规则是有限的，不可能囊括社会生活的各个方面，社会生活中相当多的问题需要通过道德教育来解决。近来一再被媒体提起的“老人摔倒扶与不扶”的问题，就是一例。不扶是有违道德的，会受到社会舆论的指责，然而这是非法律义务行为，属于公民的自治领域，并不由法律强制调整。由此可见，道德适用的范围远远大于法律，更加贴近生活。维护良好的社会秩序，形成和谐的人际关系，要靠法制，也要靠教育来提高全体公民的道德品行和文化素质。无限夸大法律惩处的作用而贬低德治的作用，或者无限夸大道德教化的作用而贬低法治的作用，都是要不得的。德治与法治相辅相成，缺一不可，忽视其中任何一个方面，都不可能达到使国家长治久安的目的。

## 四、从法治与德治的辩证统一中把握法制建设和道德建设

依法治国与以德治国相结合的治国方略，是对传统社会治理模式的扬弃，也是适

应新时代要求的创造性转换。“法治”一词在我国最早出现在《晏子春秋·谏上九》这部典籍中：“昔者先君桓公之地狭于今，修法治，广政教，以霸诸侯。”其含义虽然有强调法律权威性的意味，然而，君主却拥有制定法律和运用法律的至高权力和唯一合法性。历史事实证明，这种“君权至上”的“法治”，在实践中必然演化为专制。法家思想的弊端，在于过分夸大法律的作用而忽视道德的作用，而这个法律则是建立在过度依赖君王个人能力，以君王个人意志为依据的基础之上。法家学派的集大成者韩非子，提出法、术、势三者相结合的理论体系，强调加强君主专制。可见法家所主张的“法治”，并非现代意义上的法治。我们今天讲的法治，是“法律至上”的法治，是依据宪法和法律来治理国家。它是汲取人类政治文明的重要成果，也是对新中国成立以来的历史经验和教训进行深刻总结的结果。“依法治国”的治国方略，继承了法家思想精华，又是以现代法治理念为指导，以党的领导、人民当家做主、依法治国三者有机统一为核心，以公平正义为价值取向，以尊重和保障人权为基本原则，以法律的至高无上权威为根本要求，以监督制约为内在机制，以自由平等为理想追求的法治。历史和现实的经验都告诉我们，依法治国必须和以德治国相结合。而我们今天讲的“以德治国”，同样是在汲取儒家德治思想精华，摒弃其维护宗法等级制度、把治国希望系于君主一人、夸大德治作用而对法治重视不够等局限，适应社会主义市场经济体制要求的新型社会主义“德治”。这个新型的社会主义“德治”观，是以为人民服务为核心、以集体主义为原则，重视道德教育和道德感化的作用，强调选拔干部必须德才兼备、以德为先，要求各级领导干部和国家公务员“讲党性、重品行、作表率”，发挥示范带头作用的“德治”；是在肯定“法治”重要意义的基础上，使“德治”与“法治”互相补充，并行不悖，共同维护和保障国家长治久安的“德治”。

从“法治”与“德治”相关联的角度推进法制建设和道德建设。2013年2月23日，习近平同志在中央政治局第四次集体学习时指出：“要坚持依法治国和以德治国相结合，把法治建设和道德建设紧密结合起来，把他律和自律紧密结合起来，做到法治和德治相辅相成、相互促进。”法律与道德功能不同，调整的社会关系层面不同，应根据所要调整的各种社会关系，统筹兼顾、整体考虑。从法制建设的实践来看，法律的创制和运作必须以正确的思想道德观念为指导，立法要注意法律的道义基础，根据客观实际，把一些最重要、最基本的道德要求，直接纳入法律的规范中。从道德建设的实践来看，道德的主要功能在于“扬善”。道德作为一种规范，主要是依靠社会舆论、风俗习惯和人们的内心信念，依靠个人的自律来推动的。道德的特点在于自觉，但事实上道德自觉绝不是一开始就有的。在改革开放和社会主义市场经济环境下，在巨大的利益驱动面前，单纯的道德说教有时会显得苍白无力。良好道德品质的养成，良好社会风气的形成，一开始往往也要借助于法律、经济、行政等手段。“道德是法律的支撑，法律是道德的底线”，道德建设的一项重要任务，是要把遵纪守法作为公民最基本的要求提出来。而法律所维护的，是最基本、也是最低限度的社会道德。对于那些在社会公德、职业道德、家庭美德、个人品德等方面严重违反道德的行为和现象，客观上也必然要求运用法律来加以制裁，在立法时予以适当规范。这样，才能使法治和德治相互渗透、相辅相成，更加紧密地结合在一起。针对一个时期以来“醉酒驾驶”给群众生命安全带来的严重威胁和伤害，人大修法使“醉驾入刑”，这是运用法律手段解决严重违背社会公德问题的一个成功范例。

把推进法治中国建设和培育社会主义核心价值观紧密结合起来。法治中国，是新时期集法治国家、法治政府和法治社会为一体的法治建设新目标。推进法治中国建设，其基本路径就是坚持依法治国、依法执政、依法行政共同推进，坚持法治国家、法治政府、法治社会一体建设；其基本方针就是全面推进科学立法、严格执法、公正司法、全民守法；其基本方法就是运用法治思维和法治方式化解社会矛盾。要把这些要求落到实处，最根本的，依然是大力培育和弘扬社会主义核心价值观，提高全体公民尤其是各级领导干部的素质。国无德不兴，人无德不立。古今中外的历史充分表明，一个民族，一个国家，最持久、最深层的力量是全社会共同认可的核心价值观。社会主义核心价值观承载着中华民族的精神追求，体现着当代中国社会评判是非曲直的价值标准，是凝魂聚气、强基固本的基础工程。只有大力倡导富强、民主、文明、和谐的理念，才能把全国人民建设社会主义现代化强国，实现民族复兴的力量凝聚起来；只有大力倡导自由、平等、公正、法治的理念，才能推进社会公平正义，在全社会弘扬社会主义法治精神，引导全体人民遵守法律、有问题依靠法律来解决，形成守法光荣的良好氛围；只有大力倡导爱国、敬业、诚信、友善的理念，才能继承和弘扬中华民族传统美德，古为今用，推陈出新，以文化人，以文育人，引导人们向往和追求讲道德、尊道德、守道德的生活。社会主义核心价值观是充分反映中国特色、民族特性、时代特征的价值体系，回答了我们要建设什么样的国家、建设什么样的社会、培育什么样的公民的重大问题。在全社会培育和弘扬社会主义核心价值观，是不断促进国家治理体系和治理能力现代化的有力支撑；是维护社会主义法制的统一、尊严、权威，形成人们不愿违法、不能违法、不敢违法和自觉守法的法治环境的有力支撑；是有效整合社会意识，使社会系统得以正常运转、社会秩序得以有效维护，法治中国建设目标得以顺利推进的有力支撑。

拿破仑说过，中国是一头沉睡的狮子，当这头睡狮醒来时，世界都会为之发抖。习近平主席在中法建交 50 周年纪念大会上发表演讲时，机智而不失幽默地借用拿破仑的这句名言，表达了中国人民追求和平的强烈愿望。他说：“中国这头狮子已经醒了，但这是一只和平的、可亲的、文明的狮子。”天下太平、共享大同是中华民族绵延数千年的理想。近代以来，中国人民历经苦难，深知和平之宝贵；今天，正在崛起的中国希望同世界各国一道共谋和平、共护和平、共享和平。联合国教科文组织总部大楼前的石碑上，用多种语言镌刻着这样一句话："战争起源于人之思想，故务需于人之思想中筑起保卫和平之屏障。"以天下太平、共享大同为价值取向的中华文明，必将在21世纪为全人类在心灵中坚定和平理念、扬起和平风帆、形成维护世界和平的强大力量，做出自己应有的贡献。

# 私权抗御公权

## ——“亲亲相隐”新论

西南政法大学 俞荣根

自1977年以来，在中国法律史研究中享有持续不减之热度者，“亲亲相隐”思想及其制度问题当居于首位。观察其研究的轨迹，最令人惊叹之处在于：它是如此地契合克罗齐的名言：“一切真历史都是当代史”。[①] 换言之，它的每一次发热，都与我们时代的思想解放、传统苏醒、法治文明化，尤其是刑事法律制度文明化休戚相关、因果相连。本文通过对“亲亲相隐”思想及其制度研究的梳理，力图从家庭权利的视角揭示“亲亲相隐”的性质，它隐含着古代私权抗御公权的宝贵元素，认为其中的正面价值值得认真发掘和研讨。

## 一、30年论争：“亲亲相隐”之研究

1980年前后，在各种法学出版物中对儒家法律思想及以其为主旨的古代法的评价，负面文字居多，尤其是“亲亲相隐”，被认定为儒家思想中纯属“消极因素”的部分，[②] 断言它“是为了维护封建伦常和家族制度，巩固君主专制统治”。[③]

学界对“亲亲相隐”的研究就是在背负着这样一个沉重的负面评价中艰难起步的。追随思想解放的潮流，守望传统文化的学人们逐渐向它注入同情理解的春水，融化那个被冰封冻僵的古老法律思想和制度。这个过程十分漫长，大致经历了四个阶段。

第一个阶段。20世纪80年代，循着那个时代通行的“一分为二”、“去粗取精”的方法论，指出“亲亲相隐”的思想与制度是一种与“株连”、“缘坐”、“族刑”等酷刑

---

① （意）贝奈戴托·克罗齐：《历史学的理论和实际》，傅任敢译，北京：商务印书馆，1982年，第2页。

② 当时，持这样观点的文字比较常见，可参见法学教材编辑部审订：（高等学校法学教材）《中国法律思想史》，北京：法律出版社，1982年，第62页。

③ 参见《中国大百科全书》（法学），北京：中国大百科全书出版社，1984年，第475页。

相对立的诉讼原则与刑罚原则，是对家庭、人身和孝亲权利的一种认可，与民国时期刑诉法中亲属无举证责任的诉讼原则存在历史联系，有一定历史进步意义，“亲亲相隐”与“大义灭亲”在中国古代法中是对立统和于一体的两个方面。①

第二阶段。20世纪90年代，运用中西法律比较研究的方法，揭示“亲亲相隐”并非中国传统法律特有的原则或制度。无论中西，还是古今，法律中都存在着“亲亲相隐”之类的原则和规定。亲属容隐制度在中西法律传统中、在不同社会制度中、在不同法系中虽有一些具体规定上的差异，但在原则和原理上是相通和“暗合”的，对于“亲亲相隐”这一法律文化现象在人类文明史中的地位和价值，及其在当代社会中可能具有的功能和意义，应予积极的认识和评判。这一研究以《中国社会科学》于1997年第3期发表范忠信教授的《中西法律传统中的“亲亲相隐”》一文为代表。②

第三阶段。本世纪初，一场以哲学界为主角的“亲亲相隐”问题大讨论登上中国学术论坛。2002年，刘清平教授在《哲学研究》第2期发表《美德还是腐败？——析〈孟子〉中有关舜的两个案例》一文，开启了这场历时10年之久的辩论。辩论的另一方是武汉大学哲学教授郭齐勇先生的团队。2007年，邓晓芒教授在《学海》第1期发表长达20页的《再议“亲亲相隐”的腐败倾向》一文，力挺刘清平先生的儒学批判，把这论战推进到第二期。双方论战的内容涉及“亲亲相隐”的伦理原则、人性基础、法律制度、现代价值等。以郭齐勇为代表的当代儒家学者主张把“亲亲相隐”视为道德上的善，即视为“直德”、“圣贤典范”以及“天理人情之至”。刘、邓二位教授则将之视为道德上的恶和“社会病毒”，定性为“滋生腐败”的“温床”。在哲学界的带动下，法学学者勇猛跟进，相互呼应，其他学科纷纷卷入，使“亲亲相隐”超过传统法学中

① 参见杨景凡、俞荣根：《孔子的法律思想》，北京：群众出版社，1984年，第164页。

② 还可参考范忠信：“中西伦理合璧与法治模式的中国特色”，《法商研究》，1999年第2期；范忠信：“‘亲亲尊尊’与亲属相犯：中外刑法的暗合”，《法学研究》，1997年第3期；范忠信：《亲亲相为隐：中外法律的共同传统——兼论其根源及其与法治的关系》，《比较法研究》，1997年第2期。

的一切问题成为首要理论热点。[①]

第四阶段。2004 年人权入宪，国家法治建设有了新标高，加之佘祥林[②]、赵作

① 参见：郭齐勇主编：武汉：湖北教育出版社，2004 年；邓晓芒：《儒家伦理新批判》，重庆：重庆大学出版社，2010 年；郭齐勇主编：《〈儒家伦理新批判〉之批判》，武汉：武汉大学出版社，2011 年。相关论文在《儒家伦理争鸣集——以“亲亲互隐”为中心》一书中收录的有：郭齐勇《也谈“子为父隐”与孟子论舜——兼与刘清平先生商榷》；郭齐勇、龚建平：《“德治”语境中的“亲亲相隐”——对穆南珂先生“商榷”的商榷》；刘清平：《美德还是腐败？——析《孟子》中有关舜的两个案例》；范忠信的《中西法律传统中的“亲亲相隐”》等 3 篇文章；郑家栋：《“父为子隐，子为父隐”再议》、《中国传统思想中的父子关系及诠释的面向——从“父为子隐，子为父隐”说起》；赵文艳：《论“亲亲相隐”与“大义灭亲”》；刘军平：《儒家“亲亲相隐”的伦理依据和法律诉讼》；曾小五：《就“父子相隐”看儒家关于血缘亲情与道德法律的关系观念》等。在《儒家伦理新批判》一书中收录的有：《再议“亲亲相隐”的腐败倾向——评郭齐勇主编〈儒家伦理争鸣集〉》；《就“亲亲互隐”问题答四儒生》；《就“亲亲相隐”问题再答四儒生》；《就“亲亲相隐”问题答林桂榛先生》；《关于苏格拉底赞赏“子告父罪”的背景知识》等。在《〈儒家伦理新批判〉之批判》一书中收录的有：郭齐勇：《“亲亲相隐”“容隐制”及其对当今法治的启迪——在北京大学的演讲》；丁为祥：《反思与反省——邓晓芒〈儒家伦理新批判〉题外之思》；龚建平：《“逻辑”是否可以取代“仁德”？——答邓晓芒先生对儒家“亲亲”伦理的质询》；龚建平：《批判的前提——回邓晓芒教授》；龚建平：《“植根于身体感受”之心的“自我反思、自我批判”——邓晓芒〈儒家伦理新批判〉之我见》；胡治洪：《指“误”者之误——〈再议“亲亲相隐”的腐败倾向〉一文谬误举隅》；胡治洪：《辩误者再误——析〈就“亲亲互隐”问题答四儒生〉》；周浩翔：《为“亲亲互隐”正名——回应邓晓芒教授》；郭齐勇、陈乔见：《苏格拉底、柏拉图与孔子的“亲亲互隐”及家庭伦常观》；林桂榛：《苏格拉底对“子告父”表示赞赏吗？——就柏拉图〈欧绪弗洛篇〉的“虔敬”问题等商榷于邓晓芒教授》；范忠信：《“期待之可能性”与我国刑事法的“法治圣贤定位”——从“亲亲相隐”的角度观察》；刘斌：《“亲亲相隐”与“大义灭亲”》；留白：《“亲亲互隐”的迷局》；林桂榛：《“父子相为隐”与亲属间举证——亲情、法律、正义的伦理中道问题》；林桂榛：《关于“亲亲相隐”问题的若干辨正》；陈壁生：《孔子“父子相隐”思想新解》；崔发展：《容隐现象的发生与容隐制的建构》等。除上述三本论文集外还可参见：郭齐勇：《关于“亲亲互隐”、“爱有差等”的争鸣》，《江苏社会科学》，2005 年第 3 期；刘清平：《父子相隐、君臣相讳与即行报官——儒家“亲亲相隐”观念刍议》，《人文杂志》，2009 年第 5 期；刘水静：《重析西方文化传统中的“亲亲相隐”与“大义灭亲”之道德意涵——再评邓晓芒教授的〈儒家伦理新批判〉》，《学海》，2013 年第 6 期，等等。

② 佘祥林，男，1966 年 3 月 7 日生，京山县雁门口镇何场村九组人，捕前系京山县公安局原马店派出所治安巡逻员。1994 年 1 月 2 日，佘妻张在玉因患精神病走失失踪，张的家人怀疑张在玉被丈夫杀害。同年 4 月 28 日，佘祥林因涉嫌杀人被批捕，后被原荆州地区中级人民法院一审被判处死刑，剥夺政治权利终身。湖北省高级人民法院二审认为事实不清、证据不足发回重审。后因行政区划变更，佘祥林一案移送京山县公安局，经京山县人民法院和荆门市中级人民法院审理。1998 年 9 月 22 日，佘祥林被判处 15 年有期徒刑。在佘祥林服刑 11 年后，即 2005 年 3 月 28 日，佘妻张在玉突然从山东回到京山。4 月 13 日，京山县人民法院经重新开庭审理，宣判佘祥林无罪。自佘祥林出事后，佘母杨五香走遍了周围的村落寻找出走的儿媳。因为佘祥林跟她说过“我确实没有杀她”，这个倔强而爱子的农村妇女就开始了为儿子辩污的艰辛之路。她穷困潦倒，身无分文被人接济着四处寻找，1995 年元旦前后，杨五香寻访到了离雁门口几十公里远的天门市石河镇姚岭村，发现儿媳的线索。姚岭村副书记倪乐平给她出一个见过张在玉的证明。这份证明后来被媒体称为“良心证明”，如果没有它，也许佘祥林早已作了枪下冤魂。然而，这份证明送到有关部门后，并没有得到令佘家惊喜的结果，对方的回答是“这一套我们见得多了”。反而是杨五香因为反复上访和申诉被抓了起来，抓起来的原因是“包庇犯罪”、“妨碍司法公正”。九个月后，看守所通知佘家带上 3000 元钱去领人，看守人员把杨五香背了出来。“她变得又聋又瞎，不会走路。”佘祥林的父亲佘树生说。在病痛中挨了三个月后，佘母杨五香去世，死时才 54 岁。（参见：毛立新．拿什么纪念佘祥林的母亲［EB/OL］（2006－04－02）［2008－8－20］．http：//www.dffy.com）

海[①]等一些属于刑讯逼供“毒树之果”的重大错案曝光，且其逼供之中都有逼供家属情节，从而引发了全社会要求修改刑事诉讼法证据制度的呼声。学术界搬出刑法学中的“期待可能性理论”、“刑法谦抑主义”等武器，论证古老“亲亲相隐”原则及其制度的现代价值。[②] 2012年3月14日第11届全国人民代表大会第五次会议通过刑事诉讼法修正案。修正案增加的第一百八十八条规定：“经人民法院通知，证人没有正当理由不出庭作证的，人民法院可以强制其到庭，但是被告人的配偶、父母、子女除外。”这一“但书”，一定程度上认可主要亲属有不出庭作证权。有的学者在赞赏这一规定继承了“亲亲相隐”传统的同时，指出它并未认可亲属的“沉默权”、“拒证权”。

盘点30多年来关于“亲亲相隐”的讨论，理论收获颇丰，其集中体现为以下几点：

第一，考析“亲亲相隐”之思想流变及其法律制度化过程，梳理这一制度自汉魏经隋唐至明清的法律细节以及在司法中的运作情形。

第二，训译、释解“亲亲相隐”及“其父攘羊”、“窃负而逃”等相关故事中诸如“隐”、“攘”等词义及相关制度规定。

第三，阐明“亲亲相隐”与“不隐于亲”、“大义灭亲”在儒家思想体系中相反相成的互补关系，考论这两个方面在历代法律条款中的具体规定情形。

---

① 赵作海，河南省商丘市柘城县老王集乡赵楼村村民。1998年2月15日，赵楼村赵振晌的侄子赵作亮到公安机关报案，其叔父赵振晌于1997年10月30日离家后已失踪4个多月，怀疑被同村的赵作海杀害，公安机关当年进行了相关调查。1999年5月8日，赵楼村在挖井时发现一具高度腐烂的无头、膝关节以下缺失的无名尸体，公安机关遂把赵作海作为重大嫌疑人于5月9日刑拘。1999年5月10日至6月18日，赵作海做了9次有罪供述。2002年10月22日，商丘市人民检察院以被告人赵作海犯故意杀人罪向商丘市中级人民法院提起公诉。2002年12月5日商丘中院做出一审判决，以故意杀人罪判处被告人赵作海死刑，缓期二年执行，剥夺政治权利终身。省法院经复核，于2003年2月13日做出裁定，核准商丘中院上述判决。2010年4月30日，案中“死者”赵振晌重现人间，令该宗冤案轰动全国。河南省高院于2010年5月8日做出再审判决，宣告赵作海无罪。2010年5月13日，河南省高院宣布给予赵作海国家赔偿及生活困难补助共计65万元。随后，这宗冤案的办案细节逐渐揭露。办案机关承认“赵作海冤案”存在刑讯逼供，法院在接受央视记者采访时承认赵作海案确实存在刑讯逼供，才得出9次有效证词。当时在这个案件的审理过程中，赵作海也曾经提出来，他被刑讯逼供过。经查：从1999年5月8日至6月10日，赵作海先后被控制在柘城县老王集乡派出所和柘城县公安局刑警队，分别被铐在连椅上、床腿上或摩托车后轮上，公安办案人员分班轮流审讯和看守，这种体罚控制情况持续长达33天。赵楼村村民杜金慧和赵作海的妻子赵晓起也被传唤和长时间非法关押。（主要参见：“赵作海案”，百度百科，http：//baike.baidu.com/link? url＝qd7PSSyOgQyOyHqH6jV7qgflyMUS8fvjsPF9Vn9t8ebGUMHKByOmVg FInN1DHUQfIZQq7XpMVVFgn82e3hF9。）

② 具体参见范忠信：《“期待之可能性”与我国刑事法的“法治圣贤定位”——从“亲亲相隐”的角度观察”，《广东社会科学》，2010年第2期；范忠信：《亲属拒证权：普世与民族的重合抉择》，《中国审判》，2012年第1期；刘水静：《也谈“亲亲相隐”的法律实质、法理依据及其人性论根基——兼评邓晓芒教授的〈儒家伦理新批判〉》，《学海》，2012年第2期，等相关资料。

第四，反思“阶级斗争为纲”和“文化大革命”年代全盘否定孝道的教训。当时，宣扬“亲不亲，阶级分”，道德上片面要求“大义灭亲”，法律上规定亲属互证其罪，扭曲人性，泯灭亲情。一时间，父子乖离、夫妻反目、兄弟成仇、欺师灭祖之行得逞，诬陷暴戾之气横行，小人得志，忠良受害，造成社会道德和人文素质的民族性大倒退。

第五，辨析“亲亲相隐”的伦理、人性基础。尽管有着不同的，甚至是对立的评价，但却为正确理解“亲亲相隐”提供了哲学思维的高度和深度。

第六，论析自亚里士多德到休谟、康德、孟德斯鸠等西方思想家关于亲属的自然权利和法律权利的学说，及其与“亲亲相隐”说的异同。

第七，研究中西古今世界主要法系、主要国家法律中有关亲属权利的立法细则及其法律精神，论析它们与我国古代“亲亲相隐”之间的异同。

第八，运用“期待可能性理论”、“刑法谦抑主义”、“道德权利说”等法律学说重新释解“亲亲相隐”，并发掘其现代价值。

可以说，对“亲亲相隐”的研究是近30多年来中国学术领域具有标本意义的典范性案例。不但各学科学者纷纷参与，而且立法、司法、律师等法律实务界人士也投身其中，蔚然而成自由讨论、相互诘难、百家争鸣之风，致力于收酌古斟今、研西鉴中、综合创新之功，推动着刑事诉讼法的成功修改。回顾该问题面研究历程，如果说还有什么可以充实进去的话，那就是“亲亲相隐”以研究视角尚可更新。本文认为，“亲亲相隐”思想及其制度，其实蕴涵着私权抗御公权的法律精神。

## 二、家庭权：“亲亲相隐”之性质

人类一旦脱离丛林规则的野蛮状态而进入有组织的文明社会，就陷入私权和公权之间碰撞与对抗的困惑之中。公权往往难以避免地成为凌驾于私权之上的一个异化体、一个恶魔，成为实际掌握者手中的工具，即所谓的公器私用，吞噬人们的私权。可以说，如何处理好公权与私权关系成为几千年来一道“哥德巴赫猜想”式的难题。林林总总的政治和法律的学说及其实务，说到底，都只为求解这道难题。在中国历史上，为史家称道的成康之治、文景之治、贞观与开元之治、康乾之治，无非是公权与私权关系相比较地处理得妥当一些，显得和谐一些。而一旦这种平衡被破坏，私权被公权恣意挤压，社会就会动荡不安。

私权，其另一个常用的法律语词叫作“私权利”。现代意义上的私权利主要是人身权利和财产权利。私权利是随着社会进步、文明发展而不断丰富的。拿财产权利来说，在古代中国，私人财产以家产制的形态存在，家产权成为私权利的主要内容。在现代社会，财产权利中除了公民的物权、债权、继承权、知识产权中的物质收益权等外，还包括企业的财产权、经营权和商誉权、社会组织的财产权等。

公权，又称“公权力”，简言之，就是国家权力，包括立法权、行政权、司法权，以及外交权、军事权等。每一类公权力又可细分为许多项权力，如行政权中的执法权、处罚权、侦查权等，司法权中的审判权、刑罚权等。公权力的另一个常用的法律语词就是“权力”。所以公权力与私权利的关系，也可以简称为权力和权利的关系。在现代法治国家，实行私权优先原则。[①] 公权的终极目标是保护私权，并约束自我以维持公权与私权的平衡与和谐。

然而，正如孟德斯鸠所说，“一切有权力的人都容易滥用权力”，[②] 滥用公权力必定侵害私权利。由于公权力以国家暴力为后盾，强大无比，私权根本无法与之对抗。所以，统治集团如果追求长治久安，在公权和私权发生碰撞时，不得不约束公权、保护私权，并事先做出法律规定。行政法的“法律保留原则”是一个比较典型的例子。在这一原则下，公权力机关必须恪守“法无明文规定不得作为”。与之相对应的是“私法自治”、“契约自由”等基本原则，私法主体享有“法无明文禁止即可为之”的权利。现代法治国家则更进一步，通过制定宪法、实施宪政来维护公权与私权的平衡。

维系公权与私权平衡的最后一道防护堤便是司法。所谓司法公正，就是在一个一个具体的个案审理中救济、恢复和维系公权与私权的相对平衡。问题在于，司法权本身也存在着腐败的本能趋向。遏制其腐败的方法仍然将其纳入法律制度。诉讼法和与之相应的辩护人制度、司法鉴定制度等都为此而兴。

本文讨论的“亲亲相隐”原则及其制度问题，基本上可归属于刑事诉讼的范畴。下面，主要就刑事诉讼中公权与私权的平衡问题做一考察。

刑事案件是已然之事，时过境迁，证据灭失的可能性很大。加之犯罪嫌疑人为逃脱惩罚，会千方百计掩盖真相。所以，刑事诉讼过程的每一个阶段，都存在着办案人员与犯罪嫌疑人和其他诉讼参与人斗智、斗勇、斗法、斗理、斗情的激烈博弈。鉴于刑事案件对国家安全和社会安全的危害性很大，国家赋予办案人员的公权力相应地增大，其法定权、临时处分权、自由裁量权都会远远大于其他公务人员。一般而言，手握公权的办案人员相对于犯罪嫌疑人、涉案人和其他诉讼参与人而言，处于优势、强势地位，他们可以限制诉讼当事人和其他诉讼参与人的人身自由、冻结财产等私权。正是由于刑事诉讼中行使公权力的这种特殊性，这里存在着公权力被滥用的更大危险。

---

① 刘曙光：《论公权与私权的和谐以及私权优先原则》，爱思想网，2005－03－15。http：//www.aisixiang.com/data/6091.html 。

② （法）孟德斯鸠：《论法的精神》，张雁深译，北京：《商务印书馆》，1961年11月第1版，第154页。

历史上和现实中，刑讯逼供屡禁不止便是明证。为约束公权力使之免遭滥用，办法之一，就是在刑事诉讼制度设计中赋予公民在公权不当行使时以必要制约之权，或者说，赋予私权以抗御公权之权。

如果说，公权与私权的平衡配置是完善现代刑事诉讼法的关键，[①] 那么，它同样也是古代刑事诉讼制度中不得不考虑的一个问题。

帝制时代的中国，公权主体无疑是帝王及其皇族和官僚队伍。那么，私权主体是谁？若依移植于西方的法律理念，则应当是与公权主体相对应的黎民百姓，即私法上的个人。然而，这种认知并不符合历史实际。

前文说到，古代中国的经济结构是以农业为基础的家产制。汉以后的历代法律原则上都有这样的规定：父母在，子女不得“别籍异财”。[②] 也就是说，法律不承认自然人享有个人财产权。“家有千口，主事一人”。这“主事”之人，社会学上称之为“家长”，法律学上叫作“户主”。户，是古代中国农业经济中最基本的生产单位和经营单位，也是最基本的行政相对人和纳税人，还是最基本的法律权利主体和义务主体。[③] 在“家国一体”的古代中国，法律赋予“户”比较充分的自治权，在其尽到行政相对人和纳税人的义务的前提下，经营什么，怎么经营，对家庭成员怎样管理，乃至家产继承和析分等等，一般不予干涉。这就是一些法律教科书中说的家长握有子女的财产权、婚姻权、轻微刑事惩罚权之类，并因此而倍受诟病。其实，家长行使的是家产的管理权，并非所有权。家产的所有权属于全体家庭成员。在子子孙孙的父系血缘链条中，家是铁打的营盘，家长是个流水的兵。在血缘家庭中，一个男性成员的一生，既是子又是父。他的前半生是子，是成员，是被管理者；他的后半生是父，是家长、户主，

---

① 傅宽芝：《公权与私权平衡是完善刑诉法的关键》，《检察日报》，2007 年 07 月 23 日。

② 自西汉中期“罢黜百家，独尊儒术”后，法律逐步儒家化，秦代令父子祖孙分产析户的法律逐渐被修改、废除。三国曹魏律“除异子之科，使父子无异财也”。两晋和南北朝均有禁止别籍异财的律令。隋代旌表累世同居。唐代禁止别籍异财的法律臻于完备，《唐律·户婚》有“诸祖父母、父母在而子孙别籍异财者，徒三年”的规定，并将“父母在别籍异财”列为“十恶”中“不孝”罪的第一条。“别藉异财”法律的改易在宋代。宋初因袭唐律，宋太祖时修订的《宋刑统·户婚律》之“父母在及居丧别籍异财”条规定：“诸祖父母、父母在，而子孙别籍、异财者，徒三年。”其后，这一律条虽未更改，但在司法适用中已用敕令或指挥代替了律条。到南宋中后期，法律已认可了父母在世时的析分行为，肯定了“别立户籍”、“分异财产”的合法性。元代规定只要祖父母、父母同意则允许分产异财。明律规定：“别籍异财”的案件须经祖父母、父母告诉始受理，处罚仅为杖一百。清律规定此类案件须经期亲以上尊长告诉始成立，处罚杖八十。不过，认可子孙“别籍异财”，不等于确立子孙的个人财产权。因为从父祖大家庭中“别籍”和“异财”出去的子孙仍是一个家庭，只不过是小一些的家庭而已，这些子孙便是他们那小家庭的家长、户主，其家产制的性质没有变化。

③ 关于“户”在中国古代法中法律地位的研究，有 1998 年本人指导的周子良硕士论文《户与中国古代民法文化》。还可参见西南财经大学 2012 年邓洪燕的硕士论文《论户的民事法律地位》。

是管理者。作为家产的管理者，家长的责任重大，除了养家糊口、传宗接代，还要使家产增殖、门庭增辉、光宗耀祖。总而言之，帝制中国的民事权利主体不是作为自然人的个体，至少主要地不是个人，而是家庭、是户，家长或户主是一家或一户的民事权利的权利人，还是行政相对人。就民事权利主体和行政相对人的内涵与外延而言，基本上是与家庭权、户权相一致的。家庭自治权、家庭管理权、家产经营权、家庭财产权都属于民事权利的范畴。对家庭成员的教令权、主婚权则也包含在家庭自治权中，轻微违法和罪错行为的惩罚权也从公权分割出来成为家庭自治权的一部分。

现在再回过头来说说"亲亲相隐"，或古代法律规定中的"同居相容隐"原则。其实，它们是古代家庭权的组成部分，属于私权的范畴，是刑事诉讼方面制约公权力的一种私权利。在学界关于"亲亲相隐"的讨论中，大多认为它是一种义务本位立法。不错，"亲亲相隐"需要家庭成员，或同居成员尽到"相隐"的义务。然而，正是这种"相隐"的个体义务的共同遵循，才使这一"相隐"的家庭权利得以实现。实际上，所有的家庭权利的实现都来自这样的基础：每个家庭成员尽到应尽的义务。以家庭财产权为例，如果家庭成员都不尽到"同居共财"的义务，都闹腾着在个人名下占据一份，都热衷于挖家产的墙角，哪还有共有的家庭财产权可言?!

说到这里，又有一个中西法律的区别不得不辩。在西方近现代法中，权利与义务统一于个人，是个人本位的；在中国古代法中，权利和义务统一于家庭，是家庭本位的。在个人本位法中，对于个人而言，其权利与义务是相对应的；在家庭本位法中，对于家庭而言，其权利和义务也是相对应的，但对于家庭中的成员个人而言，就其人生的某个时段来看，权利和义务会是不尽相对应的。这种不相对应曾被我们的一些教科书夸大并贬斥为中国古代法是义务本位法、是家长特权法等等。其实，如前所述，纵观男性家庭成员的一生，其权利和义务仍然是相应的、平衡的。

总之，作为中国古代法中私权的家庭权，其家庭成员遵守共同义务是实现共有权利的基础和前提。"亲亲相隐"作为一种家庭权利也是如此，其成员的"相隐"义务尽，则家庭之"相隐"权利存；反之，其成员的"相隐"义务亡，则家庭之"相隐"权利废。

在古代中国，这样的私权构成和私权运作机制，在伦理和人性上是"合乎天理而顺乎人情"的；在经济学上是适合农业经济时代生产力发展实际的；从政府管治和社会治理上是符合效率和节约原则的；从法律关系上，是有利于公权力和私权利的相对平衡的。

对中国古代法中私权利构成及其运作机制的揭示，并不能得出"田野牧歌"式的结论。公权力的绝对优先，是中国两千多年古代法的不变原则。家产制所依托的一家一户小农经济，不用说在强大而常常带有疯狂性的公权力面前，不能不是十分脆弱的，就是遇到较严重自然灾害，也难以扛得住。

## 三、抗御公权："亲亲相隐"的价值

古代中国的"亲亲相隐"作为一项法律制度化的家庭私权利，既涵盖了我们在许多大陆法系国家刑事诉讼制度中看到的沉默权、无举证责任权和拒证权，也在一定程度上容忍了当今各国刑诉制度中不被允许的在犯罪事发后主动隐匿、藏匿和偷报消息等包庇、作伪证行为，以帮助犯罪家人逃避法律制裁。从本质上说，它是作为一种对公权力的抗御权存在的，这是"亲亲相隐"最大的法律价值。"亲亲相隐"权的实施，肯定会给官府侦查、缉捕、审判、惩罚犯罪增加难度，带来干扰，甚至会使罪犯逃脱法网。但那是官府的事，官府拥有丰富的人力、物力、财力资源，应当提高破案和侦缉的本领。美国最高法院大法官霍尔姆斯在投票否决地方法院对米兰达的有罪判决后说："罪犯逃脱法网与官府的非法行为相比，罪孽要小得多。"① 古代中国的公权主体为了维系"家国一体"的合法性统治，抓大放小，除谋反、谋叛、谋大逆重罪外，将"亲亲相隐"作为私权利纳入家庭权利之中，隐隐然有一种"罪犯逃脱法网与官府为追逃罪犯而践踏亲情、蹂躏人性相比，罪孽要小得多"的权衡。在古代帝制社会，统治集团做出这样维系人性和亲情的立法选择，确是难能可贵的。

下面，以文献资料为根据，分析一下"亲亲相隐"中隐含着哪些抗御公权力的私权利。

首先，是抗御侦查权和缉捕权。

对犯罪行为的侦查权和对罪犯的缉捕权，在国家权力位阶中居于十分强硬的地位，是仅次于军事权的警察权，仅次于甲兵暴力的国家暴力。从古人关于"亲亲相隐"的论证中，大有让国家侦查权和缉捕权在家庭权、亲属权面前止步的意思。

其中最具典型意义的，还是《孟子》书中的舜"窃负而逃"的假设。这则孟子师徒运用当时小说家手法编造出来的故事，把舜置于天子和儿子身份冲突的绝境，推到法律和伦理冲突中非此即彼的风口浪尖之上。故事的原文已为人们熟知。为了行文的完整性，还是照录一遍：

"桃应问曰：'舜为天子，皋陶为士，瞽瞍杀人，则如之何？'孟子曰：'执之而已矣。''然则舜不禁与？'曰：'夫舜恶得而禁之？夫有所受之也。''然则舜如之何？'曰：'舜视弃天下犹弃敝蹝也。窃负而逃，遵海滨而处，终身䜣然，乐而忘天下。'"②

---

① 引自陈伟：《米兰达法则与美国宪法修正案》，《读书》，2000年第7期。

② 《孟子·尽心上》。参见李学勤主编：《十三经注疏·孟子注疏》，北京：北京大学出版社，1999年，第370—371页。

本世纪初掀起的那场称为“儒家伦理问题”论争，就是由这个故事引发的。当时，有的文章曾对这个故事作过这样的续编：舜父子可以逃到海滨，国家司法人员同样可以追到海滨缉拿他们。反驳者指出，“海滨”在当时并非王法管辖之地。现在让我们跳出论争的圈子之外来看。其实，以国家公权力之强大，追到海滨捉拿两个逃犯不过小事一桩。王法管辖权也不成问题，“率土之滨，莫非王土”。那么，为什么舜父子在海滨不但可以平平安安，还能够过着“终身欣然”的快乐日子？问题不在国家公权力之不能，而在于国家公权之为不为。国家公权力对父子亲情表示敬畏和尊重，其侦查权、缉捕权止步于父子亲情之前。这才是问题的答案，才是问题的实质，也是这则故事的典型意义之所在。换言之，血缘父子天生的亲属权、家庭权抗御了国家的侦查权、缉捕权。那种以为舜将瞽瞍“窃负而逃”是开中国官场官官相护、亲亲相护的司法腐败之源的看法，恐怕未能读懂孟子师徒编排这则故事的深义及其内蕴的法律文化密码。

西汉桓宽所撰的《盐铁论》是首次从伦理和法理上系统论述“相隐”之理的一部子书。书中引“贤良文学”之言：

“自首匿相坐之法立，骨肉之恩废，而刑罪多矣。父母之于子，虽有罪犹匿之，其不欲服罪尔。闻子为父隐，父为子隐，未闻父子之相坐也。闻兄弟缓追以免贼，未闻兄弟之相坐也。闻恶恶止其人，疾始而诛首恶，未闻什伍而相坐也。”①

这里引用了“兄弟缓追以免贼”的典故。此事发生在鲁庄公三十二年至鲁僖公元年（公元前 662 年至 659 年）之间。公元前 662 年，鲁庄公去世，嗣子未定。庄公的同母弟季友拥立庄公长子——公子般即位。庄公的异母弟庆父立即派仆人邓扈乐把公子般杀了。庆公本人逃往齐国。季友又奉庄公的二子启方为国君，是为闵公。不久，庆父又谋杀了闵公。这就是“庆父不死，鲁难未已”成语的由来。季友明知弑君元凶不是邓扈乐，而是庆父。但是，庆父是他的同父异母兄弟，有亲亲情义。经过痛苦的伦理煎熬，季友选择宽容庆父，放弃跨境缉捕。庆公出逃后，各国都不收留他，于鲁僖公元年派他的儿子到鲁国请求季友容纳他，季友的回答是：“公子不可以入，入则杀矣。”《公羊传》作者何休解释道：“义不可以见贼而不杀。”庆父走投无路，只有自杀了断。《春秋》誉季子“缓追免贼”为贤。“缓追免贼”的故事把停止行使侦查权、缉捕权的范围又扩大到兄弟之间。

有“相隐”权利之同居、亲人可以向犯罪亲人通风报信，以帮助其逃脱政府侦缉人员的缉捕，是古代法中私权利抗御公权力的又一亮点。

唐律规定：

“诸同居，若大功以上亲及外祖父母、外孙，若孙之妇、夫之兄弟及兄弟妻，有罪

① （汉）桓宽撰，王利器校注：《盐铁论校注》，天津：天津古籍出版社，1983 年，第 599 页。

相为隐；部曲、奴婢为主隐，皆勿论；即漏露其事及擿语消息亦不坐。其小功以下相隐，减凡人三等。”①

在“即漏露其事及擿语消息亦不坐”一款后，“疏”文这样写道：

“议曰：假有铸钱及盗之类，事须掩摄追收，遂‘漏露其事’。‘及擿语消息’，谓报罪人所掩摄之事，令得隐避逃亡。为通相隐，故亦不坐。”②

《宋刑统·名例律》此款条文及“议曰”的文字与《唐律疏议》毫无二致。③《大明律》对此款文字稍有改动，更令人明确易懂：

“若漏泄其事，及通报消息，致令罪人隐匿逃避者，亦不坐。其小功以下相容隐，及漏泄其事，减凡人三等，无服之亲减一等……”④

清律与明律保持一致。⑤“铸钱及盗”，就是现在的私造假钞的金融犯罪和盗窃财物罪。对于此类凡谋叛以下犯罪，其同居、亲人可以“漏泄其事，及通报消息，致令罪人隐匿逃避”，显示帝制时代王朝对家庭亲属权利抗御政府侦查权、缉捕权的极大容忍。这些法律都是在各王朝建政初期制订的，说明在儒家“亲亲相隐”观念的指引下，盛唐、盛宋、盛明时期的统治者对政府治理社会的那种自信和气魄。

综上，公权力敬畏父子、兄弟亲情，让公权力在亲情面前止步、退缩，容忍同居、父子、兄弟的亲属权利抗御国家侦查权和缉捕权。在人类的中世纪时代，恐怕只有中华法系中的古代法有这样的人性张扬和制度安排。儒家“相隐”私权利的功能和价值在这里得到了理论上和制度上的极大提升。

其次，是抗御刑讯权。

“亲亲相隐”对侦查和审讯过程中的刑讯权都有一定的抗御作用。它表现在犯罪者的家属享有一定的免遭刑讯逼供的权利，哪怕他们曾经窝藏过，或帮助过犯罪亲人逃匿。在犯罪侦查过程中，刑讯罪犯家属以便于追捕罪犯，原本是实施侦查权的一部分。在审讯阶段，对罪犯家属施以刑讯以逼取证词，原本应归入审判权之中。由于古代中国在侦查和审讯中普遍存在合法的和非法的刑讯，所以将“亲亲相隐”对刑讯权的抗御从侦查和审判中提取出来，单独加以叙述。

《晋书·刑法志》载：

---

① （唐）长孙无忌等撰：《唐律疏议·名例》，刘俊文点校，北京：中华书局，1983年，第130页。

② 同前注。

③ 《宋刑统·名例律》：“诸同居，若大功以上亲及外祖父母、外孙，若孙之妇、夫之兄弟及兄弟妻有罪，相为隐，部曲奴婢为主隐，皆勿论。即漏露其事及擿语消息，亦不坐。其小功以下相隐，减凡人三等。若犯谋叛以上者，不用此律。”（吴翊立点校：《宋刑统》，北京：中华书局，1984年，第95页）

④ 怀效锋点校：《大明律》，沈阳：辽沈书社，1989年，第18－19页。

⑤ 参见田涛、郑秦点校：《大清律例》，北京：法律出版社，1999年，第121页。

“而河东卫展为晋王大理，考擿故事有不合情者，又上书曰：‘今施行诏书，有考子正父死刑，或鞭父母问子所在。近主者所称《庚寅诏书》，举家逃亡家长斩。若长是逃亡之主，斩之虽重犹可。设子孙犯事，将考祖父逃亡，逃亡是子孙，而父祖婴其酷。伤顺破教，如此者众。相隐之道离，则君臣之义废。君臣之义废，则犯上之奸生矣。秦网密文峻，汉兴，扫除烦苛，风移俗易，几于刑厝。大人革命，不得不荡其秽匿，通其圮滞。今诏书宜除者多，有便于当今，著为正条，则法差简易。’元帝令曰：‘礼乐不兴，则刑罚不中，是以明罚敕法，先王所慎。自元康已来，事故荐臻，法禁滋漫。大理所上，宜朝堂会议，蠲除诏书不可用者，此孤所虚心者也。’”①

“鞭父母问子所在”，是办案人员对犯罪人的父母进行刑讯逼供以追查其犯罪儿子的下落。“考子正父死刑”，指审判人员通过对儿子施以刑讯以获取其父亲的死罪证据。这则文献资料表明，西晋大理卫展据理力争，促成晋元帝废止了对亲属的刑讯逼供旧法，使“相隐”权利得以伸张，抗御公权力在侦查、审讯中滥用刑讯。

晋元帝的这条敕令，到唐代已发展成熟为法律条文。唐律对拷讯有严格规定，拷讯违律要以“故失”论处。《唐律疏议·断狱》称：

“诸应议、请、减，若年七十以上，十五以下及废疾者，并不合拷讯，皆据众证定罪，违者以故失论。”②

此律条之第二款规定：

“其于律得相容隐，即年八十以上，十岁以下，及笃疾，皆不得令其为证，违者，减罪人罪三等。”③

这一款的“疏”文写道：

“‘其于律得相容隐’，谓同居，若大功以上亲，及外祖父母、外孙，若孙之妇、夫之兄弟及兄弟妻，及部曲、奴婢得为主隐。其八十以上，十岁以下，及笃疾，以其不堪加刑：故并不许为证。若违律遣证，‘减罪人罪三等’，谓遣证徒一年，所司合杖八十之类。”④

这一律条及其疏议的文义十分明白，“其于律得相容隐”者不得遣证，更不得以刑讯遣证。

查《宋刑统》之“断狱律”，此条律文与唐律无异。《大明律》将此条律文系于“刑律”篇之“断狱”门下，只是将违律惩罚作了改变，由唐、宋律的“违者减罪人罪

① 《晋书·刑法志》，参见（唐）房玄龄等：《晋书》第1册，北京：中华书局，1974年，第935页。

② 刘俊文点校：《唐律疏议》，北京：中华书局，1983年，第550页。

③ 刘俊文点校：《唐律疏议》，北京：中华书局，1983年，第550页。

④ 刘俊文点校：《唐律疏议》，北京：中华书局，1983年，第551页。

三等”改为“违者笞五十”，[1] 其余与唐、宋律相同。足见，“亲亲相隐”的亲属权利是具有抗御刑讯权的价值的。

最后，是抗御审判权。

“亲亲相隐”的最终目的是使无罪的和有罪的亲属免受审判和刑罚。如果说，对侦查权、缉捕权、刑讯权的抗御是“亲亲相隐”私权利最为基本的功能与价值，那么，抗御审判权则是它的终极功能和价值指向。

前引唐律“同居相为隐”律文中，“诸同居，若大功以上亲及外祖父母、外孙，若孙之妇、夫之兄弟及兄弟妻”可以“有罪相为隐”，“部曲、奴婢”应当“为主隐”，这“隐”的涵义是什么？或曰，“隐”的法定私权利究竟包包含哪些内容？除前述的“漏露其事，及擿语消息”不受追查，更不得刑讯追查外，还有哪些？

《宋书·蔡廓传》载，蔡廓“性至孝”，南朝时在宋王室为侍中，曾上了这样一道“建议”：

“以为‘鞫狱不宜令子孙下辞明言父祖之罪，亏教伤情，莫此为大。自今但令家人与囚相见，无乞鞫之诉，使足以明伏罪，不须责家人下辞’，朝议咸以为允，从之。”[2]

“鞫狱不宜令子孙下辞明言父祖之罪”，意为，审判时不能强迫子孙出庭提供证言以证明其父祖的犯罪行为。用现代的法律语言表达，就是审讯犯罪人时，犯罪人的子孙有不到庭、无举证责任、沉默、不作证、拒证的权利。

其后，这些不到庭、无举证责任、沉默、不作证、拒证等“相隐”权利逐渐落实到法律明文之中。法律规定，不仅子孙对父祖可以如此，凡同居亲属相互间均可如此。前引唐、宋、明代法律中的“其于律得相容隐，即年八十以上，十岁以下及笃疾，皆不得令其为证”，即是关于“相隐”亲属的不到庭权、沉默权、无举证责任权、不作证权、拒证权的明文规定。

由是，从舜将瞽瞍“窃负而逃”的假设、“兄弟缓追以免贼”的《春秋》大义，到“相隐”亲属可以“漏露其事，及擿语消息”而不受追查，还可以不到庭、沉默、无举证责任、不作证、拒证，古代法中“相隐”私权利已形成一整套制度化的规定，以抗御国家的侦查、缉捕、刑讯、审判、刑罚等公权力，使公权力的行使在亲情面前变得人性一些、柔性一些、理性一些、公平一些。

关于“亲亲相隐”的私权利对国家审判权的抗御功能，还可以从其使无罪的和有罪的亲属免受审判和刑罚这样两个层面加以分析。

---

① 怀效锋点校：《大明律》，沈阳：辽沈书社，1989 年，第 211 页。

② 《宋书·卷五十七·列传第十七》，（梁）沈约，许嘉璐主编，《二十四史全译·晋书》第 2 册，上海：汉语大词典出版社，2004 年，第 1262 页。

第一个层面，使无罪亲属免受审判和刑罚。“亲亲相隐”是儒家思想家在抨击族刑、连坐、缘坐中发展完善起来的。前文引《盐铁论》贤良文学之言：“闻子为父隐，父为子隐，未闻父子之相坐也。闻兄弟缓追以免贼，未闻兄弟之相坐也。闻恶恶止其人，疾始而诛首恶，未闻什伍而相坐也。”① 即可说明。使无辜家庭成员、亲属免遭族刑、连坐、缘坐，免受审判和刑罚，是“亲亲相隐”抗御审判权和刑罚权的原初功能和价值。

第二个层面，使有罪的家庭成员、亲属免除或减轻审判和刑罚。这里的有罪的家庭成员、亲属，可分两种类型，一是因“相隐”行为而犯了藏匿罪、帮助逃匿罪等，他们的犯罪皆因被“相隐”的原犯罪人所诱发；二是诱发“相隐”行为的原犯罪人。

董仲舒“春秋决狱”中关于“父为子隐”的案例，对“亲亲相隐”原则引入法律至关重要，论者都乐于征引。它还是一个能很好说明“相隐”私权利可以抗御审判权和刑罚权的案例。

“时有疑狱曰：甲无子，拾道旁弃儿乙养之，以为子。及乙长，有罪杀人，以状语甲，甲当何论？仲舒曰：甲无子，振活养乙，虽非所生，谁与易之。诗云：螟蛉有子，蜾蠃负之。春秋之义，父为子隐，甲宜匿乙而不当坐。”②

这个案例讲的是应当认可养父的“相隐”权，免除对他藏匿养子的审判和刑罚。这个案例之所以成为“疑狱”而不得不求教于董仲舒，是因为当事人是养父。反推过去，如果不是养父而是生父，也就不成其为“疑狱”，办案官员自然懂得怎么审判，也不会追究这位父亲的藏匿之罪。③

过了大约半个世纪左右，汉宣帝地节四年（公元前66年）发布了一道诏书：

“父子之亲，夫妇之道，天性也。虽有患祸，犹蒙死而存之。诚爱结于心，仁厚之至也，岂能违之哉！自今子首匿父母，妻匿夫，孙匿大父母，皆勿坐。其父母匿子，夫匿妻，大父母匿孙，罪殊死，皆上请廷尉以闻。”④

这道诏令的核心，就是确认亲属有罪的隐匿权利。其中，卑者隐匿尊者，皆无罪；尊者隐匿卑者，死罪须“上请”，其余皆不论。换言之，隐匿权可以抗御，或部分抗御

---

① （汉）桓宽撰，王利器校注，《盐铁论校注》，天津：天津古籍出版社，1983年，第599页。

② 程树德：《九朝律考》，北京：中华书局，2006年，第164页。

③ 这里引出一个问题：“亲亲相隐”作为一种审判定罪的法律原则和规定，也许比当前学界认定的要早得多。一般认为，“亲亲相隐”原则初入法律的时间，为汉宣帝地节四年（公元前66年）的那道诏书，董仲舒的“春秋决狱”，在时间上早于宣帝诏令半个世纪左右。从董仲舒以《诗》和《春秋》经义认定养父应当与亲父一样享有“相隐”权利来分析，不排除当时就存在着亲父藏匿犯罪儿子不为罪的法律规定。鉴于对这一问题的辩证非本文主旨，仅此存疑。

④ 《汉书》卷八《宣帝纪第八》，参考（汉）班固撰，（唐）颜师古注：《汉书》，北京：中华书局，1964年，第251页。

审判权和刑罚权。

董仲舒的这一“春秋决狱”案例和汉宣帝的这道诏令，成为后世“亲亲相隐”入律的法源。它的适用对象是亲属中犯了藏匿罪、帮助逃匿罪等“相隐”行为人。藏匿犯罪亲人、帮助犯罪亲人逃匿，是由于已经犯罪的亲人所诱发的犯罪。这些被诱发而犯有藏匿罪、帮助逃匿罪的亲属，因享有“相隐”权利而可以抗御或部分抗御国家的审判权和刑罚权，从而将他们的犯罪行为除罪化。应当指出，这是古代法中“同居相为隐”法律条款的本义。

那么，亲属中诱发“相隐”行为的原犯罪人能不能因“亲亲相隐”而免罪呢？古代法律文本中无据可查。我们看到有“官当”、“八议”这样的规定，但这些规定不同于“亲亲相隐”。《华阳国志》中倒是有一个案例，一位父亲竟以“亲亲相隐”为说辞而直接帮助犯有杀人罪的儿子逃脱审判和刑罚。故事是这样的：

“李弘，字仲元，成都人。少读五经，不为章句。处陋巷，淬励金石之志，威仪容止，邦家师之。以德行为郡功曹，一月而去。子赘以见辱杀人，太守曰：‘贤者之子必不杀人。’放之。赘自以枉，语家人，弘遣亡命。太守怒，让弘，弘对曰：‘赘为杀人之贼，明府私弘枉法。君子不诱而诛也。石碏杀厚，《春秋》讥之；孔子称父子相隐，直在其中。弘实遣赘。’太守无以诘也。”①

李弘所为已属于帮助犯罪亲人逃脱审判和刑罚。这个故事颇有几分戏剧性，与前述的舜“窃负而逃”有些类似，都是帮助犯罪亲人逃脱，官府不再行使侦查权和缉捕权，从而也无从实现审判权和刑罚权。不过，舜“窃负而逃”是虚拟的，李弘的故事也许是真实的，但不具有实在法的功能与价值，只能视为一种法外特例。

## 结　语

本文从“亲亲相隐”权利视角立论，有悖素以中国古代法为义务本位法之说。笔者关注并研习儒家法30多年，对于“亲亲相隐”的认识也有一个过程。日新又新，实乃治学之本。能以今日之是知昨日之非，那是一种心灵的享受。笔者早年曾论定儒家之法为“伦理法”。“亲亲相隐”既为伦理权利又系伦理义务。这种伦理权利和伦理义务统合于家庭共同体，而不是作为自然人的个体。伦理权利是以家庭为载体的私权，它的存在以家庭成员克尽其伦理义务为前提、为条件。也许正是由于这一特点，让人误以为它是只讲义务不讲权利的法。当然，如果是抱定一个只从个体本位法律视角看问题的态度，也必然会将中国古代法判定为义务本位法。

---

① 《华阳国志》卷十上，参考《华阳国志校注》（修订版），（晋）常璩撰，刘琳校注，2007年6月，第386页。

法律是理性的结晶。古代中国统治者从统治合法性和可持续性的理性认知出发，将“亲亲相隐”作为家庭私权利确认下来，并且通过禁止和惩罚家庭成员中不履行“相隐”义务的行为来保障它的存在和实现，这就有了本文所论的“亲亲相隐”私权利具有抗御国家公权力的性质和价值，尽管这种抗御力是脆弱的。

中国的帝制社会延绵两千多年，其间经历多次改朝换代，但中华文化、中华法系之基本精神和基本形态未曾改易。观察和解密中国传统必须从家庭、家庭伦理、家庭文化入手。否则，只会南其辕而北其辙。家庭伦理，就是“父父子子”、就是“亲亲”、就是“孝”。在“家国一体”的古代中国，有“父父子子”才有“君君臣臣”。所以孔子断言“为政”基于“孝”道。① 家庭文化、家庭伦理孕育了古代中国以亲属权、家庭权作为主要私权的权利结构体系和存在方式。“亲亲相隐”，实为家庭文化、家庭伦理的理性法律选择。以历史的眼光和同情理解的态度来看，古代帝国统治集团，竟敢将亲属间的沉默、拒证、伪证、藏匿、毁证、擿漏消息、帮助逃匿等行为除罪化，打捆纳入家庭“相隐”私权利之中，且具有一定程度的抗御国家侦查权、缉捕权、刑讯权、审判权的功能，这在古代世界的私法史和刑法史上委实为难能可贵之举。

继承和弘扬中国传统文化已成举国上下共识。但若抛开悠久的家庭文化传统，中国传统文化岂不成为空壳?!“文革”中那种父子间、夫妻间、兄弟间划清界限、相互揭发的现象绝不能重演，刑侦和司法中那种迫使亲属举证的规定和做法应当坚决废绝。亲属权、家庭权或因血缘关系而天生享有，或因婚姻关系而后天获得，应当作为一种私权利纳入我们的法律保障之下。刑事诉讼中的沉默权、拒证权、不作证权和无举证责任权应当作为亲属权、家庭权的固有权利予以法律明文宣示。变古代帝制法制的公权优先为法治中国的私权优先，在现代权利制度中给予亲属权、家庭权恰当的位置。这些，当是古代“亲亲相隐”权的制度和智慧带给我们的启迪与思考。

---

① 《论语·为政》：“‘孝乎惟孝，施于有政，友于兄弟。’是亦爲政，奚其爲爲政?”参考杨伯峻校注：《论语译注》，北京：中华书局，1980年，第20—21页。

# 孝道：中国传统法律的核心价值①

西南政法大学　龙大轩

中国古代社会乃宗法伦理社会。在依此而构建的秩序体制中，伦理与法律往往难以际分。“宗法家族伦理与法律规范之间不存在严格的界限。宗法伦理是法的价值标准、法的渊源，也是罪与非罪、罚与不罚，以及罪与罚的轻重缓急的衡器。”② 由此滋生出伦理法文化。

在所有社会伦理关系中，君臣、父子这两伦，被视为人际伦常之大端，其与法律的关系更是剪不断、理还乱。君臣秩序系于忠义，为政治统治所必需；父子伦理存于孝义，亦为法律规制所依赖。故历代统治者莫不将“忠”、“孝”这两种伦理观念视为长治久安之根基，在公开标榜忠道的同时，③ 更是大力宣扬孝道，因为父母与子女之间，有着天然的血缘亲情，这种宣传容易得到民众的自发认同；同时还能达到“移孝作忠”的目的，故自汉迄清，统治者无不宣称“以孝治天下”。④ 由是之故，孝道不仅为历代所尊崇，而且与法律制度紧密结合，成为中国传统法律的核心价值。

---

①　文系国家社科基金重点项目《重新认识中华法系》（批准号：13AFX003）阶段性成果，且得到中央财政支持地方高校发展专项资金“法文化研究传播协同创新团队”建设项目、重庆市首届哲学社会科学领军人才特支计划的支持。

②　俞荣根：《儒家法思想通论》，南宁：广西人民出版社，1998年，第152页。

③　东汉经学家马融（79—166），撰《忠经》十八章，标志着春秋时期所产生的忠德观念得以系统化，对后世忠德观念的进一步牢固产生深远影响。

④　自汉及清，以孝巩固统治的思维模式，一以贯之。汉宣帝言：“导民以孝，则天下顺。”（《汉书》卷8《宣帝纪》，北京：中华书局，1962年，第250页）乃此一贯逻辑之直白表述。鲁迅先生说：“魏晋，是以孝治天下的，不孝，故不能不杀。为什么要以孝治天下呢？因为天位从禅让，即巧取豪夺而来，若主张以忠治天下，他们的立脚点便不稳，办事便棘手，立论也难了，所以一定要以孝治天下。”（《魏晋风度及文章与药及酒之关系》，载《鲁迅全集》卷3，北京：人民文学出版社，1973年，第534页。）则此又魏晋时期倡导孝道高于忠道之又一缘由。然而无论如何，以孝为治，乃历代不易之基本国策。

## 一、孝道与法律结合的演进轨迹

“传统法制中受孝道的影响非常之大，表现为孝与法的有机融合。”[1] 从某种意义上讲，中国法律史亦即孝道精神与法律制度彼此融合的历史。自上古三代而始，孝道便具有极为崇高的法律地位。汉魏以降，随着法律儒家化进程的推进，孝道伦理纷纷转化于法律制度之中，形成一套完整的孝道法律规范体系，且在唐代基本定型，进而呈现出一种独特而又一脉相承的孝道法文化现象。后历宋、元、明、清，虽略有损益，然大体上相沿不改。清末法制改革以来，西法东渐，孝道伦理逐渐退出法制领域。综而论之，孝道实为中国传统法律之核心价值，传统法律亦成长于孝道精神的熏染之下，其发展变化呈现出明显的阶段性特征。

（一）先秦时代：孝道融入法律的开端

夏商周三代以礼为法，孝道亦为其统率。经历因袭损益，逐渐而形成一套几乎涵盖所有社会领域的制度规范体系，此即周礼。以礼制为行为准则，以刑制为保障措施，违礼则入刑，用强制性刑罚辅弼礼制之权威。在三代“礼——刑”体制中，孝道得到了极大的尊崇与维护。据记载，夏后氏之时，“五刑之属三千，而罪莫大于不孝”。[2] 及至殷商，“刑三百，罪莫重于不孝”。[3] 尽管今人尚不能确知当时违背孝道有何法律后果，然而至少可以推知，自上古以来“不孝”即为重罪，必受严惩。

由于秉受夏商孝道法文化，也是出于巩固宗法制度的需要，周政权自始便极为重视用法律手段彰显孝道。周初纲领性法律文件《康诰》明确提出：“元恶大憝，矧惟不孝不友。”[4] 对此行径，须援用文王之法加以惩治，不能赦免。周公制礼，以“亲亲、尊尊”为礼之大本，作为立法和司法的根本原则。其中的亲亲原则，便是以孝道为核心，教人爱其亲属，尤其是父系尊亲，所谓“亲亲父为大”是也。推而广之，礼敬父兄、追思先祖，普遍为时人所推崇，孝道遂逐渐上升成为礼法的最高原则。

及至东周以降，礼坏乐崩，列国攻伐，臣弑君、子弑父现象大量出现。“春秋之中，弑君三十六，亡国五十二，诸侯奔走不得保其社稷者，不可胜数”。[5] 战乱纷争，功利横行，西周礼法遭到严重破坏，孝道伦理失掉法律保障，于是退而演化为纯粹的理论观念。孔子痛心于宗法社会之破坏与孝道伦常之沦丧，大力倡导并逐步充实孝道

---

① 林明：《传统法制中的孝道文化因素释义》，《法学论坛》2001年第6期。

② 《孝经·五刑章第十一》。

③ 《吕氏春秋·孝行览第二》。

④ 《尚书》卷14《周书·康诰第十一》。

⑤ 《史记》卷130《太史公自序》，北京：中华书局，1959年，第3297页。

学说。他提出“君君、臣臣、父父、子子”，强调孝道的政治与社会功用，引起统治者重视。弟子有若进一步铺陈论述：“其为人也孝悌而好犯上者，鲜矣。不好犯上而好作乱者，未之有也。君子务本，本立而道生。孝悌也者，其为仁之本与?”[①] 其后，《孟子》、《礼记》、《孝经》等经典对孝道理论进行了进一步的演绎和发扬，对孝道法律制度也进行了相应的论证和设计。例如，《礼记·王制》说：“凡听五刑之讼，必原父子之亲，立君臣之义以权之。”《孝经》称：“要君者无上，非圣人者无法，非孝者无亲。此大乱之道也。”[②]

这些论证与设计虽略显粗疏，但整个理论却根植于中国宗法伦理社会的土壤之中，有着固有的文化遗传基因和顽强的生命力，对后世法制建设产生了深远影响，成为历朝立法、司法的指导性理论。

（二）秦代：融合孝道与法律的尝试

战国时代，秦国将法家思想奉为国策，法律政策皆采极端功利主义，不甚重视亲情伦理。《商君书·开塞》认为：“亲亲则别，爱私则险，民众而以别险为务则民乱。”为增强国家军事战斗力与社会动员力，以确保秦国在战国纷争中最终胜出，商鞅主持变法时便十分注意排除孝道观念对国家综合竞争力的消极影响。汉初贾谊便认为商君在秦国变法，遗礼仪，弃仁恩，导致秦俗日败，“故秦人家富子壮则出分，家贫子壮则出赘。借父耰鉏，虑有德色。母取箕箒，立而谇语……妇姑不相说，则反唇而相稽”，[③] 孝道之风殆尽，遗俗至汉初犹存。而针对孔子所倡“父为子隐，子为父隐”的主张，法家巨子韩非更针锋相对：“君之直臣，父之暴子也……父之孝子，君之背臣也。”[④] 将忠、孝两种价值观完全对立，引导秦王用忠道抑制孝道的过分膨胀。司马谈《论六家要旨》对此概括极为精到：“法家不别亲疏，不殊贵贱，一断于法，则亲亲尊尊之恩绝矣。”[⑤]

然而，以上这些传世文献并不足以将秦代法律抛弃孝道证为定论。实则，秦代治国并非纯任法家旧说；贾谊文学家言，本多夸张之处，也不可尽信。至少出土资料显示，秦律中不仅有不孝罪，且处罚很重。《睡虎地秦墓竹简》记载，对于亲子不孝的行

---

① 《论语·学而第一》。

② 《孝经·五刑章第十一》。

③ 《汉书》卷48《贾谊传》，第2244页。

④ 《韩非子·五蠹第四十九》。

⑤ 《史记》卷130《太史公自序》，第3291页。

为，父亲甚至有权要求官府处死儿子，且此类案件官府皆当依律受理处断。[①]《法律答问》亦反映，当时殴打父母、祖父母等尊亲长辈亦当入罪，施以刑罚。[②] 此外，秦律中还有“非公室告”[③] 制度，公开修改法家“刑无等级”的一贯主张，对控告父母伤害子女的诉讼不予受理。由此可见，为了适应宗法社会的文化土壤，无论是地处西部的秦国还是统一后的秦朝，皆曾努力进行融合孝道与法律的尝试。只不过秦王朝所维护的孝道乃是功利之孝道，而非伦理之孝道。[④] 换言之，“法家是否反对‘孝’，一切以有用与否为准绳”。[⑤] 正因如此，尽管秦法严禁殴、杀、骂父母等行为，然在孝道观念淡薄之地，子不孝父、妇骂公婆之风，仍举目可见，并未因法律禁绝而自然消失。但无论如何，秦代融孝道入法律的制度成果与历史教训，后为汉所继受和吸收，此则为秦代法制之历史贡献，不可一概抹杀。

（三）汉—唐—清：孝道法律制度的定型与继承

汉代标榜以孝治天下，皇帝谥号皆加“孝”字。[⑥] 统治者一方面褒奖以孝行称誉者，一方面运用法律手段对不孝行为进行严厉惩罚，孝道俨然为汉法之指导精神与核心价值。汉武察举创“孝廉”一科，成为两汉求仕者的必由之途。汉代在乡里设置“孝悌”的官职，力倡与父祖尊亲同居共财，以在基层民间弘扬孝道观念。同时，汉代法律亦严格禁止不孝行为，犯不孝罪者要处死刑。汉武帝时，衡山王太子刘爽密报其父刘赐谋反，未得奖赏，反以“不孝”之罪而被腰斩。可见在当时，孝道甚至高于忠道，俨然成为当时至高无上、不可侵犯的金科玉律。此外，礼敬尊长、君亲无将等孝义伦理亦成为司法中“春秋决狱”的核心原则。为了彰显以父权为核心的孝道，东汉还曾出台《轻侮法》，子因父受辱而杀人竟可免于刑罚。此皆可见，汉代法律已将孝道奉为最高价值。孝道作为立法和司法的指导原则，自汉代开始逐渐向法律和社会的各个方面进行渗透。其后历代均遵循孝治天下的基本准则，孝道法文化受到广泛推崇，

---

① 《法律答问》记载，某里士五（伍）甲告曰：“甲亲子同里士五（伍）丙不孝，谒杀，敢告。”即令令史己往执。令史己爰书：与牢隶臣某执丙，得某室。丞某讯丙，辞曰：“甲亲子，诚不孝甲所，毋（无）它坐罪。”（睡虎地秦墓竹简整理小组：《睡虎地秦墓竹简》，北京：文物出版社，1990 年，第 156 页）

② 《法律答问》记载：“殴大父母，黥为城旦舂。今殴高大父母，可（何）论？比大父母。”（《睡虎地秦墓竹简》，第 111 页）

③ 《法律答问》记载：“贼杀、伤它人为公室告；子盗父母，父母擅杀、刑、髡子及奴妾，不为公室告。”（《睡虎地秦墓竹简》，第 118 页）

④ 可参看康学伟著《先秦孝道研究》（长春：吉林人民出版社，2000 年）第七章之四《法家论孝道》。

⑤ 曹峰：《睡虎地秦简所见对“孝”的重视》，《国学学刊》2009 年第 1 辑。

⑥ 《汉书》卷 2《惠帝纪》“孝惠皇帝”颜师古注曰：“孝子善述父之志。故汉家之谥，自惠帝已下皆称孝也。”第 86 页。

终于沉淀为中国传统法律之价值底色。

魏晋南北朝时期，政权更换频繁带来了几度立法高潮，加之律学研究水准日益提高，孝道的价值理念纷纷渗透到法律制度之中，成为真正引导法律体系制定和运行的灵魂性要素。

曹魏《新律》既以明文废除“异子之科”，禁止子孙与父祖分家析产；又重惩子杀继母之罪，且有条件地允许私自复仇，孝道得以更多地体现在法律之中。以至于当时出现了君父先后之争的舆论焦点，邴原公开宣扬救父不救君的观点，也未受任何法律追究。[①]

晋《泰始律》号称“尤为儒家化”，[②] 引用丧服之制以决刑罚轻重缓急，“峻礼教之防，准五服以制罪”，[③] 将孝道法律化推进至更深一层。晋人李忽杀死投敌之父亲，竟被官方定为“无从子之道”而处以死刑。[④] 时人董养感叹道：“每见国家赦书，谋反大逆皆赦，孙杀王父母、子杀父母，不赦，以为王法所不容也。”[⑤] 可见当时不孝之罪甚于谋反。同时，以孝行作为核心标准的乡党清议，亦成为九品官人法的主要考量因素和仕途进退之重要依据。

南北朝虽是乱世，但是孝道观念对法律仍起支配作用，子女孝行即便违法亦得宽待，不孝行为即便于法有据亦当严惩。《北魏律》创设存留养亲之制，将司法中屈法而伸伦理的权宜做法明确化、制度化。而《北齐律》则进一步吸纳孝道精神，将不孝行为总结归入“恶逆”、“不孝”两大类罪，定为“重罪十条”之列，给予严厉打击，为隋唐以后惩治不孝行为铺就了最后一块基石。

法律儒家化至唐代初告完成，孝道精神也已完全融入法律之中，成为法律的核心价值。唐律号为“一准乎礼”，[⑥] 明确宣称“德礼为政教之本，刑罚为政教之用”。[⑦] 作为德礼之本的孝道成为立法和司法必须尊奉之圭臬，在法律中得到淋漓尽致的体现。在“十恶”罪中，关乎孝道的恶逆、不孝、不睦这三大类罪占据其三；在刑罚制度中，大力贯彻矜恤老幼原则；在民事家庭制度中，极力强化父权，并以无子、不顺公婆作

---

① 《三国志》卷11《魏书·邴原传》裴松之注引《原别传》记载曹操太子曹丕曾经聚客讨论忠孝之事：太子建议曰：“君父各有笃疾，有药一丸，可救一人，当救君耶？父耶？”众人纷纭，或父或君。时（邴）原在座，不与此论。太子谘之于原。原勃然对曰：“父也！”太子亦不复难之。北京：中华书局，1971年，第353—354页。

② 陈寅恪：《隋唐制度渊源略论稿》，北京：三联出版社，2001年，第111页。

③ 《晋书》卷30《刑法志》，北京：中华书局，1974年，第927页。

④ 《太平御览》卷647引王隐《晋书》。

⑤ 《太平御览》卷595《文部十一·论》。

⑥ 《钦定四库全书提要》卷38《政书类二·唐律疏义解》。

⑦ 《唐律疏议》卷1《名例》。

为丈夫休妻的法定理由；在国家政策上，大肆褒奖、宣扬孝子贤孙，如此种种做法，充分彰显出孝道在唐代法律制度中的核心价值地位。孝道与法律高度结合，孝道法制化在此时宣告完成。

宋、元、明、清法典继承唐律的基本精神和制度规定，孝道观念更因理学的论证和发扬而益加根深蒂固，相关的法律条文虽因时代变迁而有所损益，但孝道作为法律的指导原则之地位则牢不可破，始终在法律的制定和实施中发挥着核心作用。直到清末修律，始有剧变。

（四）清末以来：孝道在法律中的衰微

清季以降，中国文明遭遇西方文明之强劲挑战。作为中国传统法律之核心价值观和精神旨趣，孝道首当其冲受到强烈冲击。清末沈家本主持修律过程中引发的“礼法之争”的几大焦点中，干名犯义、存留养亲、子孙违反教令、子孙卑幼的正当防卫权，无一不牵扯孝道问题。法理派骁将杨度更是将这场争论定位为代表现代文明方向的国家主义与代表旧有势力的家族主义的对抗。似乎在法理派眼中，欲改造旧律则必须首先排除孝道观念在法律中的影响。此次论争虽然双方互有妥协，但是自此以后，孝道便日渐与法律拉开距离。中华民国的刑法典、民法典虽然还有一些遗留下来的制度规范略微体现一点孝道文化，但其核心价值则是西方传入的法学理论和价值观念，不复有古代法律以孝道为精神旨趣的风采了。虽如此，孝道作为数千年的文化积淀，亦难因制度变革而消失殆尽，依然遗传在民族心理之中。时至今日，孝道仍然在中国社会各个领域包括法律领域发挥着自身的作用。

## 二、孝道与传统立法

中国传统法律以孝道为核心价值展开其制度设计，进行立法。一方面逐步明确孝道的内涵，并以法律手段对其加以倡导与鼓励；另一方面渐次完善对不孝行为的严厉惩罚。中国古代孝道文化可以从三个层面加以理解，即利亲、善事、慎终。经过漫长的历史演进，孝道与法律彼此渗透，逐步融合而为一体。孝道的这三层含义也逐渐沉淀为凝练的法律语言，明确规定在古代法律之中。

（一）利亲

1. 利亲的法定内涵

利亲乃孝道在物质层面的要求，也是最低层次的要求。

《墨子·经上》说：“孝，利亲也。”《贾子·道术》曰：“子爱利亲谓之孝。”《礼记·祭统》中也说：“孝者，畜也。”可见，传统学说都把赡养父母作为孝道之基本内容。欲尽赡养之责，则须尽力保证父母衣食无忧、物资皆不匮乏。依照礼义，“孝有三：大孝不匮，中孝用劳，小孝用力。思慈爱忘劳，可谓用力矣。尊仁安义，可谓用劳矣。博施备物，可谓不匮矣”。[①] 当然，所谓利亲亦非定要追求锦衣玉食，而应依据子女经济状况及物质条件而加以判断。如《盐铁论·孝养》所说：“善养者不必刍豢也，善供服者不必锦绣也。以己之所有尽事其亲，孝之至也。”唐律对此两方面含义全面接纳，规定：“礼云：‘孝子之养亲也，乐其心，不违其志，以其饮食而忠养之。’其有堪供而阙者，祖父母、父母告乃坐。”[②] 当然，仅能利亲还远非尽到孝道，孝道还有更高要求。

2. 惩治有违利亲的不孝行为之规定

利亲为孝道最基本的要求，有违此者则为不孝，为法律所禁止。法律循此精神而设计出两种禁止性行为模式：供养有阙、别籍异财。

在汉代，“有生父而弗食三日”，廷尉议定，处其子以弃市之刑。[③] 如其行为主体为官员，其处罚方式则为免官。西汉时丞相薛宣，因不供养后母而被两次免官。[④] 西晋庾纯亦因“父老不归供养”遭人揭发而被迫辞官。[⑤] 凡此种种，皆为司法实践之一般惯例，唐以前历朝并无统一而又明确的法律规定。

至唐朝，则将“供养有阙”及其法律后果明文规定在律典之中，供养有阙者须处两年徒刑。[⑥] 法律同时规定，“供养有阙”应为“堪供而阙”。依《唐律疏议》之说法：“《礼》云‘七十，二膳；八十，常珍’之类，家道堪供，而故有阙者，各徒二年。”[⑦] 可见此罪乃针对有条件行孝而故意不尽孝道之人而设。如果确实家境贫寒无法做到供养充足，则不能一概视为犯罪。故“堪供而阙”实为区分罪与非罪的关键。此后，供养有阙皆为刑法所制裁，各朝代大体沿袭不变。

儒家历来重视家族主义，提倡“父母存，不有私财”，[⑧] 这既是对父母供养周备的思想基础，亦为孝道的应有之义。然而秦法则不用此意，严厉推行分户析居政策。[⑨] 至汉初，有些地区“生分”习俗仍然盛行。[⑩] 故汉惠帝特意下诏鼓励同居共财。[⑪] 东汉时，

---

① 《大戴礼记·曾子大孝第五十二》。

② 《唐律疏议》卷1《名例·十恶》“不孝”条。

③ 《张家山汉墓竹简（第二四七号墓）》，第227页。

④ 《汉书》卷83《薛宣传》，第3393－3396页。

⑤ 《晋书》卷50《庾纯传》，第1397－1401页。

⑥ 《唐律疏议》卷24《斗讼四》“子孙违犯教令”条。

⑦ 《唐律疏议》卷24《斗讼四》“子孙违犯教令”条。

⑧ 《礼记》卷2《曲礼上第一》。

⑨ 《史记》卷68《商君列传》记载有商君之法：“民有二男以上不分异者，倍其赋。”第2230页。

⑩ 《汉书》卷28下《地理志下》：“（河内）薄恩礼，好生分。”第1647页。

⑪ 《汉书》卷2《惠帝纪》：“今吏六百石以上父母妻子与同居，及故吏尝佩将军都尉印将兵及佩二千石官印者，家唯给军赋，他无有所与。”第85－86页。

聚族而居现象已广为存在，且为时尚所趋。如应劭所言，“凡同居，上也”。[①] 然而法律之于别籍异财行为，尚未明文禁止。直到曹魏《新律》，始有明确立场，“除异子之科，使父子无异财”。[②]

及至唐朝，禁止别籍异财的法律规定更加完善。依唐律，“别籍”指另立户籍，“异财”指分割财产。祖父母、父母在世时，子孙有别籍或异财者，皆处徒三年之刑。[③] 但如长辈强令分家，则子孙不受法律制裁。如此，对别籍异财制裁与否，全视尊长意志为转移，其弘扬孝道之义昭然可见。至于父母死后，丧期未尽，兄弟分家则处徒刑一年。[④] 唐朝以后，禁止别籍异财之法律宗旨一以贯之，唯量刑稍有增减。比如，宋时曾重为死刑，[⑤] 明时则减为杖刑。[⑥] 直到清末法制改革后，别籍异财才不被视为犯罪。

（二）善事

1. 善事的法定内涵

善事乃孝道在精神层面的要求，属于较高层次的孝道。

《尔雅》曰：“善父母为孝。”[⑦]《说文》曰：“孝，善事父母者也。从老省，从子，子承老也。”[⑧] 孝道此层含义亦得到法律确认，《唐律疏议》曰：“善事父母曰孝。”[⑨] 如此，则善事父母亦成为孝道义务的法定内容。而其具体含义又可从两方面加以考察。

首先，态度须恭敬，故曰孝敬。孟子曰：“孝之至，莫大于尊亲。”[⑩] 孝乃是由内而外自发生成的真情流露，故须有内心之恭敬始成孝道。孔子曰：“今之孝者，是谓能养。至于犬马，皆能有养；不敬，何以别乎！”[⑪] 由其义，尽孝应超越赡养层面，饱含情感关怀与虔敬态度，力求父母内心能感受到子孙恭敬之意，以获得精神慰藉。恭敬是孝道最可宝贵之处，也是最难始终贯彻之处。子夏问孔子尽孝如何最难，孔子答曰“色难”。[⑫] 意即对父母时刻保持恭敬，言语表情温和礼敬，最难做到。俗云“久病床前无孝子”，意即此理。尽孝最难的是“色难”，故恭敬之态度在孝道中最为要义。

---

① 《风俗通义》卷4《过誉第四》。

② 《晋书》卷30《刑法志》，第925页。

③ 《唐律疏议》卷12《户婚一》“子孙别籍异财”条。

④ 《唐律疏议》卷12《户婚一》“居父母丧生子”条。

⑤ 《宋史》卷2《太祖纪二》载，宋太祖曾诏川陕诸州，“察民有父母在而别籍异财者，论死”。北京：中华书局，1977年，第30页。

⑥ 《大明律》卷4《户律一》“别籍异财”条。

⑦ 《尔雅·释训第三》。

⑧ 《说文解字·老部》。

⑨ 《唐律疏议》卷1《名例·十恶》“不孝”条。

⑩ 《孟子》卷9《万章上》。

⑪ 《论语·为政第二》。

⑫ 《论语·为政第二》。

其次，行为须顺从，故曰孝顺。一方面要顺从父母意志，对父母之意既不能有所违背，更不可口出骂詈之语，手为伤殴之举。另一方面又不能无原则地顺从。曾参任凭父亲打骂，孔子即斥其陷亲不义。东汉赵岐更将“阿意曲从，陷亲不义”定为大不孝之首。即便父母确实有过，对其进行劝谏亦应注意表达方式。训蒙读物《弟子规》将之通俗地表达为：“亲有过，谏使更。怡吾色，柔吾声。”举止如此方为孝顺。除此之外，还要顺从并继承父母的价值观念，甚至父母过世之后也要将其发扬光大。所以孔子说：“父在观其志，父没观其行，三年无改于父之道，可谓孝矣。”[①]《礼记·中庸》亦曰：“夫孝者，善继人之志，善述人之事者也。”即为此意。孝道含义如此，律典亦承该说。如《唐律疏议》曰：“礼云：‘孝子之养亲也，乐其心，不违其志。’”[②] 此条法律规定，兼及于态度恭敬、行为顺从两种要求。

2. 惩治有违善事的不孝行为之规定

善事较之利亲，为更高层次的孝道，其主旨在于给予父母精神礼敬。落实到具体行为模式上，则又有孝敬与孝顺之别。而现实中，违背善事要求的行为，不仅有不敬、不顺行为；更有甚者，则难免有出手杀害、伤殴父母之行为。凡此种种，皆为法律明文所禁止。传统法律对此类不孝行为，一一加以列举。子孙杀、殴、骂父母、祖父母，告父母、祖父母以及违反教令等等，皆属其类。

汉重孝道，杀、殴、詈祖父母、父母为一科。子杀、殴、詈直系尊亲属，妇贼伤、殴詈夫之直系尊亲属，皆处弃市刑。其后，各类行为在主观恶性和客观效果上之差异逐步在律典中有所体现。

南朝宋律文规定：“子贼杀伤殴父母，枭首；骂詈，弃市；谋杀夫之父母，亦弃市。”[③] 在特定案件中，司法官则会依孝道精神对此类不孝行为的罪刑采用加重主义。刘宋时张江陵骂母致其自尽，在遇大赦的情形下，仍判以枭首之刑。[④] 北魏时“律不逊父母，罪止髡刑”。[⑤] 随着孝道观念深入人心，南北朝时人逐渐认识到对父母的人身伤害已然超出通常意义上的不孝范畴，将之升格为“恶逆罪”，与“不孝”、“内乱”等罪名加以区分。《北齐律》更是将“恶逆”纳入“重罪十条”严加惩处，不在八议、论赎之限。

唐律则通过系统整理，对恶逆罪做出完整规定：“殴及谋杀祖父母、父母，杀伯叔父母、姑、兄姊、外祖父母、夫、夫之祖父母、父母，皆处斩刑。”此处需注意者有

① 《论语·学而第一》。

② 《唐律疏议》卷1《名例·十恶》“不孝”条。

③ 《宋书》卷54《孔季恭传附渊之传》，北京：中华书局，1974年，第1534页。

④ 《宋书》卷54《孔季恭传附渊之传》，第1534页。

⑤ 《魏书》卷111《刑罚志》，北京：中华书局，1974年，第2878页。

三：其一，对于父母、祖父母之人身伤害，只要有谋杀的意图即构成犯罪，不要求一定有实际行为。其二，媳妇亦可成为该罪的主体，杀夫之父母祖父母亦属“恶逆”。其三，“恶逆”之罪行“穷恶尽逆，绝弃人理”，[①] 故而处以斩刑，且为常赦所不免，不在议、赎之列，行刑亦决不待时。唐以后法律对“恶逆”规定大体沿袭不变，只是在刑罚上日渐加重。宋代以后，五刑之外又设“凌迟”酷刑，专门针对谋反、恶逆等重罪。清末修订《现行刑律》，将杀父母改为斩刑，殴父母改为绞刑。此外，唐律将诅咒、骂詈祖父母、父母行为一并归入“不孝罪”，处绞刑，位列“十恶”之中。[②] 其后各朝，骂詈父母、祖父母皆为绞罪。清末《现行刑律》将之改为绞监候。

控告父母亦为传统法律所不容。周代禁止卑幼控告尊长，告者有罪。儒家向来以“父为子隐、子为父隐”为人性之“直”。[③] 秦代强制告奸，然而亦有“非公室告”之制，卑亲属对尊亲属在家族内部的犯罪行为不能向官府控告。汉初明文禁止子告父母。[④] 汉宣帝时更颁布“亲亲得相首匿”的诏令，明确倡导子为父母、祖父母隐匿罪行，为从法律角度否定子告父母的行为另造声势。[⑤] 魏晋南北朝时期法律对此规定进一步细化。首先，除特殊情况外，子告父母有罪。北魏《麟趾格》规定：“父谋反大逆子得告。”还规定：“母杀其父，子不得告，告者死。”[⑥] 但是该条因受到廷尉卿窦瑗的质疑而被废止。其次，父母犯罪子女不能出庭作证。东晋元帝采纳晋王大理卫展的建议，废除了以刑讯强迫子女证其父母有罪的做法。[⑦] 刘宋时蔡廓也建议：“鞫狱不宜令子孙下辞明言父祖之罪，亏教伤情，莫此为大。”[⑧] 廷议以为有理，遂下令废禁此制。

唐人总结前代经验，对此做出全面法律规定。唐律一方面确立“同居相为隐”制度，允许亲属之间相互包庇隐瞒犯罪；一方面明确规定：“诸告祖父母、父母者绞。”[⑨] 但若父母所犯为“十恶”中之谋反、谋大逆、谋叛罪，则不得适用“亲属相隐”。以后各朝基本沿袭这一法律规定，将告发父母犯罪、证明父母有罪之行为视为“干名犯义”，给予严厉打击。

---

① 《唐律疏议》卷1《名例·十恶》“恶逆”条。

② 《唐律疏议》卷1《名例·十恶》“不孝”条。

③ 《论语·子路第十三》。

④ 《二年律令》规定：“子告父母，妇告威公，勿听而弃告者市。”（《张家山汉墓竹简（二四七号墓）》，第151页）

⑤ 《汉书》卷8《宣帝纪》载：“自今子首匿父母，妻匿夫，孙匿大父母，皆勿坐。其父母匿子，夫匿妻，大父母匿孙，罪殊死，皆上请廷尉以闻。”第251页。

⑥ 《魏书》卷88《良吏传·窦瑗传》，第1909页。

⑦ 《晋书》卷30《刑法志》，第939页。

⑧ 《宋书》卷57《蔡廓传》，第1570页。

⑨ 《唐律疏议》卷23《斗讼三》“告祖父母父母”。

孝顺乃孝道之基本要求，不听从父母教令向来为儒家伦理所反对。《礼记·内则》曰："父母怒、不说，而挞之流血，不敢疾怨，起敬起孝。"汉代以后，子孙违犯教令行为为法律所禁止，其刑罚或重至死刑，或免官夺爵。南朝宋法律规定："违犯教令，敬恭有亏，父母欲杀，皆许之。"[①] 时人向植，继承其父侯爵，因"不受母训"，被罚以夺爵。[②]

及至唐朝，子孙违反教令之法律规定得以统一。《唐律·斗讼》规定："诸子孙违反教令"，徒二年。但违反教令须是"可从而违"方可构成犯罪。如孔子所说："故当不义，则子不可以不争于父。"[③] 如果父母之命着实无法遵从，违反教令亦不构成犯罪。此即赵岐"阿意曲从，陷亲不义"理论之法律化。唐以后，惩治子孙违反教令之制得以继承，只是量刑时有变化。清末法制改革，"子孙违反教令"等罪名，曾引起激烈争论，后终被移出法典。

（三）慎终

1. 慎终的法定内涵

慎终乃宗教层面的要求，为孝道最后表现形式与最高层次要求。

父母过世，当以礼送葬，以时祭祀。无论葬礼、祭礼皆应遵循一定规制，不能违礼，此即慎终之意。因而孔子解"无违"为"生，事之以礼；死，葬之以礼，祭之以礼"。[④] 无论父母生前抑或死后，尽孝皆应遵礼而有所节制，使丧亲之痛和一片孝心以恰当方式表达出来。唯其如此，方可使民风归于厚朴。故曾参曰："慎终追远，民德归厚矣。"[⑤] 此点意见，《唐律疏议》亦照章采纳："依《礼》：'闻亲丧，以哭答使者，尽哀而问故。'父母之丧，创巨尤切，闻即崩殒，擗踊号天。"[⑥] 法律竟将闻丧之哭规定得详细如斯，尤显法律对慎终观念的遵奉。

此外，娶妻生子、传宗接代，传承祖先血脉香火亦为敬孝父祖、慎终追远的重要内容。此亦为家族宗法之基本诉求，体现出孝道在宗教层面的理想渴望。《礼记·昏义》曰："婚姻者，合二姓之好，上以事宗庙，下以继后世。"故而在汉唐明清的法律制度中，"无子"遂成为丈夫出妻的七大法定理由之一。七出之制从先秦礼制到汉晋实践一脉相承，唐朝更将之明确规定于律令之中，无子又排在七出之首。[⑦] 传统法律对夫

---

① 《宋书》卷64《何承天传》，第1702页。

② 《宋书》卷45《向靖传》，第1374页。

③ 《孝经·谏诤章第十五》。

④ 《论语·为政第二》。

⑤ 《论语·学而第一》。

⑥ 《唐律疏议》卷1《名例·十恶》"不孝"条。

⑦ 《唐律疏议》卷14《户婚》"妻无七出而出之"条曰："七出者，依令：'一无子，二淫逸，三不事舅姑，四口舌，五盗窃，六妒忌，七恶疾。'"

妇传宗以尽孝道之重视，由此可见一斑。当然，唐律对无子出妻还有人性化设计，其中明确规定，“四十九以下无子，未合出之”。[①] 意即，无子出妻的规定必须在女子达到特定年龄而后方可适用。

2. 惩治有违慎终的不孝行为之规定

慎终追远乃孝道之宗教要求，违背此道亦属不孝。中国古代丧礼发达，正欲借此弘扬孝亲之道。丧期最初为三年，其后渐改为二十七个月。丧期之内，礼制要求繁芜严格，这些要求被法律吸纳后，便形成惩治有违丧礼之不孝犯罪的相关规定。数其要者，有匿不举哀，丧期违礼，冒哀求仕等。

匿不举哀是指闻父母死而不办丧。依儒家孝道精神，父母过世之后应依礼治丧，不能隐匿拖延。《礼记》规定：“奔丧之礼。始闻亲丧，以哭答使者，尽哀；问故，又哭；尽哀，遂行。”[②] 唐代礼法合一，此条礼义自然被法律采纳。诚如前述，唐律甚至对如何哭丧都规定得十分详细，其对闻丧不哭、匿不举哀的行为，更是要加以重罚，其中规定：“诸闻父母若夫之丧，匿不举哀者，流二千里”。[③] 依当时刑制，流放二千里仅次于斩刑和绞刑，已属重刑之列。将匿不举哀者流放二千里，是唐宋法律的通行规定，其后亦大体沿袭不改。明代“闻父母及夫之丧匿不举哀”亦属“十恶”，只是刑罚有所减轻，仅处杖六十、徒一年。[④]

丧期违礼包括居丧作乐、婚嫁、生子等行为。依儒家孝道理论，为父母服丧当至悲至哀，不得作乐，不得婚嫁，更不得生子，否则即为不孝。“父母之丧，终身忧戚，三年从吉，自为达礼。”[⑤] 法律本此孝道精神，遂将此类丧期违礼行为定为不孝之罪。

汉魏六朝，此类行为已被法律所否定，只是各朝的做法尚不统一。汉律规定：“夫父母死，未葬，奸丧旁者，当不孝，不孝弃市；不孝之次，当黥为城旦舂。”[⑥] 东汉赵宣，为父母守孝期间生有五个儿女，“遂致其罪”。[⑦] 丧期违礼不仅为国法所禁止，社会舆论也对之给予强烈谴责。十六国后秦时京兆韦高“居母丧，弹琴饮酒”，给事黄门侍郎古成诜闻之曰：“吾当私刃斩之，以崇风教。”[⑧] 古人重视慎终之孝，由此可见一斑。

至唐代时，法律对丧期违礼行为的惩罚得以统一。唐律规定，在父母丧期之内，“丧制未终，释服从吉，若忘哀作乐，徒三年；杂戏，徒一年；即遇乐而听及参预吉席

---

① 《唐律疏议》卷14《户婚》“妻无七出而出之”条。

② 《礼记》卷56《奔丧第三十四》。

③ 《唐律疏议》卷10《职制二》“匿父母夫丧”条。

④ 《大明律例》卷12《礼律二·仪制》。

⑤ 《唐律疏议》卷13《户婚二》“居父母夫丧嫁娶”条。

⑥ 《张家山汉墓竹简（二四七号墓）》，第227页。

⑦ 《后汉书》卷66《陈蕃传》，北京：中华书局，1965年，第2159－2160页。

⑧ 《日知录》卷15《居丧饮酒》。

者，各杖一百”。[①] 此外，居丧饮酒食肉亦为非法，比照“释服从吉”，徒三年。司法实践中，刑罚甚至会有所加重。唐宪宗时，陆慎馀与陆博文在居丧期间身穿华服在闹市饮酒食肉，诏“各决四十，慎馀流循州，博文递归本贯。”[②] 唐律还规定，诸居父母丧而嫁娶者徒三年，且婚姻无效，须“各离之。”[③] 而且居父母丧为人主婚也属犯罪，要受到杖一百的刑罚。不仅如此，依照唐律，即便是父母犯罪待刑、身被囚禁之时，子女作乐、嫁娶也要受到刑罚惩处。[④] 当然，此时嫁娶如是奉祖父母、父母之命为之，则不为罪。即便如此，依照唐令，嫁娶时也不得铺张宴会、大肆庆祝，以示心忧父祖。除此以外，“诸居父母丧，生子及兄弟别籍、异财者，徒一年。”[⑤]不过所谓居丧生子，须是在丧期内怀孕生子才算犯罪。

冒哀求仕是指在为父母守丧期间，置孝道于不顾，贪图爵禄，出仕为官。“自古忠孝难两全”，为国尽忠与在家尽孝本具有天然的内在冲突，而传统法律选择了优先成全孝道。尤其是，在服丧期间不能出仕做官是一项普遍的法律规定。此规定最早见于汉代法律。首先，不为父母守丧者，不能被选拔或推荐出仕为官。“汉律以不为亲行三年服不得选举。”[⑥] 其次，作为汉代官僚集团后备力量的博士弟子亦须依礼服丧，否则即剥夺其官员备选资格。[⑦] 再次，在任官员必须依礼为父母守丧，否则革除官职。[⑧] 其后，仍有人因贪恋禄位、冒哀求仕，而遭到法律严厉惩戒。如北魏时偏将军乙龙虎“居三年之丧而冒哀求仕”，“依律处刑五岁”。[⑨]

唐之前对“冒哀求仕”的惩处，历朝各有不一，到唐朝始得统一，分三种情况：一曰诈言余丧。《唐律疏议·诈伪》：“诸父母死应解官，诈言余丧不解者，徒二年半。”二曰释服求仕。守丧不满二十五个月，释服从吉，出来任官的，为释服求仕，徒刑三年。三是冒哀求仕。《唐律疏议·职制》规定：“冒哀求仕者：徒一年。”[⑩] 已满二十五

---

① 《唐律疏议》卷 10《职制二》“匿父母夫丧”条。

② 《日知录》卷 15《居丧饮酒》。

③ 《唐律疏议》卷 13《户婚二》“居父母夫丧嫁娶”条。

④ 《唐律疏议》卷 10《职制二》“府号官称犯父祖名”条：“若祖父母、父母及夫犯死罪，被囚禁，而作乐者，徒一年半。”《唐律疏议》卷 13《户婚二》：“祖父母、父母既被囚禁，固身囹圄，子孙嫁娶，名教不容。”

⑤ 《唐律疏议》卷 12《户婚一》“居父母丧生子”条。

⑥ 《汉书》卷 87 下《扬雄传下》颜师古注引应劭曰，第 3569 页。

⑦ 《汉书》卷 11《哀帝纪》记载，汉哀帝绥和二年诏曰：“博士弟子父母死，予宁三年。”颜师古注曰：“宁谓处家持丧服。”第 336－337 页。

⑧ 《后汉书》卷 46《陈宠传附陈忠传》记载，东汉安帝时下诏，要求“大臣得行三年丧，服阕还职”。第 1560 页。

⑨ 《魏书》卷 108 之四《礼志四》，第 2796 页。

⑩ 《唐律疏议》卷 10《职制二》“府号官称犯父祖名”条。

个月，未满二十七个月，禫制未除，出来任官的，为冒哀求仕，徒刑一年。由此还演化出官员如何为父母守丧服孝的“丁忧”之制，以后各朝沿用不改。

从上述三种情形可知，传统法律对孝道中利亲、善事、慎终这三个层次的具体内涵做了详尽界定，同时也对违背其要求的种种不孝行为规定了相应的惩罚措施。由汉到清的两千年中，国家立法始终围绕着孝道这一中心来进行论证设计，足以证明孝道实为传统立法的核心价值。

## 三、孝道与传统司法

前已述及，孝道作为核心价值贯穿于中国传统法律的制定过程，指导着整个立法活动，从而设计出各项繁杂而又周密的制度。在多数情况下，遇有侵犯孝道之案件发生，但须依法律规定处置即可。然而法律终究不能与伦理等同，当有体现孝道的极端行为出现而又恰与法律发生直接冲突之时，孝道便会突破法律的一般规定，从而催生出屈法律以全孝道的做法，进而固定为相应的司法制度或司法惯例，斯又为中国传统法律之一大特色。此类司法制度和惯例，既体现了伦理对法律的冲击，又展现了孝道之为传统司法的核心价值，一切司法活动皆须围绕着这一价值运转而不敢有所违背。兹以实例证之。

（一）存留养亲

“存留养亲”又称“留养”。即罪犯被判死刑或流刑，其父母年老无人赡养，且家中又无其他成年子孙，在这种情况下，可暂不执行刑罚，令其在家赡养老人。待父母去世后，再执行刑罚。存留养亲作为明确的司法制度，最早见于南北朝。北魏孝文帝时下诏：“犯死罪，若祖父母、父母年老，更无成人子孙，又无期亲者，仰案后列奏以待报，著之令格。”[①] 此诏被视为存留养亲制度的初始。该制度出现后，历朝相沿不改，到唐朝得到了进一步完善。宋、元、明、清诸政权，法律中皆有此项司法制度。

存留养亲实为屈法以全孝道的特殊司法制度，不能随意滥用，故而须满足严格条件方可实施。首先，祖父母、父母年龄须是七十以上。其次，罪犯家中没有其他成年子孙赡养老人。第三，祖父母、父母没有“期亲”如同辈兄弟可以依靠。同时具备此三条，方可适用存留养亲。

此外，欲启动存留养亲制度，还需根据不同情形依照特定程序行事。如若罪犯所犯为死罪，应“具状上请”。意即逐层上报，请示皇帝裁决是否给罪犯减刑。对此皇帝处理有两种：一是不减刑，仍判死刑。此时即可令罪犯回家赡养，待老人百年归世后，

① 《魏书》卷111《刑罚志》，第2878页。

再来执行死刑；二是减刑，免去死刑，减为流刑。如若罪犯所犯为流罪，或由死罪减为流罪者，则先行鞭打，而后令其回家为父母养老送终，之后再执行流刑。流刑之所以也要留养，是因为古代交通不便，信息闭塞，一旦流放，如泥牛入海全无消息，故无法承担孝道义务。

需要特别注意的是，存留养亲是一种刑罚延期执行制度，罪犯为老人养老送终后，还得继续执行刑罚，及至清朝，则变为一种永久性减刑制度——“留养承祀”。决定适用留养承祀的罪犯，老人死后，原判死刑，也不再执行死刑；原判流刑，亦不再流放。前者要改处枷号两月、责板四十、罚交银两的处罚（十两至五十两不等）；后者改为“止杖一百，余罪收赎”，就是打一百杖，再缴些银子即可。清代创设该制度，其目的在于保留罪犯生命以便承担传宗接代之任务，故称“留养承祀”。[①] 此制体现了古人“不孝有三，无后为大”的孝道观念对法律的冲击，致生矫枉过正之弊。

（二）代父母受刑

在传统社会，司法实践中普遍存在“代父母受刑”的现象，亦称“代刑”，先秦时已有其例。《列女传》中记载：春秋末年，晋国卿大夫赵简子执政，欲渡河攻打楚国。结果河津吏因醉酒耽误渡河。赵简子欲将其正法，其女请求代父受死，河津吏因而得免死罪。[②] 汉朝以后，受儒家孝道观念影响，此类现象屡见不鲜。或代替父母受刑，或代替父母受死。

司法机关在长期处理此类案件的过程中，渐而形成惯例。凡其种类有三：

1. 允许代刑

现有史料显示，司法中允许代刑的规定最早出现在东汉。汉明帝下诏将一些死刑罪犯迁徙到朔方、五原等边境地区屯田开荒，同时规定，如有“父母同产欲相代者，恣听之”。[③] 这是代替一般的刑罚。汉安帝时，律家陈忠建议：“母子兄弟相代死，听，赦所代者。”[④] 得到朝廷的采纳。汉朝以后，当事人申请代替亲人接受刑罚，且国家也准许的情况，时有所见。例如，清朝雍正五年，浙江上虞新宅村农民陈某误杀本村孩童，其子陈福德大义报官。官府将陈某缉拿归案，判令斩首示众。陈福德自觉不孝，跪求县令以身代父受刑，县令感其孝心，同意替刑，并将代刑决定上报朝廷，得到批准后释放陈某，将陈福德斩首。

---

① 《大清律例·名例律上之三》“犯罪存留养亲”条。

② 《列女传》卷6《辩通传》。

③ 《后汉书》卷2《明帝纪》，第121页。

④ 《后汉书》卷46《陈宠传附陈忠传》，第1556页。

2. 赦免

实践中，司法官对代父受刑的请求，处于社会舆论与法律规定的冲突之中。两难之际，往往上报朝廷，请求给罪犯免刑。例如，三国时吴国赤乌元年（238年），廷尉史伟触怒孙权，身被死罪。其长子史从、次子史敦联名上书，请求代父受死。朝廷恩准任选一子替父代刑。而在刑场上，一个要代父死，一个要为兄死，兄弟两人争执不已。孙权闻讯，感叹两子年纪虽幼而能明晓孝义，于是赦免史伟罪行，恢复官职。其二子被赐姓斯氏，意为孝敬父母者当如斯；旌表门间，其地赐名为斯孝乡。①

3. 减刑

代刑案件，更多的处理结果乃是司法官通过特定程序操作，最后经皇帝认可，使得被代刑的当事人得以减轻刑罚。比较而言，因代刑而给身为罪犯的父母减刑的最多，这方面的例子不胜枚举。例如，北魏时期，山西代县人长孙真误杀妻子，被判死刑。其子长孙虑以家中弟、妹尚幼为由，请求代父受死。最终，朝廷虑其“于父为孝子，于弟为仁兄”，② 于是下诏，免去长孙真死刑，改成流刑执行。

由上可以看出，处置代刑案件的司法惯例呈现出这样的规律：真正允许代刑者较少，因代刑而赦免罪犯刑罚的较多，因代刑而给罪犯减刑的则最为普遍。“代刑”的观念和举动，对传统司法影响非常深远。自汉至清，凡遇代刑案件，司法机关大都会给予相当重视，很少有法官对其置之不理、视而不见的。这种对正常司法程序构成干扰的现象，体现了孝道对法律之冲击。而对此类案件的处置方式，则可谓屈法以全孝道的典型代表。

（三）宽容复仇

古代复仇杀人，是一个法律问题，更是一个文化问题。中国古代社会素有“崇尚复仇”的文化心理，复仇亦为儒家所推崇和鼓励。而且儒家学者还对其进行理论论证与制度设计。首先，为父母复仇具有当然的正当性。《春秋公羊传》的说法：“子不复仇，非子也。”③《礼记·曲礼上》云：“父之仇，弗与共戴天。”其次，为父母复仇应具备坚决、果敢之态度。《周礼》有“父母之仇，避之海外，虽遇市朝，斗不反兵”④ 的说法。准备复仇期间，要“寝苫、枕干、不仕”，⑤ 须时刻做好准备复仇。其三，复仇

① 《三国志》卷57《虞翻传》，第1326页注引《会稽典录》。另见清斯献德等纂修《东阳白石斯氏宗谱》，清道光28年木活字本；并见《东阳斯氏宗谱》，2011重修本，第243－244页。

② 《魏书》卷86《孝感·长孙虑传》，第1882页。

③ 《春秋公羊传·隐公十一年》。

④ 《宋书》卷51《宗室·临川武烈王道规传附刘义庆传》，第1475页。

⑤ 《礼记·檀弓》。

亦须遵循特定道义原则与国法限制。例如，“恶恶止其身”，[①] 不能滥及无辜；复仇时不能乘人之危，须讲究正大光明；父母之死非因国法，[②] 如此等等。

崇尚复仇之文化心理一旦形成，就很难消除，给古代法律带来深刻影响。秦朝奉行法家思想，禁止私相复仇。汉朝以后，国家推行“孝治”政策。为父母报仇虽有碍于社会秩序，却是尽孝的极端表现，以致此类行为在生活中层出不穷。国家对此亦不得不拿出相应的对策，于是崇尚复仇、敬重复仇的文化心理便顺理成章地渗透到法制实践中来。

就成文法典而言，对复仇的态度时有变化。有时明文允许复仇，例如东汉章帝时颁布的《轻侮法》；有时则明文禁止复仇，例如曹魏文帝曹丕曾下诏严禁之；[③] 有时则又采折中办法，对血亲复仇进行有条件的默许，例如曹魏明帝时颁布的《新律》。国家法律这种闪烁其词、欲说还休的态度，既给理论界带来了长久的争论，[④] 又给实务界带来了极大的操作空间。

就司法实践而言，对复仇案件多采宽容之策。自汉代以来，国家奉儒家学说为指导思想，出现“春秋决狱”的新型审判方式，实务界常常以此方式来宽容复仇者。所谓“春秋决狱”，即当遇有疑难案件，严格依法判案会背离人情常理，则改用《春秋》等儒家经典的经义来进行变通，以便得出法律与情理相融通的判决。众所周知，儒家《春秋》经传是崇尚“复仇大义”的，以此来审理复仇案件，当事人自然能得到有利的判决。例如，汉灵帝时赵娥为父报仇杀人，深受孝道观念熏染的司法官便千方百计为其寻求免罪理由。最终，与皇帝赦免诏书一道而至的还有十匹束帛与一座孝烈牌坊。[⑤] 唐代以后，“春秋决狱”虽退出历史舞台，然实践中对复仇案件的宽容之策不改，即便在受儒家伦理思想影响较小的蒙元时代，“因孝枉法”的案例也并不少见。[⑥]

细加条分，司法中对复仇案件的处理结果大致有四：一为判决无罪。引用春秋大

---

① 《春秋公羊传·昭公二十年》。

② 《春秋公羊传·定公四年》曰：“父不受诛，子复仇可也。”《周礼·地官·调人》云：“凡杀人而义者，不同国，勿令仇，仇之则死。”《周礼·秋官·朝士》则说：“凡报仇者，书于士，杀之无罪。”

③ 《三国志》卷2《魏书·文帝纪》记载，曹魏文帝时下诏：“今海内初定，敢有私复仇者皆族之。”第82页。

④ 如东汉张敏、桓谭等人明确主张国法禁断复仇，刘宋傅隆、南齐孔稚珪主张对复仇法外开恩。而后又有数篇重要的文章围绕复仇的法律问题展开深入地讨论。例如唐代陈子昂的《复仇议状》、柳宗元的《驳复仇议》、韩愈的《复仇状》和宋代王安石的《复仇解》，围绕礼治与法治关系、法律与人情的关系各自提出了不同的见解。

⑤ 详见《三国志》卷18《庞淯传》正文及裴注引皇甫谧《烈女传》，第548—550页。《三国志》称“赵娥”，《烈女传》称“庞娥亲”，实乃一人。

⑥ 参见赵文坦《儒家孝道与蒙元政治》，《孔子研究》2008年第3期。

义，认定复仇杀人行为不是犯罪行为，直接判无罪，当庭释放。此为汉唐间春秋决狱宽容复仇的基本方式。二为减轻刑罚。上报朝廷，由文武大臣讨论后进行减刑，这是唐朝春秋决狱消失后出现的宽贷复仇之新方式。因为唐朝已形成严格的律令格式体系，法官审案必须严格引用法律条文，否则构成犯罪。遇到复仇案件，法官自己不敢定夺，遂逐级上报。并附之以《春秋》、《礼记》复仇大义，以求为复仇者减刑。唐宪宗时梁悦复仇案即为其例。① 三为免除刑罚。上报朝廷，皇帝直接下诏进行赦免。例如，清初李复新为父报仇，杀死已被判处徒刑的仇人。县官为其孝行感动，上报朝廷，终免其刑罚；地方政府还专门为其修造孝烈牌坊，以为榜样。② 四为依律处刑，而后又表彰其孝义，这以唐代武则天时期徐元庆复仇案为其代表。但这种自相矛盾的做法也遭到了后世非议，故效法者甚少。

历史上，为亲报仇者前赴后继，司法界的宽容亦一以贯之，遂形成了“宽容复仇”的司法惯例，“体现了中华法系所带有的浓厚的伦理特征”。③

综观由汉到清两千年的司法史，除存留养亲、代父母受刑、宽容复仇这些典型的司法制度和惯例外，其他屈法以伸孝道的做法更是俯首即是。可见传统法律的实际施行，也是始终围绕着孝道这一精神灵魂来运转的，如有冲突，则法律必须为伦理让路，以进一步弘扬孝道。此足以明证孝道亦为传统司法的核心价值。

## 四、孝道法文化之价值评判

孝道既为传统立法之核心价值，亦为传统司法之核心价值，固有的中国法律，无可回避地浸染在孝道文化之中，形成一套完整的孝道法律体系，进而呈现出独具特色而又一脉相承的孝道法文化。这样的文化有如空气一般无时不有，无处不在，弥漫在传统中国人的日用常行之中。有美国学者称：“若不牢牢记住孝道是中国人的家族，社会，宗教乃至政治生活的根据的这一事实，即终究不能理解中国及中国人的真相。”④抛开孝道亦无法真正理解中国传统法律。在漫漫历史长河之中，孝道法文化对国民性格之养成，社会秩序之构建，均有着举足轻重的作用；于今日建设和谐社会与法治社会，亦当有推陈出新之功用。

---

① 事在《新唐书》卷195《孝友·张琇传》，北京：中华书局，1975年，第5587—5588页。

② 《清史稿》卷498《孝义二·李复新传》，北京：中华书局，1977年，第13780—13781页。

③ 唐红林、邹剑锋：《儒家“孝治”对“血亲复仇”的扬抑》，《宁波大学学报（人文科学版）》第18卷第6期，2005年11月。

④ 转引自徐复观：《中国孝道思想的形成、演变及其在历史中的诸问题》，文载氏著：《中国思想史论集》，上海：上海书店出版社，2004年，第131页。

（一）对人性之矫正与扭曲

既有的社会生命经验显示，人类情感呈向下趋势。父母对子女多为无条件、无保留的情感输出。如《诗经》所说："父兮生我，母兮鞠我。拊我畜我，长我育我。顾我复我，出入腹我。欲报之德，昊天罔极。"[①] 而同时，幼年子女大多无法体谅父母苦心，及其成家育子之后，又会将更多情感输出给其子女。如此下去，为父母者始终是付出多于回报。有鉴于此人性弱点，中国先哲自古就提倡孝道，强调子女对父母的情感反哺，欲借此对人性加以矫正。其后国家亦大力提倡孝道，并将其精神注入法律之中，以法律维护、成全孝道，无疑极大增强了孝道文化的贯彻效果。于是在中国，就形成了"甲代抚育乙代，乙代赡养甲代，乙代抚育丙代，丙代又赡养乙代"这种"下一代对上一代都要反馈的模式"。[②]

而且这种反馈应是物质、精神、宗教三方面的，要发之于心，形之于色，并付之于言行。一念一色、一言一行皆须毕恭毕敬，不离于孝道。如此等等，都在法律制度上一一加以确认，并辅之以宣传教化、行政强制乃至严刑重罚。遂使孝道文化在中国绵远流长，代代不息，将中国人融化在一派血浓于水的温情之中。其温情有三：

一曰，强调情感反哺。孝道乃报恩之举，年幼受之父母，成年后反哺双亲。然而此时父母皆已年老，身体、精神日益衰弱，欲行孝道便不可有嫌弃之心。因此，孝道要求既要尽量保证衣食无缺，又要善事父母，言行温和礼敬，不可使父母年老体衰之身心更受情感伤害，晚景凄凉，心灰意冷。国法遂依此意将杀、殴、骂、告父母、别籍异财、供养有阙等行为列为打击对象。二曰，顾及人伦纽带。孝慈亲情乃天性禀赋，与生俱来。《孝经》曰："父子之道，天性也。"[③] 此非法律可以强制逆转之事。况且，"法者，非从天下，非从地出，发乎人间，合乎人心而已"。[④]《韩非子·八经》更明确地说："法通乎人情关乎治理。"为了顾及这种情感纽带，于是实践中出现了宽容复仇、存留养亲等屈法以伸孝道之司法惯例与制度。三曰，注重精神传递。父母过世之后，对其追念亦属孝道情感应有之义。一方面要尽心服丧，依循礼制恰当地表达丧亲之痛；另一方面要传递香火，使前代尊亲不至绝祀。国家法律于是对丧期违礼的种种行为加以禁止，对官员服丧进行系统规定，对无子休妻制度加以确认。观其要旨，乃在于代际之间精神传递，灵魂沟通。

然而孝究为人类朴素情感，应出自血缘亲情之自然流露。如纯以伦理观念加以宣

---

① 《诗经》卷13之一《小雅·蓼莪》。

② 费孝通：《生育制度》，北京：北京大学出版社，1998年，第228页。

③ 《孝经·圣治章第九》。

④ 《慎子》佚文。

扬倡导，或不至于出离孝道本旨。然而其后孝道法文化日渐强化，以法律强制手段要求人人皆要按照特定礼制履行孝道，实践过程中则难免有矫枉过正或流于形式之嫌。其流弊亦有三：

一曰，诱发人性虚伪矫饰。孝与不孝皆源自内心情感，法律无法拘束人心，只能对外在形式加以统一规定，乃至强求一律。如此就难免出现虽有其情而不愿为繁文缛礼束缚以致违法犯罪的情形，或出现徒有其表而内心虚伪的现象。如前述东汉赵宣一案即为其例。汉末更有“察孝行，父别居”[①] 之讽谣。二曰，漠视个体价值。孝道乃自下向上之情感要求，偏重强调子女对父母无微不至的尊崇与顺从，本为矫正人性向下之弊。然而以法律相强制，久之则必然导致父权过度膨胀，相对而言子女自身正当之权利则极度萎缩。例如，其婚姻自主权要交由父母，遵循“父母之命、媒妁之言”；其生命健康权亦不得对抗父母之教令权；乃至于以身代刑这种愚孝行为都得到了法律认可与社会褒奖。个体价值在父权、孝道面前全无地位，亦遭到法律之漠视。三曰，造成屈服之国民性格。孝道法文化过度强调子女恭顺、父祖权威，自幼生于此种家庭教育和文化渲染之中的国民，其性格中遂生出一种屈服、顺从、依赖权威之属性。少年老成、谨慎持重、禁锢保守、全无创造思维竟成为社会舆论推崇褒扬之优良德行。此实为对健全国民性格之压抑与扭曲。

（二）对秩序之匡扶与异化

孝道法文化之发扬光大，不唯对人性构成其亦正亦反之影响，而且对古代中国之家国社会秩序，也有着深刻而又复杂的意义。

一方面，孝道法文化以父权为核心，强调卑幼对尊长的顺从与维护，由此促成家族组织之完备与族权之膨胀。

凡此数义皆得到国家法律的确认与强力支持，这无疑大大增强了家族内部凝聚力。于是以强有力之父权、族权为核心的大家族组织模式在古代中国基层社会普遍推广开来。如同汉哀帝诏书所称：“汉家之制，推亲亲以显尊尊。”[②] 古代国家之所以大力提倡孝道，乃至于不惜以法律手段彰显孝道，亦有其功利目的。他们试图通过鼓吹孝道以增强个体与家族之连带关系，并进而为国家通过家族控制社会做好铺垫，此即忠孝一体、移孝于忠的统治逻辑。统治者和社会舆论一致认为，弘扬孝道会使民心归于厚朴，世风日臻淳净，秩序自然达致和谐。孔子曰：“《书》云：‘孝乎为孝，友于兄弟，施于有政’，是亦为政。”[③] 汉代以后，县级以下的社会组织基本上处于乡间自治的状态，国

① 《抱朴子·外篇》卷2《审举第十五》。

② 《汉书》卷11《哀帝纪》，第339页。

③ 《论语·为政第二》。

家机构对其活动不多干预。其中，由孝道法文化所着力维护而构建起来的家族主义观念，在推进社会稳定和谐方面，贡献尤多。其表现有三：

其一，以孝道为家族秩序之支撑。法律以明文维护父亲之权威，不仅杀伤、殴打、骂詈、控告父母为法律所严惩，而且即便是违反教令、不顺舅姑、别籍异财等行为皆被列入不孝之条目，为法律明令禁止和严厉打击。而且法律还将父权无限扩大，一家之内的教令权、财产权、主婚权全部囊括在内。父权亦因此而成为家庭组织的权力支柱和核心力量。并以此构建出一整套维护家庭秩序稳定的伦理规范。家庭为社会之基础因子，家庭伦理秩序之稳定实为社会和谐之基础。其二，以家族伦理为基层规约之主要内容。传统社会的地方秩序，即有国法加以调控，更主要的则是由自发而成的村规民约所维系。而乡间规约的形成过程中，亦往往以地方上势大族众的宗族为主导。因而村规民约通常为家族伦理规范的扩展，孝道法文化仍为其核心价值。其三，以家族关系为基层社会之控制途径。中国古代基层社会的行政控制较为疏松，大体上以乡间血缘关系网为主要依托。即便是地方乡绅和普通民众之间，往往皆被夹裹在特定的亲缘关系中，因而尊卑长幼的孝道伦理关系在其间发挥着重要作用。

另一方面，孝道法文化在过分强化父权、族权之同时，又抹杀了个体价值，增强了中国社会的专制主义色彩。

以孝道为核心价值的宗法家长制形成特定的尊卑等级秩序，要求晚辈对长辈绝对服从，其婚姻、财产、人身乃至精神人格均由长辈绝对掌控。乃至于宣扬“天下无不是之父母”、“父要子亡，子不得不亡”等愚孝观念。在家国一体的逻辑观念下，历代统治者奉行“以孝治天下”的治国原则，将国家组织拟作放大的家族，皇帝则俨然以全国大家长自居。孝道与忠道由之合二为一，父权与皇权紧密结合，润物无声地将对父权的愚孝转化成为对皇帝的愚忠，强化了中国社会秩序的专制主义色彩。在专制社会之环境下，父权至上的家庭培养出来的是缺乏个性和个体价值的臣民，更增强了帝制的权威。

总而言之，孝道法文化导致传统社会、政治、文化秩序之异化。究其根本，孝道本为质朴的血亲情感，其价值在于维护家庭尊卑长幼之间的伦理关系。以法律方式维护孝道，其效能亦应仅限于家族内部。然而，古代统治者基于巩固国家秩序之需要，极力宣扬孝道，强调“以孝治天下”，使得孝道承载过多政治责任，被赋予过高政治期许。孝道法文化的过度伸张，既扭曲了孝道文化，又异化了政治秩序。

（三）孝道法文化之推陈出新

中国数千年孝道法文化之渊源流变、功过是非已如前述。然而无论如何，自清末法制变革以来，传统法律制度已然崩溃，中华法系亦渐告解体，作为其核心价值和精神灵魂的孝道法文化遂戛然而止。经历清末修律、五四运动以及新中国成立以来历次运动之不断冲刷，不惟孝道法文化几乎消失殆尽，社会上一般孝道观念乃至于道德价值亦如雨后彩虹雨后残，不堪摧凌。孝道法文化之迷失亦造成了严重的后果。

首先，孝道法文化衰落，造成老人现实境遇的普遍恶化。孝道既源自人类自觉的情感反馈，又是对人情向下习惯之矫正。尽孝乃纯粹的义务行为，所以人性会本能地选择逃避和摆脱。近代以来中国的法制变革沿着区分法律与道德的思维一路走来，法律不再与道德混同，道德亦无复法律之保障。作为传统道德价值观念之核心的孝道，便从法律中剥离出来。失去法律强力支撑的孝道观念遂迅疾滑落，以致日渐淡薄。观今日之社会，不孝现象较为常见，甚至虐老的行为也时有所见，而现有法律调控能力却十分有限。尽管现行民事法中规定子女对父母负有赡养义务，但又仅限于物质赡养范围之内，而这其实只是孝道最低层次的要求。尽管刑法中也设置有虐待罪、遗弃罪等罪名，对严重的不孝行为进行刑事追责，但定性标准太严，不孝行为须达到“情节恶劣”的程度，即长期虐待老人，或因遗弃造成老人重伤或死亡，才构成犯罪，这样的法律规定在实践中很难真正发挥惩治不孝的作用。在人口老龄化日益严重的当下之中国，在社会养老保障体制尚未建成的既有国情下，现有法律制度远不能给老人群体颐养天年提供充分的制度保障。长此以往，势必造成极其严重的社会问题，对社会秩序的稳定和谐亦将形成极大的挑战。

其次，孝道法文化衰落，造成社会个体之间情感淡漠与社会责任感的减弱。孝道文化属于报答文化，其中既有人情上的知恩图报，也有功利上的付出回报。一方面为代际之间提供温情脉脉之精神慰藉，另一方面也可消弭长辈心中老无所依之现实顾虑。因而，孝道之弘扬有增进人际情感、消减人际隔阂之大功用。孟子说：“老吾老以及人之老，幼吾幼以及人之幼。”① 推己及人，由近及远，孝道由此而成为社会责任感与社会公德之渊薮。和谐社会必定是道德秩序井然之社会。反之，道德衰败之社会亦绝非和谐社会。而当今之现实，孝道再无法律制度之维护与保障，遭到社会普遍漠视。其结果，子女在家不尽孝道，在外则无社会公德与公共责任感。此亦为和谐社会之大敌。

由是观之，孝道法文化之衰落确乎为和谐社会之大障碍。但同时，时代变迁也需要孝道法文化与传统法律制度进行创造性转化，以推陈出新。

建基于传统宗法社会基础之上的孝道法文化，以生硬强制、一厢情愿之法律手段推行孝道方式。这在社会平等观念、个体意识大为普及之今天，当然不能如法炮制。无论逻辑内容抑或规范模式，传统孝道皆需一番自我扬弃。对于传统法律中有些依据礼制而形成的不孝罪名，如别籍异财、子孙违反教令、丧期作乐、冒哀求仕等条款，自不可能重拾旧章；对于古代屈法律而全孝道之司法制度与惯例，如存留养亲、代父

① 《孟子》卷1《梁惠王上》。

受刑、宽容复仇等，亦不可能再加恢复。但是孝道精神则可用充满人性关怀之方式，重见新意于今日之法律条文与司法实践之中。

例如，子女对父母之人身伤害与精神侮辱，可否较之常人加重处罚？子女出于孝道亲情对父母违法犯罪行为包庇隐瞒，可否较之常人减轻处罚？在子女对父母尽赡养义务之外，可否再增加更高要求？对尽孝之人物、事迹，可否在精神褒奖之外再加物质奖励并将其制度化？对因孝道而产生之犯罪行为，可否给予必要的法律上之宽容与执行上之变通？如此等等问题，要完满解决，既需要创造性的制度设计，亦需要对传统孝道精神进行深刻体悟，还需要对现代法治精神有精准的把握。目前，我国立法和司法界已经对此类问题展开有益尝试。2011 年《刑法修正案（八）》中对老年人犯罪从轻处刑之新规定，2012 年《刑事诉讼法修正案》关于近亲属享有拒证权之新规定，2013 年开始实施的《老年人权益保障法》中要求子女常回家看看的规定，可说已经迈出重要一步。这是对传统孝道法文化的呼应，也是对传统法律价值的回归。

孝亲情感出于人性而自然生发，“具有超越时代的普适性和共通性”。[①] 基于中国传统孝道文化之绵绵不息，基于其在中国社会文化中之勃勃生机，基于中华民族在孝道与法律之间积累数千年之经验与教训，我们有理由相信，孝道法文化必能推陈出新，必将为今日构建和谐社会和法治社会做出殊凡贡献。

---

① 林明：《传统法制中的孝道文化因素释义》，《法学论坛》2001 年第 6 期。

# 儒家，“将权力关进笼子”的先驱

山西大学 白 平

拥有权力而不受监督，权力就会被滥用，所以必须将权力关进笼子。这个道理现代人都懂得，其实中国的古人也是懂得的，整个儒家思想的主旋律，就是要将权力关进笼子。

晚清以来，儒家形象被污化得很厉害，所以常听人说儒家认可专制，维护等级，要求绝对服从云云。这些看法都不符合事实，应予澄清。

## 一

古人认为，“天”是世间万物的主宰，是宇宙间掌握最高权力的神。儒家将这尊神进行了理想化的塑造，使它成了正义和公理的化身，是百姓利益的靠山。

《左传·僖公五年》：“故《周书》曰：皇天无亲，惟德是辅。”意思是说，天对人不论亲疏，只帮助有德者。

《尚书·泰誓上》：“惟天地万物父母，惟人万物之灵。亶聪明，作元后，元后作民父母。”意思是说，天地是万物的父母，为百姓选择了君主和官吏，让官吏当百姓的父母。

《孟子·梁惠王下》：“《书》曰：天降下民，作之君，作之师，惟曰其助上帝宠之。四方有罪无罪惟我在，天下曷敢有越厥志?”意思是说，天降生了百姓，为他们设置了君主，设置了各级官员，只是为了让君主和官员帮助上帝保护好百姓。四方的人们有罪或无罪，由君主和官员来审察，天下的人们哪敢违背天的旨意?

《尚书·泰誓上》：“以尔有众，厎天之罚。天矜于民，民之所欲，天必从之。”这话是周武王说的，意思是说，我率领你们大家，对纣执行天的惩罚。天心疼百姓，百姓的意愿，天一定会成全。

《尚书·泰誓中》：“天视自我民视，天听自我民听。”意思是说，百姓的眼睛就是天的眼睛，百姓的耳朵就是天的耳朵。换言之：民意就是天意。

这些材料说明，君主和官吏必须正派，他们必须像父母保护子女一样为天保护好百姓。谁违反了天的这一意旨，人们就可以对他执行天的惩罚。天和正义保持一致，和百姓保持一致，不和君主与官吏保持一致。

由此可见，“天”就是个笼子，其圈禁对象就是君主和官吏。顺天者昌，逆天者亡。“天”是谁？儒家说：“天视自我民视，天听自我民听。”又说：“民之所欲，天必从之。”答案很明确：“民”就是“天”。儒家实际上是给“民权”施加了“神权”的包装，企图对君主和官吏予以震慑。

《孟子·梁惠王下》：“左右皆曰贤，未可也；诸大夫皆曰贤，未可也；国人皆曰贤，然后察之；见贤焉，然后用之。左右皆曰不可，勿听；诸大夫皆曰不可，勿听；国人皆曰不可，然后察之；见不可焉，然后去之。左右皆曰可杀，勿听；诸大夫皆曰可杀，勿听；国人皆曰可杀，然后察之，见可杀焉，然后杀之，故曰国人杀之也。如此，然后可以为民父母。”

孟子的这段话说得很啰唆，但啰唆自有啰唆的道理，他是要掰开了，揉碎了，苦口婆心地说明一个道理：国君，你一切都要听下层民众的，一切都要听大多数人的。有人说儒家没有民主理念，那么，孟子这里讲的是不是民主理念？周武王讲的“民之所欲，天必从之”是不是民主理念？

## 二

儒家希望士人能“仁以为己任”，理想的发展模式是“修身齐家治国平天下”。修身的目标是成为百行齐备的君子，这是要求人们自律，不得突破道德的藩篱。

“道德”是一般社会成员的笼子，更是君主和官吏的笼子，在任何社会，人们对君主和官吏的道德要求都会高于平民。

《论语·为政》：“为政以德，譬如北辰，居其所而众星共之。”意思是说，执政者依靠品德来治理国家，就像北极星，安坐在自己的位置上，所有的星星都围绕着它运行。

《论语·颜渊》：“政者，正也。子帅以正，孰敢不正？”意思是说，政治的目标就是正确合理，您用正确合理的行为做出表率，鲁国上下谁的行为敢不正确合理？

《论语·泰伯》：“禹，吾无间然矣。菲饮食而致孝乎鬼神，恶衣服而致美乎黻冕，卑宫室而尽力乎沟洫。”意思是说，禹，我没有任何批评了。自己吃的很简单，却对鬼神很孝敬；平时穿得很简朴，却将在正式场合的礼服礼帽做得很华美；住的房子很简陋，却全力以赴地兴修水利设施。

《论语·颜渊》：“出门如见大宾，使民如承大祭。己所不欲，勿施于人。”意思是说，出门见了别人像见到贵宾一样尊敬，役使百姓像负责重要的祭祀一样认真谨慎。自己所不愿意的事情，不要施加到别人身上。

儒家对于“君子”的论述车载斗量，就是要对世人进行驯化，让人们都自觉进入“道德”的笼子。所谓“将权力关进笼子”，不就是要关进法律、道德的笼子吗？

## 三

将“天”设为笼子，能起到一定的恐吓作用。将“道德”作为笼子，能起到一定的驯化作用。然而对于君主和官吏的监督干预，最终还得靠社会的每一个人。儒家主张以道义为原则，谏阻君主的过失，规范君主的行为。

《论语·宪问》：“子路问事君，子曰：‘勿欺也，而犯之。’”意思是说，子路问如何侍奉君主，孔子说：“不要欺骗君主，但可以当面抵触他。”

《荀子·子道》：“从道不从君，从义不从父，人之大行也。”意思是说，能听命于道义而不是机械地听命于君父，这才是人的最高层级的品行。

《孝经·谏诤》：“士有争友则身不离于令名，父有争子则身不陷于不义。故当不义，则子不可以不争于父，臣不可以不争于君。故当不义则争之，从父之令又焉得为孝乎！”意思是说，士人有诤友，才能保持好名声。父亲有诤子，才不会做出不道义的事。在不道义的事情面前，儿子不可以不谏阻父亲，臣民不可以不谏阻君主。所以在不道义的事情面前就应该谏阻，机械地听从父亲的指令，哪能算是孝呢？

现代的人读古书，对“忠”字很敏感，会想到奴性。其实“忠”的意思是“在道义的原则下对人诚实负责”。人们都希望来自别人的诚实负责，人们也应该对别人诚实负责。

《论语·八佾》：“君使臣以礼，臣事君以忠。”意思是说，君主按照礼的规定役使臣民，臣民用忠的态度侍奉君主。

《论语·宪问》：“爱之，能勿劳乎？忠焉，能勿诲乎？”意思是说，既然爱他们，能不对他们的劳苦予以关怀和救助吗？既然对他们负责，能不教诲他们吗？这里的“忠”，恰恰说的是君主和官吏对百姓的“忠”。《孟子·滕文公上》：“分人以财谓之惠，教人以善谓之忠。”可见“忠”不是绝对服从的意思。

郭店楚简：“鲁穆公问于子思曰：‘何如而可谓忠臣？’子思曰：‘恒称其君之恶者，可谓忠臣矣。’公不悦，揖而退之。……成孙弋曰：‘噫，善哉言乎！夫为其君之故杀其身者，尝有之矣；恒称其君之恶者，未之有也。夫为其君之故杀其身者，效禄爵者也。恒称其君之恶者，远禄爵者也。为义而远禄爵，非子思，吾恶闻之矣？’”所谓“恒称其君之恶”，意思就是对君主只批评而不赞美。

《孟子·公孙丑下》："天下有达尊三：爵一，齿一，德一。朝廷莫如爵，乡党莫如齿，辅世长民莫如德，恶得有其一以慢其二哉？故将大有为之君必有所不召之臣，欲有谋焉则就之。其尊德乐道不如是，不足与有为也。"孟子要求君主要"尊德乐道"，他想用"德"压倒"爵"，逼得君主屈其尊，这都是儒家企图用道义圈禁君主的努力。

儒家千方百计地想将权力关进笼子，但权力最终没能有效地被圈禁起来，这责任并不能由儒家来负。夏代以来中国一直是世袭制的"家天下"社会，权柄不在儒家手里，儒家不是政党，没有组织，不能在社会制度的建设方面有所作为，所以对于权力的滥用不能形成有效的阻遏。

事实证明，儒家从来都是社会弱势群体的代言人，无论是在理论建设方面还是在实践斗争方面，都做出了杰出的贡献。

# 传统文化参与修复性司法的实践及思考

海南省政协常委、社会和法制委员会主任 张 发

《监狱法》指出："监狱是国家刑罚执行机关，监狱对罪犯实行惩罚与改造相结合、教育和劳动相结合的原则，将罪犯改造成守法公民。"这段话不仅阐明了监狱的性质、执法工作原则，更阐明了监狱工作的终极目标。作为在监狱工作的领导和警察们，最关心关注的是两个问题：一是监管安全；二是如何将罪犯改造成守法公民，换句话说，如何使监狱成为"新公民孵化器"？自2006年以来，海南省监狱管理机关在海南省司法厅主要领导的支持下，以修复性司法理念为指导，积极探索大胆实践，将中华优秀传统文化植入监狱，对服刑人员进行教育改造，并遵循教育者首先受教育的原则，对监狱警察进行学习教育，收到了意想不到的效果。特别是2008年3月4日，中央电视台12频道《第一线》栏目以《迟来的爱》为题报道了海南监狱开展传统文化的专题，在社会各界引起了高度的关注和广泛的反响。《迟来的爱》在全国流通几百万套，充分彰显了修复性司法的实践成果。从视频片中可以看出，传统文化植入监狱，有效地修复了服刑人员与家人曾经冷漠的人伦关系，监狱警察与服刑人员改造与被改造的关系更加融合。那么什么叫修复性司法呢？所谓修复性可法，就是指社会犯罪行为的发生损害了被害人、社区、伤害行为人自身以及涉及被害人双方的亲属朋友及他们所在的社会之间各种关系，必须通过调动一切相关因素，积极参加与解决权利侵害冲突，并最终使犯罪被损坏的各种关系得以修复，进而达到社会和谐的目标。日前我国社会上大力倡导的社会治安综合治理、人民调解、非监禁型的社区矫正以及2013年正式实施的新刑诉法中的"刑事和解"程序等都体现了修复性司法的精神。然而监狱是修复性司法所追求的犯罪关系破坏修复链中的一个关键环节。传统的刑事司法秉承的理念是：由于犯罪侵害了他人的合法权利，使被害人遭受了肉体和精神上的痛苦以及财产上损失。因此，犯罪人也必须被施以同等的痛苦和做出同等的补偿，根据情节甚至还可以加深犯罪人的痛苦和经济赔偿。这种刑事司法充分体现了社会公平法律正义的价值。然而，这种报应惩罚性的司法模式效果并不理想，服刑人员所面临的各种关系没有得到很好修复。一是与家人及亲属的关系。一个人犯罪，首先是自毁前程，接着是毁掉

了家庭的幸福，家庭矛盾由此凸显。有些服刑人员被家人抛弃妻离子散，有些服刑人员无视家人的痛苦，向家里索钱要物，亲情会见时父母爱人哭泣，有的犯人说“我还没死呢？哭什么!”有些服刑人员刑满释放时遭到家人及亲属的冷漠，情绪低落甚至失控。二是与被害人关系，一场官司埋下了仇恨的种子，受害人时时受到犯罪人刑满释放后报复担忧的困扰。三是与公检法机关的关系。很多服刑人员都存在一种对判决本能的敌视，因对判决不满，进而对司法人员不满。在海南省就曾发现过被假释的罪犯杀害检察官的悲剧。四是与监狱警察的关系，对个别抗改的服刑人员，依法严管、关禁闭，可能激化矛盾，发生意想不到的事情。五是与在押犯之间的关系，在监狱因刑期和地域等因素，容易产生牢头狱霸的问题，打架斗殴时有发生，造成监管上的难度。六是与社区的关系，由于一个人犯罪，给他们生活过的社区抹了黑，社区对他们不愿接纳。种种社会歧视的问题使很多刑满释放人员丧失了融入社会的信心，再加上就业难，生活无着落等各种实际困难，加重了他们对社会的仇视，“重操旧业”的可能性不断增大。以上这些服刑人员所面临的种种人伦社会司法等关系，如若不能得到有效修复，监狱法中将“将罪犯改造成守法公民”的目标就不可能实现。重新犯罪率高的问题就不可能解决，就为社会的安全和稳定留下很大地隐患。

海南省监狱坚持把修复性司法与传统文化有机结合，纠正重监管改造、重劳动改造、轻教育改造的偏差，在教育改造方面克服以往政治说教强行灌输的问题，瞄准监狱教育人改造人目标不放松，以“铸造新灵魂、培育新公民、重塑新生命”为己任，坚持把传统文化植入监狱。主要采取了以下措施：一是拿出海口监狱作为试点单位，并把该监狱定位为教育型监狱；二是把全省的新犯入监集训监区调整到海口监狱，新犯教育从以往的两个月增加到三个月，让罪犯一入监就开始接受优秀传统文化教育；三是每所监狱指派十名警察到海口监狱进行专题培训，为各监狱培养学习力行传统文化的种子老师；四是编印传统文化经典教材；五是聘请海口孝廉国学启蒙中心的老师到监狱指导教育并授课；六是编写警察及服刑人员学习传统文化感悟的书籍。经过几年实践，我们的工作取得了阶段性成果，把优秀传统文化植入罪犯教育改造工作让我们尝到甜头。

我们的主要做法是：

一是选好教材，系统熏修。在浩瀚如烟的传统文化中，精选了《弟子规》、《了凡四训》、《太上感应篇》作为基础教材，制定了“三年一周期、每年一本经典，循环进行”的教育规划，其中《弟子规》贯穿整个教育始终。为什么说把《弟子规》贯穿整个教育的始终？《弟子规》是“天下第一规”，是做人之规。我们的基本目标是：以《弟子规》为主要内容。通过“五伦八德”的教育使服刑人员耻于犯罪；以《了凡四训》为主要内容，通过改过迁善的教育，使服刑人员悔于犯罪；以《太上感应篇》为主要内容，通过畏果断恶的教育，使服刑人员畏惧再犯罪。围绕这一目标，我们把三本经典的教学纳入服刑人员年度教学计划，坚持每年系统课堂讲授不少于96课时，并通过常态化的制度和强有力的考核手段，保证教学计划的落实，从而取得了意想不到的效果。

有一位服刑人员刘某因放火罪被判有期徒刑九年，他以“行善勿作恶就是福”为题，反思自己学习传统文化的感悟。他说，“两年多来，通过学习，我觉得优秀传统文化就是做人的法宝。《弟子规》以一个‘孝’字为核心延展到人际关系‘悌’，从日常生活规范总结出一个‘谨’字，从言行为人得出‘信’，进而提高自己的修养使自己具备大爱之心‘泛爱众’，并使自己成为一个亲近仁德的人。一个人只要按照《弟子规》的指引去立身处世就一定会成为一个合格的公民。《了凡四训》破解了一个很多服刑人员都深信不疑的关于坐牢是因为自己的命不好的观念。了凡先生以自己的实际行动力行善事，终于改变了自己的命运，使‘一切皆是命，半点不由人’的迷信成为谎言，印证了‘命由我作，福自己求’的道理。《太上感应篇》将人生的因果律解剖得一清二楚。怎样才有幸福人生？很简单，坚持‘诸恶莫做，众善奉行。’为何命苦？人世间175种恶业，你只要作了，就一定会有恶果在等着你，幸福和不幸福就这么简单，行善勿作恶！谁都知道，服刑是痛苦的，一个像我这样青春年少的人自然也不例外。可是这两年来，我的痛苦和以前完全是两回事。以前是痛恨自己笨，居然作案被抓到了，以至于失去了自由。现在是恨自己为什么不早点学习优秀传统文化，读书时为什么不好好学习这些道理，为什么不将父母的教诲记在心里；以前痛苦是因为自己被关在监狱里不能自由地吃喝玩乐；现在痛苦是因为自己犯罪让父母蒙羞，牵挂父母的身体；以前痛苦觉得服刑之后人生没有希望了；现在痛苦是因为自己的罪行给受害者留下的伤害让自己愧疚不安……我虽然现在也觉得自己痛苦，但我从内心深处觉得自己这种痛苦是在接受优秀传统文化教育之后良心发现后的痛苦，是一种人生觉醒的痛苦，是一种改造成功的痛苦，也是我走向新生应有的痛苦。”这位服刑人员结合自己的实际，对《弟子规》、《了凡四训》、《太上感应篇》三部经典学得融会贯通，围绕自己的前后痛苦在忏悔中认识到了传统文化的魅力所在，在忏悔中修复了他与家人和被害人之间的人伦关系。还有一个案例发人深省，唐某因犯抢劫罪判有期徒刑四年，他说：通过学习《弟子规》我幡然悔悟，原来走到今天这一步都是因为自己愚昧无知造成的。我记得《弟子规》中有一句，‘见人善，即思齐，纵去远，以渐跻，见人恶，即内省，有则改，无加警’。意思是看见他人的优点和义举要学习，即使相差比较大也要努力学习，逐渐地赶上；看到别人的不良行为，要自我反省，检讨自己青少年的时候很容易受到他人和环境的影响，所谓‘近朱者赤近墨者黑’就是这道理，如何能做到近墨不黑呢？这对我们每个人都是一种考验。一个人要时刻对自己警钟长鸣，要对自己进行约束，怎样才能约束自己呢？最好的方式就是用孝悌忠信礼义廉耻。作为一名罪犯，在监狱这所特殊的学校我们要以优秀传统文化作为改造自己思想品德的武器，努力戒除恶习，为将来重新规划人生目标。我们只能通过洗涤心灵的污垢，以从事上改，从理上改，从心上改的改造态度收获改造成果。这些道理说起来很简单，但是要付诸行动并不容易，要具有坚强的毅力和持之以恒的决心。进步慢，不可怕，怕的是原地踏步。只要目标坚定，心志坚定总会有所建树。我的经验就是每天都从心里向父母汇报自己一天的得失，以此作为行孝的实践。每天都检讨自己一天与人相处的得失，看看自己有没有不符合“出则悌”的地方。每天都将日常行为梳理一遍，看看自己有没有违背谨信的言语行动。每天当我实践了这些的时候，就觉得自己一天特别的充实，这一天吃得香，睡得好。如果认为自己当天有些事做得不好的时候，就罚自己静坐思过，找出犯错误的原因。一年多来，我始终坚持着这样做，因为我发现自己每天都在进步。我深信绝大多数服刑人员都良心未泯。有的人是一时失足，心底还保存有善恶之心，进取之心，有的人是因为无知冲动，也有的人是因为受骗上当。一个人不管过去怎样无法无天，也不管他怎样声名狼藉，到了监狱这所特殊学校能够猛回头的话，就一定还会有自己幸福的明天。我诚恳地希望每一位服刑朋友，把一切杂念都抛得远远的，快点拿起能够拯救我们心灵的传统经典，这才是我们这些失足者的必由之路。

二是明伦倡孝，开启心智。《群书治要》（卷九·孝经）有一句话“子曰，夫孝，德之本也，教之所由生也。”意思是说，孝道，是德行的根本，一切教化都是从孝道的基础上产生出来的。中华文化特别是孝道文化，是开启人生心灵的万能钥匙，孝：誉为“天之经、地之义、人之行、德之本。”我深深地感受到中华文化具有极强的渗透力、穿透力，学了会在心里发酵。文化不仅是一种价值体系，而且是一种行为规范系统，它给整个国家和民族提供了是非、善恶、美丑、真伪、好坏的判断标准，并通过社会教育使其内化为整个民族的正义感、羞耻感、审美感、是非感和责任感，从而有效塑造国民健全的人格，使民族精神得以延续传承，不断深化升华。文化是骨髓里的东西，流淌着是道德的血液。现在我们很难找到一种让人痛哭流涕的教育，我们从中华文化中特别是孝道文化找到了这种教育真谛。孝道文化是中华传统道德文化积淀的一种文明，一种文化基因，它是建立在血缘和亲情基础上的道德情感。孝道教育培养的是一种恩义情义，如果恩义情义的处世原则培养不起来，就会形成一种仅以利害取舍的处事原则，这样的人往往就会做出见利忘义、忘恩负义的事情来。孝道文化最能触及服刑人员心理和情感中最脆弱的那个点，犯罪是最大的不孝。孝是所有人共同认知的价值观，世间的人再坏也不会反对孝道，没有任何人接受不了孝道。

衡量教育效果有六个字：动情—入心—践行。我们对服刑人员遵了忏悔—改过—感恩—重新站起来的路子进行中华文化的教育，教育效果非常好。服刑人员张某说

《弟子规》读起来让人心血喷涌啊！老师讲解《弟子规》“入则孝”部分的一声一句都如火山般燃烧我的心肺，如地震般震撼着我的灵魂。正像《群书治要》（卷九·孝经）所说“孝悌之至，通于神明，光于四海，无所不通。”

三是知行合一，贵在力行。话不能践行，万卷徒空虚。学习中华文化就是要学一句，做一句，学中思，思中行，内化于心，外践于行。关于学习方法在经典《中庸》一书中有过明确的阐述“博学之、审问之、慎思之、明辨之、笃行之。”［译文］广泛的学习，详尽的询问，慎重的思考，明确的辨析，坚定的实行。为了给使服刑人员创造一个力行中华传统文化修复与家人关系的机会，除了亲情会见与服刑人员家人双向互动外，我们还做出了一个大胆的决定，清明节放部分服刑人员回家祭祖。海口监狱职务罪犯黎某清明节回家祭祖的感言是这么写的“按传统说法，我算是归于孝子的那一类。我的祖辈向来有着清明扫墓的习俗，沿袭下来，到了我这一代，此风似乎还浓盛一些。我从小可说是逢节必事，从未间断过。即便是后来有了公干，虽公事缠身，可到了这一天，我还是设法抽出身来，回家尽一份孝的义务。服刑之后，此念早已灭绝。不过，就在今年清明节即将来到之际，我的那种固有的‘清明意识’竟然日趋强烈起来，有时甚至到了情不自禁的地步。我想必是监狱里开展的中华文化教育给我的熏陶所致吧。也许是天遂人愿吧，节前一天，我突然接到监区长的通知，说是监狱同意我清明节回家探亲。我顿时惊喜万分！感激之余，我沉浸在监狱人文管理的温暖之中。很快，我梦幻般地踏上了归程。按理说，见到如此众多的亲人，我应该高兴才是，可我心里却很沉重，还不时有眼泪流出，而流的更多的是心泪！看着那些漫山遍野扫墓的人群，我心中涌出了无限的感慨。同是在扫墓，感受各异。无论是从外地回来的，还是在家乡创业的，人家显扬出来的是尽孝奉先，承传祖业，甚至是光宗耀祖，可我该算是什么呢？站在祖宗面前我无法抬起头来，惭愧中有着一种无地自容的感觉。家祭时，我足足地跪了一刻钟，以至于我的长跪引起了亲人们的一片哭泣声。告别老家时，我依然没有感觉出来半点的欣慰和轻松，只是在想着自己应该做的事情。末了，我在心里反复说着一句话：不管以往做过什么，但我的一切还可以重来！”这个服刑人员说自己流出的是心泪，心泪是什么？心泪就是忏悔之泪、改过之泪、感恩之泪！这心泪就是一种文化在一个人心底沉淀后的本能反应。为了配合修复性司法与传统文化卓有成效的开展，我们还在全省监狱系统成立了高墙之声艺术团，以犯人为主体，自编自导自演一台文艺节目，服刑人员以他们特殊的身份、特殊的情感、演出的特殊节目催人泪下。修复性司法理念在文艺节目中充分体现，例如，《妈妈，我错啦》演绎的是未成年犯向妈妈的忏悔；《孩子，妈妈在等你》一位母亲反思自己对子女教育上的教训。《除夕接见》演绎的是一个未成年犯对受害人老奶奶的忏悔及老奶奶对这位过失杀害她孙子的罪犯的接纳；《狱中告白》则是一对职务罪犯夫妇对家人、对党和人民的忏

悔，发人深省！（播放《狱中告白》）

刑释人员吴某，在出监狱前认真地学习中华文化，力行《弟子规》，做到了与人为善，礼貌待人。他在刑满释放后，到海口市美兰区公安局办理户口注册时主态度谦和恭敬，给民警行了鞠躬礼，使得在场的民警惊讶万分地说：“你这不像从监狱出来人啊！”

刑释人员张强，家里兄弟三人争家产闹得鸡犬不宁，他把在监狱中学到的《弟子规》中“财物轻，怨何生，言语忍，忿自泯。兄道友，弟道恭，兄弟睦，孝在中”的道理。对兄弟耐心地进行劝解，并自己表明了态度，决不能为了争财产伤害母亲的心，断送手足情。由于他的一片真情，终于化解了一场家庭风波，使一家人又生活在天伦之乐中。一个刑满释放人员通过在监狱里学习力行《弟子规》，化解了家庭的矛盾，我相信如果有可能，他一定能够担当起人民调解员的责任。

海口监狱刑满释放人员符某以“离别前的心里话”为题写下了这么一段发人深省的感言：就要出监了，即将踏上拥抱故乡的归程，如果说我已然做好了“从头再来”准备的话，那么应当得益于在海口监狱对我人生的补课。这课补得就是一中华文化的教育。面对一张张亲切的脸庞，我心中油然生出一些难分难舍的思绪。其实，这世上距离最远的是人心之间的距离。我有幸参加中华文化的学习，老师把古人那些孝顺父母的故事讲给我们听的时候，真是五味缠心，流下了不知是感动和愧疚的泪水，人的心灵之间就明显感到亲近多了。“凡是人，皆须爱，天同覆，地同载。”每个人都有自己的个性，每个人都有自己的活法，每个人都拥有自己的人格和尊严，我们每个人心中都有亲情的种子，都有求生的欲望，只有经过中华文化乳汁的哺育，才能催生发芽，回顾往事不堪回首的是自己做人的失败，是对父母的不孝。忏悔之后的信心支撑就在“知耻而后勇”。当你对人懂得感恩时，对事学会尽心尽责时，对物知道珍惜时，对己能够克制时，你就会感到是传统文化的力量时时在提醒和鞭策着你……人生失败的原因可以找出百十条，但共性的一点就是没能守住规矩，尤其是到了我这把年纪的人，生活中的确有许多‘明规则’和‘潜规则’，可真正要守得住规矩，还得靠修身养性，学会慎独。传统文化告诉我们，学习圣贤之道在于明（智慧）诚（老实），当你把学懂的《弟子规》真正变为实际的时候，你就扎下规矩的根。我真切地感受到中华文化的学习，提升了自己内心约束的档次，再也不会去做‘己所不欲强施于人’的蠢事了。只要用心体察一下就会发现，在自律中，我们中国人同外国人很不一样的观念有两处：一是经常问一下自己的行为对得起父母、对得起祖先吗？二是经常问一下自己的行为对得起儿女吗？服刑的五年半时光，我对家人欠缺的已经太多，再也不能像过去那样活，再也不能像过去那样过，我会带着这两把戒尺经常拷问自己，做一个循分称家的儿子，一个称职的父亲、一个合格的公民。这位刑满释放人员告诫我们社会上一个重要的人生课题，就是守规矩，守规矩是人生的消防栓、阀门锁！规矩是一个人做人的底线，必须坚守，因为一旦超越人生规矩就不再是你，甚至会使自己全线崩溃！中华优秀传统文化进监狱，不仅使监狱教育改造的主体地位得到有力彰显，使教育改造的针对性实效性得到明显胡增强，更重要的使监狱在构建和谐社会方面发挥出重要作用。从法律意义上讲，监狱通过关押惩罚罪犯，减少了社会层面上的压力，但从更深的意义上讲，监狱对每个罪犯的成功改造，实质是为社会减少不稳定因素做贡献。如果监狱不把犯人改造好，他们在监狱互相学习犯罪的伎俩，回归社会后将给社会带来更大的危害。

四点感受：

（一）无论是党政机关、司法部门、企事业单位，所在单位的“一把手”对中华文化的认知程度具有决定意义。特别是在上级领导既没说行也没有说不行的情况下，下级的一把手你怎么办，持什么态度？海南监狱系统开展中华文化教育，是在党的十七大（2007年10月15日召开的）提出“弘扬中华文化，建设中华民族共有精神家园”之前进行的，即2006年上半年。时任海南司法厅厅长施文和副厅长兼监狱管理局长的我，都是修复性司法和中华文化植入监狱的决策者倡导者。特别是我，本是军人出身，行胜于言，认准的事排除干扰，一抓到底。

（二）教育者必须首先受教育。开始在监狱学习中华文化的初衷是针对犯人群体的，学着学着感觉不对劲。一是监狱民警对中华文化比较陌生，知之甚少。如果不先学一步，体会和感悟不深刻，根本无法承担教育者的重任。二是道德教育的特殊性，教育者必须注重自己的身教作用。监狱工作的性质，决定了监狱民警既是国家刑罚权力的执行者，又是把服刑人员改造成为守法公民的教育者。监狱民警的特殊身份，要求他们在对服刑人员教育改造过程中要学为人师，做力行的表率。我们必须有这样基本的认知，学习中华传统文化，例如《弟子规》、《了凡四训》、《太上感应篇》等经典，不是修理别人的，而是修理自己的。《群书治要》（卷四十九·傅子）提到：“秉常以化下，下服常而应上，其不化者，百未有一也。”这句话的意思是，在上位者如果能依循伦常大道来教化下位者，下位者自然会服从常道而顺应上位者，如此上行下效，还有不被教化的人，一百个里面也找不到一个。为此，我们对监狱民警做出了全员培训的计划，并付诸实施。在监狱里最受服刑人员爱戴的是学习力行中华文化比较好的警察。民警学习中华文化，使家庭也发生了变化，有一位民警的爱人说：“我真的有了换了一个老公的感觉”。

（三）无论是党政机关、企事业单位，中华文化的引入是一个富有挑战性的课题。我切身地感受到，当今社会，无论是家庭、学校、党政机关、企事业单位，我认为更多的是做事的教育，缺的是做人的教育。例如政治教育、知识教育、职业技能培训等都是做事的教育，当下最重要的是更新教育理念，若能把思想政治教育向思想道德教育转变，就是做人的教育。中华优秀传统文化就是做人的再教育。总结古今中外，对人最有效的教育是十个字：伦理、道德、法律、因果、宗教。具体说：伦理教育是指五伦十义的教育，五伦是指父子有亲、君臣有义、夫妇有别、长幼有序、朋友有信，十义是指父慈子孝、君仁臣忠、夫义妇顺、兄友弟恭、朋谊友信。道德教育是指“八德”的教育，即孝悌忠信礼义廉耻。孝为德之根，悌为德之序，忠为德之正，信为德之固，礼为德之范，义为德之宜，廉为德之节，耻为德之基。法律，一半是做人的教育一半是做事的教育。法律作为行为规范是做人的教育，作为知识是做事的教育。因果教育是做人的根本教育，因果法则是事物的根本法则之一。首先，因果是哲学观点。什么叫因果？因果就是事物和现象之间引起和被引起的关系。唯物辩证法关于世界联系和发展的问题，讲了五对范畴，即原因和结果，必然性和偶然性，可能性和现实性，内容和形式，现象和本质。其中，因果的范畴处于首位。其特点：一是前因后果。二是原因和结果是一种引起和被引起的关系。三是因果联系的客观性是不以人的意志为转移的。因果联系的普遍性是说任何事物或现象无不存在一定的因果关系当中，即没有无因之果，也没有无果之因。因果联系的多样性是一果多因，一因多果。其次，因果是自然规律。种瓜得瓜、种豆得豆。第三，由人组成的社会，种善得善，种恶得恶。仅举一例，监狱里关押的罪犯就是因果及因果报应。现实社会中因果报应的事例所在多有。讲因果报应，听着容易接受，有畏惧感。因果及因果报应教育，应是对人的一种非常巧妙的劝善方法，这是我们老祖宗的智慧所在，对人的教育，最有效的方法就是因果教育。要克服重果轻因的倾向。绝大多数人都是善恶掺杂的，通过因果教育，让恶念贪念止于起心动念之间。在独处时，不敢随心所欲，为所欲为。人生路漫漫，因因果果伴随行。

宗教在中国是一个敏感的话题。西方国家主要靠宗教提高人们的道德品行。在宗教上我说三句话：(1) 党的宗教工作基本方针就是充分发挥宗教界人士和信教群众在促进文化繁荣发展中的积极作用。(2) 防止宗教狂热和邪教，不能反动社会和政府，“法轮功”等邪教的教训值得我们深思。(3) 从构建和谐稳定社会，提升社会道德品行角度，我认为多一个信徒总比多一个歹徒更有意义，多一个信徒就少一个囚徒，多一个孝子就少一个浪子。

（四）注重培养本单位学习传承中国文化的种子老师。选择种子老师的条件：一是学习中华文化感悟深刻，二是力行中华文化具有榜样作用，二是具备一定教学实践经验。

海南省监狱管理局现任郑学海局长，非常重视修复性司法和传统文化的有机结合，坚持在继承中创新，不断提升对服刑人员教育改造的质量。一是加强监狱信息化建设，为提升教育改造质量搭建高档次平台；二是努力做好刑满释放人员的后续安置帮教工作，在解决刑满释放人员就业、社会保障、社会歧视等问题上做出更多努力。

# 從一個西方漢學家的角度
# 看“依法治國”與“以德治國”

德国慕尼黑大学 葉 翰

我收到紀念孔子誕辰2565週年國際學術研討會邀請函的時候，真的先吃了一驚——對我來講，幾個議題都很難。（1）“儒學與當代經濟和社會發展”是中國人所應該探討的題目，在歐洲企業家對於儒學基本上沒有什麼了解。中國自己當然有儒商的傳統，但是歷史上儒和商的關係也很矛盾。我當然理解“儒商問題”是很熱的研究題目，但是自己從來沒有做過這方面的研究，只是記得在宋代，如果某位理學家來自商家，他自己都不敢承認。馬克斯. 韋伯儘管並沒說過中國未來不會有成功的企業家，但是他說他那個時代，即是清末，資本主義不符合清王朝的思想。儒家的價值在企業裡面肯定會有積極作用，但是這個題目不一定符合海外洋人的專業。（2）“儒學與當代政治和國際關係”有可能是亞洲有儒學傳統國家的很有意義的課題，但是我恐怕西方的政治家不會注意到，孔子的思想是我們西方漢學家所感興趣的。（3）“儒學與當代文化的發展和不同文明的對話”是個很大的題目，圖賓根大學的孔漢斯教授長期從事全球倫理的計劃，我知道在北大現在也有全球倫理的研究所，但是作為一個普通的漢學家，我儘管可能了解一點點中國儒學，但是不敢探討世界倫理。我當然同意“己所不欲勿施于人”應該是全世界各地文化共同的遺產，而且我相信儒學當中還有許多和西方傳統共同的地方，可是這也不是適合我研究題目。（4）“儒學與當代學校教育和社會教育”還是中國自己要解決的問題，我們西方學者不一定能在這個方面做出貢獻。（5）“生態環境保護”是世界各地很重要的問題。我想這個題目在我們西方國家當然已經有意識形態的意義。解決環境的問題我們需要自然科學的方法。我不太相信儒家、道家或者其他的思想家真正在這個方面會有幫助。（6）關於“儒學與世界和平和地區和平”，我知道這個世界的問題很多。中國、日本和南亞洲的國家都有儒學傳統的背景，我很希望在釣魚台和南海問題上這些國家都能記住這個傳統并共同尋找合適的解決方案。西方國家在這個方面沒有很好的做法，希望中國不要模仿我們西方在伊拉克和其他地區的態度。但是這也不是我所熟練的領域。（8）“儒學在世界各地的研究、教育、普及情況”，我當然應該會說幾句話。可惜的是德國很多大學這幾年因為中國經濟發展得很快，對教中國古代傳統的課題不太感興趣，很多大學的漢學系改講中國當代政治、社會和經濟學，不太做儒家思想的研究了。所以在這個方面也沒有很多可以說的。

最後我決定看一看第七個題目：“德治与法治的辩证关系”。我一看就覺得很有意思，所以選擇了這個題目。然後我開始在網上搜索，又是很吃驚：中國學術輯刊全文數據庫裏面，關於“依法治國與以德治國”，從 2000 年開始已經有八百零一篇文章了，網上一共四十一頁。關於“依法治國”的文章更多，有兩萬八百六十六篇文章，一共一千四十四頁。《以德治國》的文章少一點，只有九千二百零六篇文章，一百八十五頁。所以在這個領域上提出新的想法也不容易。

這個課題受到重視的原因，當然是 1997 年 9 月，江澤民主席在党的十五大报告中阐述了“依法治国”的思想。他指出：“依法治国，就是廣大人民群眾在黨的領導下，依照憲法和法律规定，通過各種途徑和形式管理國家事務，管理經濟文化事業，管理社會事務，保證國家各项工作都依法進行，逐步實現社會主義民主的制度化、法律化，使這種制度和法律不因領導人的改變而改變，不因領導人看法和注意力的改變而改變。依法治國，是黨領導人民治理國家的基本方略，是發展社會主義市場經濟的客觀需要，是社會文明進步的重要標誌，是國家長治久安的重要保障。”

當時中國國民經濟快速發展，人民生活水平大幅度提高，西方公司在中國投資額也很高，中國也願意加入世界貿易組織，所以中國政府、西方國家的政府和企業界都希望中國在法律領域也會做一些改革。但是，由於經濟發展很快，社會文明進步的速度也很快同時，社會內部的問題也大了。2001 年 9 月 20 日中共中央引頒佈的《公民道德建設實施綱要》指出：“我國公民道德建設方面仍然存在着不少問題。社會的一些領域和一些地方道德失范，是非、善惡、美丑界限混淆，拜金主義、享樂主義、極端個人主義有所滋長，見利忘義、損公肥私行為時有發生，不講信用、欺騙欺詐成為社會公害，以權謀私、腐化墮落现象嚴重存在。”因此江澤民主席《在中央思想政治工作會議上的講話》中指出：“法律与道德作為上層建築的组成部分，都是維護社會秩序、规范人們思想和行為的重要手段，它們互相聯繫、互相補充。法治以其權威性和强制手段规范社會成员的行為。德治以其說服力和勸導力提高社會成员的思想認識和道德覺悟。道德规范和法律规范應該互相结合，统一發揮作用。”2001 年 1 月，中國加入世界貿易組織幾個月之前，江澤民在全國宣傳部長會議上，提出了“把依法治國與以德治國緊密结合起来”的治國方略。“以德治國”就是要以馬列主義、毛澤東思想、鄧小平理論為指导，積極建立適應社會主義市場經濟發展的社會主義思想道德體系，并使之成為全體人民普遍認同和自覺遵守的规范。“依法治國”和“以德治國”理念的提出是中国共產黨人政治理論的一個創舉，是符合鄧小平多次強調的搞好兩個文明（即物質文明和精神文明）建設的思想的。習近平去年也強調把法治建設和道德建設緊密结合起来。共産黨到今天仍然遵循著江澤民“依法治國与以德治國”的原則。

當然，“法治與德治”本來不是一個學術問題，而是政治問題，因此已經發表了這麼多論文。對一個西方的漢學家來說，好像所有的關於法治與德治方面的研究在中國已經做得夠好了，可謂百花已經齊放。

不過，我這次準備報告的時候發現了，法治與德治這個題目跟馬克思主義與儒學的關係這個問題很接近。有一些中國學者以為在這個領域中，要區分宣傳和學術層面的研究。實際上對一個西方漢學家來講，有意思的是中國官方的宣傳文獻裏面提到“以德治國就是要以馬列主義、毛澤東思想、鄧小平理論為指導，積極建立適應社會主義市場經濟發展的社會主義思想道德體系”，但是沒提到“法治”與“德治”在儒學乃至中國傳統思想中的基礎。

江澤民主席沒有指出法治與德治原來是儒家的範疇，雖然他說：“講學習，歷來十分重要。我們這個國家和民族，自古以來就以重視學習、講究學問之道而著稱。我國歷史上出現了許多有作為的政治家、志士仁人和著名學者，他們的建樹都是同勤于學習，具有豐富的知識分不開的。（《論黨的建設》，中央文獻出版社，2001年11月，第188－189頁）不過，可以很容易看出來，他這句話跟儒家思想一致。學習當然是古代所有重要儒家學者的第一個原則。

中國大陸90年代已經開展關於馬克思主義與儒學問題的討論和研究，概括說來，形成了三種比較有代表性的觀點（阮青，《孔子研究》1998.3）：對立說、並存說和融合說。雖然有一些馬克思主義者反對封建主義的儒學傳統，也有一些新儒家完全反對和拒絕社會主義，但是從我所看到的文章來判斷，很多學者同意第三個看法，即融合說。當然還有方可立先生的“主導意識說”和“支援意識說”，馬克思主義是主導意識，儒學是支援意識。方可立的想法基本上是儒學可以當作經典依據或者學術依據，就是說儒家經典可以作為社會主義建設的傳統資源。張小平和陸信禮在《論儒學價值觀在社會主義核心價值體系中的作用》一文說：“孟子在《孟子．盡心下》中曾指出‘民為貴，社稷次之，君為輕’。在此基礎上他還提出了‘與民同樂’的觀點。傳統儒家價值觀中的此類‘愛民’、‘惠民’和‘民本’思想，都是可以作為‘為人民服務’價值觀的思想資源的。”（《馬克思主義研究》2012.5）

按照我的理解，“支援意識說”基本上認為儒學本身沒有什麼重要的內容，但是我不知道這個想法是不是完全對。郝鐵川在《依法治國與以德治國》一文中（《求是》雜誌2001.3）說：“馬克思主義認為，法和道德都是由一定經濟關係決定并為其服務的上層建築。社會主義法制和社會主義道德作為上層建筑，都產生于社會主義經濟基础之上，是社會主義經濟關係的反映，共同為社會主義經濟基础服務。……社會主義法律意識是社會主義道德的重要组成部分。我國思想道德建設的主要目標之一是提高公民的素質。……上層建筑可以反作用于經濟基础，良好的治國方略可以促進經濟文化發展和社會秩序的稳定。中國封建社會之所以能够長期延續與發展，原因固然很多，但與其‘德主刑輔’、‘霸王道雜之’的治國方略不無關係。‘德主刑輔’的思想肇始于周公的‘明德慎罰’，孔子則明确地把德治放在第一位，把法（刑）治放在第二位。用他的話來說，就是‘道之以政，齊之以刑，民免而無恥；道之以德，齊之以禮，有恥且格。’（《論語·為政》）孟子繼承并發揮了孔子的‘德主刑輔’思想，突出強調實施德政的重要性，認為只有實行德治，重禮義教化，方能統一天下（見《孟子·公孫丑上》）。既‘隆禮’又重法的荀子，主張先禮後法，先教後刑（見《荀子·富国》）。董仲舒用陰陽學說闡釋‘德主刑輔’思想，提出‘天道之大者在陰陽。陽為德，陰為刑；刑主殺而德主生。’（《漢書·董仲舒傳》）因此，要‘大德而小刑’。（《春秋繁露·陽尊陰卑》）至此，‘德主刑輔’成為封建社會的正统的指導思想。此後一些著名的思想家、政治家的主張，如王充的‘文武張設’；李世民的‘明刑弼教’；韓愈的‘德禮為先而輔以政刑’；丘睿的‘禮教刑辟交相為用’；康熙的‘以德化民，以刑弼教’，等等，都在一定程度上反映了‘德主刑輔’的思想。而漢宣帝所說的‘漢家自有制度，本以霸王道雜之’，則表明‘德（王道）主刑（霸道）輔’的思想已轉化為统治者的治國方略。并且歷史告訴我們，凡是只用德治或只用法治的王朝，都走向了衰落、滅亡。戰國時期的魯國和齊國單純用‘德治’，很快被吞并；秦国‘專任刑罰”，則二世而亡。’”郝鐵川這篇文章指出“德主刑輔”、“霸王道雜之”的治國方略是中國傳統特色的方略。因此可以看出，儒家傳統思想不一定只是資源，而有其主旨。

過去很多學者做過馬克思主義跟儒家傳統思想的比較。他們找到了很多相同的地方，發現馬克思主義對資本的警示與儒學對逐利的鄙視，儒家的“家國同構”觀念及其對個人的影響，與馬克思主義學說中的革命集體主義似有所相通。（王傑、馮建輝《馬克思主義與儒學的關係研究綜述》，《中共中央黨校學報》第12卷第六期，2008）阮青在《90年代關於馬克思主義與儒學關係問題的研究》一文中指出：“有的學者認為二者在哲學世界觀，政治思想和大同社會理想三方面有相同點，有的則指出，二者的相似相同之處共有七个方面：唯物論、無神論、辯證法、歷史觀中的唯物論因素、民主主義、人道主義、大同的社會理想；還还有的條分縷析出八个具體的相同點：大同、小康的社會理想與社會主義、共產主義理想；民本思想與群眾路線；禮法结合、德刑相参與正确處理兩類不同性質的矛盾和兩手抓；選賢任能思想與黨的干部路線；警世致用思想與實事求是的思想路線；知行統一觀與理論聯繫實際的原則；修身思想與批評自我批評作風：朴素辯證法與馬克思主義的思想方法。”

在這裏有一個重要的問題：對一個西方漢學家來講，這些相同點表明中國古代傳統世界觀跟馬克思思想是完全符合的，還是相同點的存在證明中國化的社會主義由於有古代傳統特別是儒學傳統的影響，從而跟歐洲的社會主義是不一樣的思想體系？

一個跟我們今天的題目特別有關係的課題，就是“禮法结合、德刑相参與正确處理兩類不同性質的矛盾和兩手抓”。王鵬飛在《古代禮法結合的治國思想及啟示》一文中指出：“中國傳統治國理念乃是在儒家思想與法家思想的對立和交融中形成和發展的。從儒家的‘禮治’、‘德治’，到法家的‘法治’，再到‘德主刑輔’的禮法结合的辯證否定過程，大致勾勒出中國傳統治國思想的發展輪廓。”（《理論探索》2007年第三期）王鵬飛還指出：“不論從邏輯上還是從歷史上看，‘法治’與‘德治’並不是必然對立的。”西方不少專家以為中國古代只有刑法，沒有司法。我不同意這個說法，認為中國古代法律是從“禮”和“法”的矛盾中發展出來的，“德主刑輔”的說法是完全成立的。郝鐵川說：“馬克思主義認為，法和道德都是由一定經濟關係決定并為其服務的上層建築。社會主義法制和社會主義道德作為上層建筑。”但是有意思的是，按我所了解的馬克思，并沒有把法律和道德對立起來。這也完全屬於中國傳統思想和傳統社會裡面的矛盾。在當今的社會主義國家或過去的歐洲社會主義國家，沒有一個存在從儒家的“禮治”、“德治”，到法家的“法治”，再到“德主刑輔”的禮法结合的辯證否定過程，也不存在“依法治國”與“以德治國”的矛盾和辯證邏輯。這也證明“依法治國”與“以德治國”完全是受到儒家傳統思想影響的中國特色社會主義的口號。

最後我想討論一下“德”的翻譯。研討會英語的邀請函把“德”翻譯成“virtue”。這是西方傳教士的翻譯，有著非常強烈的宗教性色彩。但是我早在開始學漢語的時候，就已經意識到實際上“德”是非常不好翻譯的。有可能今天的中國人都會覺得“德”就是“道德”。但是，對一個對儒家傳統感興趣的西方漢學家來說，“德”的內涵當然更豐富，也是很有中國特色的一個詞（內含魅力、威信、聲望、勢力等等），跟馬克思所說的“道德”（Moral）本來就沒有很大的關係，所以我不能贊同“儒學支援意說”。

## 四、儒学的现代价值

# 孔子儒学的价值理念与精神追求

西北大学 张岂之

孔子（约前551—前479年）是儒学的创始者，他对中华文化的传承发展做出了重大贡献。今年是孔子诞辰2565年。我们正在建设富强、民主、文明、和谐的社会主义现代化国家，实现中华民族伟大复兴。这个时候纪念孔子，需要继续研究孔子和儒学的价值理念与精神追求，从中汲取丰富营养。

笔者认为，我们不是讨论如何将儒学用于今天的中国社会，而是研讨孔子和儒学对中华文化的贡献在哪里？这个问题解决得好，自然就会知道应如何继承发展儒学丰厚的文化遗产。

### 一、孔子的理想与实践：用教育文化去改造社会

孔子关注西周宗法礼制的存亡，他认为，这种礼制是以夏商两代为依据而制定的，在西周时期曾经结出丰硕的文化果实。由此，他主张沿用西周的礼制。事实上，孔子生活在春秋末期，西周宗法礼制已经变形，出现摇摇欲坠的局面。

孔子在感情上不认同这样的变化，但是他以实际行动冲破了宗法礼制传统，办起了“私学”（用私学代替西周时的官学），倡导“有教无类”，学生不分贵贱亲疏，更不论出生何地，都可以平等地接受儒家的教育。由此可见，孔子在社会发生重大变化的历史阶段，选定了这样的道路：用教育和文化去改造社会。

在中国春秋战国时期（前770—前221年）产生了许多思想学派，有儒家、道家、阴阳家、法家、名家（逻辑学家）、墨家、纵横家、杂家、农家、小说家，号称“百家争鸣”，反映了这个时期中国思想文化的巨大成就。后来的中华文化都可以从诸子百家中找到文化传承的基因，其中的儒学不但对中国，而且对世界都有影响。

孔子说：“吾十有五而志于学，三十而立，四十而不惑，五十而知天命，六十而耳

顺，七十而从心所欲不逾矩。”[①] 这里表述的不是孔子的“学历”和“知识水平”，而是他在长期教育和文化传承实践中对于人生境界、即价值观的追求所达到的高度。

孔子以前及其同时，许多人都讲“仁”。《国语·周语》：“言仁必及人。”“仁”必涉及人与人的关系。《论语》多处为“仁”规定界说，着眼于人与人、人与社会如何相处？孔子不赞成把“亲亲”与“爱人”对立起来，认为这是爱人的起点。讲“仁”不能离开“亲亲”，同时也不局限于此，应面向社会。《论语·颜渊》云：樊迟问“仁”，孔子答“爱人”。一方面是“己所不欲，勿施于人”，[②] 另一方面是“己欲立而立人，己欲达而达人”[③]；将这两方面结合起来，就体现了“忠恕之道”。

两千五百多年来，孔子的“忠恕之道”被古今中外学者、思想家们誉为做人的准则，是孔子价值理念的集中体现。第一，“己所不欲，勿施于人”的道德准则并非高不可攀，人们经过努力，是可以达到的。第二，人际关系并非只有“自己”这个主体，应同时兼顾到客体，即“他人”；孔子倡导的道德准则都是从两方面来说的，比如：父亲以慈爱对待儿子，儿子以孝道对待父亲，这样才真正达到了“爱人”的高度。第三，忠恕之道平实深刻，便于笃行。

孔子认为，人的思想行动符合“仁”的标准，可称之为“仁人”。“仁人”超越了人的本能，是具有高尚理想、深厚道德修养的人。这样的人，当他的理想与现实发生冲突，二者不能兼顾的时候，他会牺牲个人生命，去殉他的理想。对此，孔子给予很高评价：“志士仁人，无求生以害仁，有杀身以成仁。”[④] 在中华历史上，这样的理念熔铸成为中华民族志士仁人的共同信念，成为民族前进发展的动力之一。

孔子所说的“仁”是各种德目的总称。他曾提出其他德目，如：恭、宽、信、敏、惠，认为：“能行五者于天下为仁矣。”[⑤] 恭即庄重、自尊，宽即宽厚，信即诚信，敏即勤快，惠即乐于助人。

孔子重视孝道，认为人们心里尊敬父母，这才是真正的孝。他说，一般人认为“孝”就是养活父母，这很不够，如果没有孝心，这和饲养犬马又有什么区别呢？[⑥]

孔子的道德观具有深刻的理论基础，提到了人的认识论高度加以论述。他不仅说君子应当如何做，而且阐述了为何要维护道德伦理的尊严，因为只有这样，才符合人的认识法则。这个法则，孔子称之为“中庸”。

---

① 《论语·颜渊》。

② 《论语·颜渊》。

③ 《论语·雍也》。

④ 《论语·卫灵公》。

⑤ 《论语·阳货》。

⑥ 《论语·卫灵公》。

何谓“中庸”?《论语·先进》中有这样的表述：“子贡问曰：‘师与商也孰贤?’子曰：‘师也过，商也不及。’曰：‘然则师愈与?’子曰：‘过犹不及。’”子贡问孔子：颛孙师（子张）和卜商（子夏）都是孔子的学生。他们两人谁强一些呢？孔子回答说：子张有些过头，子夏有些赶不上，这两者都不是中庸之道。

还有，“子曰：‘……见义不为，无勇也。’”① ——勇敢应当与正义的行动相结合。

“子曰：‘人而不仁，如礼何？人而不仁，如乐何?’”② ——“仁”应当和“礼”、“乐”相结合。

“子曰：‘《关雎》，乐而不淫，哀而不伤。”③ ——《诗经》中的诗使人快乐而不至于无节制，悲哀而不至于伤害身心。

“子曰：‘知者乐水，仁者乐山。知者动，仁者静。知者乐，仁者寿。’”④ ——有智慧的人乐于水，不断流动，永不衰竭；有道德的人乐于山，不断积善成人，积善成家，积善成国。

还有，“子温而厉，威而不猛，恭而安。”⑤ ——孔子待人温和，对弟子有严格要求，有威严而不凶猛，恭重而冷静。

此外，《论语》中多处记述了多与寡、有与无、实与虚、惠与不费、劳与不怨、泰与不骄等方面的统一，反映出中国古代辩证思维的特色，将道德规范与认识论密切结合，力求避免“过”与“不及”。南宋时二程（程颐、程颢）指出，“中”指的是平常的道理，而“庸”则是“和”，君子做事与待人接物都力求不偏不倚，恰到好处，达到和谐的高度，这就是“庸”。“中庸”是中国儒学追求的精神境界。达到这个境界，毋需成神成仙，在现实世界中，人们经过努力学习就可以达到。《中庸》⑥ 指出：一个讲诚信的君子，在学习上应该注意五个方面：“博学之”——广博地学习；“审问之”——详细地向别人请教；“慎思之”——周密地思考；“明辨之”——清楚地辨别是非、辨别善恶、辨别美丑等；“笃行之”——切实地身体力行，做到知行合一。

孔子讲道德操守，没有空洞说教的味道，合情合理，易于深入人心。孔子提出，

---

① 《论语·为政》。

② 《论语·八佾》。

③ 《论语·八佾》。

④ 《论语·雍也》。

⑤ 《论语·述而》。

⑥ 《中庸》原来是《礼记》（秦、汉之际）中的一篇。《史记·孔子世家》认为《中庸》是孟子的老师子思写的。唐代文学家韩愈很推崇《中庸》。历经北宋时几位思想家的阐发，到南宋时思想家朱熹在前人研究基础上将《礼记》中的《大学》、《中庸》提取出来，与《论语》、《孟子》编在一起，称为《四书》。朱熹用了很长时间为《四书》作注，称为《四书章句集注》。

君子要有“欲而不贪”[①]（有欲望但不贪婪）的品德。如果不是这样，让贪婪膨胀，其结果是“损矣”[②]、使自己走上了毁灭的道路，这是必须加以警惕的。

孔子的价值观，成为中华儒学的共同准则。孔子以后儒家学派的代表人物结合他们所处时代的特点加以发展。战国中期孟子（约前372—前289年）在这方面也有很大贡献。他强调说，讲道德、重仁义，不仅是个人的事，而且事关天下国家。他说：“人有恒言，皆曰‘天下国家’。天下之大本在国，国之本在家，家之本在身。”[③] 道德修养应从个人做起，从而对天下国家产生影响。

为此，孟子提出“养气”说。所谓“养气”是指人们经过学习磨炼，培育出一种基于高尚理想和志向的精神。它催人奋进，百折不挠。孟子称这种精神为“浩然之气”或“正气”。

关于“浩然之气”，孟子这样描述：

“这种气最伟大，最刚强。用正义去培育它，丝毫不加伤害，就会充满上下四方，无所不在。这种气，需要与道义配合，缺少道义，就失去了力量。这种气，是由道义的日积月累而成，不是偶然的正义行动所取得的。”[④]

在孟子看来，这种“浩然之气”是长期学习、磨炼的结果。对此，孟子说了一段富有哲理性的名言：

“一个人要挑起重担，他的身体和思想都要经受长期的锻炼，饥饿、困乏经常袭来，思想矛盾不断，不如意事时时遇到。只有这样，才能坚定他的意志，提高他的能力，使他更加冷静、成熟。……”[⑤]

孟子还提出“大丈夫”理念，其标准，按照他的说法是：“富贵不能淫，贫贱不能移，威武不能屈，此之谓大丈夫。”[⑥] 一个人身处富贵温柔之乡，不能丧失志向；身处贫贱困苦之地，不能改变人格；身处强暴威胁之时，不能丢掉气节，这才是真正的“大丈夫”（高尚的人格）。这是中华传统美德的集中体现，历代相传，成为中华民族精神追求的目标之一。

---

① 《论语·尧曰》。

② 《论语·季氏》。

③ 《孟子·离娄上》。

④ 《孟子》书的原文是：“……其为气也，至大至刚，以直养而无害，则塞于天地之间。其为气也，配义与道；无是，馁也。是集义所生者，非义袭而取之也。”（见《孟子·公孙丑上》）。

⑤ “……故天将降大任于斯人也，必先苦其心志，劳其筋骨，饿其体肤，空乏其身，行拂乱其所为，所以动心忍性，曾（增）益其所不能。”（《孟子·告子下》）。

⑥ 《孟子·滕文公下》。

## 二、孔子“和而不同”文化观的理论意义

关于人的价值观不仅探讨人与人、人与社会的关系，也离不开人与自然的关系。《论语》中记载有孔子与弟子们关于“天”的对话。他说：“天何言哉？四时行焉，百物生焉，天何言哉？”① 这里强调天是自然。孔子要弟子们“不怨天，不尤人”，② 要靠自身的努力。

《论语》中有孔子和弟子们对于自然认识的材料，大部分以自然知识为譬喻，说明政治、伦理和做人的道理，而不是自然本身。

但是，从孔子“和而不同”的文化观来看，他坚持用事物多样性的“和”来观察世界，反对单一的“同”，从而提出“君子和而不同，小人同而不和”。③ 对此，我们可以从两方面加以阐释。其一，“和而不同”倡导博采众家之长的文化会通精神；其二，从先秦时期儒学的天人之学来看荀子论述人与自然相互关系的价值观问题。

先说会通精神。这里以我国第一部编撰于战国时期，在西汉时写定的中医药学经典《黄帝内经》为例略加说明。

《黄帝内经》的作者们对春秋战国时期的诸子百家学说不抱门户之见，凡有可取之处都加以吸取。其中有儒家思想，有墨家主张，有道家观点，还有法家的若干见解。名家、兵家，甚至阴阳五行学说中的某些成分也被吸纳。博采众家之长，因而《黄帝内经》奠定了与中华儿女繁衍发展密切相关的中医药学的坚实理论基础。

再举一例：中华文化中比较完整的关于“大同”社会的学说，主要见于《礼记·礼运篇》，这是战国末年或秦汉之际儒家学者的著作，阐述了从据乱世到小康再到大同的历史进化观。其中关于大同社会有一段描述：

“大同”社会以“天下为公”为最高准绳，不同于“天下为家”的社会。

在“大同”社会中，社会财富不是私人所藏有的，而是为大家所共同享有的（“货，恶其弃于地也，不必藏于己”）。

在“大同”社会中，人人都要为了全体的利益而进行劳动（“力，恶其不出于身也，不必为己”）。

在“大同”社会中，育幼、养老都有很好的安排，能劳动的人从事劳动，而失去劳动条件的人由集体供养（“故人不独亲其亲，不独子其子，使老有所终，壮有所用，幼有所长，矜、寡、孤、独、废、疾者皆有所养；男有分，女有归”）。

---

① 《论语·阳货》。
② 《论语·宪问》。
③ 《论语·子路》。

在“大同”社会中，大家相爱，没有权谋欺诈和盗贼掠夺，和平地生活而没有战争（“是故谋闭而不兴，盗窃乱贼而不作，故外户而不闭”）。

在“大同”社会中，公共事务由大家来办理，可以选出人们信赖的人来担任必要的工作（“选贤与能，讲信修睦”）。

像这样的“大同”理想，不但继承了早期儒家思想，而且在不少地方继承了墨家思想，例如“选贤与能”就和墨家的“尚贤”原则相似；“老有所终”一段又相似于《墨子·兼爱中》里的一节，甚至“大同”这一名称也可能从墨家所说“尚同”沿袭而来。同时，《礼记·礼运篇》有些地方也受了老子思想的影响，如“大同”世界为“大道之行”，“大道”就是道家的术语。可见，“大同”理想主要来源于儒家，同时也吸取了墨家和道家的某些思想。

再看“和而不同”文化观的第二个特点，即战国末期儒者荀子关于天人之学的基本论点。

战国末期有些儒者研究《周易》的论述，保存在《易大传》中。其书基本上属于儒家学派，也吸收了道家的一些观点。《易大传》有十篇，又名《十翼》，其中《系辞》上、下在于发掘《周易》的哲学潜质，文中关于天人之学的论述，对儒家和中华文化的发展有较大的影响。

《易大传》阐述的事物变易之理不同于《老子》书主张柔弱、无为，强调刚健中正。《乾卦·象传》曰：“天行健，君子以自强不息。”不过，《易大传》在强调刚健的同时，并不否认柔弱的作用，主张刚柔相济、二者相互为用。

《周易》讲天、地、人三才之道的统一，《易大传》加以发挥，提出“生生之谓易”，人们以此指导践行，除旧更新。又要人们笃信天地为万物之母、生养之源，应当加以礼敬，不可毁坏。

在上述思想影响下，战国末期，儒学集大成者荀子（前298—前238年）本着孔子的思路，赞成“和”而否定“同”，写出了名篇《天论》，把“和而不同”的道理阐发得深刻而清晰。

荀子写道：“天行有常，不为尧存，不为桀亡。应之以治则吉，应之以乱则凶。”认为天有常规，不受人的意愿支配。顺应天（自然）的法则，人们将从天那里取得养生之资，如粮食等。如果人们违反天的法则，将受到它的惩罚。荀子在《天论》中写下一大段关于加强农业生产的文字：“强本而节用，则天不能贫。养备而动时，则天不能病。修（循）道而不贰，则天不能祸。”认为人们抓住农业这个根本，厉行节约，天就不能使人贫困，有充分的养生之资，并按照季节进行农事，天就不能使人患病；遵循农业生产本身的法则而行动，天也不能使人遭到祸患。可见人在自然的面前不是完全无能为力的。荀子又说：“错人而思天，则失万物之情”，如果看不到人的作用，只是企求天的恩赐，就和天人关系的真实情况相背离。基于上述分析，荀子的结论是："故明于天人之分，则可谓至人矣。"

荀子"天人相分"的观点阐述了一个客观真理：当人从自然界分离出来，成为与自然相对的认识主体的时候（也就是认识到天人相分），人才有可能成为有智慧的人，而不是一般意义上的人；而是能认识并按照自然法则去行动的人；荀子称之为"至人"，用今天的话讲就是"真正的人"。

强调"人"的地位与作用，这是儒学和中华文化及其理论的特色之一。中华文化以"人"为核心，进行探索，产生了"天人之学"（探讨什么是天？什么是人？人与天有何关系?）、变易之学（探讨世界万物变化的道理）、为人之学（即人的道德伦理标准）、会通之学（即博采众家之长的文化观）方面构筑了丰富的理论体系。在这方面，荀子的"天人相分"论做出了重要的贡献。

荀子在《天论》中着重论述了天人相分，就是看到天和人各自的特点，呈现于人面前的是千姿百态的自然世界，不是一个色彩、一种声音的单调死板的存在。在异中求同，达到和而不同。由此荀子在《天论》中写下这样的话："万物为道一偏，一物为万物一偏，愚者为一物一偏，而自以为知'道'，无知也。"在荀子看来，万物只是"道"的一个方面，个别事物是整体的部分，人们往往以偏概全，以部分替代整体。从"分"到"合"，从个别到一般，这才是人们认识的正确途径。

荀子的天人相合论是通过人的生产活动来实现的。他认为，人能适应天时、顺应地利；人的这种努力，叫作"能参"；人们发挥自身的能动性，叫作"所以参"。这二者结合才达到天人相合的高度。由此荀子强调人能"群"、人是社会的动物。总之，荀子从天人相分到天人相合观，在中国先秦时期达到很高的理论水平。

"天人之学"渗透于中国古代的科学技术，从天文历算、中医药学、古地理学、古建筑学中均可看到它的思想影响。我国古代文学与史学更加离不开天人之学的滋养。关于天人之学的丰富史料，从古代史学中可以见到。西汉时大史学家司马迁有一句名言："究天人之际，通古今之变，成一家之言。"（《汉书·司马迁传》）在他看来，只有研究天人之间的关系，才能在学术上有所建树。

中国有自己独特的价值观，和西方不同。古希腊哲学是从探讨自然开始的，前苏格拉底的希腊哲学家包括米利都学派（约前6世纪产生）、毕达哥拉斯（Pythagoras，约前580—前500）、爱利亚学派（约前6世纪产生）、赫拉克利特（Heraclitus，约前535—约前475）等，对自然现象及其形成的原因进行研究，一般都留下一篇《论自然》的作品。到巴门尼德（Parmenides，约前514—?），他区分了感觉和理性、存在和非存在、本质和表象、真理和意见，由此，希腊哲学的抽象思辨能力大大提升，这是西方哲学最高命题即思维和存在关系问题的起点。在西方，后来也没有像中国哲学那样探讨天人关系。到20世纪中叶，西方思想家由于生态环境危机，才开始注意中国古代天人之学的理论及其实践意义。

## 三、儒家的“民本”观与“忧患”意识

孔子和儒家的“民本”思想源于西周礼乐文明。为西周制礼作乐的周公提出“人无于水监，当于民监”① 的理念。古代的镜子称为“监”，周公要求执政者不要用水做镜子，而以“民”为镜，时时对照，检查自己，反省为政的得失。类似的理念常见于周人的文献，可见在距今三千多年前中国历史上已经产生了“民本”思想。至于西周时“民”指什么，可在学术研讨中加以讨论解决，这里不论。

孔子和儒家继承发扬了周公的“民监”思想，这是事实，但这和做官与否并无直接联系。孔子的弟子子夏说过：“学而优则仕。”② 这只是一种愿望，并非实现“民本”一定要有官位。孔子本人除去在鲁国做过短时间的“司寇”外，周游列国，宣传自己的思想，没有做官。他的弟子中虽有做官的，但也有很多与官位无缘。因而儒家的“民本”观并非鼓励人们都去做官。

在孔子思想中，“民本”体现在如何对待“民”这个重大问题上。据《论语·公冶长》记载：“子路曰：‘愿闻子之志。’子曰：‘老者安之，朋友信之，少者怀之。’”孔子把有利于“民”而解除他们患难的行动称之为“圣”，认为像尧、舜这样的“圣王”也没有达到。孔子把为“圣”的标准与利“民”联系在一起，极大地影响了后来儒学思想的发展。

孟子论述了“民贵君轻”的思想，这在《孟子·尽心下》有一段完整的说明：“民为贵，社稷次之，君为轻。是故得乎丘民而为天子，得乎天子为诸侯，得乎诸侯为大夫。诸侯危社稷，则变置。牺牲既成，粢盛既洁，祭祀以时，然而旱干水溢，则变置社稷。”③

在国家中，百姓最重要，社稷（土神和谷神，国家的象征）其次，君主又其次。得到百姓的拥戴可以做天子。得到天子、诸侯的赞赏，只能做诸侯、大夫。一个国家的执政者要把百姓都赶出国境，另换一批百姓，在事实上是做不到的。但变换天子、诸侯，是可行的。孟子认为这在历史上有“禅让”和“征诛”两说。“禅让”是他从民族社会历史传说中得出的认识，而“征诛”则是孟子对夏商周三代交替历史的认识。

---

① 《尚书·酒诰》。

② 《论语·子张》。

③ 《孟子·尽心下》。

他说汤伐桀，是“为匹夫匹妇复仇也”[1]；武王伐纣，是“救民于水火之中”。如果君不行仁义，残害百姓，就不成其为君，虽然他还占据着君位，但实际上已经成为“一夫”，并不是真正的“君”。齐宣王问孟子：对于汤伐桀、武王伐纣这两件事应如何看？武王以臣的身份而杀纣，是否“弑君”？孟子的回答是：“闻诛一夫纣矣，未闻弑君也。”[2]

当中国历史演变至十七世纪，明末清初之际，儒学思想家黄宗羲（1610－1695年）在《明夷待访录》一书中提出：三代以下是“以君为主，天下为客”，君主把天下视为己有，独占天下之利，“为天下大害者，君而已矣”。他宣传“天下为主，君为客”的反命题。从表面看，这个命题和孟子“民为贵，社稷次之，君为轻”相同，但还有差别。孟子的命题是在战国中期提出的，劝说诸侯贵族实施“仁政”，创造统一天下的条件，而黄宗羲的命题则包含有批判君主专制主义的因素。秦汉以降，随着君主中央集权制度建立，统治者认为“国家”即皇帝。秦始皇出巡，刻石记功，声称“六合之内，皇帝之土……人迹所至，无不臣者。”[3] 由秦始皇开创的“朕即国家”的君主专制制度为历代统治者所承袭。到明末清初之际，有些思想家（儒学是他们遵循的基本原则）举起“天下”的旗帜，力求说明“天下”与君主的区别。除黄宗羲之外，他的挚友顾炎武（1613－1682年）也力求区别“亡国”和“亡天下”。他说：“易姓改号，谓之亡国。仁义充塞，而至于率兽食人，人将相食，谓之亡天下。”他强调“得天下”具有更加深刻的内涵，他说：“得天下者，匹夫之贱，与有责焉耳矣。”[4] 这样的爱国主义多少突破了易姓改号和朝代兴亡的观念。

还要谈到儒家的“忧患”意识。忧乐观实际是价值观。孔子多次讲述自己的“忧”与“乐”。他说：“德之不修，学之不讲，闻义不能徙，不善不能改，是吾忧也。”[5] 作为“君子”，不注意自己道德品质的提高，不切磋学问，不按照道义的原则去行事，有了过错不能及时改正——这些就是孔子目睹春秋末期社会现实情况而产生的忧虑。

“忧”与“乐”相互依存，孔子有“忧”也有“乐”。他的名言：“学而时习之，不亦说乎？有朋自远方来，不亦乐乎？人不知而不愠，不亦君子乎？”[6] 孔子夸赞自己的学生颜回：他身居陋巷，生活艰苦，在“人不堪其忧”的状况下能够“不改其乐”，[7]

---

① 《孟子·滕文公下》。
② 《孟子·滕文公下》。
③ 《史记·秦始皇本纪》。
④ 《日知录》卷13“正始”条。
⑤ 《论语·学而》。
⑥ 《论语·学而》。
⑦ 《论语·雍也》。

坚持追求道德和学业上的进步，实在是一位贤明的君子呵！孔子说自己“发愤忘食，乐以忘忧，不知老之将至”。[1] 可见，孔子区别“忧”与“乐”，其标准是人的道德修养和精神状态，这在中华文化中简称为“尚德”精神。

孔子关心社会的安定与和谐，这在《论语·季氏》中有详细的记载。当时鲁国公室衰微，在鲁国掌管实权的是所谓“三桓”（鲁庄公弟庆父、叔孙氏、季孙氏三家）。“颛臾”附属于鲁国，主东蒙山祭祀，季孙氏企图讨伐颛臾。面对这种形势，孔子讲了关于社会和谐的政治哲学，他说：“不患寡而患不均，不患贫而患不安。盖均无贫，和无寡，安无倾。”东汉经学家包咸（前7—65年）《论语章句》、南宋思想家朱熹（1130—1200年）《论语集注》认为，孔子在这里强调的是“上下和同”、“小大安宁”[2]、“上下相安”。[3] 归总一句话，在孔子看来，国家的忧患不在于经济实力是否充实，人力资源是否充沛，而在于对这些财物的占有和处理是否合理，能否使社会安宁有序；他强调人的作用大于物的因素。“政者，正也”，[4] 对于执政者来说，要求他们端正、公正。后来，中国古代的许多政治家、思想家，大都是沿着孔子的这个思路去看社会问题的。

“忧患”一词出于《易·系辞下》：“《易》之兴也，其于中古乎？作《易》者，其有忧患乎？”《系辞》的作者认为《易经》可能是文王时期的忧患之作。《易·明夷卦·彖传》举例说，殷纣王时期，天下无道，当时周文王被囚，蒙受大难，但是文王内存阳刚之德，外用柔顺之道，终于化险为夷。

在《易·系辞》作者们看来，《周易》主要讲天地、人事变化的道理，这简称为“变易之学”；人们通过占卜，就会知道如何趋利避害。正如《系辞下》所云：“《易》，穷则变，变则通，通则久。是以自天祐之，吉无不利。”这说明自然界和人类社会无一不在变化，礼仪刑法也是如此。当事物达到极限，会发生变化；变化了就能发展；发展了就能畅通；畅通了就能长久。基于此，《易·系辞》的作者们用“生生”、“日新”等来指称事物变化的过程，肯定它，赞美它。《系辞》还从历史角度阐明事物的变易之理，如黄帝、尧、舜时期的各种文明创造，给社会带来福祉，就是很好的例证。

《易·系辞》进一步研究了事物变易的内在根源，认为阴阳、刚柔、动静、吉凶、祸福、存亡等对立方面的相推相摩，引发了自然和社会的变化，用“穷神知化，德之盛也”八个字来说明：人们认识事物变化之奇妙，赞之为“盛德”。洞察此，君子们才能够做到“安而不忘危，存而不忘亡，治而不忘乱，是以身安而国家可保”。[5]

---

① 《论语·学而》。

② （清）刘宝楠撰，高流水点校：《论语正义》卷十九《季氏》，中华书局，1990年，第649页。

③ （宋）朱熹：《四书章句集注》，中华书局，1983年，第170页。

④ 《论语·颜渊》。

⑤ 《易·系辞下》。

忧患意识历代相传。唐代政治家魏征（580－643年）将“忧患”解为人的精神状态，据《新唐书·魏征传》载，他说：“‘思’所以危则安矣，‘思’所以乱则治矣，‘思’所以亡则存矣。”治国理政者能够不忘国家的危险因素，从而采取预防的措施，社会有望趋向安全；能够考虑明白混乱的原因，社会才能逐渐太平；能够思考清楚灭亡的原因，社会就能变得稳固。在魏征的论述中，包含有忧患意识与社会和谐这二者互相依存的某种要点。如果没有忧患意识，也就看不到社会矛盾，找不到解决矛盾的妥善方法，建造不了社会和谐。因此，对于治国理政者来说，即或是在非常顺利和取得很大胜利的时刻，仍然要谦虚谨慎，牢记“自强不息”这个中华文化的古训。

关于忧患意识，人们经常将北宋时期政治家范仲淹（989－1052）的《岳阳楼记》一文作为代表，要人们去诵读，指导自己的行动，这是很有见地的。

范仲淹有丰富的政治和实践经验，曾在延州（今陕西省延安市）率军遏止西夏军的侵扰。访问过岳州（今湖南省岳阳市）岳阳楼。此楼唐朝时初建，宋仁宗时重修。范仲淹应友人之邀，著文以记其事。首叙岳阳西著名大湖洞庭景观，次叙在淫雨霏霏的日子里登楼感物而悲，再叙春和景明之际登楼览物而喜。最后问如何才能“不以物喜，不以己悲”，回答是：“居庙堂之高，则忧其民；处江湖之远，则忧其君。是进亦忧，退亦忧。然则，何时而乐耶？其必曰：先天下之忧而忧，后天下之乐而乐。”

这里提出了问题：政治家们怎样才能不因环境变迁而改变自己的志向？不因个人得失而转移自己的信念？范仲淹对此做出了明确回答：在朝廷做官，要情系黎民百姓；不在庙堂之上，仍然要有对于国家的忧患情怀。当天下人都有了快乐和幸福，这个时候才有个人的幸福。范仲淹把儒家的忧患意识提升到忧国、忧民的高度，产生了深远影响。

## 四、中华文化传承与儒家经学

《诗》、《书》、《礼》、《易》、《春秋》是孔子思想产生的文化源头，也是他创立儒学所依据的思想资料。[①] 孔子对这些西周的古文献都做过深入的研究，自称“述而不作”，其实这是谦辞，他在传承中有创造，并赋予这些文献以新的生命力，否则也不会有儒学的产生。从孔子开始，经过儒家学者自身对古文献整理研究经验的总结，产生了儒家特殊的经学诠释方法。

经学是指解释和阐述儒家经典的学问，其名称始见于《汉书·兒宽传》。经学本义指丝织物的纵线，《说文解字》：“经，织从（纵）丝也。”在这里经引申为书籍的含义，

① 原本为“六经”，其中有“乐经”，失传，故称为“五经”。

称重要书籍为“经”，以与一般书籍相区别，或将文章中的提纲部分成为经，与阐述的部分分开来。汉武帝时，《诗》、《书》、《礼》、《易》、《春秋》始称为“五经”，后逐渐增加其他儒家著作。经学包括文字学、历史学、天文历算、鸟兽草木之训释，政治思想、哲学思想、宗教思想则是经学的重要内容。这些门类在经书中都没有明确区分，要求学人们从会通和整体上加以全面理解。

《易·系辞上》云：“圣人有以见天下之动，而观其会通。”近代学者高亨在《周易大传今注》中说：“此言圣人有以见到天下事物之运动变化，而观察其会合贯通之处，从而推行社会之典章制度。”由此引申，会通是整体性、全面性研究，要求从异中求同，从部分中求统一，是文化学术的融合贯通。

儒家经学与政治有密切关系。汉武帝时期是经学成为统治思想的开端。建元元年（前140年），武帝令大臣、诸侯举贤良，丞相卫绾奏请“所举贤良，或治申、商、韩非、苏秦、张仪之言，乱国政，请皆罢”，[①] 得到武帝认可。这件事显示出武帝有用儒家取代法家和纵横家等的意图。建元五年（前136年）立“五经”博士，表明经学已被提到官方学术的地位。但当时的经学并不完全适合武帝建立“大一统”国家的政治需要。元光元年（前134年），武帝诏问：“何行而可以章先帝之洪业休德，上参尧舜，下配三王？”[②] 春秋公羊学派经学大师董仲舒建议：“诸不在六艺之科、孔子之术者，皆绝其道，勿使并进”，[③] 被武帝采纳，这是当时多民族统一大国汉朝统治的需要，儒学成为统治思想，但这只是经学中的春秋公羊学，而不是整个经学。

东汉章帝时建立了统一的经学。章帝建初四年（79年）召开白虎观会议，这是中国经学史上一次盛大的会议。会上对经学的理解虽有多种，但经过皇帝亲自裁决，加以统一。统一的思想基础是：共同维护“君臣之正义”和“父子之纲纪”，即所谓“三纲五常”思想，[④] 还有谶纬神学思想。尽管这个时代的经学有其历史的局限性，但是经学家们保存整理儒家著作，为中华文化传承做出了贡献。

中国封建社会一般说来，政教分离，没有形成像西欧那样的宗教黑暗时期。当时占统治地位的是儒家经学中的三纲五常说。皇权统治以此为准则，而民间也用经学来维护、巩固社会关系（家庭关系、宗族关系、人际关系等）。历代官方版刻经籍、社会启蒙读本、民间乡约村规，在思想观念上都同经学有关。西汉时有“五经”，东汉时加《孝经》、《论语》成为“七经”。唐时，《礼》分《周礼》、《仪礼》、《礼记》；《春秋》分

---

① 《汉书·武帝纪》。

② 《汉书·武帝纪》。

③ 《汉书·董仲舒传》。

④ 三纲五常：君为臣纲、父为子纲、夫为妻纲为三纲，仁、义、礼、智、信为五常。

为《左传》、《公羊》、《谷梁》，加上《周易》、《尚书》、《诗经》，成为“九经”。“九经”再加《论语》、《孝经》、《尔雅》、《孟子》到宋代成为“十三经”。

儒学经书从“五经”到“十三经”，反映了中国社会演进的需要，也是中华文化传承的展示。社会各个阶层都可从其中找到自己需要的价值观和文化要素。总体来看，儒家经书既维护社会尊卑贵贱的分野，又引导人们遵守道德规范，对君子的正心、诚意、修身、齐家、治国平天下的立志修养过程都有详细论述，说《十三经》是中华中古时期的文化百科全书，并不为过。

经学成为中国传统社会的统治思想，但它并没有妨碍其他学派思想的传承发展。从魏晋南北朝到隋代，有“三教合一”说，主张儒、释、道融合渗透，或称为三教“会通”。唐朝初，可以看到三教并举的文化现象。当历史演进到北宋时期，由于书院建立，促进了学人们的独立思考。学人们对经学笺注提出了怀疑，呼唤新思想出现。理学应时而生，它立足于儒学，兼采佛、道思想。

论述儒家经学，不能忽视清朝中叶出现的“专门汉学”思潮。其代表们①以实事求是的态度和严谨学风，精心研究、整理中华古代文化典籍，纠正了2000年来关于古代文献的若干谬误，为中华学术史、文化史的研究做出了贡献。他们掌握了一套严密的搜集、排比、分类以及识别文献资料的方法。他们知识渊博，研究的内容不局限于经学、史学，而扩展至天文、历算、音韵、训诂、金石、辞章等各个方面。他们中有些人不仅是文献学家，而且是具有开拓精神的思想家。

这里简要介绍清代汉学思潮中的代表人物之一阮元（1764－1849年）在经书汇刻编纂方面的贡献：

1.《经籍纂诂》，106卷。这部书将唐以前散在群书中的古代传注按音韵编排。取材广泛，群经、诸子、史部、集部旧注以及古代字书如《尔雅》、《方言》、《说文》、《释名》等，几乎囊括了唐以前的训诂著述。

2. 重刻《十三经注疏》并附校勘记。《十三经注疏》合刻自南宋即开始，明清均有刻本，阮元根据宋本重刊并撰写校勘记，成为《十三经注疏》最规范的版本。

3.《皇清经解》（又称《学海堂经解》）。此书搜集清初至乾隆、嘉庆年间的经学著作74家，收书180余种，是对乾嘉汉学成果的汇集。

以上三部大书汇集了清代乾嘉汉学的研究成果，也是我们研究儒家经学不可缺少的著作。

---

① 阎若璩、胡渭、毛斯大、万斯同、顾祖禹等人，还有戴震、汪中、章学诚、焦循、阮元。

## 五、从佛教儒学化看中华文化强劲的生命力

中华文化不是封闭的文化，她之所以有悠久的生命力，由于她具有开放的特色。这一方面表现为中国境内各民族间的文化交流和共同创造。另一方面则体现在中外文化交流上。中国的丝绸，改变了西方人的穿着；而西域的物产和音乐，也改变着中国人的日用习惯和音乐风格。中国儒学影响了日本、朝鲜的学术发展；南亚的佛教，也影响了中华文化。汉唐时期对外域文化的吸收消化，促进了汉唐灿烂文明的出现，而唐宋时期中华文化的远播，也影响了东南亚诸国的发展进程。时至明清之际，尽管官方采取了“海禁”政策，民间的海外交往并未止步。明代郑和下西洋，未侵占外国的一寸土地。此后民间通过海上线路的中外交通日益发达。中国的一些商人和平民，在海上往来贸易，甚至到东南亚以及世界各地定居，成为今天海外华侨的祖先。他们为远播中华文化做出了很大贡献。

这里以印度佛教传入中土，与儒学融合为例来看中华文化的强劲生命力。

两汉之际，佛教传入中国以后，中国僧人为寻求佛教梵本，解答佛法中的疑难，不畏旅途艰苦，远赴印度取经，在中国思想文化史上写下“舍身求法”的光辉篇章。唐代玄奘（602—664年）本姓陈，深得唐太宗李世民的信任，为深入了解印度佛教，决心去那里取经，得到唐太宗的支持。玄奘于贞观三年（629年）从长安出发，历经千辛万苦到达印度，在著名的那烂陀寺学习五年，在印度各地游学交流四年，往返路程走了八年，于贞观十九年（645年）回到长安，先后在弘福寺、慈恩寺从事译著。

玄奘的精神，鲁迅在《中国人失掉自信力了吗?》一文中说：“中国自古以来，就有埋头苦干的人，就有拼命硬干的人，就有为民请命的人，就有舍身求法的人。……他们是中国的脊梁。”

佛教传入中国后，和中华本土文化相融合，经历了很长时间。我国前辈学术大家汤用彤先生在《汉魏两晋南北朝佛教史》和《隋唐佛教史论》中指出，佛教传入中国后，经历了三个阶段：从形似到传神再到会通，即“格义”、“玄化”到“儒化”。

两汉之际至三国、两晋，佛教始传，为沟通中外文化在语言、概念上的障碍，用中华文化中的名词概念，去比附解释佛教经文。这种方法往往牵强附会，背离佛经原义。到南北朝时，玄学盛行，佛教逐渐与玄学合流，史称“佛玄”时期，这当然不可能准确地解说佛教。到隋唐时期，佛教传入已有七八百年，佛教儒学化终于实现，主要表现在佛性与儒家心性说结合。隋唐时期，佛教各宗派大多以心性论为本派学说的重点。特别是禅宗，更是着重讲心性。六祖慧能在《坛经》中说：“佛向性中作，莫向身外求。”并作一偈语：“菩提只向心觅，何劳向外求玄？所说依此修行，西方只在眼

前。”这不仅是儒家心性论的佛教版，而且在唐代盛行的道教内丹术中也有这方面的影响。

其次，出世并不反对经世。隋唐时期中华各佛教宗派的创始人一方面接受皇权的支持和保护，另一方面也为皇权祈福效力，他们中许多人被诏封为“国师”，亦可成佛。

还有，偈语与语录并用。语录体，本是中华早期儒学著作中的一种文体，如《论语》，言简意赅，朴实无华。这是《易传・系辞》所提倡的“易则易知，简则易从”的思维方式。这种文体也影响了隋唐时期的中土佛教，慧能《坛经》以语录体为主，穿插若干宗教偈语，这体现了中国古代语录文体的“简易”，而且启发了宋明时期的理学家们。

隋唐时期，佛教儒学化程度决定了他们传播佛教的力度。“化”得比较好的，如天台、华严和禅宗，它们的影响随之扩大，邻国朝鲜、日本等国也开始建立天台、华严、禅宗等佛教宗派。总之，佛教的儒学化，引起深刻而广泛的文化影响，并带来艺术、音乐、建筑、雕塑、文学等方面的文化交流。[①]

文化交流是双向的。唐朝安史之乱后，文人学士们在坚守儒学理论和社会政治思想的同时，广泛吸收佛教和道教思想，充实自己的理论体系。韩愈（768—824 年）、李翱（772—841 年）、柳宗元（773—819 年）、刘禹锡（772—842 年）等人，在个人修养和政治上推崇儒学，在思想上和学术爱好上出入佛老，居庙堂之高讲修齐治平，处江湖之远则“栖心释梵，浪迹老庄”。[②] 柳宗元声称要“统合儒释，宣涤疑滞”，针对韩愈批评他“不斥浮图”的指责，他回答说：“浮图诚有不可斥者。”[③] 近世学者陈寅恪指出：“南北朝时，即有儒释道三教之目，至李唐之世，遂成固定之制度。如国家有庆典，则召集三教之学士，讲论于殿廷，是其一例。故自晋至今，言中国之思想，可以儒释道三教代表之。”[④]

宋代，佛教思想对学术的影响更加显著。理学大家朱熹的思想，反映了华严宗的印迹。陆九渊（1139—1193 年）的心学思想，明显接受了禅宗的影响。周敦颐（1017—1073 年）的《爱莲说》显然与佛教莲华自性清净的论述有关。朱熹的《中庸章句》的《序说》，脱胎于华严宗的理事说，而又受到程颐的影响。

道教的影响也不可低估。宋代先天图、河图洛书、太极图的传授，均出自道教。

---

① 参看张岂之主编《中国思想史》（修订本），西北大学出版社，2012 年，第 497—500 页。

② 《病中诗十五首并序》，《白居易集》卷 35，中华书局，1979 年，第 787 页。

③ 《柳宗元集》卷 25，第 668、674 页。

④ 《金明馆丛稿二编》，三联书店，2001 年，第 282 页。

不过在不同的理学家那里，这种情况并不完全相同。周敦颐的《太极图说》，受道教影响较多。朱熹著《参同契考异》，主要在研究道教的经典。

从中国思想史来看，宋代理学家们都受佛教、道教的影响，这使他们的思想更加开阔，理论更加深邃；在价值观和人生境界的精神追求上又有所提升。

## 六、结束语

中华文化源远流长，5000多年没有中断过，其中积淀着民族智慧、民族价值尺度、民族的思维方式和生活方式。汉族文化与少数民族文化相互交流、融合，构成中华文化的整体，即中华民族的精神家园。

儒学不是神的文化，而是以“人”为核心的道德文化，讲如何做人，做有道德、有理想、有作为的人；与人讲诚信友善，讲互相尊重，讲己所不欲，勿施于人；讲忠恕之道。

儒学不是宗教，它是中华的人文文化，它在发展过程中吸取了佛、道宗教思想中的某些优质，又加以改造，使自身更加丰富。

儒学是讲爱心的文化，爱国、爱亲、爱大众、爱自然、爱一草一木，即所谓“泛爱众而亲仁”。

儒学竭力排除极端，是主张践行“中庸”辩证思维的文化，反对“过头”与“不及”。

儒学引导人们追求和谐，鼓励人们营造人与社会、人与自然、人与人以及自己内心的和谐，主张用和谐取代社会冲突。儒学讲“王道”，反对“霸道”，主张道义、和平。

儒学不排斥外来的优秀文化，主张“和而不同”，倡导博采众家之长的文化会通精神。

儒学十分重视教育和人才培养，认为人们经过教育和自己的努力皆可以成才；它不是少数天才的文化，而是中华民族整体的文化。

儒学是中华历史的产物，不可能没有历史的某些局限；但这些并不影响它成为中华民族丰富深刻的精神财富。我们建设社会主义小康社会与和谐世界，要有包括儒学在内的中华民族优秀传统文化作为精神的活水源头。

# 孔子仁爱思想的现代意义

台湾元培科技大学 朱荣智

## 一、前言

每一个历久不衰的伟大民族，都有其文化的特色和值得骄傲的民族精神，我们中华民族所赖以生存的精神依据，就是以孔子为代表的儒家思想。人在天地之间，不管是中国人或是外国人，不管是古代人或是现代人，第一重要的事，便是要懂得做人的道理，懂得如何在天地之间扮演自己的角色，知道生而为人的意义和价值。

中华文化源远流长，博大精深，是我国立国精神之所寄，也是国脉民命之所系，中国人创造了中华文化，中华文化更孕育了中华儿女的民族性格。中国传统文化的特色，强调以人为本，这个观念的建立，来自孔子的人文思想。孔子是儒家思想的代表，中国传统文化是以儒家思想为主流，换言之，孔子的人文关怀成为中国传统文化最大的特质。

近代西方文化最大的成就，在于尽物之性，对于科技文明有高度的发展与贡献，但是西方文明高度的发展，却也使世变日亟，人性湮灭，对于全体人类产生极大的危机。以孔子思想为基础的中华文化，长久以来最大的贡献，是尽人之性，强调以人为本，物为末，所以中华文化能够培养和谐的人生，推其极致，可以赞天地之化育而与天地参。孔子的思想是中华文化珍贵的瑰宝，永恒的真理，超越时空，我们应该努力发扬光大。

英国学者李约瑟在所著《中国之科学与文明》一书中，认为中国社会数千年来，虽有朝代的转换，外族的侵略，内乱的频兴，但是社会的基本形式是相当永恒的，这完全是因为中华文化有稳固性，有其超越的性质，有其深厚的基础。[①] 李约瑟先生所谓的“深厚基础”，就是指孔子的儒家思想。

① 参见台湾文化大学三民主义研究所出版《三民主义与中语文化》第348页。

## 二、大哉孔子

孔子，名丘，字仲尼，生于周灵王21年（公元前551），出生于春秋时期鲁国陬邑昌平乡（今山东省曲阜）。孔子是全世界最著名的思想家、教育家及政治家，宋朝的儒者赞美孔子说："天不生仲尼，万古如长夜。"孔子的学说有如日月经天，江河行地，影响非常深远，两千多年来一直是中华文化的主流。

孔子并不是天生的圣人，孔子和我们一样，也有各种的烦恼与痛苦。孔子三岁丧父，家境贫困，但是他十分好学，孔子自述："吾十有五而志于学。""十室之邑，必有忠信如丘者也，不如丘之好学也。"同时，孔子有聪明睿智，他能超越个人的悲苦，为芸芸众生提供宝贵的人生智慧，让芸芸众生转悲为喜、转苦为乐。孔子周游列国的时候，很多隐士对孔子的批评是："知其不可而为之。"形容孔子不屈不挠、永不放弃的奋斗精神。

孔子五十五岁带领弟子周游列国，经过十四年的奔波，可惜他的政治理想没有受到诸侯国君的重用。孔子的晚年，专心于学术的研究和教育的工作，删诗书、订礼乐、赞周易、修春秋，孔子成为一位非常了不起的学者，对中华文化的发展有十分杰出的贡献，而在教育工作的成就，孔子也是倍受尊崇，被誉为"至圣先师"、"万世师表"。

美国当代史学家杜兰博士着《世界文化史》十巨册，在第一册《我们的东方传统》一书说："中国历史的形成，是受了孔子学说的影响，孔子的著述，历代相传，成为学校课本，所有儿童入学之后，即熟读其书，心领神会。这一古代圣哲所创的光明大道，灌输到全民族，使中语文化的强固，能历经外力入侵而巍然不坠，并使入侵者受其影响而改造。即在今日，犹如往昔，欲医疗任何民族因唯智主义教育，以致道德坠落，个人及民族衰弱，因而产生混乱者，最有效的补救之方，实无过于使青年们接受孔子学说的熏陶。"① 这一段话是对孔子思想价值最好的诠释。

## 三、孔子的人格特质

孔子是全世界十大思想家之一，孔子是万世师表，孔子也是伟大的政治家。孔子的伟大，一方面他是在平凡中表现不平凡，一方面他不只是理论家，也是实践家，他的言行举止，道德文章，都足为世人的楷模。

《论语·学而》："子禽问于子贡曰：夫子至于是邦也，必闻其政，求之与？抑与之与？子贡曰：夫子温、良、恭、俭、让以得之。夫子之求之也，其诸异乎人之求之与！"

---

① 参见台湾文化大学三民主义研究所出版《三民主义与中语文化》第3页。

孔子的人格特质，除了子贡所描述的温和、善良、恭敬、节约、谦让，我们还可以归纳为：勤学、乐观、爱心、谦虚、自得、宏伟的抱负。

孔子的勤学，从他自述“发愤忘食，乐以忘忧，不知老之将至。”[①] 一段话，可以领略一二；孔子的乐观，则从“畏于匡”[②]、“在陈绝粮”，[③] 以及在宋国差一点被桓・杀害[④]等危难，孔子一直抱持乐观的态度，令我们深深体会。孔子长相像阳虎，阳虎曾经欺暴匡人，孔子经过匡城的时候，被匡人误以为是阳虎，居留了五天；孔子在陈绝粮，生活困顿，弟子都忍不住了，孔子强调“君子固穷”。

孔子的爱心见于《论语・述而》：“子食于有丧者之侧，未尝饱也，子于是日哭则不歌。”孔子在丧家之侧，不忍心吃饱，当日参加丧礼悲哭，则不忍心再欢歌，可见其恻隐悲悯之心。另外，“子钓而不纲，弋不射宿。”孔子用钓竿钓鱼，不用网子网鱼，孔子射鸟，也不射夜宿没有防备的鸟，孔子的爱心，不只及于一般人，也及于天下地万物。

孔子的谦虚，《论语・子罕》：“吾少也贱，故多能鄙事。”又：“吾有知乎？无知也。有鄙夫问于我，空空如也，我叩其两端而竭焉。”《论语・述而》：“德之不修，学之不讲，闻义不能徙，不善不能改，是吾忧也。”

孔子一生不戚戚于贫贱，也不汲汲于富贵，他曾说：“富而可求，虽执鞭之士，吾亦为之，如不可求，从吾所好。”又说：“饭疏食，饮水，曲肱而枕之，乐亦在其中矣！不义而富且贵，于我如浮云。”《论语・述而》：“子之燕居，申申如也，夭夭如也。”这章是记述孔子闲居的时候，容态舒适，神色愉快。

孔子一生，志在淑世，他不愿像避世之人，只求自己的平安过日子。《论语・微子》：“长沮、桀溺耦而耕。孔子过之，使子路问津焉。长沮曰：夫执舆者为谁？子路曰：为孔丘。曰：是鲁孔丘与？曰：是也。曰：是知津矣！问于桀溺，桀溺曰：子为谁？曰：为仲由。曰：是鲁孔丘之徒与？对曰：然。曰：滔滔者，天下皆是也，而谁以易之？且而与其从辟人之士也，岂若从辟世之士哉？而不辍。子路行以告，夫子怃然曰：鸟兽不可与同群！吾非斯人之徒与而谁与？天下有道，丘不与易也。”

孔子的人生理想，是要能做到博施于民而能济众的“圣人”。孔子的人生理想，不只是做个自了汉，自求修养很好就够了，而且要能普度众生，福泽遍及天下苍生百姓，

---

① 见《论语・学而》篇，台湾学海出版社。

② 《论语・子罕》篇：“子畏于匡，曰文王既没，文不在兹乎？天之将丧斯文也，后死者不得与斯文也，天之未丧斯文也，匡人其如予何？”

③ 《论语・卫灵公》篇：“（孔子）在陈绝粮，从者病，莫能兴。子路愠见曰：君子亦有穷乎？子曰：君子固穷，小人穷斯滥矣。”

④ 《论语・述而》篇：“天生德于予，桓其如予何？”

所谓“老者安之，朋友信之，少者怀之。”[①] 孔子所关心的是天下人、天下事，而不只是一己之私，他是以救世为目标。孔子要使全天下的老年人都能得到安养，朋友之间都能以诚信相待，年少的人都得到关怀照顾，这是何等高尚的胸襟与抱负，这正是“博施于民而能济众”的写照。

## 四、孔子的仁爱思想

仁是孔子的中心思想。什么叫仁？《中庸》：“仁者，人也。”仁是人德的总称，东汉许慎《说文解字》：“人，亲也。从人二。”亲，就是爱。从人二，是指仁德的表现，是要有二人，仁德要在人际关系中才能显现出来，鲁滨孙一个人漂流在荒岛，跟谁谈道德呢？道是人的行为规范，德是行道而有所得，道德的呈现，是人与人的相互对待。古代人际关系十分单纯，儒家思想把各种人际关系归结为五伦，包括君臣、父子、夫妇、兄弟、朋友，现代社会人际关系复杂，有所谓的第六伦，称为群己关系。重视伦理是中华文化的特色。

孔子对仁的阐述很多。仁是一个人圆满人格的展现，孔子以一仁字统摄众德。孔子说：“苟志于仁，无恶也。”一个人如果能够立志行仁，就不会做不好的行为。

仁是人之所以为人的道理，仁是人德的总称，在《论语》中，论仁的有58章，仁字出现105次，可见孔子对仁的重视。孔子对仁的解释很多，其中以《论语·颜渊》樊迟问仁，子曰：“爱人”，最为简要圆满。仁是一个人人格圆满的表现，而人格必须在人群中才能呈现出来。一个能爱人的人，一定能够在人群中与别人维持良好的人际关系，一定能够时时关心别人、照顾别人、体谅别人、包容别人，也一定会是具有良好品德的好人。

人生的痛苦，往往因为心里只有自己而没有别人。孔子非常了不起的地方，是他告诉我们做人的道理，要懂得推己及人。其积极意义是“己欲立而立人，己欲达而达人”，人生在世不只要追求自己的成功，也要能够乐于助人。另外，其消极意义是“己所不欲，勿施于人。”一个人要有同理心，凡是能够感同身受，同苦共悲。因为乐于助人，就不会被忌妒、被伤害，而且心存感恩、感激，共同创造和谐富裕的社会；因为有同理心，自己不愿意吃苦，也不愿意别人吃苦，人与人之间，就不会互相争执、侵害，人间自然是充满祥和幸福。

颜渊问仁。孔子回答说：“克己复礼为仁。”[②] 颜渊接着又问如何做到“克己复礼”呢？孔子说：“非礼勿视，非礼勿听，非礼勿言，非礼勿动。”礼是行为的规范，我们

---

① 见《论语·公冶长》篇。

② 见《论语·颜渊》篇。

虽然有一颗善良的心，但是常常会经不起各种的诱惑，而做出一些不正当的行为，伤人伤己。行仁之道，最重要的是要能克制自己的私欲，不为情牵，不受物累，不合于礼的事，勿视、勿听、勿言、勿动，言行举止都要中规中矩，一切以礼为依归。

孝悌是行仁的根本。孔子说:“弟子入则孝，出则弟 悌，谨而信，泛爱众，而亲仁。”中国自古以孝悌传家，便是受孔子思想的影响，孔子主张要亲近有仁德的人，物以类聚，孟子也说:“一乡之善士，斯友一乡之善士;一国之善士，斯友一国之善士;天下之善士，斯友天下之善士。”孔子说:“里仁为美，择不处仁，焉得知。”不止要亲近有仁德的人，选择住家，也要选在有仁厚风俗的地方。

齐家之道，不外父慈、子孝、兄友、弟恭。“父母唯其疾之忧。”父母爱护子女无微不至，父母之恩，为人子女当然要尽心尽力报答，“入则孝，出则弟”，儿女孝顺父母，不在口体之养，最重要的是敬心与顺意。“子游问孝。子曰:今之孝者，是谓能养，至于犬马皆能有养，不敬，何以别乎?”“子夏问孝。子曰:色难。有事弟子服其劳，有酒食先生馔，曾是以为孝乎?”行孝当及时，子女孝顺父母，是一辈子的责任，一颗真挚的心，诚心诚意，是最重要的。善事父母为孝，善事兄长为弟，孝、弟二者是做人的根本。

孔子鼓励大家做一位仁者，孔子说:“仁远乎哉?我欲仁，斯仁至矣!”作为一位仁者并不难，只要有心就有力，不必舍近求远，更不能舍本而逐末。“君子无终食之间违仁，造次必于是，颠沛必于是。”一个人无论在得意的时候，或是失意的时候，甚至是颠沛流离，非常困顿的时候，都不能离开仁德。君子所以为君子，是因为能够时时刻刻以仁为本，不管是得意的时候，或是失意的时候，甚至是颠沛流离的时候，都不会失其初衷。孔子感叹世人不用心行仁，孔子说:“回也其心三月不违仁，其余则日月至焉而已矣。”又说:“我未见好仁者，恶不仁者，好仁者，无以尚之;恶不仁者，不使不仁者加乎其身。有能一日用其力于人矣乎?我未见力不足者。盖有之矣，我未之见也。”孔子认为，真正喜爱仁德的人，他会觉得世界上没有比仁德更重要的事;真正憎恶不仁德的人，会努力行仁德，不会使不仁德的事加在自己身上。孔子强调，没有人会因为没有能力而不能行仁德。

## 五、孔子仁爱思想的影响

孔子的思想博大精深，“至广大而尽精微，极高明而道中庸”，[①] 可以作为五千年中华文化的代表，他是我们中国人的骄傲。日本近代实业界之父涩泽荣一（1840—1931）

① 见《中庸》。

出版《论语与算盘》一书，提出伦理道德与经济发展的统一，即“富”与“仁”，“义”与“利”的统一，不合乎伦理道德的经济成就是不会长久的，他的理论对日本的现代化有很大的影响。

近几年十分畅销的韩国崔仁浩着《商道》一书，叙述1800年代朝鲜时期大商人林尚沃一生传奇的故事。林尚沃本来只是一名杂货店的员工，后来努力成为朝鲜人大王，林尚沃的成功，受儒家讲诚信、重仁义的影响很大。

新加坡政府在李光耀总理执政的时代，把儒家思想列入中学课程。李光耀总理认为：“这样做的目的，是要在我们孩子的思想还未定型，而且可以熏陶时，把这些价值观念灌输给他们，以便这些处事待人的态度，能够在他们长大后，根深蒂固，终身不忘。”

孔子的思想不只影响日本、韩国、新加坡，一九八二年八月二十八日，美国旧金山侨界举行祭孔大典，孔德成先生担任正献官，有中美人士一千两百多人参加观礼。当时的美国总统里根特派代表出席，并表示：“孔子对人类行为与伦理的标准，不但影响了中国人民，并且影响了全世界。他的教训已一代接一代地流传下来，使世界获得了丰富的文化遗产。”美国加州州长布朗先生也赞誉孔子是一位伟大的教师，说他的教训已使世界所有人民获益。

## 六、孔子是仁爱思想的启示

### 1. 仁爱是基本的人性

心中有爱，人生最美，美是心中有大爱，孔子当年提倡仁爱的思想，实在非常了不起，这是他对全人类最大的贡献。爱是生命的价值，生命中如果没有爱，生命就成了黑白而没有色彩；生命中如果没有爱，生命就失去活力，失去生机。

爱是人类最珍贵的品质，因为有爱，才有夫妻的结合；因为有爱，才有儿女的孕育；因为有爱，才有手足的亲情；因为有爱，才有朋友的扶持；因为有爱，才有对国家、对社会、对工作的热情。爱是信心，爱是力量，爱是人与人之间的坦诚相待；爱是生命迸发出来的熊熊烈火；因为有爱，生命才有意义和价值，我们要努力发扬孔子的仁爱思想。

### 2. 爱与被爱是人生中最幸福的事

爱与被爱是人生中最幸福的事，爱是心有所主，被爱是心有所属。一个人心里有所爱的人，人生有了目标，生命便充满活力、冲劲、热情、希望，再多的苦难、挑战，都愿意甘之如饴。为了所爱的人，可以牺牲一切；为了所爱的人，可以放弃所有。

一个人心里成了被爱的人，人生变得亮丽起来，心中有了归属，就有了安全感。

有人呵护、有人关心、有人细腻照料、有人嘘寒问暖，不是很甜美很幸福吗？有了爱，就有了一切；有了爱，就天长地久。

世界上最悲惨的人，是没有人爱的人，以及没有可以爱的人。

3. 爱人从自爱开始

爱人从自爱开始，没有一个不爱自己的人而能够去爱别人，唯自爱者才有能力爱人，唯自爱者才有条件被爱，自爱不是自私而是自尊自重。

爱是一份关怀，爱是一份体贴，爱是一份包容，爱是一份接纳。爱不只是自爱而已，更重要的是要爱别人，一个人成就的大小，不在于得到多少，而在于付出多少。学习孔子的仁爱思想，就是要善待自己，宽待别人。孔子教我们做人，要从“修己以敬”[①] 开始，然后“修己以安人”最后“修己以安天下”。人人做到“己立立人，己达达人。”“己所不欲，勿施于人。”才能追求圆满的人生。

4. 慈悲喜舍就是仁爱精神

人生只有两件事，一是提起，一是放下。人生所以有很多烦恼与痛苦，主要是舍不得、想不开、提不起、放不下。放下自己是智慧，放下别人是慈悲。智慧不起烦恼，慈悲没有敌人。

台湾慈济功德会是当今全世界最大规模的宗教救助团体，是慈济证严上人于1966年创立，当初是由30位志工发起，每人每天捐献5毛钱，而且热心到菜市场、街上劝募、集腋成裘，如今已逾千万个会员，推动慈善、医疗、教育、人文四大志业，这些年又增加骨髓捐赠、社区志工、环保、国际赈灾等项目，学习观音菩萨闻声救苦的慈悲胸怀，以智慧相结合，以爱心相扶持，“力邀天下善士同耕一方福田，勤植万蕊心莲同造爱的社会。”慈济的志工，人人都是智者、仁者、勇者，充分配挥孔子的仁爱精神。

大爱无国界，一个有仁爱之心的心，抱持慈、悲、善、舍的精神，无私、无求、无怨、无悔，享受布施助人的喜悦，正是孔子所谓仁者的特质。

5. 企业文化要以爱为核心

一个企业家生意做很大，是大企业家，一个企业家能有社会责任，愿意服务、奉献，捐助财富，才是伟大的企业家。台湾润泰集团总裁尹衍梁，他是海峡两岸知名的企业家，媒体关注的焦点，但是他行事非常低调，2011年底，他承诺捐出95%的财产，他常讲留太多钱会害了子孙，金钱对他来说，初期是用来满足兴趣，到了晚年受到信仰的影响，金钱是用来完成梦想的工具。尹衍梁是典型的伟大企业家。

企业的发展与中华传统文化有什么关联？尤其是孔子的仁爱思想能对企业的发展

---

① 见《论语·宪问》篇。

产生什么作用呢？中国大陆汇源集团董事长朱新礼曾经应邀来台访问，在一项学术研讨会中，他提到汇源的企业文化饱含着儒家文化的底蕴。汇源集团是大陆非常成功的果汁饮料公司，朱新礼强调儒家思想对中国历代人才的养成有重要的贡献，对当代企业的发展，也有深远的影响，是当代中国企业成长的重要基础。汇源集团的成功，主要来自孔子“泛爱众”、“博施于民”的思想，朱新礼不只追求企业利益，也要追求果农的利益和消费者的利益，他所生产的果汁产品，讲求严格的品管，安全、卫生、营养、可口，所以受全大陆人的喜爱。

## 七、结语

人文相对于科技，十八世纪西方工业革命以来，科技的快速发展，带动人类生活的重大改变与改善，各种高科技产品的发明与运用，以机器代替人力，提高了生产的质与量，对人类的物质文明，确实有很大的贡献。不过，人类的生活，除了追求物质的满足与享受，还有精神上的需求，譬如爱的需求、被尊重的需求、被社会接纳的需求，以及自我理想的实现，这些方面的需求，不全是物质可以一一取得，而是要从心灵上得到平和、愉悦、认同、提高。钱可以买很多东西，钱不能买一切东西。人从物质上得到满足，只是一时的、短暂的，因为物质的欲望，永无止境，没有求有，有求多、求好、求更多。人只有从内心得到自由开放、自得自足，才能获得真正的、持久的快乐与幸福。

甲午鸦片战争之后，中国门户洞开，很多人鉴于外国船坚炮利对国家的伤害，有人提出“中学为体，西学为用”的口号，甚至高唱“德先生”（Democracy）、“赛先生”（Science），打倒孔家店，孔子的思想被视为阻碍中国的现代化，是中国不能进步的主因。其实，发展科技与提倡人文是不冲突的，“科技始终来自于人性”，不只是一句广告词，人为主，物为末，物是为人所用，科技是配合人性需求而发明的。

孙中山先生讲民族主义的时候，一再强调，我们要恢复民族的地位，除了大家联合起来做成一个国族团体之外，最重要的，就是要把国有的旧道德恢复起来。他说：“一般醉心新文化的人，便排斥旧道德，以为有了新文化，便可以不要旧道德。不知道我们固有的东西，如果是好的，当然要保持，不好的才可以放弃。”孙中山先生的见解非常正确。

爱是生命的价值，爱是生活的动力，爱是在别人需要的时候，发现自己的责任与能力。孔子最伟大的地方，就是他提倡仁爱，鼓舞人类奋发向上，因为有爱，人类充满信心与希望，天地无情，人间有爱。大自然常常给人类带来浩劫、灾难、地震、水灾、旱灾、台风、瘟疫，每次的天灾加上人为的暴乱、战争，都造成人类生存的危机，幸好人类天生有一颗爱心，拯救无数无辜受害的生灵。

孔子的仁爱思想，从自爱而爱人，是达到个人幸福、家庭和乐、社会安详的不二法门。

**参考书目：**

[1] 于丹. 于丹《论语》心得. 台湾联经出版公司，2008.
[2] 王熙元. 论语精髓. 台湾黎明文化出版公司，1994.
[3] 傅佩荣. 孔子新说. 台湾幼狮文化出版公司，2003.
[4] 朱荣智. 孔孟伦理思想与四书教学. 台湾南岳出版公司，1985.
[5] 朱荣智. 孔子管理哲学. 台湾师大书院出版公司，1999.
[6] 朱荣智. 改变一生的孔子名言. 台湾德威出版公司，2008.

# 孔子与人的“形上自由”

四川唐君毅研究所　邵　明

在数千年的人类文明史中，不同文化形态间的交织相遇往往带来多种复杂的结果：有的文化发展依旧甚至更加强势，而有的却逐渐衰弱甚至或快或慢地消失了，还有时一种新的文化形态会随之出现，并或隐或显地呈现出某一方的文化特征。这些不同文化形态的变迁过程构成了人类文明史中的重要内容，对人类文明的发展有着最为关键的影响，而且经常还是其中最为波澜壮阔、引人入胜的部分。华夏文明与西方文明的激烈碰撞已经百年有余，但是最终的结果究竟会怎样，我们目前似乎还不得而知。对此，无数学者已经做了大量的理论思考和探讨，无数有志之士也在历史实践中进行了艰难的尝试，这无疑都给了我们深刻的启发。不过鉴于问题的复杂性和重要性，我们仍需进一步的深入研究。

## 一、“形上选择”与“形上迷失”

对美好事物的追求构成了人的经验性特征之一。这些美好事物既可以是人们日常生活当中的各种具体对象，如衣食住行中的食物、用品器械或能够满足人们情感需求的某种事物等等，也可以是各种社会文化活动中的某些抽象对象，如语言、艺术或社会伦理关系等等。同时，这些抽象对象还可以表现为更加一般性的观念，如我们在哲学史中所见到的那些“理念”、“实体”、“上帝”、“心”、“物”、“道”、“理”、“气”、“性”、“无”、“空”、“梵”、“真”、“善”、“美”等等具有形上意义的实体范畴。在现实经验生活中，对美好事物或抽象观念的追求，或隐或显地支配或影响着人们的思想和行为，构成着个人或现实社会的生存方式。信仰不同的“形上实体”，也往往导致各种文明形态或文化共同体呈现出十分不同的鲜明特色来。

那么，究竟哪一个或哪几个“形上实体”应该成为人们思想和行为规范的最终根据，成为人们值得追求或信奉的对象呢？这个“形上选择”的问题在三千年以来的人类思想史中始终处于激烈争论之中，至今悬而未决，成为一个令人倍感困惑的理论和实践难题。例如，柏拉图主义者喜欢追求某种完美无缺的理想对象，一元论或一神论者信奉某个独一无二的至上实体，而多元论或多神论者则主张各个实体间具有不可还原性，共同发挥本体作用；先验论者虽然否认这些“形上实体”的本体论地位，却认为它们构成了人的经验的可能性根据，是实践理性的必然伴随物；而当代自然主义者与相对主义者类似，几乎否定任何“形上实体”的存在意义，只愿意认可物理或生物性因果法则，如此等等。形上问题的混乱状况或“形上迷失”似乎已经给深具形上情怀的人们造成了许多思想或实践上的障碍，并在社会现实中引起意想不到的人为灾难，阻碍着人们获得真实的幸福美好的生活，特别是在历史上往往导致不同的文明或文化共同体之间产生互不理解和信任，并出现持续的争端、冲突甚至战争。可见，“形上选择”的问题需要我们给以特别地关注和思考。

如果柏拉图主义是对的，即确实有某个或某些“神”创造了这个世界，或者有某个或某些“形上实体”也具有“神”一般的超然地位，那么人们似乎就不得不接受其至尊的权威，对之顶礼膜拜以获得思想和行为的规范或关于事物的知识，同时还能使自己的身心得到安顿和幸福。这种“神”或“形上实体”无疑将会以某种方式“决定”人们的思想和行为，而消除他们承担命运的责任，并使他们只能在与其关联中得到自身的认同和意义。不过人类文明的历史现实表明，这一点尽管一度被某些时代的人们所认可，却尚未成为确凿的普遍性事实。

如果先验论是对的，那么有着相似经验历程的人类群体将也会有着相似的形而上学理念，并产生出几乎相同的文化成就，如社会伦理、政治经济、文学艺术或宗教活动等等，因为构成历史经验的先验根据是相同的，具有必然性的普遍特征。但是我们看到，历史现实也同样否证了这一点。更为重要的是，那些“形上实体”的价值和意义似乎是人类经验的产物，而并非其所以可能的根据，也不是历史实践的必然伴随物，反而具有偶然的现实情境特征。

如果自然主义或相对主义是对的，那么人类与自然万物一样，就都处于一个闭合的物理或生物因果链条之中，而没有意义的无限生发。可是，如此一来，自然主义或相对主义者是如何“洞见”到这一点的，却令人匪夷所思了。这不能以其自身的理论加以解释，构成了该理论视域的“盲点”，恐怕一时难以消除。而这一“洞见”的能力，似乎与上述那些“形上实体”有着相同的经验意义和价值内涵，正是需要我们加以阐释的对象，不能轻易地忽略。

对形上对象的追求固然是令人着迷的，获得某个外在权威的支撑似乎总是能够给人一种踏实轻松之感，但是如果深陷其中缺乏反省，就很容易固执拘泥于上述某种观念而难免僵化或失去独立人格和意志。而在由孔子所创立的儒家思想之中，却有着充分的思想资源足以化解此种拘执，从而开拓出无限的形上空间和意义世界。

## 二、“仁”的意义空间

孔子虽然敬畏天（命、道），却更重视人道，如“子贡曰：夫子之文章，可得而闻也；夫子之言性与天道，不可得而闻也。”（《论语·公冶长》）说明他不愿多谈天道，而更多的是谈论人事。从中我们也可看到，子贡很明显地是有那种形上情怀的，似乎期待着孔子能够把现实中的道理追溯到更本原的根据上。

但是孔子始终没有如他所愿，而总是以历史或现实中的人物为其榜样，从侧面加以描述，如“子曰：大哉尧之为君！巍巍乎！唯天为大，唯尧则之。荡荡乎！民不能名焉。巍巍乎！其有成功也。焕乎！其有文章！”（《论语·泰伯》）。在孔子看来，只有尧舜禹的丰功伟业才是令人赞叹的，值得效法的，而不必去追寻某个“神”或某种完美无缺的纯粹“理念”。所以，“子不语怪、力、乱、神”（《论语·述而》），且“敬鬼神而远之”（《论语·雍也》）。这与上古至先秦时期人们热衷于祭祀鬼神、拜奉天地神明的习俗和观念并不一致。但是他的弟子们就难免这些俗念，因此需要孔子的一再纠正。例如，当弟子季路来向孔子请教祭祀鬼神的事情时，“子曰：未能事人，焉能事鬼？曰：敢问死？曰：未知生，焉知死？”（《论语·先进》），主张应该把关注点从虚无缥缈的天上拉回人间。

看来孔子的文章智慧并非来源于某种神启，也非“分有”了某些完美对象的属性，更不是与生俱来的本能习惯。那么，缺乏“形上实体”的引导，孔子又是如何规范其思想和行为的呢？他给出的答案是：日常的学习和实践。“子曰：学而时习之，不亦乐乎？”（《论语·学而》），这是《论语》开篇第一句，富含深意，可以说确立了儒家甚至华夏文明的基本格调。孔子的“学”和“习”是向什么学呢？当然不是向现实世界之外的“他神”或“他物”去学，而是就向现实生活中的“他人”或“他事”去学。这个“他人”或“他事”既包括自己所能够遇到的任何人和事，也包括自己所能够了解到的古代圣贤及其事迹。于是《论语》紧接着第一句后的就是：“有朋自远方来，不亦乐乎？”为什么高兴呢？因为他们能够给自己带来文章或智慧，“三人行，必有我师焉：择其善者而从之，其不善者而改之。”（《论语·述而》）周围的人身上就总有我可以学习的地方，学习好的东西，而改掉坏的东西。这难得不就是最基本的获得学识智慧的方式吗？于是孔子说自己“吾十有五而志于学”（《论语·为政》）。他还评价说“我非生而知之者，好古，敏以求之者也。”（《论语·述而》）这说明历史的经验教训也是最好的老师，“子曰：温故而知新，可以为师矣。”（《论语·为政》）还有“子曰：盖有不知而作之者，我无是也。多闻，择其善者而从之，多见而识之，知之次也。”（《论语·述而》）以及“子曰：默而识之，学而不厌，诲人不倦，何有于我哉！”（同上）孔子认为起码自己不是依据本能或天赋得到的智慧，而是在日常生活中不断地“学”和“习”，通过多听多看再加以不断反省体悟得到的。他似乎完全不热衷于去追求某种理想的形上对象。

但是“如何学习”与“向谁学习”同样重要。如果把学习的对象视为某种完美、神圣、绝对真实的、不可变易的偶像，那么这种学习就难免会走入歧路了。所以孔子十分强调学习的方法，提出为学要有“四忌”：“子绝四：毋意，毋必，毋固，毋我。”（《论语·子罕》）不能顽固拘泥，偏执一见，而应博学，并多加思考和体悟。博学是指“礼、乐、射、御、书、数”六艺，“子曰：君子博学于文，约之以礼，亦可以弗畔矣夫。”（《论语·雍也》）。思考和体悟是指对所学习到的东西和自己的观念行为不断加以反省，以发现和纠正有错误的地方。“子曰：学而不思则罔，思而不学则殆。”（《论语·为政》）“学”和“思”不能分开，要使外来的知识化为自己的智慧，如“子夏曰：博学而笃志，切问而近思，仁在其中矣。”（《论语·子张》）可见“学问致思”是获得“仁”的重要途径。“子曰：见贤思齐焉，见不贤而内自省也。”（《论语·里仁》）这是要通过学习和内思自省而不断提高自己的精神境界，以使自己成就为“仁者”或“君子”。

指出了“向谁学习”和“如何学习”之后，就是“学习什么”的问题。孔子一再强调的就是要学习如何成为“仁者”或“君子”的“为人之道”。在他看来，通过向周围和古代的圣贤君子学习，力求博学、致思和反省，这样才能“得仁达义识礼致知”。在他看来，是否具有“仁德”是评价圣贤君子的最重要尺度，也是衡量一个人“学”和“习”达到了什么程度的最重要标准。但是，对于何者为“仁”，孔子却并没有给出一个确定的答案，而是在各种不同的描述中刻画“仁”的内涵。例如，在《论语》中，孔子的弟子们曾多次专门向孔子请教“何者为仁”或“如何为仁”的问题，孔子的解释每每不同：

樊迟问仁。曰：“仁者先难而后获，可谓仁矣。”（《雍也》）

颜渊问仁。子曰：“克己复礼为仁。一日克己复礼，天下归仁焉。为仁由己，而由人乎哉？”颜渊曰：“请问其目？”子曰：“非礼勿视，非礼勿听，非礼勿言，非礼勿动。”（《颜渊》）

仲弓问仁。子曰：“出门如见大宾，使民如承大祭。己所不欲，勿施于人。在邦无怨，在家无怨。”（同上）

司马牛问仁。子曰：“仁者，其言也讱。”曰：“其言也讱，斯谓之仁乎？”子曰：“为之难，言之得无讱乎？”（同上）

樊迟问仁。子曰：“爱人。”（同上）

樊迟问仁。子曰：“居处恭，执事敬，与人忠。虽之夷狄，不可弃也。”《子路》

子贡问为仁。子曰：“工欲善其事，必先利其器。居是邦也，事其大夫之贤者，友其士之仁者。”《卫灵公》

子张问仁于孔子。孔子曰：“能行五者于天下为仁矣。”请问之。曰：“恭、宽、信、敏、慧。恭则不侮，宽则得众，信则人任焉，敏则有功，惠则足以使人。”《阳货》

《论语》中还有其他一些言论也是关于“仁”的，例如“子曰：刚毅木讷近仁。”（《子路》）“子曰：巧言令色，鲜矣仁。”（《学而》）等等。还有许多是描述“仁者”的，如“夫仁者，己欲立而立人，己欲达而达人。能近取譬，可谓仁之方也已。”（《雍也》）、“仁者无忧”、“仁者乐山”、“仁者静”等等。

看起来“仁”有许多意义，不是能够轻易给出一个明确定义的：既可以指从自然情感中升华出来的一种超越性情感，如“爱人”；也可以是某种个人的品格或德性，如“刚毅木讷”或“讱”（持重）；还可以是某种与他人相待的为人原则，如“己所不欲，勿施于人”、“己欲立而立人，己欲达而达人”；还可以是自身应该遵循的行为准则，如“克己复礼”、“恭、敬、忠”或“恭、宽、信、敏、慧”等等。孔子对“仁”的多种解释并不表示“仁”有多么神秘，他也说：“仁远乎哉？我欲仁，斯仁至矣。”（《述而》）可见“仁”并不是远不可及的，而就在人们身心的切近之处，随处可得。尽管要想真正地得到“仁”，还需要下许多“学”和“习”的工夫。

“仁”是孔子思想中的核心概念，是他终身努力“学”和“习”的目标和理想，也是他终身遵循的行为规范和处事原则，还是他评价和判断人事的标准和尺度。可是，这个“仁”尽管被孔子反复陈说，却并没有一个明确的含义。这一点能给予我们什么启示呢？

## 三、“仁”与“道德努力”

关于孔子对“仁”的真实理解究竟是怎样的，尽管有很多猜测，现在恐怕已经不可考了。他可能是因材施教，视不同弟子的资质情况而加以不同的阐释；也可能是先秦时期的“仁”这个概念本身就具有如此多重的含义，与我们现在的理解大为不同；还可能是他的弟子后学们对《论语》的不断添加，导致“仁”这一概念出现了多种含义；甚至还可能是孔子自己就尚未思考清楚这个“仁”究竟应该如何解释更好，才试探着以各种方式加以分说；或者，他本人对“仁”的想法就始终在变化，也未可知。

不过，我们似乎不必去过度猜测或考证孔子对“仁”的真实理解，而只根据《论语》中孔子围绕着对“仁”的追求的刻画，已经可以看出“仁者”或“君子”的“道德努力”，内在地包含了一个人的某种美好情感、精神倾向、高尚品德、独立人格、意志力量以及立身处事的观念和行为规范，也内在地显示一个社会的价值取向或伦理原则。因此，这种“道德努力”可以说构成了一个人或社会具有“仁心仁性”的本质特征，也是其内在的生存方式。

首先，“仁”或“仁者”是人们应该追求的理想和目标。孔子一再教育弟子们应该努力学做一个“仁者”或“君子”，并总是在“君子”与“小人”的对比中阐释“得仁”的重要性。而且他还认为“仁”也是人们能够学好“礼”、“乐”的基本前提，如“子曰：人而不仁，如礼何？人而不仁，如乐何？”（《论语·八佾》）这表明一个人要能够承担社会性职责，首要的是培养自己的“仁德”品格。没有这样的美好品德，是不可能真正做好这些社会性工作的，而只会产生“伪君子”或“小人”。

其次，不论“仁”是作为一种美好情感、高尚品德，还是作为某种待人处事或自我立身的原则，都不是单纯的一种生物性本能，而有了某种超越的意义。尽管“仁”与人的自然生物本性有着内在的关联，却不是能够被完全地还原到生物本性之上，即可归结为某种求生意志、趋利避害的本能、繁殖欲望和性冲动、刺激—反应的行为模式、由微粒子或某种结构所产生的因果机制，以及基于这些生物性因素的群体生存性因果法则等等。所有这些生物属性似乎都不能充分解释掉“仁”所具有的某种规范性意义，因为它们都不必然地蕴含着人一定要去追求“仁”或“仁者”。

第三，“仁”并非“形上实体”，没有本体论地位，而是人类社会历史实践的经验性产物。在孔子这里，“仁”不是创造事物的本原，不是构成万事万物的基本要素或结构，也不是事物存在和运行所遵循的、最终的必然根据，更不是如“神”或太阳般的“至善”那样，属于先天而有、万事万物的原始基础或意义根源，而是具有情境性特征的经验事物，可以有不同的内涵和特征。因此，“仁”或“仁者”不是那种能够为人们消灾解难的万能之主，也不会成为人们必须绝对服从的某种至上权威，更不会成为人们不得不崇拜奉祀的神圣偶像。“仁”或“仁者”只不过是人们应该加以学习和效仿的对象，可以做人们的“师”而不是“神”。即使一个人不去求“仁”，不想当“仁者”，或其言行明显“不仁”，孔子对他也往往只是“哀其不争”，感叹其只愿做“小人”、“野人”或“鄙夫”，“不求上进”而已，而并不是以“罪孽”或“邪恶”等加以指责，甚至一定要诉诸某种严厉的惩罚不可。

第四，“仁”并不构成人们经验历程的可能性条件。或者说，“仁”既不构成经验对象的可能性条件，也不构成经验的可能性条件，其本身反而是经验的产物，来源于人们在经验历程中的努力追求，是人们通过“学”和“习”逐步获得的，伴随着“学”和“习”的实践过程偶然出现。因此，没有“仁”或“仁者”的社会也是社会，只不过是“乱世”而已；没有“仁心仁性”的个人也是人，只不过属于普通的“凡夫俗子”而已，最多也不过是“小人”、“野人”或“鄙夫”。

同时，作为经验产物的“仁”或“仁者”，在不同的人或社会就会体现出不同的内涵和特征，这也导致在不同的时空条件下，“仁”或“仁者”也都会有不同的外在表现，并由此产生出不同的历史文化成就，例如出现在不同历史时代的各种文明形态中，那些各具特色、丰富多彩的社会伦理、政治经济、文学艺术、宗教活动或民俗风情等等。

第五，个人或社会只有持续地做出“道德努力”才能逐渐具有“仁心仁性”。一方面，这意味着并不是每个人都会主动地、自觉自愿地去追求“仁”或“仁者”，那需要他不断地“学”和“习”，还需要他始终能够“思”和“省”，并且还要一直保持“恭谨诚敬”的态度。要做到这些对一般人而言是很不容易的，需要积极的努力才有可能达到，甚至要“发愤忘食，乐以忘忧，不知老之将至”（《论语·述而》）才行。同时，这样的人还要能够抵御各种外来的诱惑，安贫乐道，就像颜回那样，“子曰：贤哉回也！一箪食，一瓢饮，在陋巷，人不堪其忧，回也不改其乐，贤哉回也!”（《论语·雍也》）。又如“子曰：饭疏食，饮水，曲肱而枕之，乐亦在其中矣。不义而富且贵，于我如浮云。”（《论语·述而》）

另一方面，这还意味着，即使是一个“仁者”也往往不能在所有时间和地点都呈现其“仁”的情感、品德或原则，时时都难免出现“违仁”的情况，如“子曰：回也，其心三月不违仁，其余则日月至焉而已矣。”（《论语·雍也》）即使是孔子自己也不敢说已经达到了完全的“仁者”境界，如他说：“若圣与仁，则吾岂敢？抑为之不厌，诲人不倦，则可谓云尔已矣。”（《论语·述而》）直到古稀之年他才敢说自己“七十而从心所欲不逾矩”。（《论语·为政》）

这表明“仁”是一个人在积极、持续地现实努力中出现和获得的，即使是古代圣贤的代表性人物如尧舜禹文王周公等等，他们所具有的“仁心仁性”也是在“博施济众”、“立人达人”或“修己以安百姓”等等实践过程中才得以呈现的。这种“道德努力”没有完结的时候，是一个永远持续的经验历程，“士不可以不弘毅，任重而道远。仁以为己任，不亦重乎？死而后已，不亦远乎?”（《论语·泰伯》）我们甚至可以说，永恒持续的“道德努力”就是一个“仁者”或“君子”的本质特征和生存方式。

第六，尽管“仁”或“仁者”是值得人们追求的理想和目标，具有超越意义，但并不与其他事物隔离在两个完全不同的世界。这是由“仁”的经验性特征所决定的，即，“仁”或“仁者”并非如“神”或“上帝”一般只居住在神界天堂之中；也不是像纯粹的“形上实体”那样属于某个本体世界，而与此现象世界完全隔绝；更不仅仅是某种预设的逻辑前提或先验根据，可以推导出人们所有的思想和行为，或者可以规定万物的运行和发展。这意味着现实生活中的人们与“仁”或“仁者”之间不存在绝对的“本体障碍”，也没有绝对的“认知鸿沟”。也就是说，“仁心仁性”与现实生活之间不存在绝对不可逾越的间隔，人们都可以通过不断地“学”和“习”而达到“不违仁”的境界，都可以成为“仁人”或“君子”。

同时，更为重要的是，这也意味着在这两者之间无需任何中介物就可以得到恰当的沟通，即没有必然的理由需要某种特别的人、物或事来联结两个不同的领域，例如某类神职人员、寺庙教堂及偶像或祭祀活动等等这些通常的沟通渠道。对许多一般人的“学”和“习”而言，只是需要“师”的启发、引导或榜样的作用来帮助人们获得“仁”，“博之以文，约之以礼”。在“学问致思”的同时，也需要“见贤思齐”，虽然人们的“学”和“习”最终还是要在自身的“思”和“省”之中，才能逐渐完成品德和人格的培养。

最后，“仁”作为人们追求的理想和目标并不是一个单纯的追求对象，而更多地体现为这一追求过程本身，即人的“道德努力”。如果把“仁”视为某种外在的目标，就失去其本初的意义了。实际上“仁”就内在于人的理想追求这一过程本身之中，如“博学而笃志，切问而近思，仁在其中矣”。（《论语·子张》）“仁”也在“爱人”、“克己复礼”、“恭敬”、“立人达人”或“事贤友仁”等等日常的积极行为之中。对权力、地位或富贵等等外在对象的追求，也要看其是否“以其道得之”。这说明追求的过程才内含着“仁心仁性”，而不是这些外在对象本身。

由于“得仁”并非外在目标的获得，因而“得仁”之后一般不会引起他人的注意。不过“人不知而不愠，不亦君子乎？”（《论语·学而》）说明社会名声是不会影响一个人是否成为“仁者”或“君子”的结果的。孔子还说：“君子去仁，恶乎成名？君子无终食之间违仁，造次必于是，颠沛必于是。”（《论语·里仁》）如果没有了“仁”，一个人还会有什么真正的名声呢？在孔子看来，作为君子，不管有多么辛劳艰苦，都应该随时随地做出自己的“道德努力”。

## 四、“仁”与“形上自由”

根据孔子，人的“道德努力”即是对“仁”的理想追求过程，是“仁者”或“君子”在日常生活中持续地、积极地生存方式。

“仁”是一种理想目标，具有超越性意义，但是同时又是经验性产物，是人们在日常的“道德努力”中逐渐获得的。“仁”不是单纯的自然本能或生物性的冲动欲望，也不是某种完美无瑕的“形上实体”或“神”，高居于一个远离现实人世的空灵世界，也不是形成我们这个现象世界的可能性条件，在经验过程中必然地出现。因此，“仁”所开创出来的是一个独特的意义空间，不会被生物因果链条、“形上实体”或“神”、逻辑法则等等，限制在一个闭合的系列、结构或范围之内，而是能够立足于历史和现实的生活世界，面向未来或未知的领域无限开放。

由此，追求“仁”的“道德努力”，因其同时具有超越性和经验性而揭示了人所具有的“形上自由”：在现实的经验历程中，人们可根据社会情境条件来选择各种美好的或有益于开拓其意义空间的事物，作为理想对象加以追求，如“理念”、“实体”、“上帝”、“心”、“物”、“道”、“理”、“气”、“性”、“无”、“空”、“梵”、“真”、“善”、“美”等等。但是，这些“形上观念”不应被视为某种外在的权威或异质的对象来作为人们思想和行为的最终根据，更不应被视为神圣对象而加以无限地景仰崇拜，而应视为人们在“学”和“习”的实践历程中所赋予的价值对象和意义来源，将其纳入于自身的“道德努力”过程之中，以此提升自己的精神境界和扩充自己的意义空间。由此，人们将不会轻易地被某一个或某几个“形上实体”或“神”所左右和控制，也不会长久地陷入某种“形上迷失”之中无法自拔，而总能在持续地“道德努力”中，把握自身的命运。这意味着历史意识、现世性和理想追求将融合而形成为一种开放视域，为人类文明的永恒持续提供无限的可能性。

可见，正是孔子的“仁”所刻画出的这种意义空间，赋予了“道德努力”中的人一种“形上自由”，从使儒家具备了真正的开放性和包容性。不过，在孔子之后两千多年华夏文明的现实历程中，人们并非能够始终保持那种谨慎的“形上自由”，而总是难免因为强烈的本能冲动或“形上情怀”导致自己困顿于某种“形上实体”或“形上迷失”之中，失去其本有的开放性和包容性。尽管如此，借助于道家、佛教和西方文明的帮助，儒家学者也总是能够“返归本心”、“重拾大本”，开拓出更为广阔和丰富的意义空间来。

# 孔孟学说的贵族文化性格及其当代意义

集美大学　肖仕平

## 一

立足于当代西方世界，法国社会学家皮埃尔·布迪厄（Piere Bourdieu）所著的《区隔：趣味判断的社会批判》总结了这样的社会法则：不同阶级的成员总会进入到不同品味的场域，通过自己的生活方式和消费行为，展现他有形或无形社会等级和社会位置。[①] 布迪厄分析的对象是当代西方社会，但如果将它的观点用以思考中国文化史上的现象，也是有相当启发的。我们看到，布迪厄关于不同阶层有着互异的文化品位的观点，可以在中国文化史上得到印证，中国西周时期的上层社会的生活样态尤其生动而强烈地体现出布迪厄的观点。

《礼记》的不少文篇描述西周时期上层贵族的生活面貌，《礼记·内则》说：

子能食食，教以右手。能言，男唯女余。男鞶革，女鞶丝。六年，教之数与方名。七年，男女不同席，不共食。八年，出入门户，及席饮食，必后长者，始教之让。九年，教之数日。十年，出就外传，居宿于外，学书计。衣不帛襦袴。礼帅初，朝夕学幼仪，请肄简谅。十有三年，学乐，诵诗，舞《勺》。成童，舞象，学射御。二十而冠，始学礼，可以衣裘帛，舞《大夏》，惇行孝弟博学不教，内而不出……女子十年不出，姆教婉娩听从，执麻枲，治丝划茧，织纴组纠，学女事，以共衣服。观于祭祀，纳酒、浆、笾、豆、菹、醢，礼相助奠。十有五而笄。二十而嫁，有故，二十三而嫁。聘则为妻，奔则为妾。凡女拜，尚右手。

根据以上一段说话，我们看到西周时期上层社会的贵族要接受精致的文化教养：在幼儿能吃饭时，即教其用右手，学说话时，教男孩说“唯”，教女孩说“俞”，分别给男孩和女孩佩戴皮革制的和丝制的小囊；孩子六岁时，教其识数和辨认方向；七岁

---

① Piere Bourdieu. Distinction ; A Social Critique of th Judgement of Taste ; Harvard University Press，1984.

时，男女分席而坐，分别吃饭；八岁时，教孩子出门、进门，以及就席吃饭，学会敬长和谦让；九岁时，教其计算日期；十岁时男孩出外求学，住宿于外，学习写字和记事，不穿帛制的衣裤，遵循在家学得的谦让之礼，每天又学习初级的礼仪；十三岁时，学习音乐，诵读诗篇，习《勺》舞；成童时，习《象》舞，并学习射箭、驾车；二十岁时举行冠礼，开始学正式的礼，穿皮和帛制的衣服，习《大夏》舞等等。而女孩十岁以后就不再出门，由傅姆教她温婉柔顺、听从尊长的教诲，教以纺麻织布，煮茧缫丝等女工，并教她们观察祭祀，学习捧入酒、浆、笾、豆、菹、醢等祭品和祭器，按照祭礼的要求帮助大人放置祭品和祭器，年十五行加笄礼……

西周早期的教育文武不分，《内则》所谓“学射御”即为武事，但随文明的发展，其“文”的色彩与日俱增。《礼记·王制》说称乐正“顺先王诗、书、礼、乐以造士，春秋教以礼乐，冬夏教以诗书”，《礼记·文王世子》说：“瞽宗秋学礼，执礼者诏之；冬读书，典书者诏之。”礼乐是维系贵族社会的纽带，为贵族所必须掌握，诗书则与礼乐是相辅相成的。这样，经长期而严格的诗、书、礼、乐教育，熏陶出了贵族阶级崇尚诗书，讲求礼乐的那种精致优雅的风貌，延及春秋时期，此种贵族精神风貌依然突出，对此，我们可以从《左传》的情节中加以感受。

我们先看诗、书。春秋时期，了解诗书以及对诗书的熟悉程度，成了贵族是否具备他们所属社会阶层所应有的品味的一个标准。当时各诸侯国在政治上和外交上的来往，贵族平时的各种社交活动往往用诗书来应对。具体就《左传》的记载看，就诗而论，贵族在朝聘、会盟、宴会等场合中，往往引诗述怀，赋诗喻志，乃至借诗冷嘲热讽、钩心斗角。如《左传·昭公十六年》记载：韩起离别郑国时，郑国六卿为他饯行，行前韩起请求六卿赋诗，于是，子齹赋《野有蔓草》，子产赋《羔裘》，子太叔赋《褰裳》，子游赋《风雨》，子旗赋《有女同车》，子柳赋《萚兮》。韩起听完六人赋诗之后，大赞郑国，称道：“郑其庶乎！二三君子以君命贶起，赋不出郑志，皆昵燕好也。二三君子，数世之主也，可以无惧矣。”之后还献马还礼，又对赋《我将》一首。昭公十六年离左传纪年结束的时间还有三十多年，这里记载着故事当时的贵族如何根据场合，根据听者的具体情况选择合适的诗篇，如何优雅地将其诵咏出来，而作为听者，又如何通过诗句及其诵咏理解赋诗者的心志和感情并做出得体的反应，如何揖让进退，做出恰当评价，这些是贵族之间交往方式生动写照。

就书而论，贵族也常常引书之文句或说明已见，或驳斥对手。《左传·僖公二十七年》载：晋文公要找一位元帅，赵衰对他说：“郤縠可，臣亟闻其言，说礼乐而敦诗书。诗书，义之府也……君其试之。”对诗书的熟知成了郤縠能被举荐为元帅一个原因，这大概是《左传》记载的最能反映贵族社会崇尚诗书的例子了。

我们再看礼乐，在西周春秋的贵族社会，礼乐涉及贵族生活的各个方面，构成了他们生活的重要内容。《礼记·昏义》说："夫礼，始于冠，本于昏，重于丧、祭，尊于朝、聘，和于乡、射，此礼之大体。"如前所述，贵族从孩提时代起就需要接受行为细节方面的教育，他们的面貌神色、穿戴配饰、举手投足、聘问交游、宴享嬉戏以至言谈歌咏都当循礼仪的要求，当时的贵族如果不懂礼，或有越礼的行为，都会被嘲笑，甚至引来争斗杀伐，春秋时期的外交斗争就有不少就是在礼的名义下展开的。所以《左传·昭公七年》载：

"九月，公至自楚。孟僖子病不能相礼，乃讲学之，苟能礼者从之。及其将死也，召其大夫，曰：'礼，人之干也。无礼，无以立。吾闻将有达者曰孔丘，圣人之后也，而灭于宋。……臧叔纥有言曰："圣人有明德者，若不当世，其后必有达人。"今其将在孔丘乎？我若获没，必属说与何忌于夫子，使事之，而学礼焉，以定其位。'故孟懿子与南宫敬叔师事仲尼。"

这位孟僖子是鲁国掌握实权的三大贵族（即"三桓"）之一，鲁昭公七年，他曾陪昭公到楚国参加诸侯会盟，担任相礼之职，结果却不能胜任引起列国耻笑。那次的教训使他要遍访知礼者，以求深造。昭公二十四年，孟僖子卒前，又安排自己的两个儿子向孔子学礼。这个事例很能说明礼乐对贵族确立其社会地位、形象的重要意义。

## 二

春秋后期，贵族阶级崇尚诗书，讲求礼乐的那种精致优雅的精神风貌随着春秋贵族社会的瓦解而开始衰落。钱穆先生在《国史大纲》中评价说：

"春秋二百四十二年，一方面是一个极混乱嚣张的时期；但另一方面，则古代的贵族文化，实到春秋而发展到它的最高点。春秋时代常为后世所想慕与敬重。春秋时代，实可说是中国古代贵族文化已发展到一种极优美、极高尚、极细腻雅致的时代。"①

在经过春秋时期的充分展示之后，贵族精神风貌随着时代变迁而开始衰落。生活在春秋晚期的孔子则运时而生，他把这种贵族精神风貌引入自己的思想学说中，由此开启一种具有贵族文化性格的文化体系，这就是他开创的儒家思想体系。

孔子博学广知，本人又是贵族后裔，他盛赞周代贵族文化，声言："周监于二代，郁郁乎文哉，吾从周。"（《论语·八佾》）因此，就诗、书论，他不仅"雅言《诗》、《书》"（《论语·述而》），认为"人而不为《周南》、《召南》，其犹正墙面而立与？"（《论语·阳货》）而且把收集到的《诗》、断简残篇的《书》加以编排，传徒授学，称："不学《诗》，无以立。"（《论语·季氏》）"小子何莫学乎《诗》？"（《论语·阳货》）他

① 钱穆：《国史大纲》（上册），商务印书馆，1994年，第69页。

甚至还将《诗》、《书》用于诠释自己的思想主张，如《论语·八佾》中，子夏问《诗》："巧笑倩兮，美目盼兮，素以为绚兮。"孔子答："绘事后素。"就礼乐而论，孔子也倡导人们投入礼乐生活。《论语·宪问》说：

"子路问成人。子曰：'若臧武仲之知，公绰之不欲，卞庄子之勇，冉求之艺，文之以礼乐，亦可以为成人矣。'"

在这里，子路请教什么样才算成人。孔子的回答是，要有如臧武仲的智慧、孟公绰的寡欲、卞庄子的勇敢、冉求的才艺，最后还要加上礼乐之文饰，这样的人才称得上"成人"。

孔子在对怎样才是"成人"的这个回答时，提到要有"知"、"不欲"、"勇"和"艺"，孔子对四者的谈论都联系到具体的人物，但孔子最后又再加上礼乐，这说明，在孔子眼里，对于"成人"来说，"知"、"不欲"、"勇"和"艺"都应具备，但"礼乐"是最基本，最起点的要求，单有前四者却没有礼乐，那一切都无从谈起。因此孔子坚称："君子博我以文，约我以礼。"（《论语·雍也》）

由此可见，贵族以谈诗书为时尚，孔子同样喜好诗书；贵族讲求礼乐，孔子亦重视礼仪。总的来说，孔子欣赏一种诗书兼备、彬彬有礼、温文尔雅的人格类型，孔子通过思想学说极力提倡养育此种人格。显然，孔子的见解契合于贵族社会的思想品味。

## 三

孔子学说里有上述内容，然作为一个有创见性的思想家，他并非局限于对贵族行为、思想的亦步亦趋地、刻意地逢迎上，他理论里还具有一种春秋贵族未曾触及，但却又是可以溯源于贵族意识的独特思想，这种思想的提出使孔子学说所蕴含的贵族精神和文化性格更显现出来，也正是因为有这种思想，孔子才是被德国哲学家雅斯贝尔斯提出的"轴心时代"的伟大的精神导师。在孔子那里，这是一种什么样的思想呢？

西周春秋时期，习惯于贵族生活方式的社会上层自认为自己有君子风度，故他们明确地将自己和平民区别开来。他们认为，平民不具有自我道德约束力，应是法刑管制的对象，而自己不同于平民，他们本已有靠礼仪教育形成的内在涵养，故他们是毋需法刑的，《礼记·曲礼》"礼不下庶人，刑不上大夫"之说正是这种思想的产物。孔子对当时"礼不下庶人，刑不上大夫"观念的回应很特别。

《孔子家语·五刑解》里，孔子的学生冉有问孔子："先王制法，使刑不上大夫，礼不下庶人，然则大夫犯罪不可加以刑，庶人之行事不可治于礼乎？"孔了回答：

不然。凡治君子，以御其心，所以厉之以廉耻之节也。故古之大夫，有坐不廉污秽而退放之者，不谓之不廉污秽而退放，则曰簠簋不伤；有坐淫乱男女无别者，不谓之淫乱男女无别，则曰帷幕不修也；有坐罔上不忠者，不谓之罔上不忠，则曰臣节未著；有坐罢软不胜任者，不谓之罢软不胜任，则曰下官不职；有坐干国之纪者，不谓之干国之纪，则曰行事不请。此五者，大夫既自定有罪名矣，而犹不忍斥然正以呼之也。既而为之讳，所以愧耻之。是故大夫之罪，其在五刑之域者，闻而谴发，则白冠釐缨，盘水加剑，造乎阙而自请罪，君不使有司执缚牵掣而加之也。[①]

这段回答的要点是，大夫犯有贪污、淫乱、不忠、废政软弱、干犯国纪等五种罪过时，不直呼其罪名，而以委婉之名代之，分别叫作“簠簋不饬”—— 簠簋这两种器具没有修饬好；“帷幕不修”——帷幕没有修饰清；“臣节未著”——臣节没有得到彰显；“下官不职”——下官没有胜任职务；“行事不请”——行事不擅行，以此让犯罪者感到自愧自耻。对那些需要给予惩处的大夫则以“白冠釐缨”——让触犯五刑的大夫戴上用兽尾作缨的白帽，表示自己有罪，“盘水加剑”——在盛了清水盘子上横放利剑使大夫本人自感愧耻然后自裁。

如果考虑到《孔子家语》成书较晚，前段文字有可能为后人伪托，那么在《左传》里还可以找到另外一则能同样显示孔子思想的文字。昭公二十九年，晋国赵鞅铸刑鼎，孔子大为不满，他说：

“晋其亡乎！失其度矣。……今弃其度，而为刑鼎，民在鼎矣，何以尊贵？贵何业之守？贵贱无序，何以为国?”（《左传·昭公二十九年》）

铸刑鼎明确使“民在鼎矣”，这含有在刑法面前贵族和平民一律平等的意味，以往的“刑不上大夫”被这里的刑可上大夫的见解所代替。孔子反对铸刑鼎，他认同“刑不上大夫”。前文已言，贵族讲的是风度、内在涵养，故他们对法刑不以为然，而在这里，孔子也不屑于谈论法刑，然而相比于当时贵族的看法，孔子思想是有创发性的，他不只是期待人们通过礼的操持提升涵养，他更注重人本有的内在德性，主张人依靠对自我心性的挖掘和提升，获得道德自觉，以此养成人格，造就风度。

当子夏问及对“巧兮倩兮，美目盼兮，素以为绚兮”的理解时，孔子答：“绘事后素。”以为正如先有白绢才能作画一样，礼应是内心情感的表达。同样的思想在孔子对守丧三年之礼的解释中讲得更直接，《论语·阳货》载：

“宰我问：‘三年之丧，期已久矣。君子三年不为礼，礼必坏；三年不为乐，乐必崩。旧谷既没，新谷既升，钻燧改火，期可已矣。’子曰：‘食夫稻，衣夫锦，于女安乎?’曰：‘安。’‘女安，则为之！夫君子之居丧，食旨不甘，闻乐不乐，居不安，故不为也。今女安，则为之！’宰我出，子曰：‘予之不仁也！子生三年，然后免于父母之怀。夫三年之丧，天下之通丧也。予也有三年之爱于其父母乎?’”

① 王肃撰：《孔子家语》，辽宁教育出版社，1997年，第80页。

“三年之丧”之所以成为“天下之通丧”，这源于“子生三年，然后免于父母之怀”的经历在人们情感世界积淀成的对亲长的感怀之情。在这里，礼的规范意被孔子淡化了，体现为丧礼的这种孝成了血亲之爱，即人本有之“仁”的心理流露，贵族原来被要求的对礼的遵循，在这里成了心性问题，孔子把礼看作是人际亲情的自然引申，由此他实现了对以往贵族文化的超越。对比之下，否定法刑，讲求通过礼的教养提升涵养，达到自我约束，这是贵族的思想观念；而孔子否定法刑，要求心性完善，成就君子风度，这也当是孔子思想的贵族文化性格的体现。与当时普遍的贵族观念相比，孔子学说超越之处在于，孔子立足于新的思想起点——心性问题提出贵族君子风度的培养。

《论语》称孔子“有教无类”，的确，孔子打破以往上层社会对文化的独享，去掉贵族文化对血缘、身份的讲求，把教育面向普通大众，广泛传播礼乐文化，但他崇奉诗书，讲求礼乐教养，这依然展示出其思想上的贵族性，更重要的是，孔子倡导人们通过心性追求培养起特殊的人格风范，“今之学者为己”（《论语·宪问》），成为心性上的贵族，可见，孔子学说不是简单地承袭西周贵族文化，而是提炼和升华了原有的贵族文化，在这种升华之中，他的学说不仅没有丧失，反而具备更浓烈的贵族精神和气概——有了一种思想上的贵族气质。

## 四

我们再看孟子。

同孔子，他的思想亦带有贵族性。由传本《孟子》看，《诗》、《书》中的文句常常为孟子引用，《孟子》一文令人印象深刻的是孟子口齿犀利的雄辩，在众多回合的辩论中，孟子经常对《诗》、《书》脱口而出，出奇制胜。如同孔子，孟子也要求成就礼仪与德性兼备的君子。孟子说：

“君子所以异于人者。以其存心也。君子以仁存心，以礼存心。仁者爱人，有礼者敬人。……非仁无为也，非礼尢为也，若有一朝之患，则君子不患矣。”（《孟子·离娄上》）

以往贵族讲求通过礼的规范以提升涵养，孔子转而主张依靠对人心性的挖掘，培育的君子风度。在孟子那里，这种心性追求则成了他思想的中心，也构成了他的理论创新点。

上文谈到孔子从人际亲情引申出“三年之丧”，孟子之时，亦有一个叫夷子的人被评为“葬其亲厚”，“葬其亲厚”是对夷子在葬亲时合“礼”做法的描述，对于夷子的行为，孟子评论和发挥说：

"盖上世尝有不葬其亲者。其亲死，则举而委之于壑。他日过之，狐狸食之，蝇蚋咕嘬之，其颡有泚，睨而不见。夫泚也，非为人泚，中心达于面目，盖反蘽梩而掩之。掩之诚是也，则孝子仁人之掩其亲，亦必有道矣。"（《孟子·滕文公上》）

由将死去的亲人"举而委之于壑"，发展到"掩之"，孟子以为，这种丧葬之礼的形成也是由发自内心而显于面目的自然亲情所促成的。

孟子强调人的自然情感，在此基础上，他比起孔子又迈进了一步，他认人性为善，提出性善论：

"人皆有不忍人之心。"（《孟子·公孙丑上》）

"恻隐之心，人皆有之；羞恶之心，人皆有之；恭敬之心，人皆有之；是非之心，人皆有之。恻隐之心，仁也；羞恶之心，义也；恭敬之心，礼也；是非之心智也。仁义礼智，非由外铄我也，我固有之也，弗思耳矣。"（《孟子·告子上》）

在他看来，"人皆有不忍人之心"，"恻隐之心"、"羞恶之心"、"恭敬之心"和"是非之心"是"人皆有之"的四"心"，按照他的说法，先天之善成了普遍存在的、具体的生命个体无由回避的本性。孔子心性追求的思想主张凸现了儒学的贵族精神气息，对比而言，孟子的这种性善论理论则是儒家学说所蕴含贵族精神最极致的表现。

为什么说性善论是儒家学说所蕴含的贵族精神最极致的表现呢？为了说明这一点，我们不妨先行挖掘孟子性善论的深刻内涵。香港学者劳思光先生曾这样评论孟子的性善论：

"孟子之言"性"，实指人之'Essence'而言（注意，此处所说之"Essence"乃依亚里士多德之法——作者原注）。孟子认为，人与其他存在有一不同条件，此条件称之为人之'性'。而此条件非它，即有'价值自觉'是。人之'性'为'有价值自觉'，因'有价值自觉'乃人之心灵所独具的条件，换言之，价值自觉为人之Essence。……性善论所言之'性'，与通常所谓生而具有之'性'，截然不同。盖孟子之'性'取本质义，非通常以人之初生时所具之本能为'性'，是事实义。"①

劳思光先生以为孟子的"性"取的是"本质义"，非"事实义"，他对孟子性善论定性恰当，评价精到，但问题是，何以孟子不以"事实义"，而非要以"本质义"来谈"性"呢？

孔子以来的儒家立意于心性贵族的造就、道德君子的培养，他们确信人是可以通过心性修养获得对肉体生命的超越的，而且，也唯有实现这种生命超越的理想人物才是不枉费生命的人。既此，在厘定人的本质时，他们就不能不以"本质义"，即是否具备德性作为标准来评价、判别人，他们不理会现实中的芸芸众生生具有的种种生理欲

---

① 劳思光：《中国哲学史》（卷一），台北：三民书局，1982年，第278页。

求和实际生存现实，而是以更高的德行标准来拔擢人，提升人。这样的思考便决定了他们最终要在超越经验的层面上去评定人，并断定只有德性才是人区隔于物的特质。孟子由这条思路出发来构作人性理论，“善”就被顺理成章地看作是人之为人的本质规定了。

弄明了孟子的这条思路，我们就不难弄懂性善论是儒家学说所蕴含贵族精神最极致的表现这个结论了。周作人曾说：

“平民的精神可以说是淑本好耳（即叔本华——笔者注）所说的求生意志，贵族的精神便是尼采所说的求胜意志了。前者是要求有限的平凡的存在，后者是要求无限的超越的发展；前者完全是入世的，后者却几乎有点出世的了。”①

这段文字言说精当，平民精神要求“有限的平凡的存在”，贵族精神“要求无限的超越的发展”，杨春时先生曾对此分析：“这里把贵族精神确定为自由的超越精神，……贵族精神肯定精神的自由和人格的高贵。”② 结合这些评论我们分析孟子提出性善论的思路。

实际上，孟子在事实层面也是肯定“人之所以异于禽兽者几希”（《孟子·离娄下》）的，孟子知晓人同动物一样具有自然本性和种种生理欲求，但他却不以人生而具有的自然本性谈论人的本质，他寻求用超越事实层面的“价值自觉”去设定人，从而以“善”为人之“性”。如此可见，孟子弃绝囿于感性和生理层面对人的描述，因为确信人是可以通过心性修养获得对肉体生命的超越的，所以他就直接从超越的层面来理解人，因此可以说，孟子首先抓住的就是人的“精神的自由和人格的高贵”，徐复观先生在《中国人性论史》中的一段评论所言甚确，他说：

“孟子性善之说，是人对自身惊天动地的伟大发现……有了这一伟大发现之后，每一个人的自身，即是一个宇宙，即是一个普遍，即是一个永恒。可以透过一个人的性，一个人的心，以看出人类的命运，掌握人类的命运，解决人类的命运。每一个人即在他的性、心的自觉中，得到无待外求、圆满自足的安顿，更用不上在夸父追日似的在物质生活中，在精神陶醉中去寻求安顿。”③

孟子在意和抓住人“精神的自由和人格的高贵”，而对照周作人、杨春时有关贵族精神的说法，显然，孟子的性善论当然是最极致地表现了儒家学说的贵族精神。

通过以上所论，可以认为，孟子思想的贵族文化性格色彩是鲜明的，如果说孔孟之间存在差别的话，那么可以说，孔子提出心性问题，让人借此养成君子风度，孟子

---

① 周作人：《贵族的与平民的》，载周作人著《自己的园地》，岳麓书社，1987年，第22页。

② 杨春时：《贵族精神和现代性批判》，《厦门大学学报》，2005年第3期。

③ 徐复观：《中国人性论史》（先秦篇），上海三联书店，1993年，第159页。

则以性善论深化了儒家的心性理论，从而使早期儒学的贵族精神最极致地表现出来。

要言之，孔孟的思想目标是一致的，对比孔孟，孟子借性善说为孔子养育君子人格的思想确立人性论理论基础。如果说，孔子崇奉诗书，讲求礼乐教养，尤其是成就人格德性之说都不乏鲜明的贵族情结，因而孔子学说有着贵族文化性格的话，那么，孟子的性善说则大大凸显了创建之初的儒学的这种文化性格。

## 五

孔子倡导人们通过心性追求培养起特殊的人格风范，在思想风貌上体现出浓烈的贵族气质，孟子继而以性善论深化了儒家的心性理论，从而使早期儒学的贵族精神最极致地表现出来。

在文化上，贵族性格和平民性格相对，前者产生于贵族高贵、世袭的社会地位和生活方式。贵族享受世卿世禄，衣食无忧，细腻雅致，淡泊功利，从而形成了他们对礼乐仪法的重视，心性问题的关注和超越世俗的精神追求，孔子的儒家思想就是由对周代贵族这样一种文化传统总结、提炼和升华而来的。历史以来，具有这种贵族性格的儒家文化重视德性，讲求礼仪，注重心性，挖掘人性之善，彰扬了高雅的生活格调和超越和崇高的生命追求。

孔孟开启的儒家传统源远流长，在中国传统的思想谱系里，儒学思想无疑是最具贵族文化性格的了。同样，中国传统以来的不少思想家推进儒学发展，也伴随着对儒学贵族文化性格的再洗练。儒学经秦火之厄，历汉代经学之兴起，魏晋玄学之显扬，及佛学之大盛，终从唐朝渐有复兴，步入佳境，在宋明展现出新局，我们宋明看到，诸儒的思想重心都是在讲求礼仪，注重心性，挖掘人性之善上，正因如此，所以才有《大学》、《中庸》被确定为进学之阶，才有“天地之性”、“气质之性”，“人心”、“道心”的辨证；才有对“致良知”的顿悟……

斗转星移，构作先秦汉初儒学的时代已远去，但讨论儒家的文化性格对我们当代文化的建设无疑是有启发意义的。

处于现实中的社会大众有其功利性、世俗性的一面，但就可能性言，人又是具备理想性、超越性的。功利性和世俗性、理想性和超越性构成了现实社会大众发展的两个面向，其中的功利性和世俗性显示的是平民性格，而理想性和超越性则是贵族性格。儒家文化重视德性，讲求礼仪，注重心性，挖掘人性之善，体现了高雅、超越和崇高的生命追求，练就出一种理想性和超越性的追求。

回顾长期以来的文化建设，也是因为现代以来的社会结构的变迁，较长时间里，我们对具贵族文化性格的礼乐仪法、典雅风范、情趣心性等等不以为意，而对更彰显世俗性的文化面向有较多的推重。最近三十多年来，中国与世界接轨，我们又置身于一个文化多元的时代，在这个文化多元化的时代里，因有广泛的覆盖面和巨大的影响力，所以大众文化流行开来，但大众文化的一般方向是世俗性、功利性以及消费性的，具有浓厚的平民文化性格，这样的大众文化当然有其价值，在市场经济极大地解放出人的感官欲望的今天尤为如此，它符合社会大众的普遍和基本的需求，问题在于，一个民族不能完全陷于世俗性、消费性、功利性，否则，社会易流于庸俗，文化生命易于枯萎。为此，一个社会应当重视具备贵族文化精神的思想资源的开发，追求高尚的精神生活，汲取贵族精神，建设贵族文化。以贵族文化的高雅性、超越性和精神性成为大众文化的制约力量。

回望传统，儒家思想就为我们的文化重建提供了启发。抚平近代以来民族历史的创痛，呼唤传统的贵族文化，有助于中华民族文化的当代建设！

# 礼乐：中国传统文化之心

清华大学 彭 林

1963 年 7 月，美国学者邓尔麟前往台北拜访著名史学家钱穆先生，教中国文化的有关请益。钱先生指出，中国文化可以归结为一个“礼”字，这是中西文化相区别的关键之所在。他说，“在西方语言中没有‘礼’的同义词。它是整个中国人世界里一切习俗行为的准则，标志着中国的特殊性”，“中国人之所以成为民族，因为‘礼’为全中国人民树立了社会关系准则”；“要了解中国文化必须站得更高来看到中国之心。中国的核心思想就是礼”。① 钱先生的论述非常精辟，不如此看问题，就无法从总体上把握中国文化的精神。

## 一、周公“制礼作乐”是历史的选择

以礼乐为一国文化的核心，在全世界堪称独一无二。中国人之所以走上这样一条道路，有其深刻的历史原因。

在洪荒时代，人类为了生存，首要的任务是解决物质需求，于是，人类渐次发明了农业。两河流域的居民最早培育成功了小麦和大麦，中国人最早培育成功了小米和大米，印第安人则最早培育成功了玉米。这是农业文明的三大发祥地。中国地域辽阔，小米是中国北方旱作农业的产物，大米则是南方稻作农业的产物。考古学家在河北武安的磁山遗址，以及浙江余姚的河姆渡遗址，分别发现了小米与大米的遗存，数量都达十几万斤。两个遗址的年代，都是距今七千年，证明南北两大农业文明发煌甚早。它们经过几千年的交流与融合，汇合成为夏朝的青铜文明。又经过四百年进入商朝，物质文化进一步发展，青铜文明臻于鼎盛，社会生活进入繁荣期，

中国传统文化是礼乐文化，通常省称为礼。认识礼乐文化，要从周公“制礼作乐”说起。历史上的殷、周两朝，性质判然有别：“殷人尊神，率民以事神，先鬼而后礼。”

---

① 邓尔麟：《钱穆与七房桥世界》，社会科学文献出版社，1995 年，第 7 页。

（《礼记·表记》）殷代的青铜文化高度发达，可惜迷信鬼神，怠于民生，尤其到了纣王，更是自信有天佑神助，过着酒池肉林的糜烂生活，并用酷刑镇压反抗者，激起天怨人怒。

周武王顺应民意，在牧野与纣王决战，腐朽的商王顷刻覆亡。武王克商不是以暴易暴，而是一场全新的革命。西周初建不久，武王撒手人寰；继位的成王尚在襁褓之中，不能亲政。周公摄政临朝，开创了他的以道德为灵魂的新政，制定了一套体现道德理性的典章制度，史称周公“制礼作乐”。著名学者王国维先生说，“中国政治与文化的变革，莫剧于殷、周之际”；周公制礼作乐，是“旧制度废而新制度兴”，具有划时代的意义；“其旨则在纳上下于道德，而合天子、诸侯、卿、大夫、士、庶民以成一道德之团体”，“周代之制度典礼，实皆为道德而设”。[1] 中国礼乐文化的底蕴由此奠定，其后经过孔子的提倡，用礼乐化民成俗，成为古代中国经邦治国的基本模式。

## 二、礼乐文化的学理

一个国家、一个民族，人口众多，人的性格、好恶、习性各异。人有精神家园，人的思维活动极其活跃，如何凝聚人心、管理民众，是社会发展的最大课题。国家不同，文化传统不同，管理模式也就不同。世界上有相当一部分国家依靠宗教管理社会，如阿拉伯地区主要以伊斯兰教的教义治国；印度曾经以佛教思想治国，欧美地区则主要以基督教的教义统一民心。这些地区的文化，都以神为中心。例如基督教文化中，有一个无所不在、无所不能的上帝在主宰一切。《圣经》说，每个人的心灵里都有邪恶，没有一刻不想做坏事，所以人性是恶的。这邪恶是与生俱来的，不学就会，不教而能的，尽人皆然，故称之为“原罪”。这种邪恶如果得不到抑止，人就会无恶不作，最后成为恶魔，被打入地狱，永世不得翻身。只有基督的血，才能洗涮你的灵魂。为此，人要把灵魂交给上帝管理，每天祷告，做错了事要忏悔，若是一错再错，则要受到法律的惩处。

中国文化是以人为中心的文化。几千年来，中国人坚信天地之间有道德，有公理，有正义，得道多助，失道寡助，相信人有良知，人性本善。在中国文化里，人的灵魂是要由自己来管理的，通过终身的道德修为，可以成为君子，甚至成圣成贤。道德是抽象的范畴，如同空气，看不见，摸不着，无色无臭，但它确实存在，不言而喻，如果长时间失去它，就会出大问题。《礼记》说：“礼者，理之不可易者也。”礼是根据道德理性的要求制定出来的制度与规范，是道德理性的体现，遵守礼，就是遵循道德理

---

① 王国维：《观堂集林》卷十，《殷周制度论》，中华书局，1959年。

性，两者是一而二，二而一的关系。

儒家的任何理念都是通过礼来展现的，他们不是空喊道德理想，而是把它融化、落实到社会生活的每个层面上。离开了礼，中国文化就成了空谈。试看：

中国人的理想社会是天下为公的大同世界，有关的权威表述，是在《礼记》的《礼运》篇，可见是属于礼的范围。国家的典章制度称为礼制，建立一个好的国家制度叫“制礼作乐”，这个制度破坏了，就叫“礼崩乐坏”。

人如何自处，人生如何度过，更是礼的重点之一。人生是漫长的，但关键之点只有几个。在人生的关键点上，寓教于礼，通过“人生礼仪”来进行人生教育，是中国礼义文化的重要特色。例如，在男子年满二十岁时，为之举行成年礼，教育孩子从此负起对家庭和社会的责任；在孩子结婚时，为之举办婚礼，教给懂得他们“合二姓之好”的道理。在亲人逝世之后，举行丧祭之礼以表哀思，教育后人慎终追远。如此等等。在学习和践行礼的过程中涵养德性，变化气质，涵养德性。

下面我们来看乐。

音乐是全人类共有的文化现象，凡是文明达到某种高度，音乐便随之产生。对于世界绝大多数民族而言，音乐的功用是表达情感，主要是娱乐，娱己或者娱神。但音乐到了中国人手里，却成为最好的教化工具。

儒家认为，乐由心生。人不能没有快乐，因而就一定会有音乐。音乐是人的心声的流露，与人心的关系最为密切。今人所说的音乐，儒家分解为声、音、乐三个层次。声的层次最低，是指各种自然界的声响，或者是低级的人为之声，其特点是没有内在的乐理，没有审美价值。第二个层次是音，相当于今人所说的“音乐”。人比动物高明的地方在于，人能够发现包括七声音阶、十二律、调门、旋律等在内乐理，然后创做出各种风格的乐曲，借此表达内心丰富而复杂的情感，这一点只有人才能做到，禽兽则只能感知各种声，所以《礼记·乐记》说：“禽兽知声而不知音。”

音包罗万象，其中既有健康的，也有不健康的；既有清新向上的，也有颓废消沉的；它们取决于作曲者的心境、情趣、格调等因素。曲子一经表演，就会给听者之心以直接的影响，既可能是正面的，也可能是负面的。负面影响累积到一定程度，轻则损害自己的人生，重则会造成亡国之灾，据司马迁的《史记·殷本纪》记载，促使商纣王腐败覆亡的因素中就有音乐，他曾命令一位叫师涓的乐官“作新淫声，北里之舞，靡靡之乐”。到春秋时期，这种淫声在郑卫之地依然存在，人们称之为“亡国之音”。因此，分辨音的好坏，让民众多听高雅的音乐，远离颓废暴虐的音乐，意义极为重大。为此，要儒家将“音”进一步区分，把其中内容纯正健康、风格庄重典雅，能够起到道德教化作用的部分称之为“乐”。乐是音当中最优秀的部分，既有共性，又有差别，所以《乐记》说：“乐与音相近而不同。”又说：“德音之谓乐。”这一区分，普通人由于受教育的程度不足，很难理解。唯有洞察乐理的人方能明白，所以《乐记》说：“众庶知音而不知乐。”“惟君子为能知乐。”

古人所说的乐，通常包括歌词与舞蹈在内。歌词就是诗。流传至今的《诗经》原本都配有曲子。相传《诗经》三百篇，是孔子从众多的诗篇中挑选出来的，孔子用它做教材，教育弟子。《诗经》的核心价值在于，把人们的心性引导到正确的轨道上。《论语·八佾》引孔子的话说：“《关雎》乐而不淫，哀而不伤。”朱子《论语集注》解释说：“淫者，乐之过而失其正者也。伤者哀之过而害于和者也。……有以识其性情之正也。”“《诗》本性情，有邪有正。其为言既易知，而吟咏之间，抑扬反复，其感人又易入。故学者之初，所以兴起其好善恶恶之心而不能自已者，必于此而得之。”可见，《诗》教之旨在导性情、心志之正。所以《毛诗序》说：“发乎情，止乎礼义。发乎情，民之性也。止乎礼义，先王之泽也。”真是精辟之极。

礼与乐的作用，各有侧重，湖北荆门郭店出土的楚国竹书说：“礼，外也。乐，内也。礼、乐，共也。”就是说，礼旨在规范人的外在行为；乐，旨在端正人的心志。两者一起抓，则可内外兼修，成就你的君子风范。

古人把礼、乐、政、刑作为治国经邦的大经大法。《礼记·乐记》说：“礼以道其志，乐以和其声，政以一其行，刑以防其奸。”礼、乐是治国的方针与内涵。政，指行政系统，是推行礼、乐的组织机构。刑，是惩处破坏礼乐教育的害群之马的手段。所以，《礼记》又说：“礼、乐、刑、政，四达而不悖，则王道备矣。”

《乐记》亟言礼乐的重要，屡屡以天地相比喻：“乐由天作，礼以地制。”“大乐与天地同和，大礼与天地同节。”认为只有功成治定的王者，才配制礼作乐：“王者功成作乐，治定制礼。其功大者其乐备，其治辩者其礼具。”

## 三、礼乐的人文内涵

如何经邦治国，最主要的意见有两种：法治或德治。孔子主张德治，认为法治只能安定于一时，德治方能长治久安，他说：“道之以政，齐之以刑，民免而无耻。道之以德，齐之以礼，有耻且格。”① 用行政手段来引导民众，用刑罚来整齐他们，民众都远离了刑罚，但他们的羞耻之心并没有树立起来。如果用道德来引导民众，用礼来整齐他们，民众不但树立起了羞耻心，不仅能远离刑罚，而且有上进心。有人认为儒家，只讲礼治，反对法治，其实儒家断然不会迂腐到这种程度。儒家反对不教而诛，而是主张德主刑辅，“礼用之于未然之先，法施之已然之后”。礼的作用是在教育，法的作

① 《论语·为政》。

用是在防范。礼是提振社会向上的引绳，法是维护社会安定的底线，不能用底线来替代人格标准。秦二世而亡的历史证明，仅仅依靠法律手段，不可能根本解决社会矛盾，也不可能造就社会的真正和谐。

礼是为政者不可须臾或离的大经大法，这并非孔子的独创。我们读《左传》可知，早在孔子之前，它就已经成为许多社会贤达的共识：如“礼，经国家、定社稷、序民人、利后嗣者也”（隐公十一年）；“礼，国之干也（僖公十一年）”；“礼，政之舆也（襄公21年）”；“礼，王之大经也（昭公十五年）”；“礼，身之干也。（成公十三年）”；等等。

对于个体而言，礼乐双修旨在引导人内外兼善。《礼记·曲礼》说：“修身践言，谓之善行。行修言道，礼之质也。”《荀子·修身》说“礼者，所以正身也”。儒家所说的修身，必须是内外兼具的，既要把握礼的内涵与形式，又要把握“质”与“文”的关系，做到形神兼备，内外一致。

礼有形式与内涵两大要素。形式或称为仪式，是为表达礼的内涵服务的。内涵是礼的灵魂，是制订仪式的依据。举行某个礼仪，为什么要在这样的场所、穿这样的服饰、用这样的器物、走这样的程序、说这样的语言？其背后都有深刻的寓意，而不是随心所欲的。礼的外在形式比较直观，容易引起注意；礼的内涵难以把握，容易为人忽略。礼一旦失去了内涵，仪式再完美，也没有实际意义。春秋乱世，纲纪颓败，弑篡成风，司马迁说：“《春秋》之中，弑君三十六，亡国五十二，诸侯奔走不得保其社稷者不可胜数。[①]”这些篡位的君主丧心病狂，廉耻全无，但是，他们照样把各种仪式做得非常体面。孔子用反诘的语气质问道：“礼云礼云，玉帛云乎哉！乐云乐云，钟鼓云乎哉！”[②] 礼啊礼啊，难道就是供桌上的玉器与丝帛吗？乐啊乐啊，难道就是那些钟鼓之类的乐器吗？显然不是。

礼的主旨是培养人的博爱之心。爱，是人类的最高道德，无论是佛教、伊斯兰教，还是基督教，都以爱号召，以为标榜。儒家对爱的提倡，不亚于任何宗教。孔子希冀实现“天下为公”的“大同社会”，在孔子看来，这不是虚无缥缈的海外仙境，而是可以逐步接近的理想社会，而走向大同的途径，则是培养人的爱心。培养爱心，要从孝敬父母开始。父母给予自己生命，时刻呵护自己成长，血缘加上亲情，所以子女孝敬父母最为自然。但是，儒家提倡的孝行，并非局限于一家一户的狭隘亲情，而是要从它出发，把爱心推广到天下人的父母身上，因为“四海之内皆兄弟也”。只要人人都能推己及人，把爱心加于四海，就可以达到天下大治的目的，所以孟子说的“老吾老以

---

① 《史记·太史公自序》。

② 《论语·阳货》。

及人之老，幼吾幼以及人之幼，天下可运于掌”。[①] 孝行离不开礼，从父母的饮食起居到生老病死，每一个细节的体贴与关照，都要通过礼来体现和落实。只要每个家庭、每个人都这样做了，并且代代相传，大同世界就离我们越来越近。

礼的主旨是表达对他人的敬爱之心，《孝经》说：“礼者，敬而已矣”。礼是以对方的存在为前提，并且多多少少怀有一些敬意的。在孟子看来，有没有爱心，懂不懂得通过礼来传递爱心，是区别于君子与常人的主要标志：“君子所以异于人者，以其存心也。君子以仁存心，以礼存心。仁者爱人，有礼者敬人。爱人者，人恒爱之；敬人者，人恒敬之。”[②] 把仁放在心上，就会去爱人；把礼放在心上，就会去敬人。我以恭敬之心待人，同时也希望人以同样之心待我。人心相通，你爱他人，他人就会“恒爱之”；你敬他人，他人就会“恒敬之”；这就是民间常说的：“人敬我一尺，我敬人一丈。”儒家倡导用这样的方式来树立博爱的社会风气，实现社会的和谐。

儒家所说的爱是大爱，认为每个人都有人格尊严。有些人生活贫穷、社会地位低下，但这不一定是由于它自己的原因，对于这些属于弱势群体的人，同样要怀有敬意，《礼记》说：“夫礼者，自卑而尊人。虽负贩者，必有尊也，而况富贵乎？富贵而知好礼，则不骄不淫；贫贱而知好礼，则志不慑。”[③] 礼的原则是，对自己要自我谦卑，低调为人，但要尊重他人。即使是肩挑背负、沿街叫卖的小贩，也必定有尊严，都要以礼相待，何况富贵之人呢！富贵了而懂得好礼，就能做到不骄奢淫逸；贫贱而懂得好礼，心志就不会畏缩。

## 四、礼乐文明当代意义与普世价值

杨振宁先生说，人类在21世纪最伟大的事件，将是中华民族的复兴。一个民族的复兴，最重要的是文化的复兴，因为民族复兴离不开文化精神的引领。如果只有经济上的强大，文化上则是西方的附庸，那就表明我们民族已经被西方文化征服，离开西方文化，我们已经不会独立思考。因此，这种经济上的强大既不是严格意义上的民族复兴，也不可能持久。

中国正面临着百年不遇的发展机遇，处在国家发展的重要关口，我们理应冷静思考中华崛起中的文化问题，其核心则是如何建立“中国模式”？如果中华民族能向人类提供一种不同于西方文化的社会发展模式，并且用事实证明，不通过宗教，同样可以使社会走向和谐、博爱、正义，以及经济的高度繁荣，那将是古老的中华文明在21世

---

① 《孟子·梁惠王上》。
② 《孟子·离娄下》。
③ 《礼记·曲礼》。

纪对人类做出的最大贡献。

中华礼乐文明超越宗教文化，具有更大的普世价值，是东方文明的典范。在历史上，礼乐不仅成就了中华的灿烂文明，而且远播于朝鲜、日本、越南等地，推动了当地文明发展的进程。时至今日，礼乐文明是否还有存在的价值呢？回答是肯定的。礼乐文明对于当代社会的价值，至少有以下几点。

首先，礼乐文明有利于和谐社会的建设。近年，政府提出建设和谐社会的目标，与礼乐文明所要追求的目标完全一致。《论语》说："礼之用，和为贵。"《礼记》说："大乐与天地同和。"经典所说的"和"，就是今人所说的和谐，所以《说文解字》说："谐，和也。"儒家礼乐文明完全可以成为我们建设和谐社会的理论资源。

其次，礼乐文明有利于人心的和谐。实现和谐社会的基础，是人的和谐。人的和谐主要是身与心的和谐，只有每个社会成员的身心都和谐了，社会的和谐才能全面实现。儒家经典《中庸》《礼记》等，有关心性和谐的论述内涵相当丰富，论述极其深刻，我们理应充分吸收。

第三，礼乐文明有利于改变当今社会的无序状态。由于种种复杂的原因，当今的社会秩序存在不少乱象，最突出的是无序。要改变现状，最忌讳的是喊口号，说空话，落不到实处。礼乐文明强调有序，提倡礼让，并有许多具体而明确的规定，有很强的操作性，便于我们推广与使用。

第四，有利于树立中华的民族形象。改革开放以来，中国与海外的交流日益频繁，但是毋庸讳言，无论是内地的人文生态，还是去海外观光的游客，给外界的观感都比较差，从而损害了我们的民族形象，影响了我们的进一步发展。礼乐文明不仅可以帮助我们重塑民族形象，而且可以担当起中华文化领航者的角色，为东方文明走向世界做出更大贡献。

# 论儒学的普适性

国防大学　朱康有

“儒学在世界和平与发展中的作用和影响”，这样一个主题本身即蕴含了儒学一定程度上的普适性。作为全球化的主体，各民族和国家在相互交流乃至碰撞中，文明、文化的融合与冲突是深层次的交锋。为了解决价值观差异的死结，人类不得不多少次返回深入到支配其千百年的精神内核中，寻找历史的原典智慧。遗憾的是，当代世界主流的价值导向只是承认部分时空之域形成的知识模式，比如它认定西方近代以来提出的“自由、民主、人权”乃全人类都要走向的目标，即对任何国家和民族而言，这些内容都是普世的，甚至不惜强力推广和应用。而对于非西方民族长期以来积淀的智慧，则武断地根据物质性文明的进步标准，一概斥之为落后、封闭、反动、愚昧，认为其他文明不适合当今时代。建立在欲望、性和暴力基础上的近代西方工业化文明，就这样以其偏狭的理念，简单否定了人类历史长河中遗留下来的经验和智慧。

有必要区分一下“普适性”与“普世性”两个术语。前者是普遍的适用性，意味不仅在空间上亦在时间上能够“用”。其中的“适”，含有结合一定的时空、主客体条件来“用”，非简单地、机械地“搬用”。从字面意思看，后者更谓指空间的普遍使用，意味不论国家和民族，不论时代发展的阶段，皆可管用——我们从有些人惯用的“普世文明”、“普世价值”等字眼来看，似可作如此理解。吾以为，从哲学观念分析，“普适性”为与特殊性相对应的普遍性范畴的延伸性应用，价值中立且合法性强——你可以说，任何事物都是特殊性和普遍性的统一，为此它自有其不同于他者的个体性一面，亦有其共性的一面而彰显出特定空域和时域的“用”的存在合理性。但是，“普世性”抛弃了时域的因素、条件的选择、主客体的介入，单纯自外在强行进入，“放之四海而皆准”，则是一个虚假的概念，为此形成的所谓“普世文明”、“普世价值”亦是站不住的。我们可以说，西方近代文明有“普适”的一面，当然你也不能否认非西方文明亦没有“普适”的一面。正是立足于此，本文展开论述的儒学“普适性”便有了基石。

## 一、从“道”的规律性到“道义”的普适性

儒学追求的目标是什么？这里可以借用道家的一句话：“以道莅天下”。我们说“儒学的普适性”，是言其“道”的适用性。这个“道”究竟在多大范围和多长时间能够适用？不但体现在人的类个体上而且也体现在整个群体上，不只是一朝一夕而且是千秋万代，以“先王”或“圣人”之言与行来表明其“行之四海”、“传之万世”而不悖谬。且不论儒学能否达到这一目标，然其胸怀的志向和境界的指向即是如此。它不局限于一己一时，其眼界之开阔、胸怀之博大，令人神往而不可即也。

自然科学常常自认为追求和探索“自然规律”，社会科学亦是自认为追求和探索人类社会运行的“规律”。西方文明自古以来贯穿着求“道”即“逻各斯”的理念，到了近现代结出了它的“硕果”。东方文明同样也贯穿着求“道”或“理”的历程，其中自有其不可置疑的内在之“宝”，待人挖掘和发扬以适于今日。一些国家和民族的精英，往往基于其“私利”的需要，鼓吹前者的普世性而否定后者的价值，暴露出其文化帝国主义者和文化殖民主义者的险恶用心。时至今日，自然科学和工业文明异化使用的恶果，近代殖民化史、20世纪两次世界大战，乃至当代的霸权、强权以及世界性经济危机等事实证明，其所求之“道”之“理”的偏狭与不当，美化其“普世性”，是枉顾历史之验证也。这并不是说，我们否认另一面西方近世以来取得的积极成果及其对人类世界造成的巨大进步事实，我们只是基于另一面的后果、恶果认为，它有“偏狭”的成分而并不是“普世”的，更非是“永恒”“终极”的。即使有很多不断的“调整”，仍有局限之所在。况且，以一时一地形成的似乎很有力的“说法”，置之于人类历史长河的评判中，极可能显得可笑与片面。我们也不否认自身文明中存在着消极的因素、落后的成分，但其中的精华如果不能理解其“真实义”而众口铄金，则非但障碍认识的头脑，也绝不能发挥其功能大用一丝一毫。一百多年来，我们批判得够多了，我们抛弃得也够多了，失掉了精神家园，没有了精神自信。我们在不断追赶他者中迷失，已经不知道自己是谁、自己身在何处。我们将今人的失误和错误，强加于古人头上，非但不能解脱自己的责任，亦使问题趋于延迟解决。

曲解其内涵，不会、不能用之于当今，此乃我们今人之惜错。但殊不知，“道”还在那里，还在经典给我们的提示和启示中。这是我们仍然自信的根基。你翻开儒学的“四书五经”，就会发现，超越于利益与力量本身的束缚（西方之优势，正是奠定在现实的“利”与“力”之上，即今所说的金融与武力），先祖关于天道、人道的论述满篇皆是。从洒扫应对到尽心知性，从人道到天道，有关于形而下的，有关于形而上的。经过千百年来学人的不断筛选和史实验证，奉之为经，是因为其中所论之道之理，经

史合参，确有其不可疑、不可移的真理性。以天道推演出人道，以人道归本为天道，出乎性德之自然，返乎自然之本常。此情此理，断非凡智所度。所谓“大学之道，在明明德，在亲民，在止于至善”，修齐治平次第，内圣外王兼赅，体用俱足，万善一源。

儒学在创立之初期，即定位于人道的发明。孔子把“仁”作为核心，孟子将仁与人合一，提出“义”的原则，荀子又融铸礼法的外在规范，始将儒学的精蕴阐发披露。在个人至社会和国家的层面，摆脱了“帝”和“神”、“命”的因素，用合乎理性的方法去修身、去治国（“王道”）。抽象出来的儒学之“道”，不拘泥于一事一理，具有最大程度的普适性（“天下”）。经过后世儒者对经典的反复阐发，同时容纳吸收道家、佛家的合理思想，儒学“道”的意蕴遂又加以扩充和深度化，并能适应不断发展的外在形势需要。阐新邦以维旧命，儒学的道统命脉意识延续下来，“绝学”不绝，成为中华民族生生不息的深层意识。

儒学之“道”在形而下的层面，几乎等同于近人所说的“规律”。既是规律，即不能违背：守之则正常运行，违之则受惩罚。正如自然科学发现的“规律”有其适用的边界一样，人文之“道”亦有其适用的条件。这种对边界和条件的要求，并没有否定规律之道的普适性，毋宁可以认为它们乃普适性的生存“土壤”和“环境”。儒学之道正是如此。“道”不可以“悬空”和“搁置”，必须联系活生生的现实，附之于具体的人或事、民族或国家，才能体现出来。华夏与“蛮夷”身份的区分，主要不是地域的划界，而是文化的转换。虽为汉族后裔，如不能承继人伦文明之道，亦可退化为“蛮夷”；虽曾为未开化的“蛮夷”，如能将人伦文明发明广大，亦将转化为“华夏”。在东亚近代体系中，谁才是华夏文明的正统？按照上述原则，这一争论似乎显得没有必要。当儒学早已走出国门，辐射东北亚、东南亚地域，“东学西渐”，甚至影响到近代西方文明，其普适性自然不言而喻。

由“道”延伸的“道义性”，为中华儒学文化最大的特征之一。认同“道”，认为应当按照其原则去行事，是谓道义性。翻开世界伦理学史，几乎没有哪个民族能像华夏一样如此重视道义。先祖认为，即使进行战争，亦不是赤裸裸的利益掠夺与力量抗衡，这与西方历史上形成了极其鲜明的对比。在中国历史上，以义止战、以道取胜、以理评战，从一场战争的开始到战争进行，最后到战争结束以后，伦理的制约和评价贯穿始终。受正统儒家思想的影响，王道观念占据了主流话语系统。与此相对比的是，以追求权力与利益为核心的功利主义从一开始便在西方战争伦理中占据了主导性的地位，从而使其总体上表现出更为重视利害的判断而不是道德的判断；在民族或国家关系上，功利主义以自我利益为中心，强调适者生存的“丛林规则”，以“圣战”或维护国家利益为“幌子”，进行赤裸裸的血腥侵略战争，表现出某种非道义化的倾向。

重视和平手段，慎用战争手段，是中国军事价值取向的一个明显特征。历代战略家无一例外地将“天下太平，长治久安”作为最高战略目标。春秋时期楚庄王说：“止戈为武。”对“武”字作这样的结构分析，本身已昭示了中国传统文化热爱和平这一特征。《管子》中最早出现了“和平”一词：“致德，其民和平以静”（施之以德，老百姓就和平而安定），从中可以看出，中国人认为和平本质上是消除战争的一种安定平和的状态。华夏文明得以源远流长，经久不衰。这与中国人历来追求和平，谋求统一的传统不无关联。在处理人与人、民族与民族、国家与国家关系的过程中，儒家把“修身”与“平治天下”紧密联结在一起，主张走一条由“仁”而“和”的和平之路。和平发展道路的选择，是中国文化历史的“内生规定”。与此相关的，是西方主流战略文化对“强者法则”的推崇，以及对“暴力”与“强权”价值的认同。希腊哲学家赫拉克里特认为：“战争是万物之父，也是万物之王。”古希腊军事历史学家修昔底德关于“和平不过是两次战争的间歇”的论断，成为西方对和平本质的经典论述。近代思想家尼采甚至认为：“人若放弃了战争，也就放弃了高尚的生活。”在中国漫长的历史中，找不到像日本《明治遗训》、德国《德皇雄图秘著》、俄国《彼得一世遗嘱》那种具有侵略扩张传统的文字依据。社会达尔文主义之所以能在十九世纪末二十世纪初流行，它依据的不只是自然界的“天演”，从某种程度上反映了西方文明的实质。把人降低到动物的水平，映射的是人的动物性——这当然也具有“普世性”，不过它不能代表走向真正人的存在——后者只能是奠基在道义基础上的“普适性”。

## 二、从东亚的普适性到全球的普适性

如果从普适性的空间维度来说，西方文明可以说大获全胜：它超出地理学意义上的局限，越过国家和民族的屏障，在经济全球化的浪潮裹挟中，在互联网的大肆普及推广中，至今还在不断扩张其“边界”。但是我们不要忘记，穿上“绅士”外套的西方文明，几百年来造成的殖民化灾难、累堆起来的大量历史遗留问题，远未得到根治。不平等的国际规则、异化资本的“攻城略地”，同样不亚于血淋淋军事武力的侵占。今天，对不发达国家、发展中国家的剥夺，手段更加多样和隐蔽。只是停留于教堂祈祷中的“原罪”意识，在国际关系中却颐指气使，指手画脚，非但没有丝毫的“悔罪”感觉，而且自认为高人一等，充满高傲的优越感。和平的本意是“和谐相处，平等相待”，西方文明骨子里的种族优越意识，本质上是反和平的，其鼓吹的“自由、平等、人权”只能是少部分人，至多是少数民族、少数国家的“专利品”。实现真正的平等任重道远。果要如此，那些自我感觉良好的所谓“世界领导者”，首先即应放下身段。动辄以武力威胁或耍阴谋手段，早已丧失掉道义的制高点，遑论领导世界——若说“领导”，那就是领世人以万劫不复之地，导大众于毁灭之途。二战以后，人类长期笼罩在“蘑菇云”恐怖下的均势“和平”，从这个意义上讲，我们的文明确实已接近“世界的末日”，根本不值得推崇和赞许。无原则的实用主义作祟，甚至挑拨离间，趁火打劫，火上浇油，无所不用其极。“只许州官放火，不许百姓点灯”，双重标准，多重评断。自诩为“老大”，主持公道，但离其炫耀的正义和公平相去甚远。观其所做，视其所行，不是如此，又是何为？不深切反思己之所作所为，却变本加厉。这一切，皆源于“好斗式”文明的弱点；不正视这一点，目之为“普世性”，轻或是自欺欺人的怪谈，如真正强力推广，则给世界造成的乱局更大。

儒学在东亚的普适性表明，它可以和近代的新学（西学）融合得很好，并不失去自己的精华。比如，韩国在现代化中极好地吸纳了儒学的孝道，日本的企业文化将儒学“忠”的精髓诠释发挥，新加坡大力推行儒家伦理文化，等等。倒是国内部分人恨不能将儒学踏在脚底，指斥其落后和愚昧而与现代性不符。经济复兴起来之后，文化的建设提上议事日程。最近几年，由于党的最高领导人的大力倡导，从政府到教育部门，从个人到社会，对传统文化尤其是儒学的核心价值理念的认识逐渐正面化。把传统文化提高到领导干部“世界观、人生观、价值观”的高度，这在中国共产党的历史上还是第一次。伴随着中华民族复兴即“中国梦”的宣扬，对中华文化从社会价值观特别是道德价值观的定位，将迎来儒学“创新性发展、创造性转换”的再度辉煌。

其实，儒学作为世界精神文化遗产的重要组成部分，正在被越来越多的国家和人民所认知。儒学的当代复兴，除了经济复兴带来的民族文化自觉复归意识原因之外，还有就是全球化的国际环境的召唤。在全球化的多元文化、多元文明相处中，缺少一种可以协调不同文明关系的国际理念——西方文明的“丛林规则”仍然“绑架”着国际社会。提出构建“和谐世界”的外交主张，倡导“合作、共赢”的旗帜，最鲜明地体现了人类走向21世纪的新要求。这一主张和旗帜，实际上是中华儒学“贵和”文明的现代表达。人类世界要生存和发展下去，不能不摆脱长期以来国际关系中的“零和博弈”、“均势”理论与实践，不能不摆脱大国复兴的历史“魔咒”和“怪圈”。另一方面，中华民族的复兴，可以视作是一种新的文明的复兴——它不只是简单的“生态文明”，处理好人与自然关系，实现人与自然关系的和解，更重要的是它或许是中华民族历史内含的广义“有机文明”的复兴——不能以消耗过多的物质资源和能耗为环境代价（否则只是区域的昙花一现），不是以满足人的无节制的自私欲望消费为发展的动力（否则必然引起竞争和冲突）；发展不是物质文明的“堆积”，而主要是人性的进步和精神的提升。

儒学在满足现代人精神需要、解决现代性问题等方面具有重要的文化资源。比如，它的以仁爱为核心的理论架构，以和谐为功能的“礼用”之说，恰恰是弥合人与人、人与社会乃至民族与民族、国家与国家之间最好的“黏合剂”；它提倡做人层序的进步依次展开体现为凡人、贤人、圣人——其中主要是精神境界的进化，与人于己、安身立命、生死归宿皆有次第着落。尽管儒学对象性知识层面的东西可能不多，但它所浸染的人伦教化洋洋大观，煌煌烛明。现在有人认为，儒学产生于农业社会的“熟人”机制，处理当代工商社会的“陌生人”需用西方的“契约”规范。其实，我倒觉得，儒学把处理亲近关系推演后，更显得富有人情味和亲和力。尤其是它将“信”作为做人和交友的信条，在父母与儿女、上级与下级、个人与众人等复杂人际展开中，有一系列的对等义务和责任。一个富有儒家情理的社会氛围，并不是冷冰冰的法的“原子式”孤独关系；人们皆重视自我修养和约束，博文约礼，一定处处充满着浓厚的人文情致、人道关怀。

## 三、从历史的普适性到当代的普适性

如果从普适性的时间维度看，以儒学为核心的中华文明无疑不亚于古希腊的文明。连续不断的五千年文明史，其顽强的生命力、凝聚力得到了历史的反复核验，为他者提供了绝好的生存和发展例证。几近两千年作为正统官方意识形态的儒学价值观，经过一代代士人的阐释解读，为社会大众所接受。正如上文指出的，重视和平，保持相对的稳定，就使中华民族的长期稳步发展有了一个良好的基础。尽管近代遭逢一百多年的外辱内乱，但不能不承认，我们至今坐享着千年文明带来的“红利”。

很多人并没有意识到这一点，受近现代长期批判史的影响，绝大部分人可以说丧失了文化自信——不但没有自信，而且将其“污名化”，充斥教科书和占据头脑的即是简单的“封建、落后、专制”等字眼。数典忘祖，隔断“母体”，甚至以呵儒骂祖为荣，喊出“打倒孔家店”、“批林批孔”不伦不类的口号，动不动就将错误、失误归结到老祖宗头上，如释重负，推卸责任，好像今天的我们都是石头缝中跳蹦出来的。需知如果中华文明在历史上任何一个“环节”断档了，就没有肉身的我们存在。几代人身上传统的影踪几乎荡然无存，连最基本的国学知识都无从了解。不知对象为何物，就根本谈不上对之敬意。有学者用现代的系统方法证实，中国超稳定的传统社会结构很难打破——殊不知这也许从另一个侧面看，恰恰是我们的优势所在。还有人用“农民起义——坐上皇位——农民起义”的简单历史周期和循环，概括整个中国社会演变，否定其进步和发展。将所有历史人物都贴上阶级分析方法的标签，进行归类排队；把任何观点纳入西方唯心唯物、形而上学辩证法的套路，肢解古人精辟的见解。文化史上的拨乱反正将是一个长期的工作，非如此，民族的自信心何来？自豪感何来？一个没有历史感的民族、一个忘记了自己历史的民族，就失掉了自己的“魂”和“根”。

“历史是最好的教科书”，言下之意，恢复我们正确的历史记忆非常重要。“辉煌”增进自信，“屈辱”令人奋进。历史的存在及其合理性是普适性最主要的“证据”。用几千年的文明与几百年的文明相比，用几百年的文明与几十年的文明相比，哪个更有说服力？结论自然不言而喻。人的肉身局限性就在于眼光只是盯在当下，不愿去用头脑做深入的理性分析，偏激和偏执造就了很多人只看到横断面看不到历史的纵剖面，只看到虚假繁荣的表面而看不到血淋淋的本质内核。以小人之心度君子之心，以凡人之思虑圣人之思，肤浅的理解极大歪曲了圣贤的本意。

历史的普适性当然不等于当代的普适性。道不远人，人自远道。历史的普适性，是由于从精英到民间、从制度化到民俗民情，认同并注重在社会生活中去践履和实证。当代的“非普适性”，是由于从精英到底层、从社会到学校不但不提倡，甚至在一些极端时期不时地拿出来批它几下、踩它几脚。知行分离、两面人生、外荣内腐的现象大量存在。有时候不打破便不能进步革新，但要看打破的是什么，还应放到历史的长河去检验。一时的痛快可能带来的是长久的伤痛。附加在历史上的尘灰过于丰厚，以至于历史的真实面目反而被掩盖。历史无法为自身去辩解，只待后人去为它拭去蒙尘、抹去眼泪。无论是历史的经验，还是历史的教训，沉沉往矣！道不弘人，人能弘道。为谁纷说？逝者往矣，留待今者已也荷负重担。在一个思想文化自上而下推动的氛围中，幸时逢位高者大力倡导，吾辈当跟得上这一良苦用心，真正解放思想，厘清模糊认识，内外俱动，推动进展。如不能采取大规模的有效措施，仅停留于行政口号层面，很可能时过境迁，烟消云散。没有为儒学创造一个“适用”的环境，它就从学者的殿堂上很难走下来，从博物馆的展厅里很难出得来。目前，倒是民间的资源较为活跃，也更为大胆；巨大的政府资源谨慎展开，教育部门确定了计划：如是稳定地上下联动，儒学乃至传统的有益教化有望慢慢展开。冰冻三日，又遇外来文化冲击，险途重重，知障屏隔，需要耐心恒心。历史的普适性为当代的普适性不只是提供了佐证。当代是历史进化的结果，其正常的、合理的状态一定是容纳了历史的精华。

贯穿从历史到当代背后的动力是什么呢？早期《尚书》在论述天下之大政时，反复强调“德”在朝代更替中的作用。我们从孔子著《春秋》“微言大义”的评判中，可以发现儒学伦理的精髓往往即蕴含在对一件事理、一个人物、一个行为的简短字眼里——或褒或贬，映射出善与恶的价值判断，影响到后世的价值选择。中国传统史学承继了孔子开创的这一“笔法”。所以，我认为史学的精神并不完全在于它的“求真”，客观地、忠实地记录历史事实，而重要地体现在它的谨慎评判上。司马迁讲自己著《史记》是为“究天人之际”，此“际”吾以为不只是事实之“真”，还有行为“善”的边界含义在内。从周易的经传开始，“积善之家必有余庆，积不善之家必有余殃”的因果观，就深深地影响到人们的日常生活，亦深深地影响到史学家的世界观。支配大多数人信念的，简单地说，就是俗话“善有善报，恶有恶报；不是不报，时候未到”，这种信念与周易所说的道理一样，并不一定是“当下就报”的因果观：它承认因果的复杂性，甚至与佛家的“三世因果”（实质是多世因果）极其相似。清乾隆年间，彭希涑居士有感于诸多阐发因果道理之故事多杂引稗官小说，不足以征信于世。于是遍阅“二十二史”，从中取事迹感应显著者，汇录而成《二十二史感应录》，由于系正史事实，最具说服力。此等感应，非“命”所定，乃善恶之因果流转。推而广之，国家和民族的前途，亦是其造善为恶之结果。自命自造，因果自负，切勿怨天尤人。这是一种独特的“历史决定论”，既不同于归结为物质生产方式的最终“推手”，亦不同于离开人自身的精神动因论，毋宁说它是一种贯穿从动机到行为实施、完成的善恶决定论。儒家学说，也包括道家和佛家思想在内的整个中国传统文化，皆信仰善恶因果论——此亦为前文所说的“道义”普适性作了一个最佳注脚和说明。如果释“道”为规律，那么它就是善恶的因果决定律。任何国家和民族都逃不过这一“铁律”。昨天的所作所为决定了今天的状况；今天的所作所为又为明天的结果埋下了伏笔。我们必须战战兢兢，戒惧恐慎，为自己的言、行、思负起责任，减少未来“偿还”的代价。

人类能够借鉴的最大经验乃是自己的历史。把历史看作“婊子”也好，把任何历史都看作“当代史”也好，背后都是人自身想从中获取点什么，折射、映像出我们今天的需求。在当今“世界历史”整体演化中，各个国家和民族的相互融入，既要保留和吸取人类文明的共同智慧遗产，又要冲破各自历史哲学中单向度的自命不凡、自以为是的束缚，走出唯自己国家利益是尊的封闭圈子，携手发掘出符合道义和善性的价值观引领旗帜。

# 儒学在当代中国的价值

中国孔子研究院 孔祥林

2013年11月26日，习近平主席专程到曲阜考察，并在孔子研究院召开了座谈会，就儒家思想的研究、继承和传播做了重要讲话。联系到习近平近年一系列关于传统思想文化的讲话，许多学者认为，习近平主席将更多地采用儒家的治国方略。其实，从改革开放以来，中国逐渐加强了对传统思想文化的重视，早在1980年，邓小平就发起开展了五讲四美三热爱活动。进入21世纪，儒家思想更加受到重视。2001年，江泽民主席提出“把依法治国与以德治国紧密结合起来”的治国方略，2005年，胡锦涛主席提出建设和谐社会与和谐世界的目标，2006年胡锦涛主席提出大力建设社会主义核心价值体系，2012年，习近平总书记提出了实现中华民族伟大复兴的中国梦理想。从中国三位领导人的治国理念和目标不难看出，中国正不断从传统思想和文化中汲取营养，更好地借鉴儒家传统，对内建设和谐社会，实现国家富强、民族振兴、人民幸福的中国梦；对外坚持和平、发展、合作、共赢的方针，与世界各国人民共同建造和谐世界。儒家思想在当代中国将会发挥越来越大的作用。

## 以德治国与依法治国相结合——借鉴儒家治国传统

2000年6月，江泽民主席《在中央思想政治工作会议上的讲话》中阐述了法律和道德在国家管理中的作用：“法律与道德作为上层建筑的组成部分，都是维护社会秩序、规范人们思想和行为的重要手段，它们互相联系，互相补充。法治以其权威性和强制手段规范社会成员的行为，德治以其说服力和劝导力提高社会成员的思想认识和道德觉悟。道德规范和法律规范应该互相结合，统一发挥作用”。次年1月，在全国宣传部长会议上，江泽民明确提出了“把依法治国与以德治国紧密结合起来”的治国方略：“我们在建设有中国特色社会主义，发展社会主义市场经济的过程中，要坚持不懈地加强社会主义法制建设，依法治国，同时也要坚持不懈地加强社会主义道德建设，以德治国。对一个国家的治理来说，法治和德治从来都是相辅相成、互相促进的。二者缺一不可，也不可偏废。法治属于政治建设，属于政治文明，德治属于思想建设，属于精神文明。二者范围不同，但其地位和功能都是非常重要的。我们要把法制建设与道德建设紧密结合起来，把依法治国与以德治国紧密结合起来”。在“七一讲话”中，江泽民再次强调，“要把依法治国同以德治国结合起来，为社会保持良好的秩序和风尚营造高尚的思想道德基础”。

以德治国与依法治国相结合其实就是中国儒家的治国传统，此外还应包括以礼治国，儒家主张的是德治、礼治、法治三结合的治国方式。

孔子主张采用以德治国、以法治国与以礼治国三结合的治国方式。他说“道之以政，齐之以刑，民免而无耻；道之以德，齐之以礼，有耻且格”[①]（《为政》）。三者之中，孔子尤其提倡以德治国，“为政以德，譬如北辰，居其所而众星拱之”（《为政》），以德治国很容易治理好国家。

孔子一直重视道德，主张依据道德来处理政事，进而形成了系统的德治思想。他主张德治，提倡进行教化，反对严刑峻法，但他并不否定刑罚，刑罚还是需要的。孔子说“名不正则言不顺，言不顺则事不成，事不成则礼乐不兴，礼乐不兴则刑罚不中，刑罚不中则民无所措手足”（《子路》），法治要有礼乐教化作保证，先进行礼乐教化，才能使刑罚得当，刑罚得当，人民才不会手足无措。

虽然赞同法治，但孔子反对不进行教育就严厉处罚，他说“不教而杀谓之虐”（《尧曰》），不加教育就进行杀戮就是对人民的虐待。孔子任鲁国大司寇时，“有父子讼者，夫子同狴执之，三月不别。其父请止，夫子赦之”。季孙氏责怪孔子不“戮一不孝以教民孝”，孔子则认为“上失其道而杀其下，非理也。不教以孝而听其狱，是杀不辜”，“上教之不行，罪不在民也”，[②] 管理者失去了正确治理国家的方法却杀害人民是不合乎道理的，不进行孝道教育就进行处罚就是杀害无辜的人。管理者不对人们进行教育，人民犯了罪，责任不在人民而在管理者。在对人民进行处罚前，要首先进行教育。

孔子虽然主张法治，但他主张省刑罚，对人民少用刑律处罚。他说“‘善人为邦百年，亦可以胜残去杀矣。’诚哉是言也！”（《子路》）季康子问孔子“如杀无道以就有道”时，孔子就明确反对，“子为政，焉用杀？子欲善，而民善矣！君子之德风；小人之德草；草上之风必偃”（《颜渊》），执政者以自己的善行就能改善社会，哪里用得着杀人呢？所以孔子认为法治的最高标准是“威厉而不试，刑错而不用”，[③] 国家需要制

① 凡《论语》引文，以下均只注篇名。
② 《孔子家语·始诛》。
③ 《孔子家语·始诛》。

定严格的法律，但要通过教化提高人民的道德水平，使人民不去犯罪，法律备而不用。

孔子提倡以礼治国，主张“道之以德，齐之以礼”，用道德引导人民，用礼仪规范人民。按照礼仪规范去治理国家，国家就很容易治理。“上好礼，则民莫敢不敬”（《子路》），“上好礼，则民易使也”（《宪问》），管理者崇尚礼仪规范，老百姓就不敢不尊敬，就容易使用。即使是国君，也要按照礼仪规范使用臣子，“君使臣以礼，臣事君以忠”（《八佾》）。“齐之以礼”就是用礼仪来规范人们的行为，通过教育使人民自觉地使自己的行动符合社会规范。孔子主张以礼治国，所以一再教育弟子要“约之以礼”（《雍也》），“非礼勿视，非礼勿听，非礼勿言，非礼勿动”（《颜渊》），要“克己复礼”，努力克制自己使自己的行为合乎礼的规定。对于礼的作用，孔子的弟子有若说得很明白，“礼之用，和为贵”（《学而》），礼的使用就在于创造和谐的环境。和谐是社会发展的基本条件，只有在和谐的环境下才能更好地发展。

现在人们一般都认为中国历史上是以德治国与以法治国治国相结合，其实中国历史上是以德治国、以法治国和以礼治国三者相结合。

用道德治理国家主要是对人民进行思想教化，它没有强制性，是软的；用法律治理国家，法律是强制性的，强迫人民必须执行，否则就会受到惩罚，是硬的；而礼介于两者之间，礼仪规范没有法律的强制性，违背礼仪除非大逆不道（已经属于法律的内容），一般不会受到法律的惩罚，但会受到社会舆论的监督，所以礼是约束人们行为的外在规范。在古代社会早期，法律并不健全，礼在某些方面承担了法律的作用。即使到了封建社会，礼仍然作为法律的补充承担了重要的社会作用。每当新的王朝建立后，首要的任务就是定正朔，易服色，制定本朝的礼仪制度，很多礼仪就是法律的补充。

中国人很早就知道治乱世必用重典，在社会动乱、道德水准低下的时期，法律尤其显得重要，但是社会整体道德水平低下，执法者的道德水平能高吗？社会上犯罪的人众多，执法者也难以成为圣人，司法不公，执法者道德败坏、贪赃枉法，种种丑恶现象丛生。严刑峻法，作为阶段性的措施也许是有效的，但要治理好国家，还必须依靠德治和礼治。既要制定完善的法律，也要制定完备的礼仪制度，通过教育提高人们的道德水准，使人们自觉执行法律，遵守礼仪规范。人们自觉约束自己的行动，不去触犯法律，法律备而无用，达到孔子所说的“刑错而不用”的境界，这才是最高的治理标准。

以德治国，以礼治国，提高人民的道德水平，人民以犯罪为可耻，自觉避免犯罪，就能减少犯罪。中国传统的德治、法治、礼治二结合的治理方式是非常科学的，它比西方以法治国要高明得多。

中国是一个法制不够健全的国家，现在提倡依法治国，健全完善法律体系，由人治转向法治是完全必要的。但是，要知道，仅仅依靠法治是不够的，以法治国只能治末，不能治本，治本还必须依靠德治和礼治。在21世纪，中国应该回归传统，采用以法治国与以德治国、以礼治国相结合的方式。对人民群众广泛进行思想道德教育，以道德治心，提高人民的道德水准，人民明辨是非，就会从内心去避免犯罪；制定必要的行为规范，用礼仪治行，以礼仪来规范人民的行为，通过礼仪约束人民的行为不去违背社会规范，"克己复礼"，人民自觉地克制自己的行为使之合乎礼仪的规定，行为上就不会触犯法律；完善法律，普及法律常识，提高人民的道德水准和守法意识，人们就不会去触犯法律；提高人民的道德水准、和守礼、守法意识，才能从根本上减少犯罪。

## 建设和谐社会，借鉴儒家社会理念

2005年2月，胡锦涛主席对构建社会主义和谐社会进行了阐释："我们要建设的社会主义和谐社会，应该是民主法治、公平正义、诚信友善、充满活力、安定有序、人与自然和谐相处的社会"，"民主法治，就是社会主义民主得到充分发扬，依法治国基本方略得到切实落实，各方面积极因素得到广泛调动；公平正义，就是社会各方面的利益关系得到妥善协调，人民内部矛盾和社会其他矛盾得到正确处理，社会公平和正义得到切实维护和实现；诚实友爱，就是全社会互帮互助、诚实守信、全体人民平等友爱、融洽相处；充满活力，就是能够使一切有利于社会进步的创造愿望得到尊重，创造活动得到支持，创造才能得到发挥，创造成果得到肯定；安定有序，就是社会组织机制健全，社会管理完善，社会秩序良好，人民群众安居乐业，社会保持安定团结；人与自然和谐相处，就是生产发展，生活富裕，生态良好。"同年，胡锦涛在美国耶鲁大学演讲中提出建设和谐世界的主张："中国坚持实施互利共赢的对外开放战略，真诚愿意同各国广泛开展合作，真诚愿意兼收并蓄，博采各种文明之长，以合作谋和平，以合作促发展，推动建设一个持久和平、共同繁荣的和谐世界"，向世界各国人民表达了建设和谐世界的良好愿望。

建设和谐社会与和谐世界，一直是中国的历史传统。孔子的政治理想就是要建设一个和谐的社会。孔子生活的春秋时期，大一统的周王朝已经名存实亡，周天子虽然名义上还是天下共主，但已经失去了管理国家的能利，诸侯各自为政，大夫掌握了国家的命运，家臣掌握了大夫的实权，社会严重失序，"君不君、臣不臣、父不父、子不子"成为那个时代的显著特点。孔子为了重整社会秩序，针对当时的社会现实，通过考察古代政治制度的兴废、社会的治乱和国家兴亡的历史，从仁爱的人本哲学思想出发，以怀古的方式憧憬未来，提出了大同世界和小康社会两个不同档次的政治理想。

大同世界是孔子的最高理想：

大道之行也，天下为公，选贤与能，讲信修睦。故人不独亲其亲，不独子其子，使老有所终，壮有所用，幼有所长，矜寡孤独废疾者皆有所养，男有分，女有归。货，恶其弃于地也不必藏于己；力，恶其不出于身也不必为己。是故谋闭而不兴，盗窃乱贼而不作，故外户而不闭，是谓大同。[①]

在天下大同的社会，天下为人民所共有，选举德才兼备的人进行管理，人们讲究信用，互相关爱，和睦相处，不仅亲爱自己的亲人，抚养自己的子女，而是使所有的老年人都能得到赡养，成年人都能施展自己的才能，儿童都能得到抚养，光棍、寡妇、残疾人都能得到照顾，没有阴谋诡计，没有盗窃和作乱的现象，社会安定，夜不闭户，这是一幅多么美好的和谐社会的景象。

小康社会是孔子较低的社会理想：

今大道既隐，天下为家，各亲其亲，各子其子，货力为己。大人世及以为礼，城郭沟池以为固，礼义以为纪，以正君臣，以笃父子，以睦兄弟，以和夫妇，以设制度，以立田里，以贤勇知，以功为己。故谋用是作，而兵由此起。禹、汤、文、武、成王、周公，由此其选也。此六君子者，未有不谨于礼者也。以著其义，以考其信，著有过，刑仁讲让，示民有常。如有不由此者，在执者去，众以为殃，是谓小康。

在小康社会中，天下变成了私人的天下，官位世袭，人们只亲爱自己的亲人，只抚养自己的子女，施展权谋，挑起战争，但是制定典章制度和伦理道德，用来端正君臣关系，加深父子感情，使兄弟和睦，夫妻和顺；制定礼仪来表彰道义，提倡诚实守信，仁爱谦让，使人们遵守法规，可以称为小康社会。小康社会虽然有了等级的差别，没有大同世界那样完美，但仍然是和谐有序的社会。

为了创建和谐社会，实现自己的政治理想，改变社会失序的局面，孔子提出了一系列的主张。在政治方面主要是维护统一，推行仁政，实行德治，富民教民，减少刑罚，选用贤才，为政公平廉洁；经济方面要减少赋税，减少劳役，使民以时，多给人民好处，合理分配社会财富，要让人民富裕起来，对人民进行教育；对外关系方面，反对战争，主张和平相处，“远人不服，则修文德以来之”（《季氏》）。

孔子不仅提出了构建和谐社会的政治主张，还提出了构建和谐社会与和谐世界的原则。

孔子说：“君子和而不同，小人同而不和”（《子路》），君子和谐却不同一，小人同一却不和谐。和是多种因素的统一与和谐，是在综合不同意见之上的和谐与一致，是允许不同意见存在的和谐与协调。和谐而不同一，是孔子理想的境界。

---

① 《礼记·礼运》。

中国自古就是遵循和而不同原则建设和谐社会的。中国思想界在春秋时期是百家争鸣，百花齐放，汉代以后虽然罢黜百家，独尊儒术，儒家思想占据了指导地位，但儒家思想是一种宽容的思想，对其他思想、文化、宗教（如佛教、道教、伊斯兰教以及后期传入的西方宗教等）都能抱持宽容的态度，在中国历史上儒家思想与其他宗教思想基本上是和平共处的，中国从来没有就发生过宗教战争。正因为中国长期坚持了和而不同的原则，社会才能长期稳定和谐，中国的思想、文化、经济等各方面才能不断发展，多民族、大一统的国家才能不断发展和巩固。

20世纪以来，中国继续坚持和而不同的原则，妥善处理国内的各种矛盾和事件，最为典型的是发明了“一国两制”的方针，收回了被外国长期占领的领土香港和澳门，并成功实现了香港、澳门的平稳过渡和持续发展。“一国两制”这种中国人的智慧获得了世界的赞许，只要坚持和而不同的原则，中国的完全和平统一、中国的繁荣昌盛都是一定能实现的。

现在的中国是拥有50多个民族、13亿人口的大国，不同的民族拥有不同的宗教信仰，不同的文化，不同的风俗习惯，改革开放以来，东西方各种思想大量涌入，人们的思想异常活跃，而改革开放以来，贫富差距加大，东西部发展不平衡，各种矛盾日渐突出，建设和谐社会更需要坚持和而不同的原则。

在对外关系中，中国政府也是主张和而不同的。早在20世纪50年代就提出了和平共处的五项原则：“互相尊重主权和领土完整，互不侵犯，互不干涉内政，平等互利，和平共处”。和平共处五项原则被认为是国际关系史上的创举，它使不同社会制度、不同意识形态的国家在和而不同的原则下求同存异，和谐相处。2002年10月，江泽民主席在美国乔治·布什总统图书馆发表的演讲中说：“孔子提出的‘和而不同’思想，和谐又不千篇一律，不同而又不相互冲突。和谐以共生共长，不同以相辅相成。和而不同是社会事物和社会关系发展的一条重要规律，也是人们处世行事应该遵循的准则，是人类多种文明发展的真谛”。2003年12月10日，中国总理温家宝在美国哈佛大学所作题为“把目光投向中国”的演讲中也说：“中华民族具有极其深厚的文化底蕴，历来酷爱和平。‘和而不同’是中国古代思想家提出的一个伟大思想……用‘和而不同’的观点观察问题，处理问题，不仅有利于我们善待邻邦，也有利于国际社会化解矛盾”。中国政府主张将和而不同作为处理国际关系的准则。

从公元前2世纪起，中国就确定孔子思想作为国家的指导思想，孔子的政治理念成为治国的圭臬，和而不同成为治国的原则，孔子的伦理思想成为修身的准则。正是在孔子思想的指导下，中国历史上和谐多于动乱，动乱之后很快恢复和谐。

和而不同的原则不仅有助于建设和谐中国，而且有助于建设和谐世界。

人类是由不同的种族组成的，种族又分成了不同的民族。不同的民族有不同的信仰、不同的文化、不同的艺术；世界是由不同的国家组成的，不同国家有不同的社会制度，不同的意识形态，不同的价值观念。随着现代科学的发展，地球变得越来越小，人与人之间的距离也越来越小，各种文化、思想、宗教的接触也越来越多。伴随着距离的越来越小，各个民族、各种宗教、各种思想、各种文化产生冲突的可能性也越来越大，但是伴随着越来越多的接触，各个民族、各种宗教、各种思想、各种文化的了解也会越来越多，只要各个民族、各种宗教、各种思想、各种文化都能本着和而不同的原则，求和存异，世界就会变成一个和而不同的世界，一个和谐的世界。

## 建立社会主义核心价值体系，汲取儒家伦理精华

改革开放以来，传统美德日益受到重视。1980 年 5 月，邓小平在给《中国少年报》和《辅导员》杂志题词时提出了希望青少年做四有新人，“希望全国的小朋友，立志做有理想、有道德、有知识、有纪律的人，立志为人民作贡献，为祖国作贡献，为人类作贡献”。有理想，有道德，有知识，有纪律，作贡献，这是儒家一再所提倡，而被中国知识分子所信奉的金科玉律。2006 年 3 月，胡锦涛提出了“八荣八耻”的社会主义荣辱观，“以热爱祖国为荣，以危害祖国为耻；以服务人民为荣，以背离人民为耻；以崇尚科学为荣，以愚昧无知为耻；以辛勤劳动为荣，以好逸恶劳为耻；以团结互助为荣，以损人利己为耻；以诚实守信为荣，以见利忘义为耻；以遵纪守法为荣，以违法乱纪为耻；以艰苦奋斗为荣，以骄奢淫逸为耻”，内容包括了儒家倡导的忠、公、勤、群、信、义、礼、俭等传统美德。

如果说上述活动只是逐步开始重视传统伦理的话，那么从 2006 年开始，中国日益重视全面汲取儒家伦理思想精华。是年 10 月，中国共产党第十六届中央委员会第六次全体会议通过的《中共中央关于构建社会主义和谐社会若干重大问题的决定》中明确提出，“建设社会主义核心价值体系，形成全民族奋发向上的精神力量和团结和睦的精神纽带”，提出“用民族精神和时代精神凝聚力量、激发活力，倡导爱国主义、集体主义、社会主义思想”，“树立社会主义荣辱观，培育文明道德风尚。坚持依法治国与以德治国相结合，树立以‘八荣八耻’为主要内容的社会主义荣辱观，倡导爱国、敬业、诚信、友善等道德规范，开展社会公德、职业道德、家庭美德教育，加强青少年思想道德建设，在全社会形成知荣辱、讲正气、促和谐的风尚，形成男女平等、尊老爱幼、扶贫济困、礼让宽容的人际关系”，“反对拜金主义、享乐主义、极端个人主义。弘扬我国传统文化中有利于社会和谐的内容，形成符合传统美德和时代精神的道德规范和行为规范。加强政务诚信、商务诚信、社会诚信建设，增强全社会诚实守信意识”。2012 年召开的中国共产党第十八次代表大会政治报告指出，要“大力弘扬民族精神和

时代精神，深入开展爱国主义、集体主义、社会主义教育。倡导富强、民主、文明、和谐，倡导自由、平等、公正、法治，倡导爱国、敬业、诚信、友善，积极培育社会主义核心价值观”，“要全面提高公民道德素质。要坚持依法治国和以德治国相结合，加强社会公德、职业道德、家庭美德，个人品德教育，弘扬中华传统美德，弘扬时代新风。推进公民道德建设工程，弘扬真善美，贬斥假恶丑，引导人民自觉履行法定义务、社会责任、家庭责任，营造劳动光荣、创造伟大的社会氛围，培育知荣辱、讲正气、作奉献、促和谐的良好风尚”，“建设优秀传统文化传承体系，弘扬中华优秀传统文化”。

建立社会主义核心价值体系，一再强调弘扬中华传统美德，更加重视从传统伦理中汲取精华。中国传统文化最大的特点是伦理思想特别发达，伦理思想的作用特别明显。伦理思想包括仁、义、礼、智、信、忠、恕、孝、悌、敬、温、良、恭、俭、让、宽、敏、惠、廉、耻、勇、直、让、中、公等五六十个德目，其中仁义礼智信被称作五常，孝悌忠信、礼义廉耻被称作八德，是人们必须信守的道德规范。传统伦理观念绝大多数都是修身做人的准则，都具有促进社会和谐的功能。人们具有仁德，就能关爱他人，帮助他人，促进友爱互助、团结和睦的良好社会关系；人们讲义，就能纠正重利轻义、见利忘义的弊端；人们讲诚信，就能形成互相信任的社会氛围；人们讲忠，就能对朋友尽心竭力，真诚专一，忠于国家，就能上下齐心；人们讲孝，就能促进家庭和谐，进而促进社会的安定；人们讲恕，就能相互尊重、包容与体谅；等等。

儒家伦理思想造就了中华民族的优秀品格，国家兴亡、匹夫有责的以天下为己任的担当意识，富贵不能淫、贫贱不能移、威武不能屈的大丈夫品格，不屈不挠、自强不息的人生态度，孝悌忠信、礼义廉耻的道德自律，敬敏公明、勇直笃毅的工作态度，仁恕和惠、温良恭让的待友原则，和而不同的处事原则，修文来远的睦邻方针，等等。大部分传统伦理都可以在当代社会中发挥作用。

## 中国梦肯定儒家思想在历史上发挥的重要作用

2012年11月29日，习近平总书记首次提到中国梦的设想，“实现中华民族伟大复兴，就是中华民族近代以来最伟大的梦想”。2013年3月，在第十二届全国人民代表大会第一次全体会议闭幕式上，习近平对中国梦作了详细的阐释：“实现中华民族伟大复兴的中国梦，就是要实现国家富强、民族振兴、人民幸福，共同享有人生出彩的机会”。6月7日，习近平在美国会见记者时进一步阐释了中国梦：“中国梦要实现国家富强、民族复兴、人民幸福，是和平、发展、合作、共赢的梦，与包括美国梦在内的世界各国人民的美好梦想相通”。综合来看，中国梦就是要实现中华民族的伟大复兴，使国家富强，民族振兴，人民幸福，人人享有人生出彩的机会，对外和平、发展、合作、共赢，促进人类和平与发展。

中国梦要实现的是中华民族的伟大复兴，说明中华民族历史上曾经有过兴盛，这就肯定了儒家思想在历史上发挥的重要作用。

19世纪以来，中国遭到资本主义列强的入侵，凡战必败，割地赔款，饱受欺凌，深受西方思想影响的学者和政治家们将其归罪于孔子，归罪于儒家思想，指责儒家思想导致了中国的贫穷和落后。一百多年里，孔子及儒家思想成为罪恶的渊薮。其实这种观点以偏概全，是完全错误的。自西汉武帝罢黜百家、独尊儒术以来，儒家思想在大部分时间里一直是中国社会的指导思想，除去严重混乱时期，中国经济不断繁荣，文明不断发展，大一统国家不断发展与巩固。

从西汉到19世纪70年代，两千年间，中国在大部分时间里一直是世界经济总量最大的国家，即使到1820年，中国国民生产总值仍占世界的三分之一，而那时欧洲才占26%，1872年，中国国民生产总值世界第一的位置才被美国所取代。中国不仅是经济总量最大的国家，人均国民生产总值也曾经长期占据世界最高位置。有西方学者认为，世界进入第二个千年时，也就是北宋初年，中国的人均国民生产总值是欧洲的1.2倍。

中国不仅经济发达，科技和工业水平也非常发达。据西方学者研究，在西方文艺复兴前的上千年中，世界重大科学成果大约300项，其中中国的发明约有175项，火药、造纸、指南针、印刷术、铸铁、手推车等这些促进人类文明进步的发明都是中国人创造的，使用和推广都早于西方几个世纪。中国经济的繁荣主要依靠工业的发展，从汉代开始，中国丝绸就成为世界贸易的宠儿，以后又增加了瓷器和茶叶，中国工业产值长期世界第一。美国学者肯尼迪在《大国的兴衰》一书中说，在18世纪，中国的工业产量仍占世界的32%，而全欧洲才占23%。中国的落伍是从西方工业革命开始的，到19世纪末，中国工业总值已经下降到世界工业总值的6%，而欧洲已经上升到62%，此消彼长，中国已经远远落后了。中国落伍的原因主要是没有追赶历史的潮流，发展现代工业。造成这种失误的是颟顸自大的满族统治者，他们自认为天朝大国，物华天宝，根本看不起现代工业那些雕虫小技，致使中国错失了发展良机。早期受到西方影响的知识分子不敢归罪满族统治者，却将责任完全推给儒家思想，致使儒家思想长期受到排斥批判，中国在落后的道路上越滑越远。

世界四大古代文明中，古埃及文明、两河流域文明、古印度文明由于异族的入侵都已中断，中国历史上虽然也多次遭到少数民族的入侵，中华文明不仅延续下来而且不断发展，最主要的原因就是中华文明是先进的文明，儒家思想包容性很强，具有强大的同化力。

孔子以创办教育起家，目的就是要培养治理国家的人才。在孔子贤人政治的影响下，汉代采用察举制度，隋代开始采用科举制度选拔官员，形成了文官主政的传统。文人主政，当然重视文化，促进文化的发展。中国文化一直在不断地发展，汉赋、乐府、唐诗、宋词、元曲、明清小说，不同的朝代产生了不同的文学体裁，并达到那个时代的高峰。中国文化高度发达而且不断发展，以致有些西方学者认为中国更像是一个文明实体。90多年前，英国著名学者罗素就说："中国与其说是一个政治实体，还不如说是一个文明实体——唯一幸存至今的文明。孔子以来，埃及、巴比伦、波斯、马其顿、包括罗马帝国都消亡了，但是中国以持续的进化生存下来了。最先是佛教，现在是西方的科学，但是佛教没有把中国人变成印度人，西方科学也不会将中国人变成欧洲人"。罗素的观点抓住了中国历史的特点，也指出了中国文化发展的方向。

世界历史上曾经出现过古埃及、古巴比伦、波斯、马其顿、罗马、拜占庭等庞大帝国，这些帝国盛极一时，有的很快土崩瓦解，有的持续一段时间后才分崩离析，但都已经灰飞烟灭，并没有延续到现在的大国。世界上唯独中国，虽然历经改朝换代，庞大的统一帝国一脉相承，多民族、大一统的国家一直延续到现在。分析其原因，是孔子思想促进了多民族大一统国家的巩固和发展。

从西汉开始，孔子思想成为社会的正统思想，历代王朝无不推行孔子思想，即使是少数民族建立的政权也无不如此。最为典型的是五胡十六国时期，尊孔习儒较之此前的汉晋中原王朝有过之而无不及。学习儒家思想的结果，使少数民族逐步接受了大一统和华夏正统观念，文化认同，血缘归宗，政治上生活上逐步汉化。少数民族入主中原，提倡孔子思想，固然是他们巩固统治的需要，但客观上也加快了民族的融合。少数民族入主中原，从政治上、军事上看，他们是胜利者，但是，文化上落后的游牧民族一进入文化发达的中原地区，面临强大的儒家思想，就注定了他们是失败者，入主中原的少数民族很快就被融合，融入华夏民族。

血缘是一个民族的根，宗教信仰是一个民族最明显的特性，没有宗教信仰的民族最明显的特性是就思想文化。汉族其实是一个由许多民族不断融合而形成的族群，并非像大多数民族那样有一个共同的始祖，人们常说中华民族是炎黄子孙，这个说法本身就说明中华民族的祖先来自两个不同的部落。中华民族是一个没有共同祖先的族群，也没有共同的宗教信仰，维系这个族群的纽带就是以孔子思想为主干的传统思想文化。

对中国历史进行纵向的全面考察，可以说，孔子思想促进了民族经济的发展，民族文化的繁荣和民族融合，促进了多民族国家的形成和发展。当然，将中国的强盛全部归功于孔子思想也许并不合适，但是历史上将孔子思想作为国家的指导思想并没有影响中国成为世界上最为发达的国家，相反，抛弃孔子思想以后，中国每况愈下，到肆无忌惮地批判孔子的时期，中国经济已濒临崩溃的边缘，国民生产总值不到世界的

2%。改革开放以来，不再批判孔子，中国经济稳步发展，国民生产总值由1978年的3410亿美元激增到2013年的9.3万亿美元，占世界经济总量的比例也由不到3%激增到14%，成为世界第二大经济体。

承认中国历史上的兴盛，将能从一个多世纪以来否定儒家思想思潮中解放出来，肯定儒家思想在中国历史上发挥的重大作用，肯定儒家思想在历史上的贡献，将会理直气壮地从儒家思想中汲取有益成分，将会提高民族自信心。

## 结　论

上述分析足以证明，随着中国的发展，中国将越来越回归传统，越来越注意从儒家思想中汲取营养。儒家思想能够促进中国历史的发展，也一定能促进现代社会的发展，促进中华民族的伟大复兴，实现国家富强、民族振兴、人民幸福的中国梦。21世纪的中国，经济将会越来越发达，文化越来越繁荣，社会越来越和谐与稳定。中国越来越重视从儒家思想中汲取营养，将会更加继承儒家传统，致力建设和谐世界，坚持对外和平、发展、合作、共赢的方针，与世界各国人民一起促进人类和平与发展。

# 儒学道统思想与中华民族精神

四川省中国哲学史研究会　蔡方鹿

## 一、儒学道统思想的发展演变

儒学道统思想是中华文化的重要组成部分，站在整个中国文化发展的大传统的角度看，道统思想的发展促进了中国文化的不断发展。此文化传统既是以儒学为主导，又反映了中国文化是多元复合体的综合型文化的性质，因而是客观连续存在着的，而不是主观易断的。它作为中国历史文化的积淀，尽管有糟粕和过时的思想因素，但其中包涵着的中华民族精神和优秀文化传统是不容抹杀的。

道统是内容和形式的统一，从形式上讲，圣人之道的传授统绪日益完善并发展演变；从内容上讲，道范畴的内涵日益丰富，并随着时代的发展不断上升到新的理论高度。形式与内容的结合，构成了儒学道统思想的历史发展。道统之道一以贯之，从产生到现代，历数千年而不衰。自伏羲开创中国文化的大传统以来，历代圣人为中华文明和文化的发展做出了贡献。至孔子继承文王仁政，损益周公周礼，以仁释礼，把周公之礼发展为仁道，这奠定了儒学道统思想的基本内涵和基础，代代相传，为后世道统论所认同。

孔子仁道成为儒学道统思想的根基，广泛深刻地影响了包括各家思想在内的整个中国传统文化，形成中华文化的鲜明特色。儒学道统思想经历了时代的发展，各个时代的道统论不仅继承了孔子的仁道，而且体现了各个时代的精神，反映了各自时代思想文化的特质和一定的发展方向。同时每个时代的道统论都吸取了先前道统思想的资料和积累起来的成果，并结合社会发展和时代的要求，在此基础上加以创新，给原有的道统论注入新的内涵，使道统的发展绵延不绝，从而从一个侧面体现了中国文化发展和中华大道发展的方向。通观儒学道统思想的历史发展和演变，大致可分为以下几个互相联系又互相区别由古到今的发展阶段：

（一）早期追溯，从伏羲到周公，以文王仁政和周公之礼为代表

根据先秦典籍的记载和历代学者的追述，儒学道统论把道统的起源追溯到伏羲，即道统溯源于伏羲、神农、黄帝。从上溯至伏羲起，则道统文化有了悠久的历史，这实际是指中华民族自伏羲画八卦以来悠久灿烂的文明和文化。经尧、舜、禹、汤、文、武，到周公，道统传承中的圣人，他们创造性的活动，为中华民族文化的形成发展和相传授受，做出了卓越的贡献。此阶段除周公外，均为上古帝王（周公亦为摄政王），被后世儒家尊为圣人。其圣王行事，多为事迹，还未形成有体系的思想，但透过他们的事迹，也体现了一定的思想，足以为后人所效法。或被认为从伏羲、神农、黄帝、尧、舜、禹、汤、文、武、周公一代代传下来的外王的业绩，必定有创造这些外王业绩的内圣之道为之依据，这就形成了早期的道统，而周公是早期道统的总结者，形成了较为系统的思想。周公以前的历代圣王，其道一脉相承，尽管考诸史籍，缺乏系统的文字记载，但通过外在的事迹和外王业绩，仍可考出其内圣之道来。

在道统发展的溯源阶段，伏羲被认为是首出庶物的大圣人，他顺应天地之自然，观象取物，始作八卦，以象征八类不同属性的事物，把易象建立在自然物象的基础上，开易学之先河。后世在伏羲画八卦的基础上，逐渐形成了《周易》及易学，这在中国文化史上占有举足轻重的地位。

神农被视为继伏羲之后，道统的传人，其时代的特点是“农作”，发明农具，从事农耕以养民，解决众多民众的生存问题，以此与古民“皆食禽兽肉”的时代相区别。这是神农对中华文明发展做出的贡献。

黄帝是道统的发祥者之一，历来被认为是中华民族的共同祖先，或认为炎帝、黄帝同为中华民族的祖先。黄帝不仅文治武功超群，而且有许多发明创造，《国语·鲁语》说：“黄帝能成百物，以明民共财。”为中华文明的进步贡献很大。

尧在道统中的地位与早期的圣人相比，更为明晰，其思想言行对后世的影响也更大。这集中体现在他本于大公，于民间选择了一位至孝至悌的贤人，名曰舜，不仅相传以“允执其中”的中道原则，而且把帝位也禅让给舜。尧舜禅让，实行公天下的大同政治，反对家天下，这被儒家看作王道的最高理想境界。尧在外王即外而在政治上行王道方面，为后世树立了典范。其王道政治表现在尚贤、辞让、重义轻利、为民、兼爱、均施恩德、上下有别、贵贱有等、君臣有序、慎用武力等方面，为后世儒家所效法。

舜在孝亲和举贤用人方面，为后世树立了榜样。舜有一个不慈的父亲和不悌的兄弟，加上继母，多次加害于他。但舜却依然事父母以孝，为孔子所称颂。舜治理天下，举贤任能，包括举用鲇陶，使众人归化于仁；使契为司徒以之教民；任用禹以治水，并以“允执厥中”传之于禹。自己也是执其两端，而用其中于民。这体现了道统之中

道原则。舜亦出于大公至德，把帝位禅让给禹。孔孟往往将尧舜并论，对两人备加称颂，《今文尚书·尧典》也把尧舜结合起来介绍，表明尧舜在中国文化史上历来有崇高的地位。

其后，禹治水十三年，三过家门而不入，公而忘私，治平水患，造福于人民；又划分天下为九州，为大一统的中华国家奠定了基础。汤反对暴政，施行仁义，革残暴不仁的夏桀之命；又执中，立贤无方，体现了尧舜禹汤均相传以“执中”的原则，这成为道统相传的重要理论。文王之子武王继承文王的遗志，革商纣之命，成为继汤伐桀之后，中国历史上第二次伟大的革命，不仅《易传》对此作了充分的肯定，而且儒学代表人物孟子、荀子、朱熹均认同于文武之道，尤其是孟子、朱熹直把汤武革命的对象桀纣称之为独夫，认为贼仁贼义的独夫可诛，诛独夫不是“臣弑其君”，反对不行仁义的暴君。说明仁义之道高于君主之位，这是儒家道统思想的一个基本出发点，并以此来垂戒后世帝王。

在道统发展的溯源阶段以文王仁政和周公之礼为代表，其对后世的道统论尤其对孔子的思想产生了非常重要的影响。

周文王实行仁政是对尧舜王道之治的继承，并顺应时代潮流和民心向背，以仁政反对商纣王的暴政。文王实行仁政的内容包括：“即康功田功”（《今文尚书·无逸》）的重农思想、“怀抱小民”（《今文尚书·无逸》）的爱民观念、“咸和万民”（《今文尚书·无逸》）的安民精神，这成为儒家民本主义的思想来源。文王的仁政从“制其田里”入手，即“制民之产”，百姓有了田产，从事生产劳动，满足其衣食生活需求，老人妻子儿女有所养，从而安居乐业。文王“修德行善”（《史记·殷本纪》）、“视民如伤”（《孟子·离娄下》）、“发政施仁”（《孟子·梁惠王下》），受到儒家的高度赞扬，孔子说：“文王既没，文不在兹乎?”（《论语·子罕》）认为文王之道在文王之后仍然继续流传，以自己为继承文王之道者，可见道统传授之脉络。后世儒家在文王仁政的基础上，逐渐形成系统的道统思想来。

周公制礼作乐，其礼治思想对儒家道统影响很大。周礼的内容集中体现在亲亲和尊尊上。孔子效法周公，崇尚周礼。他说：“周监于二代，郁郁乎文哉！吾从周。”（《论语·八佾》）以周文作为其思想的基础，也就是以亲亲和尊尊作为礼的根本要求，认为植根于血缘基础的亲亲与维护宗法等级制的尊尊是相互依存的。孔孟儒家遂从亲亲中推导发展出仁来，从尊尊中发展出义来。可见儒家仁义之道与周礼之亲亲、尊尊有密切联系，这也是道统早期发展阶段的主要成果。周公还在政治、宗教方面提出了系统的敬德保民思想、天命变化尽人事的思想，它们同周礼一起共同构成周公之道，对儒家学说及道统论产生了重要影响，奠定了道统思想形成和发展的基础。

（二）从孔子到汉儒，以孔孟仁义之道为代表

道统发展的第二阶段从儒家创始人孔子起，经孟子、荀子，到汉儒董仲舒、扬雄等，其中包括儒家经典《易传》、《大学》、《中庸》等所表达的思想。这一阶段是儒家道统思想的发端期，儒家道统的基本理论在这一阶段已经提出，后世道统论就是在这个基础上发展的。孔子仁道以及孟子把仁义连用，提出仁义之道不仅是这一阶段道统思想的主要代表，而且是整个儒学道统思想的根基，不论后世道统思想发生了多少变化，也不论道统理论有多少发展创新，都没有改变孔孟仁义之道作为道统核心和基本内涵这一事实。程朱以天理论道，陆王以本心为道，现代新儒家以内圣心性之学为道统，其天理、本心、内圣心性之学无一不是以仁义为内涵，只不过是在仁义之道的基础上，从形式到内容对其加以发展罢了。

孔子继承文王仁政和周公周礼，创儒家学派，提出了以仁为核心的一整套学说，把仁与礼相结合，以仁释礼，以仁、礼为道。并提出“中庸之为德”的思想，强调“允执其中”，倡无过无不及的中道观；注重人事，以人弘道，重视发挥人的主观能动性；宣扬上古圣人，整理儒家经典，为道的传授和推广做出了旁人不可替代的贡献。由此而确立了其在道统思想发展史上十分重要的地位。

孟子的仁义之道及心性说对后世道统思想影响很大，尤其是陆王和现代新儒家之新心学一系的道统论对孟子思想吸取甚多。与孔子相比，孟子更为明确地提出了圣人之道相传授受的统绪，这为后世所遵循，由此而奠定了他在道统思想发展史上开道统传授之端绪的地位。

《易传》提出“一阴一阳之谓道”的思想，以阴阳作为道的内涵，阴阳之道一以贯之，体现在天、地、人三方面；并以形而上下分道器，这些方面丰富了道统之道的内涵。《易传》又扩大圣人的范围，《系辞》提出伏羲、神农、黄帝、尧、舜一脉相传的五帝系统，这为道统的起源提供了经典和资料的依据。

荀子虽不为宋明儒之大家所看重，但他在道统史上应占有一席之地。这是因为荀子继承发展孔子的思想，又吸取改造道家的思想，提出“天有常道”（《荀子·天论》）的命题，以礼义忠信为道，强调天道自然，人道有为；引用《道经》“人心之危，道心之微”的话，以说明主体之心存在着人心与道心的区别。这为《古文尚书·大禹谟》所吸取，开道统“十六字心传”之先河。

《大学》提出明明德之道和三纲领八条目，充分体现了儒家内圣而外王的精神。唐代韩愈以《大学》之道批佛老，建立道统论思想体系；程朱把《大学》列入“四书”之中，以之发明道统，并强调治“四书”以《大学》为先，《大学》是修身治学的纲领；王阳明也以《大学》发明“致良知”说；唯有牟宗三认为程颐、朱熹以《大学》为主，未讲出本有之心性，有违本心即性的原则，故为宋明儒学之“旁枝”，对《大

学》不予充分的重视。这些方面表现出《大学》在道统史上的重要性。

《中庸》在继承发展孔子的中庸思想并将其系统化、哲理化的同时，又提出中和之道和一系列重要命题和理论，如“天命之谓性，率性之谓道，修道之谓教。”“修身以道，修道以仁。”“尊德性而道问学”等。为道统思想的确立和完善，提供了丰富的思想资料。朱熹在对《中庸》的集注中，正式提出了“道统”二字，并对道统展开了系统深入的论述。这对道统思想的确立和发展具有重要意义。

董仲舒虽为宋明儒之道统论所超越，以周敦颐、二程直接孔孟，然而仍不能抹杀其在广义的儒学道统思想发展史上的地位和作用。董仲舒提出“罢黜百家，独尊儒术”的思想，为汉武帝所采纳，儒学遂成为中国文化的正统。这为儒家思想包括道统论的发展，创造了有利条件。董仲舒提出的“圣人法天而立道”（《汉书·董仲舒传》）的思想，不仅丰富了传统儒学的道论，而且启发了后世儒学的道统论和道统史观。

董仲舒之后，汉儒扬雄推崇儒家圣人，把圣人与道相联系，并以“五经”济道，认为“舍‘五经’而济乎道者，末矣。”（《扬子法言·吾子篇》）把道与儒家经典相结合。隋代王通有志于恢复先王之道，认为“杨墨之言出而孔子之道塞；佛老之教行而尧舜之道潜”，[1] 佛老异端与儒家圣人之道不并存。程朱的道统谱系虽不列扬雄、王通之名，但“宋初三先生”中的孙复、石介二人却在自己的道统论里树立了扬雄、王通的地位。

道统发展的第二阶段儒学代表人物和儒家经典提出了诸多的理论，丰富了道统思想的内涵，其中孔孟的仁义之道作为道统之道的核心，在道统史上的影响最大。

（三）从韩愈到程朱陆王，以超越时代的心传说和天理论为代表

道统发展的第三阶段，即道统论的正式提出和确立以及发展演变的阶段，此阶段从韩愈起，经孙复、石介、周敦颐、张载，到二程、朱熹、陆九渊、王阳明，以及吴澄等。这一阶段是道统论发展的高潮，蔚为大观，左右了当时的思想界，这具有历史的必然性。之所以把此一阶段说成是道统论的正式提出和确立时期，是因为虽然道统思想的成分在先秦、孔孟及汉代儒家思想体系里已经具有，但未成系统，尚未明确提出，其理论针对性也不明显。至唐代韩愈及宋代程朱，面对儒学发展停滞，佛老冲击儒学，动摇了其在思想文化领域的主导地位，而旧儒学墨守师说，严守家法，“疏不破注”，拘于训诂，限于名物与辞赋，已经僵化，不能与佛教精致的思辨哲学相抗衡。韩愈、程朱及宋儒学者力转此风，面对佛老思想的挑战和儒家伦理扫地而造成人无廉耻、纲常失序及社会动荡的局面，以弘扬儒家圣人之道为己任，对抗佛教宗派传道的法统，明确提出了儒家圣人之道传授的系统，并详尽论述道统之道的内涵。韩愈著《原道》，

---

① 石介：《徂徕石先生文集》卷七，《录蠹书鱼辞》引，北京：中华书局，1984 年，第 81 页。

标志着道统论的正式提出。以二程朱熹为代表的宋代理学家则以天理论道，把道统之道提升为宇宙本体，与天理等同；并提出超越时代的心传说，把传道与传心联系起来，以《古文尚书·大禹谟》“十六字传心诀”和《论语·尧曰》、《中庸》里的论述作为经典的依据，以《中庸》阐发“十六字心传”。这成为程朱道统的重要理论。其后，陆王提出心学道统观，仍讲超越时代的心传，只不过把程朱也作为超越的对象，以自己直接孟子。王阳明虽然以“致良知”说取代道统论，但他仍以“十六字传心诀”作为心学之源，这说明陆王与程朱在道统心传问题上有相同之处。此外，陆王道统虽以心为道，将道统与心学相结合，然而他们并不反对天理，只不过把天理与心等同，提倡“心即理”，心性一元，本心即性，以此与程颐朱熹的天理即道的天理论相沟通，而与其心理为二、心性有别的思想有异。在共同提倡心传，认同于天理的前提下，因其各自思想的特点，陆王与程朱的道统论又存在着一定的差异。

韩愈的道统论启发了宋儒之道统论，这是不可否认的历史事实。程朱的道统论又在韩愈道统的基础上，有了大的发展。从内容上讲，韩愈道统之道的内涵是仁义，程朱在仁义之道的基础上，以天理论道，把哲学本体论与儒家伦理学结合起来，这是对韩愈及传统道统论的发展；从形式上看，韩愈提出的道统传授谱系说为宋儒所吸取，孙复、石介不仅继承了韩愈的道统，而且在他们的传道谱系中，增加了荀子、扬雄、王通、韩愈等先秦汉唐诸儒，对韩愈备加推崇，而程朱虽然在表面上不多提韩愈，声称是由周敦颐、二程直接从孟子那里得千年不传之绝学，把圣人之道接续下来，但实际上他们受到了韩愈道统说的影响。程朱均对韩愈表示一定的尊重，只是由于他们认为《原道》中的言语有病，所以不多提韩愈在道统中的作用。

张载以气化论道，这是他思想的特点，并成为儒学道统思想发展史上以气论道的理论代表。张载提出完整的道统论，倡道于千年不传之后，他继承发挥《易传》提出的伏羲等“五帝”的系统，形成圣人一脉相传的传道次第，以回应佛老对儒学的冲击。并认为儒家圣人之道在北宋时复明，自有其复明昭显的历史必然性，观察到道统论的崛起，具有深刻的社会历史根源和思想根源。

朱熹在继承二程确立的道统论的基础上，建构精致的道的哲学，完善了道统思想体系；集注“四书”，集道统论之大成；并与陈亮展开关于道统问题的争论，在辩论中明确提出超越时代的心传思想；把道学与道统相结合，赋予道统论以时代的新义，使道学成为道统论历史发展的一个重要阶段。

自朱熹集道统思想之大成后，道统论逐渐心学方向发展演变，这也有其时代的必然性。陆九渊提出心学道统观，以心论道统，对程朱道统论加以心学化的改造，他以继孟子之后道统第一人自居，把韩愈、周敦颐、二程、朱熹均排斥在道统之外。虽然陆九渊站在心一元论哲学的立场，不同意程朱对《尚书·大禹谟》“十六字传心诀”的解释，但他以自己上接孟子而自得其道，仍然是以程朱的超越时代的心传理论为依据的。

吴澄道统论的特点是把心学与道统紧密结合，扩大心学的内涵，把朱熹道统中的众多人物及其学说都包括到心学里来，而不把心学仅限于陆氏心学。吴澄并针对朱学末流的弊端，超越朱学，向心学转化，体现了道统论演变的趋势。

王阳明直接把圣人相传授受之学称之为“心学”，把“十六字传心诀”视之为“心学之源”。[①] 提出“致良知之外无学矣”，[②] 以“致良知”说取代程朱道统论，从而把圣人相传的道统说改造为心学。完成了道统心学化的过程，这为现代新儒学之新心学一系所继承，并以之作为“源头活水”，而吸取甚多。

除上以外，明清时期，道统论继续流传，并产生了重要影响。这一时期，朱学与阳明学之争，理学道统论的流弊对思想界亦产生了影响，并反映到对道统思想的评价上。孙奇逢的道统思想和费密对理学道统论的批评，反映了时代变迁对道统思想的影响。也与整个时代社会转型、思想发展的实际紧密相连。

明清时期，由于道统思想的重要影响，出现对儒家道统传承脉络整理的风气，如周汝登（1547—1629）著《圣学宗传》，过庭训（？—1629）著《圣学嫡派》，魏裔介（1616—1686）著《圣学知统录》和《圣学知统翼录》，范鄗鼎（1626—1705）著《理学备考》，熊赐履（1635—1709）著《学统》，万斯同（1638—1702）著《儒林宗派》等。

孙奇逢（1585—1675）著《理学宗传》，对道统传承脉络加以整理，从中阐发自己的道统思想。该书融合程朱道统与心学道统，体现了孙奇逢兼采朱王，一并推崇程朱陆王，融合理学两大家的特点。

费密（1625—1701）提出帝王统道的“道脉谱论”，以代替儒生统道的理学道统论；并提出“舍经无所谓圣人之道”[③] 的思想，主张不受宋儒说经的束缚，从汉唐诸儒对儒家经典的注疏中求得圣门本旨。由此尊崇汉儒，重视训诂注疏，开清朝汉学之风气，给后来的汉学复兴以重要影响。

（四）20世纪20年代以来的现代新儒家，以由内圣心性之学开出科学民主新外王说为代表

道统发展的第四阶段即是现代新儒学之道统论阶段，此阶段现代新儒学人物中讲道统的有熊十力、冯友兰、钱穆、唐君毅、牟宗三等。其中冯友兰和牟宗三讲的较多，

---

① 《王阳明全集》卷七，《象山文集序》，上海：上海古籍出版社，1992年，第245页。

② 《王阳明全集》卷八，《书魏师孟卷》，第280页。

③ 费密：《弘道书》卷上，《道脉谱论》，怡兰堂丛书，1920年刊本。

而以牟宗三为现代新儒学之道统论的代表人物。此一阶段道统论的特点是重内圣心性之学，又吸取西学，援西学入道统，这在牟宗三的道统思想里表现的比较突出。因而形成了不同于传统道统论的特点，这也是对儒学道统思想的发展，使之与现代文化接轨，体现了现代新儒学道统论的时代意义。

熊十力认为宋儒确立道统之说，有回应宗教冲击儒家人文的作用，使人们不惑于出世主义的宗教。又指出宋儒论道不广，遂从广义的角度把道统视为一国学术的中心思想。①

冯友兰既承认在中国思想史上有儒家圣贤一脉相承的道统存在，又提出广义的道统观，以道统为社会居主导支配地位的哲学。并认为这个道统是发展的，以超越的中国哲学精神作为道统哲学发展的主线，追求"极高明而道中庸"的最高境界，从而标立"新统"，把吸取了西方哲学的新理学视为接续了中国哲学各方面最好传统的全新的形上学的新道统。②

钱穆早期肯定韩愈朱熹提出的道统说，后来则认为宋明儒之道统是一种"主观的道统"，是孤立易断的道统，从而提出广义的道统观，以中国历史文化的大传统为道统。强调应多一点包容精神，讲中国文化不能光讲儒家，讲儒家也不能只讲宋明道统，主张从更宽广的角度来弘扬中国文化。③

牟宗三提出道统、学统、政统三统之说，④ 企图通过提出一个安定人生建立制度的思想系统，来作为人们安身立命的根本和社会生活的指导思想，把时代民主政治、现代科学精神与中国文化基本的道德宗教结合起来，从而贯通中西，发展中国文化。与三统说密切联系，牟宗三提出由内圣心性之学开出科学民主新外王的思想，即通过道统之肯定，肯定道德理性即内圣心性之学的价值，开出学统与政统，由德性主体转出知性主体和政治主体，发展民主政治与科学。牟宗三所谓的"新外王"的内容是指民主政治与科学，这体现了对西学的吸取，用以作为重建儒学道统的有机组成部分。⑤

唐君毅肯定在中国文化史上有一道的传授系统，面对西方文化的传入，主张应对儒学道统文化重加研究考察，以回应西方学术文化的冲击，从而弘扬道统文化。唐君毅在由他起草，以牟宗三、徐复观、张君劢、唐君毅四人联名发表的《为中国文化敬告世界人士宣言》中论述了新儒家的道统观，指出中国文化具有一本性，其道统一脉

---

① 参见熊十力：《读经示要》，台北：明文书局，1984年，第463—464页。

② 参见冯友兰：《新原道》，《三松堂全集》第五卷，郑州：河南人民出版社，1986年，第148页。

③ 参见钱穆：《中国学术通义》，台北：台湾学生书局，1993年，第94—96页。

④ 参见牟宗三：《道德的理想主义》，台北：台湾学生书局，1992年，第6页。

⑤ 参见牟宗三：《生命的学问》，台北：三民书局，1984年，第63页。

相传，一以贯之，构成中国文化的一大特色，而与文化来源为多元的西方文化相区别。进而唐君毅把道统说与心性之学相联系，认为宋明儒之所以深信《古文尚书·大禹谟》的“十六字心传”为中国道统的来源，是因为宋明儒者均以心性之学为中国学术文化的本原。故唐君毅把心性之学作为“中国学术思想之核心”，其心性之学与道统中圣人相传之心法合一，而以儒家圣人传道为主，其道的相传又以心传为主，并以此为主体来吸收、融会西学，这体现了现代新儒学道统论的特色。

综观以上儒学道统思想的发展阶段，可以看出，儒学道统思想的发展与中国社会及文化的发展相伴随而始终，道统思想的发展集中反映了中国社会文化发展的本质和各个时代精神的精华。道统之道作为中国哲学的核心和最普遍范畴，它的演变和发展，反映了中国文化演变与发展的大趋势；道统之传授谱系又为道的延续和发展提供了基本的理论形式。道的哲学与道统传授谱系的结合及发展，体现了儒学道统思想的历史发展及其过程。总的来讲，道统文化起源于伏羲，当时未形成思想，只有业绩，经神农、黄帝、尧、舜、禹、汤的发展，至周文王实行仁政，周公提出周礼，体现为道统早期发展的主要成果，尤其是周公之道已初具较系统的思想，为道统理论的提出奠定了基础。孔子继承文王仁政和周公之礼，创造性地提出仁道，经孟子发展为仁义之道，成为道统论的理论根基，又经《易传》、《大学》、《中庸》、荀子、董仲舒等的发展，使道统内涵日益丰富。唐代韩愈面对佛老思想的挑战和旧儒学发展停滞，著《原道》，正式提出儒学之道统论。经二程朱熹以天理论道，讲超越时代的心传，集道统思想之大成，把道统论发展到一个前所未有的理论高度。而张载以气论道，陆王以心论道，形成宋明儒之道统论的不同流派。尤其是陆王把心学与道统相结合，使道统论向心学转化。这为现代新儒家之道统论所继承，把道统论与心性之学相结合，由内圣心性之学开出科学民主新外王，从而援西学入道统，把道统论发展到具有现代文化与哲学精神的新阶段，使儒学道统思想在现代社会的背景下得以继续发展。

## 二、受道统思想影响形成的中华民族精神

儒学道统思想是中华文化的重要组成部分，它的形成、发展演变与传承对中国文化产生了重要影响，对中华民族精神的塑造做出了重要贡献。受道统思想影响形成的中华民族精神主要包括：

### （一）仁爱精神

孔孟仁义思想是道统之道最基本的内涵。孔子从周礼的亲亲、尊尊的原理中发展出仁礼之道，至孟子把仁义连用，发展出儒家的仁义之道。孔子以“爱人”来解释仁，“樊迟问仁，子曰‘爱人’。”（《论语·颜渊》）孟子亦讲“仁者爱人”（《孟子·离娄

下》)，以爱来体现仁。其仁包括了忠恕之道、恻隐之心，仁体现在爱上，通过爱人、助人表现出来。由此仁爱精神成为中华民族精神的重要构成。

以“仁者爱人”、“泛爱众而亲仁”（《论语·学而》)、“君子学道则爱人”（《论语·阳货》)、“仁民而爱物”（《孟子·尽心上》)、“以爱己之心爱人则尽仁”（《正蒙·中正》)、“仁者无不爱也”（《孟子·尽心上》）等为内涵的儒家仁爱思想，以“仁”为根基，以“爱人”为主旨，是民族精神的重要组成部分，体现了中华民族优秀伦理道德的本质，至今仍有重要的现代价值，而值得吸取继承和发扬光大。

爱是人类社会的崇高价值和真挚的情感，任何社会都应把爱作为道德核心价值观，以对治社会丑陋的一面。但是爱不是抽象的情感，爱中凝结着历史与文化的传承，因而不同社会、不同文明形态中的爱的形式与爱的内涵存在着不同。但既然整个人类、各个国家，各个学派都讲爱，那么爱就具有一定的共性。其中儒家讲仁爱，墨家讲“兼爱”，佛教讲“慈悲”之爱，基督教讲“博爱”。虽然儒家的“以爱己之心爱人则尽仁”，即爱人如己才能体现仁的本质的仁爱思想，可视为人类道德的最高境界，但其他的“兼爱”、“慈悲”之爱、“博爱”等既然是历史时代的产物，就有它存在的理由和价值，而值得借鉴。当今时代，应建立以仁爱为基础的大爱。把仁爱作为当代中国社会的核心价值，贯穿在物质文明、精神文明、政治文明、生态文明建设之中，将民族精神与时代精神有机结合起来。

儒家的伦理道德学说，体系完备，思想丰富、寓意深刻，其思想的核心是“仁爱”。“仁”是德性的实践和行动，是儒学文化的精髓，也是道德价值的根本，在历史上为维系世道人心、维持社会生活的正常运转，发挥了重大作用。然而自近现代以来，儒家的仁说受到片面的批判，把“仁者爱人”直斥之为“仁者吃人”，致使人们的道德水准普遍下降。加上儒家的道德人文遭到工业化和西化思潮以及“文革”反儒批孔运动的冲击，其社会影响已经削弱。加之当今社会，功利主义、个人主义、工具理性盛行，追求表面的数据和“形象工程”，崇尚拜金主义，一切为了钱，追逐名利，社会浮躁，信仰缺失，物欲横流，人心不古，道德沦丧，世风日下。可谓重整伦理，提倡仁爱，势在必行。

一视同仁为大仁，公正无私为大爱。大仁大爱为儒家道统思想所崇尚，也是当今社会存续和发展所亟须的价值。

（二）中道和谐精神

执中、中道是道统思想的重要内涵，也即是以中庸为道统的内涵。受此影响，形成了中道和谐的民族精神。

《论语·尧曰》云：“咨！尔舜，天之历数在尔躬，允执其中”，强调执中。《论语·雍也》指出：“中庸之为德也。”孟子云：“孔子岂不欲中道。”（《孟子·尽心下》）朱熹云："盖自上古圣神继天立极，而道统之传有自来矣。其见于经，则'允执厥中'者，尧之所以授舜也；'人心惟危，道心惟微，惟精惟一，允执厥中"者，舜之所以授禹也。"① 执中、中道作为道统思想的重要内涵对中华民族精神产生了重要影响。

与执中、中道密切相关，儒家中和思想亦贯穿着和谐的原则，这在历史上产生了重要影响。《礼记·中庸》云："喜怒哀乐之未发，谓之中；发而皆中节，谓之和。中也者，天下之大本也；和也者，天下之达道也。致中和，天地位焉，万物育焉。"意即喜怒哀乐等人的感情未发之前，谓之中，此中作为思想和伦理原则，存在于内，是天下万物的根本、人的感情的发源地。人的感情表现出来，符合了中的原则，就是和。掌握了中和的道理，天地万物便有其根据，人的道德也才能达到尽善尽美的境界。

其后，历代学者都很重视《中庸》提出的中和之义，把它作为思想方法论及道德修养论的基本原则，强调一切事物都要符合中，中的运用要贯彻到人的感情流露等各种事物中去，防止违背中和的原则而出现种种偏激、不适当的行为。

儒家道统强调执其两端取其中，讲中和，不走极端，办事恰到好处，不偏不倚，既不过头，也无不及，对矛盾双方都提出规范和要求，不过分偏向一方，否则将导致统一体的破裂，这是儒家精神所反对的。由此而产生"和为贵"、"仇必和而解"的重和谐思想，在历史上影响深远。重和谐，重矛盾双方的统一，反对极端，不随意打破有机统一体，这不仅成为人们普遍遵循的思想方法，而且成为中华文化精神的重要组成部分之一。持中重和，以中为原则，来实现天下和谐，这是儒家文化所注重和维护的。

中和精神强调社会稳定，重视和谐统一，这使得中国社会与中国文化的发展具有稳定性和长期性，不至于被过度的动荡所破坏和中断，也使中国人形成求同存异、礼让克制、温和内向的心理性格。

因此在先秦时期，和合文化得以产生和发展。概而言之，所谓和合的和，指和谐、和平、祥和；合指结合、融和、合作。和合连起来讲，指在承认"不同"事物之矛盾、差异的前提下，把彼此不同的事物统一于一个相互依存的和合体中，并在不同事物和合的过程中，吸取各个事物的优长而克其短，使之达到最佳组合，由此促进新事物的产生，推动事物的发展。在此和谐精神的指导下，中华文化不断创新，同时也推动了中国社会的不断发展。

由此可见，和谐、和合文化并不否认矛盾、差异和必要的斗争，它本身就是矛盾的对立统一体，只是把矛盾、差异和斗争限定在相互依存的统一体中，防止因过度的矛盾斗争而破坏了不同事物共同存在的基础，而使事物的发展停滞不前。这表明，和

---

① 朱熹：《四书章句集注》，《中庸章句序》，北京：中华书局，1983 年，第 14 页。

谐文化有两个基本的要素，一是客观地承认不同，比如阴阳、天人、男女、父子、上下等等，相互不同；二是把不同的事物有机地合为一体，如阴阳和合、天人合一、五教和合、五行和合等等。中国古代的先哲们正是通过对天地自然界、人类社会普遍存在的和合现象作大量观察和探索，从而提出了和合、和谐的概念，对和合现象做出本质的概括，由此促进事物的发展和新事物的产生。在这个过程中，中华和谐、和合文化得以产生、流传和发展，成为人们普遍认同的观念。而孔子“和而不同”的思想较能够反映和谐文化的本质，而不仅限于人与人之间的关系，包括国与国、人与社会、人与自然之间，都可以用“和而不同”，或不同而和，来加以概括。

秦汉以来，和谐概念被普遍运用，中国文化的发展也呈现出一种融和的趋势。把和视为价值的标准。由此，振兴儒学，继承并弘扬儒学道统思想中的中道和谐理念，确有利于促进现代化事业的发展，以为和谐社会的构建，促进经济与文化的协调发展做出贡献。孔子提倡“和为贵”（《论语·学而》），《周易》重视人与自然、人与人之间的和谐统一关系。尽管人与自然相比，人的地位更为重要，但儒学道统思想并不把自然看作异己力量，而是主张人与自然和谐相处，认为天道与人道是相通的，倡“天人合一”，“万物与吾一体”之说。这与西方文化重视人与自然，以及人与人之间的分别对立的观念确有不同。故中国文化十分注重和谐局面的保持。求大同存小异，成为人们普遍接受的思维原则。主张爱其所同，敬其所异。发扬此种精神，有利于维护世界和平及环境保护，也有助维护民族团结和社会稳定。

受道统之执中、中道思想影响而形成的中道和谐精神，不仅是儒学的重要特征和内涵，亦是中华民族特有的精神。科学理解和大力弘扬中道和谐精神，加强对中华和谐思想的研究和推广，是社会发展的客观需要。这对于全面建成小康社会，促进中华民族的伟大复兴和中国的和平崛起，建设和谐世界，具有重要的现实意义。

（三）民族文化的主体精神

受道统思想之超越时代的心传说、内圣心性之学等理论的影响，传统价值观念重视内在精神的价值，具有强烈而鲜明的主体意识。这对中华民族主体精神的形成和塑造，产生了重要影响。

历史一再证明，无法守住自己的民族之魂，丧失了主体性的民族或国家只会被列强同化直至消失。世界上还没有一个抛弃了自己的民族文化而能够生存和发展的国家。相反，坚持自己民族文化的以色列，国灭而复兴。只有挺立民族文化的主体性，珍惜和发扬自己民族的优秀文化传统，才能够自立于世界民族之林。

在文化交流和吸取外来文化优长，实现现代化的过程中，存在着文化交流的主体问题。即以本民族的文化为主体来融合、吸收其他文化，并在文化交流中起着主导的作用，这须结合时代发展的社会实践来进行。中华民族在悠悠五千年历史发展的长河中创造出来的灿烂文化应视为中外文化交流中的主体。而具有强烈而鲜明的主体意识的儒学道统思想则是中华民族文化传统的重要体现，它对中国文化的形成、发展和演变，产生了深远的影响，在中国文化发展史上占有重要的地位。

像中国这样一个人口众多、历史悠久的文明大国，如果要抛弃她几千年的文化传统，投向“蓝色文明”，全部引进西方文化，那只能造成一种屈俯在帝国主义面前的殖民地文化，而失去中华民族的主体性和特性。因此，系统深入地整理研究儒学道统思想，揭示其所具有的重视主体能动性的发挥、强烈而鲜明的主体意识的基本特征，有利于挺立民族文化的主体性，以弘扬中华民族文化。

任何一个有影响的民族，如果抛弃自己的文化传统，失去民族的自性，不在发扬自己民族优秀文化的基础上去学习、吸收、借鉴外来文化的优长，而是“全盘西化”，盲目地“一切照搬”外来文化，其结果只能是民族文化的衰落、灭亡，以致整个民族的衰亡。只有珍惜和发扬自己民族的优秀文化，以本民族的文化为主体参与文化交流，才能够吸取外来文化的优长以丰富发展自身，并对世界文明的发展，做出自己的新贡献。

因此，我们应该认真思考我们的民族魂、我们的主体精神和主体意识。从这个角度讲，继承和创造性地发扬儒学道统之主体意识，具有重要意义。由伏羲、神农、黄帝，尧、舜、禹、汤，文、武、周公一脉相承而来的中华道统由孔子集大成，后经过颜子、曾子、子思、孟子的传承，再到程、朱、陆、王，以及现代新儒家的相传授受，这未曾断绝的道统应结合时代发展和现代化的需要而继承和发展创新。

受儒学道统影响而形成的民族文化的主体精神，既是民族、国家的主体意识，又是以斯文斯道为主体的文化主体意识。其中所蕴含的中华民族精神具有促进社会发展和实现现代化的内在动力和源泉，而不可缺失。以此面对外来文化及西学的挑战，坚持从民族文化的根源处挺立主体意识，以此来融合、吸收外来文化，发挥主体意识的能动性，使中国文化在吸取外来文化的优长，排除其不适合部分的过程中得到发展。并结合时代发展和现代化的需要，将民族性与时代性有机结合起来。

随着中国等非西方的新兴国家的崛起，我们已迈入了一个新的发展时代。西化和现代化理论所预设的以启蒙精神为主的欧美文明被奉为人类进步和发展的典范已受到了质疑，在新的发展时代，现代化可以具有不同的文化形式。只有通过对话才能为全球社群开辟一条和平共存、同舟共济的康庄大道。构建和谐世界，加强世界合作之哲理应出乎中国道统思想之“中道”，这与西方进化论所主张的“物竞天择，适者生存”之丛林野兽原则截然不同，前者讲求互助合作，救弱扶倾；后者讲求适者生存，弱肉强食。应发扬我中华文化几千年来所讲求之“中道”，挖掘中华文明与中国价值的世界意义，探寻人类共同价值体系。从儒学道统思想中发掘人类的普世价值，为世界文明的进步和社会发展增添新的内涵。

（四）包融涵盖精神

广义的道统思想，是以儒学为主导，吸取融合了各家各派的思想，形成中国文化发展的大传统。孔子创儒家学派，提出仁礼、中庸之道，梳理圣人相传授受之系统，奠定了道统思想的基础。其后，儒学学者在道统发展的历史过程中，以儒学道统为主体，广泛大量吸收包容了道、法、阴阳、名、墨、杂、黄老、佛，以至西方学术等各家各派的思想，用以丰富自身，并加以一定的批评和改造，结合时代的发展予以创新，使道统思想一以贯之，一脉相承，体现为中华文化发展的大传统。

与此相关，道统思想包涵甚广，其道统之道的主要内涵包括仁义之道，以执中、中道为基础的中庸和谐思想，以及将孔孟仁义之道推广开来的修齐治平之道等。道涵盖并主宰天、地、人、物，是永恒的、超时空的本体。

道统思想的一个基本特征是以道的传授和发展来体现和维系中国文化的延续和发展。因此，道统思想的发展不仅促进了中国文化的发展，而且丰富了中国文化的内涵，使之以道为核心，在哲学、政治、伦理、文学、艺术、宗教、价值观等各个文化思想领域展示出丰富多彩的内容。

儒家道统既有排他性，更具包容性，其所体现的具有涵盖性的人文精神是中华民族可以提供全球社群的丰富资源。因此，除了大家熟悉的普世价值如自由、法治、市场经济、民主和市民社会主要来自西方外，这些体现人类文明的成分，有的已被纳入当代中国社会主义核心价值观的内容。而道统中影响深远的儒家传统价值如中道、和谐精神，“推己及人”的仁道，“和而不同”的共生共处之道，以及“己所不欲，勿施于人”的恕道，仁义礼智信等人文精神亦是价值重构和文明对话不可或缺的基本原则。这些儒学道统思想中的精华亦应成为普世价值，而对世界文明的发展和现代化做出贡献。值得肯定的是，这些精华有的已被纳入了当今社会主义核心价值观，如和谐、诚信、友善等。道统思想与现代思想文化的融合，是在当代文化语境中传承和发展中华优秀传统文化，促使其走进新的社会和文化境界的重要途径。

中华文化走向世界中的道统，可提供全球性的价值，如中道、仁义、仁爱思想、和谐合作等。中国的崛起是中华文明包括道统思想的复兴，而与西方普世价值观有别。儒家道统思想值得发掘，并随时代发展而与时俱进、不断创新。

当今世界，在多元宗教与文明文化并存的现实中，儒学道统思想与各宗教、文化除存在着差异外，也有共同之处，其相近之处表现在，它们都讲爱，这具有普世价值。如儒家讲仁爱，仁者爱人，其仁包括忠恕之道、恻隐之心；基督教讲博爱，以善意和情感平等对待他人；伊斯兰教讲仁慈，行善惩恶；道家讲慈爱，无所不包容；佛教讲慈悲，主动去关爱或怜悯所有的人乃至一切生物，使他们获得快乐。总之，爱是全人类的共同情感和追求，也是人类的普遍本性而贯通于世界各文明和宗教之中。可以说，以仁慈友爱之心做人做事，是构建和谐世界的基础。

展望新时期人类社会的发展，应是东方文化、儒家文明继续崛起的时代，是从西方文化主导的世界走向多元文化并存共荣的世界，也是东西文化进一步交融的时代。各民族文化及其宗教、人文精神虽千差万别，但却是彼此平等的，应在平等的基础上，开展对话和交流，求同存异，妥善解决它们之间的分歧。

东西方及其各种文化各有所长，应加强彼此的对话、交流与合作，相互吸取优长而共同发展，提倡相兼互补而不应彼此排斥。同时应把现代文化与优秀传统文化结合起来，而不是互相脱离。加强国际文化交流与合作，以促进东西方文化的融通与发展。

我们也应客观地看到道统思想在流传过程中出现的流弊，正确处理其排他性与继承性的关系问题，道统的排他性等流弊虽遭到五四新文化运动的批判，但仍有其体现中华民族精神的内在的价值，而不可抹杀和否定。在文化认同与道统重构问题上，应批判其所遗留的旧传统，发扬其所体现的中华民族精神，使其与现代化和现代社会发展的实践相结合，从而使儒学道统思想在现代化进程和当代中国新文化建设中发挥其应有的积极作用，重光道统，以东方文化深厚的人文功能造福于世界和人类未来。

# 仁义信和　民本大同

## ——中华核心价值“新六德”论

中国人民大学　肖群忠

习近平总书记指出：“培育和弘扬社会主义核心价值观必须立足中华优秀传统文化。牢固的核心价值观，都有其固有的根本。抛弃传统、丢掉根本，就等于割断了自己的精神命脉。”① 这一论述，着力强调了中华优秀传统文化对于培育和弘扬社会主义核心价值观的基础地位、根本作用。中国的社会主义是建立在中国的现实土壤和历史传统基础上的，社会主义的核心价值观也绝不可能离开中华优秀传统文化的思想资源。这体现出我们党高度的民族文化自信，体现了尊重历史传统的正确态度。社会主义核心价值观离开了优秀传统文化这个根，就等于失去吸取营养的活头源水；如不立足于本民族的优秀传统文化，就“等于割断了自己的精神命脉”，更谈不上开创未来了。

中国社会主义必须具有中国特色，社会主义的核心价值观也必须具有鲜明的中国特色。究竟应该继承中国古代哪些优秀的、核心的优秀传统文化呢？习近平总书记要求我们，“深入挖掘和阐发中华优秀传统文化讲仁爱、重民本、守诚信、崇正义、尚和合、求大同的时代价值，使中华优秀传统文化成为涵养社会主义核心价值观的重要源泉。”②

核心价值观为什么要具有民族特色？习近平总书记提出的上述中华核心价值“新六德”的核心意蕴及其内在关系是怎样的？它与社会主义核心价值观的关系是怎样的？这是本文欲加以讨论的问题。

### 一、中华核心价值观的民族特色

习近平总书记最近指出：“价值观是人类在认识、改造自然和社会的过程中产生与发挥作用的。不同民族、不同国家由于其自然条件和发展历程不同，产生和形成的核

① 习近平2014年2月24日在中央政治局第十三次集体学习会上的讲话。

② 习近平2014年2月24日在中央政治局第十三次集体学习会上的讲话。

心价值观也各有特点。一个民族、一个国家的核心价值观必须同这个民族、这个国家的历史文化相契合，同这个民族、这个国家的人民正在进行的奋斗相结合，同这个民族、这个国家需要解决的时代问题相适应。世界上没有两片完全相同的树叶。一个民族、一个国家、必须知道自己是谁，是从哪里来的，要到哪里去，想明白了，想对了，就要坚定不移朝着目标前进。”① 习总书记的上述讲话精神特别强调指出核心价值观要有民族特色，体现了高度的道路自信、理论自信与制度自信和民族文化自信心。

一定民族国家的核心价值观是自己的文化身份标识、文化内核和文化符号，有没有属于自己的核心价值观是中国道路是否成立的前提条件，核心价值观有无鲜明的民族特色也是其能否具有中国或中华特色，从而影响世界的重要基础。越是民族的，越是世界的。也许正是在这一思想基础上，习总书记要求我们深入挖掘和阐发中华优秀传统文化讲仁爱、重民本、守诚信、崇正义、尚和合、求大同的时代价值，使中华优秀传统文化成为涵养社会主义核心价值观的重要源泉。

习总书记提出的这六个核心价值观念与德目无疑是中华文化自古以来长期追求的核心价值与德目，无论是从内容还是表达话语形式上看，它确实都是具有中国特色的中华核心价值和德目，是中华民族和中国人民长期追求并实践的。

“讲仁爱、重民本、守诚信、崇正义、尚和合、求大同”6 个方面，体现了传统美德、政治理念、社会理想、民族精神方面的根本要求，一般来说各民族核心价值观的要素往往都是由上述几个方面构成的。

一定的价值观总是把自己认为有价值的东西作为目标去追求，这一方面表现为社会理想，而一定社会理想的实现都离不开整个民族全体成员的民族精神、德性，也离不开通过一定的政治理念与政治实践去努力实现目标。正如习近平总书记 2014 年 5 月 4 日在北京大学师生座谈会上讲话“青年要自觉践行社会主义核心价值观”中指出：“核心价值观，其实就是一种德，既是个人的德，也是一种大德，就是国家的德、社会的德。国无德不兴，人无德不立，如果一个民族、一个国家没有共同的核心价值观，莫衷一是，行无依归，那这个民族、这个国家就无法前进。”这段话，明确地论述了价值观与道德的关系，强调价值观就是一种德，不仅是个人的德，也是国家、民族、社会的德，强调了价值目标与德行实践的一致性，价值目标给道德指出了前进的方向，道德是实现价值目标的精神动力。因此，从实践层面看，价值观确实就是一种德，强调了核心价值观的主体性、实践性。

习近平总书记提出的上述六个方面，既是中华民族长期以来形成的核心价值观，

---

① 习近平：《青年要自觉践行社会主义核心价值观——在北京大学师生座谈会上的讲话》，2014 年 5 月 4 日。

也是中华民族个体与群体长期践行的个人美德与民族道德、民族精神，因此，我将之概括为中华核心价值“新六德”。

## 二、“新六德”的核心意蕴及其内在关系

在20世纪初期，孙中山先生在追求民族独立、民族解放的过程中，也深刻认识到道德问题的重要性，他在其《三民主义·民族主义》中指出：“要维持民族和国家的长久地位还有道德问题，有了很好的道德，国家才能长治久安。……所以穷本极源，我们要恢复民族的地位，除了联合起来做成一个国族团体以外，就要把固有的旧道德先恢复起来。有了固有的道德，然后固有的民族地位才可以恢复。”① 基于这种认识，他批判吸收了中华传统美德的核心内容，并根据当时的时代需要，提出了“忠孝仁爱、信义和平”的新八德以区别于宋代提出的“孝悌忠信、礼义廉耻”的旧八德，后来，在30年代，国民政府将“礼义廉耻”和“忠孝仁爱、信义和平”结合在一起称为“四维八德”，长期作为他们的核心价值观与道德加以提倡。

一定的价值观不仅仅是要宣传提倡的，而且是要实践的，因此，其表达就应该简明扼要，易记才能易行，因此，为了达到这个目的，我将习总书记提出的上述六条目十八字按其内在逻辑缩减为八个字即“仁义信和、民本大同”来概括表达，认为这是习总书记根据优秀文化传统和中华民族伟大复兴的时代需要而提出的中华核心价值“新六德”。

“新六德”的内在关系，在我看来，可以分为两大类：道德德目和政治理念与社会理想。其讲仁爱、崇正义、守诚信，主要是传统美德的几个最主要方面，即传统“五常”德中的其中三德。尚和合包括和谐目标与合作精神两个方面，是社会目标与道德精神的统一。而重民本、求大同则是基本政治理念和社会理想。前四条都具有“德性”性质，都可以简化为一个字来表达，后两者省去其动词，并不影响其意义，因此，用“仁义信和、民本大同”八个字来概括中华核心价值“新六德”是恰当的。

《易传·说卦》有言：“立天之道曰阴与阳，立地之道曰柔与刚，立人之道曰仁与义。”仁与义是儒家立人道德的核心，在中国人的口头语中也有一个常常连用的辞，叫“仁义道德”。按照韩愈的思想，“道德”只是一个范畴概念，而“仁义”才是道德的实质，因此在某种意义上，“仁义”就是道德的代名词。比如，我们经常所说的“仁至义尽”“杀身成仁”“舍生取义”等都体现了这一点。这也说明，仁义是传统美德中最核心的、源发性的两个基本道德。仁是一个情感性的源头，是仁者爱人的道德情感，是

① 孙中山：《三民主义》，广东人民出版社，2007年第72、76页。

忠恕之道的思维方式和行仁之方，是奉行克己复礼的实践规范，是追求“博施济众”的奉献精神和高尚境界。让世界充满爱，按中国传统概念表达就是让世界充满仁。义，则是传统道德的另一精神渊薮，它是一种理性精神，它是对社会秩序的追求，是对道义为先的价值观的追求，是对义务为本的人伦责任的追求。仁义之所以是立人之道，就在于二者构成了道德的最根本的源发性的要素，其他道德可以说都是从这两种道德中拓展出来的。相较于“爱国”、“敬业”“友善”等具体领域的德目，仁义是更为基本的道德。没有爱人之情感何谈对人“友善”？没有责任感、义务感，何谈“爱国”“敬业”？

诚信，也属传统“五常”德之一，内诚于己，外信于人。诚者，天之道也，诚之者，人之道也。信德在传统中国就受到高度重视，它是做人、处世、治国的根本，它是道德的坚守与完成，是否有内在道德，都要表现在言行上是否有诚信。讲诚信，不仅是中华优秀传统，而且在现代社会条件下显得更加重要。现代社会市场经济的间接性、社会生活的陌生人化、人际交往的公共化，使诚信成了现代社会正常运转的基础。而且诚信之德在现代社会不仅是一种美德，而且要通过加强诚信体系建设，用制度来加以强化。

中国古代政治理念往往以伦理观念为价值基础，又要求政治为实现一定的道德目标服务。因此，讲仁爱、崇正义，守诚信就不仅是道德，也必须贯彻体现在政治治理过程中，如要以仁爱之心行仁政，重民本。崇正义不仅是对正义精神与美德的追求，同时也要在政治治理上追求一种公平正义的社会秩序、道义为先的正义精神和每个民族成员以天下为己任的责任担当。守诚信也是一样，它不仅是做人之首务，更要贯彻在政治生活中去。人无信，固然不知其可，但政治也是无信不立。“子贡问政。子曰：‘足食，足兵，民信之矣。’子贡曰：‘必不得已而去，于斯三者何先？’曰：‘去兵。’子贡曰：‘必不得已而去，于斯二者何先？’曰：‘去食。自古皆有死，民无信不立。’”（《论语·颜渊》）可见，孔夫子是多么重视信用在政治与社会生活中的重要性。

和谐是人和社会生存与发展的最高价值目标，历史经验证明社会在经济、文化上的进步必须以一个稳定祥和的社会秩序为基础，另外，社会利益分配公平正义，人与人之间诚信友爱，社会风俗祥和淳美，甚至是人与自然万物和谐相处，这正是人们世代追求的价值目标和社会理想。这是因为和谐可以促进社会进步，保证人的幸福和个性得到自由全面发展。在中国社会实现从革命－建设时代向改革－发展时代转型的过程中，在我们党从革命党转变为执政党的过程中，我们扬弃了过去的斗争哲学，而适时提出建设和谐社会的重要决策，得到了广大人民群众的衷心拥护和国际社会的普遍赞赏，也是历史的必然。和谐的目标必须通过人的合作精神来实现，培养和德是实现人和为贵的实践途径。和谐社会的形成与建立，固然离不开诸多经济、政治、文化等客观因素，比如经济上的富裕和公平分配，制度上的合理安排，文化上的礼乐教化等，当然同样也离不开公民身上所具有的和合道德品质。人是社会生活的主体，更是社会和谐的主体，离开了人的交往关系，社会和谐就无从谈起。和谐社会的本质仍然是人与人之间的和谐，最终要体现为公民的行为方式和修养境界，有此才会有社会祥和、人民幸福、世风和美的那样一种和谐社会的气象。因此当我们努力建设和谐社会的时候，也应该加强公民的和德建设。

人的道德品质是一种经常的、持久的行为方式，是主体身上体现出来的某种境界和精神气象，和德在我看来，主要体现为：公民主体自我修养的中庸温和；公民在人与人之间的友善亲和；公民在组织与团体生活中的团结求和；公民在社会生活中的守礼达和。中庸、友善、团结、守礼就是和德在公民行为方式上的体现，也可作为社会建设和德的主要行为准则和善恶评价标准；而温和、亲和、求和、达和就成为公民和德的一种修养境界、性格特点甚至是社会状态。做事不要走极端，待人要友善，在集体生活中要注意加强团结，在社会生活中要守礼遵守规矩，这样，就会形成一个人的温和性格，交往中的亲和力，群体生活中的求和心，而最终达到社会与人际的和谐目标，从而通过和德把和谐真实落到实处。

建设和谐社会是我们社会治理的目标，以人为本或以民为本是我们基本的执政理念，实现中国梦，世界大同、协和万邦则是我们的理想和处理中国和世界关系的根本理念。

民本是中国古代政治思想的基本理念，重民本是中国优良政治传统，是政治活动最终追求的目标，是实现天下大治、社会和谐的根本。孟子曰："民为贵，社稷次之，君为轻"。相比于国家社稷、君主，人民是最应优先受到重视的，"天视自我民视、天听自我民听"，为人民是一切政治活动的根本目的、价值标准。民本思想不仅是思想家们的核心政治理念，更是很多清明的政治家所实际奉行的执政理念与政治实践。如范仲淹之"居庙堂之高则忧其民，处江湖之远则忧其君"，"先天下之忧而忧，后天下之乐而乐"，很多仁人志士都为民请命，为民谋利，天下为公，即使戏剧"乔老爷上骄"中的县官乔老爷也有一句著名口头禅即"当官不为民做主，不如回家卖红薯"，体现着古代官员自觉的政治担当意识。民本思想的当代价值何在？在我们看来：第一，重民本有助于进一步深化以人为本的执政理念。第二，重民本可以进一步强化官员为人民服务的思想，提高执政道德责任感。弘扬民本思想要求干部要进一步强化为人民服务的思想，"情为民所系、权为民所用、利为民所谋"。第三，重民本可以促进现代民主建设，密切干群关系，提高执政水平。我们党历来重视"从群众中来，到群众中去"的群众路线，注重密切联系群众，开展调查研究等工作方法，坚持以民为本是中国共产党取得政权和巩固政权的有力法宝，干部树立重民本意识，必然会自觉密切干群关系，保障民众的民主权利，促进民众利益的实现，促进服务型政府形成，不断提高社会治理水平和执政水平。

“大同”则是古人最高的社会政治理想，曾经激励多少仁人志士为其矢志不移，奋斗不息，它是中国古人的“中国梦”，正如习近平总书记最近指出的那样：“实现中华民族伟大复兴的中国梦，就是要实现国家富强、民族振兴、人民幸福，既深深体现了今天中国人的理想，也深深反映了中国人自古以来不懈追求进步的光荣传统。”① 按照习总书记的上述论述，中国梦的理想也一定是植根于中华优秀文化的深刻土壤中的，换句话说，“大同”理想是中国梦的优秀传统文化根基，弘扬“求大同”的优秀文化传统不仅能增强全民对“中国梦”的历史意义的认同，而且会体现出“中国梦”的和而不同与和平主义的本质。

古人在求大同的社会理想方面有着很多价值共识，这即是：追求人际关系的融洽，社会的均平和谐以及国家的和平强盛。孙中山在民族主义、民主主义、民生主义的“三民主义”之中，首先特别强调“民生主义”。即完成民族解放和实现政治民主之后特别强调把以平均地权为基础的“民生主义”作为落脚点。他要建成的是“民有、民治、民享”的现代社会，而“民享”则显示了他对传统中崇尚均平和共享的“大同社会”的价值理念的继承。另一方面，孙中山更是坚持了世界大同的和平主义思想理念。他指出：“中国更有一种极好的道德，是爱和平。现在世界上的国家和民族止有中国是讲和平，外国都是讲战争，主张帝国主义去灭人的国家。……这种特别好的道德，便是我们民族的精神。我们以后对于这种精神不但要保存，并且要发扬光大，然后我们民族的地位才可以恢复。”② 他明确把“和平”作为他所提倡的“忠孝仁爱、信义和平”的“新八德”的重要内容。

中国梦不仅是富裕梦、强国梦，而且是公平梦、和谐梦、幸福梦；是文化梦、道德梦；正如习近平总书记在最近的演讲中明确出的那样：“实现中国梦，是物质文明和精神文明均衡发展、相互促进的结果。没有文明的继承和发展，没有文化的弘扬和繁荣，就没有中国梦的实现。中华民族的先人们早就向往人们的物质生活充实无忧、道德境界充分升华的大同世界。中华文明历来把人的精神生活纳入人生和社会理想之中。所以，实现中国梦，是物质文明和精神文明比翼双飞的发展过程。随着中国经济社会不断发展，中华文明也必将顺应时代发展焕发出更加蓬勃的生命力。”③ 中国梦更是和平梦、世界梦。中国的大同理想，在追求天下邦国文明的态度上，一直主张王道、反

---

① 习近平在联合国教科文组织总部的演讲，2014年3月27日，巴黎。

② 孙中山：《三民主义》，广东人民出版社，2007年第76页。

③ 习近平在联合国教科文组织总部的演讲，2014年3月27日，巴黎。

对霸道，追求和平主义，因此，中国梦所追求的崛起与发展是一种和平崛起、和平发展，而不会走逢强必霸的某些西方列强的老路。中国的和平发展只会为世界带来机遇与发展，而不是威胁与危害。协和万邦一直是中国人的追求，和平主义一直是中国的民族特性。中国的和平梦正因为其对和平价值的珍视与实践，也必将成为受世界人民认同和欢迎的世界梦，同一个世界，同一个梦想，这就是2008年北京奥运会向世界发出的中国声音。习近平最近在德国的演讲中明确指出："中华民族是爱好和平的民族。一个民族最深沉的精神追求，一定要在其薪火相传的民族精神中来进行基因测序。有着5000多年历史的中华文明，始终崇尚和平，和平、和睦、和谐的追求深深植根于中华民族的精神世界之中，深深溶化在中国人民的血脉之中。中国自古就提出了'国虽大，好战必亡'的箴言。'以和为贵'、'和而不同'、'化干戈为玉帛'、'国泰民安'、'睦邻友邦'、'天下太平'、'天下大同'等理念世代相传。中国历史上曾经长期是世界上最强大的国家之一，但没有留下殖民和侵略他国的记录。我们坚持走和平发展道路，是对几千年来中华民族热爱和平的文化传统的继承和发扬。"①

## 三、"新六德"与社会主义核心价值观的关系

"在当代中国，我们的民族、我们的国家应该坚守什么样的核心价值观？这个问题，是一个理论问题，也是一个实践问题。经过反复征求意见，综合各方面认识，我们提出要倡导富强、民主、文明、和谐，倡导自由、平等、公正、法治，倡导爱国、敬业、诚信、友善，积极培育和践行社会主义核心价值观。富强、民主、文明、和谐是国家层面的价值要求，自由、平等、公正、法治是社会层面的价值要求，爱国、敬业、诚信、友善是公民层面的价值要求。这个概括，实际上回答了我们要建设什么样的国家、建设什么样的社会、培育什么样的公民的重大问题。"②

那么，如何理解社会主义核心价值观与上述中华民族核心价值观的关系？按照习总书记的相关论述，一方面社会主义核心价值观是对中华优秀传统文化、世界文明有益成果的继承与超越。他说："我们提出的社会主义核心价值观，把涉及国家、社会、公民的价值要求融为一体，既体现了社会主义本质要求，继承了中华优秀传统文化，也吸收了世界文明有益成果，体现了时代精神。富强、民主、文明、和谐，自由、平等、公正、法治，爱国、敬业、诚信、友善，传承着中国优秀传统文化的基因，寄托着近代以来中国人民上下求索、历经千辛万苦确立的理想和信念，也承载着我们每个

① 习近平在德国科尔伯基金会的演讲（2014年3月28日），柏林。

② 习近平：《青年要自觉践行社会主义核心价值观——在北京大学师生座谈会上的讲话》，2014年5月4日。

人的美好愿景。”①

另一方面，社会主义核心价值观必须立足于中华优秀文化传统这个民族文化土壤之上，从中汲取营养，否则就不会有生命力和影响力。习总书记指出：“中华文明绵延数千年，有其独特的价值体系。中华优秀传统文化已经成为中华民族的基因，植根在中国人内心，潜移默化影响着中国人的思想方式和行为方式。今天，我们提倡和弘扬社会主义核心价值观，必须从中汲取丰富营养，否则就不会有生命力和影响力。比如，中华文化强调‘民惟邦本’、‘天人合一’、‘和而不同’，强调‘天行健，君子以自强不息’、‘大道之行也，天下为公’；强调‘天下兴亡，匹夫有责’，主张以德治国、以文化人；强调‘君子喻于义’、‘君子坦荡荡’、‘君子义以为质’；强调‘言必信，行必果’、‘人而无信，不知其可也’；强调‘德不孤，必有邻’、‘仁者爱人’、‘与人为善’、‘己所不欲，勿施于人’、‘出入相友，守望相助’、‘老吾老以及人之老，幼吾幼以及人之幼’、‘扶贫济困’、‘不患寡而患不均’，等等。像这样的思想和理念，不论过去还是现在，都有其鲜明的民族特色，都有其永不褪色的时代价值。这些思想和理念，既随着时间推移和时代变迁而不断与时俱进，又有其自身的连续性和稳定性。我们生而为中国人，最根本的是我们有中国人的独特精神世界，有百姓日用而不觉的价值观。我们提倡的社会主义核心价值观，就充分体现了对中华优秀传统文化的传承和升华。”②

实际上，习总书记的上述论述就是对他所提出的中华核心价值“新六德”相关内容的展开论述。如“仁者爱人”、“与人为善”、“己所不欲，勿施于人”就是讲仁爱；“民惟邦本”就是重民本；“言必信，行必果”、“人而无信，不知其可也”就是守诚信；“君子喻于义”、“君子坦荡荡”、“君子义以为质”、“天下兴亡，匹夫有责”就是崇正义；“天人合一”、“和而不同”、“德不孤，必有邻”、“出入相友，守望相助”就是尚和合；”大道之行也，天下为公”、“老吾老以及人之老，幼吾幼以及人之幼”、“扶贫济困”、“不患寡而患不均”等就是求大同。

可见，社会主义核心价值与中华民族核心价值“新六德”是一个相互支持的关系，前者是对后者的继承超越，后者是前者的源头活水和生命力、影响力所系，因此，在培育和弘扬社会主义核心价值观的过程中，注重弘扬培育中华民族核心价值“新六德”，会进一步增强民众对社会主义核心价值观的认同、接受并推动实践走向深入。

博大精深的中华优秀传统文化是我们在世界文化激荡中站稳脚跟的根基。只有中

---

① 习近平：《青年要自觉践行社会主义核心价值观——在北京大学师生座谈会上的讲话》，2014年5月4日。

② 习近平：《青年要自觉践行社会主义核心价值观——在北京大学师生座谈会上的讲话》，2014年5月4日。

国的，才是世界的。“我们要虚心学习借鉴人类社会创造的一切文明成果，但我们不能数典忘祖，不能照抄照搬别国的发展模式，也绝不会接受任何外国颐指气使的说教。”[①]让我们在培育和践行社会主义核心价值观的过程中，更加自觉和鲜明地体现当代中国核心价值观的民族特色，我们才会向世界发出中国独特的声音，对人类文明做出我们的独特贡献。

① 习近平：《青年要自觉践行社会主义核心价值观——在北京大学师生座谈会上的讲话》，2014年5月4日。

# 传统儒学价值观的创造性转化与当代中国价值观的重塑

河南郑州大学 魏 涛

习近平总书记在系列讲话中多次强调，培育和弘扬社会主义核心价值观必须立足中华优秀传统文化。牢固的核心价值观，都有其固有的根本。抛弃传统、丢掉根本，就等于割断了自己的精神命脉。要认真汲取中华优秀传统文化的思想精华和道德精髓，大力弘扬以爱国主义为核心的民族精神和以改革创新为核心的时代精神，深入挖掘和阐发中华优秀传统文化讲仁爱、重民本、守诚信、崇正义、尚和合、求大同的时代价值，使中华优秀传统文化成为涵养社会主义核心价值观的重要源泉。要处理好继承和创造性发展的关系，重点做好创造性转化和创新性发展。培育和践行社会主义核心价值观，就要从中华优秀传统文化中充分汲取思想道德营养，结合时代要求加以延伸阐发，既使中华民族最基本的文化基因与当代文化相适应、与现代社会相协调，又让社会主义核心价值体系之树深深植根于中华优秀传统文化的沃土之上。儒学是中国传统文化的思想主流，探究传统儒学价值观与当代价值观重构之关系，在返本开新中彰显价值观建设之中国特色，是赓续中国文化血脉，深入推进中国社会改革稳步前进的必由之路。

## 一、传统儒学的现代困境与价值转型探索

作为中国传统思想主流的儒学，是一个以伦理道德观念为核心的思想体系。按照崔大华先生的理解，它是一个以“仁”、“礼”、“天命”三个基本范畴所体现的、由心性的、社会的、超越的三个理论层面所构成的比较周延的思想体系。[①] 但是，应该看到，历史上的儒家并不单纯展现出其伦理道德性的一面，而且是适应当时社会发展，逐渐获得越来越广泛的社会认同，在“罢黜百家，独尊儒术”之后，被历代统治者所

① 崔大华:《儒学的现代命运》，人民出版社，2012年，第247页。

利用，演变为历史上的国家意识形态。其功能逐渐扩展，不再仅止于引领人们价值取向的道德功能，而且也增加了带有一定的法律性和宗教性的功能。南宋以后，儒学的意识形态性质被进一步强化，在当时国家政策的推动下，通过从科举考试到通俗读物的多渠道方式，广泛地影响了士、农、工、商等各个社会群体，对整个社会的价值观的形塑方面发挥了主导性的作用。其独特的理论品格和价值特点，不止对中国文化产生了深远的影响，而且远播异域，成为凝聚文化中国力量的重要精神依托。

自鸦片战争以来，在西方工业文明的挑战中，政治上一次次挫折、失败和经济上相对滞后的不争事实，促使着国人在启蒙与救亡的双重变奏中开始对儒学的现代价值和意义进行深入思考。在五四以来激进的反传统浪潮中，儒学一次次被视为是铸成中华千年未有之祸的根源，受到社会各方的严厉责难和否定性批判。深受西方文化濡染的现代国人，往往将中国文化和现代生活视为两个截然不同而且相互对立的实体。在围绕这所谓的两个实体进行讨论的过程中，问题逐渐聚焦于数千年积累下来的旧文化传统和价值观与源于西方的新生活方式之间的激烈冲突。致使自五四以来，关于文化问题的争论几乎都是围绕这一主题而展开。全盘西化论和文化保守主义者则成为其中的极端化论调，此外还存在着程度不同的西化论和本位论，及模式各异的调和论。[①] 综观历史可见，在所有非西方的文明体系中，儒家化文明所受西方的冲击与影响最为强烈。而儒学在这些文化中的地位，尤其在其原生的中国文明区，可用“摇摇欲坠”四字来形容。在这样的国人批判声浪中儒学逐渐从国家意识形态中剥离出来，在晚清以来的新教育体系中逐渐被肢解。许多华人甚至认为，如今还有什么儒学传统可谈，这东西早已过时且彻底崩溃了。相对而言，在伊斯兰教、印度教，乃至佛教文明地区，这些由宗教所主导的文化所受西方文明的影响便小得多。奠基于宗教系统的价值体系，除非抛弃或改变信仰，否则难以改变。而对这些文明来说，抛弃传统信仰几乎等于抛弃自己的一切。大概是出于从宗教性缺失的视角力图对儒学在近代艰难处境的挽救，康有为的立孔教为国教的理论和活动在清末民初的社会思潮中崭露出来，但在民主共和渐入人心的时代逐渐被质疑、否定。在蔡元培、章炳麟、陈独秀等人的激烈反对声中，以失败而告终。章炳麟则将儒学视为一种子学，让儒学以其“义理”内容在哲学的学术领域里获得了自己的安身立命之地。这一定位，后来成为迄今为止，人们对儒学的主流定位。20世纪上半期，还有一种为梁漱溟所论说的，与康有为、章炳麟皆不同的儒学定位，即将儒学理解为一种生活、一种文化。[②] 在他看来，不应将孔子儒学简单地视为是一种静态的思想观念形态，而应深入地理解为是一种鲜活的、生命的存在

① 余英时：《中国思想传统的现代诠释》，江苏人民出版社，2003年，第1页。

② 梁漱溟：《东西方文化及其哲学》，商务印书馆，1921年，第316页。

表现。与这些学者的做法相映成趣的是，包括牟宗三、徐复观、冯友兰、余英时、杜维明等人在内的学者，对于五四所提出和构建的中国现代化走向“民主”和“科学”的目标，立足于儒学进行了更为自觉的回应，力图解决儒学与这两个目标相对立的问题。他们从不同的角度对儒学可以响应或转换出“民主”和“科学”的精神资源进行了深入挖掘。提出传统民本思想与西方民主思想中的平等思想具有兼容性，如冯友兰在《中国哲学中之民主思想》中云：“孟子和荀子都主张人类是平等的，这就是民主思想中的重要核心。”① 此亦明显地体现在唐君毅等四位学者发表的《为中国文化敬告世界人士宣言》中。牟宗三进一步认定，儒学的进一步发展的文化使命就是要在儒学的道德理性中“转出”民主与科学，即“内圣开出新外王”。徐复观则更为清醒的提出：“民主、科学未曾在传统中出现……必须彻底加以接承。”② 提出儒学应该利用各种资源实现在当代实现其在历史上所缺乏的民主与科学。尽管20世纪这些学者在儒学面临现代化的困境中给我们提出了不同的诠释与发展路径，但并未根本上改变儒学从国人价值认同上与现代社会似乎对立乃至断裂的格局。2004年北京文化高峰论坛上，包括杜维明先生在内的70位学者共同签署的《甲申文化宣言》昭告世人，“注重人格、注重伦理、注重利他、注重和谐”的中华文化品格，对于解决有全球化所带来的一系列问题都具有重要的思想启示意义。③ 这样的提法固然让我们对于儒学的现代意义充满乐观，但我们应该清醒地意识到，如若儒学不能随着时代的变革而作适时地调整，这样一个曾经在中国传统社会发挥重要作用的理论资源终会被消耗殆尽，只能沦落到成为“历史博物馆的陈列品”的境地。

积极促动儒家思想现代转型的研究目前在学界已屡见不鲜，以余英时为代表的很多学者在市场经济的中国面临道德危机的情境下，提出了从价值视角审视包括儒学在内的中国文化的视角，为儒学在新时期的发展与价值的展现开辟了一个崭新的方向。余先生于中西文化价值比较的视角挺立出中国文化的价值。在他看来，中国文化只对价值的超越源头作一般性的肯定，而不特别努力去建构另外一个完善的形而上的世界以安顿价值，然后再用这个世界来反照和推动实际的人间世界。④ 并且提出，中国人的行上超越世界和形下的现实世界是不即不离的，天与人是合德的，尽性即知天，所以要求之于内。⑤ 在这一观点的基础上，余先生提出了其著名的中国文化“内在超越说”。对于我们深入思考儒学的特质和尤其所奠定的中国传统主流价值观的现代意义具有很

① 冯友兰:《三松堂学术文集》，北京大学出版社，1984年，第640页。

② 徐复观:《论传统》,《徐复观文录选粹》，台湾学生书局，1980年，第113页。

③ 《甲申文化宣言》,《大地》，2004年第8期。

④ 余英时:《中国思想传统的现代诠释》，江苏人民出版社，2003年，第13页。

⑤ 余英时:《中国思想传统的现代诠释》，江苏人民出版社，2003年，第16页。

大的启发。自本世纪初，社会主义核心价值观问题提出以来，很多学者即是从余英时所深度揭示的中国文化价值特色的角度进行了有效的回应。对于中国特色社会主义核心价值观的凝练和明确提出，发挥了重要作用。加之近年来，尤其是十七届六中全会以来官方层面的积极推动，借由包括儒学在内的中国传统文化中挺立出中国特色的声音越来越强烈。这也为我们对儒学价值观与社会主义核心价值观的融通理解提出了新的挑战。

## 二、传统儒学价值观与社会主义核心价值观的融通与涵摄

从思想发生的视角来看，传统儒学价值观成为形构社会主义核心价值观的重要渊源。人类历史是在连续性与非连续性的统一中不断前进的，价值观念的发展也是如此。任何时代的社会价值观，都与前一时代的社会价值观存在联系，新的社会价值观要建立在前人所积累的思想材料基础上，在特定的民族文化环境中产生和发展起来。作为社会主义制度的内在精神，社会主义核心价值观是引领社会思想道德建设的一面旗帜，是全民族团结和睦、奋发向上的精神纽带。要建立健全新的思想价值体系，重点在于创新和发展。社会主义核心价值观作为一种社会意识形态，来源于诸多方面，而中国传统文化正是中国特色社会主义核心价值观建构的思想源泉。社会主义核心价值观并非是对中国传统文化的全盘继承，而是取其精华去其糟粕，对中国传统文化进行升华和再创新。传统文化是文化在历史的发展中一代代的积淀，是文化的“活灵魂”。中国传统文化为社会主义核心价值观建设提供了文化基础和思想传统。社会主义核心价值观作为中国特色社会主义主导价值观的理论体系，其中的各个方面都必然贯穿着中国传统文化。而社会主义核心价值观正是植根于中国传统文化的沃土中，吸收了其精髓，才形成和发展起来的。社会主义核心价值观纳入了中国传统文化的核心价值观的一些要素，也就具备了中国文化特色。作为中国文化核心价值观承载的儒学价值观与社会主义核心价值观更是存在着千丝万缕的联系。包括儒学在内的优秀传统文化蕴含着中华民族深厚的思想底蕴，体现着中华民族独特的精神气质，凝练社会主义核心价值观既体现时代精神又植根于中华优秀传统文化的沃土之中，蕴含民族精神，体现民族特色。优秀传统文化是我国各族人民在长期的生产生活过程中逐渐形成并经过历史检验和人民认同的思想品格、价值取向、行为规范和道德准则的精髓和内核，是维系中华民族薪火相传、繁荣进步的精神纽带和不竭动力。在20世纪上半期，中国共产党人在民族独立和国家解放的斗争中，继承和弘扬了中国民族文化的优秀传统。毛泽东思想不仅是中国革命经验的总结，而且也继承和发展了包括儒学在内的中国传统文化，是中国民族智慧的结晶。毛泽东思想在形成过程中对中国传统文化的吸收和改造表现得

非常充分。党中央提出的“构建社会主义和谐社会”和“建设社会主义和谐文化”的主张，也吸收和改造了传统儒学中“贵和尚中”思想。充分认识中国传统文化中的现代价值，提炼出适合当代社会发展的“和谐文化”，是社会主义核心价值观结合传统儒学文化精髓的创造代表。

其次，基于价值共识的视角可以促使我们对儒学价值观与社会主义价值观的融通可能性有一个深度的理解。人类在创造自己的历史中，价值的多元和一元永远不可分割地联系在一起，从而在价值创造的过程中，不仅不断地形成关于社会价值观念之间的差异，同时也在追求价值一致的基础上，不断地形成关于社会价值观念之间的共识。[①] 为了解释在各种不相容却合理的各类学说与公民的普遍共识的关系问题，罗尔斯在《政治自由主义》一书中提出了“重叠共识”的理解范式。在他看来：“社会统一的本性是通过一种稳定的诸合乎理性的完备学说之重叠共识所给定的”，依此即可达致“多元条件下的有正当理由的稳定。”[②] 这对我们理解儒学价值观的现代意义具有重要的启示。不可否认的是，在当代社会中，人们必然从自己的角度来进行评价活动，由个体认同差异所带来的关于社会价值观念的不同态度，形成了社会价值观念共识的丰富资源。[③] 尽管我们说罗尔斯所谓的“重叠共识”在实质上看来并不是由不同的完备性学说中的不同的理念或判断达成的，而是由其中的共同的理念或判断构成的。虽然也可以将其所讲的“重叠共识法”推广到其他领域，但我们应该清醒地看到，它仍然也只能帮助人们找寻既已存在而又尚未凸显的共识，并非是由异而同，达成了新的共识。故此，用重叠共识法来消除价值争端，达成价值共识是不可能的。[④] 尽管如此，我们还是应该看到，人们在价值观念上所达成的共识应该说离不开现实中任何一种理论和学说的参与作用。从这个意义上来说，作为在现代社会对民众还有着一定影响的儒学价值观亦当因存在着与其他价值观念的“交集”或“重叠”而使我们在价值观的重塑中不可忽视其重要的理论贡献。

此外，从现实观念呈现的客观事实上，我们亦应看到，传统儒学的价值观正在不断地进行着自我调适，推动自身的创造性转化，实现与社会主义核心价值观的交融互渗。崔大华先生曾指出，儒学是中华民族精神生命之所在，中华民族的兴衰荣辱都能从不同维度上体现出与儒学不同程度的关联。尽管在 20 世纪初至改革开放前，儒学备受责难和批判。但自改改开放以来，尤其是进入新世纪以来，在中华民族迈上复兴之

---

① 陈新汉：《哲学视域中社会价值观念的共识机制》，《哲学动态》，2014 年第 4 期。

② 罗尔斯：《政治自由主义》，万俊人译，译林出版社，2000 年，第 45 页。

③ 陈新汉：《哲学视域中社会价值观念的共识机制》，《哲学动态》，2014 年第 4 期。

④ 韩东屏：《如何达成价值共识》，《河北学刊》，2010 年第 1 期。

路时，儒学应当有新的定位。在崔先生看来，即应“蜕去它在历史上被附着的有权利因素的那种国家意识形态性质，而以其固有的伦理道德思想特质、以其作为中国传统文化中之具有久远价值的基本精神来表现其功能时，人们发现，儒学还是珍贵的，仍在支持着、模塑着我们中华民族作为一种悠久历史的文化类型和独立的生活方式的存在。”① 在走向现代化的过程中，人类达成了基本的共识，即要在人与自然、人与人、当代与未来的三个关系维度上设计缓解、消除这一现代性社会危机的原则、方案，这一原则和方案既要有平等、正义的人类社会伦理法则，还要有尊重自然、对自然富有责任的新的道德理念基础。②在这一点上，儒家所本有的“民胞物与”“与万物同体”“万物各得其所”的生态伦理、“己所不欲，勿施于人”“仁者爱人”倡导仁义礼智信的生活伦理的观念也在不断融纳现代性的理论资源，从容地应对着不断深化的现代性问题。应该看到，当今世界除了处于强势的西方文化外，还有影响较大的以伊斯兰教为核心的阿拉伯文化和同样具有悠久历史的印度文化。它们在世俗生活的层面亦有着与儒家伦理相容的道德原则和观念。深处全球化、现代化中的中国儒学，在多元文化对话与融通中，本着“道通为一”的天下观念和充分的道德自觉，不断实现对当代人们的价值观的优化与整合作用。实际上这样的创造性转化与对当代社会价值问题的基于儒家立场的回应，正是在不断实现着与包蕴有当今人类一切优秀价值观的社会主义核心价值观的融通与涵摄，从生活世界发挥着对当今中国价值观重要的形塑作用。

## 三、儒学现代价值的激活与当代中国价值观的重塑

面对世界范围思想文化交流交融交锋形势下价值观较量的新态势，我们需要全力打造对全世界有竞争力、影响力、吸引力和凝聚力的有中国特色的价值观。随着全球化和文化多元化时代的到来，世界各国都在致力于构建自己国家的价值观，而且努力扩大自己价值观的国际影响。当代世界经济、政治、文化的竞争从根本上可以说是不同国家价值观之间的竞争。面对世界范围思想文化交流交融交锋形势下价值观较量的新态势，我们也要全力打造对全世界有竞争力、影响力、吸引力和凝聚力的中国价值观。这里我们所说的“中国价值观”实际上是指当代中国社会的主流价值观。它既不是中国的传统价值观，也不是当代中国社会现实存在的各种价值观的总称，而是体现当前中国根本性质和基本特征的中国特色社会主义价值观。③ 对当代中国价值观的重构

① 崔大华：《儒学的现代命运》，人民出版社，2012年，《自序》第2页。

② 崔大华：《儒学的现代命运》，人民出版社，2012年，《自序》第2页。

③ 江畅：《培育和践行社会主义核心价值观与中国价值观构建》，《中国社会科学报》，2014年1月13日第6版。

与建设，自然离不开长期以来对挺立中国文明特色发挥重要影响的儒学价值观营养的汲取。与以往的研究不同，我们既要看到儒家思想在现代社会人们生活领域的价值，亦应看到儒学价值观在历史时期传播层面的一些经验和有价值的做法，在活化儒学价值观，积极推进儒学价值观与马克思主义价值观、西方现代价值观的融通中，推进中国价值观的建设。

众所周知，儒家思想是适应传统农业社会、宗法社会应运而生的思想，它与我们的现代化进程到底呈现出怎样的关系。进入全面深入推进改革的时期，我们需要对这一问题进行理性地思考，避免五四的过激，亦要避免过分推崇的极端化。对此，崔大华先生借由艾森斯塔德的现代化理论给我们进行了深入回应。他从社会的转变、体制的转换、社会震荡与破坏的适应能力等方面提出，中国现代化的进程和实现的独特性，正是由儒家传统在以上三个方面所表现出的功能所铸就。① 这一结论对于我们理解儒家思想的现代意义无疑具有很大的启发。但应该看到，儒家思想对于由传统的农业社会向现代社会转变、传统体制向现代体制的转换中所彰显的主要是其价值的功能。对于中国现代化独特性的促成，也主要发挥的是其价值观的作用。根据马克思韦伯在《新教伦理与资本主义精神》和余英时先生的观点及晚近以来包括杜维明在内的儒学现代价值的研究与传播者对工业东亚复兴的伦理价值视角的思考，对儒学价值观的现代意义便不难理解。教育部刚刚颁布的《完善中华优秀传统文化的指导纲要》中更是明确指出，加强中华优秀传统文化教育，对于引导青少年学生增强民族文化自信和价值观自信，自觉践行社会主义核心价值观具有重要作用。这体现了我们国家对于中国传统文化基于充分的文化自信基础上的对其现代价值认识的一种文化自觉。综观当前社会价值状况，我们在推进传统儒学价值观的现代性转化中，关键要注意如下几个方面：其一，是要在辩证分析传统儒学的现代价值中推动其完成创造性转化。一方面，传统儒学中既包含着讲仁爱、重民本、守诚信、崇正义、尚和合、求大同等有利于修炼道德人格、促进社会和谐稳定的积极优秀成分，同时也包含着君臣父子、男尊女卑、长幼有别、贵贱之差等禁锢人的思想、阻碍社会进步的消极落后成分。我们应厘清传统儒学中的精华与糟粕，批判地继承。另一方面，传统儒学中蕴含一些与当今时代发展和社会进步相互冲突的价值理念，这需要我们根据时代特征对传统文化进行革新，处理好继承与创新的关系。伴随市场经济的深入发展和现代化建设的不断推进，传统儒学中的等级观念、专制保守等落后思想与现代的自由平等、民主法治、公平正义等观念格格不入，培育和践行社会主义核心价值观，应该善于将传统儒学与时代精神相结合，根据时代发展需要对传统儒学进行创造性转化。其二，要将儒学置于世界文化发展的

① 崔大华：《儒学的现代命运》，人民出版社，2012 年，第 382－383 页。

潮流中推动其创造性转化。在全球化的发展浪潮中，我们的国际交往更加频繁和深化，需要合理地吸收借鉴世界上其他国家和民族有益的文化成果，为我所用。传统儒学历来具有兼收并蓄、容纳天下的开放视野和博大胸怀，总能不断地从外来文化中汲取营养，滋润自身以求发展进步。当代价值观的重塑既要弘扬这种优秀品格，既植根于传统，彰显着浓厚的民族气息，又要具备全球视野。其三，关键是处理好与马克思主义价值观的融通关系。马克思主义与儒学，产生的时代背景、文化源头、社会目标、历史任务、实践的方式方法和在中国现代化进程中的地位等方面的差异，在相遇初期发生碰撞则是不可避免的现象，尤其在排他性较强的文化激进主义主导社会思潮的年代，把两者对立起来、全盘否定儒学的观点既酿成了儒学发展的悲剧，也使得马克思主义中国化理论止步不前，甚至发生严重的倒退。当回归理性的开放的时代之后，人们逐渐意识到了马克思主义与儒学的相通互补之处，并不断致力于推动两者的深度融合。从本有理论内质来看，共产主义的社会理想与儒家大同理想有近似之处，都以追求人的解放和幸福为目标；哲学上两者都是人学而非神学，都讲对立统一、与时俱进、变化日新；社会治理上都重视民众力量；在群己观和义利观上，皆提倡先人后己、以义导利等等。马克思主义对资本主义的研究和批判，可以帮助儒学在准确地把握好自我定位后有效实现当代的转型；在中国的现代化进程中，也需要吸收儒家社会管理、道德教化、人格养成的智慧，在实现中华华民族伟大复兴的事业中真正挺立出中国特色。继续推动马克思主义与儒学的会通是今后中国文化建设的一项重要任务。①

另一方面，我们应该从儒学价值观的传播经验中汲取营养，有效推进社会主义核心价值观的培育与践行。应该看到，自社会主义核心价值观问题提出以来，很多地方很多行业其实已经在结合自身实际自发地进行着培育和践行工作，有许多成功的经验需要在经验概括的基础上进行理论层面的提升和表达，以形成具有当代中国风格和气派的培育和践行核心价值观的理论话语；另一方面，对培育和践行社会主义核心价值观中产生的问题和教训，也需要进行超越就事论事的具有普遍意义的解释和建构，以形成可普遍化的规则和规范体系。② 从现实出发汲取经验固然非常可贵，但也需要植根于中国历史，对传统价值观尤其是传统儒学价值观在培育和践行方面的优势进行有益地借鉴。价值观传播的关键在于如何实现由精英价值向民众价值的转换，即实现价值观念的大众化。对于中国传统儒家文化而言，由精英儒学到大众儒学的重要转折过程主要体现在宋明儒学的转化过程。宋明两代朝廷不仅通过国家机器将儒学经典纳人科

---

① 牟钟鉴：《马克思主义与儒学会通之路》，《光明日报》，2012年4月23日理论版。

② 李兰芬：《“家风家规”：社会主义核心价值观的“知行场”》，《中国社会科学报》，2014年5月19日第6版。

举考试的内容，而且还大力在幼学的教育中普及儒家经典，用诗歌等通俗化的方式传播普及儒家学说的一些核心价值理念。至今依然为人们所广为传诵的《三字经》、《幼学琼林》、《增广贤文》等启蒙书籍既是童蒙教育的重要教材，也是传播儒学价值观念的重要著作。其中的“人之初，性本善”等观念已经成为中国文化的根据以上关于价值观念传播普及的有关规律或机制，核心内容流传至今。可见，中国传统儒家的核心价值理念之所以能够深入民心，一方面在于把高深理论转化为普及的内容，另一方面在于其选择了符合大众接受要求和接受心理的各种传播方式。从本质上来看，儒家思想核心价值理念的传播普及就是其核心价值理念转化为适当的内容通过适当形式深入民心成为广大人民群众的一种文化自觉的过程，其实质是儒学精神的大众化。这就启示我们，只要方式得当，一种抽象的价值理念是完全可以得以成功传播普及的。当然我们也应该看到，一种价值观念从传播到接受普及一般要经历一个从学院书斋的理论创造再到理论的通俗化解释，通过通俗化解释转化为大众化的内容，这实际上也是一个再创造过程，通过这个过程才能使之能够传播亦即大众化。在此基础上，以大众易于接受的艺术手段传播已经大众化的内容，这种内容最后为大众接受，也就是内化为大众文化心理的过程。这个过程决非如一些学者或大众传媒所认为的只是理论的通俗化而已，是借由深度地理解和通俗的诠释之后实现其生命力的再现与复活。恩格斯在《反杜林论》中曾指出：“我们不知道有任何一种力量能够强制外在健康清醒状态的每一个人接受某种思想。”① 这些启发我们在我们在社会主义核心价值观的传播过程中，应该注意如下几个方面：首先，一定要考虑到每一个受众的内心认同问题，否则可能导致个体认同与基于多个个体主体认同的相互作用中所形成的社会认同之间的分离与断裂。通过对价值传播过程的研究可见，理论的通俗化其实只是完成了价值观念传播普及的一半，而且还是在理论化阶段，并未进入真正的大众化阶段。一种价值观念的成功传播与普及必须要结合受众的需求与心理。事实证明，不同的社会群体对社会主义核心价值的接受认同的程度以及认识的方式不尽相同，为此应当有不同的传播策略。要紧紧抓住受众的文化心理和审美情趣，寓教于乐，让广大受众在愉快的过程中接受社会主义核心价值观念。从受众的心理来看，要让接受文化理念的过程成为一个快乐的过程、愉快的过程，为此，就应当把握好受众的审美情趣，自觉避免把传播普及活动搞成一种简单政治说教的过程。其次，在传播方式的选择方面必须用一切可能有效的方式。中国传统文化的核心价值观念的传播可谓用尽了当时能够利用的一切先进的传播手段，对识字的人通过书籍，对不能识字的人通过平话以及通过绘画艺术等，但是都有一个特点，即形象生动地反映传播者所想表达的理念和精神。这要求我们在推进社会主义核心价值的传播普

① 恩格斯：《反杜林论》，《马克思恩格斯全集》第3卷，人民出版社，2002年，第211页。

及工作时，一定要把握不同受众的特点和需求，有针对性地编写适当的传播内容，采取不同的传播方式，进行有效传播和普及。再次，还要适时推进传播平台和载体的更新，充分利用一切现代传播平台与载体，如电视、报纸、广播、网络、微信、微博等。传播平台与载体在今天的大众传媒时代显得尤为重要，对于包括价值观在内的文化传播效果将产生至关重要的影响。一方面要注意传播内容与形式的通俗化，另一方面要注意传播内容的准确以及不失真，要在传播内容的真实准确与通俗化之间寻找一个合适的度。实现了与传统儒学价值观融通涵摄的社会主义价值观的有效传播，实际上也就意味着在当代中国价值观的重塑之路上迈出了坚实的步伐。

培育和践行社会主义核心价值观就是要构建不同层次、不同维度的价值观，从而构建完整系统的中国价值观，并使之现实化为中国社会的制度和文化，内在化为中国人民的信念和准则。[①] 梁启超在《新民说》中早已经昭示我们，作为重塑中国价值观的"新民德"理论和实践，尽管需要学习西方的所谓"公德"，"采补其所本无而新之"，但更需要发扬光大"吾祖宗遗传固有之旧道德"。[②] 二十世纪以来的中国价值观念变迁实际充分说明，梁启超的这一观点乃是一种基于深刻的文化和道德自觉的思考。正像有学者指出的那样，社会主义核心价值观要从执政党的倡导真正转化为亿万人民的自觉意识和自愿行为，离不开主要蕴涵在儒学中的文化生态、文化传统、文化心理和文化语言条件。[③] 从中国传统儒学价值观面临的现代化困境及其转型中看到构建当代中国价值观的有益路径，并对儒学价值观的传播经验有所借鉴，我们在当代中国价值观的重塑中才能真正解决中国语境中的关键问题，推动社会主义核心价值观的良性培育和有效践行。

---

① 江畅：《培育和践行社会主义核心价值观与中国价值观构建》，《中国社会科学报》，2014 年 1 月 13 日第 6 版。

② 梁启超：《梁启超文存》，江苏人民出版社，2012 年，第 330 页。

③ 陈泽环：《儒学创新与人权》，《哲学动态》，2014 年第 5 期。

# 以德为本，知行合一

## ——培育践行社会主义核心价值观的理论思考

浙江省儒学学会　吴　光

### 一、提出社会主义核心价值观的时代背景

1. 是全球化时代文明互动的需要

我们现在所处的时代，是经济全球化、社会现代化、政治民主化潮流席卷世界的时代，在这个既充满竞争又需要合作的时代，我们拿什么与世界各国进行文明对话？我们能对世界文明的发展做出怎样的贡献？如何才能问心无愧地立于世界文明之林？恐怕最有说服力和影响力的莫过于传承与弘扬五千年中华优秀文化，特别是孔子思想与儒家文明。习近平总书记在去年11月考察曲阜的讲话中说："这些年来，西方资本主义动摇了，他们出了一些问题，社会主义的中国却越来越好。他们也在反省……我们是马列主义中国化，他们不承认我们的马列主义，却承认中国文化。这就是我们中国的软实力。非常好。"又说："我接待过许多国家元首，他们总是谈到孔子思想，说孔子思想怎么好，怎么适合当代社会，他们一个个简直是'言必称孔子'。这说明孔子在世界上已被许多人认可。在世界上，应该传播儒学，伊斯兰教、基督教人家传播，我们也应传播。"党的十七届六中全会决议提出了"文化强国"战略。实现这个战略的中心任务是提升文化软实力。而文化软实力中最核心最具凝聚力的东西是核心价值观。所以，党的十八大政治报告明确提出倡导社会主义核心价值观的论述，而培育和践行社会主义核心价值观正是"建设社会主义文化强国"的根本要求。

2. 是中国进入和平崛起新阶段形势发展的需要

中国自1978年实行改革开放以来经过30多年，经济高速发展，国家实力大大增长。不但超过亚洲四小龙，而且超过了日本，自2010年起发展成为世界第二大经济体（中国2010年GDP58786亿美元，比日本多4044亿美元），从而进入了和平崛起新阶段。但经济总量位居世界第二不等于就是世界第二强国，还必须有政治军事的强大，

尤其是文化软实力的强大。在这个转折关头，习近平总书记适时地提出了“实现中华民族伟大复兴的中国梦”的论述，既得天时地利，也得民心。

习总书记说：“古往今来，一个国家、一个民族的强盛，总是以文化兴盛为支撑的。中华民族伟大复兴同样需要以中华文化繁荣发展为条件。”

3. 是纠正文革毁坏中华美德的错误、抵制外来腐朽文化的需要

文化大革命虽然过去了近四十年，但文革对传统优秀文化、中华美德的破坏至今没有纠正与恢复，一些中老年人至今仍受“文革”遗风影响，仍在把儒家思想、儒家道德当作封建主义批判、排斥，一些年轻人根本不知礼义廉耻、孝悌忠信为何物，因此很容易受外来腐朽文化、腐朽生活方式的影响，成了中华传统美德的“德盲”。再者，对外开放以后，大家一心搞经济，竞相发财致富，却忽略了道德修养，一些腐朽东西（如黄、赌、毒，尔虞我诈，唯利是图）也伴随着开放大潮涌进国门，造成普遍性的道德滑坡、贪腐、奢靡、欺诈之风，扭曲了社会风尚，腐蚀了人们的良知。所以，道德教育成为当务之急。所谓“八荣八耻”荣辱观与社会主义核心价值观的提出是非常适时的，正所谓“衣食足而知荣辱，仓廪实而知礼节”也。

## 二、社会主义核心价值观的内容与重点

十八大政治报告首次系统地论述了社会主义核心价值观的理论系统，即24字价值观，理论系统分为三个层面，每层面八个字：

1. 国家层面的价值目标：富强、民主、文明、和谐

2. 社会层面的价值取向：自由、平等、公正、法治

3. 公民层面的价值准则：爱国、敬业、诚信、友善

只要认真分析一下24字核心价值体系的思想来源就可以明白，其中有十六个字是来自儒家为主导的中华传统文化的核心价值体系，即富强、文明、和谐、公正、爱国、敬业、诚信、友善。另外八个字即“民主、自由、平等、法治”则主要来自于西方文化传统的价值体系。而民主、平等、公正、法治这八个字同时也属于传统社会主义的核心价值体系。这说明中国特色社会主义的核心价值体系是吸收和综合了“全人类智慧”而形成的有别于“美国梦”的中国梦的核心价值体系，而儒家思想则是这个核心价值体系的主要思想来源。

这三个层面24字的核心价值体系，既体现了中华民族五千年传统所积淀的人文精神，也体现了中华民族在走向伟人复兴的历史进程中所应有的现代人文精神——民主法治精神。

其传统人文精神的重点就是“以人为本，以德为体”的仁爱德治精神。

儒家学派从孔子开始，历代大儒都把“仁爱”作为最核心的价值观念。孔子讲“仁者爱人”、“克己复礼为仁”；孟子讲“仁，人心也”，“道二，仁与不仁而已矣”，荀子也主张“王者先仁而后礼”，可见在孔孟荀那里，“仁”是最核心的价值观念，是普世性道德。韩愈所谓“博爱之谓仁”，是对孔孟“仁爱”之道的最佳阐发。宋儒程颢、程颐说“仁者，全体；四者，四支。仁，体也；义，宜也；礼，别也；智，知也；信，实也”，说明二程是将仁与其他常德提升到体用高度看待的。仁是道之体，义、礼、智、信是道之用。可见，在历代儒家那里，“仁”是根本之道，是最核心的价值观念，也是儒学传统的精神基础，其他德目诸如义、礼、智、信、勇、廉、和、敬之类都是由“仁”统率的。①

儒家以“仁”为根本之道，辅之以“义、礼、智、信、勇、廉、和、敬”等常用大德的核心价值体系，实际上已经成为中国特色社会主义核心价值体系的重要思想来源。且不说改革开放以来所提倡的“实事求是”、“以德治国”、“以人为本”、“小康”、“和谐”这些“中国特色社会主义”的关键词，实际上都来自儒家理想，就连胡锦涛同志提出的以“八荣八耻”为内容的社会主义荣辱观，也可以说是儒家仁、义、礼、智、信加上忠、勤、廉、耻等核心价值观念的现代扩充版。

习近平总书记关于“中国梦”的论述，充分体现了儒家传统的民本思想与仁爱精神。例如，他在十八大闭幕当天的记者见面会上强调说：“我们一定要始终与人民心心相印、与人民同甘共苦、与人民团结奋斗，夙夜在公，勤勉工作，努力向历史、向人民交一份合格的答卷。”在 2014 年 2 月 24 日在中共中央政治局第十三次集体学习时的讲话中指出：“要深入挖掘和阐发中华优秀传统文化讲仁爱、重民本、守诚信、崇正义、尚和合、求大同的时代价值。”他把“讲仁爱、重民本”放在中华优秀传统文化的第一、第二位，体现了习近平同志坚持以“仁爱”为核心价值、坚持以民为本和执政为民的思想，也揭示出儒家传统的民本思想与仁爱精神，正是习近平“中国梦”论述的思想来源之一，是中国梦的精神基础。因此，我们可以将习近平“中国梦”的核心价值观的形上道体概括为“仁爱为本”。“仁爱为本”所继承的正是中华文化传统的道德人文精神，也是儒家传统核心价值观的现代转型。这是“中国梦”区别于“美国梦”的根本所在，也是最具特色的中华民族的根本精神。

社会主义核心价值观所蕴含的现代人文精神的重点就是追求“自由、民主、平等、公正”的民主法治精神。其民主精神与中华仁爱精神是可以融合的，其法治精神即集中体现了社会主义核心价值观的现代精神。

---

① 关于“仁”与“义、礼、智、信”等常用大德的体用关系，可参阅拙文：《重塑儒学核心价值观——“一道五德”论纲》，载《哲学研究》2010 年第 6 期。

重视“法治”建设，强调依法治国、依法执政，是习近平同志一贯的执政理念，也是他阐述“中国梦”与社会主义核心价值观时强调的一个核心理念。根据报刊网络媒体报道的习近平同志关于“法治”思想的多次讲话，我们大致可以整理出如下要点：

第一，论述了法治建设的重要意义，指出“法治建设是政治文明建设的重要内容，法治进步是社会文明进步的重要标志，法治社会是人民梦寐以求的理想社会”①；

第二，论述了宪法的重要性和依宪执政的重要意义。他在首都各界纪念现行宪法公布施行30周年大会上说：“宪法是国家的根本大法，是治国安邦的总章程，具有最高的法律地位、法律权威、法律效力，任何组织或者个人，都不得有超越宪法和法律的特权。”“依法治国首先是依宪治国，依法执政关键是依宪执政”。

第三，推行廉政，惩治贪腐。他在十八届中央政治局集体学习会上说：“腐败问题越演越烈，最终必然会亡党亡国！我们要警醒啊！”又在十八届中纪委第二次全体会议上说：“党风廉政建设和反腐败斗争，是党的建设的重大任务。为政清廉才能取信于民，秉公用权才能赢得人心”，并说：“要坚持‘老虎’、‘苍蝇’一起打，既坚决查处领导干部违纪违法案件，又切实解决发生在群众身边的不正之风和腐败问题。”

第四，健全法制，加强监督。他在首都各界纪念现行宪法公布施行30周年大会上说：“我们要健全权力运行制约和监督体系，有权必有责，用权受监督，失职要问责，违法要追究，保证人民赋予的权力始终用来为人民谋利益”，在十八届中纪委第二次全体会议上说：“要加强对权力运行的制约和监督，把权力关进制度的笼子里，形成不敢腐的惩戒机制、不能腐的防范机制、不易腐的保障机制”。

综合以上论述，我们可以将习近平论述“中国梦”与社会主义核心价值观的思想概括为“仁爱为本，法治为用”八个字，简称“仁本法用”。“仁”与“法”的关系是道、器关系，是体、用关系，“仁”是道、是体；“法”是器、是用。它是一个观念结构，是一种理论形态，也是中国梦的根本价值导向。“仁爱为本”所继承的是中华民族优秀文化传统的道德人文精神，所体现的是从传统民本仁爱走向现代民主仁政的治国之道；“法治为用”所体现的，则是现代社会的有效治理方式。

“仁爱为本，法治为用”，既是以中华民族伟大复兴为目标的“中国梦”的核心价值观，也是当代“中国特色社会主义”的核心价值观。坚持“仁爱为本”，就具有了热爱祖国、热爱人民的大爱之心，就能时时处处以人民群众的根本利益为至高无上的目标追求，就能自觉实行权力在民、执政为民、取信于民的民主仁政，做一个真正的人民公仆；坚持“法治为用”，就能具有“治大国若烹小鲜”的治国情怀，举重若轻，法简政清，精心治理，恰到好处，就能出以公心，善用利器，真正做到以法治国，依法

① 《研究社会主义法治 推进“法治浙江”建设》，《浙江日报》2006年2月6日。

行政，从而达到社会的和谐，国家长治久安，人民快乐幸福。

## 三、中华优秀传统文化是社会主义核心价值观的重要源泉

习近平总书记对于中华优秀传统文化与社会主义核心价值观的关系有非常精辟的论述。他于 2014 年 2 月 24 日在中央政治局第十三次集体学习时的讲话指出："培育和弘扬社会主义核心价值观必须立足中华优秀传统文化。牢固的核心价值观，都有其固有的根本。抛弃传统、丢掉根本，就等于割断了自己的精神命脉。博大精深的中华优秀传统文化是我们在世界文化激荡中站稳脚跟的根基。中华文化源远流长，积淀着中华民族最深层的精神追求，代表着中华民族独特的精神标识，为中华民族生生不息、发展壮大提供了丰厚滋养。……大力弘扬以爱国主义为核心的民族精神和以改革创新为核心的时代精神，深入挖掘和阐发中华优秀传统文化讲仁爱、重民本、守诚信、崇正义、尚和合、求大同的时代价值，使中华优秀传统文化成为涵养社会主义核心价值观的重要源泉。"这段讲话提出了三大启示：第一，培育和弘扬社会主义核心价值观必须立足中华优秀传统文化，而不应将二者分离或对立起来；第二，中华优秀传统文化是中华民族生生不息、发展壮大的精神命脉，也是中华民族自立于世界民族之林的独特而稳固的根基；第三，中华优秀传统文化在其发展长河中形成了爱国主义为核心的民族精神，形成了讲仁爱、重民本、守诚信、崇正义、尚和合、求大同的优良传统，这些思想精华，正是涵养社会主义核心价值观的重要源泉。

在 12 组 24 字社会主义核心价值观的核心词中，有 8 组 16 字（即"富强、文明、和谐、公正、爱国、敬业、诚信、友善"）直接来自于中华传统文化；另外 4 组 8 个字（即"自由、民主、平等、法治"）主要来自西方文化核心价值词，但在中华文化传统中也有这些元素（如道家讲自由、黄宗羲讲民主、佛法讲平等、法家讲法治）。说明中华传统文化的核心价值是社会主义核心价值观的主要思想源泉。

## 四、培育社会主义核心价值观应以道德人文教育为中心

在当今物欲横流、熙熙争利、贪腐成风、道德沦丧的社会风气背景下，在广大干部群众中广泛开展以培育践行社会主义核心价值观为中心的道德教育已成为当务之急。

习近平总书记在多次讲话中特别强调深入开展道德教育的重要性与紧迫性。2013 年 11 月 26 日，他《在山东考察时的讲话》特别强调："国无德不兴，人无德不立。必须加强全社会的思想道德建设，激发人们形成善良的道德意愿、道德情感，培育正确的道德判断和道德责任，提高道德实践能力尤其是自觉践行能力，引导人们向往和追求讲道德、尊道德、守道德的生活，形成向上的力量、向善的力量。只要中华民族一

代接着一代追求美好崇高的道德境界，我们的民族就永远充满希望。”他在2014年2月24日《在中央政治局第十三次集体学习时的讲话》强调说：“中华传统美德是中华文化精髓，蕴含着丰富的思想道德资源。不忘本来才能开辟未来，善于继承才能更好创新。”

这些话，强调了道德对于国家兴旺、人格确立的强大力量，强调了道德教育的重要性与紧迫性，强调了尊崇道德与践行道德对中华民族伟大复兴的深远影响。

以儒学为主导的中华传统文化的根本精神，是确立道德主体性而以人生意义与价值的实现为终极关怀的道德人文精神。其基本特性表现为道德性、人文性、实用性、开放性、兼容性五大特性，这是中华文化的特色，也是中华文化软实力的优势所在。我们要把握优势、发扬优势，创造转化，立德兴国。

必须认识到，培育社会主义核心价值观须以道德人文教育为中心。其重点是持续开展社会公德、职业道德、家庭美德、个人品德的“四德”教育和崇尚“知行合一”的人文素质教育。

## 五、学习王阳明的“知行合一”论，努力践行社会主义核心价值观

习近平同志十分重视王阳明的“知行合一”思想，并号召大家学习王阳明。2011年5月9日，他在《与贵州大学中国文化研究院师生座谈时的讲话》中指出：“王阳明龙场悟道，就在你们贵州。不仅中国人敬仰他、学习他，而且陆王心学传播到东北亚地区，影响日韩。王阳明一生真正做到了知行合一。他既是一个伟大的哲学家、思想家，又是一个伟大的政治家、军事家。他在龙场讲学时向学生提了‘立志、勤学、责善、改过’四点基本要求，首要的是立志。他说‘志不立，天下无可成之事’。对今天的学生来说，要成才，必先立志。……要自强不息，止于至善，追求永恒!”2014年3月7日，他《在全国人大十二届二次会议贵州代表团审议会议的讲话》中又说：“明朝时，王守仁曾经在贵州参学悟道，贵州在这方面还是很有优势，希望在这方面继续深入探索。”这是对王阳明及其“知行合一”思想的高度肯定。

王阳明在被贬龙场驿的第二年，提出了著名的“知行合一”之说。《传习录》对王阳明的“知行合一”学说记载比较详细。他说：“知是行的主意，行是知的工夫；知是行之始，行是知之成。”“知者行之始，行者知之成。圣学只一个工夫，知行不可分作两事。”“今人学问，只因知行分作两件，故有一念发动，虽是不善，然却未尝行，便不去禁止。我今说个知行合一，正要人晓得一念发动处，便即是行了。发动处有不善，

就将这不善的念克倒了。须要彻根彻底，不使那一念不善潜伏胸中。此是我立言宗旨。"①

概括地说，王阳明的"知行合一"说有三个要点：第一，知行只是一个工夫，不能割裂。而所谓"工夫"，就是认知与实践的过程。第二，知行关系是辩证的统一：知是行的出发点，是指导行的，而真正的"知"不但能"行"，而且是已在"行"了；行是知的归宿，是实现知的，而真切笃实的"行"已自有明觉精察的"知"在起作用了。第三，知行工夫中"行"的根本目的，只是要彻底克服那"不善的念"而达于至善。就本质而言，王阳明所说的"知"是"吾心之良知"，或曰"道德自觉"，其所谓"行"是"致吾心良知之天理于事事物物"的道德实践。但由此道德自觉行之于社会政治实践，便是《论语》强调的"修己以安百姓"、《大学》所说的"明德、亲民、至于至善"和"修身齐家治国、平天下"的政治大业。王阳明的这些思想对于今天提倡清廉政治、践行社会主义核心价值观具有极为现实的启示意义，

尤其是其"知行合一"思想为我们践行社会主义核心价值观提供了科学务实的思维方法和精神动力，其"明德亲民"思想为执政者推行民主仁政、为人民谋利益指示了正确方向。现在有些官员说的是一套，做的是另一套，满嘴马列主义、三个代表，满肚子贪污受贿、男盗女娼，"知"与"行"完全脱节。其结果是政府官员失去民众信任，怨声载道。在这种情况下，尤其有必要提倡王阳明的"知行合一"、"致良知"和"明德亲民"思想。我们应积极响应习近平总书记的号召，敬仰王阳明，学习王阳明，像王阳明那样真正做到知行合一，力行实践，自强不息，止于至善，为践行社会主义核心价值观、实现中华民族伟大复兴的中国梦而努力奋斗！

---

① 王阳明：《传习录下》，载《王阳明全集》卷三，上海古籍出版社，2012年简体字标点本上册，第109—110页。

# 弘揚儒家“務本尚德”之教化精神以促進社會和諧發展

台湾义守大学　方俊吉

《禮記·學記》載:“君子如欲化民成俗，其必由學乎！玉不琢，不成器。人不學，不知道。是故，古之王者，建國君民，教學為先。”誠不誣也。放眼古今中外，明智之領導者，無不以教育事業為首要之政務。

儒家的宗師、孔子不僅是一位人格偉大的哲思家，也是位有遠見的政治家，更是影響至深至遠的教育家。孔子生當周室衰微，諸侯放恣，王官失守的時代，毅然奮起，開創了私人教學的風氣，藉以弘揚其“人本”思想，推展以“明人倫”、“崇道德”為主軸的教化。夫子的教育理念及法則，充分展現了“務本尚德”之精神，而樹立了中國傳統注重“人文精神”教育的典範。兩千多年來，儒家的學術思想，不僅被中國的知識份子引以為立身處世之圭臬，亦治學、為政之指南，終成中國傳統文化與學術之主流核心，而普遍影響著中華民族的“價值觀念”與“道德標準”。

然而，近百餘年來，由於科技的發達，帶動了資訊、交通與工商……，的急遽進展，造成人們的生活高度地依賴科技，同時，也促使各方面的競爭日趨劇烈。際此，“物質文明”被過度依賴，人們一昧執著於物質生活的享受，而多元文化相互衝擊且快速匯流的世代，人類良善的秉性多被掩蓋了，致使許多人的言行肆無忌憚，正義、公理也隨之而逐漸淪喪。世界普遍如此，而佔有全球近五分之一人口的華人社會，又何嘗例外？身為炎黃子孫，當如何“障百川而東之，迴狂瀾於既倒”，以促進家庭、社會乃至於人類世界的和諧，的確是當前最值得省思與探討的課題。

## 一、近百餘年來，由於重“科技、財經”而輕“人文”，而造成“價值觀”混淆、“道德標準”低落，致使文化發展的“失衡”

由於近百餘年來，科技的急遽發展，而帶動了資訊、交通與工商……，的快速進展。無形中，壓縮了人們的空間距離，致使人際、乃至於國際間往來的速度加快，頻率增高。當此之際，不僅激發了世人對於全球事務“休戚與共”的意識，面對各種問題的思維，也逐漸突破往昔疆界藩籬之侷限。所謂“地球村”（Global Village）的概念於焉形成，“全球化”（Globalization）的趨勢，終成為無法抵擋的潮流。在此同時，彼此之間的競爭，隨之而日益劇烈，人們生活的步調，也日趨快速，相互影響的層面，更日漸增廣。

存活在如此快節奏的生活環境下，人難免因迷惘而失去方向。人們也往往緣於自我迷失，而忘卻了生活的目的，從而，無視於生命崇高的真諦。同時，更由於電腦的普及，造成了許多年輕人沉溺於虛擬世界之中，而扭曲了健康的“價值觀”，與現實生活所應把握的言行分寸。終於導致了，人們的胸襟變得更為狹隘，視野更為短淺。如今，顯現在我們眼前的社會，則是“價值觀”混淆，“道德標準”也日趨低落；私心驅役了人們的思維，物慾支配著人們的言行；人性的尊嚴遭到了抹杀，人們的日常生活也被自己給“物化”[1] 了。

在中國，自“鴉片戰爭”（1840－1842）之後，一向所存在的民族自大之心態，一夕之間，被西洋人的堅船利砲所重創，連帶著民族的自信心也隨之而喪失了。加之以1919年所發起，名為青年學生“救亡圖存”的所謂“五四運動”，高舉著所謂“德先生”（即“民主”“Democracy”）與“賽先生”（即“科學”“Science”）之大纛，將兩千多年來，儒家以“倫理”、“道德”為核心的民族優良“人文精神”特質，視為迂腐、落伍。此一排斥優良“人文精神”傳統的運動，甚至於惡化，而發展成為崇洋媚外的病態心理。毋庸諱言，民族自大的心態，固不可取，然而，一個民族或國家，如果喪失了自信，甚至於崇洋媚外，則更是可悲且危險。不可否認的，科技的發展，委實可以提供人們物質生活上，許許多多的便捷與舒適。然而，人們若一昧執著於物質享受，難免造成“物質文明”被過度的依賴，相對地，“精神文明”的發展，也自然被輕忽了。

總之，當前，“科技第一”、“財經掛帥”的思維，已然成為人類世界所標榜的前衛理念。導致世人的“價值觀”逐漸混淆，“道德標準”也隨之而日趨低落。人們多顯現貪婪、霸道而肆無忌憚的心態。致使我們存活的世界，横逆取代了倫常，和諧變成了紛爭，正義與公理，也隨之而逐漸淪喪。際此“物質文明”被過度依賴，而多元文化快速匯流的浪潮，緣自於追逐物質生活所激發的貪慾與私心，已然難以抑制，相對的，“人文精神”相關的問題，當然就被輕忽了，而造成所謂整體文化發展“失調”的現

---

① 按：“物化”一詞，始見於《莊子·齊物論》：“周與蝴蝶，則必有分矣。此之謂物化。”此外，亦見於〈天道〉與〈刻意〉。唯筆者所云“物化”，非取諸莊子之意。蓋人與物之別，在於人能思想，有情感，而眾物則無。人倘若一昧沈溺於物質享受，則難免事事遷就於物質，甚至，使人逐漸失去理性與情感，終究將爲物所役，而變得十分冷漠。如此一來，人的生活必然變得更為刻板化、機械化而了無生趣，與一般的器物也就無所區別了。此即筆者所謂之“物化”。

象。如此“精神文明”與“物質文明”嚴重地失衡的發展，其後果，確實令人憂心！

## 二、儒家的宗師孔子揭櫫“人本”思想，建構“重倫理”、“崇道德”之“大道”，終使儒家學術思想，成為中華傳統文化的主流核心

中國自西周初，周公制禮作樂，開始奠定了中華文化重視“人文精神”特質的基礎。孔子紹承古昔先聖“仰觀俯察”① 於天地自然的體悟，而建構了“順乎天理”而“應乎人情”，② 著眼於引領世人體現“倫理”與“道德”的思想體系。

《中庸》載：“仲尼祖述堯、舜，憲章文、武，上律天時，下襲水土。……萬物並育而不相害，道並行而不相悖。小德川流，大德敦化。此天地之所以為大也。”

《漢書·藝文志》亦載：“儒家者流，蓋出於司徒之官，助人君，順陰陽，明教化者也。遊文於六藝之中；留意于仁義之際。祖述堯舜，憲章文武，宗師仲尼以重其言，於道爲最高。”

孔子歿後百餘年，孟子起而承襲孔子的思想，以“正人心、息邪說，距詖行、放淫辭”③ 為己任，維繫了孔道於亂世而不墜。降及漢代，孝武皇帝採董仲舒“推明孔氏，抑黜百家”④ 之議。自此，以孔、孟思想為核心的儒家學說，為代代知識份子之所傳承，而蔚成中華民族傳統優良文化與學術的主流核心，且影響於諸多鄰近的國家。

概略而言，孔子依循“天道”之精神，將之轉化成為“人道”，而建構了以“倫理”與“道德”為主軸、核心，指引人們經由“誠意”、“正心”、“修身”，到“齊家”、“治國”而“平天下”，“由本而末”的所謂儒家“大道”。換言之，以孔子的思想為宗的“儒家之道”，首重“人、我間的關係定位”，亦即明辨“長幼尊卑、親疏遠近”的所謂“倫理”。進而，強調“維繫人際倫常，及落實安身立命”之“言行規範”的所謂“道德”。此外，夫子深明於教化的重要，期盼藉由教育之功，引領世人體現由“內修己”到“外安人”，亦即所謂由“內聖”到“外王”，或謂之，由“盡性”而“推恩”之理想。析而言之，儒家之道，在指引個人先行提升自我的“品格”，以追求臻於所謂

---

① 《周易·繫辭下》：“古者，包羲氏之王天下也，仰則觀象於天，俯則觀法於地，……於是，始作八卦，以通神明之德，以類萬物之情……”

② 《禮記·禮運》載：“故聖人作則，必以天地為本……”又〈樂記〉載：“夫禮，先王以承天之道，以治人之情。”

③ 《孟子·公孫丑上》(孟子) 曰：“……乃所願則學孔子也衍。”……(孟子) 曰：“否！自有生民以來，未有孔子也。”《滕文公下》孟子曰：“……楊墨之道不息，孔子之道不著。……我亦欲正人心，息邪說，距詖行、放淫辭，以承三聖者。豈好辯哉？予不得已也。”

④ 《漢書·董仲舒傳》載：“……自武帝初立，魏其、武安侯爲相而隆儒矣。及仲舒對冊，推明孔氏，抑黜百家。立學校之官，州郡舉茂材孝廉，皆自仲舒發之。”

“贊天地之化育”，而“與天地参矣”[①] 之所謂“天人合一”的“精神生命永恆”的境界；進而，鼓勵人們進一步發揮“己立立人”、“己達達人”的精神，[②] 擴大教化的效應，以促進人類社會的和諧，而期使世界臻於所謂“大同”的理想。[③]

## 三、儒家自孔子以來，多以教化為職志，其目標崇高；原則遠大，且教育方法，靈活而多方，充分展現“務本尚德”之精神

孟子曰：“……善政不如善教之得民也。善政，民畏之；善教，民愛之。善政得民財；善教得民心。”[④] 無怪乎，歷來中外之教育專家對於教學方法及技巧之運用，無不費盡思量，多所探討，亦不乏各種理論與主張。就晚近而言，如：德國、赫爾巴特（J. F. Herbart 1776－1841）之所謂“五段教學法”[⑤]；義大利的幼兒教育學家、瑪麗亞・蒙特梭利（Maria Montessori 1870－1952）之“蒙特梭利教學法”[⑥]；美國、海倫.派克赫斯特（Helen Parkhurst 1887－1973）的所謂“道爾頓（Dalton）制”教學法；[⑦] ……。他如：所謂“啟發式教學法”；“自學輔導法”；“社會化教學法”；“魏氏（未是）教學法”；“單元教學法”，及所謂“行為目標教學法”……等，不一而足，令人目不暇給，亦各有千秋。

中國在兩千多年前，儒家宗師——孔子不僅確立了遠大的教育目標與崇高的原則，更發揮其多方且靈活的教學方法，而成功地培育出諸多賢能之士，影響至為深遠。[⑧] 以故，孔子被尊奉為“大成至聖先師”。《禮記・學記》云：“善歌者使人繼其聲，善教者使人繼其志。”夫子的教化精神，不僅為歷代儒者之所紹承，亦當今從事教育工作者，

---

① 《中庸》載：“唯天下至誠，為能盡其性。能盡其性，則能盡人之性。能盡人之性，則能盡物之性。能盡物之性，則可以贊天地之化育。可以贊天地之化育，則可以與天地參矣。”

② 《論語・雍也》：子貢曰：“如有博施於民而能濟眾，何如？可謂仁乎？”子曰：“何事於仁？必也聖乎！堯舜其猶病諸。夫仁者，己欲立而立人，己欲達而達人。能近取譬，可謂仁之方也已。”

③ 見《禮記・禮運》（《禮記注疏》卷 21－22）。

④ 見《孟子・盡心上》。

⑤ 按：德國、赫爾巴特所倡導之階段教學法，其教學過程循著一定階段，以啟發學生的思想，增進系統的知識和培養推理的能力為目的。赫爾巴特的階段教學法，原只四段。即明瞭、聯合、系統和方法，後經由齊勒（T. Ziller1817－1882）和其弟子賴恩（W. Rein1847－1929）兩次的修訂，遂成為現今一般所謂的“五段教學法”。

⑥ 按：“蒙特梭利教學法”，主張教師只是一個從旁引導者，應重視受教兒童的獨立性。此外，並著力於設計啟發性的教學情境和教具，讓兒童藉由具體操作來學習，不只是聽講。

⑦ 按：“道爾頓（Dalton）制教育法”，係由美國女教師 Helen Parkhurst 在道爾頓學校所提倡者。此教育法採“計畫原則”，學生有不同的作業表，學生必須獨自或以小組合作方式完成這些作業。

⑧ 《史記・孔子世家》載：“孔子以詩、書、禮、樂教弟子，蓋三千焉。身通六藝者，七十有二人。”

所該重視與效法者。

然則，聖人之教學之次第為何？南宋、朱熹在〈大學章句〉“篇目”下，註云：“子程子曰：《大學》孔氏之遺書，而初學入德之門也。於今可見古人為學次第者，獨賴此篇之存，而《論》、《孟》次之。學者必由是而學焉，則庶乎其不差矣。”是則，吾人欲探儒家之教育宗旨與次第，豈能捨此而他求？

《大學》云：“古之欲明明德於天下者，先治其國。欲治其國者，先齊其家。欲齊其家者，先修其身。欲修其身者，先正其心。欲正其心者，先誠其意。欲誠其意者，先致其知，致知在格物。……自天子以至於庶人，壹是皆以修身為本。”

《大學》明確指出，聖人之教，以“修身”為首要。而修身之要，則在於“明人倫，修道德”，以提昇品德，成就“人格”為根本。進而，發揮“己立立人”、“己達達人”的精神，以追求“齊家”、“治國”，乃至於“平天下”的理想。總之，儒家的教育，明顯在引導人們由“內修己”到“外安人”，而充分展現了“務本尚德”之精神。

《論語・學而》：子曰：“弟子入則孝，出則弟，謹而信，汎愛眾而親仁。行有餘力，則以學文。”又載：有子曰：“其為人也孝弟，而好犯上者鮮矣；不好犯上，而好作亂者，未之有也。君子務本，本立而道生，孝弟也者，其為仁之本與。”又載：子夏曰：“賢賢易色，事父母能竭其力，事君能致其身，與朋友交言而有信，雖曰未學，吾必謂之學矣。”

《孟子・梁惠王上》：梁惠王曰：“寡人之於國也，……”孟子對曰：“……謹庠序之教，申之以孝悌之義，頒白者不負戴於道路矣。……”又〈滕文公上〉：滕文公問為國。孟子曰：“……設為庠序學校以教之。……皆所以明人倫也。人倫明於上，小人親於下。有王者起，必來取法，是為王者師。”又載：有為神農之言者許行，……（孟子）曰：“……人之有道也，飽食煖衣，逸居而無教，則近於禽獸。聖人有憂之，使契為司徒，教以人倫。父子有親；君臣有義；夫婦有別；長幼有序；朋友有信。……”〈告子上〉載：孟子曰：“仁，人心也；義，人路也。舍其路而弗由，放其心而不知求，哀哉！……學問之道無他，求其放心而已矣。”

綜觀孔子諸多教育原則之中，最為世人所稱頌者，除“有教無類”[①] 之精神外，其所以為教者，無不著眼於日常生活中，所應秉持的分寸，即所謂“不待求之民生日用

---

① 《論語・述而》：子曰：“自行束修以上，吾未嘗無誨焉。”蓋古昔中國，封建階級分明，受教育乃貴族獨享之特權，加之以農業時代之社會，一般黎庶百姓多不重視子弟之教育。孔子生當周室衰微，諸侯競起，王官失守之世，起而以一介平民從事教化，非但開創私人從事教育之風氣，引領知識份子之崛起，亦激發諸子百家之爭鳴，從而改變當時社會之結構。是以，孔子“有教無類”之作為，最受後世所讚頌。

彝倫之外"，[1] 而避玄虛奧秘之論。[2] 這種務實而避虛的教育，教導學子從日常生活的待人接物之中，建立健康的"價值觀"與正確的"道德標準"，以提昇自我之"品德"，成就高尚的"人格"，同時也是一種"務本"的教育。職是，孔子自律甚嚴，亦不忘訓勉教育工作者，應避免空談，"以身作則"，就所傳授之道理，身體力行，以為學生之典範。

《論語·述而》：顏淵問仁。子曰："克己復禮為仁。一日克己復禮，天下歸仁焉。為仁由己，而由人乎哉？"又〈子路〉：子曰："其身正，不令而行。其身不正，雖令不從。"又：子曰："苟正其身矣，於從政乎何有？不能正其身，如正人何？"

《孟子·盡心下》：孟子曰："有事君人者，……有大人者，正己而物正者也。"實則，聖人深明"教學相長"之理，是以，除訓勉教師"以身作則"外，更不忘提醒教者，必須抱持"學而不厭，誨人不倦"之精神。且身為教師，除須孜孜不倦地自我充實、自我提昇外，在教學上，還要能不憚其煩，體現"誨人不倦"之精神。且從事教育工作者，應該持之以恆，將教化工作視為終身之志業。

《論語·述而》：子曰："默而識之，學而不厭，誨人不倦，何有於我哉？"又：子曰："若聖與仁，則吾豈敢？抑為之不厭，誨人不倦，則可謂云爾已矣。"公西華曰："正唯弟子不能學也。"（朱熹〈集註〉："聖者大而化之。……誨人，亦謂以此教人也。然不厭、不倦，非己有之則不能，所以弟子不能學也。"）

《禮記·學記》載："學然後知不足；教然後知困。知不足，然後能自反也；知困然後能自強也。故曰：教學相長也。"再者，儒家教育，固在強調"明人倫、修道德"，以成就"人格"為首要之務，然其教學之內涵，則講求"德術兼備、文武合一"，亦即所謂"內外並重、文質彬彬"之原則。

《論語·泰伯》：子曰："君子不器。"（朱熹集註云："成德之士，體無不具，故用無不周，非特為一材一藝而已。"）又：子曰："興於詩，立於禮，成於樂。"〈雍也〉則載：子曰："質勝文則野，文勝質則史，文質彬彬，然後君子。"〈述而〉：子曰："志於道，據於德，依於仁，游於藝。"又載：子以四教，文、行、忠、信。

《禮記·儒行》載："儒有忠信以為甲冑，禮義以為干櫓。戴仁而行，抱義而處。雖有暴政，不改其所，其自立有如此者。"

此外，儒家於教育初始，即注意開導弟子，面對諸多之學識，要能辨識所謂"本

---

① 朱熹《大學章句序》："……而其所以為教，則又皆本之人君躬行心得之餘，不待求之民生日用彝倫之外。"

② 《論語·述而》：子不語怪力亂神。又《中庸》子曰："素隱行怪，後世有述焉，吾弗為之矣。"

末先後、輕重緩急”，而致力於落實立身處世之根本的“孝悌忠信”之德行，亦即所謂“知類務本”之原則。

《論語・學而》：有子曰：“……君子務本，本立而道生。……”又〈先進〉：季路問事鬼神。子曰：“未能事人，焉能事鬼？”“敢問死？”曰：“未知生，焉知死？”（朱熹集註云：“問事鬼神，蓋求所以奉祭祀之意，而死者人之所必有，不可不知，皆切問也。然非誠敬足以事人，則必不能事神。”）〈子張〉則載：子游曰：“子夏之門人小子，當洒掃應對進退，則可矣，抑末也。本之則無，如之何？”子夏聞之，曰：“噫！言游過矣。君子之道，孰先傳焉，孰後倦焉。譬諸草木，區以別矣。君子之道，焉可誣也？有始有卒者，其惟聖人乎！”

《孟子・告子上》：孟子曰：“今有無名之指，屈而不信，非疾痛害事也。如有能信之者，則不遠秦楚之路，為指之不若人也。指不若人，則知惡之，心不若人，則不知惡，此之謂不知類也。”

《大學》載：“物有本末，事有終始，知所先後，則近道矣。……其本亂，而末治者否矣。其所厚者薄，而其所薄者厚，未之有也。

至於，儒家所運用的教學方法，誠可謂多方而靈活。茲就經典所載，類聚通觀，而擇其要者列述之，以窺其大端：

（一）堅守“因材而隨機”之法

聖人慮及人的資賦、性格、生長環境、背景、際遇……，不盡相同，是以，教學不能不因各別之差異而分別予以開導。

《論語・為政》：孟懿子問孝。子曰：“無違。”樊遲御，子告之曰：“孟孫問孝於我，我對曰：無違。”樊遲曰：“何謂也？”子曰：“生事之以禮，死葬之以禮，祭之以禮。”又：孟武伯問孝。子曰：“父母唯其疾之憂。”又載：子游問孝。子曰：“今之孝者，是謂能養。至於犬馬，皆能有養。不敬何以別乎？”又：子夏問孝。子曰：“色難。有事弟子服其勞，有酒食，先生饌。曾是以為孝乎？”（朱熹集註云：程子曰：“告懿子，告眾人者也。告武伯者，以其人多可憂之事。子游能養，而或失之於敬。了夏能直言，而或少溫潤之色。各因其材之高下，與其所失而告之，故不同也。”）〈雍也〉：子曰：“中人以上，可以語上也。中人以下，不可以語上也。”又〈先進〉載：子路問：“聞斯行諸？”子曰：“有父兄在，如之何聞斯行之？”冉有問：“聞斯行諸？”子曰：“聞斯行之。”公西華曰：“由也問，聞斯行諸。子曰：有父兄在。求也問，聞斯行諸。子曰：聞斯行之。赤也惑，敢問。”子曰：“求也退，故進之；由也兼人，故退之。”

《孟子・告了下》：孟子曰：“教亦多術矣。予不屑之教誨也者，是亦教誨之而已矣。”又〈盡心上〉：孟子曰：“君子之所以教者五：有如時雨化之者；有成德者；有達財者；有答問者；有私淑艾者。此五者，君子之所以教也。”

除“因材施教”之外，夫子更能在教學上，把握在適當時機予以施教。教師能把握適時開導、提點學生，則教學成效必然更佳，理甚淺白。

《禮記・學記》載：“當其可之謂時，……時過然後學，則勤苦而難成。”又：“學者有四失，教者必知之。人之學也，或失則多，或失則寡，或失則易，或失則止。此四者，心之莫同也。知其心，然後能救其失也。教也者，長善而救其失者也。”

自孔子展現其“因材而隨機”之施教以來，經歷兩千餘年之驗證，此一法則，迄今，依然備受中外教育專家之效法與推崇。

（二）秉持“啟發、輔導與鼓勵”之施教

以啟發、輔導與鼓勵之法教育學生，不僅可以防止學生排斥，同時可以讓學生有充分發揮其興趣與潛能的機會及空間。這對於教學的成效而言，確實十分重要。

《論語・述而》：子曰：“不憤不啟，不悱不發。舉一隅，不以三隅反，則不復也。”

《禮記・學記》載：“故君子之教，喻也。道而弗牽，強而弗抑，開而弗達。道而弗牽則和，強而弗抑則易，開而弗達則思。和易以思，可謂善喻矣。”

（三）引領學生“由博入約”

所謂“由博入約”之法，除在教導學子博學而不器，進而，將所學在生活中加以落實、體現之外，尚有另層意涵。由於人的潛能，誠非一時之所能盡知並開發者，以故，執教者應廣泛提供學子各種嘗試之機會，並加以觀察，從而，就其潛能及興好之所在，引導並輔助其充分發揮。〈學記〉云：“教也者，長善而救其失者也。”其此之謂也。

《論語・雍也》：子曰：“君子博學於文，約之以禮，亦可以弗畔矣夫。”[①]（朱熹集註云：“君子學欲其博，故於文無不考。守欲其要，故其動必以禮。如此，則可以不背於道矣。程子曰：博學於文而不約之以禮，必至於汗漫。博學矣，又能守禮而由於規矩，則亦可以不畔道矣。”）又〈子罕〉：顏淵喟然歎曰：“仰之彌高，鑽之彌堅。瞻之在前，忽焉在後。夫子循循然善誘人。博我以文，約我以禮。欲罷不能，既竭吾才，如有所立卓爾，雖欲從之，末由也已。”

《孟子・離婁下》：孟子曰：“博學而詳說之，將以反說約也。”

《禮記・儒行》載：“儒有博學而不窮，篤行而不倦，幽居而不淫，尚通而不困。禮以和為貴，忠信之美，優游之法，慕賢而容眾，毀方而瓦合，其寬裕有如此者。”《中庸》則云：“博學之，審問之，慎思之，明辨之，篤行之。”

（四）採循序漸進之法“欲其自得之”

朱子曰：“言君子務於深造，而必以其道者，欲其有所持循，以俟夫默識心通，自然而得之於己也。自得於己，則所以處之者安固而不搖。處之安固，則所藉者深遠而

---

① 按：本章於《顏淵》篇重出。

無盡。所藉者深，則日用之間，取之至近，無所往而不值其所資之本也。”[①]

《孟子·離婁下》：孟子曰：“君子深造之以道，欲其自得之也。自得之，則居之安。居之安，則資之深。資之深，則取之左右逢其原。故君子欲其自得之也。”

（五）訓勉學生“專致且持恆”、“盈科而後進”

俗云：“有恆乃成功之母”。學習任何知識、技能，除了必須持之以恆外，當專心致志，心不得有所旁騖，且應按部就班，不可陵節躁進或躐等。[②]

《論語·子路》：子曰：“南人有言：‘人而無恆，不可以作巫醫’善夫！不恆其德，或承之羞。……”

《孟子·梁惠王上》：齊宣王問曰：“齊桓、晉文之事，可得聞乎?”……（孟子）曰：“無恆產而有恆心者，惟士為能。若民則無恆產，因無恆心。苟無恆心，放辟邪侈，無不為已。”又〈離婁下〉：孟子曰：“原泉混混，不舍晝夜，盈科而後進，放乎四海。有本者如是，是之取爾。苟為無本，七八月之間雨集，溝澮皆盈。其涸也，可立而待也。故聲聞過情，君子恥之。”又〈盡心上〉：孟子曰：“孔子登東山而小魯，登太山而小天下。故觀於海者難為水，遊於聖人之門者，難為言。觀水有術，必觀其瀾。日月有明，容光必照。流水之為物也，不盈科不行。君子之志於道也，不成章不達。”又〈告子上〉：孟子曰：“無或乎王之不智也。雖有天下易生之物也，一日暴之，十日寒之，未有能生者也。……今夫奕之為數，小數也。不專心致志，則不得也。……”又〈盡心上〉：孟子曰：“有為者，辟若掘井。掘井九軔而不及泉，猶為棄井也。”

《中庸》則云：“有弗學，學之弗能，弗措也。有弗問，問之弗知，弗措也。有弗思，思之弗得，弗措也。有弗辨，辨之弗明，弗措也。有弗行，行之弗篤，弗措也。人一能之，己百之，人十能之，己千之。果能此道矣，雖愚必明，雖柔必強。”

（六）鼓勵學生“學思並重”、“切問近思”

朱子曰：“不求諸心，故昏而無得；不習其事，故危而不安。”程子云：“博學、審問、慎思、明辨、篤行五者，廢其一非學也。”[③]《論語·為政》：子曰：“學而不思則罔，思而不學則殆。”又〈子張〉：子夏曰：“博學而篤志，切問而近思，仁在其中矣。”

（七）訓示學生應“不恥下問”、“切磋觀摩”

《論語·述而》：子曰：“三人行必有我師焉。擇其善者而從之，其不善者而改之。”又〈里仁〉：子曰：“見賢思齊焉，見不賢而內自省也。”〈公冶長〉：子貢問曰：“孔文子何以謂之文?”子曰：“敏而好學，不恥下問。是以謂之文也。”

---

① 見《孟子·離婁下》朱熹《集註》。

② 見《禮記·學記》。

③ 見《論語·為政》朱熹《集註》。

《禮記・學記》載："……相觀而善之謂摩。……獨學而無友，則孤陋而寡聞。"〈大學〉亦載："《詩》云：'瞻彼淇澳，菉竹猗猗。有斐君子，如切如磋，如琢如磨。……'如切如磋者，道學也；如琢如磨者，自修也。"

（八）提醒學生"學而時習"、"溫故知新"

俗云："熟能生巧"，理甚淺白。朱子云："學能時習舊聞，而每有新得，則所學在我，而其應不窮。"[①]

《論語・學而》：子曰："學而時習之，不亦說乎?！有朋自遠方來，不亦樂乎?！人不知而不慍，不亦君子乎?！"又〈為政〉：子曰："溫故而知新，可以為師矣。"〈子張〉則載：子夏曰："日知其所亡，月無忘其所能，可謂好學也已矣。"

（九）教導學生體認"學以致用"的重要性

程子曰："窮經將以致用也。世之誦詩者，果能從政而專對乎？然則，其所學者章句之末耳。此學者之大患也。"[②]

《論語・子路》：子曰："誦詩三百，授之以政，不達。使於四方，不能專對。雖多，亦奚以為?"又〈公冶長〉：子路有聞，未之能行，唯恐有聞。（按：此章亦在明"盈科而後進"之義也。）

《中庸》則云："博學之，審問之，慎思之，明辨之，篤行之。"（朱熹〈章句〉："程子曰：'五者廢其一，非學也。'"[③]）

（十）指引學生品味"學習之樂趣"

聖人深明教育不止要讓學子先知曉"學習"對於人的必要性及其益處，同時，更要指引學子，懂得咀嚼學習之樂趣所在，不該給學習者有壓力感，[④] 甚或急功近利，而使用"揠苗助長"[⑤] 之法。

《論語・雍也》：子曰："知之者，不如好之者。好之者，不如樂之者。"（朱熹集註云："尹氏[⑥]曰：'知之者，知有此道也。好之者，好而未得也。樂之者，有所得而樂之也。'張敬夫曰：'譬之五穀，知者知其可食也。好者，食而嗜之者也。樂者，嗜之而飽者也。知而不能好，則是知之未至也。好之而未及於樂，則是好之未至也。此古之學者，所以自強而不息者與。'"）

---

① 見《論語・學而》朱熹《集註》。

② 見《論語・子路》朱熹《集註》。

③ 按：此章固所以明"由博入約"之道。同時，亦訓示人，所學必以能體現、篤行為目標。否則，任憑其所知淵博，終究流於虛空，毫無價值。

④ 《禮記・學記》載："故君子之教，喻也。道而弗牽，強而弗抑，開而弗達。"

⑤ 見《孟子・公孫丑上》。

⑥ 按：此尹氏即尹焞也。

《禮記·學記》載：“玉不琢，不成器；人不學，不知道。……雖有嘉肴，弗食，不知其旨也；雖有至道，弗學，不知其善也。”實則，此一法則，非但為教學之至理要道，亦人們建構“樂觀進取”人生觀的最佳門徑。蓋體會人生之意義者的境界，不如珍愛人生者，而知所珍愛人生者境界，又比不上，真正體認生命之意義與價值，進而抱持樂觀之態度，去咀嚼生命中的每一分一秒，而將追求、體現人生理想視為生活中之享受者。

此外，夫子更不忘時時提醒弟子，當知受教育之目的，非所以炫耀於人，或受知於人。以免於陷於，如曾國藩〈聖哲畫像記〉所云：“士方其佔畢咿唔，則期報於科第祿仕。或少讀古書，窺著作之林，則責報於遐邇之譽，後世之名。……朝耕而暮穫，一施而十報。”之失。

《論語·里仁》：子曰：“不患無位，患所以立。不患莫己知，求為可知也。”〈憲問〉：子曰：“古之學者為己，今之學者為人。”又：子曰：“不患人之不己知，患其不能也。”（朱熹集註云：“此章凡四見，而文皆有異。則聖人於此一事，蓋屢言之。其丁寧之意，亦可見矣。”）〈衛靈公〉：子曰：“君子病無能焉，不病人之不己知也。”又載：子曰：“君子求諸己，小人求諸人。”

《孟子·盡心上》：孟子謂宋句踐曰：“子好遊乎？吾語子遊。人知之，亦囂囂；人不知，亦囂囂。……”

綜上所述，明顯可見，儒家的教育，自孔子以降，不僅時時發揮其靈活而多方之法則，並處處訓示學生，當知力行、體現以倫理、道德為本的“立身處世”之道，遠較學習知識、技能，更為重要的道理。充分展現了儒家“務本尚德”之教化精神。此一精神，兩千多年來，已然成為中國傳統教育之特色，而迥然有別於，注重知識與技能之傳授的西方教育。概略而言，西方的教育，大多專注於知識技能之傳授，至於品德之教育，往往藉重宗教的力量，由“教會”的所謂“主日學”，以及到“教堂”禮拜時，依賴神職人員講經說教，予以輔成。

## 四、弘揚儒家“務本尚德”之教化精神，乃促進社會和諧發展之不二法門

思想、理念，乃決定一個人的“價值觀”及“道德標準”與“思維模式”的主要因素，而“價值觀”、“道德標準”與“思維模式”，則是左右人們言行作為之取向，最根本的力量。教育，對於個人而言，乃在啟發智慧、提昇人格，並指導人們建構其健康的理念與思想系統的工作；對群體而言，則是推動民族或國家發展的主要潛力之所在。一個民族或國家的盛衰、強弱，及其文化之良窳、榮枯，端視其教育之成敗，誠乃千古不易之定理。然則，完善的教育事業，除了學校教育之外，家庭與社會之教育，也應該兼顧而並進。再者，成功的教育步驟，當以生活教育與品德教育為本，進而，

再施以知識及技能之教育，所謂“本立而道生”，其此之謂也。簡而言之，教育要成功，應該以教導學生“做人”的道理為先，再傳授其“做事”的知識及技能。儒家“務本尚德”的教化，即在體現此一原則。

唐、韓昌黎先生〈原道〉云：“夫所謂先王之教者，何也？博愛之謂仁；行而宜之之謂義。由是而之焉之謂道；足乎己，無待於外之謂德。其文《詩》《書》《易》《春秋》，其法禮樂刑政。……其為道易明，而其為教易行也。是故，以之為己，則順而祥；以之為人，則愛而公；以之為心，則和而平；以之為天下國家，無所處而不當。”[①] 誠不誣也。蓋以孔、孟思想為核心的“儒學”，是一種維繫“人文精神”的大智慧；而所謂“儒家之道”，不僅是引領人們“安身立命”最便捷的坦途，同時也是教導人們由“內修己”到“外安人”最直接的門徑；儒家的教育，也兼顧了學校、家庭與社會。其“務本尚德”的教化精神，更是指引人們立身處世的明燈。人們若要提昇個人的人格，光大生命的意義，營造祥和的家庭，導正社會的風氣，優化生活之品質，進而，讓人類世界邁向和諧、安樂的境地，唯有藉由學校、家庭與社會，多管齊下、同時並進，落實儒家“務本尚德”的教化精神，以喚醒芸芸眾生正視“倫理”與“道德”的重要，教導世人將聖哲的明訓，內化成為“價值判斷”的依據與言行作為的“規範”。除此之外，實在別無他途。

## 結　語：

總之，以儒家的學術思想為核心，而重視“倫理、道德”教化的中華傳統優良文化，其思想、理念，兩千多年來，不僅為無數中國人藉以為立身、處世之圭臬；其精神，更被廣泛應用在政治、教育，甚至於藝文、經濟……等方面，也多能發揮其最直接而有效的指導功能。相較於，強調“功利”，突顯“個人英雄”，而藉重宗教的輔助力量，以維繫家庭關係及社會正義的西方文化，截然有所不同。無怪乎，英國倫敦國王學院的希臘語與歷史學的知名教授、阿諾爾得．約翰．湯恩比博士（Arnold Joseph Toynbee1889－1975）在一次國際會議中，就曾指出：“解決 21 世紀整個世界社會的問題，要靠中國的孔、孟學說與大乘佛教。”此外，公元 1988 年，七十五位諾貝爾得獎主，在巴黎所發表的“聯合宣言”中，更直截了當地指稱：“21 世紀的人類要生存下去，必須回歸到兩千多年前，汲取孔夫子的智慧。”這些振聾發聵的呼籲，對於炎黃子孫子孫而言，確實令人振奮。現在，我們可以理直氣壯地說，當前，在“學校”、“家庭”及“社會”，同步積極弘揚儒家“明人倫”、“崇道德”的思想，落實“務本尚德”的教化，乃促進家庭、社會乃至於人類世界和諧的不二法門。

---

① 見《韓昌黎集》卷十一。

# 儒教问题的讨论与儒学在新时期的发展

南京大学　洪修平

关于儒学是否宗教与儒学宗教性的讨论，是随着近代以来随着西学的东渐和中西文化的比较而慢慢地凸现出来。这种争论从一个侧面反映出人们在传统向现代的社会变迁中，对中国宗教和中国传统文化特性的不同认识，也反映了人们对儒学的历史作用和社会影响的不同评价，在新时期，更反映了人们对儒学在当代社会如何更好地发挥应有的作用而做的探讨。本文从儒教问题讨论的角度切入，对儒学在近代以来的发展进行考察，并对儒学在当下的发展与作用做初步探讨，以求教于方家。

## 一、现实关怀下儒教问题的提出

早在上个世纪初，梁启超、蔡元培、陈独秀等就曾提出过儒教非教说。例如梁启超在《保教非所以尊孔论》中明确提出儒教非教、孔子“不为宗教家”，新文化运动的重要代表人物陈独秀也提出，“孔教绝无宗教之实质与仪式，是教化之教，非宗教之教”。[①] 虽然他们主要是针对当时社会上出现的复辟帝制、要“定孔教为国教”的逆流而发表的观点，并非是从学术研究的角度来对这个问题进行专门的探讨，但这反映出西学东渐、社会变革背景下人们对传统思想文化的一种反思。这种观点对后世的学术研究有一定的影响。

20世纪70年代，随着对中国哲学和宗教研究的深入，任继愈先生较早提出了儒学是宗教的观点。其在1980年分别发表了《论儒教的形成》和《儒家与儒教》两篇文章，[②] 认为孔子学说经过汉代推行董仲舒的“罢黜百家，独尊儒术”和宋明理学的两次大的改造，最终成了宗教。虽然任继愈认为中国儒教与西方中世纪宗教在形式上有区别，“儒教这个宗教，看起来不同于其他宗教，如基督教、伊斯兰教、佛教等”，[③] 但他

---

① 陈独秀：《驳康有为致总理书》。

② 分别载于《中国社会科学》1980年第1期和《中国哲学》第3辑（三联书店1980年版）。

③ 任继愈：《论儒教的形成》，见《儒教问题争论集》，宗教文化出版社，2000年，第10页。

仍然从教主、教义、经典、神学理论、清规戒律和祭祀制度等方面做了大致的对应，例如认为儒教的教主是孔子，其经典为儒家六经，教派及传法世系即儒家的道统论，其教义和崇奉的对象是“天地君亲师”，祭天、祀孔则是儒教的宗教仪式。“其宗教组织即中央的国学及地方的州学、府学、县学，学官即儒教的专职神职人员。”儒教的教徒就是儒生，从中央到地方各州府县建立的孔庙就是孔教信徒定期聚会朝拜的场所。[①]

值得注意的是，任继愈等将儒学视为宗教，着眼点是对宗教和儒家文化的批判。在他看来，“宋明以后的儒教，提倡忠君孝亲、尊孔读经、复古守旧，都是文化遗产中的糟粕，是民族的精神赘疣。”因此，他的结论是：“儒教带给我们的是灾难、是桎梏、是毒瘤，而不是优良传统。它是封建宗法专制主义的精神支柱，它是使中国人民长期愚昧落后、思想僵化的总根源。”儒教“已成为阻碍我国现代化的极大思想障碍”，“为了中华民族的生存，就要让儒教早日消亡。”[②] 同样值得注意的是，反对儒学是宗教者，有一条重要理由是儒学在历史上是起过积极作用的，因而它不是宗教。其潜含的也是对宗教的批判，认为宗教对社会是没有进步作用的。例如有学者在认为汉武帝“独尊儒术”有助于当时社会进步时曾据此反问：如果说董仲舒的思想是宗教思想，“岂不是等于承认宗教对社会的进步作用?!”[③] 这反映了大陆当时对宗教较为普遍的一种看法。

以任继愈的“儒教是教说”为基本立论，李申在上个世纪末撰写了近一百五十万字的巨著《中国儒教史》上下卷，[④] 力图以史实来展示儒教发生发展的历史，从学术的角度弄清儒教的宗教性质。本世纪初，又撰写了《中国儒教论》，希望通过将儒教与其他公认的宗教进行比较所揭示的宗教本质来阐明儒教的宗教性质。其基本观点也很明确，“儒教，是中国封建时代的国教”，“在总体上，它就不可能适用于现代的社会生活和社会制度”。[⑤]《中国儒教史》出版后引起较大争议，有的认为“开启了儒教研究的新纪元，对于儒学研究有拓新之功”，有的则认为此书“走向了否定中国传统文化”，“会导致对中国传统文化全盘否定的民族文化虚无主义”。[⑥]

而与此形成对照的是，同样是大力主张儒教是宗教，有儒者却认为儒家思想是中国传统文化的精华，也是全人类的思想财富，希望孔子思想能够普及全人类。[⑦] 近年来，随着人们对中华文化复兴和精神文明建设的关注，更有部分学者认为，“在种种复

---

① 见《儒教问题争论集》，宗教文化出版社，2000 年，第 10—11 页、第 30—31 页、第 175 页。

② 见《儒教问题争论集》，宗教文化出版社，2000 年，第 20 页，第 21 页，第 16 页，第 21 页。

③ 李国权、何克让：《儒教质疑》，原载《哲学研究》1981 年第 7 期，见《儒教问题争论集》，宗教文化出版社，2000 年，第 43 页。

④ 分别由上海人民出版社 1999 年和 2000 年出版。

⑤ 李申：《中国儒教论》，河南人民出版社，2004 年，第 470—472 页。

⑥ 韩星：《儒教问题：争鸣与反思》，陕西人民出版社，2004 年，第 112 页、第 108 页、第 116 页。

⑦ 香港孔教学院院长汤恩佳近年来就大力宣传这一观点。

兴中华文化的呼吁和探索之中，重建儒教是一种重要的努力和尝试”，在他们看来，历史上的儒教本质上就是一种宗教，他们致力于建立一种现代宗教意义的儒教，甚至希望儒教成为“国教”，在面对基督教在中国大规模传播、即将在孔子家乡建造基督教堂的事件时，他们呼吁“政府宜尽快承认儒教的合法地位，赋予儒教与佛道回耶等宗教平等的身份，努力培育包括儒教在内的中国各宗教和谐相处的宗教文化生态”。①

可见，关于儒学是否宗教的问题，从一开始就不是一个纯粹的学术争论，不是纯理论的问题，而是有着很强的现实社会关怀，而改革开放以来，随着学术研究的深入而展开的讨论，很大程度上仍然是围绕着中国向何处去而展开的。争论的双方虽然在儒学是否宗教的问题上观点相反，其背后却是共同的希望中国顺利走上繁荣富强的现代化之路。正是循着这一理路，关于儒学是否宗教的问题，更多的人慢慢转向如何发挥儒教的作用或关心儒学是否具有宗教性以及中国传统的宗教具有哪些特性等问题。例如有学者提出了在中国历史上有一个延绵数千年的正统宗教、即以祭天祭祖为核心的“宗教法性传统宗教”的观点，认为“儒学只是有一定的宗教性，但又有更多的非宗教性”，② 儒学与宗法性传统宗教关系密切，相互影响，两者有交叉，甚至“两者价值取向一致，典籍文献合一”，③ 但两者不是一回事，儒学本身并不是宗教。论者在儒学是否宗教的争论中，另辟蹊径，通过对中国传统宗法性正统宗教的梳理，来回答儒学是不是宗教的问题，并期望以此能更好地“正确把握中华民族的性格特征和文化特征”，“认识很多外来宗教在顺化以后所具有的中国精神”。④

## 二、近代以来儒学起落中的儒教问题讨论

为什么在中华民族复兴之时，要讨论中国文化的主要代表儒学是否宗教？这与近代以来西学东渐，科学思潮传入中国有关，也与中国向何处走的关键时刻，人们对传统的反思有关。

---

① 见《尊重中华文化圣地，停建曲阜耶教教堂的意见书》，载中国儒教网（http：//www. chinarujiao. net/p _ info. asp? PID=8312）等网站。黄玉顺曾对此发表看法，认为“在这个信仰自由的时代，吸引信众不可能依赖任何强制力量、例如政府，而只能是使之心甘情愿、‘心悦而诚服之’。平心而论，你不得不承认：基督教在中国的传播，并没有借助任何强制性的力量，例如政府等等。……那么，问题究竟何在？眼下儒学存在的问题多多。”（氏著《儒教问题研究》，人民出版社，2012 年，第 144－145 页）可以补充的是，汉代以来统治者主导的“独尊儒术”和“三武一宗”灭佛，都并没能阻止外来佛教在中国的兴盛和传播发展，而佛教在宋代以后的衰落，与唐代韩愈、李翱乃至宋代儒士的吸收佛教、复兴儒学倒是有一定的关联。

② 牟钟鉴：《中国宗法性传统宗教试探》，《世界宗教研究》1990 年第 1 期。

③ 张践：《儒学与宗法性传统宗教》，《世界宗教研究》1991 年第 1 期。

④ 牟钟鉴：《中国宗法性传统宗教试探》，《世界宗教研究》1990 年第 1 期。

从历史上看，明末清初，长江流域一带商品经济得到了长足的发展，西方先进的科学技术、商品经济意识、自然科学成果和社会文化观念传入中国，导致了社会中出现了资本主义的萌芽。在这一背景下，思想界出现了“实学”思潮或曰启蒙思潮，并涌现出了方以智、顾炎武、颜元、黄宗羲、王夫之、戴震等思想家，他们抨击君主专制的政治体制、批判窒息人性的理学、讲究经世致用、关注社会现实，既使“实学”成为明清儒学思想的主流，也促进了中国古代思想学术向现代的转换。从儒学的历史发展看，明末清初的儒学开始进入一个转折期，此时的儒家思想家不仅面临着自我批判，而且还要承受从未有过的来自外部的冲击。到了近代，随着西方文化入侵，新学兴起，儒家思想在中国意识形态中的主导地位从此一蹶不振。明清之际，从形式上看，出现了对理学加以系统整理著作，著名的有黄宗羲、全祖望的《宋元学案》、《明儒学案》等，从思想上看，这个时期也对理学进行了总结批判，黄宗羲、顾炎武和王夫之，号称明清之际的三大家，代表了早期启蒙思想的出现，而王夫之、顾炎武以及颜元、戴震等人对理学的批判，标志着理学的发展走向了衰退。

而从儒学本身来看，当作为天理之流行的“三纲五常”发展为一种“吃人的礼教”时，原始儒学基于“仁”而对每个人的关注也就湮没在其对人伦关系“礼”的强调之中了。强化纲常名教导致的对人的束缚和对人性的摧残，名教伦理的异化，成为晚明李贽自然人性论的抬头、王学倡导的主体精神的流行、明清启蒙思潮以及清代戴震等人批判理学是“以理杀人”的重要原因，并一直影响到了20世纪初的社会文化思潮。伴随着对封建礼教的批判，儒学也成为人们批评的对象。

孔孟儒学从提倡仁爱、探讨人的价值、追求人在人伦关系中的实现出发，经过在封建社会中上千年的理论演化，最后却成了封建社会的意识形态，其主张的亲疏长幼有别、上下尊卑有序的人伦关系被异化为道德教条，并被统治者利用而成为一种与政治结合的统治术时，不仅导致了其人文精神的失落，更使它成为统治者维护专制、扼杀人性的工具。这样，进入20世纪之后，中国人民在进行反帝反封建的斗争时，矛头很自然地就指向了代表封建意识形态的儒学，希望通过对儒学的全面清算来表达对传统旧政治和旧道德的否定和批判。而企图维护旧秩序、旧文化者，当然也就会时时祭起孔子儒学的大旗。同时，一些看到儒学并不等同于封建礼教、儒学中有其合理因素的思想家，在新旧社会交替的过程中，也希望能发展儒学以适应新时代的文化需求。于是，在思想文化的舞台上，尊孔、批孔、守旧、开新，围绕着儒学的争论就热闹起来，并呈现出极其错综复杂的局面。

康有为在19世纪末到20世纪初，出于维新变法的政治需要，大力提倡孔学，希望借助“托古改制”的形式，来宣扬西方近代平等、自由和博爱等思想。康有为对儒学的改制，招致了章太炎的激烈反对，章太炎批评儒术是统治者的“南面之术，愚民之计”，① 由此掀开了20世纪儒学起落的序幕。辛亥革命推翻帝制，民国政府成立，实际上否定了儒学作为意识形态之指导思想的地位。但袁世凯要复辟当皇帝，又演起了尊儒祭孔的闹剧，康有为等也主张尊孔读经，甚至成立所谓“孔教会”，提出要“定孔教为国教”。这些倒行逆施，导致了五四新文化运动的蓬勃兴起。五四运动以反帝反封建为旗帜，引进西学，提倡“科学”与“民主”，喊出了“打倒孔家店”的口号，极大地冲击了儒家的政治和伦理学说。值得注意的是，新文化运动的重要代表人物在尖锐批评儒家学说不适应时代发展需要的同时，并未对儒学简单地全盘否定。例如陈独秀就曾说：“吾人不满于儒家者，以其……不合于现代社会之生活也。然其说尚平实近乎情理。”② “孔子精华，乃在祖述儒学，组织有系统之伦理学说。……虽不可行至今世，而在宗法社会封建时代，诚属名产。吾人所不满意者，以其为不适于现代社会之伦理学说，然犹支配今日之人心，以为文明改进之大阻力耳。”③甚至说：“在现代知识的评定之下，孔子有没有价值？我敢肯定的说有。”④ 这就表明，五四的“打倒孔家店”是因为孔子儒学在当时已成为社会进步的阻力，已不适合现代社会的需要，特别是已成为复辟倒退的工具，而并非是对儒学全部价值的彻底否定。但五四对儒学的正面抨击，毕竟给了儒学以沉重的打击，随着胡适、吴虞、鲁迅等一大批人对封建旧礼教的痛斥，儒学的地位更是日趋低落。

然而，有着悠久历史的儒学作为中国传统思想文化的主流，毕竟包含着对人类有价值的东西。因此，从20世纪20年代开始，就有人不断地援引西学来重构儒学，或希望通过“创造性的阐释”来发掘儒学在现代社会的意义和价值，从儒学中开出适合现代社会发展的新意，从而肇始了现代新儒学思潮。

新儒学是以西学来发挥儒家之理学，认为民族文化的复兴就是儒学的复兴，希冀“内圣开出新外王”，即从传统儒学中开出现代科学和民主政治制度。牟宗三曾明确说：“儒家学术第三期的发展，所应负的责任即是要开这个时代所需要的外王，亦即开新的外王。‘新外王’是什么意义呢？外王即是外而在政治上行王道，王道则以夏、商、周三代的王道为标准。”“儒家的理性主义在今天这个时代，要求新的外王，才能充分地表现。今天这个时代所要求的新外王，即是科学与民主政治。事实上，中国以前所要求的事功，亦只在民主政治的形态下，才能够充分的实现，才能够充分被正视。在古老的政治形态、社会形态下，瞧不起事功，故而亦无法充分实现。这种事功的精神要充分地使之实现，而且在精神上、学问上能充分地证成之，使它有根据，则必得靠民

① 章太炎：《驳康有为论革命书》。

② 陈独秀：《阴阳家》，《陈独秀文章选编》（上），三联书店，1984年，第275页。

③ 陈独秀：《答俞颂华》，《陈独秀文章选编》（上），三联书店，1984年，第211页。

④ 陈独秀：《孔子与中国》，《陈独秀著作选》第三卷，上海人民出版社，1993年，第377页。

主政治。”[①]

对于现代新儒学的观点，不管是否赞同，但现代新儒者强烈的社会责任感和历史使命感，却总是令人心生敬佩。现代新儒学的发展，国内外有三期和四期的不同说法。但不同时期的主题，都充分表现着现代新儒者的这种责任感使命感，他们都在融会中西学中来展开自己对中国文化发展问题的思考。就儒学与宗教的关系而言，如果说从20世纪20年代开始的新儒学第一期，主要是致力于“在儒学中寻找无神论的反宗教思想”，[②] 强调“周孔教化非宗教”、孔子以来走上的是“以道德代宗教之路”，[③] 以回应科学理性主义等西学的冲击，因为“五四新文化运动以来，中国知识分子，因深受西方启蒙心态的影响，对宗教多半抱着否定和排拒的态度”，[④] 那么，第二期则主要是“致力于阐发儒学即道德即宗教以及内在超越的品格”，[⑤] 强调儒学道德宗教的特质，从儒家的伦理道德与宗教超越精神“合一而不可分”[⑥] 的角度，参与到世界文明的对话中，以期从儒学中寻求普世性的价值，[⑦] 然而以西方一元宗教为参照、以西方话语为背景、以西方观念为标准的讨论，并不能充分彰显中国儒学的特质和特殊价值，因而到了新儒学发展的第三期，就开始转向了对中国民族特色的儒家文化自身特殊精神资源和精神价值的探讨，尽管这种探讨仍然是在经济全球化而文化多元化因而普遍关注文明对话的世界性话语背景下展开，但已经回归中国文化自身话语体系的本位。而中国大陆随着对文化复兴的自觉以及对“宗教热”等现象的反思，也出现了对儒家宗教性资源的重新评价。这样，儒学是否宗教的讨论，就更多地逐渐转向了儒学宗教性的讨论，亦即不再讨论儒学是不是宗教，而是致力于讨论儒学具有怎样的宗教性、究竟应该如何发挥儒学的实际作用，以为人的安身立命提供超越性的依持。有些讨论已经由“儒

---

① 牟宗三：《从儒家的当前使命说中国文化的现代意义》，《政道与治道》新版序，台湾学生书局，1996年，第1—31页。

② 刘子阳、朱寰：《杜维明对儒学宗教性问题的方法论批判》，《吉首大学学报》2007年第4期。

③ 梁漱溟：《中国文化要义》，学林出版社，1987年，第102页、第106页。

④ 杜维明：《儒家人文精神的宗教涵义》，《哲学动态》2000年第5期。

⑤ 朱寰：博士论文《对现代新儒家思想内在理路的探讨——以新儒家对儒学宗教性的思考为线索》，南京大学，2004年，第54页。

⑥ 唐君毅：《中华人文与当今世界》，《唐君毅集》，群言出版社，1993年，第488页。

⑦ 例如将儒教与基督教相比，认为其在客观方面有天道，“如果把天道加以位格化”就是上帝、就是人格神，其在主观方面有呼求之情，“此呼求之情即类乎祈祷”，但儒家的中心点和重点“并未落在上帝与祈祷上”，因此，“自事方面看，儒教不是普通所谓宗教，因它不具备普通宗教的仪式。它将宗教仪式转化而为日常生活轨道中之礼乐。但自理方面看，它有高度的宗教性，而且是极圆成的宗教精神，它是全部以道德意识道德实践贯注于其中的宗教意识宗教精神，因为它的重点是落在如何体现天道上。”（牟宗三：《中国哲学的特质》，上海古籍出版社，1997年，第100页—103页）“天道高高在上，有超越的意义。天道贯注于人身之时，又内在于人而为人的性，这时天道又是内在的。因此，我们可以康德喜用的字眼，说天道一方面是超越的，另一方面又是内在的。天道既超越又内在，此时可谓兼具宗教与道德的意味，宗教重超越义，而道德重内在义。”（同上第21页）

教是不是宗教?”转换为“儒教是怎样一种宗教?”[①] 原来习惯上把宗教和人文相对立看待，这时却出现了“人文主义宗教与宗教人文主义”[②] 或“儒家人文精神的宗教涵义”这样的论题。“在比较文明的格局之中，强调儒家人文精神的宗教性无非是要阐明儒家的人生哲学虽然入世但却有向往天道的维度。”儒家具有超越意义的“天道”被认为体现了“那种突出涵盖性和包容性的人文精神”。“严格地说，儒家在人伦日用之间体现终极关怀的价值取向正显示‘尽心知性’可以‘知天’乃至‘赞天地之化育’的信念。”[③] 为此，新儒家第三代主要代表人物之一的杜维明出版了《论儒学的宗教性》[④]

以上关于儒学宗教性的讨论，虽然回归中国文化自身话语体系的本位，但在国际化日益加深的时代，它当然仍会受到西学的影响。例如杜维明从“儒家在人伦日用之间体现终极关怀的价值取向”来谈儒学的宗教性，使我们很容易会联想到德国神学家保罗·蒂利希（1886－1965）对宗教的一个著名的定义：“宗教，就该词最宽泛、最基本的意义而论，就是终极关怀。”[⑤] 这种中西文化交互影响中的学术讨论，既是现代新儒学的一大特色，也是他们带给大陆学术界的新鲜空气。事实上，正是由于有一批富有活力的国际型海外学者以极大的使命感活动于中国大陆和港台、亚洲与欧美之间，吸收当代科学成果，比较中西文化异同，关注社会热点，在不同文明的对话中，致力于开发儒家文化资源和实现儒家文化传统的创造性再生，才使现代新儒学成为一门受人瞩目的显学。而在西方宗教学和海外新儒家的影响下，大陆学者对儒学是否宗教的争论也逐渐转向了儒学具有宗教性的讨论。

近代以来，随着中国封建制度衰落，社会危机的加深，西方异质文化的传入，有关儒学是否宗教和儒学宗教性的讨论，从一个侧面反映了人们对上千年中国主流文化儒学的关注，同时也推动了儒学的研究和儒学的发展。

## 三、儒学在当代的发展及其发挥作用

从历史上看，儒学是中国思想文化的主流和基础，儒学有其独特的文化内涵和精

---

① 陈明主编的论集《儒教新论》，“之所以名之曰‘新论’，是相对于20世纪80年代初由任继愈先生所揭橥的儒教论争，这些文章的论述主轴已经不再是‘儒教是不是宗教?’而转换成为‘儒教是怎样一种宗教?’”（《儒教新论·编序》，贵州人民出版社，2010年）

② 请参阅蒙培元、李存山和郭沂的相关笔谈，《中国哲学史》2002年第2期。

③ 杜维明：《儒家人文精神的宗教涵义》，《哲学动态》2000年第5期。

④ 武汉大学出版社1999年1版。此书英文初版原名为《中与庸：论〈中庸〉》，修订再版时增加了“论儒学的宗教性”一章，并将“论儒学的宗教性”作为书的副标题，中文版则将副标题改作正标题。

⑤ 蒂利希：《文化神学》英文本第7－8页，转引自吕大吉：《从哲学到宗教学》，宗教文化出版社，2002年，第763页。

神，这种文化内涵和精神在与诸子百家的争鸣中不断丰富和成长，在与佛道的交融中不断演变和发展。从三教关系的角度看，儒学对佛道的吸收不是无原则的，而是以丰富和促进儒学自身的发展为目的，儒学有其持之一贯的内在之道，有不同于佛道的文化精神和终极追求，正因为此，儒学在吸收融合佛道思想的同时也对佛道思想进行着批判。不管是吸收融合还是批判否定，落足点都是一致的，都是为了更好地彰显儒学自身的价值和意义。儒学正是在其动态发展过程中既吸收佛道思想，同时也在有意识地批判和否定佛道的思想中保持了自身发展的独立性，从而不断确立并推进着不同于佛道思想的文化精神和价值体系。而儒学这种既吸收融合又批判否定佛道思想的发展特点为我们今天讨论儒学的特点与精神、儒学的发展及其在世界多元文明中的地位和作用等提供了理论视角和历史借鉴。

在儒学的独特文化内涵和文化精神中，人文精神是一直为人们津津乐道的，笔者也曾撰写过专论《论儒学的人文精神及其现代意义》。[①] 但儒家的人文精神只是其文化内涵和文化精神的一方面，与此同时，儒学的宗教性同样不能忽视。从总体上看，儒学其实兼具人文性和宗教性两个方面，这正是造成儒学在上千年的历史展开中曲折而多向度的发展，并成为近现代以来在儒学是否宗教以及儒学宗教性问题讨论中异说纷纭的重要原因。在探讨儒学的特点以及儒学在当代的发展及其如何发挥更大作用时，兼顾儒学的人文性与宗教性两个方面，也许能更加全面地回归儒学自身的特质。因此，关注儒学的人文性和宗教性，从中国传统文化独特性的角度挖掘儒学中带有普适性意义的优质资源，从而开拓儒学发展及其发挥积极作用的新时代，就成为一个值得探讨的重要课题。

关于儒学的人文精神，在学界得到了比较一致的肯定，而关于儒教是教非教以及儒学宗教性的讨论，则至今仍未取得较为一致的看法，继续这样的讨论，对于今天如何更好地继承发展中华优秀传统文化仍然是有意义的，因为它对于考察中国宗教有别于西方宗教的特点、中国社会文化的特质，乃至当代中国文化建设和发展的走向以及中国文化如何更好地发挥对当下中国人的精神引领作用等，都具有重要的意义。

综观世界历史，古代各大文明传统中，其他的文明或者早已没落，或者已失去了生机，[②] 只有中华文化传承数千年而至今生生不息，其原因是多方面的。作为中华文化主体和基础的儒学，以其独特的文化内涵和文化精神满足了中国社会和人生的多种需求，并与佛、道等具有不同文化倾向和文化追求的多元文化并存，在不同民族文化、

① 载《中国社会科学》2000 年第 6 期。

② 有关这方面的最新讨论，可参阅张绪山《中国文明是世界唯一未曾中断的文明吗?》，《中国社会科学报》2014 年 8 月 13 日第 14 版。

不同文化形态之间的相互争鸣和相互借鉴中不断自我更新与发展，并推动着整个中华文化的不断更新和发展，这显然是重要原因之一。虽然近代以来，中国传统思想文化因遭遇到内在与外在的各种冲击而出现低潮，但不可否认的是，它仍然是我们今天建设新文化的重要资源。

当然，作为世界多元文明中之一元的儒学，在当代社会和文化的转型中，仍然有一个如何与时俱进、不断更新发展的问题。儒学自身的创新和发展，必须在更为广阔的文化视野下真正面向现代和未来，努力在世界多元的文化格局中寻求新的突破，更好地展示其自身的独特价值，并融入新的文化以发展自己，从而更好地发挥其积极的作用。儒学在当代的发展及其发挥作用，与儒学自身的特质及其在当代的发展密切相关。如何使儒学在现代社会中更好地发展，更好地发出自己的声音，提出自己的思想，发挥自己应有的作用？时代性和民族性依然是需要认真思考和解决的问题，处理好传统与现代、中国与世界等关系十分重要。[①] 在这过程中，深入探讨并努力挖掘儒学独特的文化内涵和文化精神，这对于儒学在今天的发展及其在社会人生中发挥更大的积极作用都具有十分重要的意义。

---

① 请参阅拙文《儒学、中国文化与世界多元文明——以儒佛道三教关系为视角》，《孔子研究》2010年第4期。

# 现代社会与儒教的作用

韩国成均馆大学 吴锡源

## 一、现代社会的特点与问题

现代社会发展迅速，瞬间万变。科学技术，信息通信的高度发达使人类超越国境和地区，浑然一体，形成了地球村。知识的大众化则是人们的知识水平日益提高，世界各国的多种文化汇聚一堂。然而，有人类社会自私，排他的姿态，新的民族，文化，宗教矛盾却越来越多。

支配当今世界的现代社会理念是文艺复兴之后出现的西方近代思想。该思潮的特点可概括为以重视人之理性的理论为基础的物质主义等等。较之共同体，重视个人；较之个人主义和精神，重视物质。

在以理性为基础的合理性思维中，对于物质与精神，个人与集体，人类与自然等互异的两种价值，通常以分析的，对立的视角来审视，而不是将之看作综合的，互补的关系。这种分析的，合理的价值认识促进了科学的思维，同时由于排他的两级逻辑，也引发了社会矛盾和斗争问题。

重视个人的价值意识促进人权的发展，扩大了自由，使人们获得了表现个性，实现自我的机会，然而，缺少责任意识的自由带来了各种问题，它发展为无限的放人注意，当无视共同体意识的个人主义失去健全，均衡的思维时，就会堕落为盲目的斗争主义和集体利己主义。

重视物质的价值意识随着科学。经济的发展，令我们的生活越发便利，物质更加富有。但是，同时也导致本应为手段的物质变为目的，带来价值观的混乱。这不仅是人们丧失了人的尊严与精神道德，对物质的无尽追求也秀发相对贫困意识所导致的匮乏与敌对情绪，令人们为了获得更多的物质财富而不择手段，从而引发了无数的社会丑恶现象和不法行为。

由于人类优越主义，利己主义，物质万能主义等，现代社会的诸多问题带来了可能导致人类灭亡的新危险。因此，20世纪60年代以法国的雅克·德里达（Jacques Derrida），米歇尔·福柯（Michel Foucault）等为中心的后现代（post-modernism）主义登上历史舞台，对近代思想的对立结构主义，人类优越主义等假象进行了批判。

政治伦理，经济伦理、社会伦理，文化伦理等是我们社会的已有问题。最近，还出现了遗传工程学导致的生命伦理，电脑发展导致的信息通信伦理，家庭快速解体过程中新的家庭伦理，叛逆青少年的教育等问题。越来越多的人既渴求富裕、稳定的生活，又渴望以新的道德，成熟的人格和信赖为基础的规范的人际关系。

不论科学与经济如何发展，运作它们的主体终归是人。因此，人具有正确的精神素养是迫在眉睫的，基本的且重要的问题。为此，我们要恢复真正的人之本质，建立起以正确的价值观和道德为基础的共存框架。我们儒学人应正确对待这样的社会要求。首先要准确理解儒家思想的本质直视被当今韩国社会忽视的儒教现实问题，深入分析其原因，指出新的未来方向。

## 二、儒教思想的本质

儒教思想是孔子（551－479 B.C.）主张的一种思想。孔子思想最大的特点是从以往“以神为中心”思维转换到“以认为本”的思维。即将宗教的天命世界内置于人类，要通过人的道德自觉来认识超越一切的神性。也就是说，如果完全重建人内在的本性，就不仅能够实现人类规范的生活，最终还将能够感受到宗教世界。

在理解儒教思想的本质特点时，必须要理解《论语》。《论语》记录有创建儒教的孔子的思想。在《论语》中，孔子强调了人的规范行动的准则——礼，正确的价值判断——义和规范的人际关系——仁。包含在这三项德行中的孔子所主张的儒教思想的本质可概括为以下五项。

第一，儒教思想是“以人为本”的思想。儒教所追求的“道”意味着“人之道”，所以更重视人的个人主体性和社会关系性。因此，可以说它与重视自然的道家或者以超越人的神为中心的普通宗教具有完全不同的立场。儒家的这种人本思想，不是“人应该支配万物”的人类优越主义思想，而是“要与宇宙万物共存，尽人类义务”的真正意义上的人道主义思想。

第二，儒教思想是肯定现实的思想。即较之已经失去的过去或是将至的未来，更主张以积极的态度为现在这一瞬间而竭尽全力，是欲在自身面对的现时日常生活中实现最高价值得生活哲学。因而，与消极看待现实的道家和佛家立场不同，认为只要在目前的情况下竭尽全力，就能到达“天道合一”的最终醒悟的世界。

第三，儒教思想是重视动机和过程的思想，较之结果本身，儒教对朝向理想不断努力的认真态度赋予更多的意义。因而，不同于比起动机更重视结果的法家。人生中，结果与目的的固然重要，但动机与过程更为重要。儒家主张以纯洁之心和认真的态度去努力，生活会日新月异，在其中追求人生的真正价值。

第四，儒教思想是“以实践为中心”的思想。在儒教中，求知和知识以正确的价值判断与道德实践为前提，不同于今日“以知识为中心”的西方学术观。宋代性理学以“理气论”为中心，深入分析了人的各种问题。然而，这种哲学分析的穷极目标在于道学的实践。所以，儒教思想强调，博学固然重要，但最重要的是不沉浸与观念，以规范的人格为基础去实践。

第五，儒教思想是实现人的自我存在的思想。追求规范生活的动机与目的就在于人类存在的自我实现。因此，儒教猛烈地批判强调来拯救的宗教祈福主义和忽视道德的功利主义。人类的存在原理本身使人能够过上有道德的生活，竭尽全力尽人之义务，从而实现自身的存在价值。因此即使他人不认可自己的行为或没有任何代价，也不可以怨天尤人。可以说，只以“人，义”来“尽人事，待天命”的姿态里包含着能够认识到自身真正存在价值的“自得处”和能够看到人生的较高境地——“自乐处”。

## 三、领袖形象的确立及实践

一般来说，东方儒教文化圈指的是韩国、中国、日本及东南亚地区。在这些国家中，韩国可以说是至今保持着高度儒教价值认识的国家。目前，在西方文化的基础上混合存在着各种宗教和思想，但韩国人的衣食结构和生活规范依然按照儒教的价值意识而形成。可以说，乳胶思想已经融入了韩国人的生活。然而，不同于社会主义国家——中国今日重新认识和强调儒教文化重要性的立场，一般来说在韩国，儒教是不被普通人所重视的。

经过达到物质文明高峰的20世纪，进入21世纪后，精神文化的重要性越来越为人们所重视。在这样的世界历史潮流中，可以说正确认识儒教的本质集体性、探索人类的新远景，是迫在眉睫的课题。也就是说，要求人们要正确认识儒教的本质，以成熟的人格为基础，实践有道德的生活；要求社会要符合普通大众的要求，实现健全的社会风俗，同时更多的关注弱势阶层及残障人士的痛苦并为他们服务。

很早以前，韩国传统社会的领导阶层——儒生就以清贫、朴素、高风亮节、诚信、先公后私、重以轻利等儒生精神积极参与社会、发挥批判精神，尽支柱作用。茶山丁若镛（1762－1836）在《牧民心书》中以国家领导者——牧民官的姿态强调过“律己。奉公、爱民”.“律己”指彻底控制自己，提高修养；“奉公”指放弃私心，一心为公，服务于社会；“爱民”则指真心深爱百胜。即强调领导者应该如此完全管理自身，一心为公，实践博爱和服务的精神。

今日，新的领袖形象不是指高高在上地引领众人，而是指以服务的姿态走近国民。在《论语》中孔子曾回答子路的提问说政治领导者应有的基本姿态是“先之，劳之”。不论过去、还是现在，优秀的领导者都是值得国民学习的榜样，懂得主动以牺牲和献身感动国民。可以说，这样的模范和献身行为将带来领导能力并能够获得国民的责任。

以往的企业将焦点聚在优秀的个人身上。即较之心灵，觉得头脑更为重要。然而，在现今的信息、知识社会，人们更重视人际网络（human network）的重要性。因为个人的信息和值 hi 与人际关系相结合时，将发挥更大的力量。所以，比起有能力却不热情的人，思想开明、善于与人相处的人更受欢迎。人的本质在于宁可牺牲自己也要真心珍惜、关心对方。因此，当今世界需要能够痛他人所痛，乐他人所乐之人。今天，为了实现儒教的现代化，我们儒学学者应该正确认识社会要求的新领袖形象，率先进行实践。

## 四、新儒教理念的创造与大众化

为了激活今日停滞不前的儒教，促进儒教的新发展，方案之一可以说是创造新的儒教理念。过去，以宋代的朱子（1130－1200）为中心的新儒学在相同东方文化圈的佛教、道教的影响下，确立了新的理论儒教。今天的现代社会已形成了一个全球文化圈。在这样的历史分界点上，我们应该整合东西文化，指出人类文化的新方向，确立第二个新儒学理论。

现代社会促进了科学技术的发展，缺乏阻止滥用的智慧；经济蒸蒸日上，却缺乏对他人和环境的关心；民主主义以深入人心，却缺少伦理。因此，德国的汉斯·约纳斯（1928－）提出面对多重价值、生活方式、行为规范、语言游戏和人生形式，应该制定更加积极、需要基本同意人类整合的“新地球伦理”。他强调，应摒弃过去抑制所有欲望的禁欲主义，遵守所有宗教和哲学都共同认可的最小限度的准则，在“人道”、“相互的原则”下，所有人都应被看作人，己所不欲，勿施于人。

为创造出适合现代社会的儒教理论，我们应该与人类普遍性相联系，能够为人类的共存和和平起到巨大的作用。为此，我们应准确分析 21 世纪面临的危机，建立概括 21 世纪所有人的要求的综合体系，创造能够解决现代社会问题的高水平理论，并进行科学的检验。当然，这是进行学术研究的学者们的责任。但是，普通儒学人也应给予关注，集思广益，积极参与，提出新的理论并将之大众化。

在进行儒教的现代化与大众化时，最重要的是要策划符合现代社会的具体的儒教项目，通过国际网络，开发多种多样的活动。同事，需要灵活利用韩国、中国等儒教相关文化遗址帮助人们体验儒生的生活。今日，越来越多的人因以物质的中心的价值观在自私的个人社会中无限制地竞争而各种压力过重，希望在忙碌不堪的生活中抽出一些时间寻找真正的自我，重新创造出新的人生。因此，为人们提供机会令他们通过这样的儒教文化体验获得生活的智慧，也是非常有意义的事情。

今天，在西方文化的影响下，家庭迅速解体，独居人士日益增加。在这种现实情况下，不可以一味地强调传统家庭或狭义的对自身父母的孝敬。应该超越传统社会的家庭概念，首先确立现代的家庭观念，在家庭解体的现代社会中，确定符合当今现实的新家庭面貌。同事，留意新的时代变化，与新时代共进，适宜地重新进行审视，扩大“孝”的意义，将“孝之爱”扩展到“人际关系之爱”。孝文化从狭义来讲是孝敬、恭敬自己的父母，从广义来看则使人的义务，是实现“人之爱”的一种爱。

此外，还应该积极探索各种其他方法，如开设各种儒教教育活动和研修课程，帮助人们具备适合现代人的新价值观和人性，将儒教文化和大众文化相结合等等。作为新的市民活动方法，应以家庭主妇们为对象开设研修课程，帮助他们把子女培养成栋梁之才；开设古典讲座等课程，提高普遍大众的素养。特别是，可以在全国范围内开展“读《论语》运动”，帮助一般大众形成新的价值观，出版并大力普及有关儒教的书籍，吸引更多的人走近儒教文化。

## 五、儒教在现代社会中的作用

21 世纪是全球共同生活、需要整合和宽容的时代。在未来社会应该追求的重要课题中，一般会提到人与人的和谐、人与自然的和谐、宗教与宗教的和谐。可以说，人本身是实现这些和谐和最重要因素。现代社会更加需要仁义、善良、正义、有勇气、有礼貌、谦虚、兼具能力与智慧的人。

儒教理念包含着追求物质以上世界的纯道德和考虑、关爱他人的高层次人格。还包含着追求规范行为的高品位礼仪意识、强烈的儒生精神—排斥丑恶和不义并实践真理、正义。我们应该以这种儒教的关爱和正义精神为基础，探索具体方案，是未来人类能够珍惜人的生命，和平共存。未来的生活应是以人的尊严和道德为基础的成熟的人、以这样的人格为基础的人类和平共存的双赢社会。孔子的“人道精神”和“大同社会”理念正是当今时期所迫切需要的。

儒教理念主张“修己”、“治人”。积极参与社会。我们应当把现在当作一个契机，为这种乳胶理念注入新的生命力并使之重生为更具活力的儒教。儒教拥有应对社会变化与要求的“中庸”哲学，一直以来在历史进程中为无数危机和批判指明了正确的方向。因此，今日的儒教应实现这种“时中之道”，确立适应现代社会的理论，指出人类未来的新远景。

孟子主张较之“天时”和“地利”，应该更重视“人和”。今日，要求我们儒学人首先要做到的就是这种和解精神。因为所有的发展方案只有在儒学人相互信任、和谐的基础上才能得以实现。最重要的不是多种多样的理论，而是直接付诸行动的实践。现在，为了重新振兴儒教，儒教人首先要各自正确地理解儒教理念的本质，从自己、从现在这一刻的日常生活开始实践、做出榜样，才能够找到未来的希望。

未来的人类社会应该恢复人的尊严，成为真正意义上的“人性化社会”，因为，无论借助多么尖端的科学实现了新的宇宙时代，操纵和运作机器的主体也永远是人，因此，新方向的课题即是：所有人都向往更为成熟的人性，并以这样的人格为基础认识人类生命的尊严，尊重对方的文化与宗教，从而实现所有人类和平共存的社会。

# 现代社会与儒家伦理

——以先秦儒家为主

韩国孔子学会　金学权

## 一、绪论

当今社会，经济的高速发展给人类带来丰富的物质生活，人类为了追求更高层次的物质生活，不断进行科技创新。科学技术已成为人类生活的支配理念，特别是交通技术的发展，使得全世界不再闭塞，人类已进入地球村时代。

因此，人类的生活方式和社会结构乃至人类的意识都在快速变化，由此带来的后果就是与过去相比，各种非人道主义行为和社会弊病急速增加，渐渐威胁到人类的生存，使人类陷入困境。现代社会，到底是什么使人类的生活陷入苦痛？如何解决这样的社会问题，开创美好未来？要解决这些问题，应先客观省察当今社会的诸多弊端，然后导入曾为中国社会精神支柱的儒家伦理加以探讨。

## 二、现代社会的诸多弊端

现代社会的众多特征中，最具代表性的当属日新月异的科学技术，在技术文明社会，科学技术已深入人类的生活，成为人类社会的支配理念。科学技术的发展使得商品的生产方式甚至人类的生活方式都渐渐变得机械化、自动化，人类的生活方式和社会结构都在快速变化，特别是交通通信技术的发展，人类得以跨越国界与民族，促进与其他文化圈的交流，使得世界变为单一的文化圈，社会进入地球村时代。由此，从衣食住行开始，全世界的生活方式与行动方式都变得单一化。

事实上，科学技术的发展带来的强大生产力，解决了人类的温饱及物质缺乏，缩短劳动时间，将人类从肉体劳动中解放出来，有了更多可以相帮互助共建合作体系的空余时间，从这点上来看，科学技术的发展是积极正面的。如今，科学技术的发展带动了医疗手段的提升，给人类带来丰饶的物质生活，成为人类文明的支配因素。然而，科学技术的发展带来的影响并不完全是积极的，其副作用也不容忽视。

科学技术的发展使得地球人口急剧增加，能源、粮食等重要资源快速枯竭，工业化、城市化带来的污染使人类面临严重生态危机；各种武器的研发给人类带来极大威胁；机械化、自动化带来的人类行为减退，人与人之间的交往越来越少，忧郁症等精神疾病发病率大幅增加；过度依赖工具导致人生失去意义，由此造成自杀、谋杀、恐怖活动等各种轻视生命的社会弊病频现。

快速发展的科学技术与生产力完美地控制和支配了人类的思想和行为，加上科学技术不知自省与节制的特性，如不受人类理性控制，将更大限度地控制人类。然而，现代人陶醉于科学技术中，殊不知自己的生活也变得机械化，物质万能主义和拜金主义的产物，是缺乏人类尊严的非人道主义社会。

如果人类不控制自己的欲望，缺乏通过相帮互助实现互利共赢的共同体意识，人类的美好未来只是天方夜谭。享受着科技发展带来的丰饶物质生活，更应着力剔除技术文明的发展招致的各种社会弊端，确立人类本性恢复人类尊严，共创美好未来。

## 三、儒家伦理的基本精神：博爱

人类与其他动物一样，具有维持生命所需的食欲与延续种族所需的性欲，也一样靠着一系列的物理化学反应延续生命。从生物进化论的角度来看，人类也仅是一种进化生物而已。但从生物学的角度来看，人类与其他动物相比，出生的时候更不成熟，通过自身的努力（汎所適應）积极地创造文化。（阿道夫·波尔特曼 Adolf Portmann）先天的行动方式并不足以延续生存，但通过后天的不断学习（社会化）能够逐渐适应，也就是说，人类需要后天的训育来完善自己。（阿尔诺德·盖伦 Arnold Gehlen）即，人类之所以是人类，并不是依靠动物普遍拥有的动物本性，而是依靠通过自身的意志与努力完善自己的创造性活动。

亚里士多德曾说过“对人类来说，理性的生活是最好最愉快的，理性是人类的象征，所以这样的生活才是最幸福的生活。”儒家伦理的基本精神也是超越动物本性，通过创造活动构建人文社会，人类践行道德的品质谓之为仁。儒家伦理中，尊崇超越动物本性关爱他人的道德品质——仁。即，仁是人类的象征，是人类的基本精神，是人类尊严的核心要素。

孔子向弟子颜渊释道“克己复礼为仁”，努力约束自己，使自己的行为符合礼的要求，这样才称得上为仁。人类的尊严是指超越动物本能、克服自身欲望，以怀仁之心关爱他人。所以孔子提倡，不做有违社会行为道德规范和损害社会和谐信赖之事。

孔子认为，将普天下皆看为拥有高贵生命和生存价值的平等的人即是仁。仁就是不把别人当做实现自己目标时的工具和手段，而是把别人放在与自己对等的位置。孔子弟子樊遲向孔子求教“仁”时，孔子答道“仁者先难而后获，可谓仁矣”，接着说到“爱人”，孔子主张平等博爱的仁心即为人道，并说道“人而不仁，如礼何．人而不仁，如乐何”强调仁是人性的根本。

继承了孔子仁学思想的孟子也将人性归于人内在的仁，孟子曰：“人皆有不忍人之心……无恻隐之心，非人也。无羞恶之心，非人也。无辞让之心，非人也。无是非之心，非人也。恻隐之心，仁之端也。羞恶之心，义之端也。辞让之心，礼之端也。是非之心，智之端也。人之有是四端也，犹其有四体也。”孟子主张，仁与四肢躯体一样，是所有人先天就有的，并发展为“仁义礼智”四德。四德并不是求取富贵功名的工具，而是能够痛人所痛、为错误感到羞愧、照顾身处困境的他人、判别是非真假的觉悟。因此孟子认为，不具备“四德”之人不配被称为人类，孟子也主张自悟及践行“四德”。

荀子曾曰“人有气有生有知，亦且有义，故最为天下贵也。”人的特性为通过对是非善恶的选择与判断来体现义，对道德价值的自悟与实践使人类成为世间最尊贵的存在。通过上述论议我们能了解到儒家伦理的基本精神为仁，即博爱，人性的尊严也是以仁德作为基础。

## 四、儒家伦理的履行：忠恕的实践

人间指的是人与人的共存，人性以及人类的尊严也是在人与人之间发现和扩散。致力于研究人类存在学的马丁·海德格尔（Martin Heidegger）曾说过“共同存在是，即使感觉不到有人在你面前，仍可以用实存论来说明现存在。即使一个人也是与世界共存。即使不能感知到他人，他人也是存在的。独存只是共存的一种缺陷形态，其可能性就是对共存的证明。”海德格尔的主张为与他人的共存才是人类最本质的状态，独存只是人类存在的一种特殊形式。即人类本质上是与他人共存的存在。

孔子将脱离人类的现实生活领域，不能通过经验与知识论证的抽象问题归到论议范围之外。在弟子请教“死”时，孔子答曰“未知生，焉知死”。孔子关心的是现实问题，而非不能以经验论证的生前死后。所以孔子思想中大部分都是关于现世的问题。孔子在与弟子曾参的对话中曾说道“参乎！吾道一以貫之。曾子曰唯。出门人问曰，何谓也。曾子曰夫子之道，忠恕而已矣。”由此可知，孔子一生中作为生活信条的行为准则为“忠恕之道”。参子参透了孔子的意思，贯穿孔子一生的“仁”是以“忠恕”的方式来实践的。

说到底，什么才是忠恕之道？孔子向弟子子贡解释道“己所不欲，勿施于人”则为“恕”。我们的日常生活与他人紧密相关。要与他人融洽相处，需要关心爱护他人。对他人的关心爱护分为两种形式：第一种为自己不愿做的，也不让别人做的消极方式；第二种为自己喜欢愿意做的，分享给别人一起做的积极方式。孔子所说的“恕”属于自己不愿意不喜欢的，也不交给别人的这种消极的方式。

“忠”指的是我想做愿意做的，也帮助别人一起做，这是实践仁德的一种积极的方式。孔子曾对子贡说：“夫仁者，己欲立而立人，己欲达而达人。能近取譬，可谓仁之方也已。”通过孔子的解释，我们可以了解到，“忠恕之道”是站在他人的立场上考虑问题，是实践仁德的道德准则。这与伊曼努尔·康德（Immanuel Kant）的见解不约而同。康德主张，在特定情况下，对我来说正确的，对他人来说也是正确的；对我来说错误的，对他人来说也是错误的。个人的欲望、感情、意见等经验上的差异与选择什么样的行为无关。确信无论何时普遍共通的道德实践准则都是存在的。“你的意识准则同时也是普遍的立法原理，妥善的选择自己的行为吧。”以此确立实践理性的基本法则，主张此为最高原理。

忠恕之道在儒家得以继承发扬并成为道德实践的普遍原理。在《大学》以“所恶于上，毋以使下，所恶于下，毋以事上，所恶于前，毋以先后，所恶于后，毋以从前，所恶于右，毋以交于左，所恶于左，毋以交于右，此之谓絜矩之道也”做出说明。这是孔子对子贡所说的“恕”，即仁德的消极实践方法的具体说明。被用作衡量人际关系的絜矩，所以也被称为絜矩之道。《中庸》中有对仁德的积极实践方法“忠”的详细说明“忠恕违道不远，施诸己而不愿，亦勿施于人。君子之道四，丘未能一焉。所求乎子，以事父未能也。所求乎臣，以事君未能也。所求乎弟，以事兄未能也。所求乎朋友，先施之未能也。庸德之行，庸言之谨。有所不足，不敢不勉，有馀不敢尽。言顾行，行顾言。君子胡不慥慥尔”。这是《论语》中孔子对子贡所说的仁德的积极实践方法“忠”的说明。结合自身事例，联系人际关系做出的详细说明。《中庸》和《大学》中对忠恕之道都有详细说明，忠恕之道作为仁德的实践方法也被称为君子之道。

孟子认为人性的根本为“仁义道德”，强调仁义道德的实践主体为人心。孟子曰“仁，人心也。义，人路也，舍其路而弗由，放其心而不知求，哀哉。人有鸡犬放，则知求之。有放心而不知求。学问之道无他，求其放心而已矣。”孟子概叹当时社会世态，将人性的根本“仁义道德”弃之不顾，沦落为世俗欲望的奴隶，追求仁义道德的人心不复存在。孟子主张，为了坚守仁义道德，连贵重的生命都可以抛弃。所以他说“仁，人心也。义，人路也。舍其路而弗由，放其心而不知求，哀哉。人有鸡犬放，则知求之。有放心而不知求。学问之道无他，求其放心而已矣。”这是说生命虽然尊贵，但为了守住生命而放弃人性尊严即仁义道德是不可取的。

孟子继承和发展了孔子的“忠恕之道”思想，认为仁义礼智的四端之心生来有之，要充实人性，只能扩充四端。由此孟子曰“人之所以異于禽兽者几希。庶民去之，君子存之”。在日常人际交往中，一直将内在的四端作为行为准则不是一件容易的事。先人后我，持之以恒坚守四端的君子才是社会平安和睦的原动力。

## 五、儒家伦理的目标：实现至善世界

亚里士多德认为幸福不是某种心理状态而是一种活动，一种非物质的精神活动，也被称为“好行为（eupraxia)”。幸福作为一种活动，这种活动的舞台则是人生，不是分段的连续的人生。幸福是一种贯穿整个人生的理性活动，有高低起伏的观照活动。孔子也认为幸福的人生无论何时都是克己复礼的道德实践理性活动，还包括在有限生命中对同类（人类）的同情与博爱。孔子曰“志士仁人，无求生以害仁，有杀身成仁”。

但是，个人的生活无法脱离社会，个人的幸福和痛苦与社会也有紧密的关系。所以，越是在太平盛世，个人越可能幸福，孔子所追求的终极目标是建立所有人都安乐的平天下社会。孔子在与弟子子贡的对话中曾说道“博施于民而能济众，……必也圣乎。”。人类作为社会的一员，无法脱离他人独立生存。反而能从包容和帮助陷入困境的人中收获快乐，体会生命的意义。孔子将深刻自悟人类本质、善于施人以恩惠、救助陷入困境的人、努力使大家都幸福的人称为圣人。

由此孔子从强调个人的道德修养发展到建立平天下社会的目标。孔子曰“修己以安百姓”。孔子从个人道德修养扩展到全社会的思想被后代继承发扬，在《大学》中也有“大学之道，在明明德，在亲民，在止于至善。”的内容。表明从自身的道德修养做起，逐步扩展到全社会，并将实现至善社会作为终极目标。

如果说个人的理想生活是人道生活的话，理想社会就是社会成员全都享有这种生活的社会。怎样的社会才算是理想社会呢？首先，要具备能让大家维持安定生活的经济基础，人人都能接受教育，各自都在与自己的能力相匹配的工作岗位上，没有劳动能力的人都能享受社会保障，人人都有先人后己的意识，充满信义与关爱，这样的社会才是理想社会，也是将人的道德水平发展到最高境界的至善世界。

孔子将充满人性、道义和关爱的道德社会的至善世界称为大同世界。《礼记》中，孔子解释道何谓大同世界“大道之行也，天下爲公。选贤与能，讲信修睦，故人不独亲其亲，不独子其子，使老有所终，壮有所用，幼有所长，矜寡孤独废疾者，皆有所养。男有分，女有归。货恶其弃于地也，不必藏于己。力恶其不出于身，不必为己。是故，谋废而不兴，盗窃乱贼而不作，故外户而不闭，是谓大同。”。大同世界描绘的社会是人人敬老，人人爱幼，无处不均匀，无人不饱暖的理想社会。儒家伦理所追求的终极目标，即是将个人保有的先天道德从个人扩展到家庭，再从家庭扩展到全社会，直至实现大同世界。仁德也是大同世界的基本要素，仁德是实现个人和全社会幸福不可或缺的基本条件。

## 结 语

近代工业革命过后，日新月异的科技发展为人类带来了前所未有的丰饶的物质生活。即便物质生活如此丰富，自杀、杀人等反人类活动激增，各种社会弊端层出不穷。由此可知，虽然物质生活极大丰富，精神层面却变得荒芜。我们人类离生存价值生存目的越来越远，不断向痛苦的深渊下坠。只追求丰富的物质生活而丧失了人性的生活不可能是幸福的生活。盲目崇信科学技术和物质万能主义，将万物根基的自然当作我们追求物质的工具，甚至将精神也理解为物质现象，轻视生命的不正之风蔓延，环境污染导致生态破碎，资源枯竭等环境危机使我们的生存面临严峻的威胁与挑战。科技为人类带来便利的同时也是使人性日渐泯灭的元凶，从而使人类陷入生存困境。正如孟子所言“祸福无不自己求之者”我们自己犯的错误也应由我们自己拨乱反正。

曾作为中国人精神支柱的传统儒家伦理，其核心思想为人生而有德，强调发扬先人后己的博爱精神，这就是儒家伦理中的人文主义。因此，人只是实现崇高价值的目的，而非达成某些目的的手段和工具。人人生而平等，以“易地思之”的方法来实践“忠恕之德”，具体来说就是自己愿意帮助他人共享，还有己所不欲勿施于人。通过实践忠恕之德追求共存共荣的幸福生活。提高个人道德涵养，并使之扩散到家庭乃至整个社会，直至实现大同世界。大同世界强调相帮互助的共同体意识。

为了解决现代社会的诸般问题，共创人类的美好未来，应致力于确立重视人内在价值和尊严的价值观。摒弃为获得一己私利而将他人当做工具的利己主义，发扬博爱思想。为了实现人人幸福的至善社会，应强化相帮互助的共同体意识。为了创造我们人类的美好明天，像张载所言“为天地立志，为生民立道，为去圣继绝学，为万世开太平。”，应通过考察中国传统儒家伦理，努力扬其所长。

# 儒学与社会的现代化

俄罗斯科学院　布罗夫

当人们谈论现代化的时候，通常所指与其说是工农业生产的增长，不如说是包括信息工业在内的国民经济现代领域的发展，是科学技术最新成果在生产中的应用。但是在我看来，把现代化归结为这些“技术参数”是不对的。现代化是一个复杂得多的社会现象。它包括如下特征：城市化的水平、居民的文化水平、职业教育体系的存在、对企业活动自由的保障、社会动员速度的增加、职业分化、国民对自己归属于所在社会的意识、独立社会组织的不断涌现，等等。

现代化要以整个社会结构和社会关系体系的改变，更重要的是人本身的改变，为前提。现代化不仅仅是物质生活水平的提高，而且也是人们观念的改变，智力的提高。住在现代公寓、拥有私家车、享用西方的食品、穿戴摩登的服装，具备所有的这些条件还不足以谈现代化。仅仅就人而言，现代化意味着拥有现代知识与观念，意味着他的行为符合现代规范。如果就整个社会而言，谈论现代化就要谈到法治国家，以及实现公正、理性、和谐的意向。

可见，现代化具有文明的、社会文化的性质，换句话说，它包括社会关系的一切领域，虽然它对这些领域的影响是不一样的。现代化的目标和意义不仅是经济增长，而且也是包括技术文化、管理文化、政治文化和社会文明在内的社会文化的发展达到一定的水平。现代化在很大程度上是对来自发达国家的挑战的回应，是对在新的世界现实诸条件中生存形式的探寻。常常有这种情况，当人们在学术著作中谈论现代化时，其实是在根据这个或那个国家接近或者进入西方文明的程度判断它的现代性，西方文明充当了文明程度的普遍尺度，也就是说，成为现代国家，意味着成为西方，被人们看作西方式的国家。

我认为这种看问题的角度是不正确的。不能说现代化就是与以往社会的或者文化的经验完全决裂。不论在什么情况下，现代化都不是反传统的或者非传统的运动，它与连续性历史过程中的传统有着继承关系。

我认为，当前中国社会的经济现代化和政治现代化问题与对中国传统哲学，首先是儒学，的准确理解有着不可分割的联系。在18世纪，欧洲启蒙思想家们把中国视为国家的典范，正是因为中国存在着孔夫子的伦理学。但是在19世纪末和20世纪初，西方社会出现了来自马克斯·韦伯的对儒学的不正确的观念。大家知道，他提出了社会伦理以及经济发展趋势依赖于宗教信仰体系的思想。按照他的意见，正是在新教伦理中包含着企业家活动的精神。新教拥有诸如勤勉、节俭、热爱创新和为人类服务这样一些价值。同时马克斯·韦伯认为，儒家社会缺少企业家活动的精神，因为它的成员是不如新教徒那样有活力、有理性。这位德国社会学家断言，儒家学说在根本上就是与经济发展以及社会现代化相敌对的。

应该说，韦伯的观点在当时对西方的史学研究，特别是美国的史学研究，产生了重大影响。Д. 列昂杰夫的《如家中国及其现代命运》和M. 赖特的《中国保守主义的最后抵抗》就是例子。按照列昂杰夫的意见，儒学是正在消失的文化现象，因为它与现代世界相抵触。他认为，儒学排除了产生科学的可能性，因为儒学家们的存在有赖于某些道德律令和普遍价值在社会中的实现，在这样的社会中出现政治问题、经济问题方面的专家是不可能的。按照赖特的意见，中国进入现代世界的主要障碍是构成儒学体系的那些因素，而不是帝国主义侵略、满清的统治、官员们的愚钝，或者历史的偶然性。

美国学者们认为儒学中没有工业和促进现代社会发展的其他因素的立足之地。儒学的基石是集体对人们活动的控制，单个人不可能是独立个人，因为他的任何行动都是由来自外面的因素左右的。由于政府对社会生活的全面干预以及与此相关的政治文化，市场结构和自由资本主义在中国社会不可能得到发展。儒学的注意力集中在利用人的那些可以使它成为自然的主宰的特点来培养人的“美德”的培养上。韦伯说，信奉儒学的人喜欢谈论美，但是很难成为考虑成功的商人。儒学不是把民族集体才智的发展过程看作知识与信息的积累，而是看作在传统观念框架中得到评价的知识、材料的简单传递。

但是韦伯的看法不符合历史现实，因为他不明白，儒学不是宗教，而是道德学说，是社会伦理规范的汇总。韦伯的错误在于他了解真正的儒家学说的原理。实际上在儒学中是可以找到伦理学和企业家活动之间的联系的，因为儒学中也包含有诸如勤勉、节俭、创新、个人主义和追求利益这样一些价值。

因此近年来有人对儒学在现代社会中的作用做了过高的评价。这与20世纪下半叶出现了人的异化、悲观主义心理、道德退化等众多社会文化问题有关。工作时人与人的关系不再具有个性，回到家里感觉就像在笼子里一样，商业化和道德相对主义成为主流倾向。在这种情况下道德价值和精神价值可以充当“建设与改造的力量”。许多学者发现，儒学不仅在东亚不少国家和地区令人印象深刻的经济成就中发挥了作用，而且还是一种能够帮助解决那些超级工业化的、原子化了的社会的众多严重问题的伦理体系，不论这样的社会地处何方。

当前的现代化自身带有一些严重的问题，这些问题在某种意义上导致人与人关系的非人道主义化，环境被破坏、给个人和整个社会的健康造成损害。出现了人与人之间的疏离与异化。在这种情况下，和谐、诚信、互相依靠、自我修养等儒学价值作为培养人的责任感和执行力的手段，可以充当现代化社会各种“疾病”与“溃疡”的解毒剂。儒学可以使人始终是人，社会始终是社会。显然，这和它的人道主义精神有关。

应该指出，并非所有的美国学者都支持马克斯·韦伯的观点。著名的美国学者成中英教授不同意韦伯对儒学的理解。在他看来，应该避免把对儒学的认识简单化。这位美国学者说，儒学对自然、人以及天的观点有许多个方面，为了实现把儒学传统和经济与技术发展的现代普适亚文化在自身结合在一起的有机现代化，它们可以被赞同、使用和研究。按照成中英的意见，这是因为儒学伦理学始终把全社会的幸福摆在中心位置。自我完善和修养的目的是为他人服务和节制自己的欲望与利益，儒学的道德规范排除了对物质生活安逸的追求，对单个的人来说，第一位的是家庭利益，而通过家庭利益追求的是整个社会的利益。孝的原则，除了要求遵守一定的行为规范，把儿子为父母提供物质方面的保障作为理所当然的目标包括在自己当中。除此而外，按照儒学的规定统治者必须关心人民，因此在儒学的实质内容中就包含有现代化的理由。一方面国家必须提高自己国民的物质幸福水平，另一方面每个人在家庭面前都负有尽力保障家庭成员物质幸福的责任。这种责任应该从更广的意义上看，它不仅服务于家庭，最终是服务于社会。

儒学中有一些有价值的东西是西方学说，包括新教，不具备的，这些有价值的东西使得儒学能够适应当前的现代化的需要。与立足于个人主义的理性主义相对立，儒学的理性主义把家庭式的集体主义看作人际关系的基础。同时儒学教导人们怎样成为人。“成人”要以不间断的自我发展、自我完善为前提。它具有两面性：一方面是掌握职业的、技术的习惯和专门知识，另一方面是认识自己这个“我”的特点，是自我认识过程的不断完善。儒学伦理学捍卫的不是人权，而是人的责任感。它立足于社会的统一，寻找每个人都可以接受的在具体的专门的社会共同体中的地位。这里说的是，人应该承担一定的义务，并且按照这些义务的要求行事。这种行为模式以人的自我修养和出于自愿的精神和心理意义上的自我节制为前提。同时，现代的儒学伦理学强调教育的重要，教育被理解为不是简单的知识积累，而是性格的锤炼和个性的形成。教育的最终目的是培养人的责任感和对伟大理想的忠诚。所有这些使儒学成为当今社会现代化过程不可缺少的因素。

从更大的背景来看，儒学伦理学的广泛传播为作为统一文化空间的中国国家的持续存在提供了基础。中国的政治论理学发挥着整个政治共同体共同意志的整合作用，而不是其成员不同利益的收集者。当然，在完成国家建设的任务是，中国的政治伦理不仅求助于儒学，它还依靠强力和法律。但是强力和法律等手段似乎不那么有效，它们的使用还要消耗许多人力和财力资源。同时运用儒学思想“花费”较少，它的功用则是多种多样的。它既是人际交往的准则，也是挑选官员的标准、政治惩罚的依据和参与政治行动的理由。依靠儒学思想，人民和政府思想意识上的一致得到保障。权力和思想的结合，对民族的整治整合，能够使任何的国家措施得到实现。

按照儒学伦理学，领导者应该具有高尚的道德品质，让人们以自己为表率，只有这时他才能够领导他们。在儒学中，理想的领导人被认为是贤王。只有养成了必需的品德并且在社会中建立起和睦气氛的统治者才能成为贤王。只有这时，他的领导权才能得到受他领导的那些人承认。但是（杜维明的一段话没有翻译）

因此，在我看来，儒学中包含的那些价值即使在今天也是有意义的。它们能够制衡西方国家民主进程发展中明显地暴露出来的两种倾向。第一种倾向与对个人自由的过度称赞有关，扩大公民自由的同时，没有相应地增加他们的责任。用索尔仁尼琴的话说：“在西方，对个人权利的保卫到了这样的程度，以致在一些人面前社会成为不受保护的了。已经到了这样的时候，应该保护的与其说是权利，不如说是义务。”第二种倾向是法律规范和社会规范之间的失衡。关于法律至上和法律面前人人平等这些就其实质而言完全正确的原理，在西方国家的实践中常常变成对调节人们行为的社会规范的遗忘：“个人能够把自由解释为可以做任何法律允许但社会不接受的事情的权利”。这里所说的是法律规范和调节家庭婚姻关系的社会规范之间的矛盾。

东方各民族的文化传统与西方式民主的各种价值有极大的不同，在建立稳定的政治体系时，这些传统首先强调整个社会的作用。尤其是儒学，它支持在个人权利和社会利益之间建立平衡。儒学的长处在于它是调节人们社会行为道德规范的汇总。孔子号召统治者遵循如下规则：“道之以政，齐之以刑，民免而无耻；道之以德，齐之以礼，有耻且格。”（《论语·为政》）

在中国的传统文化中没有“此世”和“彼世”两个世界的划分。它们因为儒学伦理学而构成一个整体。按照杰出哲学家冯友兰的说法：“四书是中国人的圣经，但是在四书中没有谈创世，也没有关于天国和地狱的回忆”。这些书是人的智慧的集中，而不是对天启的描述。因此可以说儒学具有理性主义的性质，或者谈论儒学理性主义。儒学理性主义依赖于人的经验，把人的经验视为智慧的唯一来源。人的理智的功能只在于把人的经验中有价值的东西作为对人们活动的指导来接受。

当儒学说“我”的时候，它说的不是单独的人，更不是孤立的存在物，而是在说人与周围世界的各种关系的聚集地。人存在于不断扩展着的生命空间之中，从家庭开始，以社会、国家、宇宙结束。根据儒家学说，人的形成意味着独特的“我”的实现，意味着各种独特的自然品质的发展。

最后，我不同意说儒学阻碍了科学的发展，不同意为了克服这种缺点，必须使中国思维理性化，使它西方化。正是中国发明了指南针、火药、造纸、印刷术，仅仅根据这一简单的理由，上述哪些说法就是经不住批评的。另一个证据是，有四个中国人获得了诺贝尔奖，虽然他们是在美国获得高等教育的，但是他们的学术基础是在中国奠定的。除此而外，如果说在西方宗教和科学的关系往往是势不两立的，那么在中国则没有这种情况，因为儒学信奉“中庸之道”。

当然了，儒学的历史有不同的时期，曾经有一个时期它的代表人物服务于封建阶级的利益。但是不能因为这类事实就怀疑孔子学说道德格言的永久性，这类事实无损于仁爱、义务、公正、尊老、爱智等孔子捍卫的人类普遍价值的意义。即使在今天，它们也能够在现代化过程中得到应用。

# 康有为与孙中山大同思想比较

黑龙江大学 魏义霞

“大同”一词最早出现在儒家经典《礼记·礼运篇》中，是中国人的千年梦想。在近代，康有为、谭嗣同和孙中山等人都对大同思想津津乐道。其中，康有为的《大同书》集中描述了大同社会的理想蓝图，成为近代大同思想的第一种形态；孙中山的大同理想与康有为一样源自儒家，所不同的是，作为一位革命家和辛亥革命的领导者，他将大同理想与现实的政治斗争密切联系起来，克服了康有为大同思想的空想性，将大同理想推向了一个前所未有的高度。康有为、孙中山的大同思想异同互见，对二者进行比较，透视其同，有助于深入了解近代大同和平等思想的时代内涵；透视其异，可以更加直观地理解维新派与革命派不同的政治纲领和奋斗目标。

## 一、康有为、孙中山的大同情结与平等思想

综观近代思想可以发现，推崇平等的思想家均对大同社会乐此不疲。就维新派而言，康有为、谭嗣同代表的平等派均对大同社会乐此不疲，而作为自由派代表的严复、梁启超则对大同予以保留乃至含有微词。不可否认的是，孙中山对大同的向往也与对平等的侧重相关，这使他的思想与康有为、谭嗣同具有相同之处。孙中山对大同社会的具体理解以及实现平等的途径与康有为、谭嗣同大相径庭而已。

在分析中国积贫积弱的原因时，近代思想家找到了不同的根源。拿维新派来说，康有为、谭嗣同侧重中国社会内部上下隔绝的不平等，进而将推进平等视为拯救中国的不二法门。这使两人最终都走向了平等派。因循平等思路的康有为、谭嗣同对大同社会倍加关注，这从一个侧面印证了平等与大同之间的内在联系。

按照康有为的说法，当时的中国在各方面都存在着严重的不平等，正是这些不平等造成了中国的落后和衰弱。要救亡图存，必须在中国提倡和实现平等。有鉴于此，他十分重视平等，将实现平等奉为自己的行动目标和拯救中国的不二法门。康有为的《大同书》从政治、经济、文化、宗教、公益和家庭等各个方面建构了一个绝对平等的

世界，书名《大同书》之“大同”即含有绝对平等之义。按照康有为的理解，平、同同义，取消一切差异而绝对相同、绝对平均才是平等。“‘同’字、‘平’字，先同而后能平。”[1] 如此看来，《大同书》之所以弥漫着绝对平均主义的气氛，就是为了彰显绝对平等的主题，因为《大同书》以“至公”为要义，而至平、大同才是至公：“大同之道，至平也，至公也，至仁也，治之至也，虽有善道，无以加此矣。”[2] 对于康有为来说，大同与平等相互印证：一方面，平等表现为消灭各种差异的世界大同。为了消灭国与国、种族与种族之间的不平等，他利用古代的大同理想为平等辩护，进而向往、提倡天下大同。在康有为看来，将来的世界或者说太平社会就是大同世界，那时全世界同一人种、同一国家、同一文化、同一政治乃至同一语言文字——不仅取消了国家，从根本上铲除了战争，而且消除了种族、人种之分，人与人绝对平等。于是，他断言：“地既同矣，国既同矣，种既同矣，政治、风俗、礼教、法律、度量、权衡、语言、文字无一不同。”[3] 这样的绝对平等社会就是大同世界。另一方面，只有到了大同社会，才能彻底实现平等：“全世界人类尽为平等，则太平之效渐著矣。”[4]

孙中山将“破除人类之不平等”奉为一切革命的宗旨：“夫世界古今何为而有革命？乃所以破除人类之不平等也。孔子曰：‘汤武革命，顺乎天而应乎人。’革命之时义大矣哉！”[5] 孙中山提倡三民主义，而三民主义按照他自己的解释分别对应着自由、平等、博爱。与此相一致，对于自己所领导的辛亥革命和民主革命的宗旨，他不厌其烦地表白是为了在中国建立一个自由、平等、博爱的新型国家。对此，孙中山在《军政府宣言》中解释说：“我等今日与前代殊，于驱除鞑虏，恢复中华之外，国体民生尚当与民变革，虽经纬万端，要其一贯之精神，则为自由、平等、博爱。”对于三民主义与自由、平等、博爱之间的关系，他以法国大革命的口号为例具体解释说：“用我们三民主义的口号和法国革命的口号来比较，法国的自由和我们的民族主义相同，因为民族主义是提倡国家自由的。平等和我们的民权主义相同，因为民权主义是提倡人民在政治之地位都是平等的，要打破君权。使人人都是平等的，所以说民权是和平等相对待的。此外还有博爱的口号，这个名词的原文是‘兄弟’的意思，和中国‘同胞’两个字是一样解法，普通译成博爱，当中的道理，和我们的民生主义是相通的。因为我

---

① 《万木草堂讲义·中庸》，《康有为全集》（第二集）中国人民大学出版社，2007年，第293页。

② 《大同书》，中州古籍出版社，1998年，第39页。

③ 《大同书》，中州古籍出版社，1998年，第126页。

④ 《大同书》，中州古籍出版社，1998年，第148页。

⑤ 《三民主义》，《孙中山全集》（第五卷），中华书局，2006年，第185页。

们的民生主义是图四万万人幸福的，为四万万人谋幸福就是博爱。”① 由此可见，孙中山的三民主义就是中国本土语境中的自由、平等和博爱。其中，民族主义对应的是自由，民权主义对应的平等，民生主义对应的是博爱。孙中山倡导的民主革命之所以没有直接以自由、平等、博爱而是以民族主义、民权主义和民生主义作为行动纲领是基于中国特殊的国情，不过这并不妨碍三民主义分别对应着自由、平等、博爱，奉行三民主义就是为了将中国改造成自由、平等、博爱的大同社会。

在这个前提下，必须说明的是，尽管孙中山民主革命的纲领三民主义——民族主义、民权主义和民生主义各有侧重，分别指向自由、平等、博爱，三者之间绝非并列的关系，而是以平等为中心；正如三民主义一言以蔽之即民有、民治、民享一样，对于国民来说，三民主义主要是使之从不平等之痛苦走向平等之幸福。孙中山本人对于三民主义之间的关系的解释恰好说明了这个问题："我们革命党提倡改良中国，何以要行三民主义的革命呢？……像满清征服中国，英国征服印度，法国征服安南，日本征服高丽，发生本族和异族政权上的不平等。那种不平等的民族要求平等，便用武力来反抗异族，那种对于异族的反抗，便是民族革命。至于政权都掌〈握〉在一种民族的手内，如果执政的人威权过甚，小百姓太没有能力，便发生有权势的人和平民之分，政权上还是人人不平等的。平民都要求平等，便要去反抗有权势的人。那平民对于有权势的人的反抗，便是民权革命。至于近来人类要求社会上机会平均，贫富相等，便是民生革命。明朝朱元玮〔璋〕推翻元朝，可以说是做到了民族革命，但以后各代专制太过，所以满清入关，政治宽大，中国人民还是欢迎他。由此可见，本国人专制，也是不对的。但本国人政权上不专制，社会上的贫富，还要平均，才能相安无事，否则还免不了革命。世界上起了这项革命，现在已经成功的，只有俄国。我们观察古今中外大势，默想本国将来的情形，要改良成一个完全的中华民国，行一个一劳永逸的方法，所以行了民族主义的革命、民权主义的革命，必须兼顾民生主义的革命。”② 这明白无误地表明，孙中山对自由、平等、博爱具有自己的独特理解，虽然承认民族主义、民权主义和民生主义分别对应着自由、平等和博爱，却使三者共同指向了平等：民族主义针对“本族和异族政权上的不平等”，是“民族要求平等”；民权主义是在“政权都掌〈握〉在一种民族的手内”的情况下，没有权利的“平民都要求平等”；民生主义则旨在政治上实现平等之后，在经济上实现平等，“机会平均，贫富相等”。这表明，三民主义最终都可以归结为平等，平等是三民主义一以贯之的灵魂和核心。可

① 《三民主义·民权主义》，《孙中山全集》（第九卷），中华书局，2006年，第283页。

② 《在广州欢宴各军将领会上的演说》，《孙中山全集》（第八卷），中华书局，2006年，第471页。

以作为佐证的是，相对于自由来说，孙中山更为偏袒和重视的还是平等之权，这一点从他对自由的态度中可以更明显地体现出来。例如，孙中山声称："夫自由既属可贵，如空气然，不得则死。然中西历史不同，西国政府对于人民，事事干涉，故西人重视自由，有'不自由毋宁死'之说，其历史之战争，多自由之战争。若中国则不然，中国个人向极自由，以其得之极易，故不知宝贵。历史上为自由而战者，自秦末一役以后，殆不数数覯。故吾国人之于自由，正患其多，不患其少，何则？个人有自由，则团体无自由故也。吾人既为国民之一分子，又为本党之一党员，当牺牲个人之自由，以蕲国家之安全、党务之发展。吾国自推倒满清以来，国家尚不能独立，故华侨之旅居外国者，多受外人压制，因国家不自由，而个人之自由亦不能保，其害不亦彰昭较著乎？"①

对于自由，孙中山阐明了两点主张：第一，中西国情不同，西方自古以来就没有自由，自由弥足珍贵，才有"不自由毋宁死"之说；中国太自由，自由对于中国来说并不适用，因为中国对于自由"不患其少"而"正患其多"。自由对于中西间的这种不同情况就仿佛不龟手之药在不同人的手中具有不同的效用一样。第二，自由不仅对于中国不适用，反而有害。孙中山与梁启超等人一样对个人自由与团体自由作对立解，指出中国之所以不自由，是由于个人太自由——借用孙中山本人的话说便是："个人有自由，则团体无自由"。循着这个思路，在中国近代的特殊背景之下，中国的自由要用于为团体争自由，万万不可用到个人身上去。基于这种认识，孙中山对自由予以保留，虽然将三民主义与自由、平等、博爱相提并论，其中的民族主义对应自由，那是就国家与国家之间的国权平等而言的，并不包括个人的自由在内。不仅如此，稍加留意即可发现，自由、平等、博爱之中，他更强调平等，三民主义的主导精神是平等："三民主义的精神，就是要建设一个极和平、极自由、极平等的国家。不但在政治上要谋民权的平等，而且在社会上要谋求经济上的平等。这样做去，方才可以免除种种阶级冲突、阶级竞争的苦恼。"② 在这里，孙中山虽然将自由与平等并提，却将二者都归结为平等，；由于将个人自由排除在自由之外，他始终是以平等（国家与国家、种群与种群之间的平等）来界定、诠释自由的。因此，他将民族主义与自由相对应，而民族主义主要指中国与西方列强的国权平等。同样是在对平等的强调中，孙中山关注国计民生和人民大众的生存状况，始终突出经济上和政治上的平等。

至此可见，三民主义的宗旨是自由、平等、博爱而并非只是平等。作为三民主义之首的民族主义指本族与异族之间的国权平等，这证明了孙中山所讲的平等以国家的

---

① 《在广州国民党党务会议的讲话》，《孙中山全集》（第八卷），中华书局，2006年，第267页。

② 《与戴季陶的谈话》，《孙中山全集》（第五卷），中华书局，2006年，第69页。

平等权利为第一目标，而不是侧重个人平等。民族主义印证了中国近代救亡图存的理论初衷，对民族主义的重视表明了孙中山对平等的关注和重视。自由、平等、博爱在孙中山那里并不是并列的，而是以平等为中心，正是这一点注定了他对大同社会的梦萦魂牵。

上述内容显示，鉴于中国近代日益深重的民族危机，虽然平等的主体包括国群与个人两个方面，近代思想家在讲平等时不约而同地偏向前者。这使他们所讲的平等带有其他时期以及其他国家所罕见的特点。正是基于对国群平等的期盼，康有为、孙中山把实现平等的希望寄托在大同社会。尽管在客观效果上产生了不同的影响，他们探讨中国与西方平等的初衷是毋庸置疑的。正是这一点，催生了近代的大同思想。

## 二、世界主义与民族主义

康有为、孙中山对大同社会的渴望如出一辙，通往国群平等的思路却相差悬殊：康有为主张通过取消国界走向大同，在取消国家、地球成为公政府中彻底消除国与国、人种与人种以及民族与民族之间的差别，这使他的大同思想带有浓郁的世界主义情结；孙中山虽然像康有为那样向往大同社会，将平等的最终实现定位在大同社会，却秉持民族主义立场，不仅没有将大同社会的实现寄托在取消国界上，反而关注中华民族的前途命运。

康有为所规划、设计的平等途径和归宿便是大同社会。对于大同社会的具体情况，他在《大同书》中进行了详细的描绘。大同社会取消国界，全球的政治、经济、宗教、文化皆一体化。更有甚者，大同社会不仅全球同一文化，同一语言，而且同一人种，从根本上铲除了民族、种族或人种差异。正是由于消除了所有的差异，大同社会进入绝对同一、消除差别的平均状态，这种平均状态就是平等。平等的对立面是不平等而绝非差异，试图通过绝对平均而臻于平等暴露了康有为思想的幼稚性和极端性，也使他所讲的平等和大同社会带有致命的空想性和乌托邦色彩，注定是无法实现的。尽管如此，康有为对大同社会的津津乐道正体现了他对全世界绝对平等，各民族、各国家一律平等的理想诉求。例如，对于大同社会的平等景象，康有为如是畅想："太平之世，人人平等，无有臣妾奴隶，无有君主统领，无有教主教皇。"[①]

为了进入绝对平等的大同社会，康有为提出了消灭种族差异的具体措施，企图通过与白种人通婚、饮食、迁地等办法改变中国人种，漂白中国人的肤色，作为中华民族的黄色人种也已经荡然无存。此外，由于大同社会消除了国界，全球公政府，中国

① 《大同书》，中州古籍出版社，1998年，第343页。

已经不复存在。为了平等、独立，康有为甚至劝导人“直隶于天”，呼吁人们作“天人”而不作国人，作“天民”而不作国民。这极大地消解了刻不容缓的救亡图存，在世界主义中放逐了民族主义。更有甚者，康有为对取消国界迫不及待、寄予厚望，《大同书》共十部，甲部是“入世界观众苦”，癸部是“去苦界至极乐”，中间则是由苦至乐的步骤，其中的第一部即乙部就是“去国界合大地”，接着便是“平民族”和“去种界”。这表明，中国不可能在大同社会拥有一席之地，反倒是消除中国与各国以及中华民族与其他民族的差异才是进入大同的前提条件。有鉴于此，梁启超一针见血地指出，康有为的大同思想是世界主义而不是民族主义，是宗教家不切实际的幻想甚至是梦呓：“所谓对于世界而知有国家者何也？宗教家之论，动言天国，言大同，言一切众生。所谓博爱主义、世界主义，抑岂不至德而深仁也哉？虽然，此等主义，其脱离理想界而入于现实界也，果可期乎？此其事或待至万数千年后，吾不敢知，若今日将安取之？”①

对大同社会心向往之的孙中山坚守民族主义的立场，始终将民族主义放在第一位。正是基于民族主义的立场，他将民族主义置于三民主义之首。这既突出了民族主义的地位，也使大同社会作为三民主义的最终目标带有民族主义的特征。可以看到，与康有为、谭嗣同等戊戌启蒙思想家幻想消除国界、在取消中国的前提下走向大同的思路迥异其趣，孙中山的大同理想秉持民族主义的立场，其中的爱国主义更为明确，救亡图存的宗旨也更为鲜明。换言之，孙中山不是在取消中国和中华民族中走向大同，而是在大同世界中使中华民族屹立于世界民族之林。对此，他一再断言：

“中华民族者，世界最古之民族，世界最大之民族，亦世界最文明而最大同化力之民族也。然此庞然一大民族则有之，而民族主义则向所未有也。何为民族主义？即民族之正义之精神也。惟其无正义、无精神，故一亡于胡元，再亡于满清，而不以为耻，反谓他人父、谓他人君，承命惟谨，争事之恐不及，此有民族而无民族主义者之所谓也……民族主义之范围，有以血统、宗教为归者，有以历史习尚为归者，语言文字为归者，夐乎远矣。然而最文明高尚之民族主义范围，则以意志为归者也。”②

“夫汉族光复，满清倾覆，不过只达到民族主义之一消极目的而已，从此当努力猛进，以达民族主义之积极目的也。积极目的为何？即汉族当牺牲其血统、历史与夫自尊自大之名称，而与满、蒙、回、藏之人民相见于诚，合为一炉而冶之，以成一中华民族之新主义，如美利坚之合黑白数十种之人民，而冶成一世界之冠之美利坚民族主义，斯为积极之目的也。五族云乎哉。夫以世界最古、最大、最富于同化力之民族，加以世界之新主义，而为积极之行动，以发扬光大中华民族，吾决不久必能驾美迭欧

① 《新民说》，中州古籍出版社，1998年，第70页。

② 《三民主义》，《孙中山全集》（第五卷），中华书局，2006年，第186—187页。

而为世界之冠，此固理有当然，势所必至也。国人其无馁!”①

由此可见，“发扬光大中华民族”，“驾美迭欧而为世界之冠”是孙中山领导的民主革命的最终目标，孙中山怀抱大同理想就是为了使中国屹立于世界民族之林，并且成为富强民族。在秉持民族主义立场上，孙中山的大同思想与康有为等人幻想通过消除种族、人种，取消国界而实现大同的思路天悬地隔。与此同时，孙中山的大同理想与三民主义和他所领导的民主革命互为一体，三民主义和民主革命不仅使他的大同理想从空想变成了现实的变革社会的政治运动，而且彰显了大同理想的民族主义旗帜。正是基于对国权平等的强烈诉求，孙中山在三民主义中将民族主义列在了首位。

近代思想家所讲的大同社会与平等以及中国与西方列强之间的关系密切相关，每个人对大同社会的构想却千差万别。孙中山的大同理想极富个性和中国特色，集中表现就是秉持民族主义的立场。如果说康有为在大同社会中迷失了自己本民族的立场的话，那么，民族主义则是孙中山大同社会的价值旨趣。作为中国近代大同理想的第二种形态，孙中山的大同理想将康有为的空想性转化为理想性，不仅在民主革命的实践中向大同社会靠近，而且在对民族主义的坚守中克服了康有为、谭嗣同由于大同社会取消国界对救亡图存的消解。与康有为、谭嗣同在取消国界中实现中国与西方列强的平等的消极做法迥然相异，孙中山一面对大同社会心驰神往，一面高举反帝爱国的旗帜，在大同理想中彰显中国主权的独立主题。孙中山的大同理想与康有为的根本区别在于，不再像康有为那样取消国界，而是彰显民族主义，让中华民族在世界进化的潮流中屹立于世界民族之林。三民主义具体包括民族主义、民权主义和民生主义三个主义在内，之所以将民族主义列在首位，有突出民族主义之意，旨在争取中国的主权独立，实现中国与西方列强为首的各国平等。对此，孙中山解释说，民族主义借用法国自由、平等、博爱的话语方式表达便是自由，之所以将自由称为民族主义是鉴于中国的具体国情，旨在突出中国向帝国主义争取国权自由。从这个意义上说，三民主义以民族主义为基础，反帝主题十分鲜明和突出。不仅如此，孙中山将民族主义置于三民主义之首表明他所讲的自由与平等密不可分，并且预示着平等问题最本质的是中国与西方列强之间的平等。为了与西方列强平等，孙中山提出中国必须提倡民族主义，发展中国的民族经济，超过英国，赶上美国。

## 三、千百万年之后的遐想与现实的民权运动

古代大同社会是对黄金时代的回忆，近代的大同社会是对未来社会的憧憬。康有

---

① 《三民主义》，《孙中山全集》（第五卷），中华书局，2006年，第187—188页。

为、孙中山都坚信人类历史的进化，并且将大同社会视为人类进化的最高阶段。对于两人来说，大同社会在未来，是人类社会进化的最美好、最完善的阶段。

康有为认为，孔子主张进化，《春秋》寄托了孔子托古改制的微言大义，书中记载的鲁国242年的历史包括“所见之世”“所闻之世”“所传闻之世”，分别代表了据乱世、升平世和太平世，其中，升平世是小康之世，太平世就是大同之世。由此，他坚信，大同社会在未来，并且是实现了自由、平等、博爱的理想社会。孙中山的大同理想同样在未来，并且基于世界进化的考察。孙中山是进化论的坚定信仰者，根据进化论宣称世界万物皆由进化而来，整个世界都处于进化之途，并且提出了世界由物质进化之时期到物种进化之时期，再到人类进化之时期的世界进化三阶段说。在此基础上，他进一步指出，有了人类便开始了人类社会历史的进化，人类社会是进化的，进化的轨迹便是从不平等臻于平等，正如君权时代是打破人与神之间的不平等建立起来的一样，从君与民不平等的君权时代过渡到人人平等的民权时代是历史进化的必然归宿。孙中山将人类历史的进化分为洪荒太古时代、神权时代、君权时代和民权时代四个阶段，这使民权时代作为人类历史进化的最高阶段而具有了历史必然性和正当性，而这个民权时代就是大同社会。对此，他多次强调推翻君权，在政治上、经济上实现平等的民权时代是人类历史的潮流，他之所以提倡三民主义，将三民主义奉为自己领导的民主革命的行动纲领，就是因为确信三民主义是世界进化的潮流，因为从不平等达到平等是进化的法则，势不可挡。“革命之目的，即欲实行三民主义也……中国革命何以必须行此三民主义？以在此二十世纪之时代，世界文明进化之潮流，已达于民生主义也；而中国则尚在异族专制之下，则民族之革命以驱除异族，与民权之革命以推覆专制，已为势所不能免者也。然我民族、民权之革命时机，适逢此世界民生革命之潮流，此民生革命又我所不能避也。以其既不能免，而又不能避之三大革命，已乘世界之进化潮流催迫而至，我不革命而甘于沦亡，为天然之淘汰则已。如其不然，则曷不为一劳永逸之举，以一度之革命，而达此三进化之阶级也。此予之所以主张三民主义之革命也。”① 在此基础上，孙中山将民权时代与中国古代的大同理想联系起来，致使大同理想不仅成为人类社会进化的最高阶段，而且成为三民主义的最高理想和奋斗目标。对此，他多次明确表示自己所领导的民主革命的最终目标就是建立一个儒家理想中的大同社会。下仅举其一斑：

昔文王以百里王天下，即以其能施行仁政，便万民皆蒙乐利也。故吾国人追思往古，动称唐虞三代，其时确为太平盛世，人人安居乐业，为后世所不可企及。本党目

---

① 《三民主义》,《孙中山全集》(第五卷)，中华书局，2006年，第185页。

的即在达到此种境地。①

人类进化之目的为何？即孔子所谓“大道之行也，天下为公”。②

进而言之，既然大同社会在未来，便涉及具体实现途径问题。在这个现实问题上，直观地反映了康有为与孙中山大同思想的本质区别。康有为将“男女平等各自独立”视为通往大同世界的第一步，将通往大同的全部希望寄托在废除家庭，消灭私有制上。与此同时，出于改良主义的立场，康有为借口“时之未至，不能躐等”，将大同社会推向无限遥远的未来，甚至仅仅限于对未来的遐想而与当下无关。从这个意义上说，他之所以讲平等充其量是理论上对遥远未来的畅想，仅限于纸上谈兵，一切都与现实无涉——“可为理想之空言，不能为施行之实事”。对此，康有为坦言：“地各有宜，物各有适；有宜于彼而不宜于此者，有适于前而不适于后者。今革命民主之方，适与中国时地未宜，可为理想之空言，不能为施行之实事也。不然，中国之人，创言民权者仆也，创言公理者仆也，创言大同者仆也，创言平等者仆也；然皆仆讲学著书之时，预立至仁之理，以待后世之行耳，非谓今日即可全行也。仆生平言世界大同，而今日列强交争，仆必自爱其国，此《春秋》据乱世所以内其国而外诸夏也。仆生平言天下为公，不可有家界，而今日人各自私，仆必自亲其亲、自私其子，此虽孔子，亦养开官夫人伯鱼，而不能养路人也。仆言众生皆本于天，皆为兄弟，皆为平等，而今当才智竞争之时，未能止杀人，何能戒杀兽？故仆仍日忍心害理，而食鸟兽之肉、衣鸟兽之皮，虽时时动心，曾斋一月而终不戒。此阿难戒佛饮水，而佛言不见即可饮，孔子所以仅远庖厨也。仆生平言男女平等、婚姻自由、政事同权，而今日女学未至、女教未成，仆亦不遽言以女子为官吏也。仆生平言民权、言公议，言国为民公共之产，而君为民所请代理之人，而不愿革命民主之事，以时地相反，妄易之则生大害，故孔子所以有三世三统之异也。”③ 梁启超的介绍和评价印证了康有为的这个说法。据梁启超披露，康有为完成《大同书》后，一直“秘不以示人，亦从不以此义教学者，谓今方为‘据乱’之世，只能言小康，不能言大同，言则陷天下于洪水猛兽……而有为始终谓当以小康义救今世，对于政治问题，对于社会道德问题，皆以维持旧状为职志。”④ 正是对于大同社会的矛盾态度使康有为的《大同书》作于1884年，直到现在902年才定稿，前后长达近二十年，其中的矛盾和徘徊由此可见一斑。作为内心矛盾和挣扎的直接反映，康有为一面在理论上宣传平等，一面不厌其烦地强调在操作上中国实现平

① 《在广州国民党党务会议的讲话》，《孙中山全集》（第八卷），中华书局，2006年，第269页。

② 《建国方略》中州古籍出版社，1998年，第98页。

③ 《答南北美洲诸华商论中国只可行立宪不能行革命书》，《康有为全集》（第六集），中国人民大学出版社，2007年，第321页。

④ 《清代学术概论》，东方出版社，1996年，第74页。

等为时过早、不可妄动。为此，他的理由是，由人类社会历史演变的公理来看，世界进化由专制而立宪，由立宪而民主；时之未至，不可躐等。当时中国正处于由专制向立宪过渡的阶段，只能先实行立宪，而不能进入共和，更遑论大同社会了。

与康有为将大同社会推向无限遥远的未来不同，作为革命家的孙中山不仅宣称人类历史由君权时代直接进化到民权时代，而取消了在康有为那里作为过渡环节的君主立宪阶段，而且主张像俄国十月革命那样通过暴力行动夺取国家政权，并且将国家交给国民管理和享有。正因为如此，孙中山同样向往大同社会，建立大同社会的途径与康有为对千百万年之后的遐想相去霄壤。作为中国民主主义革命的先行者，孙中山将大同社会与自己所领导的政治斗争联为一体，汇聚成当下的民主革命和民权运动。正是在这个意义上，他不止一次地断言：

至若俄国则更进步，其目的在使人人享受经济上平等之幸福，而无不均之患。语其大成，则与孔子所谓大同相类。①

夫苏维埃主义者，即孔子之所谓大同也。孔子曰："大道之行也，天下为公，选贤与能，讲信修睦。故人不独亲其亲，不独子其子，使老有所终，壮有所用，幼有所长，矜寡孤独废疾者皆有所养，男有分，女有归。货恶其弃于地也，不必藏于己；力恶其不出于身也，不必为己。是故谋闭而不兴，盗窃乱贼而不作，故外户而不闭，是为大同。"②

在这里，孙中山多次将大同社会与俄国十月革命后建立的苏维埃共和国相提并论，这使大同社会被纳入到现实的实践之中，与推翻帝制、人民当家做主密切相关。事实上，孙中山理想中的大同社会既不像明清之际的早期启蒙思想家如黄宗羲、顾炎武等人所渴望的那样恢复理想中的夏、商、周三代，也不像康有为、谭嗣同那样幻想世界主义，而是效仿苏联通过暴力革命，推翻满洲统治，赶走帝国主义，建立中华民族的共和国。正是基于这一设想，孙中山一面向往世界大同、天下为公，一面提倡民族主义，捍卫国家主权。与此相联系，他的三民主义始终高举反帝反封建的旗帜——既反对封建统治，又反对西方列强。

在将大同社会与现实的暴力革命和社会变革联为一体的前提下，孙中山将民权主义列入三民主义之中，始终强调国民应有的权利。与重视国民的权利相互印证，他将民权时代说成是人类历史的最高阶段，这使他的大同理想直接指向民权时代。民权时代与以往社会的不同特点是国民具有参政的权利，三民主义的宗旨便是"民有、民治、

---

① 《在广州大本营对各界人士的演说》，《孙中山全集》（第八卷），中华书局，2006年，第349页。

② 《致犬养毅书》，《孙中山全集》（第八卷），中华书局，2006年，第405页。

民享”，旨在使国民享受民权：“吾党之三民主义，即民族、民权、民生三种。此三种主义之内容，亦可谓之民有、民治、民享，与自由、平等、博爱无异，故所向有功。以名言之，可称民有、民治、民享……质而言之，民有即民族也。天下者，天下人之天下，非一二族所可独占。民权即民治也。从前之天下，在专制时代则以官僚武人治之，本总理则谓人人皆应有治之之责，亦应负治之之责，故余极主张以民治天下。民生即民享也。天下既为人人所共有，则天下之利权，自当为天下人民所共享。自此三民主义推行以来，无坚不入，无人不从。何者？权利为人所共好，今平均而与之，宜其无不从也。”[①] 由此可见，肯定大同理想始于足下，大同社会的实现就在当下的政治运动中，大同社会的标识之一就是国民享受权利，是孙中山的大同理想与康有为的大同空想最本质的区别。

综上所述，孙中山的大同思想与康有为具有不容忽视的明显区别：第一，秉持民族主义的立场。第二，将实现大同与平等纳入到现实的政治斗争。这些区别体现了孙中山领导的辛亥革命与康有为发起的维新变法的区别，也是孙中山大同理想的独特魅力。从这个意义上说，不理解孙中山大同理想的独特性便无法理解三民主义的实质，也就无法从根本上认识孙中山领导的辛亥革命及民主革命的历史意义。同样不可否认的是，康有为、孙中山的大同理想带有鲜明的近代特征，具有诸多相似、相同之处。这突出表现在以下几个方面：第一，在立言宗旨上，出于救亡图存的历史背景和现实需要，将大同理想置于全球化的历史背景和文化语境中，突破了中国古代“天下一家，中国一人”的模式，旨在借助大同社会解决中国与西方的平等问题。第二，在内涵界定上，将平等、自由视为大同社会的基本特征，表达了近代的价值理念和民主要求。第三，在合理证明上，将大同理想纳入进化史观之中，彰显了大同社会的必然性和正当性。这些是近代大同理想有别于古代之处，也是康有为、孙中山思想的一致性。从这个意义上说，两人的大同思想都属于近代形态。

---

① 《在广西阳朔人民欢迎会的演说》，《孙中山全集》（第五卷），中华书局，2006 年，第 628—629 页。

# 大同理想与大同之路

中国人民大学 张 践

大同理想可以说是全人类共同的理想，追求大同理想在此岸世界的实现，则是中国人民特有的价值观念。但是应当如何理解大同理想？应当如何实现大同理想？则是关系到社会发展是否和谐、顺畅的重要社会问题，需要进行历史的梳理和逻辑的探讨。

## 一、大同世界是人类的共同向往

人类自从进入文明历史之后，就一直在私有制社会中发展。虽然随着社会生产力的不断提高，人类的生活质量也在不断提升。但是私有制所造成的社会不公、两极分化、人性压抑一直存在，因此建立一个富裕、平等、自由、公正的社会，一直是世界人民的共同理想，差异主要在于，实现这个理想境界的道路。或者是出世的，把大同世界安放到死后的天国；或者是入世的，试图在人间建立太平天国，就是由世界各国人民的历史文化差异造成的。

中国人民的大同理想，最清晰的表达就是儒家《礼记·礼运》的“大同篇”，“孔子曰：大道之行也，与三代之英，丘未之逮也，而有志焉。大道之行也，天下为公，选贤与能，讲信修睦，故人不独亲其亲，不独子其子。使老有所终，壮有所用，幼有所长，矜寡孤独废疾者皆有所养，男有分，女有归。货，恶其弃于地也，不必藏于己；力，恶其不出于身也，不必为己。是故谋闭而不兴，盗窃乱贼而不作，故外户而不闭，是谓大同。”孔子开创儒学，本为制止“礼坏乐崩”的社会混乱，恢复周礼规定的尊卑等级明确，上下秩序健全的社会制度。但是儒家思想的意蕴并不仅止于此，在《礼运》篇中，甚至连礼乐昌明的“三代”都不是儒家所追求的最高理想，他们把理想的罗盘直接指向人类所能设想的最辉煌的极限。从“大同篇”的经典表述看，大同世界是财产公有的社会，因此人们才能做到“人不独亲其亲”、“选贤与能”、“讲信修睦”、“人尽其力”、“皆有其养”、“谋闭不兴”、“盗窃乱贼不作”、“天下为公”、“世界大同”。这说明古代思想家已经充分认识到，财产私有、家天下是“人各为己”、“独子其子”、“老无所养”、“壮无所用”、“残疾无着”、“男孤女寡”、“盗贼横行”、“战乱不已”等等一系统社会痼疾的总根源。儒家是以对原始社会的模糊记忆为依据的，把历史群体记忆中三皇五帝时代，人无私产，亦无私心，青壮年皆有劳动之地，老弱病残皆可得到社会的供养，天子实行“禅让制”，国家传贤不传子，没有战争也没有犯罪等等美好的记忆，作为社会发展的理想蓝图。

对于大同世界苦苦追求的，并不仅仅是中国人民的专利。由于民族文化、心理、习俗的差异，不同民族使用不同的表达方式，有世俗的，也有宗教的。宗教天国虽然是超验的，但在一定条件下却可以对现实的人生发挥巨大的调节作用。无论是佛教、伊斯兰教还是基督教，其终极寄托都是富裕、美好、平等的天国。

佛教产生于宗教氛围浓郁得古印度，尽管佛教对于古老的婆罗门教有所批判，但是在一些基本价值预设，如来世、因果等方面都有很大的继承性。佛教的基本教义“四谛”说，第一条就是讲“苦谛”，说人生、老、病、死之苦，“怨憎会苦”，“爱别离苦”，“求不得苦”。不仅现世是苦，轮回转世，仍难逃苦海。得救的唯一方法，就是听从佛祖的教诲，遵守佛门的戒律，修行善果，获得涅槃觉悟。那些难以理解涅槃境界的人，只要每日口宣“阿弥陀佛”名号，死后便可得阿弥陀佛的“接引”往生西方“净土”。“净土”也就是佛教为人类设计的大同世界。在那里“自然七宝——金、银、琉璃、珊瑚、琥珀、砗磲、玛瑙——合成为地”，“七宝诸树，周遍世界”，“讲堂、精舍、宫殿、楼观，皆七宝庄严，自然化成”，“若食时，七宝应器，自然在前，……百味饮食，自然盈满。……事已，化去；时至，复现。”（《无量寿经》）佛教设计了如此美好的极乐世界，所以才能在印度、中国、东南亚、东北亚诸国赢得大量信众，广泛传播。

伊斯兰教创生于西亚，广泛流行于中东、北非及南欧的穆斯林中间。伊斯兰教宣称：今世是短暂的，虚幻的，后世才是永久的，真实的。人活在世上，一切游戏、娱乐都是欺骗人的享受。人死之后，灵魂不灭，并且会复活，接受真主末日的审判。凡是在生前信奉真主，奉行“五功”的人，灵魂就会跟随真主进入天堂，生前作恶之人，灵魂就要下地狱，受到永久的折磨。《古兰经》说天国的乐园叫作“菲尔道斯”，那里有四条大河，即水河、蜜河、奶河、酒河，乐园周围笼罩着浓密的树荫，既无烈日，亦无严寒。天堂建筑极仅豪华，金砖、银础、麝泥、珍珠铺地。住进乐园的善者，躺在珠宝镶成的宝榻上，终日有身穿着软绸缎的少女陪伴着他，童仆捧着醴泉供他享用，每周还可拜谒真主一次。在这里当然没有人世剥削、贫困、欺诈等苦恼，只有祝寿和祝安。

基督教在欧美各国有着广泛的影响，成为西方文化的源泉之一。近代基督教在亚洲、非洲、拉美广泛传播，成为世界第一大宗教。基督教认为：天地万物都由上帝创造，按照上帝的意志运行。人类始祖亚当和夏娃也是上帝的产物，本来无忧无虑地生活在伊甸园中。但是他们不听上帝的劝告，偷吃禁果，犯了原罪，被赶出了伊甸园。所以人类从出生之日就背上了原罪的包袱，注定一世受苦，来赎清祖先的罪孽。不过基督教又认为：现实的人生是短暂的，只是灵魂朝圣旅途中不长的一段，如果在今世生活中能隐忍苦难，信奉上帝，死后灵魂就会得救，飞升天堂，永享极乐。基督教的天国，又称天堂，是一个纯粹属灵的境地。在天堂中，有三一真神，众天使，众信徒。基督徒去世后去到天堂，都要身穿白衣，手拿棕树枝，在上帝面前歌颂他（见启七 9、10）。天堂里只有善的，没有恶的，撒旦与魔鬼不能住在天堂。天堂中也无阶级之分，凡是信徒，不分男女老幼，都一律进去。天堂中也没有男女嫁娶的婚姻生活（可十二 25）。人去到那里后，得到永生，永远在天堂享乐、安息。

西方文化除了基督教背景外，还有从古希腊文化中留传下来的世俗的人文主义的传统。在这一部分传统中，追求大同的倾向更为强烈。古希腊大哲学家柏拉图写有一本名著《理想国》。在他建构的理想国中，虽然存在着严格的等级界线，但他认为在贵族等级中应实行财产公有制度，公共婚姻制度，子女由社会共同抚养，免费教育，以便从小培养他们的高尚品德。十六世纪意大利柏拉图派哲学家、诗人和作家托马斯·康帕内拉，继承并发展了柏拉图的思想，写出名著《太阳城》，进一步完善了柏拉图的共产主义空想。在他设想的太阳城中，私有财产和贫困已经消失，任何人都不能占有他人的劳动成果。国家由受过理性教育的人来治理，每个人都努力工作以增加社会的福利。大体与之同时，意大利另一著名思想家托马斯·莫尔写出了空想社会主义的又一代表作《乌托邦》。乌托邦原文由希腊文的“没有”和“地方”两词组成，意译为“无何有之乡”，是西方人梦中的“桃花源”。莫尔用文学的笔法详细描述了由异教徒建立的，各种制度和政策完全理性化的共产主义城邦，在那里，人人过着自由、平等、富裕的生活。莫尔认为：是私有制和对权力、财富的贪欲把欧洲搞得四分五裂，而共产主义是根治私人生活和公共生活中利己主义的唯一良药。《乌托邦》一书的问世在欧洲产生了很大影响，十七、十八世纪，出现了许多建立乌托邦公社的实验，其中英国工厂主欧文，法国改革家傅立叶的实验最为著名，成为马克思主义的理论来源之一。

世界各国人民的大同理想，尽管有诸多细节的差异，方法的不同，但是在反对私有制度，反对阶级压迫，要求社会公平，追求人民幸福生活等基本价值观念上，却有着极大的相似性。这一切充分说明，向往大同世界是人类的共同本性，具有超越时空的永恒价值。

## 二、向往大同是中国人特有的精神价值

关于大同世界的理想，其实并非儒家的专利，春秋战国时代的其他诸子，也多把

社会的理想坐标瞄准了远古的“共产”之世。墨家创始人墨翟，提倡“兼相爱，交相利”，“有力者疾以助人，有财者勉以分人，有道者劝以教人”（《墨子·尚贤下》），通过社会成员的协力互助实现天下大同。老子的道家宣扬“小国寡民”的政治理想，使人民群众回到原始时代没有剥削，没有压迫、没有争夺、没有战争的状态去，“甘其食，美其俗，安其居，乐其俗，邻国相望，鸡犬之声相闻，民至老死不相往来。”（《老子》八十章）两汉以后，儒道墨法诸家思想合一，大同理想成为知识分子的普遍向往。晋朝的陶渊明设计了没有战乱，没有冲突的“桃花源”，“土地平旷，屋舍俨然。有良田美池桑竹之属，阡陌交通，鸡犬相闻。其中往来种作，男女衣着悉如外人，黄发垂髫，并怡然自乐。”他们在其中自耕自食，与世无争，过得安然愉快。晋人鲍敬言主张“无君论”，希望建立一个“无君无臣，穿井而饮，耕田而食，日出而作，日入而息，泛然不系，恢而自得，不竞不营，无荣无辱”（《抱扑子·诘鲍篇》）的理想社会。尽管各家对理想社会的表达不尽相同，但都可以看出大同社会的影子。

近代社会由于西方帝国主义的侵略以及封建主义的压迫，中国人民陷入了深重的苦难之中。民族的危难激起先进的中国人寻找出路的决心和意志，通观近代以来不同阶级，不同阶层设计的各种救国方案，我们便不难发现他们的信仰罗盘是牢牢地指向大同境界的。洪秀全创立“拜上帝会”，用西方传来的基督教组织农民，发动起义。他的理想是在地上创建“太平天国”，他说：“天下多男人，尽是兄弟之辈；天下多女子，尽是姊妹之群。何得存此疆彼界之私，何得起尔吞我并之念？是故孔丘曰：‘大道之行，天下为公……是谓大同’。”（《原道醒世训》）太平天国的领袖们为了在人间实现自己的理想，还设计了一套完整的《天朝田亩制度》，规定天下百姓按人口分田，“凡分田，照人口，不论男妇，算其家人口多寡，人多则分多，人寡则分寡。”“凡天下，树墙下以桑，凡妇蚕绩缝衣裳。凡天下，每家五母鸡，二母彘，无失其时。”“务使天下共享天父上主皇上帝大福，有田同耕，有饭同食，有衣同穿，有钱同使，无处不均平，无处不饱暖。”为了防止两极分化的发生，每家收获之后，除留够一年的口粮，余者全部上缴国库，婚丧嫁娶全由国库开支。彻底消除了私有财产，便可保证社会的持久公平。不过，这种建立在小农经济基础上的农业共会主义，只能是不切实际的空想，从来也没有付诸实践。

“太平天国”的海市蜃楼刚刚散去，另一座更美好的空中楼阁又在神州大地上开始构造施工了，这就是中国资产阶级改良派领袖康有为所写的《大同书》。康有为直接借用了《礼记·礼运》中大同、小康的说法，又将其与《春秋公羊传》中据乱、升平、太平的划分相比附，认为当时的社会是孔子所说的据乱世，资产阶级改良成功以后，社会便进入了升平世，也就是小康世界。但小康社会并不是他的最高理想，他信念的罗盘仍然是对准太平世，亦即大同世界的。康有为超过洪秀全之处，在于他的大同理想已经是建立在近代大工业生产的基础上。在那里人的各种自然本性都可以得到充分的发挥，物质财富极为充足，因而人的各种欲望也都可以得到极大的满足。为了保证社会大同的性质，他指出必须“去产界，公产业”。他讲：“今欲致大同，必去人之私产而后可。凡农工商之业，必归之公，举天下之田地，皆为公有，人无得私有而买卖之。”像许多古代空想社会主义者一样，康有为也是不惜笔墨，不厌其烦地描述了大同世界人民的具体生活场景。那时的人们，居室则“珠玑今碧，光彩陆离”，行路则“飞屋飞船”，“舟皆电运”，饮食则“以备养生，而人益寿”。总之，“太平世之生人不知抽剥追敲之苦，只有领得工金，为歌舞游玩之乐”。可惜到了如何实现大同立理想的部分，康有为则显得有些力不从心，难以自圆其说了。所以毛泽东说：“康有为写了《大同书》，他没有也不可能找到一条到达大同的路。”（《论人民民主专政》，《毛泽东选集》2 版，第 4 卷，北京：人民出版社，1991 年，第 422 页。）

孙中山是中国近代资产阶级革命之父，领导着中国人民推翻了清王朝，建立了中华民国。孙中山虽然是资产阶级的领袖，但是他在领导中国资产阶级进行革命之时，西方资本主义社会的弊病已经表现得相当充分。所以他并不以在中国建立资产阶级共和国为满足，而是希望走出一条有中国特色的资本主义道路，将资本主义革命和社会主义革命“毕其功于一役”，实现国人梦寐以求的大同理想。故此他提出了“民生主义”的主张，宣传“天下为公”，“耕者有其田”，土地、铁路、邮政、矿山、森林，统统收归国有，人人都是劳动者，自食其力，社会平均分配劳动成果。因而在大同社会里，消除了贫富不均，以富欺贫，没有阶级压迫和阶级斗争，他说：“人类进化目的之为何？即孔子所谓‘大道之行也，天下为公’，耶稣所谓‘尔旨得成，在地若天’。此人类所希望，化现在之痛苦，而为极乐之天堂也。”（《孙中山选集》人民出版社 1956 年版，第 142 页）孙中山的时代，马克思主义在世界范围影响巨大，所以他又说：“故民生主义就是社会主义，又名共产主义，即是大同主义。”（《民生主义》《孙中山选集》下卷，765 页，北京，人民出版社，1966）孙中山又为实现民生主义设计了两条措施，即“节制资本”，“平均地权”，也就是通过国家资本主义的方法逐步实现财产公有。但是在当时的社会条件下，国家靠什么手段去限制私人资本的发展，用那一笔钱去赎买地主的土地，孙中山都没有回答，大约也是无法回答的。终孙中山的一生，民生主义一直也仅仅是一种理想。

以上简单的考证充分说明，在中国历史上，不论哪一个阶级的思想家，他们都不是以自己阶级的视域为限，而是把人类大同作为终极目的。造成这一现象的根本原因，则在于人性的深处，向往一种没有争夺、没有欺诈、没有杀戮的公平社会，是一切人性的共同追求。儒家作为中国传统社会的主流文化，大同篇说出了人们的共同向往，因此也就在几千的历史发展中，逐渐成为时代中国人共同的价值观念。不过在不同时代，人们表述的大同理想，其语境不同、素材不同而已。这说明对于大同世界的向往，是中国人的一种终极价值，一种永恒的追求。

## 三、追求大同的路径决定了追求者的成败

孔子提出了大同的理想，但是孔子并没有把建设大同社会当成可立即实现的实践目标。在感叹大同世界“未之逮”之后，孔子马上就提出了现实可行的小康社会蓝图。“今大道既隐，天下为家。各亲其亲，各子其子，货力为己。大人世及以为礼，城郭沟池以为固。礼义以为纪，以正君臣，以笃父子，以睦兄弟，以和夫妇，以设制度，以立田里，以贤勇知，以功为己，故谋用是作，而兵由此起。禹汤文武 成王周公，由此其选也。此六君子者，未有不谨于礼者也。以著其义，以考其信，著有过，刑仁讲让，示民有常。如有不由此者，在埶者去，众以为殃。是谓小康。”小康社会的显著特征是天下为家，孔子指出，在这一社会中，要实现社会和谐，必须通过礼义纲纪，调节、规范君臣、父子、兄弟、夫妇之间的人伦关系，树立正确的行为规范与价值导向，完善社会秩序，通过建立明确的赏罚机制，实现社会的和谐有序。小康之世虽不是孔子的理想境界，但是在当时小农经济的生产水平上，在宗法家族社会结构中，这样一种以“以礼为序”的差等社会，是最为可能的，也最现实的理想社会。

孔子和儒家学者为心目中理想世界的实现，设计了具体的路径。《大学》提出了儒家治世的“八纲目”，即“致知在格物，物格而后知至，知至而后意诚，意诚而后心正，心正而后身脩，身脩而后家齐，家齐而后国治，国治而后天下平。”《中庸》则将其发展为“九经”即“凡为天下国家有九经，曰：修身也、尊贤也、亲亲也、敬大臣也、体群臣也、子庶民也、来百工也、柔远人也、怀诸侯也。”按照儒家的路径实现“平天下”的大同世界是一种由内及外、由近及远的渐进过程。

历代儒家学者及士大夫，也都在自己的著作中设计实践回复大同世界的方案，在力所能及的范围进行一些尝试。例如儒家亚圣孟子指出：“夫仁政，必自经界始。经界不正，井地不钧，谷禄不平。是故暴君污吏必慢其经界。经界既正，分田制禄可坐而定也。”（《孟子·滕文公上》）井田也就是传说中上古大同世界的土地公有制度，在这种制度下：“方里而井，井九百亩，其中为公田。八家皆私百亩，同养公田。公事毕，然后敢治私事。”（同上）由于有了固定的井田，人人生活有保证，人心安定，“死徙无出乡，乡田同井。出入相友，守望相助，疾病相扶持，则百姓亲睦。”（同上）孟子以一种田园诗般的语言描述了井田制下一个普通农民家庭的美好生活：“五亩之宅，树墙下以桑，匹妇蚕之，则老者足以衣帛矣。五母鸡，二母彘，无失其时，老者足以无失肉矣。百亩之田，匹夫耕之，八口之家足以无饥矣。”（《孟子·尽心上》）五亩之宅、

百亩之田、五母鸡、两母彘也就是当时人们所能设想的“幸福生活”了。以后几千年，不少儒家学者、士大夫都在不同范围进行过“复井田”的实验，宋代大儒张载就是其中的典型人物。据说他与自己的学生吕大临等人，在家乡横渠镇买地一块，按照《周礼》的模式，划分为公田，私田等分给无地、少地的农民，并疏通东西二渠“验之一乡”以证明井田制的可行性和有效性。今横渠镇崖下村，扶风午井镇、长安子午镇仍保持着遗迹，至今这一带还流传着“横渠八水验井田”的故事。他还把自己关于复井田的构想写成《井田议》上奏皇帝，希望得到国家的支持，但没有下文。估计张载的井田实验也无果而终了，仅仅留下一道长长的田埂成为供人们凭吊的历史遗迹。

总体而言，儒家士大夫们对于大同理想，多是作为一种价值理想用以指导政治实践，将大同理想变成具体行动的不多，但是按照大同的原则设计政治改良方案的不少。从董仲舒到王安石，提出如限兼并、减徭役、济贫赈灾之类的改良方案，虽没有改变封建社会土地私有的性质，但是对于改善人民生活，协调社会发展机制都起到了积极的作用。在这些方案的背后，都可以看到《大同篇》的身影。不过一般士大夫都知道，立即全面实现大同世界是不现实的，甚至可能妨碍眼前可行的改良方案。康有为在1894年开始写《大同书》，但写成之后秘不示人，只是与一些最亲密的弟子分享，为的是怕人们提前追求大同世的生活，忽视了升平世的奋斗。直到1913年民国以后，康有为才陆续发表了《大同书》部分稿件，直至1927年康有为死后第8年，才由弟子全文出版，足见其慎重。

相反倒是处于社会底层的农民阶层，更主动、大胆地宣扬、追求、实践大同世界的梦想。东汉末年，张角、张陵在人民陷于水深火热之中时，组织了太平道和五斗米道在民间传播，主张平等、平均，反对地主阶级不劳而食，否定财产私有权。《太平经》认为：“天之有道，乐与人共之；地之有德，乐与人同之；中和有财，乐以养人。”“财物乃天地中和所有，以共养人也。”这种思想深受农民群众的拥护，成为农民群众进行斗争的武器。唐末黄巢领导农民大起义，自称“冲天太保均平大将军”，并建立“大齐”政权，充分体现了要把天下财富均齐，使人人一律平等的大同思想。北宋初年，王小波、李顺农民起义提出了“均贫富”的战斗口号。王小波向农民群众宣告：“我疾贫富不均，今为汝辈均之。”使农民起义的平均思想进一步具体化和明朗化。南宋钟相、杨么领导的农民起义，在群众中宣传鼓动说：“法分贵贱贫富，非善法也。我行法，当等贵贱，均贫富。”“等贵贱，均贫富”口号继承了中国传统的大同思想，集中地反映了农民阶级在政治上要求平等、经济上要求平均的愿望，深受农民群众的欢迎。明末李自成农民起义，针对当时土地高度集中、赋役繁重、民不聊生的社会现实，明确提出了“除暴恤民”、“均田免粮”、“平买平卖”、“公平交易”等战斗口号，受到广大农民的热烈拥护。不过在历史资料中，凡是建立政权的农民起义队伍，在政治实践中也仅是把“等贵贱，均贫富”当成一种鼓动农民起义的宣传口号，并不能变成革命的现实。例如洪秀全的太平天国，他的“天朝田亩制度”在建国十几年的实践中，并没有一条落到实处。他口口声声说“天下多男子，尽是兄弟之辈；天下多女子，尽是姊妹之群。”可是一进了天京城的天王府，马上过上了“称孤道寡”、“嫔妃成群”的帝王生活，看不到一点大同世界的影子。

在中国历史上，大同理想的真正实践，怕也只有毛泽东的人民公社了。毛泽东青年时代深受康有为《大同书》的影响，后来他在与斯诺的谈话中曾回忆起了这段往事时说：“新民丛报我读了又读，直到可以背下来。我崇拜康有为和梁启超。”（埃德加·斯诺：《西行漫记》，上海：三联书店，1979 年）他曾经设想与同学们在岳麓山麓建设一个新农村。这一理想在新中国建立后，终于有了“可以实现”的条件。毛泽东自认为找到了一条可以达到大同世界的真实的道路，即苏俄式的计划经济。1958 年，这种理想化的试验在神州大地上普遍开花。后人总结人民公社的特点，包括“一大二公”、“政社合一”、“吃饭不要钱”等等。因为人民公社能实现集体所有制过渡到全民所有制；实行工资制与供给制相结合的分配制度，包含了社会主义的按劳分配和共产主义的按需分配，并且能实现前者到后者的过渡；公共食堂、托儿所的建立，实现了家务劳动社会化；公社办工厂、办红专大学、建新村等，便于消除城乡差别、工农差别、体力劳动和脑力劳动的差别。因此当时社会流行的口号是“共产主义是天堂，人民公社是桥梁”，亿万中国人民包括毛泽东本人都真诚地相信，中国人几千年来苦苦追求的大同世界——共产主义马上就可以实现了。然而残酷的现实却是，在政治权力的强行推动下，使生产关系超越生产力的需要水平，只能造成生产力的巨大破坏。人民公社这座金桥并没有把中国引向共产主义的天堂，而是把六亿中国人民引向了三年困难时期的可怕深渊。

通过对历史上大同思想实践的反思，我们似乎可以得到一点启示：即大同世界在现实世界之内，不在现实世界之外。没有一个超出现实世界之外的大同世界，等着我们在某一个时间段具体到达，而是将大同理想落实于人类世世代代的发展过程中。人类社会的每一次重大的经济、科技、政治、文化的进步，都是大同理想不断趋近的表现，“大同世界”的终极理想就寓于这样每一次具体的进步之中。洪秀全设计的“五亩之宅、百亩之田、五母鸡、两母彘”式的小农“太平天国”早已不在话下，就是康有为理想的居室则“珠玑今碧，光彩陆离”，行路则“飞屋飞船”，“舟皆电运”，饮食则“以备养生，而人益寿”也都变成了我们的现实生活。至于“贫民归公政府恤养”，“病者皆归公医院治之”，“死者归孝终院料理丧葬”等等也在西方发达国家的社会民主主义的实践中完成了。这一切充分说明，按照大同理想的指引，脚踏实地进行改革和建设才是真正实现大同理想的正确之途。

然而生活于21世纪的人们，仍然要面对很多严峻的社会问题，环境污染、资源枯竭、贫富分化、政治不公、霸权主义、恐怖主义等等，严重威胁人类的生存。因此大同理想仍然是指导各国政治家进行社会改良和社会建设的价值指南。不过我们特别要注意大同理想实现道路问题，注意可行之途与人为陷阱的不同，防止国家再次走上自我毁灭之途。

# 传承儒学适应当代 文化强国圆中国梦

澳大利亚澳中文化协会 冯文玮

## 一、儒学智慧在西方的启示

当我们仔细的重温历史，作为中华儿女是自豪的。中华传统文化和中华智慧对西方有显著的影响，尤其是儒学对西方知识分子，思想家和哲学家的启示，儒学的智慧成就了他们非凡的启蒙事业及文艺复兴。启蒙思想家们虽然没有到过中国，但他们是由传教士的著作和翻译中理解儒家思想，他们认为儒学反映了当时西方的理想和精神，丰富西方文化和时代需求。

在许多启蒙思想家的眼中，孔子不仅教人如何做人，还教人如何自我调节。许多启蒙思想家认为儒学思想是反对专政的封建世袭重要的方法，他们对当时中国的政治制度和思想基础都有高度赞扬。当时西方渴望稳定，和谐社会的理想，期待仁慈，开明的君主，而在中国展示的是长期稳定和优秀的社会系统，他们认为当时中国状态是世界上管理最好的国家，中国的政治制度是合理的，因为它是在宗法社会的基础上建成的，孝敬父母的儿童是国家的基础。

18世纪法国大哲学家、启蒙运动的领袖和导师伏尔泰（1694—1778年），在他的《哲学辞典》中说："我全神贯注地读孔子的这些著作，我从中吸取了精华，除了最纯洁的道德之外，我从未在其中发现任何东西，并且没有些许的假充内行式的蒙骗的味道。"他又说，"在这个地球上曾有过的最幸福的、并且人们最值得尊敬的时代，那就是人们遵从孔子法规的时代。"。他宣称，"在道德上欧洲人应当成为中国人的徒弟"。孔子学说在17、18世纪的在欧洲风靡一时，哲学家和学者们并对这种外来文化不胜感激。

但近代中华文化的国际影响力和世界渴望了解中华文化的愿望还不相适应，为此国际儒联的各位儒学者为了广泛的传播富有独特魅力中华儒家文化做出了重大贡献，也感到了任重道远。目前，西方思想文化对我国的渗透和影响在不断加剧，因此充分挖掘和弘扬中华传统文化及儒学的有益核心价值，有利于中华文化保持民族性、时代性、先进性，有利于抵御全盘西化思想的文化渗透。

中华文化与西方文化是两种不同的意识形态和文化系统，但无论是对人的生命价值和世界的终极意义的思考和探索，他们在许多方面有着共同的存在，双方是可以互相学习，取长补短。中华文化对西方文化的不足，特别是解决目前西方文化所存在的危机是可借鉴的，中华智慧在西方的传播不仅有历史价值，在现代和当代也是有价值的。值得反省的是随着中国快速的和平崛起，有些文化沙文主义现象出现，如：“中国威胁论”“东方文化统治论”、“中国世纪论”等种种缺乏常识的理论观点，这是违背儒家核心“和而不同”和谐理念的。西方传统文化和哲学思想对人类也做出具大贡献，因此西方文化也有它传承的价值。现实证实了，未来的世界仍将是一个多极共存并进的世界，未来的世界文化，也将是一个多元文化沟通互补、和而不同，相互渗透的世界文化格局，这样儒学才能发展它的现代核心价值，才能真正为国际间不同文化相互交流、取长补短、做出新贡献。

## 二、儒学核心价值观与社会主义核心价值观探讨

进入新世纪新阶段，全球意识形态处于从未有过的大活跃、大碰撞、大交融，意识形态面临着异常复杂的新考验、新挑战和新影响，面对经济全球化、政治多极化、文化多元化、科技信息化、经济市场化的新特点新情况，社会中的原有价值理念和道德标准受到冲击 ，一些原本十分清楚的价值观受到了质疑，致使一些人在价值评判和行为准则选择上，感到迷茫困惑，甚至无所适从，世界各地的儒家学者都认为儒学必须以与时俱进的精神、不断推进儒学现代化，适应当代。事实上，社会经济上的现代化，物质生活方式的变化，生活水平的提高，最终都是服务于人，服务于生活在新世纪新阶段的人。新世纪的人必需提高人的素质，並作用于社會，利己亦利人，民生得到提高和发展。

儒家思想重于人学，因此对于儒学核心价值观的讨论和学习，如何传承儒学，如何适应当代，显得越来越迫切，越来越必要。习近平主席指出“要讲清楚中华优秀传统文化的历史渊源、发展脉络、基本走向，讲清楚中华文化的独特创造、价值理念、鲜明特色，增强文化自信和价值观自信。要认真汲取中华优秀传统文化的思想精华和道德精髓，大力弘扬以爱国主义为核心的民族精神和以改革创新为核心的时代精神，深入挖掘和阐发中华优秀传统文化讲仁爱、重民本、守诚信、崇正义、尚和合、求大同的时代价值，使中华优秀传统文化成为涵养社会主义核心价值观的重要源泉。要处理好继承和创造性发展的关系，重点做好创造性转化和创新性发展”。习主席的讲话对儒

家学者是重要的启示，大时代需要儒家学者为此做出奉献。

1. 儒学的价值观和道德精髓

价值观是一种内心尺度。它凌驾于整个人性当中，支配着人的行为、态度、观察、信念、理解等，支配着人认识世界、明白事物对自己的意义和自我了解、自我定向、自我设计等；也为人正当的行为提供充足的理由。历史告诉我们，以儒学为核心的中国传统文化中的价值观含有社会主义核心价值观的因素，我们根据儒家经典，研究那些是中华优秀传统文化的思想精华和道德精髓，基本上把儒家的核心价值观概括“仁义礼智信”。

儒家以“仁”为根本之道的理论主张，突出了“以人为本”的儒学特质。以人为本就是承认人的生存权，承认人民在政治生活中的主权，承认统治者的权利来自人民。所谓“仁爱”就是“仁者人也，仁者爱人”强调人的道德自觉，及“仁民爱物”的人文精神。“义”在生活中的实践就是立足仁道，追求合理，适时、正义、公正。“礼”就是内在修养，善性向外的落实，生活中表现在待人接物，人际关系中。在社会所处的位置上，做到恰如其分，礼敬则是每个人应有的行为态度，是和谐社会的基础。“智”是知者不惑，审物明辨，过安乐自在的生活。“信”在生活中的实践是诚实、守信、守法，它体现了实事求是，守法的精神。“诚信”是立身之本，也是立业、立国之本。

经过历代大儒的丰富发展，形成了一整套儒家价值观的观念体系，最重要的观念是就是仁爱、和谐、诚信、中庸这四大范畴。孔子谈得最多的是仁与礼，中庸等价值观念。孟子讲得最多的是仁、义、礼、智，也多次阐述了恻隐、恭敬、辞让、善恶、诚信、良知、民本等价值观念。《中庸》说：“诚者，天之道也。诚之者，人之道也”是儒家的一个中心价值。儒学讲“和为贵”，体现的是人与自然、人与社会、人与人的共生、共荣和谐精神提倡中庸之道。儒学讲“去人欲”，针对人欲横流，针对人们对物质的追求是有现代价值的。

2. 儒学思想是涵养社会主义核心价值观的重要源泉

党的十八大提出，富强、民主、文明、和谐，自由、平等、公正、法治，爱国、敬业、诚信、友善的社会主义核心价值观基本内容。从国家层面提倡富强、民主、文明、和谐，从社会层面提倡自由、平等、公正、法治，从个人层面提倡爱国、敬业、诚信、友善。

儒学的孝、悌、忠、信、礼、义、廉、耻、仁、爱、和、平，体现了我们优秀的文化和传统美德。从国家层面做到仁、爱、和、平、从社会层面做到是礼、义、廉、耻、从个人层面做到孝、悌、忠、信。由此可见中华优秀传统文化和社会主义核心价值观是与人类文明成果相承接的，是完全相应的，也是中华民族宏伟的，为之努力的目标。

孔子名言论语三宝："知者不惑、仁者不忧、勇者不惧"出自《论语·子罕》。在《论语正义》中《申鉴·杂言下》又对这句话做了进一步阐述："君子审物明辨故不惑，乐天知命故不忧，定心致公故不惧。"孔子认为知者能审物明辨，所以不迷惑；仁者最主要的是能做到乐天知命；所以不忧虑。勇者因为能定心致公，所以没有畏惧的事情。这里的知者、仁者、和勇者就是孔子用来衡量是否是君子的标准，也是衡量廿十一世纪中华民族追梦者的标准。

现在提倡的社会主义核心价值观，与儒家传统文化的核心价值观有着不可割裂的内在思想联系，也证实儒学思想是践行社会主义核心价值观的重要源泉，由此可见社会主义核心价值观，它和中华传统文化及儒学思想道德是不相悖的，这也正是儒学的现代生命力。重要的是我们必须通过教育来传承、通过对书籍的阅读来提升、通过人们的自我实践来体悟、通过努来抵达。

## 三、实践儒学思想提高国民素质

人的素质是一个包括多重丰富内涵的整体，它包含了人的道德素质，文化素质和身体素质等相互依存不可分割的三大内容。早在公元前四五百年，中国儒家已经提出过一套明智的人学，儒学教导我们如何处理人与人之间的关系，既尊重他人，又爱护自己，真正做到我为人人，人人为我。因此儒学只是朴素地指出，人与天地万物、自然界的关系、人与的人关系、人与自我关系，儒学的五伦五常八德阐述了儒学基本概念和实践方法。然而再观察如今中国，提高国民素质已是重中之重，也是实现国家富强，民族复兴，人民幸福的基础。

1. 国民素质概念

国民素质是综合概念，包括思想、修养、礼仪、文化、政治、体能、道德、教育等等都体现了国民素质，国民素质道德水平评议包括精神面貌、文化素质、道德修养、礼仪素养、全民教育、经济条件、身体素质、民族的向心力凝聚力等。中国国民素质确实在逐步提升，但我们也会发现，中国与有些国家国民素质是有差距的。

人的道德素质是人们的道德认识和道德行的综合反映，包含一个人的道德修养和道德情操，体现着一个人的道德水平和道德风貌。中国古代就十分重视人的道德素质对的社会作用，提出"德者，国家之基也"，"有才无德，其行不远"。德乃做人之首，道德是文化最基本的内容之一。

诺贝尔经济学奖获得者诺斯教授曾说过，"自由市场制度本身并不能保证效率，一个有效率的自由市场制度除了需要一个有效的产权和法律制度相配合之外，还需要在诚实、正直、合作、公平、正义等方面有良好道德的人去操作这个市场。世界范围内日趋激烈的综合国力竞赛，不仅仅是经济、科技和军事力量的竞争，同时也是国家之间精神力量的较量，民族精神的较量，归根结底是人的素质和道德风貌的竞争现代核心价值观”。

由此可见中国国民素质的全面提高是社会发展的要求和趋势，尤其是当前人类即将迈入知识经济社会，提高人的综合素质尤为迫切。这证实儒学道德思想“人无德不立，国无德不兴”的现代价值观 。

人文素质的提升是以经济和科技为基础的，我们的经济比过去有了巨大提升，人民文明程度也是逐步提高的。如果没有文化素质，就无法接受思想品德的陶冶和教育，当然人的文化素质提高，离不开道德素质的辅助和实践。坚持正确的信念、既能提高人的文化质素，又能使文化素质在现实生活中体现它的实际价值。

身体素質是人民群众最关心、最直接、最现实的利益问题之一，近年来，中国全民健身事业蓬勃发展，国民的身体素质显著改善，《2010年国民体质监测公报》结果显示，大学生的身体素质出现了下滑。大学生们是未来社会的中坚力量，他们的身体素质在一定程度上决定着国民素质，提高他们的身体素质和身体机能迫在眉睫，学校、家庭和个人都应强化体育锻炼意识，健康为人生之宝，精神乃立身之本。

儒家顺其自然体现了“天人合一”的思想。强调在养生的过程中，既不可违背自然规律，同时也要重视人与社会的统一协调性。正如《内经》主张：“上知天文，下知地理，中知人事，可以长久”。儒家提倡，养生先养心。养心就是要心胸宽阔，遇事不怒，想得开，放得下，始终保持心情的平和。对人与事，不要斤斤计较，要对他人多着想。过喜伤心，过怒伤肝，忧伤脾，悲伤肺，惊恐伤肾，要保持正常的七情。养心要心静自然，不要过分追求，要知足者常乐。当然不是不要追求的目标，而是有目标努了力就可以了，胜不骄，败不躁。人生之完善基于自觉，无论就其内在心性品质，人格心理或其外在事功、学问、在成就上而言，均要在于自身修养的优良与否。年轻人要制定一个长期的锻炼计划，长期坚持下去，这样才能达到提高自身身体素质的效果，才能为实践“中国梦”做出贡献。

2. 儒学结合当代学校教育

无论是东方或西方，教育最重要的一个功能是培植人才，中国古代聖賢孔子，孟子，西方哲学家柏拉图、亚里士多德都是重视这些问题。欧美教育的传统是如此，中国教育的传统也是如此。以前人类社会都是用道德价值来判断一切问题，但是现在科学、经济、财富成了价值判断的标准，这是值得我们深思的问题。儒学以特有的智慧观察人与人及人与宇宙的关系，希望我们能从儒学的教育中得到启示。

中华五千年文明基本上是人文来创造的，因为人文只有在时间久了之后才能产生出效果，不像科学很快就能产生出效果。把当代学校教育结合人的价值目标，结合儒家教育是可行有效的，因为儒家學說的重心在人，是一种关于人的学说，或曰“伦理哲学”。作为一种“伦理哲学”，它所探讨的主要对象，是人与人之间的相互关系，人的道德修养，人的道德修养的境界问题。儒家五德是基础，“温、良、恭、俭、让”这是作中国圣人的基础标准，如果人人能把此教义贯彻于日常生活与学习中，使人的本性、人的潜能，良知善心与慈悲澈底表现出来。不管叫“素质教育”还是叫其他，最重要的内容是教育年青一代如何做人。

要实现这个目的，教师本身非常重要。现实中我们经常看到，教师也许掌握了丰富的知识，教学技巧也不错，但是，教师本人的人品却很成问题，对于教师的道德要求，首先应该从师范学校严格做起，教师为人师表，要从自己做起，教师一定要比平常人更加遵守道德规范。同时，国家政府应该对教师，尤其是基础教育的教师提高经济待遇，让全社会形成以教师为荣，以教师为尊的风气，同时也提高教师的道德门槛和专业门槛。国家应该让教师队伍成为全社会各方面的优秀模范，要采取一切手段，努力实现这个目标。这样，中国的未来才会真正有希望。对于教师队伍的败类，应该毫不犹豫地加以谴责。教师在道德方面决不应该以普通人的要求来对待自己，教师是人类灵魂的工程师，不能只落在嘴上，更应该变成一个国家的具体实践。

3. 儒学实践及社会主义核心价值的社会普及教育

在实践社会教育这个问题上，儒家方式比较有效，因儒家完全承认人性，可用电视和互联网传播儒家的经典来教育民众。电视和互联网是导致现代社会道德堕落的重要原因之一，这种看法并非罕见，但是，我们必须认识，电视、互联网已经是现代社会必不可少的要素，社会学家们也意识到，虽然大众媒体有不好的一面，但是同样应该看到，大众媒体在宣传上的强大力量。如何利用大众媒体的宣传力量，避免不好的内容过多占据宣传领地，而让好的、善的内容更多地传达到观众面前，媒体、新闻工作者和社会各界都有重大责任

值得我们深思的是儒学如何引导社会风气与经济要求实现良性结合，以经济为主的生活方式，很容易导致重利轻义，欺骗、自私和贪欲膨胀。在中国历史上“小国寡民”的状态能够保持自身的良好经济发展，与外界不良经济模式的互动就能够减少，而事实上，现代社会在世界一体化的发展趋势下，与外界的经济互动是必然的，在这种互动中，诚信的良好社会风气是否还能延续？这个问题，它需要全社会的共同努力，甚至需要全世界的共同一致解决。

但是，这种共同性的要求如何才能实现？儒学最重要的启示就是要从人心抓起，要从教育抓起，电视和互联网传播能起到积极作用和效果。

目前民办非营利性的教育单位文化中心，诵读讲介儒家经典，旨在培养社会亟须的伦理道德教育师资力量和社会文化教育工作者，在作无私的贡献。他们以各种办班

教学活动，中心的目标，配合社区街道构建和谐社会示范点，向社会证明：人是可以教得好的，和谐社会是可以实现的。

社区学校也可以配合社会教育，有些社区公布当地优秀校长和教师名单，校长和教师获得很民众的尊敬。学校教育和各方面的社会活动中，家长都会给校长和教师提供优先的便利，与此同时，这也形成社区对校长和老师的社会舆论监督，一旦校长或老师言行不轨，就会遭到社区舆论的谴责。

## 四、“传承中华美德 共圆中国梦想”

现实世界只有一个 ，而人们心灵中的理想境界却有许多。古往今来 ，千百万不同种族、不同肤色的人们 ，沉浸在自己的理想和梦想世界里 ，世世代代为之奋斗不息，带动着一代又一代的后来人为之前赴后继，研究并传承圣贤们不同的理想和梦境界 ，对于当前的社会主义现代化建设以及未来的社会发展 ，有着极其深远的现实意义。我们与古圣先贤之间 ，纵然相隔千年，但都有圣贤共同特征的梦想境界。

“中国梦：国家富强、民族振兴、人民幸福、社会和谐。”的追求不亚于我国古代的移山愚公精神 ，足以感天动地泣鬼神。古圣先贤都有各自明确的、为之奋斗终生的最高理想境界：孔子追求圣明 ，是一个随心所欲而又不违天道的境界；佛祖追求涅般一个远离一切苦厄的清净境界；老庄追求大道，一个淡泊宁静、无私无为而又无不为的境界；基督追求永生博爱、平等、无私欲的境界。圣贤带动着我们这一代的追求和梦想，于是长江后浪推前浪 ，圣贤的理想便如那万古不息的长江大河 ，生机勃勃地从古代奔向未来，与现实世界的江河融为一体，孕育着中华大地，中华民族的共同梦想。

我们总是在说中国地方大，人口多所以不好管理，真实原因就是我们不敢承认我们的不足之处，如果真实情况比别人差，就应该虚心接受自己的不足和错误，尽其所能改过补足。我们是否能从自己做起，从小事做起，可以先把一个省，再不行，先把一个市，一个区，实在不行，我们先把一条街做到干净文明，我们能做到了什么就做什么，为祖宗争荣，为国家争光。

我们希望通过这次论坛，传承中华美德共圆中国梦，在国际儒联指导下，为实践者搭建一个公益性的交流平台，旨在传播传承中华美德，唤起各界对中华美德伦理的认知，从我做起，成为带领和谐家庭，和谐社会，经济伦理和经济发展相结合的领头人，共同行动，为传承中华美德、传播、普及和应用提供服务，为人们学习、了解传承中华美德和中国传统文化知识提供服务。

关于如何从我做起，在现实生活中有哪些可以借鉴和实践的，当然有很多不同的观察点。例如，现代和谐社会的一个重要标志是与家庭的和谐，人与人的和谐，环境的和谐，提高因此中华美德，实践社会教育，在社区，街道，文明办，社团，企业举办传承儒家道德公益讲座，通过自己以身作则，帮不相识的居民。

5月10日上海市妇联，上海公共外交协会，澳中文化协会共同成功举办了“传承中华美德，共圆中国梦想”道德讲座，此次道德讲座的指导思想是，按照习近平主席关于培育和弘扬社会主义核心价值观作为凝魂聚气、强基固本的基础工程，继承和发扬中华优秀文化和传统美德，广泛开展社会主义核心价值观宣传教育，引导人们讲道德、遵道德、守道德，追求高尚的道德理想，不断夯实中国特色社会主义的思想道德基础的讲话精神，重在传承传统道德文化，提升国民素质，对外树立良好的国民形象。会议从上午九时开始到下午五时，全场一千多位听众无一人提早离席，一百多位上海文化志愿者以身示范，为道德讲座的成功做出贡献。会后全国政协委员、上海公共外交协会陈海刚会长会说：“我们共同举办讲座非常成功，各方反响很好，听众朋友的热情投入给我留下深刻印象。最近习近平主席又强调，要重视公共外交，传播好中国声音，讲好中国故事，我衷心希望有机会再次合作。”上海市妇联领导也提议在9月份在上海举办“世界妇女论坛”时我们再次合作。

国际儒联可与国际上与志同道合者加强沟通和交流，传承中华美德精华应用到个人修养和社会教育上去，应用到经济发展上去，应用到国家和社会治理上去，应用到促进世界和平与各国共同发展上去。只有每个有机会与外国人接触的中国人都学会如何从自身的角度向外国人介绍中国，这样形成的中国形象才是丰满的、立体的，也才是真实可信、可亲可近的，能够引发国际上的文化认同和情感共鸣。

回望人类历史，道德的光辉伴随社会前进的每一个脚步。和谐社会的构建，需要社会每个分子的参与，公民道德进步能够促进社会进步。作为“追梦人”，我们对自身道德素质的追求应该是永无止境的，国家也应该加强公民道德建设力度，只有这样，社会才能不断发展，构建社会主义和谐社会的“中国梦”才能早日实现。

## 结　语

西方和东方、中国和世界、传统和现代、物质和精神、科技和人文，这些困扰着我们的时代性难题，也许能在中华文明精神之中寻找答案。

千百年来，孔子，孟子，历代学者共同创立的中华文化和儒家学说，曾对中国古代的政治、经济、文化、教育乃至社会生活和世风民俗等产生了广泛而深刻影响，儒家学说漂洋过海，传播到东亚及世界各地，与各国的文化结合起来，形成了不同文化相互取长补短、吸收融合、共同发展。儒家学说不仅是人类文化和精神的瑰实也促进了不同文明的对话与交流。其中不少符合时代需要的精华至今仍潜移默化地影响着当今人类的思维习惯及行为模式。

我们可以、也应该借鉴儒家的刚健有为精神，来激励自己发愤图强；借鉴儒家的公忠为国精神，来培育自己的爱国情怀；借鉴儒家的“以义制利”精神，来启示自己正确对待物质利益，借鉴儒家的仁爱精神，来培育自己热爱人民的高尚情操；借鉴儒家的气节观念，来培育自己的自尊、自强的独立人格；也借鉴墨家的“兼爱”、“尚贤”、“节用”；道家的“少私寡欲”、“道法自然”；法家的“废私立公”，等等思想。追本溯源，取其精华，自然大有裨益。

纵观世界优秀民族，都是严谨，认真，执着，勤奋，积极乐观，主动永不服输的这些品质，我们的祖宗前辈就是这样的！

儒家学说作为世界文化遗产的一部分，21世纪是中国人为世界做出贡献的世纪，目前美国有2000万人在学汉文，到2020年中华传统文化，汉文化会成为世界文化主流，我们用十年时间努力学习，成为21世纪20年代的汉文化老师。

古之学者为己，今之学者为人，为使我们的子孙生活在一个更加和平、友好和繁荣的世界，中华文化的优良传统，泽被后世，需要不断弘扬。我们共同努力，彰显儒学思想的影响力，因梦想而伟大 因学习而改变 因行动而成功。

**参考文献：**

［1］顾立雅．孔子中国之道．374．

［2］伏尔泰全集．1865：25、27卷．

［3］沈福伟．中西文化交流史．上海人民出版社，1985：452．

［4］中共中央政治局就培育和弘扬社会主义核心价值观、弘扬中华传统美德进行第十三次集体学习．人民日报．2014.2.26．

［5］新制度经济学”和制度变迁．美国华盛顿大学的诺斯教授，复旦大学经济学教授张军博士．

［6］古籍：《荀子》、《史记》、《论语》、《汉书》、《孟子》、《礼记》、《中庸》，《论衡》。

# 中国梦：复兴中华文化

北京师范大学　周桂钿

中国梦，就是中华民族的伟大复兴。中华民族的复兴，重点在于中华文化的复兴。这个问题，看似简单，实际上相当复杂。电视和报纸上多有误读、误解，有必要加以梳理澄清。

## 一、中国梦

做梦，有主体与内容的区别，通俗地讲，谁做梦，做什么梦，是不一样的。这个中国梦，是指主体，还是内容。如指主体，那么，所有中国人做的梦都是中国梦。如指内容，那么，不管是哪一国人，只要希望中华民族复兴，就是中国梦。中国大多数人都希望中华民族复兴，因此他们做的都是中国梦。但一小部分人，追求的是个人私利，只要对自己有利，可以放弃中国籍，入了外国籍，他们做的就不算中国梦。更有甚者，为了私利，故意出卖民族利益，即使他现在还是中国籍的人，甚至还当着什么官，他做的不是中国梦，而是汉奸梦。有所谓裸官，将家属和财富全部转移到国外，自己随时准备逃亡，他做的就不可能是中国梦。他对中华民族的复兴没有信心，也没有兴趣。社会现象是错综复杂的，一些人在对外交往中可能会产生意想不到的结果，或者造成一些损失，不一定是汉奸。我认为：只明知对中国不利，为了谋取私利，“故意”出卖民族利益，这才是汉奸。现代的经济汉奸、科技汉奸，比抗日战争的日本汉奸，危害更大。总之，有一小部分中国人做的不是中国梦。相反，有一些不是中国人，却做着中国梦，抗日战争时期的白求恩做的是中国独立、复兴的中国梦，现在也有一些外国人希望中国复兴，支持中国富强，做的也是中国梦。

## 二、复兴论

复兴的前提是曾经辉煌过，未曾辉煌，只能是崛起。如果一直辉煌，也不存在复兴，只有辉煌中断、衰落，才要复兴。

中华文化的辉煌，是世界公认的，不论东洋、西洋，许多著名思想家都高度评价过。只是在近几百年，落后挨打以后，欧洲崛起，欧洲中心主义盛行于世，极力贬低中华文化，一切辉煌都被否定了。从五四运动到“文化大革命”，国内也有人提倡全盘西化，全面否定中华文化，提出破“四旧”，大呼“与传统决裂”，形成中华文化的灾难期。

中华文化虽然有灾难，也有低潮，但从未中断。有人以为蒙古族入主中原以后，中华文化就中断了，但是元朝修《宋史》，明朝修《元史》，清朝修《明史》，民国修《清史稿》，中华文化没有中断，是基本事实，谁也否定不了。世界许多文明古国都中断了，只有中华文化数千年绵延不断，这是奇迹，《二十四史》是世界文化瑰宝。中国从秦始皇统一中国以后，汉朝董仲舒提出“大一统”论，两千多年来，国家统一成为中华民族的共同观念，谁为统一做出贡献，谁就是民族英雄，受到敬仰，永垂不朽，流芳百世，相反，谁搞分裂割据，甚至与国外敌对势力相勾结，阻挠统一事业，那就是民族败类，有的则是汉奸卖国贼，受到唾骂，遗臭万年。数千年不中断，又能维持统一大国的局面，这是中华文化中政治智慧的结晶。

中华文化有丰富的政治智慧，可以古为今用，又有宽大的包容性，能够吸取别人的优长，洋为中用。这样丰厚的思想基础，中华文化的复兴是完全可以预期的。大难兴邦，想在，正处于大难之后，兴邦指日可待。

## 三、辉煌榜

讲复兴，就是承认中华文化有辉煌内容，突出的是政治智慧，从政治体制改革和选拔人才两方面来略加分析。政治体制，在尧、舜之前是天下为公，禹以后，建立家天下。周朝建立封建制，以分片包干的方式，巩固家天下，维持了八百年。后来进入春秋战国分类割据的乱世。秦始皇用武力统一天下以后，实行郡县制，加强集中统一的家天下。汉初实行“一国两制”，封建制与郡县制并存，吴楚七国之乱时，有叛国无叛郡，说明郡县制有利于社会的统一稳定。从汉唐到明清，郡县制延续了两千多年。中国维持统一大国的政治局面，郡县制起了关键性作用。

关于选拔人才，公天下时选贤举能，家天下以后，分封建国，子弟和功臣才有资格。秦朝以军功作为选拔标准，对于提高战斗力是有意义的。乱世时代，这种办法是切实可行的，而且是有效的。建立稳定社会以后，没有战争，也就没有军功，而且治理社会，统治人民，只靠武力就不行了。因此选拔人才，就需要其他方法。汉代除了军功之外，又增加举孝廉、对策、推荐、任子、鬻爵等。推荐孝子与廉吏当官，皇帝策问，各地选拔的贤良文学之士对策，皇帝亲自根据对策选拔。各位两千石高官推荐人才，高官退休，选一儿子进入官场，叫任子。花钱买爵位，或者捐款较多，被选上任职，叫鬻爵。这种办法，让有多余粮食的人有花钱买荣誉的机会，增加政府收入，减轻贫苦百姓的负担，具有“损有余以不足”的社会效果。

先秦时代，思想家已经提出选拔贤人当官的主张，一直没有制度的保证，只是口号与愿望。隋代发明科举制度，实行了一千多年，具有巨大进步意义，被欧洲人认为是中国一大发明，引入欧洲，产生了考公务员制度。而中国却将它视为封建糟粕抛弃掉，废除自己的，又从欧洲引进考公务员制度。冷静考察，现在考公务员比当年科举制度落后很多，从考试的严格、保密以及对舞弊的处理各方面来看，都相形见绌。科举制度体现公民身份平等与机会平等，因此中国人没有提出平等的要求，而欧洲人提出平等要求，正由于缺少平等。

中华文化中的政治智慧最核心的是民本观。从最古老的典籍《尚书》就有“民为邦本”的说法，西周提出“敬天保民”，《左传》中有“民与天齐、民为神主”的说法，战国时代的孟子提出“民贵君轻”，汉代贾谊归纳为“民无不为本”，柳宗元提出“吏为民役”，就是现代所谓的“公仆”，明清之际黄宗羲提出“天下为主，君为客”，……这一系列资料说明，中华文化一直传承民本观念。

民本与西方民主做一比较，西方现代民主都是形成了一种制度，以投票方式来表达民意，中国古代民本只是一种观念，没有制度保证，也没有法律约束，明智的统治者关心人民，做点利民的事，不明智者只图自己享乐，最后，天下大乱，亡国灭身，改朝换代。远古时代，将这种现象归结为天意、天命。后人认为天意表达的是民心，所谓“民心所欲，天必从之”，因此，“得民心者得天下”，成为流传甚广的政治口号。许多皇帝都想做一些得民心的事，保住祖先留下的家天下的基业。每一任皇帝都要负责到底，绝无短期行为。但由于个人智力有限，用人不当，听信谗言，就可能毁掉江山。而西方民主制度实行选举制、任期制，可以避免这种现象发生。但是，西方民主也导致短期行为，积极在任期内干一些事，不管将来如何。

另外，民本观，首先要倾听人民的意见，进行分析，做出利民的选择，如果不能使人民满意，早晚要被人民所推翻。而投票民主，仅以简单多数决定去取，而票数又与竞选者口才有关。没有真心实意，也没有有才能的人，可能因为口才好当选，而助选的宣传也会误导民众，当政的结果与竞选的承诺，差距巨大是常有的事。美国有一教授告诉我，四年投一张票，是平等的，也是民主的。投完票以后，既不平等，也不是民主，单纯的投票民主，在中国不适用。汉族占人口94%，少数民族很难当选。共产党员八千万，其他党派不到八百万，很难有发言权。社会上有一批弱势群体，如妇女、小学教师、农民工，他们的意愿难以表达。中国现行的人民代表制度，通过协商，代表有广泛的代表性，先协商后投票这种模式更适合中国，避免了西方投票民主的弊病。协商要有共同的观念基础，这就是民本观，在为人民服务的大前提下，才会有正常的协商，也才可能形成集思广益的最佳方案。所谓民主，应该表达人民的诉求。用什么方式来表达人民的诉求，就是民主方式。东西方有很大差别，各有利弊，过去只是捧西贬东，有失偏颇。

许多人认为，西方的民主、平等、自由，都比中华文化优越。如果从世界历史宏观角度来考察，中华文化不中断，数千年仍能维持大国局面，政治智慧远比西方强。

学术是文化的主要内容。西方重在分科之学，称为科学。中国则是分派之学，先秦有诸子百家，汉唐以后，主要是儒释道，都是学派，不是学科，例如医学，有儒医、道医等。简单地说，一派中有许多学科，而西方文化是一个学科中分许多学派。因此，儒家可以分为儒学、儒教，并不奇怪。

## 四、李约瑟难题

李约瑟研究了中国科技的发展，得出这样的结论：在十五世纪以前，中国的科技发明创造，遥遥领先于西方，是同时代的欧洲所望尘莫及的。但是，近现代世界科技却产生于欧洲，为什么？这就成了李约瑟无法解答的难题。许多中国人为解答李约瑟难题，写了很多文章，提出各种见解。有的说因为中国用难认难写的方块字，有的说儒家重视道不重视技，有的说科举制度只考文科，不重视理工科，士人只想当官，不屑于研究科技，有的说中国时黄色文化，封闭、落后，地理环境不好，不如欧洲的有地中海的蓝色文化。总之，中国所有的东西，都成了中国落后的原因。如果放眼世界历史，哪一种说法能够站住脚呢？地理位置，是从来就有的，汉字从仓颉造字以来，至少三千年以上，孔子创立儒家学派也有两千多年，科举制度从隋唐到清朝也有一千多年。李约瑟说十五世纪以前，中国科技领先于西方，上面所有说法都不能成立。唐朝是东方大帝国时，英国还是不见经传的小城邦。明代郑和七下西洋的时候，中国造船业、航海业已经是世界最先进的，过了87年，哥伦布才开始航海，规模与水平都远不如郑和航海，过了一百年，欧洲航海水平也赶不上郑和。从秦朝徐福航海到郑和航海，两千多年中，欧洲都望尘莫及。而中国的海岸线，比欧洲所有国家都长，中国如何成了黄色文化，而欧洲是蓝色文化的？

物质发展规律，盛极而衰，是符合辩证法的。世界许多文明古国都衰败、灭亡了。中国在昌盛数千年以后，出现衰败，有什么奇怪的？许多文明古国中断了，只有中国延续下来。现在称霸于世的国家，如美国，才独立二百多年，究竟能维持多少年，很难预料。凡事不能只看一时一事，就下断语。美国曾是英国的殖民地，而英国在一千年以前，则是小城邦，整个欧洲的社会产值，不及中国的唐朝。就是到了清朝乾隆年间的产值在世界上的份额，比当今美国在世界的份额还大。马可波罗看到元代的宁波，认为比欧洲任何城市都更繁华，而宁波在中国却不算是大城市。

## 五、复兴中华文化三步骤

（一）领导干部带头

领导干部是群众的榜样，在复兴中华文化方面要先走一步，起带头作用。主要表现在两个方面：

1. 要学习中国历史和世界历史，正确认识中华文化的世界意义和特殊价值，纠正多年来形成的偏见，改变从五四运动以来的观念，培养文化自信，弘扬传统美德。例如贬低中华文化有许多表现，讲哲学，不论是唯物论和辩证法，只要是中国古代哲学家，都要加上“朴素”二字，为什么？张岱年先生说：“如果说的正确，朴素何妨？如果说的不正确，即使说得很巧妙，也不过善于诡辩而已。”（见《中国哲学大纲》）

毛泽东在延安时给陈伯达信中说，墨子是唯物辩证法大家。以毛泽东的权威，在哲学界却没有赞成者，李岚清副总理想找一些人编一本《中国哲学与辩证法唯物主义》，召开过一系列座谈会，第一次座谈会是在汤一介的中国文化书院里召开的。张岱年先生说，张载明确提出唯物主义和辩证法，而且将二者有机地结合在一起，为什么不能称他为辩证法唯物主义哲学家？王夫之也是把唯物主义与辩证法有机地结合在一起，也应该是辩证唯物主义哲学家。但是，哲学界不成文的规定，辩证唯物主义是马克思主义的专利。恩格斯认为马克思有两项理论发现，一是剩余价值，一是历史唯物主义。所谓阶级斗争，所谓辩证唯物主义，都是马克思以前的资产阶级哲学家的理论成果，不是马克思的发现。马克思、恩格斯从来没说自己是辩证唯物主义者，只说过自己是“实践的唯物主义”。与以前的哲学家只是解释世界不同，自己要改造世界。中国著名的马克思主义哲学家有根有据地提出马克思主义哲学是“实践唯物主义”，却遭到围攻！从苏联传过来的“辩证唯物主义”，居然如此不可动摇！甚至有人说，中国没有变“修”，全赖他们从苏联搬来马克思主义。毛泽东将马克思主义与中国革命实践相结合，领导革命取得胜利。邓小平从实际出发，提出以经济建设为中心，使中国人民富起来。而许多教条主义者仍然照搬苏联的社会主义模式，却以为自己有多大理论贡献。苏联在七十多年中，出版了许多研究马克思主义的专著，每年都有几十本获奖。这些获奖的著作究竟有多少理论价值，不得而知。真正的马克思主义者要从实际出发，领会其精神实质，深入研究，提出解决现实问题的方案，未必正确，却不会脱离实际，还是有讨论的价值。

2. 要在行政贯彻民本观念，处处为人民着想，权为民所用，利为民所谋，百姓满意度是政绩的主要内容。简单地说，就是以传统道德与百姓满意作为考核提拔的依据。同时要逐渐淘汰拉拢关系，弄虚作假上来的干部。考核提拔要自上而下，从最高层做起，上梁不正下梁歪。自身不正，如何正人？董仲舒提出，皇帝正心，心正才能正朝廷；朝廷正才能正百官；百官正，才能正万民、正四方。董子说的就是这个道理。

（二）教育领域先行

青少年是民族的未来，他们对社会还没有固化的观念，有较强的可塑性。对他们进行中华文化的传播和教育，效果好，又能长久。百年树人，说明文化教育不是一代人所能完成的，必须先培养教师，才能培养出学生。因此，要先在教育领域进行文化教育，才能实现中华文化的复兴。

先有国家主席习近平考察曲阜，多次强调复兴中华文化，山东省委宣传部组织全省高校部分教师到山东师范大学与儒学研究专家对话。济宁市教育局决定每所中小学都派一名教师作为中华文化导师到济宁教育学院参加培训，由儒学研究专家给他们讲座，讲《论语》、《大学》、《中庸》、《孟子》等，并要他们听后自己读这些书。然后辅导全校师生阅读并讲解。孔子、孟子的故乡都属于济宁市，济宁市应该成为儒学示范区。山东省也应该并有条件成为复兴中华文化大省、强省。

（三）普及大众，移风易俗

山东省、济宁市可以作为复兴中华文化的示范区，示范区的作用在于推动全面发展，要将中华文化普及到民间，普及到广大民众，全体人民的文化素质得到普遍提高，中国人所到之处，都给当地人民带去礼仪之邦的风范，带去和谐的氛围，也带去以儒学为主干的中华文化。

在将近一百年批儒以后，许多人包括耄耋之年的老人，在头脑中对儒学反感仍有深刻的印象，从小没有读过儒家的书，只有批儒留下的痕迹。以为老人的说法都是可靠的，这是没有了解特殊时代的一种误解。没有读过“四大名著”的八十岁以上老人，没有读过“四书”的九十岁以上老人，并不罕见，我们怎么能要求他们知道中华文化？

鉴于以上现实，国际儒学联合会会长叶选平先生提出：提高与普及都很重要，现在更急需普及。因此在国际儒联内成立儒学普及委员会，每年召开一次全国性的普及大会，对儒学的普及做出巨大的推动作用。

许多地方采取各种方式，教儿童读经，背诵《弟子规》，许多中小学指导学习传统经书，或者组织中华文化讲座，或者培训教师。以各种形式将中华文化融入中小学教育，这是民间兴起的普及中华文化的热潮。

无论是领导干部带头，还是教育领域先行，无论是普及，还是提高，最后目标就是为了复兴中华文化，提高全民族的文化素质。

儿童读经和于丹等人的电视讲坛，对于普及中华文化都是有贡献的。在普及的基础上，就需要提高，这就要求一些中华文化的研究专家来解读经典，与时俱进，解决现实问题，达到移风易俗的目的。总之，复兴中华文化，领导干部带头是前提，如果领导干部反对复兴中华文化，群众办个“孟母堂”，就下令取缔；有人创办私立的文化教育，就宣布是非法的，没收财物，逮捕法办；或者将中华文化教育与现代科学、西方文化对立起来，中华文化怎么能复兴？领导干部不转变观念，复兴中华文化就是空想、幻想，不能成为梦想。中华文化深入民间，普及大众是基础，有这个基础，专家的研究、提高，才有动力，才有基本条件，精英分子才有用武之地。当万事俱备的情况下，学者下功夫研究，提出不同的看法，经过长期的百家争鸣，逐渐取得共识，必将对中华文化在传承的基础上弘扬并发展中华文化，综合创新，创造出适应现代的崭新的中华文化。这个新文化必将是古为今用、洋为中用的新成果。

以上三个步骤不是截然分开的，由于发展不平衡，从全社会来看，有交叉情况；从各地来看，既有先后，也有综合，最后的结果，都要达到移风易俗、复兴中华民族的文化。

# 新文化运动对传统的否定及其影响

北京外交人员服务局　王荣华

以陈独秀1915年创办《青年杂志》为发端的新文化运动，到明年就整整100年了。新文化运动的历史功绩是毋庸置疑的，它对中国的封建思想发起了攻击，以狂风暴雨般的攻势，动摇了封建思想的统治地位；它高举民主和科学的旗帜，将一股新鲜空气注入中国的思想界；它启发了民众的民主主义觉悟，为社会改造和进步提供了思想武器。在近100年后的今天，我们应该看到，阳光下的这座新文化运动的丰碑也是有阴影的。新文化运动在语言文字、家族、孝文化和礼乐文化等方面彻底否定了传统文化，这种否定一直对中国的思想界产生着影响，其影响之一就是中国的思想界对如何看待儒学不能形成统一的认识，未能给儒学以正确的定位，让它在中国人的精神生活中起到更大的作用。

## 我们先来看看新文化运动如何在语言文字方面割断传统的

新文化运动的旗手胡适先生在其《文学改良刍议》一文中说："吾以为今日而言文学改良，须从八事入手。八事者何？一曰，须言之有物。二曰，不模仿古人。三曰，须讲求文法。四曰，不作无病之呻吟。五曰，务去滥调套语。六曰，不用典。七曰，不讲对仗。八曰，不避俗字俗语。"尽管，胡适先生是针对时弊，有感而发，但有些要求违背了汉字语文的特色，如对仗。对仗是汉语词语各种组合能产生对比、对照、承接和衬托等多种意义的特性。其实，提倡白话文何必非要强调不讲对仗呢！在这种思想的指导下，汉语的虚实字的掌握和运用、汉字平仄声调的掌握和运用，在中学和大学的语文教学中一直未得到充分的重视。

胡适先生对国语的看法并未就此止步。他在《建设的文学革命论》中得出了这样的结论："我曾仔细研究：中国这二千年何以没有真有价值真有生命的'文言的文学'？我自己回答道：'这都因为这二千年的文人所做的文学都是死的，都是用已经死了的语言文字做的。死文字决不能产出活文学。所以中国这二千年只有些死文学，只有些没有价值的死文学。”一个“死”字否定了中国二千年的文化，这不是割断是什么?

新文化运动的先锋钱玄同在《致陈独秀》一信中说他赞同陈关于推翻孔学的主张，说“玄同对于先生这个主张，认为救现在中国的唯一办法，然因此又想到一事：则欲废孔学，不可不先废汉文；欲驱除一般人之幼稚的野蛮的顽固的思想，尤不可不先废汉文。”此可谓石破天惊之语。他主张废汉文不单单因为汉文难学，更是因为“二千年来用汉字写的书籍，无论哪一部，打开一看，不到半页，必有发昏做梦的话。此等书籍，若是知识正确，头脑清晰的人看了，自然不至堕其彀中；若令初学之童读之，必致终身蒙其大害而不可就药。”他进一步解释说：“二千年来所谓学问，所谓道德，所谓政治，无非推衍孔二先生一家之学说，所谓《四库全书》者，除晚周几部非儒家的子书外，其余则十分之八都是教忠教孝之书：‘经’不待论；谓‘史’者，不是大民贼的家谱，就是小民贼杀人放火的账簿，——如所谓‘平定什么方略’之类；——‘子’、‘集’的书，大多数都是些‘王道圣功’、‘文以载道’的妄谈……欲废孔学，欲剿灭道教，惟有将中国书籍一概束之高阁之一法。何以故?因中国书籍，千分之九百九十九都是这两类之书故；中国文字，自来即专用于发挥孔门学说，及道教妖言故。”把汉文字都废了，不就是将汉文字所承载的文化和传统全都废了吗！依我们对历史的了解，怎么能说二千年的文字都是发昏做梦哪！胡、钱二位将两千年的文化一棍子打死，真是登峰造极了。汉语语言与拼音语言重大的区别之一，就是拼音文字，如欧洲的一些文字是具有离心作用的；而汉语是具备向心力的一种语言。汉字不仅仅是汉族人交流思想的工具，还是承传文化的手段。汉字本身具有丰富的文化内涵，学习汉字可以帮助人们了解古代的文化知识。

有些人认为钱玄同的主张是一个特例，不代表新文化运动的看法。若真如此我们应该能找到运动先锋们与钱进行商榷的只言片语。我们非但看不到与钱进行讨论的文字，我们看到的是鲁迅等对他的主张的附和，看到的是陈独秀为他的辩护：“但是社会上有一班人，因此怒骂他，讥笑他，却不肯发表意思和他辩驳，这又是什么道理呢?难道你们能断定汉文是永远没有废去的日子吗?”（《新青年·罪案之答辩书》）

事实上，我国有相当一部分人在钱的思想的影响下，积极地探讨了用世界语代替汉语的可行性。后来的汉语拼音字母的推出以及简化字的推行，与钱玄同的思想不无关系。我们借此机会呼吁社会重视认繁体字，因为现在的学生已经不认识繁体字了，繁体字已经与文言文一起作古了。这是非常危险的一件事情。我们还要呼吁重视汉字的书写，只说汉语，不写汉字，久而久之，汉字里的向心力就消失了。为了我们的民族，为了传承传统文化，我们提议每个成年人至少每月抄写一首诗词。

## 下面我们来看看陈独秀是如何废孔学的

陈独秀在《新青年》一直在寻找除旧的突破口。他先将老、儒、佛三说并列加以攻击，而以老子学说为害居于三者之首。但是从1916年开始，他的笔锋就指向“儒者三纲之说”了。陈在说明他的这种选择时，说在学术上、政治上国人的态度是明确的，“继今以往，国人所怀疑莫诀者，当为伦理问题……盖伦理问题不解决，则政治学术，皆枝叶问题。纵一时舍旧谋新，而根本思想，未尝变更，不旋踵而仍复旧观者，此自然必然之事也。”（《宪法与孔教》）要解决伦理问题，就要拿“儒者三纲之说”开刀了。他说：“三纲之说，为一切道德政治之大原。君为臣纲，则民于君为附属品，而无独立自主之人格矣；父为子纲，则子于父为附属品，而无独立自主之人格矣；夫为妻纲，则妻于夫为附属品，而无独立自主之人格矣。率天下之男女，为臣，为子，为妻，而不见有一独立自主之人者，三纲之说为之也。”（《一九一六年》）之后，陈独秀做的是将“三纲之说”按到孔子的头上。他是如何按的呢？他在《孔子与中国》一文中说：“孔子的……价值是建立君、父、夫三权一体的礼教……孔子……已预见封建颓势将无可挽救，当时的社会又无由封建走向民主之可能，于是乃在封建的躯壳中抽出它的精髓，即所谓尊卑长幼之节，以为君臣之义，父子之恩，夫妇之别普遍而简单的礼教，来代替那‘王臣公、公臣大夫、大夫臣士、士臣皂、皂臣舆、舆臣隶、隶臣僚，僚臣仆、仆臣台’（见昭七年《左传》）的十等制，冀图在‘礼’的大帽子之下，不但在朝廷有君臣之礼，并且在整个社会复父子、夫妻等尊卑之礼，拿这样的连环法宝，来束缚压倒那封建诸侯大夫以至陪臣，使他们认识到君臣之义，无所逃于天地之间，以维持那日就离析分崩的社会。”但是，在孔子的全部学说中，根本不存在所谓的“三纲之说”。在儒家的经典著作中也没有这样的提法。孔子自己的提法是：“君君、臣臣、父父、子子”，这是说当国君的要像格国君、做臣子的要像个臣子、做父亲的要像格父亲、做儿子的要像个儿子。这样的话与君为臣纲、父为子纲，夫为妻纲相去甚远。陈独秀说：“不但孔子自己及他的及门弟子是这样，孔子之后，孔子的嫡派大儒孟子、荀子，他们的思想无论对于天鬼，对于孔教，都是孔子的继承者。”（《孔子与中国》）他引用了孟子这样的话：当尧之时……使契为司徒，教以人伦，——父子有亲，君臣有义，夫妇有别，长幼有序，朋友有信。这个话里丝毫没有臣子绝对服从君主、儿子绝对服从父亲、妻子绝对服从丈夫的意思。同样是孟子的话，陈独秀则有选择性地省略了。如“民为重，社稷次之，君为轻。”再如：“君之视臣为手足，则臣视君子如腹心；君之视臣如草芥，则臣视君子如路人；君之视臣如犬马，则臣视君子如寇仇。”这两句话完全可以推翻陈独秀的立论，是与他所说的“儒者三纲之说”格格不入的。

对“三纲之说”是否为孔子所创的质疑，陈独秀做了这样的辩解：“三纲五常之名词，虽不见于经，而其学说之实质，非起自两汉、唐、宋以后，则不可争之事实也。”（《宪法与孔教》）此学说如何产生在两汉之前，陈并未说明。他在《孔子与中国》一文中发出了这样的质问：“孔子、孟子、荀子虽然未说‘三纲’这一名词，而其立教的实质，不是‘三纲’是什么呢?”他自己没有直接回答这个问题。他是想让读者顺着他的思路，做出肯定的回答。笔者认为是否使用了“三纲”一词，是个原则问题。提出、提倡“三纲”与没有提出，没有提倡“三纲”有着天壤之别。孔子学说的实质是礼、仁和民本思想，而不是什么“三纲”。陈独秀在《宪法与孔教》中辩解说：“尊卑贵贱之所由分，即三纲之说之所由起也。（三纲之义，乃起于礼别尊卑，始于夫妇，终于君臣……）”陈的意思说白了，就是因为礼别尊卑，则必然会产生“三纲”之说。这个因果关系的跨越也太大了。礼仪之讲究就是要表现尊敬，让接受尊敬的人感到尊贵，让表示尊敬的人以卑微之心真诚第表达情感。接受尊敬的人，或其本身却有值得尊敬的品格或业绩，或其社会地位应该得到尊敬。如同今日美国总统有权乘坐“空军一号”，而普通百姓无此权利一样。在世界上大多数国家，当其国家元首进入一个正式的场合时，在场的人员都会起立致敬。我们号称“礼仪之邦”，但是当我们的国家主席步入会堂之时，台上台下均无人起立表示欢迎。这真是大不敬。我们的国民很少有人觉得这是个问题，才真是叫人痛心的地方。生活中不讲究区别，不允许存在区别，就是不讲礼仪，就是不尊重人，也不尊重自己。陈独秀所谓“三纲”之说是由区分尊卑贵贱引起的说法，是毫无道理的。

虽然陈独秀在《孔子与中国》一文中也提到董仲舒和班固，说他们“都有‘三纲’之说”。这给人以董、班二人是在孔子礼教之说的基础上阐述他们的学说的印象。实际上，董仲舒是在阴阳学的基础上提出“三纲”之说的。他说：“君臣、父子、夫妇之义，皆取之阴阳之道。君为阳，臣为阴；父为阳，子为阴；夫为阳，妻为阴”。认为男的为阳，女的为阴，是“尽取之天”，由上天所决定，而且阳的永远是主体，阴的永远是附庸，“阳之出也，常悬于前而任事；阴之出也，常悬于后而空守处。”（以上均引自《春秋繁露·基义》）班固所纂《白虎通德论》说：“言行者，欲言为天行气之义也，地之承天，犹妻之事夫，臣之事君也。其位卑，卑者亲事，故自周于一行。尊于天也”。他说：“三纲之义，日为君，月为臣也。”（《白虎通义·日月》）他还说：“子顺父，妻顺夫，臣顺君，何法？法地顺天。”（《白虎通义·天地》）可见，班固所论述的“三纲”之说也是建立在阴阳五行的基础上的，与孔学毫无关系。以陈独秀之学识，他没有点破“三纲”之说的这层渊源，颇是耐人寻味。

在陈独秀等新文化运动的先锋对孔子动了这番手脚之后，孔子便成为中国封建思想的代表，不但遭到批判，而且几次被“打倒”。至今，没有认真读过孔子的人，很多都会人云亦云，认为孔学没有什么可学的。作为中国传统文化的精髓的儒学就这样被反复地践踏着。

家族文化遭到毁灭性打击。其原因是这个文化里有很多落后、黑暗的因素，例如女子的缠足、包办婚姻、女子在丈夫过世后不能再嫁等。这些腐朽封建的行为，在二十世纪初就遭到了猛烈的攻击，在社会上形成了根除这些恶习的力量。然而，家族文化在历史上一直发挥延续传统和教育的功能。家族文化的颓废有两个重要的标志，一是祠堂活动的终止；二是群居习惯被颠覆。家族文化之颓废与新文化运动中“矫枉过正”不无关系。鲁迅在《狂人日记》里感叹道：“我翻开历史一查，这历史没有年代，歪歪斜斜地每页上都写着‘仁义道德’几个字。我横竖睡不着，仔细看了半夜，才从字缝里看出字来，满本都写着两个字是‘吃人’!”他笔下的祥林嫂激发了人们对封建礼教的仇恨。在当时被誉为“只手打孔家店的老英雄”的吴虞说鲁迅的《狂人日记》“把礼教吃人的内容和仁义道德的表面，看得清清楚楚，那些戴着礼教假面具吃人的伎俩，都被他把黑幕揭破了。”吴虞在《吃人与礼教》一文中举了一些值得考证和推敲的“吃人”的历史事例后叫道：“孔二先生的礼教讲到极点，就非杀人吃人不成功，真是残酷极了！一部历史里面，讲道德说仁义的人，时机一到，他就直接间接的都会吃起人肉来了。就是现在的人，或者也有没做过吃人的事；但他们想吃人，想咬你几口出气的心，总未必打扫得干干净净！到了如今，我们应该觉悟：我们不是为君主而生的！不是为圣贤而生的！也不是为纲常礼教而生的！什么‘文节公’呀，‘忠烈公’呀，都是那些吃人的人设的圈套，来诳骗我们的！我们如今，应该明白了！吃人的就是讲礼教的！讲礼教的就是吃人的呀!”听到如此煽情的话，有谁还会想到家族文化的好的方面呢？我们应该看到家族文化的弱化，给我们的社会带来了一些问题。家族的教育在我国的历史上一直起着举足轻重的作用，它是社会上的课堂，是中国的教堂，它首先强调的是道德教育，首先教的是如何做人。它重视的是“首孝悌，次见闻，”然后才是“知某数，识某文”。它强调的是：“首孝悌，次谨信。泛爱众，而亲仁。有余力，则学文。”我们所面对的严酷的事实是：在“学文”之前，孝弟、谨信、爱众和亲仁的教育非常薄弱。为人师者，自己就没有学好，又怎能去教育别人呢！《中华遗产》杂志 2013 年第 11 期列出了我国历史上“一百个最具影响力的家族”是非常值得品味和思考的。由于时代的变迁，这些家族赖以生存的组织形式不复存在了，我国今后恐再也不会出现这样的家族了。面对这样的现实，我们则更要强调家庭教育和学校教育的重要性了。家族文化的另一层意义是表达对祖先的敬重。我们的祖先创造了我们家族的文化和传统，开拓了家族生育繁衍的土地，积累了生活的经验和财富。祭祖是表达我们的敬重的一种方式。对家族文化的破坏，大大地削弱了中国人敬重祖先的传统。

吴虞认为家族制度是专制主义的“根据”。在家族制度里，“孝敬忠顺，皆利于尊贵长上，而不利于卑贱，……儒家以孝弟二字为二千年来专制政治与家族制度联结之根干，而不可动摇。……夫孝之义不立，则忠之说无所附，家庭之专制既解，君主之压力亦散；如造穹窿然，去其主石，则主体坠地。”（《家庭制度为专制主义之根据论》）吴虞还在《说孝》一文中讲：“就这样看来，他们教孝，所以教忠，也就是教一般人恭恭顺顺的听他们一干在上的人愚弄，不要犯上作乱，把中国弄成一个‘制造顺民的大工厂’。孝字的大作用，便是如此!”很显然，“孝”是新文化运动先锋们的眼中钉。然而，孝道是中华文明区别于古希腊罗马文明和印度文明的重大文化现象之一。孝是中国文化的一个核心观念与首要文化精神，是中国文化的显著特色之一。因此我们可以说：否定“孝道”就是否定中国文化，就是割断中国文化的传统。实际上，中国人几千年来的行为模式可以概括为：入则孝，出则悌。我们也可以说，对“孝道”的否定，也是对中国人的否定。说到底，“孝”是中国人对生命的热爱，是朴素感情的流露，是对爱的回报。“孝”在中国人的血液里。不孝者必是中国人中的另类。

对儒学“礼”的批判淡化了社会上礼仪的意识。首先，陈独秀关于儒学的“礼”是“别尊卑明贵贱之阶级制度”的说法值得讨论。因为，孔子及其弟子的著作中所说的“礼”，是在上层社会中实行的，仅限于天子、君王、诸侯、公卿大夫和士之间的礼仪。所谓“礼不下庶人”是说在老百姓中间不推行“礼”。不是对老百姓不尊重。从这个意义上讲所谓“礼”是一个阶级内部的规定，说它是阶级制度显然是不准确的。这样看来，把孔子作为“封建礼教”的罪魁祸首是值得推敲的。从孔子的时代到二十世纪初叶，“礼”的内容在不断地变化。但是，有一点似可肯定，缠足、封烈女等的做法非自孔子的时代始。礼仪不仅是社会生活中的行为规范，而是一种道德规范。尽管我们不必照搬《礼记》中所描述的300多种礼节，我们则不必删繁就简，而是要在生活中保留一些仪式。必要的仪式是对行为和道德进行规范，是教育的一种手段。荀子曾说：“衣服有制，宫室有度，人徒有数，丧祭械用，皆有等宜。”（《荀子·王制》）也就是说，每一个社会成员从穿衣、饮食到起居、言谈，都必须按照等级身份，遵循一定的礼仪。笔者曾应邀参加某报的周年庆祝活动，这项活动对衣着没提要求，活动自始至终嘈杂纷乱。活动的组织者不重视仪式，参加者缺乏礼仪意识，其效果就很差。我们有些活动要对衣着提出要求，不能仅提“衣着整齐”，这个要求太一般了。针对活动的重要性，要提出“请着正装”，或“请着礼服”等。重大的活动，大家穿正装，可保持活动的严肃性，衬托活动的重要意义。在有些活动中讲究仪式，往往会对参加者的精神产生震撼作用。不能一味地取消、简化仪式；坚守必要的礼仪和仪式是一种教育手段，是践行礼俗，是传播文化。毛泽东同志也是主张搞必要的礼仪的，譬如，他在《为人民服务》中说：“村上的人死了，开个追悼会。用这样的方法，寄托我们的哀思，使整个人民团结起来。”过去我们礼太多，走到了某种极端，其结果就是今天礼太少，以至于“不讲礼”。我们的民族至今没有统一的，被大多数人认可的民族服装，就是“不讲礼”的表现之一。要使我们成为名副其实的“礼仪之邦”，我们有很多工作要做。认真第践行礼仪，可以净化人的心灵；虔诚地参与必要的礼仪，可以提高修养，维持全民族的文明水平；可以使道德教育落到实处；可以增进人们之间的相互尊敬；可以在社会上推广道德规范，形成良好的社会风气。

笔者提出上述看法，不是要否定新文化运动；而是希冀大家看到这个伟大的运动给我们留下的一些负面影响。笔者对这些负面影响的分析和认识可能不准确，希望大家予以指正。通过我们的分析，我们对一些问题的看法应该坚定起来。譬如，在如何看到儒学的问题上，我们不要再折腾了。尽管儒学有着自己的金刚不坏之身，折腾起来对我们是不利的。我们应该明白无误地声明：儒学是中国传统文化的精髓。儒学的基本原则，仁义礼智信应该成为中国国民基本的道德规范。

做这样的声明，是国家儒学联合会应尽的义务。

# 儒学复兴与思想巨人的出现①

山西大学 刘毓庆

关于儒学的复兴，已成为近几年的热点话题。曾为外交官的澳大利亚学者李瑞智，与黎华伦合作撰写了《儒学的复兴》一书，于20世纪末出版。日本学者村山节《东西方文明沉思录》，也提出了中国精神复兴的预言。2009年在纪念孔子诞辰2560周年学术研讨会上，汤一介先生还做了题为《论儒学复兴》的主题发言。以儒学复兴为内容的文章与评论，从20世纪末开始，即不断见于报刊。而“国学热”的出现，更为这一呼声提供了理论根据。当然，批判甚至谩骂“儒学复兴论”的声音更高。但无论如何，儒学由原初完全被批判到如今可以公开的肯定，这一变化无疑是值得关注的。而且这一过程，与历史上前两次思想革命思潮高涨时期的儒学处境基本相似，都是由被排斥甚至批判，而后走向肯定的。②

笔者之所以对儒学复兴做出肯定的回答，主要是从三个方面做出分析的。

首先，从儒学的性质，看其复兴的合理性。人类文化有正脉，有支脉。这两个系统是相互配合的。正脉如同人体主干，是从头到臀的部分；支脉如同四肢。正脉断了人必死无疑，而某一支脉断了，属身体残疾，虽生活不便，但还可以维持生命。中华文化就是人类文化的正脉，是人类几千年积累起来的文明成果。它不只是属于某一个民族的，而是属于全人类的。在周朝，儒是知礼乐射御书数、以道艺教民的人，即《周礼·天官·太宰》所说的“儒以道得民”。周之文明是从夏商文明的基础上发展来的。孔子本是殷人之后，但他在文化选择上却说：“郁郁乎文哉，吾从周。”原因就在于他认为周之礼乐文明是人类最高的文明形态，他要继承并发扬它。他一生奋斗，就是为了复兴礼乐。而在“道不行”的郁闷中，他选择了整理“六经”的事业，目的就是要把这种文明承传下去。而此后，守护并承传人类文化的正脉便成为儒者的事业。

---

① 本文是作者未发表的书稿《中国历史的三次大循环与全球化后的中国》中的一节。

② 参见刘毓庆、张小敏：《中国历史上的三次思想革命浪潮》，《社会科学战线》，2013年第9期（总219期），第124－138页。

我们之所以说这种文化是人类文化的正脉，主要在于它植根于人类道德性的自觉，是对人类善性的发现与培植，有一种向善与向上的力量在导引着。而这也是人类独具的。人类从自然界走出，依靠两种力量，一是智慧，一是道德。“智慧”使人类在力不及虎豹、捷不及禽兽的条件下，能够战胜自然，创造了人类丰富多彩的生活；“道德”使人相互之间以诚相待，协同合作，构建了人类最初的社群。而对最初的人类群体组成，起决定作用的则是道德。

就道德而言，人最初构建群体组织，信赖的便是一个“诚”字。所谓“诚”，就是“真实无妄”。《礼记・中庸》说：“不诚无物。”“诚者，天之道也；诚之者，人之道也。”“唯天下至诚为能经纶天下之大，立天下之大本，知天地之化育。”换言之，天地间若没有了诚，万物不能生，人类无以成。宋周敦颐《通书》有《诚上》《诚下》二章，是专就“诚”字而发的。他说：

诚者，圣人之本。“大哉乾元，万物资始”，诚之源也。“乾道变化，各正性命”，诚斯立焉。纯粹至善者也。故曰：“一阴一阳之谓道，继之者善也，成之者性也。”“元亨”，诚之通；“利贞”，诚之复。大哉《易》也，性命之源乎。

圣，诚而已矣。诚，五常之本，百行之源也。静无而动有，至正而明達也。五常百行，非诚，非也，邪暗塞也。故诚则无事矣。至易而行难，果而确，无难焉。故曰：“一日克己复礼，天下归仁焉。”

我们习惯上用“淳朴”、“憨厚”、“赤子之心”形容人的德性，这正是对人类初始行为状态的表述。而儒家所强调的“礼”，正是建立在作为“五常之本”的“诚”的道德意识基础上的。在政治权力出现之前，有了相互之间的诚信守诺，才有可能形成人类最初的规则和群体。人类社会才能建构。当在人类社会政治权力出现之后，是用何种思路和方法维护社会秩序，这便有了分别。在中国，则是始终把握着道德原则，并在此基础上，形成了中国独具特色的“礼制”。荀子在《礼论》篇中，开首即云：

礼起于何也？曰：人生而有欲，欲而不得，则不能无求；求而无度量分界，则不能不争；争则乱，乱则穷。先王恶其乱也，故制礼义以分之，以养人之欲，给人之求，使欲必不穷乎物，物必不屈于欲，两者相持而长，是礼之所起也。

这实际上是在强调，礼是维护社会道德秩序的纲纪。其功能一是确立尊卑秩序（注意，在这里尊卑是表示上下位置，而不表示价值），二是制止人的欲望膨胀、人性下坠，最终则实现社会的有序与和谐。“礼”之内核在一个“理”字，故《礼记・乐记》说：“礼也者，理之不可易者也。”后期儒学强调“理”，坚持的仍然是道德性原则。中国社会长期以儒学作为国家意识形态，这是历史选择的结果，是在经验和教训中，选择出的最理想的人类生存之道。在东方的历史上也曾有过放弃“礼”的时代和地区，如战国时的秦国，用“法”代替“礼”，用赤裸裸的物质利益代替道义，被中原各国视为“狼虎之国”。虽然秦国凭借着利益扇动起的国民好战热情，获得了一时的成功，完成了统一大业。然而却因道义丧失，前后兴盛不到一百五十年，便彻底消亡。其因道德丧失导致的民风败坏的后遗症，给历史留下了深刻的教训。使得汉初百余年间的士大夫群体，在对秦二世而亡的思考中，不断探讨历史的运动方向。正是在对历史的深入研究和深刻反思中，知识群体在其智慧的充分发挥中，基本达成共识，最终选择了儒学，走上了以“礼”治国的道路。正是在“礼”的坚持中，中国及东亚国家平稳地走过了两千多年。显然这是人类一条健康的生存之道，当然这条道路人类在今后的进程中还会继续完善，但大的方向不应改变，因为它代表了人类正确的发展方向，代表了人性发展的方向（我这里所说的人性，是指人独具的品性，而不是人兽共有的被当代哲学家称作“人性”的那种东西）。人类只有在这一道德原则的坚持中，才能继续生存。一旦这条主脉中断，人类就会走向消亡。

欧美文化则不同，他们代表的是人类文化的支脉。之所以说是支脉，因为 这种文化放弃了人类赖以形成的最初的道德原则，而去发挥人的创造力。这种文化以追求利益最大化、不断满足人的欲望为目标。但这种满足，是以破坏道德维系的平衡为代价的，在这种文化体系中，人性中从动物界带来的恶的东西被合理化，但在集团内部可通过失去人性温情与道德基础的社会规则——法制，给予底线制约，维护社会秩序。在集团之外，如国际社会中，则采取以物质利益最大化为原则的价值判断，认可生存竞争、优胜劣汰、以强凌弱的合理性。这就是西方目前走的路，也是曾被中国历史所淘汰的秦国之路。这种文化最能体现人类的创造力，也最能体现人类的物质文明水平，犹如人之双手与双脚最能体现人的本领一样。因此这种文化在当今世界大显神威，其在以利益为核心的价值观的导引下产生出的观念、信奉、规则，如民主、法制、科学、自由、人权、爱国等等，被作为普世价值，随着强大的经济与军事实力推向全世界。但这些所谓的普世价值，无一不是以维护、获取个人利益或集团利益为前提的，像道义、是非、情理、良知等等，在这里几乎找不到踪影，甚至被否定。只有在关涉到集团内部的稳定、和谐时，才会发出没有具体内容的“博爱”之声；也只有在掠夺别的集团或个人利益时，才会出现人类特有的羞耻感与道德感——以对方违背道义、公约为借口，为自己的侵略行径遮羞。德军入侵波兰、日军入侵中国、美国出兵伊拉克等等，无一不是在符合道义、公约的借口下进行的，但借口又无一不是编造出来的谎言。这种以利益为核心的价值判断与文化导向，永远关注的是眼下，而非未来；是自我或局部利益，而不是人类整体。在这种文化的支配下，人类很难获得安宁，甚至很难继续生存500年。这显然不是人类健康发展之路。因此这种文化只能算做人类文化的支脉，而不能成为正脉。人类要想健康、幸福的生存，必然延续正脉。因此以孔子为代表的儒学复兴，从哲学的层面上看，是有其学理上的依据的。

其次，从人类的永恒性需求，看儒学复兴的必要性。人类有两种不同性质的智慧，一种是“仁学智慧”，一种是“科学智慧”。“科学智慧”主要体现在工具性、技术性的层面上。这里所谓的科学，是西方意义上的“科学”，是在西方分析性的思维框架下，建构起来的反映事物客观规律的分科知识体系。在拉丁文中书作“scientia”，意即“知识”、“学问”，英文则用“science”来表示。这种分科的知识体系，面对的只能是具体事物、具体学科，是单一性的，因此有利于单向突破。故而在西方智慧主导的200年间，人类在物质财富方面的创造，比过去五千年的总和还要超过千百倍！交通、通讯的发达，打破了传统空间与时间的观念，地球两端相隔万里之遥的亲人，可以在半天内相聚，也可以通过视频笑脸相对。信息高速公路的开通，使信息交流几乎没有了时间差。反季节蔬菜的发明，使得夏果冬尝，季节的观念被淡化。同时人类在为利益争夺而研发的武器装备，由过去的“一刀一个人头”，进展到“一个子弹消灭一个敌人”，到现在则变成了一个指头轻动按钮，就会有成千上万生命消失。这种智慧的创造力无疑是惊人的。然而，这种智慧只能帮助人在与自然或人群的竞争中临时获胜，也只能使人在单项突破中感受到人类创造力的伟大，而却无法解决人与人、人与自然、人与社会之间的永恒冲突。这种智慧驱动下而产生的不断创新理念，把全社会卷入到了一个无休止的巨大漩涡中，使每一个灵魂都处于焦虑不安的状态。在人类劳动效率比原始人千百倍的提高后，人类一点也没有感觉到轻松，相反更加疲倦。而且使人产生了“不在竞争中站起就在竞争中死亡”的感觉。在科学智慧淋漓尽致地获得发挥时，人类的安全感、幸福感却大幅度的丧失。以食品为例，像面粉加增白剂，豆芽加无根素，牛奶加三聚氰胺，养猪用瘦肉精，养鸭用苏丹红等等，哪一项不是科学智慧的产物？哪一项没有为商家赢得巨利？又有哪一项没有给人带来恐惧？而对哪一项有害性的认识不需要过程？即今大量转基因食品、反季节蔬菜、保鲜剂、增白剂、调味剂等等，有谁敢保证300年后不出问题呢？比如威胁人类生育、导致某种怪病的出现等等。对科学的过度自信，导致了人们以技术制服技术的种种幻想，认为科学是万能的，能够解决任何难题。但就在这种自信中，人类却一步步走向了危机四伏的包围圈。

更让人担忧的是，科学智慧是在利益最大化价值观的导引下运作的。在个体、族群和集团之间都存在着利益问题，由此而形成了一个个的利益集团，集团与集团之间为利益争夺斗智斗勇，道德变得苍白无力，只有经济与武力才是最实惠的。因而几乎所有的大国都把最聪明的才智、最大的经费开销，用在了杀人武器的研发上。不可讳言，现代科技不是在人民生活需求的牵动下起步的，而是由军事上的制敌需求一路向前推进的。只有军事上解密后，才会变为民用。这样，以杀人制敌技术为最高表现形态的科学智慧，若继续向前推进，必然的结果无异于人类集体自杀。科学再万能，也无法解决战争冲突。据有关资料披露，仅20世纪，死于利益争夺战争的人口就超过了一个亿。故著名科学家霍金忧心忡忡地提出“人类如何才能继续生存一百年”的难题。

人类如何避免集体自杀，这就需要有高于科学智慧的大智慧发挥作用。这种智慧一定要能够统摄科学智慧，使其在“万物并育而不相害，道并行而不相悖”的轨道上运行。而以儒学为代表的东方智慧就是这样的一种大智慧。这种智慧我们可称之为“仁学智慧”。所谓“仁”，就是“万物一体”的感受体验。即宋儒程颢所说：“仁者，以天地万物为一体，莫非己也。”[①] 这种智慧最大特点是，把整体性利益永远放在局部之上，对事物从生态的角度考虑其相互关联、彼此相依的关系，以创造良好的生态环境和达成和谐的精神状态为最高目标。儒家学说的创始者孔子提出的“仁”学理论，便是这大智慧的最高体现。相传为孔子所撰的《易传》说：“天地之大德曰生”，“生生之为易”。又说：“乾，其静也专，其动也直，是以大生焉；夫坤，其静也翕，其动也辟，是以广生焉。”这“生”气，就是天地“仁”心的体现，世俗把饱含生机的果核称作“仁”，原因也在此。宋杨伯喦《臆乘》说：“俗称果核中子曰仁……盖仁者生意之所寓，谓百果得此为发生之基。”仁者能以己体人，故能与万物相通、相贯、相爱，共生共荣。虽然在更多的情况下，人们把这种“仁”的学说作道德性的理解。但孔子明确地说：“仁者安仁，知（智）者利仁。”把“仁”认作了大智慧。人可以通过仁的方式——相互宽容、理解、尊重、体谅、礼让、关爱，建构起和谐的良好生态。在这种生态（包括自然生态与人文生态）中，生命可以获得全面放松，从而实现全体利益的最大化。老子对这种智慧是用“道”来表述的。他说：“道者万物之奥，善人之宝，不善人之所保。”“善人”“不善人”，就是孔子所说的“仁者”“智者”。从“仁者”“善人”而言，这“仁”这“道”就是一种精神要达到的境，这是道德性的；从“智者”“不善人”言，这“仁”这“道”则是获得持久性利益所必须遵循的最高原则，这是智者的发现。从“仁”出发，孔子提出了“礼让”；从道出发，老子提出了“不争”。“不争”则“天下莫能与之争”；“礼让”则天下安宁。在“不争”“礼让”的生态环境中生存，生命不但可以处于快乐的境界，而且还不失去基本利益的保证，这可说是一种艺术的人生。

据此，以儒家文化为代表的“仁学智慧”，有利于解决人类集体自杀的难题。在当代西方“科学智慧”高度发挥作用的情况下，人类因竞争而处于焦虑、恐惧、惴惴不安之中的灵魂，极需要“仁性智慧”来解困。因而代表“仁性智慧”的儒学复兴，是非常必要的。

其三，从事物规律，看儒学复兴的必然性。物极必反是一个不可抗拒的事物变化规律。以利益最大化为价值导向、以科学技术为生存手段的西方文化，已经发展到了

---

① （宋）程颢、程颐著：《二程集·河南程氏遗书》卷二（上），中华书局，1981年，第15页。

一个顶点，它造福于人类的使命已基本完成，正在以加倍的副作用威胁着人类的健康生存。其价值系统，导致了人类道德意识的整体性丧失和人文生态的全面恶化；其智慧系统，导致了人类欲望的恶性膨胀和自然生态环境的大面积破坏。于是出现了威胁人类生存的种种危机，有人还专门写了一份25万字的《21世纪人类生存危机报告》。有人根据生态破坏导致的恶果，声称人类正在导演地球第六次生物大灭绝。有人根据世界大战潜在的危机，提出全球拥有核武器的总数量为200多亿吨，相当于全世界每人头上悬挂了10多吨的TNT炸药，可以摧毁地球25次。同时，像污染、饥饿、暴力、吸毒、自杀、非典、艾滋病、禽流感、恐怖活动等，无一不是对人类的重拳出击。尽管由这一文化系统产生的制约事物恶化的法规仍然起着一定的作用，但其法规在因贪欲调动起的聪明才智面前显得漏洞百出，合法不合理、合理不合法之事比比可见，故而奸邪之徒可从容游刃于其间。再则，法律不能处理国际冲突，如美国以萨达姆生产核武器为由出兵伊拉克，导致上百万人死亡，结果什么也没有找到，他们对伊拉克人民犯下的罪行，有谁奈何得了呢？

这是西方文化发展到“极”点的表现形态。这种“极”点形态，在精英与草根中产生了两种不同的恐惧。草根民众为“天下亡”而担忧，精英分子为“人类亡”而恐慌。为此，事物出现了“反”的动向。

所谓“天下亡”，指道德委地，人性尽失，人混同禽兽而横行于天下，即顾炎武所说的“仁义充塞，而至于率兽食人，人将相食”。[①] 目前道德大滑坡，价值观大颠倒，杀人、偷盗等等传统认为的败德行为，在虚拟世界里被合法化。正是介于“天下亡”的现实，大陆掀起了“国学热”、“少儿读经热”，一些宗教团体和个人，出资印刷《弟子规》，向路人免费赠送。一些单位和学者，免费开办国学讲坛和讲座，对民众进行传统道德教育。还有一些企业家投资办国学书院，免费向社会开放。这是自发起来拯救人类灵魂的文化行动，其发展态势，必将变为由有识之士参与和组织的自觉运动。

所谓“人类亡”，是指人类实体的消亡。这是近代西方一批顶尖级的科学家和学者，根据人类目前的发展模式和方向产生的担忧。因为这种追求物欲满足的文化，其必然的结果，就是导致资源枯竭和生态大破坏，导致战争频发和世界大战的爆发，导致人类集体自杀。因此英国著名史学家汤因比（1889－1975）博士说：“世界统一是避免人类自杀之路，在这点上现在各民族中具有最充分准备的，是两千年来培育了独特

① （明）顾炎武著，张京华校释：《日知录》卷十七“正始”条，岳麓书社，2011年，第557页。

思维方法的中华民族。”① 他在一次报告中还提出：“世界现在最需要的是中国文明的精髓——和谐。如果中国不能取代西方成为人类的主导，那么整个人类的前途是可悲的。”② 汤因比在与池田大作先生的谈话中还提到：“近代物质文明的危机，本质在于‘道德差距’。就是说，‘善性’衰退，人类的伦理、道德水准低下。要克服这些，提高人类伦理性，巨大的力量是中华民族所具有的‘世界精神’。”奥地利著名心理学家卡尔·荣格（1875—1961）在他的《东洋冥想的心理学》中指出：应该转换西方人已经偏执化了的心灵，学习整体性领悟世界的东方智慧，应该让他们放弃一些令人毛骨悚然的技术，拆穿他们拥有力量的幻象。这已导致千百万人付出生命。

在1988年巴黎召开的“面向21世纪”第一届诺贝尔奖获得者国际大会上，著名瑞典科学家汉内斯·阿尔文博士提出：“人类要生存下去，就必须回到公元前六世纪之前，去汲取孔子的智慧。”澳大利亚学者李瑞智、黎华伦在《儒学的复兴》一书序言中说：“北亚古老的神话和圣哲，看来更可能替代西方文化成为我们‘地球村’未来的中心。”③

与西方学者呼应，中国一批旧学功底深厚的学者，如季羡林、张岱年、汤一介、何兹全、张立文等先生，也提出了类同的观点。可以看出，西方文化已发展到极点，正遵循物极必反的运动规律向反面转化。而代表中国主流传统的儒家文化，经过百年的消沉，开始被越来越多的人所认识，其走向复兴，已成为必然。

需要说明的是，走向复兴的儒学，已非传统意义上的儒学，它是在吸纳各种新的文化营养之后形成的一种新的文化形态。儒学是一个开放的文化思想系统，儒家学者的志向是要为天地立心，为生民立命。这种学说的意义指向，不在个人、家庭或集团，而在人类和自然万物；不在眼下，而在未来。受这种文化思想熏陶的学者，具有“守正”与“创新”的双重理想。为了保护人类文化的正脉，他们甘作卫道者；为了人类文化的发展，他们又会以开放的胸襟对待各种学说。在春秋时代，代表人类积累千年的文明成果——华夏文明，在野蛮民族的冲击下面临断绝时，孔子起而奋臂，作《春秋》，倡导“尊王攘夷”。“攘夷”目的在守护文化正脉。到战国末，终结这个时代的儒学大师荀子，则在对各家学说进行分析、批判的基础上，以儒家所承传的传统文化为主体，融百家于一炉，铸就了以礼制为核心的儒学新形态。在唐宋时期，文化的正脉再次遭到了异端学说的冲击——以不承担人生责任（包括人种繁衍）的“出家”行为

① 汤因比著，苟春生、朱继征、陈国樑译：《展望21世纪——汤因比与池田大作对话录》，国际文化出版公司，1985年，第294—295页。

② 汤因比：《谁将继承西方在世界的主导地位》，《思潮》1994年第9期。

③ 李瑞智、黎华伦著，范道丰译：《儒学的复兴》，商务印书馆，1995年，第3页。

为表现形态的释、道两家，从强调修行的角度，对儒家“修齐治平”的人生理想与治国理念，进行了颠覆性否定。理学的先驱者韩愈即开始视佛为“夷狄之法”，起而排之。而后期的理学家及理学的集大成者朱熹，则吸纳释道的心性理气学说于理学新体系之中，建构了儒学的新形态——理学。在现代史上，自称以儒家道统为思想基础的孙中山，“驱除鞑虏，恢复中华”的革命纲领，尚表现着强烈的华夷之辨的观念与民族主义情绪。而近几十年来的儒学发展，则是在全球视野下，废弃民族文化本位主义的立场，从人类文明发展的前景，来反省人与人、人与社会、人与自然的多重关系的，并沿着宋儒“民吾同胞，物吾与也”的精神，追求着人心、天道及万物的和谐。这一表现形态，完全消除了非此即彼的对立，而成为一切爱好和平、追求和谐人们的精神资源。

严格地说，现代复兴的不是儒学，而是以儒学为主干的中国传统文化，而其由开放的态势表现出的新形态，又可称作是“新国学”。根据前两次理性时代的历史推导，在近百年将会出现与荀子、朱熹同等影响力的思想巨人。这个思想巨人的思想，是在“新国学”的基础上，将各种有益于人类健康、幸福、快乐发展的文化融为一体，建构起来的思想大厦。

这样的思想巨人产生需要有两个方面的条件，第一是文化生态环境：只有在全开放的文化环境中，而且是在新的文化思想积累到一定程度、经过一定时间的孕育，思想巨人才能出现。从前两次思想巨人诞生的情况即可以看出，无论是战国还是宋代，都是一个全开放的、文化思想十分活跃的时期。各种思想可以自由发挥并相互碰撞有个过程。同时，其孕育期从大言之，需约三百年左右；从小言之，也需百余年。荀子的出现，若从孔子创立儒学算起，将近三百年；若从孟子算起，则是一百余年。朱熹的出现，若从韩愈提出“道”算起，约三百余年；若从公认的理学开山鼻祖周敦颐算起，则是一百余年。第三轮的历史循环呈现出了加速之势，这位融通中西优秀文化传统的思想巨人有可能会提早诞生，但若从魏源倡导向西方学习算起，恐怕少说也需要二百年以上；若从“三民主义”、“共产主义”在大陆兴起算起，少说也需一百五十年。因为时间短了，难以孕育成这样的大胚胎。由此推论，这位巨人的诞生当在本世纪中期以后。

第二是个人的素质与遭际：这样的思想巨人必然要有超人的天赋，经并过坎坷的人生遭遇。因为只有具备高旷的胸襟、超人的思辨能力，才有能力对积累到一定时期的文化思想做出全面的综合、分析，并由此而形成系统、完善的思想体系。如荀子、朱熹，都是这样的人物。开创理性时代需要天才，如孔子、孟子、韩愈、周敦颐等，结束这个时代也需要天才。朱熹其影响之大人所共知，连近代之前日本、韩国的思想界，都变成了朱子的天下。荀子则因宋儒的贬抑，近千年来人鲜知其能。但从荀子体大思精的思想体系与时人“孔子弗过”（《荀子·尧问》）的评价中可以看出，其思辨天赋确实是超人的。同时，只有经过逆境，才能对人生、对政治有更多的体悟和更深刻的认识。如荀子曾遭谗于齐人，遭废于楚人，政治上始终不得其遇；朱熹在当时也曾受到政治迫害，当权派诬蔑其学说为“伪学”，其人身也曾遭到种种诬陷。荀子与朱熹，皆在郁闷中死去。新的思想巨人，也当有相类的坎坷人生，方能发出震撼历史八百年的思想力量。尽管这个巨人的思想形态现在还不能知其全貌，但有一点可以肯定，近世从西方输入的科学、民主、自由、法制等等思想，皆会融入他以人类文化正脉 为主体的博大的思想体系之中。

# 儒学成人理念及其现代价值

四川师范大学　黄开国

中国传统文化是以儒学为主导以儒释道为主体包容诸子百家的文化系统。它所包含的价值、意义、信仰，对中国人的人格铸造，中华民族的民族精神、性格的形成，起到了深远的影响。中国之为中国，中国人之为中国人，不在地域、肤色、语言，而在中国文化。中国文化的根核则在儒学。儒学的创立者是春秋末年的孔子，用历代思想家的话来说，孔子的思想集古代圣王之大成，又有合于春秋时代发展的创新（孟子称孔子为“圣之时者”），中国古代以来有价值的文化精髓多为孔子所创立的儒学所继承，在其后的历史长河中，儒学又不断与时俱进，加入了不少有价值的思想文化因素。从孔子创立儒家学派以来，儒学在先秦是最有影响的显学，从汉代以来二千余年一直是官方尊奉的统治思想，在中国历史上对社会政治经济文化的发展起着重大作用，也对中国人社会生活的方方面面发生了最为深远的影响，其中的成人理念在今天的社会尤具有不可或缺的现实意义与重要价值。

## 一、礼义是儒学成人理念的核心

儒学可以用两个字来概括，这就是“人学”：或用四个字来概括，这就是“成人之学”。儒学千言万语，不外乎教人如何做一个高尚的人、做一个有道德的人，做一个对人民、社会有用的人才。儒学的典籍无论是五经，还是四书，儒学的学派无论是汉学，还是宋学，儒学的历代大师，无不以成人理念为其思想学说的核心。

基于人是不同于禽兽的类的人类自觉，这是儒学成人理念的出发点。人的本质是什么？人与禽兽的区别何在？人为什么贵于万物？生活在中国这块土地上的远古先哲，经过长期的思考，至少在春秋时期就已经对这个问题有了较为一致的看法。他们认为，人是不同于禽兽的类，人与禽兽的区别不在人有两足无毛这些自然生理方面，而在于人的社会属性，在于人有礼义。这就是荀子说的：“故人之所以为人者，非特以其二足而无毛也，以其有辨也。夫禽兽有行父子而无父子之亲，有牝牡而无男女之别，故人道莫不有辨。”[①] 所谓辩是指辨识、分辨，辨识、分辨本来属于认识论的问题，但荀子这里并不是或至少主要不是讲认识论问题，而是讲对父子之亲、夫妇之别的礼的分辨，是讲礼义的问题。这个问题是先秦儒学的最重要的问题，集先秦汉初儒学礼论之大成的《礼记》，在第一篇《曲礼》开首就说：“鹦鹉能言，不离飞鸟。猩猩能言，不离禽兽。今人而无礼，虽能言，不亦禽兽之心乎？夫唯禽兽无礼，故父子聚麀。是故圣人作，为礼以教人，使人以有礼，知自别于禽兽。”虽然《礼记》成书在西汉中期，但将这段话置于全书之首的这一编撰无疑是深得儒学大义的，体现了对人的认识，在儒学中的中心地位。此外，在《礼记》的《乐记》等篇以及《穀梁传》等典籍中都有类似论述。以礼义为人之为人的根本，是人贵于禽兽的所在，是儒学成人理念的最早得出的最重要内容，也是儒学成人理念的基石。一个中国人，不讲礼义，就失去了人之为人的根本。

礼义有外在的礼仪规范，还有由礼仪礼节外在规范所蕴含的道德、政治与文化意义，这就是礼义的内在价值。在两个方面，先秦的儒学大师最注重的是礼义的价值意义。孔子面对春秋时期礼崩乐坏，礼义的价值意义被践踏，而发出了：“礼云礼云，玉帛云乎哉？乐云乐云，钟鼓云乎哉？”[②] 的哀叹。以至孔子说：“不学礼，无以立。”[③] 以礼义道德为主要内容的礼是人安身立命的根本，也是人之为人的根据。孟子认为人之异于禽兽几稀，就在于有仁义礼智的四端，并以有无四端，作为人禽之分的根据。孟子以仁义礼智为善，故在人性论上持性善说。性善说是儒学发展史的最大意义，在于第一次系统的对人之为人这一重大问题，做出了人性论论证，奠定儒学关于人的本质规定的基调。孟子所确立的这一思想，成为后来儒学的最根本的理念，传统启蒙读物《三字经》开首就是孟子的性善说，绝非偶然。即使被认为在人性论上与孟子相对立的荀子，也是以礼义为人的本质。荀子说：“水火有气而无生，草木有生而无知，禽兽有知而无义，人有气、行生、行知，亦且有义，故最为天下贵也。”[④] “若其义，则不可须臾舍也。为之人也，舍之禽兽也。”[⑤] 荀子多次指斥不合礼义的行为是“禽兽之行”，[⑥] 以不修礼义的人“嫌于禽兽矣”，[⑦] “是禽兽之不若也”。[⑧] 这些儒学大师的论述都贯穿着以礼义为人之为人的本质的共同认识。而他们所说的礼义，并不在形式上遵循了礼义

① 《荀子·非相》，《四库全书》本，上海古籍出版社，1987 年。

② 《论语·阳贺篇》，《四库全书》本，上海古籍出版社，1987 年。

③ 《论语·季氏》，《四库全书》本，上海古籍出版社，1987 年。

④ 《荀子·王制》，《四库全书》本，上海古籍出版社，1987 年。

⑤ 《荀子·劝学》，《四库全书》本，上海古籍出版社，1987 年。

⑥ 《荀子·荣辱》，《四库全书》本，上海古籍出版社，1987 年。

⑦ 《荀子，礼论》，《四库全书》本，上海古籍出版社，1987 年。

⑧ 《荀子，礼论》，《四库全书》本，上海古籍出版社，1987 年。

的外在规范，而在于有无礼义的精神实质。按照儒学的这一观点，一个人只要没有礼义的精神实质，即使说得再冠冕堂皇，也不具备为人的资格的。那些满口仁义道德，表面上的谦谦君子，背地里却言行不一，专门做一些见不得人下三烂的肮脏勾当的人，被老百姓斥为衣冠禽兽，正是儒学成人理念对中国人精神影响的具体体现。

从生理说，古代以年满 18 岁即为成人。但如果不懂礼义，不按礼义的规定来行为，即使年满 18 岁，也不能称为成人，也不构成人的标准。儒学典籍关于古代冠礼的记载，就清楚地说明了这一点：

古者冠礼，筮日筮宾，所以敬冠事，敬冠事，所以重礼，重礼，所以为国本也。

故冠于阼，以著代也。醮于客位，三加弥尊，加有成也。已冠而字之，成人之道也。见于母，母拜之，见于兄弟，兄弟拜之，成人而与为礼也。玄冠玄端奠挚于君，遂以挚见于乡大夫乡先生，以成人见。成人之者，将责成人礼焉也。责成人礼焉者，将责为人子、为人弟、为人臣、为人少者之礼行焉。将责四者之行于人，其礼可不重与？

故孝弟忠顺之行立，而后可以为人，可以为人，而后可以治人也。故圣王重礼。故曰："冠者，礼之始也，嘉事之重者也。"是故古者重冠，重冠故行之于庙，行之于庙者，所以尊重事。尊重事而不敢擅重事，不敢擅重事，所以自卑而尊先祖也。[①]

在儒学看来，成人礼所以要庄重盛大，是因为在其中贯穿着对成人的礼的精神要求。当举行成人礼之后，能够以礼义的规定来规范自己的一言一行，才可以称之为成人。这一以礼义为成人的本质规定，是儒学的通识。而古代对礼的重视，正是因为礼义是成人必不可少的内在要求，这就是春秋时期子大叔说的："礼，上下之纪，天地之经纬也，民之所以生也，是以先王尚之。故人之能自曲直以赴礼者，谓之成人。大，不亦宜乎？"[②]

## 二、成人理念的丰富内涵

儒学的成人，以礼义为成人之本，主要是就道德而言。但儒学讲的成人，绝不是仅仅是道德的人格，而是具有丰富的内容。《论语·宪问》第十二章载：

子路问成人。

子曰："若藏武仲之知，公绰之不欲，卞庄子之勇，冉求之艺，文之以礼乐，亦可以为成人矣。"

朱熹在《四书章句集注》中疏解此章说："言兼此四子之长，则知足以穷理，廉足

---

① 《礼记·礼器第十》，《四库全书》本，上海古籍出版社，1987 年。

② 《左传》昭公 24 年，《四库全书》本，上海古籍出版社，1987 年。

以养心，勇足以力行，艺足以泛应，而又节之以礼，和之以乐，使德成于内，而文见乎外。则材全德备，浑然不见一善成名之迹；中正和乐，猝然无复偏倚驳杂之蔽，而其为人也亦成矣。然亦之为言，非其至者，盖就子路之所可及而语之也。若论其至，则非圣人之尽人道，不足以语此。”也就是说，即使依照较低的标准来看，儒学所说成人也是具有多方面内在要求的：智慧、寡欲、勇敢、多才多艺、精通礼乐，无一缺少，涉及人的智能、人品、性格、才艺、政治、道德、音乐多方面的素养。用今天的话来讲，成人应该是一个在德、智、体、美诸方面全面发展的人。

荀子用“全”与“粹”二个特点，作为“成人”的要求。他说：

君子知夫不全不粹之不足以为美，故诵数以贯之，思索以通之，为其人以处之，除其害者以持养之，使目非是无欲见也，使耳非是无欲闻也，使口非是无欲言也，使心非是无欲虑也。及至其致好之也，目好之五色，耳好之五声，口好之五味，心利之有天下。是故权利不能倾也，群众不能移也，天下不能荡也。生乎由定，死乎由是，夫是之谓德操。德操然后能定，能定然后能应，能定能应，夫是之谓成人。①

这是《劝学篇》的最后一段话。荀子以人性恶，与禽兽无异，主张通过学习《诗》、《书》、《春秋》诸经，特别是学礼，使人性由恶变为美。而人性美即人之成人的标识，这标识又由人的视、听、言、虑等表现出来，人唯有在四个方面完全合于诸经与礼的规范，且纯粹无驳，具有“全”与“粹”的两个特点，并能在任何条件下自觉地坚守这一德操，才是合于美的要求，可以称为“成人”。荀子的“成人”观念，包含对典籍文献知识的学习，社会典章制度与人际交往礼仪规范的熟习，一心造福天下万民的追求等等，他将“全”与“粹”作为这诸方面的内行要求，以“全”与“粹”的统一才可称之为美，这说明荀子的“成人”，乃是一种完美无瑕的人格，极富美学的意义。它与孔子讲的成人应是德、智、体、美的全面发展人格一样，都是讲的一种至高至大的理想人格。讲“成人”，重在这种理想人格，是儒家“成人”理念的重要特点。

有礼义主要是讲成人的有别于禽兽，而以“全”与“粹”的完善统一才可称为成人，表明儒家所讲的成人，是一个有层次的多极观念。在这个观念中，儒家设定了不同层次的成人人格，如庶君子、贤人、圣人等等，历代儒家对此有相关的大量论说。这些成人人格各有许多规定，难以一一细论，其中论说得最多的是君子与圣人这两种成人人格。

君子是儒家所讲的成人的现实人格的主要体现。它在成人的层次上，是高于仅别于禽兽的人，又不如贤人、圣人的人格，它是经过人在现实社会的努力就可以达到的境界。所以，孔子在讲了成人的理想人格之后说：“今之成人者何必然？见利思义，见

① 《荀子·劝学篇》，《四库全书》本，上海古籍出版社，1987年。

危授命，久要不忘平生之言，亦可以为成人矣。”。[①] 从历代儒家关于君子人格的论说中，可知君子绝非一般能行礼义的成人，而是现实社会中成人的优秀楷模。根据历代儒学家与儒学经典关于君子的论述，儒学的君子人格具有如下五个特征：其一，广博的仁爱之心；其二，执著的道义追求；其三，高度的道德自觉；其四，宽容的待人胸怀；其五，豁达的人生态度。儒家看来，这种君子人格只要人努力去追求，就完全可以实现，因此，它是任何社会都可以见到的现实人格。

儒家以君子为成人的现实人格代表，这就给一般人的成人追求提供了一个可见的参照，历代儒家大师大谈特谈君子人格，就是要人们知道君子是人经过努力都可能达到的境界，从而，使人对成就君子这一成人模范人格充满信心，以形成人人争做君子的社会风尚。

圣人则是儒家成人观念中的最高理想人格。孔子说：“圣人，吾不得而见之矣，得见君子。”[②] 孟子说：“圣人，人伦之至也。”[③] 荀子说：“积善而全尽谓之圣人。”董仲舒说圣人的“至德巍巍乎不可加矣”。[④] 都是讲圣人在道德方面的完美无加。君子是现实中的成人理想人格，故可以看到。圣人则是成人的最高理想人格，所以，在现实社会中是看不见的。但是，若无这一至高至大至善的成人理想人格，成人的追求就不会完美，就有所止境，圣人又不可得见，于是，儒家就将已经过去了的历史人物予以美化，说尧、舜、禹、汤、文、武、周公如何完美并称为圣人，后儒则在周公之后，加上被儒学神圣化的孔子，构成一个至孔子而终后世无继的圣人系列。更少到西汉时，儒家所讲的圣人部不是单一的道德人格，而是内圣外王的统一。一方面，圣人是具有至高德性的完美人格，是整个社会的道德完美楷模；另一方面，圣人又是外王的最高境界，是能够造福万民，为人民带来全面而满足福祉的领袖。

儒家的圣人人格，淋漓尽致地表现了儒家心目中的理想人格，尽管这一人格并非现实的而是理想主义的，但它却在儒家成人观念中具有极大的意义。正是有了尽善尽美的圣人作为成人的最高楷模，才使儒家的成人理念成为没有止境的无限追求，人们才不会以现实的君子为满足，而不断向成人的极致作无尽的奋发努力。

## 三、儒学道德主体自觉论

儒学关于成人的规定，是要为实现成为一个有道德的人，成为对全社会有用的人，

---

① 《论语·宪问》,《四库全书》本，上海古籍出版社，1987 年。
② 《论语·述而》,《四库全书》本，上海古籍出版社，1987 年。
③ 《孟子·离娄上》,《四库全书》本，上海古籍出版社，1987 年。
④ 《春秋繁露·顺命》,《四库全书》本，上海古籍出版社，1987 年。

成为能够造福于天下人民的人，提供一个目标。如何实现这一目标，是儒学成人理念最为重要的内容。围绕着成人目标的实现，儒学提出了道德主体自觉论，以保障成人目标的顺利实现。这一道德主体自觉论，是儒学成人理论的最重要内容。在1994年举行的国际儒学联合会暨国际儒学联合会成立大会上，我提交的论文就是以“道德主体自觉论”来解读先秦儒学，以孔子、孟子、荀子的思想都以道德主体自觉为中心，《大学》、《中庸》则是儒学道德主体自觉论的完成。[①] 儒学强调道德主体自觉，目的是实现儒学的成人理想，而道德主体自觉则是实现成人目标的不二法门。

儒学道德主体自觉论在以道德为人之本的基础上，肯定人人皆具道德自觉的能力。人是否具有道德能力，是对人进行道德要求的基本前提。对此，孔子、孟子、荀子都一无例外地承认，每个人都有行使道德的主观能力。孔子说：“仁远乎哉？我欲仁，斯仁至矣。”[②]“为仁由己，而由人乎哉？”又说：“欲仁得仁。”[③] 在孔子的思想中，仁是总括道德的概念，几乎是道德的同义语。孔子的这些论述明确肯定了道德主体的“我”、“己”具有践履道德的能力。孔子还有一著名命题：“人能弘道，非道弘人。”[④] 道是行仁之路，是以道德为重要内容的，这同样是对人的道德能力的肯定。孟子对道德主体的道德能力的认定、论说最有理据。他在与梁惠王答问时，曾反复用譬喻来证明这一点，他辨析不忍之心的运用扩大，犹如折枝一样容易，是人人都能够做到的，而非挟泰山超北海那样力所不能。人未能扩充不忍之心，乃是因为自己不为，而不是不能。从而，就通过不能与不为的分别，论证了人实行道德的能力，不存在有无的问题，它是每一个人都具有的，区别只在于为与不为，即有无主观自觉性的问题。同时。孟子还用人们见小孩落井，都会自然忍不住要去打救的著名例证，有力地论证了人的道德能力是天生的内在本能，不需任何外在的原因，而自然地在那里发生作用。荀子讲人性恶，但也承认，人在后天经圣王教化，化性起伪，仍可获得道德的能力，并将其转化为人的内在要素。甚至认为，只要自我不断努力道德修养，同样可以成为圣人，所谓“一自善也，谓之圣人”。[⑤] 重视自身在道德修养中的作用，是儒学道德主体自觉论的第一要义，并由此形成了儒学的“求诸己”思想。孔子说：“不患莫己知，求为可知

---

① 参见拙著：《儒家道德主体论与21世纪个人道德修养》，《纪念孔子诞生2545周年国际儒学研讨会文集》，华夏出版社，1996年。

② 《论语·述而》，《四库全书》本，上海古籍出版社，1987年。

③ 《论语·尧曰》，《四库全书》本，上海古籍出版社，1987年。

④ 《论语·卫灵公》，《四库全书》本，上海古籍出版社，1987年。

⑤ 《荀子·君子》，《四库全书》本，上海古籍出版社，1987年。

也。”[①]“不患人之不己知，患其不能也。”[②]“君子病无能焉，不病人之不己知也。”[③] 重要的不在别人如何看，而在自己的道德修行。孟子说：“口之于味也，目之于色也，耳之于声也，鼻之于臭也，四肢之于安佚也，性也。有命焉，君子不谓性也。仁之于父子也，义之于君臣也，礼之于宾主也，知之于贤者也，圣人之于天道也，命也。有性焉，君子不谓命也。”[④] 孟子的这一著名的性命之辩，反对人对外在食色、富贵的名利追求，强调人自身的善端的扩充与道德的修养，是先秦儒学“求诸己”的精炼说明。孟子在儒学史上明确提出“身为本”的论点：“天下之本在国，国之本在家，家之本在身。君子之守，修其身而天下平。”[⑤] 这里不仅进一步论证了孔子的思想，而且直接开启了《大学》“修身为本”的观念，在儒学道德主体自觉论的发展中有着重大意义。

孔、孟、荀还提出了保证“求诸己”的自我道德修养的诸种方法。孔子有“忠恕之道”，其弟子曾子有“三省吾身”，孟子有“诚身”，荀子有“正身”，各有各的特色。曾子曾用“忠恕”二字，来作为贯穿孔子整个思想的概括。所谓忠与恕是有区别的，孔子对“恕”作过明确回答：

子贡问曰：“有一言而可以终身行之者乎？”

子曰：“其恕乎！己所不欲，勿施于人。”[⑥]

《论语·颜渊》载，仲弓问仁，孔子回答也有“己所不欲，勿施于人”之语。由此看来，恕乃是行仁之方，很为孔子所看重。“忠”是什么，孔子却无明说，一些学者认为就是孔子所说的：“己欲立而立人，己欲达而达人。”[⑦] 如此说不错，则孔子的忠恕之道乃是行仁的两种方法。忠是积极的修养方法，恕则是消极的修养办法。而忠与恕都强调一个“欲”字，欲不仅是主观动机，更是主观能动性，它必须合于仁的精神才是正当的。所以，“欲”与“不欲”都不是随心所欲，而是贯注着仁的自觉精神。忠恕之道的出发点是己，对象是人，可称为由己以推人的修养方法。孔子另有“思齐”与“内省”两种修养方法：“见贤思齐焉，见不贤而内省也。”[⑧] 看到贤的人，就向他看齐；看到不贤的人，就反省自己有没有人家的毛病。二者都是有见于人，再反于己，可看作由人及己的修养方法。而思齐重在向善，内省偏于改过。其中内省一法为曾子所笃行，而发展为“三省吾身”。曾子说：“吾日三省吾身：为人谋，而不忠乎？与朋友交，

---

① 《论语·里仁》，《四库全书》本，上海古籍出版社，1987 年。

② 《论语·宪问》，《四库全书》本，上海古籍出版社，1987 年。

③ 《论语·卫灵公》，《四库全书》本，上海古籍出版社，1987 年。

④ 《孟子·尽心下》，《四库全书》本，上海古籍出版社，1987 年。

⑤ 《孟子·离娄下》，《四库全书》本，上海古籍出版社，1987 年。

⑥ 《论语·里仁》，《四库全书》本，上海古籍出版社，1987 年。

⑦ 《论语·雍也》，《四库全书》本，上海古籍出版社，1987 年。

⑧ 《论语·里仁》，《四库全书》本，上海古籍出版社，1987 年。

而不信乎？传不习乎？’”①“三省”的内容都是就其改过而言，基本上是孔子内省法同一方向的具体化。

孟子对人的道德修养，讲求扩充善端，养浩然之气，求其放心等等，都可统摄于诚身。他说：“诚身有道，不明乎善，不诚其身矣。是故诚者，天之道也。思诚者，人之道也。至诚而不动者，未之有也；不诚，未有能动者也。”②诚身将诚与身合在一起，对道德的主体自觉精神作了最好的表达。其后，《中庸》的诚的学说，即肇端于此。诚的修养方法亦为荀子所讲。但荀子更进了一步，由孟子的“诚身”变为了“诚心”，他说：“君子养心莫善乎诚，致诚则无它事矣。唯仁之为守，唯义之为行，则心守仁则形，形则神，神则化矣。”③ 心为身之内，身之主，所以，讲求诚心较诚身，是对道德主体内在精神的深化追求，更注重道德主体的自觉精神。顺着诚心，荀子在后文又提出了“慎独”说：“夫此顺命，以慎其独者也；善之为道者，不诚则不独，不独则不形。”④诚则正，故从诚心很容易推出正心，而正心为后来《大学》八目之一，慎独则为《大学》、《中庸》所同有，所以，荀子的诚的修养观念不仅与《大学》，而且与《中庸》都有着理论上的联系。诚是成人的最重要保障，关于这一点，宋儒王开祖说：“诚者，成也，所以成人也。人而不诚，禽兽奚择焉。君子处则其身安。出则其道尊。无他，不欺而已矣。……夫诚者，微也。诚于心，人莫之见也，接于物亦莫之见也，由人服而物化之，然后见焉，及其至也，充乎天地之大，此其著可知也矣。”⑤

孔、孟、荀的“求诸己”，与其保证的各种修养方法，都贯注着自觉的精神。这种道德自觉精神不仅是对道德的理性认知，而且是一种发自内心的自觉行动。因其是发自内心的自觉活动，所以，它在人的行为中时时处处都表现出来。孔子说：“君子无终食之间违仁，造次必于是，颠沛必于是。”⑥荀子说：“君子无日不在是”，“非礼不进，非义不受。”⑦ 即使在极其丰厚的物欲引诱时，与遇到生命受到威胁的两种极端情形，有着道德自觉精神的人，也能不为利动，不惧威胁，而坚定自己的道德操守。荀子说：“义之所在，不倾于权，不顾其利，举国而与之不为视。”⑧ 又说：“行一不义，杀一无罪，而得天下，仁者不为也。”⑨从正面讲，有道德自觉精神的人信守道义，决不会因

---

① 《论语·学而》，《四库全书》本，上海古籍出版社，1987年。
② 《孟子·离娄上》，《四库全书》本，上海古籍出版社，1987年。
③ 《荀子·不苟》，《四库全书》本，上海古籍出版社，1987年。
④ 《荀子·不苟》，《四库全书》本，上海古籍出版社，1987年。
⑤ 王开祖：《儒志编》，《四库全书》本，上海古籍出版社，1987年。
⑥ 《论语·里仁》，《四库全书》本，上海古籍出版社，1987年。
⑦ 《荀子·大略》，《四库全书》本，上海古籍出版社，1987年。
⑧ 《荀子·荣辱》，《四库全书》本，上海古籍出版社，1987年。
⑨ 《荀子·王霸》，《四库全书》本，上海古籍出版社，1987年。

任何物欲的诱惑而改变；从反面讲，做一件不道德的事，就可得到天下，有道德自觉精神的也绝不会去做。而当道德与生命之间，二者必择其一时，有道德自觉精神的人，也会慨然“有杀身以成仁”,[①]“舍生取义”[②]之举。由人的道德自觉精神所生发的这种价值取向，对中华人的气节培养有着深远而重大的影响。许多民族英雄能够为了国家、民族大义舍生取义，大义凛然，不为利动，就得益于儒学的这一观念的熏陶。

人有道德自觉精神，就能在任何情况下矢志道德，这是因为道德自觉精神的实现，在孔、孟、荀来，不仅是一种伟大的勇敢精神，而且也是人生的最大快乐。孔子说：“三军可夺帅也，匹夫不可夺志也。”[③]又说：“当仁不让于师。”[④]孟子讲的大丈夫“富贵不能淫，贫贱不能移，威武不能屈”；荀子在《强国篇》论三威，在《性恶篇》论三勇，皆分三个等次，而无不以道德之威、道德之勇为上，并用“块然而独立于天地之间”来形容。都是对道德自觉精神所体现出的大无畏勇敢的论说。

道德的自觉又是人生的真正乐趣所在。孔子以为，君子是不存在忧患的，就是“饭疏食饮水，曲肱而枕之”，只要自觉躬行道德，“乐亦在其中矣”。[⑤]并且，还塑造了颜渊这样一个苦中得乐的典范，孔子说他“一箪食，一瓢饮，在陋巷，人不堪其忧，回也不改其乐”。[⑥]孔子弟子三千，高足七十，但孔门四科，以德行为第一，而以颜渊列第一，颜渊这种安贫乐道、达观自信的处世态度与人生境界，与孔子的人生境界，被后世儒学誉为“孔颜乐处”，成为人格理想与道德境界所热衷讨论的命题，被汉、宋以来的儒学大师奉为最高的人格理想与道德境界。孟子亦说：“反身而诚，乐莫大焉，”“尊德乐义，则可嚣嚣矣。”[⑦]自觉躬行道德就是人生的最大快乐。由自觉践行道德而带来的人生快乐与勇敢精神，又反过来加强了人的道德自觉力量，从而，使人时时处处自觉恪守道德，成为一种不为任何威胁、利诱所动摇的巨大精神力量。人能达到这一点，也就可以使自己逐渐成为道德的理想人格了，成就成人的理想。

在儒学看来，只有信奉道德主体自觉，才可以成为高尚的有道德的人，也才能够称之为成人。若不明成人知道，人就不会成其为人，还会一生陷入愚蠢无知的境地，朱熹说：“故徃往自幼至长，愚騃如一，由不知成人之道故也。”[⑧]

---

① 《论语·卫灵公》,《四库全书》本，上海古籍出版社，1987年。
② 《孟子·告子上》,《四库全书》本，上海古籍出版社，1987年。
③ 《论语·子罕》,《四库全书》本，上海古籍出版社，1987年。
④ 《论语·卫灵公》,《四库全书》本，上海古籍出版社，1987年。
⑤ 《论语·述而》,《四库全书》本，上海古籍出版社，1987年。
⑥ 《论语·雍也》,《四库全书》本，上海古籍出版社，1987年。
⑦ 《孟子·尽心上》,《四库全书》本，上海古籍出版社，1987年。
⑧ 朱熹：《小学集注》卷五，《四库全书》本，上海古籍出版社，1987年。

## 四、儒学成人理念的当代价值

儒学的成人理念，在中国历史发展长河中，对中国人形成重视道德修养，以讲道德为荣，不讲道德为耻的社会风气，养成中国人重义不重利，舍生取义等精神品格与价值追求，起到了积极的作用。中国人能够成为知书达礼的文明人，在很大程度上得益于儒学的成人理念。尽管儒学从近代以来，就遭遇到被冷落、被否定、被批判的命运，但只要人类存在，就存在儒学所说的成人问题，儒学的成人理念就有存在的价值。在当今社会中，儒学所说的成人理念依然是一个具有现实价值的宝贵理论。

在近两百年的时间里，我们对传统文化不正确过多否定，儒学被视为封建糟粕，受到长期的批判。尤其是最近几十年，随着中国的经济发展，西方文化价值观的冲击，传统文化中有价值的东西又没有理直气壮得到提倡，使传统文化中儒学成人理念这一极有价值的思想得不到承认，甚至被人遗忘。儒学以道德为人之本的思想，被许多人抛到脑后，道德主体自觉更无从谈起，面对物欲横流的社会现实，中国人的道德急剧堕落失滑，在很多人的眼中，只有对金钱、地位、权势的贪婪，没有一点道德羞耻心，没有一点社会的责任心，揭发出来的贪官贪污腐化，动辄数千万、数亿元，几乎都有包养数名甚至二位数情妇的肮脏记录，官员的不雅照时有泄露；在全国多地发生了多起本为教书育人的“人类灵魂”工程师奸污学生甚至幼女的令人心痛的丑剧，高等学府的中被揭发证明是白天教授夜晚禽兽的伪君子大有人在，应为白衣天使的个别医务人员也堕落为贩卖婴儿的人贩子；有的地方卖淫泛滥，制毒贩毒成灾；各个领域、各个行业假冒伪劣充斥，制假造假充斥生活衣食住行的方方面面，假酒、假药、毒大米、毒奶粉事件，不绝于耳；欺诈的传销骗局，你方唱罢我登场，不断上演；许多人不以为耻，反以为荣，只要有钱，什么道德人格都抛到一边，道德的失落成为中国当代的一大社会公害。

这固然有多方面的原因，但儒学成人理念被遗忘，应该是一个重要原因。如果现代的中国人尤其是年轻人，能够懂得一点儒学的成人理念，知道一点儒学道德主体自觉论，知晓道德是为人的根本，从而，自觉的践行道德自律，以作有道德的君子为荣，无道德的小人为耻，许多不道德的事件就可以从根本上避免，不道德的雾霾就将在礼义之邦的中国被清扫，我们的社会才会变得更加美好起来。倘若我们没有对现存社会不讲道德泛滥的反思，进行有力的矫正，对整个民族都将是灭顶之灾，而这一灭顶之灾较之近代西方的入侵的危害，只有过之而无不及。因为，对道德的崇敬，一直是中国人的精神支柱。西方入侵，可以在军事、科技等打败中国，但打不垮中国人的精神。而道德的失落，将导致中国人精神家园的失落，这才是最可怕的根本丧失。所以，在当今社会理直气壮地提倡儒学的成人理念，肯定儒学道德主体自觉论的价值，对儒学研究者是一项十分急迫而极其重要的义不容辞的义务。儒学研究者不仅要宣扬更要践行对道德的重视，而不要做满口仁义道德一肚子男盗女娼的伪君子。

# 儒家人生观及其现代价值

安徽大学　解光宇

儒家文化博大精深，而儒家的人生观又是儒学的重要内容之一。探讨儒家的人生观以及修养观、人际观，吸取其中的精华，对于我们个人的心性修养、人格的塑造以及人生观的培养，都有很好的借鉴作用。

## 一、“内圣外王”的人生观

人生观是指对人生的目的、意义和价值等看法和态度的总和。儒家的人生观是什么？儒家强调入世，强调进取，强调对社会民族担当责任的意识，所以，“自强不息”是儒家人生观的重要特征。儒家的这种人生观在不同的历史阶段有不同的表述，如在先秦为“内圣外王”的人生观；而北宋的理学家张载的“四句教”，更是将儒家的担当意识发挥得淋漓尽致，即“为天地立心，为生民立命，为往圣继绝学，为万世开太平”。张载的“四句教”是对“内圣外王”人生观的具体化。

那么，如何理解“内圣外王”呢？

“内圣外王”是儒家为人生确立了根本的方向。“内圣”即内在的知识修养和道德修养达到了较高的境界，也就是我们常说的一个有道德的人，一个高尚的人，综合素质比较高；“外王”即是用知识和道德报效国家，服务社会，也就是我们现代意义上的为人民服务。

“内圣外王”的思想原出自于儒家的经典《大学》。《大学》所提出的“三纲八目”，集中表述了儒家内圣外王的人生观。《大学》一开篇提出“三纲”，即明德、新民、至善：“大学之道，在明明德，在新民，在止于至善”。所谓“八目”，就是为了实现“三纲”所确立的具体步骤。“八目”即“格物、致知、诚意、正心、修身、齐家、治国、平天下。”一般又把“八目”分为两大方面，即“格物、致知、诚意、正心、修身”为自我内在的修养工夫，也就是“内圣”工夫；“齐家、治国、平天下”为外在的实践工夫，即服务社会，报效国家，也就是“外王”的工夫。“八目”后来简化为我们常说的

"修身、齐家、治国、平天下"，就是"修、齐、治、平"。"治国、平天下"是儒家外在努力的最高目标。这个目标的提出，应与春秋战国时代整个中国的政局有关。因为这个时代中国诸侯国林立，周王朝名存实亡，中国面临分裂。而儒家一贯主张中国的大一统，所以，维护中华民族统一的"治国、平天下"，就成为儒家外在努力的最高目标。

"三纲"和"八目"构成了一个有机的逻辑整体。"三纲"是最高境界，"八目"是具体实现步骤。"三纲"、"八目"以精练的语言揭示了儒家思想丰富的精神内涵，以及儒家理想人格修行和作为的整个过程，形成了一个由"内圣"到"外王"的缜密思想体系，展示了儒家服务社会、报效国家的远大志向和宏伟抱负。孔子所说的"修己以安人"，"修己以安百姓"，就是"内圣外王"之道，其中"修己"是"内圣"，"安百姓"是"外王"。"圣"是理想人格的最高境界，达到这一境界的就是"圣人"。只有"内圣"，才能成就"外王"的事业。"内圣"与"外王"互为表里，相辅相成，二者应是统一的。这种"外王"事业，以"博施济众"为极致，孔子将它树立为儒家的最高政治理想。

儒家"内圣外王"的人生观，体现了个人与社会、自我价值与社会价值的高度统一。儒家很重视人的社会本性，个人不脱离社会群体而生存。而要生存，就必须处理好个人与社会的关系。儒家"内圣外王"的人生观，正是建立在个人与社会关系的基础上。个人生存的意义乃是个人价值与社会价值的统一，自我满足与满足社会的统一。孔子说："夫人者，己欲立而立人，己欲达而达人"。己立、己达是起点，立人、达人是归宿，满足自己也要满足他人才是仁者情怀。人的价值与社会的价值在本质上是统一的，人的个人价值只有转化为社会价值，才有意义，也就是说，社会价值的实现也就是人的自我价值的实现。

儒家"内圣外王"的人生观，不仅对中华民族精神的形成与发展产生了巨大的推动作用，而且对我们今天塑造理想人格以及培育良好的个人修养有着重要的借鉴意义。

"内圣"即是进行道德修养，成就圣贤人格，形成正确的人生观、世界观和价值观。养成高尚的道德人格是做人的根本，是建功立业的条件。"外王"则是从事道德实践以建功立业。"内圣外王"就是正己才能正人，修己才能修人。一个道德高尚的人必然会感染他人、教育他人，激发起他人内心的道德意识，进而使他人自觉或不自觉地向往、学习、效法。如果人人都注重个人修养，起榜样示范作用，就会带动周围人相互学习，从而改善不良的社会风气。

儒家"内圣外王"就是提倡"忧国忧民"的忧患意识和献身精神。儒家的忧患意识表现出一种爱国情怀，是"天下兴亡，匹夫有责"的强烈的责任感与捍卫民族尊严、维护祖国利益的崇高品德，表现在行动上就是奉献精神。学习儒家的忧患意识和献身精神，使我们主动把自我与社会责任、义务联系起来，处处以大局和国家民族为重，激发爱国情怀。

诚然，“内圣外王”的人格模式并非十全十美，而是存在着内在的矛盾：在道德理想上要求“内圣”与“外王”统一，而在现实生活中二者往往又是相互分离的。即“内圣”未必能够“外王”，“外王”也未必就是“内圣”。当然，这主要从狭义的“外王”上所说的。但不容否认，这种人生观的理想人格、价值取向是积极的、有意义的，是中华民族文化的主体精神。尤其是其中自强不息、积极有为、以天下为己任的使命感和责任感，以及“国家兴亡，匹夫有责”的博大精神，更是中华民族精神不可分割的一部分。中国历代知识分子常常以“穷则独善其身，达则兼济天下”、“乐以天下，忧以天下”来激励自己，这和“内圣外王”的人生观思想是一致。就是在现代，这一思想体系仍然有其积极的成分，仍能为我们所借鉴。它所提出的知识的学习和道德的修养，以及“治国、平天下”的人生目标，要求我们既要有较强的知识才能，又要有较高的道德修养，更要有胸怀祖国的远大目标。为了这样的目标而去奋斗，就是一个高尚的人，一个有纯粹有道德的人，一个有远大抱负的人。在推进中华民族伟大复兴的今天，我们对于这一传统的理想人格模式应加以吸收和改造，使其在培育和弘扬当代中华民族精神的过程中发挥其积极作用。

## 二、“性善论”的修养观

《三字经》开宗就是“人之初，性本善”，就是说，“性善论”是儒家人性学说的主流，影响很大。从整个儒家人性发展史中可见，儒家主张人性善。人性虽善，人也有情，情有善有恶，所以，对不善的情要加以教化，才能成为贤人、圣人。儒家的性善学说以及性情关系说，为我们的道德修养和教化方面，提供了宝贵的理论财富。

我国古代的人性问题首先是孔子提出的。孔子虽然提出“性相近也，习相远也”的命题，但没有系统地论述。而孟子明确提出“性善说”，并且作了系统地论述，从而成为中国人性学说的主干。

“孟子道性善，言必称尧舜”，性善论是孟子整个思想的基础。孟子在与告子争论中阐述人性善的思想。

告子认为人性无所谓善或不善。孟子认为，人性之善就像水之就下，虽然也可以把水引上山，但向上却不是水的本性。所以孟子认为善是人性的表现。

孟子虽然主张人性善，但这种善并不是说人人天生就是善人，而只是“善端”，是善的萌芽，需要培养、扩充。孟子把恻隐之心、羞恶之心、辞让之心、是非之心称为仁、义、礼、智四端，“仁、义、礼、智根于心”，“非由外铄我也，我固有之”。所以，要培养“四端”、“扩而充之”，才能显示善性。

由于仁、义、礼、智四端是“我固有之”，那么，其表现为“良能”、“良知”。所谓“良知”、“良能”像“四端”一样也是天生就有的。

孟子虽然强调人的本性中有“善端”、“良知”、“良能”，但不是说人生来就是有完善的道德。社会上的人确实有不善的。不善者就是没有很好培养“善端”。人能否培养和扩充自己的“善端”，主要取决于自身的主观愿望和努力。所以向善者取决于主观的“心”，即要养心，养心才能培养、扩充“善端”。

如何“养心”？孟子以为“养心莫善于寡欲”，因为追求过多的物质欲望会使人失去善性，故孟子反对“求利”和“多欲”，以“寡欲”为养心的主要内容。

如果不能“寡欲”而丧失善性，就应努力把它找回来，恢复善之本性，这就是所谓的“求放心”。心官能思，通过思维的明辨，便能克制物欲以存善性。所以他强调要先把心中固有的“善”树立起来，以防感官因“蔽于物”而夺走善性。

孟子的“性善说”是儒家人性学说发展的逻辑起点。虽然后继者大部分都继承“性善”思想，但在论述“情”的方面发展了“性恶”的思想。中国哲学史上人性善恶争论的过程，实质上是“性”与“情”这对范畴发展和演变的过程。

孟子虽然没有提出“情”的概念，但在论述性时透露出关于“情”的思想。他从人性善出发，认为人皆有“恻隐之心”、“辞让之心”、“羞恶之心”和“是非之心”，这“四端”就是仁义礼智，恻隐、羞恶，是非与辞让就是“情”。既然人性是善的，那么情也善。

荀子首次明确地提出“情”的概念。荀子说：“性者，天之就也；情者，性之质也；欲者情之应也。”荀子把性、情、欲三者联系在一起，认为情欲是性的表现。“情”表现在哪些方面呢？荀子提出“六情说”：“性之好、恶、喜、怒、哀、乐谓之情。”特别是“好”，往往表现为恶的欲望，即所谓“目好色，耳好声，口好味，心好利，骨体肤理好愉佚”，就是说人“生而好利焉”，“生而有耳目之欲，有好声色焉”，如果“从人之性，顺人之情，必出于争夺，合于犯分乱理而归于暴”，因此，人性恶其表现的情欲也恶。

董仲舒的“性仁情贪，性有三品”，明显具有调和性的善恶色彩。他认为，人一生下来就具有“性”和“情”：“身之有性情也，若天之有阴阳也。言人之质而无其情，犹言天之阳而无其阴也”。董仲舒“性仁情贪”观点：“身之名取诸天，天两，有阴阳之施；身亦两，有贪仁之性。”就是说天有阴阳，表现在人性上也有阴阳两种属性，即性是阳的体现，其属性为“仁”，情是阴的体现，其属性为“贪”，这就是所谓“性仁情贪”。所以他认为孟子的性善说有缺陷，“谓性已善，奈其情何?”，也不同意荀子性情皆恶的观点，认为情虽然恶，但是性“仁”，恶的情最终要受到性的控制。他根据人所禀受情欲的多少而划分了三种人性，第一类是情欲极少的“圣人之性”；第二类是情欲极多的“斗筲之性”；第三类是仁贪对半、可以为善也可以为恶的“中民之性”。

董仲舒“性三品”的提出，理论上旨在调和性善和性恶、性与情的矛盾。唐代的韩愈、李翱在此基础上加以发挥，使之更加精致。

韩愈认为，不能把性和情截然分开，应该将性与情并提。他说：“性也者，与生俱生也。情也者，接于物而生也。”并且指出性的内容有五，即仁义礼智信；情的内容有七，即喜怒哀惧爱恶欲。韩愈在论述性情的基础上，把人性也分为上中下三品：“性之品有上中下三，上焉者，善焉而已矣；中焉者，可导而上下也；下焉者，恶焉而已矣。”性有三品，性情相应，情也依附而分为三种，即上品的性必发为上品的情，它基本上符合五德；中品的性必发为中品的情，它于五德虽然有违背或不足，但其中包含有合乎五德的地方；下品的性则必发为下品的情，它从本质上是与五德相违背的。性与情一一对应，二者紧密相连。韩愈性情相关联的思想则是对董仲舒割裂性情关系的修正，为宋明理学家的“天命之性”和“气禀之性”做理论上的准备。

朱熹曾就古代人性学说作评说，认为大都不得要领，仅有韩愈的“性三品”说“却是说得稍近”。然而朱熹又说韩愈的“性三品”说尚有不尽之言：“韩退之原性中说三品，说得也是，但不曾分明说是气质之性耳”，“盖人之所以有万殊不齐，只缘气禀不同”。如此看来，“气禀之性”对于解决人性问题的争端非常重要。

如果说“气禀之性”是人性学说发展过程中的一个重要纽结，那么，是程颢系起了这颗纽结。程颢在坚持孟子“性善说”的基础上，把人性理论推向一个新的高峰。程颢说：

“人生气禀，理有善恶，然不是性中元有两物相对而生也。有自幼而善，有自幼而恶，是气禀有然也。善固性也，然恶亦不可不谓之性也。……皆水也，有流而至海，终无所污，此何烦人力之为也。有流而未远，固已渐浊；有出而甚远，方有所浊；有浊之多者，有浊之少者，清浊虽不同，然不可以浊者不为水也。如此则人不可以不加澄治之功。故用力敏勇则疾清，用力缓怠则迟清。及其清也，则却只是元初水也。不是将清来换却浊，亦不是取出浊来置在一隅也。水之清则性善之谓也。故不是善与恶在性中为两物相对，各自出来。”

这段论述主要贡献在于从“气禀之性”逻辑地推导出加强道德教化的“澄治之功”。“澄治之功”实质上就是强调伦理纲常教育的重要性。

王彦霖以为：“人之为善，须是他自肯为时，方有所得，亦难强。”曰：“此言虽是，人须是自为善，然又不可为如此却都不管他，盖有教矣，‘修道之谓教’，岂可不修！”。

王彦霖是程颢的学生，认为人要自己愿意为善才行，强劝不行。但程颢认为，对不愿为善的人要管他，“修道则谓之教”，就是要加强教化。显而易见，“修道之谓教”的“澄治之功”就是要加强道德教化，通过道德教化来恢复人的善性。

上述可见，程颢以“气禀之性”为出发点，然后过渡到“修道则谓之教”的“澄治之功”，可谓逻辑严密。所以，朱熹对程子的“气禀之性”十分赞赏：“孟子未尝说气质之性，程子论性，所以有功于名教者，以其发明气质之性也。以气质论，则凡言性不同者，皆冰释矣。”“道夫问：气质之说始于何人？曰：此起于张、程，某以为极有功于圣门，有补于后学，读之使人深有感于张、程。”。即是说，朱熹非常赞赏把性区分为“天命之性”和“气质之性”，认为这种区分既解决了人性学说的种种矛盾，又为道德教化提供了理论依据。

综上所述，儒家人性学说强调“性善”与“修道之谓教”的道德教化，即强调道德他律，又强调道德自律；并且通过道德他律向道德自律的转换，达到理想道德人格的境界。这些思想可为当代的伦理建设和道德修养提供很好的借鉴。

## 三、“和为贵”的人际观

“和”是儒家文化乃至整个中华文化的核心概念。它既是一种价值观，又是一种方法论。

《易经》曾说：“保合大和，乃利贞。首出庶物，万国咸宁”。（《易·乾卦·象》）“和”即和谐、和美之意，而这里的“大和”是指事物自身天然的、最高的和谐，是一种高度和谐的状态。整句话的意思是说要保持那本来和谐的至高状态，这种高度的和谐就是万物产生的首要因素，它能够使所有的国家都稳定安宁。简单来讲，就是说天地万物都要保持一种非常和谐的状态，因为只有在和谐的状态中才能产生新的事物，国家社会也必须保持和谐的状态，因为只有在和谐安定的状态中，国家社会才能有所发展，人类才能有所进步，否则万物则不生，国家社会将停滞不前。自然界也是如此，万物只有在风调雨顺的自然和谐状态中生长，才能硕果累累。自然界如此，人类社会也是如此。只有在一个安定和谐的国家中，才能最大限度地实现我们的人生价值，实现我们的梦想，国家才能够不断繁荣富强。所以，无论是自然界，还是人类社会，“和”的意义都十分重大。

在儒家思想中，“和”的内涵广大而精微，其中“和而不同”是儒家“和”文化的一个极为重要的内涵。“和而不同”简单来讲就是说不同性质事物之间构成的一种和谐稳定的状态，或者说“和而不同”，就是追求内在的和谐统一，而不是表象上的相同和一致。《国语·郑语》中，史伯提出“和实生物，同则不继。以他平他谓之和，故能丰长而物生之；若以同裨同，尽乃弃矣。”意思是说不同事物之间的相互结合才能产生出新的事物，同一事物的相互结合只是数量上的增加，并没有产生新事物。这里主要是说事物之间的差异性、多样性才是化生宇宙万物的动力和源泉，或者说只有不同性质的事物之间在相互碰撞中才具有产生万物的生机，才能生成万物。可见，儒家思想中的“和”是一个动态的过程，是一个生生不息的过程，因事物之间的不同或者对立，从而相互运动、相互摩擦、相互配合产生新事物或者达到新的效果。

孔子说过：“君子和而不同，小人同而不和”，就是说在人际关系的处理上，“和”也是我们大家所追求的至高境界，是君子为人处世的根本方法。显然这里的“和”与“同”并不是同一个意思，“同”指的是无差别的统一，是你好我好大家好的代名词，故小人只追求相同、“一团和气”而反对差别和不同意见，认为事物的存在只有单一性，否定事物相互之间的合力。然而，“和”指的是有差别的统一，表面上看起来，君子之间会因为观点、立场、价值观上的不同而产生分歧甚至对立，但其最终的目的是要趋向于一个更高层次的和谐圆融之境，故君子认为同异相生，阴阳对立互根，才能发展壮大，其本身具有生生不息的内在价值。在我们现实的人际关系中，我们大家要容纳不同的意见，承认个性存在，不能盲目附和。只有在不同思想的碰撞中才能产生出新的思想，个人才能不断地进步。中国五十六个民族是一家，五十六个民族有五十六个不同的民族文化，我国民族政策规定要尊重少数民族的风俗习惯、尊重和保护少数民族的宗教信仰自由，在共同发展的基础上和谐相处，这是“和而不同”思想在中国政治思想中的典型表现。同时，还有“一国两制”，一国就是“和”，两制就是不“同”，“和而不同”显然体现了具有中国特色的社会主义政治文明。

在全球政治多元化的背景下，各个国家要相互承认并尊重对方的个性存在，不能以己度人，片面地认为人不如己。当今世界的繁荣发展与丰富多彩正是各个不同国家的文化、制度、价值观相互碰撞与交融的结果。可见“和而不同”思想不仅在处理我们个人关系，而且在我们处理国际关系中也发挥着极其重要的作用。

关于“和”，儒家还从哲理上、方法论上来说明。如“中庸”本意即为用中，即“执其两端，用其中于民”，（《礼记·中庸》）也就是说把握事物正反的两个方面，采取适中的方法来治理百姓。“中”就是不偏不倚，无过无不及的意思，要求我们在处理事情或者交往过程中要把握中庸的原则。孔子说：“吾有知乎哉？无知也，有鄙夫问于我，空空如也。我叩其两端而竭焉”。（《论语·子罕》）可见，“中庸”、“中和”就是要适度，无过之无不及，不偏不倚，不左不右，就是使两种不同的因素协调、配合，使之达到统一、和谐。《中庸》中讲到：“喜怒哀乐之未发，谓之中；发而皆中节，谓之和”，提到了“中”与“和”两个概念，并把二者联系起来。这句话的意思是说，每个人都有喜怒哀乐之情，当其未发时感情无所偏向，所以就是“中”；而当其已发时，或者说当感情表现出来时又能够有所节制，合乎法度，所以就是“和”。“和”包含“中节”的意思，中节并不是指在喜与怒、哀与乐之间取其中间，而是当喜则喜、当怒则怒、当哀则哀、当乐则乐；既是发自于内心的真情表露，又是合乎于当下的事理之宜。当我们的每种感情都达到了“中节”，全部感情也就自然而然达到“和”了。这就是儒家提出的“中和”原则，这种原则适用于协调一切不同事物之间的关系，包括人与人之间、物与物之间、人与物之间、人与自然之间的关系等等。把握中庸、中和的原则就是要求我们做事情不偏不倚，这就是中庸之道的内在意义。当宇宙间的一切事物相互之间都遵循“中和”的原则时，那么天地便各就其位而运行不息，万物就各得其所而生长繁衍了，用《中庸》中的话来讲即是“致中和，天地位焉，万物育焉”。

儒家“和”文化对于我们今天构建社会主义和谐社会也有重要的价值。我们知道，和谐的社会，除了要满足社会所需求的物质财富之外，还必须努力在民族文化的土壤上培植可以激励、愉悦和净化社会成员心灵的精神财富，这就是构建和谐社会不可缺少的和谐文化。我们要构建理想的和谐社会大厦，就一定要拥有与之相适应的和谐文化作为基石。可以说，儒家的和谐文化是建设和谐社会的重要理论来源。“和”就是要协调多种差异的因素，使之得到和谐统一。“和而不同”一是主张多样性，二是主张平衡性。推及施政，则必须协调各种利益，平衡各方面关系，化解矛盾，追求社会各方面平衡、协调地发展，使和谐思想成为治国的根本法则。只有这样，才能均调天下，和乐人民，国家才能可持续发展。可见，儒家“和为贵”思想，为落实科学发展观，建构和谐社会提供了很好的思想资源。

# 《四书》和《弟子规》是治国与塑造社会主义新人的经典

## ——儒学现代化刍议

徐州市文联　安启杰

### 一、问题的提起

自汉武帝接受董仲舒“罢黜百家，独尊儒术”的奏议以来，至今已两千余年，儒学尤其是《论语》一直是中国人的“圣经”，塑造了中华民族的民族性，成为中华民族的价值观、人生观和世界观；一直是历代帝王治国所遵循的指导思想和不二法门，是朝野百姓共同遵守的伦理道德规范、思想行为标准；也是维持中国大一统的社会团结统一、辽阔的国土分久必合的强大思想武器；已经融进中国人的血液和基因，虽历经风雨浩劫，永不衰败。数千年来，中国的国土从中原地区发展到今天的版图，中国的民族文化丰富多彩为世界景仰，中国的经济社会不断发展壮大，中国自立于民族之林，直到今天的改革开放，不管承认与否，都与儒学像阳光一样的照耀，像乳汁一样的滋养，像春风雨露一样的润抚分不开。

世界各国各民族，无不为本国本民族的传统文化而骄傲自豪，无不向世界夸耀和展示自己民族的文化，甚至一些并无传统文化的国家，却用坚船利炮向世界强力推送自己国家的文化；就是一些经济文化十分落后的民族，也无限热爱本民族的传统文化。只有我们这个具有灿烂文化的中国，一度把自己的民族传统文化踩在脚下，自污是“落后”“反动”“腐朽”；把自己民族的圣贤们污损得一文不值，把由于清朝统治者闭关和腐败导致的丧权辱国、沦为半殖民地，归罪于自己民族的文化。这样的民族虚无主义，这样的文化卖国主义和洋奴主义，是对自己国家民族的背叛！导致的恶果，是国人思想混乱，伦理失序，道德沦丧，不少人人性泯灭，唯钱是举，享乐腐化，奢侈浪费，暴殄天物……民族文化和传统美德，面临断代危险。语云“十年树木百年树人”，振兴民族文化，重拾民族精神，重塑国人形象，需要全国上下，齐心协力，也还需毕数年之功！

直到现在，虽然民间有识之士不断发出强烈呼吁，要振兴民族文化。但在不少党政干部思想上或潜意识中，仍然认为儒学是落后的，是中国现代化的绊脚石。

究其原因，是我国近代以来，反孔之声不绝于耳。“文革”中，更是用党政的力量，对包括儒学在内的传统文化进行摧枯拉朽的无情打击，使儒道释这些中华借以立国的国之灵魂遭到灭顶之灾，文人儒士更是被无情摧残。而“文革”后，只是注重清算政治上的影响和流毒，对在文化上的影响没有或很少触及。因此肃清“文革”影响，实事求是地评价儒学就显得尤为必要。对儒学本身，也有一个与时俱进、对一些提法和认识，有赋予新的解释的必要。马克思主义需要与时俱进，为什么儒学不能与时俱进呢！马克思主义是革命的学说，这是真理；数千年的实践证明，儒学也是革命的学说！人们不能只准马克思主义不断发展，而不准儒道释等传统文化不断进步发展吧！对待儒学的态度，不能像鲁迅笔下的假洋鬼子一样不准革命吧！

## 二、儒学是开放的学说，是与时俱进的学说

儒学并不是从孔子时代开始的，在孔子之前的文献中，例如《国语》《尚书》等都闪耀着儒家思想的光辉。在孔子之后的年代中，儒学也不断发展，吸收道家、佛家、宋明理学及各家学说，丰富自己。虽然历史上“罢黜百家，独尊儒术”，但是儒学本身并不排斥其他学说，主张“博学之，审问之，慎思之，明辨之，笃行之。有弗学，学之弗能弗措也；有弗问，问之弗知弗措也；有弗思，思之弗得弗措也；有弗辨，辨之弗明弗措也；有弗行，行之弗笃弗措也。人一能之，己百之；人十能之，己千之。果能此道矣，虽愚必明，虽柔必强。”（《中庸》）博学、审问、慎思、明辨、笃行，说明儒学是开放的学说。子夏曰：“贤贤易色；事父母，能竭其力；事君，能致其身；与朋友交，言而有信。虽曰未学，吾必谓之学矣。”（《论语》）强调“笃行”，说明儒学是实践的学问。凡是实践的学问，大都重视与时俱进，否则，就无法实践。就是在“独尊儒术”的汉代，就是汉武帝，也没有真的“罢黜百家”。

今天，把这个问题搞清楚十分必要，因为，虽然儒学是发展的学说，但是许多人，尤其是部分党政官员，把儒学看成僵死的一成不变的学说，在他们脑子里，儒学是迂腐的。戴着有色眼镜看事物，用形而上学的观点看事物，用迂腐的脑袋看任何东西，得出的结论都和他们的脑袋一样。

弄清这个问题，关系着传统文化能否继承和发展，关系着辩证唯物主义能否真正成为党的哲学思想，也关系着改革开放能否进行到底的大问题。

## 三、要从儒道释等中华传统文化中汲取治国和外交理念

以儒道释为核心的中华传统文化，对治国安邦、发展外交具有现实的指导意义。

“日若稽古，帝尧日放勋，钦明文思安安，允恭克让，光被四表，格于上下。克明俊德，以亲九族。九族既睦，平章百姓，百姓昭明，协和万邦，黎民于变时雍。”《尚书·尧典》这里回答了怎样“修身齐家治国平天下”的问题，直到今天仍有极其重要的指导意义。“克明俊德，以亲九族。”这不就是百族和睦的民族政策吗！“九族既睦，平章百姓，百姓昭明，协和万邦”，这不就是今天的和谐社会吗！对“协和万邦”应赋予新的解释，不是诸侯国，而是各省区市县，也可以解释为世界各国。时代在发展，数千年来，中国的许多词汇都发展出新的意义，传统文化当然也要跟着发展，尤其是文言文，古代不点标点符号，本来就有许多模糊概念，可以这样断句，也可以那样断句，可以作多种解释，这为我们古为今用，为儒学的发展，提供了许多方便。

历史上的汉唐雄风，就是开放的雄风，是在儒家思想指导下对外开放、对外交流的雄风。历史上凡是开放的年代，中国就发展，经济文化就异常发达，疆域也不断扩大，就受到世界各国的尊重，就“四方来朝”；反之，违背儒家的开放思想，中国就衰微，清朝闭关自守导致的落后挨打，沦为半封建半殖民地社会，几至亡国灭种，是最好的注脚。历史证明，尊重儒学的朝代，国运都较长久，一般在200年左右；反之，就短命，例如秦朝。

今天，在我们的改革开放政策中，有许多是从传统文化和儒家精神中汲取的智慧。譬如“和平共处五项原则”，“求大同存小异”，“与邻为善，以邻为伴”的睦邻友好政策，“搁置争议，共同开发”……。这些，既显示了决策人的智慧，也闪射出传统文化和儒家思想的光芒。

## 四、《四书》和《弟子规》是塑造社会主义新人的经典

这些年来，“道德滑坡”一词屡见报端，成了国人的口头禅。其实何止滑坡，伦理失序、道德沦丧已经令人触目惊心，各种丧尽天良的事情屡屡出现。究其原因，是因为传统文化的断代造成。儒家文化是中华民族的主流价值观，是中华民族的民族精神，是中华民族的灵魂。灵魂被抽掉了，就只剩下钱，剩下利益，追钱逐利就成为共同追求。马克思指出：“一旦有适当的利润，资本就胆大起来。如果有百分之十的利润，它就保证被到处使用；有百分之二十的利润，它就活跃起来；有百分之五十的利润，它就铤而走险；为了百分之一百的利润，它就敢践踏一切人间法律；有百分之三百的利润，它就敢犯任何罪行，甚至冒绞首的危险。”这句话，不幸成为一幕幕在中国上演不衰的活剧。

我们强调依法治国，这没错。但是法律是低层次的，是做人的最低要求，因而是形而下的。我们不能按照最低要求来治理国家，来教育和设计人的灵魂。对人，应当

有更高的要求，更高的标准。

《四书》和《弟子规》不仅集中了治国的理念和智慧，更集中了中国关于伦理道德的菁华，人们虽然不能全部做到成为圣贤，就像人们不能全部做到《圣经·马太福音》中所要求的一样，但是你努力按照其中的要求去做，你必定会成为一个高尚的人。《四书》和《弟子规》中的理念，至今仍是社会的亟须。

总的说，中国的伦理道德的内容，用十多个字可以概括其主要精神，这就是：忠、孝、悌、仁、义、礼、恕、节、善、廉、耻、智、信、温、良、恭、俭、让。这些是规范社会关系和社会行为的准则，不仅没有过时，而且只要人类社会在，家庭在，千秋万代不会过时。它闪射着智慧的光辉，散发着人间的温暖，规范着家庭社会的伦理，维持着人类社会的正常运行。谁触动了这些准则，就会受到惩罚，就会给国家人民造成巨大的损失。

首先，“孝”“悌”是亘古不变的原理。只要有家庭在，有父母在，只要辈分在，年龄的差距在，“孝”就在，“悌”就在。恩格斯说：“父亲子女兄弟姊妹等称谓，并不是简单的荣誉称号，而是一种负有完全确定的异常郑重的相互义务的称呼，这些义务的总和便构成这些民族的社会制度的实质部分。”可见中外皆是如此。孔子也反对愚孝，这在《论语》中有明确论述。因此，任何理由都不能否定“孝”与“悌”。在当今社会，大量违背孝悌原理的事情大量存在，造成亲情和社会的创伤。父子反目，夫妻离异，子戕其母等极端事例屡屡出现，“啃老族”已成为多发甚至普遍现象，究其根源，皆是孝悌教育缺失的结果。虽然看起来是家庭的现象，却透露出颓废、寄生、不思进取、得过且过的精神状态，这样的民族是危险的，长此以往，是没有出路的。

再说“仁”与“善”。“仁”，首先是仁政，仁政以善为基础。有法不依不是仁，违法乱纪不是仁，近年来被群众深恶痛绝的“强拆”不是仁。“仁”以善良为灵魂。见义不为不是仁，见到老人倒地不扶不是仁。在工商界，不仁的事例比比皆是。例如未经批准暗中生产销售转基因食品不是仁，“三聚氰胺”事件反映的问题不是仁，“地沟油”的制造销售者不是仁，假冒伪劣产品的生产销售者不是仁，有意污染环境赚取利润不是仁，而那些睁只眼闭只眼纵容包庇的官员们更不是仁。岂止是不仁，那是违法乱纪，丧尽天良。这方面的例子，举不胜举。《三字经》说：“人之初，性本善”，为什么善被恶打败，是因为现代教育中，对于善恶的教育太差，对“仁”的教育缺失，使人不知何为善，何为恶，形成赚钱为善不赚钱为恶的观念，这是社会“仁”与“善”缺失的根本原因；也是一些官吏为非作歹的根本原因。

综上所述，当前社会所产生的腐败、“道德滑坡”、污染环境、假冒伪劣、诚信缺失、残暴无理等等社会问题，其最终原因，皆是因为丢弃了中华民族传统美德的教育，甚至一度把这些作为“落后”、“腐朽”来批判，造成价值的缺失，人心的混乱，是非颠倒，黑白混淆。

其余恕道、诚信、礼让、廉耻、节俭等等观念，都是现代社会不能须臾离开的美德。

自五四运动以来，直至“文化大革命”，虽然对中国传统文化口诛笔伐，列举传统文化的种种“罪状”，但是直至今日，尚没有一位圣贤，没有一本书，没有一种理论，能够代替四书五经和弟子规对国人人性的塑造。四书五经经受了数千年时间的检验，证明其是颠扑不破的真理，是中华民族的“圣经”，对治国安邦，对塑造人的灵魂，有无可替代的作用，不可须臾离开。

因此，在当前的国民教育中，在各级学校里，从小学到大学，应当按照内容深浅把四书五经列为必修课，至少应把四书和弟子规列为必修课，在文化课中增加四书的内容。在对党政干部的教育中，应把四书和弟子规列为必修教材，甚至在党课教育中，也可以增加部分四书的内容，弟子规则应列为必须背诵的内容。因为，《四书》和《弟子规》不仅是塑造祖先人格的经典，也是在新时代塑造社会主义新人的经典。